CHILTON®

GENERAL MOTORS
SERVICE MANUAL
2010 EDITION
VOLUME I

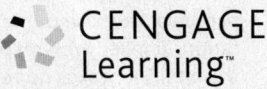
CENGAGE
Learning™

Australia • Brazil • Japan • Korea • Mexico • Singapore • Spain • United Kingdom • United States

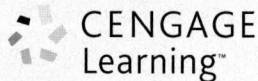
CENGAGE
Learning™

CHILTON®
General Motors Service Manual
2010 Edition
Volume I

Vice President,
Technology Professional
Business Unit:
  Gregory L. Clayton

Publisher,
Technology Professional
Business Unit:
  David Koontz

Director of Marketing:
  Beth A. Lutz

Production Director:
  Carolyn Miller

Production Manager:
  Andrew Crouth

Marketing Manager:
  Jennifer Barbic

Marketing Coordinator:
  Rachael Conover

Editorial Assistant:
  Tracey Gates

Chilton Content Specialist:
  Paula Baillie

Graphical Designer:
  Melinda Possinger

Art Director:
  Benj Gleeksman

Sr. Content Project Manager:
  Elizabeth C. Hough

Managing Editor:
  Terry L. Blomquist

Senior Editor:
  Christine L. Sheeky

Editors:
  Ken Burdette

  Sherry Burdette

  Scott Critchfield

  Nick D'Andrea

  Eugene F. Hannon, Jr., A.S.E.

  Kyla Nyjordet

  David G. Olson

  Jonathan Wallace

For product information and technology assistance, contact us at
Professional & Career Group Customer Support, 1-800-648-7450.
For permission to use material from this text or product, submit all requests online at **www.cengage.com/permissions.**
Further permissions questions can be e-mailed to **permissionrequest@cengage.com.**

ISBN-13: 978-1-1110-3658-4
ISBN-10: 1-1110-3658-6
ISSN: 1939-621X

Delmar
5 Maxwell Drive
Clifton Park, NY 12065-2919
USA

Cengage Learning is a leading provider of customized learning solutions with office locations around the globe, including Singapore, the United Kingdom, Australia, Mexico, Brazil, and Japan. Locate your local office at: **international.cengage.com/region**

Cengage Learning products are represented in Canada by Nelson Education, Ltd.

NOTICE TO THE READER

Publisher does not warrant or guarantee any of the products described herein or perform any independent analysis in connection with any of the product information contained herein. Publisher does not assume, and expressly disclaims, any obligation to obtain and include information other than that provided to it by the manufacturer.

The reader is expressly warned to consider and adopt all safety precautions that might be indicated by the activities described herein and to avoid all potential hazards. By following the instructions contained herein, the reader willingly assumes all risks in connection with such instructions.

The publisher makes no representations or warranties of any kind, including but not limited to, the warranties of fitness for particular purpose or merchantability, nor are any such representations implied with respect to the material set forth herein, and the publisher takes no responsibility with respect to such material. The publisher shall not be liable for any special, consequential, or exemplary damages resulting, in whole or part, from the readers' use of, or reliance upon, this material.

Printed in the United States of America
1 2 3 4 5 6 7 13 12 11 10 09

Table of Contents

Model Index

these instructions may result in personal injury.

• Observe all applicable safety precautions when working around fuel. Whenever servicing the fuel system, always work in a well-ventilated area. Do not allow fuel spray or vapors to come in contact with a spark, open flame, or excessive heat (a hot drop light, for example). Keep a dry chemical fire extinguisher near the work area. Always keep fuel in a container specifically designed for fuel storage; also, always properly seal fuel containers to avoid the possibility of fire or explosion. Do not smoke or carry lighted tobacco or open flame of any type when working on or near any fuel-related components.

• Fuel injection systems often remain pressurized, even after the engine has been turned OFF. The fuel system pressure must be relieved before disconnecting any fuel lines. Failure to do so may result in fire and/or personal injury.

• The evaporative emissions system contains fuel vapor and condensed fuel vapor. Although not present in large quantities, it still presents the danger of explosion or fire. Disconnect the battery ground cable from the battery to minimize the possibility of an electrical spark occurring, possibly causing a fire or explosion if fuel vapor or liquid fuel is present in the area. Failure to follow these instructions can result in personal injury.

• The EPA warns that prolonged contact with used engine oil may cause a number of skin disorders, including cancer! You should make every effort to minimize your exposure to used engine oil. Protective gloves should be worn when changing oil. Wash your hands and any other exposed skin areas as soon as possible after exposure to used engine oil. Soap and water, or waterless hand cleaner should be used.

• Some vehicles are equipped with an air bag system, often referred to as a Supplemental Restraint System (SRS) or Supplemental Inflatable Restraint (SIR) system. The system must be disabled before performing service on or around system components, steering column, instrument panel components, wiring and sensors. Failure to follow safety and disabling procedures could result in accidental air bag deployment, possible personal injury and unnecessary system repairs.

• Always wear safety goggles when working with, or around, the air bag system. When carrying a non-deployed air bag, be sure the bag and trim cover are pointed away from your body. When placing a nondeployed air bag on a work surface, always face the bag and trim cover upward, away from the surface. This will reduce the motion of the module if it is accidentally deployed.

• Electronic modules are sensitive to electrical charges. The ABS module can be damaged if exposed to these charges.

• Brake pads and shoes may contain asbestos, which has been determined to be a cancer-causing agent. Never clean brake surfaces with compressed air. Avoid inhaling brake dust. Clean all brake surfaces with a commercially available brake cleaning fluid.

• When replacing brake pads, shoes, discs or drums, replace them as complete axle sets.

• When servicing drum brakes, disassemble and assemble one side at a time, leaving the remaining side intact for reference.

• Brake fluid often contains polyglycol ethers and polyglycols. Avoid contact with the eyes and wash your hands thoroughly after handling brake fluid. If you do get brake fluid in your eyes, flush your eyes with clean, running water for 15 minutes. If eye irritation persists, or if you have taken brake fluid internally, immediately seek medical assistance.

• Clean, high quality brake fluid from a sealed container is essential to the safe and proper operation of the brake system. You should always buy the correct type of brake fluid for your vehicle. If the brake fluid becomes contaminated, completely flush the system with new fluid. Never reuse any brake fluid. Any brake fluid that is removed from the system should be discarded. Also, do not allow any brake fluid to come in contact with a painted or plastic surface; it will damage the paint.

• Never operate the engine without the proper amount and type of engine oil; doing so will result in severe engine damage.

• Timing belt maintenance is extremely important! Many models utilize an interference-type, non-freewheeling engine. If the timing belt breaks, the valves in the cylinder head may strike the pistons, causing potentially serious (also time-consuming and expensive) engine damage.

• Disconnecting the negative battery cable on some vehicles may interfere with the functions of the on-board computer system (s) and may require the computer to undergo a relearning process once the negative battery cable is reconnected.

• Steering and suspension fasteners are critical parts because they affect performance of vital components and systems and their failure can result in major service expense. They must be replaced with the same grade or part number or an equivalent part if replacement is necessary. Do not use a replacement part of lesser quality or substitute design. Torque values must be used as specified during reassembly.

USING THIS INFORMATION

Organization

To find where a particular model section or procedure is located, look in the Table of Contents. Main topics are listed with the page number on which they may be found. Following the main topics is an alphabetical listing of all of the procedures within the section and their page numbers.

Manufacturer and Model Coverage

This product covers 2008 – 2010 General Motors models that are produced in sufficient quantities to warrant coverage, and which have technical content available from the vehicle manufacturers before our publication date. Although this information is as complete as possible at the time of publication, some manufacturers may make changes which cannot be included here. While striving for total accuracy, the publisher cannot assume responsibility for any errors, changes, or omissions that may occur in the compilation of this data.

Part Numbers & Special Tools

Part numbers and special tools are recommended by the publisher and vehicle manufacturer to perform specific jobs. Before substituting any part or tool for the one recommended, you must be completely satisfied that neither your personal safety, nor the performance of the vehicle will be endangered.

ACKNOWLEDGEMENT

Portions of materials contained herein have been reprinted under license from General Motors Company, Service and Parts Operations License Agreement #0510757.

PRECAUTIONS

Before servicing any vehicle, please be sure to read all of the following precautions, which deal with personal safety, prevention of component damage, and important points to take into consideration when servicing a motor vehicle:

- Always wear safety glasses or goggles when drilling, cutting, grinding or prying.
- Steel-toed work shoes should be worn when working with heavy parts. Pockets should not be used for carrying tools. A slip or fall can drive a screwdriver into your body.
- Work surfaces, including tools and the floor should be kept clean of grease, oil or other slippery material.
- When working around moving parts, don't wear loose clothing. Long hair should be tied back under a hat or cap, or in a hair net.
- Always use tools only for the purpose for which they were designed. Never pry with a screwdriver.
- Keep a fire extinguisher and first aid kit handy.
- Always properly support the vehicle with approved stands or lift.
- Always have adequate ventilation when working with chemicals or hazardous material.
- Carbon monoxide is colorless, odorless and dangerous. If it is necessary to operate the engine with vehicle in a closed area such as a garage, always use an exhaust collector to vent the exhaust gases outside the closed area.
- When draining coolant, keep in mind that small children and some pets are attracted by ethylene glycol antifreeze, and are quite likely to drink any left in an open container, or in puddles on the ground. This will prove fatal in sufficient quantity. Always drain the coolant into a sealable container.
- To avoid personal injury, do not remove the coolant pressure relief cap while the engine is operating or hot. The cooling system is under pressure; steam and hot liquid can come out forcefully when the cap is loosened slightly. Failure to follow these instructions may result in personal injury. The coolant must be recovered in a suitable, clean container for reuse. If the coolant is contaminated it must be recycled or disposed of correctly.
- When carrying out maintenance on the starting system be aware that heavy gauge leads are connected directly to the battery. Make sure the protective caps are in place when maintenance is completed. Failure to follow these instructions may result in personal injury.
- Do not remove any part of the engine emission control system. Operating the engine without the engine emission control system will reduce fuel economy and engine ventilation. This will weaken engine performance and shorten engine life. It is also a violation of Federal law.
- Due to environmental concerns, when the air conditioning system is drained, the refrigerant must be collected using refrigerant recovery/recycling equipment. Federal law requires that refrigerant be recovered into appropriate recovery equipment and the process be conducted by qualified technicians who have been certified by an approved organization, such as MACS, ASI, etc. Use of a recovery machine dedicated to the appropriate refrigerant is necessary to reduce the possibility of oil and refrigerant incompatibility concerns. Refer to the instructions provided by the equipment manufacturer when removing refrigerant from or charging the air conditioning system.
- Always disconnect the battery ground when working on or around the electrical system.
- Batteries contain sulfuric acid. Avoid contact with skin, eyes, or clothing. Also, shield your eyes when working near batteries to protect against possible splashing of the acid solution. In case of acid contact with skin or eyes, flush immediately with water for a minimum of 15 minutes and get prompt medical attention. If acid is swallowed, call a physician immediately. Failure to follow these instructions may result in personal injury.
- Batteries normally produce explosive gases. Therefore, do not allow flames, sparks or lighted substances to come near the battery. When charging or working near a battery, always shield your face and protect your eyes. Always provide ventilation. Failure to follow these instructions may result in personal injury.
- When lifting a battery, excessive pressure on the end walls could cause acid to spew through the vent caps, resulting in personal injury, damage to the vehicle or battery. Lift with a battery carrier or with your hands on opposite corners. Failure to follow

BUICK, CHEVROLET, GMC AND SATURN

Acadia • Enclave • Outlook • Traverse

1

SPECIFICATIONS AND MAINTENANCE CHARTS

ENGINE AND VEHICLE IDENTIFICATION

Engine							Model Year	
Code ①	Liters (cc)	Cu. In.	Cyl.	Fuel Sys.	Engine Type	Eng. Mfg.	Code ②	Year
7	3.6 (3598)	217	6	SFI	DOHC	GM	8	2008
D	3.6 (3598)	217	6	SFI*	DOHC	GM	9	2009

SFI: Sequential Fuel Injection

DOHC: Double Overhead Camshafts

SFI*: Sequential Fuel Injection with High Pressure Direct Injection

36616_ACAD_C0001

GENERAL ENGINE SPECIFICATIONS

Year	Model	Engine Displacement Liters (cc)	Engine ID/VIN	Fuel System Type	Net Horsepower @ rpm	Net Torque @ rpm (ft. lbs.)	Bore x Stroke (in.)	Compression Ratio	Oil Pressure @ rpm
2008	All	3.6 (3598)	7	SFI	275@6600	251@3200	3.70x3.37	10.2:1	20@2000
2009	All	3.6 (3598)	D	SFI*	288@6300	270@3400	3.70x3.37	11.4:1	20@2000

SFI: Sequential Fuel Injection

SFI*: Sequential Fuel Injection with High Pressure Direct Injection

36616_ACAD_C0002

ENGINE TUNE-UP SPECIFICATIONS

Year	Engine Displacement Liters	Engine ID/VIN	Spark Plug Gap (in.)	Ignition Timing (deg.) MT	Ignition Timing (deg.) AT	Fuel Pump (psi) ①	Idle Speed (rpm) MT ②	Idle Speed (rpm) AT ②	Valve Clearance In.	Valve Clearance Ex.
2008	3.6	7	0.043	NA	③	50-60	NA	④	HYD	HYD
2009	3.6	D	0.044	NA	③	Variable	NA	④	HYD	HYD

NOTE: The Vehicle Emission Control Information label often reflects specification changes made during production.

The label figures must be used if they differ from those in this chart.

NA is not applicable

HYD: Hydraulic

① 2009 pressure is measured with a diagnostic scan tool

② Idle speed measured with manual transmission in Neutral; automatic transmission in D (drive)

③ Engines equipped with Distributorless Ignition System (DIS). Ignition timing is not adjustable

④ Refer to the Vehicle Emission Control Information label

36616_ACAD_C0003

CAPACITIES

Year	Engine Displacement Liters	Engine VIN	Engine Oil with Filter (qts.)	Transmission pts. ①	Transfer Case (pts.)	Front Axle (pts.)	Rear Axle (pts.)	Fuel Tank (gal.)	Cooling System (qts.)
2008	3.6	7	5.5	①	1.7	NA	1.7	22.0	11.4
2009	3.6	D	5.5	①	1.7	NA	1.7	22.0	11.4

NA Not applicable

① 6 speed: Fluid change: 4.2-6.3 qts., Overhaul: 7.4-9.5 qts.

36616_ACAD_C0004

FLUID SPECIFICATIONS

Year	Model	Engine Displacement Liters (VIN)	Engine Oil	Auto. Trans.	Drive Axle	Power Steering Fluid	Brake Master Cylinder
2008	All	3.6 (7)	5W-30	①	75W-90	Power Steering Fluid	DOT 3
2009	All	3.6 (D)	5W-30	①	75W-90	Power Steering Fluid	DOT 3

DOT: Department Of Transpotation

① DEXRON®-VI Automatic Transmission Fluid

36616_ACAD_C0010

VALVE SPECIFICATIONS

Year	Engine Displ. Liters	Engine ID/VIN	Seat Angle (deg.)	Face Angle (deg.)	Spring Test Pressure (lbs. @ in.)	Spring Free-Length (in.)	Stem-to-Guide Clearance (in.) Intake	Stem-to-Guide Clearance (in.) Exhaust	Stem Diameter (in.) Intake	Stem Diameter (in.) Exhaust
2008	3.6	7	45	44.25	①	1.6555-	0.0010	0.0014	0.2344	0.2341
					②	1.766	0.0026	0.0030	0.2352	0.2348
2009	3.6	D	45	44.25	①	1.6555-	0.0010	0.0014	0.2344	0.2341
					②	1.766	0.0026	0.0030	0.2352	0.2348

① Valve spring load closed: 247-273 N @ 56-61 lb.

② Valve spring load open: 598-662 N @ 134-149 lb.

36616_ACAD_C0006

CRANKSHAFT AND CONNECTING ROD SPECIFICATIONS

All measurements are given in inches.

| Year | Engine Displacement Liters | Engine ID/VIN | Crankshaft | | | | Connecting Rod | | |
			Main Brg. Journal Dia.	Main Brg. Oil Clearance	Shaft End-play	Thrust on No.	Journal Diameter	Oil Clearance	Side Clearance
2008	3.6	7	2.6768-2.6775	0.0004-0.0024	0.0039-0.0130	3	2.2044-2.2050	0.0004-0.0028	0.0374-0.0140
2009	3.6	D	2.6768-2.6775	0.0004-0.0024	0.0039-0.0130	3	2.2044-2.2050	0.0004-0.0028	0.0374-0.0140

36616_ACAD_C0005

PISTON AND RING SPECIFICATIONS

All measurements are given in inches.

| Year | Engine Displacement Liters | Engine ID/VIN | Piston Clearance | Ring Gap | | | Ring Side Clearance | | |
				Top Compression	Bottom Compression	Oil Control	Top Compression	Bottom Compression	Oil Control
2008	3.6	7	0.0010-0.0021	0.0059-0.0118	0.0110-0.0189	0.0059-0.0236	0.0012-0.0026	0.0006-0.0024	0.0012-0.0067
2009	3.6	D	0.0010-0.0021	0.0059-0.0118	0.0110-0.0189	0.0059-0.0236	0.0012-0.0026	0.0006-0.0024	0.0012-0.0067

36616_ACAD_C0007

TORQUE SPECIFICATIONS

All readings in ft. lbs.

| Year | Engine Displacement Liters | Engine ID/VIN | Cylinder Head Bolts | Main Bearing Bolts | Rod Bearing Bolts | Crankshaft Damper Bolts | Flexplate Bolts | Manifold | | Spark Plugs | Oil Pan Drain Plug |
								Intake	Exhaust		
2008	3.6	7	①	②	③	④	⑤	⑥	15	13	18
2009	3.6	D	①	②	③	④	⑤	⑤	15	13	18

① M8 bolt
  Step 1: 11 ft. lbs.
  Step 2: Plus 75 degrees
  M11 bolt
  Step 1: 22 ft. lbs.
  Step 2: Plus 150 degrees

② Inner Bolts
  Step 1: 15 ft. lbs.
  Step 2: Plus 80 degrees
  Outer Bolts
  Step 1: 10 ft. lbs.
  Step 2: Plus 110 degrees
  Side Bolts
  Step 1: 22 ft. lbs.
  Step 2: Plus 60 degrees

③ Step 1: 22 ft. lbs.
  Step 2: back off to zero
  Step 3: 18 ft. lbs
  Step 4: Plus 110 degrees

④ 74 ft. lbs. Plus 150 degrees

⑤ 22 ft. lbs. Plus 45 degrees

⑥ Intake manifold bolts: 17ft. lbs. Tuning valve bolts: 89 inch lbs.

36616_ACAD_C0008

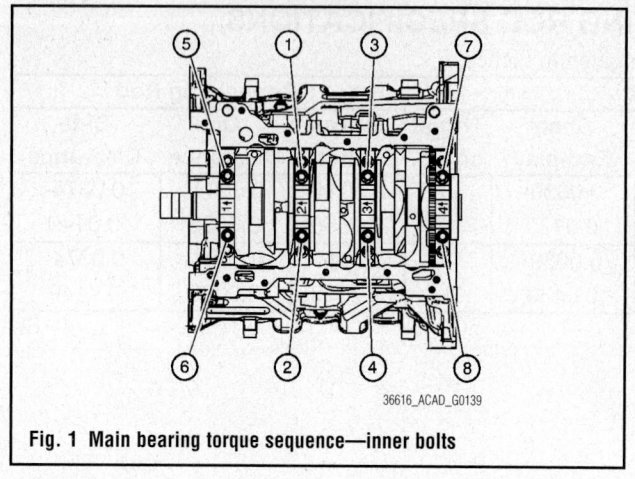

Fig. 1 Main bearing torque sequence—inner bolts

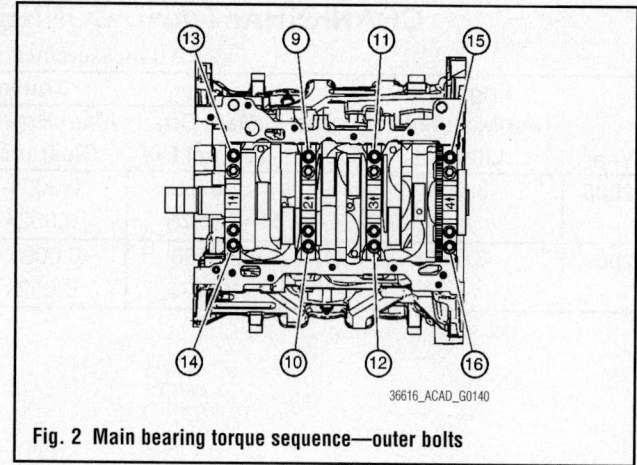

Fig. 2 Main bearing torque sequence—outer bolts

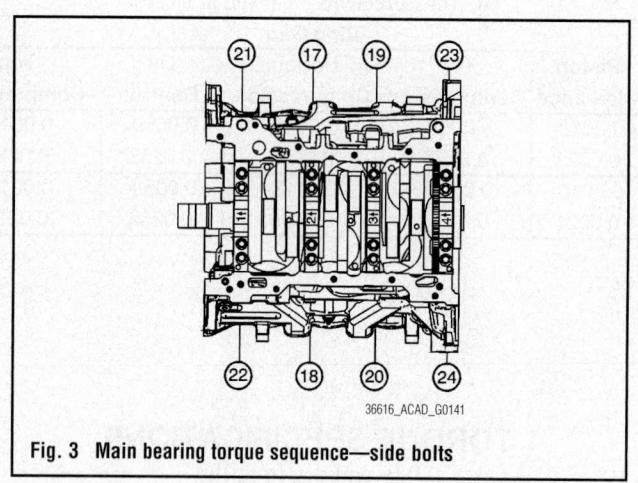

Fig. 3 Main bearing torque sequence—side bolts

WHEEL ALIGNMENT

Year	Model		Caster Range (+/-Deg.)	Caster Preferred Setting (Deg.)	Camber Range (+/-Deg.)	Camber Preferred Setting (Deg.)	Toe-in (in.)
2008	All	F	0.75	4.65	0.75	0.9	0.00 +/- 0.20
		R	NA	NA	0.75	0.85	0.10 +/- 0.20
2009	All	F	0.75	4.65	0.75	0.9	0.00 +/- 0.20
		R	NA	NA	0.75	0.85	0.10 +/- 0.20

36616_ACAD_C0009

TIRE, WHEEL AND BALL JOINT SPECIFICATIONS

| Year | Model | OEM Tires | | Tire Pressures (psi) | | Wheel Size | Ball Joint Inspection | Lug Nut (ft. lbs.) |
		Standard	Optional	Front	Rear			
2008	All	①	①	①	①	①	②	140
2009	All	①	①	①	①	①	②	140

OEM: Original Equipment Manufacturer

PSI: Pounds Per Square Inch

① For tire size and information, check the label located inside the glove compartment door.

② No noticable play should be present.

36616_ACAD_C0011

BRAKE SPECIFICATIONS

All measurements in inches unless noted

| Year | Model | | Brake Disc | | | Brake Drum Diameter | | | Minimum Lining Thickness | Brake Caliper | |
			Original Thickness	Minimum Thickness	Maximum Runout	Original Inside Diameter	Max. Wear Limit	Maximum Machine Diameter		Bracket Bolt (ft. lbs.)	Mounting Bolt (ft. lbs.)
2008	All	F	1.140	1.080	0.002	NA	NA	NA	NS	129	47
		R	0.790	0.720	0.002	NA	NA	NA	NS	151	20
2009	All	F	1.140	1.080	0.002	NA	NA	NA	NS	129	47
		R	0.790	0.720	0.002	NA	NA	NA	NS	151	20

NA: Not Applicable

NS: Not Specified

F: Front

R: Rear

36616_ACAD_C0012

SCHEDULED MAINTENANCE INTERVALS

Acaida, Enclave, Outlook, Traverse

TO BE SERVICED	TYPE OF SERVICE	VEHICLE MILEAGE INTERVAL (x1000)												
		3	6	9	12	15	18	21	24	27	30	33	36	39
Engine oil & filter ①	R	✓	✓	✓	✓	✓	✓	✓	✓	✓	✓	✓	✓	✓
Visually inspect for leaks or damage	S/I	✓	✓	✓	✓	✓	✓	✓	✓	✓	✓	✓	✓	✓
Air filter element ②	S/I													
Rotate tires	S/I	✓	✓	✓	✓	✓	✓	✓	✓	✓	✓	✓	✓	✓
Inspect brake system	S/I													
Engine cooling system ③	S/I												✓	
Inspect suspension and steering components ④	S/I		✓		✓		✓		✓		✓		✓	
Inspect the restrain system components ⑤	S/I		✓		✓		✓		✓		✓		✓	
Lubricate body components ⑥	S/I		✓		✓		✓		✓		✓		✓	
Inspect throttle body ⑦	S/I		✓				✓		✓		✓		✓	
Automatic transaxle fluid & filter	R	Every 100,000 miles												
Accessory drive belt(s)	S/I	Every 150,00 miles												
Exhaust system	S/I	Every 25,000 miles												
Spark plugs	R	Every 100,000 miles												
Ignition cables	S/I	Every 100,000 miles												
Inspect the fuel system for damage or leaks	S/I	Every 25,000 miles												

S/I: Service or Inspect

R: Replace

① Newer models are equipped with an engine life oil system. The engine oil life system calculates when to change your engine oil and filter based on vehicle use. Anytime your oil is changed, reset the system so it can calculate when the next oil change is required. If a situation occurs where you change your oil prior to the CHG OIL message being turned on, reset the system as follows:

Turn the ignition key to the ON/RUN position with the engine OFF

Fully press and release the accelerator pedal 3 times within 5 seconds.

② If you drive regularly in dusty conditions, inspect the filter at every oil change. Change the filter every 50,000 miles

③ Visually inspect hoses and have them replaced if they are cracked, swollen, or deteriorated. Inspect all pipes, fittings and clamps; replace as needed. To help ensure proper operation, a pressure test of the cooling system and pressure cap and cleaning the outside of the radiator and air conditioning condenser is recommended at least once a year. Check the coolant level t every oil change. A cooling system service should be performed at least every 5 yea

④ Visually inspect front and rear suspension and steering system for damaged, loose, or missing parts or signs of wear. Inspect electric power steering cables for proper hook-up, binding, cracks, chafing, etc. Inspect hydraulic power steering lines and hoses for proper hook-up, binding, leaks, cracks, chafing, etc

⑤ Make sure the safety belt reminder light and all your belts, buckles, latch plates, retractors, and anchorages are working properly. Look for any other loose or damaged safety belt system parts. If you see anything that might keep a safety belt system from doing its job, have it repaired. Have any torn or frayed safety belts replaced. Also look for any opened or broken airbag coverings, and have them repaired or replaced. The airbag system does not need regular maintenanc

⑥ Lubricate all key lock cylinders, door hinges and latches, hood hinges and latches, and trunk lid hinges and latches. More frequent lubrication may be required v exposed to a corrosive environment. Applying silicone grease on weatherstrips with a clean cloth will make them last longer, seal better, and not stick or squeak

⑦ Check system for interference or binding and for damaged or missing parts. Replace parts as needed. Replace any components that have high effort or excessive wear. Do not lubricate accelerator or cruise control cables

36616_ACAD_C0013

PRECAUTIONS

Before servicing any vehicle, please be sure to read all of the following precautions, which deal with personal safety, prevention of component damage, and important points to take into consideration when servicing a motor vehicle:

• Never open, service or drain the radiator or cooling system when the engine is hot; serious burns can occur from the steam and hot coolant.

• Observe all applicable safety precautions when working around fuel. Whenever servicing the fuel system, always work in a well-ventilated area. Do not allow fuel spray or vapors to come in contact with a spark, open flame, or excessive heat (a hot drop light, for example). Keep a dry chemical fire extinguisher near the work area. Always keep fuel in a container specifically designed for fuel storage; also, always properly seal fuel containers to avoid the possibility of fire or explosion. Refer to the additional fuel system precautions later in this section.

• Fuel injection systems often remain pressurized, even after the engine has been turned OFF. The fuel system pressure must be relieved before disconnecting any fuel lines. Failure to do so may result in fire and/or personal injury.

• Brake fluid often contains polyglycol ethers and polyglycols. Avoid contact with the eyes and wash your hands thoroughly after handling brake fluid. If you do get brake fluid in your eyes, flush your eyes with clean, running water for 15 minutes. If eye irritation persists, or if you have taken brake fluid internally, IMMEDIATELY seek medical assistance.

• The EPA warns that prolonged contact with used engine oil may cause a number of skin disorders, including cancer. You should make every effort to minimize your exposure to used engine oil. Protective gloves should be worn when changing oil. Wash your hands and any other exposed skin areas as soon as possible after exposure to used engine oil. Soap and water, or waterless hand cleaner should be used.

• All new vehicles are now equipped with an air bag system, often referred to as a Supplemental Restraint System (SRS) or Supplemental Inflatable Restraint (SIR) system. The system must be disabled before performing service on or around system components, steering column, instrument panel components, wiring and sensors. Failure to follow safety and disabling procedures could result in accidental air bag deployment, possible personal injury and unnecessary system repairs.

• Always wear safety goggles when working with, or around, the air bag system. When carrying a non-deployed air bag, be sure the bag and trim cover are pointed away from your body. When placing a non-deployed air bag on a work surface, always face the bag and trim cover upward, away from the surface. This will reduce the motion of the module if it is accidentally deployed. Refer to the additional air bag system precautions later in this section.

• Clean, high quality brake fluid from a sealed container is essential to the safe and proper operation of the brake system. You should always buy the correct type of brake fluid for your vehicle. If the brake fluid becomes contaminated, completely flush the system with new fluid. Never reuse any brake fluid. Any brake fluid that is removed from the system should be discarded. Also, do not allow any brake fluid to come in contact with a painted surface; it will damage the paint.

• Never operate the engine without the proper amount and type of engine oil; doing so WILL result in severe engine damage.

• Timing belt maintenance is extremely important. Many models utilize an interference-type, non-freewheeling engine. If the timing belt breaks, the valves in the cylinder head may strike the pistons, causing potentially serious (also time-consuming and expensive) engine damage. Refer to the maintenance interval charts for the recommended replacement interval for the timing belt, and to the timing belt section for belt replacement and inspection.

• Disconnecting the negative battery cable on some vehicles may interfere with the functions of the on-board computer system(s) and may require the computer to undergo a relearning process once the negative battery cable is reconnected.

• When servicing drum brakes, only disassemble and assemble one side at a time, leaving the remaining side intact for reference.

• Only an MVAC-trained, EPA-certified automotive technician should service the air conditioning system or its components.

BRAKES

ANTI-LOCK BRAKE SYSTEM (ABS)

GENERAL INFORMATION

PRECAUTIONS

• Certain components within the ABS system are not intended to be serviced or repaired individually.

• Do not use rubber hoses or other parts not specifically specified for and ABS system. When using repair kits, replace all parts included in the kit. Partial or incorrect repair may lead to functional problems and require the replacement of components.

• Lubricate rubber parts with clean, fresh brake fluid to ease assembly. Do not use shop air to clean parts; damage to rubber components may result.

• Use only DOT 3 brake fluid from an unopened container.

• If any hydraulic component or line is removed or replaced, it may be necessary to bleed the entire system.

• A clean repair area is essential. Always clean the reservoir and cap thoroughly before removing the cap. The slightest amount of dirt in the fluid may plug an orifice and impair the system function. Perform repairs after components have been thoroughly cleaned; use only denatured alcohol to clean components. Do not allow ABS components to come into contact with any substance containing mineral oil; this includes used shop rags.

• The Anti-Lock control unit is a microprocessor similar to other computer units in the vehicle. Ensure that the ignition switch is OFF before removing or installing controller harnesses. Avoid static electricity discharge at or near the controller.

• If any arc welding is to be done on the vehicle, the control unit should be unplugged before welding operations begin.

WHEEL SPEED SENSORS

REMOVAL & INSTALLATION

Front

See Figure 4.

➡**If replacing the wheel speed sensor due to a DTC, inspect the back of the wheel bearing on the encoder surface for metallic chips or metal shavings. If metallic debris is found, clean the encoder surface to prevent interference with the wheel speed sensor signal and setting of a DTC.**

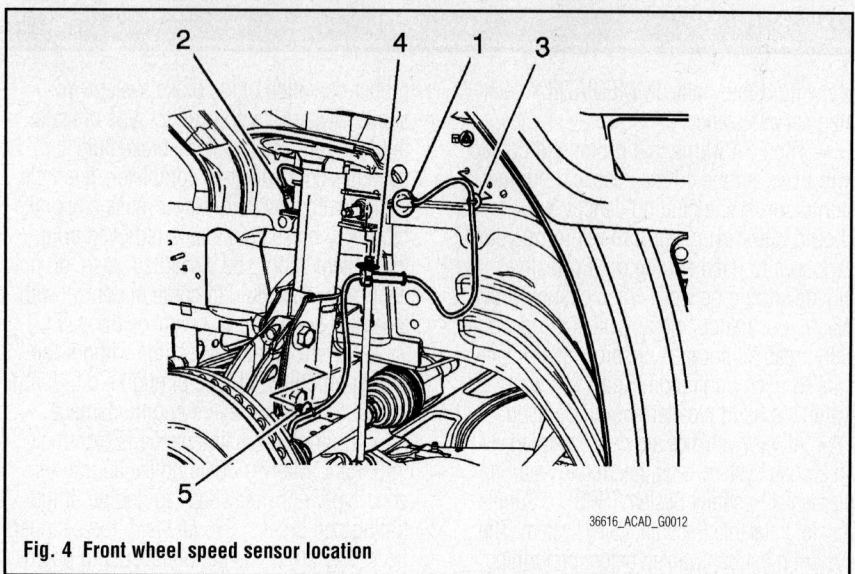

Fig. 4 Front wheel speed sensor location

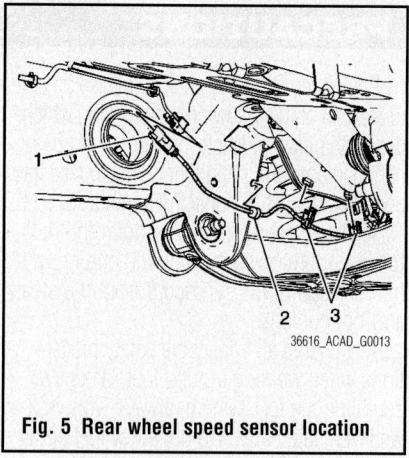

Fig. 5 Rear wheel speed sensor location

1. If replacing the left front wheel speed sensor, remove the air cleaner element.

2. If replacing the right front wheel speed sensor, disconnect and position aside the battery positive junction block cables.

3. Disconnect the wheel speed sensor electrical connector.

4. Raise and support the vehicle.

5. Remove the tire and wheel assembly.

6. Release the wheel speed sensor wire grommet (1) from the wheelhouse.

7. Carefully pull the wheel speed sensor wire and connector (2) through the wheel house.

8. Release the wheel speed sensor wire harness routing clip (3) from the wheel house.

9. Release the wheel speed sensor wire harness routing clips (4) and (5) from the suspension strut.

10. Remove the wheel speed sensor bolt.

11. Pull the wheel speed sensor straight up and out of the steering knuckle.

➡ Clean the wheel speed sensor mounting area on the steering knuckle of any accumulated dirt and debris.

To install:

12. Install the wheel speed sensor to the steering knuckle.

13. Install the wheel speed sensor bolt and Tighten the bolt to 80 inch lbs. (9 Nm).

14. Install the wheel speed sensor wire harness routing clips and to the suspension strut.

15. Insert the wheel speed sensor wire electrical connector through the wheel house hole.

16. Seat the wheel speed sensor wire harness grommet to the wheel house.

17. Connect the wheel speed sensor electrical connector.

18. Install the tire and wheel assembly.

19. If replacing the right front wheel speed sensor, connect the battery positive junction block cables.

20. If replacing the left front wheel speed sensor, install the air cleaner element.

Rear

See Figure 5.

➡ If replacing the wheel speed sensor due to a DTC, inspect the back of the wheel bearing on the encoder surface for metallic chips or metal shavings. If metallic debris is found, clean the encoder surface to prevent interference with the wheel speed sensor signal and setting of a DTC.

1. Raise and support the vehicle.

2. Remove the tire and wheel assembly.

3. Disconnect the wheel speed sensor electrical connector (1).

4. Release the wheel speed sensor wire harness grommet (2) from the lower control arm bracket.

5. Release the wheel speed sensor wire harness routing clips (3) from the upper suspension link.

6. Remove the wheel speed sensor bolt.

7. Pull the wheel speed sensor straight up and out of the wheel knuckle.

➡ Clean the wheel speed sensor mounting area on the steering knuckle of any accumulated dirt and debris.

To install:

8. Install the wheel speed sensor to the wheel knuckle.

9. Install the wheel speed sensor bolt and Tighten the bolt to 80 inch lbs. (9 Nm).

10. Install the wheel speed sensor wire harness routing clips to the upper suspension link.

11. Install the wheel speed sensor wire harness routing clips to the upper suspension link.

12. Install the wheel speed sensor wire harness grommet to the lower control arm bracket.

13. Connect the wheel speed sensor electrical connector.

14. Install the tire and wheel assembly.

BRAKES

BLEEDING THE BRAKE SYSTEM

BLEEDING PROCEDURE

BRAKE LINE BLEEDING

1. Place a clean shop cloth beneath the brake master cylinder to catch brake fluid spills.

2. With the ignition OFF and the brakes cool, apply the brakes 3–5 times, or until the brake pedal effort increases significantly, in order to deplete the brake booster power reserve.

3. If you have performed a brake master cylinder bench bleeding on this vehicle, or if you disconnected the brake pipes from the master cylinder, or if you have disconnected the brake pipes from the proportioning valve assembly or the brake modulator assembly, you must perform the following steps to bleed air at the ports of the hydraulic component:

    a. Ensure that the brake master cylinder reservoir is full to the maximum-fill level.

4. If removal of the reservoir cap and diaphragm is necessary, clean the outside of the reservoir on and around the cap prior to removal. With the brake pipes installed securely to the master cylinder, proportioning valve assembly, or brake modulator assembly, loosen and separate one of the brake pipes from the port of the component.

5. For the proportioning valve assembly or the brake modulator assembly, perform these steps in the sequence of system flow; begin with the fluid feed pipes from the master cylinder.

    a. Allow a small amount of brake fluid to gravity bleed from the open port of the component.

    b. Connect the brake pipe to the component and tighten securely.

    c. Have an assistant slowly press the brake pedal fully and maintain steady pressure on the pedal.

    d. Loosen the same brake pipe to purge air from the open port of the component.

    e. Tighten the brake pipe, then have the assistant slowly release the brake pedal.

    f. Wait 15 seconds, then repeat the steps until all air is purged from the same port of the component.

    g. With the brake pipe installed securely to the master cylinder, proportioning valve assembly, or brake modulator assembly, after all air has been purged from the first port of the compo-

nent that was bled, loosen and separate the next brake pipe from the component, until each of the ports on the component has been bled.

    h. After completing the final component port bleeding procedure, ensure that each of the brake pipe-to-component fittings are properly tightened.

6. Fill the brake master cylinder reservoir. Make sure that the brake master cylinder reservoir remains at least half-full during this bleeding procedure. Add fluid as needed to maintain the proper level.

7. Clean the outside of the reservoir on and around the reservoir cap prior to removing the cap and diaphragm.

8. Install a box-end wrench onto the right rear wheel hydraulic circuit bleeder valve.

9. Install a transparent hose over the end of the bleeder valve.

10. Submerge the open end of the transparent hose into a transparent container partially filled with brake fluid from a clean, sealed brake fluid container.

11. Have an assistant slowly press the brake pedal fully and maintain steady pressure on the pedal.

12. Loosen the bleeder valve to purge air from the wheel hydraulic circuit.

13. Tighten the bleeder valve, then have the assistant slowly release the brake pedal.

14. Wait 15 seconds, then repeat steps 8-10 until all air is purged from the same wheel hydraulic circuit.

15. With the right rear wheel hydraulic circuit bleeder valve tightened securely, after all air has been purged from the right rear hydraulic circuit, install a proper box-end wrench onto the left front wheel hydraulic circuit bleeder valve.

16. Install a transparent hose over the end of the bleeder valve and perform the same procedure used to bleed the right rear.

17. Bleed the left rear and front right in the same manner.

18. Fill the brake master cylinder reservoir to the maximum-fill level with brake fluid from a clean, sealed brake fluid container.

19. Slowly press and release the brake pedal. Observe the feel of the brake pedal.

20. If the brake pedal feels spongy, repeat the bleeding procedure again. If the brake pedal still feels spongy after repeating the bleeding procedure check for leaks in the system and pressure test the system to purge trapped air.

21. Turn the ignition key ON, with the engine OFF. Check to see if the brake system warning lamp remains illuminated.

➡ **DO NOT allow the vehicle to be driven until it is diagnosed and repaired.**

BLEEDING THE ABS SYSTEM

1. The base hydraulic brake system must be bled before performing this automated bleeding procedure. If you have not yet performed the base hydraulic brake system bleeding procedure

2. Install a scan tool to the vehicle.

3. Start the engine and allow the engine to idle.

4. Using the scan tool, begin the automated bleed procedure.

5. Follow the instructions on the scan tool to complete the automated bleed procedure. Apply the brake pedal when instructed by the scan tool.

6. Turn the ignition OFF.

7. Remove the scan tool from the vehicle.

8. Fill the brake master cylinder reservoir to the maximum-fill level with GM approved brake fluid from a clean, sealed brake fluid container. Refer to Master Cylinder Reservoir Filling.

9. Bleed the hydraulic brake system. Refer to Hydraulic Brake System Bleeding.

10. With the ignition OFF, apply the brakes 3-5 times, or until the brake pedal becomes firm, in order to deplete the brake booster power reserve.

11. Slowly depress and release the brake pedal. Observe the feel of the brake pedal.

12. If the brake pedal feels spongy, repeat the automated bleeding procedure. If the brake pedal still feels spongy after repeating the automated bleeding procedure inspect the brake system for external leaks. Refer to Brake System External Leak Inspection.

13. Turn the ignition key ON, with the engine OFF. Check to see if the brake system warning lamp remains illuminated.

14. If the brake system warning lamp remains illuminated, DO NOT allow the vehicle to be driven until it is diagnosed and repaired. Refer to Symptoms - Hydraulic Brakes.

15. Drive the vehicle to exceed 13 km/h (8 mph) to allow ABS initialization to occur. Observe brake pedal feel.

16. If the brake pedal feels spongy, repeat the automated bleeding procedure until a firm brake pedal is obtained.

BRAKES

※※ CAUTION

Dust and dirt accumulating on brake parts during normal use may contain asbestos fibers from production or aftermarket brake linings. Breathing excessive concentrations of asbestos fibers can cause serious bodily harm. Exercise care when servicing brake parts. Do not sand or grind brake lining unless equipment used is designed to contain the dust residue. Do not clean brake parts with compressed air or by dry brushing. Cleaning should be done by dampening the brake components with a fine mist of water, then wiping the brake components clean with a dampened cloth. Dispose of cloth and all residue containing asbestos fibers in an impermeable container with the appropriate label. Follow practices prescribed by the Occupational Safety and Health Administration (OSHA) and the Environmental Protection Agency (EPA) for the handling, processing, and disposing of dust or debris that may contain asbestos fibers.

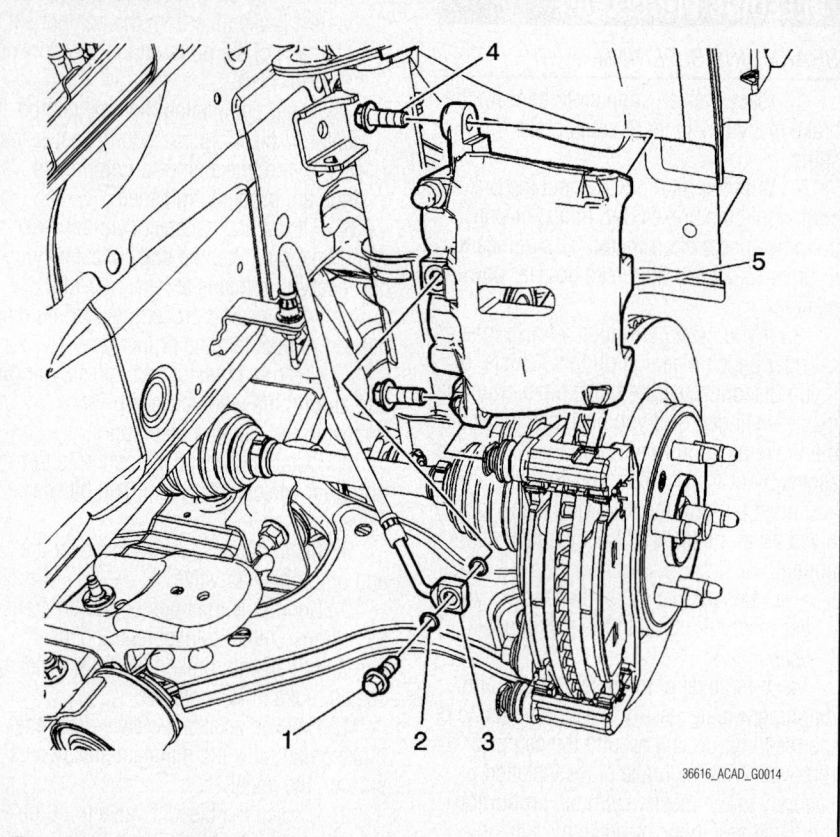

Fig. 6 Front brake caliper (5) and related components

BRAKE CALIPER

REMOVAL & INSTALLATION

See Figure 6.

1. Empty the master cylinder reservoir until it is half full.
2. Raise and support the vehicle.
3. Remove the tire and wheel assembly.
4. Install and firmly hand tighten 2 wheel nuts to opposite wheel studs in order to retain the rotor to the hub.
5. Install a large C-clamp over the body of the brake caliper with the C-clamp ends against the rear of the caliper body and against the outer brake pad.
6. Tighten the C-clamp until the caliper piston is compressed into the caliper bore enough to allow the caliper to slide past the brake rotor.
7. Remove the C-clamp from the caliper.
8. Remove the brake hose-to-caliper bolt from the brake caliper.
9. Remove the brake hose from the brake caliper.
10. Remove and discard the 2 copper brake hose gaskets. These gaskets may be stuck to the brake caliper and/or the brake hose end.

11. Cap or plug the opening in the brake caliper and the brake hose to prevent fluid loss and contamination.
12. Remove the brake caliper guide pin bolts.
13. Remove the brake caliper from the caliper bracket.
14. Inspect the brake caliper guide pins for freedom of movement, and inspect the condition of the guide pin boots.

To install:
15. Install the brake caliper to the brake caliper bracket.
16. Install the brake caliper guide pin bolts and tighten to 47 ft. lbs. (64 Nm).
17. Remove the caps or plugs from the brake caliper opening and the brake hose.

➡**Do not reuse the copper brake hose gaskets.**

18. Install NEW copper brake hose gaskets to the brake hose-to-caliper bolt and to the brake hose.
19. Install the brake hose and the brake hose-to-brake caliper bolt to the brake caliper. Tighten to 30 ft. lbs. (40 Nm).
20. Bleed the hydraulic brake system.

21. Remove the wheel nuts retaining the brake rotor to the wheel hub.
22. Install the tire and wheel assembly.
23. Lower the vehicle.
24. With the engine OFF, gradually apply the brake pedal to approximately 2/3 of its travel distance.
25. Slowly release the brake pedal.
26. Wait 15 seconds, then repeat the last 2 steps until a firm brake pedal is obtained
27. Fill the master cylinder reservoir to the proper level.

DISC BRAKE PADS

REMOVAL & INSTALLATION

See Figure 7.

1. Empty the master cylinder reservoir until it is half full.
2. Raise and support the vehicle.
3. Remove the tire and wheel assembly.
4. Install and firmly hand tighten 2 wheel nuts to opposite wheel studs in order to retain the rotor to the hub.
5. Remove the brake caliper lower guide pin bolt.

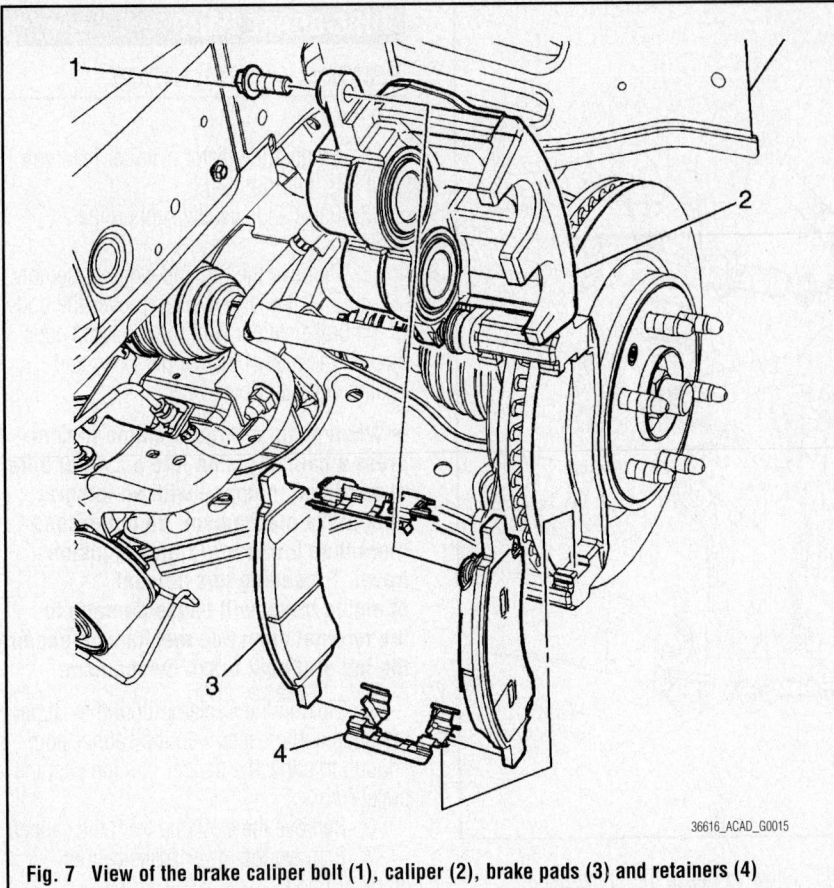

Fig. 7 View of the brake caliper bolt (1), caliper (2), brake pads (3) and retainers (4)

36616_ACAD_G0015

caliper bracket, of any debris and corrosion.

11. Inspect the brake caliper guide pins for freedom of movement, and inspect the condition of the guide pin boots.

To install:

12. Make sure the brake pad hardware mating surfaces are clean.

13. Install the brake pad retainers to the brake caliper bracket.

➡**The wear sensor equipped disc brake pad must be mounted inboard of the rotor with the leading edge of the sensor facing the brake rotor during forward wheel rotation, or at the top of the pad when installed in vehicle position.**

14. Install the brake pads to the caliper bracket.

15. Remove the support, and rotate the brake caliper into position over the disc brake pads and to the caliper mounting bracket.

16. Install the lower brake caliper guide pin bolt. Tighten to 47 ft. lbs. (64 Nm).

17. Remove the wheel nuts retaining the brake rotor to the hub.

18. Install the tire and wheel assembly. Lower the vehicle.

19. With the engine OFF, gradually apply the brake pedal to approximately ⅔ of its travel distance.

20. Slowly release the brake pedal.

21. Wait 15 seconds, then repeat the last 2 steps until a firm brake pedal is obtained

22. Fill the master cylinder reservoir to the proper level.

6. Without disconnecting the hydraulic brake flexible hose, pivot the caliper upward and secure the caliper with heavy mechanics wire, or equivalent.

7. Remove the brake pads from the caliper mounting bracket.

8. Push the disc brake caliper piston into the caliper bore using an old inner disc brake pad and a disc brake piston installation tool.

9. Remove the brake pad retainers from the caliper bracket.

10. Thoroughly clean the brake pad hardware mating surfaces of the

BRAKES

✳ CAUTION

Dust and dirt accumulating on brake parts during normal use may contain asbestos fibers from production or aftermarket brake linings. Breathing excessive concentrations of asbestos fibers can cause serious bodily harm. Exercise care when servicing brake parts. Do not sand or grind brake lining unless equipment used is designed to contain the dust residue. Do not clean brake parts with compressed air or by dry brushing. Cleaning should be done by dampening the brake components with a fine mist of water, then wiping the brake components clean with a dampened cloth. Dispose of cloth and all residue containing asbestos fibers in

an impermeable container with the appropriate label. Follow practices prescribed by the Occupational Safety and Health Administration (OSHA) and the Environmental Protection Agency (EPA) for the handling, processing, and disposing of dust or debris that may contain asbestos fibers.

BRAKE CALIPER

REMOVAL & INSTALLATION
See Figure 8.

1. Empty the master cylinder reservoir until it is half full.

2. Raise and suitably support the vehicle.

REAR DISC BRAKES

3. Remove the tire and wheel assembly.

4. Install a large C-clamp over the body of the brake caliper with the C-clamp ends against the rear of the caliper body and against the outer brake pad.

5. Tighten the C-clamp until the caliper piston is compressed into the caliper bore enough to allow the caliper to slide past the brake rotor.

6. Remove the C-clamp from the caliper.

7. Remove the brake hose to caliper bolt (1) from the brake caliper.

8. Remove the brake hose (3) from the brake caliper.

9. Remove and discard the 2 copper brake hose gaskets (2). These gaskets may be stuck to the brake caliper and/or the brake hose end.

Fig. 8 Rear brake caliper (5) removal

10. Cap or plug the opening in the brake caliper and the brake hose to prevent fluid loss and contamination.

11. Remove the 2 brake caliper pin bolts.

12. Remove the park brake cable from the caliper.

13. Remove the brake caliper from the brake caliper bracket.

To install:

14. Inspect the caliper slide boots for cuts, tears, or deterioration.

15. Install the brake caliper to the brake caliper bracket. Tighten the bolts to 20 ft. lbs. (27 Nm).

16. Install the park brake cable to the caliper.

17. Remove the caps or plugs from the brake caliper opening and the brake hose.

➡**DO NOT reuse the copper brake hose gaskets.**

18. Install NEW copper brake hose gaskets to the brake hose-to-caliper bolt and to the brake hose.

19. Install the brake hose and the brake hose-to-caliper bolt to the brake caliper. Tighten the bolts to 37 ft. lbs. (50 Nm).

20. With the engine OFF, gradually apply the brake pedal to approximately ⅔ of its travel distance.

21. Slowly release the brake pedal.

22. Wait 15 seconds, then repeat the last 2 steps until a firm brake pedal is obtained

23. Fill the master cylinder reservoir to the proper level.

DISC BRAKE PADS

REMOVAL & INSTALLATION

See Figure 9.

1. Empty the master cylinder reservoir until it is half full.

2. Raise and suitably support the vehicle.

3. Remove the tire and wheel assembly.

4. Install a large C-clamp over the body of the brake caliper with the C-clamp ends against the rear of the caliper body and against the outer brake pad.

➡**When using a large C-clamp to compress a caliper piston into a caliper bore of a caliper equipped with an integral park brake mechanism, do not exceed more than 0.039 in. (1mm) of piston travel. Exceeding this amount of piston travel will cause damage to the internal adjusting mechanism and/or the integral park brake mechanism.**

5. Tighten the C-clamp until the caliper piston is compressed into the caliper bore enough to allow the caliper to slide past the brake rotor.

6. Remove the C-clamp from the caliper.

7. Remove the lower brake caliper guide pin bolt.

8. Pivot the brake caliper upward from the caliper bracket and support the caliper out of the way with heavy mechanic's wire; ensure that there is no tension on the hydraulic brake flexible hose. Do NOT dis-

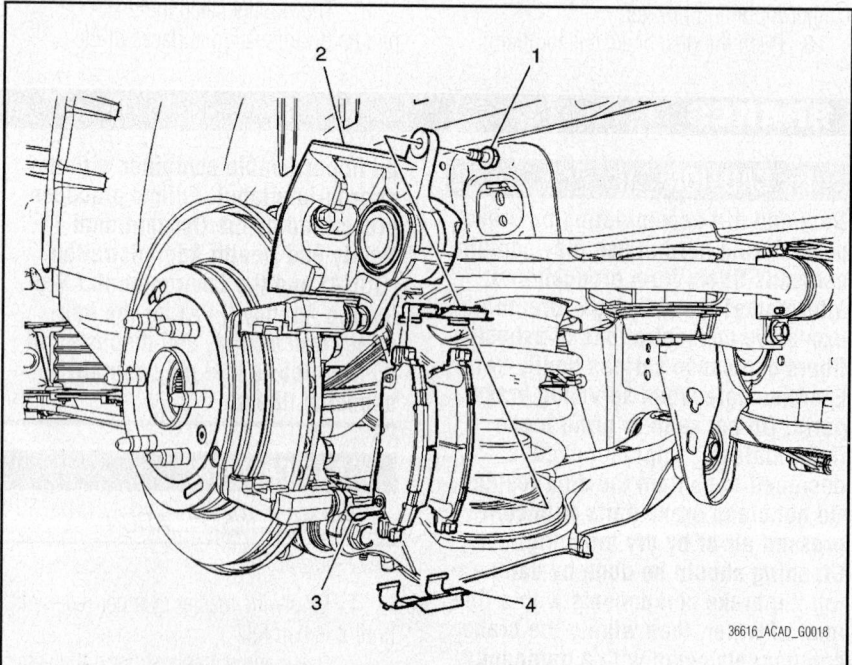

Fig. 9 Rear brake caliper guide pin bolt (1), caliper (2), brake pad (3) and retainer (4)

connect the hydraulic brake flexible hose from the caliper.

9. Remove the brake pads from the brake caliper mounting bracket.

10. Remove and the brake pad retainers from the brake caliper mounting bracket.

To install:

➡ **Do not attempt to clean away any corrosion. If damaged or corroded replace the necessary components.**

11. Inspect the brake caliper piston boot for deterioration, replace if damaged.

12. Use a piston installation tool in order to twist the brake caliper piston into the brake caliper bore.

13. Install the brake pad retainers to the brake caliper mounting bracket.

14. Install the brake pads to the brake caliper mounting bracket.

15. Pivot the brake caliper downward, over the brake pads and into the caliper bracket.

16. Install the brake caliper guide pin bolt to the brake caliper guide pin. Tighten the bolts to 20 ft. lbs. (27 Nm).

17. Install the tire and wheel assembly.

18. Lower the vehicle.

19. With the engine OFF, gradually apply the brake pedal to approximately ⅔ of its travel distance.

20. Slowly release the brake pedal.

21. Wait 15 seconds, then repeat the last 2 steps until a firm brake pedal is obtained

22. Fill the master cylinder reservoir to the proper level.

BRAKES

Park brake application is completely independent of the hydraulic brake system. The park brake system is a mechanical system which operates the rear disc brakes through the calipers. The system is activated by depressing the park brake pedal, which applies the rear disc brakes via cables. When the park brake is set and the ignition switch is on, the BRAKE warning lamp on the instrument panel will be on. The park brake is released by pushing the pedal down until a click is heard and then releasing. The pedal will click again and the BRAKE lamp in the instrument panel will go out when the park brake system is fully released.

PARKING BRAKE SHOES

REMOVAL & INSTALLATION

See Figures 10 through 12.

1. Raise and support the vehicle.
2. Remove the tire and wheel assembly.
3. Remove the rear brake rotor.
4. Retract the park brake shoe adjuster to ease removal.
5. Remove the upper park brake shoe retainer spring (1).

6. Remove the park brake shoe adjuster (2).

7. Remove the rear park brake shoe hold down spring (1) by compressing the spring and rotating ¼ turn.

8. Remove the lower park brake shoe retainer spring (2) and the rear park brake shoe (3).

9. Remove the front park brake shoe hold down spring (1) by compressing the spring and rotating ¼ turn.

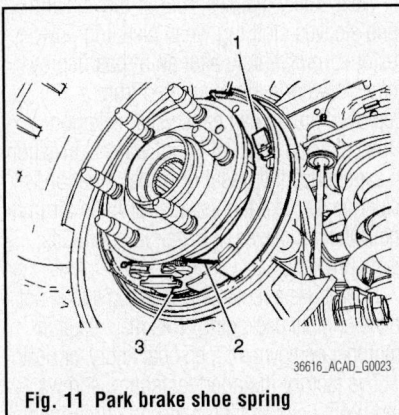

Fig. 11 Park brake shoe spring locations

36616_ACAD_G0023

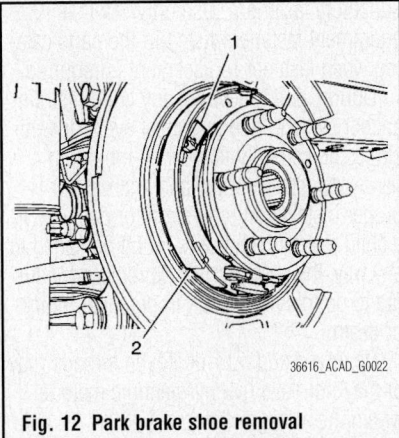

36616_ACAD_G0021

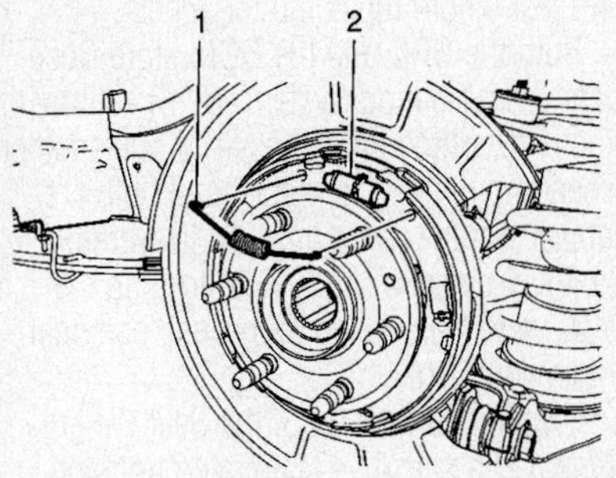

Fig. 10 Park brake shoe adjuster location

PARKING BRAKE

10. Remove the front park brake shoe (2).

11. Clean the rear brake backing plate with denatured alcohol or equivalent and allow to dry.

To install:

12. Apply a light coat of high temperature brake lubricant to the park brake shoe contact areas of the brake backing plate.

13. Install the front park brake shoe.

14. Ensure the park brake shoe is properly seated in the park brake actuator.

15. Install the front park brake shoe hold down spring by compressing the spring and rotating ¼ turn.

16. Install the rear park brake shoe and the lower park brake shoe retainer spring.

17. Ensure the park brake shoe is properly seated in the park brake actuator.

18. Install the rear park brake shoe hold down spring by compressing the spring and rotating ¼ turn.

19. Install the park brake shoe adjuster.

20. Install the upper park brake shoe retainer spring.

21. Adjust the park brake.

ADJUSTMENT

See Figure 13.

1. Apply and fully release the park brake.

2. Verify that the park brake pedal releases completely.

3. Turn ON the ignition. Verify the BRAKE indicator lamp is off.

   a. If the BRAKE indicator lamp is on, ensure the park brake pedal is in release mode and has fully returned to the stop. Remove the slack in the front park brake cable by pulling downward on the cable.

4. Raise and support the vehicle. Refer to Lifting and Jacking the Vehicle.

5. Remove the rear tire and wheel assemblies.

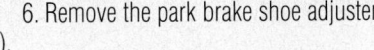

36616_ACAD_G0022

Fig. 12 Park brake shoe removal

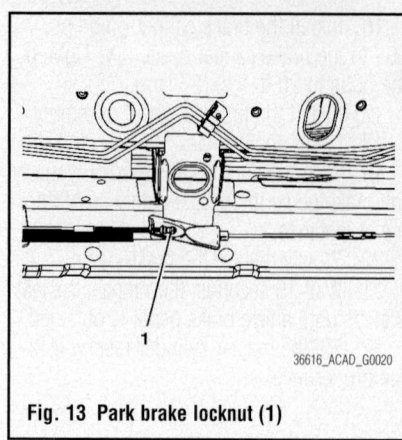

Fig. 13 Park brake locknut (1)

36616_ACAD_G0020

6. Loosen the locknut at the park brake cable equalizer to relieve tension on the park brake system.

7. Remove the rear brake rotors.
8. Set the J-21177-A drum-to-brake shoe clearance gage inside of the park brake drum at the widest point.

   a. Place the contacts on the tool to the widest point of the drum.

   b. Tighten the set screw on the tool to ensure the proper measurement when removing the tool from the drum.

9. Position the J-21177-A drum-to-brake shoe clearance gage over the park brake shoe at the widest point.

10. Turn the adjuster screw until the park brake shoe just contacts the J-21177-A drum-to-brake shoe clearance gage.

11. Repeat the previous steps for the opposite side.

12. Install the rear brake rotors.
13. Install the rear tire and wheel assemblies.
14. Adjust the park brake by turning the locknut at the equalizer while spinning both rear wheels. When either rear wheel starts to drag, back off the locknut one full turn.
15. Lower the vehicle to curb height.
16. Apply the park brake, then inspect for rotation of the rear wheels. If the rear wheels rotate during this inspection, then readjust the park brake shoes.
17. Release the park brake. Verify the rear wheels rotate freely.
18. Lower the vehicle.

CHASSIS ELECTRICAL   AIR BAG (SUPPLEMENTAL RESTRAINT SYSTEM)

GENERAL INFORMATION

✳✳ CAUTION

These vehicles are equipped with an air bag system. The system must be disarmed before performing service on, or around, system components, the steering column, instrument panel components, wiring and sensors. Failure to follow the safety precautions and the disarming procedure could result in accidental air bag deployment, possible injury and unnecessary system repairs.

SERVICE PRECAUTIONS

Disconnect and isolate the battery negative cable before beginning any airbag system component diagnosis, testing, removal, or installation procedures. Allow system capacitor to discharge for two minutes before beginning any component service. This will disable the airbag system. Failure to disable the airbag system may result in accidental airbag deployment, personal injury, or death.

Do not place an intact undeployed airbag face down on a solid surface. The airbag will propel into the air if accidentally deployed and may result in personal injury or death.

When carrying or handling an undeployed airbag, the trim side (face) of the airbag should be pointing towards the body to minimize possibility of injury if accidental deployment occurs. Failure to do this may result in personal injury or death.

Replace airbag system components with OEM replacement parts. Substitute parts may appear interchangeable, but internal differences may result in inferior occupant protection. Failure to do so may result in occupant personal injury or death.

Wear safety glasses, rubber gloves, and long sleeved clothing when cleaning powder residue from vehicle after an airbag deployment. Powder residue emitted from a deployed airbag can cause skin irritation. Flush affected area with cool water if irritation is experienced. If nasal or throat irritation is experienced, exit the vehicle for fresh air until the irritation ceases. If irritation continues, see a physician.

Do not use a replacement airbag that is not in the original packaging. This may result in improper deployment, personal injury, or death.

The factory installed fasteners, screws and bolts used to fasten airbag components have a special coating and are specifically designed for the airbag system. Do not use substitute fasteners. Use only original equipment fasteners listed in the parts catalog when fastener replacement is required.

During, and following, any child restraint anchor service, due to impact event or vehicle repair, carefully inspect all mounting hardware, tether straps, and anchors for proper installation, operation, or damage. If a child restraint anchor is found damaged in any way, the anchor must be replaced. Failure to do this may result in personal injury or death.

Deployed and non-deployed airbags may or may not have live pyrotechnic material within the airbag inflator.

Do not dispose of driver/passenger/ curtain airbags or seat belt tensioners unless you are sure of complete deployment. Refer to the Hazardous Substance Control System for proper disposal.

Dispose of deployed airbags and tensioners consistent with state, provincial, local, and federal regulations.

After any airbag component testing or service, do not connect the battery negative cable. Personal injury or death may result if the system test is not performed first.

If the vehicle is equipped with the Occupant Classification System (OCS), do not connect the battery negative cable before performing the OCS Verification Test using the scan tool and the appropriate diagnostic information. Personal injury or death may result if the system test is not performed properly.

Never replace both the Occupant Restraint Controller (ORC) and the Occupant Classification Module (OCM) at the same time. If both require replacement, replace one, then perform the Airbag System test before replacing the other.

Both the ORC and the OCM store Occupant Classification System (OCS) calibration data, which they transfer to one another when one of them is replaced. If both are replaced at the same time, an irreversible fault will be set in both modules and the OCS may malfunction and cause personal injury or death.

If equipped with OCS, the Seat Weight Sensor is a sensitive, calibrated unit and must be handled carefully. Do not drop or handle roughly. If dropped or damaged, replace with another sensor. Failure to do so may result in occupant injury or death.

If equipped with OCS, the front passenger seat must be handled carefully as well. When removing the seat, be careful when setting on floor not to drop. If dropped, the sensor may be inoperative, could result in occupant injury, or possibly death.

If equipped with OCS, when the passenger front seat is on the floor, no one should sit in the front passenger seat. This uneven force may damage the sensing ability of the seat weight sensors. If sat on and damaged, the sensor may be inoperative, could result in occupant injury, or possibly death.

DISARMING THE SYSTEM

Air Bag Fuse

1. Turn the steering wheel so that the vehicles wheels are pointing straight ahead.

Place the ignition in the OFF position.

➡**The SDM may have more than one fused power input. To ensure there is no unwanted SIR deployment, personal injury, or unnecessary SIR system repairs, remove all fuses supplying power to the SDM. With all SDM fuses removed and the ignition switch in the ON position, the AIR BAG warning indicator illuminates. This is normal operation, and does not indicate a SIR system malfunction.**

2. Locate and remove the fuse(s) supplying power to the SDM.

3. Wait 1 minute before working on the system.

Negative Battery Cable

1. Turn the steering wheel so that the vehicles wheels are pointing straight ahead.

2. Place the ignition in the OFF position.

3. Disconnect the negative battery cable from the battery.

4. Wait 1 minute before working on system.

ARMING THE SYSTEM

Air Bag Fuse

1. Place the ignition in the OFF position.

2. Install the fuse(s) supplying power to the SDM.

3. Turn the ignition switch to the ON position. The AIR BAG indicator will flash then turn OFF.

4. Perform the Diagnostic System Check - Vehicle if the AIR BAG warning indicator does not operate as described.

Negative Battery Cable

1. Place the ignition in the OFF position.

2. Connect the negative battery cable to the battery.

3. Turn the ignition switch to the ON position. The AIR BAG indicator will flash then turn OFF.

4. Perform the Diagnostic System Check - Vehicle if the AIR BAG warning indicator does not operate as described.

CLOCKSPRING CENTERING

See Figure 14.

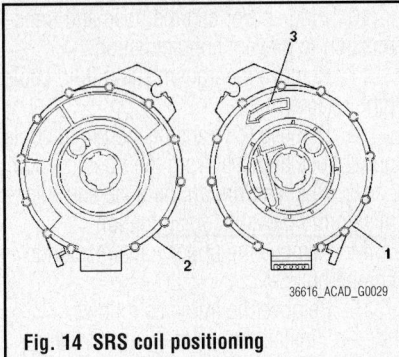

Fig. 14 SRS coil positioning

1. Verify the following conditions before centering the inflatable restraint steering wheel module coil:

a. The wheels on the vehicle are pointed straight ahead.

b. The block tooth (1) of the steering shaft is in the 12 o'clock position.

c. The ignition and start switch is in the LOCK position, or anti-rotation pin J-42640 pin is installed.

2. If the front side (3) of the inflatable restraint steering wheel module coil does NOT have a centering window, and the back side (2) does NOT have a spring service lock (1), perform the following steps:

a. Hold the coil with the face up.

b. Rotate the coil hub clockwise until the coil ribbon stops.

c. Rotate the coil hub, slowly, counter clockwise, for 2.5 revolutions. This is center position.

d. While maintaining the coil hub in center position, align the centered coil with the horn tower and slide onto the steering shaft.

DRIVE TRAIN

AUTOMATIC TRANSAXLE ASSEMBLY

REMOVAL & INSTALLATION

See Figures 15 and 16.

6T70/6T75 Transaxle

1. Remove the air cleaner assembly. See Air Cleaner Assembly in Engine Mechanical.

2. Remove the battery tray.

3. Remove the transmission range select lever cable and bracket.

4. Drain the transmission fluid.

5. Drain the transfer case fluid, if applicable.

6. Remove the wire harness retainer from the control valve body cover stud.

7. Disconnect the control valve body

Transmission Control Module (TCM) electrical connector.

8. Remove the transmission fluid cooler pipe retainer nut.

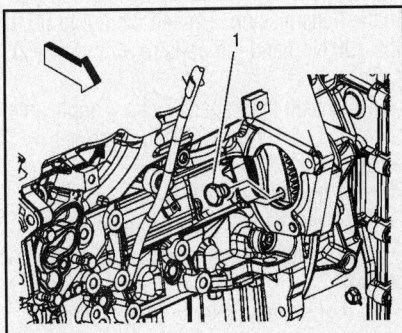

Fig. 15 Torque converter to flywheel bolt locations (1)

9. Remove the transmission fluid cooler inlet hose and seal from the transmission.

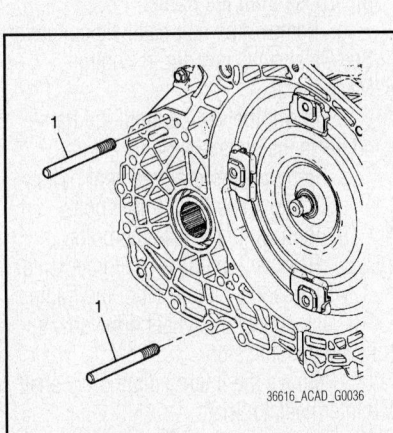

Fig. 16 Installing guide pins (1)

10. Plug and/or cap the hose and transmission to prevent contamination.

11. Remove the transmission fluid cooler pipe retainer nut.

12. Remove the transmission fluid cooler outlet hose and seal from the transmission.

13. Plug and/or cap the hose and transmission to prevent contamination.

14. Remove the upper transmission to engine bolts.

15. Remove the frame as follows:

a. Install the engine support fixture.

b. Support the radiator and condenser from above.

c. Raise the vehicle on a hoist.

d. Remove the tire and wheel assemblies.

e. Remove the front fender liner.

f. Remove the engine splash shield.

g. Remove the lower ball joints from the steering knuckles. See Lower Ball Joint in Suspension.

h. Remove the tie rod ends from the steering knuckles.

i. Remove both stabilizer links from the stabilizer bar. See Stabilizer Bar in Suspension.

j. Remove the power steering gear mounting bolts and secure the gear out of the way using mechanic's wire or equivalent, being sure not to overextend the intermediate shaft. See Power Steering Gear in Steering.

k. Remove the engine mount fasteners from the frame.

l. Remove the front transmission mount bolt from the frame.

m. Remove the left transmission mount fasteners from the frame.

n. Remove the rear transmission mount bracket fasteners from the frame.

o. Remove the brake lines from the retainers on the frame.

p. Remove the power steering outlet pipe/hose from the frame.

q. Remove the rear catalytic converter. See Catalytic Converter in Engine Mechanical.

r. Lower the vehicle until the frame contacts the engine support fixture.

s. Remove the reinforcement bolts.

t. Remove the front frame bolts.

u. Remove the rear frame bolts.

v. Remove the frame reinforcements.

w. Raise the vehicle off of the frame.

16. Disconnect the wheel drive shafts from the transmission.

17. Remove the intermediate drive shaft. See Intermediate Shaft.

18. Remove the propeller shaft taking care to matchmark the location.

19. Remove the transfer case bolts.

20. Remove the transfer case.

21. Remove the transmission brace bolts.

22. Remove the transmission brace.

23. Remove the rear transmission mount from the transmission.

24. Remove the front transmission mount from the transmission.

25. Remove the starter. See Starter in Engine Electrical.

26. Mark the relationship of the flywheel to the torque converter for reassembly.

27. Remove the torque converter to flywheel bolts.

28. Use a transmission jack in order to support the transmission.

29. Remove the flywheel inspection cover bolts.

30. Remove the flywheel inspection cover.

31. Remove the remaining transmission bolts.

➡**Ensure the torque converter remains securely in place on the transmission input shaft while separating and removing the transmission.**

32. Separate the transmission from the engine.

33. Lower the transmission with the transmission jack far enough to remove the transmission.

To install:

34. Raise the transmission with the transmission jack and position the transmission to the engine. Tighten the bolts to 55 ft. lbs. (75 Nm).

35. Install the flywheel inspection cover and bolts. Tighten the bolts to 55 ft. lbs. (75 Nm).

36. Remove the transmission jack.

37. Install the torque converter to flywheel bolts. Tighten the bolts to 46 ft. lbs. (62 Nm).

38. Install the starter.

39. Install the front transmission mount to the transmission. Tighten the nut to 66 ft. lbs. (90 Nm) and the bolts to 37 ft. lbs. (50 Nm).

40. Install the transfer case, if applicable.

a. Lubricate the O-rings with petroleum jelly.

b. Install the shaft O-ring seal.

c. Install the half shaft retainer.

d. Install the transfer case O-ring seal

e. Carefully insert a clean soft cloth into the transmission torque converter housing differential bore to prevent debris from entering the transmission.

f. Clean the oxidation from the transmission torque converter housing differential bore surface using steel wool or crocus cloth.

g. Carefully remove any debris and the cloth from the transmission torque converter housing differential bore.

h. Fabricate 2 guide pins by cutting the heads off of 2 bolts M12x1.75x75. chamfer and remove burrs from the cut end of the bolt.

i. Hand thread the guide pins into the transmission upper and lower transfer case mounting bolt holes.

j. Install the transfer case to transmission.

k. Remove the guide pins.

l. Install the transfer case bolts and tighten to 37 ft. lbs. (50 Nm).

41. Install the rear transmission mount to the transmission. Tighten the transaxle mount to transmission bolts to 37 ft. lbs. (50 Nm) and the transaxle to mount bracket through bolt to 66 ft. lbs. (90 Nm).

42. Install the transmission brace.

43. Install the transmission brace bolts. Tighten the bolts to 37 ft. lbs. (50 Nm)

44. Install the intermediate drive shaft.

45. Install the wheel drive shafts to the transmission.

46. Install the propeller shaft, if necessary. Tighten transfer case flange bolts to 25 ft. lbs.(35 Nm), center bearing mounting bolts to 19 ft. lbs. (25 Nm) and differential yolk bolts to 37 ft. lbs. (50 Nm).

47. Install the frame as follows:

a. Lower the vehicle on to the frame.

b. Install the frame reinforcements.

c. Install the front frame bolts and hand tighten only.

d. Install the reinforcement bolts and hand tighten only.

e. Tighten the rear frame bolts. Tighten to 81 ft. lbs. (110 Nm) , plus an additional 90 degrees.

f. Tighten the front frame bolts. Tighten to 81 ft. lbs. (110 Nm) , plus an additional 90 degrees.

g. Install the reinforcement bolts. Tighten to 44 ft. lbs. (60 Nm).

h. Raise the vehicle.

i. Install the power steering outlet pipe/hose to the frame. Install the brake lines to the retainers on the frame.

j. Install the rear transmission mount bracket fasteners. Tighten the transaxle mount to transmission bolts to 37 ft. lbs. (50 Nm) and the transaxle to mount bracket through bolt to 66 ft. lbs. (90 Nm).

k. Install the left transmission mount fasteners to the frame. Tighten the transaxle mount to transmission bolts to 66 ft. lbs. (90 Nm) and the transaxle to mount bracket through bolt to 66 ft. lbs. (90 Nm).

l. Install the front transmission mount bracket bolt. Tighten the transaxle mount to transmission bolts to 66 ft. lbs. (90 Nm) and the transaxle to mount bracket through bolt to 66 ft. lbs. (90 Nm).

m. Install the engine mount fasteners to the frame. Tighten the nuts/bolts to 55 ft. lbs. (75 Nm).

n. Install the power steering gear mounting fasteners.

o. Install both stabilizer links to the stabilizer bar. Tighten to 48 ft. lbs. (65 Nm) plus an additional 180 degrees.

p. Install the tie rod ends to the steering knuckles.

q. Install the lower ball joints to the steering knuckles. Tighten the ball stud to steering knuckle pinch nut to 37 ft. lbs. (50 Nm). Reverse the nut ¾ of a turn. Tighten to 37 ft. lbs. (50 Nm) plus an additional 60 degrees.

r. Install the rear catalytic converter.

s. Install the front fender liner.

t. Install the engine splash shield.

u. Lower the vehicle.

v. Remove the temporary radiator and condenser support.

w. Remove the engine support fixture.

48. Install the upper transmission to engine bolt. Tighten the bolts to 55 ft. lbs. (75 Nm).

49. Install the transmission fluid cooler outlet and inlet hoses and seal to the transmission.

50. Install the transmission fluid cooler pipe retainer nut. Tighten to 16 ft. lbs. (22 Nm).

51. Connect the control valve body Transmission Control Module (TCM) electrical connector and tighten to 106 inch lbs. (12 Nm).

52. Install the remaining components in the reverse order of removal.

53. Fill the transmission with fluid.

54. Fill transfer case fluid, if necessary, and tighten fill plug to 29 ft. lbs. (39 Nm).

a. Park the vehicle on a level surface, apply the parking brake and place the shift lever in PARK (P).

b. Start the engine.

c. Depress the brake pedal and move the shift lever through each gear range, pausing for about 3 seconds in each range. Then move the shift lever back to PARK (P).

d. Allow the engine to idle 500-800 rpm for at least 1 minute. Release the brake pedal.

e. Keep the engine running and observe the transmission fluid temperature (TFT) using the Driver Information Center or a scan tool.

➡ **If the fluid temperature is below the specified range, perform the following procedure to raise the fluid temperature to the specified range. If the TFT reading is not within the required temperature ranges, allow the vehicle to cool, or operate the vehicle until the appropriate TFT is reached.**

f. Drive the vehicle in second gear until the fluid temperature is within the specified range.

g. Check the transmission fluid level when the TFT is between 180°F and 200°F (82°C and 93°C). The fluid level rises as fluid temperature increases, so it is important to ensure the transmission fluid temperature is within range.

h. Remove the dipstick and wipe it with a clean rag or paper towel.

i. Inspect the fluid color. The fluid should be red or dark brown.

➡ **If the fluid color is very dark or black and has a burnt odor, inspect the fluid for excessive metal particles or other debris. A small amount of "friction" material is a "normal" condition. If large pieces and/or metal particles are noted in the fluid, flush the oil cooler and cooler lines and overhaul the transmission. If there are no signs of transmission internal damage noted, replace the fluid, repair the oil cooler, and flush the cooler lines.**

➡ **Fluid that is cloudy or milky or appears to be contaminated with water indicates engine coolant or water contamination.**

j. Install the dipstick and tighten. Wait three seconds and then remove it again.

➡ **Always check the fluid level at least twice. Consistent readings are important to maintaining proper fluid level. If inconsistent readings are noted, inspect the transmission vent assembly to ensure it is clean and unclogged.**

k. Check both sides of the dipstick and read the lower level.

➡ **It is not necessary to get the fluid level all the way up to the MAX mark. Anywhere within the crosshatch band is acceptable.**

l. Install and remove the dipstick again to verify the reading.

➡ **If the fluid level is not within the crosshatch band, and the transmission temperature is between 180°F and 200°F (82°C and 93°C), add or drain fluid as necessary to bring the level into the crosshatch band. If the fluid level is low, add only enough fluid to bring the level into the crosshatch band. Do not add more than one pint (0.5L) at a time without rechecking the level. Once the oil is on the dipstick bullet, it will not take much more fluid to raise the fluid level into the crosshatch band. Do not overfill. Also, if the fluid level is low, inspect the transmission for leaks.**

m. If the fluid level is in the acceptable range, install the dipstick.

n. If the fluid was changed, reset the transmission oil life monitor if applicable.

55. Road test the vehicle.

56. Check for Diagnostic Trouble Codes and

FRONT HALFSHAFTS

REMOVAL & INSTALLATION

See Figure 17.

1. Raise and support the vehicle.

2. Remove the tire and wheel assembly.

3. Remove the wheelhouse panel from the vehicle.

4. Insert a punch or brass drift in the brake rotor so that the brass drift or punch rest against the brake caliper mounting bracket.

5. Using a breaker bar and socket, loosen the wheel drive shaft nut.

➡ **DO NOT re-use the wheel drive shaft nut, discard and use NEW.**

6. Remove the wheel drive shaft nut.

7. Using the appropriate tool, remove the wheel drive shaft from the steering knuckle.

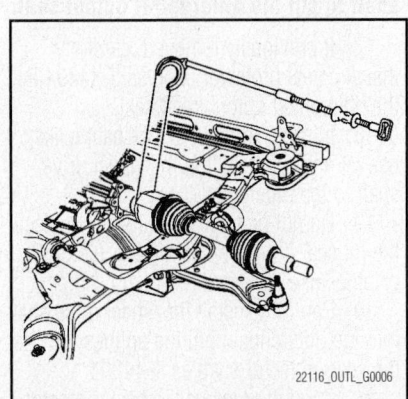

22116_OUTL_G0006

Fig. 17 Front axle shaft removal tool

➤In the following service procedure, it is NOT necessary to completely remove the tie rod end. Only remove the tie rod end from the steering knuckle.

8. Remove the outer tie rod end from the steering knuckle.

9. Remove the stabilizer shaft link at the stabilizer bar and secure.

10. Remove the lower ball joint from the steering knuckle.

11. Remove and relocate the suspension module to the side and secure.

➤The following service procedure can be used on vehicles that are Front Wheel Drive (FWD) left side only, as well as vehicles equipped with All Wheel Drive (AWD).

12. Assemble the axle shaft removal tool as illustrated.

13. Using the axle shaft removal tool, disengage the wheel drive shaft enough to install a seal protector such as J-44394.

➤A seal protector such as J-44394J-44394 must be installed into the differential output shaft seal prior to removing and installing the wheel drive shaft. Failure to install J-44394 as indicated may cause the splines of the wheel drive shaft to cut the differential output seal.

14. Carefully install a seal protector such as J-44394 over the wheel drive shaft.

15. Carefully slide a seal protector such as J-44394 into the differential output shaft seal.

16. Remove the wheel drive shaft from the vehicle.

To install:

➤A seal protector such as J-44394 must be installed into the differential output shaft seal prior to removing and installing the wheel drive shaft. Failure to install J-44394 as indicated may cause the splines of the wheel drive shaft to cut the differential output seal.

17. If previously removed, carefully install a seal protector such as J-44394 into the differential output shaft seal.

18. In order to prevent lubricant leaks, use care when installing the wheel drive shaft to the differential.

19. Do not damage the oil seal. Replace the oil seal if it becomes nicked, distorted, or otherwise damaged.

20. Carefully install the wheel drive shaft into the differential until the splines are past the seal protector such as J-44394 .

21. Carefully remove the seal protector from the differential output shaft seal.

22. Carefully continue installing the wheel drive shaft until the retaining ring is fully seated.

23. Verify the front wheel drive shaft retaining ring is properly seated. Grasp the inner housing and pull the inner housing outward. Do not pull on the front wheel drive axle shaft. The front wheel drive axle will remain in place when the front wheel drive shaft retaining ring is properly seated.

24. Install the wheel drive shaft into suspension module.

25. Install the lower ball joint in the steering knuckle.

26. Install the outer tie rod end to the steering knuckle.

27. Install the stabilizer link to the stabilizer bar.

28. Install the wheel drive shaft nut, tighten by hand.

29. Insert a brass drift or punch in the brake rotor so that it rest against the brake caliper mounting

30. Using a torque wrench and socket, tighten the wheel drive shaft nut to 173 ft. lbs. (235 Nm).

31. Install the wheel house panel on the vehicle.

32. Install the tire and wheel.

33. Remove the support and lower the vehicle.

34. Check the fluid level of the transmission

CV-BOOTS INSPECTION

Look for tears and grease leaks from CV boot area. Check the clamping rings for tightness. If boots are torn, replace boots and check CV joints for excessive wear.

INTERMEDIATE SHAFT

REMOVAL & INSTALLATION

See Figure 18.

1. Raise and support the vehicle.
2. Remove the right front wheel drive shaft.
3. Remove the intermediate drive shaft mounting bolts from the engine bracket.
4. Remove the intermediate drive shaft from the vehicle.

To install:

5. Install the intermediate drive shaft to the transaxle.
6. Position the intermediate shaft support bracket to the engine.
7. Install the support bracket bolts and tighten to 43 ft. lbs. (58 Nm).
8. Install a new wheel drive shaft retaining ring.

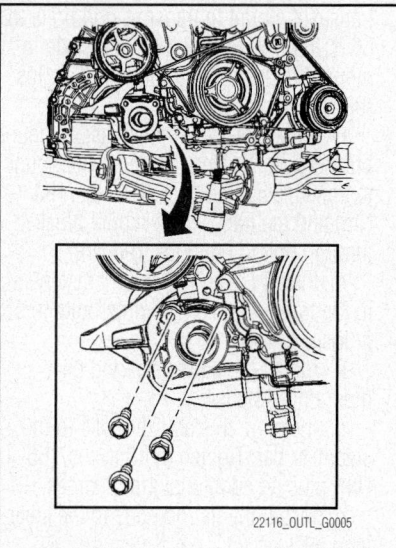

22116_OUTL_G0005

Fig. 18 Intermediate shaft support bracket to engine mounting

9. Install the right wheel drive shaft.
10. Remove the support and lower the vehicle.

REAR AXLE HOUSING

REMOVAL & INSTALLATION

See Figures 19 and 20.

1. Raise and support the vehicle.
2. Remove the tires and wheels.
3. Drain the rear differential assembly.
4. Remove the rear wheel drive shafts. See Halfshafts.
5. Remove the propeller shaft assembly. See Driveline Torque Tube in Rear Drive Axle.
6. Remove the front torque tube mounting bracket bolt.
7. Lower the front of the torque tube to gain access to the electronic clutch control module.
8. Disconnect the electrical connector from the electronic clutch control module.
9. Support the torque tube with a jack stand.

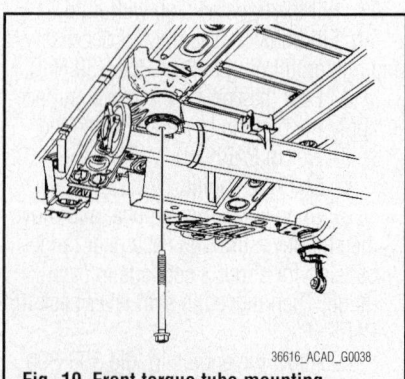

36616_ACAD_G0038

Fig. 19 Front torque tube mounting bracket bolt location

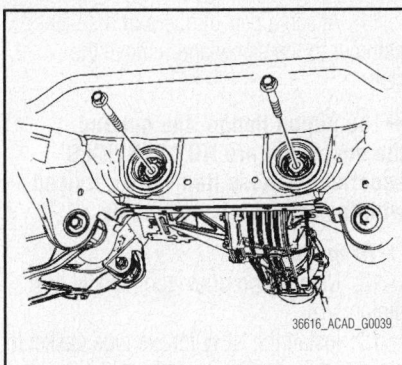

Fig. 20 Rear differential drive mounting bolt locations

10. Support the rear differential assembly with a transmission jack.

11. Remove the rear differential drive mounting bolts.

12. With the aid of an assistant, remove the rear differential assembly from the vehicle.

13. Remove the torque tube assembly mounting bolts from the rear differential assembly.

To install:

14. Install the torque tube assembly to the rear differential assembly.

15. Position the rear differential in the vehicle.

16. Install the rear differential mounting bolts. Tighten to 118 ft. lbs. (160 Nm).

17. Reconnect the electrical connector for the electronic clutch control module.

18. Lift the torque tube into position.

19. Install the torque tube bolt and tighten to 137 ft. lbs. (185 Nm).

20. Install the propeller shaft assembly.

21. Refill the rear differential assembly.

22. Install the rear wheel drive shaft.

23. Install the tires and wheels.

24. Remove the support and lower the vehicle.

REAR HALFSHAFTS

REMOVAL & INSTALLATION

See Figures 21 and 22.

1. Remove the tire and wheel assembly.

2. Insert a brass drift or punch in the brake rotor so that the brass drift or punch rest against the brake caliper mounting bracket.

3. Using the breaker bar and socket, loosen the wheel drive shaft nut.

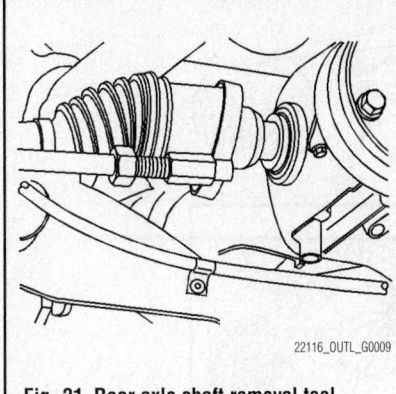

Fig. 21 Rear axle shaft removal tool

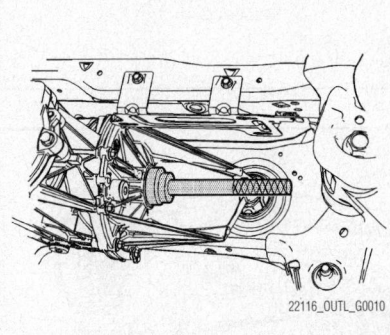

Fig. 22 Assemble an installer tool such as J 33832 and the handle J 8092

➡**DO NOT re-use the wheel drive shaft nut, discard and use NEW.**

4. Remove the wheel drive shaft nut.

5. Remove the wheel bearing/hub assembly.

6. Assemble the rear axle removal tool and position on the wheel drive shaft.

➡**Because of the design of the wheel drive shaft inner seal, the seal will be removed at the same time the wheel drive shaft is removed. Replace the seal, DO NOT re-use the seal. Replace with NEW.**

7. Using the rear axle removal tool , remove the wheel drive shaft.

➡**The rear knuckle does not have to be removed in order to service either the right or left rear the wheel drive shaft. The opening in the knuckle is large enough to allow the wheel drive shaft to pass through.**

8. Remove the wheel drive shaft through the knuckle.

9. If servicing the right wheel drive shaft, remove the muffler assembly.

➡**DO NOT re-use the retaining clip, replace with NEW.**

10. Remove the retaining ring from the tripod.

To install:

11. Position the new seal in the wheel drive shaft seal.

12. Assemble an installer tool such as J 33832 and the handle J 8092 .

13. Using the installer tool such as J 33832 and the handle J 8092, install the wheel drive shaft seal.

14. Install the wheel drive shaft through the knuckle.

15. Install the wheel bearing/hub assembly.

16. Install the wheel drive shaft nut.

17. Install the muffler assembly, if removed.

18. Insert a brass drift or punch in the brake rotor so that the brass drift or punch rest against the brake caliper mounting bracket.

19. Using a torque wrench and socket, tighten the new wheel drive shaft nut to 151 ft. lbs. (205 Nm).

20. Check the fluid level in the rear differential for any fluid loss during the service procedure.

21. Install the tire and wheel assembly.

REAR PINION SEAL

REMOVAL & INSTALLATION

See Figures 23 and 24.

1. Raise and support the vehicle.

2. Remove the propeller shaft assembly.

3. Remove the torque tube mounting bolt.

4. Disconnect the electrical connector from the clutch control module.

5. Remove the clutch control module, if needed.

6. Remove the torque tube mounting bolts from the rear differential.

7. Remove the torque tube gasket (2) from the rear differential and the alignment pins (4).

➡**DO NOT re-use the old gasket, discard and use NEW only.**

8. Remove the torque tube assembly (3) from the rear differential assembly.

9. Remove the torque tube assembly (3) from the vehicle.

10. Install a sheet metal screw into the seal.

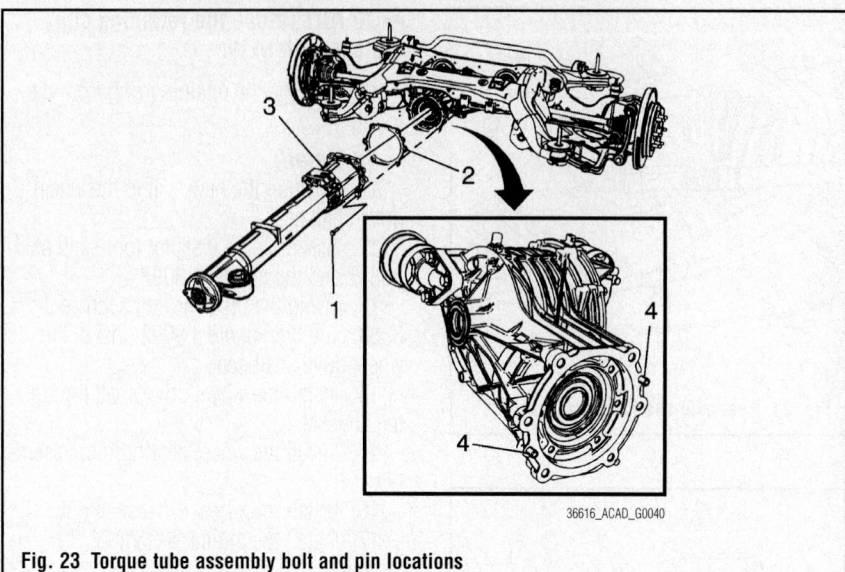

Fig. 23 Torque tube assembly bolt and pin locations

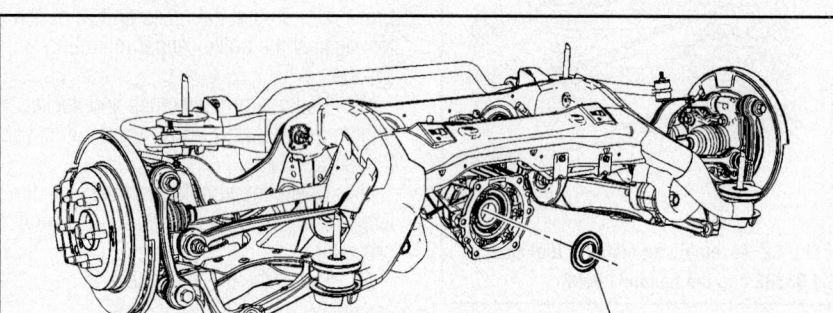

Fig. 24 Pinion seal location

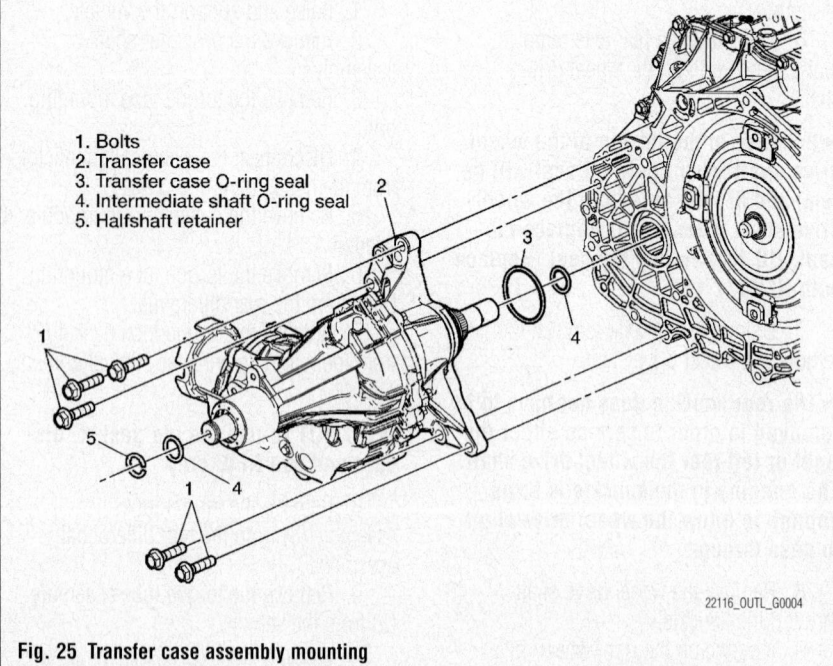

1. Bolts
2. Transfer case
3. Transfer case O-ring seal
4. Intermediate shaft O-ring seal
5. Halfshaft retainer

Fig. 25 Transfer case assembly mounting

11. Attach a pair of pliers or a slider hammer to the screw and remove the seal.

➡ **The pinion flange, the nut and the dust cover are NOT SERVICED separately. These items are serviced with the torque tube assembly.**

To install:

12. Using appropriate tool, install new pinion seal.

13. Install the NEW torque tube gasket to the rear differential assembly.

14. Position torque tube on the alignment pins on the rear differential.

15. Using a suitable jack stand support the torque tube assembly.

16. Hand tighten the torque tube to differential bolts before torquing to specifications.

17. Torque the mounting bolts to specifications. Tighten the bolts to 40 ft. lbs. (55 Nm).

18. Install the clutch control module, if needed.

19. Install the electrical connector for the clutch control module.

20. Inspect the fluid level.

TRANSFER CASE ASSEMBLY

REMOVAL & INSTALLATION

See Figure 25.

1. Raise and support the vehicle.
2. Drain the transfer case fluid.
3. Remove the propeller shaft. See Driveline Torque Tube in Rear Drive Axle.
4. Remove the right wheel drive shaft. See Halfshaft in Automatic Transaxle.
5. Remove the exhaust flexible pipe. See Catalytic Converter in Engine Mechanical.
6. Remove the engine rear mount bracket.
7. Support the transaxle with a jackstand.
8. Remove the transfer case bolts and the transfer case.
9. Remove the transfer case O-ring seal and the intermediate shaft seal.

To install:

10. Install a new intermediate shaft seal and a new transfer case O-ring seal.

11. Install the transfer case and tighten the bolts to 37 ft. lbs. (50 Nm).

12. Install the remaining components in the reverse of removal.

ENGINE COOLING

ENGINE FAN

REMOVAL & INSTALLATION

1. Disconnect electrical connector at fan shroud harness.
2. Remove front fascia upper support.
3. Remove hood latch support.
4. Remove upper radiator mounting brackets and tip radiator forward for additional clearance.
5. Remove the shroud mounting bolts and the pushpin retainers.
6. Remove the fan shroud and fan assembly. It may be necessary to tilt the assembly rearwards and upwards to remove.

To install:

7. Installation is the reverse of removal.

RADIATOR

REMOVAL & INSTALLATION

See Figure 26.

1. Drain and recycle the engine coolant.
2. Remove radiator inlet hose.
3. Remove radiator outlet hose.
4. Remove fan shroud top mounting bolts and pushpin from radiator and position fan shroud rearward.
5. Remove transmission inlet cooling line from radiator.
6. Remove transmission outlet cooling line from radiator.
7. Remove coolant reservoir hose from radiator filler neck.
8. Remove the front bumper fascia upper support.
9. Pinch fastening tabs together at top of condenser to remove from radiator and position forward.

10. Remove side rubber air deflectors from radiator tanks.
11. Remove the radiator mounting bolts and the radiator.

To install:

12. Installation is the reverse of removal, tighten the radiator mounting bolts to 89 inch lbs. (10 Nm).
13. Fill the coolant.
14. Inspect the transmission fluid level.

THERMOSTAT

REMOVAL & INSTALLATION

See Figure 27.

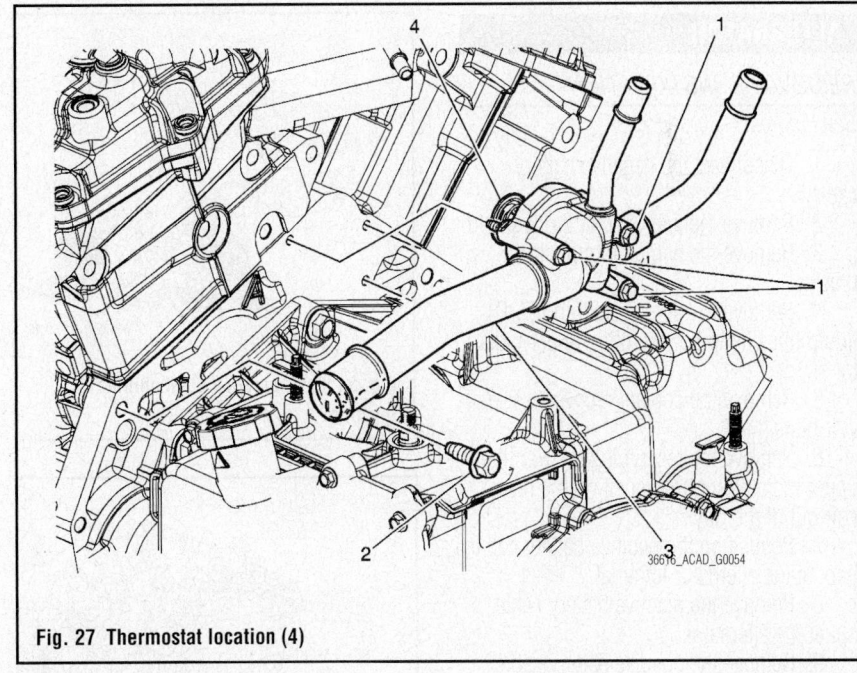

Fig. 27 Thermostat location (4)

36616_ACAD_G0054

1. Partially drain the cooling system.
2. Remove the radiator outlet hose from the thermostat housing.
3. Remove the heater inlet and outlet hoses.
4. Remove the thermostat housing bolts (1).
5. Remove the housing.

To install:

6. Install the thermostat housing bolts. Tighten the bolts to 89 in. lbs. (10 Nm).
7. Install the heater inlet and outlet hoses.
8. Install the radiator outlet hose to the thermostat housing.
9. Fill the cooling system.

WATER PUMP

REMOVAL & INSTALLATION

See Figures 28 and 29.

1. Drain and recycle the engine coolant.
2. Remove the drive belt. See Accessory Drive Belt in Engine Mechanical.
3. Use the a water pump pulley holding tool such as EN 46104 in order to retain the water pump pulley.
4. Remove the water pump pulley bolts.
5. Remove the water pump pulley.
6. Remove the water pump bolts.
7. Remove the water pump.
8. Remove and DISCARD the water pump seal.

9. Carefully clean the water pump sealing surfaces.

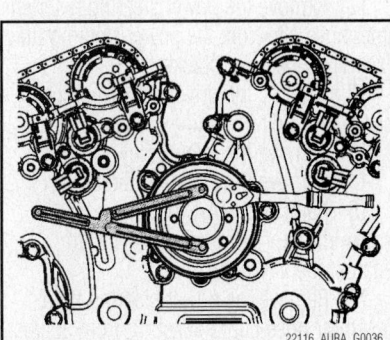

Fig. 28 Use the a water pump pulley holding tool such as EN 46104 in order to retain the water pump pulley

22116_AURA_G0036

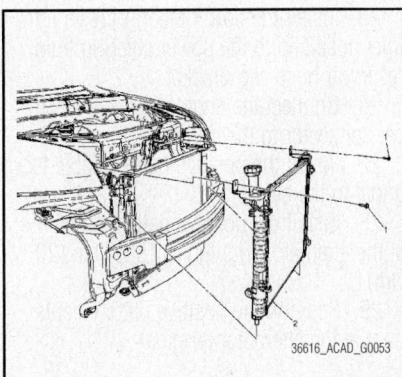

Fig. 26 Radiator location

36616_ACAD_G0053

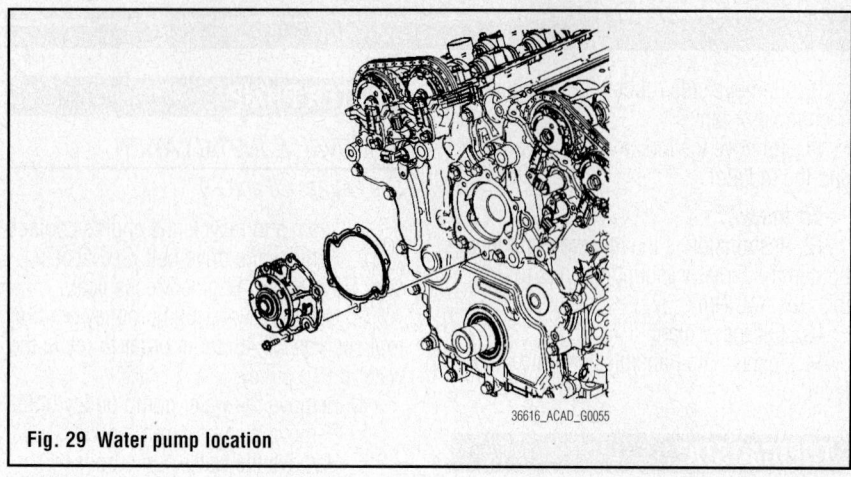

Fig. 29 Water pump location

To install:

10. Install a NEW water pump seal.

11. Install the water pump.

12. Install the water pump bolts and tighten to 89 inch lbs. (10 Nm).

13. Install the water pump pulley and the water pump pulley bolts.

14. Use the a water pump pulley holding tool such as EN 46104 in order to retain the water pump pulley.

15. Install and tighten the water pump pulley bolts to 89 inch lbs. (10 Nm).

16. Install the drive belt.

17. Fill the cooling system.

ENGINE ELECTRICAL

ALTERNATOR

REMOVAL & INSTALLATION

See Figures 31 through 33.

1. Disconnect the negative battery cable.

2. Remove the fuel injector sight shield.

3. Remove the engine mount strut bracket.

4. Remove the air conditioning (A/C) liquid line clamp bolt from the upper radiator support.

5. Remove the coolant recovery reservoir bolts.

6. Remove the reservoir tabs from the upper radiator support, position the reservoir out of the way.

7. Reposition the positive battery cable boot at the alternator terminal.

8. Remove the positive battery cable nut at the alternator.

9. Remove the positive battery cable terminal from the alternator.

10. Disconnect the engine harness electrical connector from the alternator.

11. Remove the power steering reservoir inlet hose clip from the power steering fluid reservoir hose clip bracket.

12. Remove the drive belt. See Accessory Drive Belt in Engine Mechanical.

13. Remove the idler pulley.

14. Remove the alternator bolts.

15. Remove the A/C compressor/evaporator hose bracket (1) from against the alternator.

16. Remove the power steering fluid reservoir hose clip bracket (3) from against the alternator.

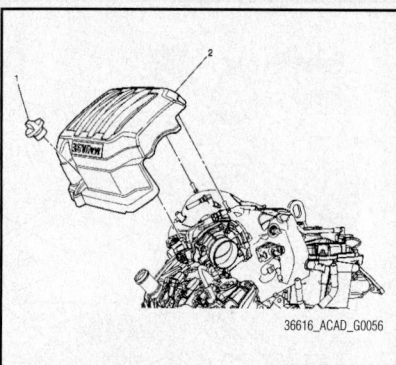

Fig. 31 Fuel injection sight shield (2) location

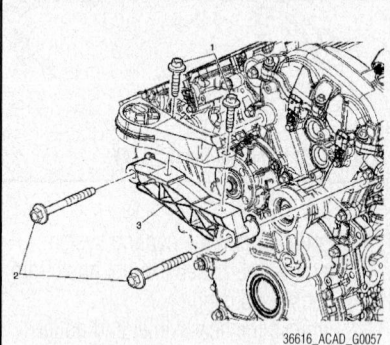

Fig. 32 Engine mount strut bracket location

17. Remove the alternator (4) and idler pulley (5) together from the vehicle.

18. Remove the idler pulley from the generator.

To install:

19. Install the alternator.

20. Loosely install the alternator bolts.

CHARGING SYSTEM

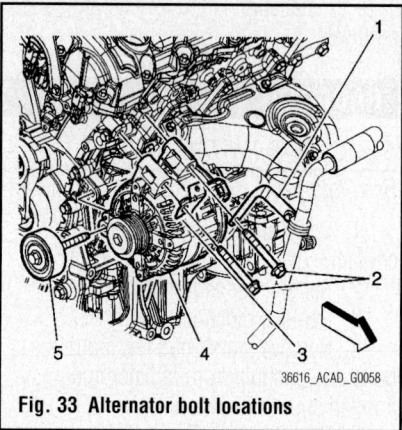

Fig. 33 Alternator bolt locations

21. Install the idler pulley. Tighten the bolts to 37 ft. lbs. (50 Nm).

22. Tighten alternator bolts to 37 ft. lbs. (50 Nm).

23. Install the power steering fluid reservoir hose clip bracket onto one of the alternator bolts, and install the bolt finger tight.

24. Install the A/C compressor/evaporator hose bracket onto the other alternator bolt, and install the bolt finger tight.

25. Install the power steering reservoir inlet hose clip to the power steering fluid reservoir hose clip bracket.

26. Connect the engine harness electrical connector to the alternator.

27. Install the positive battery cable terminal to the alternator.

28. Install the positive battery cable nut at the alternator. Tighten to 15 ft. lbs. (20 Nm).

29. Position the positive battery cable boot at the alternator terminal.

30. Install the coolant recovery reservoir tabs into the appropriate slots in the upper radiator support.

31. Install the coolant recovery reservoir bolts and tighten to 44 inch lbs. (5 Nm).

32. Install the A/C liquid line clamp bolt at the upper radiator support.

33. Install the engine mount strut bracket and tighten strut bolt to 43 ft. lbs. (58 Nm) and the strut bracket bolt to 66 ft. lbs. (90 Nm).

34. Install the fuel injector sight shield.

35. Install the drive belt.

36. Connect the negative battery cable.

ENGINE ELECTRICAL · IGNITION SYSTEM

IGNITION COIL

REMOVAL & INSTALLATION

1. Remove the fuel injector sight shield.
2. For bank 2, remove the intake manifold. See Intake Manifold in Engine Mechanical.
3. Disconnect the engine wiring harness electrical connector(s) from the ignition coil(s).
4. Remove the ignition coil bolt(s).
5. Remove the ignition coil(s).

To install:

6. Install the ignition coil(s).
7. Install the ignition coil bolt(s) and tighten to 89 inch lbs. (10 Nm).
8. Connect the engine wiring harness electrical connector(s) to the ignition coil(s).
9. For bank 2, install the intake manifold.
10. Install the fuel injector sight shield.

IGNITION TIMING

INSPECTION

The ignition timing is controlled by the Powertrain Control Module (PCM). No adjustment is necessary or possible.

SPARK PLUGS

REMOVAL & INSTALLATION

1. Remove the ignition coil(s).

➡ Clean the spark plug recess area before removing the spark plug. Failure to do so could result in engine damage because of dirt or foreign material entering the cylinder head, or by the contamination of the cylinder head threads. The contaminated threads may prevent the proper seating of the new plug. Use a thread chaser to clean the threads of any contamination.

2. Use compressed air in order to remove debris from the spark plug cavity.

➡ Allow the engine to cool before removing the spark plugs. Attempting to remove the spark plugs from a hot engine may cause the plug threads to seize, causing damage to cylinder head threads.

3. Remove the spark plug.

To install:

➡ Use only the spark plugs specified for use in the vehicle. Do not install spark plugs that are either hotter or colder than those specified for the vehicle. Installing spark plugs of another type can severely damage the engine.

➡ Check the gap of all new and reconditioned spark plugs before installation. The pre-set gaps may have changed during handling. Use a round feeler gage to ensure an accurate check. Installing the spark plugs with the wrong gap can cause poor engine performance and may even damage the engine.

4. Use a thread chaser, if necessary, to clean threads in the cylinder head. Cross-threading or failing to fully seat the spark plug can cause overheating of the plug, exhaust blow-by, or thread damage.
Install the spark plug.

5. Be sure that the spark plug threads smoothly into the cylinder head and the spark plug is fully seated.
6. Tighten the spark plug to 15 ft. lbs. (20 Nm).
7. Install the ignition coil(s).

ENGINE ELECTRICAL · STARTING SYSTEM

STARTER

REMOVAL & INSTALLATION

See Figure 34.

1. Disconnect the negative battery cable.
2. Raise the vehicle.
3. Remove the front left side catalytic converter.
4. Remove the starter heat shield bolt and shield.
5. Remove the starter solenoid BAT terminal nut.
6. Disconnect the engine harness electrical connector.

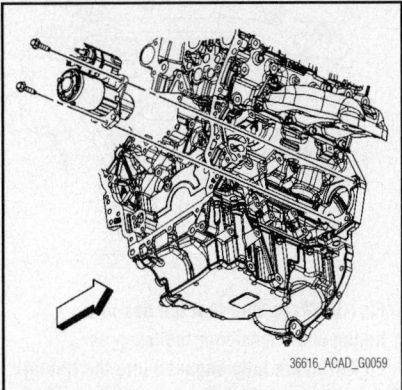

Fig. 34 Starter bolt locations

36616_ACAD_G0059

7. Disconnect the starter motor bolts and starter.

To install:

8. Position the starter motor in the engine block. Tighten the bolts to 37 ft. lbs. (50 Nm).
9. Connect the engine harness electrical connector to the starter.
10. Install the starter solenoid BAT terminal nut. Tighten the nut to 18 ft. lbs. (25 Nm).
11. Install the starter heat shield bolt and shield tighten bolt to 62 inch lbs. (7 Nm).
12. Install the front catalytic converter.
13. Lower the vehicle.
14. Connect the negative battery cable.

ENGINE MECHANICAL

➡Disconnecting the negative battery cable may interfere with the functions of the on board computer systems and may require the computer to undergo a relearning process, once the negative battery cable is reconnected.

ACCESSORY DRIVE BELTS

ACCESSORY BELT ROUTING

See Figure 35.

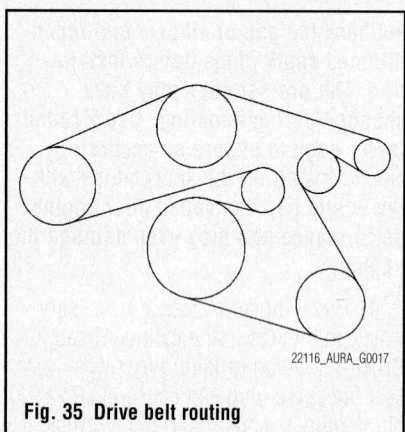

Fig. 35 Drive belt routing

INSPECTION

Inspect the drive belt for signs of glazing or cracking. A glazed belt will be perfectly smooth from slippage, while a good belt will have a slight texture of fabric visible. Cracks will usually start at the inner edge of the belt and run outward. All worn or damaged drive belts should be replaced immediately.

ADJUSTMENT

An automatic tensioner maintains a constant tension on the belt, there is no adjustment possible.

REMOVAL & INSTALLATION

See Figure 35.

1. Remove the air cleaner assembly.
2. Remove the engine mount strut.
3. Install a breaker bar to the drive belt tensioner.
4. Rotate the drive belt tensioner counterclockwise to release the spring tension.
5. Remove the drive belt.

To install:
6. Installation is the reverse of removal.

CAMSHAFT AND VALVE LIFTERS

REMOVAL & INSTALLATION

Right Side

See Figures 36 through 42.

1. Remove the lower intake manifold.
2. Remove the camshaft cover.
3. Remove the camshaft sensors.
4. Remove the intake camshaft position actuator solenoid.
5. Remove the crankshaft balancer.

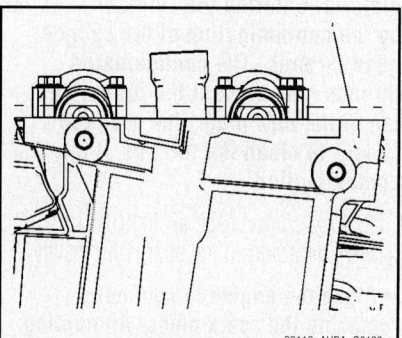

Fig. 36 Rotate the crankshaft with a camshaft rotation socket such as EN 46111 until the camshafts are in a neutral (low tension) position. The camshaft flats will be parallel with the camshaft cover rail (1)–Right side

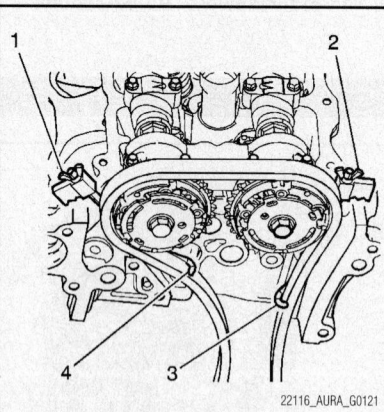

Fig. 37 Make sure that the tips of a timing chain tensioner tool such as EN 46108 are fully engaged into the timing chain (3 and 4). Install a timing chain tensioner tool such as EN 46108 (1 and 2) in order to retain the timing chain–Rights side

6. Rotate the crankshaft with a camshaft rotation socket such as EN 46111 until the camshafts are in a neutral (low tension) position. The camshaft flats will be parallel with the camshaft cover rail.
7. Use an open-end wrench at the camshaft hex to prevent camshaft/engine rotation. DO NOT remove the camshaft position actuator bolt at this time.
8. Loosen the camshaft position actuator bolt.
9. Make sure that the tips of a timing chain tensioner tool such as EN 46108 are fully engaged into the timing chain.
10. Install a timing chain tensioner tool such as EN 46108 in order to retain the timing chain. Firmly tighten the tool nuts.

➡Ensure that the camshaft timing chain and the camshaft position actuators are marked for proper assembly.

11. Mark the timing chain and the respective locations on camshaft position actuators (15-18).
12. Remove the camshaft position actuator bolt.
13. Remove the camshaft bearing caps and the camshaft.
14. Remove the valve rocker arms from the cylinder head. If the rocker arms are to be reused, keep in order so they can be reinstalled in the same position.
15. Remove the lifters.

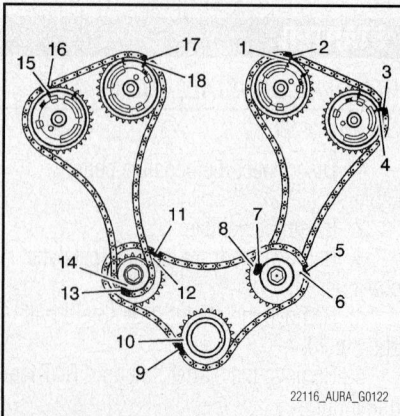

Fig. 38 Mark the timing chain and the respective locations on camshaft position actuators (15-18)–Right side

To install:

16. Make sure that the marks on the camshaft position actuators and the timing chain (15-18) are aligned. DO NOT tighten the camshaft position actuator bolt at this time.

17. Locate the camshafts to the cylinder head and assemble the camshaft actuators to the camshafts.

18. Install the lifters.

19. Install the rocker arms.

20. Install the camshafts and the camshaft bearing caps as follows:

a. Ensure that the crankshaft is in the stage one timing drive assembly position using a crankshaft rotation socket such as EN 46111 .

b. Ensure that the camshaft sealing rings are in place in the camshaft grooves. Camshaft sealing rings must be in place below the surface of the camshaft journal in order to avoid being

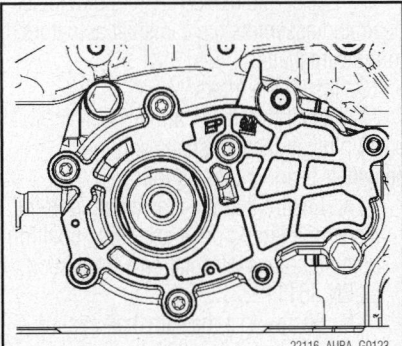

Fig. 39 Ensure that the crankshaft is in the stage one timing drive assembly position using a crankshaft rotation socket such as EN 46111—Right side

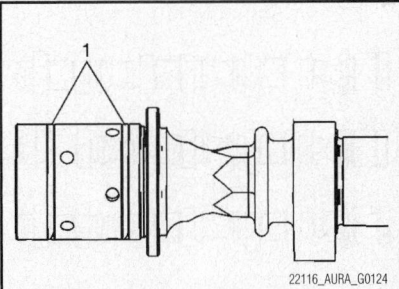

Fig. 40 Ensure that the camshaft sealing rings (1) are in place in the camshaft grooves. Camshaft sealing rings must be in place below the surface of the camshaft journal in order to avoid being pinched between the cylinder head and the camshaft caps—Right side

pinched between the cylinder head and the camshaft caps.

c. Select the proper camshaft for the particular installation location. Depending upon engine type, the ring placement may be defined as follows:

- The number 2 identification ring for the right exhaust camshaft is machined off (1) - Third Design, Camshaft Timing Drive System.
- The number 3 identification ring for the right intake camshaft is machined off (2) - Third Design and Fourth, except High Output, Camshaft Timing Drive System.
- The number 2 and 5 identification rings for the right intake camshaft

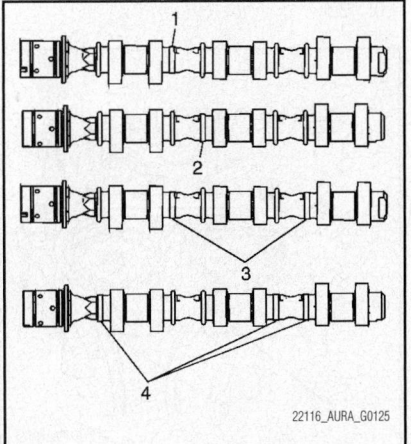

Fig. 41 Select the proper camshaft for the particular installation location—Right side

is machined off (3) - Fourth Design, Camshaft Timing Drive System.

- The number 1, 4 and 5 identification rings for the right exhaust camshaft is machined off (4) - Fourth Design High Output, Camshaft Timing Drive System.

➡ **Some engines may not posses this type of identification.**

d. Apply a liberal amount of lubricant to the camshaft journals and the right cylinder head camshaft carriers.

e. Place the right intake and right exhaust camshafts in position in the right cylinder head.

f. Position the camshaft lobes in a neutral position with the flats on the back of the camshafts up and parallel with the right cylinder head camshaft cover rail.

g. Observe the markings on the right cylinder head camshaft bearing caps. Each bearing cap is marked in order to identify its location. The markings have the following meanings:

- The raised feature must always be oriented toward the center of the cylinder head.
- The I indicates the intake camshaft
- The E indicates the exhaust camshaft
- The number 1, 3, 5 indicates the cylinder position from the front of the engine

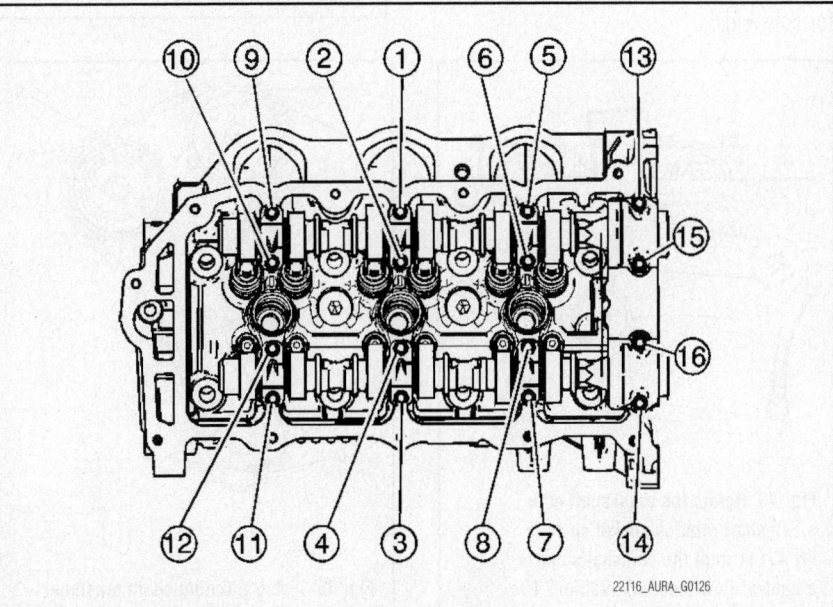

Fig. 42 Right side camshaft bearing caps torque sequence

h. Apply a liberal amount of lubricant to the camshaft bearing caps.

i. Install the camshaft bearing thrust caps in the first journal of the right cylinder head.

j. Install the remaining bearing caps with their orientation mark toward the center of the cylinder head.

k. Hand start all the camshaft bearing cap bolts.

l. Tighten the camshaft bearing cap bolts in the sequence shown to 89 in. lbs. (10 Nm).

m. Loosen the center intake camshaft bearing cap bolts (1, 2) and the center exhaust camshaft bearing cap bolts (3, 4). Retighten the center camshaft bearing cap bolts (1, 2, 3, 4) to 89 in. lbs. (10 Nm).

n. Remove the timing chain retention tool.

o. Install the crankshaft balancer.

➡Use an open-end wrench at the camshaft hex to prevent camshaft/engine rotation.

21. Install and tighten the camshaft position actuators.

22. Install the intake camshaft position actuator solenoid.

23. Install the camshaft sensors.

24. Install the camshaft cover.

25. Install the lower intake manifold.

Left Side

See Figures 43 through 48.

1. Remove the lower intake manifold.

2. Remove the left bank camshaft cover.

3. Remove the camshaft sensors.

4. Remove the camshaft position actuator solenoid.

5. Remove the crankshaft balancer.

6. Rotate the crankshaft with camshaft rotation socket such as EN 46111 until the camshafts are in a neutral (low tension) position. The camshaft flats will be parallel with the camshaft cover rail.

7. Use an open-end wrench at the camshaft hex to prevent camshaft/engine rotation. DO NOT remove the camshaft position actuator bolt at this time.

8. Loosen the camshaft position actuator bolt.

9. Make sure that the tips of a timing chain tensioner tool such as EN 46108 are fully engaged into the timing chain.

10. Install a timing chain tensioner tool such as EN 46108 in order to retain the timing chain. Firmly tighten the tool nuts.

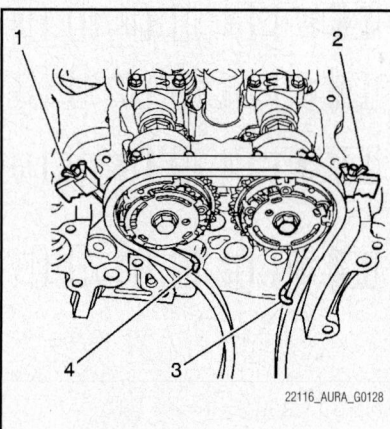

Fig. 44 Install a timing chain tensioner tool such as EN 46108 (1 and 2) in order to retain the timing chain—left side

➡Ensure that the camshaft timing chain and the camshaft position actuators are marked for proper assembly.

11. Mark the timing chain and the respective locations on camshaft position actuators (1-4).

12. Remove the camshaft position actuator bolt.

13. Remove the camshaft bearing caps and the camshaft.

14. Remove the valve rocker arms from the cylinder head. If the rocker arms are to be reused, keep in order so they can be reinstalled in the same position.

15. Remove the lifters.

To install:

16. Ensure that the marks on the camshaft position actuator and the timing chain (1-4) are aligned. DO NOT tighten the camshaft position actuator bolt at this time

17. Locate the camshafts to the cylinder head and assemble the camshaft actuators to the camshafts.

18. Install the lifters.

19. Install the rocker arms.

20. Install the camshafts and the camshaft bearing caps as follows:

a. Ensure that the crankshaft is in the stage one timing drive assembly position using a crankshaft rotation socket such as EN 46111 .

b. Ensure that the camshaft sealing rings are in place in the camshaft grooves. Camshaft sealing rings must be in place below the surface of the camshaft journal in order to avoid being pinched between the cylinder head and the camshaft caps.

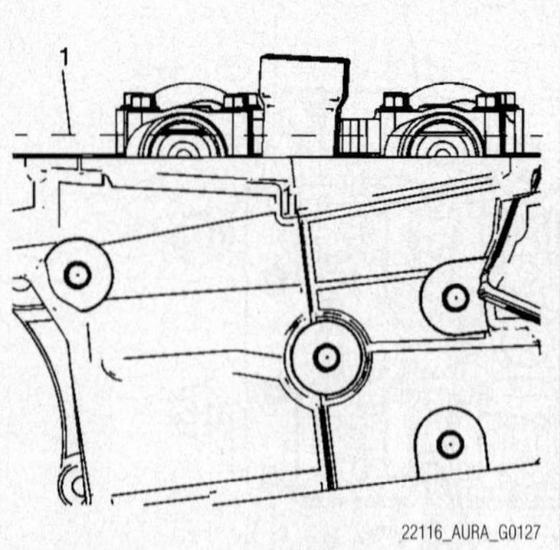

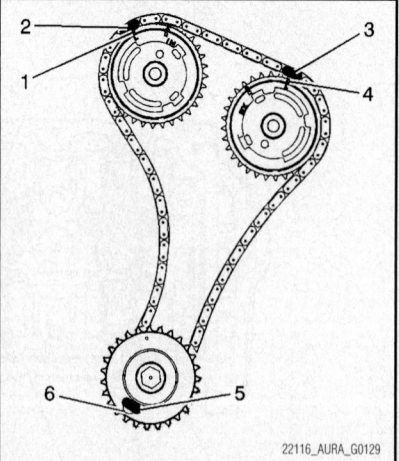

Fig. 45 Install a timing chain tensioner tool such as EN 46108 (1 and 2) in order to retain the timing chain—Left side

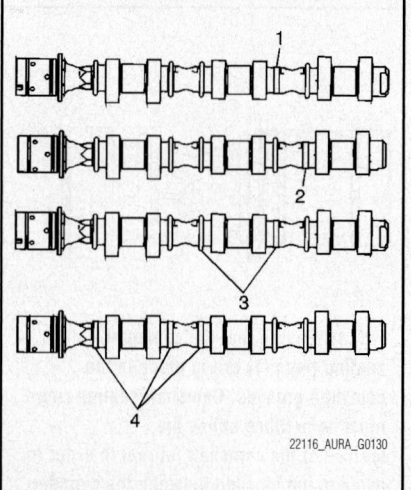

Fig. 46 Select the proper camshaft for the particular installation location—left side

Fig. 43 Rotate the crankshaft with a camshaft rotation socket such as EN 46111 until the camshafts are in a neutral (low tension) position. The camshaft flats will be parallel with the camshaft cover rail (1)

c. Select the proper camshaft for the particular installation location. Depending upon engine type, the ring placement may be defined as follows:

- The number 4 identification ring for the left intake camshaft is machined off (1) - Third Design, Camshaft Timing Drive System.
- The number 5 identification ring for the left exhaust camshaft is machined off (2) - Third Design, Fourth, except High Output, Camshaft Timing Drive System.
- The number 3 and 4 identification rings for the left intake camshaft is machined off (3) - Fourth Design, Camshaft Timing Drive System.
- The number 1, 2 and 3 identification rings for the left exhaust camshaft is machined off (4) - Fourth Design High Output, Camshaft Timing Drive System.

➡ **Some engines may not posses this type of identification.**

d. Apply a liberal amount of lubricant to the camshaft journals and the right cylinder head camshaft carriers.

e. Place the left intake and left exhaust camshafts in position in the left cylinder head.

f. Position the camshaft lobes in a neutral position with the flats on the back of the camshafts up and parallel with the right cylinder head camshaft cover rail.

g. Observe the markings on the left cylinder head camshaft bearing caps. Each bearing cap is marked in order to identify its location. The markings have the following meanings:

- The raised feature must always be oriented toward the center of the cylinder head.
- The I indicates the intake camshaft
- The E indicates the exhaust camshaft
- The number 2, 4, 6 indicates the cylinder position from the front of the engine

h. Apply a liberal amount of lubricant to the camshaft bearing caps.

i. Install the camshaft bearing thrust caps in the first journal of the left cylinder head.

j. Install the remaining bearing caps with their orientation mark toward the center of the cylinder head.

k. Hand start all the camshaft bearing cap bolts.

l. Tighten the camshaft bearing cap bolts in the sequence shown to 89 inch lbs. (10 Nm).

m. Loosen the center intake camshaft bearing cap bolts (1, 2) and the center exhaust camshaft bearing cap bolts (3, 4). Retighten the center camshaft bearing cap bolts (1, 2, 3, 4) to 89 inch lbs. (10 Nm).

n. Remove the timing chain retention tool.

o. Install the crankshaft balancer.

➡ **Use an open-end wrench at the camshaft hex to prevent camshaft/engine rotation.**

21. Install and tighten the camshaft position actuators.

22. Install the intake camshaft position actuator solenoid.

23. Install the camshaft sensors.

24. Install the camshaft cover.

25. Install the lower intake manifold.

CATALYTIC CONVERTER

REMOVAL & INSTALLATION

Left Side

1. Remove the exhaust manifold heat shield.

2. Remove the catalytic converter to exhaust manifold nuts.

3. Remove the exhaust flexible pipe.

4. Remove the catalytic converter brace bolt.

5. Remove the catalytic converter from the exhaust manifold.

6. Remove and discard the catalytic converter to exhaust manifold seal.

To install:

7. Install a NEW exhaust manifold seal onto the catalytic converter.

8. Install the catalytic converter to the exhaust manifold.

9. Install the catalytic converter brace bolt and tighten to 30 ft. lbs. (41 Nm).

10. Install the exhaust flexible pipe and tighten header flange nuts to 21 ft. lbs. (28 Nm) and exhaust flange nuts to 37 ft. lbs. (50 Nm).

11. Install the catalytic converter to exhaust manifold nuts and tighten to 37 ft. lbs. (50 Nm).

12. Install the exhaust manifold heat shield.

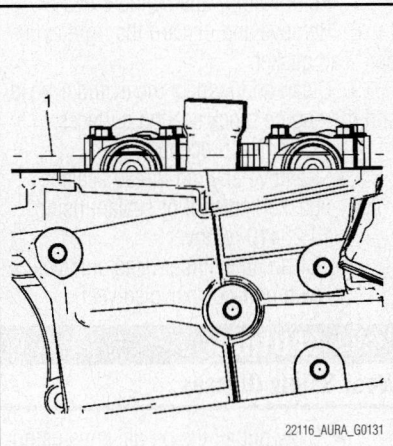

22116_AURA_G0131

Fig. 47 Position the camshaft lobes in a neutral position with the flats on the back of the camshafts up and parallel with the left cylinder head camshaft cover rail (1)—left side

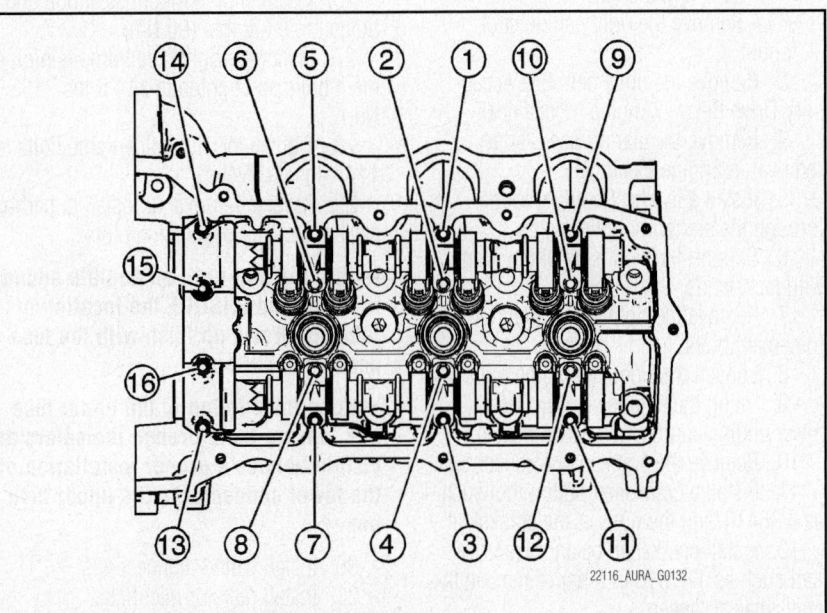

22116_AURA_G0132

Fig. 48 Left side camshaft bearing caps torque sequence

Right Side

1. Remove the exhaust flexible pipe.
2. Remove the catalytic converter to exhaust manifold nuts.
3. Remove the catalytic converter from the exhaust manifold.
4. Remove and discard the catalytic converter to exhaust manifold seal

To install:

5. Install a NEW catalytic converter to exhaust manifold seal onto the catalytic converter.
6. Install the catalytic converter to the exhaust manifold.
7. Install the catalytic converter to exhaust manifold nuts and tighten the nuts to 37 ft. lbs. (50 Nm).
8. Install the exhaust flexible pipe and tighten header flange nuts to 21 ft. lbs. (28 Nm) and exhaust flange nuts to 37 ft. lbs. (50 Nm).

CRANKSHAFT DAMPER

REMOVAL & INSTALLATION

1. Install engine support fixture.
2. Remove the engine mount strut bracket. See Engine Mount Strut in Engine Mechanical.
   a. Remove the radiator inlet hose from the water outlet tube. See Radiator in Engine Cooling.
   b. Remove the underhood fuse block bracket and fuse block.
   • Disconnect the battery.
   • Remove the junction block cover.
   • Disconnect the battery positive cable from the junction block by removing the nut.
   c. Remove the right engine strut mount.
3. Remove the drive belt. See Accessory Drive Belts in Engine Mechanical.
4. Remove the starter. See Starter removal in Engine Electrical.
5. Install a flywheel holding tool through the starter mounting hole.
6. Support the right side of the frame with jackstands.
7. Remove the right side frame reinforcement bolts.
8. Loosen the right side frame bolts.
9. Using the engine support fixture, lower engine approximately two inches.
10. Remove the crankshaft balancer bolt.
11. Install a crankshaft button tool such as J 38416-2 in the nose of the crankshaft.
12. Install crankshaft balancer remover tool such as J 41816 in order to remove the crankshaft balancer.
13. Tighten the center bolt of the crank-

shaft balancer remover tool in order to pull the crankshaft balancer off of the crankshaft.
14. Remove the crankshaft balancer remover tool from the crankshaft balancer.

To install:

➡ **The crankshaft balancer remover tool must be installed onto the flywheel.**

15. Use the tool, nut, bearing and washer to install the crankshaft balancer.

➡ **Do not lubricate the crankshaft front oil seal or crankshaft balancer sealing surfaces. The crankshaft balancer is installed into a dry seal.**

16. Apply lubricant to the inside of the crankshaft balancer hub bore.
17. Place the crankshaft balancer in position on the crankshaft.
18. Thread the tool in the crankshaft. Ensure you engage at least 10 threads of the tool before pressing the crankshaft balancer in place.
19. Push the crankshaft balancer into position by tightening the nut on the tool until the large washer bottoms out on the crankshaft end.
20. Remove the tool.
21. Install the crankshaft balancer bolt and tighten the crankshaft balancer bolt to 74 ft. lbs. (100 Nm) plus an additional 150 degrees.
22. Remove the flywheel holding tool.
23. Install the starter. See Starter installation in Engine Electrical.
24. Using engine support fixture, raise the engine into position.
25. Install the engine mount strut bracket and tighten to 43 ft. lbs. (58 Nm).
26. Install engine mount strut bolt and tighten to 66 ft. lbs. (90 Nm).
27. Install the right side frame reinforcement bolts and tighten to 114 ft lbs. (155 Nm).
28. Tighten the right side frame bolts to 114 ft lbs. (155 Nm).
29. Reverse removal to install underhood electrical center or junction block.

➡ **Turn the bolt until an audible sound is heard and ENSURE the location of tabs are drawn up flush with the fuse center top surface**

➡ **Upon installation of the upper fuse box, ensure the 2 orange indicators are visible to have a proper installation of the lower connector to the upper fuse box.**

30. Install battery connections.
31. Install radiator inlet hose.
32. Refill coolant.

33. Install drive belt. See Accessory Drive Belts in Engine Mechanical.

CRANKSHAFT FRONT SEAL

REMOVAL & INSTALLATION

1. Remove the crankshaft damper. See Crankshaft Damper in Engine Mechanical.
2. Use a flat-bladed tool to remove the seal from the front cover.

To install:

3. Use a suitable seal driver in order to install the crankshaft front oil seal to the engine front cover.
4. Install the crankshaft damper. See Crankshaft Damper in Engine Mechanical.

CYLINDER HEAD

REMOVAL & INSTALLATION

Right Side

See Figures 49 and 50.

➡ **See Timing Chain and Gears in Engine Mechanical for removal and installation.**

1. Remove the right bank secondary timing chain.
2. Remove the right side catalytic converter from the exhaust manifold. See Catalytic Converter in Engine Mechanical.
3. Remove the ground wires from the cylinder head.
4. Disconnect and unclip the heated oxygen sensor (HO2S) wiring harness.
5. Unbolt the power steering hose retainer.
6. Remove the right cylinder head bolts.
7. Remove the right cylinder head.
8. Remove and discard the right cylinder head gasket.
9. Clean and inspect the cylinder head and the engine block sealing surfaces.
   a. Cleaning procedure:
   • Remove any old thread sealant, gasket material or sealant using J 28410 remover
   • Clean all cylinder head surfaces with non-corrosive solvent

✳✳ CAUTION

Wear Safety Glasses.

• Blow out all the oil galleries using compressed air
• Remove any carbon deposits from the combustion chambers using an appropriate brush
• Clean any debris or build-up from the lifter pockets

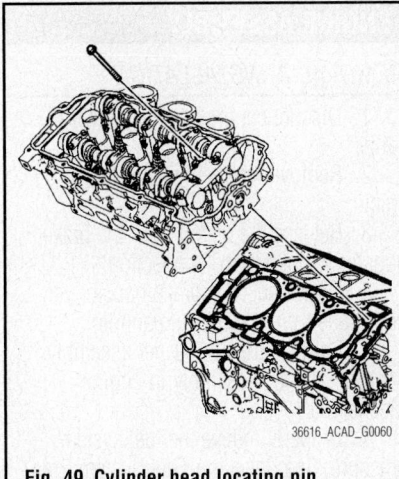

Fig. 49 Cylinder head locating pin positioning—Right

36616_ACAD_G0060

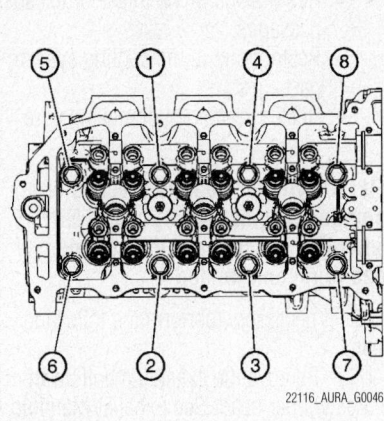

Fig. 50 Right side cylinder head bolt tightening sequence

22116_AURA_G0046

b. Visually inspect the cylinder head camshaft bearing surfaces for the following conditions:
- Excessive scoring or pitting
- Discoloration from overheating
- Deformation from excessive wear
- If the camshaft bearing journals appear to be scored or damaged, you must replace the cylinder head. DO NOT machine the camshaft bearing journals.

➡**If any of the above conditions exist on the camshaft bearing surfaces, replace the cylinder head**

c. Inspect the cylinder head for the following:
- Cracks, damage or pitting in the combustion chambers
- Debris in the oil galleries— Continue to clean the galleries until all debris is removed
- Coolant leaks or damage to the deck face sealing surface
- Burrs or any defects that would degrade the sealing of the NEW secondary camshaft drive chain tensioner gasket
- Damage to any gasket surfaces
- Damage to any threaded bolt holes
- Burnt or eroded areas in the combustion chamber
- Cracks in the exhaust ports and combustion chambers
- External cracks in the water passages
- Restrictions in the intake or exhaust passages
- Restrictions in the cooling system passages
- Rusted, damaged or leaking core plugs

➡**If the cylinder head is cracked or damaged, it must be replaced. No welding or patching of the cylinder head is recommended.**

10. If necessary, perform the following steps:
    a. Remove the exhaust manifold from the cylinder head. See Exhaust Manifold in Engine Mechanical.
    b. Remove the camshaft. See Camshaft and Valve Lifters in Engine Mechanical.
    c. Disassemble the cylinder head.

To install:

11. Ensure the cylinder head locating pins are securely mounted in the cylinder block deck face.
12. Install a NEW right cylinder head gasket using the deck face locating pins for retention.
13. Align the right cylinder head with the deck face locating pins.
14. Place the right cylinder head in position on the deck face.

➡**DO NOT allow oil on the cylinder head bolt bosses or DO NOT reuse the old cylinder head bolts.**

15. Tighten the NEW M11 cylinder head bolts using the following 2 steps:
    a. Step 1: in sequence to 22 ft. lbs. (30 Nm).
    b. Step 2: in sequence an additional 150 degrees.
16. Tighten the NEW M8 cylinder head bolts using the following 2 steps:
    a. Step 1: in sequence to 11 ft. lbs. (15 Nm).
    b. Step 2: in sequence an additional 75 degrees.
17. Install the power steering hose retainer.

18. Connect and clip the HO2 sensor wiring harness.
19. Install the ground wires to the cylinder head.
20. Install the right side catalytic converter to the exhaust manifold.
21. Install the right bank secondary timing chain.

Left Side

See Figures 51 and 52.

1. Remove the left bank secondary timing chain.
2. Remove the oil level indicator.
3. Disconnect the coolant temperature sensor electrical connector.
4. Remove the wiring harness ground from the cylinder head.
5. Remove the catalytic converter. See Catalytic Converter in Engine Mechanical.
6. Remove the camshaft position actuator solenoid valve. See Variable Camshaft Position Actuator Solenoid Valve in Engine Performance & Emission Controls.
7. Remove the two front M8 left cylinder head bolts.
8. Remove the left cylinder head bolts.
9. Remove the left cylinder head with exhaust manifold.
10. Remove and discard the left cylinder head gasket.
11. Clean and inspect the cylinder head and the engine block sealing surfaces.
    a. Cleaning procedure:
    - Remove any old thread sealant, gasket material or sealant using J 28410 remover
    - Clean all cylinder head surfaces with non-corrosive solvent

✳✳ CAUTION

Wear Safety Glasses.

- Blow out all the oil galleries using compressed air
- Remove any carbon deposits from the combustion chambers using an appropriate brush
- Clean any debris or build-up from the lifter pockets
    b. Visually inspect the cylinder head camshaft bearing surfaces for the following conditions:
    - Excessive scoring or pitting
    - Discoloration from overheating
    - Deformation from excessive wear
    - If the camshaft bearing journals appear to be scored or damaged, you must replace the cylinder head. DO NOT machine the camshaft bearing journals.

➡️**If any of the above conditions exist on the camshaft bearing surfaces, replace the cylinder head**

    c. Inspect the cylinder head for the following:

- Cracks, damage or pitting in the combustion chambers
- Debris in the oil galleries — Continue to clean the galleries until all debris is removed
- Coolant leaks or damage to the deck face sealing surface
- Burrs or any defects that would degrade the sealing of the NEW secondary camshaft drive chain tensioner gasket
- Damage to any gasket surfaces
- Damage to any threaded bolt holes
- Burnt or eroded areas in the combustion chamber
- Cracks in the exhaust ports and combustion chambers
- External cracks in the water passages

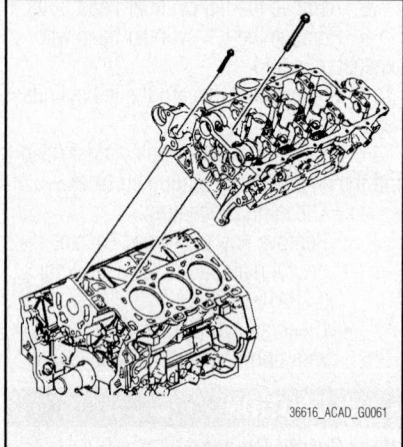

Fig. 51 Cylinder head locating pin positioning—Left

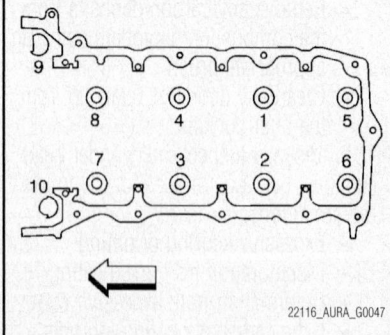

Fig. 52 Left side cylinder head bolt tightening sequence

- Restrictions in the intake or exhaust passages
- Restrictions in the cooling system passages
- Rusted, damaged or leaking core plugs

➡️**If the cylinder head is cracked or damaged, it must be replaced. No welding or patching of the cylinder head is recommended.**

    12. If necessary, perform the following steps:

    a. Remove the exhaust manifold from the cylinder head. See Exhaust Manifold in Engine Mechanical.

    b. Remove the camshaft. See Camshaft and Valve Lifters in Engine Mechanical.

    c. Disassemble the cylinder head.

    d. Remove the coolant sensor.

To install:

    13. Ensure the cylinder head locating pins are securely mounted in the cylinder block deck face.

    14. Install a NEW left cylinder head gasket using the deck face locating pins for retention.

    15. Align the left cylinder head with the deck face locating pins.

    16. Place the left cylinder head in position on the deck face.

➡️**DO NOT allow oil on the cylinder head bolt bosses or DO NOT reuse the old cylinder head bolts.**

    17. Tighten the NEW M11 cylinder head bolts using the following 2 steps:

    a. Step 1: in sequence to 22 ft. lbs. (30 Nm).

    b. Step 2: in sequence an additional 150 degrees.

    18. Install the 2 front NEW M8 left cylinder head bolts and tighten to 11 ft. lbs. (15 Nm) plus an additional 75 degrees.

    19. Install the camshaft position actuator solenoid valve.

    20. Install the catalytic converter to the exhaust manifold.

    21. Connect the wiring harness electrical connector located at the side of the cylinder head.

    22. Install the wiring harness ground to the cylinder head.

    23. Install the coolant temperature sensor electrical connector.

    24. Install the oil level indicator.

    25. Install the left bank secondary timing chain.

ENGINE ASSEMBLY

REMOVAL & INSTALLATION

    1. Disconnect the negative battery cable.

    2. Remove the fuel injector sight shield.

    3. Release the clamp from the brake booster vacuum hose connection.

    4. Disconnect the brake booster vacuum hose from the intake manifold.

    5. Remove the air cleaner assembly. See Air Cleaner Assembly in Engine Mechanical.

    6. Properly relieve the fuel system pressure. See Relieving Fuel System Pressure in Gasoline Fuel Injection System.

    7. Disconnect the Evaporative Emission (EVAP) hose/pipe from the EVAP canister purge solenoid valve.

    8. Disconnect the engine fuel hose/pipe from the chassis fuel hose/pipe using appropriate tool.

    9. Discharge the Air Conditioning (A/C) system.

    10. Remove the A/C compressor suction hose assembly from the compressor. Cap or plug the hoses and compressor to prevent contamination.

    11. Remove the A/C compressor discharge hose assembly from the compressor. Cap or plug the hoses and compressor to prevent contamination.

    12. Drain and recycle the engine coolant. See Engine Cooling.

    13. Remove the coolant recovery reservoir.

    a. Drain the coolant from the recovery reservoir.

    b. Remove the front compartment sight shield if necessary.

    14. Disconnect the inlet coolant heater hose from the engine.

    15. Disconnect the outlet coolant heater hose from the engine.

    16. Remove the radiator inlet hose.

    17. Raise and support the vehicle.

    18. Remove the radiator outlet hose.

    19. Remove the exhaust flexible pipe and secure the rear half of the exhaust system to the vehicle underbody. See Catalytic Converter in Engine Mechanical.

    20. Remove the front tires.

    21. Remove the engine splash shield.

    22. Remove the steering intermediate steering shaft pinch bolt and discard the bolt.

    23. Disconnect the steering intermediate steering shaft from the steering gear.

24. Disconnect the transaxle shift cable.

25. Disconnect the transaxle cooler lines.

26. Disconnect the negative battery extension cable.

27. Disconnect all engine electrical connectors.

28. Remove the right and left steering linkage outer tie rod ends from the steering knuckles. See Steering Linkage in Front Suspension.

29. Remove the right and left stabilizer shaft links from the stabilizer shaft. See Stabilizer Bar in Front Suspension.

30. Remove the right and left lower ball joints from the steering knuckles. See Lower Control Arms in Front Suspension.

31. Place a drain pan under the transaxle then separate the right and left front wheel drive shafts from the transaxle/transfer case. See Halfshafts in Front Drive Axle.

32. On All Wheel Drive (AWD) models, remove the driveline torque tube. See Driveline Torque Tube in Rear Drive Axle.

33. Lower the vehicle.

34. On all models, place a block of wood between the frame and the engine oil pan in order to support the engine once the bolts are removed from the right engine mount.

35. Remove the right engine mount strut. See Engine Mount Strut in Engine Mechanical.

➡ **Insure the vehicle body is secured to the hoist.**

36. Disconnect and reposition the engine harness as necessary.

37. Raise the vehicle.

38. Place a universal frame support fixture or jackstands under the frame.

39. Lower the vehicle until the frame contacts the frame support fixture or jackstands.

40. Remove the frame-to-body bolts and frame reinforcement bolts. Discard the bolts.

➡ **Inspect for areas of body to powertrain contact or entanglement of wires and hoses while separating the vehicle body and powertrain.**

41. Carefully raise the vehicle body up away from the powertrain.

42. Disconnect the engine electrical wiring harness from the following:
   • Oxygen sensor
   • EVAP purge solenoid
   • Ignition coils
   • Ground lead

43. Remove the wire harness from retainers.

44. Disconnect the left and right cylinder head engine electrical wiring harness from the Camshaft Position (CMP) sensors and actuators.

45. Disconnect the engine electrical wiring harness from the following:
   • Alternator
   • Retainer clips
   • A/C compressor hose
   • Oil pressure switch
   • A/C compressor
   • Battery cable
   • Retainer clips
   • Transmission module

46. If equipped with an engine coolant heater, disconnect the coolant heater cord.

47. Remove the throttle body assembly.

48. Remove the starter motor. See Starter in Engine Electrical.

49. Remove the torque converter bolts. See Flywheel in Engine Mechanical.

50. Install an engine lift chain to the engine lift brackets.

51. Support the engine weight with an engine hoist.

52. Remove the engine and transmission mount nuts from the frame.

53. Raise the engine and transmission assembly off the frame.

54. Remove the automatic transaxle bolts.

55. Separate the automatic transaxle from the engine.

56. Lift the engine away from the frame and the automatic transaxle.

57. Secure the engine to an engine stand.

58. Remove any additional engine components as necessary. Refer to appropriate component sections in manual if needed.

To install:

59. Remove the engine from the engine stand.

60. Align the engine to the frame and automatic transaxle.

61. Install the transaxle-to-engine bolts. Tighten to 55 ft. lbs. (75 Nm).

62. Place a block of wood between the frame and the engine oil pan in order to support the engine on the frame once the engine hoist is removed.

63. Remove the engine hoist and lift chain.

64. Install the torque converter bolts. Tighten to 44 ft. lbs. (60 Nm).

65. Install the starter motor.

66. Install the throttle body assembly.

67. If equipped with an engine coolant heater, connect the coolant heater cord.

68. Connect the engine electrical wiring harness to the following:

   • Transmission module
   • Retainer clips
   • Battery cable. Tighten to 80 inch lbs. (9 Nm).
   • A/C compressor
   • Oil pressure switch
   • A/C compressor hose
   • Retainer clips
   • Alternator

69. Connect the left and right cylinder head engine electrical wiring harness to the CMP sensors and actuators.

70. Connect the engine electrical wiring harness to the following:

71. Retainers.
   • Ground lead
   • Ignition coils
   • EVAP purge solenoid
   • Oxygen sensor

72. Install NEW frame-to-body bolts and reinforcement bolts. Tighten to 114 ft. lbs. (155 Nm).

73. Raise the vehicle up away from the frame support fixture or jackstands and remove the support fixture or jackstands from under the vehicle.

74. Connect the power steering hoses to the power steering fluid cooler.

75. Lower the vehicle.

76. Install the left transaxle mount bracket.

77. Install the engine mount strut.

78. Remove the block of wood.

79. Raise the vehicle.

80. On AWD models, install the driveline torque tube.

81. On FWD models, install the right and left front wheel drive shafts into the transaxle.

82. Install the right and left lower ball joints to the steering knuckles.

83. Install the right and left stabilizer shaft links to the stabilizer shaft.

84. Install the right and left steering linkage outer tie rod ends to the steering knuckles.

85. Connect all engine electrical connectors.

86. Connect the negative battery extension cable.

87. Connect the transaxle shift cable.

88. Connect the transaxle cooler lines.

89. Connect the steering intermediate steering shaft to the steering gear.

90. Install a NEW pinch bolt to the steering intermediate steering shaft. Tighten to 16 ft. lbs. (22 Nm).

91. Install the front tires.

92. Install the exhaust flexible pipe.

93. Install the radiator outlet hose.

94. Lower the vehicle.

95. Install the radiator inlet hose.

96. Connect the outlet coolant heater hose to the engine.

97. Connect the inlet coolant heater hose to the engine.

98. Install the coolant recovery reservoir.

99. Install the A/C compressor discharge hose assembly to the compressor.

100. Install the A/C compressor suction hose assembly to the compressor.

101. Connect the engine fuel hose/pipe to the chassis fuel hose/pipe.

102. Connect the EVAP hose/pipe to the EVAP canister purge solenoid valve.

103. Install the air cleaner assembly.

104. Connect the brake booster vacuum hose to the intake manifold.

105. Position the clamp on the brake booster vacuum hose connection.

106. Install the fuel injector sight shield.

107. Fill the engine with engine oil.

108. Fill the engine with coolant.

109. Check the transaxle fluid level.

110. Charge the AC system.

111. Cycle the ignition ON for 5 seconds then OFF for 10 seconds. Repeat cycling twice.

112. Crank the engine until it starts. The maximum starter motor cranking time is 20 seconds.

113. If the engine does not start, repeat the steps.

EXHAUST MANIFOLD

REMOVAL & INSTALLATION

Right Side

1. Remove the right exhaust manifold heat shield bolts. See Exhaust Manifold Heat Shield in Engine Mechanical.

2. Remove catalytic converter. See Catalytic Converter in Engine Mechanical.

3. Remove the right exhaust manifold heat shield.

4. Remove the right exhaust manifold lower bolts from the right cylinder head.

5. Remove the right exhaust manifold upper bolts from the right cylinder head.

6. Remove the right exhaust manifold.

To install:

7. Install a NEW right exhaust manifold gasket.

8. Install the right exhaust manifold.

9. Loosely install the right exhaust manifold bolts into the right cylinder head.

10. Tighten the right exhaust manifold bolts to 15 ft. lbs. (20 Nm).

11. Install catalytic converter.

12. Install the exhaust manifold heat shield and bolts, tighten to 89 in. lbs. (10 Nm).

Left Side

1. Remove the exhaust manifold heat shield. See Exhaust Manifold Heat Shield in Engine Mechanical.

2. Remove the oil level indicator.

3. Remove the catalytic converter. See Catalytic Converter in Engine Mechanical.

4. Remove the exhaust manifold bolts.

5. Remove the exhaust manifold and gasket. Discard the gasket.

To install:

➡If replacing exhaust manifold, see Heater Oxygen Sensor in Engine Performance & Emission Controls.

6. Install one exhaust manifold bolt to the exhaust manifold.

7. Install the NEW exhaust manifold gasket onto the exhaust manifold and bolt.

8. Install the exhaust manifold (with gasket) to the cylinder head and the catalytic converter.

9. Install the remaining exhaust manifold bolts and tighten to 15 ft. lbs. (20 Nm).

10. Install the catalytic converter.

11. Install the oil level indicator.

12. Install the exhaust manifold heat shield.

EXHAUST MANIFOLD HEAT SHIELD

REMOVAL & INSTALLATION

Right side

See Figure 53.

1. Remove the heated oxygen sensor. See Heater Oxygen Sensor in Engine Performance & Emission Controls.

2. Remove the exhaust flexible pipe. See Catalytic Converter in Engine Mechanical.

3. Remove the exhaust manifold heat shield bolts (1).

4. Remove the exhaust manifold heat shield.

To install:

5. Install the exhaust manifold heat shield.

6. Install the exhaust manifold heat shield bolts and tighten to 89 inch lbs. (10 Nm).

7. Install the exhaust flexible pipe.

8. Install the HO2S.

Left Side

See Figure 54.

1. Remove the fuel injector sight shield.

2. Disconnect the engine wiring harness electrical connector (2) from the heated oxygen sensor (HO2S) electrical connector (3). See Heater Oxygen Sensor in Engine Performance & Emission Controls.

3. Remove the HO2S electrical connector retainer from the engine wiring harness clip (1).

4. Remove the exhaust manifold heat shield bolts.

5. Remove the exhaust manifold heat shield, sliding the shield up over the HO2S pigtail.

To install:

6. Install the exhaust manifold heat shield, sliding the shield down over the HO2S pigtail.

7. Install the exhaust manifold heat shield bolts and tighten to 89 inch lbs. (10 Nm).

8. Connect the engine wiring harness electrical connector to the HO2S electrical connector.

9. Install the HO2S electrical connector retainer to the wiring harness clip.

10. Install the fuel injector sight shield.

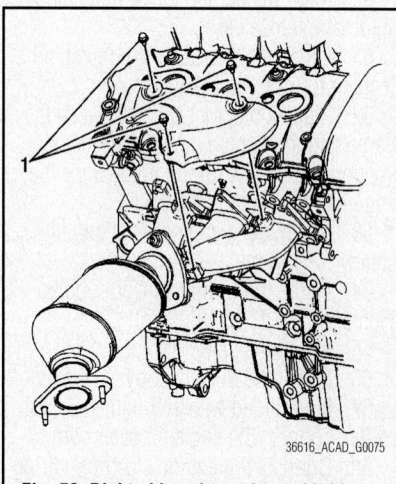

36616_ACAD_G0075

Fig. 53 Right side exhaust heat shield

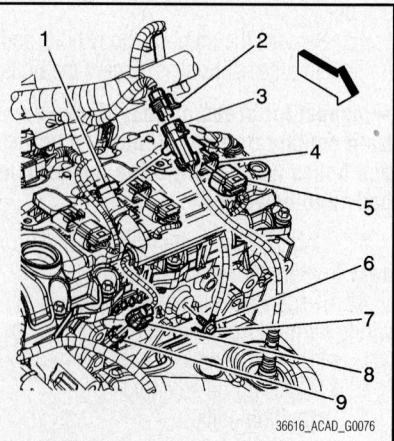

36616_ACAD_G0076

Fig. 54 Left side heated oxygen sensor and related components

INTAKE MANIFOLD

REMOVAL & INSTALLATION

2008 ModelsModels

Upper

See Figures 55 through 57.

1. Remove the fuel injector sight shield.
2. Remove the air cleaner outlet duct.
3. Remove the intake manifold insulator.

   a. Remove the manifold absolute pressure (MAP) sensor. See Manifold Absolute Pressure Sensor in Engine Performance & Emission Controls.

   b. Remove the positive crankcase ventilation (PCV) hose.

   c. Remove the brake booster hose from the intake manifold.

   d. Lift upward on the front intake manifold insulator.

   e. Disconnect the purge tube assembly from the evaporative emission (EVAP) canister connector.

   f. Remove the right side intake manifold insulator bolts.

   g. Remove right side intake manifold insulator.

   h. Remove the left side insulator.

4. Disconnect the evaporative emissions (EVAP) canister purge line (1) and reposition aside.

5. Disconnect the PCV line (2) from the top of the intake manifold and reposition aside.

6. Disconnect the intake manifold tuning valve electrical connector (3).

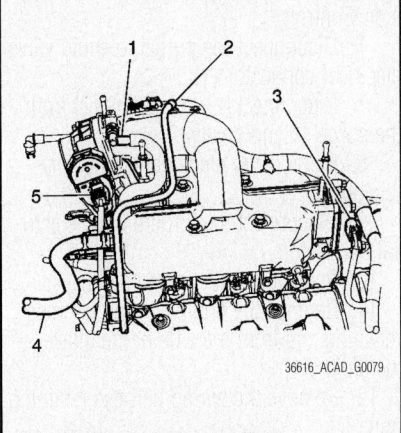

Fig. 56 Upper intake manifold

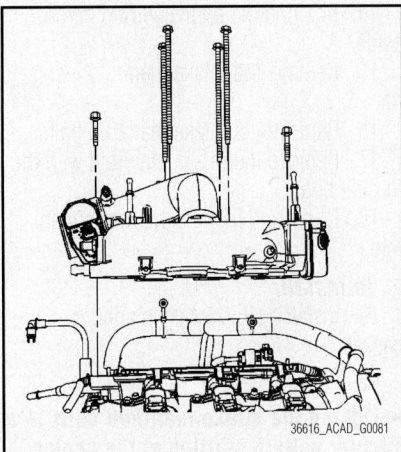

Fig. 57 Upper intake manifold bolt locations

7. Remove the brake booster vacuum hose (4) from the intake manifold.

8. Disconnect the electronic throttle control (ETC) electrical connector (5).

9. Remove the engine harness bracket retaining bolt.

10. Disconnect the map sensor electrical connector.

11. Completely loosen but do not remove upper intake retaining bolts.

12. Remove the upper intake manifold, gasket and bolts together. Discard gasket.

13. If replacing the upper intake manifold complete the following steps:

To install:

14. Install the upper intake manifold gaskets to the lower intake manifold and install the fir tree retainers to retain the upper intake manifold gasket position.

15. Install the bolts into the upper intake manifold.

16. Install the upper intake manifold with bolts and tighten to 17 ft. lbs. (23 Nm).

17. Connect the map sensor electrical connector.

18. Install the engine harness bracket retaining bolt.

19. Connect the ETC electrical connector.

20. Install the brake booster vacuum hose to the intake manifold.

21. Connect the intake manifold tuning valve electrical connector.

22. Connect the PCV line to the top of the intake manifold.

23. Connect the EVAP canister purge line.

24. Install the intake manifold insulator.

25. Install the air cleaner outlet duct.

26. Install the fuel injector sight shield.

Lower

See Figure 58.

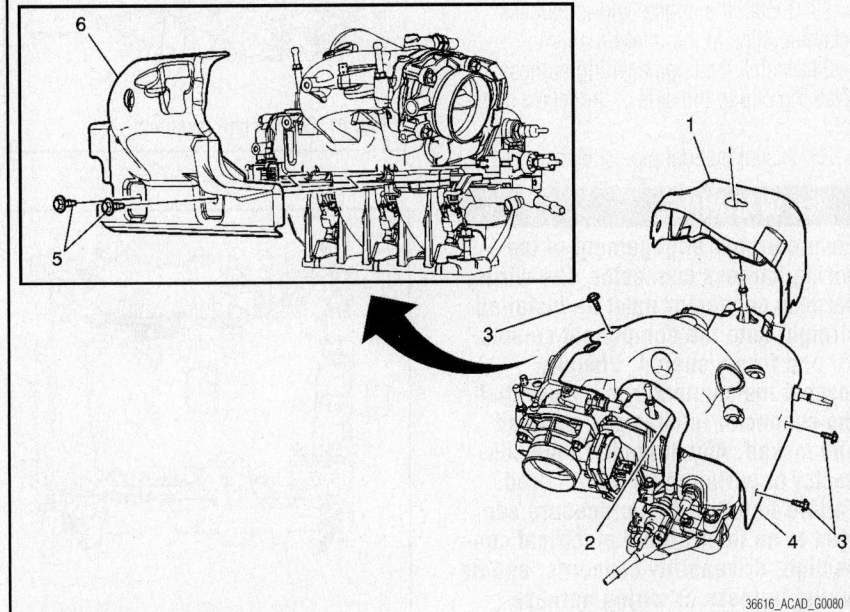

Fig. 55 Intake manifold insulator

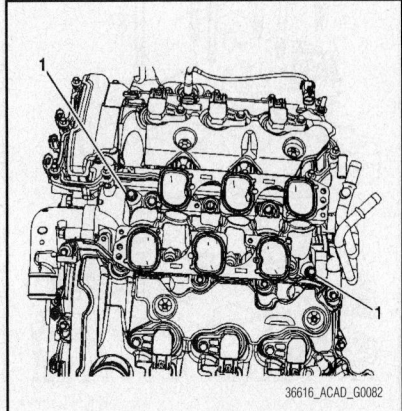

Fig. 58 Lower intake manifold bolt locations (1)

1. Remove the fuel injectors and fuel rail. See Fuel Rail & Injectors in Fuel System.

2. Remove the lower intake manifold bolts.

3. Remove the lower intake manifold and gasket from engine. Discard the gasket.

4. Clean and inspect the intake manifold and the sealing surfaces.

To install:

5. Install the lower intake manifold gasket.

6. Install the lower intake manifold bolts and tighten to 17 ft. lbs. (23 Nm).

7. Install the fuel injectors and fuel rail.

2009 Models

See Figures 59 and 60.

1. Turn the ignition OFF.

2. Remove the fuel injector sight shield.

3. Remove the air cleaner outlet duct.

4. Disconnect the brake booster vacuum hose from the intake manifold.

5. Remove the rear positive crankcase ventilation hose. See Positive Crankcase

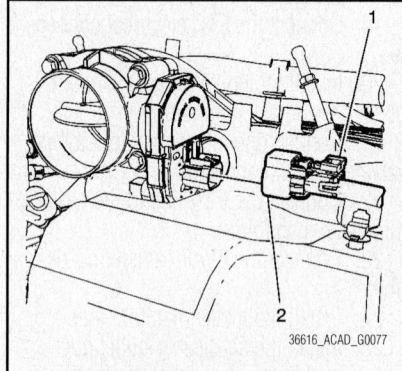

Fig. 59 Purge solenoid location (1, 2)

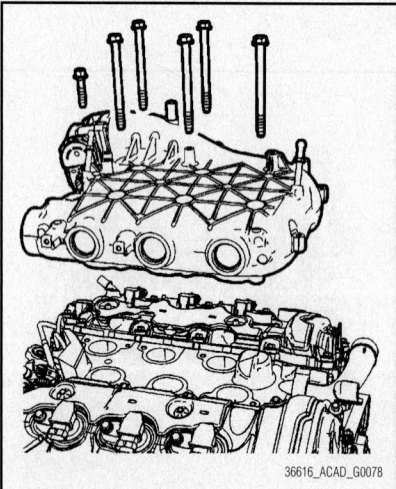

Fig. 60 Intake manifold bolt locations—2009

Ventilation in Engine Performance & Emission Controls

6. Disconnect the purge solenoid valve electrical connector (1).

7. Disconnect the purge line (2) from the purge solenoid valve.

8. Remove the electrical connector retainer.

9. Disconnect the throttle body electrical connector.

10. Remove the fuel pipe shield.

11. Remove the engine wiring harness retaining clip from the side of the intake manifold.

12. Remove the wiring harness retaining bolt.

13. Remove the engine wiring harness retaining clips from the intake manifold.

14. Position the engine wiring harness aside.

15. Remove the intake manifold insulator.

16. Remove the intake manifold bolts.

17. Remove the intake manifold with the throttle body.

18. Clean and inspect the intake manifold.

To install:

19. Install a NEW intake manifold gasket.

20. Install the intake manifold.

➡ **Tighten the intake manifold bolts in a circular pattern starting at the center (long bolts) and moving outward.**

21. Install the intake manifold bolts and tighten to 17 ft. lbs. (23 Nm).

22. Position the engine wiring harness in place.

23. Install the engine wiring harness retaining clips to the intake manifold.

24. Install the engine wiring harness retaining clip to the side of the intake manifold.

25. Install the fuel pipe shield.

✳✳ WARNING

Ensure proper engagement of the wiring harness connector. The wiring harness connector must be installed straight onto the component connector and firmly seated. Visually inspect the connector to ensure that the connector latches are engaged and locked. Any damage to the connector or wiring must be repaired. Failure to follow this procedure can lead to an intermittent electrical connection, driveability concerns, and/or wiring harness or wiring harness connector damage or failure.

26. Connect the electrical connector to the throttle body.

27. Install the electrical connector retainer.

28. Connect the purge line to the purge solenoid valve.

29. Connect the purge solenoid valve electrical connector.

30. Install the rear positive crankcase ventilation hose.

31. Connect the brake booster vacuum hose to the intake manifold.

32. Install the air cleaner outlet duct.

33. Install the fuel injector sight shield.

OIL PAN

REMOVAL & INSTALLATION

See Figures 61 through 65.

1. Drain the engine oil and remove the oil filter.

2. Remove the exhaust flexible pipe. See Catalytic Converter in Engine Mechanical

3. Remove the engine. See Engine Assembly in Engine Mechanical.

4. Remove the engine front cover. See

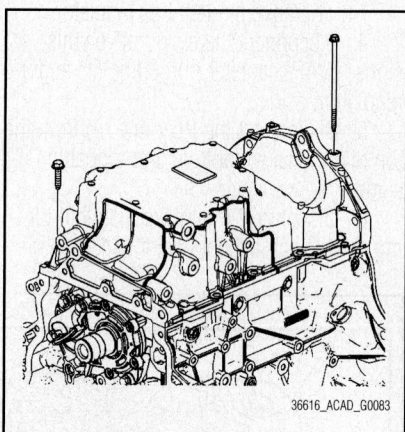

Fig. 61 Oil pan bolt locations

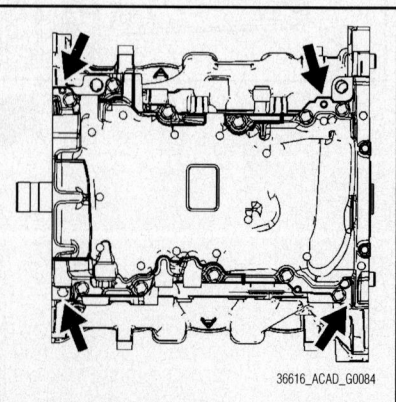

Fig. 62 Oil pan pry points

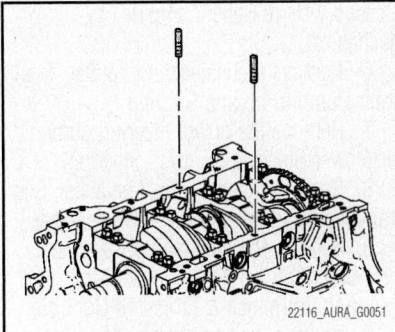

Fig. 63 Install the 0.315 in. (8mm) guides from the a guide pin set such as EN 46109 into the center oil pan rail bolt hole on each side of the engine block

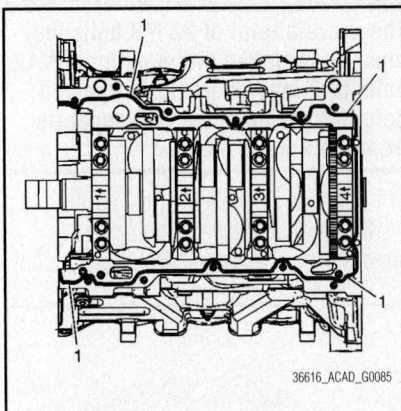

Fig. 64 Sealant application (1)

Timing Chain and Sprockets in Engine Mechanical.

5. Remove the oil pan bolts.

6. Using the pry points located at the edge of the oil pan separate the RTV sealant.

7. Remove the oil pan from the block.

8. Clean the oil pan and the engine block gasket surface.

To install:

9. Install the 0.315 in. (8mm) guides from the a guide pin set such as EN 46109 into the center oil pan rail bolt hole on each side of the engine block.

10. Place a 0.118 in. (3mm) bead of RTV sealant on the block pan rail and the crankshaft rear oil seal housing.

11. Position the oil pan onto the block.

12. Remove guide pin set guides from the engine block.

13. Loosely install the oil pan bolts.

14. Tighten the oil pan bolts in sequence.

    a. 8 mm bolts 1 through 11 to 17 ft. lbs. (23 Nm).

    b. 6 mm bolts 12 and 13 to 89 in. lbs. (10 Nm).

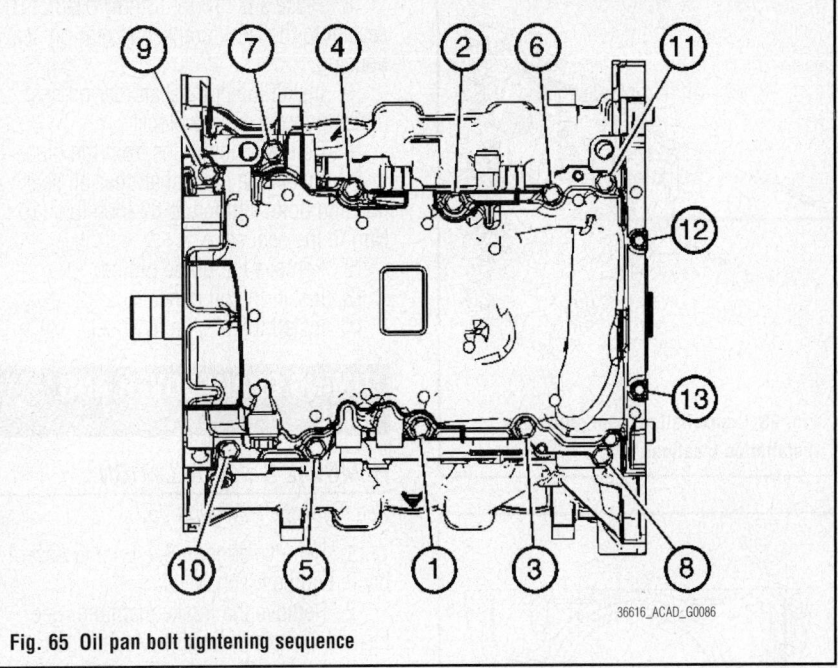

Fig. 65 Oil pan bolt tightening sequence

15. Install the engine front cover.

16. Install the engine.

17. Install the exhaust flexible pipe.

18. Refill the engine oil.

19. Start the vehicle and inspect for leaks.

OIL PUMP

REMOVAL & INSTALLATION

See Figure 66.

1. Remove the primary timing chain.

2. Remove the oil pump bolts and the oil pump.

To install:

3. Align the oil pump drive gear with the crankshaft flats and install the oil pump to the engine block.

4. Align the pump body with the mounting holes in the cylinder block.

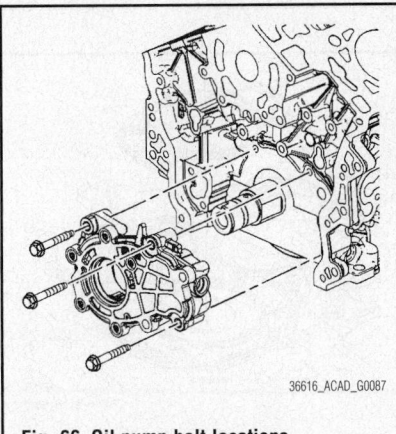

Fig. 66 Oil pump bolt locations

5. Install the oil pump bolts and tighten to 17 ft. lbs. (23 Nm).

6. Install the primary timing chain.

REAR MAIN SEAL

REMOVAL & INSTALLATION

See Figures 67 through 70.

1. Remove the engine flywheel. See Flywheel in Engine Mechanical.

2. Remove the oil pan. See Oil Pan in Engine Mechanical.

3. Remove the crankshaft rear oil seal housing bolts.

4. Use the pry points located at the edge of the crankshaft rear oil seal housing to separate the RTV sealant.

5. Remove and discard the crankshaft rear oil seal housing.

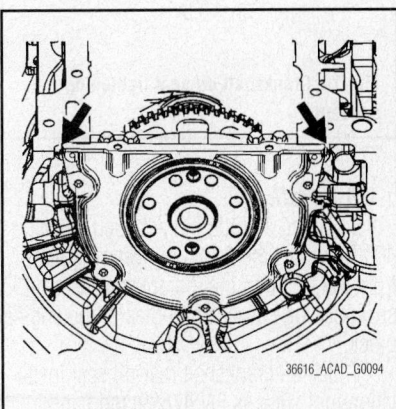

Fig. 67 Crankshaft oil seal pry locations

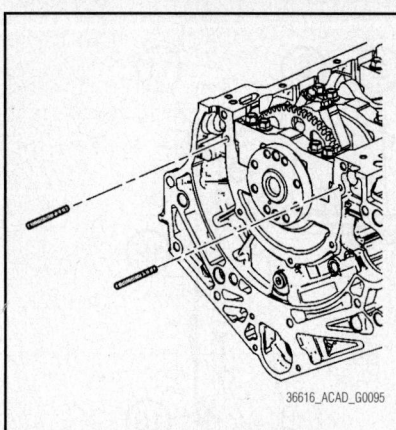

Fig. 68 Crankshaft oil seal guide pin installation locations

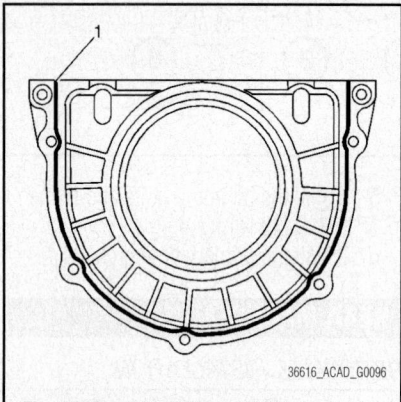

Fig. 69 Crankshaft oil seal RTV application (1)

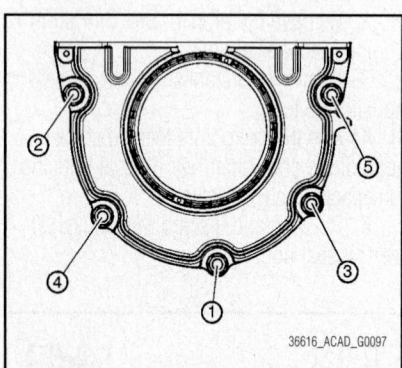

Fig. 70 Crankshaft oil seal tightening sequence

To install:

6. Using a guide pin set such as EN 46109, install the 0.236 in. (6mm) guides from the tool into the 2 crankshaft rear oil seal housing corner bolt holes of the engine block.

7. Install crankshaft rear oil seal installation tool such as EN 47839 and handle onto the rear of the crankshaft flange.

8. Place a 0.118 in. (3mm) bead of RTV sealant to the NEW crankshaft rear oil seal housing.

9. Install the crankshaft rear oil seal housing to the engine block

10. Remove the guides from the block.

11. Install the crankshaft rear oil seal housing bolts, tighten to 89 inch lbs. (10 Nm) in the sequence.

12. Remove the guide pin set.

13. Install the oil pan.

14. Install the engine flywheel.

TIMING CHAIN COVER AND SEAL

REMOVAL & INSTALLATION

See Figures 71 through 75.

1. Remove engine. See Engine Assembly in Engine Mechanical.

2. Remove the intake manifold. See Intake Manifold in Engine Mechanical.

3. Remove the valve covers. See Valve Covers in Engine Mechanical.

4. Remove the water outlet housing assembly.

5. Remove the drive belt tensioner. See Accessory Drive Belts in Engine Mechanical.

6. Remove the water pump pulley. See Water Pump in Engine Cooling.

7. Remove the power steering pump. See Power Steering Pump in Steering.

8. Remove the crankshaft balancer. See Crankshaft Damper in Engine Mechanical.

9. Remove the camshaft position sensors. See Camshaft Position Sensor in Engine Performance & Emission Controls.

10. Remove the camshaft position actuator solenoid valves from the front cover. See Camshaft Position Actuator Solenoid Valves in Engine Performance & Emission Controls.

11. Remove the alternator. See Alternator in Engine Electrical.

✳✳ WARNING

There are a total of 22 M8 bolts that must be removed and 3 optional M12 bolts that may need to be removed before the front cover will separate from the engine block.

12. Remove the engine front cover.

13. Use a flat-bladed tool in order to remove the crankshaft oil seal. Use care not

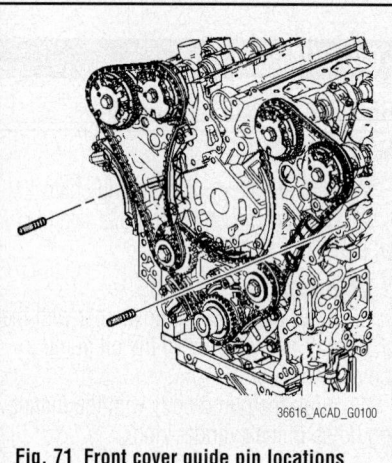

Fig. 71 Front cover guide pin locations

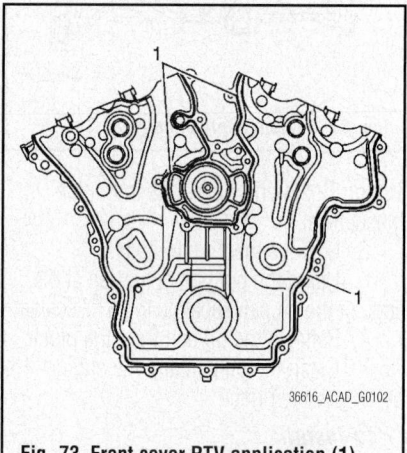

Fig. 73 Front cover RTV application (1)

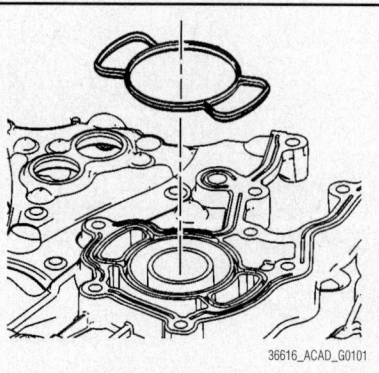

Fig. 72 Front cover block seal location

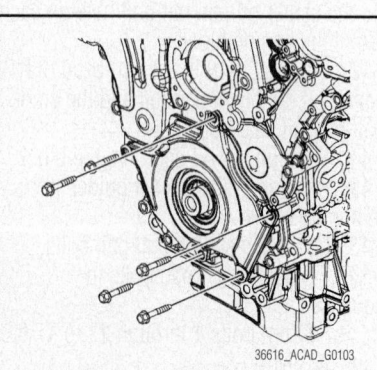

Fig. 74 Front cover deadener bolt locations

to damage the engine front cover or the crankshaft.

To install:

14. Use the J 29184 or equivalent to install the crankshaft front oil seal.

15. Install front cover:

a. Install the 8 mm (0.315 in) guide from the EN-46109 pins into the cylinder block positions as shown.

b. Install the NEW engine front cover to cylinder block seal.

c. Place a 3 mm (0.118 in) bead of RTV sealant, GM P/N 12378521 (Canadian P/N 88901148) or equivalent, on the engine front cover.

d. Place the engine front cover onto the EN-46109 pins and slide into position.

e. Remove the EN-46109 pins from the cylinder block.

f. Install the engine front cover deadener.

➡ **The front cover and deadener may vary in appearance depending on application but are retained by the same number of bolts.**

g. Loosely install the engine front cover bolts to hold the engine front cover deadener into position.

h. Loosely install the remaining engine front cover bolts.

➡ **Engine front cover bolts in the number (23) location are model dependent and may not apply.**

i. Tighten the engine front cover bolts (1-22) in sequence shown to 14 ft lbs. (20 Nm).

j. Tighten the engine front cover bolts (1-22) a second pass in sequence an additional 60 degrees.

k. Tighten the engine front cover bolts (23) to 48 ft. lbs. (65 Nm).

16. Install the alternator.

17. Install the camshaft position actuator solenoid valves to the front cover.

18. Install the camshaft position sensors.

19. Install the crankshaft balancer.

20. Install the power steering pump.

21. Install the water pump pulley.

22. Install the water outlet housing assembly.

23. Install the drive belt tensioner.

24. Remove the EN-48383 from the right camshafts.

25. Remove the EN-48383 from the left camshafts.

26. Install the valve covers.

27. Install the intake manifold.

28. Install engine.

29. Start engine and check for leaks.

TIMING CHAIN AND SPROCKETS

REMOVAL & INSTALLATION

See Figures 76 through 110.

1. Remove the spark plugs in order to ease crankshaft/engine rotation.

2. Remove front cover. See Timing Chain Cover and Seal in Engine Mechanical.

3. Using the EN-48589 , rotate the crankshaft until the left cylinder head camshafts align with the EN-48383 and the right cylinder head camshafts align with the EN-48383

4. Install the EN-48383-1 to the left camshafts.

5. Remove the right bank secondary camshaft drive chain tensioner.

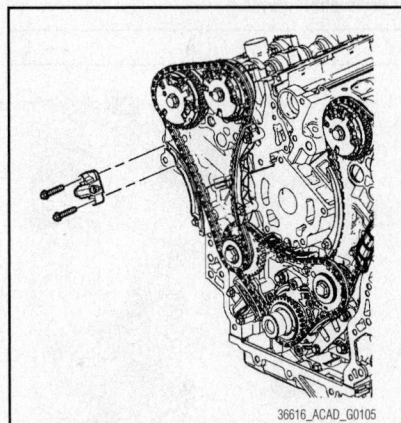

36616_ACAD_G0105

Fig. 76 Right bank secondary camshaft drive chain tensioner

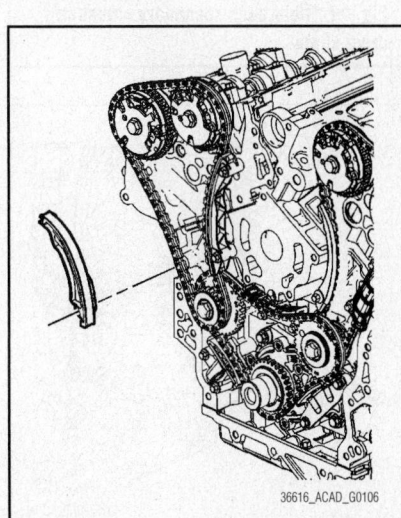

36616_ACAD_G0106

Fig. 77 Right bank secondary camshaft drive chain shoe

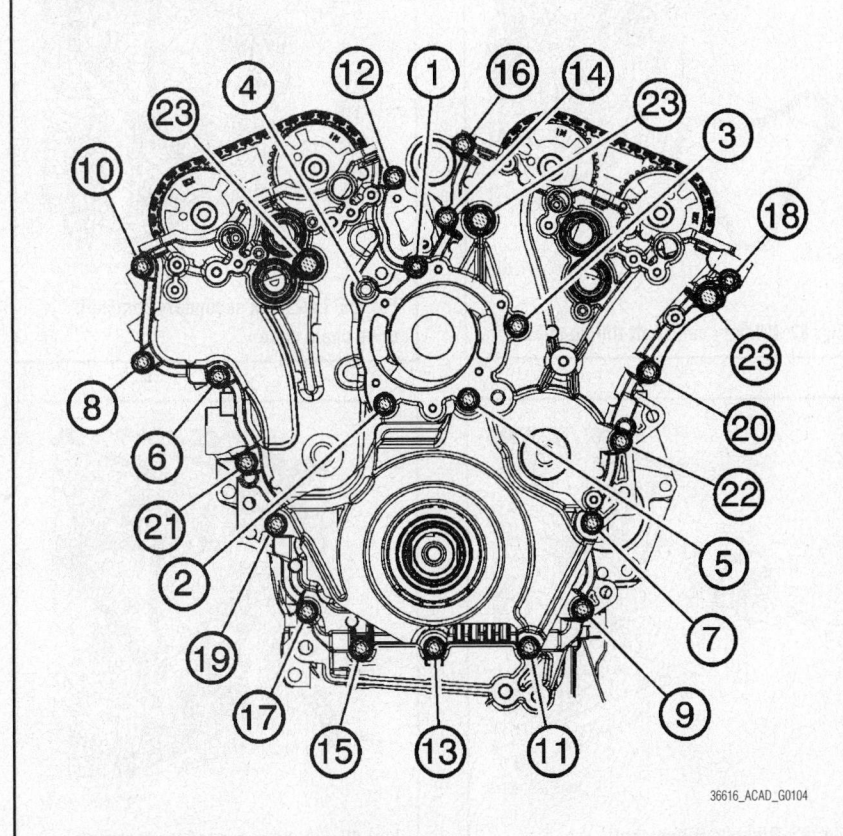

36616_ACAD_G0104

Fig. 75 Front cover bolt tightening sequence

6. Remove and discard the right secondary camshaft drive chain tensioner gasket.

7. Remove the right bank secondary camshaft drive chain shoe.

8. Remove the right bank secondary camshaft drive chain guide.

9. Remove the right secondary camshaft drive chain from the right camshaft position actuators and the right camshaft intermediate drive chain idler sprocket.

10. Remove the primary camshaft drive chain tensioner.

11. Remove and discard the primary camshaft drive chain tensioner gasket.

12. Remove the primary camshaft drive chain upper guide.

13. Remove the primary camshaft timing chain.

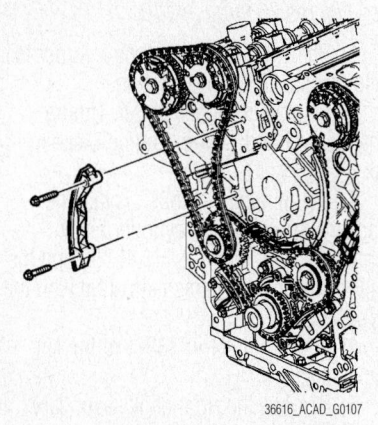

Fig. 78 Right bank secondary camshaft drive chain guide

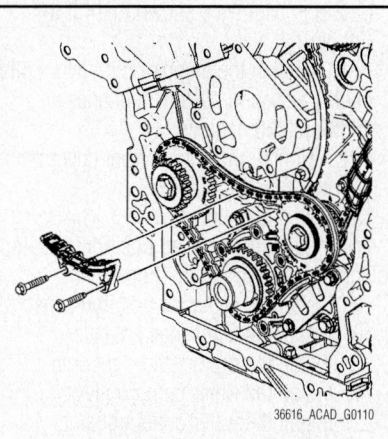

Fig. 81 Primary camshaft drive chain upper guide

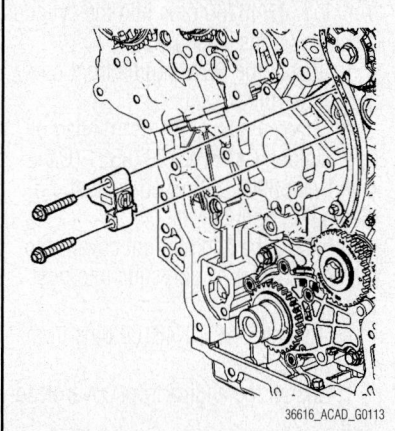

Fig. 84 Left bank secondary camshaft drive chain tensioner

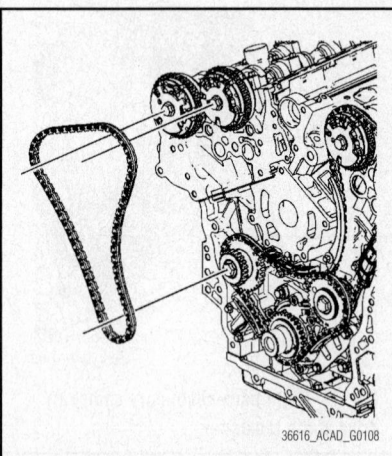

Fig. 79 Right bank secondary camshaft drive chain

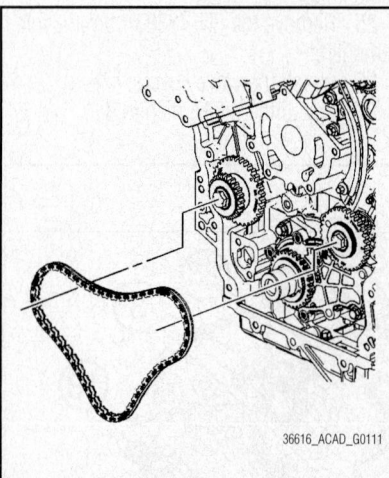

Fig. 82 Primary camshaft timing chain

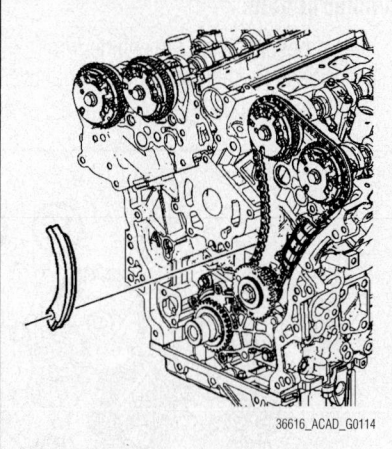

Fig. 85 Left bank secondary camshaft drive chain shoe

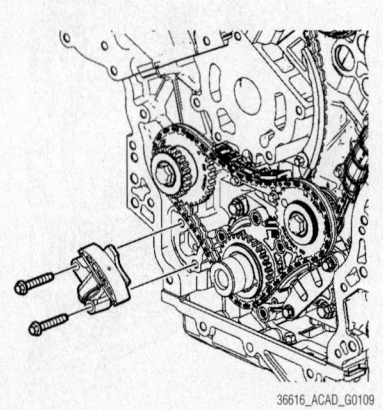

Fig. 80 Primary camshaft drive chain tensioner

Fig. 83 Right bank camshaft intermediate drive chain idler

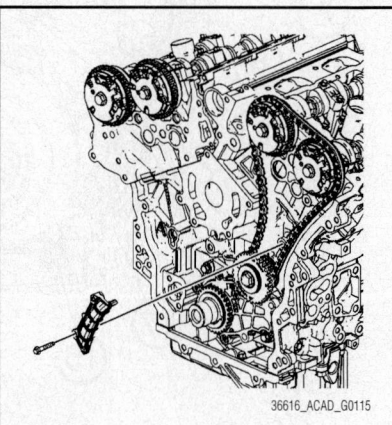

Fig. 86 Left bank secondary camshaft drive chain guide

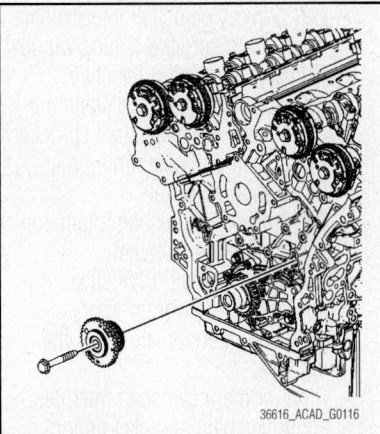

Fig. 87 Left bank camshaft intermediate drive chain idler

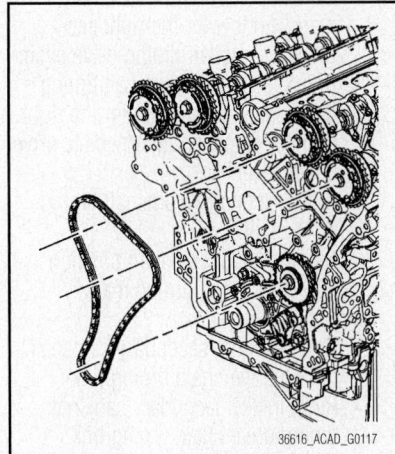

Fig. 88 Left bank secondary camshaft drive chain

14. Remove the right bank camshaft intermediate drive chain idler

15. Remove the left bank secondary camshaft drive chain tensioner.

16. Remove and discard the left secondary camshaft drive chain tensioner gasket.

17. Remove the left bank secondary camshaft drive chain shoe.

18. Remove the left bank secondary camshaft drive chain guide.

19. Remove the left bank camshaft intermediate drive chain idler.

20. Remove the left bank secondary camshaft drive chain.

21. Clean and inspect all of the camshaft timing drive components. Replace components as necessary.

To install:

✳✳ WARNING

All camshafts must be locked in place before installation of any camshaft drive chains.

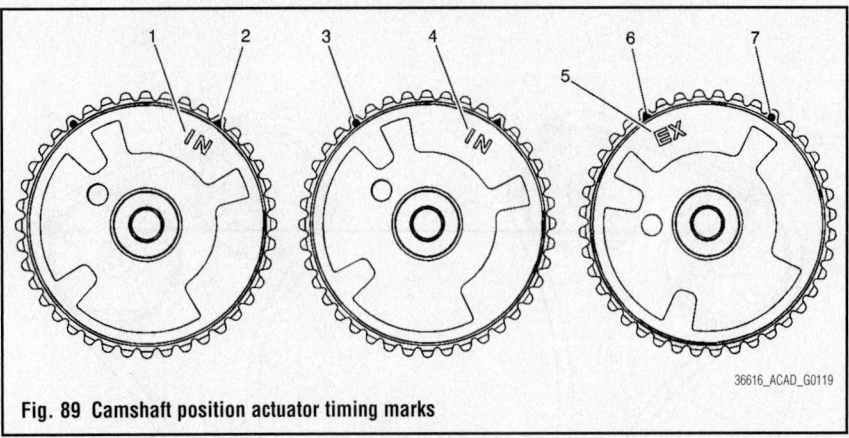

Fig. 89 Camshaft position actuator timing marks

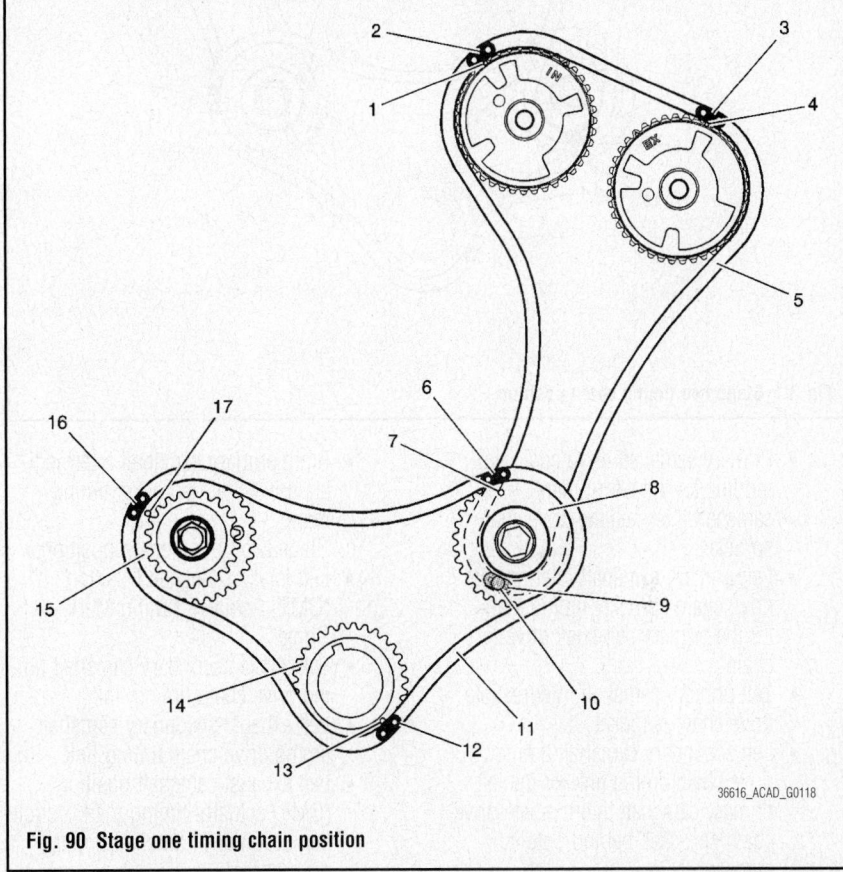

Fig. 90 Stage one timing chain position

22. Camshaft and timing chain positioning:

a. Camshaft position actuator timing marks
- Right intake camshaft position actuator identifier
- Right intake camshaft position actuator right side timing mark - triangle
- Left intake camshaft position actuator left side timing mark - circle
- Left intake camshaft position actuator identifier
- Exhaust camshaft position actuator identifier
- Exhaust camshaft position actuator right side timing mark - triangle
- Exhaust camshaft position actuator left side timing mark - circle

b. Stage one timing chain position:
- Left intake camshaft position (CMP) actuator timing mark - circle
- Left intake secondary camshaft timing drive chain timing link
- Left exhaust secondary camshaft timing drive chain timing link
- Left exhaust camshaft position (CMP) actuator timing mark - circle
- Left secondary camshaft timing drive chain

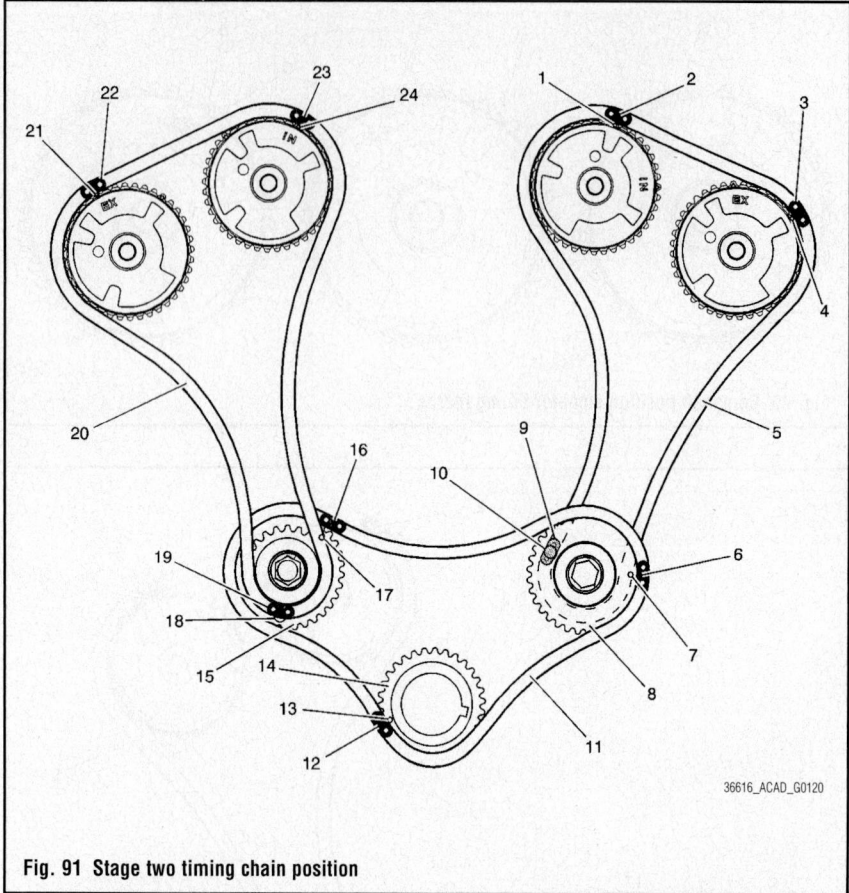

Fig. 91 Stage two timing chain position

- Primary camshaft drive chain timing link for the left primary camshaft intermediate drive chain sprocket
- Left primary camshaft intermediate drive chain sprocket timing mark for the primary camshaft drive chain
- Left primary camshaft intermediate drive chain sprocket
- Left secondary camshaft timing drive chain timing link for the left primary camshaft intermediate drive chain sprocket, behind hole in sprocket
- Left primary camshaft intermediate drive chain sprocket timing window for the left secondary camshaft timing drive chain timing link
- Primary camshaft drive chain
- Primary camshaft drive chain timing link for the crankshaft sprocket
- Crankshaft sprocket timing mark
- Crankshaft sprocket
- Right primary camshaft intermediate drive chain sprocket
- Primary camshaft drive chain timing link for the right primary camshaft intermediate drive chain sprocket

- Right primary camshaft intermediate drive chain sprocket timing mark
- c. Stage two timing chain position:
- Left Intake Camshaft Position (CMP) Actuator Timing Mark - Circle
- Left intake secondary camshaft timing drive chain timing link
- Left exhaust secondary camshaft timing drive chain timing link
- Left exhaust camshaft position (CMP) actuator timing mark - circle
- Left secondary camshaft timing drive chain
- Primary camshaft drive chain timing link for the left primary camshaft intermediate drive chain sprocket
- Left primary camshaft intermediate drive chain sprocket timing mark for the primary camshaft drive chain
- Left primary camshaft intermediate drive chain sprocket
- Left secondary camshaft timing drive chain timing link for the left primary camshaft intermediate drive chain sprocket, behind hole in sprocket

- Left primary camshaft intermediate drive chain sprocket timing window
- Primary camshaft drive chain
- Primary camshaft drive chain timing link for the crankshaft sprocket
- Crankshaft sprocket timing mark
- Crankshaft sprocket
- Right primary camshaft intermediate drive chain sprocket
- Primary camshaft drive chain timing link for the right primary camshaft intermediate drive chain sprocket
- Right primary camshaft intermediate drive chain sprocket timing mark for the primary camshaft drive chain
- Right primary camshaft intermediate drive chain sprocket timing mark/window for the right secondary camshaft timing drive chain
- Right secondary camshaft timing drive chain timing link for the right primary camshaft intermediate drive chain sprocket
- Right secondary camshaft timing drive chain
- Right exhaust camshaft position (CMP) actuator timing mark - triangle
- Right exhaust secondary camshaft timing drive chain timing link
- Right intake secondary camshaft timing drive chain timing link
- Right intake camshaft position (CMP) actuator timing mark - triangle

23. Ensure the crankshaft is in the stage one timing position with the crankshaft sprocket timing mark (1) aligned to the stage one timing mark on the oil pump cover (2).

24. Install the left secondary camshaft drive chain.

a. Place the left secondary camshaft

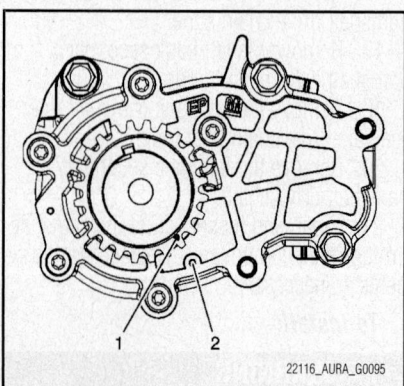

Fig. 92 Crankshaft sprocket timing mark (1) aligned to the stage one timing mark on the oil pump cover (2)

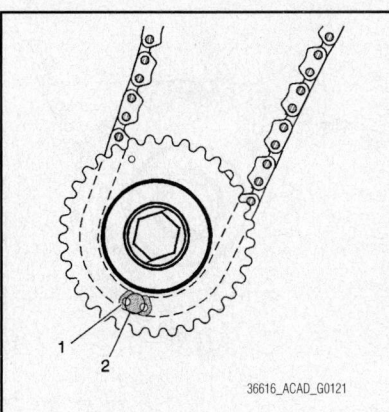

Fig. 93 Secondary camshaft drive chain positioning—bottom

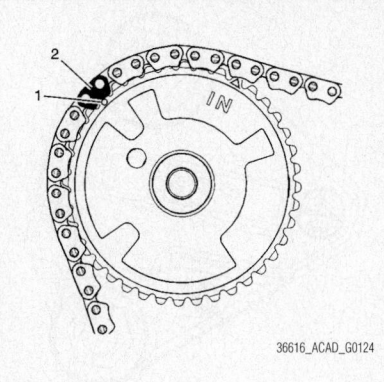

Fig. 96 Left intake camshaft position actuator sprocket alignment

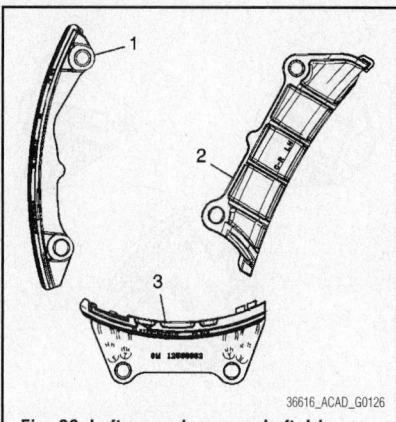

Fig. 98 Left secondary camshaft drive chain guide view

drive chain around the inner sprocket of the left camshaft intermediate drive chain idler with the timing camshaft drive chain link (1) aligned to the alignment access hole (2) made in the left camshaft intermediate drive chain idler outer sprocket.

b. Wrap the secondary camshaft drive chain around both left actuator drive sprockets.

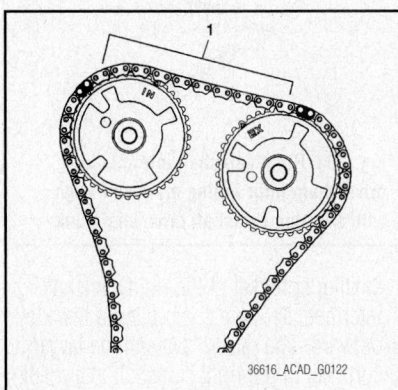

Fig. 94 Secondary camshaft drive chain positioning—top

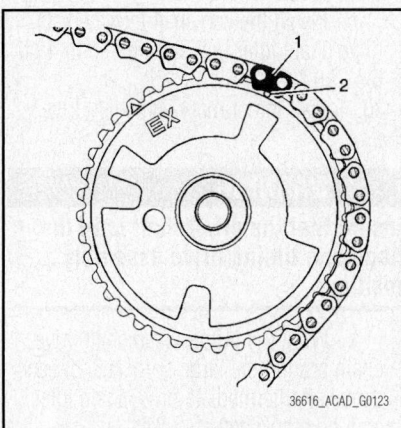

Fig. 95 Left exhaust camshaft position actuator sprocket alignment

c. Ensure there are 10 links (1) between the timing camshaft drive chain links for the camshaft position actuator sprockets.

d. Align the left exhaust camshaft position actuator sprocket alignment circle mark (2) with the timing camshaft drive chain link (1).

e. Align the left intake camshaft position actuator sprocket alignment circle mark (1) with the timing camshaft drive chain link (2).

25. Install the left bank camshaft intermediate drive chain idler.

a. Ensure that the left camshaft intermediate drive chain idler (2) is being installed. The recessed hub (3) and the larger sprocket of the left camshaft intermediate drive chain idler is installed outward. The raised hub and the smaller sprocket of the left camshaft intermediate drive chain idler is installed towards the block.

b. Place the left camshaft intermediate drive chain idler to the cylinder block.

c. Install the camshaft intermediate drive chain idler bolt and tighten to 43 ft. lbs. (58 Nm).

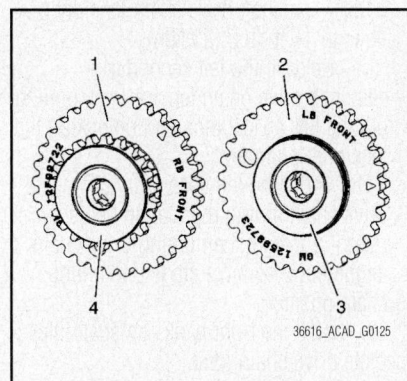

Fig. 97 Left camshaft intermediate drive chain idler view

26. Install the left bank secondary camshaft drive chain guide.

a. Ensure that the left secondary camshaft drive chain guide (2) is being installed.

b. Position the left secondary camshaft drive chain guide.

c. Install the secondary camshaft drive chain guide bolts and tighten to 17 ft. lbs. (23 Nm).

27. Install the left bank secondary camshaft drive chain shoe.

a. Ensure that the left secondary camshaft drive chain shoe (2) is being installed.

b. Position the left secondary camshaft drive chain shoe.

c. Install the secondary camshaft drive chain shoe bolt and tighten to 17 ft. lbs. (23 Nm).

28. Install the left bank secondary camshaft drive chain tensioner.

a. Ensure that the left secondary camshaft drive chain tensioner (2) is being installed.

b. Using the J-45027 tool , reset the left secondary camshaft drive chain tensioner plunger.

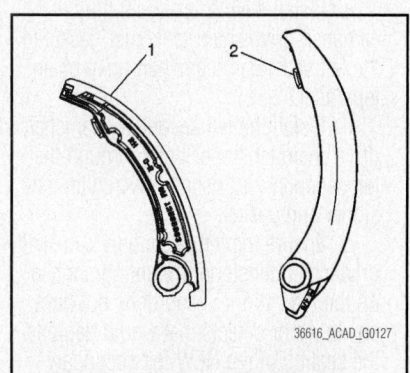

Fig. 99 Left secondary camshaft drive chain shoe view

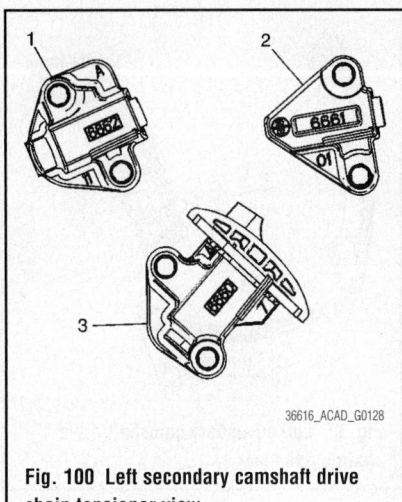

Fig. 100 Left secondary camshaft drive chain tensioner view

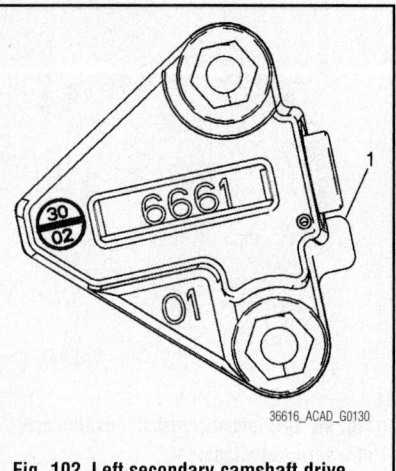

Fig. 102 Left secondary camshaft drive chain tensioner gasket tab

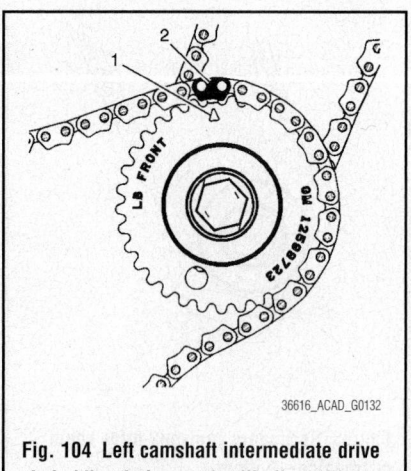

Fig. 104 Left camshaft intermediate drive chain idler timing mark will align with a timing camshaft drive chain link

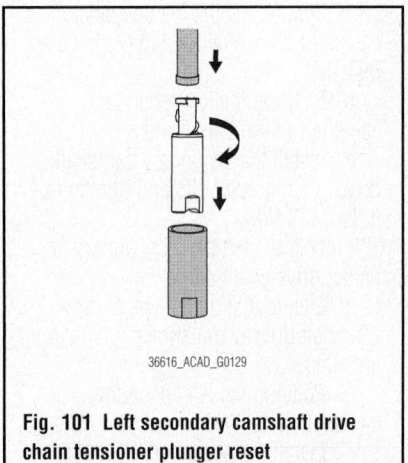
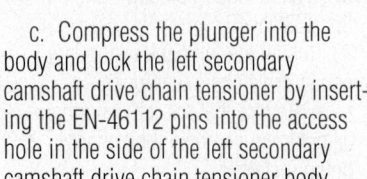

Fig. 101 Left secondary camshaft drive chain tensioner plunger reset

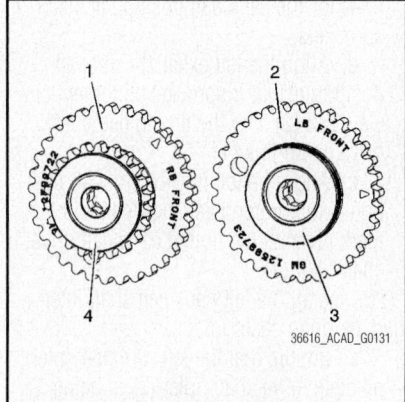

Fig. 103 Right camshaft intermediate drive chain idler view

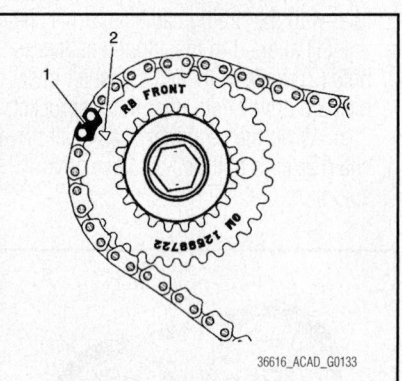

Fig. 105 Right camshaft intermediate drive chain idler timing mark will align with a timing camshaft drive chain link

c. Compress the plunger into the body and lock the left secondary camshaft drive chain tensioner by inserting the EN-46112 pins into the access hole in the side of the left secondary camshaft drive chain tensioner body.

d. Slowly release pressure on the left secondary camshaft drive chain tensioner. The left secondary camshaft drive chain tensioner should remain compressed.

e. Install a NEW left secondary camshaft drive chain tensioner gasket to the left secondary camshaft drive chain tensioner.

f. Install the left secondary camshaft drive chain tensioner bolts through the left secondary camshaft drive chain tensioner and gasket.

g. Ensure the left secondary camshaft drive chain tensioner mounting surface on the left cylinder head does not have any burrs or defects that would degrade the sealing of the NEW left secondary camshaft drive chain tensioner gasket.

h. Place the left secondary camshaft

drive chain tensioner into position and loosely install the bolts to the block.

i. Verify the proper placement of the left secondary camshaft drive chain tensioner gasket tab (1).

j. First pass, tighten the left secondary camshaft drive chain tensioner bolts to 44 inch lbs. (5 Nm).

k. Second pass, tighten the left secondary camshaft drive chain tensioner bolts to 17 ft. lbs. (23 Nm).

l. Release the left secondary camshaft drive chain tensioner by pulling out the EN-46112 pins and unlocking the tensioner plunger.

m. Verify the left secondary camshaft drive chain timing mark alignments by referring to camshaft timing drive chain alignment diagram - stage one timing chain position.

29. Install the right bank camshaft intermediate drive chain idler.

a. Ensure that the right camshaft intermediate drive chain idler (1) is being installed. The recessed hub (4) and the

smaller sprocket of the right camshaft intermediate drive chain idler is installed outward. The raised hub and the larger sprocket of the right camshaft intermediate drive chain idler is installed towards the block.

b. Install the right camshaft intermediate drive chain idler.

c. Install the camshaft intermediate drive chain idler bolt and tighten to 43 ft. lbs. (58 Nm).

30. Install the primary camshaft drive chain.

✳✳ WARNING

Ensure that the crankshaft is in the stage one timing drive assembly position.

a. Wrap the primary camshaft drive chain around the large sprockets of each camshaft intermediate drive chain idler and the crankshaft sprocket.

b. The left camshaft intermediate drive chain idler timing mark (1) will

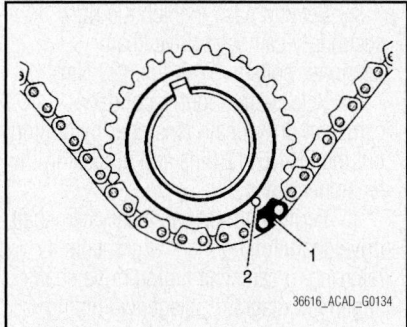

Fig. 106 Crankshaft sprocket timing mark will align with a timing camshaft drive chain link

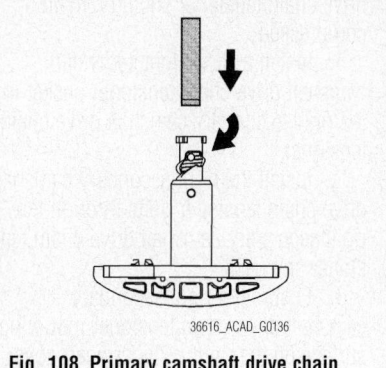

Fig. 108 Primary camshaft drive chain tensioner reset

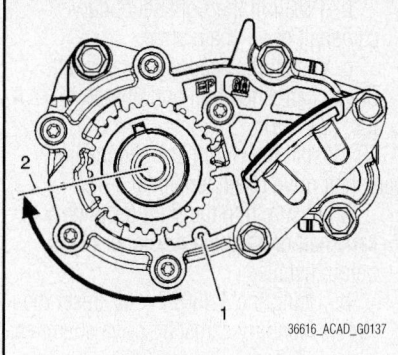

Fig. 109 Crankshaft sprocket stage 2 position

align with a timing camshaft drive chain link (2).

c. The right camshaft intermediate drive chain idler timing mark (2) will align with a timing camshaft drive chain link (1).

d. The crankshaft sprocket timing mark (2) will align with a timing camshaft drive chain link (1).

e. Ensure all the timing marks (2, 3, 6) are properly aligned with the timing camshaft drive chain links (1, 4, 5).

31. Install the primary upper camshaft drive chain guide.

a. Ensure the upper primary camshaft drive chain guide (3) is being installed.

b. Install the upper primary camshaft drive chain guides.

c. Install the upper primary camshaft drive chain guide bolts and tighten to 17 ft. lbs. (23 Nm).

32. Install the primary camshaft drive chain tensioner.

a. Ensure that the primary camshaft drive chain tensioner (3) is being installed.

b. Using the J-45027 tool , reset the primary camshaft drive chain tensioner plunger.

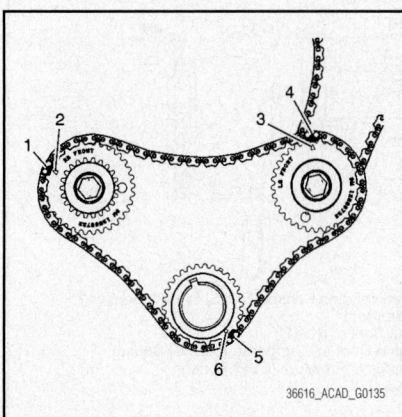

Fig. 107 Primary camshaft drive chain alignment

c. Install the plunger into the primary camshaft drive chain tensioner body.

d. Compress the plunger into the body and lock the primary camshaft drive chain tensioner by inserting the EN-46112 pins into the access hole in the side of the primary camshaft drive chain tensioner body.

e. Slowly release pressure on the primary camshaft drive chain tensioner. The primary camshaft drive chain tensioner should remain compressed.

f. Install a NEW primary camshaft drive chain tensioner gasket to the primary camshaft drive chain tensioner.

g. Install the primary camshaft drive chain tensioner bolts through the primary camshaft drive chain tensioner and gasket.

h. Ensure the primary camshaft drive chain tensioner mounting surface on the engine block does not have any burrs or defects that would degrade the sealing of the NEW primary camshaft drive chain tensioner gasket.

i. Place the primary camshaft drive chain tensioner into position and loosely install the bolts to the block.

j. Verify the proper placement of the primary camshaft drive chain tensioner gasket tab (1).

k. First pass, tighten the primary camshaft drive chain tensioner bolts to 44 inch lbs. (5 Nm).

l. Second pass, tighten the primary camshaft drive chain tensioner bolts to 17 ft. lbs. (23 Nm).

m. Release the primary camshaft drive chain tensioner by pulling out the EN-46112 pins and unlocking the tensioner plunger.

n. Verify the primary camshaft drive chain timing mark alignments by referring to camshaft timing drive chain align-

ment diagram - stage one timing chain position.

33. Remove the EN 48383-1 from the rear of the left camshafts.

34. Using the EN-48589 socket , rotate the crankshaft and crankshaft sprocket from the stage 1 alignment position (1) to the stage 2 alignment position (2), 115 crankshaft degrees, in order to install the right secondary camshaft drive chain components.

35. Install the EN-48383-2 onto the rear of the left camshafts.

36. Install the EN 48383-3 onto the rear of the right camshafts.

37. Install the right bank secondary camshaft drive chain guide.

38. Ensure that the right secondary camshaft drive chain guide (1) is being installed.

a. Position the right secondary camshaft drive chain guide.

b. Install the secondary camshaft drive chain guide bolts and tighten to 17 ft. lbs. (23 Nm).

39. Install the right bank secondary camshaft drive chain shoe.

a. Ensure that the right secondary camshaft drive chain shoe (1) is being installed.

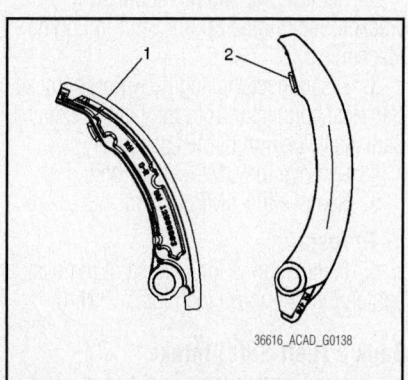

Fig. 110 Right secondary camshaft drive chain shoe

b. Position the right secondary camshaft drive chain shoe.

c. Install the secondary camshaft drive chain shoe bolt and tighten to 17 ft. lbs. (23 Nm).

40. Install the right bank secondary camshaft drive chain tensioner.

a. Ensure that the right secondary camshaft drive chain tensioner (1) is being installed.

b. Using the J 45027 tool , reset the right secondary camshaft drive chain tensioner plunger.

c. Install the plunger into the right secondary camshaft drive chain tensioner body.

d. Compress the plunger into the body and lock the right secondary camshaft drive chain tensioner by inserting the EN 46112 pins into the access hole in the side of the right secondary camshaft drive chain tensioner body.

e. Slowly release pressure on the right secondary camshaft drive chain tensioner. The right secondary camshaft drive chain tensioner should remain compressed.

f. Install a NEW right secondary camshaft drive chain tensioner gasket to the right secondary camshaft drive chain tensioner.

g. Install the right secondary camshaft drive chain tensioner bolts through the right secondary camshaft drive chain tensioner and gasket.

h. Ensure the right secondary camshaft drive chain tensioner mounting surface on the right cylinder head does not have any burrs or defects that would degrade the sealing of the NEW right secondary camshaft drive chain tensioner gasket

i. Place the right secondary camshaft drive chain tensioner into position and loosely install the bolts to the block.

j. Verify the proper placement of the right secondary camshaft drive chain tensioner gasket tab (1).

k. First pass, tighten the right secondary camshaft drive chain tensioner bolts to 44 inch lbs. (5 Nm).

l. Second pass, tighten the right secondary camshaft drive chain tensioner bolts to 17 ft. lbs. (23 Nm).

m. Release the right secondary camshaft drive chain tensioner by pulling out the EN-46112 pins and unlocking the tensioner plunger.

n. Verify the right secondary camshaft drive chain timing mark alignments by referring to camshaft timing drive chain alignment diagram - stage two timing chain position.

41. Remove the EN-48383 from the right camshafts.

42. Remove the EN-48383 from the left camshafts.

43. Install the engine front cover. See Timing Chain Cover and Seal in Engine Mechanical.

VALVE LASH

ADJUSTMENT

All engines utilize hydraulic lash adjusters; no adjustment is necessary.

ENGINE PERFORMANCE & EMISSION CONTROLS

COMPONENT LOCATIONS

See Figures 111 through 114.

CAMSHAFT POSITION (CMP) SENSOR

LOCATION

See Figure 115.

REMOVAL & INSTALLATION

Bank 2 (Left Side) Exhaust

1. Remove the air cleaner assembly, if necessary.

2. Remove the engine mount strut bracket. See Engine Mount Strut in Engine Mechanical.

3. Disconnect the engine wiring harness electrical connector from the bank 2 exhaust Camshaft Position (CMP) sensor.

4. Remove the CMP sensor bolt.

5. Remove the CMP sensor.

To install:

6. Installation is the reverse of removal, tighten the bolt to 89 inch lbs. (10 Nm).

Bank 2 (Left Side) Intake

1. Remove the air cleaner assembly, if necessary.

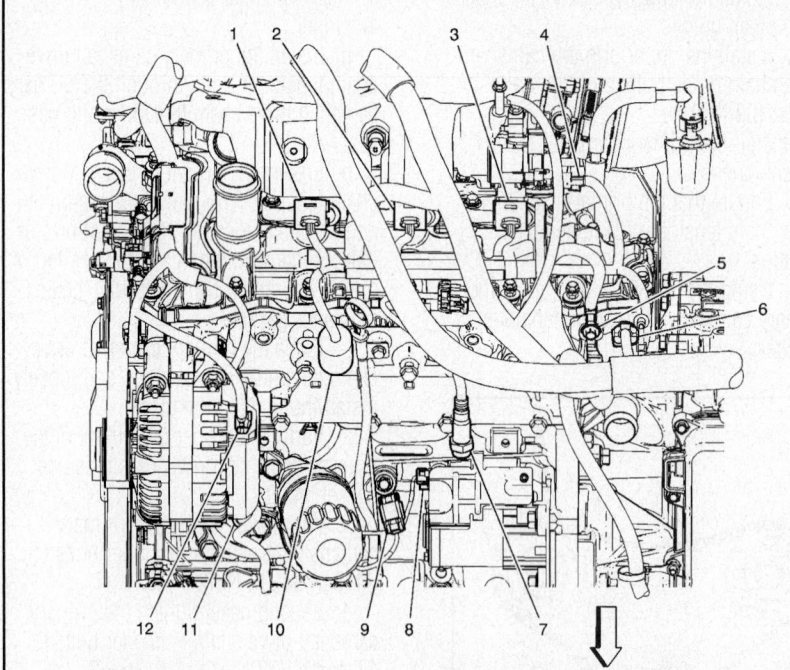

1. Ignition Coil 2
2. Ignition Coil 4
3. Ignition Coil 6
4. Evaporative Emission (EVAP) Canister Purge Solenoid Valve
5. G114
6. High Pressure Fuel Pump (2009)
7. Heated Oxygen Sensor (HO2S) Bank 2 Sensor 1
8. Starter Motor
9. Knock Sensor (KS) 2
10. Engine Coolant Temperature (ECT) Sensor
11. Engine Oil Pressure (EOP) Sensor
12. Generator

36616_ACAD_G0047

Fig. 111 Engine component view—front

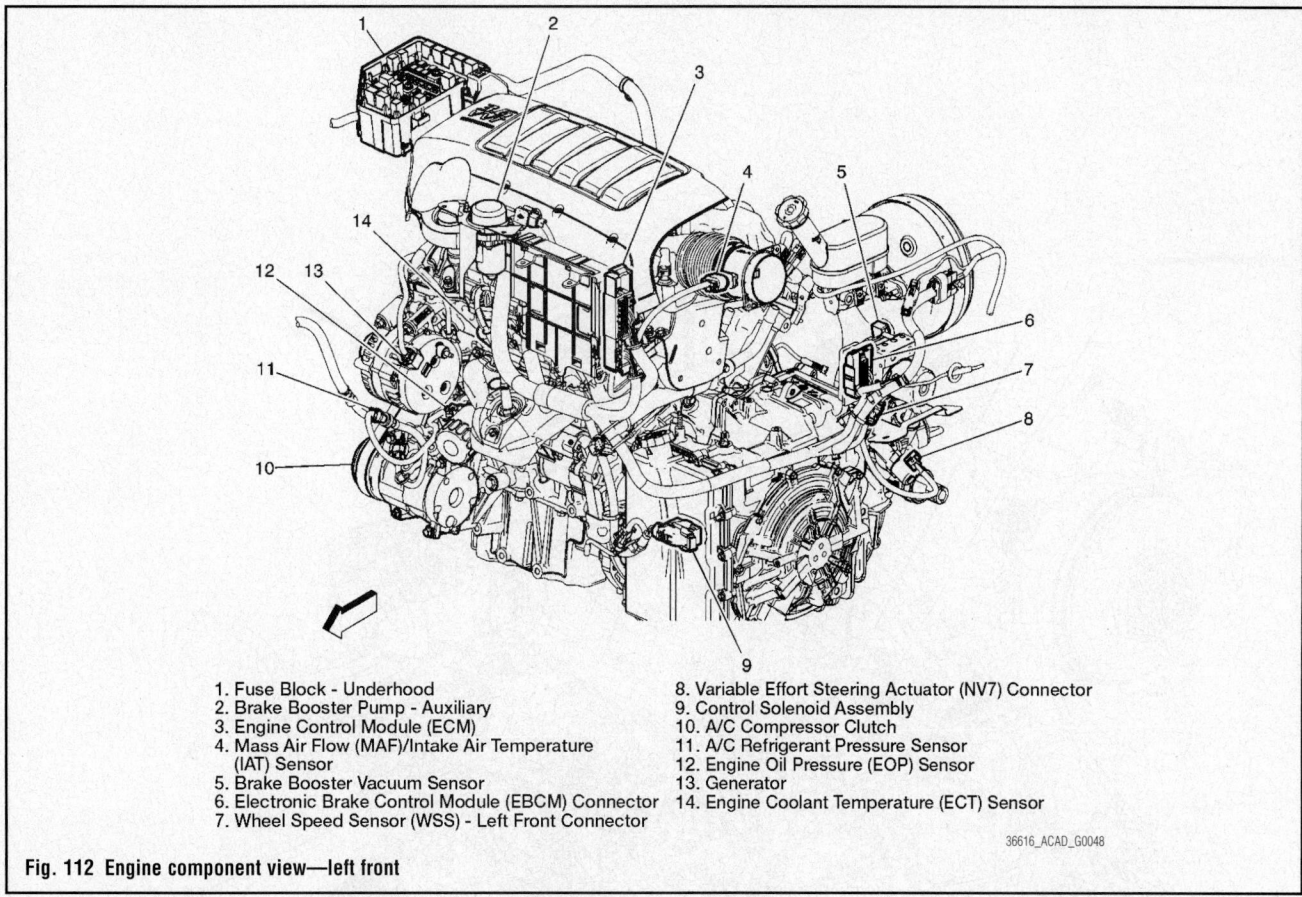

1. Fuse Block - Underhood
2. Brake Booster Pump - Auxiliary
3. Engine Control Module (ECM)
4. Mass Air Flow (MAF)/Intake Air Temperature (IAT) Sensor
5. Brake Booster Vacuum Sensor
6. Electronic Brake Control Module (EBCM) Connector
7. Wheel Speed Sensor (WSS) - Left Front Connector
8. Variable Effort Steering Actuator (NV7) Connector
9. Control Solenoid Assembly
10. A/C Compressor Clutch
11. A/C Refrigerant Pressure Sensor
12. Engine Oil Pressure (EOP) Sensor
13. Generator
14. Engine Coolant Temperature (ECT) Sensor

36616_ACAD_G0048

Fig. 112 Engine component view—left front

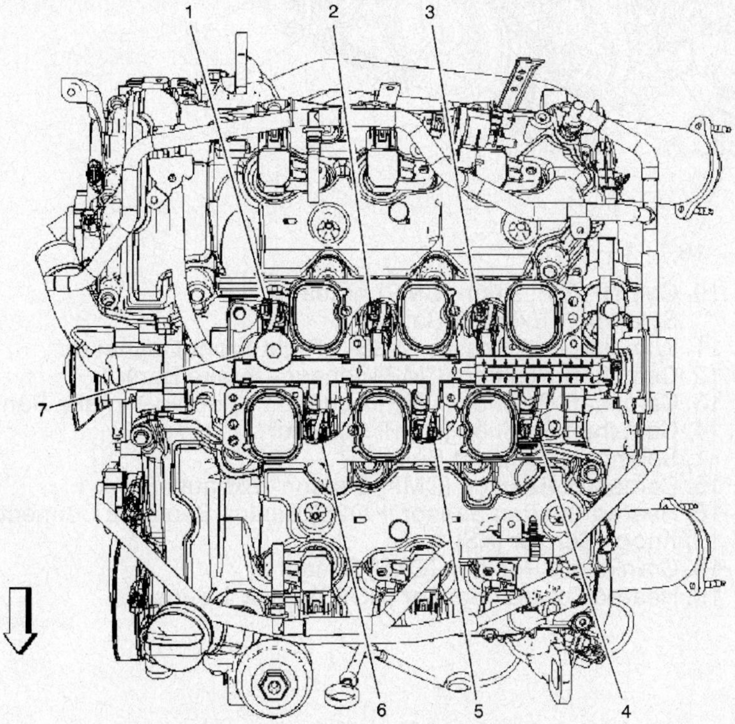

1. Fuel Injector 1
2. Fuel Injector 3
3. Fuel Injector 5
4. Fuel Injector 6
5. Fuel Injector 4
6. Fuel Injector 2
7. Fuel Rail Pressure (FRP) Sensor

36616_ACAD_G0049

Fig. 113 Engine component view—top

2. Remove the engine mount strut bracket. See Engine Mount Strut in Engine Mechanical.

3. Remove the radiator inlet hose from the water outlet.

4. Remove the power steering fluid reservoir bracket bolts. See Power Steering Pump in Steering.

5. Remove and reposition the power steering fluid reservoir bracket (2) out of the way.

6. Disconnect the engine wiring harness electrical connector from the bank 2 intake Camshaft Position (CMP) sensor.

7. Remove the CMP sensor bolt.

8. Remove the CMP sensor.

To install:

9. Installation is the reverse of removal, tighten the bolt to 89 inch lbs. (10 Nm).

Bank 1 (Right Side) Exhaust

1. Remove the air cleaner assembly, if necessary.

2. Remove the engine mount strut bracket. See Engine Mount Strut in Engine Mechanical.

3. Disconnect the engine wiring harness electrical connector from the bank 1 exhaust Camshaft Position (CMP) sensor.

4. Remove the CMP sensor bolt.

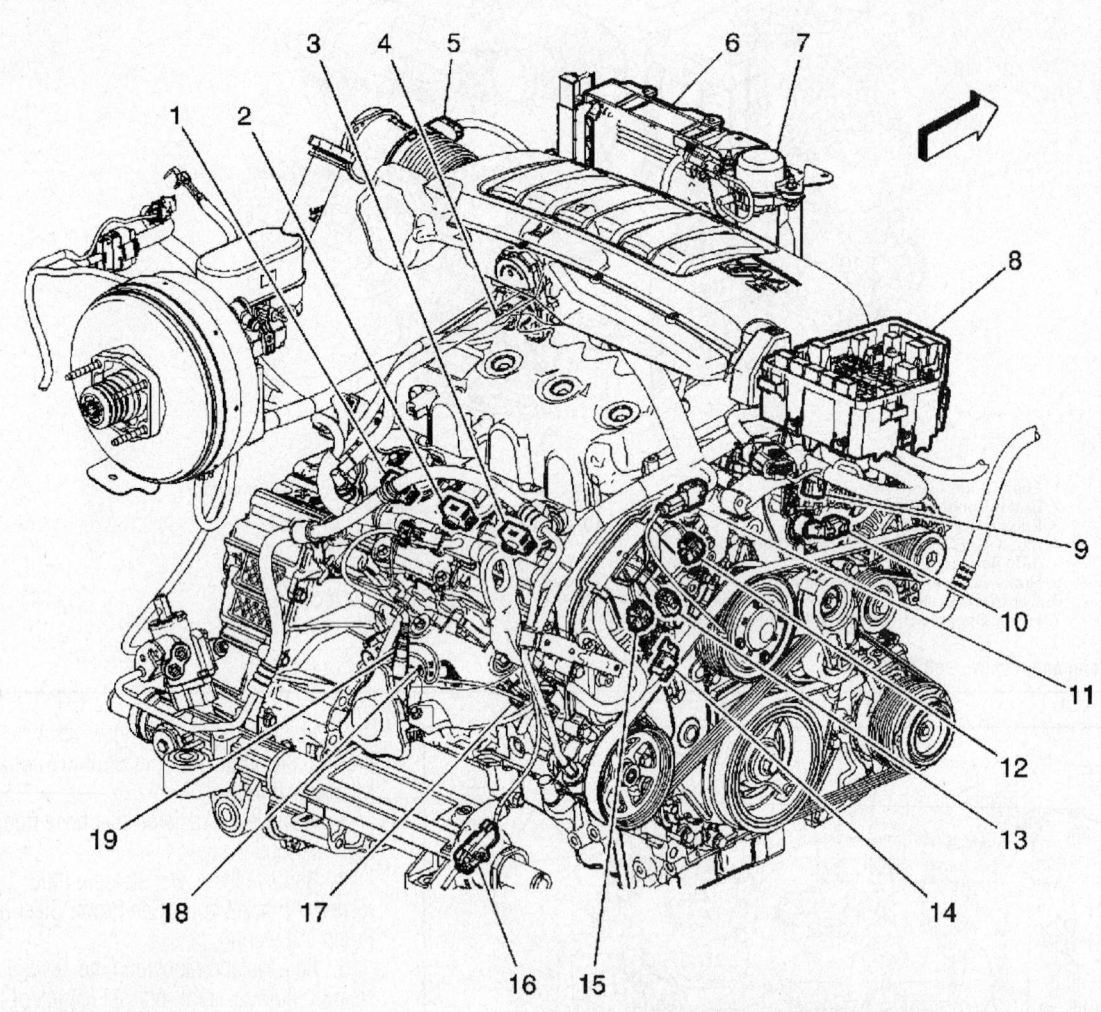

1. Ignition Coil 5
2. Ignition Coil 3
3. Ignition Coil 1
4. Throttle Body
5. Mass Air Flow (MAF)/Intake Air Temperature (IAT) Sensor
6. Engine Control Module (ECM)
7. Brake Booster Pump - Auxiliary
8. Fuse Block - Underhood
9. Camshaft Position (CMP) Actuator Solenoid - Intake Bank 2
10. Camshaft Position (CMP) Actuator Solenoid - Exhaust Bank 2
11. Wheel Speed Sensor (WSS) - Right Front Connector
12. Camshaft Position (CMP) Sensor - Intake Bank 1
13. Camshaft Position (CMP) Actuator Solenoid - Intake Bank 1
14. Camshaft Position (CMP) Actuator Solenoid - Exhaust Bank 1
15. Camshaft Position (CMP) Sensor - Exhaust Bank 1
16. Heated Oxygen Sensor (HO2S) Bank 1 Sensor 2 Connector
17. Knock Sensor (KS) 1
18. Crankshaft Position (CKP) Sensor
19. Heated Oxygen Sensor (HO2S) Bank 1 Sensor 1

36616_ACAD_G0050

Fig. 114 Engine component view—right rear

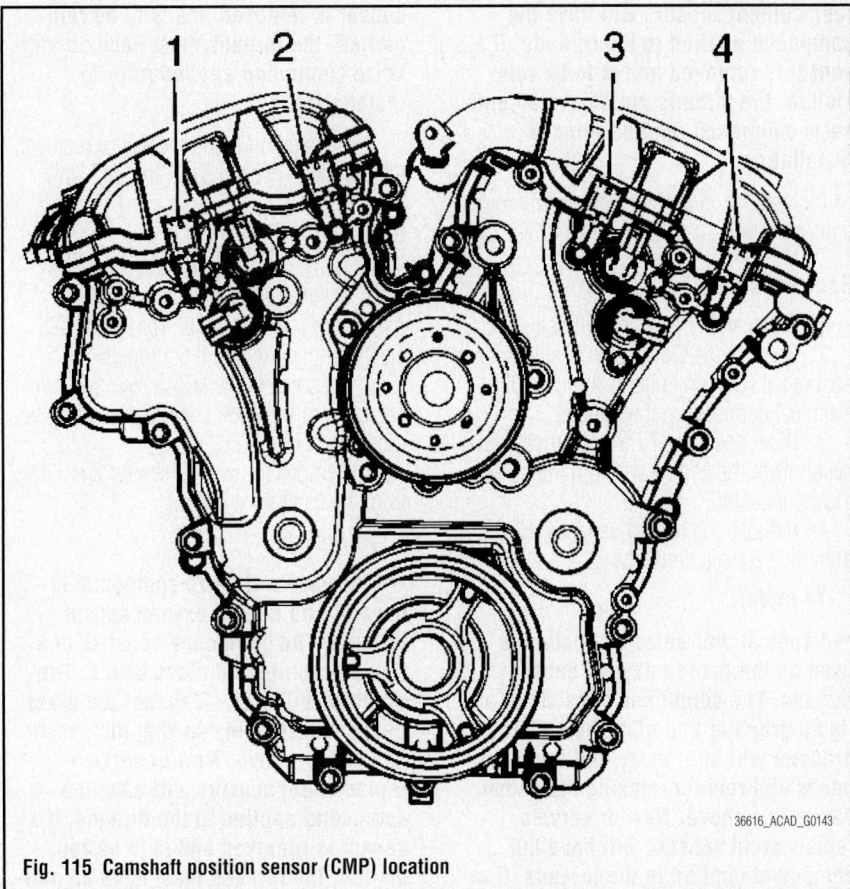

Fig. 115 Camshaft position sensor (CMP) location

5. Remove the CMP sensor.

To install:

6. Installation is the reverse of removal, tighten the bolt to 89 inch lbs. (10 Nm).

Bank 1 (Right Side) Intake

1. Remove the air cleaner assembly, if necessary.

2. Remove the engine mount strut bracket. See Engine Mount Strut in Engine Mechanical.

3. Disconnect the engine wiring harness electrical connector from the bank 1 intake Camshaft Position (CMP) sensor.

4. Remove the CMP sensor bolt.

5. Remove the CMP sensor.

To install:

6. Installation is the reverse of removal, tighten the bolt to 89 inch lbs. (10 Nm).

CRANKSHAFT POSITION (CKP) SENSOR

LOCATION

See Figure 116.

REMOVAL & INSTALLATION

See Figure 116.

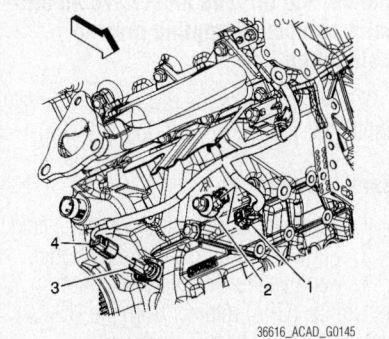

Fig. 116 Disconnect the electrical connector (3) from the Crankshaft Position (CKP) sensor (4)

1. Remove the exhaust manifold lower heat shield.

2. Disconnect the engine wiring harness electrical connector from the Crankshaft Position (CKP) sensor.

3. Remove the crankshaft sensor bolt.

4. Remove the crankshaft sensor.

To install:

5. Installation is the reverse of removal, tighten the bolt to 89 inch lbs. (10 Nm).

6. Lubricate the sensor O-ring seals with clean engine oil.

ENGINE COOLANT TEMPERATURE (ECT) SENSOR

LOCATION

See Figure 117.

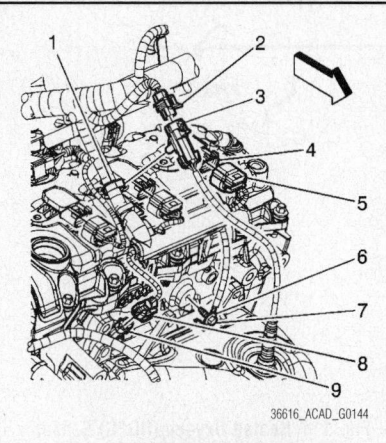

Fig. 117 Disconnect the electrical connector (8) from the Engine Coolant Temperature (ECT) sensor (9)

REMOVAL & INSTALLATION

See Figure 117.

1. Drain the cooling system.

2. Slide the electrical connector heat shield up the wiring harness.

3. Disconnect the engine wiring harness electrical connector from the engine coolant temperature (ECT) sensor.

4. Remove the ECT sensor.

To install:

➡**Replacement components must be the correct part number for the application. Components requiring the use of the thread locking compound, lubricants, corrosion inhibitors, or sealants are identified in the service procedure. Some replacement components may come with these coatings already applied. Do not use these coatings on components unless specified. These coatings can affect the final torque, which may affect the operation of the component. Use the correct torque specification when installing components in order to avoid damage.**

5. Install the ECT sensor and tighten to 16 ft. lbs. (22 Nm).

6. Connect the engine wiring harness electrical connector to the ECT sensor.

7. Slide the electrical connector heat shield down over the connector.

8. Fill the cooling system.

HEATED OXYGEN (HO2S) SENSOR

LOCATION

See Figure 118.

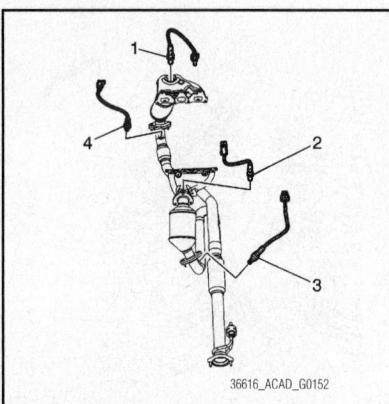

Fig. 118 Heated Oxygen (HO2S) Sensor locations (1-4)

36616_ACAD_G0152

REMOVAL & INSTALLATION

See Figure 118.

➡**When replacing the HO2S perform the following:**

1. A code clear with a scan tool, regardless of whether or not a DTC is set
2. HO2S heater resistance learn reset with a scan tool, where available.
3. Perform the above in order to reset the HO2S resistance learned value and avoid possible HO2S failure.

Bank 1 Sensor 1

1. Remove the fuel injector sight shield.
2. Remove the engine wiring harness Heated Oxygen sensor (HO2S) electrical connector clip from the engine harness.
3. Remove the Connector Position Assurance (CPA) retainer from the HO2S electrical connection, if equipped.
4. Disconnect the engine wiring harness electrical connector from the HO2S electrical connector.
5. Raise and support the vehicle to an appropriate height to reach the HO2S.
6. Remove the HO2S from the exhaust manifold.

To install:

➡A special anti-seize compound is used on the heated oxygen sensor threads. The compound consists of a liquid graphite and glass beads. The graphite will burn away, but the glass beads will remain, making the sensor easier to remove. New or service replacement sensors will have the compound applied to the threads. If a sensor is removed and is to be reinstalled, the threads must have an anti-seize compound applied prior to installation.

7. Installation is the reverse of removal, tighten the sensor to 31 ft. lbs. (42 Nm).

Bank 1 Sensor 2

1. Raise and support the vehicle.
2. Remove the Connector Position Assurance (CPA) retainer from the HO2S electrical connection, if equipped.
3. Disconnect the HO2S electrical connector from the engine wiring harness electrical connector.
4. Remove the bank 1 sensor 2 HO2S from the catalytic converter

To install:

➡A special anti-seize compound is used on the heated oxygen sensor threads. The compound consists of a liquid graphite and glass beads. The graphite will burn away, but the glass beads will remain, making the sensor easier to remove. New or service replacement sensors will have the compound applied to the threads. If a sensor is removed and is to be reinstalled, the threads must have an anti-seize compound applied prior to installation.

5. Installation is the reverse of removal, tighten the sensor to 31 ft. lbs. (42 Nm).

Bank 2 Sensor 1

1. Remove the fuel injector sight shield.
2. Remove the air cleaner outlet duct.
3. Remove the Connector Position Assurance (CPA) retainer from the HO2S electrical connection, if equipped.
4. Disconnect the engine wiring harness electrical connector from the HO2S electrical connector.
5. Remove the HO2S electrical connector clip from the engine wiring harness tab.
6. Remove the HO2S from the exhaust manifold.

To install:

➡A special anti-seize compound is used on the heated oxygen sensor threads. The compound consists of a liquid graphite and glass beads. The graphite will burn away, but the glass beads will remain, making the sensor easier to remove. New or service replacement sensors will have the compound applied to the threads. If a sensor is removed and is to be reinstalled, the threads must have an anti-seize compound applied prior to installation.

7. Installation is the reverse of removal, tighten the sensor to 31 ft. lbs. (42 Nm).

Bank 2 Sensor 2

1. Raise and support the vehicle.
2. Remove the Connector Position Assurance (CPA) retainer from the HO2S electrical connection, if equipped.
3. Disconnect the HO2S electrical connector from the engine wiring harness electrical connector.
4. Remove the bank 2 sensor 2 HO2S from the catalytic converter.

To install:

➡A special anti-seize compound is used on the heated oxygen sensor threads. The compound consists of a liquid graphite and glass beads. The graphite will burn away, but the glass beads will remain, making the sensor easier to remove. New or service replacement sensors will have the compound applied to the threads. If a sensor is removed and is to be reinstalled, the threads must have an anti-seize compound applied prior to installation.

5. Installation is the reverse of removal, tighten the sensor to 31 ft. lbs. (42 Nm).

INTAKE AIR TEMPERATURE (IAT) SENSOR

LOCATION

See Figure 119.

REMOVAL & INSTALLATION

See Figure 119.

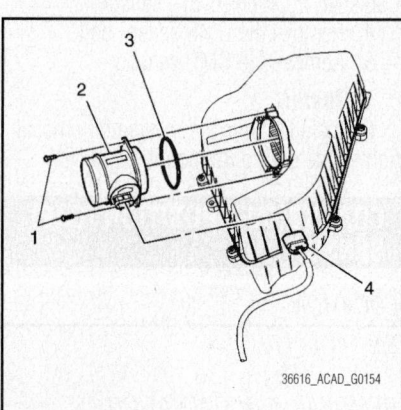

Fig. 119 MAF/IAT sensor screws (1), sensor (2), seal (3) and connector (4)

36616_ACAD_G0154

1. Remove the air cleaner outlet duct. Refer to Air Cleaner Outlet Duct Replacement.

2. Disconnect the engine wiring harness electrical connector from the mass air flow (MAF)/Intake Air Temperature (IAT) sensor.

3. Remove the MAF/IAT sensor screws.

4. Remove the MAF/IAT sensor from the air cleaner assembly.

5. Remove the MAF/IAT sensor seal.

To install:

6. Install the MAF/IAT sensor seal onto the MAF/IAT sensor.

7. Install the MAF/IAT sensor to the air cleaner assembly.

8. Install the MAF/IAT sensor screws and tighten to 35 inch lbs. (4 Nm)

9. Connect the engine wiring harness electrical connector to the MAF/IAT sensor.

10. Install the air cleaner outlet duct.

KNOCK SENSOR (KS)

LOCATION

See Figures 120 and 121.

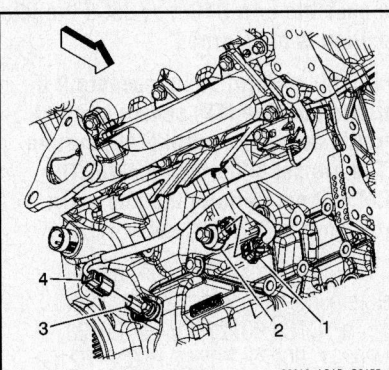

Fig. 120 Knock Sensor (KS) location—bank 1

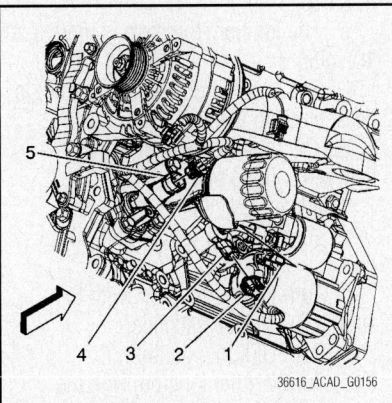

Fig. 121 Knock Sensor (KS) location—bank 2

REMOVAL & INSTALLATION

Bank 1

See Figure 120.

1. Disconnect the negative battery cable.

2. Remove the exhaust manifold lower heat shield.

3. Disconnect the engine wiring harness electrical connector from the Knock Sensor (KS).

4. Remove the knock sensor bolt and sensor.

To install:

5. Installation is the reverse of removal. Tighten the KS bolt to 17 ft. lbs. (23 Nm).

Bank 2

See Figure 121.

1. Disconnect the negative battery cable.

2. Raise and support the vehicle.

3. Remove the engine oil filter.

4. Lower the vehicle.

5. Disconnect the engine wiring harness electrical connector from the Knock Sensor (KS).

6. Remove the knock sensor bolt and sensor.

To install:

7. Installation is the reverse of removal. Tighten the KS bolt to 17 ft. lbs. (23 Nm).

8. Install a new oil filter.

MANIFOLD ABSOLUTE PRESSURE (MAP) SENSOR

LOCATION

See Figure 122.

REMOVAL & INSTALLATION

See Figure 122.

1. Remove the fuel injector sight shield.

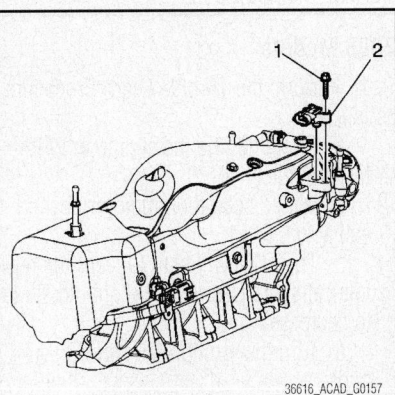

Fig. 122 MAP sensor connector (1) and sensor (2) location (—2008

2. Disconnect the engine wiring harness electrical connector from the Manifold Absolute Pressure (MAP) sensor.

3. Remove the MAP sensor bolt and sensor.

To install:

4. Installation is the reverse of removal, Lubricate a new sensor seal with clean engine oil prior to installation. Always replace the seal.

5. Tighten attaching screws to 89 inch lbs. (10 Nm).

POWERTRAIN CONTROL MODULE (PCM)

LOCATION

See Figure 123.

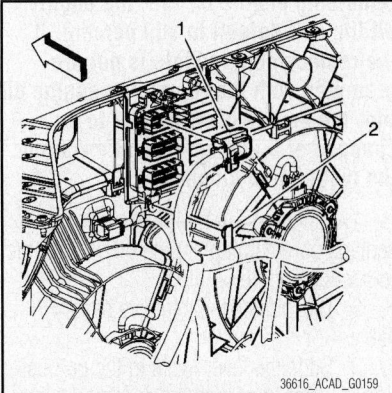

Fig. 123 Powertrain Control Module (PCM) location, connector (1) and harness clip (2)

REMOVAL & INSTALLATION

See Figure 123.

➡Turn the ignition OFF when installing or removing the control module connectors and disconnecting or reconnecting the power to the control module (battery cable, powertrain control module (PCM)/engine control module (ECM)/transaxle control module (TCM) pigtail, control module fuse, jumper cables, etc.) in order to prevent internal control module damage.

➡Control module damage may result when the metal case contacts battery voltage. DO NOT contact the control module metal case with battery voltage when servicing a control module, using battery booster cables, or when charging the vehicle battery.

➡In order to prevent any possible electrostatic discharge damage to the control module, do not touch the connector pins or the soldered components on the circuit board.

➡Remove any debris from around the control module connector surfaces before servicing the control module. Inspect the control module connector gaskets when diagnosing or replacing the control module. Ensure that the gaskets are installed correctly. The gaskets prevent contaminant intrusion into the control module.

➡The replacement control module must be programmed with proprietary equipment.

➡It is necessary to record the remaining engine oil life. If the replacement module is not programmed with the remaining engine oil life, the engine oil life will default to 100 percent. If the replacement module is not programmed with the remaining engine oil life, the engine oil will need to be changed at 5,000 km (3,000 mi) from the last engine oil change.

1. Using a scan tool, retrieve the percentage of remaining engine oil. Record the remaining engine oil life.
2. Disconnect the negative battery cable.
3. Slide the lever locks to the up position in order to release the engine wiring harness electrical connectors.
4. Disconnect the engine wiring harness electrical connectors from the engine control module (ECM).
5. Release the retaining tab located in the battery tray using a small screwdriver or other suitable tool.
6. Remove the ECM by lifting upward after releasing the tab.

To install:
7. Slide the ECM into the bracket on the battery tray.
8. Push down on the ECM until the retaining tab snaps into place.
9. Connect the engine wiring harness electrical connectors to the ECM.
10. Slide the lever locks to the down position in order to engage the engine wiring harness electrical connectors.
11. Connect the negative battery cable.

RESET PROCEDURE

The replacement control module must be programmed with proprietary tools and should not be attempted without proper training and equipment.

THROTTLE POSITION SENSOR (TPS)

LOCATION

See Figure 124.

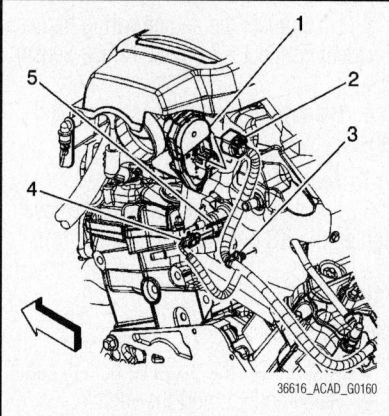

36616_ACAD_G0160

Fig. 124 Throttle Position Sensor (TPS) location

REMOVAL & INSTALLATION

See Figure 124.

1. Remove the air cleaner outlet duct.
2. Disconnect the engine wiring harness electrical connector from the Electronic Throttle Control (ETC).
3. Remove the throttle body bolts.
4. Remove the throttle body and gasket. Discard the gasket.

To install:
5. Clean the gasket mating surfaces.
6. Install a new gasket.
7. Install the throttle body. Tighten the bolts to 89 inch lbs. (10 Nm).
8. Connect the engine wiring harness electrical connector to the ETC.
9. Install the air cleaner outlet duct.

LEARN PROCEDURE

2008 Models

1. Perform the Throttle Learn Procedure as follows:
   a. Start and idle the engine in PARK for 3 minutes.
   b. With a scan tool, monitor desired and actual RPM.
   c. The ECM will start to learn the new idle cells and Desired RPM should start to decrease.
   d. Turn the ignition OFF for 60 seconds.
   e. Start and idle the engine in PARK for 3 minutes.

f. After the 3 minute run time the engine should be idling normal.

➡During the drive cycle the check engine light may come on with idle speed DTCs. If idle speed codes are set, clear codes so the ECM can continue to learn. If the engine idle speed has not been learned the vehicle will need to be driven at speeds above 70 km/h (44 mph) with several decelerations and extended idles.

   g. After the drive cycle, the engine should be idling normally. If the engine idle speed has not been learned, turn OFF the ignition for 60 seconds repeat the throttle learn procedure.
   h. Once the engine speed has returned to normal, clear DTCs.

2009 Models

➡The engine control module (ECM) learns the idle position of the throttle body to ensure the correct idle operation. Anytime the ECM or the throttle body is replaced, the ECM must learn the idle position. The engine idle may be unstable or a DTC may set if the idle position is not learned.

➡Do not perform this procedure if a throttle position (TP) sensor or other throttle actuator control (TAC) system DTCs are set other than P2176. The ECM will not perform the idle learn procedure with a DTC set.

1. Ensure these conditions are met before performing with this procedure:
   a. DTCs P0121, P0122, P0123, P0221, P0222, P0223, P0638, P2100, P2101, P2105, and P2119 are not set.
   b. The engine speed is less than 40 RPM.
   c. The vehicle speed is 0 km/h (0 mph).
   d. The accelerator pedal position is less than 14.9 percent.
   e. The ignition 1 voltage is more than 10 volts.
   f. The engine coolant temperature is between 5-85°C (41-185°F).
   g. The intake air temperature is between 5-60°C (41-140°F).
2. Idle learn procedure:
   a. Turn OFF the ignition for 30 seconds.
   b. Turn ON the ignition, with the engine OFF for 60 seconds.
   c. Turn OFF the ignition.
   d. Turn ON the ignition, with the engine OFF.
   e. Clear the DTCs with a scan tool.

FUEL   **GASOLINE FUEL INJECTION SYSTEM**

Safety is the most important factor when performing not only fuel system maintenance but any type of maintenance. Failure to conduct maintenance and repairs in a safe manner may result in serious personal injury or death. Maintenance and testing of the vehicle's fuel system components can be accomplished safely and effectively by adhering to the following rules and guidelines.

• To avoid the possibility of fire and personal injury, always disconnect the negative battery cable unless the repair or test procedure requires that battery voltage be applied.

• Always relieve the fuel system pressure prior to disconnecting any fuel system component (injector, fuel rail, pressure regulator, etc.), fitting or fuel line connection. Exercise extreme caution whenever relieving fuel system pressure to avoid exposing skin, face and eyes to fuel spray. Please be advised that fuel under pressure may penetrate the skin or any part of the body that it contacts.

• Always place a shop towel or cloth around the fitting or connection prior to loosening to absorb any excess fuel due to spillage. Ensure that all fuel spillage (should it occur) is quickly removed from engine surfaces. Ensure that all fuel soaked cloths or towels are deposited into a suitable waste container.

• Always keep a dry chemical (Class B) fire extinguisher near the work area.

• Do not allow fuel spray or fuel vapors to come into contact with a spark or open flame.

• Always use a back-up wrench when loosening and tightening fuel line connection fittings. This will prevent unnecessary stress and torsion to fuel line piping.

• Always replace worn fuel fitting O-rings with new. Do not substitute fuel hose or equivalent where fuel pipe is installed.

Before servicing the vehicle, make sure to also refer to the precautions in the beginning of this section as well.

RELIEVING FUEL SYSTEM PRESSURE

Without High Pressure System

✳✳ **CAUTION**

Remove the fuel tank cap and relieve the fuel system pressure before servicing the fuel system in order to

reduce the risk of personal injury. After you relieve the fuel system pressure, a small amount of fuel may be released when servicing the fuel lines, the fuel injection pump, or the connections. In order to reduce the risk of personal injury, cover the fuel system components with a shop towel before disconnection. This will catch any fuel that may leak out. Place the towel in an approved container when the disconnection is complete.

1. If the fuel system requires repair, prevent fuel spillage by removing the fuel pump fuse.
2. Loosen the fuel fill cap in order to relieve the fuel tank vapor pressure.
3. Remove the engine cover, if required.
4. Remove the fuel rail service port cap.
5. Wrap a shop towel around the fuel rail service port and using a small flat bladed tool, depress (open) the fuel rail test port valve.
6. Remove the shop towel from around the fuel rail service port, and place in an approved gasoline container.
7. Install the fuel rail service port cap.
8. Install the engine cover, if required.
9. Tighten the fuel fill cap.

With High Pressure System

✳✳ **CAUTION**

Remove the fuel tank cap and relieve the fuel system pressure before servicing the fuel system in order to reduce the risk of personal injury. After you relieve the fuel system pressure, a small amount of fuel may be released when servicing the fuel lines, the fuel injection pump, or the connections. In order to reduce the risk of personal injury, cover the fuel system components with a shop towel before disconnection. This will catch any fuel that may leak out. Place the towel in an approved container when the disconnection is complete.

1. If the fuel system requires repair, prevent fuel spillage by removing the fuel pump fuse.
2. Remove the engine cover, if required.
3. Loosen the fuel fill cap in order to relieve the fuel tank vapor pressure.
4. Remove the fuel rail service port cap.

✳✳ **CAUTION**

Wrap a shop towel around the fuel pressure connection in order to reduce the risk of fire and personal injury. The towel will absorb any fuel leakage that occurs during the connection of the fuel pressure gage. Place the towel in an approved container when the connection of the fuel pressure gage is complete.

5. Wrap a shop towel around the fuel rail service port.
6. Connect the CH-48027-3 to the fuel rail service port.
7. Connect the CH-48027-2 to the CH-48027-3.
8. Place the hose on the CH-48027-2 into an approved gasoline container.
9. Open the valve on the CH-48027-2 in order to bleed any fuel from the fuel rail.
10. Close the valve on the CH-48027-2.
11. Remove the hose on the CH-48027-2 from the approved gasoline container.
12. Clean all of the following areas before performing any disconnections in order to avoid possible contamination in the system:
• The fuel pipe connections
• The hose connections
• The areas surrounding the connections
13. If relieving the fuel pressure for the fuel pressure gage installation and removal, it is NOT necessary to proceed with the following steps.
• Disconnect the CH-48027-2 from the CH-48027-3.
• Disconnect the CH-48027-3 from the fuel rail service port.
• Remove the shop towel from around the fuel rail service port, and place in an approved gasoline container.
• Install the fuel rail service port cap.
• Install the engine cover, if required.
• Tighten the fuel fill cap.

FUEL FILTER

REMOVAL & INSTALLATION

The fuel filter is part of the fuel pump module and is not individually replaceable.

FUEL PUMP

REMOVAL & INSTALLATION

See Figure 125.

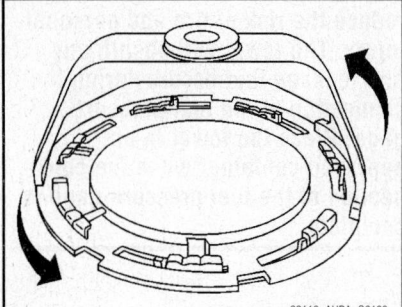

Fig. 125 Install a fuel pump lock ring wrench such as J 45722 to the fuel pump module lock ring

1. Remove the fuel tank.
2. Disconnect the fuel tank fuel pump module wiring harness electrical connectors from the fuel pressure sensor and the pump.
3. Disconnect the fuel tank vent pipe quick connect fittings from the pump.
4. Install a fuel pump lock ring wrench such as J 45722 to the fuel pump module lock ring.

➡**Avoid damaging the lock ring. Use only a fuel pump lock ring wrench such as J 45722 to prevent damage to the lock ring.**

➡**Do Not handle the fuel sender assembly by the fuel pipes. The amount of leverage generated by handling the fuel pipes could damage the joints. Do NOT use impact tools. Significant force will be required to release the lock ring. The use of a hammer and screwdriver is not recommended. Secure the fuel tank in order to prevent fuel tank rotation.**

5. Using a fuel pump lock ring wrench such as J 45722 and a long breaker-bar, rotate the lock ring in a counterclockwise direction in order to unlock the lock ring.
6. Remove the fuel pump lock ring wrench such as J 45722 from the fuel pump module lock ring.
7. Lift the fuel pump module up slightly in order to disconnect the fuel tank vent pipe quick connect fitting from the pump cover.
8. Raise the fuel pump up from the fuel tank. Tilt the pump in order to allow the fuel level sensor arm and float to clear the pump opening.

9. Remove the fuel pump.
10. Remove and discard the fuel pump module seal.
11. Clean the fuel pump sealing surfaces.

To install:

> ❊❊ **CAUTION**
>
> **Drain the fuel from the fuel sender assembly into an approved container in order to reduce the risk of fire and personal injury. Never store the fuel in an open container.**

➡**Some lock rings were manufactured with "DO NOT REUSE" stamped into them. These lock rings may be reused if they are not damaged or warped. Inspect the lock ring for damage due to improper removal or installation procedures. If damage is found, install a NEW fuel pump module. Inspect the lock ring for flatness as best as possible. If the lock ring is warped, replace the fuel pump module.**

12. Clean any contamination from the male pipe ends of the fuel pump.
13. Place a NEW fuel tank pump seal onto the fuel tank.
14. Insert the fuel pump into the fuel tank allowing the sensor arm and float to clear the module opening.
15. Lower the pump down into the fuel tank until the fuel tank vent pipe quick connect fitting can be connected.
16. Connect the fuel tank vent pipe quick connect fitting at the pump cover.
17. Press the fuel tank pump downward.
18. Install the pump lock ring wrench such as J 45722 to the fuel pump module lock ring.

➡**Ensure that the lock ring is installed with the correct side facing upward. A correctly installed lock ring will only turn in a clockwise direction.**

19. Using the pump lock ring wrench such as J 45722 and a long breaker-bar, rotate the lock ring in a clockwise direction in order the lock the lock ring.
20. Remove the pump lock ring wrench from the fuel pump module lock ring.
21. Connect the fuel tank vent pipe quick connect fittings to the pump.
22. Connect the fuel tank fuel pump module wiring harness electrical connectors to the fuel pressure sensor and the pump.
23. Install the fuel tank.

FUEL TANK

REMOVAL & INSTALLATION

See Figure 126.

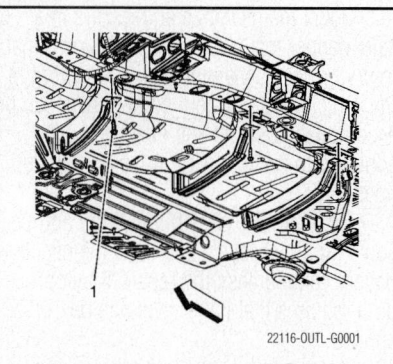

Fig. 126 Location of the fuel tank straps (1)

> ❊❊ **CAUTION**
>
> **Do not allow smoking or the use of open flames in the area where work on the fuel or EVAP system is taking place. Anytime work is being done on the fuel system, disconnect the negative battery cable, except for those tests where battery voltage is required.**

> ❊❊ **CAUTION**
>
> **Fuel supply lines will remain pressurized for long periods of time after the engine is shutdown. This pressure must be relieved before servicing the fuel system.**

1. Properly relieve the fuel system pressure.
2. Drain the fuel tank.

> ❊❊ **CAUTION**
>
> **Whenever fuel lines are removed, catch fuel in an approved container. Container opening must be a minimum of 300 mm (12 in) diameter to adequately catch the fluid.**

➡**Clean all fuel pipe connections and surrounding areas before disconnecting the fuel pipes to avoid contamination of the fuel system.**

3. Disconnect the fuel pump fuel feed line quick connect fitting from the chassis fuel line.
4. Disconnect the fuel tank Evaporative Emission (EVAP) canister vent front pipe quick connect fitting from the chassis EVAP line.

5. Disconnect the vent hose from the left rear of the fuel tank.

6. Disconnect the fuel sender wiring harness electrical connector from the body wiring harness electrical connector.

7. Remove the fuel sender wiring harness clip from the underbody side rail extension.

8. Remove the left underbody side rail.

9. Support the fuel tank with a suitable adjustable jack.

10. Remove the fuel tank strap bolts. Allow the fuel tank straps to hang.

➡**Do not bend the fuel tank straps. Bending the fuel tank straps may cause damage to the straps.**

11. Push up on the rear of the strap slightly and rotate the strap towards the rear of the vehicle, in order the remove the fuel tank straps.

12. Using the adjustable jack and the aid of an assistant, lower the fuel tank from the underbody of the vehicle.

13. With the aid of the assistant, remove the fuel tank from the adjustable jack, and place on a flat work surface.

To install:

14. With the aid of an assistant, remove the fuel tank from the work surface and place on the adjustable jack.

15. With the aid of the assistant, raise the fuel tank into position under the vehicle.

16. Install the fuel tank straps and tighten the bolts to 37 ft. lbs. (50 Nm).

17. Remove the adjustable jack from under the fuel tank.

18. Install the left underbody side rail.

19. Connect the fuel sender wiring harness electrical connector to the body wiring harness electrical connector.

20. Install the fuel sender wiring harness clip to the underbody side rail extension.

21. Connect the vent hose to the left rear of the fuel tank.

22. Connect the fuel tank EVAP canister vent front pipe quick connect fitting to the chassis EVAP line.

23. Connect the fuel pump fuel feed line quick connect fitting to the chassis fuel line.

➡**Ensure that the notch in the fill hose aligns with the tab on the fuel tank.**

24. Position and install the fuel tank fill pipe to the fuel tank.

25. Connect the EVAP canister vent rear pipe quick connect fitting to the recirculation line on the fuel fill pipe.

26. Tighten the fuel tank fill hose clamp at the fuel tank to 29 inch lbs. (3.3 Nm).

27. Lower the vehicle.

28. Refill the fuel tank.

29. Tighten the fuel fill cap.

30. Inspect for fuel leaks using the following procedure:

   a. Turn ON the ignition, with the engine OFF for 2 seconds.

   b. Turn OFF the ignition for 10 seconds

   c. Turn ON the ignition

   d. Inspect for fuel leaks.

31. Install the fuel injector sight shield.

FUEL RAIL & INJECTORS

REMOVAL & INSTALLATION

2008 Models

1. Remove the fuel injector sight shield.

2. Disconnect the engine wiring harness electrical connector from the fuel injector wiring harness electrical connector.

3. Disconnect the fuel feed pipe quick connect fitting from the fuel rail.

4. Remove the upper intake manifold.

✳✳ CAUTION

Wear safety glasses while using the compressed air to avoid eye injury.

5. Use compressed air in order to remove any debris from the around the area where the fuel injectors enter the lower intake manifold.

6. Remove the fuel rail bolts.

➡**Remove the fuel rail assembly carefully in order to prevent damage to the injector electrical connector terminals and the injector spray tips. Support the fuel rail after the fuel rail is removed in order to avoid damaging the fuel rail components. Cap the fittings and plug the holes when servicing the fuel system in order to prevent dirt and other contaminants from entering open pipes and passages.**

7. Remove the fuel rail with fuel injectors from the lower intake manifold.

8. Lift up the fuel injector electrical connector retainer.

9. Push in the fuel injector electrical connector tab in order to disconnect the connector from the injector.

10. Remove the fuel injector retainer clip.

11. Remove the fuel injector.

12. Remove and discard the fuel injector seals.

To install:

13. Install NEW fuel injector seals.

14. Install the fuel injector.

15. Install the fuel injector retainer clip.

16. Install the fuel injector electrical connector.

17. Push down on the fuel injector electrical connector retainer, securing the electrical connector.

18. Install the fuel rail with fuel injectors to the lower intake manifold. Tighten the bolts to 89 in. lbs. (10 Nm).

19. Install the upper intake manifold.

20. Connect the fuel feed pipe quick connect fitting to the fuel rail.

21. Connect the engine wiring harness electrical connector to the fuel injector wiring harness electrical connector.

22. Inspect for fuel leaks using the following procedure:

   a. Turn ON the ignition, with the engine OFF for 2 seconds.

   b. Turn OFF the ignition for 10 seconds

   c. Turn ON the ignition

   d. Inspect for fuel leaks.

23. Install the fuel injector sight shield.

2009 Models

See Figures 127 through 130.

➡**This procedure requires proprietary tools to complete.**

1. Relieve the fuel system pressure. See Relieving Fuel System Pressure in Fuel Systems.

2. Remove the fuel pipe shield.

   a. Remove the fuel injection sight shield.

   b. Remove the air cleaner assembly.

3. Remove the intake manifold. See Intake Manifold in Engine Mechanical..

4. Remove the high pressure fuel pipe. Discard the pipe. Refer to Fuel Feed Intermediate Pipe

   a. Remove the foam insulator from the pipes.

   b. Loosen the high pressure pipe fitting to the high pressure fuel pump.

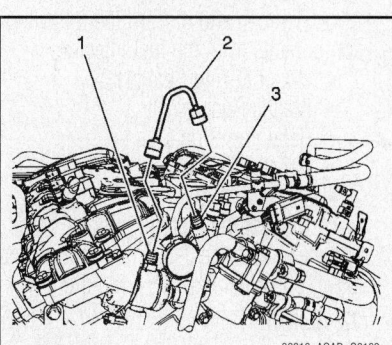

Fig. 127 Fuel feed intermediate pipe location (2)

36616_ACAD_G0162

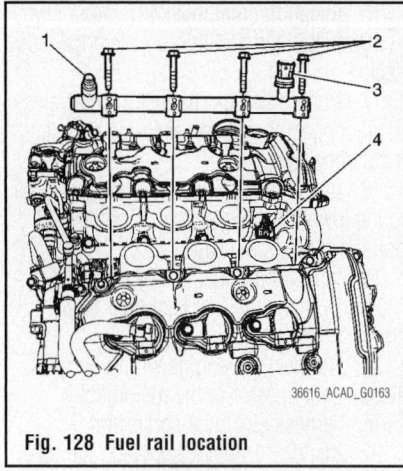

Fig. 128 Fuel rail location

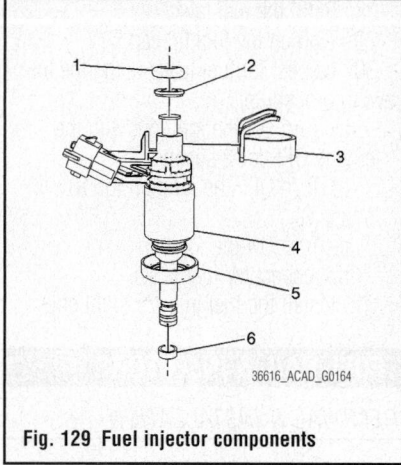

Fig. 129 Fuel injector components

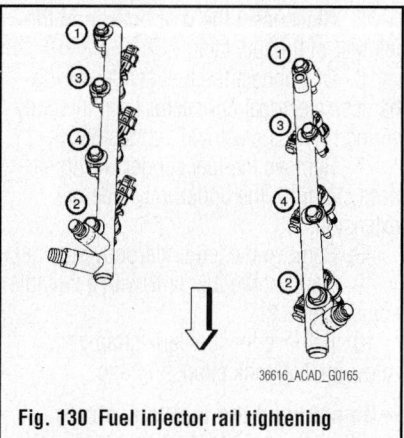

Fig. 130 Fuel injector rail tightening sequence

c. Loosen the high pressure pipe fitting to the left fuel rail.

d. Remove the high pressure fuel pipe from the vehicle. Discard the pipe.

5. Remove the fuel rail crossover pipe and discard the pipe.

6. Disconnect the fuel pressure sensor electrical connector and cut the wire harness tie straps.

7. Remove the fuel rail (1) bolts (2).

8. Remove the fuel pressure sensor.

9. Remove and discard the direct fuel injector hold down clamps.

➡**The direct fuel injectors must be rebuilt whenever the injector has been released from the fuel rail or cylinder head.**

10. Once the fuel rail is removed, remove the fuel injectors and rebuild them.

a. Remove and discard the three fuel injector retaining rings

b. Remove the direct fuel injectors and harness as an assembly, and disconnect the electrical connector.

➡**If necessary, use the J 2619-01 slide hammer with the J-37281-A injector remover in order to remove the direct fuel injectors evenly.**

c. Remove and discard the following components from the fuel injectors.
- Upper O-ring Seal (1)
- Plastic Spacer (2)
- Retaining Ring (3)
- Isolator Cup (5)
- Teflon Seal (6)

d. Inspect the fuel rail injector bores and clean with the J-39313 adapter , and EN-47909 cleaning kit , if required.

To install:

➡**Lubricate a NEW O-ring seal with silicon free engine oil GM P/N 36616610 (Canadian P/N 993193) or equivalent.**

11. Install the following new components to the fuel injectors. Use steps 2 through 8 to install these components.
- Upper O-ring Seal (1)
- Plastic Spacer (2)
- Retaining Ring (3)
- Isolator Cup (5)
- Teflon Seal (6)

12. From the EN-48266 Installer , position the EN 48266-1 to the injector tip.

➡**DO NOT lubricate the NEW Teflon seal.**

13. Install a NEW Teflon seal onto the EN 48266-1.

14. Pull the NEW Teflon seal by hand over the EN 48266-1 and into the groove in the injector.

15. Remove the EN 48266-1 from the injector tip.

16. From the EN-48266 Installer , install the EN 48266-2 to the injector tip.

17. Using the EN 48266-2, resize the Teflon seal. Install the EN 48266-2, until it bottoms out against the injector body, and rotate the EN 48266-2 while applying only moderate force 180 degrees in one direction and then 180 degrees back in the other direction.

18. Remove the EN 48266-2.

19. Install the rebuilt direct fuel injectors to the cylinder heads.

20. Install NEW direct injector hold down clamps to the injector.

21. On a new fuel rail, lubricate the fuel injector cups with silicon free engine oil GM P/N 36616610 (Canadian P/N 9931930) or equivalent.

22. Carefully place the fuel rail into position, placing the front into the fuel rail over the front injector and rotating the rear downward.

23. Install the 2 outer fuel rail bolts first, then the 2 inner bolts, and hand tighten.

24. Tighten the fuel rail bolts in the sequence shown:

a. Tighten the Bank 1 fuel rail bolts first pass to 106 inch lbs. (12 Nm).

b. Tighten the Bank 1 fuel rail bolts final pass to 17 ft. lbs. (23 Nm).

25. Install a NEW fuel rail crossover pipe.

a. Position the fuel rail crossover pipe to the right fuel rails fitting and left fuel rail fitting and tighten the fuel rail crossover pipe fittings to:

b. Tighten the fittings first pass to 12 ft. lbs. (16 Nm).

c. Tighten the fittings final pass to 24 ft. lbs. (32 Nm).

26. Install a NEW high pressure fuel pipe.

a. Ensure that the high pressure fuel pipe, fuel rail fitting and fuel pump fitting are clean and dry prior to assembly.

b. Lubricate the pipes with silicon free engine oil GM P/N 36616610 (Canadian P/N 993193) or equivalent.

c. Position the high pressure fuel pipe to the high pressure fuel pump fitting and left fuel rail. Initially hand tighten the fitting then tighten the high pressure fuel pipe fitting to:

d. Tighten the fitting a first pass to 12 ft. lbs. (16 Nm).

e. Tighten the fitting a final pass to 24 ft. lbs. (32 Nm).

27. Install the high pressure fuel sensor and tighten to 25 ft. lbs. (33 Nm).

28. Connect the fuel injector wiring harness electrical connector to the fuel injectors, fuel rail and fuel pressure sensor.

29. Inspect for fuel leaks using the following procedure:

a. Turn ON the ignition, with the engine OFF for 2 seconds.

b. Turn OFF the ignition, for 10 seconds.

c. Turn ON the ignition, with the engine OFF.

d. Inspect for fuel leaks.

30. Install the foam insulator from the fuel rails.

31. Install the intake manifold.

32. Install the fuel pipe shield.

33. Install the low side fuel pressure service port cap.

34. Install the fuel tank cap.

35. Repair any leaks, as necessary.

IDLE SPEED

ADJUSTMENT

There is no idle speed possible or necessary.

THROTTLE BODY

REMOVAL & INSTALLATION

1. Remove the air cleaner outlet duct.

2. Disconnect the engine wiring harness electrical connector from the Electronic Throttle Control (ETC).

3. Remove the throttle body bolts.

4. Remove the throttle body and gasket. Discard the gasket.

To install:

5. Clean the gasket mating surfaces.

6. Install a new gasket.

7. Install the throttle body. Tighten the bolts to 89 inch lbs. (10 Nm).

8. Connect the engine wiring harness electrical connector to the ETC.

9. Install the air cleaner outlet duct.

10. Perform the Throttle Learn Procedure. See Throttle Position Sensor in Components.

HEATING & AIR CONDITIONING SYSTEM

BLOWER MOTOR

REMOVAL & INSTALLATION

1. Remove the instrument panel insulator - right side.

2. Remove the blower motor screw.

3. Disconnect the electrical connectors.

4. Rotate the blower motor counterclockwise to remove.

To install:

5. Installation is the reverse of removal.

6. Tighten screws to 18 inch lbs. (2 Nm).

HEATER CORE

REMOVAL & INSTALLATION

See Figure 131.

1. Drain the coolant.

2. Remove heater inlet hose from heater core.

3. Remove heater outlet hose from heater core.

4. Remove left front floor console extension panel.

5. Remove the floor outlet air duct.

6. Reposition any wiring harness to access heater core cover.

7. Remove the heater core cover screw and cover.

8. Remove the heater core tube clips. Cap or plug heater core, hoses and tubes to prevent any fluid leakage. Position tube forward to release from heater core and slide rearward to remove.

9. Reposition the heater core outward from the heater case to ease in removal.

10. Mark the location of the center foam seal from the old heater core to the new heater core.

To install:

11. Installation is the reverse of removal, please note the following:

   a. Press on foam seals to activate adhesive.

   b. Keep the heater core horizontal and straight when inserting into the HVAC module in order to prevent foam seal damage.

   c. Push heater core until the foam seal around the heater core tank is inserted into the HVAC module and the heater core is fully seated.

   d. Always use new seals when connecting hoses and covers.

HVAC MODULE ASSEMBLY

REMOVAL & INSTALLATION

See Figure 132.

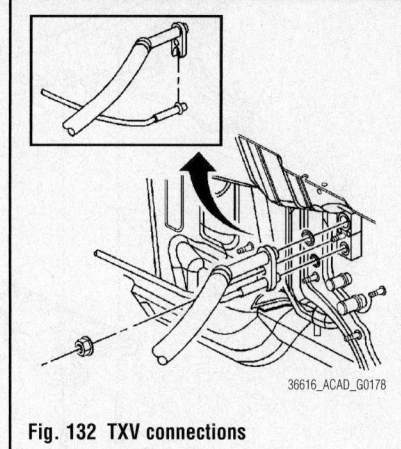

36616_ACAD_G0178

Fig. 132 TXV connections

1. Drain the coolant.

2. Recover the refrigerant.

3. Remove the air cleaner outlet duct.

4. Remove heater inlet hose from heater core.

5. Remove heater outlet hose from heater core.

6. If equipped, remove the windshield washer solvent heater.

7. Remove A/C lines from Thermal Expansion Valve (TXV).

8. Remove I/P Carrier Assembly.

9. Remove HVAC module assembly nuts and bolts.

10. Remove HVAC module assembly.

11. Cap or plug A/C and heater pipe openings to prevent spillage of fluids upon removal.

To install:

12. Installation is the reverse of removal.

13. Tighten HVAC module bolts to 53 inch lbs. (6 Nm).

14. Install new TXV sealing washers.

15. Tighten TXV bolts to 44 inch lbs. (5 Nm).

16. Refill coolant and check for leaks.

17. Recharge A/C system.

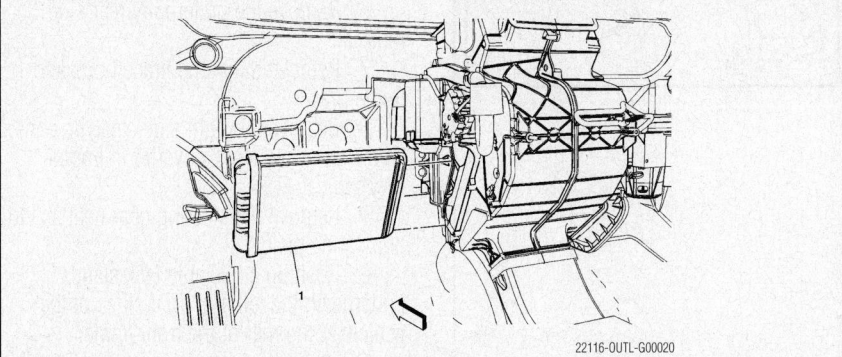

22116-OUTL-G00020

Fig. 131 View of the heater core assembly mounting

STEERING

POWER RACK & PINION STEERING GEAR

REMOVAL & INSTALLATION

See Figures 133 through 136.

➡Secure the steering wheel utilizing a strap to prevent rotation. Locking of the steering column will prevent damage and a possible malfunction of the SIR system. The steering wheel must be

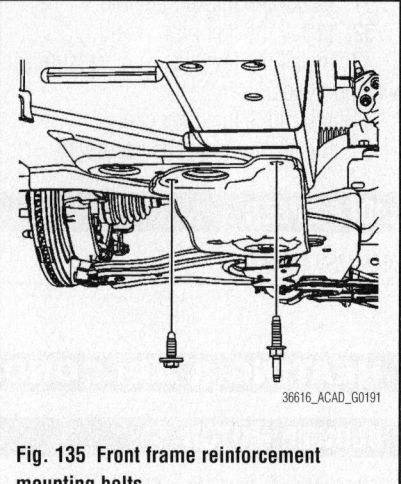

Fig. 135 Front frame reinforcement mounting bolts

secured in position before disconnecting the following components:

- The steering column
- The intermediate shaft
- The steering gear

➡After disconnecting these components, do not move the front tires and wheels. Failure to follow these procedures may cause improper alignment of some components during installation and result in possible damage to the SIR coil.

1. Remove as much power steering fluid from the remote power steering fluid reservoir as possible.

2. Disconnect the steering linkage outer tie rods from the steering knuckles.

3. Disconnect the stabilizer shaft links at the stabilizer shaft. See Control Links in Front Suspension.

4. Disconnect the intermediate steering shaft from the steering gear. See Intermediate Shaft.

5. Remove the rear propeller shaft, if equipped. See Driveline Torque Tube in Rear Drive Axle.

6. Remove the underbody rear side rails.

7. Remove the frame brace bolts and frame brace.

8. Remove the right side catalytic converter. See Catalytic Converter in Engine Mechanical.

9. Remove the steering gear heat shield bolts and shields.

10. Position adjustable jack stands underneath the left and right sides of the vehicle at the rear of the front frame.

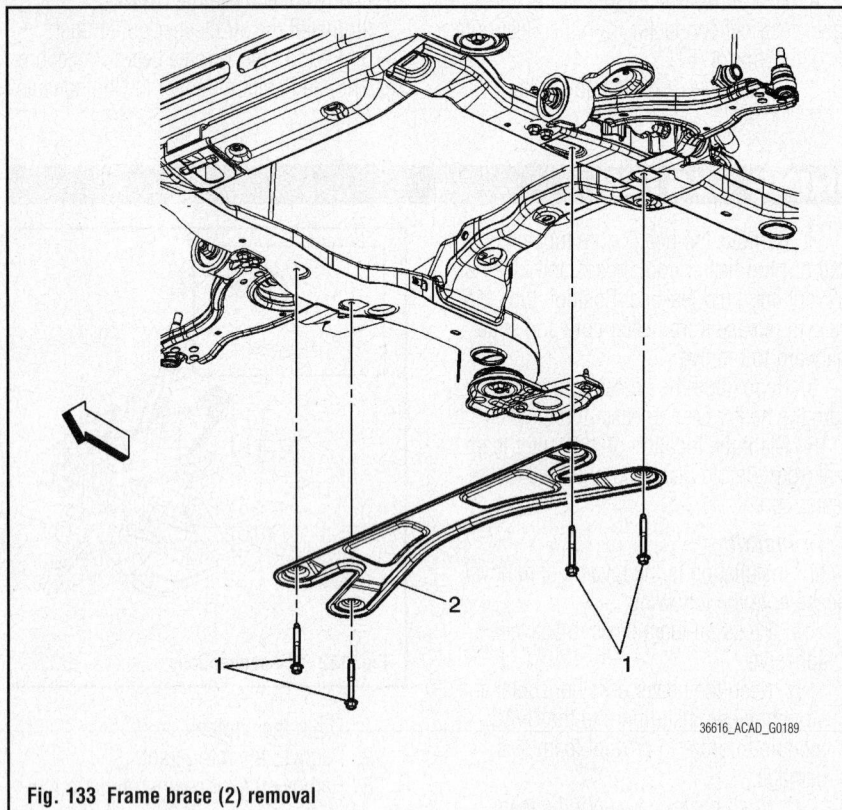

Fig. 133 Frame brace (2) removal

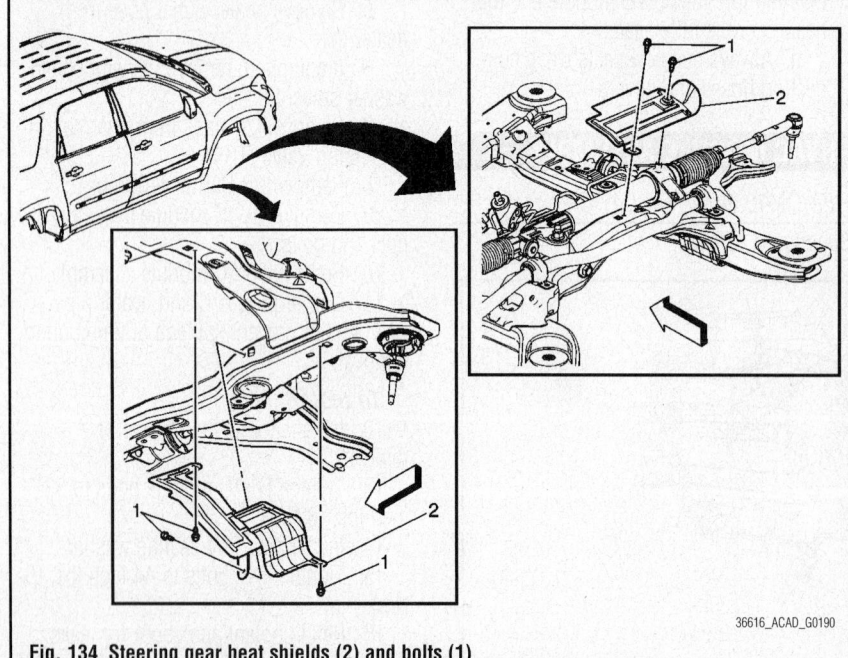

Fig. 134 Steering gear heat shields (2) and bolts (1)

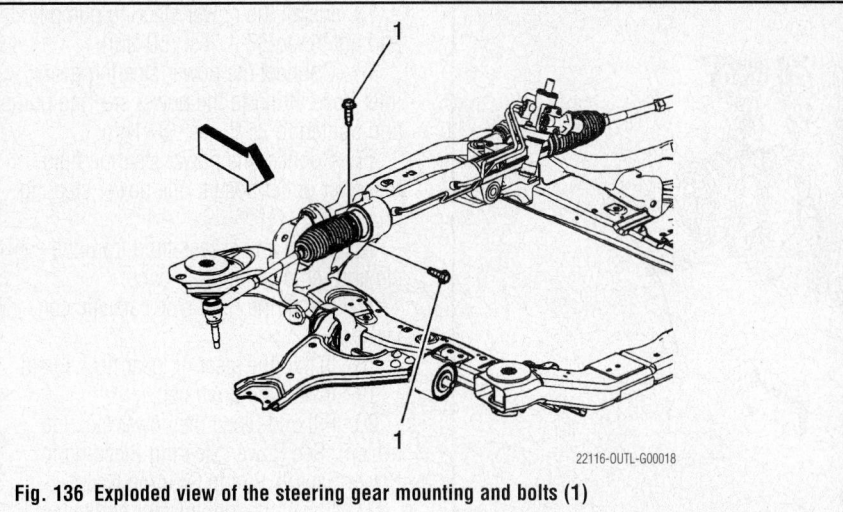

Fig. 136 Exploded view of the steering gear mounting and bolts (1)

11. Place drain pans under the vehicle as needed.

12. Remove the left and right front frame reinforcement mounting bolts.

13. Loosen the front frame reinforcement mounting bolts.

14. Loosen the front frame mounting bolts.

15. Loosen the rear front frame mounting bolts.

16. Lower the frame from the frame rail until enough clearance is gained to remove the steering gear.

17. Remove the power steering gear inlet hose retaining plate bolt and the power steering gear inlet and outlet pipe clip bolt.

18. Pull the power steering gear inlet and outlet hoses out of the steering gear and power steering gear inlet and outlet pipe clip.

19. Remove the left side steering gear nuts and bolts.

20. Remove the right side steering gear bolts.

21. Remove the steering gear from the vehicle through the driver side of the vehicle.

To install:

22. Install the steering gear to the vehicle through the driver's side.

➥**Start all bolts by hand before finalizing any torques.**

23. Install the right side steering gear bolts. Tighten to 74 ft. lbs. (100 Nm).

24. Install the left side steering gear nuts and bolts. Tighten to 55 ft. lbs. (75 Nm).

25. Install the power steering gear inlet and outlet hoses to the steering gear.

26. Install the power steering gear inlet hose retaining plate bolt and the power steering gear inlet and outlet pipe clip bolt.

27. Raise the front frame to the vehicle body leaving approximately a half inch gap.

28. Install the left and right front frame reinforcement mounting bolts. Tighten to 37 ft. lbs. (50 Nm).

29. Tighten the rear front frame mounting bolts. Tighten to 74 ft. lbs. (100 Nm) plus an additional 90 degrees.

30. Tighten the front frame mounting bolts. Tighten to 74 ft. lbs. (100 Nm) plus an additional 90 degrees.

31. Tighten the front frame reinforcement mounting bolts. Tighten to 37 ft. lbs. (50 Nm).

32. Remove the adjustable jack stands from underneath the vehicle.

33. Clean any excess fluid from the vehicle and remove the drain pans.

34. Install the underbody rear side rails.

35. Install the rear propeller shaft, if equipped.

36. Install the steering gear heat shields.

37. Install the right side catalytic converter.

38. Install the frame brace.

39. Connect the intermediate steering shaft to the steering gear. Tighten the retainers to 16 ft. lbs. (22 Nm).

40. Connect the stabilizer shaft links at the stabilizer shaft.

41. Connect the steering linkage outer tie rods to the steering knuckles.

42. Fill and bleed the power steering system.

43. Adjust the front toe.

POWER STEERING BLEEDING PROCEDURE

※※ WARNING

Use clean, new power steering fluid type only. Refer to Fluid and Lubricant Recommendations.

- Hoses touching the frame, body or engine may cause system noise. Verify that the hoses do not touch any other part of the vehicle.
- Loose connections may not leak, but could allow air into the steering system. Verify that all hose connections are tight.
- Maintain the power steering fluid level throughout the bleed procedure.

1. With the engine OFF, fill the pump reservoir to the MAX mark on cap-stick fluid level indicator.

2. Raise the vehicle until the front wheels are off the ground.

3. Start the engine and turn the steering wheel from stop to stop 4 times.

4. Verify power steering fluid level.

5. Rotate steering wheel from left to right another 8 times. Check for signs of cavitation or fluid aeration (pump noise/whining).

6. Verify the fluid level. Repeat the bleed procedure, if necessary.

POWER STEERING PUMP

REMOVAL & INSTALLATION

See Figures 134 and 137.

1. Remove the fuel injector sight shield.

2. Remove as much power steering fluid from the remote power steering fluid reservoir as possible.

3. Place drain pans under the vehicle as needed.

4. Remove the drive belt. See Accessory Drive Belt in Engine Mechanical.

5. Remove the steering gear heat shield.

6. Remove the right side catalytic converter. See Catalytic Converter in Engine Mechanical.

7. Disconnect the power steering fluid reservoir outlet hose from the power steering pump.

8. Disconnect the power steering gear inlet hose from the power steering pump.

9. Remove the power steering pump bolts (1).

10. Remove the power steering pump (2) from the vehicle.

11. Transfer any parts as needed.

To install:

12. Install the power steering pump to the vehicle.

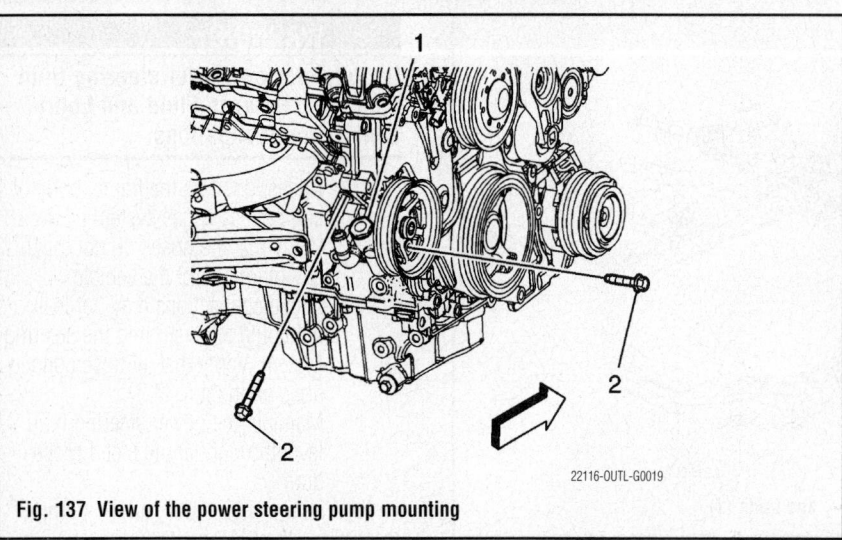

Fig. 137 View of the power steering pump mounting

13. Install the power steering pump bolts and tighten to 37 ft. lbs. (50 Nm).

14. Connect the power steering gear inlet hose fitting to the power steering pump and tighten to 25 ft. lbs. (34 Nm).

15. Connect the power steering fluid reservoir outlet hose to the power steering pump.

16. Clean any excess fluid from the vehicle and remove the drain pans.

17. Install the right side catalytic converter.

18. Install the steering gear heat shield.

19. Install the drive belt.

20. Fill and bleed the power steering system. See Power Steering Bleeding in Power Rack & Pinion Steering Gear

21. Install the fuel injector sight shield.

SUSPENSION

CONTROL LINKS

REMOVAL & INSTALLATION

See Figure 138.

1. Raise and support the vehicle.
2. Remove the tire and wheel.
3. Use a wrench to prevent the stub link from rotating.
4. Using the proper size wrench, remove the retaining nut for the upper stabilizer shaft link stub link.
5. Repeat the previous steps to remove the lower stabilizer shaft stub link retaining nut.
6. Remove the stabilizer shaft link from the vehicle.

To install:

7. Installation is reverse of removal.
8. Tighten the stabilizer link to strut nut to 52 ft. lbs. (70 Nm).
9. Tighten the stabilizer link to stabilizer shaft nut to 55 ft. lbs. (75 Nm).

LOWER BALL JOINT

REMOVAL & INSTALLATION

See Figures 139 and 140.

1. Remove the lower control arm assembly. See Lower Control Arm
2. Install the lower control arm in a vise.

FRONT SUSPENSION

➡Use a center punch to aid in starting the drill if drilling the rivet.

3. Drill or grind off the head of the rivet.
4. Use a punch and a hammer to loosen the rivets from the lower control arm.

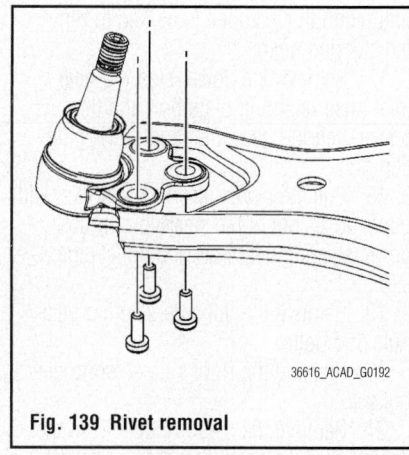

Fig. 139 Rivet removal

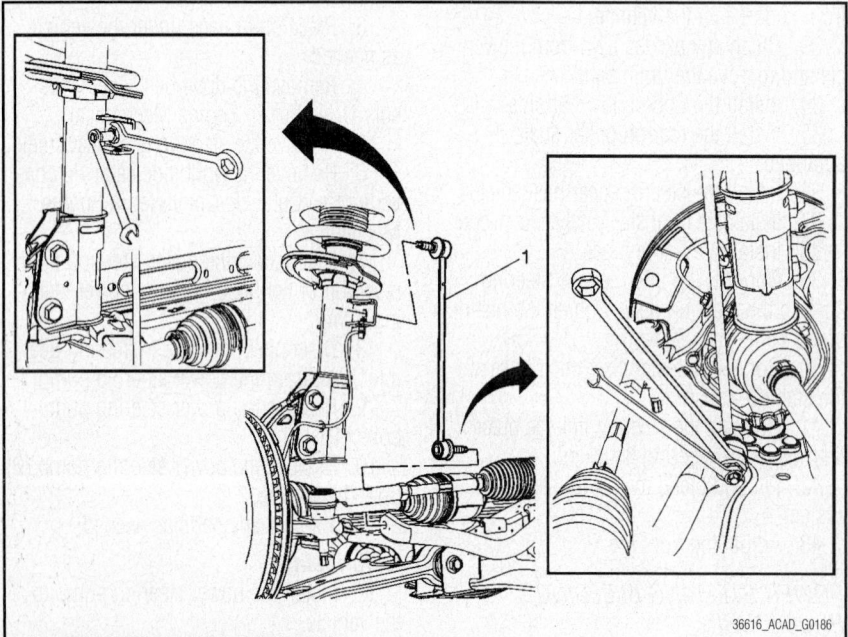

Fig. 138 Stabilizer shaft stub link (1)

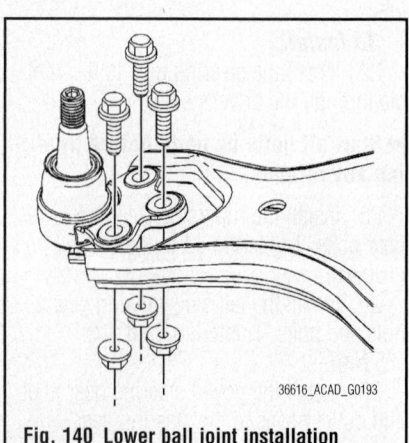

Fig. 140 Lower ball joint installation

5. Remove the rivets from the lower control arm.

6. Remove the ball joint from the lower control arm.

To install:

7. Position the ball joint on the lower control arm.

➡**When tightening the mounting nuts and bolts for the ball joint, hold the bolt and torque the nut for the proper torque measure.**

8. Install the ball joint mounting nuts and bolts . Tighten to 50 ft. lbs. (68 Nm).

9. Remove the lower control arm assembly from the vise.

10. Install the lower control arm.

11. Check the front end alignment of the vehicle.

LOWER CONTROL ARM

REMOVAL & INSTALLATION

See Figure 141.

1. Raise and support the vehicle.
2. Remove the tire and wheel assembly.
3. Remove the outer tie rod end from the steering knuckle.

4. Turn the knuckle assembly to left.

5. Using a Allen wrench and the proper size wrench, remove the lower ball joint retaining nut.

6. Using the ball joint separator remove the lower ball joint from the control arm.

7. Remove the tool from the lower ball joint.

8. Remove the front control arm mounting nut and stud.

9. Remove the rear control arm mounting bolt and nut.

10. Remove the lower control arm from the vehicle.

To install:

11. Position the lower control arm in the front bushing and the rear mounting bracket.

12. Install and hand tighten the rear lower control arm mounting bolt and nut.

13. Install the front lower control arm nut and stud. Tighten to 144 ft. lbs. (195 Nm).

14. Install the rear control arm mounting bolt and nut. Tighten to 111 ft. lbs. (150 Nm).

15. Install the lower ball joint in steering knuckle.

16. Install the ball joint mounting nut.

17. Using an Allen wrench with the proper size wrench, tighten the mounting

nut to 30 ft. lbs. (40 Nm) plus an additional 90 degrees.

18. Install outer tie rod. Tighten to 22 ft. lbs. (30 Nm). plus 120 degrees (2 flats).

19. Install the tire and wheel assembly.

20. Remove the support and lower the vehicle.

STABILIZER BAR

REMOVAL & INSTALLATION

See Figure 142.

1. Raise and support the vehicle.

2. Remove the front tires and wheels.

3. Remove the bolt from the intermediate shaft bracket to the front cradle. See Intermediate Shaft in Steering.

4. Remove the rear propeller shaft, if equipped. See Driveline Torque Tube in Rear Drive Axle.

5. Remove the outer tie rod ends from the steering knuckle. See Tie Rod End in Steering.

6. Remove the stabilizer shaft links at the stabilizer bar. See Control Links.

7. Position adjustable jack stand underneath the left and right side at the rear of the front cradle.

8. Remove the left and right frame reinforcement mounting bolts. See Power Steering Gear in Steering.

9. Loosen the front frame reinforcement mounting bolts.

10. Loosen the front frame mounting bolts.

11. Loosen the rear frame mounting bolts.

12. Lower the frame from the frame rail until enough clearance is gained to remove the stabilizer shaft.

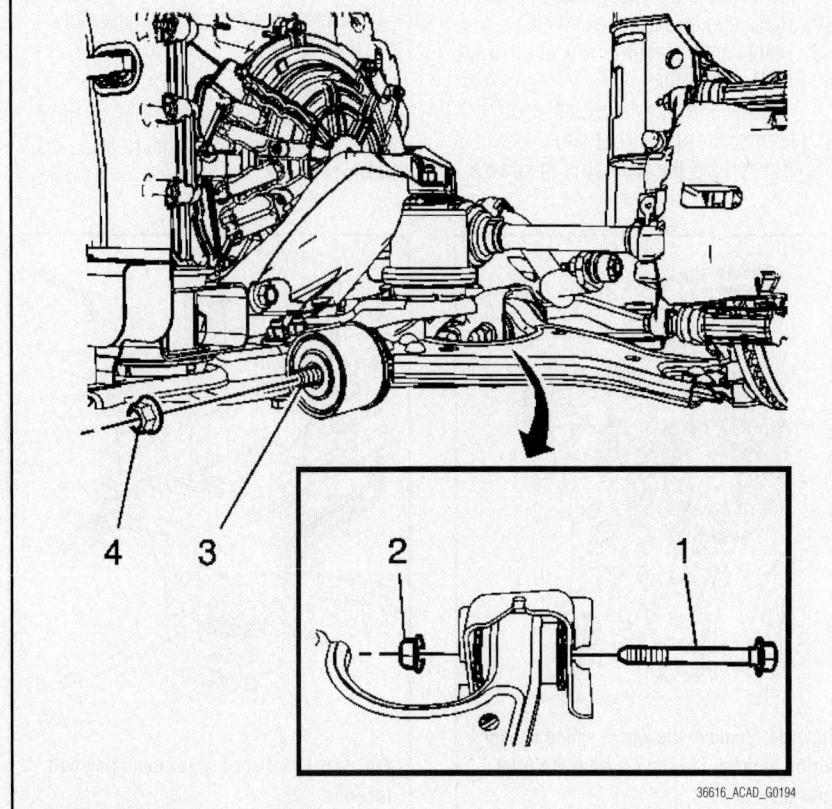

36616_ACAD_G0194

Fig. 141 Lower control arm bolt location

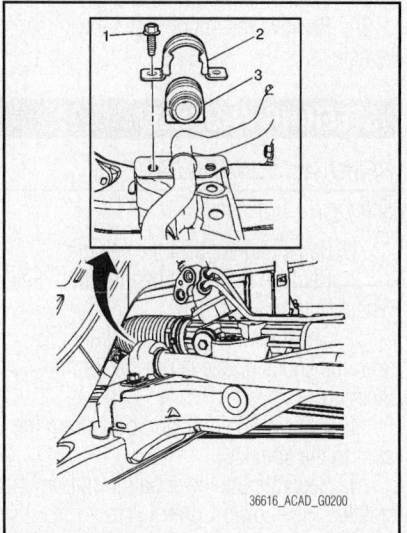

36616_ACAD_G0200

Fig. 142 Stabilizer shaft insulator location

➡️If replacing the stabilizer shaft, use NEW insulators.

13. Remove both left and right stabilizer shaft insulators.

➡️It may be necessary to maneuver the stabilizer shaft in such a way to remove it from the front cradle.

14. Remove the stabilizer shaft from the vehicle.

To install:

15. Position the stabilizer shaft on the frame.

16. Install the left and right stabilizer shaft insulators and brackets and tighten to 37 ft. lbs. (50 Nm).

17. Install the stabilizer shaft links to the stabilizer shaft.

18. Using the jack stands, raise the front cradle into position.

19. Tighten the front frame bolts.

20. Tighten the frame to body bolts to 74 ft. lbs. (100 Nm) plus an additional 90 degrees.

21. Tighten the front frame reinforcement mounting bolts to 37 ft. lbs. (50 Nm).

22. Tighten the rear frame mounting bolts to 74 ft. lbs. (100 Nm) plus an additional 90 degrees.

23. Tighten the rear reinforcement bolts to 37 ft. lbs. (50 Nm).

24. Remove the adjustable jack stands.

25. Install the bolt from the intermediate shaft bracket to the front cradle.

26. Install the outer tie rod ends to the knuckle. Tighten to 22 ft. lbs. (30 Nm) plus an additional 120 degrees.

27. Install the rear propeller shaft, if equipped.

28. Install the front tires and wheels.

29. Remove the support and lower the vehicle.

STEERING KNUCKLE

REMOVAL & INSTALLATION

See Figure 143.

1. Raise and support the vehicle.

2. Remove the wheel bearing/hub. See Wheel Hub and Bearings.

3. Separate the outer tie rod end from the knuckle. See Outer Tie Rod in Steering.

4. Remove the nuts and bolts from the strut to the knuckle.

5. Separate the lower ball joint from the knuckle. See Lower Control Arm.

6. Remove the knuckle assembly.

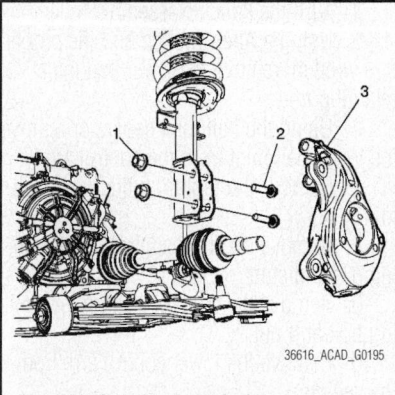

Fig. 143 Steering knuckle (3) removal

➡️Support the wheel drive shaft with mechanics wire after the knuckle has been removed.

To install:

7. Installation is the reverse of removal.

8. Tighten the strut to knuckle nuts/bolts to 144 ft. lbs. (195 Nm).

9. Tighten tie rod end to knuckle to 22 ft. lbs. (30 Nm) plus an additional 120 degrees.

STRUT

REMOVAL & INSTALLATION

See Figures 144 through 146.

1. Remove the air inlet grille.

2. Raise and support the vehicle.

3. Remove the stabilizer link at the front strut. See Control Links.

4. Remove the wheel speed sensor wiring harness from the front strut.

5. If removing the front strut to service

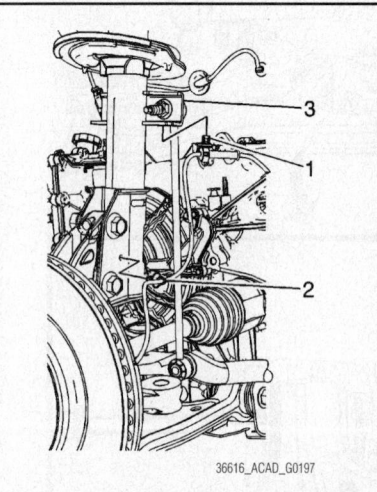

Fig. 144 Remove the wheel speed sensor wiring harness (1) and (2) from the front strut (3)

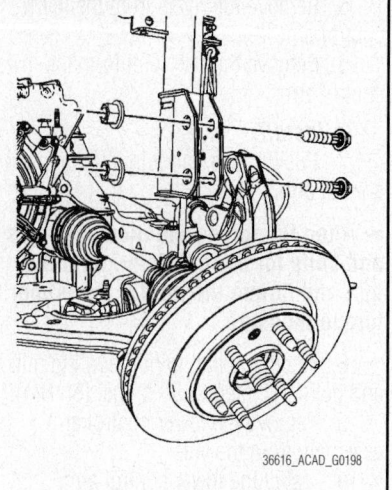

Fig. 145 Front strut lower mounting bolt location

any other suspension or steering component, scribe a line in the steering knuckle against the front strut. This will aid in the realigning the front suspension.

6. Lower the vehicle to gain access to the upper strut mounting bolts.

7. Remove the front strut mounting bolts and nuts.

8. Remove the upper strut mounting nuts.

9. Separate the front strut from the steering knuckle.

10. Remove the front strut assembly from the vehicle.

To install:

11. Position the front strut in the strut tower. Tighten the upper nuts to 33 ft. lbs. (45 Nm).

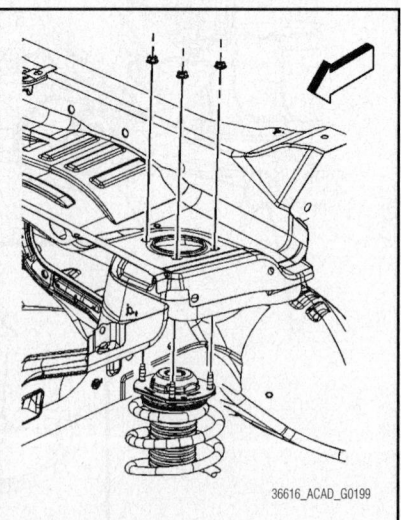

Fig. 146 Front strut upper mounting bolt location

12. Raise the vehicle.

➡ **If installing the front strut after servicing another steering or suspension component, align the front strut to the scribe mark on the steering knuckle.**

13. Position the front strut on the steering knuckle.

14. Install the front strut to steering knuckle mounting nuts and bolts. Tighten to 144 ft. lbs. (195 Nm).

15. Install the stabilizer link at the front strut.

16. Install the wheel speed sensor wiring harness on the front strut.

17. Install the air inlet grille.

18. Align the front end.

OVERHAUL

1. Remove the strut from the vehicle.

2. Install the strut (a spring compressor tool.)

➡ **The spring is compressed when the strut moves freely.**

3. Turn the spring compressor forcing screw until the coil spring is compressed.

4. Use a 45 TORX® socket in order to hold the strut shaft. Use a strut rod socket such as J 42991 to remove the upper strut mount nut.

5. Remove the strut from the compressor

6. Loosen the compressor forcing screw until the upper strut mount and coil spring may be removed.

7. Remove the upper strut mount and the coil spring from the compressor.

To install:

8. Install the coil spring and upper strut mount to the compressor.

9. Turn the spring compressor forcing screw until the coil spring is compressed.

10. Install the strut to the coil spring and upper strut mount.

11. Loosely install the strut retaining nut.

12. Use a 45 TORX® socket in order to hold the strut shaft. Use a strut rod socket such as J 42991 to install the upper strut mount nut. Tighten to 63 ft. lbs. (85 Nm).

13. Remove the strut from the compressor.

14. Install the strut to the vehicle.

WHEEL HUB AND BEARING

REMOVAL & INSTALLATION
See Figure 147.

1. Raise and support the vehicle.

2. Remove the tire and wheel.

3. Remove the front brake rotor. See Front Brakes in Brakes.

4. Remove the wheel drive shaft retaining nut and washer.

5. Install the a wheel hub puller such as J 42129 to the wheel bearing and hub.

6. Using a wheel hub puller such as J 42129, separate the wheel drive shaft from the wheel bearing and hub.

7. Remove the wheel hub puller from the wheel bearing and hub assembly.

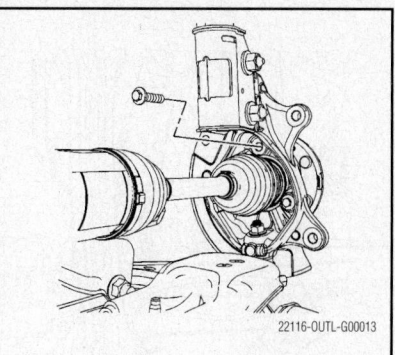

22116-OUTL-G00013

Fig. 147 Wheel hub and bearing mounting

8. Remove the retaining bolts for the wheel bearing and hub.

9. Remove the wheel bearing and hub assembly.

To install:

10. Position the wheel bearing and hub assembly in the knuckle.

11. Install the retaining bolts for the wheel bearing and hub. Tighten to 103 ft. lbs. (140 Nm).

12. Install the front brake rotor.

13. Install the wheel drive shaft retaining nut and washer and tighten to 173 ft. lbs. (235 Nm).

14. Install the tire and wheel.

15. Remove the support and lower the vehicle.

ADJUSTMENT

The wheel bearing are sealed at the factory and do not require any adjustment or maintenance

SUSPENSION

COIL SPRING

REMOVAL & INSTALLATION
See Figure 148.

1. Raise and support the vehicle.

2. Remove the rear tire and wheel.

3. Position an adjustable jack stand under the lower control arm .

4. Remove the lower stabilizer shaft link bushing and nut. See Stabilizer Bar.

5. Remove the lower shock absorber bolt. See Shock Absorber.

6. Remove the lower bolts from the knuckle. See Knuckle.

7. Using the adjustable jack stand, slowly lower the vehicle until the rear spring, insulator jounce bumper and the spring seat can be removed.

To install:

8. Position the spring seat, jounce bumper, rear spring and the insulator on the lower control arm.

9. Using the adjustable jack stand,

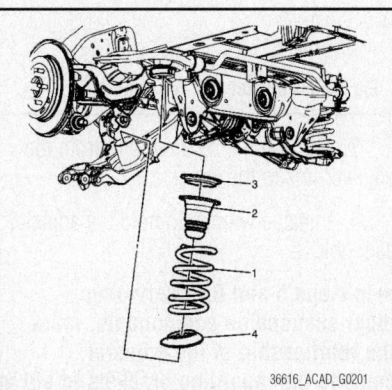

36616_ACAD_G0201

Fig. 148 Rear spring (1), insulator (4), jounce bumper (2), and spring seat (3)

REAR SUSPENSION

raise the lower control arm until the lower bolts for the knuckle can be installed.

10. Remove the adjustable jack stand.

11. Install the lower stabilizer shaft link bushing and nut.

12. Install the lower shock absorber bolt. Tighten to 74 ft. lbs. (100 Nm) plus an additional 60 degrees.

13. Install the rear tire and wheels.

14. Remove the support and lower the vehicle.

CONTROL ARMS/LINKS

REMOVAL & INSTALLATION
See Figures 149 through 153.

1. Raise and support the vehicle. Refer to Lifting and Jacking the Vehicle.

2. Remove the rear shock absorber. See Shock Absorber.

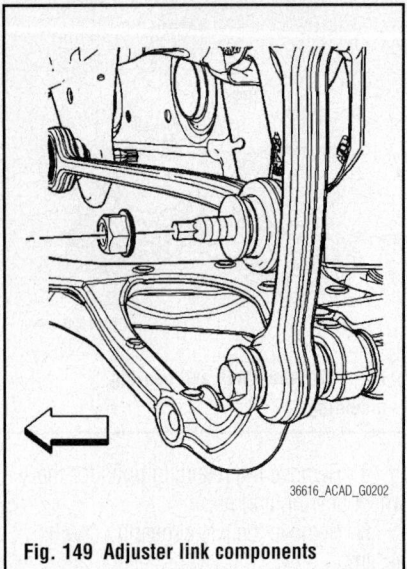

Fig. 149 Adjuster link components

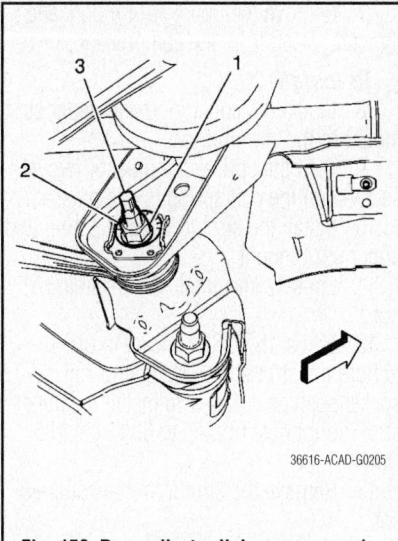
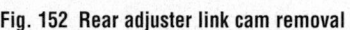

Fig. 152 Rear adjuster link cam removal

5. Mark a point of reference on the adjuster cam and the mounting bracket.

6. Remove the front adjuster nut (1) and the adjuster cam (2).

7. Remove the rear adjuster nut (1), adjuster cam (2).

8. Maneuver the adjuster bolt (3) so as to remove it from the mounting bracket.

9. Remove the adjuster link from the knuckle and the mounting bracket.

To install:

10. Install the adjuster link on the knuckle and in the mounting bracket.

11. Install the adjuster bolt in the mounting bracket and adjuster link.

12. Install the rear adjuster cam and adjuster nut. Finger tighten the nut at this time.

13. Install the front adjuster cam and the adjuster nut. Finger tighten the nut at this time.

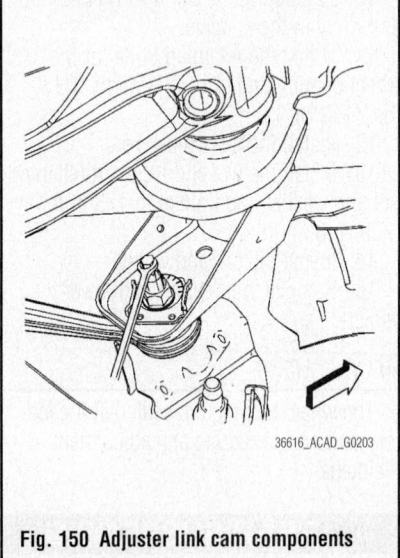

Fig. 150 Adjuster link cam components

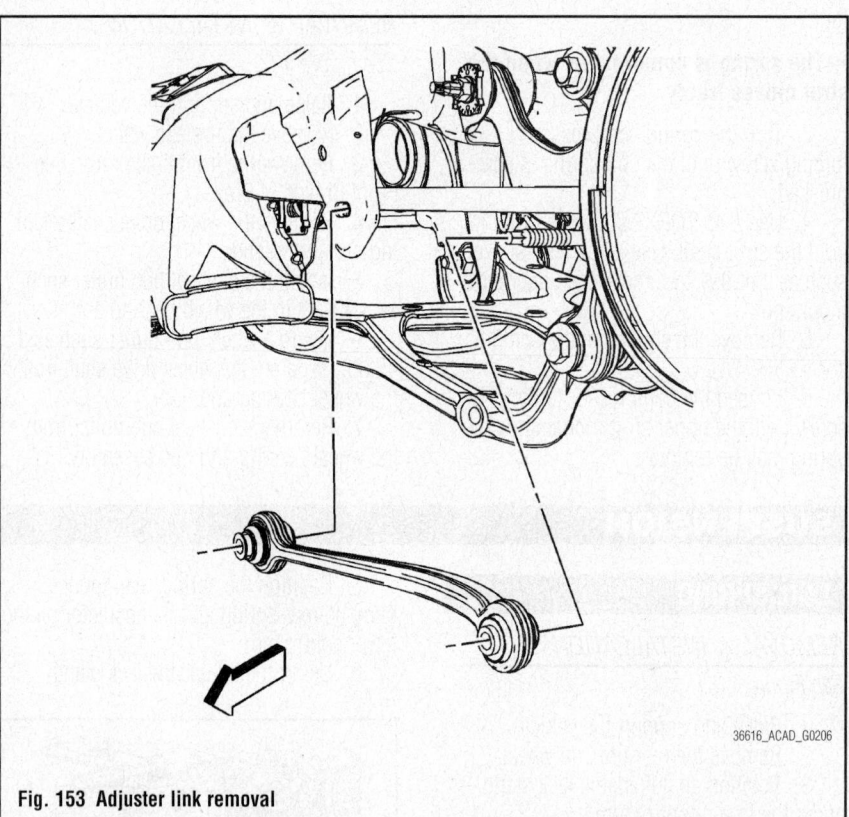

Fig. 153 Adjuster link removal

Fig. 151 Front adjuster link cam removal

3. Remove the retaining nut from the adjuster link to the knuckle.

4. Install a wrench to hold the adjuster cam bolt.

➡**In steps 5 and 6, if servicing other suspension components, mark the relationship of the adjuster cams to the mounting brackets to aid in the re-installation of the adjustment link.**

14. Install the retaining nut for the adjuster link and tighten to 55 ft. lbs. (75 Nm) plus 60 degrees.

15. Install the rear shock absorber.

➡**If servicing other suspension components, align the relationship marks on the adjuster cam and the mounting brackets to aid in the re-installation of the adjustment link.**

16. Align the reference marks on the adjuster cam and the mounting bracket.

17. Install a wrench to hold the adjuster cam bolt and tighten the adjuster cam nuts to 103 ft. lbs. (140 Nm).

18. Remove the support and lower the vehicle.

19. Align the rear suspension.

LATERAL LINK

REMOVAL & INSTALLATION

See Figure 154.

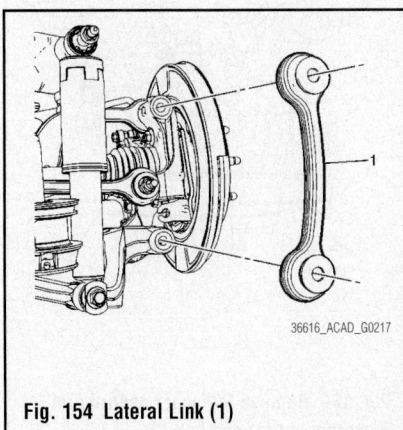

Fig. 154 Lateral Link (1)

1. Raise and support the vehicle.
2. Remove the rear tire and wheel.
3. Support the lower control arm with a jack stand.
4. Remove the upper control arm bolt. See Upper Control Arm.
5. Remove the lower control arm bolt. See Lower Control Arm.
6. Remove lateral link.

To install:

7. Installation is the reverse of removal.

8. Install the bolt from the upper control arm to the knuckle and finger tighten the nut. Tighten the bolt to 74 ft. lbs. (100 Nm) plus an additional 90 degrees.

9. Install the bolt from the lower control arm to the knuckle and finger-tighten. Tighten the bolt to 74 ft. lbs. (100 Nm) plus an additional 90 degrees.

LOWER CONTROL ARMS

REMOVAL & INSTALLATION

See Figure 155.

1. Remove the rear coil spring and related parts. See Coil Spring.
2. Rear lower control arm nut.
3. Rear lower control arm bolt.
4. Rear lower control arm.

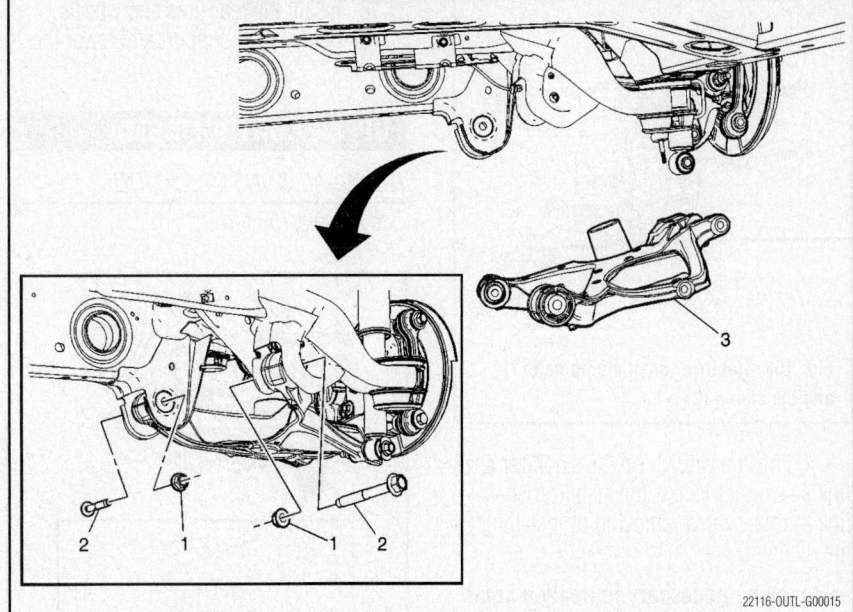

Fig. 155 Rear lower control arm mounting (and mounting nuts (1) and bolts (2))–Outlook

To install:

5. Installation is the reverse of removal.

6. Tighten the front bolt/nut to 81 ft. lbs. (110 Nm) plus an additional 45 degrees.

7. Tighten the rear bolt/nut to 89 ft. lbs. (120 Nm) plus an additional 60 degrees.

8. Inspect the wheel alignment and adjust as needed.

SHOCK ABSORBER

REMOVAL & INSTALLATION

See Figure 156.

1. Remove the tire and wheel.
2. Using a suitable jack stand, raise the rear knuckle to remove spring tension.
3. Remove the lower shock bolt.
4. Remove the upper shock nuts.
5. Remove the shock from the vehicle.

To install:

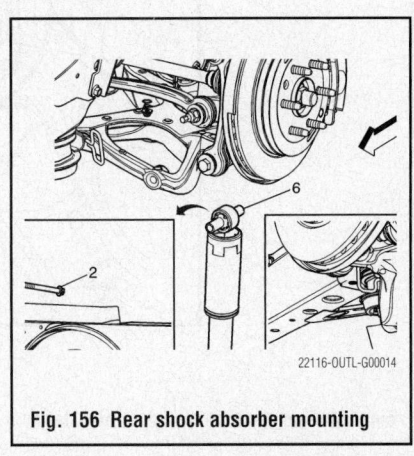

Fig. 156 Rear shock absorber mounting

6. Place the shock in the vehicle.

7. Install the shock absorber to body nuts. Tighten to 52 ft. lbs. (70 Nm).

8. Install the shock absorber to knuckle bolt. Tighten to 74 ft. lbs. (100 Nm) plus an additional 60 degrees.

9. Remove the jack stand from the rear knuckle.

10. Install the tire and wheel.

11. Lower the vehicle.

STABILIZER BAR

REMOVAL & INSTALLATION

See Figures 157 and 158.

1. Raise and support the vehicle.
2. Remove the rear tires and wheels.
3. Remove the spare tire.

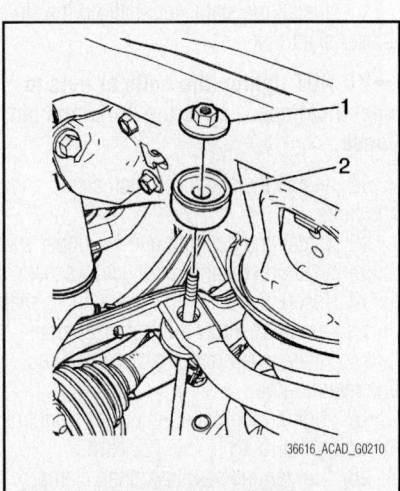

Fig. 157 Upper stabilizer shaft link retaining nut with washer and bushing

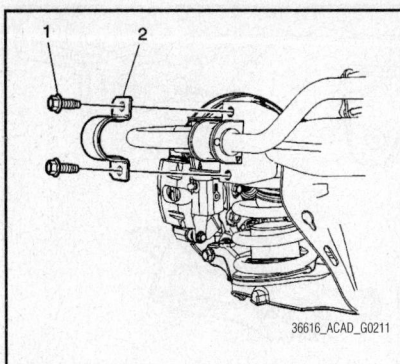

Fig. 158 Stabilizer shaft clamp bolt (1) and the clamp (2)

4. Insert a wrench on the stabilizer shaft link so as not to allow the stabilizer shaft link to rotate when removing or installing the retaining nut.

➡It may be necessary to apply a small amount of penetrating oil to the stabilizer shaft link retaining nut prior to removal.

5. Remove the upper stabilizer shaft link retaining nut with washer and bushing.
6. Remove the stabilizer shaft clamp bolt and the clamp.
7. Remove the stabilizer shaft from the stabilizer shaft link.

➡It may be necessary to maneuver the stabilizer shaft in such away to remove it from the vehicle.

8. Remove the stabilizer shaft and bushing from the vehicle.

To install:
9. Install the bushing on the stabilizer shaft.
10. Maneuver the stabilizer shaft in such away to properly install it on the frame.
11. Install the stabilizer shaft on the stabilizer shaft link.

➡DO NOT tighten the bolts or nuts to specifications. Leave the bolts and nut loose.

12. Install the stabilizer shaft clamp and the bolts.
13. Install the bushing and the upper stabilizer shaft link retaining nut with washer.
14. Insert a wrench on the stabilizer shaft link so as not to allow the stabilizer shaft link to rotate when removing or installing the retaining nut.
15. Tighten the upper stabilizer shaft link retaining nut to 16 ft. lbs. (22 Nm).
16. Tighten the stabilizer shaft clamp bolts to 37 ft. lbs. (50 Nm).
17. Install the spare tire.

18. Install the rear tires and wheels.
19. Remove the support and lower the vehicle.

UPPER CONTROL ARMS

REMOVAL & INSTALLATION
See Figures 159 through 163.

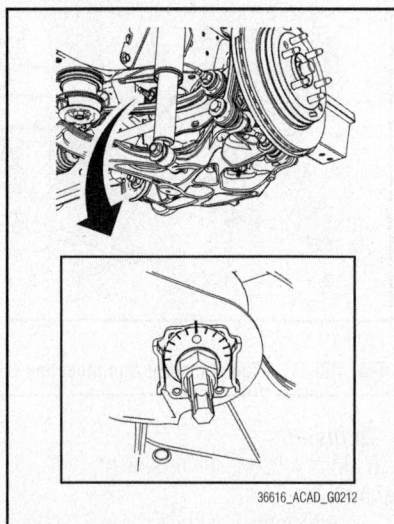

Fig. 159 Adjuster cam and the bracket scribe mark

1. Remove the tire and wheel assembly.

➡If removing the upper control arm to service scribe a line on the front adjuster cam to aid in the realignment of the control arm.

2. Scribe a reference mark on the adjuster cam and the bracket to aid in installing the upper control arm.

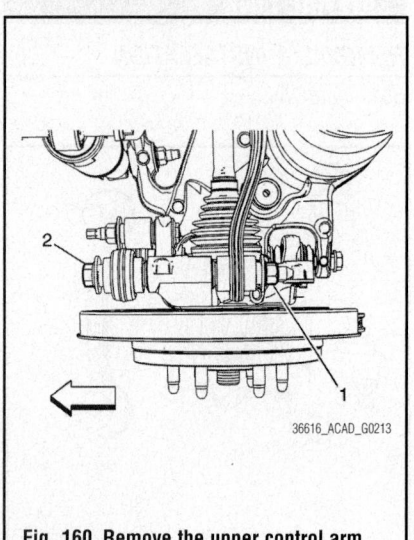

Fig. 160 Remove the upper control arm mounting nut (1) and bolt (2)

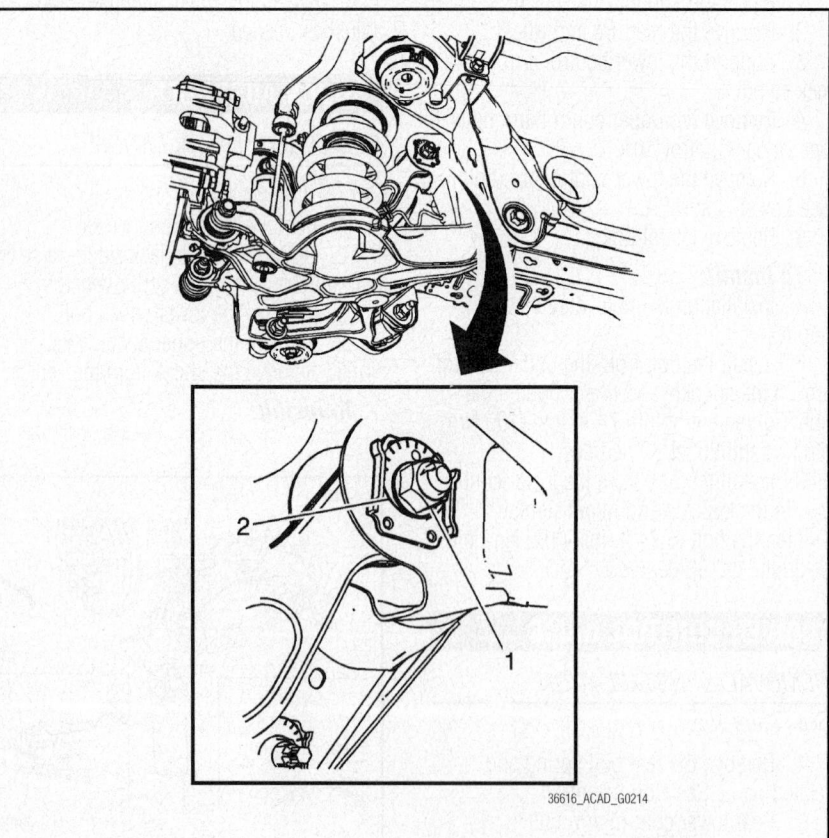

Fig. 161 Remove the rear upper adjuster cam bolt (1) and the rear upper adjuster cam (2)

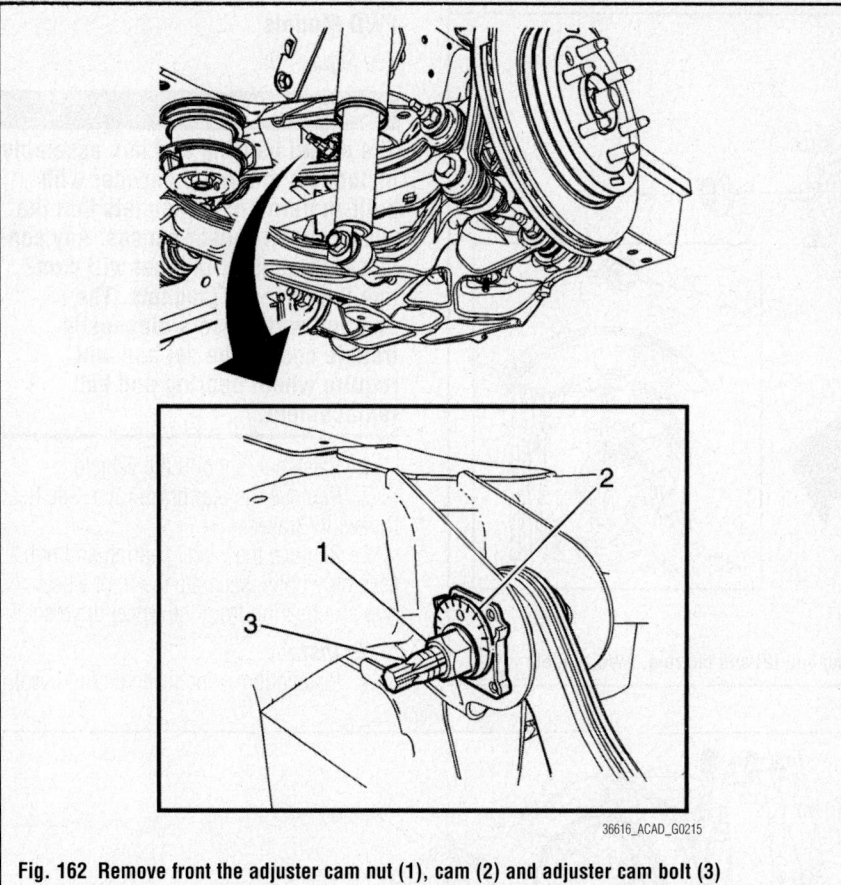

Fig. 162 Remove front the adjuster cam nut (1), cam (2) and adjuster cam bolt (3)

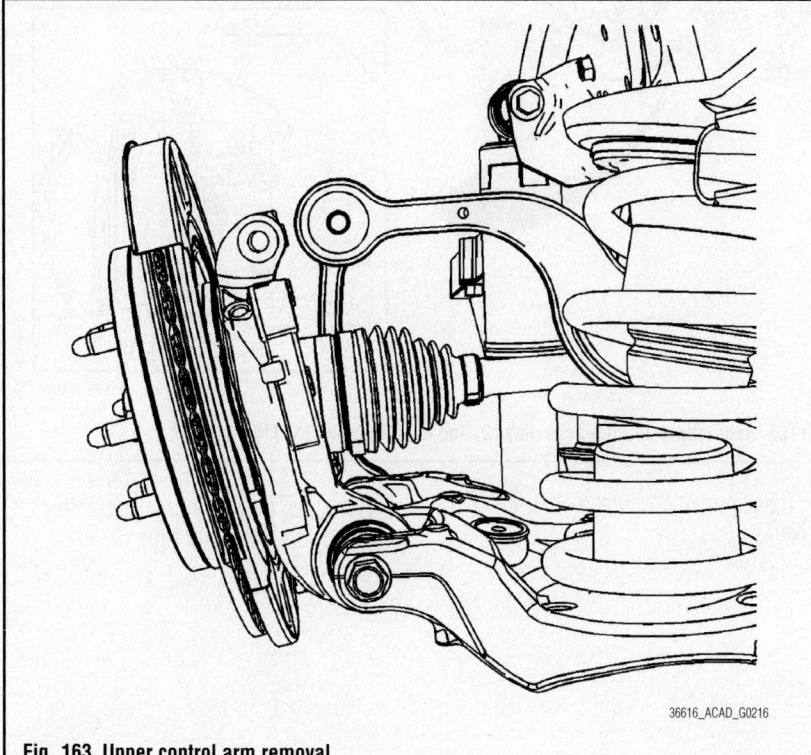

Fig. 163 Upper control arm removal

3. Remove the speed sensor wiring harness retaining clips and from the upper control arm.

4. Position a jack stand under the lower control arm.

5. Remove the upper control arm mounting nut and bolt.

6. Use a wrench to hold the adjuster cam bolt.

7. Remove the rear upper adjuster cam bolt.

8. Remove the rear upper adjuster cam.

9. Remove front the adjuster cam nut.

10. Remove the adjuster cam.

11. Remove the adjuster cam bolt.

12. Rotate the rear knuckle down to gain removal clearance for the upper control arm.

13. Remove the upper control arm.

To install:

14. Install the upper control arm in the mounting bracket.

15. Rotate the knuckle assembly back into the proper position.

16. Position the front adjuster cam in the mounting bracket.

17. Install the adjuster cam bolt.

18. Finger tighten the front adjuster cam nut.

19. Position the rear adjuster cam in the mounting bracket.

20. Finger tighten the rear adjuster cam nut.

21. Install the upper control arm bolt and nut. Tighten to 74 ft. lbs. (100 Nm) plus an additional 90 degrees.

22. Remove the jack stand from under the lower control arm.

23. Install the speed sensor wiring harness retaining clips and on the upper control arm.

24. Align the reference marks on the adjuster cam and bracket.

25. Using a wrench to hold the adjuster cam bolt in place, tighten all the adjuster cam nuts. Tighten to 103 ft. lbs. (140 Nm).

26. Install the tire and wheel assembly.

27. Verify wheel alignment.

WHEEL HUB AND BEARING

REMOVAL & INSTALLATION

AWD Models

See Figure 164.

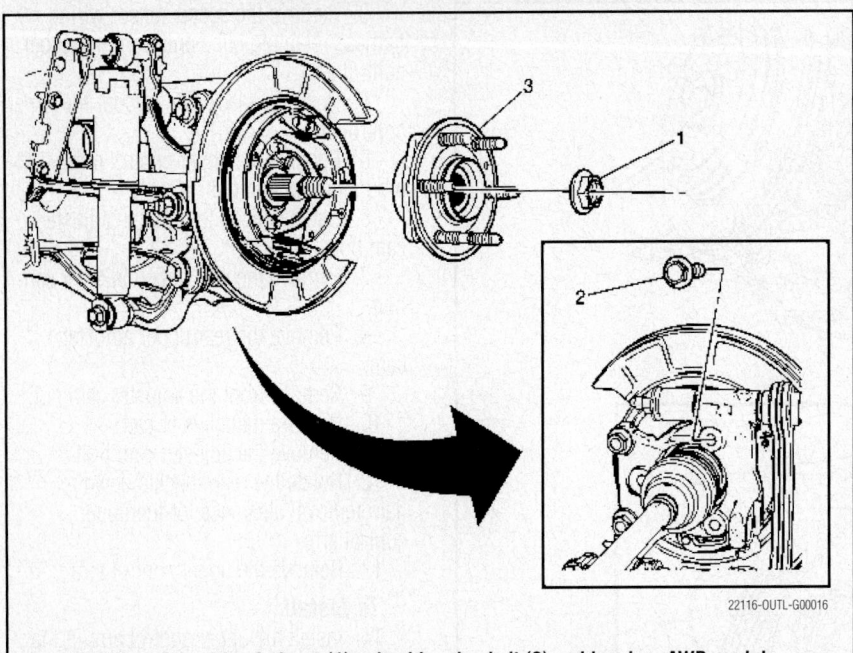

Fig. 164 View of the driveshaft nut (1), wheel bearing bolt (2) and bearing, AWD models

✳✳ WARNING

The wheel bearing and hub assembly includes a magnetic encoder with built-in permanent magnets that the wheel speed sensor senses. Any contact with another magnet will damage the encoder magnets. The damage will cause a diagnostic trouble code to be set and will require wheel bearing and hub replacement.

1. Raise and support the vehicle.
2. Remove the rear brake rotor. See Rear Brakes in Brakes.
3. Remove the drive shaft nut.
4. Remove the wheel bearing and hub assembly bolts, separate the front wheel hub and bearing from the wheel drive shaft.

To install:
5. Installation is the reverse of removal.
6. Tighten the bearing/hub assembly bolts to 103 ft. lbs. (140 Nm)

FWD Models

See Figure 165.

✳✳ WARNING

The wheel bearing and hub assembly includes a magnetic encoder with built-in permanent magnets that the wheel speed sensor senses. Any contact with another magnet will damage the encoder magnets. The damage will cause a diagnostic trouble code to be set and will require wheel bearing and hub replacement.

1. Raise and support the vehicle.
2. Remove the rear brake rotor. See Rear Brakes in Brakes.
3. Remove the wheel bearing and hub assembly bolts, separate the front wheel hub and bearing from the wheel drive shaft.

To install:
4. Installation is the reverse of removal.

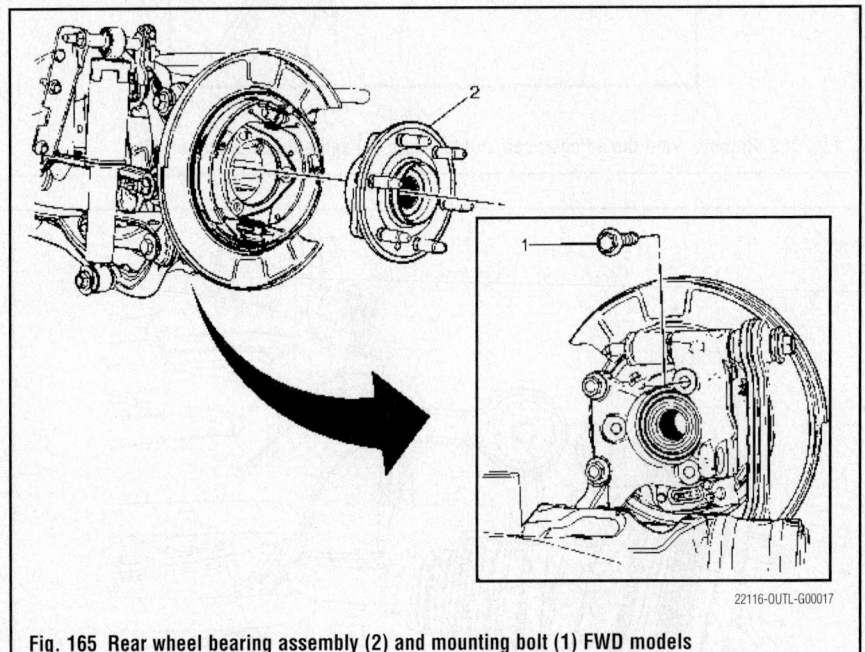

Fig. 165 Rear wheel bearing assembly (2) and mounting bolt (1) FWD models

7. Tighten drive shaft nut to 151 ft. lbs. (205 Nm).

5. Tighten the bearing/hub assembly bolts to 103 ft. lbs. (140 Nm).

BUICK

Allure • LaCrosse

SPECIFICATIONS AND MAINTENANCE CHARTS

ENGINE AND VEHICLE IDENTIFICATION

			Engine					Model Year	
Code ①	Liters (cc)	Cu. In.	Cyl.	Fuel Sys.	Engine Type	Eng. Mfg.		Code ②	Year
G	3.0 (2,999)	183	6	SIDI	DOHC	GM		8	2008
7	3.6 (3,564)	217	6	SFI	DOHC	GM		9	2009
V	3.6 (3,564)	217	6	SIDI	DOHC	GM		A	2010
1	3.8 (3,791)	231	6	SFI	OHV	GM			
2	3.8 (3,791)	231	6	SFI	OHV	GM			
C	5.3 (5,328)	325	8	SFI	OHV	GM			

SFI: Sequential Multiport Fuel Injection   DOHC: Dual Overhead Camshafts

SIDI: Spark Ignition Direct Injection   OHV: Overhead Valves

① 8th position of Vehicle Identification Number (VIN)

② 10th position of VIN

36616_LACR_C0001

GENERAL ENGINE SPECIFICATIONS

All measurements are given in inches.

Year	Model	Engine Displacement Liters	Engine Series ID/VIN	Net Horsepower @ rpm	Net Torque @ rpm (ft. lbs.)	Bore x Stroke (in.)	Compression Ratio	Oil Pressure @ rpm
2008	Allure, LaCrosse	3.6	7	240@6000	225@2000	3.70 x 3.37	10.2:1	20@2000
		3.8	1	200@5200	230@4000	3.80 x 3.40	9.4:1	60@1850
		5.3	C	300@5600	323@4000	3.78 x 3.62	9.9:1	18@2000
2009	Allure, LaCrosse	3.8	2	200@5200	230@4000	3.80 x 3.40	9.4:1	60@1850
		5.3	C	300@5600	323@4000	3.78 x 3.62	9.9:1	18@2000
2010	Allure, LaCrosse	3.0	G	255@6900	217@5100	3.50 x 3.16	11.7:1	20@2000
		3.6	V	280@6300	259@4800	3.70 x 3.37	11.4:1	20@2000

36616_LACR_C0002

GASOLINE ENGINE TUNE-UP SPECIFICATIONS

Year	Engine Displacement Liters	Engine VIN	Spark Plug Gap (in.)	Ignition Timing (deg.)	Fuel Pump (psi)	Idle Speed (rpm)	Valve Lash Clearance	
							Intake	Exhaust
2008	3.6	7	0.043	①	55-60 ②	③	HYD	HYD
	3.8	1	0.060	①	50-60 ②	③	HYD	HYD
	5.3	C	0.040	①	50-60 ②	③	HYD	HYD
2009	3.8	2	0.060	①	50-60 ②	③	HYD	HYD
	5.3	C	0.040	①	50-60 ②	③	HYD	HYD
2010	3.0	G	0.043	①	50-60 ②	③	HYD	HYD
	3.6	V	0.043	①	50-60 ②	③	HYD	HYD

NOTE: The Vehicle Emission Control Information label often reflects specification changes made during production.

The label figures must be used if they differ from those in this chart.

HYD: Hydraulic

① Ignition timing is controlled by the PCM and is not adjustable

② With key ON and engine OFF

③ Idle speed is controlled by the PCM and is not adjustable

36616_LACR_C0003

CAPACITIES

Year	Model	Engine Displacement Liters	Engine VIN	Engine Oil with Filter (qts.)	Transmission (pts.) Manual	Auto. ①	Transfer Case (pts.)	Drive Axle Front (pts.)	Rear (pts.)	Fuel Tank (gal.)	Cooling System (qts.)
2008	Allure, LaCrosse	3.6	7	5.5	NA	14.8	NA	NA	NA	17.0	11.2
		3.8	1	4.5	NA	14.8	NA	NA	NA	17.5	11.2
		5.3	C	6.0	NA	14.8	NA	NA	NA	17.5	13.3
2009	Allure, LaCrosse	3.8	2	4.5	NA	14.8	NA	NA	NA	17.0	11.2
		5.3	C	6.0	NA	14.8	NA	NA	NA	17.5	13.3
2010	Allure, LaCrosse	3.0	G	6.0	NA	19.0	1.4	NA	②	③	9.9
		3.6	V	5.5	NA	19.0	1.4	NA	②	③	9.9

NA: Not Applicable

NOTE: All capacities are approximate. Add fluid gradually and check to be sure a proper fluid level is obtained.

① Drain and refill

② Differential clutch without Limited Slip Differential (LSD) clutch: 1.1 pts.

    Differential clutch with LSD clutch: 1.18 pts.

    LSD without LSD clutch: 1.26 pts.

    LSD with LSD clutch: 1.48 pts.

③ AWD: 19.5 gallons

    FWD: 18.6 gallons

36616_LACR_C0004

FLUID SPECIFICATIONS

Year	Model	Engine Displacement Liters	Engine VIN	Engine Oil	Manual Trans.	Auto. Trans.	Power Steering Fluid	Brake Master Cylinder	Cooling System
2008	Allure, LaCrosse	3.6	7	5W-30	NA	Dexron VI	①	DOT-3	②
		3.8	1	5W-30	NA	Dexron VI	①	DOT-3	②
		5.3	C	5W-30	NA	Dexron VI	①	DOT-3	②
2009	Allure, LaCrosse	3.8	2	5W-30	NA	Dexron VI	①	DOT-3	②
		5.3	C	5W-30	NA	Dexron VI	①	DOT-3	②
2010	Allure, LaCrosse	3.0	G	5W-30	NA	Dexron VI	①	DOT-3	②
		3.6	V	5W-30	NA	Dexron VI	①	DOT-3	②

NA: Not Applicable

DOT: Department Of Transportation

① GM Power Steering Fluid (GM Part No. 89021184)

② 50/50 mixture of clean water and DEXCOOL Antifreeze/Coolant

36616_LACR_C0005

VALVE SPECIFICATIONS

Year	Engine Displacement Liters	Engine VIN	Seat Angle (deg.)	Face Angle (deg.)	Spring Test Pressure (lbs. @ in.)	Spring Installed Height (in.)	Stem-to-Guide Clearance (in.)		Stem Diameter (in.)	
							Intake	Exhaust	Intake	Exhaust
2008	3.6	7	45.0	44.25	134-149@ 0.9449	0.945-1.378	0.0010-0.0026	0.0014-0.0030	0.2344-0.2352	0.2341-0.2348
	3.8	1	45.0	46.0	228@ 1.277	1.690-1.750	0.0012-0.0028	0.0014-0.0029	0.3129-0.3136	0.3129-0.3136
	5.3	C	46.0	45.0	220@ 1.320	1.800	0.0010-0.0026	0.0010-0.0026	0.3130-0.3140	0.3130-0.3140
2009	3.8	2	45.0	46.0	228@ 1.277	1.690-1.750	0.0012-0.0028	0.0014-0.0029	0.3129-0.3136	0.3129-0.3136
	5.3	C	46.0	45.0	220@ 1.320	1.800	0.0010-0.0026	0.0010-0.0026	0.3130-0.3140	0.3130-0.3140
2010	3.0	G	45.0	44.25	134-149@ 0.9449	0.945-1.378	0.0010-0.0026	0.0014-0.0030	0.2344-0.2352	0.2341-0.2348
	3.6	V	45.0	44.25	134-149@ 0.9449	0.945-1.378	0.0010-0.0026	0.0014-0.0030	0.2344-0.2352	0.2341-0.2348

36616_LACR_C0006

CAMSHAFT AND BEARING SPECIFICATIONS CHART
All measurements are given in inches.

Year	Engine Displ. Liters	Engine VIN	Journal Dia.	Brg. Oil Clearance	Shaft End-play	Runout	Journal Bore	Lobe Lift	
								Intake	Exhaust
2008	3.6	7	①	0.0016-0.0033	0.0018-0.0085	②	0.0016-0.0033	1.6687-1.6805	1.6703-1.6821
	3.8	1	1.8462-1.8448	0.0016-0.0047	NA	0.00025	NA	0.2580	0.2580
	5.3	C	2.1640-2.1660	0.0009-0.0038	0.0010-0.0120	0.0020	③	④	④
2009	3.8	2	1.8462-1.8448	0.0016-0.0047	NA	0.00025	NA	0.2580	0.2580
	5.3	C	2.1640-2.1660	0.0009-0.0038	0.0010-0.0120	0.0020	③	④	④
2010	3.0	G	①	0.0016-0.0033	0.0018-0.0085	②	0.0016-0.0033	1.6687-1.6805	1.6703-1.6821
	3.6	V	①	0.0016-0.0033	0.0018-0.0085	②	0.0016-0.0033	1.6687-1.6805	1.6703-1.6821

① Front number 1 diameter: 1.3754 - 1.3764 in.
Middle and rear number 2-4 diameter: 1.0605 - 1.0614 in.

② Front and rear number 1 and 4 runout: 0.0010 in.
Middle number 2 and 3 runout: 0.0020 in.

③ Cam Bearing Bore 1 and 5: 2.345-2.347 inches
Bore 2 and 4: 2.325-2.327 inches
Bore 3: 2.306-2.308 inches

④ Active Fuel Management Cylinders: 0.2890 inch
Non-active Fuel Management Cylinders: 0.2830 inch

36616_LACR_C0007

CRANKSHAFT AND CONNECTING ROD SPECIFICATIONS

All measurements are given in inches.

Year	Engine Displacement Liters	Engine VIN	Crankshaft				Connecting Rod		
			Main Brg. Journal Dia.	Main Brg. Oil Clearance	Shaft End-play	Thrust on No.	Journal Diameter	Oil Clearance	Side Clearance
2008	3.6	7	2.6768-2.6775	0.0004-0.0024	0.0039-0.0130	3	2.2044-2.2050	0.0004-0.0028	0.0037-0.0140
	3.8	1	2.4988-2.4998	①	0.0030-0.0110	2	2.2487-2.2499	0.0005-0.0026	0.0040-0.0200
	5.3	C	2.5580-2.5590	0.0008-0.0021	0.0015-0.0078	5	2.0991-2.0999	0.0009-0.0025	0.0043-0.0200
2009	3.8	2	2.4988-2.4998	①	0.0030-0.0110	2	2.2487-2.2499	0.0005-0.0026	0.0040-0.0200
	5.3	C	2.5580-2.5590	0.0008-0.0021	0.0015-0.0078	5	2.0991-2.0999	0.0009-0.0025	0.0043-0.0200
2010	3.0	G	2.6768-2.6775	0.0004-0.0024	0.0039-0.0130	3	2.2044-2.2050	0.0004-0.0028	0.0037-0.0140
	3.6	V	2.6768-2.6775	0.0004-0.0024	0.0039-0.0130	3	2.2044-2.2050	0.0004-0.0028	0.0037-0.0140

① Journal 1: 0.0007-0.0016 inch

  Journals 2, 3, 4: 0.0009-0.0018 inch

36616_LACR_C0008

PISTON AND RING SPECIFICATIONS

All measurements are given in inches.

Year	Engine Displ. Liters	Engine VIN	Piston Clearance	Ring Gap			Ring Side Clearance		
				Top Compression	Bottom Compression	Oil Control	Top Compression	Bottom Compression	Oil Control
2008	3.6	7	0.0010-0.0021	0.0059-0.0118	0.0110-0.0189	0.0059-0.0236	0.0012-0.0026	0.0006-0.0024	0.0012-0.0067
	3.8	1	0.0020-0.0036	0.0100-0.0180	0.0230-0.0330	0.0100-0.0300	0.0013-0.0031	0.0013-0.0031	0.0009-0.0079
	5.3	C	-0.0014-0.0006	0.0090-0.0196	0.0173-0.0300	0.0070-0.0320	0.0016-0.0034	0.0016-0.0031	0.0005-0.0078
2009	3.8	2	0.0020-0.0036	0.0100-0.0180	0.0230-0.0330	0.0100-0.0300	0.0013-0.0031	0.0013-0.0031	0.0009-0.0079
	5.3	C	-0.0014-0.0006	0.0090-0.0196	0.0173-0.0300	0.0070-0.0320	0.0016-0.0034	0.0016-0.0031	0.0005-0.0078
2010	3.0	G	0.0010-0.0021	0.0059-0.0118	0.0110-0.0189	0.0059-0.0236	0.0012-0.0026	0.0006-0.0024	0.0012-0.0067
	3.6	V	0.0010-0.0021	0.0059-0.0118	0.0110-0.0189	0.0059-0.0236	0.0012-0.0026	0.0006-0.0024	0.0012-0.0067

36616_LACR_C0009

TORQUE SPECIFICATIONS
All readings in ft. lbs.

Year	Engine Displacement Liters	Engine VIN	Cylinder Head Bolts	Main Bearing Bolts	Rod Bearing Bolts	Crankshaft Damper Bolts	Flywheel Bolts	Manifold Intake	Manifold Exhaust	Spark Plugs	Oil Pan Drain Plug
2008	3.6	7	①	②	③	④	⑤	⑥	⑦	13	18
	3.8	1	⑧	⑨	⑩	⑪	⑫	⑬	⑭	11	22
	5.3	C	⑮	⑯	⑰	⑱	⑲	⑳	㉑	11	18
2009	3.8	2	⑧	⑨	⑩	⑪	⑫	⑬	⑭	11	22
	5.3	C	⑮	⑯	⑰	⑱	⑲	⑳	㉑	11	18
2010	3.0	G	①	②	③	④	⑤	⑥	⑦	15	18
	3.6	V	①	②	③	④	⑤	⑥	⑦	15	18

① M8 bolts:
  Step 1: 10 ft. lbs.
  Step 2: plus 60 degrees
  M11 bolts:
  Step 1: 33 ft. lbs.
  Step 2: plus 120 degrees

② Inner:
  Step 1: 15 ft. lbs.
  Step 2: plus 80 degrees
  Outer:
  Step 1: 10 ft. lbs.
  Step 2: plus 110 degrees
  Side:
  Step 1: 22 ft. lbs.
  Step 2: plus 60 degrees

③ Step 1: 22 ft. lbs.
  Step 2: back off to zero
  Step 3: 18 ft. lbs.
  Step 4: plus 110 degrees

④ Step 1: 74 ft. lbs.
  Step 2: plus 150 degrees

⑤ Step 1: 22 ft. lbs.
  Step 2: plus 45 degrees

⑥ Intake manifold bolts: 17 ft. lbs.
  Tuning valve bolt: 89 in. lbs.

⑦ Exhaust manifold bolts: 15 ft. lbs.
  Heat shield bolt: 89 in. lbs.
  Studs: 53 in. lbs.

⑧ Step 1: Tighten all bolts to 37 ft. lbs.
  Step 2: Turn all bolts 120 degrees

⑨ Cap bolts: 30 ft. lbs. plus 110 degrees
  Side bolts: 11 ft. lbs. plus 45 degrees

⑩ 20 ft. lbs. plus 50 degrees

⑪ 111 ft. lbs. plus 76 degrees

⑫ 11 ft. lbs. plus 50 degrees

⑬ Upper manifold: 8 ft. lbs.
  Lower manifold: 11 ft. lbs.
  Upper manifold cover nut 27 in. lbs.

⑭ Exhaust manifold bolt/nut: 22 ft. lbs.
  Heat shield bolt & manifold stud: 89 in. lbs
  Heat shield nut: 18 ft. lbs.
  Manifold pipe stud nut: 24 ft. lbs.

⑮ Refer to procedure for torque sequence/bolt ID
  M11 bolts Step 1: 22 ft. lbs.
  M11 bolts Step 2: 90 degrees
  M11 bolts Step 3: 70 degrees
  M8 bolts: 22 ft. lbs.

⑯ Refer to procedure for torque sequence/bolt identification
  M10 bolts Step 1: 15 ft. lbs.
  M10 bolts Step 2: 80 degrees
  M10 studs Step 1: 15 ft. lbs.
  M10 studs Step 2: 51 degrees
  M8 bolts: 18 ft. lbs.

⑰ Step 1: 15 ft. lbs.
  Step 2: 85 degrees

⑱ Step 1: 110 ft. lbs.
  Step 2: loosen 360 degrees
  Step 3: 37 ft. lbs.
  Step 4: 230 degrees

⑲ Step 1: 15 ft. lbs.
  Step 2: 37 ft. lbs.
  Step 3: 74 ft. lbs.

⑳ Refer to procedure for torque sequence/bolt identification
  Step 1: 44 inch lbs.
  Step 2: 89 inch lbs.

㉑ Bolts Step 1: 11 ft. lbs.
  Bolts Step 2: 15 ft. lbs.
  Heat shield bolts: 80 inch lbs.
  Manifold studs: 15 ft. lbs.

36616_LACR_C0010

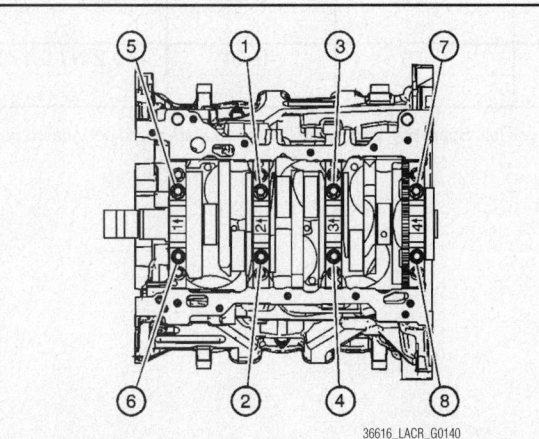

36616_LACR_G0140

Fig. 1 Main bearing inboard bolt tightening sequence—3.0L and 3.6L engines

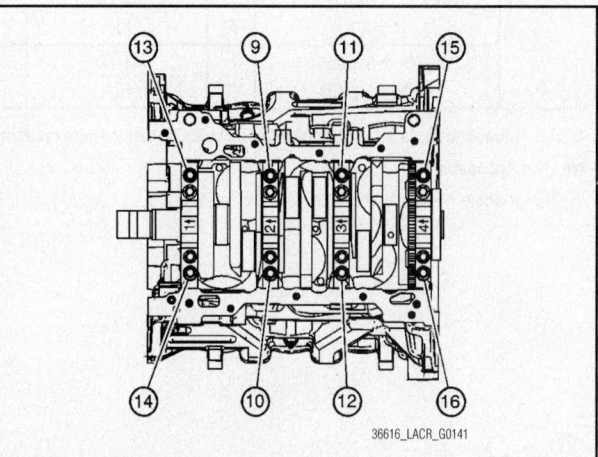

36616_LACR_G0141

Fig. 2 Main bearing outboard bolt tightening sequence—3.0L and 3.6L engines

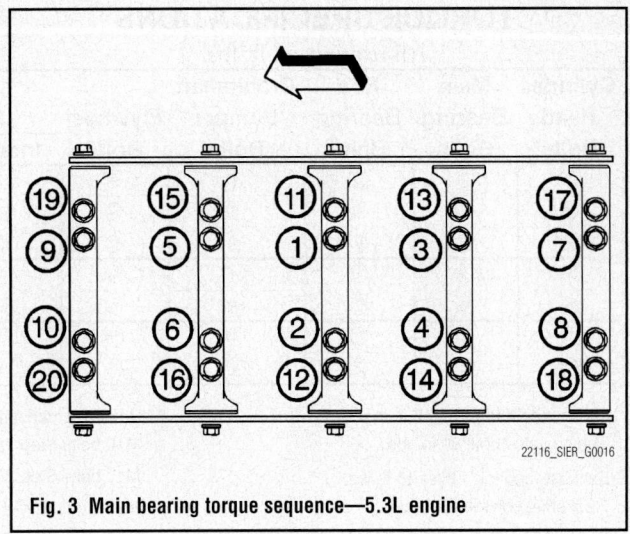

Fig. 3 Main bearing torque sequence—5.3L engine

WHEEL ALIGNMENT

Year	Model		Caster Range (+/-Deg.)	Caster Preferred Setting (Deg.)	Camber Range (+/-Deg.)	Camber Preferred Setting (Deg.)	Toe-in (Deg.)
2008	Allure, LaCrosse	F	0.75	3.00	0.75	-0.8	+0.10+/-0.20
	Base	R	NA	NA	-0.75	-0.80	+0.10+/-0.20
	Allure, LaCrosse	F	0.75	3.00	0.75	-1.0	+0.10+/-0.20
	Super	R	NA	NA	-0.75	-1.3	+0.10+/-0.20
2009	Allure, LaCrosse	F	0.75	3.00	0.75	-0.8	+0.10+/-0.20
	Base	R	NA	NA	-0.75	-0.80	+0.10+/-0.20
	Allure, LaCrosse	F	0.75	3.00	0.75	-1.0	+0.10+/-0.20
	Super	R	NA	NA	-0.75	-1.3	+0.10+/-0.20
2010	Allure, LaCrosse	F	0.75	4.72	0.75	-0.42	+0.26+/-0.17
	Standard	R	NA	NA	①	①	①
	Allure, LaCrosse	F	0.75	4.85	0.75	-0.55	+0.24+/-0.17
	Sport	R	NA	NA	①	①	①
	Allure, LaCrosse	F	0.75	4.59	0.75	-0.27	+0.26+/-0.17
	AWD	R	NA	NA	①	①	①
	Allure, LaCrosse	F	0.75	4.70	0.75	-0.44	+0.24+/-0.17
	AWD Sport	R	NA	NA	①	①	①

NOTE: Measurements are given for unladen vehicle: fuel, engine coolant, and fluid levels are full. Spare tire, jack, hand tools, and mats are in designated positi

NA: Not Applicable

① Thrust angle measurement: 0.0 +/- 0.1 degrees

36616_LACR_C0011

TIRE, WHEEL AND BALL JOINT SPECIFICATIONS

Year	Model	OEM Tires		Tire Pressure (psi)		Wheel Size	Ball Joint Inspection	Lug Nut Torque (ft. lbs.)
		Standard	Optional	Front	Rear			
2008	Allure, LaCrosse CX	P225/60R16	NA	①	①	16 in.	②	100
	Allure, LaCrosse CXL	P225/60R16	NA	①	①	16 in.	②	100
	Allure, LaCrosse Super	P235/50R18	NA	①	①	18 in.	②	100
2009	Allure, LaCrosse CX	P225/60R16	NA	①	①	16 in.	②	100
	Allure, LaCrosse CXL	P225/60R16	NA	①	①	16 in.	②	100
	Allure, LaCrosse Super	P235/50R18	NA	①	①	18 in.	②	100
2010	Allure, LaCrosse CX	P245/50R17	NA	①	①	17 in.	②	111
	Allure, LaCrosse CXL FWD	P235/50R18	NA	①	①	18 in.	②	111
	Allure, LaCrosse CXL AWD	P235/50R18	NA	①	①	18 in.	②	111
	Allure, LaCrosse CXS	P235/50R18	P245/40R19	①	①	18 in. / 19 in. opt.	②	111

OEM: Original Equipment Manufacturer

PSI: Pounds Per Square Inch

NA: Not Applicable

① See the tire placard on the vehicle

② No more than 0.02 inch of vertical lash in the ball joint

36616_LACR_C0012

BRAKE SPECIFICATIONS

All measurements in inches unless noted

Year	Model		Brake Disc			Minimum Lining Thickness	Brake Caliper	
			Original Thickness	Minimum Thickness	Maximum Runout		Bracket Bolts (ft. lbs.)	Guide Pin Bolts (ft. lbs.)
2008	Allure, LaCrosse CX/CXL	F	1.27	1.21	0.002	①	133	27
		R	0.55	0.49	0.002	①	89	②
	Allure, LaCrosse Super	F	1.181	1.126	0.002	①	133	27
		R	0.433	0.354	0.002	①	89	②
2009	Allure, LaCrosse CX/CXL	F	1.27	1.21	0.002	①	133	27
		R	0.55	0.49	0.002	①	89	②
	Allure, LaCrosse Super	F	1.181	1.126	0.002	①	133	27
		R	0.433	0.354	0.002	①	89	②
2010	Allure, LaCrosse (All models)	F	1.18	1.07	0.002	③	④	21
		R	0.827	0.905	0.002	③	⑤	20

F: Front

R: Rear

① Replace the disc brake pads when the friction surface is worn to within 0.030 inch (0.76mm) of the mounting plates.

② JL9: 32 ft. lbs.

   J65: 25 ft. lbs.

③ Replace the disc brake pads when the friction surface is worn to within 0.08 inch (2mm) of the mounting plates.

④ 111 ft. lbs. + 45 degrees + 15 degrees

⑤ 74 ft. lbs. + 60 degrees

36616_LACR_C0013

MAINTENANCE I AND II SERVICE SCHEDULES
Buick Allure, LaCrosse

When the CHANGE ENGINE OIL light appears, certain services and inspections are required.

Required services are described as Maintenance I and Maintenance II.

The first service of a vehicle should be Maintenance I, and the second service should be Maintenance II.

Alternate between the 2 services thereafter. However, in some cases, Maintenance II may be required more often.

Maintenance I: Use Maintenance I if the CHANGE ENGINE OIL light comes on within 10 months since the vehicle was purchased or, if Maintenance II was performed.

Maintenance II: Use Maintenance II if the previous service performed was Maintenance I. Always use Maintenance II whenever the CHANGE ENGINE OIL light comes on 10 months or more since the last service, or, if the CHANGE ENGINE OIL light has not come on at all for one year.

Service	Maintenance I	Maintenance II
Change the engine oil and filter. Reset the oil life system	✓	✓
Visually inspect the vehicle for leaks or damage. A fluid loss in the vehicle system could indicate a problem. Inspect, repair, and add fluid to the system as necessary.	✓	✓
Inspect the engine air cleaner filter. If necessary, replace the filter.	—	✓
Rotate the tires. Inspect the tire inflation pressures and the tire wear.	✓	✓
Visually inspect the brake lines and hoses for proper hook-up, binding, leaks, cracks, chafing, etc. Inspect the disc brake pads for wear and the rotors for surface condition. Inspect wheel cylinders, calipers, parking brake (incl. adjustment)	✓	✓
Check the engine coolant and windshield washer fluid levels and add fluid as needed.	✓	✓
Inspect the suspension and steering components. Inspect for damaged, loose or missing parts, or signs of wear. Inspect the power steering lines and the hoses for proper hook-up, binding, leaks, cracks, chafing, etc.	—	✓
Inspect the coolant hoses and replace the hoses if they are cracked, swollen, or deteriorated. Inspect all pipes, fittings, and clamps; replace with GM parts as needed. To help ensure proper operation, a pressure test of the cooling system and pressure cap. Cleaning the outside of the radiator and air conditioning condenser is recommended at least once a year.	—	✓
Inspect the wiper blades for wear or cracking.	—	✓
Inspect the restraint system components. Ensure that the safety belt reminder light and all the belts, buckles, latch plates, retractors, and anchorages are working properly. Look for any other loose or damaged safety belt system parts. Repair or replace the damaged part. Inspect for any opened or broken air bag coverings and repair or replace, as needed. The air bag system requires regular maintenance.	—	✓
Lubricate all key lock cylinders, hood latch assemblies, secondary latches, pivots, spring anchor and release pawl, hood and door hinges, and trunk hinges. Frequent lubrication may be required when exposed to a corrosive environment. Apply dielectric silicone grease, on the weatherstrips with a clean cloth.	—	✓
Inspect the transmission fluid level and add fluid as needed.	—	✓
Inspect the throttle system for interference or binding and for damaged or missing parts. Replace the parts as needed. Replace any components that have high effort or excessive wear.	—	✓
Replace the passenger compartment air filter.	—	✓

To reset the CHANGE ENGINE OIL light:

Vehicles with Driver Information Center (DIC)

1. Press the option button on the DIC until ENGINE OIL MONITOR appears on the DIC screen.

2. Press the set/reset button to reset the system. The next screen indicates that the CHANGE OIL SOON message message has been reset. If the vehicle has the uplevel DIC, when the gages button is pressed and the OIL LIFE REMAINING mode appears, it should read 100 percent OIL LIFE REMAINING

3. Turn the key to OFF.

Vehicles without Driver Information Center (DIC)

1. With the engine OFF, turn the ignition key to RUN.

2. Fully press and release the accelerator pedal slowly 3 times within 5 seconds.

3. Turn the key to OFF, then start the vehicle.

NOTE: If the light or message comes back on when starting the vehicle, the oil life system has not reset. Repeat the procedure.

ADDITIONAL MAINTENANCE SERVICES

Buick Allure, LaCrosse

TO BE SERVICED	TYPE OF SERVICE	VEHICLE MILEAGE INTERVAL (x1000)					
		25	50	75	100	125	150
Air cleaner filter	R		✓		✓		✓
Accessory drive belt	I						✓
Automatic transmission fluid ①	R				✓		
Engine coolant ②	R	Every 5 years or 150,000 miles					
Evaporative control system ③	I		✓		✓		✓
Fuel system (for damage or leaks)	I	✓	✓	✓	✓	✓	✓
Exhaust system	S/I	✓	✓	✓	✓	✓	✓
Spark plugs	R				✓		
Spark plug wires	I				✓		

R: Replace

S/I: Inspect and service, if necessary

FREQUENT OPERATION MAINTENANCE (SEVERE SERVICE)

If a vehicle is operated under any of the following conditions, it is considered severe service:

- Extremely dusty areas

- 50% or more of the vehicle operation is in 90°F (32°C) or higher temperatures, or constant operation in temperatures below 32°F (0°C)

- Prolonged idling (vehicle operation in stop and go traffic)

- Frequent short running periods (engine does not warm to normal operating temperatures)

- Police, taxi, delivery usage, or trailer towing usage

- Driving in hilly or mountainous terrain

① Replace the fluid every 50,000 miles under Severe Service

② Drain, flush, and refill the cooling system. Inspect hoses. Clean the radiator, condenser, pressure cap, and filler neck. Pressure test the cooling pressure cap.

③ Check all fuel and vapor lines and hoses for proper hook-up, routing, and condition. Check that the purge valve works properly, if equipped. Replace

36616_LACR_C0015

PRECAUTIONS

Before servicing any vehicle, please be sure to read all of the following precautions, which deal with personal safety, prevention of component damage, and important points to take into consideration when servicing a motor vehicle:

• Never open, service or drain the radiator or cooling system when the engine is hot; serious burns can occur from the steam and hot coolant.

• Observe all applicable safety precautions when working around fuel. Whenever servicing the fuel system, always work in a well-ventilated area. Do not allow fuel spray or vapors to come in contact with a spark, open flame, or excessive heat (a hot drop light, for example). Keep a dry chemical fire extinguisher near the work area. Always keep fuel in a container specifically designed for fuel storage; also, always properly seal fuel containers to avoid the possibility of fire or explosion. Refer to the additional fuel system precautions later in this section.

• Fuel injection systems often remain pressurized, even after the engine has been turned **OFF**. The fuel system pressure must be relieved before disconnecting any fuel lines. Failure to do so may result in fire and/or personal injury.

• Brake fluid often contains polyglycol ethers and polyglycols. Avoid contact with the eyes and wash your hands thoroughly after handling brake fluid. If you do get brake fluid in your eyes, flush your eyes with clean, running water for 15 minutes. If eye irritation persists, or if you have taken brake fluid internally, IMMEDIATELY seek medical assistance.

• The EPA warns that prolonged contact with used engine oil may cause a number of skin disorders, including cancer. You should make every effort to minimize your exposure to used engine oil. Protective gloves should be worn when changing oil. Wash your hands and any other exposed skin areas as soon as possible after exposure to used engine oil. Soap and water, or waterless hand cleaner should be used.

• All new vehicles are now equipped with an air bag system, often referred to as a Supplemental Restraint System (SRS) or Supplemental Inflatable Restraint (SIR) system. The system must be disabled before performing service on or around system components, steering column, instrument panel components, wiring and sensors. Failure to follow safety and disabling procedures could result in accidental air bag deployment, possible personal injury and unnecessary system repairs.

• Always wear safety goggles when working with, or around, the air bag system. When carrying a non-deployed air bag, be sure the bag and trim cover are pointed away from your body. When placing a non-deployed air bag on a work surface, always face the bag and trim cover upward, away from the surface. This will reduce the motion of the module if it is accidentally deployed. Refer to the additional air bag system precautions later in this section.

• Clean, high quality brake fluid from a sealed container is essential to the safe and proper operation of the brake system. You should always buy the correct type of brake fluid for your vehicle. If the brake fluid becomes contaminated, completely flush the system with new fluid. Never reuse any brake fluid. Any brake fluid that is removed from the system should be discarded. Also, do not allow any brake fluid to come in contact with a painted surface; it will damage the paint.

• Never operate the engine without the proper amount and type of engine oil; doing so WILL result in severe engine damage.

• Timing belt maintenance is extremely important. Many models utilize an interference-type, non-freewheeling engine. If the timing belt breaks, the valves in the cylinder head may strike the pistons, causing potentially serious (also time-consuming and expensive) engine damage. Refer to the maintenance interval charts for the recommended replacement interval for the timing belt, and to the timing belt section for belt replacement and inspection.

• Disconnecting the negative battery cable on some vehicles may interfere with the functions of the on-board computer system(s) and may require the computer to undergo a relearning process once the negative battery cable is reconnected.

• When servicing drum brakes, only disassemble and assemble one side at a time, leaving the remaining side intact for reference.

• Only an MVAC-trained, EPA-certified automotive technician should service the air conditioning system or its components.

BRAKES

GENERAL INFORMATION

PRECAUTIONS

• Certain components within the ABS system are not intended to be serviced or repaired individually.

• Do not use rubber hoses or other parts not specifically specified for and ABS system. When using repair kits, replace all parts included in the kit. Partial or incorrect repair may lead to functional problems and require the replacement of components.

• Lubricate rubber parts with clean, fresh brake fluid to ease assembly. Do not use shop air to clean parts; damage to rubber components may result.

• Use only DOT 3 brake fluid from an unopened container.

• If any hydraulic component or line is removed or replaced, it may be necessary to bleed the entire system.

• A clean repair area is essential. Always clean the reservoir and cap thoroughly before removing the cap. The slightest amount of dirt in the fluid may plug an orifice and impair the system function. Perform repairs after components have been thoroughly cleaned; use only denatured alcohol to clean components. Do not allow ABS components to come into contact with any substance containing mineral oil; this includes used shop rags.

• The Anti-Lock control unit is a microprocessor similar to other computer units in the vehicle. Ensure that the ignition switch is **OFF** before removing or installing con-

ANTI-LOCK BRAKE SYSTEM (ABS)

troller harnesses. Avoid static electricity discharge at or near the controller.

• If any arc welding is to be done on the vehicle, the control unit should be unplugged before welding operations begin.

WHEEL SPEED SENSORS

REMOVAL & INSTALLATION

The wheel speed sensors are integral with the hub and bearing assemblies. If a speed sensor or a ring needs replacement, replace the entire hub and bearing assembly. Do not service the harness pigtail individually because the harness pigtail is part of the sensor. Refer to Wheel Hub and bearing (sealed unit), removal & installation.

BLEEDING PROCEDURE

Manual Bleeding

1. Before servicing the vehicle, refer to the Precautions Section.

2. Place a clean shop cloth beneath the brake master cylinder to prevent brake fluid spills.

3. With the ignition OFF and the brakes cool, apply the brakes 3–5 times, or until the brake pedal effort increases significantly, in order to deplete the brake booster power reserve.

4. If you have performed a brake master cylinder bench bleeding on this vehicle, or if you disconnected the brake pipes from the master cylinder, you must perform the following steps:

   a. Ensure that the brake master cylinder reservoir is full to the maximum-fill level. If necessary, add GM approved brake fluid from a clean, sealed brake fluid container. If removal of the reservoir cap and diaphragm is necessary, clean the outside of the reservoir on and around the cap prior to removal.

   b. With the rear brake pipe installed securely to the master cylinder, loosen and separate the front brake pipe from the front port of the brake master cylinder.

   c. Allow a small amount of brake fluid to gravity bleed from the open port of the master cylinder.

   d. Reconnect the brake pipe to the master cylinder port and tighten securely.

   e. Have an assistant slowly depress the brake pedal fully and maintain steady pressure on the pedal.

   f. Loosen the same brake pipe to purge air from the open port of the master cylinder.

   g. Tighten the brake pipe, then have the assistant slowly release the brake pedal.

   h. Wait 15 seconds, then repeat the above 5 steps until all air is purged from the same port of the master cylinder.

   i. With the front brake pipe installed securely to the master cylinder, after all air has been purged from the front port of the master cylinder, loosen and separate the rear brake pipe from the master cylinder, then repeat the above 6 steps.

   j. After completing the final master cylinder port bleeding procedure, ensure that both of the brake pipe-to-master cylinder fittings are properly tightened.

5. Fill the brake master cylinder reservoir with GM approved brake fluid from a clean, sealed brake fluid container. Ensure that the brake master cylinder reservoir remains at least half-full during this bleeding procedure. Add fluid as needed to maintain the proper level. Clean the outside of the reservoir on and around the reservoir cap prior to removing the cap and diaphragm.

6. Install a proper box-end wrench onto the RIGHT REAR wheel hydraulic circuit bleeder valve.

7. Install a transparent hose over the end of the bleeder valve.

8. Submerge the open end of the transparent hose into a transparent container partially filled with GM approved brake fluid from a clean, sealed brake fluid container.

9. Have an assistant slowly depress the brake pedal fully and maintain steady pressure on the pedal.

10. Loosen the bleeder valve to purge air from the wheel hydraulic circuit.

11. Tighten the bleeder valve, then have the assistant slowly release the brake pedal.

12. Wait 15 seconds, then repeat steps 9–11 until all air is purged from the same wheel hydraulic circuit.

13. With the right rear wheel hydraulic circuit bleeder valve tightened securely, after all air has been purged from the right rear hydraulic circuit install a proper box-end wrench onto the LEFT REAR wheel hydraulic circuit bleeder valve.

14. Install a transparent hose over the end of the bleeder valve, then repeat steps 9–13.

15. With the left rear wheel hydraulic circuit bleeder valve tightened securely, after all air purged from the left rear hydraulic circuit, install a proper box-end wrench onto the RIGHT FRONT wheel hydraulic circuit bleeder valve.

16. Install a transparent hose over the end of the bleeder valve, then repeat steps 9–13.

17. With the right front wheel hydraulic circuit bleeder valve tightened securely, after all air has been purged from the right front hydraulic circuit, install a proper box-end wrench onto the LEFT FRONT wheel hydraulic circuit bleeder valve.

18. Install a transparent hose over the end of the bleeder valve, then repeat steps 9–13.

19. After completing the final wheel hydraulic circuit bleeding procedure, ensure that each of the 4 wheel hydraulic circuit bleeder valves are properly tightened.

20. Fill the brake master cylinder reservoir to the maximum-fill level with GM approved brake fluid from a clean, sealed brake fluid container.

21. Slowly depress and release the brake pedal. Observe the feel of the brake pedal.

22. If the brake pedal feels spongy, repeat the bleeding procedure again. If the brake pedal still feels spongy after repeating the bleeding procedure, perform the following steps:

   a. Inspect the brake system for external leaks.

   b. Pressure bleed the hydraulic brake system in order to purge any air that may still be trapped in the system.

23. Turn the ignition key ON, with the engine OFF. Check to see if the brake system warning lamp remains illuminated.

✳✳ CAUTION

If the brake system warning lamp remains illuminated, DO NOT allow the vehicle to be driven until it is diagnosed and repaired.

➡**If the brake system warning lamp remains illuminated, refer to Diagnostic Trouble Codes.**

Pressure Bleeding

Special Tools:
- J-29532: Diaphragm Pressure Bleeder, or equivalent
- J-35589-A Brake Pressure Bleeder Adapter

1. Before servicing the vehicle, refer to the Precautions Section.

2. Place a clean shop cloth beneath the brake master cylinder to prevent brake fluid spills.

3. With the ignition OFF and the brakes cool, apply the brakes 3–5 times, or until the brake pedal effort increases significantly, in order to deplete the brake booster power reserve.

4. If you have performed a brake master cylinder bench bleeding on this vehicle, or if you disconnected the brake pipes from the master cylinder, you must perform the following steps:

   a. Ensure that the brake master cylinder reservoir is full to the maximum-fill level. If necessary add GM approved brake fluid from a clean, sealed brake fluid container. If removal of the reservoir cap and diaphragm is necessary, clean the outside of the reservoir on and around the cap prior to removal.

b. With the rear brake pipe installed securely to the master cylinder, loosen and separate the front brake pipe from the front port of the brake master cylinder.

c. Allow a small amount of brake fluid to gravity bleed from the open port of the master cylinder.

d. Reconnect the brake pipe to the master cylinder port and tighten securely.

e. Have an assistant slowly depress the brake pedal fully and maintain steady pressure on the pedal.

f. Loosen the same brake pipe to purge air from the open port of the master cylinder.

g. Tighten the brake pipe, then have the assistant slowly release the brake pedal.

h. Wait 15 seconds, then repeat the above 5 steps until all air is purged from the same port of the master cylinder.

i. With the front brake pipe installed securely to the master cylinder, after all air has been purged from the front port of the master cylinder, loosen and separate the rear brake pipe from the master cylinder, then repeat the above 6 steps.

j. After completing the final master cylinder port bleeding procedure, ensure that both of the brake pipe-to-master cylinder fittings are properly tightened.

5. Fill the brake master cylinder reservoir to the maximum-fill level with GM approved brake fluid from a clean, sealed brake fluid container. Clean the outside of the reservoir on and around the reservoir cap prior to removing the cap and diaphragm.

6. Install the J-35589-A, Brake Pressure Bleeder Adapter, to the brake master cylinder reservoir.

7. Check the brake fluid level in the J-29532, Diaphragm Pressure Bleeder, or equivalent. Add GM approved brake fluid from a clean, sealed brake fluid container as necessary to bring the level to approximately the half-full point.

8. Connect the J-29532, Diaphragm Pressure Bleeder, or equivalent, to the J-35589-A Brake Pressure Bleeder Adapter.

9. Charge the J-29532 Diaphragm Pressure Bleeder, or equivalent, air tank to 25–30 psi (175–205 kPa).

10. Open the J-29532, Diaphragm Pressure Bleeder, or equivalent, fluid tank valve to allow pressurized brake fluid to enter the brake system.

11. Wait approximately 30 seconds, then inspect the entire hydraulic brake system in order to ensure that there are no existing external brake fluid leaks. Any brake fluid

leaks identified require repair prior to completing this procedure.

12. Install a proper box-end wrench onto the RIGHT REAR wheel hydraulic circuit bleeder valve.

13. Install a transparent hose over the end of the bleeder valve.

14. Submerge the open end of the transparent hose into a transparent container partially filled with GM approved brake fluid from a clean, sealed brake fluid container.

15. Loosen the bleeder valve to purge air from the wheel hydraulic circuit. Allow fluid to flow until air bubbles stop flowing from the bleeder, then tighten the bleeder valve.

16. With the right rear wheel hydraulic circuit bleeder valve tightened securely, after all air has been purged from the right rear hydraulic circuit, install a proper box-end wrench onto the LEFT REAR wheel hydraulic circuit bleeder valve.

17. Install a transparent hose over the end of the bleeder valve, then repeat steps 15–16.

18. With the left rear wheel hydraulic circuit bleeder valve tightened securely, after all air has been purged from the left rear hydraulic circuit, install a proper box-end wrench onto the RIGHT FRONT wheel hydraulic circuit bleeder valve.

19. Install a transparent hose over the end of the bleeder valve, then repeat steps 15–16.

20. With the right front wheel hydraulic circuit bleeder valve tightened securely, after all air has been purged from the right front hydraulic circuit, install a proper box-end wrench onto the LEFT FRONT wheel hydraulic circuit bleeder valve.

21. Install a transparent hose over the end of the bleeder valve, then repeat steps 15–16.

22. After completing the final wheel hydraulic circuit bleeding procedure, ensure that each of the 4 wheel hydraulic circuit bleeder valves are properly tightened.

23. Close the J-29532, Diaphragm Pressure Bleeder, or equivalent, fluid tank valve, then disconnect the J-29532, Diaphragm Pressure Bleeder, or equivalent, from the J-35589-A, Brake Pressure Bleeder Adapter.

24. Remove the J-35589-A, Brake Pressure Bleeder Adapter, from the brake master cylinder reservoir.

25. Fill the brake master cylinder reservoir to the maximum-fill level with GM approved brake fluid from a clean, sealed brake fluid container.

26. Slowly depress and release the brake pedal. Observe the feel of the brake pedal.

27. If the brake pedal feels spongy perform the following steps:

a. Inspect the brake system for external leaks.

b. Using a scan tool, perform the antilock brake system automated bleeding procedure to remove any air that may have been trapped in the Brake Pressure Modulator Valve (BPMV). Refer to Bleeding the ABS System.

28. Turn the ignition key ON, with the engine OFF. Check to see if the brake system warning lamp remains illuminated.

✳✳ CAUTION

If the brake system warning lamp remains illuminated, DO NOT allow the vehicle to be driven until it is diagnosed and repaired.

➡**If the brake system warning lamp remains illuminated, refer to Diagnostic Trouble Codes.**

ABS AUTOMATED BLEED PROCEDURE

✳✳ WARNING

When adding fluid to the brake master cylinder reservoir, use only DOT-3 brake fluid from a clean, sealed brake fluid container. The use of any type of fluid other than the recommended type of brake fluid, may cause contamination which could result in damage to the internal rubber seals and/or rubber linings of hydraulic brake system components.

✳✳ WARNING

Avoid spilling brake fluid onto painted surfaces, electrical connections, wiring, or cables. Brake fluid will damage painted surfaces and cause corrosion to electrical components. If any brake fluid comes in contact with painted surfaces, immediately flush the area with water. If any brake fluid comes in contact with electrical connections, wiring, or cables, use a clean shop cloth to wipe away the fluid.

➡**The base hydraulic brake system must be bled before performing this automated bleeding procedure. Refer to Bleeding The Brake System.**

1. Before servicing the vehicle, refer to the Precautions Section.

2. Install a scan tool to the vehicle.

3. Start the engine and allow the engine to idle.

4. Depress the brake pedal firmly and maintain steady pressure on the pedal.

5. Using the scan tool, begin the automated bleed procedure.

6. Follow the instructions on the scan tool to complete the automated bleed procedure. Release the brake pedal between each test sequence.

7. Turn the ignition OFF.

8. Remove the scan tool from the vehicle.

9. Fill the brake master cylinder reservoir to the maximum-fill level with Delco Supreme 11® GM P/N 12377967, or equivalent DOT-3 brake fluid, from a clean, sealed brake fluid container.

10. Bleed the hydraulic brake system.

11. With the ignition OFF, apply the brakes 3–5 times, or until the brake pedal becomes firm, in order to deplete the brake booster power reserve.

12. Slowly depress and release the brake pedal. Observe the feel of the brake pedal.

13. If the brake pedal feels spongy, repeat the automated bleeding procedure. If the brake pedal still feels spongy after repeating the automated bleeding procedure, inspect the brake system for external leaks. Refer to Brake System External Leak Inspection.

14. Turn the ignition key ON, with the engine OFF; check to see if the brake system warning lamp remains illuminated.

15. If the brake system warning lamp remains illuminated, DO NOT allow the vehicle to be driven until it is diagnosed and repaired.

16. Drive the vehicle to exceed 8 mph (13 km/h) to allow ABS initialization to occur. Observe brake pedal feel.

17. If the brake pedal feels spongy, repeat the automated bleeding procedure until a firm brake pedal is obtained.

BRAKES

FRONT DISC BRAKES

✳✳ CAUTION

Dust and dirt accumulating on brake parts during normal use may contain asbestos fibers from production or aftermarket brake linings. Breathing excessive concentrations of asbestos fibers can cause serious bodily harm. Exercise care when servicing brake parts. Do not sand or grind brake lining unless equipment used is designed to contain the dust residue. Do not clean brake parts with compressed air or by dry brushing. Cleaning should be done by dampening the brake components with a fine mist of water, then wiping the brake components clean with a dampened cloth. Dispose of cloth and all residue containing asbestos fibers in an impermeable container with the appropriate label. Follow practices prescribed by the Occupational Safety and Health Administration (OSHA) and the Environmental Protection Agency (EPA) for the handling, processing, and disposing of dust or debris that may contain asbestos fibers.

BRAKE CALIPER

REMOVAL & INSTALLATION

See Figure 4.

1. Before servicing the vehicle, refer to the Precautions Section.

2. Inspect the fluid level in the brake master cylinder reservoir.

3. If the brake fluid level is midway between the maximum-full point and the minimum allowable level, then no brake fluid needs to be removed from the reservoir before proceeding. If the brake fluid level is higher than midway between the maximum-full point and the minimum allowable level, then remove brake fluid to the midway point before proceeding.

4. Raise and support the vehicle

5. Remove the tire and wheel.

6. Install a large C-clamp over the body of the brake caliper with the C-clamp ends against the rear of the caliper body and against the outer brake pad.

7. Tighten the C-clamp until the caliper piston is compressed into the caliper bore enough to allow the caliper to slide past the brake rotor.

8. Remove the C-clamp from the caliper.

9. Remove the brake hose fitting bolt and the 2 gaskets. Use NEW gaskets for installation.

10. Remove the brake hose and cap the brake hose fitting to prevent brake fluid loss and contamination.

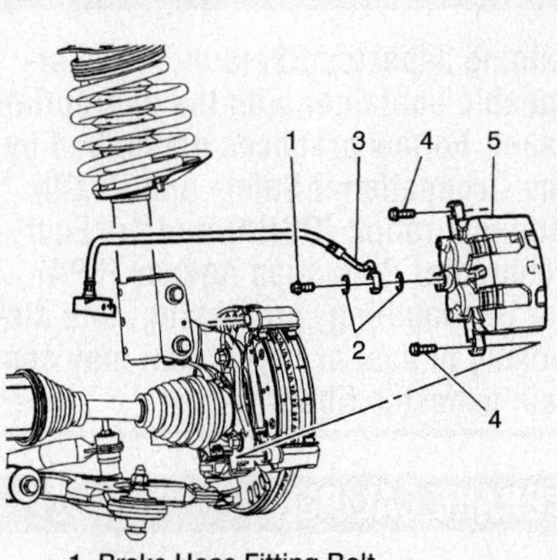

1. Brake Hose Fitting Bolt
2. Brake Hose Fitting Gasket (Qty: 2)
3. Brake Hose
4. Guide Pin Bolts (Qty: 2)
5. Brake Caliper

36616_LACR_G0105

Fig. 4 Removing the front brake caliper

11. Remove the brake caliper guide pin bolts.

12. Remove the brake caliper from the caliper bracket.

13. Inspect the brake caliper guide pins for freedom of movement, and inspect the condition of the guide pin boots. Move the guide pins inboard and outboard within the bracket bores, without disengaging the slides from the boots, and observe the following:

- Restricted caliper guide pin movement
- Looseness in the brake caliper mounting bracket
- Seized or binding caliper guide pins
- Split or torn boots

14. If any of the conditions listed exist, the brake caliper guide pins and/or boots require replacement.

To install:

15. Installation is the reverse of the removal procedure.

16. Tighten the guide pin bolts to 27 ft. lbs. (36 Nm).

17. Use new brake hose fitting gaskets and tighten the bolt to 40 ft. lbs (54 Nm).

18. Bleed the hydraulic brake system. Refer to Bleeding The Brake System.

19. With the engine OFF, gradually apply the brake pedal to approximately ⅔ of its travel distance.

20. Slowly release the brake pedal.

21. Wait 15 seconds, then repeat steps 5–6 until a firm brake pedal is obtained. This will properly seat the brake caliper pistons and brake pads.

22. Fill the master cylinder reservoir to the proper level.

23. Burnish the pads and rotors.

DISC BRAKE PADS

REMOVAL & INSTALLATION

See Figure 5.

1. Before servicing the vehicle, refer to the Precautions Section.

2. Inspect the fluid level in the brake master cylinder reservoir.

3. If the brake fluid level is midway between the maximum-full point and the minimum allowable level, then no brake fluid needs to be removed from the reservoir before proceeding. If the brake fluid level is higher than midway between the maximum-full point and the minimum allowable level, then remove brake fluid to the midway point before proceeding.

4. Raise and support the vehicle.

5. Remove the tire and the wheel assembly.

6. Hand-tighten 2 wheel lug nuts in order to retain the rotor to the hub.

7. Install a large C-clamp over the top of the caliper housing and against the back of the outboard pad.

8. Slowly tighten the C-clamp until the piston pushes into the caliper bore enough to slide the caliper off the rotor.

9. Remove the C-clamp from the caliper.

10. Remove the lower guide pin bolt.

✳✳ WARNING

Use care to avoid damaging the pin boot when rotating the caliper.

11. In order to access the pads, rotate the caliper upward and suitably support it.

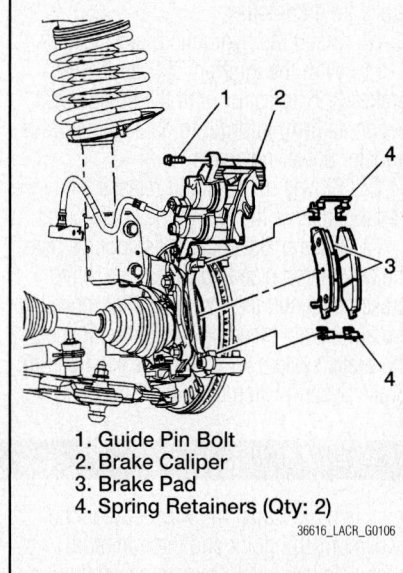

1. Guide Pin Bolt
2. Brake Caliper
3. Brake Pad
4. Spring Retainers (Qty: 2)

36616_LACR_G0106

Fig. 5 Removing the front brake pads

✳✳ WARNING

Support the brake caliper with heavy mechanic wire, or equivalent, whenever it is separated from its mount and the hydraulic flexible brake hose is still connected. Failure to support the caliper in this manner will cause the flexible brake hose to bear the weight of the caliper, which may cause damage to the brake hose and in turn may cause a brake fluid leak.

12. Remove the pads from the caliper bracket.

13. Remove the 2 retainer slides from the caliper bracket.

14. Inspect all parts for cuts, tears, or deterioration. Replace any damaged parts.

15. Inspect the guide pin bolts for corrosion or damage. If corrosion is found, use new bolts when installing the caliper.

16. Place a block of wood or an old disc brake pad against the brake caliper pistons.

17. Using a brake pad spreader or a C-clamp, slowly compress the brake caliper pistons squarely into the caliper bores.

18. If installing the original brake pads, note the brake pad location for proper installation.

19. When replacing the brake pads, ensure the brake pad with the wear indicator is positioned inboard of the brake rotor and the wear indicator is pointing down.

20. Clean the friction surfaces of the brake rotor with denatured alcohol.

To install:

21. Installation is the reverse of the removal procedure.

22. Tighten the guide pin bolt to 27 ft. lbs. (36 Nm) on 2008–09 vehicles and 21 ft. lbs. (28 Nm) on 2010 vehicles.

23. If replacing the brake pads, DO NOT reuse the spring retainers. Install NEW spring retainers.

24. With the engine OFF, gradually apply the brake pedal to approximately ⅔ of its travel distance.

25. Slowly release the brake pedal.

26. Wait 15 seconds, then repeat steps 4–5 until a firm brake pedal is obtained. This will properly seat the brake caliper pistons and the brake pads.

27. Fill the master cylinder reservoir to the proper level.

28. Burnish the pads and rotors.

BRAKES

✳✳ CAUTION

Dust and dirt accumulating on brake parts during normal use may contain asbestos fibers from production or aftermarket brake linings. Breathing excessive concentrations of asbestos fibers can cause serious bodily harm. Exercise care when servicing brake parts. Do not sand or grind brake lining unless equipment used is designed to contain the dust residue. Do not clean brake parts with compressed air or by dry brushing. Cleaning should be done by dampening the brake components with a fine mist of water, then wiping the brake components clean with a dampened cloth. Dispose of cloth and all residue containing asbestos fibers in an impermeable container with the appropriate label. Follow practices prescribed by the Occupational Safety and Health Administration (OSHA) and the Environmental Protection Agency (EPA) for the handling, processing, and disposing of dust or debris that may contain asbestos fibers.

BRAKE CALIPER

REMOVAL & INSTALLATION

See Figures 6 and 7.

1. Before servicing the vehicle, refer to the Precautions Section.

2. Inspect the fluid level in the brake master cylinder reservoir.

REAR DISC BRAKES

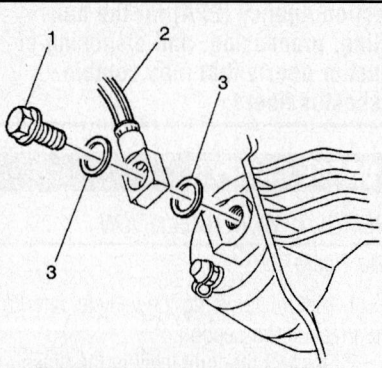

1. Brake hose-to-caliper bolt
2. Rear brake hose
3. Copper brake hose gaskets

36616_LACR_G0108

Fig. 6 View of the brake hose bolt (1), hose (2) and gaskets (3)

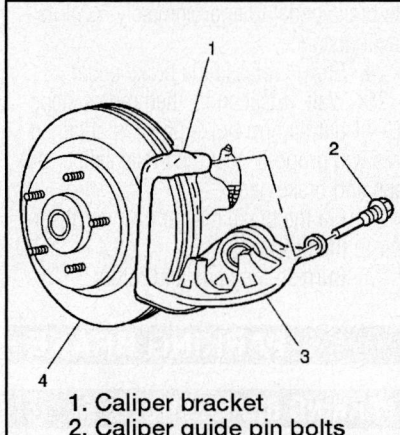

1. Caliper bracket
2. Caliper guide pin bolts
3. Rear brake caliper
4. Rear brake rotor

36616_LACR_G0109

Fig. 7 Removing the rear brake caliper

3. If the brake fluid level is midway between the maximum-full point and the minimum allowable level, then no brake fluid needs to be removed from the reservoir before proceeding. If the brake fluid level is higher than midway between the maximum-full point and the minimum allowable level, then remove brake fluid to the midway point before proceeding.

4. Raise and suitably support the vehicle.

5. Remove the rear tire and the wheel assembly.

6. Hand-tighten 2 wheel lug nuts to retain the rotor to the hub.

7. Install a large C-clamp over the top of the brake caliper and against the back of the outboard brake pad.

8. Tighten the C-clamp until the caliper piston is pushed into the caliper bore enough to slide the caliper off the rotor.

9. Remove the C-clamp from the caliper.

10. Remove the brake hose-to-caliper bolt from the caliper.

11. Discard the 2 copper brake hose gaskets. These gaskets may be stuck to the brake caliper and/or the brake hose end.

12. Plug the opening in the rear brake hose to prevent excessive brake fluid loss and contamination.

13. Remove the 2 brake caliper guide pin bolts.

14. Remove the caliper from the rotor and the caliper bracket.

15. Inspect the caliper bracket bolt boots on the caliper bracket for the following conditions:

- Cuts
- Tears
- Deterioration

16. Replace any damaged caliper bracket bolt boots.

17. Inspect the caliper bolts for corrosion or damage. If corrosion is found, use NEW caliper bolts, including bushings, when installing the caliper.

To install:

18. Install the caliper over the rotor and the caliper bracket. Ensure that the bushings are in place.

19. Using high temperature, silicone brake lubricant, lubricate the caliper guide pin bolts. Do not lubricate the threads.

20. Using high temperature, silicone brake lubricant, lubricate the 2 bolt boots in the caliper bracket.

➡**Ensure the bolt boots fit securely in the groove of the caliper bolts. Do not to pinch or tear the boots. If the boots are damaged, they must be replaced.**

21. Install the caliper guide pin bolts and tighten to 32 ft. lbs. (44 Nm) on 2008–09 vehicles and 20 ft. lbs. (27 Nm) on 2010 vehicles.

22. Assemble the brake hose bolt and the NEW copper brake hose gaskets to the brake hose.

23. Install the brake hose fitting bolt to the brake caliper and tighten to 40 ft. lbs. (54 Nm) on 2008–09 vehicles and 30 ft. lbs. (40 Nm) on 2010 vehicles.

24. Bleed the hydraulic brake system. Refer to Bleeding The Brake System.

25. Remove the 2 wheel lug nuts retaining the rotor to the hub.

26. Install the rear tire and the wheel assembly.

27. Fill the master cylinder to the proper level with clean brake fluid.

DISC BRAKE PADS

REMOVAL & INSTALLATION

See Figure 8.

1. Before servicing the vehicle, refer to the Precautions Section.

2. Inspect the fluid level in the brake master cylinder reservoir.

3. If the brake fluid level is midway between the maximum-full point and the minimum allowable level, then no brake fluid needs to be removed from the reservoir before proceeding. If the brake fluid level is higher than midway between the maximum-full point and the minimum allowable level, then remove brake fluid to the midway point before proceeding.

4. Raise and suitably support the vehicle.

5. Remove the rear tire and the wheel assembly.

6. Hand install a wheel nut to retain the rotor to the hub.

7. Using a large C-clamp placed against the outer brake pad and the back of the caliper, compress the brake caliper piston.

8. Remove the upper caliper guide pin bolt.

✳✳ WARNING

Support the brake caliper with heavy mechanic wire, or equivalent, whenever it is separated from its mount and the hydraulic flexible brake hose is still connected. Failure to support the caliper in this manner will cause the flexible brake hose to bear the weight of the caliper, which may cause damage to the brake hose and in turn may cause a brake fluid leak.

9. Pivot the caliper downward and support with heavy mechanics wire or equivalent.

10. Remove the brake pads from the caliper bracket.

11. Remove the 2 pad clips from the caliper bracket.

12. Inspect the brake caliper mounting hardware for damage and replace if necessary.

13. Inspect the brake caliper for damage and repair if necessary.

To install:

14. Install the 2 retainers to the caliper bracket.

➡**The wear sensor is on the outer pad. The sensor is positioned at the trailing or downward edge of the pad during forward wheel rotation.**

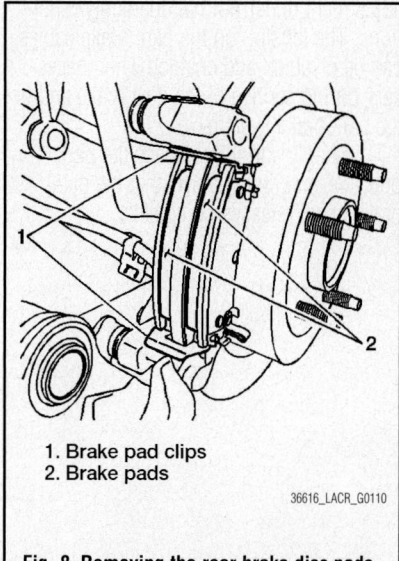

1. Brake pad clips
2. Brake pads

36616_LACR_G0110

Fig. 8 Removing the rear brake disc pads

15. Install the pads to the caliper bracket.

16. Position the caliper to the brake caliper bracket.

17. Apply a light coat of high temperature silicone brake lubricant to the brake caliper guide pin bolt and the guide pin bolt seal.

18. Install the upper caliper bolt and tighten to 32 ft. lbs. (44 Nm) on 2008–09 vehicles and 20 ft. lbs. (27 Nm) on 2010 vehicles.

19. Remove the wheel lug nut retaining the rotor to the hub.

20. Install the rear tire and the wheel assembly.

21. Align the previous marks on the wheel, hub, and bearing.

22. Lower the vehicle.

23. With the engine OFF, gradually apply the brake pedal to approximately ⅔ of its travel distance.

24. Slowly release the brake pedal.

25. Wait 15 seconds, then repeat steps 10–11 until a firm brake pedal is obtained. This will properly seat the brake caliper pistons and brake pads.

26. Fill the brake master cylinder reservoir to the proper level.

27. Burnish the pads and rotors.

BRAKES

The parking brake application is completely independent of the hydraulic brake system. The park brake system is a mechanical system which operates the rear disc brakes through the calipers. The system is activated by depressing the park brake pedal, which applies the rear disc brakes via cables. When the park brake is set and the ignition switch is on, the BRAKE warning lamp on the instrument panel will be on. The park brake is released by pushing the pedal down until a click is heard and then releasing. The pedal will click again and the BRAKE lamp in the instrument panel will go out when the park brake system is fully released.

PARKING BRAKE CABLES

ADJUSTMENT

The parking brake pedals are equipped with automatic adjusters. The Park Brake Cable Equalizer evenly distributes input force to both the left and right park brake units and the threaded park brake cable equalizers are also used to remove slack in park brake cables.

The park brake system does not require adjustment under normal operating conditions. The tension on the park brake cables can be disabled and enabled when necessary during service of the disc brake and/or the park brake system.

1. Apply and fully release the park brake several times. Verify that the park brake pedal releases completely.

2. Turn ON the ignition. Verify the red BRAKE warning lamp is not illuminated.

3. If the red BRAKE warning lamp is illuminated, check that the park brake pedal is in the fully released position and against the stop or that there is no slack in the cables.

4. If the BRAKE warning light is on and park brake appears to be fully released, pull the pedal back by hand and continue with the adjustment procedure.

5. Turn OFF the ignition.

6. Raise and support the vehicle.

7. With the park brake pedal fully released, check the park brake levers on the rear calipers. The levers should be against the stops on the caliper housings. If the levers are not against the stops, binding may exist.

8. Fully apply and release the park brake pedal 3–5 times in order for the cable tensioner to take up any slack in the park brake cables.

9. Fully apply the park brake pedal, a firm pedal should be obtained by depressing the pedal less than one full stroke.

10. Attempt to rotate the rear tire and wheel assemblies. There should be no rotation forward or rearward.

11. Fully release the park brake pedal.

12. Verify the park brake is released by rotating the rear tire and wheel assemblies. The rear tire and wheel assemblies should rotate freely and exhibit no brake drag.

13. Lower the vehicle.

PARKING BRAKE

PARKING BRAKE SHOES

REMOVAL & INSTALLATION

The rear disc brake pads serve as the parking brake pads. For replacement, refer to Rear Disc Brakes, Disc Brake Pads, removal & installation.

ADJUSTMENT

➡ **Plastic-coated park brake cables do not need periodic lubrication.**

Coated park brake cables are used to reduce apply effort and increase corrosion protection. The cables are coated with a plastic material which slides against nylon seals inside the conduit end fittings.

The park brake lever has an indicator switch which closes when the park brake is set, thus illuminating the red BRAKE lamp.

Park brake application is completely independent of the hydraulic brake system. The park brake system is a mechanical system which operates the rear disc brakes through the calipers. The system is activated by depressing the park brake pedal, which applies the rear disc brakes via cables. When the park brake is set and the ignition switch is ON, the BRAKE warning lamp on the instrument panel will be on. The park brake is released by pushing the pedal down until a click is heard and then releasing. The pedal will click again and the BRAKE lamp in the instrument panel will go out when the park brake system is fully released.

CHASSIS ELECTRICAL   AIR BAG (SUPPLEMENTAL RESTRAINT SYSTEM)

GENERAL INFORMATION

These vehicles are equipped with an air bag system. The system must be disarmed before performing service on, or around, system components, the steering column, instrument panel components, wiring, and sensors. Failure to follow the safety precautions and the disarming procedure could result in accidental air bag deployment, possible injury, and unnecessary system repairs.

SERVICE PRECAUTIONS

To avoid serious or fatal injury on vehicles equipped with the Supplemental Restraint System (SRS), never attempt to repair the electrically conductive circuits or wiring components related to the SRS. Such repairs can compromise the conductivity and current carrying capacity of those critical electrical circuits which may cause the SRS components not to deploy when required, or to deploy when not required. Any wire harness containing broken, cut, burned, or otherwise damaged electrically conductive SRS wiring, terminals, or connector components must be removed and replaced with an entire new wire harness. Only minor cuts or abrasions of wire and terminal insulation where the conductive material has not been damaged, or connector insulators where the integrity of the latching and locking mechanisms have not been compromised may be repaired using appropriate methods. Failure to follow these instructions may result in possible serious or fatal injury.

When performing service on or near the Supplemental Inflatable Restraints (SIR) components or the SIR wiring, the SIR system must be disabled. Failure to observe the correct procedure could cause deployment of the SIR components, personal injury, or unnecessary SIR system repairs.

The inflatable restraint Sensing and Diagnostic Module (SDM) maintains a reserved energy supply. The reserved energy supply provides deployment power for the air bags. Deployment power is available for as much as 1 minute after disconnecting the vehicle power. Disabling the SIR system prevents deployment of the air bags from the reserved energy supply.

When carrying an undeployed inflator module: Do not carry the inflator module by the wires or connector. Make sure the air bag opening points away from you. Failure to observe these guidelines may result in personal injury.

When storing an undeployed inflator module: Make sure the air bag opening points away from the surface on which the inflator module rests. Provide free space for the air bag to expand in case of an accidental deployment. When storing a steering column, do not rest the column with the air bag opening facing down and the column vertical. Lay the column on its side. Failure to observe these guidelines may result in personal injury.

The following are general service instructions which must be followed in order to properly repair the vehicle and return it to its original integrity:

• Do not handle the inflatable restraint vehicle rollover sensor when connected to vehicle power

• Do not expose inflator modules to temperatures above 150° F (65° C)

• Verify the correct replacement part number. Do not substitute a component from a different vehicle

• Use only original GM replacement parts available from your authorized GM dealer. Do not use salvaged parts for repairs to the SIR system

Discard any of the following components if dropped from a height of 3 feet (91cm) or greater:

• Inflatable restraint front end sensor
• Inflatable restraint Instrument Panel (I/P) module
• Inflatable restraint Passenger Presence System (PPS)
• Inflatable restraint roof rail module
• Inflatable restraint SDM
• Inflatable restraint Side Impact Sensor (SIS)
• Inflatable restraint steering wheel module
• Inflatable restraint steering wheel module coil
• Inflatable restraint vehicle rollover sensor
• Seat belt pre-tensioner

Wear safety glasses, rubber gloves, and long-sleeved clothing when cleaning powder residue from vehicle after an airbag deployment. Powder residue emitted from a deployed airbag can cause skin irritation. Flush affected area with cool water if irritation is experienced. If nasal or throat irritation is experienced, exit the vehicle for fresh air until the irritation ceases. If irritation continues, see a physician.

Do not use a replacement airbag that is not in the original packaging. This may result in improper deployment, personal injury, or death.

The factory installed fasteners, screws, and bolts used to fasten airbag components have a special coating and are specifically designed for the airbag system. Do not use substitute fasteners. Use only original equipment fasteners listed in the parts catalog when fastener replacement is required.

During, and following, any child restraint anchor service, due to impact event or vehicle repair, carefully inspect all mounting hardware, tether straps, and anchors for proper installation, operation, or damage. If a child restraint anchor is found damaged in any way, the anchor must be replaced. Failure to do this may result in personal injury or death.

Deployed and non-deployed airbags may or may not have live pyrotechnic material within the airbag inflator.

Do not dispose of driver/passenger/curtain airbags or seat belt tensioners unless you are sure of complete deployment.

Dispose of deployed airbags and tensioners consistent with state, provincial, local, and federal regulations.

After any airbag component testing or service, do not connect the battery negative cable. Personal injury or death may result if the system test is not performed first.

If the vehicle is equipped with the Occupant Classification System (OCS), do not connect the battery negative cable before performing the OCS Verification Test using the scan tool and the appropriate diagnostic information. Personal injury or death may result if the system test is not performed properly.

Never replace both the Occupant Restraint Controller (ORC) and the Occupant Classification Module (OCM) at the same time. If both require replacement, replace one, then perform the Airbag System test before replacing the other.

Both the ORC and the OCM store OCS calibration data, which they transfer to one another when one of them is replaced. If both are replaced at the same time, an irreversible fault will be set in both modules and the OCS may malfunction and cause personal injury or death.

If equipped with OCS, the Seat Weight Sensor is a sensitive, calibrated unit and must be handled carefully. Do not drop or handle roughly. If dropped or damaged, replace with another sensor. Failure to do so may result in occupant injury or death.

If equipped with OCS, the front passenger seat must be handled carefully as well. When removing the seat, be careful not to drop the seat when setting it on the floor. If dropped, the sensor may be inoperative. This could result in occupant injury or possibly death.

If equipped with OCS, when the passenger front seat is on the floor, no one should sit in the front passenger seat. This uneven force may damage the sensing ability of the seat weight sensors. If sat on and damaged, the sensor may be inoperative. This could result in occupant injury or possibly death.

DISARMING THE SYSTEM

Disabling Procedure—Air Bag Fuse

1. Before servicing the vehicle, refer to the Precautions Section.
2. Turn the steering wheel so that the vehicles wheels are pointing straight ahead.
3. Place the ignition in the OFF position.

➡ **The SDM may have more than one fused power input. To ensure there is no unwanted SIR deployment, personal injury, or unnecessary SIR system repairs, remove all fuses supplying power to the SDM. With all SDM fuses removed and the ignition switch in the ON position, the AIR BAG warning indicator illuminates. This is a normal operation, and does not indicate a SIR system malfunction.**

4. Locate and remove the fuse(s) supplying power to the SDM.
5. Wait 1 minute before working on the system.

Disabling Procedure—Negative Battery Cable

1. Before servicing the vehicle, refer to the Precautions Section.
2. Turn the steering wheel so that the vehicle wheels are pointing straight ahead.
3. Place the ignition in the OFF position.
4. Disconnect the negative battery cable from the battery.
5. Wait 1 minute before working on the system.

ARMING THE SYSTEM

Enabling Procedure—Air Bag Fuse

✶✶ CAUTION

As an added precaution, make sure no one is in the vehicle when reconnecting the negative battery cable.

1. Before servicing the vehicle, refer to the Precautions Section.
2. Place the ignition in the OFF position.
3. Install the fuse(s) supplying power to the SDM.
4. Turn the ignition switch to the ON

position. The AIR BAG indicator will flash then turn OFF.
5. If the AIR BAG warning indicator does not operate as described, perform and diagnostic system check.

Enabling Procedure—Negative Battery Cable

✶✶ CAUTION

As an added precaution, make sure no one is in the vehicle when reconnecting the negative battery cable.

1. Before servicing the vehicle, refer to the Precautions Section.
2. Place the ignition in the OFF position.
3. Connect the negative battery cable to the battery.
4. Turn the ignition switch to the ON position. The AIR BAG indicator will flash then turn OFF.
5. If the AIR BAG warning indicator does not operate as described, perform a diagnostic system check.

CLOCKSPRING CENTERING

See Figures 9 and 10.

✶✶ CAUTION

To avoid serious or fatal injury on vehicles equipped with airbags, disable the Supplemental Inflatable Restraint (SIR) before attempting any steering wheel, steering column, airbag, seat belt tensioner, impact sensor, or instrument panel component diagnosis or service. Disconnect and isolate the battery negative (ground) cable, then wait 1 minute for the system capacitor to discharge before performing further diagnosis or service. Failure to take the proper precautions could result in accidental airbag deployment.

➡ **Before starting this procedure, be certain to turn the steering wheel until the front wheels are in the straight-ahead position.**

1. Before servicing the vehicle, refer to the Precautions Section.
2. Place the front wheels in the straight-ahead position.

✶✶ WARNING

The new SIR coil assembly will be centered. Improper alignment of the SIR coil assembly may damage the unit, causing an inflatable restraint malfunction.

3. Verify the following conditions before centering the SIR steering wheel module coil:
4. The wheels on the vehicle are straight ahead.
5. The centering mark of the steering shaft is in the 6 o'clock position.
6. Turn the lobe of the clockspring clockwise until the coil ribbon stops. Do not use excessive force.
7. Turn the lobe of the clockspring counterclockwise approximately 3 turns to the Neutral position.
8. Properly align until the centering window turns yellow. This indicates the CENTER position.

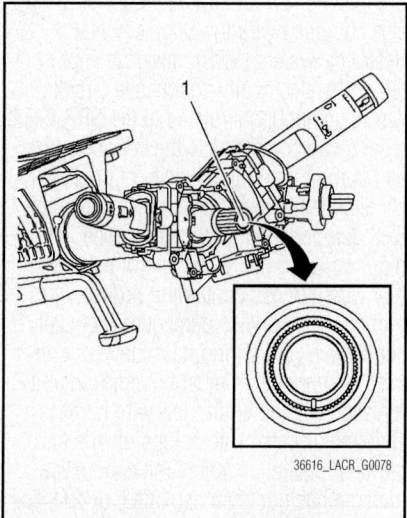

36616_LACR_G0078

Fig. 9 Align the centering mark (1) of the steering shaft to the 6 o'clock position

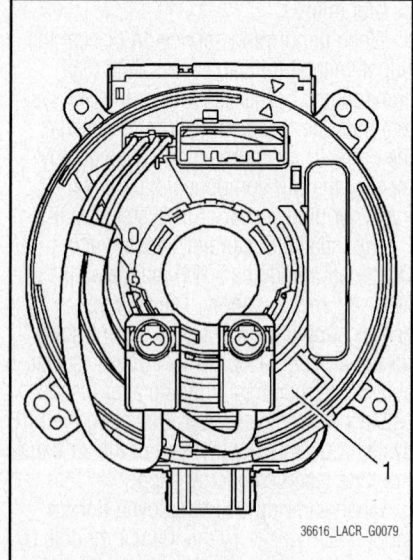

36616_LACR_G0079

Fig. 10 Properly align the clockspring until the centering window turns yellow (1). This indicates the CENTER position

DRIVE TRAIN

AUTOMATIC TRANSAXLE ASSEMBLY

REMOVAL & INSTALLATION

4T65-E Transaxle

See Figures 11 through 14.

Special Tools:
- J 37096: Flywheel Holder
- J 28467-B: Universal Engine Support Fixture (3.8L engine)
- J 36462-A: Engine Support Adapter Leg Set (3.8L engine)
- J-28467-501: Engine Support Fixture Adapters (3.8L engine)
- J 28467-B: Universal Engine Support Fixture (5.3L engine)
- J 28467-501: Engine Support Fixture Adapters (5.3L engine)
- J 42451-1: Engine Support Adapter (5.3L engine)

1. Before servicing the vehicle, refer to the Precautions Section.
2. Disconnect the negative battery cable.

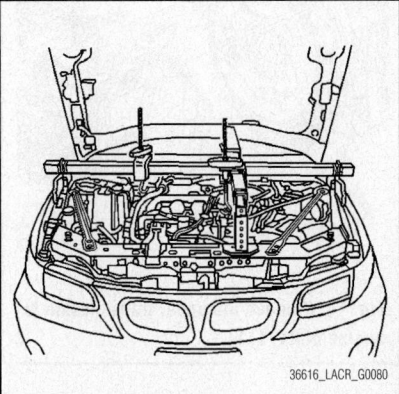

Fig. 11 Engine support fixture installed—3.8L engine

3. Remove the air cleaner intake duct.
4. Remove the starter motor. Refer to Starter, removal & installation.
5. Remove the exhaust crossover pipe.
6. Disconnect the transaxle wiring harness electrical connector.
7. Remove the wiring harness ground nut from the transaxle.
8. Remove the wiring harness grounds from the transaxle.
9. Remove the wiring harness ground bolt from the transaxle.
10. Remove the wiring harness grounds from the transaxle.
11. Remove the wiring harness bracket bolt and reposition the wiring harness.
12. Remove the range selector cable from the transaxle shift lever.
13. Remove the range selector retainer from the cable.
14. Remove the range selector cable from the transaxle.
15. Disconnect the wiring harness connectors from the top of the transaxle.
16. Remove the upper transaxle bolts and the stud.
17. Install the engine support fixture. Refer to Engine Support Fixture for the 3.8L engine or Engine Support Fixture for the 5.3L engine.
18. Raise and support the vehicle.
19. Remove the front wheels.
20. Remove the left and the right engine splash shields.
21. Remove the frame from the vehicle.
22. Install J 37096 in order to gain access to the torque converter bolts and to prevent the flywheel from turning.
23. Remove the torque converter bolts.
24. Remove the oil cooler pipes from the transaxle.

➡**Position and secure the wheel half-shafts out of the way.**

25. Remove the left and the right wheel halfshafts from the transaxle.
26. Secure the halfshafts to the steering knuckles.
27. Disconnect the electrical connector from the vehicle speed sensor.

➡**Ensure that the transmission jack is properly secured to the transaxle.**

28. Position a transmission jack under the transaxle and secure the jack firmly to the transaxle.
29. Remove the transaxle brace.
30. Remove the lower transaxle bolt and the stud.
31. Remove the transaxle from the vehicle.
32. Transfer all necessary parts as needed.
33. Flush the transmission cooler and lines. Refer to Transmission Fluid Cooler Flushing and Flow Test.

To install:

➡**Ensure that the transaxle is secured properly to the transmission jack.**

34. Position the transaxle onto a transmission jack and secure the transaxle to the jack.
35. Install the transaxle into the vehicle.
36. Install the lower transaxle bolt and the stud. Tighten the bolt and the stud to 55 ft. lbs. (75 Nm).
37. Install the transaxle brace.
38. Install J 37096 in order to gain access to install the torque converter bolts and to prevent the flywheel from turning.
39. Install the torque converter bolts. Tighten the bolts to 46 ft. lbs. (63 Nm).
40. Install the wheel drive shafts into the transaxle.
41. Install the oil cooler pipes to the transaxle.

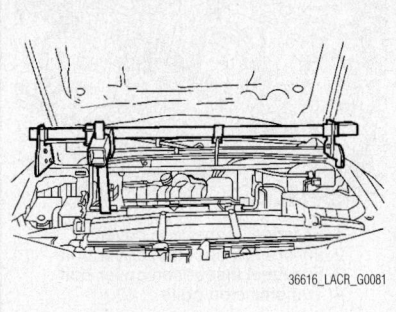

Fig. 12 Engine support fixture installed—5.3L engine

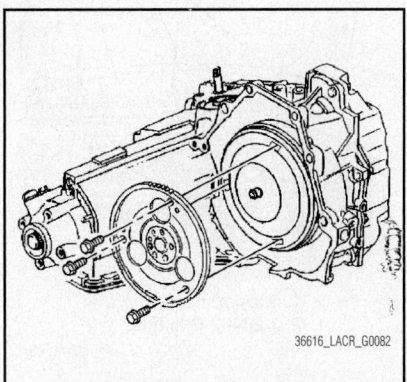

Fig. 13 Torque converter bolt removal

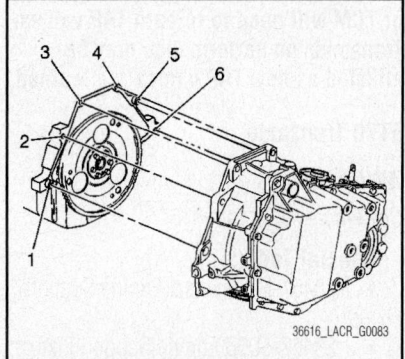

Fig. 14 Remove the transaxle from the vehicle—4T65-E

42. Remove the transmission jack from the transaxle.

43. Install the frame to the vehicle.

44. Connect the electrical connector to the vehicle speed sensor.

45. Install the left and the right engine splash shield.

46. Install the front wheels.

47. Lower the vehicle.

48. Remove the engine support fixture.

49. Install the upper transaxle bolts and the stud. Tighten the bolts and the stud to 55 ft. lbs. (75 Nm).

50. Install the cable to the transaxle range selector cable bracket.

51. Install the A/T range selector cable retainer to the cable.

52. Install the transaxle range selector cable to the transaxle shift lever.

53. Reposition the wiring harness and install the wiring harness bracket and the bolt. Tighten the bolt to 18 ft. lbs. (25 Nm).

54. Install the wiring harness grounds to the transaxle.

55. Install the transaxle wiring harness ground bolt to the transaxle. Tighten the bolt to 18 ft. lbs. (25 Nm).

56. Install the wiring harness grounds to the transaxle.

57. Install the wiring harness ground nut to the transaxle. Tighten the nut to 33 ft. lbs. (45 Nm).

58. Install the starter motor. Refer to Starter, removal & installation.

59. Connect the transaxle wiring harness electrical connector.

60. Install the engine crossover pipe.

61. Install the air cleaner intake duct.

62. Connect the negative battery cable.

63. Fill the transaxle with the proper type and amount of transmission fluid.

64. Inspect the transaxle for fluid leaks.

➡ It is recommended that Transmission Adaptive Pressure (TAP) information be reset. Resetting the TAP values using a scan tool will erase all learned values in all cells. As a result, the ECM, PCM, or TCM will need to relearn TAP values. Transmission performance may be affected as new TAP values are learned.

6T70 Transaxle

AWD Vehicles

See Figures 15 through 17.

Special Tools:
• J-28467-B Universal Engine Support Fixture
• J-28467-500B Engine Support Fixture Adapters
• J-36857 bracket

1. Before servicing the vehicle, refer to the Precautions Section.

2. Disconnect the battery cables.

3. Remove the battery tray.

4. Remove the transmission range select lever cable and bracket.

5. Drain the transmission fluid.

6. Remove the wire harness retainer from the control valve body cover stud.

7. Disconnect the control valve body Transmission Control Module (TCM) electrical connector.

8. Remove the transmission fluid cooler pipe retainer nut.

9. Remove the transmission fluid cooler inlet hose and seal from the transmission.

10. Plug and/or cap the hose and transmission to prevent contamination.

11. Remove the transmission fluid cooler pipe retainer nut.

12. Remove the transmission fluid cooler outlet hose and seal from the transmission.

13. Plug and/or cap the hose and transmission to prevent contamination.

14. Disconnect both pipes from the retainer.

15. Install the engine support fixture.

16. Remove the left catalytic converter and pipe assembly. Refer to Catalytic Converter, removal & installation.

17. Use a transmission jack in order to support the transmission.

18. Remove the rear transmission mount from the transmission.

19. Remove the front transmission mount from the transmission.

20. Remove the left transmission mount from the transmission.

21. Remove the upper transmission-to-engine bolts.

22. Remove the frame.

23. Disconnect the wheel halfshafts from the transmission and transfer case.

24. Remove the transfer case from the transmission. Refer to Transfer Case, removal & installation.

25. Remove the starter. Refer to Starter, removal & installation.

26. Mark the relationship of the flywheel to the torque converter for reassembly.

27. Remove the torque converter-to-flywheel bolts.

28. Remove the flywheel inspection cover bolts.

29. Remove the flywheel inspection cover.

30. Remove the remaining transmission bolts.

➡ Ensure the torque converter remains securely in place on the transmission input shaft while separating and removing the transmission.

Fig. 16 Remove the upper transmission to engine bolts (1, 2).

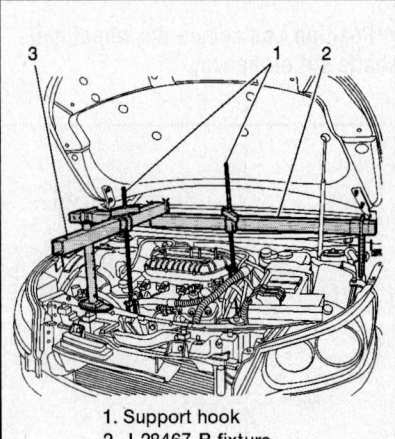

1. Support hook
2. J-28467-B fixture

36616_LACR_G0084

Fig. 15 Engine support fixture installed

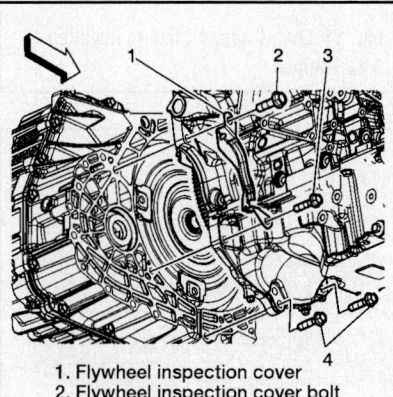

1. Flywheel inspection cover
2. Flywheel inspection cover bolt
3. Flywheel inspection cover bolt
4. Transmission bolts

36616_LACR_G0086

Fig. 17 Transmission removal—6T70 (AWD)

31. Separate the transmission from the engine.

32. Lower the transmission with the transmission jack far enough to remove the transmission.

To install:

33. Raise the transmission with the transmission jack and position the transmission to the engine.

34. Install the transmission bolts and tighten to 55 ft. lbs. (75 Nm).

35. Install the flywheel inspection cover.

36. Install the flywheel inspection cover bolts and tighten to 55 ft. lbs. (75 Nm).

37. Install the transfer case to the transmission. Refer to Transfer Case, removal & installation.

38. Remove the transmission jack.

➡**If reusing the torque converter bolts, clean the threads and apply LOCTITE® 242, GM P/N 12345382 (Canadian P/N 10953489), or equivalent, to the threads prior to installation.**

39. Install the torque converter to flywheel bolts and tighten to 46 ft. lbs. (62 Nm).

40. Install the starter. Refer to Starter, removal & installation.

41. Install the front transmission mount to the transmission.

42. Install the rear transmission mount to the transmission.

43. Install the left transmission mount to the transmission.

44. Install the wheel halfshafts to the transmission.

45. Install the frame.

46. Install the upper transmission to engine bolts and tighten to 55 ft. lbs. (75 Nm).

47. Install the left catalytic converter and pipe assembly. Refer to Catalytic Converter, removal & installation.

48. Remove the engine support fixture.

49. Lower the vehicle.

50. Install the transmission fluid cooler outlet hose and seal to the transmission.

51. Install the transmission fluid cooler pipe retainer nut and tighten to 16 ft. lbs. (22 Nm).

52. Install the transmission fluid cooler inlet hose and seal to the transmission.

53. Install the transmission fluid cooler pipe retainer nut and tighten to 16 ft. lbs. (22 Nm).

54. Connect the control valve body TCM electrical connector. Install the wire harness retainer to the control valve body cover stud and tighten the nut to 106 inch lbs. (12 Nm).

55. Install the transmission range select lever cable and bracket.

56. Install the battery tray.

57. Adjust the automatic transmission range selector lever cable, as necessary.

58. Fill the transmission with the proper type and amount of fluid.

➡**After an internal transmission repair or internal part replacement the service fast learn adapt procedure should be performed.**

59. Perform the service fast learn adapt procedure. Refer to Service Fast Learn Adapt Procedure.

60. Road test the vehicle.

FWD Vehicles

See Figures 15, 16 and 18.

Special Tools:

• J-28467-B Universal Engine Support Fixture
• J-28467-500B Engine Support Fixture Adapters
• J-36857 bracket

1. Before servicing the vehicle, refer to the Precautions Section.

2. Disconnect the battery cables.

3. Remove the battery tray.

4. Remove the transmission range select lever cable and bracket.

5. Drain the transmission fluid.

6. Remove the wire harness retainer from the control valve body cover stud.

7. Disconnect the control valve body Transmission Control Module (TCM) electrical connector.

8. Remove the transmission fluid cooler pipe retainer nut.

9. Remove the transmission fluid cooler inlet hose and seal from the transmission.

10. Plug and/or cap the hose and transmission to prevent contamination.

11. Remove the transmission fluid cooler pipe retainer nut.

12. Remove the transmission fluid cooler outlet hose and seal from the transmission.

13. Plug and/or cap the hose and transmission to prevent contamination.

14. Disconnect both pipes from the retainer.

15. Install the engine support fixture.

16. Remove the rear transmission mount from the transmission.

17. Remove the front transmission mount from the transmission.

18. Remove the left transmission mount from the transmission.

19. Remove the upper transmission-to-engine bolts.

20. Remove the frame.

21. Disconnect the wheel halfshafts from the transmission.

22. Remove the intermediate drive shaft.

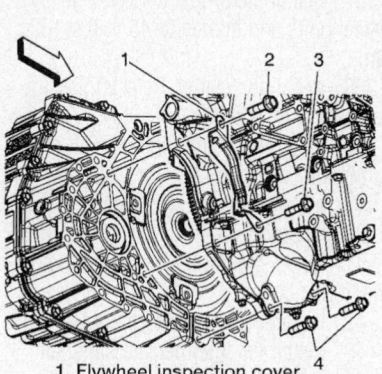

1. Flywheel inspection cover
2. Flywheel inspection cover bolt
3. Flywheel inspection cover bolt
4. Transmission bolts

36616_LACR_G0087

Fig. 18 Transmission removal—6T70 (FWD)

23. Remove the starter. Refer to Starter, removal & installation.

24. Mark the relationship of the flywheel to the torque converter for reassembly.

25. Remove the torque converter to flywheel bolts.

26. Use a transmission jack in order to support the transmission.

27. Remove the flywheel inspection cover bolts.

28. Remove the flywheel inspection cover.

29. Remove the remaining transmission bolts.

➡**Ensure the torque converter remains securely in place on the transmission input shaft while separating and removing the transmission.**

30. Separate the transmission from the engine.

31. Lower the transmission with the transmission jack far enough to remove the transmission.

To install:

32. Raise the transmission with the transmission jack and position the transmission to the engine.

33. Install the transmission bolts and tighten to 55 ft. lbs. (75 Nm).

34. Install the flywheel inspection cover.

35. Install the flywheel inspection cover bolts and tighten to 55 ft. lbs. (75 Nm).

36. Remove the transmission jack.

➡**If reusing the torque converter bolts, clean the threads and apply LOCTITE® 242, GM P/N 12345382 (Canadian P/N 10953489), or equivalent, to the threads prior to installation.**

37. Install the torque converter-to-fly-wheel bolts and tighten to 46 ft. lbs. (62 Nm).

38. Install the starter. Refer to Starter, removal & installation.

39. Install the front transmission mount to the transmission.

40. Install the rear transmission mount to the transmission.

41. Install the left transmission mount to the transmission.

42. Install the transmission brace.

43. Install the intermediate halfshaft.

44. Install the wheel halfshafts to the transmission.

45. Install the frame.

46. Install the upper transmission to engine bolt and tighten to 55 ft. lbs. (75 Nm).

47. Remove the engine support fixture.

48. Install the transmission fluid cooler outlet hose and seal to the transmission.

49. Install the transmission fluid cooler pipe retainer nut and tighten to 16 ft. lbs. (22 Nm).

50. Install the transmission fluid cooler inlet hose and seal to the transmission.

51. Install the transmission fluid cooler pipe retainer nut and tighten to 16 ft. lbs. (22 Nm).

52. Connect the control valve body TCM electrical connector. Install the wire harness retainer to the control valve body cover stud and tighten the nut to 106 inch lbs. (12 Nm).

53. Install the transmission range select lever cable and bracket.

54. Install the battery tray.

55. Adjust the automatic transmission range selector lever cable, as needed.

56. Fill the transmission with the proper type and amount of fluid.

➡**After an internal transmission repair or internal part replacement the service fast learn adapt procedure should be performed.**

57. Perform the service fast learn adapt procedure. Refer to Service Fast Learn Adapt Procedure.

58. Road test the vehicle.

SERVICE FAST LEARN ADAPT PROCEDURE

Service Fast Learn Adapts is a procedure for 6-speed automatic transmissions in which a series of tests are run to allow the Transmission Control Module (TCM) to learn individual clutch characteristics. Once the clutch data is learned, Service Fast Learn Adapts translates it into the adaptive data cells, which the TCM uses for clutch control during shifts. The scan tool provides initiation of the Service Fast Learn Adapts procedure. This procedure is to be used following transmission repair.

The Service Fast Learn Adapts procedure must be performed when one of the following repairs have been made to the vehicle. Failure to perform the procedure after one of the following repairs may result in poor transmission performance, as well as transmission DTC's being set:

• Transmission internal service/overhaul
• Valve body repair or replacement
• Control solenoid (w/body and TCM) valve assembly replacement
• TCM software/calibration update
• Any service in response to a shift quality concern

Ensure the following conditions are met before performing the Service Fast Learn Adapts procedure:

• Drive wheels are blocked
• Parking brake is applied
• Service brake is applied
• Zero percent throttle and no external engine RPM control
• Transmission Fluid Temperature (TFT) is between 158–239°F (70–115°C)
• Transmission gear selector has been cycled from Park to Reverse 3 times in order to purge air from the reverse clutches.

1. Use the scan tool to navigate to Service Fast Learn Adapts by selecting the following commands:
   a. F1: Transmission Control Module
   b. F5: Module Setup
   c. F0: Fast Learn Adapts Process

If at any time during the procedure, required conditions are not met, Service Fast Learn Adapts may abort and the process may need to be started again from the beginning. If this occurs, the transmission will be left in a neutral state until the controller is shut down, key OFF and remove the Tech 2 and wait for more than 30 seconds prior to re-try procedure. If the procedure repeatedly fails, a limit that engineering set is being exceeded and there is possibly a transmission hardware issue.

2. Use the scan tool to perform the Service Fast Learn Adapts procedure.

3. As the procedure is being performed, the scan tool data display will provide operator instructions. Follow the scan tool instructions as required.

4. Once the procedure is complete, shut OFF the engine and power down the TCM. You will lose communication to the scan tool.

5. Ensure you exit back to the main screen in the Tech 2, shut the Tech 2 OFF, and unplug it from the DLC or the controller will not shut down leaving the vehicle in a neutral state.

6. Restart the engine. This will complete the Service Fast Learn Adapts procedure.

➡**When the Service Fast Learn Adapts procedure is completed, the transmission will remain in a neutral state until the controller shuts down. If after 1–2 minutes of sitting, with the key OFF and scan tool removed, the vehicle remains in a neutral state, disconnect the battery and wait 5–10 minutes and then reconnect the battery. Reverse and drive should return.**

7. If the Service Fast Learn Adapts will not run and the above stated conditions have been met, ensure the following:
   a. TFT is between –239°F (70–115°C).
   b. Brakes and brake switch are functioning properly.
   c. No active DTC's.
   d. Closed throttle and engine RPM increases above 1,500 RPM while at entrance of the test.
   e. Park/Neutral position switch is properly adjusted and functioning.
   f. Line pressure control is able to provide 1,000 kPa and is within specifications.
   g. Vehicle is not moving, or vibrating excessively.
   h. Clutches are properly assembled.

TRANSFER CASE ASSEMBLY

REMOVAL & INSTALLATION

AWD Vehicles

See Figures 19 and 20.

Special Tools:
• DT-49064: Puller
• DT-49030: Fork, Cardan Removal

1. Before servicing the vehicle, refer to the Precautions Section.

2. Raise and safely support the vehicle.

3. Remove the rear catalytic converter. Refer to Catalytic Converter, removal & installation.

4. Remove the muffler.

5. Mark a reference point between the propeller shaft and the flange.

6. Using the appropriate tools, remove the flange bolts and the retainers.

7. Use the DT-49064 puller to remove the propeller shaft, if needed.

➡**Support the support bearings of the propeller shaft assembly with jack stands.**

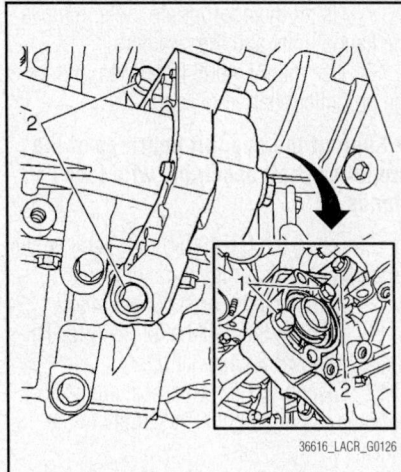

Fig. 19 Remove the support bracket fasteners (1) and the support bracket-to-engine fasteners (2)

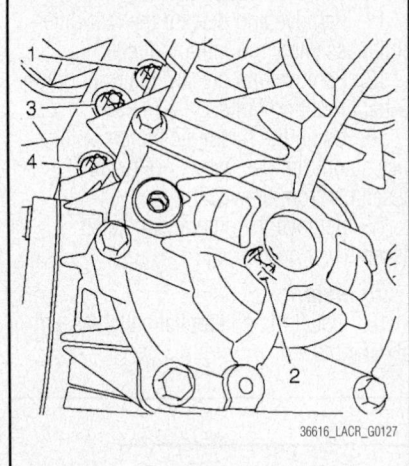

Fig. 20 Transfer case bolt tightening sequence

8. Using the DT-49030 fork, remove the propeller shaft from the transfer case.

9. Drain the oil from the transmission.

10. Remove the right front halfshaft. Refer to Halfshafts, removal & installation.

11. Remove the drivetrain and front suspension frame.

12. Remove the transmission rear mount bracket.

13. Remove the support bracket fasteners.

14. Remove the support bracket-to-engine fasteners.

15. Support the transfer case with a suitable jack, and secure with suitable straps.

16. Remove the transfer case fasteners.

17. Lower and ease out the transfer case from the vehicle.

To install:

18. Clean the contact surfaces between the transfer case and the gearbox. Fit a new O-ring into position.

19. Raise and align the transfer case in the correct position in relation to the gearbox.

20. Install the transfer case. Tighten the bolts in the correct order, as illustrated, to 81 ft. lbs. (110 Nm).

21. Fit the support bracket between the transfer case and the engine carefully in 3 steps to avoid breakage.

22. Tighten the support bracket fasteners to 44 inch lbs. (5 Nm)

23. Tighten the support bracket-to-engine fasteners to 44 ft. lbs. (60 Nm)

24. Tighten the support bracket fasteners to 44 ft. lbs. (60 Nm).

25. Install the transmission rear mount bracket.

26. Install the drivetrain and front suspension frame.

27. Install the right front halfshaft. Refer to Halfshafts, removal & installation.

28. Apply grease on the spline and position the propeller shaft into the transfer case. Use the matchmarks made during removal.

29. Install the flange bolts and the retainers to 22 ft. lbs. (30 Nm).

30. Install the support bearing mounting bolts and tighten to 15 ft. lbs. (20 Nm).

31. Install the muffler.

32. Install the rear catalytic converter. Refer to Catalytic Converter, removal & installation.

33. Check the fluid level of the rear differential assembly.

34. Fill the transmission with the proper amount and type of oil.

FRONT HALFSHAFTS

REMOVAL & INSTALLATION

See Figure 21.

Special Tools:
- J 2619-01: Slide Hammer
- J 29794: Axle Shaft Remover Extension
- J 33008-A: Axle Shaft Remover
- J 42129: Hub Spindle Remover

✳✳ CAUTION

To prevent personal injury and/or component damage, do not allow the weight of the vehicle to load the front wheels, or attempt to operate the vehicle, when the halfshaft(s) or halfshaft nut(s) are removed. To do so may cause the inner bearing race to separate, resulting in damage to brake and suspension components and loss of vehicle control.

Fig. 21 Front halfshaft removal

✳✳ WARNING

Halfshaft boots, seals and clamps should be protected from sharp objects any time service is performed on or near the halfshaft(s). Damage to the boot(s), the seal(s) or the clamp(s) may cause lubricant to leak from the joint and lead to increased noise and possible failure of the halfshaft.

1. Before servicing the vehicle, refer to the Precautions Section.

2. Raise and suitably support the vehicle.

3. Remove the tire and wheel assembly.

4. Insert a drift or punch in the cooling fins of the brake rotor.

5. Rotate the brake rotor until the drift or punch contacts the brake caliper mounting bracket.

6. Using a breaker bar, loosen the halfshaft nut.

7. Using the appropriate tool, separate the halfshaft from the knuckle.

8. Remove the halfshaft nut.

9. Remove the lower control arm from the knuckle. Refer to Lower Control, removal & installation.

10. Remove the outer tie rod end from the knuckle.

➡It may be necessary to have an assistant hold the knuckle assembly while removing the halfshaft. If removing the halfshaft to service other suspension or driveline components, use care when removing or installing the halfshaft so as not to damage the halfshaft boots.

11. Remove the halfshaft from the vehicle.

To install:

12. Position the halfshaft in the vehicle.

13. Insert the halfshaft in the knuckle.

14. Install the lower control arm in the knuckle.

15. Install the outer tie rod end in the knuckle.

16. Install the halfshaft nut.

17. Insert a drift or punch in the cooling fins of the brake rotor.

18. Rotate the brake rotor until the drift or punch contacts the brake caliper mounting bracket.

19. Using a torque wrench, tighten the halfshaft nut.

   a. For 2008–09 vehicles: Tighten the halfshaft nut to 118 ft. lbs. (160 Nm).

   b. For 2010 vehicles:

   • First pass tighten to 111 ft. lbs. (150 Nm), plus 45°, plus another 45°

   • Second pass tighten to 184 ft. lbs. (250 Nm)

20. Install the tire and wheel assembly.

21. Remove the support and lower the vehicle.

FRONT PINION SEAL

REMOVAL & INSTALLATION

AWD Vehicles

See Figure 22.

Special Tools:

• DT-49061: Entry Cone

• DT-49097: Seal Installer

1. Before servicing the vehicle, refer to the Precautions Section.

2. Raise and safely support the vehicle.

3. Remove the drive shaft, also called the propeller shaft.

4. Remove the dust shield from the output shaft using a suitable tool.

5. Remove the pinion seal or output shaft seal.

To install:

6. Install the shaft seal using DT-49097 installer and DT-49061 cone.

7. Install the dust shield using DT-49095 installer.

8. Install the drive shaft.

9. Add the proper type and amount of fluid as necessary.

10. Check for fluid leaks, repair as needed.

REAR AXLE HOUSING

REMOVAL & INSTALLATION

AWD Vehicles

See Figures 23 through 26.

Special Tools:

• DT-49064: Puller

• DT-49030: Fork, Cardan Removal

1. Before servicing the vehicle, refer to the Precautions Section.

2. Raise and safely support the vehicle.

3. If replacing the rear differential assembly, drain the rear differential fluid.

4. Remove the rear catalytic converter. Refer to Catalytic Converter, removal & installation.

5. Remove the muffler.

6. Mark a reference point between the propeller shaft and the flange.

7. Using the appropriate tools, remove the flange bolts and the retainers.

8. Use the DT-49064 puller to remove the propeller shaft, if needed.

➡**Support the support bearings of the propeller shaft assembly with jack stands.**

9. Using the DT-49030 fork, remove the propeller shaft from the transfer case.

10. Remove the rear stabilizer shaft.

11. Remove the halfshafts. Refer to Halfshafts, removal & installation.

12. Disconnect the electrical connectors from the rear differential assembly to the chassis.

➡**Ensure that the rear differential is securely fastened to the hydraulic jack stand.**

13. Support the rear differential assembly with a transmission jack.

14. Remove and discard the rear differential assembly mounting bolts.

15. Remove and discard the front differential mounting bolts.

16. Using the hydraulic transmission jack stand, remove the rear differential assembly from the vehicle.

17. Remove the differential clutch assembly, if needed.

To install:

18. Install the differential clutch assembly, if removed.

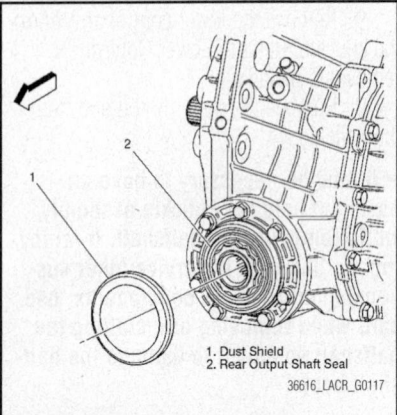

1. Dust Shield
2. Rear Output Shaft Seal

36616_LACR_G0117

Fig. 22 Removing the rear output shaft seal

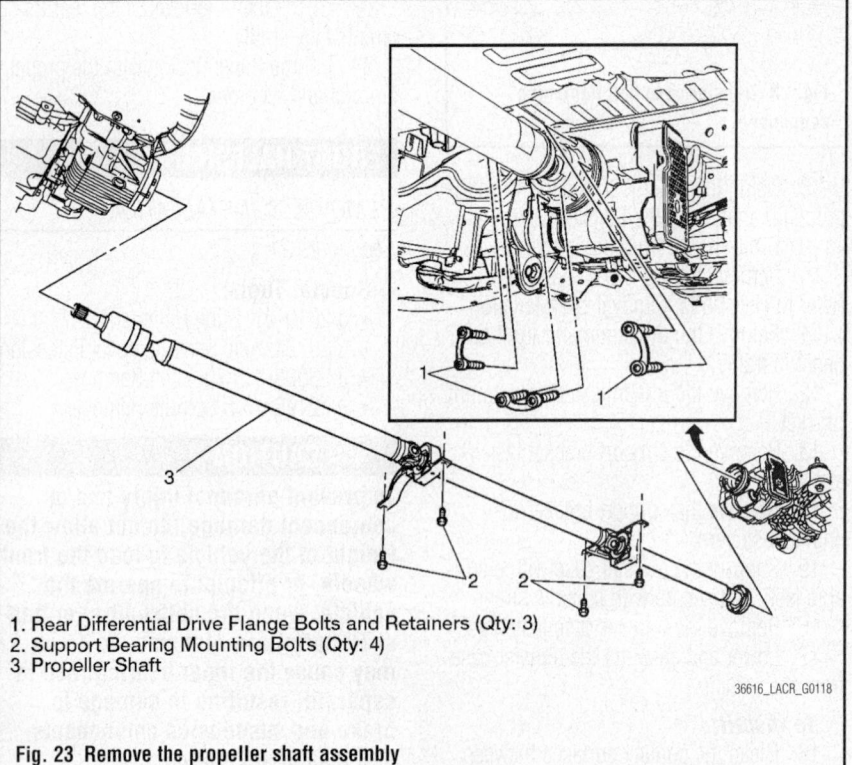

1. Rear Differential Drive Flange Bolts and Retainers (Qty: 3)
2. Support Bearing Mounting Bolts (Qty: 4)
3. Propeller Shaft

36616_LACR_G0118

Fig. 23 Remove the propeller shaft assembly

19. Using the hydraulic jack stand, position the rear differential assembly in the vehicle.

20. Install the NEW front differential mounting bolts and tighten to 92 ft. lbs. (125 Nm).

21. Install the NEW rear differential assembly mounting bolts and tighten to 92 ft. lbs. (90 Nm), plus 100°.

22. Remove the hydraulic jack stand.

23. Install the wheel drive shafts. Refer to Halfshafts, removal & installation.

24. Install the rear stabilizer shaft.

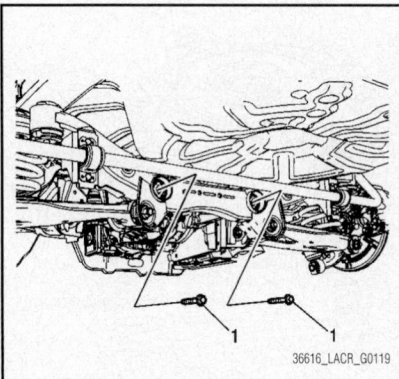

Fig. 24 Remove and discard the rear differential assembly mounting bolts (1)

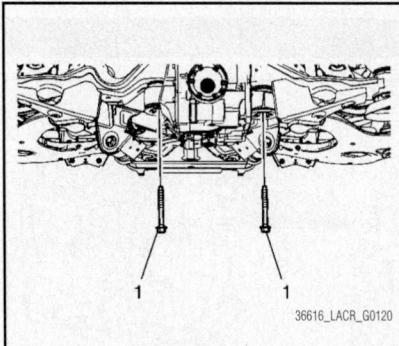

Fig. 25 Remove and discard the front differential mounting bolts (1)

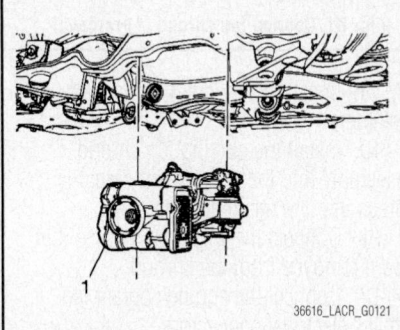

Fig. 26 Removing the rear differential assembly (1)

25. Connect the electrical connectors to the rear differential assembly and the chassis.

26. Apply grease on the spline and position the propeller shaft into the transfer case. Use the matchmarks made during removal.

27. Install the flange bolts and the retainers to 22 ft. lbs. (30 Nm).

28. Install the support bearing mounting bolts and tighten to 15 ft. lbs. (20 Nm).

29. Install the muffler.

30. Install the rear catalytic converter. Refer to Catalytic Converter, removal & installation.

31. Check the fluid level of the rear differential assembly.

32. If installing a NEW rear differential assembly, fill with the proper amount and type of fluid.

33. Remove the supports and lower the vehicle.

34. Check for fluid leaks, repair as necessary.

REAR AXLE SHAFT, BEARING & SEAL

REMOVAL & INSTALLATION

AWD Vehicles

See Figure 27.

Special Tools:
- J-23907: Slide Hammer
- J-29369-1: Drive Shaft Seal Puller

1. Before servicing the vehicle, refer to the Precautions Section.

2. Raise and safely support the vehicle.

3. Remove the halfshaft of side to be repaired. Refer to Halfshafts, removal & installation.

4. Remove the seal using J-29369-1 and J-23907.

To install:

5. Installation is the reverse of the removal procedure.

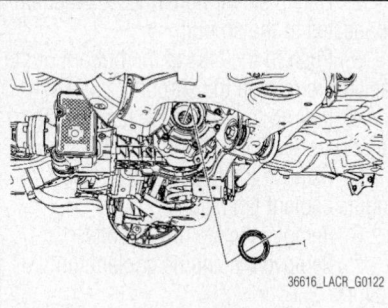

Fig. 27 Removing the rear axle shaft seal (1)—left side (right side is similar)

6. Check the lubricant level and adjust as needed.

REAR HALFSHAFTS

REMOVAL & INSTALLATION

AWD Vehicles

See Figures 28 and 29.

✸✸ WARNING

To prevent personal injury and/or component damage, do not allow the weight of the vehicle to load the front wheels, or attempt to operate the vehicle, when the halfshaft(s) or halfshaft nut(s) are removed. To do so may cause the inner bearing race to separate, resulting in damage to brake and suspension components and loss of vehicle control.

✸✸ WARNING

Halfshaft boots, seals, and clamps should be protected from sharp objects any time service is performed on or near the halfshaft(s). Damage to the boot(s), the seal(s), or the clamp(s) may cause lubricant to leak from the joint and lead to increased noise and possible failure of the halfshaft.

1. Before servicing the vehicle, refer to the Precautions Section.

2. Raise and safely support the vehicle.

3. Remove the tire and wheel.

4. Remove the rear wheel bearing and hub. Refer to Wheel Hub and Bearing (sealed unit), removal & installation.

5. Support the lower control arm with a suitable jack stand.

6. Remove the link from the upper and lower control arms.

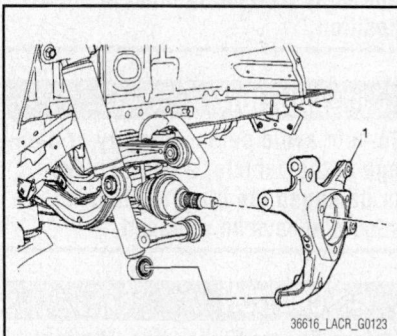

Fig. 28 Removing the rear wheel hub bracket (1)

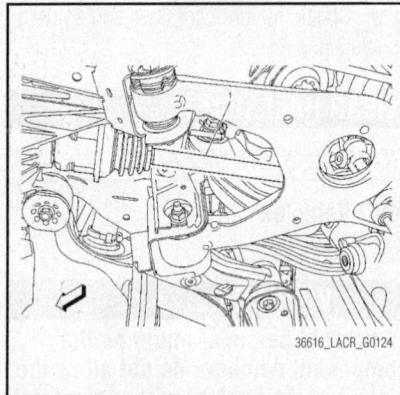

Fig. 29 Removing the rear halfshaft

7. Remove the bolt from the adjust link to the rear wheel hub bracket.

8. Remove the bolt from the shock absorber to the rear wheel hub bracket.

9. Place drain pans underneath the vehicle, as needed.

10. Tap out the rear halfshaft from the rear axle using a brass drift and a mallet.

To install:

11. Lubricate the rear halfshaft splines with rear axle lubricant to help ease in installation. Press in the shaft until the circlip engages.

12. Installation continues in the reverse of the removal procedure.

13. Check the rear axle lubricant level. Adjust as needed with the proper type and amount of lubricant.

REAR PINION SEAL

REMOVAL & INSTALLATION

AWD Vehicles

See Figure 30.

Special Tools:
- DT- 50022: Seal Installer
- J-8092: Universal Handle

1. Before servicing the vehicle, refer to the Precautions Section.

2. Raise and safely support the vehicle.

3. Using a flat-bladed screwdriver, remove the differential clutch.

4. Remove the differential clutch seal.

To install:

5. Apply a small amount of lubricant to the seal prior to installing it in the differential clutch.

6. Using the DT- 50022 installer and the J-8092 handle, install the differential clutch seal.

➡ **The seal must be flush with the axle.**

7. Installation continues in the reverse of the removal procedure.

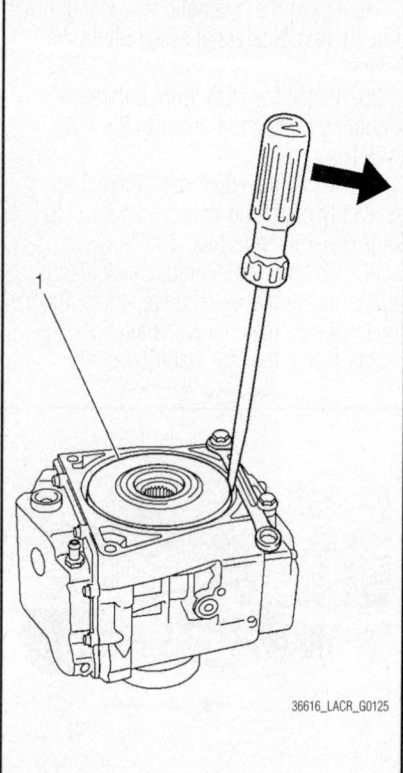

Fig. 30 Removing the differential clutch seal (1)

ENGINE COOLING

ENGINE FAN

REMOVAL & INSTALLATION

See Figures 31 and 32.

✳✳ CAUTION

Keep hands, tools, and clothing away from the electric engine coolant fans in order to help prevent personal injury. These fans are electric and can turn on whether or not the engine is running. The fans can start automatically with the ignition in the **ON** position.

✳✳ CAUTION

To help avoid personal injury or damage to the vehicle, a bent, cracked, or damaged fan blade or housing should always be replaced.

✳✳ CAUTION

Unless directed otherwise, the ignition and start switch must be in the **OFF** or **LOCK** position, and all electrical loads must be OFF before servicing any electrical component. Disconnect the negative battery cable to prevent an electrical spark should a tool or equipment come in contact with an exposed electrical terminal. Failure to follow these precautions may result in personal injury and/or damage to the vehicle or its components.

1. Disconnect the engine coolant fan motor electrical connectors.

2. Unclip all wiring harnesses that are connected to the shroud.

3. Push in the tabs at the bottom of the radiator to release the shroud.

4. Pull up to remove the cooling fan shroud assembly from the vehicle.

5. Remove the retainers from the engine coolant fan blades.

6. Remove the fan motor bolts.

7. Remove the engine coolant fan motors.

To install:

8. Install the engine coolant fan motors. Tighten the bolts to 89 inch lbs. (10 Nm).

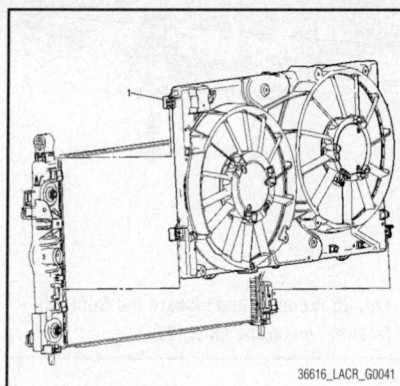

Fig. 31 Cooling fan shroud (1) removal

9. Install the coolant fan blades and the retainers.

10. Install the cooling fan shroud assembly into the vehicle and carefully press into the retaining tabs.

11. Connect the wiring harnesses that were removed from the shroud.

12. Connect the engine coolant fan motor electrical connectors.

13. Check for proper operation of the engine cooling fans.

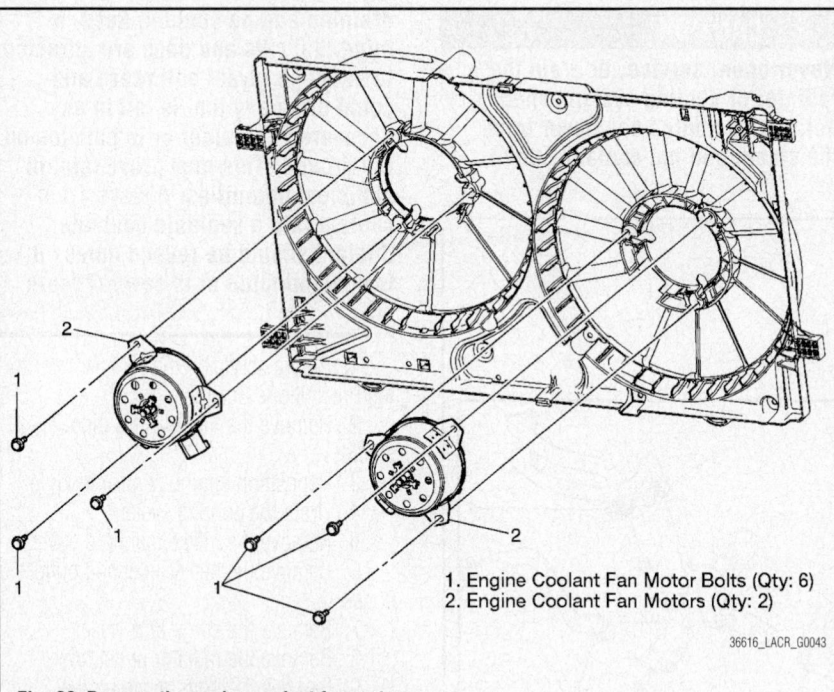

1. Engine Coolant Fan Motor Bolts (Qty: 6)
2. Engine Coolant Fan Motors (Qty: 2)

36616_LACR_G0043

Fig. 32 Remove the engine coolant fan motors

RADIATOR

REMOVAL & INSTALLATION

See Figures 31 and 33.

✷✷ CAUTION

Never open, service, or drain the radiator or cooling system when hot; serious burns can occur from the steam and hot coolant. When draining engine coolant, keep in mind that cats and dogs are attracted to ethylene glycol antifreeze and could drink any that is left in an uncovered container or in puddles on the ground. This may prove fatal in sufficient quantities. Always drain coolant into a sealable container. Coolant should be reused unless it is contaminated or is several years old.

1. Before servicing the vehicle, refer to the Precautions Section.
2. Disconnect the negative battery cable.
3. Remove the air cleaner assembly.
4. Drain the cooling system.
5. Remove the right and the left engine mount struts.
6. Remove the inlet hose from the radiator.
7. Remove the Powertrain Control Module (PCM) harness clip from the fan shroud.
8. Remove the transaxle oil cooler lines from the retainer clip at the bottom of the cooling fan shroud.

36616_LACR_G0042

Fig. 33 Radiator removal

9. Remove the fan shroud clip from the condenser tubes.
10. Remove the bolt that connects the fan shroud to the condenser hold down bracket.
11. Remove the air deflectors from the top of the radiator.
12. Remove the cooling fan shroud bolts.
13. Remove the coolant reservoir hose from the radiator overflow neck.
14. Remove the radiator upper support brackets and bolts that connect to the fan shroud.
15. Disconnect the engine cooling fan motors electrical connectors.

16. Remove the cooling fan motors electrical harness from the fan shroud clips.
17. Remove the cooling fan shroud.
18. Remove the outlet hose from the radiator.
19. Disconnect the transaxle oil cooler pipes from the radiator.
20. Tilt the top of the radiator rearward.
21. Remove the condenser hold down bracket from the radiator.
22. Lift the condenser from the mounting tabs on the radiator and position the condenser aside.
23. Remove the radiator.

To install:

24. Install the radiator to the lower mounts.

➡**Verify that the condenser is fully seated in the radiator mounting tabs.**

25. Install the condenser to the mounting tabs on the radiator.
26. Install the condenser hold down bracket to the radiator and condenser.
27. Install the outlet hose to the radiator.
28. Connect the transaxle oil cooler pipes to the radiator.

➡**Ensure the lower edge of the fan shroud engages the clip at the bottom of the radiator.**

29. Install the cooling fan shroud.
30. Install the cooling fan motors electrical harness to the fan shroud clips.
31. Connect the engine cooling fan motors electrical connectors.
32. Install the fan shroud clip to the condenser tubes.
33. Install the cooling fan shroud bolts and tighten to 89 inch lbs. (10 Nm).
34. Install the radiator upper support brackets and bolts that connect to the fan shroud.
35. Install the air deflectors to the top of the radiator.
36. Install the bolt that connects the fan shroud to the condenser hold down bracket.
37. Install the PCM harness clip on to the fan shroud.
38. Install the inlet hose to the radiator.
39. Install the air cleaner assembly.
40. Install the coolant reservoir hose to the radiator overflow neck.
41. Install the right and the left engine mount struts.
42. Install the transaxle oil cooler lines to the retainer clip at the bottom of the cooling fan shroud.
43. Fill the cooling system.
44. Connect the negative battery cable.
45. Adjust the transaxle fluid level.

THERMOSTAT

REMOVAL & INSTALLATION

3.0L and 3.6L Engines
See Figures 34 and 35.

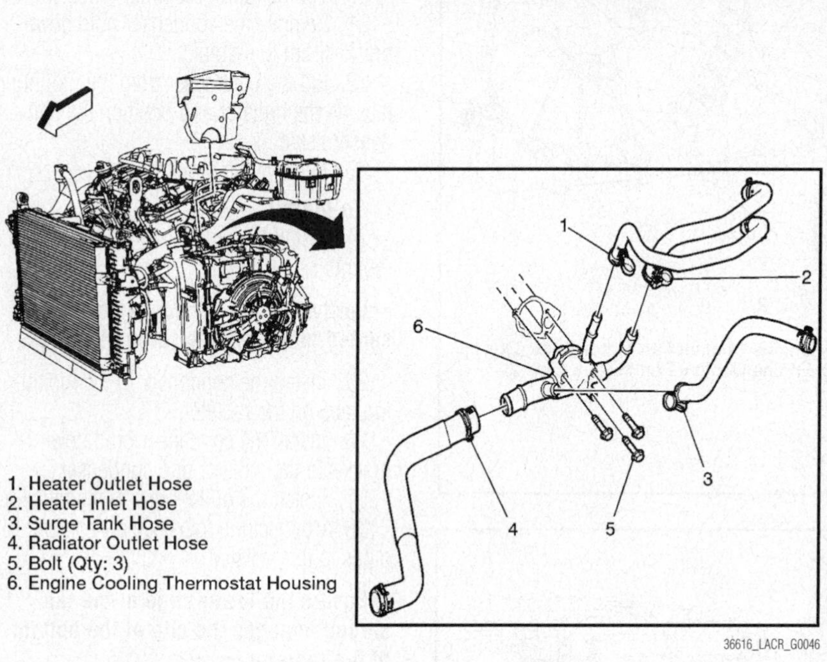

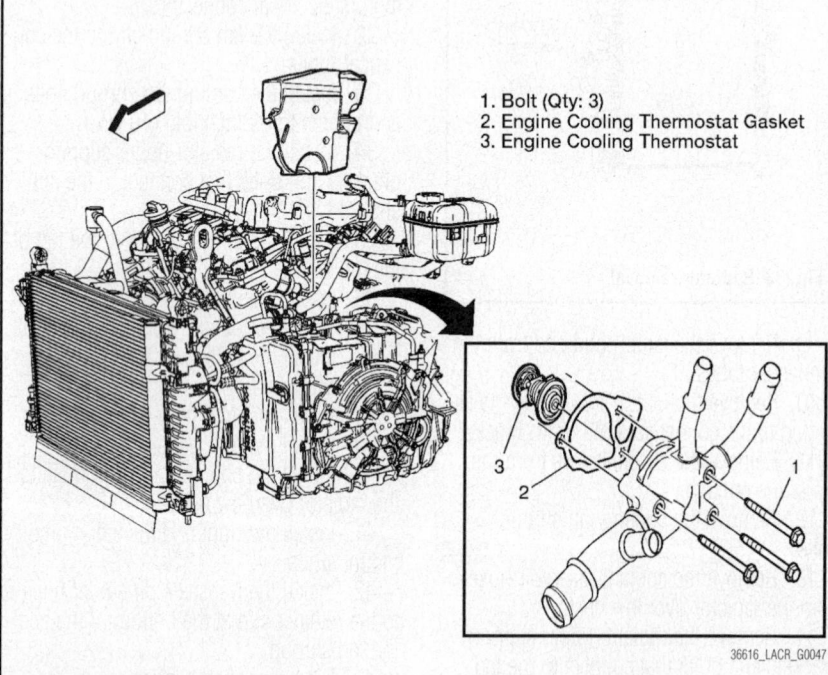

1. Heater Outlet Hose
2. Heater Inlet Hose
3. Surge Tank Hose
4. Radiator Outlet Hose
5. Bolt (Qty: 3)
6. Engine Cooling Thermostat Housing

36616_LACR_G0046

Fig. 34 Engine coolant thermostat housing removal—3.0L and 3.6L engines

1. Bolt (Qty: 3)
2. Engine Cooling Thermostat Gasket
3. Engine Cooling Thermostat

36616_LACR_G0047

Fig. 35 Engine coolant thermostat removal—3.0L and 3.6L engines

✻✷ CAUTION

Never open, service, or drain the radiator or cooling system when hot; serious burns can occur from the steam and hot coolant. When draining engine coolant, keep in mind that cats and dogs are attracted to ethylene glycol antifreeze and could drink any that is left in an uncovered container or in puddles on the ground. This may prove fatal in sufficient quantities. Always drain coolant into a sealable container. Coolant should be reused unless it is contaminated or is several years old.

1. Before servicing the vehicle, refer to the Precautions Section.
2. Remove the fuel injector pipe shield.
3. Reposition engine control module.
4. Drain the cooling system.
5. Remove the intake manifold cover.
6. Remove the heater inlet and outlet hoses.
7. Remove the surge tank hose.
8. Remove the radiator outlet hose.
9. Remove the bolts retaining the engine coolant thermostat housing.
10. Remove the thermostat housing.
11. Remove the thermostat gasket and discard.
12. Remove the engine cooling thermostat from the thermostat housing.

To install:
13. Replace the thermostat gasket and any worn hoses.
14. Clean the engine block and thermostat gasket surfaces.
15. Install the thermostat and a new gasket.
16. Installation is the reverse of the removal procedure.
17. Tighten the thermostat housing bolts to 88 inch lbs. (10 Nm).
18. Fill the cooling system with the proper type and amount of fluid.
19. Run the engine and check for fluid leaks.

3.8L Engine
See Figure 36.

Special Tool:
• J 38185: Hose Clamp Pliers

✻✷ CAUTION

Never open, service, or drain the radiator or cooling system when hot; serious burns can occur from the steam and hot coolant. When draining engine coolant, keep in mind that cats and dogs are attracted to ethylene glycol antifreeze and could drink any that is left in an uncovered container or in puddles on the ground.

This may prove fatal in sufficient quantities. Always drain coolant into a sealable container. Coolant should be reused unless it is contaminated or is several years old.

1. Before servicing the vehicle, refer to the Precautions Section.
2. Remove the fuel injector sight shield.
3. Partially drain the cooling system.
4. Use the J 38185 in order to reposition the hose clamp from the water outlet housing.
5. Remove the radiator inlet hose from the water outlet housing.
6. Reposition the wiring harness from the water outlet housing stud.
7. Remove the water outlet housing bolt and the stud.
8. Remove the water outlet housing and the gasket.
9. Remove the thermostat.

To install:

10. Clean and inspect the water outlet housing gasket mating surfaces.
11. Install the thermostat.
12. Install the gasket and the water outlet housing.
13. Install the water outlet housing bolt and the stud to the water outlet housing. Tighten the bolt and the stud to 20 ft. lbs. (27 Nm).
14. Install the wiring harness to the water outlet housing stud.
15. Install the radiator inlet hose to the water outlet housing.
16. Use the J 38185 in order to reposition and install the hose clamp to the water outlet housing.

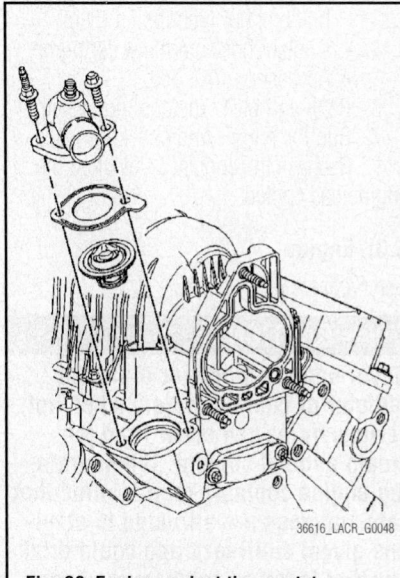

36616_LACR_G0048

Fig. 36 Engine coolant thermostat removal—3.8L engine

17. Fill the cooling system with the proper type and amount of fluid.
18. Install the fuel injector sight shield.
19. Run the engine and check for fluid leaks.

5.3L Engine

See Figure 37.

Special Tool:
- J 38185: Hose Clamp Pliers

❋❋ CAUTION

Never open, service, or drain the radiator or cooling system when hot; serious burns can occur from the steam and hot coolant. When draining engine coolant, keep in mind that cats and dogs are attracted to ethylene glycol antifreeze and could drink any that is left in an uncovered container or in puddles on the ground. This may prove fatal in sufficient quantities. Always drain coolant into a sealable container. Coolant should be reused unless it is contaminated or is several years old.

1. Before servicing the vehicle, refer to the Precautions Section.
2. Remove the radiator air lower baffle and deflector.
3. Reposition the radiator inlet hose.
4. Partially drain the cooling system.
5. Use the J 38185 in order to reposition the hose clamp from the water outlet housing.
6. Remove the radiator inlet hose from the water outlet housing.
7. Remove the water outlet housing bolts.
8. Remove the water outlet housing and O-ring seal.

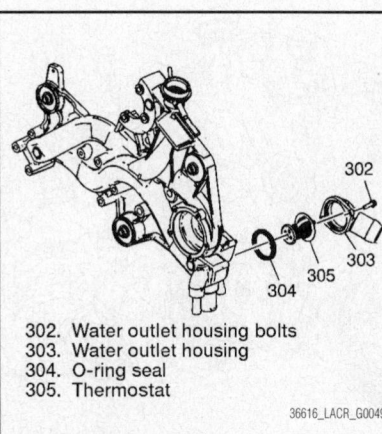

302. Water outlet housing bolts
303. Water outlet housing
304. O-ring seal
305. Thermostat

36616_LACR_G0049

Fig. 37 Engine coolant thermostat removal—5.3L engine

9. Remove the thermostat.
10. Clean and inspect the water outlet housing O-ring seal mating surfaces.

To install:

❋❋ WARNING

DO NOT use cooling system seal tabs, or similar compounds, unless otherwise instructed. The use of cooling system seal tabs, or similar compounds, may restrict coolant flow through the passages of the cooling system or the engine components. Restricted coolant flow may cause engine overheating and/or damage to the cooling system or the engine components/assembly.

11. Install the thermostat.
12. Install the O-ring seal and water outlet housing.
13. Install the water outlet housing bolts and tighten to 11 ft. lbs. (15 Nm).
14. Install the radiator inlet hose to the water outlet housing.
15. Use the J 38185 in order to reposition and install the hose clamp to the water outlet housing.
16. Fill the cooling system with the proper type and amount of fluid.
17. Install the radiator inlet hose.
18. Install the radiator air lower baffle and deflector.
19. Run the engine and check for fluid leaks.

WATER PUMP

REMOVAL & INSTALLATION

3.0L and 3.6L Engines

See Figures 38 and 39.

❋❋ CAUTION

Never open, service, or drain the radiator or cooling system when hot; serious burns can occur from the steam and hot coolant. When draining engine coolant, keep in mind that cats and dogs are attracted to ethylene glycol antifreeze and could drink any that is left in an uncovered container or in puddles on the ground. This may prove fatal in sufficient quantities. Always drain coolant into a sealable container. Coolant should be reused unless it is contaminated or is several years old.

1. Before servicing the vehicle, refer to the Precautions Section.
2. Drain the cooling system.

3. Remove the accessory drive belt. Refer to Accessory Drive Belts, removal & installation.

4. Use tool EN 46104 in order to retain the water pump pulley.

5. Remove the water pump pulley bolts.

6. Remove the water pump pulley.

7. Remove the water pump bolts.

8. Remove the water pump.

9. Remove and DISCARD the water pump seal.

10. Carefully clean the water pump sealing surfaces.

To install:

11. Install a NEW water pump seal.

12. Install the water pump.

13. Install the water pump bolts. Tighten the water pump bolts to 89 inch lbs. (10 Nm).

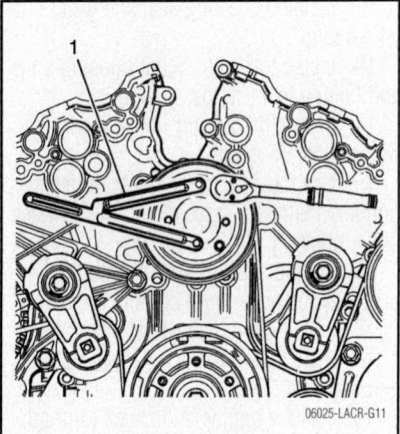

Fig. 38 Use tool EN 46104 (1) in order to retain the water pump pulley

14. Install the water pump pulley and the water pump pulley bolts.

15. Install the water pump pulley bolts. Tighten the water pump pulley bolts to 106 inch lbs. (12 Nm).

16. Install the alternator drive belt. Refer to Accessory Drive Belts, removal & installation.

17. Fill the cooling system with the proper type and amount of fluid.

18. Run the engine and check for fluid leaks.

3.8L Engine

See Figure 40.

> ❋❋ **CAUTION**
>
> **Never open, service, or drain the radiator or cooling system when hot; serious burns can occur from the steam and hot coolant. When draining engine coolant, keep in mind that cats and dogs are attracted to ethylene glycol antifreeze and could drink any that is left in an uncovered container or in puddles on the ground. This may prove fatal in sufficient quantities. Always drain coolant into a sealable container. Coolant should be reused unless it is contaminated or is several years old.**

1. Before servicing the vehicle, refer to the Precautions Section.

2. Drain the cooling system.

3. Remove or disconnect the following:
   • Negative battery cable

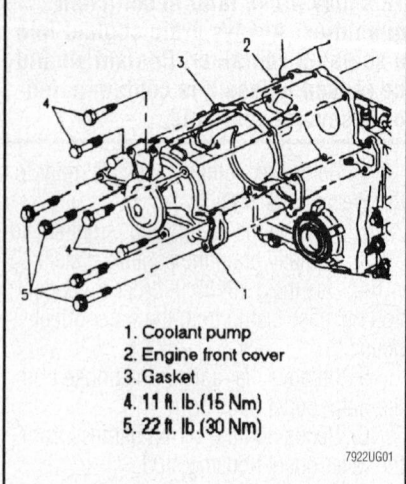

1. Coolant pump
2. Engine front cover
3. Gasket
4. 11 ft. lb.(15 Nm)
5. 22 ft. lb.(30 Nm)

7922UG01

Fig. 40 Exploded view of the water pump—3.8L engine

• Accessory drive belt
• Coolant hoses from the water pump
• Water pump pulley bolts

➡The long bolt can be removed by aligning the bolt head up with the hole in the frame rail.

• Pulley
• Water pump bolts
• Water pump

To install:

4. Apply a thin bead of sealer around the outside edge of the water pump.

5. Install or connect the following:
   • Water pump with new gasket. Torque the water pump short bolts to 11 ft. lbs. (15 Nm) and the long bolts to 22 ft. lbs. (30 Nm)
   • Water pump pulley. Torque the bolts to 115 inch lbs. (13 Nm)
   • Coolant hoses to the water pump
   • Accessory drive belt

6. Refill and bleed the cooling system.

7. Run the engine and check for leaks.

8. Recheck the coolant level when the engine has cooled.

5.3L Engine

See Figure 41.

> ❋❋ **CAUTION**
>
> **Never open, service, or drain the radiator or cooling system when hot; serious burns can occur from the steam and hot coolant. When draining engine coolant, keep in mind that cats and dogs are attracted to ethylene glycol antifreeze and could drink any that is left in an uncovered container or in puddles on the ground.**

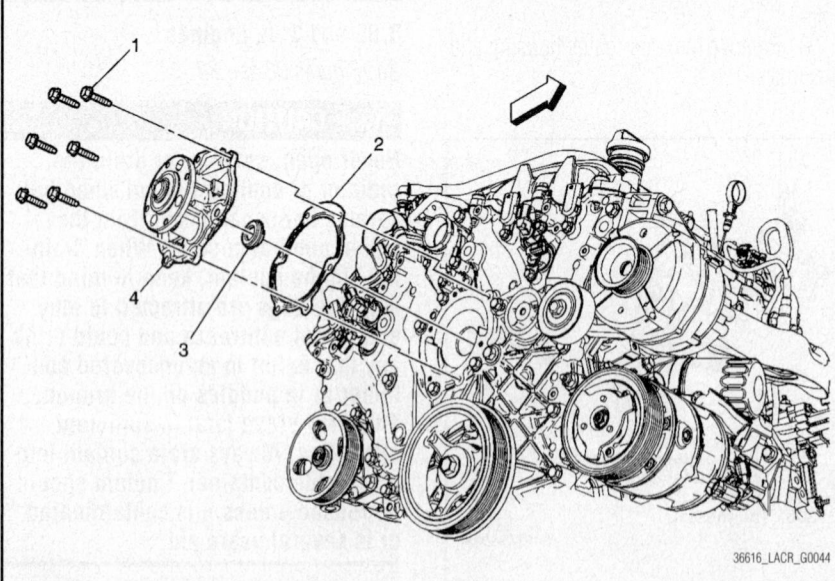

36616_LACR_G0044

Fig. 39 Water pump mounting bolts (1), seal (2) and water pump (4)—3.0L and 3.6L engines

This may prove fatal in sufficient quantities. Always drain coolant into a sealable container. Coolant should be reused unless it is contaminated or is several years old.

1. Before servicing the vehicle, refer to the Precautions Section.
2. Disconnect the negative battery cable.

➡️**Align the notched area of the water pump flange with the locating tab on the manifold assembly.**

3. Drain the cooling system.
4. Remove the battery and battery tray.
5. Remove the drive belt. Refer to Accessory Drive Belts, removal & installation.

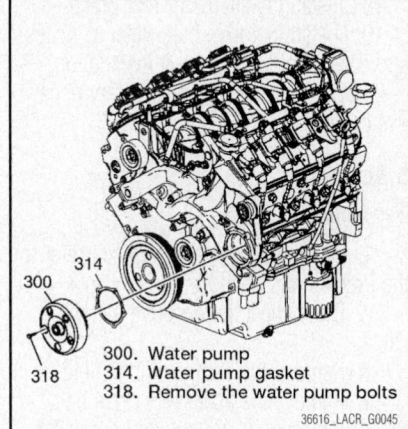

300. Water pump
314. Water pump gasket
318. Remove the water pump bolts

36616_LACR_G0045

Fig. 41 Water pump removal—5.3L engine

6. Remove the water pump bolts.
7. Remove the water pump and gasket. Discard the gasket.

To install:

8. Clean and inspect the water pump gasket mating surfaces.
9. Install the water pump and a NEW gasket.
10. Tighten the water pump bolts to 89 inch lbs. (10 Nm).
11. Install the drive belt. Refer to Accessory Drive Belts, removal & installation.
12. Install the battery tray and battery.
13. Fill the cooling system with the proper type and amount of fluid.
14. Run the engine and check for fluid leaks.

ENGINE ELECTRICAL

ALTERNATOR

REMOVAL & INSTALLATION

3.0L and 3.6L Engines

See Figure 42.

1. Before servicing the vehicle, refer to the Precautions Section.
2. Disconnect the battery ground (negative) cable from the battery.
3. Remove the air cleaner outlet duct.
4. Reposition the positive battery cable boot at the alternator terminal.
5. Remove the positive battery cable nut at the alternator.
6. Remove the positive battery cable terminal from the alternator.
7. Disconnect the engine harness electrical connector from the alternator.

8. Remove the drive belt. Refer to Accessory Drive Belts, removal & installation.
9. Remove the idler pulley.
10. Remove the alternator bolts.

➡️**When removing the alternator from the vehicle, it may be necessary to maneuver the alternator to remove it from the vehicle.**

11. Remove the alternator.

To install:
12. Install the alternator.
13. Loosely install the alternator bolts.
14. Install the idler pulley. Tighten the bolts to 43 ft. lbs. (58 Nm).
15. Tighten the alternator bolts in the sequence shown to 37 ft. lbs. (50 Nm).
16. Install the drive belt. Refer to Accessory Drive Belts, removal & installation.
17. Connect the engine harness electrical connector to the alternator.
18. Install the positive battery cable terminal to the alternator.
19. Install the positive battery cable nut at the alternator. Tighten to 15 ft. lbs. (20 Nm).
20. Position the positive battery cable boot at the alternator terminal.
21. Connect the negative battery cable.

3.8L Engine

See Figure 43.

1. Before servicing the vehicle, refer to the Precautions Section.
2. Disconnect the battery ground (negative) cable from the battery.
3. Remove the drive belt from the alter-

CHARGING SYSTEM

nator. Refer to Accessory Drive Belts, removal & installation.
4. Remove the alternator rear brace.
5. Remove the bolts and the stud from the alternator.
6. Disconnect the electrical connector from the alternator.
7. Position aside the protective boot from the alternator output BAT terminal for access.

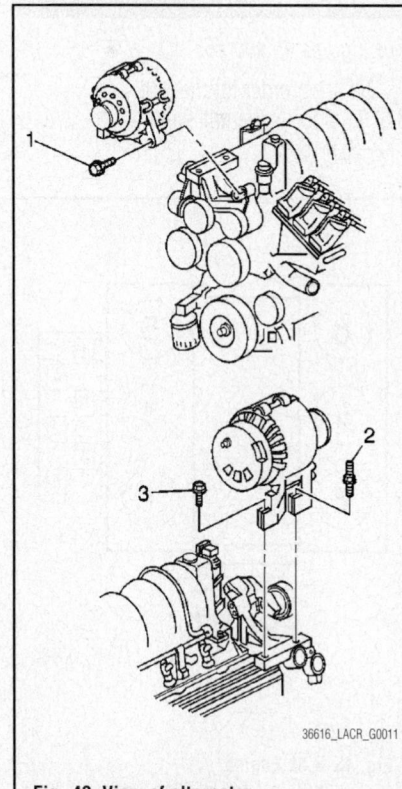

36616_LACR_G0011

Fig. 43 View of alternator removal/installation—3.8L engine

36616_LACR_G0010

Fig. 42 Alternator bolt tightening sequence—3.0L and 3.6L engines

8. Remove the alternator output BAT terminal nut and remove the positive battery lead from the alternator.

9. Remove the alternator.

To install:

10. Position the alternator to the engine.

11. Install the positive battery lead to the alternator.

12. Install the alternator output BAT terminal nut and tighten to 15 ft. lbs. (20 Nm).

13. Install the protective boot to the alternator output BAT terminal.

14. Connect the electrical connector to the alternator. Do not tighten the stud.

15. Install the alternator stud to the alternator bracket. Do not tighten the bolts.

16. Install the alternator bolts to the alternator bracket.

17. Tighten the alternator bolts and stud in the order described. The following is a mandatory torque sequence:

 a. Tighten the alternator bolt to 37 ft. lbs. (50 Nm).

 b. Tighten the alternator stud to 37 ft. lbs. (50 Nm).

 c. Tighten the alternator rear bracket bolt to 37 ft. lbs. (50 Nm).

18. Install the alternator rear brace.

19. Install the drive belt. Refer to Accessory Drive Belts, removal & installation.

20. Connect the negative battery negative cable.

5.3L Engine

See Figure 44.

1. Before servicing the vehicle, refer to the Precautions Section.

2. Disconnect the negative battery cable.

3. Remove the engine sight shield.

4. Remove the accessory drive belt. Refer to Accessory Drive Belts, removal & installation.

5. Disconnect the electrical connectors from the alternator.

6. Remove the alternator retaining bolts.

7. Remove the component from its mounting.

To install:

➡**Be sure to use new fasteners, as required.**

8. Position the alternator to its mounting.

Fig. 44 View of alternator and related components

9. Tighten the retaining bolts to 41 ft. lbs. (55 Nm).

10. Connect the electrical connectors to the alternator and tighten the cable nuts to 80 inch lbs. (9 Nm).

11. Continue the installation in the reverse order of the removal procedure.

12. Connect the battery cable.

13. Check for proper system operation. Correct as required.

ENGINE ELECTRICAL

FIRING ORDERS

See Figures 45 and 46.

The firing order for the 3.0L and 3.6L engines is the following: 1-2-3-4-5-6.

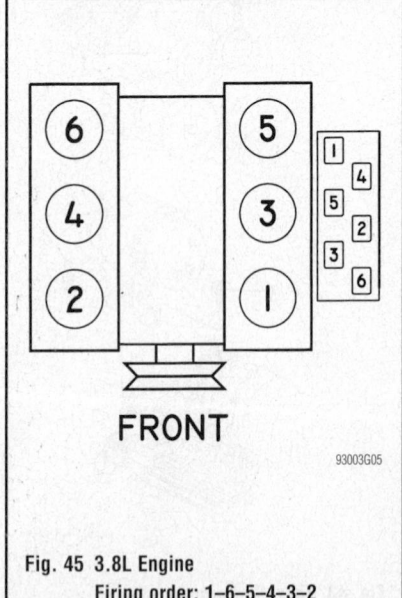

Fig. 45 3.8L Engine
Firing order: 1-6-5-4-3-2
Distributorless ignition system

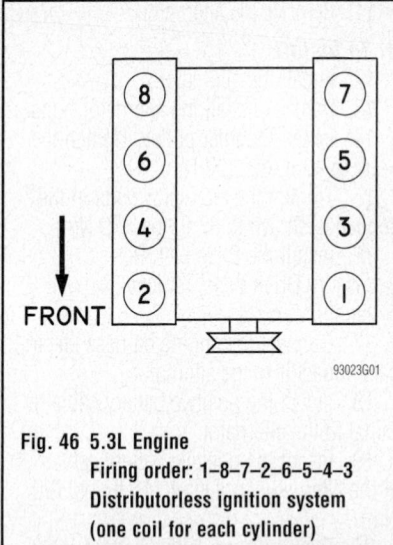

Fig. 46 5.3L Engine
Firing order: 1-8-7-2-6-5-4-3
Distributorless ignition system
(one coil for each cylinder)

IGNITION COILS

REMOVAL & INSTALLATION

3.0L and 3.6L Engines

Bank 1

See Figure 47.

1. Before servicing the vehicle, refer to the Precautions Section.

IGNITION SYSTEM

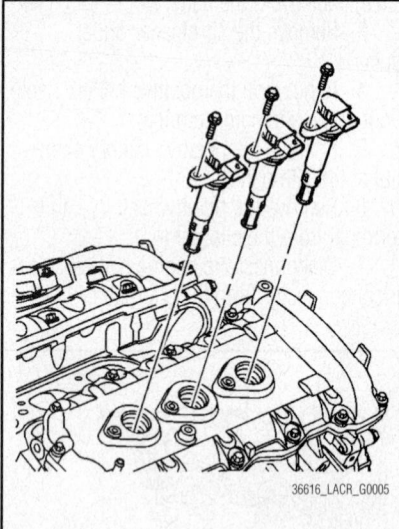

Fig. 47 Removing and installing the ignition coils (bank 1)—3.0L and 3.6L engines

2. Remove the fuel injector sight shield.

3. Disconnect the engine wiring harness electrical connector(s) from the ignition coil(s).

4. If removing the number 5 cylinder ignition coil, remove the Evaporative Emission (EVAP) canister purge tube.

5. If removing the number one ignition coil, remove the canister purge solenoid.

6. Remove the ignition coil bolt(s).

7. Remove the ignition coil(s).

To install:

8. Install the ignition coil(s).

9. Install the ignition coil bolt(s) and tighten to 89 inch lbs. (10 Nm).

10. If the number 5 cylinder ignition coil was removed, install the EVAP canister purge tube.

11. If the number one ignition coil was removed, install the canister purge solenoid.

12. Connect the engine wiring harness electrical connector(s) to the ignition coil(s).

13. Install the fuel injector sight shield.

Bank 2

See Figure 48.

1. Before servicing the vehicle, refer to the Precautions Section.

2. Remove the fuel injector sight shield.

3. Disconnect the engine wiring harness electrical connector(s) from the ignition coil(s).

4. Remove the ignition coil bolt(s).

5. Remove the ignition coil(s).

To install:

6. Installation is the reverse of the removal procedure.

7. Tighten the ignition coil bolts to 89 inch lbs. (10 Nm).

3.8L Engine

See Figure 49.

1. Before servicing the vehicle, refer to the Precautions Section.

2. Disconnect the negative battery cable.

3. Disconnect the spark plug wires from the ignition coil.

4. Remove the ignition coil screws.

5. Remove the ignition coil.

To install:

6. Install the ignition coils and tighten to 40 inch lbs. (5 Nm).

7. Connect the spark plug wires.

8. Connect the negative battery cable.

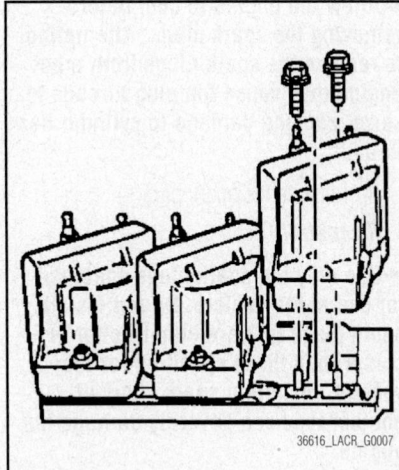

36616_LACR_G0007

Fig. 49 Removing and installing the ignition coils—3.8L engine

5.3L Engine

See Figures 50 through 52.

1. Before servicing the vehicle, refer to the Precautions Section.

2. Disconnect the negative battery cable.

3. Remove the engine sight shield.

4. Disconnect the spark plug wires at the ignition coils.

5. Disconnect the coil harness connector.

6. Remove the coil mounting bolts. Remove the coil from its mounting.

➡**Two different manufacturers of ignition coils are used on this vehicle. Refer to the illustrations for identification.**

To install:

➡**Be sure to use new fasteners, as required.**

7. Position the component on its mounting.

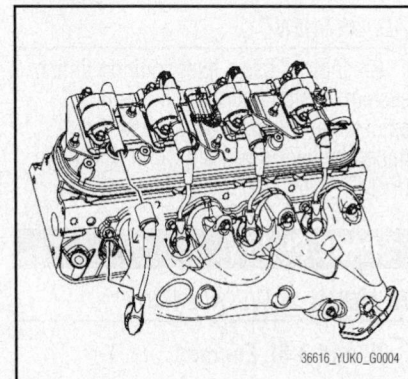

36616_YUKO_G0004

Fig. 50 View of ignition coil and related components

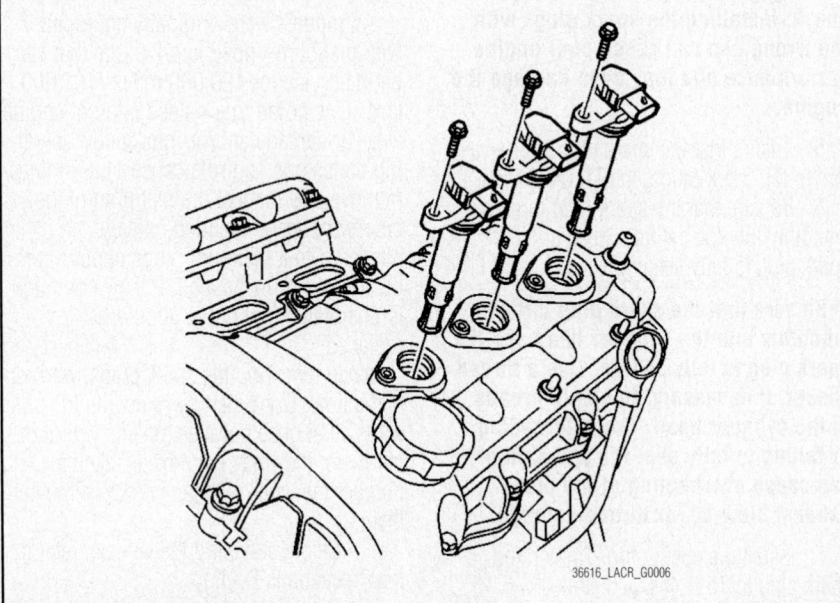

36616_LACR_G0006

Fig. 48 Removing and installing the ignition coils (bank 2)—3.0L and 3.6L engines

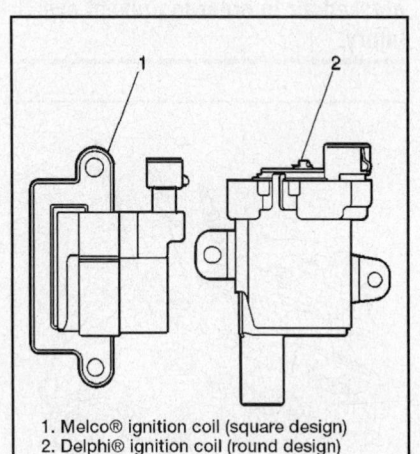

1. Melco® ignition coil (square design)
2. Delphi® ignition coil (round design)

36616_YUKO_G0006

Fig. 51 Ignition coil identification

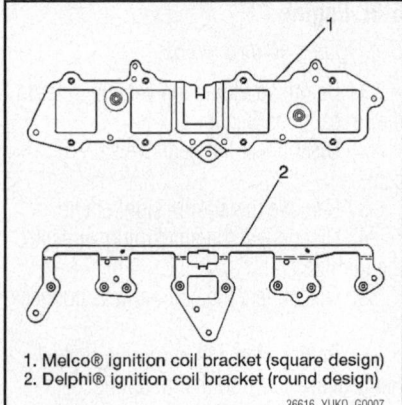

1. Melco® ignition coil bracket (square design)
2. Delphi® ignition coil bracket (round design)

36616_YUKO_G0007

Fig. 52 Ignition coil bracket identification

8. Tighten the retaining bolts to 89 inch lbs. (10 Nm).
9. Continue the installation in the reverse order of the removal procedure.
10. Connect the negative battery cable.

IGNITION TIMING

ADJUSTMENT

All engines use a fixed ignition timing system. Basic ignition timing is not adjustable. All spark advance is determined by the Powertrain Control Module (PCM).

SPARK PLUGS

REMOVAL & INSTALLATION

3.0L and 3.6L Engines
See Figure 53.

✳✳ CAUTION

Wear safety glasses when using compressed air in order to prevent eye injury.

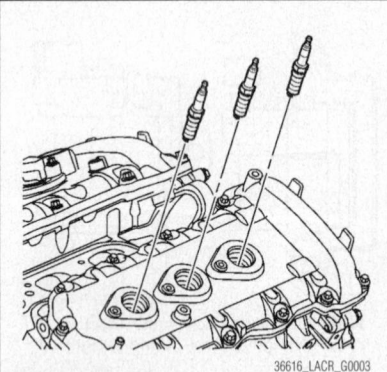

36616_LACR_G0003

Fig. 53 Removing the spark plugs—3.0L and 3.6L engines

➡Clean the spark plug recess area before removing the spark plug. Failure to do so could result in engine damage because of dirt or foreign material entering the cylinder head, or by the contamination of the cylinder head threads. The contaminated threads may prevent the proper seating of the new plug. Use a thread chaser to clean the threads of any contamination.

1. Before servicing the vehicle, refer to the Precautions Section.
2. Remove the ignition coil(s). Refer to Ignition Coils, removal & installation.
3. Use compressed air in order to remove debris from the spark plug cavity.

➡Allow the engine to cool before removing the spark plugs. Attempting to remove the spark plugs from a hot engine may cause the plug threads to seize, causing damage to cylinder head threads.

4. Remove the spark plug(s).

To install:

➡Use only the spark plugs specified for use in the vehicle. Do not install spark plugs that are either hotter or colder than those specified for the vehicle. Installing spark plugs of another type can severely damage the engine.

➡Check the gap of all new and reconditioned spark plugs before installation. The pre-set gaps may have changed during handling. Use a round feeler gage to ensure an accurate check. Installing the spark plugs with the wrong gap can cause poor engine performance and may even damage the engine.

5. Ensure that the spark plug is equivalent to the spark plug gap of 0.0433 inch.
6. Be sure that the spark plug threads smoothly into the cylinder head and the spark plug is fully seated.

➡Be sure that the spark plug threads smoothly into the cylinder head and the spark plug is fully seated. Use a thread chaser, if necessary, to clean threads in the cylinder head. Cross-threading or failing to fully seat the spark plug can cause overheating of the plug, exhaust blow-by, or thread damage.

7. Install the spark plug. Tighten the spark plug to 15 ft. lbs. (20 Nm).
8. Install the ignition coil(s). Refer to Ignition Coils, removal & installation.

3.8L Engine

➡When removing the spark plugs, work on 1 at a time. Don't start by removing the plug wires all at once because, unless you number them, they may get mixed. Take time to number the wires with tape before removing them.

✳✳ WARNING

If the vehicle has been run recently, allow the engine to thoroughly cool. Attempting to remove the plugs from a hot cylinder head could cause the plugs to seize and damage the threads in the cylinder head.

1. Before servicing the vehicle, refer to the Precautions Section.
2. Carefully twist the spark plug wire boot to loosen it, then pull upward and remove the boot from the plug. Be sure to pull on the boot and not on the wire, otherwise the connector located inside the boot may become separated.

➡A spark plug wire removal tool is recommended as it will make removal easier and help prevent damage to the boot and wire assembly.

3. Disconnect the spark plug wires.
4. Remove the spark plugs.

To install:
5. To install, reverse the removal procedure.
6. Tighten the spark plugs to 11 ft. lbs. (15 Nm).

5.3L Engine

All models were originally equipped with platinum-tipped spark plugs that can be in service for 100,000 miles (161,000 km). This holds true unless internal engine wear or damage and/or improperly operating emissions controls cause plug fouling. Remove and inspect the platinum plugs before the recommended mileage, as needed. Most platinum plugs should not be cleaned or re-gapped. If their condition is unsuitable, the plugs should be replaced.

When removing the spark plugs, work on 1 at a time. Don't start by removing the plug wires all at once because, unless you number them, they may get mixed. Take time to number the wires with tape before removing them.

1. Before servicing the vehicle, refer to the Precautions Section.
2. Disconnect the negative battery cable.

※※ WARNING

If the vehicle has been run recently, allow the engine to thoroughly cool. Attempting to remove the plugs from a hot cylinder head could cause the plugs to seize and damage the threads in the cylinder head.

3. Check for access to the plugs on your vehicle. The wheel wells of some vehicles covered by this manual are designed to allow access to the sides of the engine. A rubber cover may be draped over the opening, and it may require removal of 1 or more plastic body snap fasteners before you can move it aside for clearance. If this is your best access point, raise and support the vehicle safely then remove the front tire and wheel assemblies.

➡ **On some models, the engine cover may be removed to provide additional access to the spark plugs.**

4. Carefully twist the spark plug wire boot to loosen it, then pull upward and remove the boot from the plug. Be sure to pull on the boot and not on the wire, otherwise the connector located inside the boot may become separated.

➡ **A spark plug wire removal tool is recommended as it will make removal easier and help prevent damage to the boot and wire assembly.**

5. Using compressed air (and SAFETY GLASSES), blow any water or debris from the spark plug well to assure that no harmful contaminants are allowed to enter the combustion chamber when the spark plug is removed. If compressed air is not available, use a rag or a brush to clean the area.

➡ **Remove the spark plugs when the engine is cold, if possible, to prevent damage to the threads. If plug removal is difficult, apply a few drops of penetrating oil or silicone spray to the area around the base of the plug, and allow it a few minutes to work.**

6. Using a spark plug socket (usually a ⅝ inch socket on these engines) equipped with a rubber insert to properly hold the plug, turn the spark plug counterclockwise to loosen and remove the spark plug from the bore.

※※ WARNING

AVOID the use of a flexible extension on the socket. Use of a flexible extension may allow a shear force to be applied to the plug.

To install:

7. Inspect the spark plug boot for tears or damage. If a damaged boot is found, the spark plug wire must be replaced. Check the spark plug wires for proper resistance and/or damage.

8. Using a wire feeler gauge, check and adjust the spark plug gap. When using a gauge, the proper size should pass between the electrodes with a slight drag. The next larger size should not be able to pass while the next smaller size should pass freely.

9. Carefully thread the plug into the bore by hand. If resistance is felt before the plug is almost completely threaded, back the plug out and begin threading again. In small, hard to reach areas, an old spark plug wire and boot could be used as a threading tool. The boot will hold the plug while you twist the end of the wire and the wire is supple enough to twist before it would allow the plug to cross-thread.

※※ WARNING

Do not use the spark plug socket to thread the plugs. Always carefully thread the plug by hand or using an old plug wire to prevent the possibility of cross-threading and damaging the cylinder head bore.

10. Carefully tighten the spark plug. Refer to the Torque Specifications chart for tightening torque.

11. Apply a small amount of silicone dielectric compound to the end of the spark plug lead or inside the spark plug boot to prevent sticking, then install the boot to the spark plug and push until it clicks into place. Gently pull back on the boot to assure proper contact.

ENGINE ELECTRICAL

STARTER

REMOVAL & INSTALLATION

3.0L and 3.6L Engines
See Figure 54.

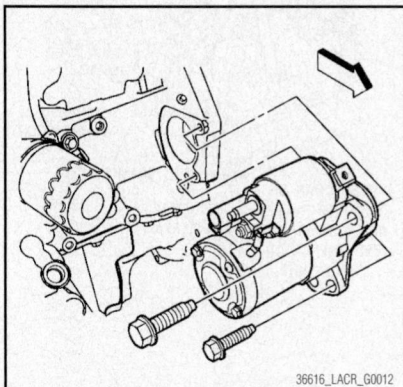

36616_LACR_G0012

Fig. 54 Starter removal—3.0L and 3.6L engines

1. Before servicing the vehicle, refer to the Precautions Section.
2. Turn OFF the ignition.
3. Disconnect the negative battery cable.
4. Remove the heat shield from the starter.
5. Raise and safely support the vehicle.
6. Disconnect the knock sensor connector.
7. Remove the battery positive nut and the engine harness connector, from the starter solenoid.
8. Remove the starter motor bolts.
9. Remove the starter motor.

To install:
10. Install the starter motor.
11. Install the starter motor mounting bolts. Tighten to 43 ft. lbs. (58 Nm).
12. Install the battery positive cable and engine harness connector to the starter. Tighten the battery positive cable nut to 18 ft. lbs. (25 Nm).

STARTING SYSTEM

13. Install the engine harness connector to the starter solenoid.
14. Install the starter heat shield and tighten the bolt to 62 inch lbs. (7 Nm).
15. Connect the knock sensor connector.

3.8L Engine
See Figure 55.

1. Before servicing the vehicle, refer to the Precautions Section.
2. Remove or disconnect the following:
   - Negative battery cable
   - Flexplate inspection cover
   - Splash shield, if equipped
   - Electrical connectors
   - Transaxle cooler line clip from the transaxle, if necessary
   - Starter motor wiring
   - Starter motor bolts
   - Starter

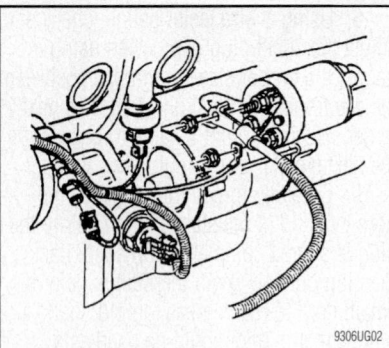

Fig. 55 Starter in place with wiring—3.8L engine

To install:

3. Install or connect the following:
- Starter and torque the bolts to 32 ft. lbs. (43 Nm)
- Wiring and torque the B-terminal nut to 89 inch lbs. (10 Nm) and the S-terminal nut to 22 inch lbs. (3 Nm).
- Flexplate inspection cover and torque the bolts to 62 inch lbs. (7 Nm)

- Splash shield
- Negative battery cable

5.3L Engine

See Figure 56.

1. Before servicing the vehicle, refer to the Precautions Section.
2. Disconnect the negative battery cable.
3. Remove the starter solenoid BAT terminal nut and remove the positive battery cable from the starter motor.
4. Remove the engine harness terminal from the starter motor.
5. Disconnect the starter motor electrical connector.
6. Remove the air cleaner assembly.
7. Remove the starter motor bolts and starter motor.

To install:

8. Position the starter motor to the engine.
9. Install the starter bolts and tighten the bolts to 37 ft. lbs. (50 Nm).
10. Connect the starter motor electrical connector.

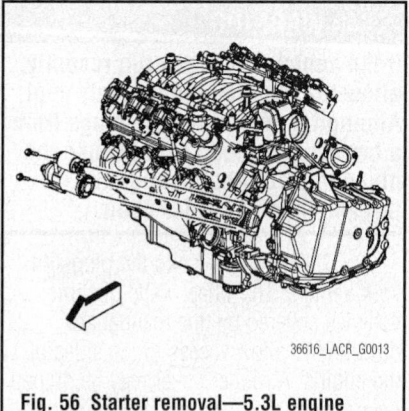

Fig. 56 Starter removal—5.3L engine

11. Install the engine harness terminal to the starter motor.
12. Install the positive battery cable (2) and the starter solenoid BAT terminal nut to the starter motor and tighten the terminal nut to 89 inch lbs. (10 Nm).
13. Install the air cleaner assembly.
14. Connect the negative battery cable.

ENGINE MECHANICAL

ACCESSORY DRIVE BELTS

ACCESSORY BELT ROUTING

See Figures 57 through 59.

INSPECTION

Inspect the drive belt for signs of glazing or cracking. A glazed belt will be perfectly smooth from slippage, while a good belt will have a slight texture of fabric visible. Cracks will usually start at the inner edge of the belt and run outward. All worn or damaged drive belts should be replaced immediately.

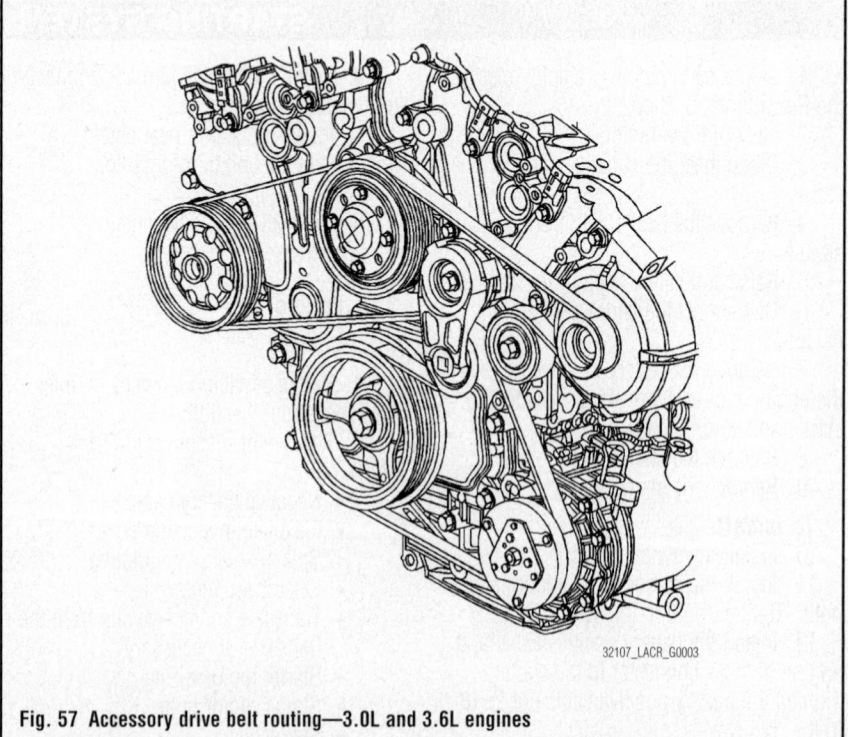

Fig. 57 Accessory drive belt routing—3.0L and 3.6L engines

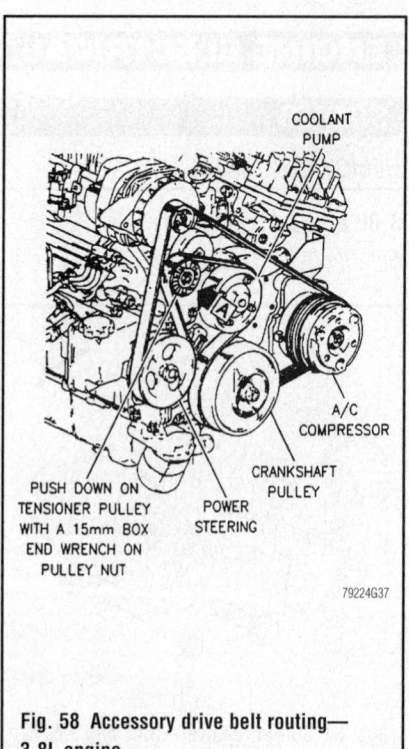

Fig. 58 Accessory drive belt routing—3.8L engine

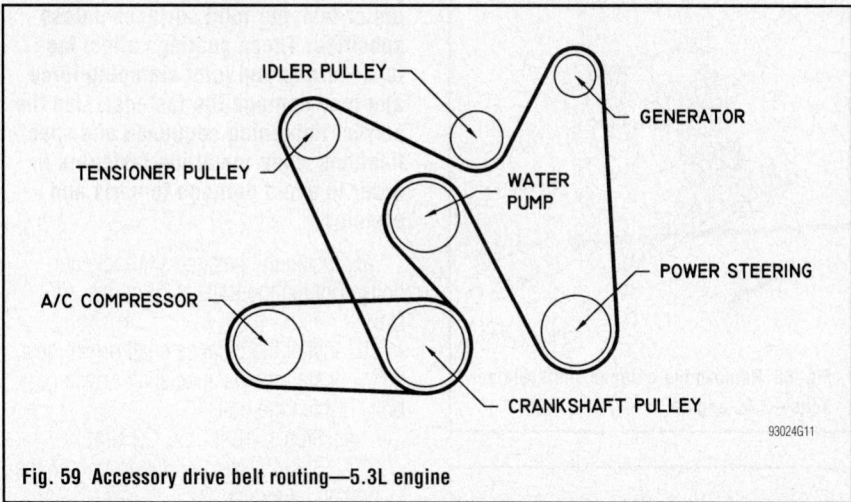

Fig. 59 Accessory drive belt routing—5.3L engine

ADJUSTMENT

These vehicles are equipped with a single serpentine belt and spring loaded tensioner. The proper belt adjustment is automatically maintained by the tensioner, therefore, no periodic adjustment is needed. If the pointer is past the scale on the tensioner gauge, replace the belt. If the correct belt tension cannot be achieved, make sure the correct belt is installed. If the correct tension is still not achieved, check for proper mounting on all accessory drive pulleys.

REMOVAL & INSTALLATION

3.0L and 3.6L Engines

See Figure 60.

1. Before servicing the vehicle, refer to the Precautions Section.
2. Remove the air cleaner assembly.
3. Remove the right engine mount bracket.
4. Install a breaker bar to the drive belt tensioner.

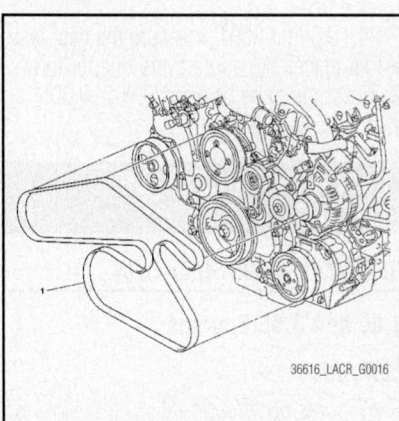

Fig. 60 Accessory drive belt removal—3.0L and 3.6L engines

5. Rotate the drive belt tensioner counterclockwise to release the spring tension.
6. Remove the accessory drive belt from the alternator.
7. Slowly release the accessory drive belt tensioner.
8. Remove the accessory drive belt from the accessory drive pulleys.

To install:

9. Install the accessory drive belt to the accessory drive pulleys.
10. Rotate the accessory drive belt tensioner clockwise.
11. Install the accessory drive belt to the alternator.

➡**Ensure the accessory drive belt is properly aligned and seated into the grooves of the accessory drive pulleys.**

12. Slowly release the accessory drive belt tensioner
13. Install the right engine mount bracket and tighten to 74 ft. lbs. (100 Nm).
14. Install the air cleaner assembly.

3.8L Engine

See Figure 58.

1. Before servicing the vehicle, refer to the Precautions Section.
2. Install a 15mm box end wrench to the drive belt tensioner pulley nut.
3. Rotate the drive belt tensioner to release the spring tension.
4. Remove the accessory drive belt from the alternator.
5. Slowly release the accessory drive belt tensioner.
6. Remove the accessory drive belt from the accessory drive pulleys.

To install:

7. Install the accessory drive belt to the accessory drive pulleys.

8. Rotate the accessory drive belt tensioner with a 15mm box end wrench.
9. Install the accessory drive belt to the alternator.

➡**Ensure the accessory drive belt is properly aligned and seated into the grooves of the accessory drive pulleys.**

10. Slowly release the accessory drive belt tensioner

5.3L Engine

See Figures 59 and 61.

Special Tools:
• EN-47988: Serpentine Belt Tension Unloader

1. Before servicing the vehicle, refer to the Precautions Section.
2. Remove the passenger side diagonal brace, if more clearance is required.
3. Reposition the Underhood Bussed Electrical Center (UBEC), if more clearance is required.
4. Install the EN-47988, to the drive belt tensioner.
5. Rotate the EN-47988 clockwise in order to relieve the tension on the belt tensioner.
6. Remove the drive belt from over the power steering pump pulley.
7. Slowly release the EN-47988.
8. Remove the EN-47988 from the belt tensioner.
9. Remove the drive belt from around all the other pulleys.
10. Clean and inspect the belt surfaces of all the pulleys.

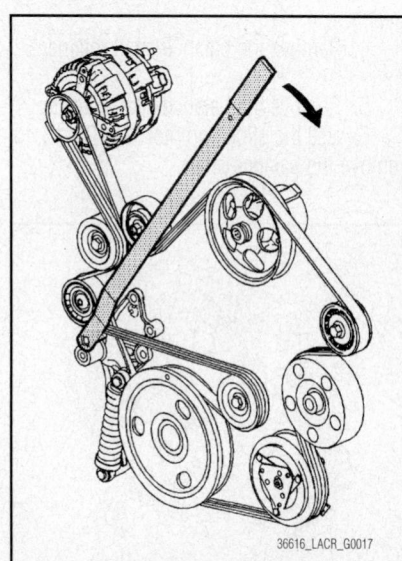

Fig. 61 Using the EN-47988, Serpentine Belt Tension Unloader, to remove the accessory drive belt—5.3L engine

To install:

11. Install and route the drive belt around all the pulleys except for the power steering pump pulley.

➡Ensure that when installing the EN-47988 to the belt tensioner that the EN-47988 is NOT installed above the drive belt.

12. Ensure that when installing the EN-47988, to the belt tensioner that the EN-47988 is installed below the drive belt.

13. Rotate the EN-47988 clockwise in order to relieve the tension on the belt tensioner.

14. Ensure that the drive belt is still properly routed around all the other pulleys, then install the drive belt over the power steering pump pulley.

15. Slowly release the EN-47988.

16. Remove the EN-47988 from the belt tensioner.

17. Inspect the drive belt for proper installation and alignment.

18. Position the UBEC, if required.

19. Install the passenger side diagonal brace, if required.

BALANCE SHAFT

REMOVAL & INSTALLATION

3.8L Engine

See Figures 62 through 65.

1. Before servicing the vehicle, refer to the Precautions Section.

2. Remove the balance shaft driven gear bolt.

3. Remove the balance shaft driven gear.

4. Remove the balance shaft retainer bolts.

5. Remove the balance shaft retainer.

6. Use the slide hammer, J 6125-1B, to remove the balance shaft.

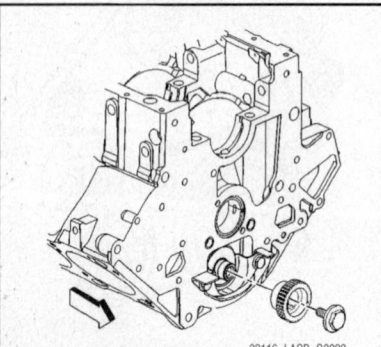

Fig. 62 Remove the balance shaft driven gear bolt—3.8L engine

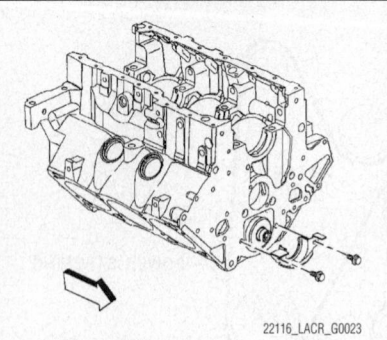

Fig. 63 Remove the balance shaft retainer bolts—3.8L engine

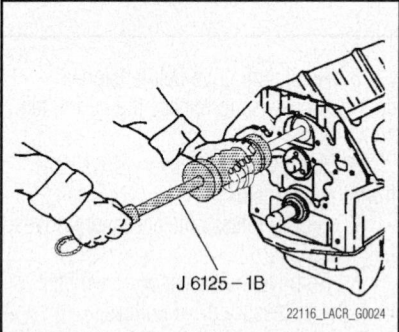

Fig. 64 Use J 6125-1B to remove the balance shaft—3.8L engine

To install:

7. Use J 21465-13 and J 36996 to install the balance shaft into the engine block.

8. Install the balance shaft retainer.

➡Use the correct fastener in the correct location. Replacement fasteners must be the correct part number for that application. Fasteners requiring replacement or fasteners requiring the use of thread locking compound or sealant are identified in the service procedure. Do not use paints, lubricants, or corrosion inhibitors on fasten-

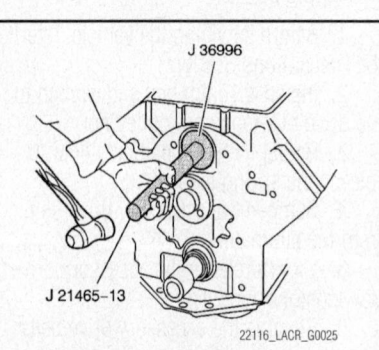

Fig. 65 Use J 21465-13 and J 36996 to install the balance shaft into the engine block—3.8L engine

ers or fastener joint surfaces unless specified. These coatings affect fastener torque and joint clamping force and may damage the fastener. Use the correct tightening sequence and specifications when installing fasteners in order to avoid damage to parts and systems.

9. Install the balance shaft retainer bolts. Tighten the bolts to 22 ft. lbs. (30 Nm).

10. Install the balance shaft driven gear.

11. Install the balance shaft driven gear bolt. Tighten the bolt:

a. Step 1: 16 ft. lbs. (22 Nm).

b. Step 2: Use J 45059 to tighten the bolt an additional 70°.

12. Using J 8001, measure the balance shaft end play. End play must not exceed 0.008 inch (0.028mm).

13. Using J 8001, measure the balance shaft radial play at the rear. Radial play must be between 0.0005–0.0047 inch (0.0127–0.119mm).

14. Install the balance shaft drive gear.

15. Install the camshaft sprocket.

16. Turn the camshaft so the timing mark on the camshaft sprocket is straight down.

17. Remove the camshaft sprocket and balance shaft drive gear.

18. Turn the balance shaft so the timing mark on the balance shaft driven gear points straight down.

19. Partially install the balance shaft drive gear so the gear teeth are not engaged.

20. Align the marks on the balance shaft driven gear and the balance shaft drive gear. Do this by turning the balance shaft.

21. Once the marks are aligned, fully seat the balance shaft drive gear and engage the gear teeth.

22. Turn the crankshaft so the number one piston is at Top Dead Center (TDC).

23. Install the timing chain and camshaft sprocket.

24. Using J 8001, measure the gear lash at four places. Measure every quarter turn. Gear lash must be between 0.002–0.005 inch (0.050–0.127mm).

CAMSHAFT AND VALVE LIFTERS

REMOVAL & INSTALLATION

3.0L and 3.6L Engines

Left Side

See Figures 66 through 74.

1. Before servicing the vehicle, refer to the Precautions Section.

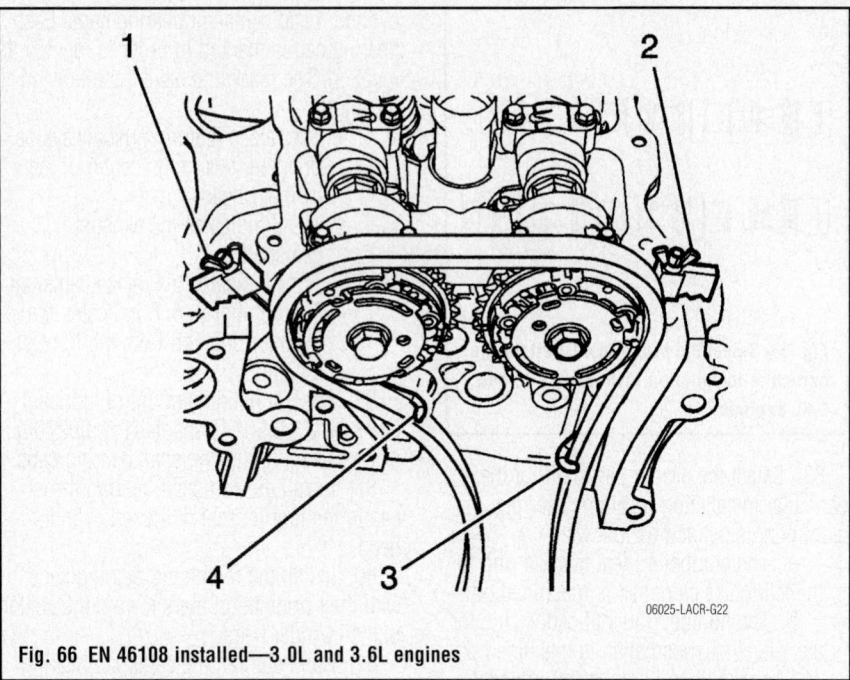

Fig. 66 EN 46108 installed—3.0L and 3.6L engines

2. Remove the upper intake manifold with the lower intake manifold.

3. Disconnect the ignition coil electrical connectors.

4. Remove the wiring harness from the side of the camshaft cover by sliding the conduit down and outboard.

5. Remove the wiring conduit retainers from the camshaft cover by rotating the wiring harness conduit retainers counterclockwise.

➡It is not necessary to disconnect the engine front cover electrical connectors.

6. Remove the wiring harness from the front of the camshaft cover.

7. Reposition and secure the wiring harnesses away from the camshaft cover in order to provide clearance.

8. Remove the ignition coils.

9. Loosen the left engine strut bracket.

10. Loosen the left engine strut bracket to cylinder head bolts.

11. Remove the camshaft cover bolts and camshaft cover.

12. Remove and discard the camshaft cover seal and grommets. DO NOT reuse.

13. Remove the camshaft sensors.

➡Do not disconnect the power steering fluid lines/hoses from the reservoir.

14. Remove the power steering fluid reservoir bolts and reposition the power steering fluid reservoir in order to provide access.

15. Remove the Camshaft Position (CMP) actuator valve electrical connector.

16. Remove the camshaft position actuator solenoid.

17. Remove the crankshaft damper.

18. Rotate the crankshaft until the camshafts are in a neutral (low tension)

position. The camshaft flats will be parallel with the camshaft cover rail

✸✸ WARNING

A wrench must be used on the hex of the camshaft when loosening or tightening in order to prevent component damage. Failure to prevent the torque reaction against the timing drive chain can lead to timing drive chain failure.

➡Use an open-end wrench at the camshaft hex to prevent camshaft/engine rotation. DO NOT remove the camshaft position actuator bolt at this time.

19. Loosen the camshaft position actuator bolt.

➡Ensure that the tips of tool EN 46108 are fully engaged into the timing chain.

20. Install tool EN 46108 in order to retain the timing chain. Firmly tighten the tool nuts.

➡Ensure that the camshaft timing chain and the camshaft position actuators are marked for proper assembly.

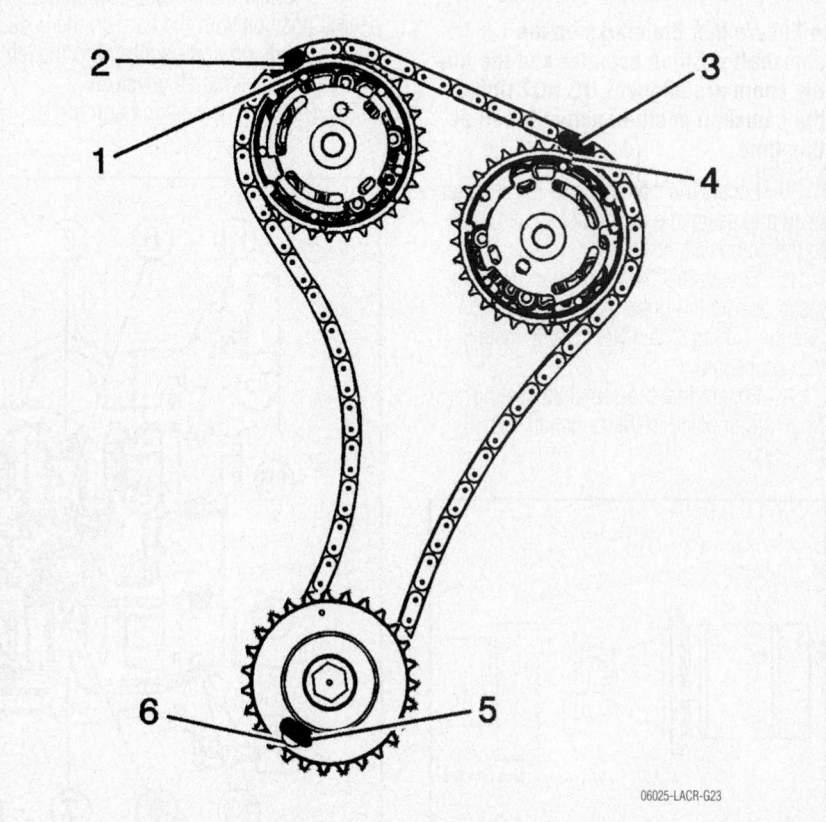

Fig. 67 Mark the timing chain and the respective locations on the camshaft position actuators—3.0L and 3.6L engines

21. Mark the timing chain and the respective locations on the camshaft position actuators.

22. Remove the camshaft position actuator bolt.

23. Remove the timing chain from the sprockets.

24. Position the camshaft lobes in a neutral position.

25. Observe the markings on the bearing caps. Each bearing cap is marked in order to identify its location. The markings have the following meanings:
- The raised feature must always be oriented toward the center of the cylinder head
- The E indicates the exhaust camshaft
- The I indicates the intake camshaft
- The number indicates the journal position from the front of the engine

26. Remove the camshaft bearing cap bolts.

27. Remove the camshaft bearing caps.

28. Remove the camshafts.

29. Replace the camshaft bearing caps and bolts.

To install:

➡**Ensure that the marks on the camshaft position actuator and the timing chain are aligned. DO NOT tighten the camshaft position actuator bolt at this time.**

30. Locate the camshafts to the cylinder head and assemble the camshaft actuators to the camshafts.

31. Ensure that the crankshaft is in the stage one timing drive assembly position. See the Timing Chain Removal & Installation procedure.

32. Ensure that the camshaft sealing rings are in place in the camshaft grooves.

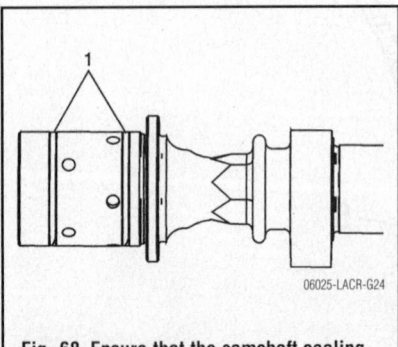

Fig. 68 Ensure that the camshaft sealing rings (1) are in place in the camshaft grooves—3.0L and 3.6L engines

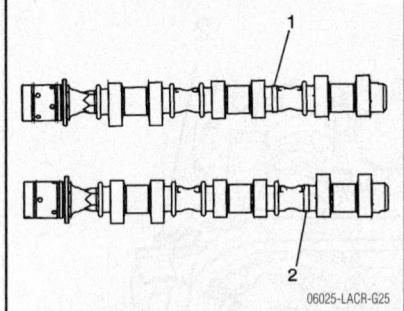
06025-LACR-G25

Fig. 69 Select the proper camshaft for the particular installation location—3.0L and 3.6L engines

33. Select the proper camshaft for the particular installation location. The ring placement is defined as follows:

a. The number 4 identification ring for the left intake camshaft is machined off.

b. The number 5 identification ring for the left exhaust camshaft is machined off.

34. Apply a liberal amount of lubricant GM P/N 12345501 (Canadian P/N 992704), or equivalent, to the camshaft journals and the left cylinder head camshaft carriers.

35. Place the left intake and left exhaust camshafts in position in the left cylinder head.

36. Position the camshaft lobes in a neutral position with the flats on the back of the camshafts up and parallel with the left cylinder head camshaft cover rail.

37. Observe the markings on the left cylinder head camshaft bearing caps. Each bearing cap is marked in order to identify its location. The markings have the following meanings:
- The raised feature must always be oriented toward the center of the cylinder head.
- The E indicates the exhaust camshaft.
- The I indicates the intake camshaft.
- The number 2, 4, 6 indicates the cylinder position from the front of the engine.

38. Apply a liberal amount of lubricant GM P/N 12345501 (Canadian P/N 992704) or equivalent to the camshaft bearing caps.

39. Install the camshaft bearing thrust cap in the first journal of the left cylinder head.

40. Install the remaining bearing caps with their orientation mark toward the center of the cylinder head.

41. Hand start all the camshaft bearing cap bolts.

42. Tighten the camshaft bearing cap bolts in the sequence shown. Tighten the camshaft bearing cap bolts in sequence to 89 inch lbs. (10 Nm).

43. Loosen the center intake camshaft bearing cap bolts 1, 2 and the center exhaust camshaft bearing cap bolts 3, 4.

44. Retighten the center camshaft bearing cap bolts 1, 2, 3, 4. Retighten the camshaft bearing cap bolts to 89 inch lbs. (10 Nm).

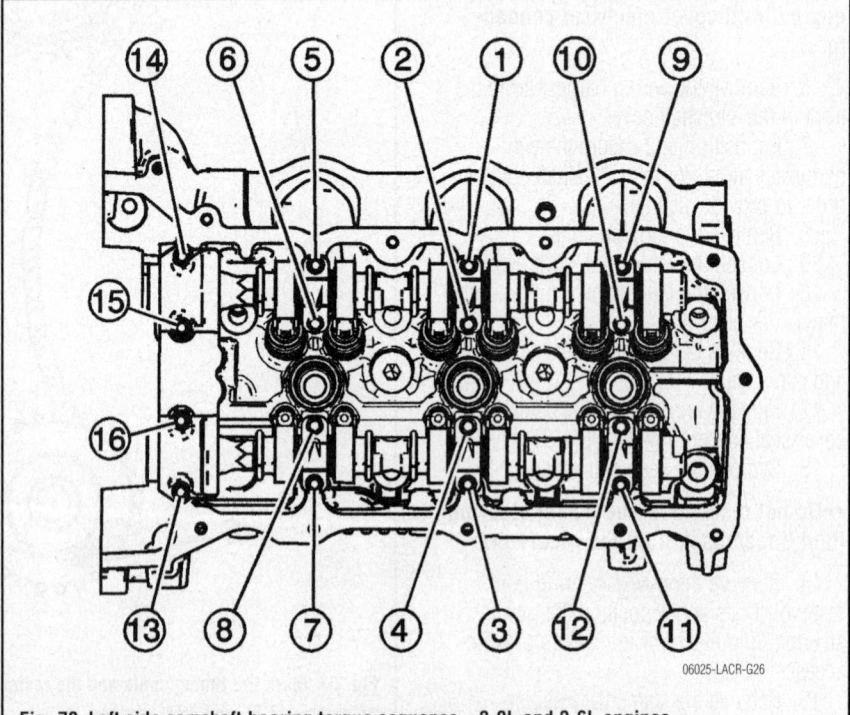
06025-LACR-G26

Fig. 70 Left side camshaft bearing torque sequence—3.0L and 3.6L engines

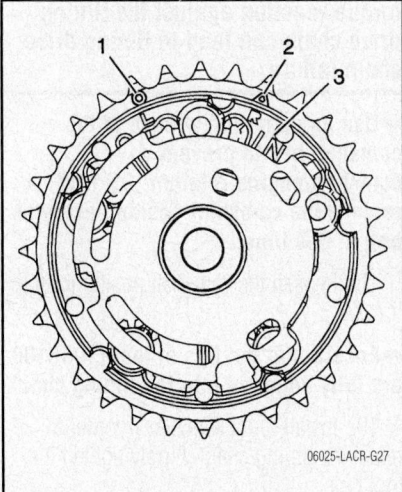

Fig. 71 Left intake CMP actuator position—3.0L and 3.6L engines

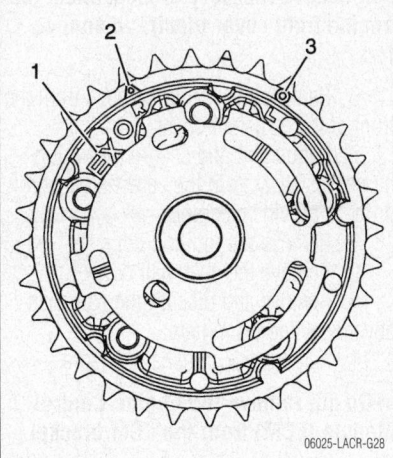

Fig. 72 Left exhaust CMP actuator position—3.0L and 3.6L engines

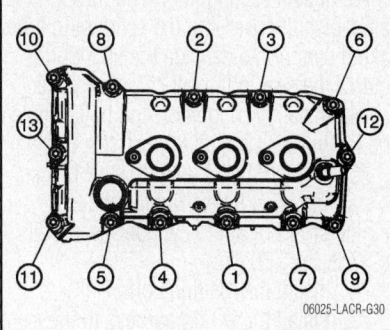

Fig. 74 Left side camshaft cover torque sequence—3.0L and 3.6L engines

✷✷ WARNING

Notice: A wrench must be used on the hex of the camshaft when loosening or tightening in order to prevent component damage. Failure to prevent the torque reaction against the timing drive chain can lead to timing drive chain failure.

➡ **Use an open-end wrench at the camshaft hex to prevent camshaft/engine rotation.**

45. Install and tighten the camshaft position actuators. Tighten the camshaft position actuator bolt to 43 ft. lbs. (58 Nm).

46. Install the CMP sensor.

47. Install the CMP sensor bolt. Tighten the CMP sensor bolt to 89 inch lbs. (10 Nm).

48. Install the CMP sensor electrical connector.

49. Install the power steering fluid reservoir. Tighten the M6 bolt to 80 inch lbs. (9 Nm). Tighten the M8 bolt to 18 ft. lbs. (25 Nm).

50. Install the CMP actuator valve.

51. Install the CMP actuator valve bolt. Tighten the CMP actuator valve bolt to 89 inch lbs. (10 Nm).

52. Install the CMP actuator valve electrical connector.

53. Install the camshaft sensors.

54. Install the crankshaft damper.

55. Install a NEW camshaft cover seal and NEW grommets.

56. Install a NEW camshaft cover seal and NEW grommets.

57. Install the camshaft cover.

58. Tighten the left engine strut bracket to cylinder head bolts. Tighten the left engine strut bracket to cylinder head bolts to 37 ft. lbs. (50 Nm).

59. Install the ignition coils.

60. Install the wiring harness to the front of the camshaft cover.

61. Install the wiring harness conduit retainers to the wiring harness conduit.

62. Install the wiring harness to the side of the camshaft cover.

63. Connect the ignition coil electrical connectors.

64. Install tool EN 46101 onto the spark plug tubes of the left cylinder head.

65. Install the camshaft cover bolt grommets prior to installing the camshaft cover bolts.

66. Wipe the camshaft cover sealing surface on the left cylinder head with a clean, lint-free cloth.

67. Place a bead 0.3150 inch (8mm) in diameter by 0.1575 inch (4mm) in height of RTV sealant, GM P/N 12378521 (Canadian P/N 88901148) or equivalent, on the engine front cover split lines.

68. Place the left camshaft cover into position onto the left cylinder head.

69. Loosely install the left camshaft cover bolts.

70. Tighten the left camshaft cover bolts in the sequence shown. Tighten the left camshaft cover bolts in the sequence to 89 inch lbs. (10 Nm).

71. Remove the tool from the spark plug tubes of the left cylinder head.

72. Install the NEW spark plugs into the left cylinder head. Tighten the spark plugs to 15 ft. lbs. (20 Nm).

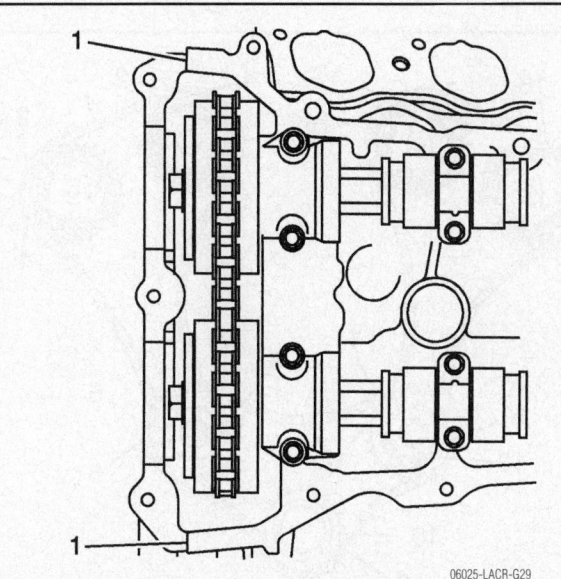

Fig. 73 Place a bead 0.3150 inch (8mm) in diameter by 0.1575 inch (4mm) in height of RTV sealant, GM P/N 12378521 (Canadian P/N 88901148) or equivalent, on the engine front cover split lines (1)—3.0L and 3.6L engines

73. Install each ignition coil through the left camshaft cover into the spark plug tube taking care not to damage the spark plug and/or the seal in the left camshaft cover.

74. Install each ignition coil bolt. Tighten the ignition coil bolt to 89 inch lbs. (10 Nm).

75. Tighten the left engine strut bracket to cylinder head bolts. Tighten the left engine strut bracket to cylinder head bolts to 37 ft. lbs. (50 Nm).

76. Install the ignition coils.

77. Install the wiring harness to the front of the camshaft cover.

78. Install the wiring harness conduit retainers to the wiring harness conduit.

79. Install the wiring harness to the side of the camshaft cover.

80. Connect the ignition coil electrical connectors.

81. Install the upper intake manifold with the lower intake manifold.

Right Side

See Figures 75 through 77.

1. Before servicing the vehicle, refer to the Precautions Section.

2. Remove the upper intake manifold with the lower intake manifold.

3. Disconnect the ignition coil electrical connectors.

4. Remove the wiring harness from the side of the camshaft cover by sliding the conduit down and outboard.

5. Remove the wiring conduit retainers from the camshaft cover by rotating the wiring harness conduit retainers counter-clockwise.

➡It is not necessary to disconnect the engine front cover electrical connectors.

6. Remove the wiring harness from the front of the camshaft cover.

7. Reposition and secure the wiring harnesses away from the camshaft cover in order to provide clearance.

8. Remove the ignition coils.

9. Remove the camshaft cover.

10. Remove and discard the camshaft cover seal and grommets.

11. Remove the camshaft sensors.

➡Do not remove the Engine Control Module (ECM) from the ECM bracket.

Do not remove the ECM redundant ground wire from the ECM.

12. Remove the ECM bracket bolts and reposition the ECM bracket in order to provide access.

13. Remove the Camshaft Position (CMP) actuator valve electrical connector.

14. Remove the CMP actuator valve bolt.

15. Remove the CMP actuator valve.

16. Remove the crankshaft damper.

17. Rotate the crankshaft until the camshafts are in a neutral (low tension) position. The camshaft flats will be parallel with the camshaft cover rail.

✳✳ WARNING

A wrench must be used on the hex of the camshaft when loosening or tightening in order to prevent component damage. Failure to prevent the

torque reaction against the timing drive chain can lead to timing drive chain failure.

➡Use an open-end wrench at the camshaft hex to prevent camshaft/engine rotation. DO NOT remove the camshaft position actuator bolt at this time.

18. Loosen the camshaft position actuator bolt.

➡Ensure that the tips of tool EN 46108 are fully engaged into the timing chain.

19. Install tool EN 46108 in order to retain the timing chain. Firmly tighten the tool nuts.

➡Ensure that the camshaft timing chain and the camshaft position actuators are marked for proper assembly.

20. Mark the timing chain and the respective locations on camshaft position actuators.

21. Remove the camshaft position actuator bolt.

22. Position the camshaft lobes in a neutral position.

23. Observe the markings on the bearing caps. Each bearing cap is marked in order to identify its location. The markings have the following meanings:

- The raised feature must always be oriented toward the center of the cylinder head
- The I indicates the intake camshaft
- The E indicates the exhaust camshaft
- The number indicates the journal position from the front of the engine

24. Remove the camshaft bearing cap bolts.

25. Remove the camshaft bearing caps.

26. Remove the camshafts.

27. Replace the camshaft bearing caps and bolts.

To install:

➡Ensure that the marks on the camshaft position actuators and the timing chain are aligned. DO NOT tighten the camshaft position actuator bolt at this time.

28. Locate the camshafts to the cylinder head and assemble the camshaft actuators to the camshafts.

29. Ensure that the crankshaft is in the stage one timing drive assembly position. Refer to the Timing Chain Removal & Installation procedure.

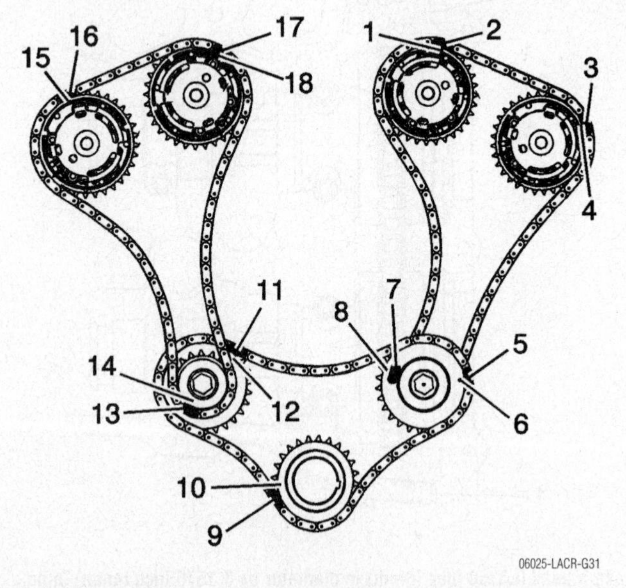

06025-LACR-G31

Fig. 75 Ensure that the camshaft timing chain and the camshaft position actuators are marked for proper assembly—3.0L and 3.6L engines (right side)

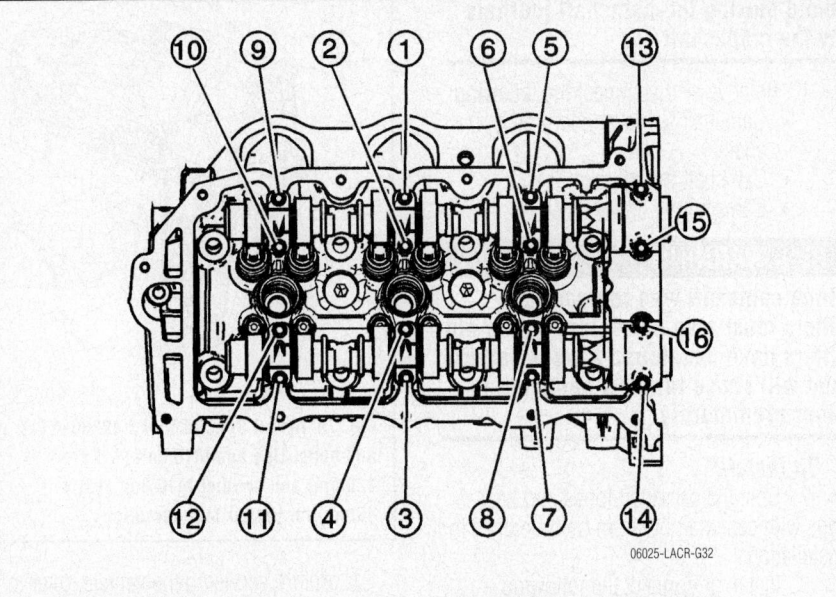

Fig. 76 Right side camshaft bearing cap torque sequence—3.0L and 3.6L engines

30. Ensure that the camshaft sealing rings are in place in the camshaft grooves.

31. Select the proper camshaft for the particular installation location. The ring placement is defined as follows:

    a. The number 2 identification ring for the right exhaust camshaft is machined off.

    b. The number 3 identification ring for the right intake camshaft is machined off.

32. Apply a liberal amount of lubricant GM P/N 12345501 (Canadian P/N 992704), or equivalent, to the camshaft journals and the right cylinder head camshaft carriers.

33. Place the right intake and right exhaust camshafts in position in the right cylinder head.

34. Position the camshaft lobes in a neutral position with the flats on the back of the camshafts up and parallel with the right cylinder head camshaft cover rail.

35. Observe the markings on the right cylinder head camshaft bearing caps. Each bearing cap is marked in order to identify its location. The markings have the following meanings:

- The raised feature must always be oriented toward the center of the cylinder head
- The I indicates the intake camshaft
- The E indicates the exhaust camshaft
- The number 1, 3, 5 indicates the cylinder position from the front of the engine

36. Apply a liberal amount of lubricant GM P/N 12345501 (Canadian P/N 992704), or equivalent, to the camshaft bearing caps.

37. Install the camshaft bearing thrust caps in the first journal of the right cylinder head.

38. Install the remaining bearing caps with their orientation mark toward the center of the cylinder head.

39. Hand start all the camshaft bearing cap bolts.

40. Tighten the camshaft bearing cap bolts in the sequence shown. Tighten the camshaft bearing cap bolts in sequence to 89 inch lbs. (10 Nm).

41. Loosen the center intake camshaft bearing cap bolts and the center exhaust camshaft bearing cap bolts.

42. Retighten the center camshaft bearing cap bolts. Retighten the camshaft bearing cap bolts to 89 inch lbs. (10 Nm).

43. Install the crankshaft damper.

✳✳ WARNING

A wrench must be used on the hex of the camshaft when loosening or tightening in order to prevent component damage. Failure to prevent the torque reaction against the timing drive chain can lead to timing drive chain failure.

➡**Use an open-end wrench at the camshaft hex to prevent camshaft/engine rotation.**

44. Install the CMP actuator valve.

45. Install the CMP actuator valve bolt. Tighten the CMP actuator valve bolt to 89 inch lbs. (10 Nm).

46. Install the CMP actuator valve electrical connector.

47. Install the ECM bracket with the ECM.

48. Ensure the proper camshaft position actuator is installed. Observe the body of the camshaft position actuator for the IN or EX marking.

49. Ensure the proper timing mark is used. Observe the outer ring of the camshaft position actuator for the R and triangle marking. The marking is for alignment to the highlighted timing chain link on the right side of the engine.

50. Use an open wrench on the hex cast into the camshaft in order to prevent camshaft rotation when tightening the camshaft position actuator bolt.

51. Install the right intake camshaft position actuator.

52. Install the camshaft position actuator bolt. Tighten the camshaft position actuator bolt to 43 ft. lbs. (58 Nm).

53. Install the intake camshaft position actuator solenoid.

54. Install the camshaft sensors.

55. Install a NEW camshaft cover seal and NEW grommets.

56. Install tool EN 46101 onto the spark plug tubes of the right cylinder head.

57. Install the camshaft cover bolt grommets prior to installing the camshaft cover bolts.

58. Wipe the camshaft cover sealing surface on the right cylinder head with a clean, lint-free cloth.

59. Place a bead 0.3150 inch (8mm) in diameter by 0.1575 inch (4mm) in height of RTV sealant, GM P/N 12378521 (Canadian P/N 88901148), or equivalent, on the engine front cover split lines.

60. Place the right camshaft cover into position onto the right cylinder head.

61. Loosely install the right camshaft cover bolts.

62. Tighten the right camshaft cover bolts in the sequence shown. Tighten the right camshaft cover bolts in the sequence to 89 inch lbs. (10 Nm).

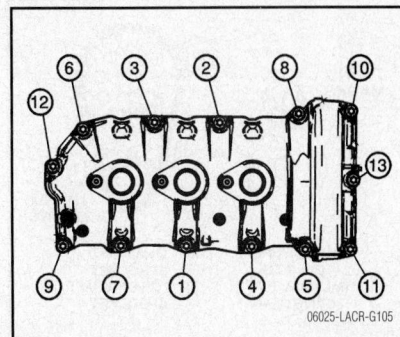

Fig. 77 Right side camshaft cover torque sequence—3.0L and 3.6L engines

63. Remove tool EN 46101 from the spark plug tubes of the right cylinder head.

64. Install the NEW spark plugs into the right cylinder head. Tighten the spark plugs to 15 ft. lbs. (20 Nm).

65. Install each ignition coil through the right camshaft cover into the spark plug tube taking care not to damage the spark plug and/or the seal in the right camshaft cover.

66. Install each ignition coil bolt. Tighten the ignition coil bolt to 89 inch lbs. (10 Nm).

67. Install the upper intake manifold with the lower intake manifold.

3.8L Engine

See Figure 78.

1. Before servicing the vehicle, refer to the Precautions Section.

2. Relieve the fuel system pressure.

3. Remove the engine and mount it on an engine stand.

4. Remove or disconnect the following:
- Negative battery cable
- Intake manifold
- Rocker arm covers
- Rocker arm assemblies
- Pushrods
- Lifters and guides

➡ **A magnet may be helpful when pulling the lifters out of their bores. Identify all parts as they are removed, so they can be reinstalled in their original locations.**

- Crankshaft damper
- Timing chain front cover

5. Set the engine to Top Dead Center (TDC) No. 1 cylinder (firing position) to align the timing marks, before disassembling the timing chain and sprockets.

☀☀ WARNING

Align the timing marks of the camshaft and crankshaft sprockets to

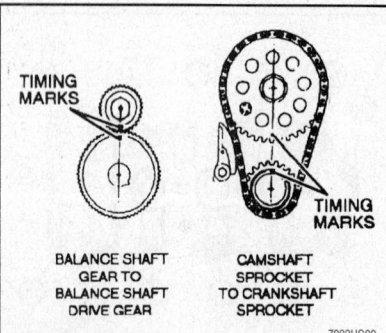

Fig. 78 The timing marks should face each other when the chain and gears are installed properly—3.8L engine

avoid burring the camshaft journals by the crankshaft.

6. Remove or disconnect the following:
- Camshaft sprocket and timing chain
- Camshaft thrust plate
- Camshaft

☀☀ WARNING

If the camshaft was replaced the lifters must also be replaced. The old lifters have developed a wear pattern and will cause the new camshaft to wear prematurely.

To install:

7. Coat the camshaft lobes and bearings with camshaft break-in prelube prior to installation.

8. Install or connect the following:
- Camshaft
- Camshaft thrust plate. Torque the bolts to 10 ft. lbs. (14 Nm).
- Camshaft sprocket and timing chain with timing marks aligned. Torque the camshaft sprocket bolt to 74 ft. lbs. (100 Nm), plus an additional 90° turn.
- Timing chain front cover
- Crankshaft damper. Torque the mounting bolt to 111 ft. lbs. (150 Nm). plus an additional 76° turn.

9. Coat the valve lifters with camshaft break-in prelube.

10. Install or connect the following:
- Valve lifters
- Lifter guides and lifter guide retainer. Torque the retainer mounting bolts to 22 ft. lbs. (30 Nm).
- Pushrods and rocker arms. Torque the rocker arm bolts to 11 ft. lbs. (15 Nm) plus an additional 90° turn.
- Rocker arm covers
- Intake manifold
- Engine
- Negative battery cable

11. Verify that all fluid levels are full and correct.

12. Start the engine and check for leaks. Check engine operation.

5.3L Engine

See Figures 79 through 88.

Special Tools:
- EN 46330: Timing Belt Tensioner Retaining Pin
- J 42386-A: Flywheel Holding Tool
- J 45059: Angle Meter

➡ **If camshaft replacement is required, the valve lifters must also be replaced.**

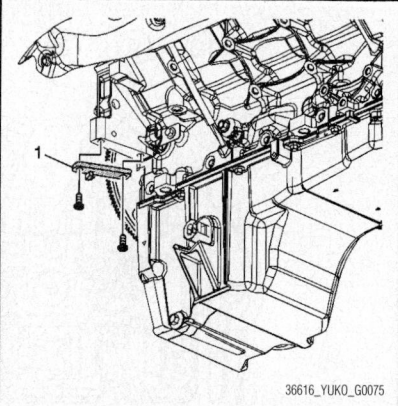

36616_YUKO_G0075

Fig. 79 Install Special Tool J 42386-A (1) and bolts. Use one M10 bolt (1.5 x 120mm) and another M10 bolt (1.5 x 45mm) for proper tool operation

1. Before servicing the vehicle, refer to the Precautions Section.

2. Remove the negative battery cable.

3. Remove the radiator support.

4. Remove the valve lifters, as follows:

a. Remove the cylinder head and gasket. Refer to Cylinder Head, removal & installation.

b. Remove the valve lifter guide bolts.

c. Remove the valve lifter guides with the lifters. Note the installed position of the guides. The notched area of the guides is to align with the locating tab on the engine block.

d. Remove the valve lifters from the guide.

e. Organize or mark the components so that they can be installed in the same location from which they were removed, if required.

f. Clean and inspect the valve lifters, if required.

5. Remove the engine front cover. Refer to Timing Chain Cover and Seal, removal & installation.

6. Remove the starter motor. Refer to Starter, removal & installation.

7. Install Special Tool J 42386-A and bolts. Use one M10 bolt (1.5 x 120mm) and another M10 bolt (1.5 x 45mm) for proper tool operation. Tighten the J 42386-A bolts to 37 ft. lbs. (50 Nm).

➡ **Ensure that the teeth of the J 42386-A mesh with the teeth of the engine flywheel.**

8. Rotate the crankshaft sprocket until the Camshaft Position (CMP) actuator alignment mark and the crankshaft sprocket alignment mark are aligned.

9. Remove and discard the CMP actuator solenoid valve.

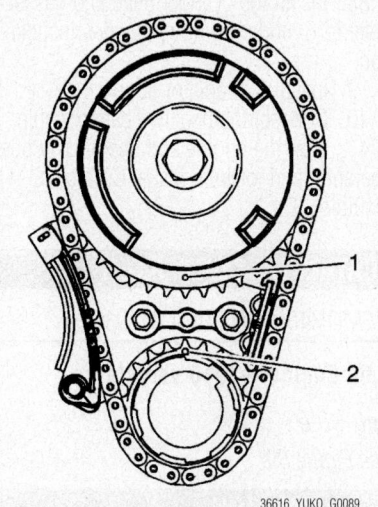

Fig. 80 Ensure the timing marks are properly aligned. The mark on the camshaft sprocket (1) should be located in the 6 o'clock position and the mark on the crankshaft sprocket (2) should be located in the 12 o'clock position

✳✳ WARNING

Do not turn the crankshaft assembly after the timing chain has been removed in order to prevent damage to the piston assemblies or the valves.

10. Remove the CMP actuator and timing chain.
11. Remove the camshaft retainer bolts and retainer.

✳✳ WARNING

All camshaft journals are the same diameter, so care must be used in removing or installing the camshaft to avoid damage to the camshaft bearings.

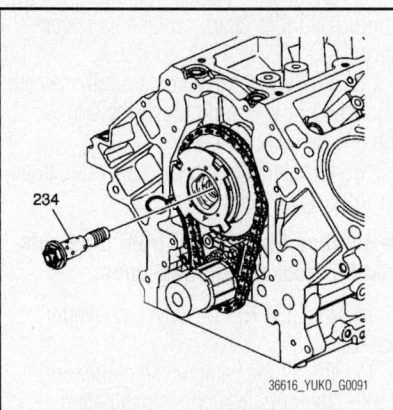

Fig. 81 Remove and discard the CMP actuator solenoid valve (234)

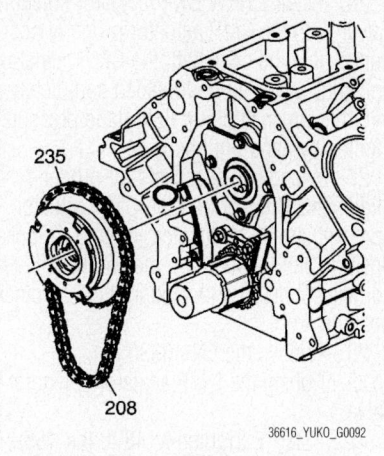

Fig. 82 Remove the CMP actuator (235) and timing chain (208)

12. Install the camshaft sprocket bolt into the camshaft front bolt hole.
13. Using the bolt as a handle, carefully rotate and remove the camshaft from the engine block.
14. Remove the bolt from the camshaft.

To install:

15. Lubricate the camshaft journals and the bearings with clean engine oil.
16. Install the camshaft sprocket bolt into the camshaft front bolt hole.
17. Using the bolt as a handle, carefully install the camshaft into the engine block.
18. Remove the bolt from the front of the camshaft.
19. Install the camshaft retainer and bolts. Install the retainer with the sealing gasket facing the engine block.

➡The gasket surface on the engine block should be clean and free of dirt and/or debris.

20. Tighten the camshaft retainer bolts:
   a. Tighten the first design hex head bolts to 18 ft. lbs. (25 Nm).

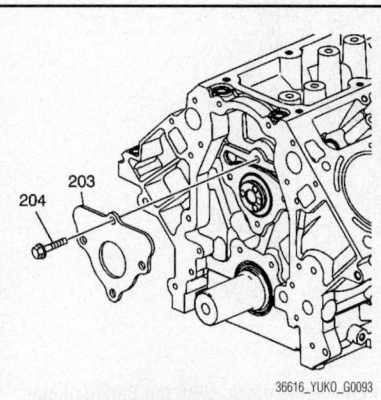

Fig. 83 Remove the camshaft retainer bolts (204) and retainer (203)

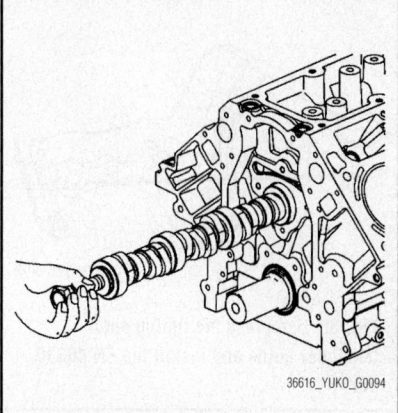

Fig. 84 Using the bolt as a handle, carefully rotate and remove the camshaft from the engine block

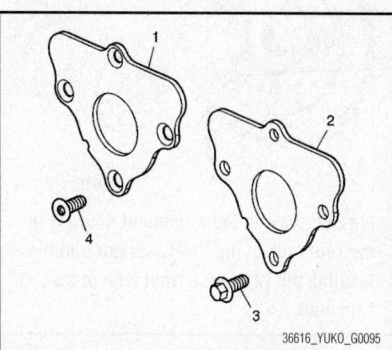

Fig. 85 Tighten the camshaft retainer bolts to specification, according to design illustrated

   b. Tighten the second design TORX® head bolts to 11 ft. lbs. (15 Nm).
21. Compress the timing chain tensioner guide and install the EN 46330 pin.

➡Properly locate the CMP actuator onto the locating pin of the camshaft. The sprocket teeth and timing chain teeth must mesh. The camshaft and the crankshaft sprocket alignment mark MUST be aligned properly.

➡Do not use the CMP solenoid valve again. Install a NEW valve during assembly.

22. Identify the alignment hole in the rear face of the CMP actuator and the locating pin on the front face of the camshaft.
23. Align the CMP actuator so the timing mark is in the 6 o'clock position.
24. Install the CMP actuator and timing chain. Align the hole in the face of the CMP actuator with the locating pin on the front face of the camshaft.
25. Place a straight edge across the front face of the engine block and inspect for

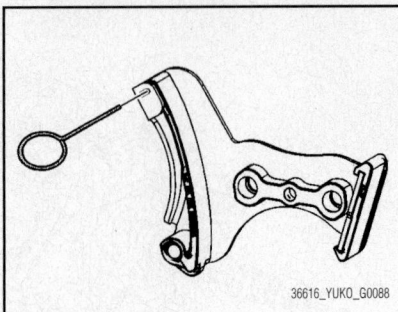

Fig. 86 Compress the timing chain tensioner guide and install the EN 46330 pin

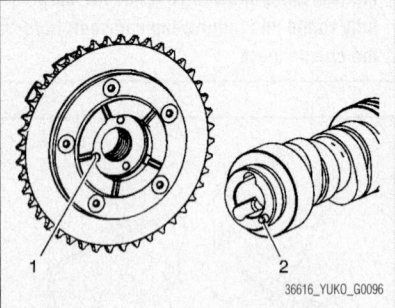

Fig. 87 View of the alignment hole (1) in the rear face of the CMP actuator and the locating pin (2) on the front face of the camshaft

proper installation of the CMP actuator and timing chain. With the CMP actuator properly and completely installed onto the front of the camshaft, the timing chain will not protrude beyond the front face of the engine block.

26. Install a NEW CMP actuator solenoid valve. With the CMP actuator properly positioned onto the camshaft, the CMP actuator solenoid valve can be threaded completely into the camshaft using light hand pressure. Tighten by hand until snug.

27. Inspect the sprockets for proper alignment. The mark on the CMP actuator sprocket should be located in the 6 o'clock position and the mark on the crankshaft sprocket should be located in the 12 o'clock position.

28. Remove the EN 46330 pin.

29. Tighten the CMP actuator solenoid valve:

   a. Step 1: Tighten to 48 ft. lbs. (65 Nm).

   b. Step 2: Tighten an additional 90° using the J 45059.

30. Remove the J 42386-A and bolts.

31. Install the starter motor. Refer to Starter, removal & installation.

32. Install the engine front cover. Refer to Timing Chain Cover and Seal, removal & installation.

33. Install the valve lifters, as follows:

34. Lubricate the valve lifters and engine block valve lifter bores with clean engine oil.

35. Insert the valve lifters into the lifter guides. Align the flat area on the top of the lifter with the flat area in the lifter guide bore. Push the lifter completely into the guide bore.

36. Install the valve lifters and guide to the engine block.

37. Install the valve lifter guide bolts and tighten to 106 inch lbs. (12 Nm).

38. Install the cylinder head and gasket. Refer to Cylinder Head, removal & installation.

39. Install the radiator support.

40. Connect the negative battery cable.

41. Start the engine and check for proper operation and for fluid leaks. Correct as required.

CATALYTIC CONVERTER

REMOVAL & INSTALLATION

3.0L Engine—2010 vehicle

Left Side
See Figure 89.

✳✳ CAUTION

In order to avoid being burned, do not service the exhaust system while it is still hot. Service the system when it is cool.

✳✳ CAUTION

Always wear protective goggles and gloves when removing exhaust parts as falling rust and sharp edges from worn exhaust components could result in serious personal injury.

1. Before servicing the vehicle, refer to the Precautions Section.

2. Raise and safely support the vehicle.

3. Remove the exhaust front pipe.

4. Disconnect the oxygen sensor electrical connector.

5. Remove the catalytic converter attaching nuts.

6. Remove the catalytic converter and the gasket.

To install:

7. Clean and inspect the studs on the engine cylinder head, replace as necessary.

8. Verify that the studs are fully seated. The stud collar should touch the surface of the engine cylinder head.

9. If replacing catalytic converter, transfer the oxygen sensor.

➡**Replace the exhaust front pipe nuts and the gasket with new ones.**

10. Install a NEW catalytic converter gasket.

11. Install the catalytic converter and tighten the nuts in a crisscross pattern.

   a. First Pass to 15 ft. lbs. (20 Nm).

   b. Final Pass to 34 ft. lbs. (46 Nm).

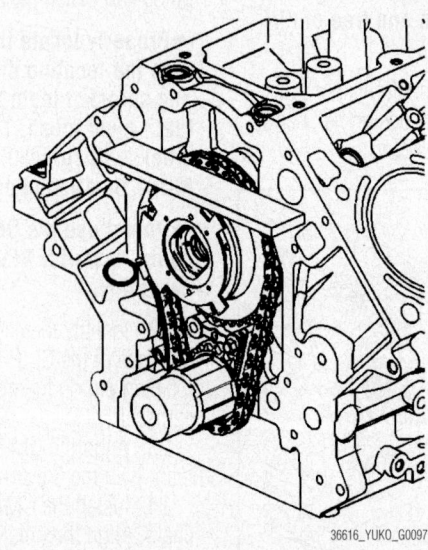

Fig. 88 Place a straight edge across the front face of the engine block. With the CMP actuator properly installed onto the front of the camshaft, the timing chain will not protrude beyond the front face of the engine block

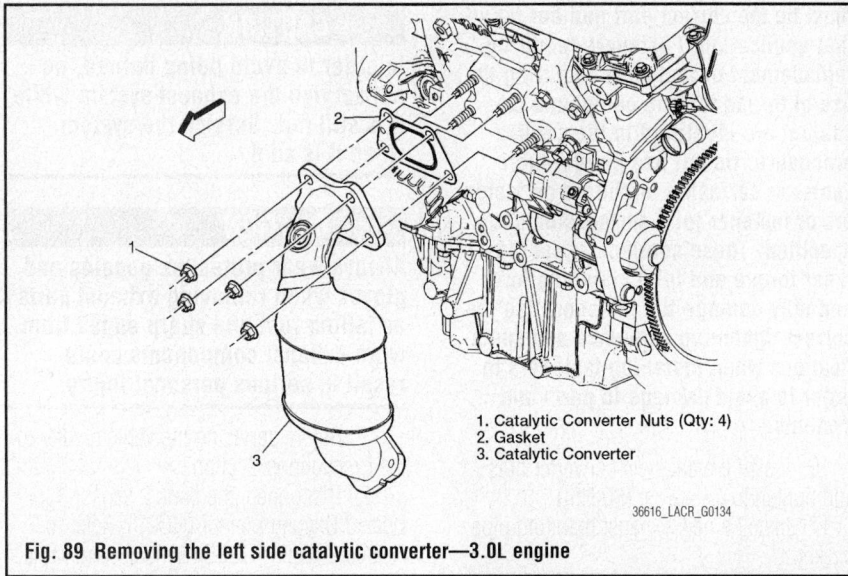

1. Catalytic Converter Nuts (Qty: 4)
2. Gasket
3. Catalytic Converter

36616_LACR_G0134

Fig. 89 Removing the left side catalytic converter—3.0L engine

12. Connect the oxygen sensor electrical connector.

13. Install the exhaust front pipe.

14. Lower the vehicle.

15. Inspect the exhaust system for leaks and possible underbody contact. Repair as needed.

➡Improperly installed and/or leaking exhaust manifold gaskets may affect vehicle emissions and/or On-Board Diagnostics (OBD) II system performance.

Right Side

See Figure 90.

> **✳✳ CAUTION**
>
> **In order to avoid being burned, do not service the exhaust system while it is still hot. Service the system when it is cool.**

> **✳✳ CAUTION**
>
> **Always wear protective goggles and gloves when removing exhaust parts as falling rust and sharp edges from worn exhaust components could result in serious personal injury.**

1. Before servicing the vehicle, refer to the Precautions Section.

2. Raise and safely support the vehicle.

3. Remove the exhaust front pipe.

4. Remove the exhaust front pipe. Refer to Exhaust Front Pipe Replacement.

5. Remove the catalytic converter attaching nuts.

6. Remove the catalytic converter and the gasket.

To install:

7. Clean and inspect the studs on the engine cylinder head, replace as necessary.

8. Verify that the studs are fully seated. The stud collar should touch the surface of the engine cylinder head.

9. If replacing catalytic converter, transfer the oxygen sensor.

➡**Replace the exhaust front pipe nuts and the gasket with new ones.**

10. Install a NEW catalytic converter gasket.

11. Install the catalytic converter and tighten the nuts in a crisscross pattern.
   a. First Pass to 15 ft. lbs. (20 Nm).
   b. Final Pass to 34 ft. lbs. (46 Nm).

12. Install the exhaust front pipe.

13. Lower the vehicle.

14. Inspect the exhaust system for leaks and possible underbody contact. Repair as needed.

➡Improperly installed and/or leaking exhaust manifold gaskets may affect vehicle emissions and/or On-Board Diagnostics (OBD) II system performance.

3.6L Engine—2008 vehicles

See Figure 91.

> **✳✳ CAUTION**
>
> **In order to avoid being burned, do not service the exhaust system while it is still hot. Service the system when it is cool.**

> **✳✳ CAUTION**
>
> **Always wear protective goggles and gloves when removing exhaust parts as falling rust and sharp edges from worn exhaust components could result in serious personal injury.**

➡**The catalytic converter is serviced by replacing the entire assembly. Always replace the gaskets at the front and rear flanges when servicing the catalytic converter. Never install the original gasket.**

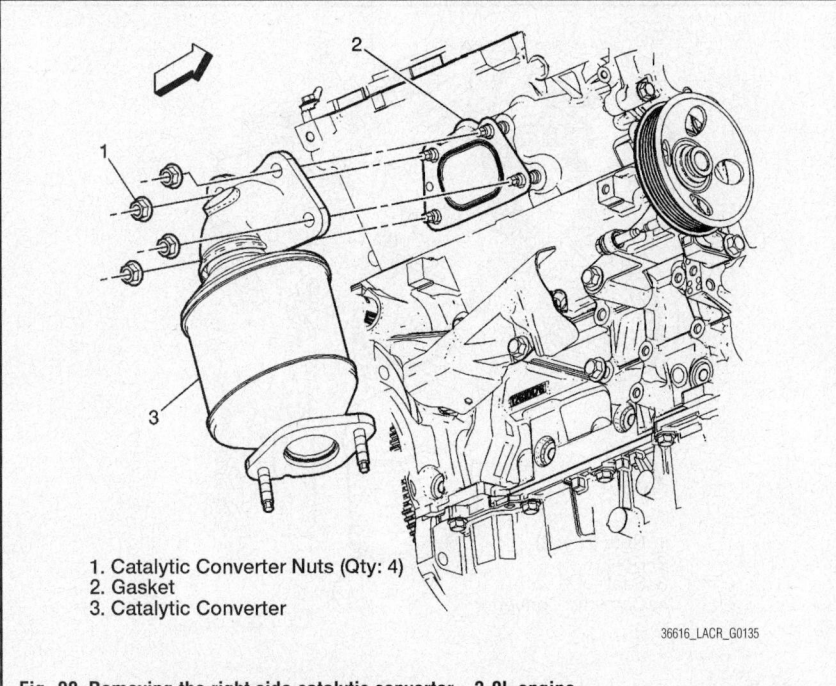

1. Catalytic Converter Nuts (Qty: 4)
2. Gasket
3. Catalytic Converter

36616_LACR_G0135

Fig. 90 Removing the right side catalytic converter—3.0L engine

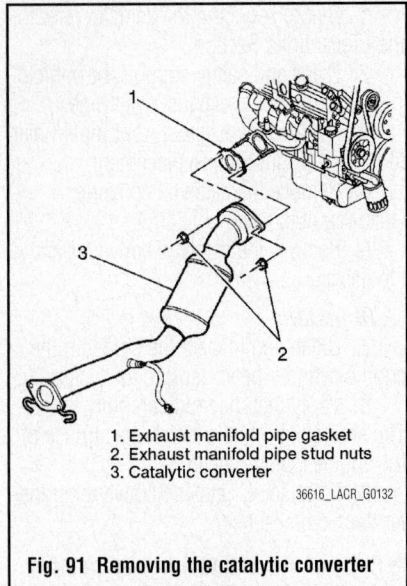

1. Exhaust manifold pipe gasket
2. Exhaust manifold pipe stud nuts
3. Catalytic converter

36616_LACR_G0132

Fig. 91 Removing the catalytic converter

1. Before servicing the vehicle, refer to the Precautions Section.
2. Raise and support the vehicle.
3. Disconnect the Heated Oxygen Sensor (HO2S) electrical connector.
4. Remove the exhaust manifold pipe stud nuts.
5. Remove the exhaust manifold pipe gasket.
6. Support the exhaust system.
7. Remove the catalytic converter nuts.
8. Remove the catalytic converter hangers.
9. Remove the catalytic converter.
10. Remove the catalytic converter gasket.
11. Clean and inspect the exhaust manifold and the exhaust pipe gasket mating surfaces.
12. Remove the HO2S, if required. Refer to Heated Oxygen (HO2S) Sensor, removal & installation.

To install:

❋❋ WARNING

To prevent internal damage to the flexible coupling of the catalytic converter assembly, the converter must be supported. The vertical movement at the rear of the catalytic converter assembly must not exceed 6° up or down.

13. Install the HO2S, if required.
14. Install a new gasket to the exhaust pipe studs.
15. Install and support the catalytic converter.

➡Use the correct fastener in the correct location. Replacement fasteners

must be the correct part number for that application. Fasteners requiring replacement or fasteners requiring the use of thread locking compound or sealant are identified in the service procedure. Do not use paints, lubricants, or corrosion inhibitors on fasteners or fastener joint surfaces unless specified. These coatings affect fastener torque and joint clamping force and may damage the fastener. Use the correct tightening sequence and specifications when installing fasteners in order to avoid damage to parts and systems.

16. Install the catalytic converter nuts and tighten to 44 ft. lbs. (60 Nm).
17. Install a new exhaust manifold pipe gasket.
18. Install the exhaust manifold pipe stud nuts and tighten to 26 ft. lbs. (35 Nm).
19. Install the catalytic converter hangers.
20. Remove the support from the exhaust system.
21. Connect the HO2S electrical connector.
22. Lower the vehicle.
23. Inspect the exhaust system for leaks and possible underbody contact. Repair as needed.

3.6L Engine—2010 vehicles

Left Side

See Figure 92.

❋❋ CAUTION

In order to avoid being burned, do not service the exhaust system while it is still hot. Service the system when it is cool.

❋❋ CAUTION

Always wear protective goggles and gloves when removing exhaust parts as falling rust and sharp edges from worn exhaust components could result in serious personal injury.

1. Before servicing the vehicle, refer to the Precautions Section.
2. Disconnect the bank 2 sensor 1 Heated Oxygen Sensor (HO2S). Refer to Heated Oxygen (HO2S) Sensor, removal & installation.
3. Remove the exhaust manifold heat shield bolts.
4. Remove the exhaust manifold heat shield.
5. Remove the exhaust front pipe.
6. Remove the catalytic converter attaching nuts/bolt.
7. Remove the catalytic converter and seal.

To install:

8. Install the catalytic converter seal and catalytic converter.
9. Install the attaching nuts/bolt to the catalytic converter and tighten to 36 ft. lbs. (50 Nm).

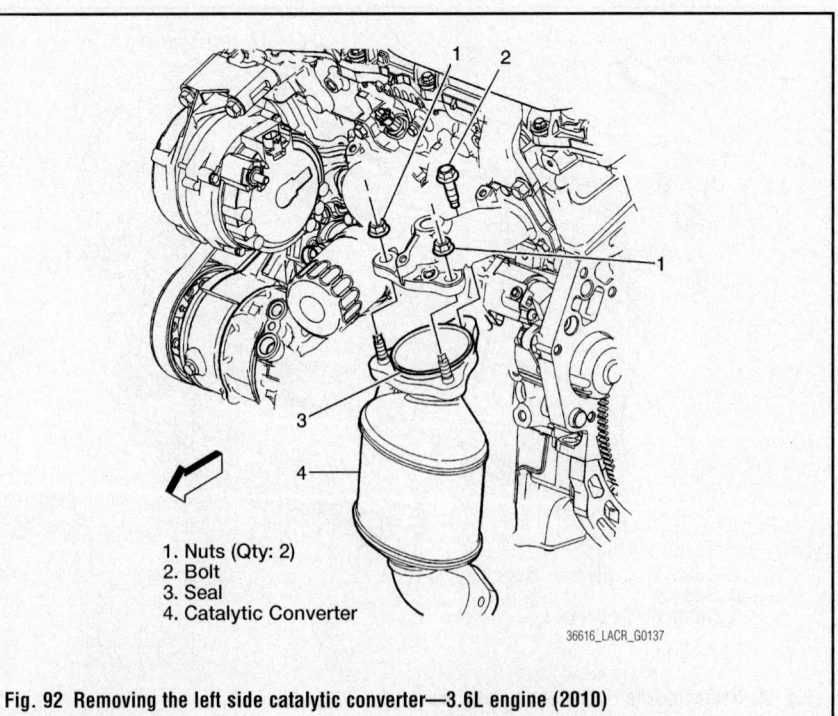

1. Nuts (Qty: 2)
2. Bolt
3. Seal
4. Catalytic Converter

36616_LACR_G0137

Fig. 92 Removing the left side catalytic converter—3.6L engine (2010)

10. Install the exhaust front pipe.

11. Install the exhaust manifold heat shield. Tighten the bolts to 89 inch lbs. (10 Nm).

12. Connect the bank 2 sensor 1 HO2S connector.

13. Inspect the exhaust system for leaks and possible underbody contact. Repair as needed.

Right Side

See Figures 93 and 94.

> ✳✳ **CAUTION**
>
> **In order to avoid being burned, do not service the exhaust system while it is still hot. Service the system when it is cool.**

> ✳✳ **CAUTION**
>
> **Always wear protective goggles and gloves when removing exhaust parts as falling rust and sharp edges from worn exhaust components could result in serious personal injury.**

1. Before servicing the vehicle, refer to the Precautions Section.

2. Disconnect the bank 1 sensor 1 Heated Oxygen Sensor (HO2S). Refer to Heated Oxygen (HO2S) Sensor, removal & installation.

3. Raise the vehicle to an appropriate height to reach the heat shield bolts.

4. Remove the exhaust manifold heat shield bolts.

➡ **It may be necessary to gently pull down on the catalytic converter in order to remove the heat shield.**

5. Remove the exhaust manifold heat shield.

6. Remove the exhaust front pipe.

7. Remove the catalytic converter attaching nuts.

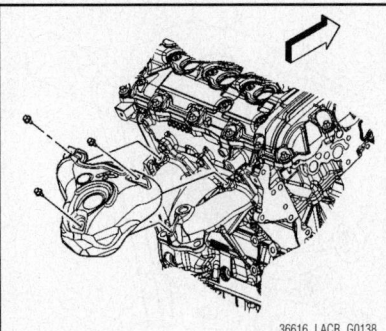

Fig. 93 Removing the right side exhaust manifold heat shield—3.6L engine (2010)

36616_LACR_G0138

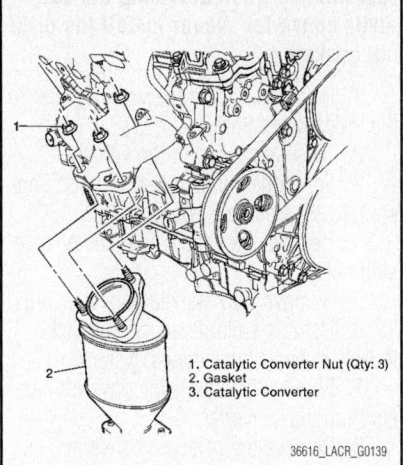

1. Catalytic Converter Nut (Qty: 3)
2. Gasket
3. Catalytic Converter

36616_LACR_G0139

Fig. 94 Removing the right side catalytic converter—3.6L engine (2010)

8. Remove the catalytic converter and gasket.

To install:

9. Install the catalytic converter gasket and catalytic converter.

10. Install the attaching nuts to the catalytic converter and tighten to 36 ft. lbs. (50 Nm).

11. Install the exhaust front pipe.

12. Install the exhaust manifold heat shield. Tighten the bolts to 89 inch lbs. (10 Nm).

➡ **It may be necessary to gently pull down on the catalytic converter in order to install the heat shield.**

13. Connect the bank 1 sensor 1 HO2S connector.

14. Inspect the exhaust system for leaks and possible underbody contact. Repair as needed.

3.8L Engine

See Figure 91.

> ✳✳ **CAUTION**
>
> **In order to avoid being burned, do not service the exhaust system while it is still hot. Service the system when it is cool.**

> ✳✳ **CAUTION**
>
> **Always wear protective goggles and gloves when removing exhaust parts as falling rust and sharp edges from worn exhaust components could result in serious personal injury.**

➡ **The catalytic converter is serviced by replacing the entire assembly. Always replace the gaskets at the front and rear flanges when servicing the catalytic converter. Never install the original gasket.**

1. Before servicing the vehicle, refer to the Precautions Section.

2. Raise and support the vehicle.

3. Disconnect the Heated Oxygen Sensor (HO2S) electrical connector.

4. Remove the exhaust manifold pipe stud nuts.

5. Remove the exhaust manifold pipe gasket.

6. Support the exhaust system.

7. Remove the catalytic converter nuts.

8. Remove the catalytic converter hangers.

9. Remove the catalytic converter.

10. Remove the catalytic converter gasket.

11. Clean and inspect the exhaust manifold and the exhaust pipe gasket mating surfaces.

12. Remove the HO2S, if required. Refer to Heated Oxygen (HO2S) Sensor, removal & installation.

To install:

> ✳✳ **WARNING**
>
> **To prevent internal damage to the flexible coupling of the catalytic converter assembly, the converter must be supported. The vertical movement at the rear of the catalytic converter assembly must not exceed 6° up or down.**

13. Install the HO2S, if required. Refer to Heated Oxygen (HO2S) Sensor, removal & installation.

14. Install a new gasket to the exhaust pipe studs.

15. Install and support the catalytic converter.

➡ **Use the correct fastener in the correct location. Replacement fasteners must be the correct part number for that application. Fasteners requiring replacement or fasteners requiring the use of thread locking compound or sealant are identified in the service procedure. Do not use paints, lubricants, or corrosion inhibitors on fasteners or fastener joint surfaces unless specified. These coatings affect fastener torque and joint clamping force and may damage the fastener. Use the correct tightening sequence and specifications when installing fasteners in** order to avoid damage to parts and systems.

16. Install the catalytic converter nuts and tighten to 44 ft. lbs. (60 Nm).

17. Install a new exhaust manifold pipe gasket.

18. Install the exhaust manifold pipe stud nuts and tighten to 26 ft. lbs. (35 Nm).

19. Install the catalytic converter hangers.

20. Remove the support from the exhaust system.

21. Connect the HO2S electrical connector.

22. Lower the vehicle.

23. Inspect the exhaust system for leaks and possible underbody contact. Repair as needed.

5.3L Engine

See Figure 95.

❊❊ CAUTION

In order to avoid being burned, do not service the exhaust system while it is still hot. Service the system when it is cool.

❊❊ CAUTION

Always wear protective goggles and gloves when removing exhaust parts as falling rust and sharp edges from worn exhaust components could result in serious personal injury.

➡ The catalytic converter is serviced by replacing the entire assembly. Always replace the gaskets at the front and rear flanges when servicing the catalytic converter. Never install the original gaskets.

1. Before servicing the vehicle, refer to the Precautions Section.

2. Raise and support the vehicle.

3. Disconnect the Heated Oxygen Sensor (HO2S) electrical connector.

4. Remove the catalytic converter pipe stud nuts.

5. Remove the catalytic converter nuts.

6. Using a suitable adjustable jack, loosely support the exhaust system.

7. Remove the catalytic converter hangers from the converter.

8. Remove the catalytic converter.

9. Remove and discard the catalytic converter gaskets.

10. Remove the HO2S, if required. Refer to Heated Oxygen (HO2S) Sensor, removal & installation.

11. Clean and inspect the exhaust manifold and the exhaust pipe mating surfaces.

To install:

❊❊ WARNING

To prevent internal damage to the flexible coupling of the catalytic converter assembly, the converter must be supported. The vertical movement at the rear of the catalytic converter assembly must not exceed 6° up or down.

12. Install the HO2S, if required. Refer to Heated Oxygen (HO2S) Sensor, removal & installation.

13. Install NEW gaskets to the exhaust manifold and muffler studs.

14. Position the catalytic converter into place.

15. Install the catalytic converter hangers to the converter.

➡ Use the correct fastener in the correct location. Replacement fasteners must be the correct part number for that application. Fasteners requiring replacement or fasteners requiring the use of thread locking compound or sealant are identified in the service procedure. Do not use paints, lubricants, or corrosion inhibitors on fasteners or fastener joint surfaces unless specified. These coatings affect fastener torque and joint clamping force and may damage the fastener. Use the correct tightening sequence and specifications when installing fasteners in order to avoid damage to parts and systems.

16. Install the catalytic converter pipe stud nuts and tighten to 26 ft. lbs. (35 Nm).

17. Install the catalytic converter nuts and tighten to 44 ft. lbs. (60 Nm).

18. Remove the exhaust system support.

19. Connect the HO2S electrical connector.

20. Lower the vehicle.

21. Run the vehicle and inspect the exhaust system for leaks and underbody contact.

CRANKSHAFT DAMPER

REMOVAL & INSTALLATION

3.0L and 3.6L Engines

See Figures 96 and 97.

1. Before servicing the vehicle, refer to the Precautions Section.

2. Remove the drive belt. Refer to Accessory Drive Belts, removal & installation.

3. Install the engine support fixture.

4. Remove the engine mount strut bracket.

5. Remove the engine mount.

6. Remove the starter.

7. Install a flywheel holding tool through the starter mounting hole.

8. Using the engine support fixture, lower the engine approximately 2 inches.

9. Remove the crankshaft balancer bolt.

10. Install a crankshaft button tool such as J 38416-2 in the nose of the crankshaft.

11. Install crankshaft balancer remover tool such as J 41816 in order to remove the crankshaft balancer.

12. Tighten the center bolt of the crankshaft balancer remover tool in order to pull the crankshaft balancer off of the crankshaft.

13. Remove the crankshaft balancer remover tool from the crankshaft balancer.

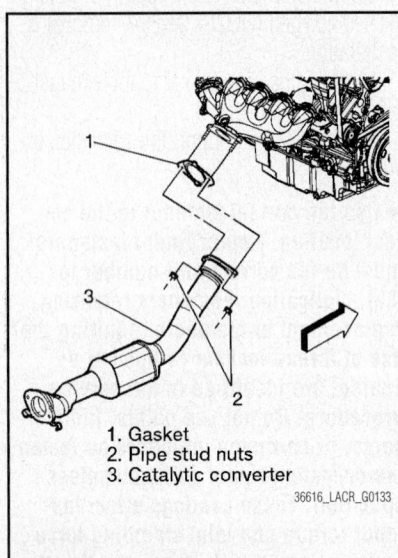

1. Gasket
2. Pipe stud nuts
3. Catalytic converter

36616_LACR_G0133

Fig. 95 Removing the catalytic converter—5.3L engine

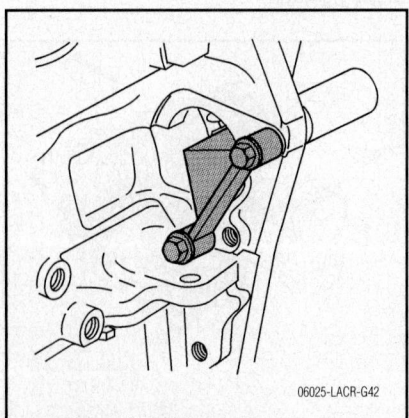

06025-LACR-G42

Fig. 96 Flywheel holding tool—3.0L and 3.6L engines

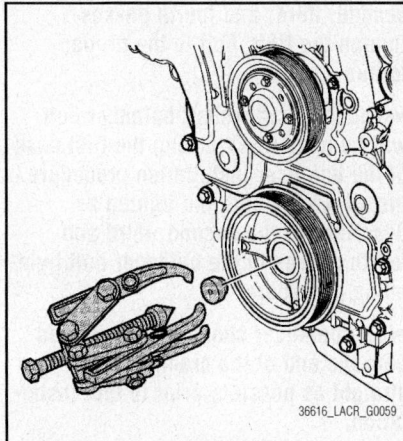

Fig. 97 Removing the crankshaft balancer—3.0L and 3.6L engines

To install:

➥**The crankshaft balancer remover tool must be installed onto the flywheel.**

14. Use the tool, nut, bearing, and washer to install the crankshaft balancer.

➥**Do not lubricate the crankshaft front oil seal or crankshaft balancer sealing surfaces. The crankshaft balancer is installed into a dry seal.**

15. Apply lubricant to the inside of the crankshaft balancer hub bore.
16. Place the crankshaft balancer in position on the crankshaft.
17. Thread the tool in the crankshaft. Ensure you engage at least 10 threads of the tool before pressing the crankshaft balancer in place.
18. Push the crankshaft balancer into position by tightening the nut on the tool until the large washer bottoms out on the crankshaft end.
19. Remove the tool.
20. Install the crankshaft balancer bolt.
21. Tighten the crankshaft balancer bolt and tighten to 74 ft. lbs. (100 Nm), plus an additional 150°.
22. Remove the flywheel holding tool.
23. Install the starter. Refer to Starter, removal & installation.
24. Using engine support fixture, raise the engine into position.
25. Install the engine mount.
26. Install the engine mount strut bracket.
27. Install the drive belt. Refer to Accessory Drive Belts, removal & installation.

3.8L Engine

See Figures 98 and 99.

1. Before servicing the vehicle, refer to the Precautions Section.

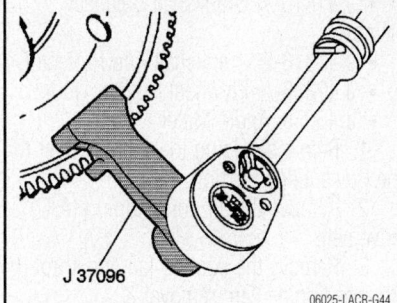

Fig. 98 Use tool J 37096 to secure the flywheel in order to prevent the crankshaft from rotating

2. Disconnect the negative battery cable.
3. Remove the accessory drive belt. Refer to Accessory Drive Belts, removal & installation.
4. Raise and support the vehicle.
5. Remove the right front tire and wheel.
6. Remove the right engine splash shield retainers and the engine splash shield.
7. Remove the torque converter covers.
8. Use tool J 37096 to secure the flywheel in order to prevent the crankshaft from rotating.
9. Remove the crankshaft damper bolt and discard the balancer bolt.

➥**Do not separate the crankshaft pulley from the crankshaft damper. Service the crankshaft pulley and the crankshaft damper as an assembly.**

10. Remove the crankshaft balancer (damper) using tool J 38197-A.

To install:

11. Coat the engine front cover seal con-tact area on the crankshaft damper, and the seal surface with engine oil.
12. Install the crankshaft damper.
13. Prevent the crankshaft from rotating.
14. Install the NEW crankshaft damper bolt. Tighten the bolt to 111 ft. lbs. (150 Nm), plus 76°.
15. Install the torque converter covers.
16. Install the right engine splash shield and the engine splash shield retainers.
17. Install the right front tire and wheel.
18. Lower the vehicle.
19. Install the accessory drive belt. Refer to Accessory Drive Belts, removal & installation.

➥**The following CKP System Variation Learn Procedure must be performed.**

20. Install a scan tool.
21. Monitor the Powertrain Control Module (PCM) for DTC's with a scan tool.
22. Select the crankshaft position variation learn procedure with a scan tool.
23. The scan tool instructs you to perform the following:
   a. Accelerate to Wide Open Throttle (WOT).
   b. Release the throttle when fuel cut-off occurs.
   c. Observe the fuel cut-off specifications for the applicable engine.
   d. The engine should not accelerate beyond the calibrated RPM value.
   e. Release the throttle immediately if the value is exceeded.
   f. Block the drive wheels.
   g. Set the parking brake.
   h. DO NOT apply the brake pedal.
   i. Cycle the ignition from OFF to ON.
   j. Apply and hold the brake pedal.
   k. Start and idle the engine.

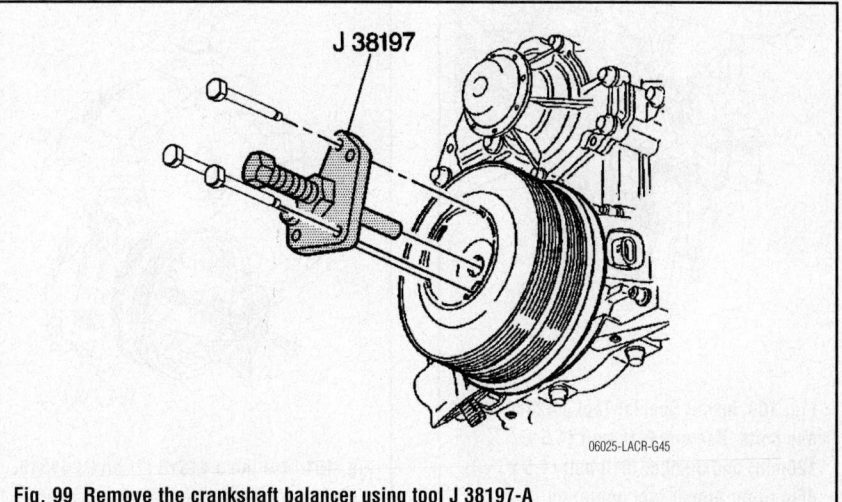

Fig. 99 Remove the crankshaft balancer using tool J 38197-A

l. Turn the A/C OFF.

m. The vehicle must remain in Park or Neutral.

24. The scan tool monitors certain component signals to determine if all the conditions are met to continue with the procedure. The scan tool only displays the condition that inhibits the procedure.

25. Enable the crankshaft position system variation learn procedure with the scan tool and perform the following:

➡While the learn procedure is in progress, release the throttle immediately when the engine starts to decelerate. The engine control is returned to the operator and the engine responds to throttle position after the learn procedure is complete.

26. Accelerate to WOT.

a. Release when fuel cut-off occurs.

b. Test in progress.

27. The scan tool displays Learn Status: Learned this ignition.

a. If the scan tool indicates that DTC P0315 ran and passed, the CKP variation learn procedure is complete.

b. If the scan tool indicates DTC P0315 failed or did not run, refer to DTC P0315.

28. Turn OFF the ignition for 30 seconds after the learn procedure is completed successfully.

5.3L Engine

See Figures 100 through 103.

Special Tools:

• J 41478: Crankshaft Front Oil Seal Installer

• J 41665: Crankshaft Balancer and Sprocket Installer

• J 41816-A: Crankshaft Balancer Remover

• J 41816-2: Crankshaft End Protector

• J 42386-A: Flywheel Holding Tool

• J 45059: Angle Meter

1. Before servicing the vehicle, refer to the Precautions Section.

2. Remove the air conditioning (A/C) drive belt.

3. Remove the cooling fan and shroud. Refer to Engine Fan, removal & installation.

4. Remove the starter motor. Refer to Starter, removal & installation.

5. Install Special Tool J 42386-A and bolts. Use one M10 bolt (1.5 x 120mm) and another M10 bolt (1.5 x 45mm) for proper tool operation. Tighten the J 42386-A bolts to 37 ft. lbs. (50 Nm).

➡Ensure that the teeth of the J 42386-A mesh with the teeth of the engine flywheel.

6. Remove the crankshaft balancer bolt. Do not discard the crankshaft balancer bolt at this time. The old balancer bolt will be used during the balancer installation procedure.

7. Install the J 41816 and J 41816-2 to remove the crankshaft balancer.

➡The crankshaft balancer is balanced as an individual component. It is not necessary to mark the balancer prior to removal.

To install:

➡The crankshaft balancer installation and bolt tightening involves a 4-stage tightening process. The first pass ensures that the balancer is installed completely onto the crankshaft. The second, third, and fourth passes tighten the NEW bolt to the proper torque.

➡The used crankshaft balancer bolt will be used ONLY during the first pass of the balancer installation procedure. Install a NEW bolt and tighten as described in the second, third and fourth passes of the balancer bolt tightening procedure.

➡The balancer should be positioned onto the end of the crankshaft as straight as possible prior to tool installation.

8. Position the crankshaft balancer onto the end of the crankshaft.

9. Install the J 41665 and the threaded rod from the J 41478 to crankshaft balancer and install the balancer.

a. Assemble the threaded rod, nut, washer, and installer. Insert the smaller end of the installer into the front of the balancer.

b. Use a wrench and hold the hex end of the threaded rod.

c. Use a second wrench and rotate the installation tool nut clockwise until the balancer is started onto the crankshaft.

d. Remove the tool and reverse the installation tool.

➡Position the larger end of the installer against the front of the balancer.

e. Use a wrench and hold the hex end of the threaded rod.

f. Use a second wrench and rotate the installation tool nut clockwise until the balancer is installed onto the crankshaft.

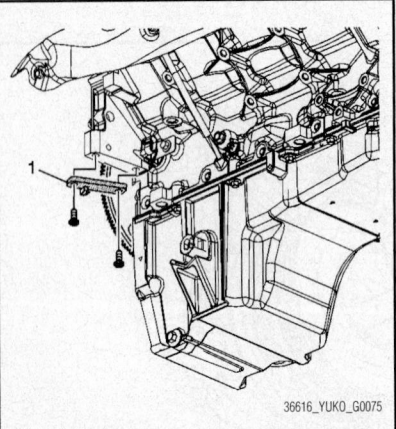

36616_YUKO_G0075

Fig. 100 Install Special Tool J 42386-A (1) and bolts. Use one M10 bolt (1.5 x 120mm) and another M10 bolt (1.5 x 45mm) for proper tool operation

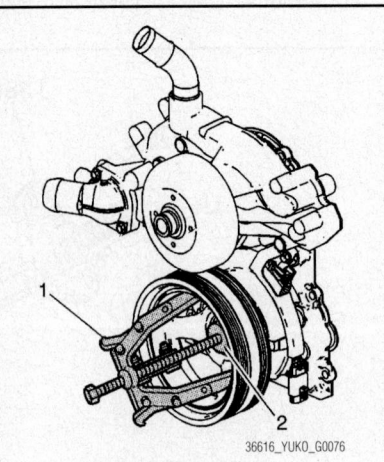

36616_YUKO_G0076

Fig. 101 Use the J 41816 (1) and J 41816-2 (2) to remove the crankshaft balancer

36616_YUKO_G0077

Fig. 102 Use the J 41665 and the threaded rod from the J 41478 to install the crankshaft balancer

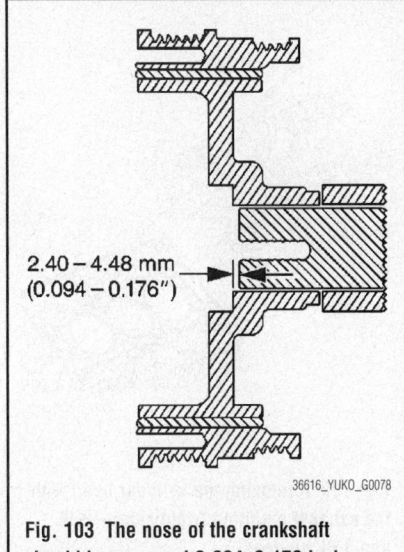

Fig. 103 The nose of the crankshaft should be recessed 0.094–0.176 inch (2.4–4.48mm) into the balancer bore

g. Remove the J 41665 and the threaded rod.

10. Install the USED crankshaft balancer bolt. Tighten the USED bolt to 240 ft. lbs. (330 Nm).

11. Remove the USED crankshaft balancer bolt.

➡The nose of the crankshaft should be recessed 0.094–0.176 inch (2.4–4.48 mm) into the balancer bore.

12. Measure for a correctly installed balancer. If the balancer is not installed to the proper dimension, install the J 41665 and repeat the installation procedure.

13. Install the NEW crankshaft balancer bolt and tighten the bolt:
   a. Step 1: 37 ft. lbs. (50 Nm).
   b. Step 2: 140° using J 45059.

14. Remove the J 42386-A and bolts.

15. Install the starter motor. Refer to Starter, removal & installation.

16. Install the cooling fan and shroud. Refer to Engine Fan, removal & installation.

17. Install the A/C drive belt.

18. Perform the Crankshaft Position (CKP) system variation learn procedure. Refer to Crankshaft Position System Variation Learn.

CRANKSHAFT FRONT SEAL

REMOVAL & INSTALLATION

3.0L and 3.6L Engines

1. Before servicing the vehicle, refer to the Precautions Section.

2. Remove the crankshaft damper. Refer to Crankshaft Damper, removal & installation.

3. Use J 45000 in order to remove the crankshaft oil seal.

To install:

➡Do not lubricate the crankshaft front oil seal or the crankshaft damper sealing surfaces.

4. Use the J 29184, or equivalent, to install the crankshaft front oil seal.

5. Install the crankshaft damper. Refer to Crankshaft Damper, removal & installation.

3.8L Engine

1. Before servicing the vehicle, refer to the Precautions Section.

2. Remove the crankshaft damper. Refer to Crankshaft Damper, removal & installation.

⚹⚹ WARNING

Be careful not to damage the crankshaft.

3. Pry out the crankshaft front oil seal with a flat bladed tool such as a large screwdriver. Use care to avoid damaging the crankshaft front oil seal bore or the crankshaft front oil seal contact surfaces.

4. Inspect the crankshaft damper and engine front cover for scratches.

To install:

5. Install the crankshaft front oil seal in the engine front cover using the J 35354-A.

6. Tighten the bolt until the crankshaft front oil seal is seated in the engine front cover.

7. Remove the J 35354-A.

8. Install the crankshaft damper. Refer to Crankshaft Damper, removal & installation.

9. Inspect for leaks.

10. Perform the Crankshaft Position (CKP) system variation learn procedure. Refer to Crankshaft Position System Variation Learn.

5.3L Engine

See Figures 104 and 105.

Special Tool:
• J 41478: Crankshaft Front Oil Seal Installer

1. Before servicing the vehicle, refer to the Precautions Section.

2. Remove the crankshaft balancer. Refer to Crankshaft Damper, removal & installation.

3. Remove the crankshaft front oil seal from the front cover.

To install:

➡Do not lubricate the oil seal sealing surface.

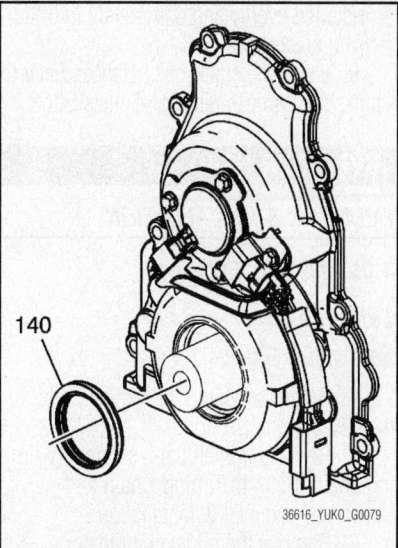

Fig. 104 Remove the crankshaft front oil seal (140) from the front cover

➡Do not reuse the crankshaft front oil seal.

4. Lubricate the outer edge of the oil seal with clean engine oil.

5. Lubricate the front cover oil seal bore with clean engine oil.

6. Install the crankshaft front oil seal onto the J 41478 guide.

7. Install the J 41478 threaded rod (with nut, washer, guide, and oil seal) into the end of the crankshaft.

8. Use the J 41478 in order to install the oil seal into the cover bore.
   a. Use a wrench and hold the hex on the installer bolt.
   b. Use a second wrench and rotate the installer nut clockwise until the seal bottoms in the cover bore.
   c. Remove the J 41478.
   d. Inspect the oil seal for proper installation. The oil seal should be

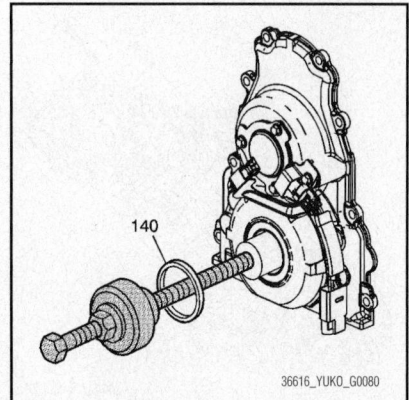

Fig. 105 Use the J 41478 in order to install the oil seal (140) into the cover bore

installed evenly and completely into the front cover bore.

9. Install the crankshaft balancer. Refer to Crankshaft Damper, removal & installation.

CYLINDER HEAD

REMOVAL & INSTALLATION

3.0L and 3.6L Engines

Left Side

See Figures 106 and 107.

1. Before servicing the vehicle, refer to the Precautions Section.

2. Remove the left bank secondary timing chain. Refer to Timing Chain and Sprockets, removal & installation.

3. Remove the oil level indicator.

4. Disconnect the coolant temperature sensor electrical connector.

5. Remove the wiring harness ground from the cylinder head.

6. Remove the catalytic converter. Refer to Catalytic Converter, removal & installation.

7. Remove the cylinder head with the exhaust manifold.

8. Remove and discard the left cylinder head gasket.

To install:

9. Clean and inspect the cylinder head and the engine block sealing surfaces.

10. Ensure the cylinder head locating pins are securely mounted in the cylinder block deck face.

11. Install a NEW left cylinder head gasket using the deck face locating pins for retention.

12. Align the left cylinder head with the deck face locating pins.

13. Place the left cylinder head in position on the deck face.

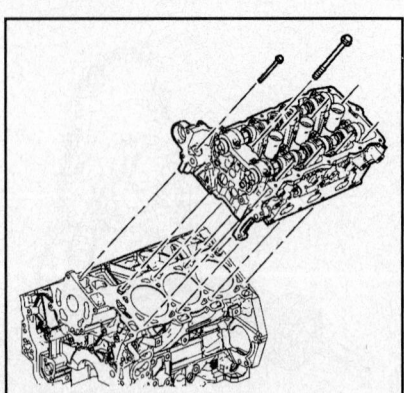

Fig. 106 Removing the cylinder head with the exhaust manifold (left side)—3.0L and 3.6L engines

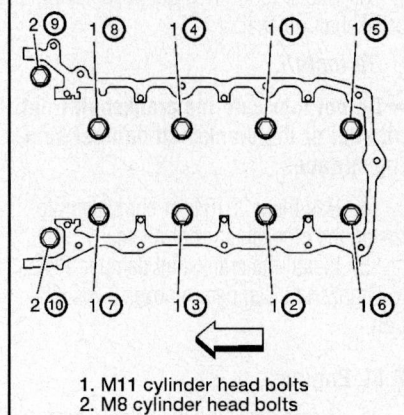

1. M11 cylinder head bolts
2. M8 cylinder head bolts

36616_LACR_G0051

Fig. 107 Cylinder head bolt tightening sequence (left side)—3.0L and 3.6L engines

➡**DO NOT allow oil on the cylinder head bolt bosses. Do not reuse the cylinder head bolts.**

14. Install the NEW M11 cylinder head bolts and tighten:

   a. First pass in sequence to 22 ft. lbs. (30 Nm).

   b. Second pass an additional 150° using an angle meter (J 45059).

15. Install 2 NEW front M8 left cylinder head bolts and tighten:

   a. First pass in sequence to 11 ft. lbs. (15 Nm).

   b. Second pass an additional 75° using an angle meter (J 45059).

16. Install the catalytic converter to the exhaust manifold. Refer to Catalytic Converter, removal & installation.

17. Connect the wiring harness electrical connector located at the side of the cylinder head.

18. Install the wiring harness ground to the cylinder head.

19. Install the coolant temperature sensor electrical connector.

20. Install the oil level indicator.

21. Install the left bank secondary timing chain. Refer to Timing Chain and Sprockets, removal & installation.

Right Side

See Figures 108 and 109.

1. Before servicing the vehicle, refer to the Precautions Section.

2. Remove the hood.

3. Remove the right bank secondary timing chain. Refer to Timing Chain and Sprockets, removal & installation.

4. With the aid of an assistant, remove the cylinder head with the exhaust manifold.

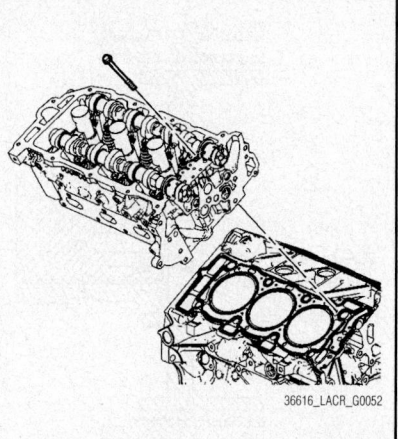

36616_LACR_G0052

Fig. 108 Removing the cylinder head with the exhaust manifold (right side)—3.0L and 3.6L engines

5. Remove and discard the cylinder head gasket.

To install:

6. Clean and inspect the cylinder head and the engine block sealing surfaces.

7. Install a NEW cylinder head gasket.

8. With the aid of an assistant, carefully install the cylinder head with the exhaust manifold to the engine.

9. Ensure the cylinder head locating pins are securely mounted in the cylinder block deck face.

10. Install a NEW right cylinder head gasket using the deck face locating pins for retention.

11. Align the right cylinder head with the deck face locating pins.

12. Place the right cylinder head in position on the deck face.

➡**DO NOT allow oil on the cylinder head bolt bosses or DO NOT reuse the old M11 cylinder head bolts.**

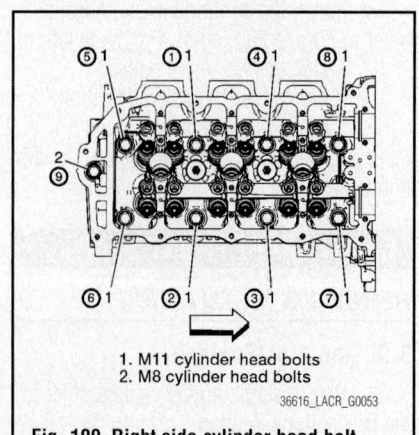

1. M11 cylinder head bolts
2. M8 cylinder head bolts

36616_LACR_G0053

Fig. 109 Right side cylinder head bolt tightening sequence–3.0L and 3.6L engines

13. Tighten the NEW M11 cylinder head bolts:

a. First pass in sequence to 22 ft. lbs. (30 Nm).

b. Second pass in sequence an additional 150°.

14. Install and tighten the NEW M8 cylinder head bolt:

a. First pass to 11 ft. lbs. (15 Nm).

b. Second pass an additional 75°.

15. Install the right bank secondary timing chain. Refer to Timing Chain and Sprockets, removal & installation.

16. Install the hood.

3.8L Engine

See Figure 110.

1. Before servicing the vehicle, refer to the Precautions Section.

2. Disconnect the negative battery cable.

3. Relieve the fuel system pressure.

4. Drain the cooling system.

5. Remove or disconnect the following:

- Intake manifold
- Exhaust manifold
- Valve covers
- Ignition wires and ignition coil/module assembly
- Alternator front mounting bracket and alternator
- Air conditioning bracket to cylinder head bolt
- Power steering pump
- Accessory drive belt tensioner
- Fuel pipe heat shield
- Rocker arm assemblies, note their original position
- Pushrods and guide plate
- Cylinder head bolts
- Cylinder head

To install:

6. Place the new cylinder head gasket on the engine block dowels with the note

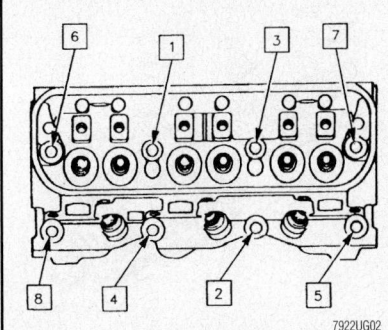

Fig. 110 Cylinder head bolt torque sequence—3.8L engine

THIS SIDE UP facing the cylinder head and the arrow facing the front of the engine. Position the cylinder head on the engine block.

➡The head gasket is identified by either a L or a R stamped on it next to the arrow.

➡This engine uses special torque to yield head bolts. The procedure must be followed carefully and new bolts must be used whenever the head is removed. Total bolt torque should not exceed 60 ft. lbs. (81 Nm).

7. Install new cylinder head bolts and torque them in sequence as follows:

a. Step 1: 37 ft. lbs. (50 Nm).

b. Step 2: Plus 120°.

8. Install or connect the following:

- Pushrods and guide plate
- Rocker arm assemblies into their original location

➡Apply a thread lock compound to the rocker arm pedestal bolts before assembly.

- Valve covers
- Fuel pipe heat shield
- Accessory drive belt tensioner
- Power steering pump
- Air conditioning compressor bracket bolt. Torque it to 52 ft. lbs. (70 Nm)
- Alternator front mounting bracket, and alternator
- Ignition coil/module assembly and spark plug wires
- Exhaust manifold. Torque the bolts to 22 ft. lbs. (30 Nm)
- Intake manifold
- Negative battery cable

9. Refill and bleed the cooling system.

10. Start the engine and check for leaks and proper operation.

5.3L Engine

Left Side

See Figures 111 through 113.

Special Tools:

- J 45059: Angle Meter
- J 42385-200: Common Thread Repair Kit

1. Before servicing the vehicle, refer to the Precautions Section.

2. Release the fuel system pressure.

3. Disconnect the negative battery cable.

4. Remove the alternator bracket. Refer to Alternator, removal & installation.

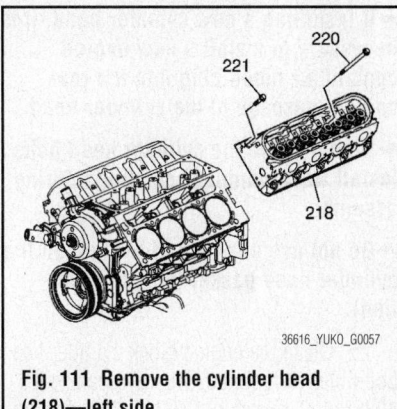

Fig. 111 Remove the cylinder head (218)—left side

5. Remove the intake manifold. Refer to Intake Manifold, removal & installation.

6. Remove the coolant air bleed pipe.

7. Remove the left exhaust manifold. Refer to Exhaust Manifold, removal & installation.

8. Remove the pushrods. Refer to Rocker Arms/Shafts, removal & installation.

9. Remove the engine ground strap bolt from the rear of the cylinder head.

10. Remove the ground strap from the cylinder head.

➡The cylinder head bolts are of a torque-to-yield design and are NOT to be reused.

11. Remove and discard the cylinder head bolts.

✳✳ WARNING

After removal, place the cylinder head on 2 wood blocks in order to prevent damage to the sealing surfaces.

12. Remove the cylinder head.

13. Remove and discard the cylinder head gasket.

14. If required, clean and inspect the cylinder head.

To install:

✳✳ CAUTION

Wear safety glasses in order to avoid eye damage.

✳✳ WARNING

Clean all dirt, debris, and coolant from the engine block cylinder head bolt holes. Failure to remove all foreign material may result in damaged threads, improperly tightened fasteners or damage to components.

➡If installing a new cylinder head, it is necessary to install a new engine coolant air bleed plug into the rear coolant passage of the cylinder head.

➡Do not reuse the cylinder head bolts. Install NEW cylinder head bolts during assembly.

➡Do not use any type of sealant on the cylinder head gasket (unless specified).

15. Clean the engine block cylinder head bolt holes, if required. Thread repair tool J 42385-107, found in J 42385-200, may be used to clean the threads of old thread-locking material.

16. Spray cleaner GM P/N 12346139, or equivalent into the hole.

17. Clean the cylinder head bolt holes with compressed air.

18. Check the cylinder head locating pins for proper installation using the following illustration. The specified measurement (a) from flush is 0.327 inch (8.3mm).

➡When properly installed, with FRONT on the left side, the tab on the cylinder head gasket should be located left of center.

19. Install the NEW cylinder head gasket onto the locating pins.

20. Install the cylinder head onto the locating pins.

21. Install the NEW cylinder head bolts.

22. Tighten the cylinder head bolts in the sequence illustrated.

a. Tighten the M11 cylinder head bolts (1–10) a first pass to 22 ft. lbs. (30 Nm).

b. Tighten the M11 cylinder head bolts (1–10) a second pass to 90° using J 45059.

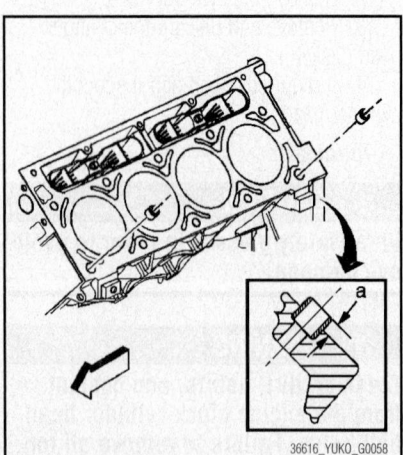

Fig. 112 Check the cylinder head locating pins for proper installation

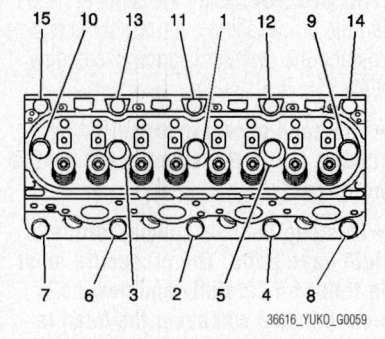

Fig. 113 Cylinder head bolt tightening sequence—left side

c. Tighten the M11 cylinder head bolts (1–10) a final pass to 70° using J 45059.

d. Tighten the M8 cylinder head bolts (11–15) to 22 ft. lbs. (30 Nm). Begin with the center bolt and alternating side-to-side, work outward tightening all of the bolts.

23. Position the ground strap to the rear of the left cylinder head. Tighten the bolt to 12 ft. lbs. (16 Nm).

24. Install the pushrods. Refer to Rocker Arms/Shafts, removal & installation.

25. Install the left exhaust manifold. Refer to Exhaust Manifold, removal & installation.

26. Install the coolant air bleed pipe.

27. Install the intake manifold. Refer to Intake Manifold, removal & installation.

28. Install the alternator bracket. Refer to Alternator, removal & installation.

Right Side

See Figures 112, 114 and 115.

Special Tools:
- J 45059: Angle Meter
- J 42385-200: Common Thread Repair Kit

1. Before servicing the vehicle, refer to the Precautions Section.

2. Release the fuel system pressure.

3. Disconnect the negative battery cable.

4. Remove the oil level indicator.

5. Remove the intake manifold. Refer to Intake Manifold, removal & installation.

6. Remove the coolant air bleed pipe.

7. Remove the right exhaust manifold. Refer to Exhaust Manifold, removal & installation.

8. Remove the pushrods. Refer to Rocker Arms/Shafts, removal & installation.

9. Remove the negative battery cable stud from the front of the right cylinder head.

10. Remove the negative battery cable

terminal and the engine harness terminal from the cylinder head.

➡The cylinder head bolts are of a torque-to-yield design and are NOT to be reused.

11. Remove and discard the cylinder head bolts.

※※ WARNING

After removal, place the cylinder head on 2 wood blocks in order to prevent damage to the sealing surfaces.

12. Remove the cylinder head.

13. Remove and discard the cylinder head gasket.

14. If required, clean and inspect the cylinder head.

To install:

※※ CAUTION

Wear safety glasses in order to avoid eye damage.

※※ WARNING

Clean all dirt, debris, and coolant from the engine block cylinder head bolt holes. Failure to remove all foreign material may result in damaged threads, improperly tightened fasteners, or damage to components.

➡If installing a new cylinder head, it is necessary to install a new engine coolant air bleed plug into the rear coolant passage of the cylinder head.

➡Do not reuse the cylinder head bolts. Install NEW cylinder head bolts during assembly.

➡Do not use any type of sealant on the cylinder head gasket (unless specified).

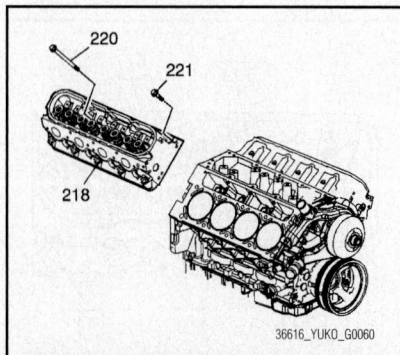

Fig. 114 Remove and discard the cylinder head bolts (220, 221) from the cylinder head (218)—right side

15. Clean the engine block cylinder head bolt holes, if required. Thread repair tool J 42385-107, found in J 42385-200, may be used to clean the threads of old thread-locking material.

16. Spray cleaner GM P/N 12346139, or equivalent, into the bolt holes.

17. Clean the cylinder head bolt holes with compressed air.

18. Check the cylinder head locating pins for proper installation using the following illustration. The specified measurement (a) from flush is 0.327 inch (8.3mm).

➡When properly installed, with FRONT on the right side, the tab on the cylinder head gasket should be located right of center.

19. Install the NEW cylinder head gasket onto the locating pins.

20. Install the cylinder head onto the locating pins.

21. Install the NEW cylinder head bolts.

22. Tighten the cylinder head bolts in the sequence illustrated.

   a. Tighten the M11 cylinder head bolts (1–10) a first pass to 22 ft. lbs. (30 Nm).

   b. Tighten the M11 cylinder head bolts (1–10) a second pass to 90° using J 45059.

   c. Tighten the M11 cylinder head bolts (1–10) a final pass to 70° using J 45059.

   d. Tighten the M8 cylinder head bolts (11–15) to 22 ft. lbs. (30 Nm). Begin with the center bolt (11) and alternating side-to-side, work outward tightening all of the bolts.

23. Position the negative battery cable terminal to the cylinder head.

24. Install the negative battery cable stud to the front of the right cylinder head and tighten the stud to 18 ft. lbs. (25 Nm).

25. Install the pushrods. Refer to Rocker Arms/Shafts, removal & installation.

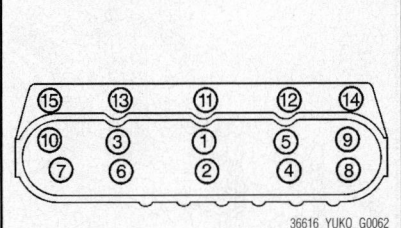

Fig. 115 Cylinder head bolt tightening sequence—right side

26. Install the right exhaust manifold. Refer to Exhaust Manifold, removal & installation.

27. Install the coolant air bleed pipe.

28. Install the intake manifold. Refer to Intake Manifold, removal & installation.

29. Install the oil level indicator.

ENGINE ASSEMBLY

REMOVAL & INSTALLATION

3.0L and 3.6L Engines

See Figure 116.

1. Before servicing the vehicle, refer to the Precautions Section.

2. Disconnect the negative battery cable.

3. Remove the intake manifold cover.

4. Drain the cooling system.

5. Drain the engine oil.

6. Remove the air cleaner assembly.

7. Remove the hood.

8. Remove the drive belt. Refer to Accessory Drive Belts, removal & installation.

9. Disconnect the front Knock Sensor (KS).

10. Disconnect the rear KS and the crank sensor. Refer to Crankshaft Position (CKP) Sensor, removal & installation.

11. Re-position the plastic wire loom/shield on each valve cover, then disconnect the Camshaft Position (CMP) sensor.

12. Disconnect the Manifold Absolute Pressure (MAP) sensor.

13. Disconnect the Evaporative Emission (EVAP) canister purge solenoid.

14. Disconnect the front and rear ignition coils.

15. Disconnect the A/C compressor.

16. Disconnect the coolant temperature sensor.

17. Disconnect the electrical connectors from the Heated Oxygen Sensor HO2S and Electronic Throttle Control (ECT).

18. Unclip harness as necessary and lay the harnesses off to the side.

19. Raise and support the vehicle.

20. Remove the catalytic converters. Refer to Catalytic Converter, removal & installation.

21. Remove the left exhaust manifold only.

22. Remove the engine wiring harness grounds and negative cable from the cylinder head.

23. Remove the starter motor. Refer to Starter, removal & installation.

24. Remove the torque converter bolts.

25. Remove the Air Conditioning (A/C) compressor. DO NOT discharge the A/C system. Support the compressor.

26. Remove the power steering pump and position aside. Refer to Power Steering Pump, removal & installation.

27. If equipped with FWD, remove the transaxle-to-oil pan brace bolts and brace.

28. If equipped with AWD, remove the transfer case bracket and unbolt transfer case from the engine and set aside.

29. Remove the lower transaxle-to-engine bolts.

30. If equipped with FWD, unbolt the intermediate shaft support frame from the engine block and rotate the support away from the block leaving the intermediate shaft and axle in place.

31. Remove the radiator outlet hose from the engine.

32. Remove the engine coolant thermostat housing from the engine.

33. Remove the vacuum hoses from the upper intake manifold.

34. Remove the radiator inlet hose from the engine.

35. Install the engine lifting device to the engine.

36. Remove the upper transaxle-to-engine bolts.

37. Remove the engine from the vehicle.

38. Remove the flywheel. Refer to Engine Flywheel Replacement.

39. Install the engine to the engine stand.

40. Disconnect all electrical connectors, as needed.

41. Transfer parts, as needed.

To install:

42. Remove the engine from the engine stand.

43. Install the flywheel. Refer to Flywheel/Flexplate, removal & installation.

44. Install the engine to the vehicle.

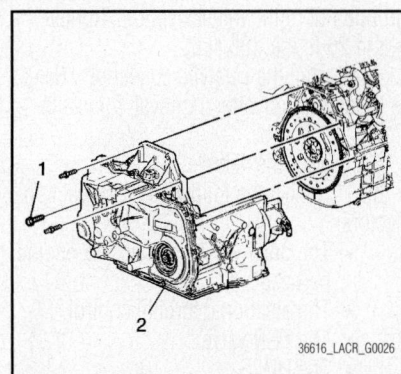

Fig. 116 Remove the lower transaxle-to-engine bolts (1)—3.0L and 3.6L engines

45. Install the upper transaxle-to-engine bolts and tighten to 55 ft. lbs. (75 Nm).

46. Remove the engine lifting device.

47. Install the radiator inlet hose to the engine.

48. Install the battery ground to the rear of engine.

49. Install the fuel lines to the fuel rail.

50. Install the brake booster vacuum hose to the upper intake manifold.

51. Install the vacuum hoses to the upper intake manifold.

52. Install the engine coolant thermostat housing to the engine.

53. Raise the vehicle and remove the transaxle support.

54. Install the radiator outlet hose to the engine.

55. Install the lower transaxle-to-engine bolt and the stud and tighten to 55 ft. lbs. (75 Nm).

56. Position the transaxle to oil pan brace and install the bolts. Tighten the bolts to 50 ft. lbs. (50 Nm).

57. If equipped with AWD, install the transfer case bracket and bolt and tighten the support bracket fasteners to 44 inch lbs. (5 Nm).

   a. Tighten the support bracket-to-engine fasteners to 44 ft. lbs. (60 Nm).

   b. Tighten the support bracket fasteners to 44 ft. lbs. (60 Nm).

58. Install the engine mount.

59. Install the torque converter bolts.

60. Install the power steering pump. Refer to Power Steering Pump, removal & installation.

61. Install the A/C compressor. Refer to Compressor, removal & installation.

62. Install the starter motor. Refer to Starter, removal & installation.

63. Install the torque converter covers.

64. Install the engine wiring harness grounds to the transaxle.

65. Install the engine wiring harness ground nut to the transaxle stud. Tighten the nut to 26 ft. lbs. (35 Nm)

66. Install the catalytic converters. Refer to Catalytic Converter, removal & installation.

67. Lower the vehicle.

68. Connect the following electrical connectors:

   • The body wiring harness-to-engine harness
   • The electronic throttle control
   • The EGR valve
   • The HO2S

69. Connect the coolant temperature sensor.

70. Connect the A/C compressor.

71. Connect the front and rear ignition coils.

72. Connect the EVAP canister purge solenoid.

73. Connect the MAP sensor.

74. Connect the CMP sensor, then reposition the plastic wire loom/shield on each valve cover.

75. Connect the rear KS.

76. Connect the front KS and the crank sensor.

77. Install the drive belt. Refer to Accessory Drive Belts, removal & installation.

78. Install the hood.

79. Install the air cleaner assembly.

80. Connect the negative battery cable.

81. Fill the crankcase with the proper amount and type of engine oil.

82. Fill cooling system with the proper amount and type of fluid.

83. Perform a Crankshaft Position System Variation Learn procedure. Refer to Crankshaft Position System Variation Learn in the Engine Performance Section, under Crankshaft Position (CKP) sensor.

84. Install the intake manifold cover.

85. Inspect for leaks. Correct as necessary.

3.8L Engine

See Figures 117 through 119.

1. Before servicing the vehicle, refer to the Precautions Section.

2. Disconnect the negative battery cable.

3. Remove the hood.

4. Remove the fuel injector sight shield.

5. Raise and support the vehicle.

6. Drain the engine oil.

7. Drain the cooling system.

8. Remove the torque converter covers.

9. Remove the engine ground nut and the engine ground wire from the transaxle stud.

10. Remove the oil level sensor harness retainer bolt.

11. Remove the oil level harness retainer from the engine.

12. Disconnect and reposition the electrical connectors from the following components:

   • Vehicle Speed Sensor (VSS)
   • Oil pressure sensor
   • Oil level sensor
   • Knock sensors
   • Heated Oxygen Sensor (HO2S)

13. Remove the starter motor. Refer to Starter, removal & installation.

14. Remove the engine flywheel-to-torque converter bolts.

15. Scribe the torque converter to the flywheel for installation.

16. Remove the transaxle brace.

17. Remove the engine mount lower nuts.

18. Remove the exhaust manifold pipe stud nuts and reposition the catalytic converter from the exhaust manifold.

19. Remove the right side halfshaft. Refer to Halfshafts, removal & installation.

20. Remove the oil filter adapter housing.

21. Remove the lower transaxle-to-engine bolt and the stud.

22. Lower the vehicle while supporting the transaxle.

23. Remove the air cleaner assembly.

24. Disconnect the fuel line from the fuel rail.

25. Disconnect the fuel vapor line.

26. Loosen the water pump pulley bolts.

27. Remove the drive belt. Refer to Accessory Drive Belts, removal & installation.

28. Remove the water pump pulley bolts and the water pump pulley.

29. Remove the right and the left engine mount struts.

30. Remove the engine mount brackets from the radiator support.

Fig. 117 Remove the transaxle brace—3.8L engine

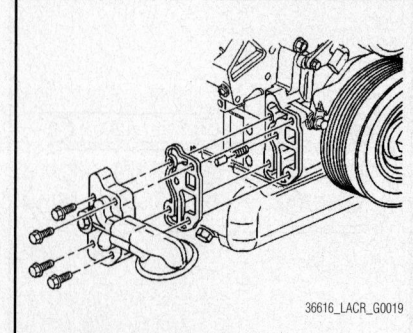

Fig. 118 Remove the oil filter adapter housing—3.8L engine

31. Disconnect the positive battery cable.

32. Remove the engine cooling fans. Refer to Engine Fan, removal & installation.

33. Remove the vacuum booster hose from the engine.

34. Disconnect the A/C vacuum hose from the engine.

35. Remove the power steering pump bolts and pump from the engine. Lay the power steering pump aside.

36. Disconnect the upper engine electrical connectors from the following components:

- Electronic Throttle Control (ETC)
- Fuel injectors
- EVAP purge solenoid
- Exhaust Gas Recirculation (EGR) valve
- Manifold absolute pressure (MAP) sensor
- BARO sensor, if equipped

➡**Note the position of the engine wiring harness during removal.**

37. Remove the upper engine wiring harness from the retaining clips and reposition the engine wiring harness for engine removal.

38. Remove the radiator inlet hose from the engine.

39. Remove the radiator outlet hose from the engine.

40. Remove the heater hoses.

41. Remove the A/C compressor from the engine.

42. Install the engine lifting device.

43. Remove the upper transaxle-to-engine bolts.

44. With the aid of an assistant, remove the engine from the vehicle.

45. Remove the flywheel. Refer to Flywheel/Flexplate, removal & installation.

46. Install the engine to the engine stand.

To install:

47. Remove the engine from the engine stand.

48. Install the flywheel. Refer to Flywheel/Flexplate, removal & installation.

49. With the aid of an assistant, install the engine to the vehicle.

50. Install the upper transaxle-to-engine bolts and tighten the bolts to 55 ft. lbs. (75 Nm).

51. Remove the engine lifting device.

52. Install the A/C compressor to the engine.

53. Install the heater hoses.

54. Install the radiator outlet hose to the engine.

55. Install the radiator inlet hose to the engine.

56. Reposition and install the engine wiring harness to the engine as noted during removal.

57. Connect the upper engine electrical connectors to the following components:

- BARO sensor, if equipped
- MAP sensor
- EGR valve
- EVAP purge solenoid
- Fuel injectors
- Electronic Throttle Control (ETC)

58. Install the upper engine wiring harness to the retaining clips.

59. Install the power steering pump to the engine.

60. Install the power steering pump bolts and tighten the bolts to 25 ft. lbs. (34 Nm).

61. Connect the A/C vacuum hose to the engine.

62. Install the vacuum booster hose to the engine.

63. Install the engine cooling fans.

64. Connect the positive battery cable. Tighten the cable terminal bolt to 11 ft. lbs. (15 Nm).

65. Install the engine mount brackets to the upper radiator support.

66. Install the engine mount struts to the engine mount strut brackets.

67. Install the water pump pulley.

68. Install the water pump pulley bolts and tighten the bolts to 116 inch lbs. (13 Nm).

69. Install the drive belt. Refer to Accessory Drive Belts, removal & installation.

70. Connect the fuel vapor line.

71. Connect the fuel line to the fuel rail.

72. Install the air cleaner assembly.

73. Raise the vehicle and remove the transaxle support.

74. Install the lower transaxle-to-engine bolt and the stud. Tighten the bolt and the stud to 55 ft. lbs. (75 Nm).

75. Install the oil filter adapter housing.

76. Install a new gasket and the catalytic converter to the right exhaust manifold.

77. Install the exhaust manifold pipe stud nuts and tighten the nuts to 26 ft. lbs. (35 Nm).

78. Install the engine mount lower nuts and tighten the nuts to 35 ft. lbs. (47 Nm).

79. Install the transaxle brace.

80. Install the engine flywheel-to-torque converter bolts.

81. Install the starter motor. Refer to Starter, removal & installation.

82. Reposition and connect the electrical connectors to the following components:

- HO2S
- Knock sensors
- Oil level sensor
- Oil pressure sensor
- VSS

83. Install the oil level sensor harness retainer to the engine.

84. Install the oil level sensor harness retainer bolt and tighten the bolt to 89 inch lbs. (10 Nm).

85. Install the engine ground wire and the engine ground wire nut to the transaxle stud. Tighten the nut to 26 ft. lbs. (35 Nm).

86. Install the torque converter covers.

87. Lower the vehicle.

88. Install the fuel injector sight shield.

89. Install the hood.

90. Connect the negative battery cable.

91. Fill the crankcase with the proper amount and type of engine oil.

92. Fill the cooling system with the proper amount and type of fluid.

93. Inspect for leaks.

94. Perform a Crankshaft Position System Variation Learn procedure. Refer to Crankshaft Position System Variation Learn

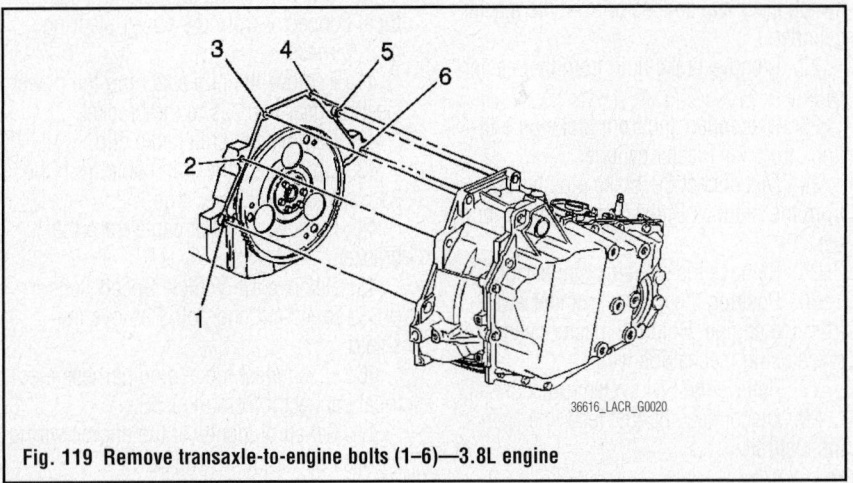

36616_LACR_G0020

Fig. 119 Remove transaxle-to-engine bolts (1–6)—3.8L engine

in the Engine Performance Section, under Crankshaft Position (CKP) sensor.

Variation Learn.

5.3L Engine

See Figures 120 through 124.

Special Tools:

- J 38185: Hose Clamp Pliers
- J 39580: Universal Engine Support Table

1. Before servicing the vehicle, refer to the Precautions Section.
2. Disconnect the negative battery cable.
3. Remove the engine sight shield.
4. Evacuate the (A/C) system.
5. Remove the front tires and wheels.
6. Drain the cooling system.
7. Drain the engine oil.
8. Lower the vehicle.
9. Using the J 38185, reposition the inlet hose clamp at the radiator.
10. Remove the inlet hose from the radiator.
11. Using the J 38185, reposition the outlet hose clamp at the radiator.
12. Disengage the outlet hose clips from the fan shroud.
13. Remove the outlet hose from the radiator.
14. Remove the A/C compressor hose nut at the A/C receiver/dehydrator tube.
15. Remove the A/C compressor hose.
16. Remove the A/C compressor hose nut at the A/C condenser.
17. Remove the A/C compressor hose.
18. Remove the brake booster vacuum hose from the brake booster.
19. Remove the brake booster vacuum hose from the intake manifold.
20. Disconnect the engine harness electrical connectors from the Instrument Panel (I/P) harness electrical connectors.
21. Disconnect the brake fluid level switch electrical connector from the master cylinder.
22. Remove brake fluid from the master cylinder.
23. Disconnect the from brake pipe fittings from the master cylinder.
24. Disconnect the brake pipe fittings from the Antilock Brake System (ABS) module.
25. Remove the master cylinder nuts.
26. Position the master cylinder away from the engine. Hold the master cylinder in place using mechanic's wire.
27. Relieve the fuel system pressure.
28. Disconnect the fuel feed line from the fuel rail.

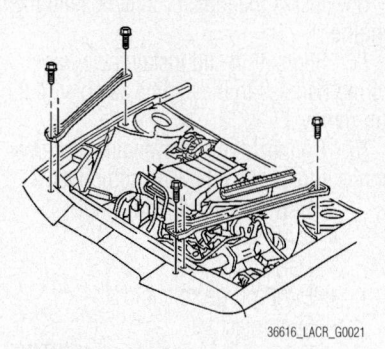

Fig. 120 Remove the right front fender diagonal brace—5.3L engine

29. Disconnect the evaporative emission (EVAP) line from the purge solenoid.
30. Remove the right front fender diagonal brace.
31. Remove the underhood electrical center cover.
32. Loosen the 4 integral bolts attaching the fuse block. Reposition the fuse block.
33. Loosen the engine harness connector bolt. Remove the engine harness connector from the bracket.
34. Disconnect the camshaft position sensor lead.
35. Disconnect the engine harness electrical connector from the ABS module.
36. Disconnect the engine harness electrical connector from the Electronic Brake Control Module (EBCM).
37. Remove the air cleaner assembly.
38. Disconnect the following electrical connectors:

- Transmission Control Module (TCM)
- Engine Control Module (ECM)
- A/C pressure sensor

39. Disconnect the engine harness electrical connector from the Crankshaft Position (CKP) sensor harness.
40. Disconnect the engine harness electrical connector from the power steering gear harness.
41. Remove the clip attaching the power steering gear harness to the bracket.
42. Remove the shift cable clip.
43. Disconnect the shift cable from the transaxle selector lever stud.
44. Remove the shift cable from the bracket.
45. Remove the Vehicle Speed Sensor (VSS) shield nut and bolt. Remove the shield.
46. Disconnect the engine harness electrical connector from the VSS.
47. Set all branches of the engine wiring harness on top of the engine.

48. Reposition the intermediate shaft lower boot.
49. Remove the intermediate shaft to steering gear bolt.
50. Separate the intermediate shaft from the steering gear.
51. Disconnect both front wheel speed sensors.
52. Unclip the ABS wire harness from the lower control arm.
53. Using the J 38185, reposition the heater inlet and outlet hose clamps.
54. Remove the heater inlet and outlet hoses from the heater inlet/outlet pipe.
55. Raise and support the vehicle.
56. Disconnect the stabilizer links from the stabilizer shaft.
57. Disconnect the ball joints from the steering knuckles.
58. Disconnect the power steering pressure hose from the steering gear.
59. Disconnect the power steering pressure line clips from the frame.
60. Disconnect the outer tie rod ends from the steering knuckles.
61. Loosen the power steering hose clamp at the inlet pipe.
62. Remove the power steering hose from the inlet pipe.
63. Remove the left and right wheel drive shafts from the transaxle.
64. Support the wheel drive shafts using mechanic's wire.
65. Remove the transaxle oil cooler line bracket bolt/stud.
66. Disconnect the transaxle oil cooler lines from the transaxle.
67. Remove the positive battery cable nut from the starter.

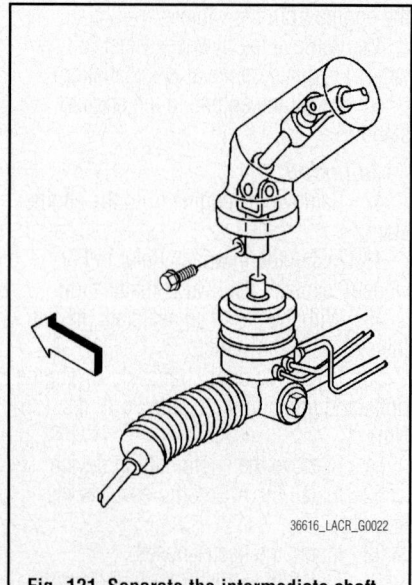

Fig. 121 Separate the intermediate shaft from the steering gear—5.3L engine

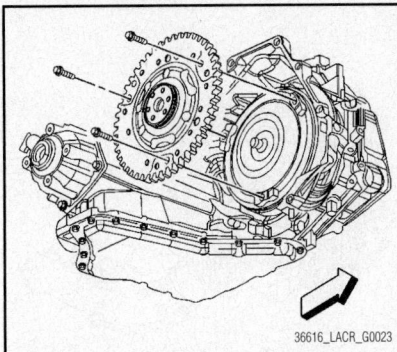

Fig. 122 Remove the flywheel bolts—5.3L engine

68. Remove the cable terminal from the starter.

69. Remove the battery cable ground nut.

70. Remove the cable ground terminal from the stud.

71. Remove the battery cable retainers from the engine frame.

72. Disconnect the exhaust system.

73. Disconnect the O2 sensor harness pigtail.

74. Remove the transaxle converter cover bolt/stud.

75. Remove the converter cover.

76. Remove the flywheel bolts.

77. Remove the front air deflectors.

78. Raise the vehicle enough to place J 39580 under the engine, frame, and front suspension.

79. Support the rear of the vehicle with suitable jackstand.

80. Strap the front of the vehicle to the hoist.

81. Raise the J 39580, Universal Engine Support Table, or lower the vehicle to preload the weight of the engine, frame, and front suspension.

82. Remove the radiator to frame brackets.

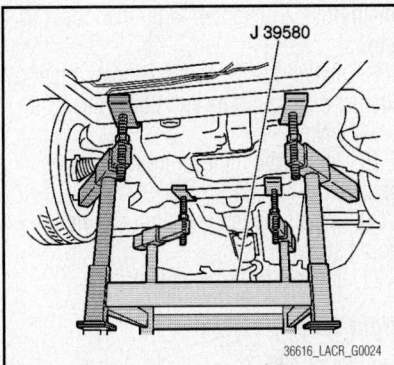

Fig. 123 Positioning the J 39580, Universal Engine Support Table, beneath the vehicle—5.3L engine

83. Remove the engine frame front bolts.

84. Remove the engine frame rear bolts.

85. With the aid of an assistant, lower the J 39580 and/or raise the vehicle to remove the engine and the frame from the vehicle.

86. Ensure that all hoses, wires, and pipes clear the vehicle during the removal process.

87. Use a suitable engine lift to support the engine.

88. Remove the front engine mount to frame nuts.

89. Remove the rear engine mount to frame nuts.

90. Remove the transaxle-to-engine bolts and stud.

91. Separate the engine from the transaxle.

92. Using a suitable engine lift, remove the engine from the frame.

93. Install the engine onto a suitable engine stand.

To install:

94. Using a suitable engine lift, remove the engine from the engine stand.

95. Position and install the engine to the frame and the transaxle.

96. Install the transaxle to engine bolts and stud. Tighten the bolts/stud to 55 ft. lbs. (75 Nm).

97. Install the rear engine mount-to-frame nuts and tighten to 37 ft. lbs. (50 Nm).

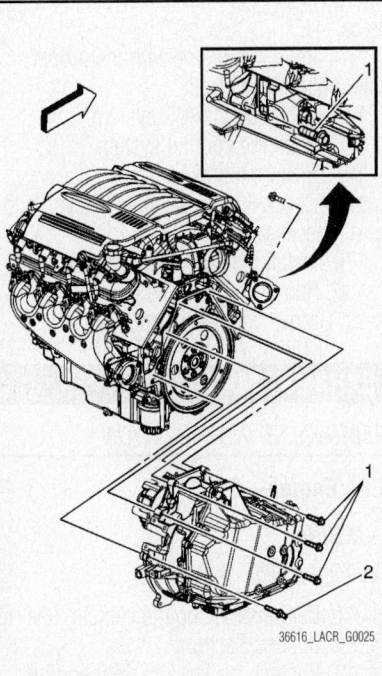

Fig. 124 Remove the transaxle-to-engine bolts (1) and stud (2)—5.3L engine

98. Install the front engine mount-to-frame nuts and tighten to 37 ft. lbs. (50 Nm).

99. Ensure that all hoses, wires, and pipes clear the vehicle during the installation process.

100. With the aid of an assistant, raise the J 39580 and/or lower the vehicle to install the engine and frame to the vehicle.

101. Install the engine frame rear bolts and tighten to 118 ft. lbs. (160 Nm).

102. Install the engine frame front bolts and tighten to 107 ft. lbs. (145 Nm).

103. Install radiator-to-front frame brackets.

104. Lower the J 39580, or raise the vehicle to preload the weight of the engine, frame, and front suspension.

105. Remove the support from under the rear of the vehicle.

106. Raise the vehicle enough to remove the J 39580 from under the engine, frame, and front suspension.

107. Connect the exhaust system and connect the O2 sensor harness pigtail.

108. Install the flywheel bolts and tighten to 47 ft. lbs. (63 Nm).

109. Install the converter cover.

110. Install the transaxle converter cover bolt/stud. Tighten the bolt/stud to 89 inch lbs. (10 Nm).

111. Install the left and right wheel drive shafts into the transaxle.

112. Install the battery cable retainers to the engine frame.

113. Install the front air deflector.

114. Install the cable ground terminal to the stud.

115. Install the battery cable ground nut and tighten to 22 ft. lbs. (30 Nm).

116. Install the cable terminal to the starter.

117. Install the positive battery cable nut to the starter. Tighten the nut to 89 inch lbs. (10 Nm).

118. Connect the transaxle oil cooler lines to the transaxle.

119. Install the transaxle oil cooler line bracket bolt/stud. Tighten the bolt/stud to 18 ft. lbs. (25 Nm).

120. Install the power steering hose to the inlet pipe.

121. Tighten the power steering hose clamp at the inlet pipe to 53 inch lbs. (6 Nm).

122. Connect the power steering pipe to the steering gear.

123. Connect the power steering pipe to the frame clips.

124. Lower the vehicle.

125. Position and install the ball joint nuts.

126. Install the sway links to the stabilizer shaft.

127. Install the tie rod ends to the steering knuckles.

128. Connect the wheel speed sensor electrical connectors.

129. Connect the wheel speed sensor wiring harness to the lower control arm.

130. Install the heater inlet and outlet hoses to the heater inlet/outlet pipe.

131. Using the J 38185, position the heater inlet and outlet hose clamps.

132. Install the intermediate shaft to the steering gear.

133. Install the intermediate shaft to steering gear bolt. Tighten the bolt to 35 ft. lbs. (48 Nm).

134. Position the intermediate shaft lower boot.

135. Route all branches of the engine wiring harness to the correct locations.

136. Connect the engine harness electrical connector to the VSS.

137. Install the VSS shield. Install the VSS shield nut and bolt. Tighten the bolt/nut to 18 ft. lbs. (25 Nm).

138. Install the shift cable to the bracket.

139. Connect the shift cable to the transaxle selector lever stud.

140. Install the shift cable clip.

141. Install the clip attaching the power steering gear harness to the bracket.

142. Connect the engine harness electrical connector to the CKP sensor harness.

143. Connect the engine harness electrical connector to the power steering gear harness.

144. Connect the camshaft position sensor lead to the sensor.

145. Connect the following electrical connectors:
- The TCM
- The ECM
- The A/C pressure sensor

146. Install the air cleaner assembly.

147. Connect the engine harness electrical connector to the EBCM.

148. Connect the engine harness electrical connector to the ABS module.

149. Install the engine harness connector to the bracket. Tighten the engine harness connector bolt to 89 inch lbs. (10 Nm).

150. Position the fuse block. Tighten the 4 integral bolts attaching the fuse block to 89 inch lbs. (10 Nm).

151. Install the electrical center cover.

152. Connect the fuel feed line to the fuel rail.

153. Connect the EVAP line to the purge solenoid.

154. Remove the mechanic's wire holding the master cylinder. Position the master cylinder to the brake booster.

155. Install the master cylinder nuts and tighten the nuts to 24 ft. lbs. (33 Nm).

156. Connect the brake pipe fittings to the ABS module. Tighten the fittings to 11 ft. lbs. (15 Nm).

157. Connect the brake pipe fittings to the master cylinder. Tighten the fittings to 22 ft. lbs. (30 Nm).

158. Connect the brake fluid level switch electrical connector to the master cylinder.

159. Connect the engine harness electrical connectors to the I/P harness electrical connectors.

160. Install the brake booster vacuum hose to the intake manifold.

161. Install the brake booster vacuum hose to the brake booster.

162. Install the A/C compressor hose.

163. Install the A/C compressor hose nut at the A/C condenser. Tighten the nut to 12 ft. lbs. (16 Nm).

164. Install the A/C compressor hose.

165. Install the A/C compressor hose nut at the A/C receiver/dehydrator tube. Tighten the nut to 12 ft. lbs. (16 Nm).

166. Install the outlet hose to the radiator.

167. Connect the outlet hose clips to the fan shroud.

168. Using the J 38185, position the outlet hose clamp at the radiator.

169. Install the inlet hose to the radiator.

170. Using the J 38185, position the inlet hose clamp at the radiator.

171. Install the front tires and wheels.

172. Connect the negative battery cable.

173. Install the right fender diagonal brace.

174. Refill the engine with the proper amount and type of oil.

175. Recharge the A/C system.

176. Refill the cooling system.

177. Bleed the brake system.

178. Check the transaxle fluid level, add fluid if necessary.

179. Install the engine sight shield.

180. Run the engine and inspect for leaks. Correct as necessary.

EXHAUST MANIFOLD

REMOVAL & INSTALLATION

3.6L Engine—2008

Left Side
See Figure 125.

1. Before servicing the vehicle, refer to the Precautions Section.

2. Remove the left and right engine mount struts.

3. Remove the oil level indicator and tube.

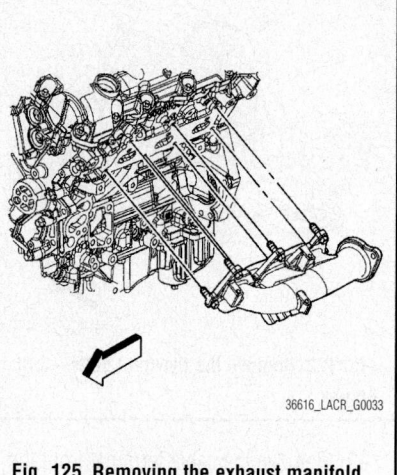

36616_LACR_G0033

Fig. 125 Removing the exhaust manifold (left side)—3.6L engine (2008)

4. Remove the exhaust crossover pipe to left exhaust manifold nuts.

5. Remove the exhaust manifold heat shield bolts.

6. Remove the exhaust manifold heat shield.

7. Remove the exhaust manifold bolts.

8. Remove the exhaust manifold.

9. Remove and discard the exhaust manifold gasket.

10. Clean and inspect the exhaust manifold sealing surfaces.

To install:

11. Install one exhaust manifold bolt through a bolt hole in the manifold.

12. Install the NEW exhaust manifold gasket onto the bolt.

13. Position the exhaust manifold to the cylinder head.

14. Install the exhaust manifold using the one installed bolt until snug.

15. Install the remaining exhaust manifold bolts and tighten to 22 ft. lbs. (30 Nm).

16. Install the exhaust manifold heat shield.

17. Install the exhaust manifold heat shield bolts and tighten to 89 inch lbs. (10 Nm).

18. Install the exhaust crossover pipe to exhaust manifold nuts and tighten to 18 ft. lbs. (25 Nm).

19. Install the oil level indicator and tube.

20. Install the left and right engine mount struts.

21. Inspect for exhaust leaks.

Right Side
See Figure 126.

1. Before servicing the vehicle, refer to the Precautions Section.

2. Remove the air inlet duct.

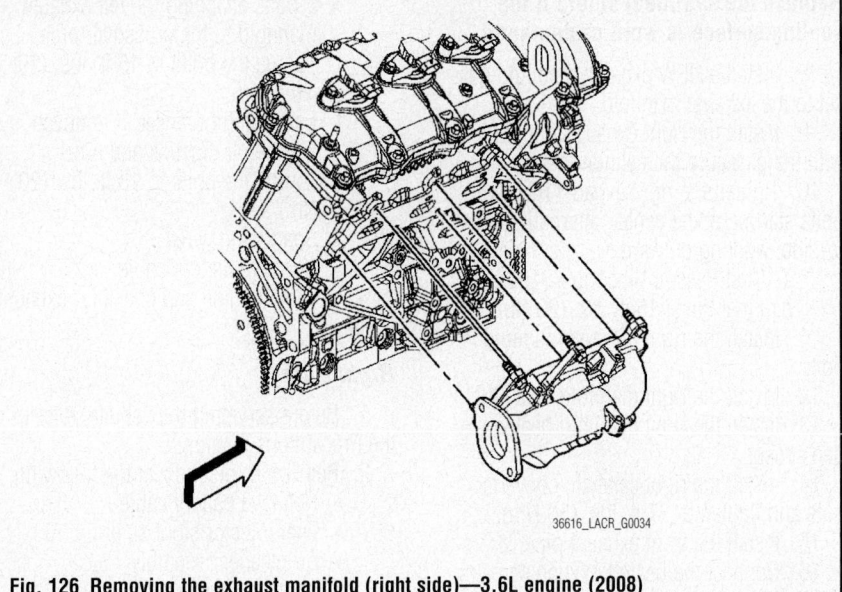

Fig. 126 Removing the exhaust manifold (right side)—3.6L engine (2008)

3. Remove the master cylinder fluid level sensor in order to provide clearance for lowering the powertrain.

4. Remove the engine mount struts.

5. Raise and support the vehicle.

6. Remove the catalytic converter. Refer to Catalytic Converter, removal & installation.

➡**Use a long extension in order to remove the exhaust crossover pipe nuts.**

7. Remove the exhaust crossover pipe to right bank exhaust manifold nuts.

8. Remove the exhaust manifold bolts.

9. Remove the exhaust manifold.

10. Remove and discard the exhaust manifold gasket.

11. If replacing the exhaust manifold, remove the exhaust manifold heat shield bolts and the heat shield.

12. Clean the exhaust manifold sealing surfaces.

To install:

13. If the exhaust manifold was replaced, position the exhaust manifold heat shield to the exhaust manifold.

14. Install the exhaust manifold heat shield bolts and tighten to 89 inch lbs. (10 Nm).

15. Insert one bolt through a bolt hole in the exhaust manifold.

16. Position the NEW exhaust manifold gasket over the bolt.

17. Position the exhaust manifold to the cylinder head.

18. Tighten the bolt until snug.

19. Install the remaining exhaust manifold bolts and tighten to 15 ft. lbs. (20 Nm).

20. Install the exhaust crossover pipe to right bank exhaust manifold nuts and tighten to 25 ft. lbs. (34 Nm).

21. Install the catalytic converter. Refer to Catalytic Converter, removal & installation.

22. Connect the intermediate steering shaft to the steering gear.

23. Lower the vehicle.

24. Install the engine mount struts.

25. Install the master cylinder fluid level sensor.

26. Install the air inlet duct.

27. Inspect for exhaust leaks.

3.0L and 3.6L Engines—2010

Left Side

See Figure 127.

✷✷ CAUTION

While the engine is operating, the exhaust system will become extremely hot. To prevent burns, avoid contacting a hot exhaust system.

1. Before servicing the vehicle, refer to the Precautions Section.

2. Remove the front exhaust pipe.

3. Disconnect the left manifold heated oxygen sensor.

4. Remove the left exhaust manifold heat shield.

5. Remove the left catalytic converter nuts, bolt and seal, to the left exhaust manifold.

6. Remove the left exhaust manifold bolts and gasket from the cylinder head. Discard the old gasket.

7. If reusing the exhaust manifold, clean and inspect the exhaust manifold sealing surfaces.

To install:

➡**Inspect the catalytic converter seal/heat shield sealing surface. Replace the seal/heat shield if the sealing surface is worn or damaged.**

8. Install a NEW exhaust manifold gasket to the exhaust manifold.

9. Install the left exhaust manifold with the gasket to the cylinder head.

10. Tighten the left exhaust manifold bolts starting at the center, alternating side-to-side, working outward.

a. First Pass: 84 inch lbs. (10 Nm).

b. Final Pass: 15 ft. lbs. (20 Nm).

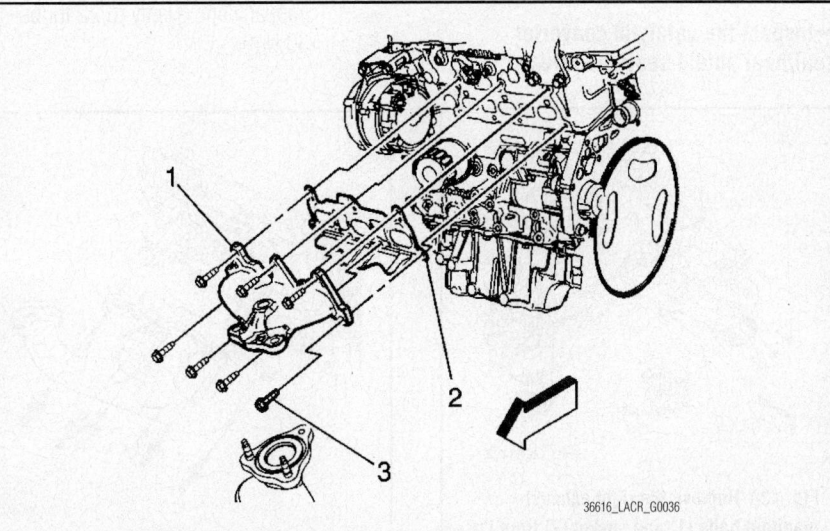

Fig. 127 Remove the left exhaust manifold bolts (3) and gasket (2) from the cylinder head—3.0L and 3.6L engines (2010)

11. Install the left exhaust manifold bolts.

12. Install the left manifold heat shield.

13. Connect the left exhaust manifold heated oxygen sensor.

14. Install the left catalytic converter nuts, bolt and gasket. Tighten to 37 ft. lbs. (50 Nm).

15. Install the right catalytic converter nuts and gasket. Tighten to 37 ft. lbs. (50 Nm).

16. Install the front exhaust pipe.

17. Connect the heated oxygen sensors.

18. Inspect the exhaust system for leaks.

Right Side

See Figure 128.

✳✳ CAUTION

While the engine is operating, the exhaust system will become extremely hot. To prevent burns, avoid contacting a hot exhaust system.

1. Before servicing the vehicle, refer to the Precautions Section.

2. Remove the front exhaust pipe.

3. Disconnect the right exhaust manifold heated oxygen sensor.

4. Remove the right exhaust manifold heat shield.

5. Remove the right catalytic converter nuts and seal to the right exhaust manifold.

6. Remove the right exhaust manifold bolts and gasket from the cylinder head. Discard the old gasket.

7. If reusing the exhaust manifold, clean and inspect the exhaust manifold sealing surfaces.

To install:

➡Inspect the catalytic converter seal/heat shield sealing surface.

Replace the seal/heat shield if the sealing surface is worn or damaged.

8. Install a NEW exhaust manifold gasket to the exhaust manifold.

9. Install the right exhaust manifold with the gasket to the cylinder head.

10. Tighten the right exhaust manifold bolts starting at the center, alternating side-to-side, working outward.

  a. First Pass: 84 inch lbs. (10 Nm).

  b. Final Pass: 15 ft. lbs. (20 Nm).

11. Install the right exhaust manifold bolts.

12. Install the right manifold heat shield.

13. Install the right manifold heated oxygen sensor.

14. Install the right catalytic converter nuts and tighten to 37 ft. lbs. (50 Nm).

15. Install the front exhaust pipe.

16. Connect the heated oxygen sensors.

17. Inspect the exhaust system for leaks.

3.8L Engine

Left Side

See Figure 129.

1. Before servicing the vehicle, refer to the Precautions Section.

2. Remove or disconnect the following:
- Negative battery cable
- Spark plug wires
- Engine oil dipstick and tube
- Left side lift bracket, if necessary
- 2 bolts attaching the left exhaust manifold to the crossover pipe
- Exhaust manifold

To install:

3. Install or connect the following:
- Exhaust manifold with a new gasket. Torque the studs and bolts gradually and evenly to 22 ft. lbs. (30 Nm).

- 2 bolts attaching the left exhaust manifold to the crossover pipe. Torque the bolts to 15 ft. lbs. (20 Nm).
- Left side lift bracket, if removed
- Engine oil dipstick and tube. Torque the bolts to 15 ft. lbs. (20 Nm).
- Spark plug wires
- Negative battery cable

4. Run the engine and check for exhaust leaks.

Right Side

1. Before servicing the vehicle, refer to the Precautions Section.

2. Remove or disconnect the following:
- Negative battery cable
- Fuel injector sight shield
- Air cleaner assembly
- Spark plug wires
- Brake booster heat shield
- Crossover pipe
- Engine harness from the right hand engine lift hook bracket
- Transaxle fluid dipstick and tube
- Oxygen (O_2S) sensor
- Exhaust Gas Recirculation (EGR) feed pipe bolt from the manifold
- Transaxle oil level tube and seal
- Exhaust manifold flange nuts
- Front exhaust pipe
- Engine lift bracket
- Exhaust manifold

To install:

3. Install or connect the following:
- Manifold to the cylinder head and crossover pipe using new gaskets
- Manifold mounting studs. Torque the studs and bolts to 22 ft. lbs. (30 Nm), beginning at the center and working outwards.
- Engine lift bracket
- Front exhaust pipe
- Front exhaust pipe to manifold nuts. Torque the nuts to 22 ft. lbs. (30 Nm).
- Transaxle dipstick tube seal and the tube
- EGR feed pipe to the manifold
- O_2S sensor
- Spark plug wires to the spark plugs
- Engine harness to the right hand engine lift hook bracket
- Crossover pipe
- Brake booster heat shield
- Air cleaner assembly
- Fuel injector sight shield
- Negative battery cable

4. Run the engine and check for exhaust leaks.

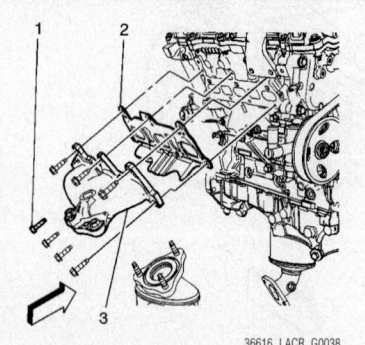

36616_LACR_G0038

Fig. 128 Remove the right exhaust manifold bolts (1) and gasket (2) from the cylinder head—3.0L and 3.6L engines (2010)

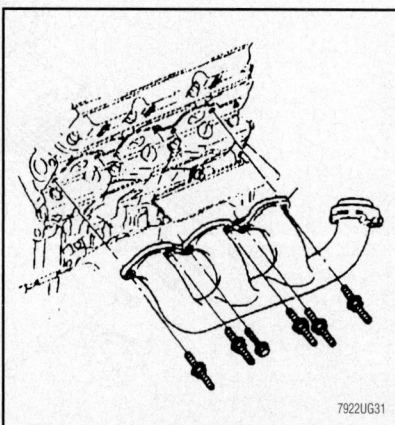

7922UG31

Fig. 129 Exploded view of the left exhaust manifold mounting—3.8L engine

5.3L Engine

Left Side

See Figure 130.

1. Before servicing the vehicle, refer to the Precautions Section.
2. Remove the engine sight shield.
3. Remove the exhaust crossover pipe heat shield in order to access the cross pipe to the exhaust manifold nuts.
4. Remove the exhaust crossover pipe nuts from the left exhaust manifold.
5. Remove the left side spark plugs.
6. Remove the oil level indicator tube.
7. Remove the exhaust manifold heat shield bolts.
8. Remove the exhaust manifold heat shield.
9. Remove the heater hose retainer bolts in order to be able to remove the manifold.
10. Remove the exhaust manifold bolts.
11. Remove the exhaust manifold.
12. Remove and discard the exhaust manifold gasket.

To install:

➡Tighten the exhaust manifold bolts as specified in the service procedure. Improperly installed and/or leaking exhaust manifold gaskets my affect vehicle emissions and/or On Board Diagnostic (OBD) II system performance.

➡The cylinder head exhaust manifold bolt hole threads must be clean and free of debris or thread-locking material.

➡DO NOT apply threadlock to the first 3 threads of the bolts.

13. Apply a 0.2 inch (5mm) wide band of threadlock GM P/N 12345493 (Canadian

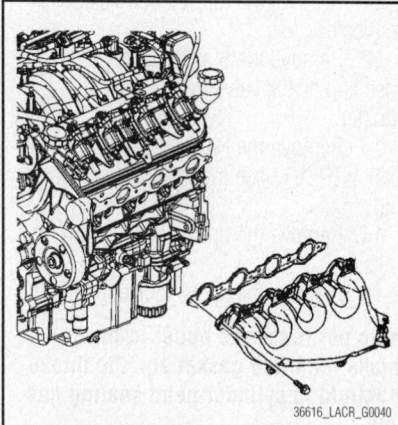

Fig. 130 Removing the left exhaust manifold—5.3L engine

36616_LACR_G0040

P/N 10953488), or equivalent, to the threads of the exhaust manifold bolts.

14. Install a NEW exhaust manifold gasket.
15. Install the exhaust manifold and bolts. Tighten the bolts by alternating from side to side, and work toward the outside. Tighten the bolts beginning with the center 2 bolts.
    a. First pass to 11 ft. lbs. (15 Nm).
    b. Final pass to 15 ft. lbs. (20 Nm).
16. Using a flat punch, bend over the exposed edge of the exhaust manifold gasket at the rear of the left cylinder head.
17. Install the exhaust manifold heat shield.
18. Install the exhaust manifold heat shield bolts. Tighten the bolts to 80 inch lbs. (9 Nm).
19. Install the oil level indicator tube.
20. Install the left side spark plugs.
21. Install the exhaust crossover pipe nuts to the left exhaust manifold. Tighten the nuts to 18 ft. lbs. (25 Nm).
22. Install the exhaust crossover pipe heat shield.
23. Install the heater pipe retainer bolts and tighten bolts to 12 ft. lbs. (16 Nm).
24. Install the engine sight shield.

Right Side

1. Before servicing the vehicle, refer to the Precautions Section.
2. Remove the engine sight shield.
3. Remove the spark plugs.
4. Remove the exhaust crossover pipe nuts from the right exhaust manifold.
5. Disconnect the catalytic converter from the exhaust manifold. Refer to Catalytic Converter, removal & installation.
6. Support the catalytic convertor and exhaust system with the mechanics wire.
7. Lower the vehicle.
8. Remove the ignition coil.
9. Remove the Heated Oxygen Sensor (HO2S).
10. Remove the exhaust manifold heat shield bolts.
11. Remove the exhaust manifold heat shield.
12. Remove the exhaust manifold bolts.
13. Remove the exhaust manifold.
14. Remove and discard the exhaust manifold gasket.

To install:

➡Tighten the exhaust manifold bolts as specified in the service procedure. Improperly installed and/or leaking exhaust manifold gaskets my affect vehicle emissions and/or On Board

Diagnostic (OBD) II system performance.

➡The cylinder head exhaust manifold bolt hole threads must be clean and free of debris or thread-locking material.

➡DO NOT apply threadlock to the first 3 threads of the bolts.

15. Apply a 0.2 inch (5mm) wide band of threadlock GM P/N 12345493 (Canadian P/N 10953488), or equivalent, to the threads of the exhaust manifold bolts.
16. Install a NEW exhaust manifold gasket.
17. Install the exhaust manifold and bolts. Tighten the bolts beginning with the center 2 bolts. Alternate from side to side, and work toward the outside.
    a. First pass to 11 ft. lbs. (15 Nm).
    b. Final pass to 15 ft. lbs. (20 Nm).
18. Using a flat punch, bend over the exposed edge of the exhaust manifold gasket at the rear of the right cylinder head.
19. Install the exhaust manifold heat shield.
20. Install the exhaust manifold heat shield bolts. Tighten the bolts to 80 inch lbs. (9 Nm).
21. Install the HO2S sensor. Refer to Heated Oxygen (HO2S) Sensor, removal & installation.
22. Raise the vehicle.
23. Remove the mechanics wire from the exhaust system and connect the catalytic converter. Refer to Catalytic Converter, removal & installation.
24. Install the exhaust crossover pipe nuts to the right exhaust manifold. Tighten the nuts to 18 ft. lbs. (25 Nm).
25. Install the ignition coil
26. Install the spark plugs.
27. Install the fuel injector sight shield.

FLYWHEEL

REMOVAL & INSTALLATION

3.0L and 3.6L Engines

See Figure 131.

1. Before servicing the vehicle, refer to the Precautions Section.
2. Remove the transaxle.
3. Lock the flywheel from moving and remove the engine flywheel bolts and the flywheel.
4. Clean and inspect the flywheel. If the flywheel teeth are damaged, inspect the starter for proper operation. Replace the starter if there is excessive wear or damage to the starter drive.

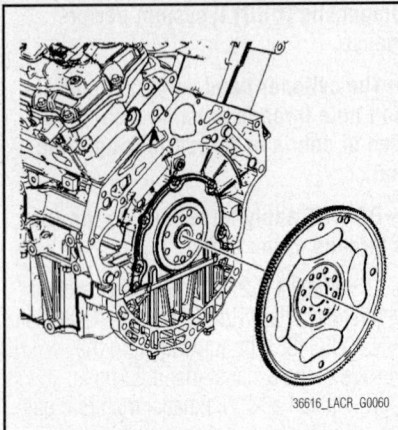

Fig. 131 Removing the flywheel—3.0L and 3.6L engines

36616_LACR_G0060

To install:

5. Place the engine flywheel in position on the crankshaft.

6. Install 2 NEW bolts in location at the top and bottom of the engine flywheel bolt pattern allowing the engine flywheel to hang in position.

7. Install the remaining NEW engine flywheel bolts.

8. Tighten the engine flywheel bolts to 22 ft. lbs. (30 Nm), plus an additional 45°.

3.8L Engine

1. Before servicing the vehicle, refer to the Precautions Section.

2. Remove the transaxle.

3. Lock the flywheel from moving and remove the engine flywheel bolts and the flywheel.

4. Loosen the 8 engine flywheel bolts.

5. Remove 7 of the 8 engine flywheel bolts, leaving one bolt at the top of the crankshaft rotation.

6. Firmly grasp the engine flywheel and remove the remaining bolt. Do not drop the engine flywheel when removing the final bolt.

7. Remove the engine flywheel.

To install:

8. Place the engine flywheel in position on the crankshaft.

9. Hold the flywheel from turning and install the new engine flywheel bolts.

10. Tighten the engine flywheel bolts to 11 ft. lbs. (15 Nm), plus an additional 50°.

11. Install the transaxle.

5.3L Engine

See Figures 132 and 133.

1. Before servicing the vehicle, refer to the Precautions Section.

2. Remove the transmission. Refer to Automatic Transmission Assembly, removal & installation.

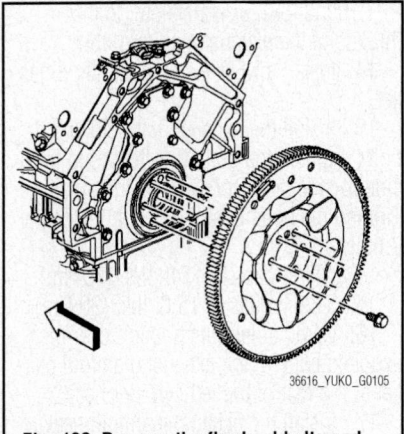

Fig. 132 Remove the flywheel bolts and the flywheel

36616_YUKO_G0105

➡ Note the position and direction of the engine flywheel before removal.

3. Remove the flywheel bolts.

4. Remove the flywheel.

5. Install two M11 x 1.5mm bolts to the threaded holes of the spacer, if applicable.

6. Rotate the bolts clockwise to remove the spacer.

7. Remove the spacer from the rear of the crankshaft, if applicable.

To install:

➡ The flywheel does not use a locating pin for alignment and will not initially seat against the crankshaft flange or spacer, if applicable, but will be pulled onto the crankshaft by the engine flywheel bolts. This procedure requires a 3-stage tightening process.

8. Install the spacer, if applicable, onto the rear of the crankshaft.

➡ Longer flywheel bolts must be used on applications using a flywheel spacer.

9. Install the flywheel and bolts to the crankshaft.

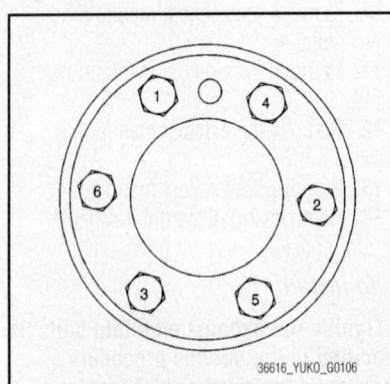

Fig. 133 Flywheel bolt tightening sequence

36616_YUKO_G0106

10. Apply thread-lock to the threads of the flywheel bolts.

11. Tighten the flywheel bolts according to the sequence shown.

  a. Step 1: Tighten the bolts to 15 ft. lbs. (20 Nm).

  b. Step 2: Tighten the bolts to 37 ft. lbs. (50 Nm).

  c. Step 3: Tighten the bolts to 74 ft. lbs. (100 Nm).

12. Install the transmission. Refer to Automatic Transmission Assembly, removal & installation.

INTAKE MANIFOLD

REMOVAL & INSTALLATION

3.6L Engine—2008

Lower Manifold

See Figure 134.

1. Before servicing the vehicle, refer to the Precautions Section.

2. Turn the ignition OFF.

3. Remove the air inlet duct.

4. Remove the fuel pressure and Evaporative Emission (EVAP) hoses from the engine.

5. Disconnect the BARO sensor electrical connector, if equipped.

➡ Do not disconnect the Engine Control Module (ECM) electrical connectors.

6. Remove the ECM bracket with the ECM and reposition aside.

7. Disconnect the purge solenoid electrical connector.

8. Disconnect the purge solenoid electrical connector.

9. Remove the wiring harness from the right side of the intake manifold.

10. Disconnect the fuel injector electrical connector.

11. Remove the throttle body electrical connector.

12. Remove the brake booster vacuum hose and check valve from the brake booster.

13. Remove the Positive Crankcase Ventilation (PCV) hose from the intake manifold.

14. Remove the upper intake manifold bolts.

15. Remove the upper intake manifold.

➡ Do not reuse the upper to lower intake manifold gasket and the intake manifold to cylinder head sealing gaskets.

16. Remove the upper to lower intake manifold bolts.

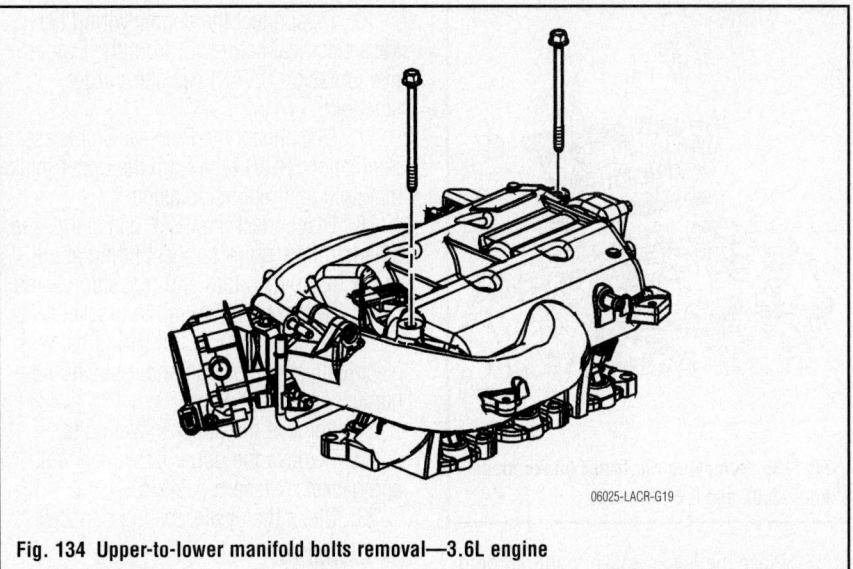

Fig. 134 Upper-to-lower manifold bolts removal—3.6L engine

17. Remove the fuel rail feed hose bracket bolts from the upper intake manifold.

18. Remove the fuel injector wiring harness bracket bolt from the upper intake manifold.

19. Remove the upper intake manifold from the lower intake manifold.

20. Remove and discard the upper to lower intake manifold gaskets.

21. Clean and inspect the intake manifold and the sealing surfaces.

To install:

→**Do not reuse the upper to lower intake manifold gasket and the intake manifold to cylinder head sealing gaskets.**

22. Install the NEW upper to lower intake manifold gaskets.

23. Install the upper intake manifold to the lower intake manifold.

24. Install the fuel injector wiring harness bracket bolts to the upper intake manifold. Tighten the fuel injector wiring harness bracket bolts to 89 inch lbs. (10 Nm).

25. Install the fuel rail feed hose bracket bolt to the upper intake manifold. Tighten the fuel rail feed hose bracket bolt to 89 inch lbs. (10 Nm).

26. Install the upper to lower intake manifold bolts. Tighten the upper to lower intake manifold bolts to 17 ft. lbs. (23 Nm).

27. Install the intake manifold.

28. Install the PCV hose to the intake manifold.

29. Install the brake booster vacuum hose and check valve to the brake booster.

30. Install the throttle body electrical connector.

31. Connect the fuel injector electrical connector.

32. Install the wiring harness to the right side of the intake manifold. Tighten the wiring harness bracket bolts to 89 inch lbs. (10 Nm).

33. Connect the purge solenoid electrical connector.

34. Install the ECM bracket with the ECM.

35. Connect the BARO sensor electrical connector.

36. Install the fuel pressure and EVAP hoses to the engine.

37. Install the air inlet duct.

Upper Manifold

See Figure 135.

1. Before servicing the vehicle, refer to the Precautions Section.

2. Turn the ignition OFF.

3. Remove the air inlet duct.

4. Relieve the fuel system pressure.

5. Remove the fuel pressure and Evaporative Emission (EVAP) hoses from the engine.

6. Remove the purge line from the purge line retainer.

7. Remove the fuel feed hose bracket bolt and reposition the fuel feed hose.

→**Do not disconnect the Engine Control Module (ECM) electrical connectors. Do not remove the ECM from the ECM bracket.**

8. Remove the ECM bracket with the ECM and position it aside.

9. Disconnect the purge solenoid electrical connector.

10. Remove the wiring harness from the right side of the intake manifold.

11. Disconnect the fuel injector electrical connector.

12. Remove the fuel injector electrical connector from the fuel injector electrical connector bracket.

13. Remove the throttle body electrical connector.

14. Remove the brake booster vacuum hose and check valve from the brake booster.

15. Remove the electrical connector for the BARO sensor.

16. Remove the Positive Crankcase Ventilation (PCV) hose from the intake manifold.

17. Remove the intake manifold bolts.

18. Remove the upper intake manifold.

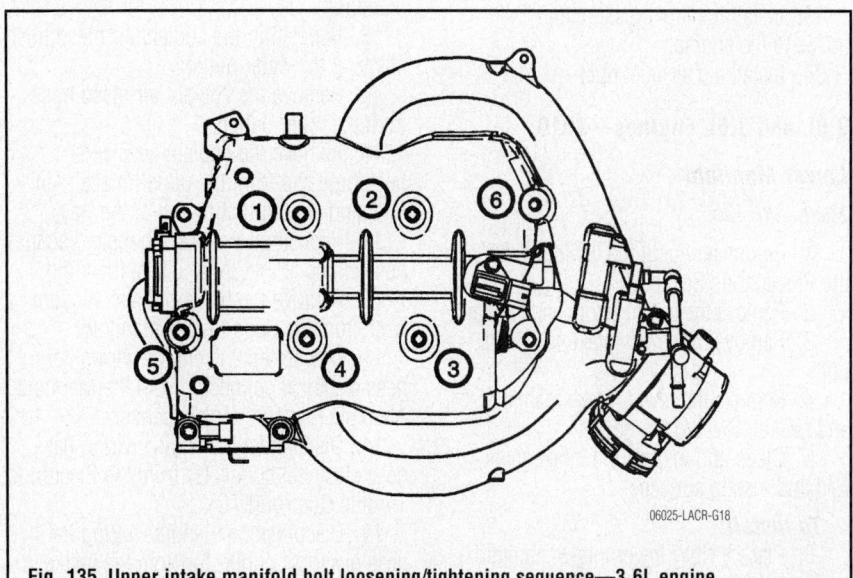

Fig. 135 Upper intake manifold bolt loosening/tightening sequence—3.6L engine

19. Remove and discard the upper intake manifold gasket.

20. Clean and inspect the intake manifold and the sealing surfaces.

To install:

21. Install the intake manifold bolts. Tighten the intake manifold bolts in the order shown to 17 ft. lbs. (23 Nm).

22. Install the PCV hose to the intake manifold.

23. Install the brake booster vacuum hose and check valve to the brake booster.

24. Install the throttle body electrical connector.

25. Reconnect the electrical connector for the BARO sensor, if equipped.

26. Install the fuel injector electrical connector to the fuel injector electrical connector bracket.

27. Install the ECM bracket.

28. Connect the fuel injector electrical connector.

29. Install the wiring harness and bracket to the right side of the intake manifold. Tighten the wiring harness bracket bolts to 89 inch lbs. (10 Nm).

30. Connect the purge solenoid electrical connector.

✳✳ WARNING

In order to prevent any possible electrostatic discharge damage to the ECM, do not touch the connector pins.

31. Install the fuel feed hose bracket and the fuel feed hose bracket bolt. Tighten the fuel feed hose bracket bolt to 89 inch lbs. (10 Nm).

32. Install the purge line to the purge line retainer.

33. Install the fuel pressure and EVAP hoses to the engine.

34. Install the air inlet duct.

3.0L and 3.6L Engines—2010

Lower Manifold

See Figure 136.

1. Before servicing the vehicle, refer to the Precautions Section.

2. Remove the fuel injectors and fuel rail.

3. Remove the lower intake manifold bolts.

4. Remove the lower intake manifold and gasket. Discard the gasket.

5. Clean and inspect the intake manifold and mating surfaces.

To install:

6. Place a NEW lower intake manifold gasket onto the cylinder heads.

Fig. 136 Removing the lower intake manifold—3.0L and 3.6L engines

7. Place the lower intake manifold onto the cylinder heads.

8. Install the lower intake manifold bolts and tighten to 17 ft. lbs. (23 Nm).

9. Install the fuel injectors and fuel rail.

Upper Manifold

See Figure 137.

1. Before servicing the vehicle, refer to the Precautions Section.

2. Remove the fuel injector sight shield.

3. Remove the air cleaner outlet duct.

4. Disconnect the fuel feed line quick connect fitting from the fuel rail.

5. Remove the fuel feed pipe line nut and remove the fuel feed line clip from the stud.

6. Reposition the fuel feed line out of the way.

7. Remove the coolant air bleed hose/pipe clip bolt from the upper intake manifold.

8. Reposition the coolant air bleed hose clamp at the water outlet.

9. Remove the coolant air bleed hose from the water outlet.

10. Remove the coolant air bleed hose/pipe clip from the upper intake manifold stud and reposition out of the way.

11. Reposition the brake booster vacuum hose clamp at the upper intake manifold.

12. Remove the brake booster vacuum hose from the upper intake manifold.

13. Disconnect the engine wiring harness electrical connector from the Manifold Absolute Pressure (MAP) sensor.

14. Disconnect the engine wiring harness electrical connector from the Electronic Throttle Control (ETC).

15. Disconnect the engine wiring harness electrical connector from the intake manifold tuning valve.

16. Disconnect the engine wiring harness electrical connector from the Evaporative Emission (EVAP) canister purge solenoid.

17. Disconnect the Positive Crankcase Ventilation (PCV) tube from the upper intake manifold and reposition aside.

18. Disconnect the EVAP canister purge solenoid tube quick connect fitting at the upper intake manifold and reposition aside.

19. Remove the fuel rail to bracket bolt.

20. Remove the fuel rail wiring harness electrical connector bolt and reposition the harness out of the way.

21. Remove the upper intake bolts.

22. Remove the upper intake manifold and gaskets. Discard gaskets.

23. Clean the gasket mating surfaces.

To install:

24. Place NEW upper intake manifold gaskets onto the lower intake manifold.

25. Place the upper intake manifold onto the lower intake manifold.

26. Install the upper intake bolts and tighten to 17 ft. lbs. (23 Nm).

27. Position the fuel rail wiring harness and install the fuel rail wiring harness electrical connector bolt Tighten to 89 inch lbs. (10 Nm).

28. Install the fuel rail to bracket bolt. Tighten to 89 inch lbs. (10 Nm).

29. Position and install the EVAP canister purge solenoid tube quick connect fitting to the upper intake manifold.

30. Position and install the PCV tube to the upper intake manifold.

31. Connect the engine wiring harness electrical connector to the EVAP canister purge solenoid.

32. Connect the engine wiring harness electrical connector to the intake manifold tuning valve.

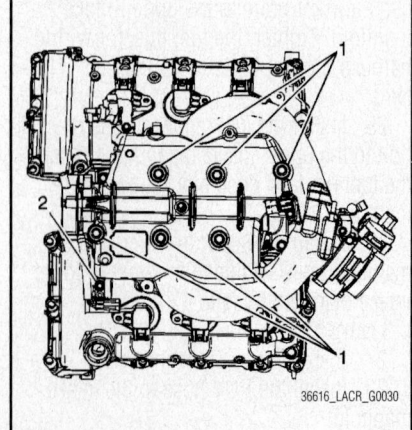

Fig. 137 Removing the upper intake bolts—3.0L and 3.6L engines

33. Connect the engine wiring harness electrical connector to the ETC.

34. Connect the engine wiring harness electrical connector to the MAP sensor.

35. Install the brake booster vacuum hose to the upper intake manifold.

36. Position the brake booster vacuum hose clamp at the upper intake manifold.

37. Position and install the coolant air bleed hose/pipe clip to the upper intake manifold stud.

38. Install the coolant air bleed hose to the water outlet.

39. Position the coolant air bleed hose clamp at the water outlet.

40. Install the coolant air bleed hose/pipe clip bolt to the upper intake manifold. Tighten to 89 inch lbs. (10 Nm).

41. Position the fuel feed line and install the fuel feed line clip to the stud.

Install the fuel feed line nut. Tighten to 89 inch lbs. (10 Nm).

42. Connect the fuel feed line quick connect fitting to the fuel rail.

43. Install the air cleaner outlet duct.

44. Install the fuel injector sight shield.

3.8L Engine

See Figures 138 through 140.

1. Before servicing the vehicle, refer to the Precautions Section.

2. Disconnect the negative battery cable.

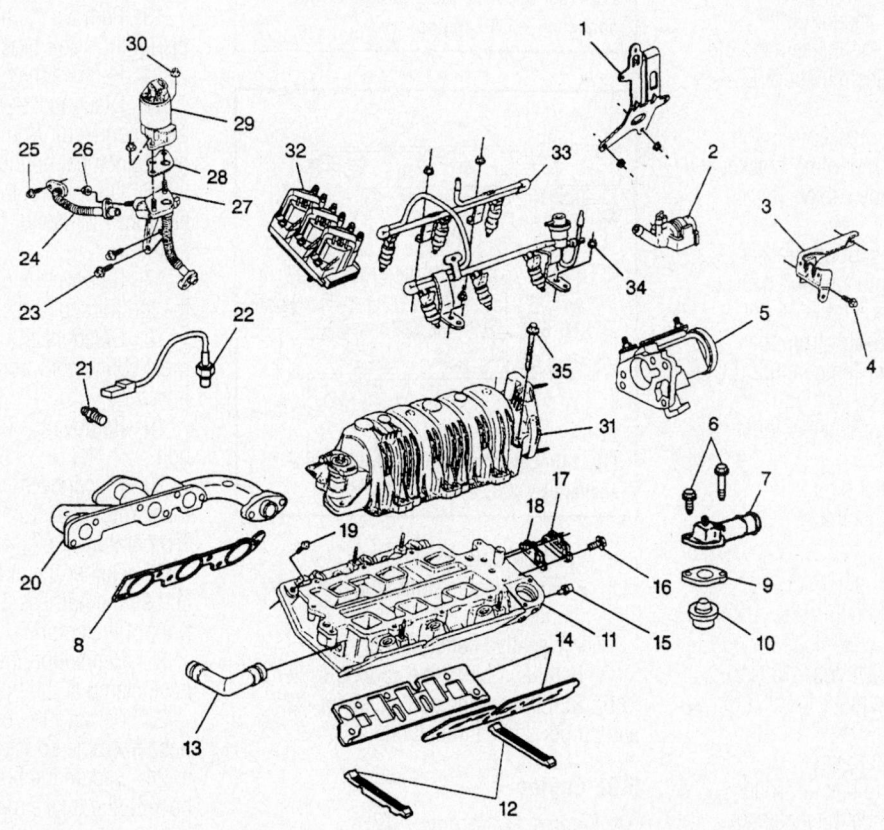

1 Fuel Injector Sight Shield Bracket	19 Lower Intake Manifold Bolt
2 Vacuum Source Manifold	20 Exhaust Manifold (Right)
3 Accelerator Cable Control Bracket	21 Exhaust Manifold Bolt/Stud
4 Throttle Body Support Bolt	22 Exhaust Oxygen Sensor
5 Throttle Body	23 EGR Valve Adapter Bolt
6 Water Outlet Bolt	24 EGR Valve Outlet Pipe
7 Water Outlet	25 EGR Valve Outlet Pipe Bolt
8 Exhaust Manifold Gasket	26 EGR Valve Outlet Pipe Nut
9 Water Outlet Gasket	27 EGR Valve Adapter
10 Thermostat	28 EGR Valve Gasket
11 Lower Intake Manifold	29 EGR Valve
12 Intake Manifold Seal	30 EGR Valve Nut
13 Heater Water Inlet Pipe	31 Upper Intake Manifold
14 Lower Intake Manifold Gasket	32 ICM
15 Coolant Temperature Sensor	33 Fuel Injection Rail
16 Engine Coolant Manifold Bolt	34 Fuel Injector Rail Nut
17 Engine Coolant Manifold	35 Upper Intake Manifold Bolt
18 Engine Coolant Manifold Gasket	

9300UG02

Fig. 138 Exploded view of the intake manifold and related components—3.8L engine

3. Drain the cooling system.
4. Relieve the fuel system pressure.
5. Remove or disconnect the following:
- Fuel injector sight shield
- Air inlet duct
- Spark plug wires from the right side
- Manifold Absolute Pressure (MAP) sensor
- Vacuum lines from the intake manifold
- Fuel lines
- Fuel injector electrical connectors
- Fuel regulator vacuum line
- Fuel rail from the intake manifold
- Exhaust Gas Recirculation (EGR) heat shield
- Throttle cable bracket from the cylinder head mounting bracket and the throttle body cables, if equipped
- Throttle body support bracket
- Upper intake plenum and gasket
- Thermostat housing
- Electrical connector from the Engine Coolant Temperature (ECT) sensor
- Accessory drive belt tensioner assembly
- EGR valve outlet pipe
- Lower intake manifold

To install:

6. Install or connect the following:
- Intake manifold using new manifold gaskets. Torque the bolts in sequence to 11 ft. lbs. (15 Nm); then, re-torque to 11 ft. lbs. (15 Nm)
- EGR valve outlet pipe
- Accessory drive belt tensioner assembly. Torque the tensioner bolts to 37 ft. lbs. (50 Nm)
- Electrical connector to the ECT sensor
- Thermostat housing
- Upper intake plenum. Torque the intake plenum bolts to 88 inch. lbs. (10 Nm)
- Throttle body support bracket
- Throttle cable bracket to the cylinder head mounting bracket and the cables to the throttle body lever, if equipped
- EGR heat shield
- Fuel rail. Torque the fuel rail bolts to 88 inch. lbs. (10 Nm)
- Fuel lines
- Fuel regulator vacuum line
- Fuel injector electrical connectors
- Vacuum lines to the intake manifold
- MAP sensor

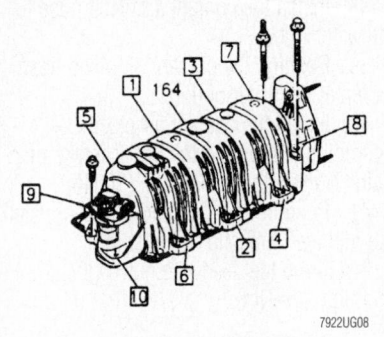

Fig. 139 Upper intake manifold torque sequence—3.8L engine

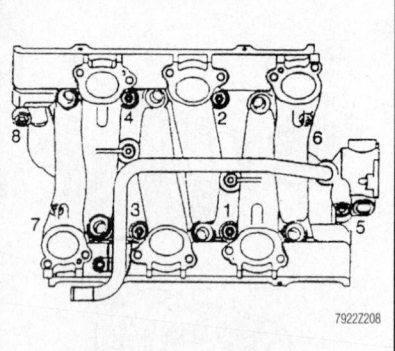

Fig. 140 Lower intake manifold torque sequence—3.8L engine

- Spark plug wires
- Fuel injector sight shield and air inlet duct
- Negative battery cable
7. Refill and bleed the cooling system.
8. Run the engine and check for leaks and proper engine operation.

5.3L Engine

See Figures 141 through 143.

➡The intake manifold, throttle body, fuel injection rail, and fuel injectors may be removed as an assembly. If not servicing the individual components, remove the manifold as a complete assembly.

1. Before servicing the vehicle, refer to the Precautions Section.
2. Relieve the fuel system pressure.
3. Disconnect the negative battery cable.
4. Remove the air cleaner outlet duct.
5. Remove the alternator. Refer to Alternator, removal & installation.
6. Remove the engine harness retainer nut.
7. Remove the engine harness retainer from the stud and locator pin.
8. Disconnect the engine harness elec-

trical connector from the Evaporative Emission (EVAP) canister purge solenoid.
9. Disconnect the engine wiring harness electrical connector from the Manifold Absolute Pressure (MAP) sensor.
10. Remove the Connector Position Assurance (CPA) retainer.
11. Disconnect the engine harness electrical connector from the ignition coil harness electrical connector.
12. Disconnect the engine harness electrical connectors from the left side fuel injectors.
13. Remove the engine harness clip from the ignition coil bracket stud.
14. Remove the CPA retainer.
15. Disconnect the engine harness electrical connector from the ignition coil harness electrical connector.
16. Disconnect the engine harness electrical connector from the throttle actuator.
17. Remove the engine harness clip from the ignition coil bracket stud.
18. Disconnect the engine harness electrical connectors from the right side fuel injectors.
19. Remove the engine harness clip and bolt.
20. Disconnect the engine harness electrical connector from the Engine Coolant Temperature (ECT) sensor.
21. Gather the engine harness branches and tie the harness up out of the way to the front of the engine compartment.
22. Reposition the brake booster vacuum hose clamp at the booster.
23. Remove the brake booster vacuum hose from the booster fitting.
24. Secure the brake booster vacuum hose to the intake manifold.

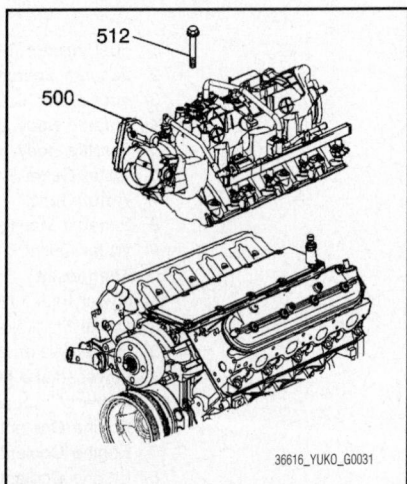

Fig. 141 Remove the intake manifold bolts (512) and the intake manifold (500)—5.3L engine

25. Disconnect the EVAP canister purge tube quick connect fitting from the EVAP canister purge solenoid.

26. Disconnect the fuel feed line quick connect fitting from the fuel rail.

27. Remove the Positive Crankcase Ventilation (PCV) hose from the intake manifold fitting.

28. Position the hose out of the way.

29. Loosen the intake manifold bolts.

➡**The aid of an assistant may be helpful in holding the engine harness up out of the way so the upper intake manifold cover does not get caught against the engine harness.**

30. Remove the intake manifold.

31. Cover the cylinder head passages in order to prevent dirt or debris from entering the passages.

32. Remove and discard the intake manifold gaskets.

33. If replacing the intake manifold, perform the following steps, otherwise proceed to step 21 of the installation procedure.

34. Place the intake manifold on a clean work surface.

35. Reposition the brake booster vacuum hose clamp at the intake manifold.

36. Remove the brake booster vacuum hose from the intake manifold nipple.

37. Remove the upper intake manifold cover nut.

38. Remove the upper intake manifold cover.

39. Remove the MAP sensor retainer.

40. Remove the MAP sensor.

41. Disconnect the EVAP tube quick connect fitting at the intake manifold.

42. Disengage the retainer securing the EVAP canister purge solenoid to the fuel rail.

43. Remove the EVAP tube and purge solenoid.

44. Remove the throttle body bolts/nuts.

45. Remove the throttle body.

46. Remove and discard the throttle body gasket.

47. Remove the fuel rail bolts.

➡**Lift evenly on both sides of the fuel rail until all injectors are removed from their bores.**

48. Remove the fuel rail.

49. Remove and discard the fuel injector lower O-ring seals.

➡**Evenly push in the RED collar in order to remove the nipple.**

50. Remove the brake booster vacuum hose nipple.

To install:

51. If the intake manifold was replaced, perform the following steps, otherwise proceed to step 21.

➡**Evenly push in the RED collar in order to install the nipple.**

52. Install the brake booster vacuum hose nipple to the NEW intake manifold.

53. Install NEW fuel injector lower O-ring seals onto the injectors.

54. Lubricate the NEW O-ring seals with clean engine oil.

➡**Push down firmly on both sides of the rail until all the injectors have been seated into their bores.**

55. Install the fuel rail.

56. Install the fuel rail bolts and tighten to 89 inch lbs. (10 Nm).

57. Install a NEW throttle body gasket to the intake manifold.

58. Install the throttle body.

59. Install the throttle body bolts/nuts and tighten to 89 inch lbs. (10 Nm).

60. Install the EVAP tube and purge solenoid.

61. Install the EVAP canister purge solenoid to the fuel rail bracket and engage the retainer.

62. Connect the EVAP tube quick connect fitting at the intake manifold.

63. Lubricate the MAP sensor seal with clean engine oil.

64. Install the MAP sensor.

65. Install the MAP sensor retainer.

66. Install the upper intake manifold cover.

67. Install the upper intake manifold cover nut until snug

68. Install the brake booster vacuum hose to the intake manifold nipple.

69. Position the brake booster vacuum hose clamp at the intake manifold.

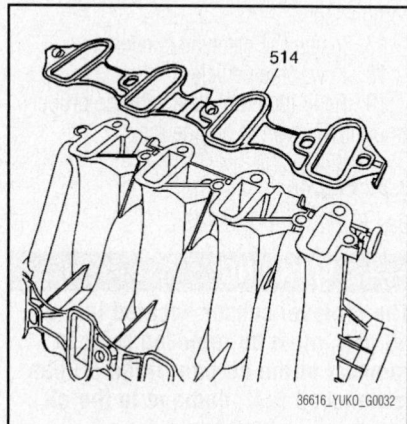

Fig. 142 Install NEW intake manifold gaskets to the intake manifold—5.3L engine

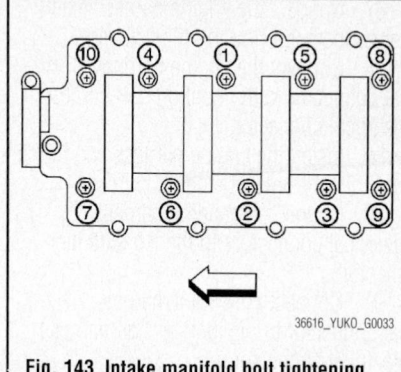

Fig. 143 Intake manifold bolt tightening sequence—5.3L engine

70. Secure the brake booster vacuum hose to the intake manifold.

71. Install NEW intake manifold gaskets to the intake manifold.

72. Remove the covers from the cylinder head passages.

73. Install the intake manifold.

➡**The aid of an assistant may be helpful in holding the engine harness up out of the way so the upper intake manifold cover does not get caught against the engine harness.**

74. Tighten the intake manifold bolts until snug.

75. Tighten the intake manifold bolts to specifications:

   a. Tighten the bolts a first pass, in the sequence shown, to 44 inch lbs. (5 Nm).

   b. Tighten the bolts a final pass, in the sequence shown, to 89 inch lbs. (10 Nm).

76. Position and install the PCV hose to the intake manifold fitting.

77. Connect the fuel feed line quick connect fitting to the fuel rail.

78. Connect the EVAP canister purge tube quick connect fitting to the EVAP canister purge solenoid.

79. Secure the brake booster vacuum hose to the intake manifold.

80. Install the brake booster vacuum hose to the booster fitting.

81. Position the brake booster vacuum hose clamp at the booster.

82. Untie the engine harness branches from the front of the engine compartment and position them over the engine.

83. Connect the engine harness electrical connector to the ECT sensor.

84. Position the engine harness clips to the bracket.

85. Connect the engine harness electrical connectors to the right side fuel injectors.

86. Install the engine harness clip to the ignition coil bracket stud.

87. Connect the engine harness electrical connector to the throttle actuator.

88. Connect the engine harness electrical connector to the ignition coil harness electrical connector.

89. Install the engine harness clip to the ignition coil bracket stud.

90. Connect the engine harness electrical connectors to the left side fuel injectors.

91. Connect the engine harness electrical connector to the ignition coil harness electrical connector.

92. Install the CPA retainer.

93. Connect the engine wiring harness electrical connector to the MAP sensor.

94. Connect the engine harness electrical connector to the EVAP canister purge solenoid.

95. Install the engine harness retainer to the stud and locator pin.

96. Install the engine harness retainer nut and tighten to 44 inch lbs. (5 Nm).

97. Install the alternator. Refer to Alternator, removal & installation.

98. Install the air cleaner outlet duct.

OIL PAN

REMOVAL & INSTALLATION

3.0L and 3.6L Engines

See Figures 144 and 145.

1. Before servicing the vehicle, refer to the Precautions Section.

2. Raise and support the vehicle.

3. Drain the engine oil and remove the oil filter.

4. Remove the catalytic converter.

5. Remove the Air Conditioning (A/C) compressor.

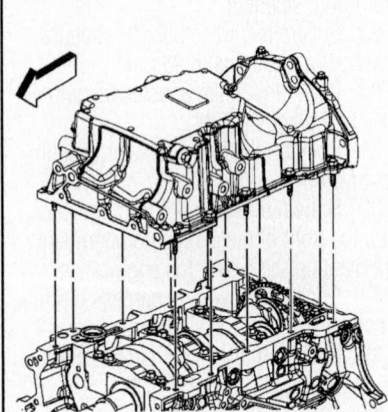

Fig. 144 Removing the oil pan—3.0L and 3.6L engines

36616_LACR_G0054

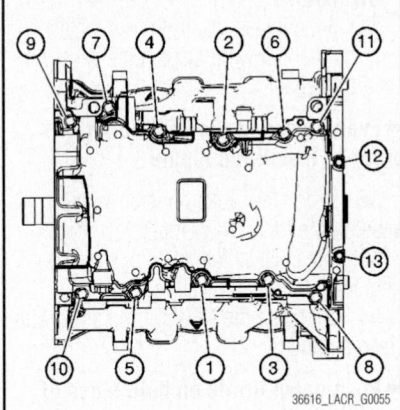

36616_LACR_G0055

Fig. 145 Oil pan bolt tightening sequence—3.0L and 3.6L engines

6. Remove the transmission bell housing bolts.

7. Remove the oil pan bolts.

8. Remove the oil pan.

9. Clean the oil pan and the engine block gasket surface.

To install:

10. Install the 0.315 inch (8mm) guides from the a guide pin set such as EN 46109 into the center oil pan rail bolt hole on each side of the engine block.

11. Place a 0.118 inch (3mm) bead of RTV sealant on the block pan rail and the crankshaft rear oil seal housing.

12. Position the oil pan onto the block.

13. Remove guide pin set guides from the engine block.

14. Loosely install the oil pan bolts.

15. Tighten the oil pan bolts in sequence shown as follows:

    a. 8mm bolts 1–11 to 17 ft. lbs. (23 Nm).

    b. 6mm bolts 12 and 13 to 89 inch lbs. (10 Nm).

16. Install the Air Conditioning (A/C) compressor.

17. Install the catalytic converter.

18. Lower the vehicle.

19. Refill the crankcase with the proper amount and type of engine oil.

3.8L Engine

See Figures 146 and 147.

✷✷ WARNING

The oil level sensor, located in the oil pan, must be removed prior to removal of the oil pan. If the oil pan is removed first, damage to the oil level sensor may occur.

1. Before servicing the vehicle, refer to the Precautions Section.

2. Disconnect the negative battery cable.

3. Remove the fuel injector sight shield.

4. Remove the air cleaner intake duct.

5. Install the engine support fixture.

6. Raise and support the vehicle.

7. Drain the engine oil and remove the oil filter.

8. Remove the power steering oil cooler pipe brackets from the frame.

9. Disconnect the oil level sensor electrical connector.

10. Remove the oil level sensor wiring harness bolt and reposition the oil level sensor wiring harness.

11. Remove the catalytic converter to the right exhaust manifold pipe stud nuts and reposition the catalytic converter.

12. Remove the left and right engine mount struts.

13. Remove the torque converter covers.

14. Lower the vehicle.

15. Using the engine support fixture, raise the engine to gain access for the oil pan removal.

16. Raise the vehicle.

✷✷ WARNING

Remove the oil level sensor, located in the oil pan, before the oil pan is removed. The sensor may be damaged if the oil pan is removed first.

17. Remove the oil level sensor.

18. Remove the oil pan bolts.

19. Remove the oil pan.

20. Remove the oil pump pipe screen assembly.

21. Clean the following parts:
- Oil pump screen mating surfaces
- Oil pan flanges
- Oil pan rail
- Front cover
- Rear main bearing cap
- Threaded holes

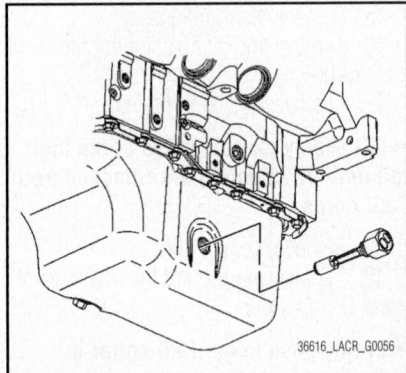

36616_LACR_G0056

Fig. 146 Remove the oil level sensor—3.8L engine

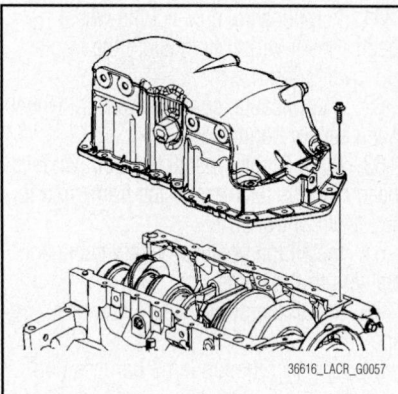

Fig. 147 Oil pan removal—3.8L engine

To install:

22. Install the oil pump pipe screen assembly and gasket.

23. Install the oil pump pipe screen bolts. Tighten the bolts to 11 ft. lbs. (15 Nm).

24. Apply a continuous bead 0.19 inch (3.0mm) thick of RTV sealer to the oil pan flange on the block as well as an additional drop to all four corners of the block where the front and rear covers meet.

➡**Install the oil level sensor, located in the oil pan, after the oil pan is installed. The sensor may be damaged if the oil level sensor is installed first.**

25. Install the oil pan.

26. Clean the oil pan bolts and apply one drop of threadlock compound to the oil pan bolt threads.

27. Install the oil pan bolts. Tighten the oil pan bolts to 125 inch lbs. (14 Nm).

28. Install the oil level sensor. Tighten the sensor to 15 ft. lbs. (20 Nm).

29. Install the torque converter covers.

30. Install the engine mount and the engine mount bracket.

31. Install the catalytic converter to the right exhaust manifold.

32. Install the catalytic converter pipe stud nuts and tighten to 24 ft. lbs. (32 Nm).

33. Install the oil level sensor wiring harness and the oil level sensor wiring harness bolt to the engine. Tighten the bolt to 89 inch lbs. (10 Nm).

34. Connect the oil level sensor electrical connector.

35. Install the power steering oil cooler pipe brackets to the frame.

36. Install the engine oil filter.

37. Lower the vehicle.

38. Remove the engine support fixture.

39. Install the right and left engine mount strut.

40. Fill the crankcase with the proper type and amount of engine oil.

41. Install the air cleaner intake duct.

42. Install the fuel injector sight shield.

43. Connect the negative battery cable.

44. Inspect for leaks.

5.3L Engine

See Figures 148 and 149.

Special Tool:

• J 39580: Power Pack Stand Engine And Transaxle Assembly Support Remove/Installer

1. Before servicing the vehicle, refer to the Precautions Section.

2. Install the engine support fixture.

3. Raise and support the vehicle.

4. Remove the front tires and wheels.

5. Remove the radiator air lower baffle and deflector.

6. Remove the positive battery cable and the retainers from the frame and position aside.

7. Disconnect the power steering return hose from the frame.

8. Secure the power steering return hose.

9. Remove the stabilizer shaft links and rotate the stabilizer shaft upward to gain access to the mounting bolts in the power steering gear. Refer to Control Link, removal & installation.

10. Remove the mounting bolts from the power steering gear. Refer to Steering Gear, removal & installation.

11. Secure the power steering gear.

12. Remove the nuts that secure the engine mount to the frame.

13. Remove the nuts which secure the transaxle mount to the frame.

14. If applicable, disconnect the front wheel speed sensor harness connectors.

15. If applicable, disconnect the wheel speed sensor harness from the frame and lower control arms.

16. If applicable, remove the retainers at the front wheel speed harness from the frame and from the lower control arms.

17. Separate both of the lower ball joints from the steering knuckle.

18. Remove both front drivetrain reinforcements using the following procedure:

   a. Remove the drivetrain reinforcement to support brace bolts.

   b. Remove the drivetrain reinforcement to front frame mounting stud nut.

   c. Remove the drivetrain reinforcement from the vehicle.

19. Lower the vehicle until the frame contacts the J 39580.

20. Remove the radiator-to-front frame brackets.

21. Remove the bolts which secure the front frame to the body.

22. Remove the bolts which secure the rear frame to the body.

23. Raise the vehicle in order to separate the frame from the body.

24. Drain the engine oil and remove the engine oil filter.

25. Reinstall the drain plug and oil filter until snug.

26. Remove the transaxle converter cover bolt/stud and cover.

27. Disconnect the oil level sensor electrical connector.

28. Remove engine harness retainer from the front of oil pan.

29. Position the drive belt tensioner aside in order to access the oil pan bolt.

30. Remove the oil pan bolts.

31. Remove the oil pan.

➡**DO NOT allow foreign material to enter the oil passages of the oil pan, cap or cover the openings as required.**

32. Drill out the oil pan gasket retaining rivets, if required.

33. Remove the gasket from the pan.

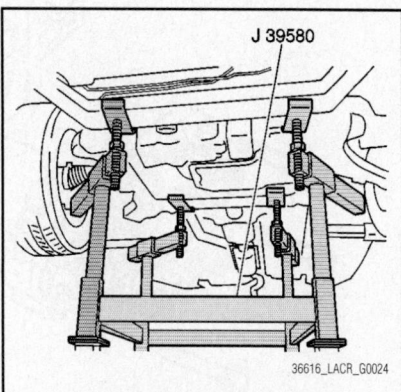

Fig. 148 Positioning the J 39580, Universal Engine Support Table, beneath the vehicle—5.3L engine

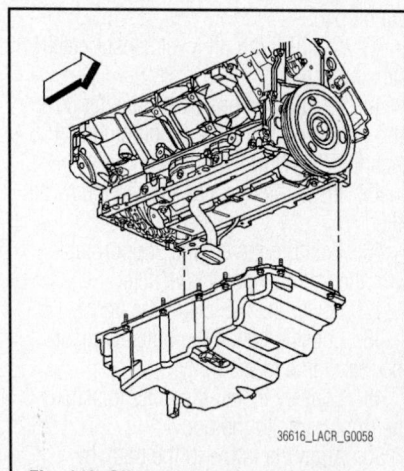

Fig. 149 Oil pan removal—5.3L engine

34. Discard the gasket and rivets.
35. Clean and inspect the engine oil pan.

To install:

➡ **The alignment of the structural oil pan is critical. The rear bolt hole locations of the oil pan provide mounting points for the transmission housing. To ensure the rigidity of the powertrain and correct transmission alignment, it is important that the rear of the block and the rear of the oil pan are flush, or even. The rear of the oil pan must NEVER protrude beyond the engine block and transmission housing plane.**

➡ **Do NOT reuse the oil pan gasket. It is NOT necessary to rivet the NEW gasket to the oil pan.**

36. Apply a 0.20 inch (5mm) bead of sealant to the engine block. Apply the sealant directly onto the tabs of the front/rear cover gasket that protrudes into the oil pan surface.

➡ **Be sure to align the oil gallery passages in the oil pan and engine block properly with the oil pan gasket.**

37. Pre-assemble the oil pan gasket to the pan.
   a. Install the gasket onto the pan.
   b. Install the oil pan bolts to the pan and through the gasket.
38. Install the oil pan, gasket, and bolts to the engine block. Tighten the oil pan and oil pan-to-front cover bolts to 18 ft. lbs. (25 Nm).
39. Tighten the oil pan-to-rear cover bolts to 106 inch lbs. (12 Nm).
40. Tighten the transmission housing, converter cover, and transmission bolts/stud to 37 ft. lbs. (50 Nm).
41. Install the drive belt tensioner.
42. Install engine harness to the front of the oil pan.
43. Connect the oil level sensor electrical connector.
44. Install the transaxle converter cover and bolt/stud. Tighten the bolt/stud to 106 inch lbs. (12 Nm).
45. Install new engine oil and a new oil filter.
46. Position the engine support table with the frame under the vehicle.
47. Lower the vehicle to the frame.
48. Loosely install the bolts to secure the rear frame to the body.
49. Loosely install the bolts to secure the front frame to the body.
50. Align the frame to the body by inserting two 0.74 x 8 inch (19 x 203mm)

pins in the alignment holes on the right side of the frame.
51. Install the front and rear frame bolts. Tighten the front bolts to 107 ft. lbs. (145 Nm).
52. Tighten the rear bolts to 118 ft. lbs. (160 Nm).
53. Install the drivetrain reinforcements using the following procedure:
   a. Position the drivetrain reinforcements to the front frame mount stud to the support brace.
   b. Loosely install the drivetrain reinforcement to support brace bolts.
   c. Install the drivetrain reinforcement to cradle mount nut. Tighten the drivetrain reinforcement brace nut to 37 ft. lbs. (50 Nm).
54. Tighten the drivetrain reinforcement brace bolts to 18 ft. lbs. (25 Nm).
55. Install the radiator-to-front frame brackets.
56. Connect both the lower ball joints to the steering knuckle.
57. Install the nuts that secure the engine mount to the frame.
58. Install the nuts which secure the transaxle mount to the frame.
59. Install the steering gear mounting bolts. Refer to Steering Gear, removal & installation.
60. Install the stabilizer shaft links. Refer to Control Link, removal & installation.

61. If applicable, connect the wheel speed sensor wiring harness to the frame and lower control arm.
62. If applicable, connect the front wheel speed sensor connectors.
63. If applicable, install the front wheel speed harness retainers to the frame and to the lower control arm.
64. Install the positive battery cable and retainers to the frame.
65. Install the power steering cooler pipe.
66. Connect the fog lamp harness connectors.
67. Install the front tires and wheels.
68. Install the radiator air lower baffle and deflector.
69. Lower the vehicle.
70. Remove the engine support fixture.
71. Inspect the front wheel alignment, adjust as needed.

OIL PUMP

REMOVAL & INSTALLATION

3.0L and 3.6L Engines

See Figure 150.

1. Before servicing the vehicle, refer to the Precautions Section.

➡ **Do not remove the left bank idler sprocket.**

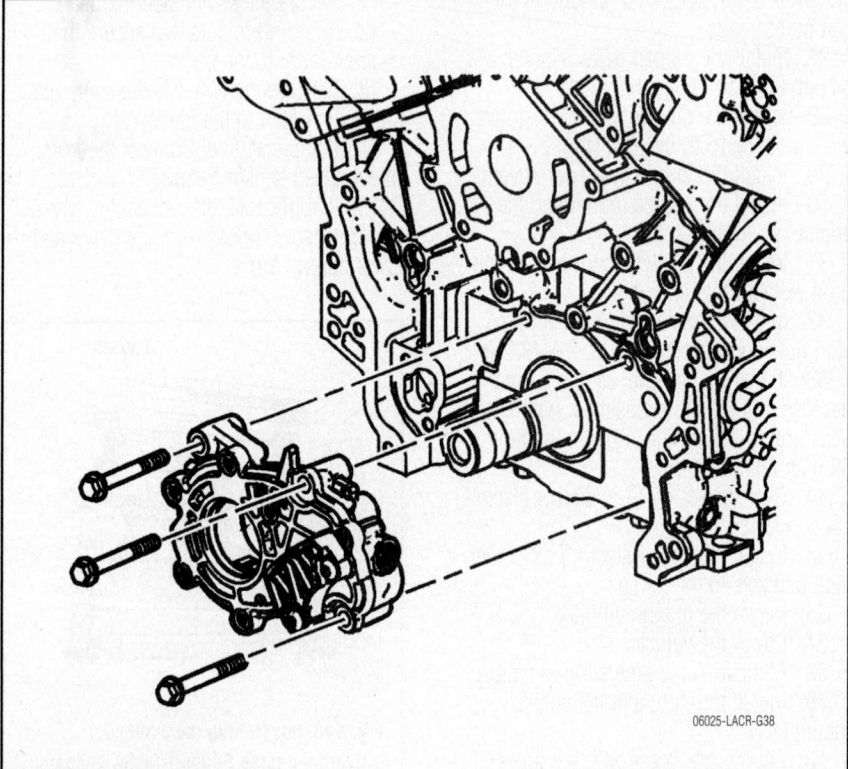

Fig. 150 Oil pump removal—3.6L engine

06025-LACR-G38

2. Remove the primary timing chain.

3. Remove the crankshaft sprocket.

➡**There are no serviceable components within the oil pump. Disassemble the pump only to diagnose an oiling concern. A disassembled oil pump must not be reused. A disassembled oil pump must be replaced.**

4. Remove the oil pump bolts and the oil pump.

To install:

5. Align the oil pump gerotor with the crankshaft flats and install the oil pump to the engine block.

6. Align the pump body with the mounting holes in the cylinder block.

7. Install the oil pump bolts. Tighten the oil pump bolts to 17 ft. lbs. (23 Nm).

8. Install the crankshaft sprocket.

9. Install the primary timing chain.

3.8L Engine

See Figure 151.

1. Before servicing the vehicle, refer to the Precautions Section.

2. Support the engine using an engine support fixture.

3. Remove or disconnect the following:
   • Negative battery cable
   • Engine drive belts and tensioner assembly
   • Drive belt idler pulley and bracket
   • Torque axis mount bracket, if necessary
   • Engine front cover assembly
   • Oil filter adapter with pressure regulator valve and spring
   • Oil pump cover
   • Inner and outer pump gears

To install:

4. Lubricate the oil pump gears with petroleum jelly.

5. Install the gears into the oil pump housing.

6. Pack the gear cavity with petroleum jelly after the gears have been installed in the housing.

7. Install or connect the following:
   • Oil pump cover. Torque the screws to 97 inch lbs. (11 Nm).
   • Oil filter adapter with new gasket, pressure regulator valve and spring. Torque the bolts to 11 ft. lbs. (15 Nm).
   • Front cover assembly
   • Tensioner assembly
   • Drive belt idler pulley and bracket, if removed
   • Drive belts
   • Torque axis mount bracket
   • Negative battery cable

8. Remove the engine support fixture.

9. Verify the correct engine oil level.

10. Start the vehicle and verify no leaks and proper oil pressure.

5.3L Engine

See Figures 152 through 154.

1. Before servicing the vehicle, refer to the Precautions Section.

2. Remove the oil pan. Refer to Oil Pan, removal & installation.

3. Remove the engine front cover. Refer to Timing Chain Cover and Seal, removal & installation.

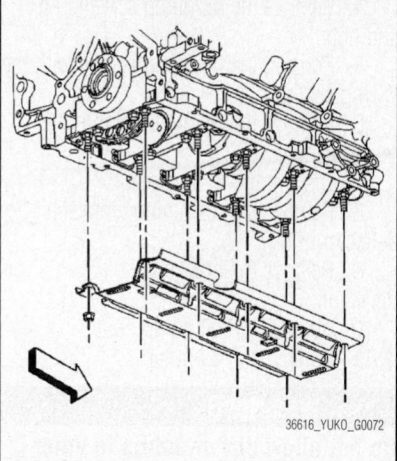

Fig. 153 Remove the crankshaft oil deflector

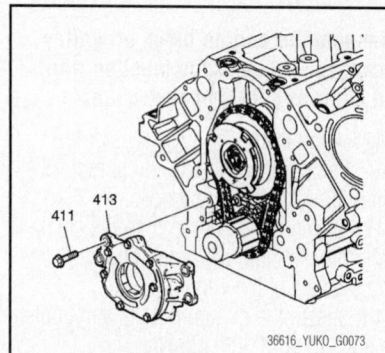

Fig. 154 Remove the oil pump bolts (411) and the oil pump (413)

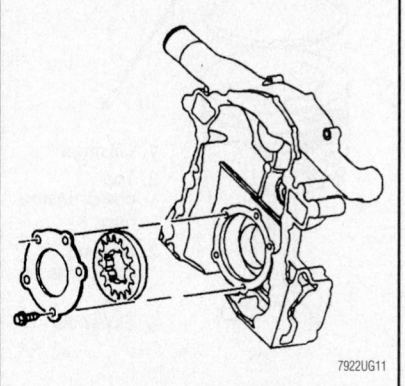

Fig. 151 The oil pump is located inside the front engine cover—3.8L engines

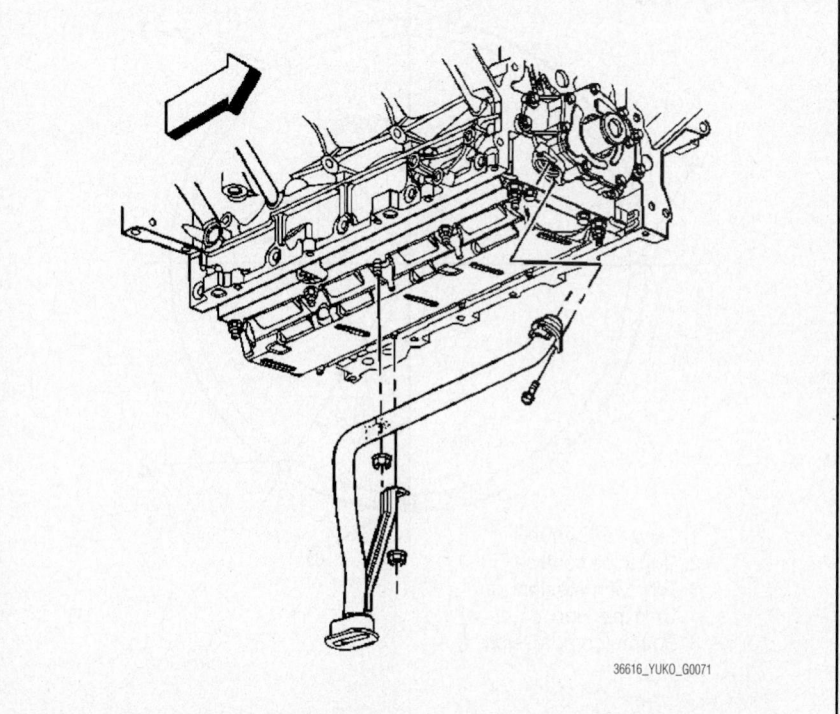

Fig. 152 View of oil pick-up tube and screen

4. Remove the oil pump screen bolt and nuts.

5. Remove the oil pump screen with the O-ring seal.

6. Remove the O-ring seal from the pump screen.

7. Discard the O-ring seal.

8. Remove the remaining crankshaft oil deflector nuts.

9. Remove the crankshaft oil deflector.

10. Remove the oil pump bolts.

11. Remove the oil pump.

❊❊ WARNING

Do not allow dirt or debris to enter the oil pump assembly, cap as necessary.

To install:

➡ **Inspect the engine block oil galley passages. These areas must be free and clear of debris or restrictions.**

12. Align the splined surfaces of the crankshaft sprocket and the oil pump drive gear and install the oil pump.

13. Install the oil pump onto the crankshaft sprocket until the pump housing contacts the face of the engine block.

14. Install the oil pump bolts and tighten the bolts to 18 ft. lbs. (25 Nm).

15. Position the crankshaft oil deflector and install the nuts until snug.

16. Lubricate a NEW oil pump screen O-ring seal with clean engine oil and install it onto the oil pump screen.

❊❊ WARNING

Push the oil pump screen tube completely into the oil pump prior to tightening the bolt. Do not allow the bolt to pull the tube into the pump.

17. Align the oil pump screen mounting brackets with the correct crankshaft bearing cap studs.

18. Install the oil pump screen.

19. Install the oil pump screen bolt and nuts.

   a. Tighten the bolt to 106 inch lbs. (12 Nm).

   b. Tighten the nuts to 18 ft. lbs. (25 Nm).

20. Install the engine front cover. Refer to Timing Chain Cover and Seal, removal & installation.

21. Install the oil pan. Refer to Oil Pan, removal & installation.

PISTON AND RING

POSITIONING

See Figures 155 through 159.

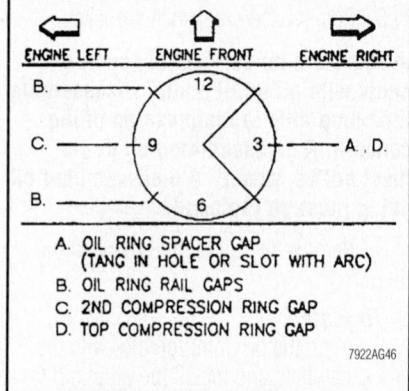

Fig. 156 Piston ring end-gap spacing—3.8L engines

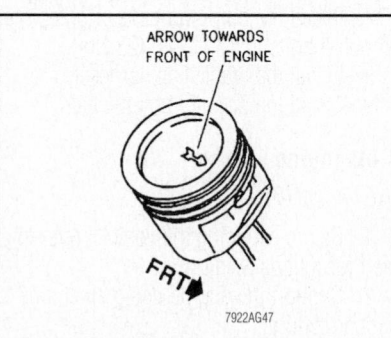

Fig. 157 Piston positioning. Often the arrow is replaced by a notch, which also must face toward the front of the engine—3.8L engines

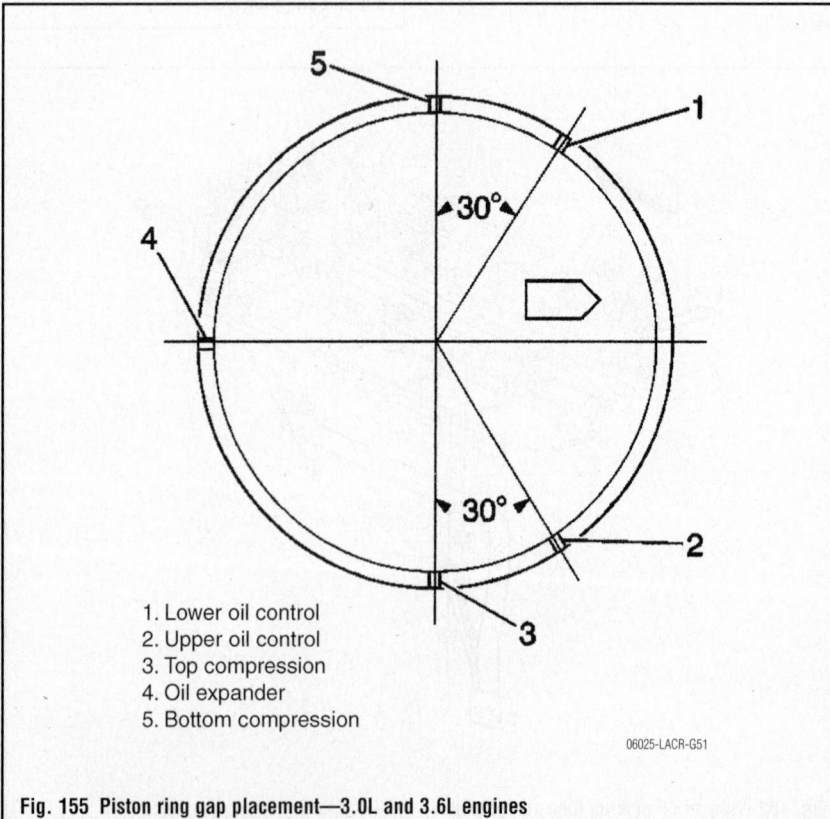

1. Lower oil control
2. Upper oil control
3. Top compression
4. Oil expander
5. Bottom compression

Fig. 155 Piston ring gap placement—3.0L and 3.6L engines

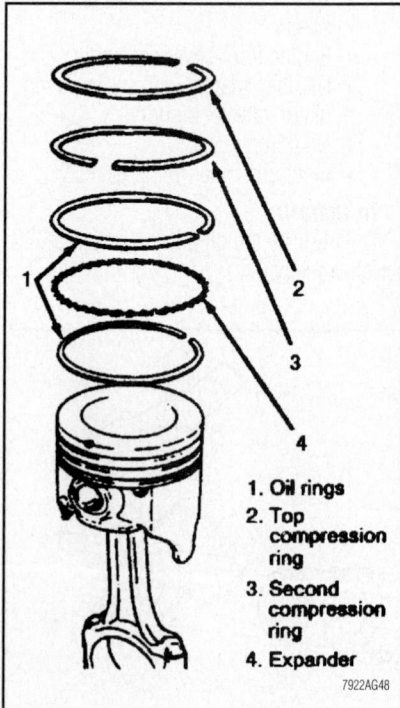

1. Oil rings
2. Top compression ring
3. Second compression ring
4. Expander

Fig. 158 Piston ring positioning—3.8L engines

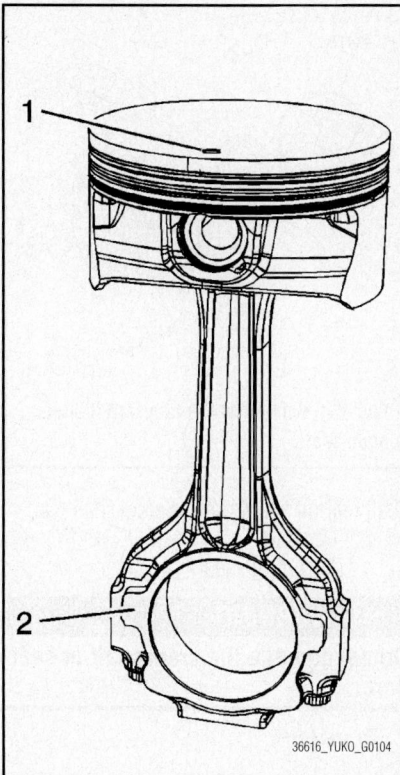

Fig. 159 Piston and ring positioning—place the ring gaps 180 degrees apart; the mark on the top of the piston (1) and the tab (2) on the side of the connecting rod should face the front of the engine

REAR MAIN SEAL

REMOVAL & INSTALLATION

3.0L and 3.6L Engines

See Figures 160 through 162.

1. Before servicing the vehicle, refer to the Precautions Section.
2. Remove the transaxle.
3. Remove the engine flywheel bolts and discard.
4. Remove the engine flywheel from the crankshaft.
5. Remove the oil pan.
6. Remove the crankshaft rear oil seal housing bolts.
7. Using the pry points located at the edge of the crankshaft rear oil seal housing shear the RTV sealant.
8. Remove and discard the crankshaft rear oil seal housing.

To install:

9. Install the 0.236 inch (6mm) guides from kit EN 46109 into the 2 crankshaft rear oil seal housing corner bolt holes of the engine block.

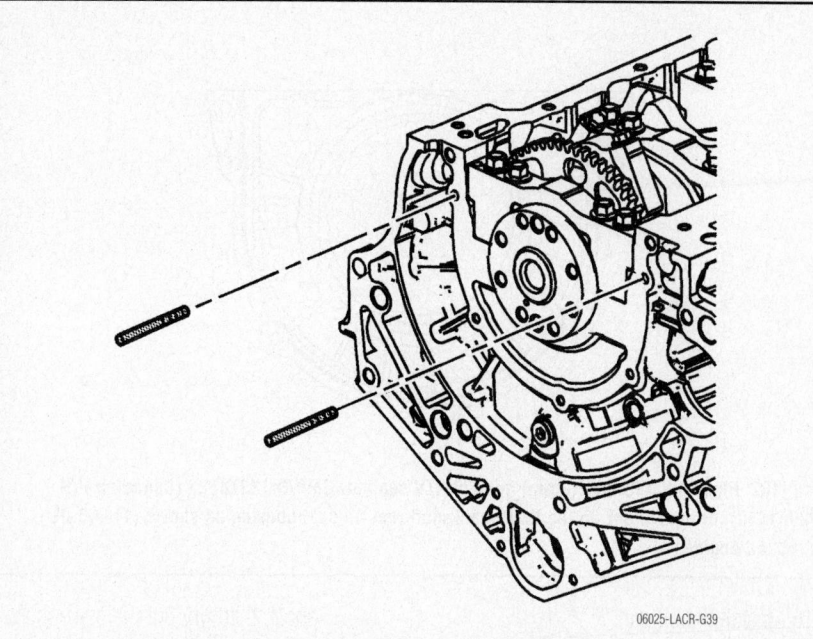

Fig. 160 Install the 0.236 inch (6mm) guides from kit EN 46109 into the 2 crankshaft rear oil seal housing corner bolt holes of the engine block—3.0L and 3.6L engines

10. Install seal tools EN-47839 with the J-42183 onto the rear of the crankshaft flange.
11. Place a 0.118 inch (3mm) bead of RTV sealant, GM P/N 12378521 (Canadian P/N 88901148), or equivalent, to the NEW crankshaft rear oil seal housing as shown.

➡**DO NOT allow any engine oil on the area where the crankshaft rear oil seal housing is to be installed.**

12. Install the crankshaft rear oil seal housing to the engine block.
13. Remove the guides from the engine block.
14. Install the crankshaft rear oil seal housing bolts. Tighten the crankshaft rear oil seal housing bolts to 89 inch lbs. (10 Nm).
15. Remove the seal tool from the crankshaft flange.

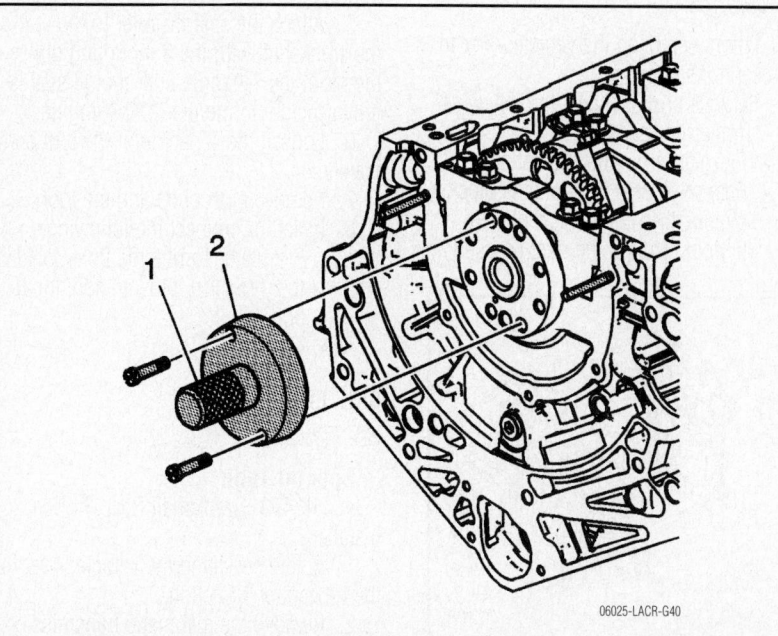

Fig. 161 Install seal tools EN-47839 with the J-42183 (1, 2) onto the rear of the crankshaft flange—3.0L and 3.6L engines

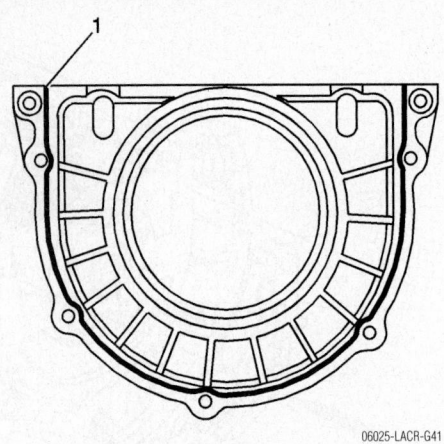

Fig. 162 Place a 0.118 inch (3mm) bead of RTV sealant, GMP/N 12378521 (Canadian P/N 88901148), or equivalent, to the NEW crankshaft rear oil seal housing as shown (1) —3.0L and 3.6L engines

16. Install the oil pan.

17. Place the engine flywheel in position on the crankshaft.

18. Install 2 NEW bolts in location at the top and bottom of the engine flywheel bolt pattern allowing the engine flywheel to hang in position.

19. Install the remaining NEW engine flywheel bolts.
- Tighten the NEW engine flywheel bolts to 22 ft. lbs. (30 Nm)
- Tighten the NEW engine flywheel bolts an additional 45°

20. Install the transaxle.

3.8L Engine

See Figure 163.

1. Before servicing the vehicle, refer to the Precautions Section.

2. Remove or disconnect the following:
- Transaxle assembly
- Flexplate from the crankshaft
- Rear main seal from engine block by inserting a small flat-bladed prytool through the dust lip at an

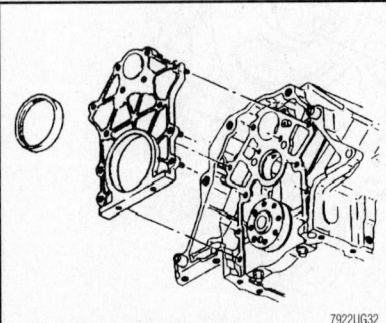

Fig. 163 Rear main oil seal and rear cover—3.8L engine

angle, then pry out the crankshaft rear oil seal. Repeat as necessary around the seal until it is removed.

> ※※ **WARNING**
>
> **Do not damage or scratch the sealing surface of the crankshaft or the seal bore.**

To install:

3. Lubricate new rear main with clean engine oil prior to installation.

4. Slide the oil seal on the mandrel of seal installer tool J-38196 until the back of the seal is seated squarely against the collar of the tool.

5. Attach the seal installer to the rear of the crankshaft with the 2 mounting bolts, then turn the T-handle until the oil seal is fully seated into the rear of the engine.

6. Loosen the T-handle of the tool completely.

7. Remove both bolts and the tool.

8. Install or connect the following:
- Flexplate. Torque the bolts to 11 ft. lbs. (15 Nm), plus an additional 50°.
- Transaxle

5.3L Engine

See Figure 164.

Special Tool:
- J 41479: Crankshaft Rear Oil Seal Installer

1. Before servicing the vehicle, refer to the Precautions Section.

2. Remove the automatic transmission flywheel. Refer to Flywheel, removal & installation.

3. Using a suitable tool, pry the crank-

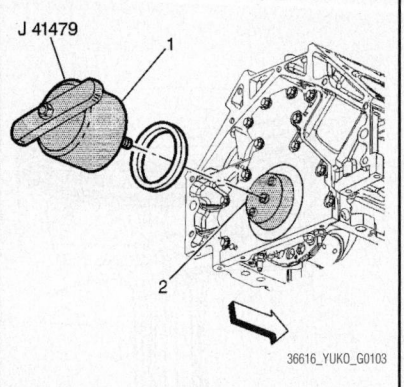

Fig. 164 Using J 41479 to install the rear main seal

shaft rear oil seal from the crankshaft rear oil seal housing.

4. Discard the seal.

> ※※ **WARNING**
>
> **Do not damage the crankshaft or seal bore.**

To install:

➡For proper orientation, note the installation direction of the oil seal. The oil seal is a reverse-lip design. The part number is applied to the outside face of the seal.

5. Inspect the seal and identify the part number markings for proper orientation.

6. Install the J 41479 cone and bolts onto the rear of the crankshaft.

7. Tighten the bolts until snug. Do not over-tighten.

8. Install the rear oil seal onto the tapered cone and push the seal to the rear seal bore.

9. Install the oil seal with the part number markings facing away from the engine.

10. Thread the J 41479 threaded rod into the tapered cone until the tool contacts the oil seal.

11. Align the oil seal into the tool.

12. Rotate the handle of the tool clockwise until the seal enters the rear cover and bottoms into the cover bore.

13. Remove the J 41479.

14. Install the automatic transmission flexplate. Refer to Flexplate, removal & installation.

ROCKER ARMS/SHAFTS

REMOVAL & INSTALLATION

3.0L and 3.6L Engines

See Figures 165 and 166.

1. Before servicing the vehicle, refer to the Precautions Section.

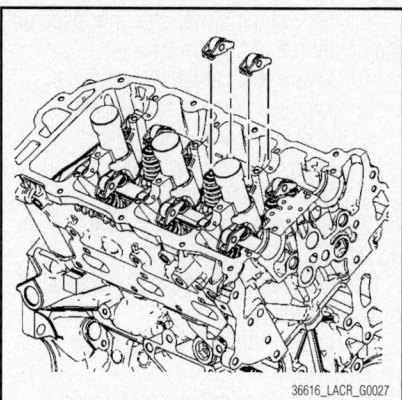

Fig. 165 Removing the rocker arms (right side)—3.0L and 3.6L engines

2. Remove the applicable camshaft(s). Refer to Camshaft, removal & installation.

3. Remove the rocker arms.

4. Clean and inspect the camshafts and the rocker arms. Repair or replace as necessary.

To install:

5. Apply a liberal amount of lubricant GM P/N 12345501 (Canadian P/N 992704), or equivalent, to the pivot pocket, roller, and valve slot areas of the camshaft followers.

➡**The follower must be positioned squarely on the valve tip so that the full width of the roller will completely contact the camshaft lobe. If the followers are being reused, they must be put back in the original location.**

6. Place the camshaft followers in position on the valve tip and the Stationary Hydraulic Lash Adjuster (SHLA).

7. The rounded head end of the follower goes on the SHLA while the flat end goes on the valve tip.

8. Clean the camshaft journals and carriers with a clean, lint-free cloth.

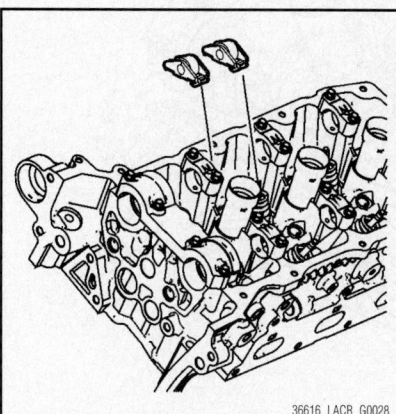

Fig. 166 Removing the rocker arms (left side)—3.0L and 3.6L engines

3.8L Engine

See Figure 167.

➡**When removing valvetrain components, it is very important that they are marked for installation reference, so that they can be reinstalled in their original location.**

1. Before servicing the vehicle, refer to the Precautions Section.

2. Remove or disconnect the following:
   - Negative battery cable
   - Spark plug wires
   - Rocker arm cover(s)
   - Rocker arm pedestal bolts and assemblies
   - Pushrods

To install:

3. Lubricate the pushrod tips and put them in their proper locations.

4. Lubricate the rocker arms and pedestals and install them. Be sure the pushrod tips are properly seated in the rocker arms.

5. Apply thread-locking compound to the rocker arm pedestal bolt threads. Torque the bolts to 11 ft. lbs. (15 Nm), plus an additional 90° turn.

6. Apply suitable thread-locking compound to the rocker arm cover bolts.

7. Install or connect the following:
   - Rocker arm cover using a new gasket. Torque the bolts to 89 inch lbs. (10 Nm)
   - Spark plug wires

- Accessory drive belt
- Negative battery cable

8. Run the engine and check for leaks and proper engine operation.

5.3L Engine

See Figures 168 and 169.

1. Before servicing the vehicle, refer to the Precautions Section.

2. Remove the valve rocker arm cover. Refer to Valve Cover, removal & installation.

➡**The engine firing order is 1, 8, 7, 2, 6, 5, 4, 3. Cylinders 1, 3, 5, and 7 are the left bank.**

3. Remove the number one cylinder spark plug.

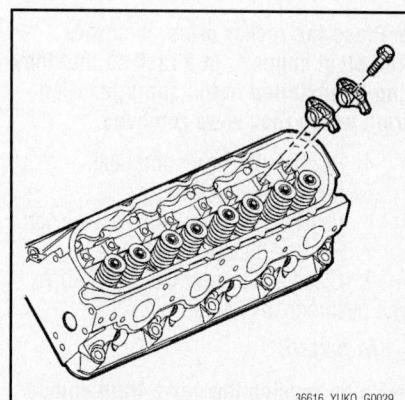

Fig. 168 Remove the rocker arm bolts and the rocker arms—5.3L engine

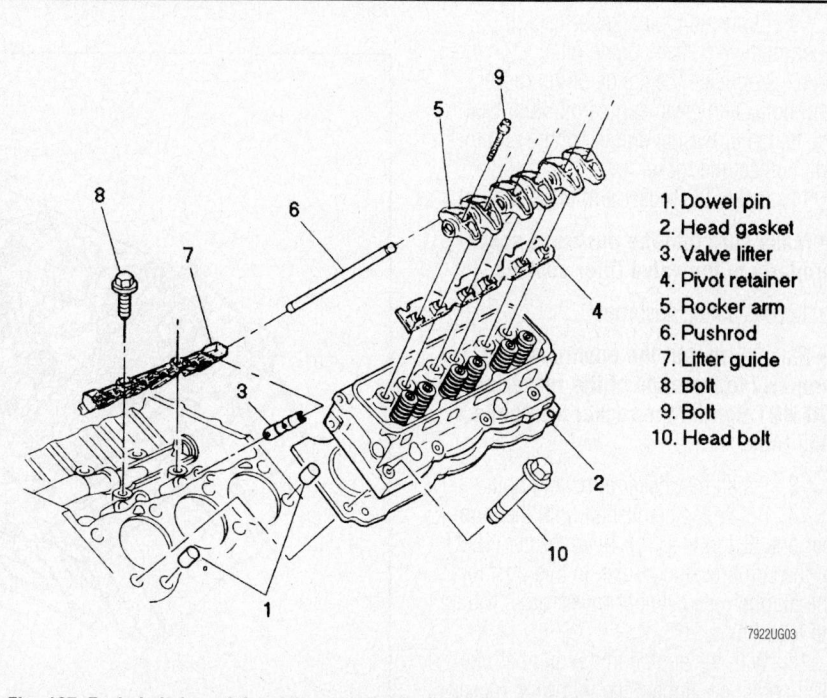

1. Dowel pin
2. Head gasket
3. Valve lifter
4. Pivot retainer
5. Rocker arm
6. Pushrod
7. Lifter guide
8. Bolt
9. Bolt
10. Head bolt

Fig. 167 Exploded view of the rocker arms and related components—3.8L engine

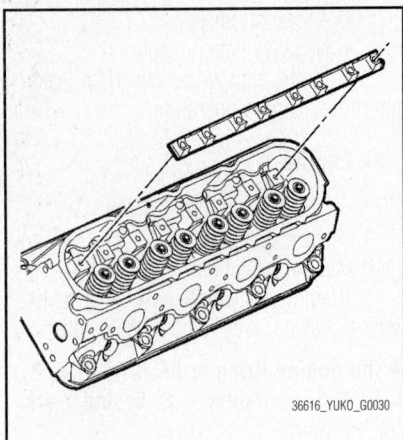

Fig. 169 Remove the rocker arm pivot support—5.3L engine

➡Place the rocker arms, pushrods, and pivot support, in a rack so that they can be installed in the same location from which they were removed.

4. Remove the rocker arm bolts.
5. Remove the rocker arms.
6. Remove the rocker arm pivot support.
7. Remove the pushrods.
8. Clean and inspect the rocker arms and pushrods, if required.

To install:

➡When reusing the valve train components, always install the components into the original location and position.

➡The valve lash is net build; no valve adjustment is required.

9. Lubricate the rocker arms and pushrods with clean engine oil.
10. Lubricate the flange of the rocker arm bolts with clean engine oil. Lubricate the flange or washer surface of the bolt that will contact the rocker arm.
11. Install the rocker arm pivot support.

➡Make sure that the pushrods seat properly to the valve lifter sockets.

12. Install the pushrods.

➡Make sure that the pushrods seat properly to the ends of the rocker arms. DO NOT tighten the rocker arm bolts at this time.

13. Install the rocker arms and bolts.
14. Rotate the crankshaft until the number one piston is at Top Dead Center (TDC) of the compression stroke. In this position, the number one cylinder rocker arms will be off lobe lift.
15. With the engine in the number one firing position, tighten the following rocker arm bolts:

a. Tighten cylinders 1, 2, 7, and 8 exhaust valve rocker arm bolts to 22 ft. lbs. (30 Nm).
b. Tighten cylinders 1, 3, 4, and 5 intake valve rocker arm bolts to 22 ft. lbs. (30 Nm).
16. Rotate the crankshaft 360°.
17. Tighten the following rocker arm bolts:

a. Tighten cylinders 3, 4, 5, and 6 exhaust valve rocker arm bolts to 22 ft. lbs. (30 Nm).
b. Tighten cylinders 2, 6, 7, and 8 intake valve rocker arm bolts to 22 ft. lbs. (30 Nm).
18. Install the number one cylinder spark plug.
19. Install the valve rocker arm cover. Refer to Valve Cover, removal & installation.

TIMING CHAIN COVER AND SEAL

REMOVAL & INSTALLATION

3.0L and 3.6L Engines

See Figures 170 through 174.

1. Before servicing the vehicle, refer to the Precautions Section.
2. Disconnect the negative battery cable.
3. Remove the ECU module bracket. Position it out of the way. DO NOT remove the ECU or disconnect it.
4. Remove the alternator assembly.
5. Remove the coolant overflow reservoir.

6. Remove the power steering reservoir and position it out of the way.
7. Remove the camshaft covers.
8. Remove the upper radiator hose.
9. Remove the water pump.
10. Remove the engine splash shield.
11. Remove the crankshaft damper.
12. Remove the accessory drive belt tensioner.
13. Remove the camshaft position actuator valve bolts.
14. Remove the camshaft position actuator valves from the front cover.
15. Remove the engine front cover bolts.

✳✳ WARNING

Do not pry between the engine front cover and the camshaft position sensors or the camshaft position actuators in order to shear the RTV. Use the pry points and a bolt in the jackscrew hole in order to remove the engine front cover. Damage to the camshaft position sensors or the camshaft position actuators may occur if the camshaft position sensors or the camshaft position actuators are used to pry against in order to remove the engine front cover.

16. Loosely install a 10 x 1.5mm bolt in the jackscrew hole.
17. Using the pry points located at the edge of the front cover and the jackscrew, shear the RTV sealant.
18. Remove the engine front cover.

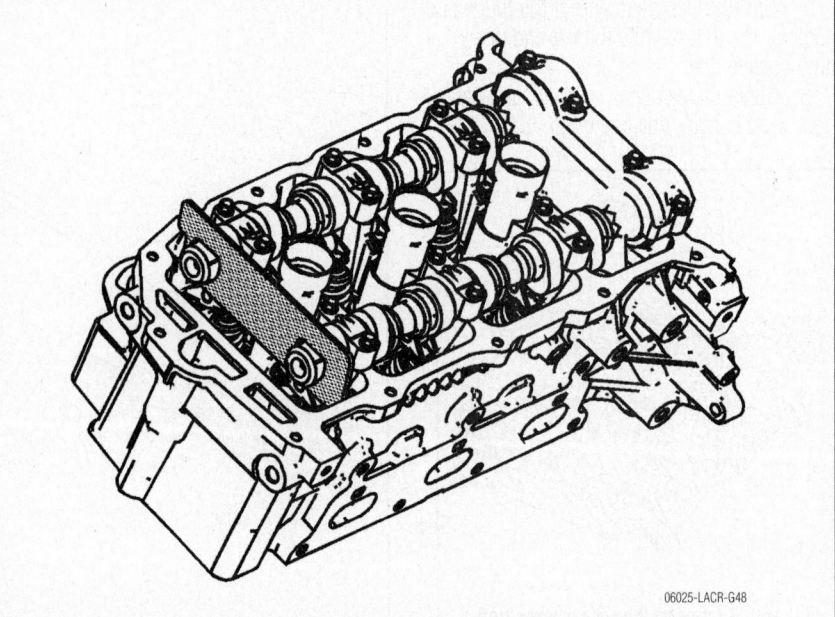

Fig. 170 Install the EN 46105-1 to the right camshafts—3.0L and 3.6L engines

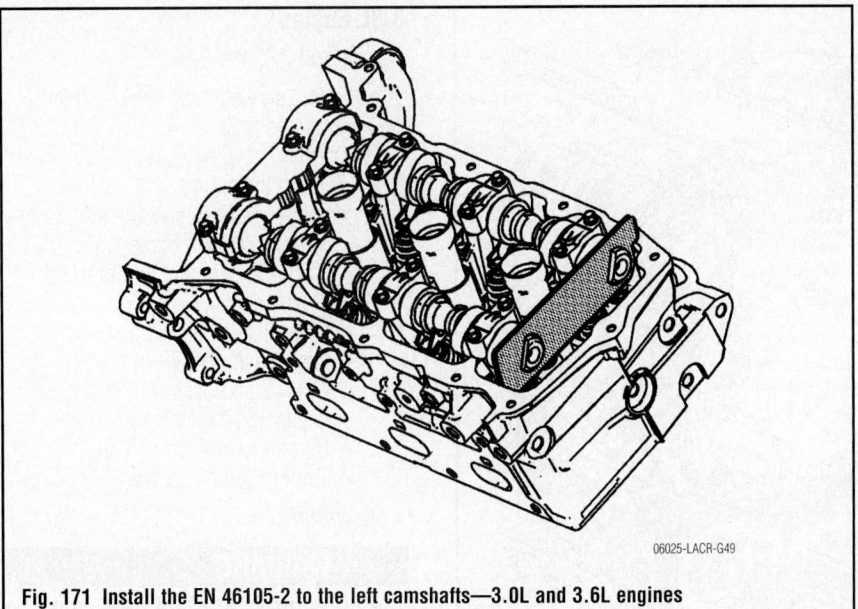

Fig. 171 Install the EN 46105-2 to the left camshafts—3.0L and 3.6L engines

19. Rotate the crankshaft until the left cylinder head camshafts align with the EN 46105-2 and the right cylinder head camshafts align with the EN 46105-1.

20. Install the EN 46105-1 to the right camshafts.

21. Install the EN 46105-2 to the left camshafts.

To install:

➡ **Do not lubricate the crankshaft front oil seal or crankshaft damper sealing**

surfaces. **The crankshaft damper is installed into a dry seal.**

22. Install the NEW crankshaft front oil seal into the engine front cover using a seal driver.

23. Place the seal into position with the notches in the seal down. The notches will face in board when properly installed.

24. Install the NEW camshaft position actuator valve oil seals into the engine front cover.

25. Install the 0.315 inch (8mm) guide from kit EN 46109 into the cylinder block positions as shown.

26. Install the NEW engine front cover to cylinder block seal.

27. Place a 0.118 inch (3mm) bead of RTV sealant, GM P/N 12378521, (Canadian P/N 88901148), or equivalent, on the engine front cover as shown.

28. Place the engine front cover onto the guide pins and slide into position.

29. Remove the guide pins from the cylinder block.

30. Hand start all the front cover bolts.

31. Tighten the engine front cover bolts in the sequence shown. Tighten the engine front cover bolts in sequence to 17 ft. lbs. (23 Nm).

32. Install NEW O-rings on the camshaft position sensor.

33. Place the camshaft position sensors in position on the front cover.

34. Install the camshaft position sensor bolts. Tighten the camshaft position sensor bolts to 89 inch lbs. (10 Nm).

35. Place the camshaft position actuator valves in position on the front cover.

36. Install the camshaft position actuator valve bolts. Tighten the camshaft position actuator valve bolts to 89 inch lbs. (10 Nm).

37. Install the water pump.

38. Install the camshaft covers.

39. Install the accessory drive belt tensioner. Install the accessory drive belt tensioner bolts. Tighten the accessory drive belt tensioner center bolts to 37 ft. lbs. (50 Nm). Tighten the accessory drive belt tensioner outer bolts to 17 ft. lbs. (23 Nm).

40. Install the crankshaft damper.

41. Install the coolant overflow reservoir.

42. Install the power steering reservoir. Tighten the M6 bolt to 80 inch lbs. (9 Nm). Tighten the M8 bolt to 18 ft. lbs. (25 Nm).

43. Install the upper radiator hose.

44. Install the alternator assembly.

45. Install engine splash shield.

46. Install the ECU module bracket. Tighten the ECM bracket bolts to 89 inch lbs. (10 Nm).

47. Connect the negative battery cable.

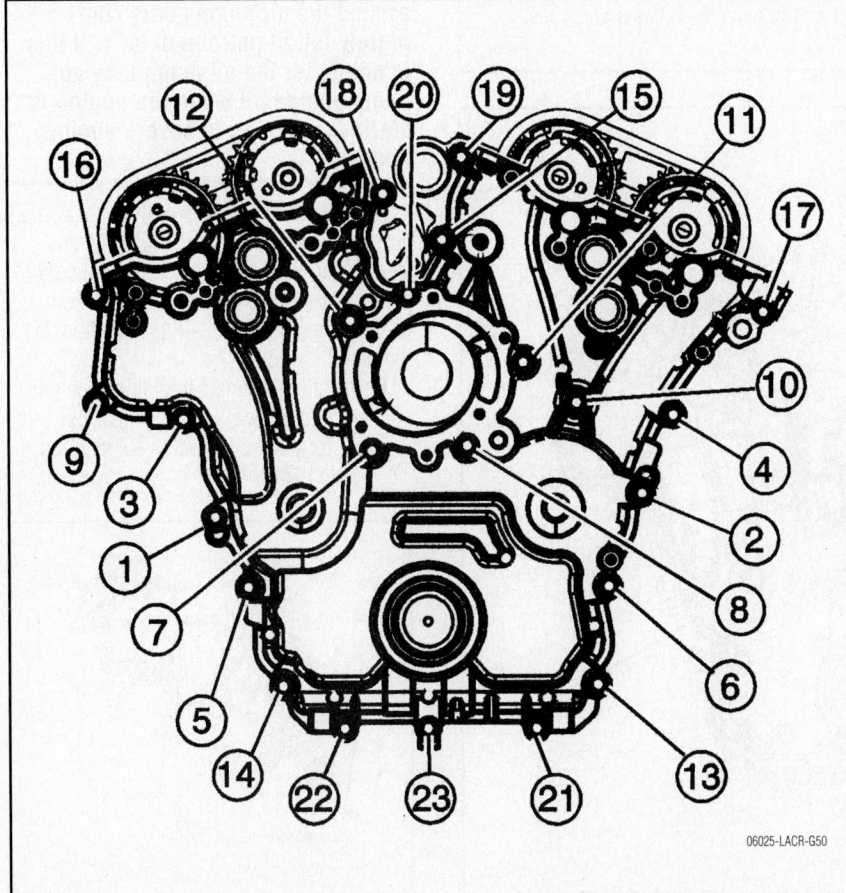

Fig. 172 Front cover torque sequence—3.0L and 3.6L engines

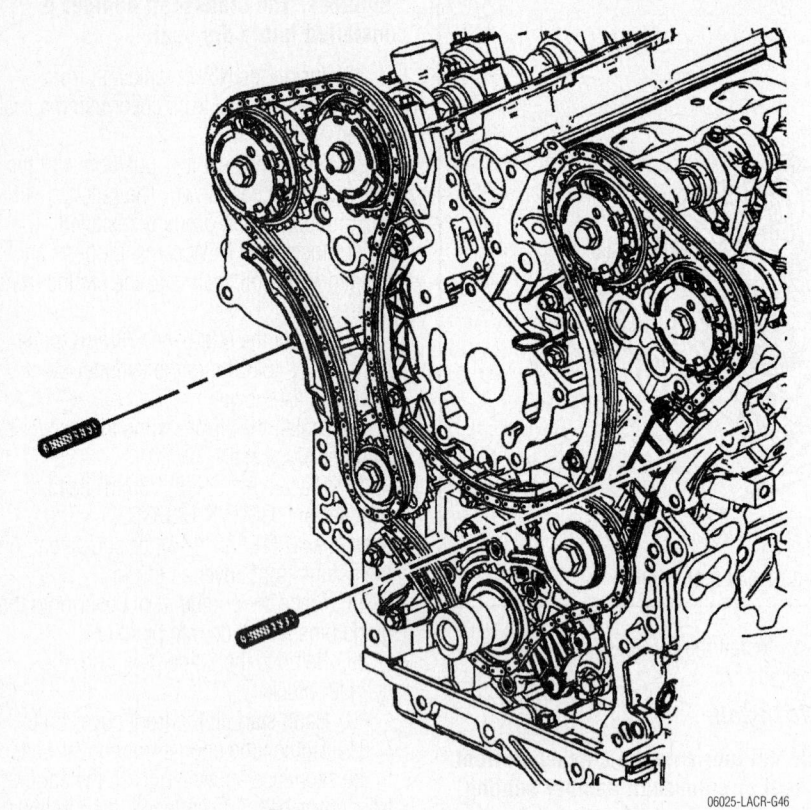

Fig. 173 Install the 0.315 inch (8mm) guide from kit EN 46109 into the cylinder block positions as shown—3.0L and 3.6L engines

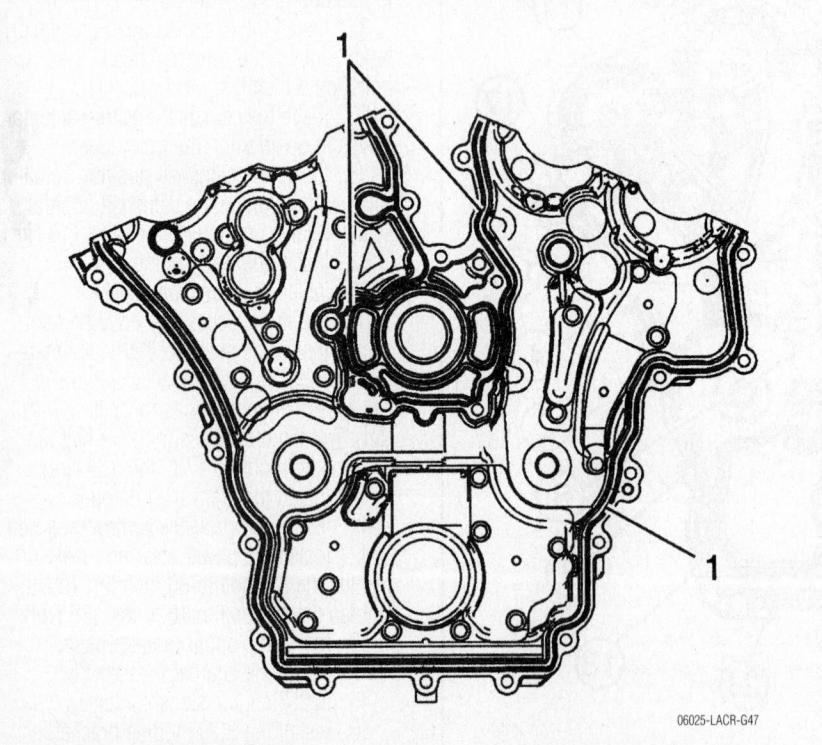

Fig. 174 Place a 0.118 inch (3mm) bead of RTV sealant on the engine front cover as shown (1)—3.0L and 3.6L engines

3.8L Engine

See Figures 175 and 176.

1. Before servicing the vehicle, refer to the Precautions Section.
2. Drain the cooling system.
3. Support the engine.
4. Remove or disconnect the following:
   - Negative battery cable
   - Torque axis mount and bracket
   - Drive belt
   - Drive belt tensioner
   - Crankshaft damper
   - Crankshaft Position (CKP) sensor shield and the CKP sensor
   - Oil pan to front cover bolts
   - Timing chain front cover

To install:

✻✻ WARNING

The oil pump is built into the front cover. When the cover is removed, oil drains from the pump. Since the pump loses its prime, it may not establish oil pressure as soon as the engine starts. Therefore, it is important to remove the oil pump cover from the back of the timing chain front cover and pack the space around the oil pump gears completely full of petroleum jelly. If this is not done, the oil pump may not pump engine oil when the engine is started, resulting in severe engine damage.

5. Remove the screws and the oil pump cover from the back of the timing chain front cover. Pack the space around the oil pump gears completely full of petroleum jelly. There must be no air space left inside the pump.
6. Install or connect the following:
   - Pump cover with new gaskets. Torque the screws to 97 inch lbs. (11 Nm).

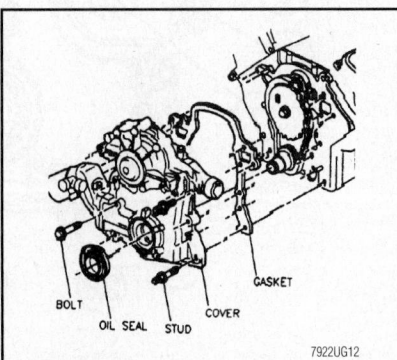

Fig. 175 Timing chain front cover—3.8L engine

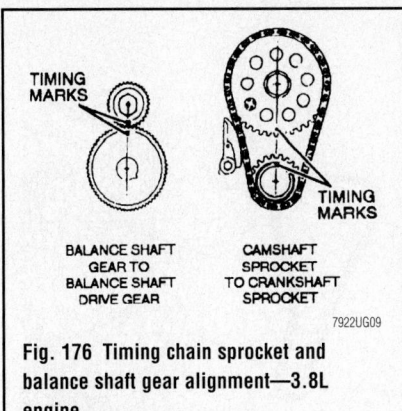

Fig. 176 Timing chain sprocket and balance shaft gear alignment—3.8L engine

- Timing chain front cover. Torque the front cover to engine bolts to 11 ft. lbs. (15 Nm), plus an additional 40°.
- Oil pan to front cover bolts. Torque the bolts to 125 inch lbs. (14 Nm).
- CKP sensor. Torque the bolts to 14–28 ft. lbs. (20–40 Nm).
- CKP sensor shield
- Crankshaft damper. Torque the bolt to 111 ft. lbs. (150 Nm), plus an additional 76° turn.
- Drive belt tensioner assembly
- Right inner fender access panel and the right front wheel
- Drive belt(s)
- Engine mount
- Coolant hoses
- Negative battery cable

7. Remove the engine support fixture.

8. Refill and bleed the cooling system.

9. Start the vehicle and check for leaks and proper engine operation.

5.3L Engine

See Figures 177 through 179.

Special Tool:

- J 41476: Front and Rear Cover Alignment Tool

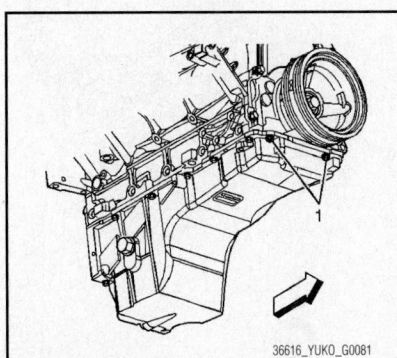

Fig. 177 Remove the oil pan-to-front cover bolts (1)

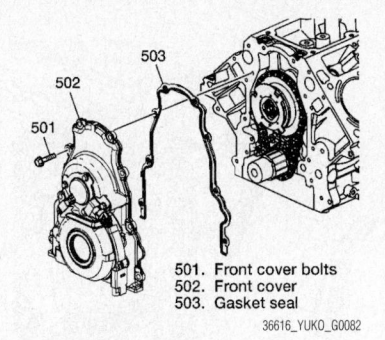

501. Front cover bolts
502. Front cover
503. Gasket seal

Fig. 178 Remove the front cover and gasket seal

1. Before servicing the vehicle, refer to the Precautions Section.

2. Remove the water pump. Refer to Water Pump, removal & installation.

3. Remove the crankshaft balancer. Refer to Crankshaft Damper, removal & installation.

4. Disconnect the engine harness electrical connector from the Camshaft Position (CMP) sensor wire harness electrical connector.

5. Remove the oil pan-to-front cover bolts.

6. Remove the front cover bolts.

7. Remove the front cover and gasket seal.

8. Discard the front cover gasket.

9. Remove the crankshaft front oil seal. Refer to Crankshaft Front Seal, removal & installation.

10. If replacing the engine front cover, perform the following steps:

    a. Remove the CMP sensor wire harness bolts.

    b. Disconnect the CMP sensor wire harness from the CMP sensor.

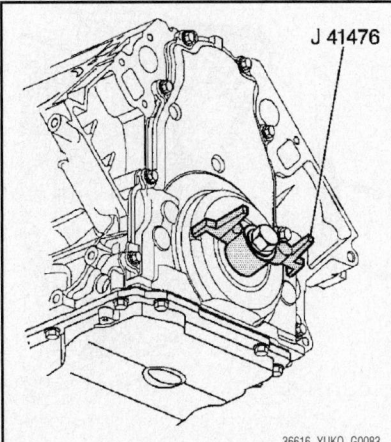

Fig. 179 Align the tapered legs of the J 41476 with the machined alignment surfaces on the front cover

    c. Remove the CMP sensor wire harness and the CMP sensor.

    d. Remove the CMP actuator magnet bolts and magnet.

    e. Remove and discard the CMP actuator magnet gasket.

To install:

➡ Do not reuse the crankshaft oil seal or front cover gasket. Do not apply any type of sealant to the front cover gasket, unless specified.

✳✳ WARNING

The special tool in this procedure is used to properly center the front crankshaft front oil seal. All gasket surfaces should be free of oil or other foreign material during assembly. The crankshaft front oil seal MUST be centered in relation to the crankshaft. An improperly aligned front cover may cause premature front oil seal wear and/or engine oil leaks.

11. If replacing the front cover, perform the following steps:

    a. Install a NEW CMP actuator magnet gasket onto the magnet.

    b. Install the CMP actuator magnet and bolts. Tighten the bolts to 106 inch lbs. (12 Nm).

    c. Inspect the CMP sensor O-ring seal for cuts or damage. If the seal is not cut or damaged, it may be reused.

    d. Lubricate the O-ring seal with clean engine oil.

    e. Install the CMP sensor. Position the CMP sensor wire harness to the front cover.

    f. Connect the CMP sensor wire harness to the CMP sensor.

    g. Install the CMP sensor wire harness bolts and tighten to 106 inch lbs. (12 Nm).

12. Apply a 0.20 inch (5mm) bead of sealant, 0.80 inch (20mm) long, to the oil pan-to-engine block junction.

13. Position the NEW engine front cover gasket and front cover to the engine.

14. Install the front cover bolts until snug. Do not over-tighten.

15. Install the oil pan-to-front cover bolts until snug. Do not over-tighten.

16. Install J 41476 to the front cover.

17. Align the tapered legs of the J 41476 with the machined alignment surfaces on the front cover.

18. Install the crankshaft balancer bolt until snug. Do not over-tighten.

19. Tighten the oil pan-to-front cover bolts to 18 ft. lbs. (25 Nm).

20. Tighten the engine front cover bolts to 18 ft. lbs. (25 Nm).

21. Remove the J 41476.

22. Connect the engine harness electrical connector to the CMP sensor wire harness electrical connector.

23. Install a NEW crankshaft front oil seal. Refer to Crankshaft Front Seal, removal & installation.

24. Install the water pump. Refer to Water Pump, removal & installation.

TIMING CHAIN AND SPROCKETS

REMOVAL & INSTALLATION

3.0L and 3.6L Engines

See Figures 180 through 198.

1. Before servicing the vehicle, refer to the Precautions Section.

2. Remove the timing chain cover and seal. Refer to Timing Chain Cover and Seal, removal & installation.

3. Remove the right bank secondary camshaft drive chain tensioner:

   a. Remove the right secondary camshaft drive chain tensioner bolts.

   b. Remove the right secondary camshaft drive chain tensioner.

   c. Remove and discard the right secondary camshaft drive chain tensioner gasket.

   d. Inspect the right secondary camshaft drive chain tensioner mounting surface on the right cylinder head for burrs or any defects that would degrade the sealing of the NEW right secondary camshaft drive chain tensioner gasket.

4. Remove the right bank secondary camshaft drive chain shoe:

   a. Remove the right secondary camshaft drive chain shoe bolt.

   b. Remove the right secondary camshaft drive chain shoe.

5. Remove the right bank secondary camshaft drive chain guide:

   a. Remove the right secondary camshaft drive chain guide bolts.

   b. Remove the right secondary camshaft drive chain guide.

6. Remove the right secondary camshaft drive chain from the right camshaft position actuators and the right camshaft intermediate drive chain idler sprocket.

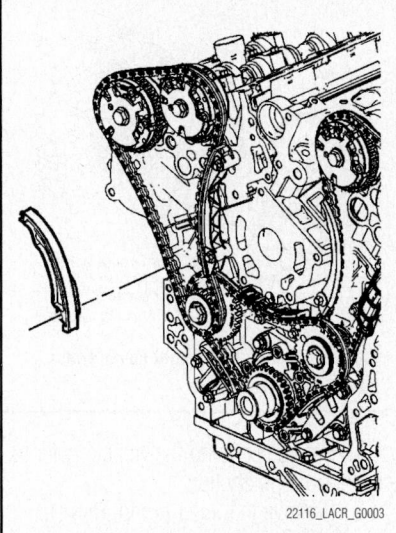

Fig. 181 The right secondary camshaft drive chain shoe bolt and drive chain shoe—3.0L and 3.6L engines

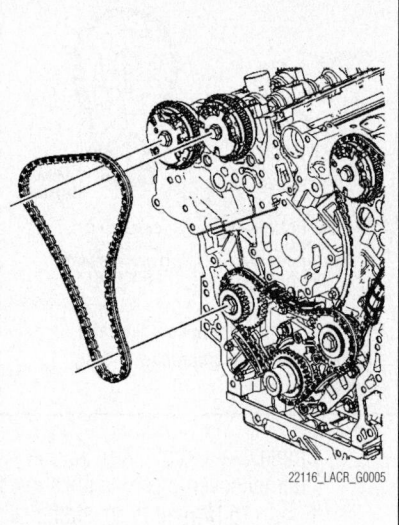

Fig. 183 The right bank secondary camshaft drive chain—3.0L and 3.6L engines

Fig. 184 The primary camshaft drive chain tensioner—3.0L and 3.6L engines

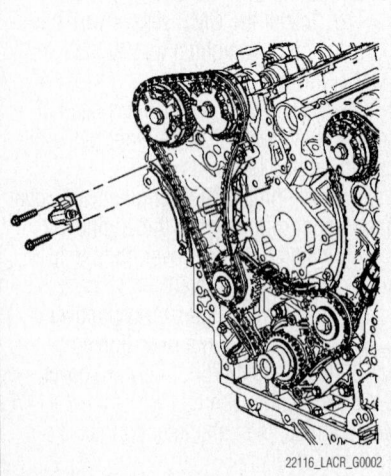

Fig. 180 The right bank secondary camshaft drive chain tensioner—3.0L and 3.6L engines

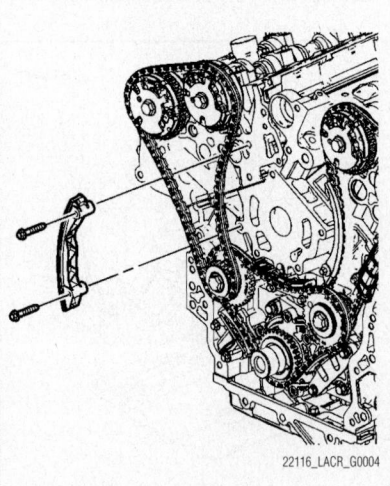

Fig. 182 The right bank secondary camshaft drive chain guide—3.0L and 3.6L engines

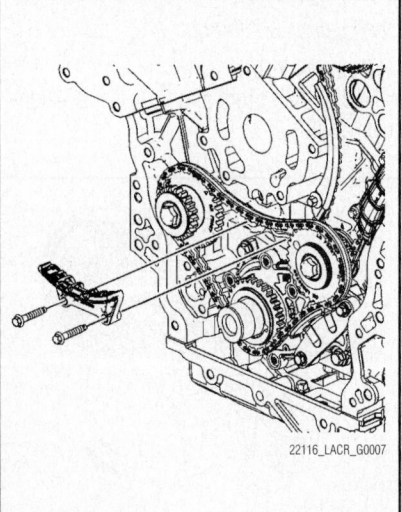

Fig. 185 The primary camshaft drive chain upper guide—3.0L and 3.6L engines

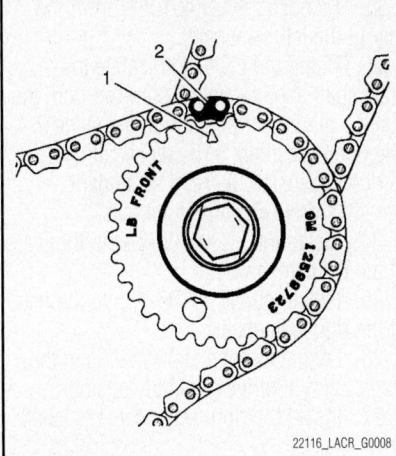

Fig. 186 Line up the left camshaft intermediate drive chain idler timing mark and the timing camshaft drive chain link—3.0L and 3.6L engines

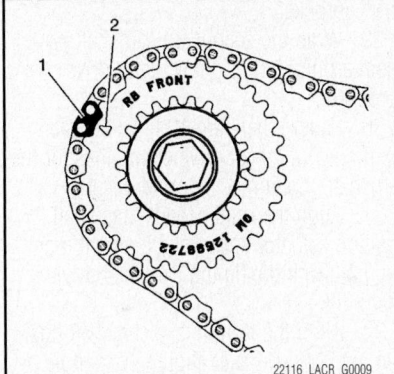

Fig. 187 Line up the right camshaft intermediate drive chain idler timing mark and the timing camshaft drive chain link—3.0L and 3.6L engines

7. Remove the primary camshaft drive chain tensioner:

    a. Remove the primary camshaft drive chain tensioner bolts.

    b. Remove the primary camshaft drive chain tensioner.

    c. Remove and discard the primary camshaft drive chain tensioner gasket.

    d. Inspect the primary camshaft drive chain tensioner mounting surface on the engine block for burrs or any defects that would degrade the sealing of the NEW primary camshaft drive chain tensioner gasket.

8. Remove the primary camshaft drive chain upper guide:

    a. Remove the primary camshaft drive chain upper guide bolts.

    b. Remove the primary camshaft drive chain upper guides.

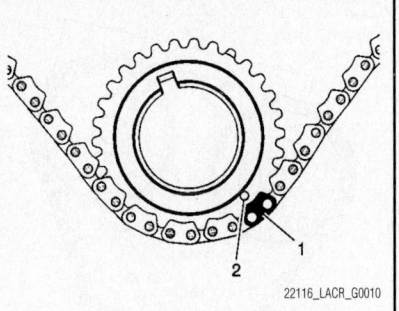

Fig. 188 The crankshaft sprocket timing mark will align with a timing camshaft drive chain link—3.0L and 3.6L engines

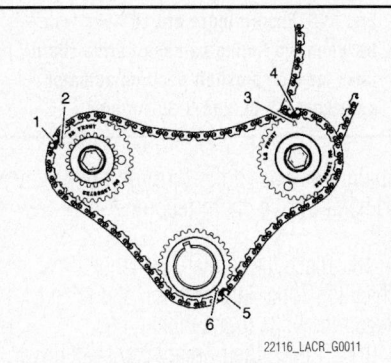

Fig. 189 Ensure all the timing marks are properly aligned with the timing camshaft drive chain links—3.0L and 3.6L engines

To install:

➡Ensure that the crankshaft is in the stage one timing drive assembly position.

9. Install the primary camshaft drive chain:

    a. Wrap the primary camshaft drive chain around the large sprockets of each camshaft intermediate drive chain idler and the crankshaft sprocket.

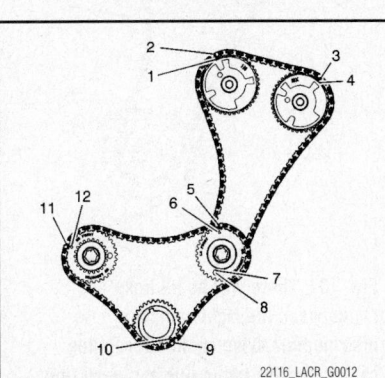

Fig. 190 Verify the primary and left secondary camshaft drive chain timing mark alignments—3.0L and 3.6L engines

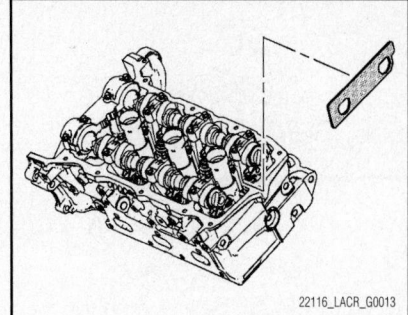

Fig. 191 Remove the EN 46105-1 from the rear of the left camshafts—3.0L and 3.6L engines

    b. The left camshaft intermediate drive chain idler timing mark will align with a timing camshaft drive chain link.

    c. The right camshaft intermediate drive chain idler timing mark will align with a timing camshaft drive chain link.

    d. The crankshaft sprocket timing mark will align with the timing camshaft drive chain link.

    e. Ensure all the timing marks are properly aligned with the timing camshaft drive chain links.

10. Install the primary upper camshaft drive chain guide.

11. Install the upper primary camshaft drive chain guide bolts. Tighten bolts to 17 ft. lbs. (23 Nm).

12. Using the J 45027, reset the primary camshaft drive chain tensioner plunger.

13. Install the plunger into the primary camshaft drive chain tensioner body.

14. Compress the plunger into the body and lock the primary camshaft drive chain tensioner by inserting the EN 46112 into the access hole in the side of the primary camshaft drive chain tensioner body.

15. Slowly release pressure on the primary camshaft drive chain tensioner. The

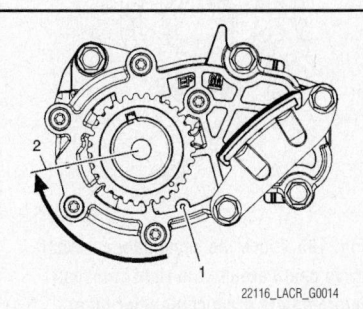

Fig. 192 Using the EN 46111, rotate the crankshaft and crankshaft sprocket from the stage 1 alignment position (1) to the stage 2 alignment position (2)—3.0L and 3.6L engines

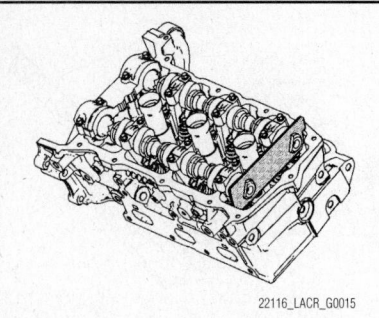

Fig. 193 Install the EN 46105-2 onto the rear of the left camshafts—3.0L and 3.6L engines

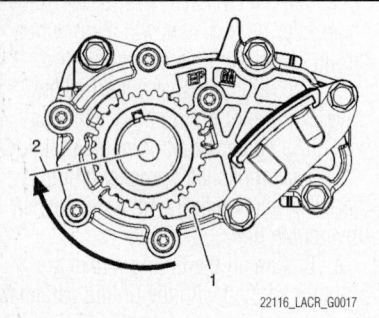

Fig. 194 Ensure that the crankshaft is in the stage 2 timing drive assembly position (2)—3.0L and 3.6L engines

primary camshaft drive chain tensioner should remain compressed.

16. Install a NEW primary camshaft drive chain tensioner gasket to the primary camshaft drive chain tensioner.

17. Install the primary camshaft drive

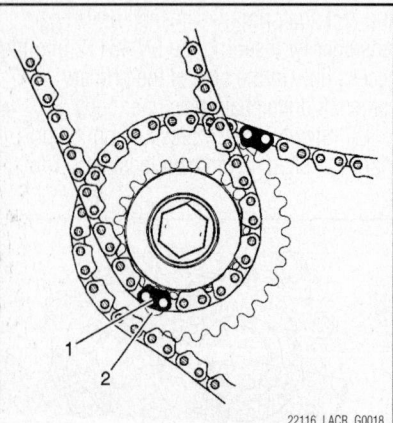

Fig. 195 Place the secondary camshaft drive chain around the right camshaft intermediate drive chain idler outer sprocket, aligning the timing camshaft drive chain link (1) with the alignment access hole (2) made in the right camshaft intermediate drive chain idler inner sprocket—3.0L and 3.6L engines

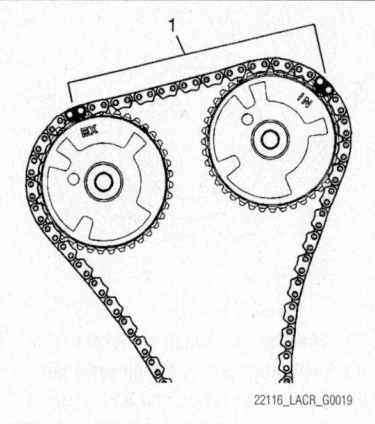

Fig. 196 Ensure there are 10 links (1) between the timing camshaft drive chain links for the camshaft position actuator sprockets—3.0L and 3.6L engines

chain tensioner bolts through the primary camshaft drive chain tensioner and gasket.

18. Place the primary camshaft drive chain tensioner into position and loosely install the bolts to the block.

19. Tighten the primary camshaft drive chain tensioner bolts:

    a. Step 1: 44 inch lbs. (5 Nm).

    b. Step 2: 17 ft. lbs. (23 Nm).

20. Release the primary camshaft drive chain tensioner by pulling out the EN 46112 and unlocking the tensioner plunger.

21. Verify the primary and left secondary camshaft drive chain timing mark alignments.

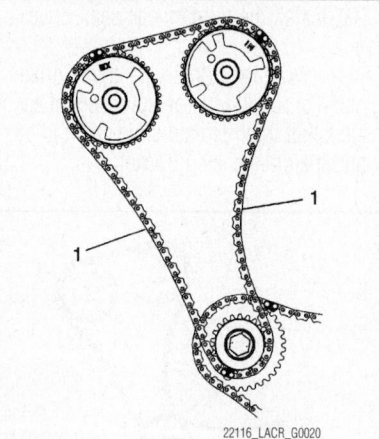

Fig. 197 There will be 22 links (1) between the right camshaft intermediate drive chain idler timing camshaft drive chain link and each right camshaft position actuator sprocket timing camshaft drive chain link—3.0L and 3.6L engines

22. Remove the EN 46105-1 from the rear of the left camshafts.

23. Using the EN 46111, rotate the crankshaft and crankshaft sprocket from the stage 1 alignment position to the stage 2 alignment position, 115 crankshaft degrees, in order to install the right secondary camshaft drive chain components.

24. Install the EN 46105-2 onto the rear of the left camshafts.

25. Install the EN 46105-1 onto the rear of the right camshafts.

26. Ensure that the crankshaft is in the stage 2 timing drive assembly position.

27. Install the right secondary camshaft drive chain.

28. Place the secondary camshaft drive chain around the right camshaft intermediate drive chain idler outer sprocket, aligning the timing camshaft drive chain link with the alignment access hole made in the right camshaft intermediate drive chain idler inner sprocket.

29. Wrap the secondary camshaft drive chain around both right actuator drive sprockets.

30. Ensure there are 10 links between the timing camshaft drive chain links for the camshaft position actuator sprockets.

31. Align the right exhaust camshaft position actuator sprocket alignment triangle mark with the timing camshaft drive chain link.

32. Align the right intake camshaft position actuator sprocket alignment triangle mark with the timing camshaft drive chain link.

33. Ensure that there are 22 links between the right camshaft intermediate drive chain idler timing camshaft drive chain link and each right camshaft position actuator sprocket timing camshaft drive chain link.

34. Position the right secondary camshaft drive chain guide.

35. Install the secondary camshaft drive chain guide bolts. Tighten the bolts to 17 ft. lbs. (23 Nm).

36. Position the right secondary camshaft drive chain shoe.

37. Install the secondary camshaft drive chain shoe bolt. Tighten the bolt to 17 ft. lbs. (23 Nm).

38. Using the J 45027, reset the right secondary camshaft drive chain tensioner plunger.

39. Install the plunger into the right secondary camshaft drive chain tensioner body.

40. Compress the plunger into the body and lock the right secondary camshaft drive chain tensioner by inserting the EN 46112 into the access hole in the side of the right

secondary camshaft drive chain tensioner body.

41. Slowly release pressure on the right secondary camshaft drive chain tensioner.

➡**The right secondary camshaft drive chain tensioner should remain compressed.**

42. Install a NEW right secondary camshaft drive chain tensioner gasket to the right secondary camshaft drive chain tensioner.

43. Install the right secondary camshaft drive chain tensioner bolts through the right secondary camshaft drive chain tensioner and gasket.

➡**Ensure the right secondary camshaft drive chain tensioner mounting surface on the right cylinder head does not have any burrs or defects that would degrade the sealing of the NEW right secondary camshaft drive chain tensioner gasket.**

44. Place the right secondary camshaft drive chain tensioner into position and loosely install the bolts to the block.

45. Verify the proper placement of the right secondary camshaft drive chain tensioner gasket tab.

46. Tighten the right secondary camshaft drive chain tensioner bolts:
   a. Step 1: 44 inch lbs. (5 Nm).
   b. Step 2: 17 ft. lbs. (23 Nm).

47. Release the right camshaft drive chain tensioner by pulling out the EN 46112 and unlocking the tensioner plunger.

✳✳ WARNING

Ensure that all timing chain tensioners are completely released. A timing chain tensioner that is not properly released can lead to serious engine damage.

48. Verify all primary and secondary camshaft drive chain timing mark alignments.

49. Install the timing chain cover and seal. Refer to Timing Chain Cover and Seal, removal & installation.

3.8L Engine

See Figures 199 and 200.

1. Before servicing the vehicle, refer to the Precautions Section.

2. Drain the cooling system.

3. Support the engine.

4. Remove or disconnect the following:
   • Negative battery cable
   • Torque axis mount and bracket
   • Drive belt
   • Drive belt tensioner
   • Crankshaft damper
   • Crankshaft Position (CKP) sensor shield and the CKP sensor
   • Oil pan to front cover bolts
   • Timing chain front cover

5. Align the timing marks on the camshaft and crankshaft sprockets so they are as close together as possible.
   • Timing chain damper
   • Camshaft sprocket bolt, the camshaft sprocket and timing chain
   • Crankshaft sprocket

✳✳ WARNING

Do not rotate the camshaft or crankshaft while the timing chain and sprockets are removed.

To install:

6. Install or connect the following:
   • Timing chain and sprockets with the timing marks aligned
   • Camshaft sprocket bolt. Torque the bolt to 74 ft. lbs. (100 Nm), plus an additional 90° turn.
   • Timing chain damper. Torque the bolts to 16 ft. lbs. (22 Nm).

✳✳ WARNING

The oil pump is built into the front cover. When the cover is removed, oil drains from the pump. Since the pump loses its prime it may not establish oil pressure as soon as the engine starts. Therefore, it is important to remove the oil pump cover from the back of the timing chain front cover and pack the space around the oil pump gears completely full of petroleum jelly. If this is not done, the oil pump may not pump engine oil when the engine is started, resulting in severe engine damage.

7. Remove the screws and the oil pump cover from the back of the timing chain front cover. Pack the space around the oil pump gears completely full of petroleum jelly. There must be no air space left inside the pump.

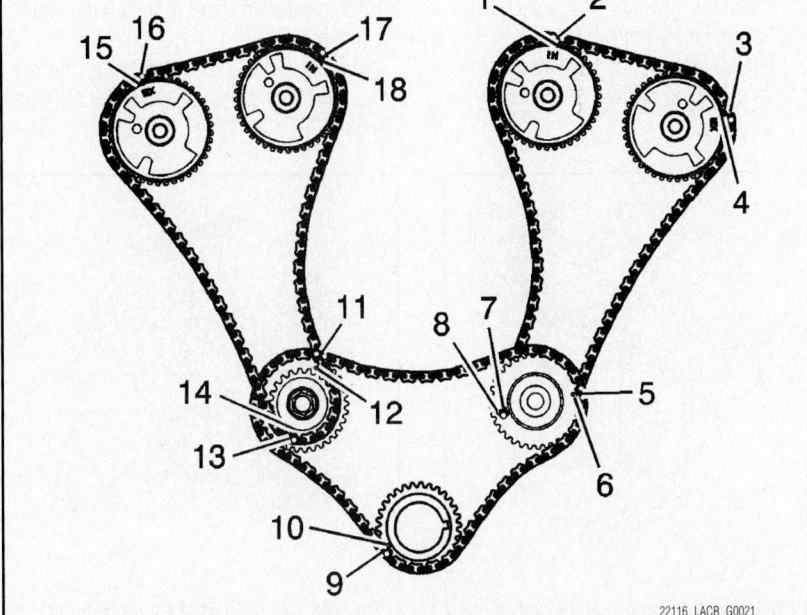

22116_LACR_G0021

Fig. 198 Verify all primary and secondary camshaft drive chain timing mark alignments—3.0L and 3.6L engines

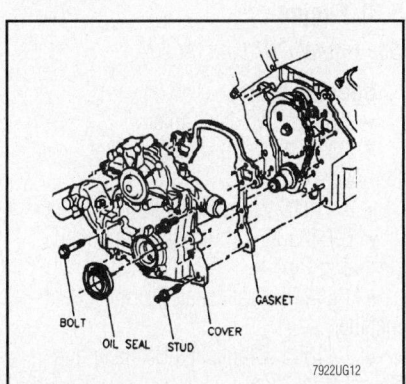

7922UG12

Fig. 199 Timing chain front cover—3.8L engine

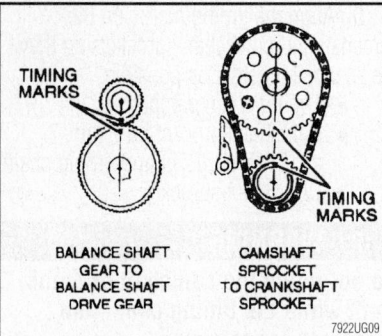

Fig. 200 Timing chain sprocket and balance shaft gear alignment—3.8L engine

8. Install or connect the following:
- Pump cover with new gaskets. Torque the screws to 97 inch lbs. (11 Nm)
- Timing chain front cover. Torque the front cover to engine bolts to 11 ft. lbs. (15 Nm), plus an additional 40°
- Oil pan to front cover bolts. Torque the bolts to 125 inch lbs. (14 Nm)
- CKP sensor. Torque the bolts to 14–28 ft. lbs. (20–40 Nm)
- CKP sensor shield
- Crankshaft damper. Torque the bolt to 111 ft. lbs. (150 Nm) plus an additional 76° turn
- Drive belt tensioner assembly
- Right inner fender access panel and the right front wheel
- Drive belt(s)
- Engine mount
- Coolant hoses
- Negative battery cable

9. Remove the engine support fixture.

10. Refill and bleed the cooling system.

11. Start the vehicle and check for leaks and proper engine operation.

5.3L Engine

See Figures 201 through 207.

Special Tools:
- J 8433: Two Jaw Puller
- J 41558: Crankshaft Sprocket Remover
- J 41816-2: Crankshaft End Protector
- EN 46330: Timing Belt Tensioner Retaining Pin
- J 41478: Crankshaft Front Oil Seal Installer
- J 41665: Crankshaft Balancer and Sprocket Installer
- J 42386-A: Flywheel Holding Tool
- J 45059: Angle Meter

✱✱ WARNING

Do not turn the crankshaft assembly after the timing chain has been removed in order to prevent damage to the piston assemblies or the valves.

1. Before servicing the vehicle, refer to the Precautions Section.
2. Disconnect the negative battery cable.
3. Drain the cooling system.
4. Remove the front cover and seal. Refer to Timing Chain Cover and Seal, removal & installation.
5. Remove the starter.
6. Install the J 42386-A tool and bolts. Use one M10 bolt (1.5 x 120mm) and another M10 bolt (1.5 x 45mm) for proper tool operation. Tighten the J 42386-A tool bolts to 37 ft. lbs. (50 Nm).
7. Remove and discard the camshaft sprocket bolt.
8. Remove the camshaft sprocket and timing chain.
9. Remove the bolts and timing chain tensioner.
10. Use the J 41816-2 protector, the J 41558 remover, bolts, and the J 8433 puller in order to remove the crankshaft sprocket.
11. Remove the crankshaft sprocket.
12. Remove the crankshaft sprocket key, as required.
13. Remove the J 42386-A tool and bolts.

To install:
14. Install the key into the crankshaft keyway, if previously removed.
15. Tap the key into the keyway until both ends of the key bottom onto the crankshaft.

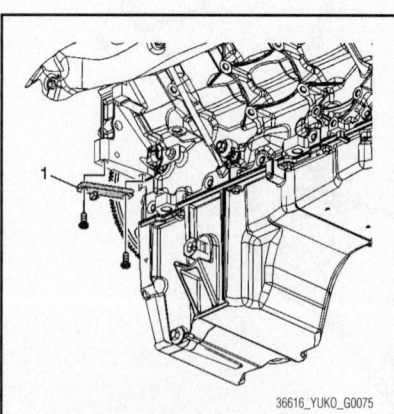

Fig. 201 Install Special Tool J 42386-A (1) and bolts. Use one M10 bolt (1.5 x 120mm) and another M10 bolt (1.5 x 45mm) for proper tool operation

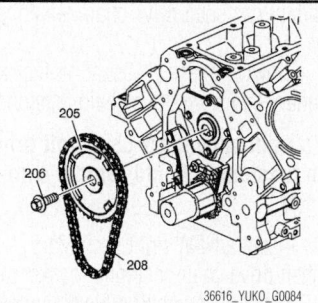

Fig. 202 Remove and discard the camshaft sprocket bolt (206). Remove the camshaft sprocket (205) and timing chain (208)

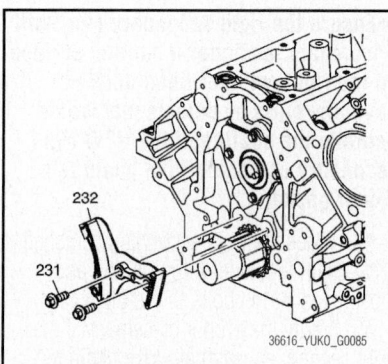

Fig. 203 Remove the bolts (231) and timing chain tensioner (232)

16. Position the crankshaft sprocket onto the front of the crankshaft. Align the crankshaft key with the crankshaft sprocket keyway.
17. Use the J 41478 installer and the J 41665 installer in order to install the crankshaft sprocket.
18. Install the sprocket onto the crankshaft until fully seated against the crankshaft flange.

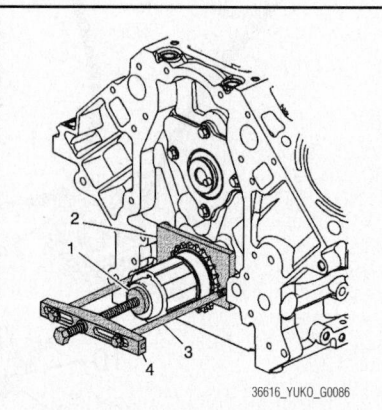

Fig. 204 Use the J 41816-2 protector (1), the J 41558 remover (2), bolts (3), and the J 8433 puller (4) in order to remove the crankshaft sprocket

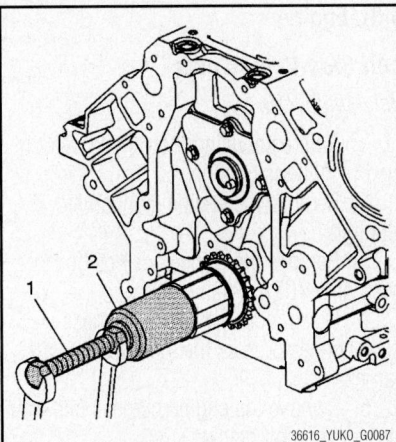

Fig. 205 Use the J 41478 installer (1) and the J 41665 installer (2) in order to install the crankshaft sprocket

19. Rotate the crankshaft sprocket until the alignment mark is in the 12 o'clock position.

20. Compress the timing chain tensioner guide and install the EN 46330 pin.

21. Install the timing chain tensioner and bolts. Tighten the timing chain tensioner bolts to 18 ft. lbs. (25 Nm).

➡**Do not use the camshaft sprocket bolt again. Install a NEW bolt during assembly. The sprocket teeth and timing chain must mesh and the camshaft and the crankshaft sprocket alignment marks MUST be aligned properly.**

22. Install the camshaft sprocket, timing chain, and NEW bolt.

23. Inspect the sprockets for proper alignment. The mark on the camshaft sprocket should be located in the 6 o'clock position and the mark on the crankshaft sprocket should be located in the 12 o'clock position.

24. Remove the EN 46330 pin.

25. Install the J 42386-A tool and bolts. Use one M10 bolt (1.5 x 120mm) and

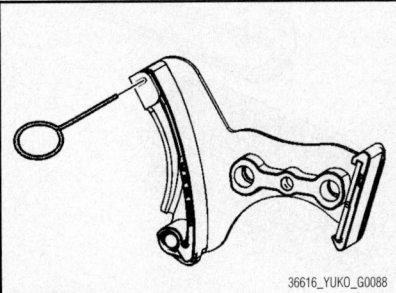

Fig. 206 Compress the timing chain tensioner guide and install the EN 46330 pin

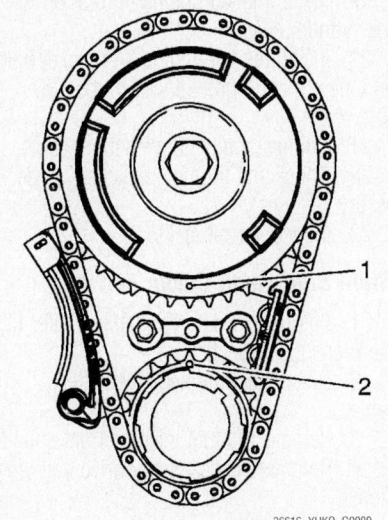

Fig. 207 Ensure the timing marks are properly aligned. The mark on the camshaft sprocket (1) should be located in the 6 o'clock position and the mark on the crankshaft sprocket (2) should be located in the 12 o'clock position

another M10 bolt (1.5 x 45mm) for proper tool operation. Tighten the J 42386-A tool bolts to 37 ft. lbs. (50 Nm).

26. Tighten the camshaft sprocket bolt.

   a. Step 1: Tighten to 55 ft. lbs. (75 Nm).

   b. Step 2: Tighten an additional 50° using the J 45059 meter.

27. Remove the J 42386-A tool and bolts.

28. Install the starter.

29. Install the front cover. Refer to Timing Chain Cover and Seal, removal & installation.

30. Start the engine and check for proper operation. Correct as required.

31. Check for leaks, correct as required.

VALVE COVERS

REMOVAL & INSTALLATION

3.0L and 3.6L Engines
See Figures 208 and 209.

1. Before servicing the vehicle, refer to the Precautions Section.

2. Remove the upper intake manifold with the lower intake manifold.

3. Disconnect the ignition coil electrical connectors.

4. Remove the wiring harness from the side of the valve cover by sliding the conduit down and outboard.

5. Remove the wiring conduit retainers from the valve cover by rotating the wiring harness conduit retainers counterclockwise.

6. Remove the wiring harness from the front of the valve cover.

7. Reposition and secure the wiring harnesses away from the valve cover in order to provide clearance.

8. Remove the ignition coils.

9. On the left side, loosen the left engine strut bracket and strut bracket to cylinder head bolts.

10. On both sides, remove the valve cover bolts and valve cover.

11. Remove and discard the valve cover seal and grommets. DO NOT reuse.

To install:

12. Install a NEW valve cover seal and NEW grommets.

13. Place an 8mm in diameter bead by 4mm bead in height of RTV sealant on the engine front cover split lines.

14. Place the left valve cover into position onto the left cylinder head.

15. Loosely install the left valve cover bolts.

16. Tighten the left valve cover bolts to 89 inch lbs. (10 Nm) in the sequence shown.

17. Place the right valve cover into position onto the left cylinder head.

18. Loosely install the right valve cover bolts.

19. Tighten the right valve cover bolts to 89 inch lbs. (10 Nm) in the sequence shown.

20. On the left side, tighten the left engine strut bracket and strut bracket-to-cylinder head bolts.

21. Install the ignition coils.

22. Position and secure the wiring harnesses to the valve cover.

23. Install the wiring harness to the front of the valve cover.

24. Install the wiring conduit retainers to the valve cover by rotating the wiring harness conduit retainers clockwise.

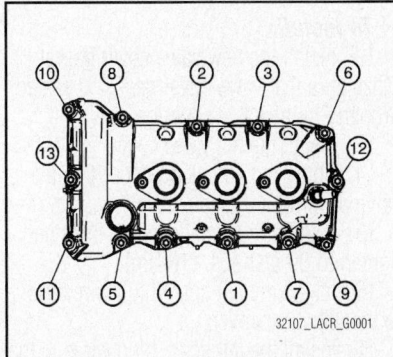

Fig. 208 Left valve cover bolt tightening sequence—3.0L and 3.6L engines

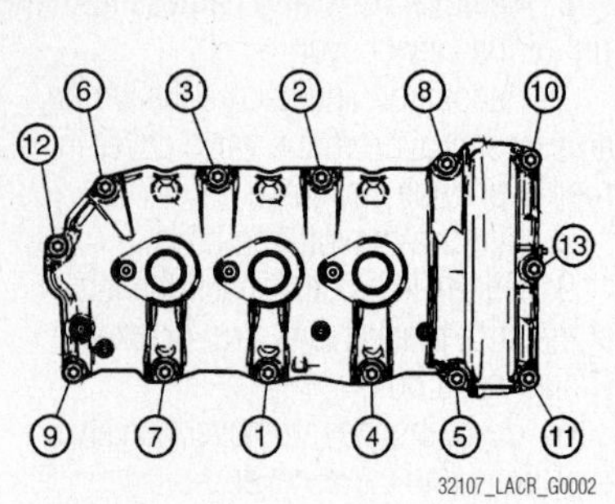

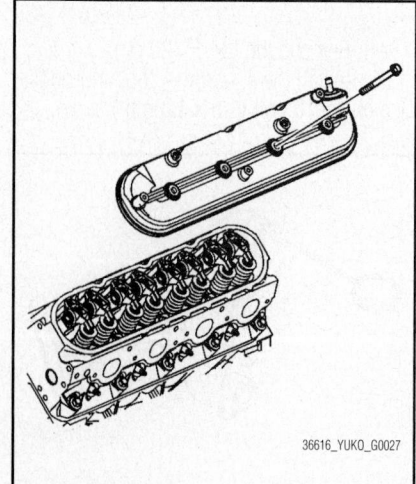

Fig. 209 Right valve cover bolt tightening sequence—3.0L and 3.6L engines

25. Install the wiring harness to the side of the valve cover by sliding the conduit up and inboard.

26. Connect the ignition coil electrical connectors.

27. Install the upper intake manifold with the lower intake manifold.

3.8L Engine

Left Side Valve Cover

1. Before servicing the vehicle, refer to the Precautions Section.

2. Disconnect the negative battery cable.

3. Remove the left engine lift bracket bolt and nut from the engine lift bracket.

4. Remove the left engine lift bracket from the cylinder head.

5. Remove the right engine mount strut bracket.

6. Remove the left spark plug wires from the spark plugs.

7. Remove the left spark plug wire cover from the left valve cover.

8. Remove the left valve cover bolts.

9. Remove the left valve cover and gasket.

10. Clean the valve rocker arm mating surfaces.

11. Clean the valve cover bolts of all thread-locking adhesive.

To install:

12. Install the new valve cover gasket. Make sure that valve cover gasket is seated properly in the valve cover groove.

13. Install the left valve cover.

14. Apply threadlock compound to the valve cover bolt threads.

15. Install the left valve cover bolts and tighten to 89 inch lbs. (10 Nm).

16. Install the left spark plug wire cover to the left valve cover.

17. Install the left spark plug wires to the spark plugs.

18. Install the right engine mount strut bracket.

19. Install the left engine lift bracket to the cylinder head.

20. Install the left engine lift bracket bolt and the nut and tighten to 22 ft. lbs. (30 Nm).

21. Connect the negative battery cable.

22. Check and fill the crankcase, as necessary.

23. Inspect for oil leaks.

Right Side Valve Cover

1. Before servicing the vehicle, refer to the Precautions Section.

2. Disconnect the negative battery cable.

3. Remove the fuel injector sight shield.

4. Remove the accessory drive belt tensioner.

5. Remove the right spark plug wires from the spark plugs.

6. Remove the fuel injector sight shield bracket nuts.

7. Remove the fuel injector sight shield bracket.

8. Remove the right engine lift bracket bolt and the nut from the engine lift bracket.

9. Remove the right engine lift bracket from the exhaust manifold.

10. Remove the right valve cover bolts.

11. Remove the right valve cover and gasket.

12. Clean the valve cover gasket mating surfaces.

13. Clean the valve cover bolts of all thread locking adhesive.

To install:

14. Install the new valve cover gasket.

15. Install the right valve cover.

16. Apply threadlock compound to the valve cover bolt threads.

17. Install the right valve cover bolts and tighten to 89 inch lbs. (10 Nm).

18. Install the right engine lift bracket to the exhaust manifold.

19. Install the right engine lift bracket bolt and the nut and tighten to 22 ft. lbs. (30 Nm).

20. Install the fuel injector sight shield bracket to the exhaust manifold.

21. Install the fuel injector sight shield bracket nuts and tighten to 22 ft. lbs. (30 Nm).

22. Install the right spark plug wires to the right spark plugs.

23. Install the accessory drive belt tensioner.

24. Install the fuel injector sight shield.

25. Connect the negative battery cable.

26. Check and fill the crankcase, as necessary.

27. Inspect for oil leaks.

5.3L Engine

Left Side Valve Cover

See Figure 210.

1. Before servicing the vehicle, refer to the Precautions Section.

2. Remove the engine sight shield, if required.

3. Remove the Connector Position Assurance (CPA) retainer.

4. Disconnect the engine harness electrical connector from the ignition coil wire harness.

5. Remove the engine harness clip from the ignition coil bracket stud.

6. Reposition the engine harness, as necessary.

7. Remove the spark plug wires from the ignition coils. Twist each plug wire ½ turn. Pull only on the boot in order to remove the wire from the ignition coil.

8. Remove the ignition coil bracket studs.

9. Remove the ignition coil bracket.

10. Remove the Positive Crankcase Ventilation (PCV) hose.

11. Loosen the valve rocker arm cover bolts.

12. Remove the valve rocker arm cover.

13. Remove and discard the old gasket.

To install:

➡**All gasket surfaces should be free of oil and/or other foreign material during assembly.**

➡**DO NOT reuse the valve rocker arm cover gasket.**

➡**If the PCV valve grommet has been removed from the rocker cover, install a NEW grommet during assembly.**

Fig. 210 Remove the valve rocker arm cover—left side

14. Install a NEW rocker cover gasket.

15. Install the valve rocker arm cover.

16. Tighten the rocker arm cover bolts to 106 inch lbs. (12 Nm).

17. Install the PCV hose.

18. Apply threadlock to the threads of the ignition coil bracket studs.

19. Position the ignition coil bracket onto the rocker cover.

20. Install the ignition coil bracket studs and tighten to 106 inch lbs. (12 Nm).

21. Install the spark plug wires to the ignition coils.

22. Position the engine harness, as necessary.

23. Install the engine harness clip to the ignition coil bracket stud.

24. Connect the engine harness electrical connector to the ignition coil wire harness.

25. Install the CPA retainer.

26. Install the engine sight shield, if required.

Right Side Valve Cover

See Figure 211.

1. Before servicing the vehicle, refer to the Precautions Section.

2. Remove the engine sight shield, if required.

3. Remove the Connector Position Assurance (CPA) lock.

4. Disconnect the main electrical connector to the ignition coil wire harness.

5. Remove the harness clips.

6. Reposition the engine harness, if necessary.

7. Remove the spark plug wires from the ignition coils. Twist each plug wire ½ turn. Pull only on the boot in order to remove the wire from the ignition coil.

8. Remove the surge tank outlet hose from the heater hose bracket.

9. Remove the heater hose bracket bolt from the front of the right cylinder head.

10. If necessary, remove the ignition coil bracket studs from the rocker arm cover.

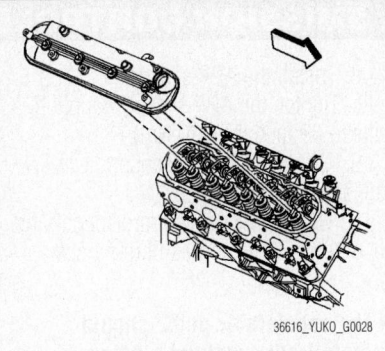

36616_YUKO_G0028

Fig. 211 Remove the valve rocker arm cover—right side

11. If necessary, remove the ignition coils and bracket from the rocker cover.

12. Remove the vent hose from the valve rocker arm cover.

13. Remove the valve rocker arm cover bolts.

14. Remove the valve rocker arm cover.

15. Remove the gasket from the rocker cover.

16. Discard the OLD gasket.

17. Remove the oil fill cap from the oil fill tube.

18. Remove the oil fill tube from the rocker cover, if required.

19. Discard the oil fill tube, if necessary.

To install:

➡**All gasket surfaces should be free of oil or other foreign material during assembly.**

➡**DO NOT reuse the valve rocker arm cover gasket.**

➡**The valve rocker arm cover bolt grommets may be reused.**

➡**If the oil fill tube has been removed from the rocker arm cover, install a NEW fill tube during assembly.**

20. Lubricate the O-ring seal of the NEW oil fill tube with clean engine oil.

21. Insert the NEW oil fill tube into the

rocker arm cover. Rotate the tube clockwise until locked in the proper position.

22. Install the oil fill cap into the tube. Rotate the cap clockwise until locked in the proper position.

23. Install a NEW rocker cover gasket into the valve rocker arm cover.

24. Install the valve rocker arm cover onto the cylinder head.

25. Install new rocker arm cover grommets, if necessary.

26. Install the rocker arm cover bolts and grommets and tighten the bolts to 106 inch lbs. (12 Nm).

27. Install the vent hose to the valve rocker arm cover.

28. Apply threadlock, GM P/N 12345382, or equivalent, to the threads of the bracket bolts.

29. If necessary, install the ignition coils and bracket to the rocker arm cover.

30. If necessary, install the ignition coil bracket studs to the rocker cover and tighten the studs to 106 inch lbs. (12 Nm).

31. Install the heater hose bracket and nut to the front of the right cylinder head and tighten to 80 inch lbs. (9 Nm).

32. Install the surge tank outlet hose to the heater hose bracket.

33. Install the spark plug wires to the ignition coils.

34. Position the engine harness, if necessary.

35. Install the harness clips.

36. Connect the main electrical connector feeding the ignition coils.

37. Install the CPA lock.

38. Install the engine sight shield, if required.

VALVE LASH

ADJUSTMENT

These engines use hydraulic lifters, which require no periodic adjustment.

ENGINE PERFORMANCE & EMISSION CONTROLS

ACCELERATOR PEDAL POSITION (APP) SENSOR

LOCATION

See Figure 212.

The Accelerator Pedal Position (APP) sensor is located at the top of the accelerator pedal.

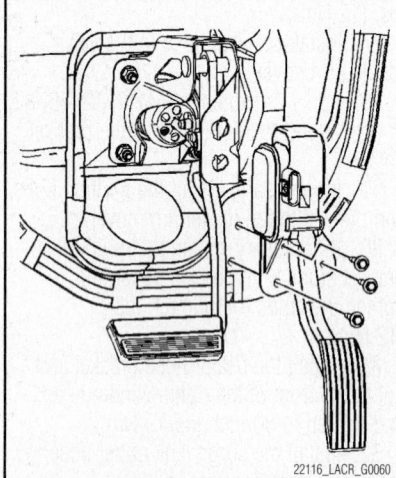

Fig. 212 Accelerator Pedal Position (APP) sensor location

REMOVAL & INSTALLATION

See Figure 212.

1. Before servicing the vehicle, refer to the Precautions Section.
2. Turn the ignition OFF.
3. Remove the insulator panel from under the dashboard on the driver's side.

✱✱ WARNING

Handle the electronic throttle control components carefully. Use cleanliness in order to prevent damage. Do not drop or roughly handle the electronic throttle control components. Do not immerse the electronic throttle control components in cleaning solvents of any type.

4. Disconnect the Accelerator Pedal Position (APP) sensor electrical connector from the accelerator pedal module.
5. Remove the APP sensor mounting bolts.
6. Remove the APP sensor from the vehicle.

To install:

7. Position the APP sensor to the mounting plate.

8. Install the APP sensor mounting bolts. Tighten the APP sensor mounting bolts to 89 inch lbs. (10 Nm).
9. Connect the APP sensor electrical connector.
10. Operate the accelerator pedal and observe the APP angles using a scan tool.

➡**The accelerator pedal should operate freely, without binding, between closed throttle and Wide Open Throttle (WOT).**

11. Install the insulator panel under the dashboard on the driver's side.

CAMSHAFT POSITION (CMP) SENSOR

LOCATION

See Figures 213 through 219.

REMOVAL & INSTALLATION

3.0L and 3.6L Engines

Intake—Bank 1 (Right Side)

See Figure 213.

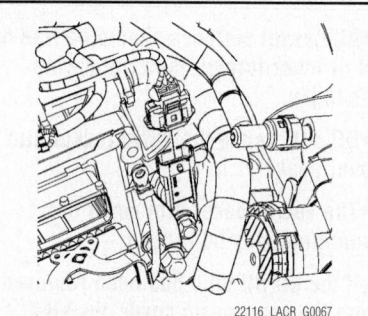

Fig. 213 Camshaft Position (CMP) sensor, intake, bank 1 (right side)—3.6L engine

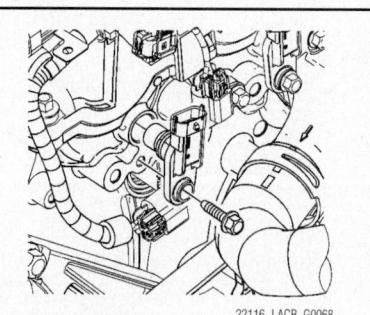

Fig. 214 Camshaft Position (CMP) sensor, exhaust, bank 1 (right side)—3.6L engine

1. Before servicing the vehicle, refer to the Precautions Section.
2. Turn the ignition OFF.
3. Remove the Camshaft Position (CMP) sensor electrical connector.
4. Remove the CMP sensor bolt.
5. Remove the CMP sensor.

To install:

6. Install the CMP sensor.
7. Install the CMP sensor bolt. Tighten the CMP sensor bolt to 89 inch lbs. (10 Nm).

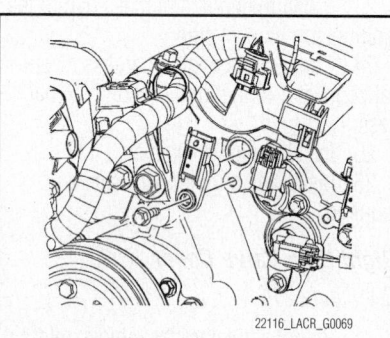

Fig. 215 Camshaft Position (CMP) sensor, intake, bank 2 (left side)—3.6L engine

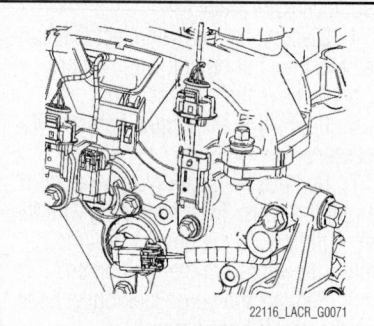

Fig. 216 Camshaft Position (CMP) sensor, exhaust, bank 2 (left side)—3.6L engine

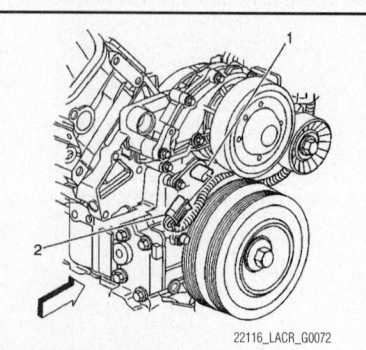

Fig. 217 Camshaft Position (CMP) sensor—3.8L engine

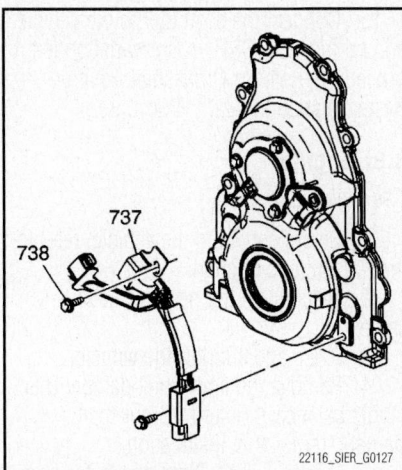

Fig. 218 Camshaft Position (CMP) sensor location and harness mounting (type one)—5.3L engine

8. Install the CMP sensor electrical connector.

Exhaust—Bank 1 (Right Side)

See Figure 214.

1. Before servicing the vehicle, refer to the Precautions Section.
2. Turn the ignition OFF.

➡**Do not remove the Engine Control Module (ECM) from the ECM bracket. Do not remove the ECM redundant ground wire from the ECM.**

3. Remove the ECM bracket bolts and reposition the ECM bracket in order to provide access.
4. Remove the Camshaft Position (CMP) sensor electrical connector.

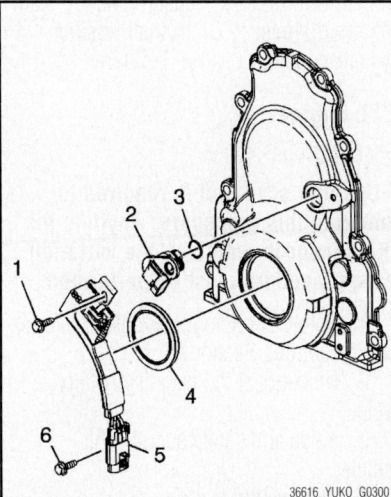

Fig. 219 Camshaft Position (CMP) sensor location and harness mounting (type two)—5.3L engine

5. Remove the CMP sensor bolt.
6. Remove the CMP sensor.

To install:

7. Install the CMP sensor.
8. Install the CMP sensor bolt. Tighten the CMP sensor bolt to 89 inch lbs. (10 Nm).
9. Install the CMP sensor electrical connector.
10. Install the ECM bracket with the ECM.

Intake—Bank 2 (Left Side)

See Figure 220.

1. Before servicing the vehicle, refer to the Precautions Section.
2. Turn the ignition OFF.

➡**Do not disconnect the power steering fluid lines/hoses from the reservoir.**

3. Remove the Power Steering (PS) fluid reservoir bolts and reposition the PS fluid reservoir in order to provide access.
4. Remove the Camshaft Position (CMP) sensor electrical connector.
5. Remove the CMP sensor bolt.
6. Remove the CMP sensor.

To install:

7. Install the CMP sensor.
8. Install the CMP sensor bolt. Tighten the CMP sensor bolt to 89 inch lbs. (10 Nm).
9. Install the CMP sensor electrical connector.
10. Install the PS fluid reservoir.
   a. Tighten the PS pump bracket bolt to 80 inch lbs. (9 Nm).
   b. Tighten the PS pump bracket bolt to 18 ft. lbs. (25 Nm).

Exhaust—Bank 2 (Left Side)

See Figure 216.

1. Before servicing the vehicle, refer to the Precautions Section.
2. Turn the ignition OFF.

➡**Do not disconnect the power steering fluid lines/hoses from the reservoir.**

3. Remove the Power Steering (PS) fluid reservoir bolts and reposition the PS fluid reservoir in order to provide access.
4. Remove the Camshaft Position (CMP) sensor electrical connector.
5. Remove the CMP sensor bolt.
6. Remove the CMP sensor.

To install:

7. Install the CMP sensor.
8. Install the CMP sensor bolt. Tighten the CMP sensor bolt to 89 inch lbs. (10 Nm).
9. Install the CMP sensor electrical connector.

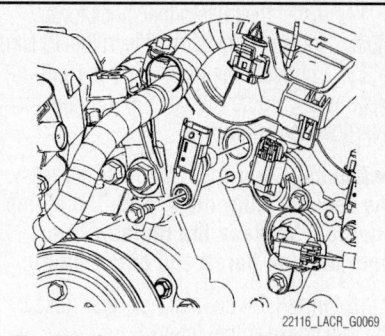

Fig. 220 Camshaft Position (CMP) sensor, intake, bank 2 (left side)—3.0L and 3.6L engines

10. Install the PS fluid reservoir.
   a. Tighten the PS pump bracket bolt to 80 inch lbs. (9 Nm).
   b. Tighten the PS pump bracket bolt to 18 ft. lbs. (25 Nm).

3.8L Engine

See Figure 217.

1. Before servicing the vehicle, refer to the Precautions Section.
2. Reposition the coolant reservoir hose clamp aside at the radiator overflow fitting.
3. Remove the coolant reservoir hose from the radiator overflow fitting.
4. Disconnect the coolant reservoir hose support retainer from the electrical harness.
5. Remove the coolant reservoir nuts from the shock tower studs.
6. Remove the coolant recovery reservoir from the lower retainer and the shock tower studs.
7. Drain the coolant from the recovery reservoir into a clean container.
8. Remove the accessory drive belt. Refer to Accessory Drive Belts, removal & installation.
9. Disconnect the electrical connector from the Camshaft Position (CMP) sensor.
10. Remove the CMP sensor bolt.
11. Remove the CMP sensor from the engine front cover.

To install:

12. Install the CMP sensor to the engine front cover.
13. Install the CMP sensor bolt. Tighten the bolt to 89 inch lbs. (10 Nm).
14. Connect the electrical connector to the CMP sensor.
15. Install the accessory drive belt. Refer to Accessory Drive Belts, removal & installation.
16. Install the coolant recovery reservoir to the lower retainer and the shock tower studs.

17. Install the nuts to the shock tower studs. Tighten the nuts to 29 inch lbs. (3 Nm).

18. Lubricate the reservoir hose with clean water. Route the hose to the radiator overflow neck fitting.

➥**The hose end must be flush against the radiator filler neck. Seat the clamp squarely between the radiator filler neck and the flared end of the fitting.**

19. Install the coolant reservoir hose to the radiator overflow fitting.

20. Connect the coolant reservoir hose support retainer to the electrical harness.

21. Position the coolant reservoir hose clamp to the radiator overflow fitting.

22. Fill the coolant recovery reservoir to the proper level.

5.3L Engine

See Figures 218 through 219.

1. Before servicing the vehicle, refer to the Precautions Section.

2. Disconnect the negative battery cable.

3. Raise and support the vehicle safely.

4. Unplug the harness connector from the CMP sensor.

5. Remove the CMP sensor harness bolts, then remove the sensor from the engine.

To install:

➥**Be sure to use new fasteners, as required.**

6. Installation is the reverse of removal.

7. Lubricate a new O-ring with clean engine oil. Tighten the bolt to 106 inch lbs. (12 Nm).

CRANKSHAFT POSITION (CKP) SENSOR

LOCATION

See Figures 221 through 223.

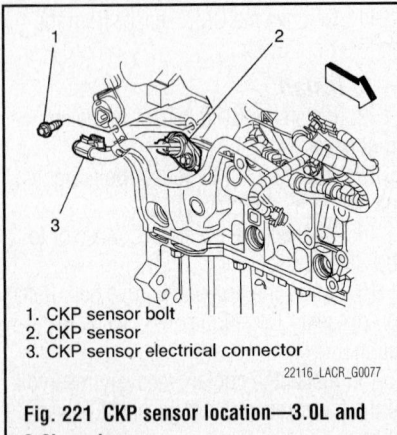

1. CKP sensor bolt
2. CKP sensor
3. CKP sensor electrical connector

22116_LACR_G0077

Fig. 221 CKP sensor location—3.0L and 3.6L engines

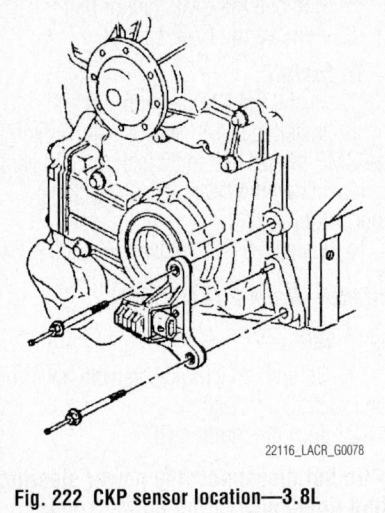

22116_LACR_G0078

Fig. 222 CKP sensor location—3.8L engine

REMOVAL & INSTALLATION

3.0L and 3.6L Engines

See Figure 221.

1. Before servicing the vehicle, refer to the Precautions Section.

2. Turn the ignition OFF.

3. Raise and support the vehicle.

4. Reposition the wiring harness heat shield to obtain access.

5. Disconnect the Crankshaft Position (CKP) electrical connector.

6. Remove the crankshaft sensor bolt.

7. Remove the crankshaft sensor.

To install:

8. Install the crankshaft position sensor.

9. Install the crankshaft position sensor bolt. Tighten the crankshaft position sensor bolt to 89 inch lbs. (10 Nm).

10. Connect the CKP electrical connector.

11. Install the wiring harness heat shield to the oil level indicator tube.

12. Lower the vehicle.

13. Connect the scan tool to the vehicle and perform the CKP sensor variation learn procedure. Refer to Crankshaft Position System Variation Learn Procedure.

3.8L Engine

See Figure 222.

1. Before servicing the vehicle, refer to the Precautions Section.

2. Disconnect the negative battery cable.

3. Raise and support the vehicle.

4. Remove the crankshaft damper (harmonic balancer). Refer to Crankshaft Damper, removal & installation.

5. Disconnect the Crankshaft Position (CKP) sensor electrical connector.

❈❈ WARNING

Do not use a pry bar when removing the CKP sensor shield.

6. Remove the CKP sensor shield.

7. Remove the CKP sensor studs.

8. Remove the CKP sensor.

To install:

9. Install the CKP sensor.

10. Install the CKP sensor studs. Tighten the studs to 22 ft. lbs. (30 Nm).

11. Install the CKP sensor shield.

12. Connect the CKP sensor electrical connector.

13. Install the crankshaft damper. Refer to Crankshaft Damper, removal & installation.

14. Lower the vehicle.

15. Connect the negative battery cable.

16. Connect the scan tool to the vehicle and perform the CKP sensor variation learn procedure. Refer to Crankshaft Position System Variation Learn Procedure.

5.3L Engine

See Figure 223.

➥**Use of a scan tool is required to complete this procedure. Anytime the CKP sensor is replaced, the variation learn procedure must be performed.**

1. Before servicing the vehicle, refer to the Precautions Section.

2. Disconnect the negative battery cable.

3. Raise and safely support the vehicle.

4. Remove the starter.

5. Clean the area around the sensor to prevent debris from entering the engine.

6. Remove the bolt securing the sensor, then remove it from the engine.

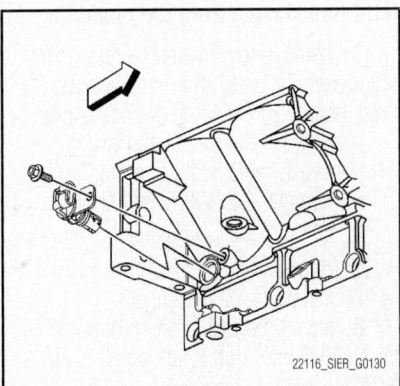

22116_SIER_G0130

Fig. 223 Crankshaft Position (CKP) sensor location—5.3L engine

To install:

➡**Be sure to use new fasteners, as required.**

7. Installation is the reverse of removal.

8. Lubricate a new O-ring with clean engine oil.

9. Tighten the bolt to 18 ft. lbs. (25 Nm).

10. Connect the scan tool to the vehicle and perform the CKP sensor variation learn procedure. Refer to Crankshaft Position System Variation Learn Procedure.

CRANKSHAFT POSITION SYSTEM VARIATION LEARN PROCEDURE

1. Before servicing the vehicle, refer to the Precautions Section.

2. Install a scan tool.

3. Monitor the Engine Control Module (ECM) for Diagnostic Trouble Codes (DTC's) with a scan tool. If other DTC's are set, except DTC P0315, refer to Diagnostic Trouble Codes for the applicable DTC that set.

4. Select the CKP variation learn procedure with a scan tool.

5. The scan tool instructs you to perform the following:

a. Accelerate to Wide Open Throttle (WOT).

b. Release throttle when fuel cut-off occurs.

c. Observe fuel cut-off for applicable engine.

d. Engine should not accelerate beyond calibrated RPM value.

e. Release throttle immediately if value is exceeded.

f. Block drive wheels.

g. Set parking brake.

h. DO NOT apply brake pedal.

i. Cycle ignition from OFF to ON.

j. Apply and hold brake pedal.

k. Start and idle engine.

l. Turn A/C OFF.

m. Vehicle must remain in Park or Neutral.

n. The scan tool monitors certain component signals to determine if all the conditions are met to continue with the procedure. The scan tool only displays the condition that inhibits the procedure. The scan tool monitors the following components:

- CKP sensors activity: If there is a CKP sensor condition, refer to the applicable DTC that set.
- Camshaft Position (CMP) sensor activity: If there is a CMP sensor condition, refer to the applicable DTC that set.

- Engine Coolant Temperature (ECT): If the ECT is not warm enough, idle the engine until the engine coolant temperature reaches the correct temperature.

6. Enable the CKP System Variation Learn Procedure with a scan tool.

➡**Important: While the learn procedure is in progress, release the throttle immediately when the engine starts to decelerate. The engine control is returned to the operator and the engine responds to throttle position after the learn procedure is complete.**

7. Accelerate to WOT.

8. Release when the fuel cut-off occurs.

9. Test in progress.

10. The scan tool displays Learn Status: Learned this ignition. If the scan tool indicates that DTC P0315 ran and passed, the CKP Variation Learn Procedure is complete. If the scan tool indicates DTC P0315 failed or did not run, refer to DTC P0315. If any other DTC's set, refer to Diagnostic Trouble Codes for the applicable DTC that set.

11. Turn OFF the ignition for 30 seconds after the learn procedure is completed successfully.

12. The CKP Variation Learn Procedure is also required when the following service procedures have been performed, regardless of whether DTC P0315 is set:

- A CKP sensor replacement
- An engine replacement
- An ECM replacement
- An harmonic balancer replacement
- A crankshaft replacement
- Any engine repairs which disturb the CKP sensor relationship

ENGINE CONTROL MODULE (ECM)

LOCATION

See Figures 224 and 225.

REMOVAL & INSTALLATION

3.0L and 3.6L Engines

See Figure 224.

✳✳ WARNING

Turn the ignition OFF when installing or removing the control module connectors and disconnecting or reconnecting the power to the control module (battery cable, Powertrain Control Module (PCM)/Engine Control Module (ECM)/Transaxle Control Module (TCM) pigtail, control module

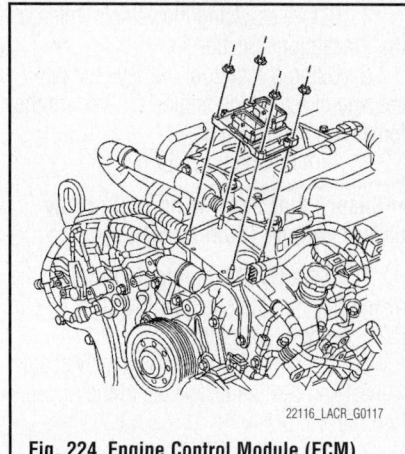

22116_LACR_G0117

Fig. 224 Engine Control Module (ECM) location—3.0L and 3.6L engines

fuse, jumper cables, etc.) in order to prevent internal control module damage.

✳✳ WARNING

Control module damage may result when the metal case contacts battery voltage. DO NOT contact the control module metal case with battery voltage when servicing a control module, using battery booster cables, or when charging the vehicle battery.

✳✳ WARNING

In order to prevent any possible electrostatic discharge damage to the control module, do not touch the connector pins or the soldered components on the circuit board.

➡Remove any debris from around the control module connector surfaces before servicing the control module. Inspect the control module connector gaskets when diagnosing or replacing the control module. Ensure that the gaskets are installed correctly. The gaskets prevent contaminant intrusion into the control module.

➡The replacement control module must be programmed.

➡It is necessary to record the remaining engine oil life. If the replacement module is not programmed with the remaining engine oil life, the engine oil life will default to 100 percent. If the replacement module is not programmed with the remaining engine oil life, the engine oil will need to be changed at 3,000 miles (5,000 km) from the last engine oil change.

1. Before servicing the vehicle, refer to the Precautions Section.

2. Using a scan tool, retrieve the percentage of remaining engine oil. Record the remaining engine oil life.

3. Turn the ignition OFF.

➡**Ensure that there is no main relay circuit voltage (ECM Fuse).**

4. Use a DVOM in order to measure the main relay circuit voltage at the ECM fuse in the underhood fuse block.

5. Disconnect the battery negative cable.

6. Remove the ECM fuse in the underhood fuse block.

7. Remove the TCM/Instrument Panel Cluster (IPC) fuse in the underhood fuse block.

8. Remove the ECM/TCM fuse in the underhood fuse block.

9. Unlock the body side (outboard) ECM electrical connector:

   a. Depress the ECM electrical connector lever lock.

   b. Simultaneously rotate the ECM connector clamp lever and depress the lock slide.

✻✻ **WARNING**

In order to prevent any possible electrostatic discharge damage to the ECM, do not touch the connector pins.

10. Remove the body side (outboard) ECM connector.

11. Unlock and remove the engine side (inboard) ECM connector.

12. Remove the ECM redundant ground wire and bolt from the ECM.

13. Remove the ECM bolts.

14. Remove the ECM.

15. If necessary, perform the following steps:

   a. Remove the ECM bracket bolts.

   b. Remove the ECM bracket.

To install:

16. Install the ECM bracket, as necessary.

17. Install the ECM bracket bolts, as necessary. Tighten the ECM bracket bolts to 89 inch lbs. (10 Nm).

✻✻ **WARNING**

In order to prevent any possible electrostatic discharge damage to the ECM, do not touch the connector pins.

18. Install the ECM.

19. Install the ECM bolts. Tighten the ECM bolts to 89 inch lbs. (10 Nm).

20. Install the ECM redundant ground and bolt to the ECM. Tighten the ECM redundant ground wire bolt to 44 inch lbs. (5 Nm).

21. Install the engine side (inboard) ECM connector.

22. Install the body side (outboard) ECM connector.

23. Install the ECM/TCM fuse in the underhood fuse block.

24. Install the TCM/IPC fuse in the underhood fuse block.

25. Install the ECM fuse in the underhood fuse block.

26. Connect the negative battery cable to the battery.

27. If a new ECM is being installed, the ECM must be programmed.

28. Turn the ignition OFF for at least 5 seconds after the programming event is complete.

5.3L Engine

See Figure 225.

Service of the Engine Control Module (ECM) should normally consist of either replacement of the ECM or Electrically Erasable Programmable Read Only Memory (EEPROM) programming. If the diagnostic procedures call for ECM replacement, inspect the ECM first to see if the replacement is the correct part. If the ECM is faulty, remove the ECM and install the new service ECM.

The new service ECM will not be programmed. You must program the new ECM. DTC P0602 indicates the EEPROM is not programmed or has malfunctioned.

✻✻ **WARNING**

In order to prevent any possible electrostatic discharge damage to the ECM, do not touch the connector pins or the soldered components on the circuit board.

✻✻ **WARNING**

Control module damage may result when the metal case contacts battery voltage. DO NOT contact the control module metal case with battery voltage when servicing a control module, using battery booster cables, or when charging the vehicle battery.

✻✻ **WARNING**

Always turn the ignition OFF when installing or removing the ECM connectors in order to prevent damage to the components.

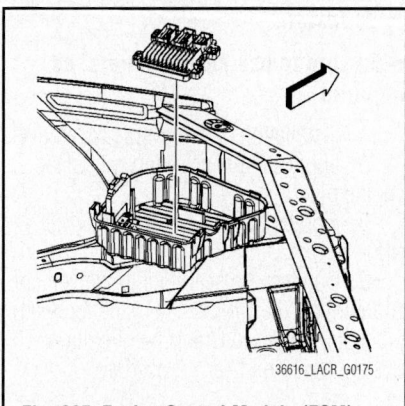

36616_LACR_G0175

Fig. 225 Engine Control Module (ECM) location—5.3L engine

➡**It is necessary to record the remaining engine oil life. If the replacement module is not programmed with the remaining engine oil life, the engine oil life will default to 100 percent. If the replacement module is not programmed with the remaining engine oil life, the engine oil will need to be changed at 3,000 miles (5,000 km) from the last engine oil change.**

1. Before servicing the vehicle, refer to the Precautions Section.

2. Using a scan tool, retrieve the percentage of remaining engine oil. Record the remaining engine oil life.

3. Disconnect the negative battery cable.

4. Disengage the engine wiring harness upper and lower electrical connector retainers and remove the connectors from the ECM.

5. Remove the air cleaner assembly.

6. Disengage the retainer tabs securing the ECM to the bracket.

7. Remove the ECM.

To install:

8. Install the ECM to the air cleaner lower housing.

9. Install the bottom ECM tabs into the bracket.

10. Push the ECM in securing the ECM to the bracket.

11. Position the engine wiring harness lower and upper electrical connectors and engage the retainers securing the connectors to the ECM.

12. Connect the negative battery cable.

13. If a NEW ECM was installed, program the ECM. Refer to Reset Procedure.

RESET

Special Tool:

• EL-49642: Service Programming System (SPS) Programming Support Tool

If the ECM is replaced, the following procedures must be performed:
1. ECM Reprogramming.
2. The CKP System Variation Learn.
3. The Throttle/Idle Learn procedure.
4. Theft Deterrent reprogramming.
5. Fuel Composition Diagnostic.
6. Engine Oil Life Remaining. When available, use a scan tool to reset the engine oil life remaining back to the original percentage recorded before the module was replaced.
7. Transmission Fluid Life Remaining. When available, use the scan tool to reset the Transmission Fluid Life Remaining back to the original percentage recorded before the module was replaced.

Review the information below to ensure proper programming protocol.

• DO NOT program a control module unless you are directed by a service procedure or you are directed by a General Motors Corporation service bulletin. Programming a control module at any other time will not permanently correct for a fault or DTC being set.

• It is essential that the TIS terminal, MDI, and/or Scan Tool, is equipped with the latest software before performing service programming.

• Due to the time requirements of programming a controller, install EL-49642 SPS Programming Support Tool to maintain system voltage. Stable battery voltage is critical during programming. Any fluctuation, spiking, over voltage, or loss of voltage will interrupt programming. If the above tool is not available, connect a fully charged 12 volt jumper or booster pack disconnected from the AC voltage supply.

• Some modules will require additional programming/setup events to be performed before or after programming.

• Some vehicles may require the use of a CANDi or MDI module for programming.

• Review the appropriate service information for these procedures. DTC's may set during programming. Clear DTC's after programming is complete. Clearing powertrain DTC's will set the Inspection/Maintenance (I/M) system status indicators to NO.

Ensure the following conditions are met before programming a control module:
8. Vehicle system voltage:
  a. There is not a charging system concern. All charging system concerns must be repaired before programming a control module.
  b. Battery voltage is greater than 12 volts, but less than 16 volts. The battery must be fully charged before programming the control module.

c. Turn OFF or disable any system that may put a load on the vehicles battery, such as the following components:
• Interior lights
• Twilight sentinel
• Daytime Running Lights (DRL)—Applying the parking brake, on most vehicles, disables the DRL system
• Heating, Ventilation, and Air Conditioning (HVAC) systems
• Engine cooling fans, radio, etc.
9. The ignition switch must be in the proper position. SPS prompts you to turn ON the ignition, with the engine OFF. DO NOT change the position of the ignition switch during the programming procedure, unless instructed to do so.
10. Make certain all tool connections are secure, including the following components and circuits:
  a. Scan Tool.
  b. The RS-232 communication cable port.
  c. The connection at the Data Link Connector (DLC).
  d. The voltage supply circuits (MDI).
  e. The USB, Ethernet, or Wireless communication port
  f. The connection at the Data Link Connector (DLC)
11. DO NOT disturb the tool harnesses while programming. If an interruption occurs during the programming procedure, programming failure or control module damage may occur.
12. DO NOT turn OFF the ignition if the programming procedure is interrupted or unsuccessful. Ensure that all control module and DLC connections are secure and the TIS terminal operating software is up to date. Attempt to reprogram the control module.
  a. If the control module cannot be programmed, turn the ignition OFF for at least 1 minute.
  b. Turn the ignition ON and attempt to reprogram the control module. The control module should program.
  c. If the control module cannot be programmed, replace the control module.
13. After programming, perform the following to avoid future misdiagnosis:
  a. Turn the ignition OFF for 30 seconds.
  b. Turn the ignition ON, with the engine OFF.
  c. Use the scan tool in order to retrieve history DTC's from all modules.
  d. Clear all history DTC's.

ENGINE COOLANT TEMPERATURE (ECT) SENSOR

LOCATION

See Figures 226 through 228.

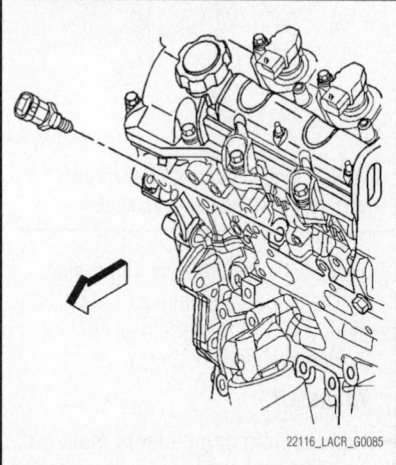

Fig. 226 Engine Coolant Temperature (ECT) sensor location—3.0L and 3.6L engines

22116_LACR_G0085

REMOVAL & INSTALLATION

3.0L and 3.6L Engines
See Figure 226.

✳✳ CAUTION

Allow sufficient time for the engine to cool before removing the Engine Coolant Temperature (ECT) sensor. A hot engine may cause excessive coolant loss or personal injury.

1. Turn the ignition OFF.
2. Partially drain the cooling system.
3. Remove the ECT sensor electrical connector.
4. Remove the ECT sensor.

To install:
5. Install the ECT sensor. Tighten the sensor to 16 ft. lbs. (22 Nm).
6. Install the ECT sensor electrical connector.
7. Inspect and fill the cooling system as necessary.

3.8L Engine
See Figure 227.

✳✳ WARNING

Use care when handling the coolant sensor. Damage to the coolant sensor will affect the operation of the fuel control system.

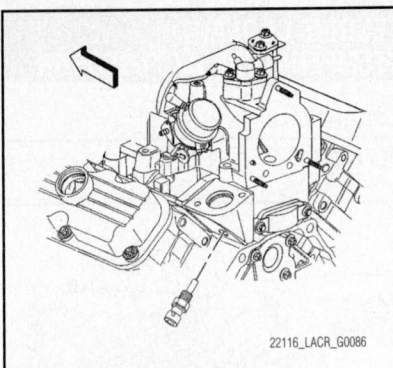

Fig. 227 Engine Coolant Temperature (ECT) sensor location—3.8L engine

1. Partially drain the cooling system.
2. Disconnect the Engine Coolant Temperature (ECT) sensor electrical connector.
3. Remove the ECT sensor.

To install:

➡Replacement components must be the correct part number for the application. Components requiring the use of the thread locking compound, lubricants, corrosion inhibitors, or sealants are identified in the service procedure. Some replacement components may come with these coatings already applied. Do not use these coatings on components unless specified. These coatings can affect the final torque, which may affect the operation of the component. Use the correct torque specification when installing components in order to avoid damage.

4. Coat the threads with sealer GM P/N 12346004 (Canadian P/N 10953480), or equivalent.
5. Install the ECT sensor. Tighten the sensor to 18 ft. lbs. (25 Nm).
6. Connect the ECT sensor electrical connector.

7. Inspect and fill the cooling system as necessary.

5.3L Engine
See Figure 228.

1. Before servicing the vehicle, refer to the Precautions Section.
2. Disconnect the negative battery cable.
3. Drain the cooling system to a level below the ECT sensor.
4. Unplug the harness connector from the ECT sensor.
5. Remove the ECT sensor from the engine.

To install:

➡Be sure to use new fasteners, as required.

6. Installation is the reverse of removal.
7. If reusing the old sensor, coat the threads with sealant GM P/N 12346004, or equivalent. New sensors are already coated; additional sealant is not needed.
8. Tighten the sensor to 15 ft. lbs. (20 Nm).

EVAPORATIVE EMISSIONS (EVAP) CANISTER

LOCATION
See Figure 229.

The Evaporative Emissions (EVAP) Canister is located on the fuel tank.

REMOVAL & INSTALLATION
See Figure 229.

1. Before servicing the vehicle, refer to the Precautions Section.
2. Remove the fuel tank. Refer to Fuel Tank, removal & installation.

3. Disconnect the EVAP vent hose, the EVAP purge pipe, and the EVAP vapor pipe from the EVAP canister.

➡Replace the retaining strap when replacing the EVAP canister.

4. Release the EVAP canister retaining strap.
5. Remove the EVAP canister from the fuel tank.

To install:
6. Position the EVAP canister on the fuel tank.
7. Install the new EVAP canister retaining strap.

➡Do not attempt to straighten kinked nylon pipes. Replace any kinked nylon pipes in order to prevent damage to the vehicle. Do not attempt to repair sections of nylon pipes. Replace damaged nylon pipes. Replace the vapor pipes and hoses with original equipment or parts that meet GM specifications. Use only reinforced fuel-resistant hose identified with the word Fluoroelastomer, or GM 6163M, on the hose.

8. Connect the EVAP vent hose, the EVAP purge pipe, and the EVAP vapor pipe to the EVAP canister.
9. Install the fuel tank. Refer to Fuel Tank, removal & installation.

EXHAUST GAS RECIRCULATION (EGR) VALVE

LOCATION
See Figure 230.

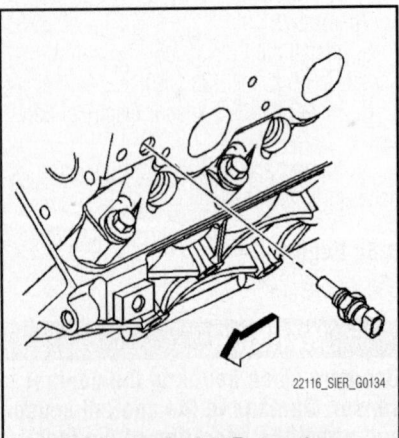

Fig. 228 Engine Coolant Temperature (ECT) sensor location—5.3L engine

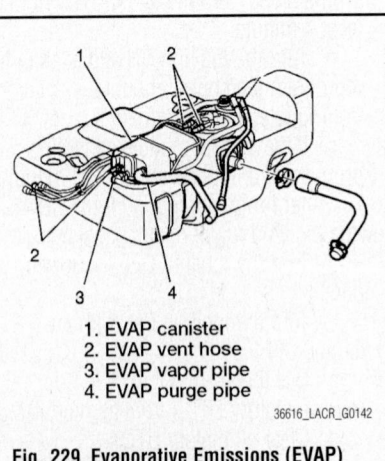

1. EVAP canister
2. EVAP vent hose
3. EVAP vapor pipe
4. EVAP purge pipe

Fig. 229 Evaporative Emissions (EVAP) Canister location

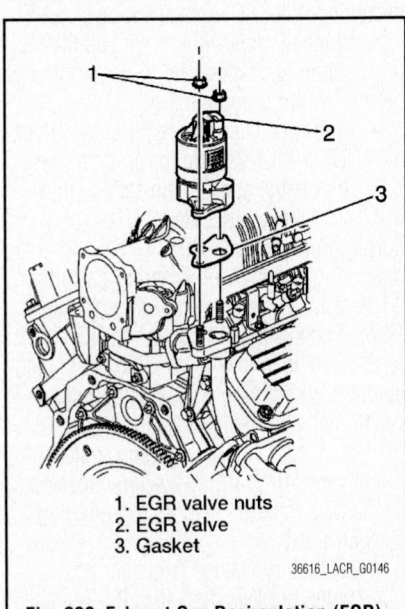

1. EGR valve nuts
2. EGR valve
3. Gasket

Fig. 230 Exhaust Gas Recirculation (EGR) Valve location—3.8L engine

REMOVAL & INSTALLATION

See Figure 230.

1. Before servicing the vehicle, refer to the Precautions Section.
2. Disconnect the Exhaust Gas Recirculation (EGR) valve electrical connector.
3. Remove the EGR valve nuts.
4. Remove the EGR valve.
5. Remove the gasket from the EGR valve adapter.
6. Clean the EGR valve gasket mating surfaces.

To install:

7. Install a new EGR valve gasket.
8. Install the EGR valve.
9. Install the EGR valve nuts and tighten to 18 ft. lbs. (25 Nm).
10. Connect the EGR valve electrical connector.

HEATED OXYGEN (HO2S) SENSOR

LOCATION

See Figures 231 through 236.

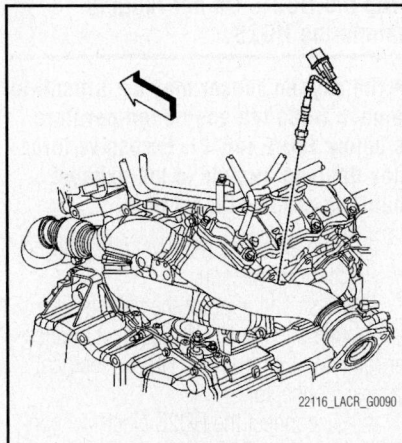

Fig. 231 Location of the heated oxygen sensor 1—3.6L engine

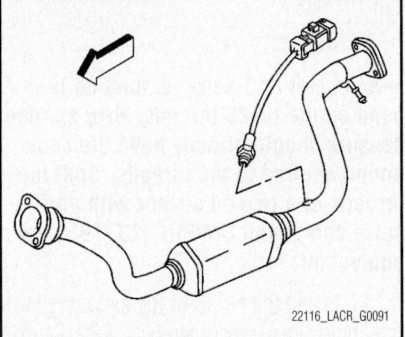

Fig. 232 Location of the heated oxygen sensor 2—3.6L engine

REMOVAL & INSTALLATION

3.0L and 3.6L Engines

Heated Oxygen Sensor—1

See Figure 231.

> ✳✳ **WARNING**
>
> **The Heated Oxygen Sensor (HO2S) uses a permanently attached pigtail and connector. Do not remove this pigtail from the HO2S. Damage or the removal of the pigtail or the connector could affect the proper operation of the sensor. Take care when handling the HO2S. Keep the in-line electrical connector, and the louvered end, free of grease, dirt, or other contaminants. Also avoid using cleaning solvents of any type. Do not drop the HO2S. Do not roughly handle the HO2S.**

1. Before servicing the vehicle, refer to the Precautions Section.
2. Disconnect the HO2S electrical connector.

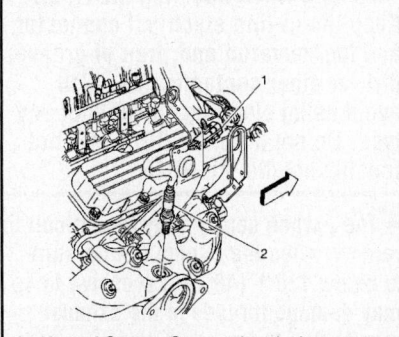

1. Heated Oxygen Sensor electrical connector
2. Heated Oxygen Sensor

Fig. 233 Location of the heated oxygen sensor 1—3.8L engine

> ✳✳ **WARNING**
>
> **The use of excessive force may damage the threads in the exhaust manifold/pipe.**

➡️If the engine temperature is not above 120°F (48°C), the oxygen sensor may be difficult to remove.

3. Remove the HO2S.

To install:

➡️A special anti-seize compound is used on the oxygen sensor threads. New service sensors should already have the compound applied to the threads. Coat the threads of a reused sensor with anti-seize compound P/N 5613695, or equivalent.

4. Install the HO2S. Tighten the HO2S 1 to 31 ft. lbs. (42 Nm).
5. Connect the HO2S electrical connector.

Heated Oxygen Sensor—2

See Figure 232.

> ✳✳ **WARNING**
>
> **The Heated Oxygen Sensor (HO2S) uses a permanently attached pigtail and connector. Do not remove this pigtail from the HO2S. Damage or the removal of the pigtail or the connector could affect the proper operation of the sensor. Take care when handling the HO2S. Keep the in-line electrical connector, and the louvered end, free of grease, dirt, or other contaminants. Also avoid using cleaning solvents of any type. Do not drop the HO2S. Do not roughly handle the HO2S.**

1. Before servicing the vehicle, refer to the Precautions Section.
2. Raise and support the vehicle.

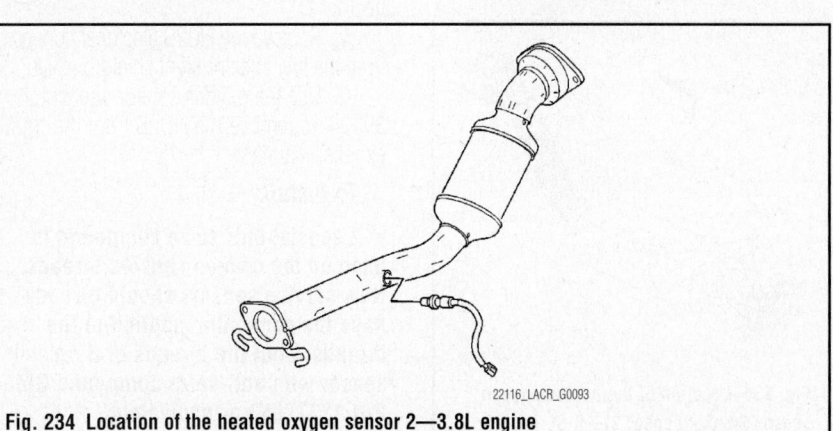

Fig. 234 Location of the heated oxygen sensor 2—3.8L engine

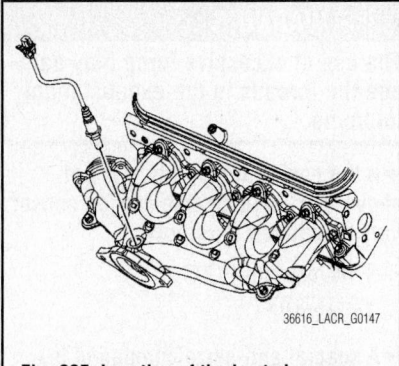

Fig. 235 Location of the heated oxygen sensor (bank 1 sensor 1)—5.3L engine

3. Disconnect the HO2S electrical connector.

✱✱ WARNING

The use of excessive force may damage the threads in the exhaust manifold/pipe.

➡️If the engine temperature is not above 120°F (48°C), the oxygen sensor may be difficult to remove.

4. Remove the HO2S.

To install:

✱✱ WARNING

Use the correct fastener in the correct location. Replacement fasteners must be the correct part number for that application. Fasteners requiring replacement or fasteners requiring the use of thread locking compound or sealant are identified in the service procedure. Do not use paints, lubricants, or corrosion inhibitors on fasteners or fastener joint surfaces unless specified. These coatings affect fastener torque and joint clamping force and may damage the fastener. Use the correct tightening sequence and specifications when

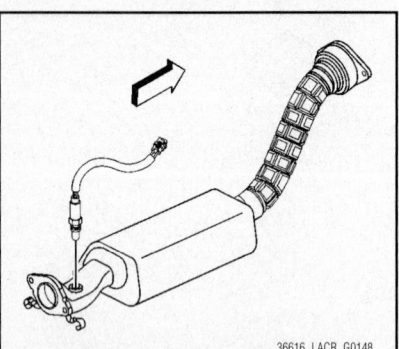

Fig. 236 Location of the heated oxygen sensor (bank 2 sensor 2)—5.3L engine

installing fasteners in order to avoid damage to parts and systems.

➡️A special anti-seize compound is used on the oxygen sensor threads. New service sensors should already have the compound applied to the threads. Coat the threads of a reused sensor with anti-seize compound P/N 5613695, or equivalent.

5. Install the HO2S. Tighten the HO2S 2 to 31 ft. lbs. (42 Nm).
6. Connect the HO2S electrical connector.
7. Lower the vehicle.

3.8L Engine

Heated Oxygen Sensor—1
See Figure 233.

✱✱ WARNING

The Heated Oxygen Sensor (HO2S) uses a permanently attached pigtail and connector. Do not remove this pigtail from the HO2S. Damage to the pigtail or the connector could affect the proper operation of the sensor. Take care when handling the HO2S. Keep the in-line electrical connector, and the louvered end, free of grease, dirt, or other contaminants. Also avoid using cleaning solvents of any type. Do not drop the HO2S. Do not roughly handle the HO2S.

➡️The oxygen sensor may be difficult to remove when the engine temperature is below 120°F (48°C). Excessive force may damage threads in the exhaust manifold or the exhaust pipe.

1. Before servicing the vehicle, refer to the Precautions Section.
2. Remove the fuel injector sight shield.
3. Remove the HO2S retaining clip.
4. Disconnect the HO2S electrical connector.
5. Remove the HO2S electrical connector from the fuel injector sight shield bracket.
6. Use the oxygen sensor wrench, J 39194, to remove the HO2S from the right exhaust manifold.

To install:

➡️A special anti-seize compound is used on the oxygen sensors threads. New service sensors should already have the compound applied to the threads. Coat the threads of a reused sensor with anti-seize compound GM P/N 12377953 or equivalent.

7. Install the HO2S to the right exhaust manifold. Use the oxygen sensor wrench, J 39194, to tighten the HO2S to 31 ft. lbs. (42 Nm).
8. Install the HO2S electrical connector to the fuel injector sight shield bracket.
9. Connect the HO2S electrical connector.
10. Install the HO2S retaining clip.
11. Install the fuel injector sight shield.

Heated Oxygen Sensor—2
See Figure 234.

✱✱ WARNING

The Heated Oxygen Sensor (HO2S) uses a permanently attached pigtail and connector. Do not remove this pigtail from the HO2S. Damage to or the removal of the pigtail or the connector could affect the proper operation of the sensor. Take care when handling the HO2S. Keep the in-line electrical connector, and the louvered end, free of grease, dirt, or other contaminants. Also, avoid using cleaning solvents of any type. Do not drop the HO2S. Do not roughly handle the HO2S.

➡️The oxygen sensor may be difficult to remove when the engine temperature is below 120°F (48°C). Excessive force may damage threads in the exhaust manifold or the exhaust pipe.

1. Before servicing the vehicle, refer to the Precautions Section.
2. Raise and support the vehicle.
3. Remove the HO2S electrical connector retaining clip from the HO2S electrical harness connector.
4. Disconnect the HO2S electrical connector from the HO2S electrical harness connector.
5. Use the oxygen sensor wrench, J 39194, to remove the HO2S from the exhaust pipe.

To install:

➡️A special anti-seize compound is used on the HO2S threads. New service sensors should already have the compound applied to the threads. Coat the threads of a reused sensor with anti-seize compound GM P/N 12377953, or equivalent.

6. Install the HO2S to the exhaust pipe. Use the oxygen sensor wrench, J 39194, to tighten the HO2S to 31 ft. lbs. (42 Nm).
7. Connect the HO2S electrical connec-

tor to the HO2S electrical harness connector.

8. Install the HO2S electrical connector retaining clip to the HO2S electrical harness connector.

9. Lower the vehicle.

5.3L Engine

Heated Oxygen Sensor—1

See Figure 235.

Do not remove the pigtail from the Heated Oxygen Sensor (HO2S). Removing the pigtail or the connector will affect sensor operation. Handle the oxygen sensor carefully. Do not drop the HO2S. Keep the inline electrical connector and the louvered end free of grease, dirt, or other contaminants. Do not use cleaning solvents of any type. Do not repair the wiring, connector or terminals. Replace the oxygen sensor if the pigtail wiring, connector, or terminal is damaged. This external clean air reference is obtained by way of the oxygen sensor signal and heater wires. Any attempt to repair the wires, connectors, or terminals could result in the obstruction of the air reference and degraded sensor performance.

The following guidelines should be used when servicing the heated oxygen sensor:

• Do not apply contact cleaner or other materials to the sensor or vehicle harness connectors. These materials may get into the sensor causing poor performance

• Do not damage the sensor pigtail and harness wires in such a way that the wires inside are exposed. This could provide a path for foreign materials to enter the sensor and cause performance problems

• Ensure the sensor or vehicle lead wires are not bent sharply or kinked. Sharp bends or kinks could block the reference air path through the lead wire

• Do not remove or defeat the oxygen sensor ground wire, where applicable. Vehicles that utilize the ground wired sensor may rely on this ground as the only ground contact to the sensor. Removal of the ground wire will cause poor engine performance

• Ensure that the peripheral seal remains intact on the vehicle harness connector in order to prevent damage due to water intrusion. The engine harness may be repaired using Packard's Crimp and Splice Seals Terminal Repair Kit. Under no circumstances should repairs be soldered since this could result in the air reference being obstructed

1. Before servicing the vehicle, refer to the Precautions Section.

2. Remove the intake manifold sight shield.

3. Remove the Connector Position Assurance (CPA) retainer.

4. Disconnect the bank 1 sensor 1 electrical connector.

5. Remove the bank 1 sensor 1 from the exhaust manifold.

To install:

➡A special anti-seize compound is used on the HO2S threads. The compound consists of liquid graphite and glass beads. The graphite tends to burn away, but the glass beads remain, making the sensor easier to remove. New or service replacement sensors already have the compound applied to the threads. If the sensor is removed from an exhaust component and if for any reason the sensor is to be reinstalled, the threads must have anti-seize compound applied before reinstallation.

6. If re-installing the old sensor, coat the threads with anti-seize compound P/N 12377953, or equivalent.

7. Install the bank 1 sensor 1 to the exhaust manifold. Tighten the sensor to 31 ft. lbs. (42 Nm).

8. Connect the bank 1 sensor 1 electrical connector.

9. Install the CPA retainer.

10. Install the intake manifold sight shield.

Heated Oxygen Sensor—2

See Figure 236.

Do not remove the pigtail from the Heated Oxygen Sensor (HO2S). Removing the pigtail or the connector will affect sensor operation. Handle the oxygen sensor carefully. Do not drop the HO2S. Keep the inline electrical connector and the louvered end free of grease, dirt, or other contaminants. Do not use cleaning solvents of any type. Do not repair the wiring, connector or terminals. Replace the oxygen sensor if the pigtail wiring, connector, or terminal is damaged. This external clean air reference is obtained by way of the oxygen sensor signal and heater wires. Any attempt to repair the wires, connectors, or terminals could result in the obstruction of the air reference and degraded sensor performance.

The following guidelines should be used when servicing the heated oxygen sensor:

• Do not apply contact cleaner or other materials to the sensor or vehicle harness connectors. These materials may get into the sensor causing poor performance

• Do not damage the sensor pigtail and harness wires in such a way that the wires inside are exposed. This could provide a path for foreign materials to enter the sensor and cause performance problems

• Ensure the sensor or vehicle lead wires are not bent sharply or kinked. Sharp bends or kinks could block the reference air path through the lead wire

• Do not remove or defeat the oxygen sensor ground wire, where applicable. Vehicles that utilize the ground wired sensor may rely on this ground as the only ground contact to the sensor. Removal of the ground wire will cause poor engine performance

• Ensure that the peripheral seal remains intact on the vehicle harness connector in order to prevent damage due to water intrusion. The engine harness may be repaired using Packard's Crimp and Splice Seals Terminal Repair Kit. Under no circumstances should repairs be soldered since this could result in the air reference being obstructed

1. Before servicing the vehicle, refer to the Precautions Section.

2. Raise and support the vehicle.

3. Remove the Connector Position Assurance (CPA) retainer.

4. Disconnect the bank 2 sensor 2 electrical connector.

5. Remove the bank 2 sensor 2 from the catalytic converter.

To install:

➡A special anti-seize compound is use on the heated oxygen sensor (HO2S) threads. The compound consists of liquid graphite and glass beads. The graphite tends to burns away, but the glass beads remain, making the sensor easier to remove. New or service replacement sensors already have the compound applied to the threads. If the sensor is removed from an exhaust component and if for any reason the sensor is to be reinstalled, the threads must have anti-seize compound applied before reinstallation.

6. If re-installing the old sensor, coat the threads with the anti-seize compound P/N 12377953, or equivalent.

7. Install the bank 2 sensor 2 to the catalytic converter. Tighten the sensor to 31 ft. lbs. (42 Nm).

8. Connect the bank 2 sensor 2 electrical connector.

9. Install the CPA retainer.

10. Lower the vehicle.

INTAKE AIR TEMPERATURE (IAT) SENSOR

LOCATION

See Figures 237 through 239.

REMOVAL & INSTALLATION

3.0L and 3.6L Engines

See Figure 237.

1. Before servicing the vehicle, refer to the Precautions Section.
2. Turn the ignition OFF.

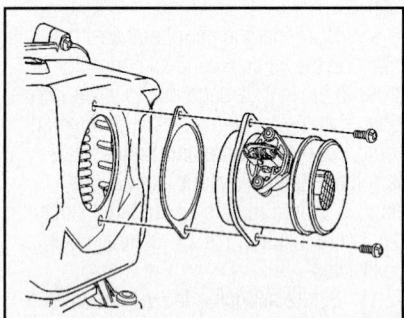

Fig. 237 Intake Air Temperature (IAT)/Mass Air Flow (MAF) sensor location—3.0L and 3.6L engines

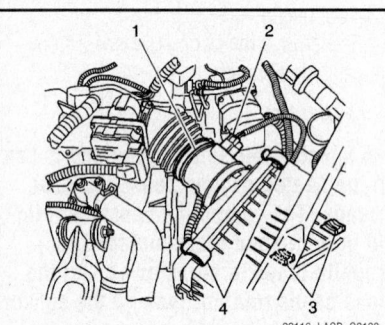

Fig. 238 Intake Air Temperature (IAT)/Mass Air Flow (MAF) sensor location—3.8L engine

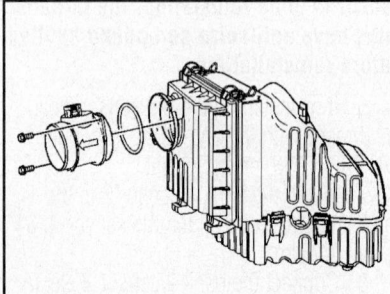

Fig. 239 Intake Air Temperature (IAT)/Mass Air Flow (MAF) sensor location—5.3L engine

3. Remove the Intake Air Temperature (IAT)/Mass Air Flow (MAF) electrical connector.
4. Remove the air cleaner intake duct.
5. Remove the IAT/MAF sensor fasteners.
6. Remove the IAT/MAF sensor and the IAT/MAF sensor seal.

To install:

7. Install the new IAT/MAF sensor seal and the IAT/MAF sensor.
8. Install the IAT/MAF sensor screws. Tighten the IAT/MAF sensor screws to 35 inch lbs. (4 Nm).
9. Install the air cleaner intake duct.
10. Install the IAT/MAF electrical connector.

3.8L Engine

See Figure 238.

1. Before servicing the vehicle, refer to the Precautions Section.
2. Remove the fuel injector sight shield.

➡**The Intake Air Temperature (IAT) sensor and the Mass Air Flow (MAF) sensor are combined as one sensor.**

3. Disconnect the MAF/IAT sensor electrical connector.
4. Loosen the air cleaner intake duct clamps.
5. Remove the air cleaner intake duct from the air cleaner housing cover and the throttle body assembly.
6. Remove the MAF/IAT sensor from the air cleaner intake duct.

To install:

7. Install the MAF/IAT sensor to the air cleaner intake duct.
8. Install the air cleaner intake duct to the air cleaner housing cover and the throttle body assembly.
9. Tighten the air cleaner intake duct clamp screws. Tighten the duct clamps to 27 inch lbs. (3 Nm).
10. Connect the MAF/IAT sensor electrical connector.
11. Install the fuel injector sight shield.

5.3L Engine

See Figure 239.

1. Before servicing the vehicle, refer to the Precautions Section.
2. Remove the air intake duct.
3. Disconnect the Mass Air Flow (MAF)/Intake Air Temperature (IAT) sensor electrical connector.
4. Remove the MAF/IAT sensor bolts.

5. Remove the MAF/IAT sensor from the air cleaner housing.
6. Remove the MAF/IAT sensor seal, if necessary.

To install:

7. Install the MAF/IAT sensor seal, if necessary.
8. Install the MAF/IAT sensor to the air cleaner housing.
9. Install the MAF/IAT sensor bolts and tighten to 89 inch lbs. (10 Nm).
10. Connect the MAF/IAT sensor electrical connector.
11. Install the air intake duct.

KNOCK SENSOR (KS)

LOCATION

See Figures 240 through 245.

The Knock Sensor (KS) is located on the side of the engine block.

REMOVAL & INSTALLATION

3.0L and 3.6L Engines

Knock Sensor (KS)—Bank 1

See Figure 240.

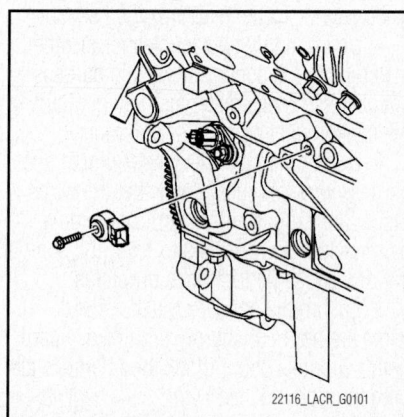

Fig. 240 Knock Sensor (KS) location bank 1—3.0L and 3.6L engines

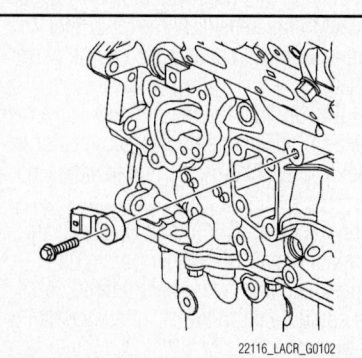

Fig. 241 Knock Sensor (KS) location bank 2—3.0L and 3.6L engines

1. Before servicing the vehicle, refer to the Precautions Section.
2. Turn the ignition OFF.
3. Raise and support the vehicle.
4. Reposition the wiring harness heat shield to obtain access.
5. Remove the Knock Sensor (KS) electrical connector.
6. Remove the KS bolt.
7. Remove the KS.

To install:

8. Install the KS.
9. Install the KS bolt. Tighten the KS bolt to 17 ft. lbs. (23 Nm).
10. Install the KS electrical connector.
11. Install the wiring harness heat shield to the original position.
12. Lower the vehicle.

Knock Sensor (KS)—Bank 2

See Figure 241.

1. Before servicing the vehicle, refer to the Precautions Section.
2. Turn the ignition OFF.
3. Raise and support the vehicle.
4. Remove the catalytic converter.
5. Remove the left engine splash shield.
6. Disconnect the intermediate steering shaft to the steering gear:

   a. Position the seal in order to provide access to the lower pinch bolt on the intermediate steering shaft.

✳✳ WARNING

The front wheels of the vehicle must be maintained in the straight ahead position and the steering column must be in the LOCK position before disconnecting the steering column or intermediate shaft. Failure to follow these procedures will cause improper alignment of some components during installation and result in damage to the SIR coil assembly.

   b. Remove the lower pinch bolt from the power steering gear stub shaft.

   c. Insert the steering column lock pin, J 42640, into the steering column access hole in order to lock the steering column. This will maintain the orientation.

   d. Disconnect the intermediate steering shaft from the power steering gear stub shaft. Note the shaft to gear alignment for installation.

7. Position jack under rear of frame.
8. Remove the bolts that secure the rear frame to the body.
9. Lower the frame to gain access to the crankshaft position sensor lower heat shield.

10. Remove the crankshaft position sensor lower heat shield bolts and position shield out of the way.
11. Remove the Knock Sensor (KS) electrical connector.
12. Remove the KS bolt.
13. Remove the KS.

To install:

14. Install the KS.
15. Install the KS bolt. Tighten the KS bolt to 17 ft. lbs. (23 Nm).
16. Install the KS electrical connector.
17. Install the crankshaft position sensor lower heat shield bolts.

   a. Tighten the crankshaft position sensor lower heat shield M6 bolt to 89 inch lbs. (10 Nm).

   b. Tighten the crankshaft position sensor lower heat shield M10 bolt to 37 ft. lbs. (50 Nm).

18. Raise the frame.
19. Install the bolts which secure the rear frame to the body.
20. Install the rear frame bolts. Tighten the bolts to 118 ft. lbs. (160 Nm).
21. Remove the jack from under the frame.
22. Connect the intermediate steering shaft to the steering gear:

   a. Connect the intermediate steering shaft to the power steering gear stub shaft as noted during removal.

   b. Install the lower intermediate steering shaft pinch bolt. Tighten the pinch bolt to 35 ft. lbs. (48 Nm).

   c. Connect the intermediate steering shaft seal onto the power steering gear. Rotate the lower seal as necessary to gain maximum clearance.

23. Install the left engine splash shield.
24. Install the catalytic converter.
25. Lower the vehicle.

3.8L Engine

Knock Sensor (KS)—Bank 1

See Figure 242.

✳✳ CAUTION

Hot engine coolant may cause severe burns. Although the cooling system has been drained, coolant still remains in the engine water jacket. This coolant will drain with the removal of the knock sensor.

1. Before servicing the vehicle, refer to the Precautions Section.
2. Raise and support the vehicle.
3. Drain the cooling system.
4. Disconnect the Knock Sensor (KS) electrical connector.
5. Remove the KS.

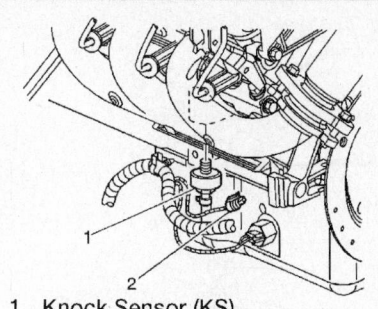

1. Knock Sensor (KS)
2. KS electrical connector

22116_LACR_G0103

Fig. 242 Knock Sensor (KS) location bank 1—3.8L engine

To install:

✳✳ WARNING

Use the correct fastener in the correct location. Replacement fasteners must be the correct part number for that application. Fasteners requiring replacement or fasteners requiring the use of thread locking compound or sealant are identified in the service procedure. Do not use paints, lubricants, or corrosion inhibitors on fasteners or fastener joint surfaces unless specified. These coatings affect fastener torque and joint clamping force and may damage the fastener. Use the correct tightening sequence and specifications when installing fasteners in order to avoid damage to parts and systems.

✳✳ WARNING

DO NOT apply thread sealant to sensor threads. The sensor is coated at factory and applying additional sealant will affect the ability of the sensor to detect detonation.

6. Install the KS. Tighten the sensor to 14 ft. lbs. (19 Nm).
7. Connect the KS electrical connector.
8. Lower the vehicle.
9. Fill the cooling system.

Knock Sensor (KS)—Bank 2

See Figure 243.

✳✳ CAUTION

Hot engine coolant may cause severe burns. Although the cooling system has been drained, coolant still remains in the engine water jacket. This coolant will drain with the removal of the knock sensor.

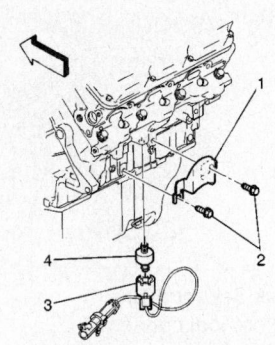

1. Knock Sensor (KS) heat shield
2. KS heat shield bolts
3. KS electrical connector
4. KS

22116_LACR_G0104

Fig. 243 Knock Sensor (KS) location bank 2—3.8L engine

1. Before servicing the vehicle, refer to the Precautions Section.
2. Raise and support the vehicle.
3. Drain the cooling system.
4. Disconnect the Knock Sensor (KS) electrical connector from the KS.
5. Remove the KS.

To install:

❋❋ WARNING

DO NOT apply thread sealant to sensor threads. The sensor is coated at factory and applying additional sealant will affect the sensors ability to detect detonation.

6. Install the KS. Tighten the sensor to 14 ft. lbs. (19 Nm).
7. Connect the KS electrical connector.
8. Lower the vehicle.
9. Fill the cooling system.

5.3L Engine

Knock Sensor (KS)—Bank 1

See Figure 244.

1. Before servicing the vehicle, refer to the Precautions Section.
2. Disconnect the negative battery cable.
3. Raise and safely support the vehicle.
4. Disconnect the engine wiring harness electrical connector from the knock sensor.
5. Remove the knock sensor bolt and knock sensor.

To install:
6. Position the knock sensor to the engine block and install the knock sensor bolt. Tighten the bolt to 18 ft. lbs. (25 Nm).
7. Connect the engine wiring harness electrical connector to the knock sensor.

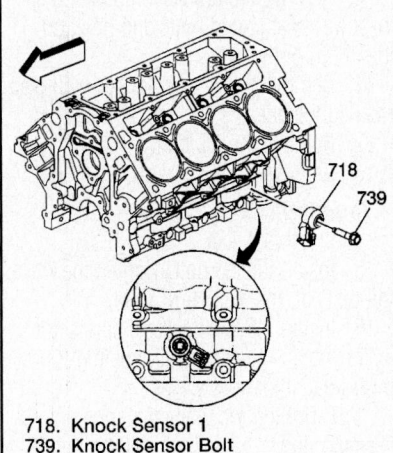

718. Knock Sensor 1
739. Knock Sensor Bolt

36616_YUKO_G0304

Fig. 244 Knock Sensor (KS) location bank 1—5.3L engine

8. Position the engine wiring harness sleeve over the knock sensor electrical connection.

Knock Sensor (KS)—Bank 2

See Figure 245.

1. Before servicing the vehicle, refer to the Precautions Section.
2. Disconnect the negative battery cable.
3. Raise and safely support the vehicle.
4. Remove the knock sensor bolt and knock sensor.

To install:
5. Position the knock sensor to the engine block and install the knock sensor bolt. Tighten the bolt to 18 ft. lbs. (25 Nm).
6. Connect the engine wiring harness electrical connector to knock sensor.

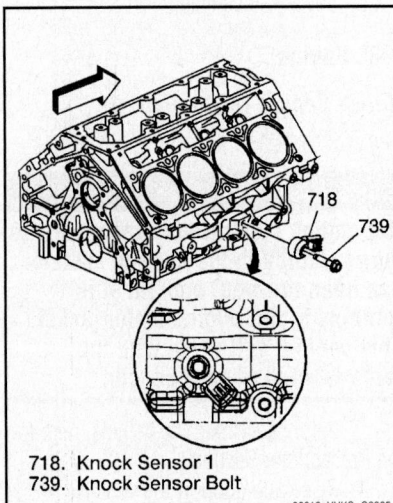

718. Knock Sensor 1
739. Knock Sensor Bolt

36616_YUKO_G0305

Fig. 245 Knock Sensor (KS) location bank 2—5.3L engine

MALFUNCTION INDICATOR LIGHT (MIL)

RESET PROCEDURE

1. Proper operation of the Malfunction Indicator Light (MIL):
   - The MIL will illuminate with the ignition switch ON and the engine OFF
   - The MIL will turn OFF when the engine is started
   - The MIL will remain ON if the self-diagnostic system has detected a malfunction
   - The MIL may turn OFF if the malfunction is no longer present
   - If the MIL is illuminated and then the engine stalls, the MIL will remain illuminated as long as the ignition switch is ON
   - If the MIL is not illuminated and the engine stalls, the MIL will not illuminate until the ignition switch is cycled OFF, then ON
2. Resetting the MIL:
   - The control module turns OFF the MIL after 3 consecutive ignition cycles that the diagnostic system runs and does not fail
   - The control module turns OFF the MIL after a current Diagnostic Trouble Code (DTC) clears when the diagnostic cycle runs and passes
   - There may still be a history of DTC's stored in the system. These will clear after 40 consecutive warm-up cycles, if no failures are reported by any other related diagnostic system
   - Manual resetting of the MIL and any DTC stored in the system, requires the use of an OBD2 scan tool connected to the Data Link Connector (DLC) for communication with the vehicle. Follow the instructions of the scan tool for both retrieval and resetting of DTC's. The scan tool can be used to command the MIL off.

➡ If the error symptoms causing the MIL to illuminate have been corrected, the MIL will return to normal operation.

MASS AIR FLOW (MAF) SENSOR

For information on the Mass Air Flow (MAF) sensor, please refer to Intake Air Temperature (IAT) sensor.

MANIFOLD ABSOLUTE PRESSURE (MAP) SENSOR

LOCATION

See Figures 246 and 247.

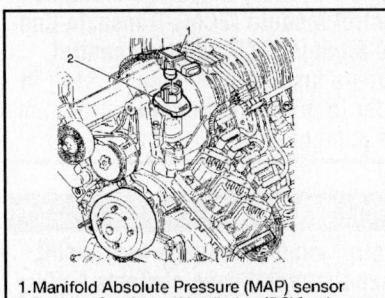

1. Manifold Absolute Pressure (MAP) sensor
2. Positive Crankcase Ventilation (PCV) valve cover

22116_LACR_G0115

Fig. 246 Manifold Absolute Pressure (MAP) sensor location—3.8L engine

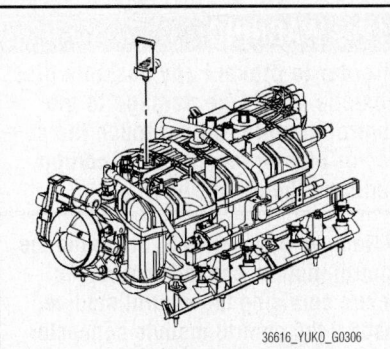

36616_YUKO_G0306

Fig. 247 Manifold Absolute Pressure (MAP) sensor location—5.3L engine

REMOVAL & INSTALLATION

3.8L Engine

See Figure 246.

The Manifold Absolute Pressure (MAP) sensor is mounted to the Positive Crankcase Ventilation (PCV) valve cover.

1. Before servicing the vehicle, refer to the Precautions Section.
2. Remove the fuel injector sight shield.
3. Disconnect the MAP sensor electrical connector.
4. Carefully release the locking tabs holding the MAP sensor to the PCV valve cover just enough to remove the MAP sensor.
5. Pull the MAP sensor straight out of PCV valve cover.

To install:

6. Ensure that the seal is installed on the MAP sensor and that the seal is not damaged.

7. Position and install the MAP sensor to the PCV valve cover. Ensure that the locking tabs engage to hold the MAP sensor to the PCV valve cover.
8. Connect the MAP sensor electrical connector.
9. Install the fuel injector sight shield.

5.3L Engine

See Figure 247.

1. Before servicing the vehicle, refer to the Precautions Section.
2. Remove the engine sight shield.
3. Disconnect the engine wiring harness electrical connector from the Manifold Absolute Pressure (MAP) sensor.
4. Remove the MAP sensor retainer.
5. Remove the MAP sensor.

To install:

➡ **Lightly coat the MAP sensor seal with clean engine oil before installing the sensor.**

6. Install the MAP sensor.
7. Install the MAP sensor retainer.
8. Connect the engine harness wiring electrical connector to the MAP sensor.
9. Install the engine sight shield.

POSITIVE CRANKCASE VENTILATION (PCV) VALVE

LOCATION

See Figures 248 through 250.

REMOVAL & INSTALLATION

3.0L and 3.6L Engines

See Figure 248.

1. Before servicing the vehicle, refer to the Precautions Section.

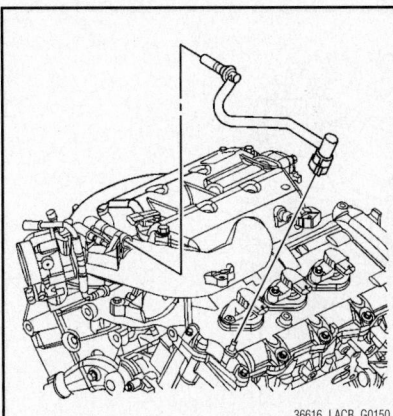

36616_LACR_G0150

Fig. 248 Positive Crankcase Ventilation (PCV) location—3.0L and 3.6L engines

2. Remove the Positive Crankcase Ventilation (PCV) fresh air tube from the left camshaft cover.
3. Remove the PCV fresh air tube from the air inlet duct.
4. Remove the PCV dirty air tube from the right camshaft cover.
5. Remove the PCV dirty air tube from the intake manifold.

To install:

6. Install the PCV dirty air tube to the intake manifold.
7. Install the PCV dirty air tube to the right camshaft cover.
8. Install the PCV fresh air tube to the air inlet duct.
9. Install the PCV fresh air tube to the left camshaft cover.

3.8L Engine

See Figure 249.

1. Before servicing the vehicle, refer to the Precautions Section.
2. Remove the fuel injector sight shield.
3. Disconnect the MAP sensor electrical connector.
4. Remove the MAP sensor.
5. Use a ⅝ inch (16mm) socket to press the access cover down and rotate ¼ turn counterclockwise.

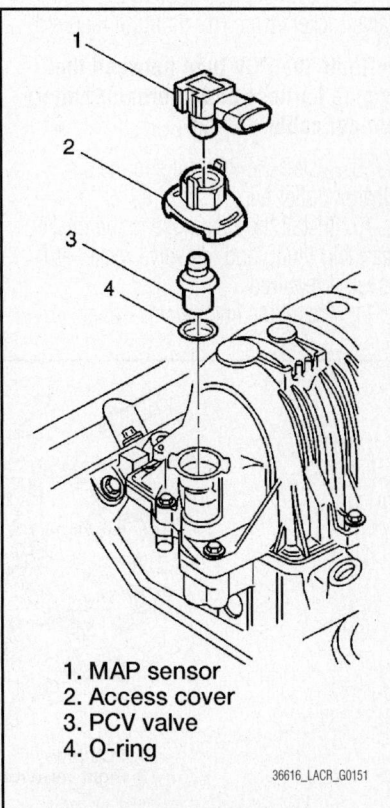

1. MAP sensor
2. Access cover
3. PCV valve
4. O-ring

36616_LACR_G0151

Fig. 249 Positive Crankcase Ventilation (PCV) location—3.8L engine

6. Remove the access cover.

7. Remove the PCV valve and the O-ring from the intake manifold.

To install:

8. Install the new O-ring and the PCV valve.

9. Install the access cover.

10. Install the MAP sensor.

11. Connect the MAP sensor electrical connector.

12. Install the fuel injector sight shield.

5.3L Engine

See Figure 250.

1. Before servicing the vehicle, refer to the Precautions Section.

2. Remove the engine sight shield.

3. Remove the Positive Crankcase Ventilation (PCV) hose from the intake manifold fitting and left valve rocker arm cover, if required.

4. Remove the PCV tube from the air cleaner outlet duct, if required.

5. Remove the PCV tube from the right valve rocker arm cover fitting, if required.

6. Remove the appropriate PCV hose and tube assembly.

To install:

7. Install the PCV hose/tube to the vehicle.

8. Install the PCV tube to the right valve rocker arm cover fitting, if required.

➡Route the PCV tube between the engine harness and alternator battery jumper cable.

9. Install the PCV tube to the air cleaner outlet duct, if required.

10. Install the PCV hose to the intake manifold fitting and left valve rocker arm cover, if required.

11. Install the engine sight shield.

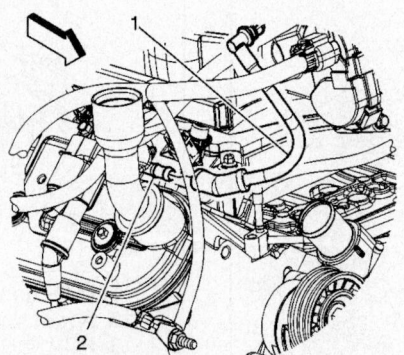

1. PCV tube
2. Right valve rocker arm cover fitting

36616_YUKO_G0364

Fig. 250 Positive Crankcase Ventilation (PCV) location—5.3L engine

POWERTRAIN CONTROL MODULE (PCM)

LOCATION

See Figure 251.

REMOVAL & INSTALLATION

3.8L Engine

See Figure 251.

➡Service of the Powertrain Control Module (PCM) should normally consist of either replacement of the PCM or Electrically Erasable Programmable Read Only Memory (EEPROM) programming. If the diagnostic procedures call for the PCM to be replaced, the PCM should be inspected first to see if the correct part is being used. If the correct part is being used, remove the faulty PCM and install the new service PCM.

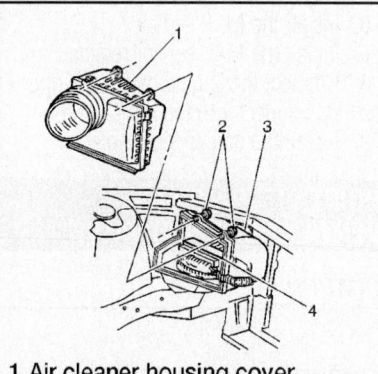

1. Air cleaner housing cover
2. Air cleaner housing cover screws
3. Air cleaner housing assembly
4. Powertrain Control Module (PCM)

22116_LACR_G0120

Fig. 251 Powertrain Control Module (PCM) location—3.8L engine

✳✳ WARNING

Turn the ignition OFF when installing or removing the control module connectors and disconnecting or reconnecting the power to the control module (battery cable, PCM/Engine Control Module (ECM)/Transaxle Control Module (TCM) pigtail, control module fuse, jumper cables, etc.) in order to prevent internal control module damage.

✳✳ WARNING

Control module damage may result when the metal case contacts battery voltage. DO NOT contact the control module metal case with battery voltage when servicing a control module, using battery booster cables, or when charging the vehicle battery.

✳✳ WARNING

In order to prevent any possible electrostatic discharge damage to the control module, do not touch the connector pins or the soldered components on the circuit board.

➡Remove any debris from around the control module connector surfaces before servicing the control module. Inspect the control module connector gaskets when diagnosing or replacing the control module. Ensure that the gaskets are installed correctly. The gaskets prevent contaminant intrusion into the control module.

➡The new service PCM will not be programmed. You must program the new PCM. DTC P0602 indicates the EEPROM is not programmed or has malfunctioned.

➡It is necessary to record the remaining engine oil life. If the replacement module is not programmed with the remaining engine oil life, the engine oil life will default to 100 percent. If the replacement module is not programmed with the remaining engine oil life, the engine oil will need to be changed at 3,000 miles (5,000 km) from the last engine oil change.

1. Before servicing the vehicle, refer to the Precautions Section.

2. Using a scan tool, retrieve the percentage of remaining engine oil life. Record the remaining engine oil life.

3. Remove or disconnect the following:

- The negative battery cable
- The left front inner fender brace
- The air cleaner intake duct
- The air cleaner housing cover screws
- The air cleaner housing cover

4. Without disconnecting the PCM electrical connectors, remove the PCM and the wiring harness from the air cleaner housing assembly.

5. Disconnect the PCM electrical connectors and remove the PCM.

To install:

6. Install or connect the following:
- The PCM to the PCM electrical connectors. Tighten the connectors to 71 inch lbs. (8 Nm)
- The PCM and the wiring harness to the air cleaner housing assembly
- The air cleaner housing cover
- The air cleaner housing cover screws. Tighten the screws to 35 inch lbs. (4 Nm)
- The air cleaner intake duct
- The left front inner fender brace
- The negative battery cable

7. If a new PCM is being installed, the PCM must be programmed.

RESET PROCEDURE

Special Tool:

- EL-49642: Service Programming System (SPS) Programming Support Tool

If the PCM is replaced, the following procedures must be performed:

1. PCM Reprogramming.
2. The CKP System Variation Learn.
3. The Throttle/Idle Learn procedure.
4. Theft Deterrent reprogramming.
5. Fuel Composition Diagnostic.
6. Engine Oil Life Remaining. When available, use a scan tool to reset the engine oil life remaining back to the original percentage recorded before the module was replaced.
7. Transmission Fluid Life Remaining. When available, use the scan tool to reset the Transmission Fluid Life Remaining back to the original percentage recorded before the module was replaced.

Review the information below to ensure proper programming protocol.

- DO NOT program a control module unless you are directed by a service procedure or you are directed by a General Motors Corporation service bulletin. Programming a control module at any other time will not permanently correct for a fault or DTC being set.
- It is essential that the TIS terminal, MDI, and/or Scan Tool, is equipped with the latest software before performing service programming.
- Due to the time requirements of programming a controller, install EL-49642 SPS Programming Support Tool to maintain system voltage. Stable battery voltage is critical during programming. Any fluctuation, spiking, over voltage, or loss of voltage will interrupt programming. If the above tool is not available, connect a fully charged 12 volt jumper or booster pack disconnected from the AC voltage supply.
- Some modules will require additional programming/setup events to be performed before or after programming.
- Some vehicles may require the use of a CANDi or MDI module for programming.
- Review the appropriate service information for these procedures. DTC's may set during programming. Clear DTC's after programming is complete. Clearing powertrain DTC's will set the Inspection/Maintenance (I/M) system status indicators to NO.

Ensure the following conditions are met before programming a control module:

8. Vehicle system voltage:

a. There is not a charging system concern. All charging system concerns must be repaired before programming a control module.

b. Battery voltage is greater than 12 volts, but less than 16 volts. The battery must be fully charged before programming the control module.

c. Turn OFF or disable any system that may put a load on the vehicles battery, such as the following components:

- Interior lights
- Twilight sentinel
- Daytime running lights (DRL)–Applying the parking brake, on most vehicles, disables the DRL system
- Heating, Ventilation, and Air Conditioning (HVAC) systems
- Engine cooling fans, radio, etc.

9. The ignition switch must be in the proper position. SPS prompts you to turn ON the ignition, with the engine OFF. DO NOT change the position of the ignition switch during the programming procedure, unless instructed to do so.

10. Make certain all tool connections are secure, including the following components and circuits:

a. Scan Tool.

b. The RS-232 communication cable port.

c. The connection at the Data Link Connector (DLC).

d. The voltage supply circuits (MDI).

e. The USB, Ethernet, or Wireless communication port

f. The connection at the Data Link Connector (DLC)

11. DO NOT disturb the tool harnesses while programming. If an interruption occurs during the programming procedure, programming failure or control module damage may occur.

12. DO NOT turn OFF the ignition if the programming procedure is interrupted or unsuccessful. Ensure that all control module and DLC connections are secure and the TIS terminal operating software is up to date. Attempt to reprogram the control module.

a. If the control module cannot be programmed, turn the ignition OFF for at least 1 minute.

b. Turn the ignition ON and attempt to reprogram the control module. The control module should program.

c. If the control module cannot be programmed, replace the control module.

13. After programming, perform the following to avoid future misdiagnosis:

a. Turn the ignition OFF for 30 seconds.

b. Turn the ignition ON, with the engine OFF.

c. Use the scan tool in order to retrieve history DTC's from all modules.

d. Clear all history DTC's.

THROTTLE ACTUATOR CONTROL (TAC)

LOCATION

The throttle body mounts to the intake manifold. The throttle position sensor and Throttle Actuator Control (TAC) DC motor are integral to the throttle body. The throttle body is a non-serviceable item, replace the throttle body as an assembly if found faulty.

REMOVAL & INSTALLATION

The throttle body mounts to the intake manifold. The throttle position sensor and throttle actuating motor are integral to the throttle body. The throttle body is a non-serviceable item, replace the throttle body as an assembly if found faulty. Refer to Throttle Body, removal & installation.

THROTTLE POSITION SENSOR (TPS)

LOCATION

The Throttle Position Sensor (TPS) is integral to the throttle body. If it is determined, that the TPS signal is faulty, the throttle body assembly must be replaced. Refer to Throttle Body, removal & installation.

REMOVAL & INSTALLATION

The throttle body position sensor is not serviceable as a stand-alone part. The throttle body position sensor is an integral part of the throttle body. If the throttle position sensor requires replacement, replace the throttle body assembly. Refer to Throttle Body, removal & installation.

VEHICLE SPEED SENSOR (VSS)

LOCATION

See Figures 252 and 253.

REMOVAL & INSTALLATION

4T65-E Transaxle

See Figure 252.

1. Before servicing the vehicle, refer to the Precautions Section.
2. Raise and support the vehicle.
3. Remove the right front tire and wheel.
4. Disconnect the Vehicle Speed Sensor (VSS) electrical connector.

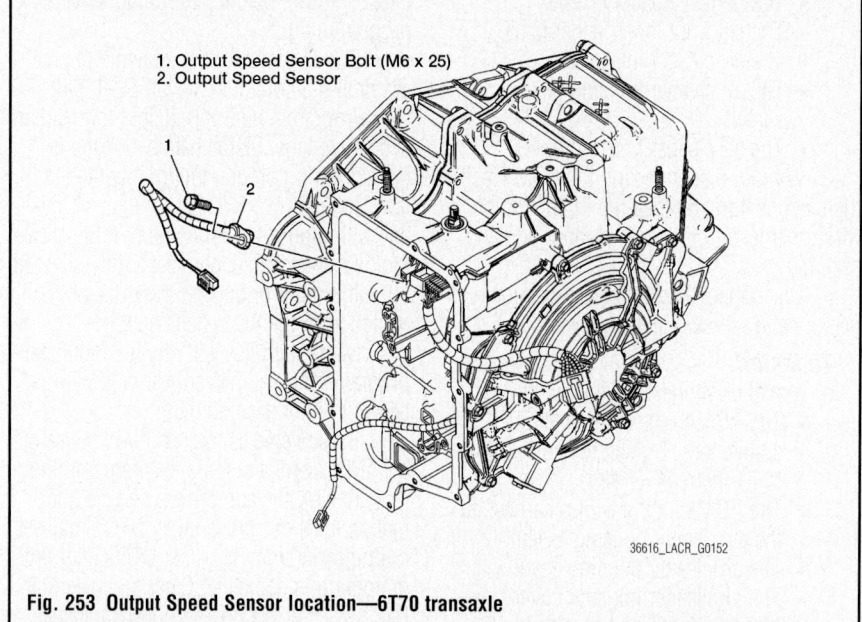

1. Output Speed Sensor Bolt (M6 x 25)
2. Output Speed Sensor

36616_LACR_G0152

Fig. 253 Output Speed Sensor location—6T70 transaxle

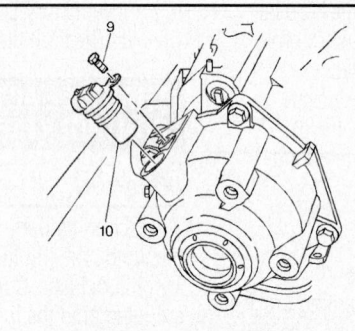

9. Vehicle Speed Sensor bolt
10. Vehicle Speed Sensor

22116_LACR_G0127

Fig. 252 Vehicle Speed Sensor (VSS) location—4T65-E transaxle

5. Remove the VSS bolt.
6. Remove the VSS from the extension case.
7. Remove the O-ring from the VSS.

To install:

8. Install the O-ring to the VSS.
9. Install the VSS.

10. Install the VSS bolt. Tighten the bolt to 106 inch lbs. (12 Nm).
11. Connect the VSS electrical connector.
12. Install the right front tire and wheel. Tighten the wheel lug nuts to 100 ft. lbs. (140 Nm).
13. Lower the vehicle.

6T70 Transaxle

See Figure 253.

1. Before servicing the vehicle, refer to the Precautions Section.
2. Raise and support the vehicle.
3. Remove the control valve lower body and upper body.
4. Remove the output speed sensor bolt.
5. Remove the output speed sensor.

To install:

6. Installation is the reverse of the removal procedure.
7. Tighten the output speed sensor bolt to 106 inch lbs. (12 Nm).

FUEL SYSTEM SERVICE PRECAUTIONS

Safety is the most important factor when performing, not only fuel system maintenance, but any type of maintenance. Failure to conduct maintenance and repairs in a safe manner may result in serious personal injury or death. Maintenance and testing of the vehicle's fuel system components can be accomplished safely and effectively by adhering to the following rules and guidelines.

• To avoid the possibility of fire and personal injury, always disconnect the negative battery cable unless the repair or test procedure requires that battery voltage be applied.

• Always relieve the fuel system pressure prior to disconnecting any fuel system component (injector, fuel rail, pressure regulator, etc.), fitting, or fuel line connection. Exercise extreme caution whenever relieving fuel system pressure to avoid exposing skin, face, and eyes to fuel spray. Please be advised that fuel under pressure may penetrate the skin or any part of the body that it contacts.

• Always place a shop towel or cloth around the fitting or connection prior to loosening to absorb any excess fuel due to spillage. Ensure that all fuel spillage (should it occur) is quickly removed from the engine surfaces. Ensure that all fuel soaked cloths or towels are deposited into a suitable waste container.

• Always keep a dry chemical (Class B) fire extinguisher near the work area.

• Do not allow fuel spray or fuel vapors to come into contact with a spark or an open flame.

• Always use a back-up wrench when loosening and tightening fuel line connection fittings. This will prevent unnecessary stress and torsion to the fuel line piping.

• Always replace worn fuel fitting O-rings with new. Do not substitute fuel hose or equivalent where fuel pipe is installed.

Before servicing the vehicle, make sure to also refer to the precautions in the beginning of this section.

RELIEVING FUEL SYSTEM PRESSURE

✳✳ CAUTION

Gasoline or gasoline vapors are highly flammable. A fire could occur if an ignition source is present. Never drain or store gasoline or

diesel fuel in an open container, due to the possibility of fire or explosion. Have a dry chemical (Class B) fire extinguisher nearby.

✳✳ CAUTION

Remove the fuel tank cap and relieve the fuel system pressure before servicing the fuel system in order to reduce the risk of personal injury. After you relieve the fuel system pressure, a small amount of fuel may be released when servicing the fuel lines, the fuel injection pump, or the connections. In order to reduce the risk of personal injury, cover the fuel system components with a shop towel before disconnection. This will catch any fuel that may leak out. Place the towel in an approved container when the disconnection is complete.

1. Remove the engine cover, if required.
2. Loosen the fuel fill cap in order to relieve the fuel tank vapor pressure.
3. Remove the fuel rail service port cap.
4. Wrap a shop towel around the fuel rail service port.
5. Connect the adapter to the fuel rail service port.
6. Connect service port adapter to pressure tester.
7. Place the relief hose on the tester into an approved gasoline container.
8. Open the valve on the tester in order to bleed any fuel from the fuel rail.
9. Close the valve on the tester.
10. Remove the relief hose on the tester from the approved gasoline container.
11. Disconnect service port adapter and tester.
12. Install the fuel rail service port cap.
13. Install fuel cap.

FUEL FILTER

REMOVAL & INSTALLATION

The fuel filter is part of the fuel pump module located in the fuel tank. It is serviced as part of the fuel pump module. Refer to Fuel Pump Module, removal & installation.

FUEL PUMP MODULE

REMOVAL & INSTALLATION

See Figures 254 through 256.

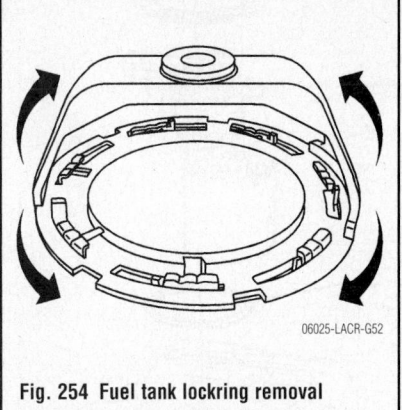

Fig. 254 Fuel tank lockring removal

Special Tool:
• J 45722: Fuel Sender Lock Ring Wrench

✳✳ CAUTION

Gasoline or gasoline vapors are highly flammable. A fire could occur if an ignition source is present. Never drain or store gasoline in an open container, due to the possibility of fire or explosion. Have a dry chemical (Class B) fire extinguisher nearby.

➡ Clean the fuel and Evaporative Emission (EVAP) connections and surrounding areas prior to disconnecting the lines in order to avoid possible system contamination.

1. Before servicing the vehicle, refer to the Precautions Section.
2. Relieve the fuel system fuel pressure.
3. Drain the fuel tank.
4. Raise and support the vehicle.
5. Loosen the fuel fill hose clamp at the fuel tank.
6. Remove the fuel tank fill hose from the fuel tank.
7. Disconnect the EVAP vent solenoid hose on the tank from the EVAP vent valve solenoid hose.
8. Disconnect the EVAP vent pipe quick-connect fitting from the fill pipe EVAP vent pipe quick-connect fitting.
9. Disconnect the fuel feed, and the EVAP lines from the fuel tank lines.
10. Support the exhaust system.
11. Remove the rubber exhaust pipe hangers in order to allow the exhaust system to drop slightly.
12. Remove the fuel tank shield retainers.
13. Remove the fuel tank shield.

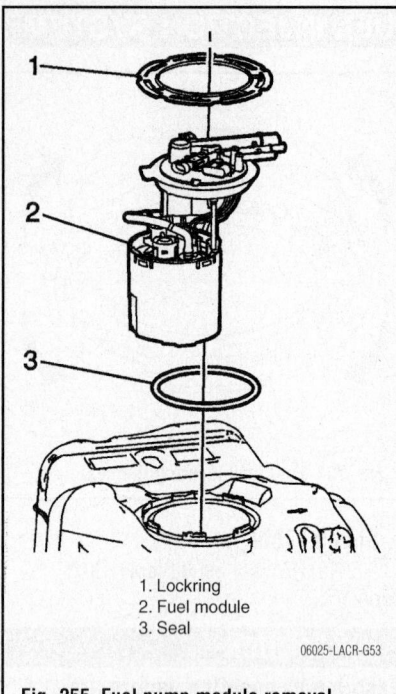

1. Lockring
2. Fuel module
3. Seal

06025-LACR-G53

Fig. 255 Fuel pump module removal

※※ WARNING

Do not bend the fuel tank straps as this may damage the straps.

14. Support the fuel tank with a suitable adjustable jack.

15. Remove the fuel tank strap bolts.

16. Using the jack lower the fuel tank.

17. Disconnect the fuel sender jumper harness electrical connector.

18. Remove the fuel tank and place the tank in a suitable work area.

19. Disconnect and remove the fuel pressure sensor and fuel sender jumper harness electrical connectors.

➡**Note the routing of the lines for installation.**

20. Disconnect and remove the fuel feed line, and the EVAP lines.

21. Remove the EVAP canister.

22. Remove the insulator pads from the fuel tank. Note the location of the insulator pads for installation.

23. Disconnect the fuel sender module electrical connectors.

※※ WARNING

Do Not handle the fuel sender assembly by the fuel pipes. The amount of leverage generated by handling the fuel pipes could damage the joints.

24. Disconnect the fuel pipes from the fuel sender.

※※ WARNING

Avoid damaging the lockring. Use only the J 45722 to prevent damage to the lockring.

※※ WARNING

Do Not handle the fuel sender assembly by the fuel pipes. The amount of leverage generated by handling the fuel pipes could damage the joints.

➡**Do NOT use impact tools. Significant force will be required to release the lockring. The use of a hammer and screwdriver is not recommended. Secure the fuel tank in order to prevent fuel tank rotation.**

25. Use tool J 45722 and a long breaker-bar in order to unlock the fuel sender lockring. Turn the fuel sender lockring in a counterclockwise direction.

26. Remove the fuel sender lockring and the fuel sender from the fuel tank.

27. Remove and discard the fuel sender seal.

28. Remove the fuel level sensor from the fuel sender module.

➡**Some lockrings were manufactured with DO NOT REUSE stamped into them. These lockrings may be reused if they are not damaged or warped.**

➡**Inspect the lockring for damage due to improper removal or installation procedures. If damage is found, install a NEW lockring.**

➡**Check the lockring for flatness.**

29. Place the lockring on a flat surface. Measure the clearance between to lockring and the flat surface using a feeler gage at 7 points.

a. If warpage is less than 0.016 inch (0.41 mm), the lock ring does not require replacement.

b. If warpage is greater than 0.016 inch (0.41 mm), the lock ring must be replaced.

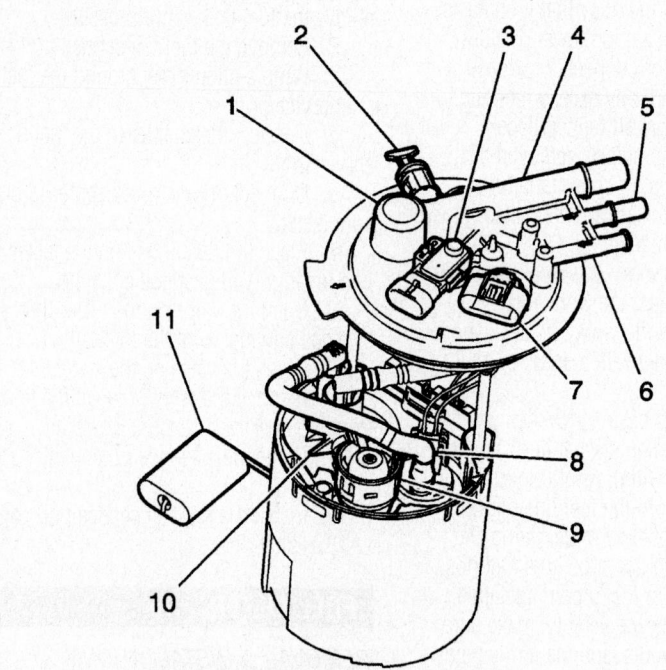

1. Fill Limit Vent Valve (FLVV)
2. T-connector for vapor hose/pipes to vent/rollover valve and fill tube
3. Fuel Tank Pressure (FTP) sensor
4. FLVV outlet to Evaporative Emission (EVAP) canister
5. Fuel feed outlet
6. Fuel return inlet-not used
7. Fuel sender assembly connector
8. Fuel pump
9. Fuel pressure regulator
10. Fuel filter assembly
11. Fuel level sensor float

06025-LACR-G54

Fig. 256 Fuel module components

To install:

30. Install the fuel level sensor to the fuel sender module.
31. Clean the fuel sender sealing flange.

➡Always replace the fuel sender seal when installing the fuel sender assembly.

32. Install the NEW fuel sender seal to the fuel tank seal groove.
33. Install the fuel sender and the fuel sender lockring.

➡Always replace the fuel sender seal when installing the fuel sender assembly. Replace the lockring if necessary. Do not apply any type of lubrication in the seal groove. Ensure the lockring is installed with the correct side facing upward. A correctly installed lockring will only turn in a clockwise direction.

34. Use tool J 45722 in order to install the fuel sender lockring. Turn the fuel sender lockring in a clockwise direction.
35. Install the fuel pipes to the fuel sender.
36. Install the fuel sender sensor electrical connectors.
37. Install the insulator pads to the fuel tank.
38. Install the EVAP canister.

✳✳ WARNING

Do not attempt to straighten kinked nylon pipes. Replace any kinked nylon pipes in order to prevent damage to the vehicle. Do not attempt to repair sections of nylon pipes. Replace damaged nylon pipes. Replace the vapor pipes with original equipment or parts that meet GM specifications. Replace the vapor hoses with original equipment or parts meeting GM specifications. Use only reinforced fuel-resistant hose identified with the word Fluoroelastomer or GM 6163M on the hose.

39. Install and connect the fuel feed line, and the EVAP lines.
40. Install and connect the fuel pressure sensor and fuel sender jumper harness electrical connectors.
41. Install the fuel tank onto a suitable jack.
42. Partially raise the fuel tank until the electrical connection can be made.
43. Connect the fuel sender jumper harness electrical connector.
44. Completely raise the tank.
45. Install the fuel tank strap bolts. Tighten the bolts to 35 ft. lbs. (48 Nm).
46. Remove the jack from the fuel tank.
47. Position the fuel tank shield to the fuel tank.
48. Install the shield retainers.
49. Install the rubber exhaust pipe hangers.
50. Remove the support from the exhaust system.
51. Connect the fuel feed, and EVAP lines to the fuel tank lines.
52. Connect the EVAP vent pipe quick-connect fitting to the fill pipe EVAP vent pipe quick-connect fitting.
53. Connect the EVAP vent pipe quick-connect fitting to the fill pipe EVAP vent pipe quick-connect fitting.
54. Install the fuel tank fill hose onto the fuel tank. Install the hose over the orientation feature on the tank until fully seated to the tank.
55. Tighten the fuel fill hose clamp at the fuel tank. Tighten the clamp to 22 inch lbs. (3 Nm).
56. Lower the vehicle.
57. Add fuel and install the fuel fill cap.
58. Connect the negative battery cable.
59. Inspect the fuel system for leaks by performing the following steps:
    a. Turn ON the ignition for 2 seconds.
    b. Turn OFF the ignition for 10 seconds.
    c. Turn ON the ignition.
    d. Inspect for fuel leaks.
60. Install the engine sight shield.

FUEL RAIL & INJECTORS

REMOVAL & INSTALLATION

3.6L Engine—2008

See Figures 257 and 258.

1. Before servicing the vehicle, refer to the Precautions Section.
2. Relieve the fuel system pressure.
3. Remove the upper intake manifold.
4. Remove the fuel pipe retaining clip.
5. Disconnect the fuel feed pipe from the fuel injector rail.

✳✳ CAUTION

Wear safety glasses.

6. Use compressed air in order to remove debris from the area where the fuel injectors enter the intake manifold.
7. Remove the fuel rail bolts.

✳✳ WARNING

Remove the fuel rail assembly carefully in order to prevent damage to the injector electrical connector terminals and the injector spray tips. Support the fuel rail after the fuel rail is removed in order to avoid damaging the fuel rail components. Cap the fittings and plug the holes when servicing the fuel system in order to prevent dirt and other contaminants from entering open pipes and passages.

8. Remove the fuel rail with the fuel injectors.
9. Disengage the fuel injector electrical connector lock.
10. Disconnect the fuel injector electrical connector.
11. Remove the fuel injector retainer clip.
12. Remove the fuel injector.
13. Remove and discard the fuel injector seals.

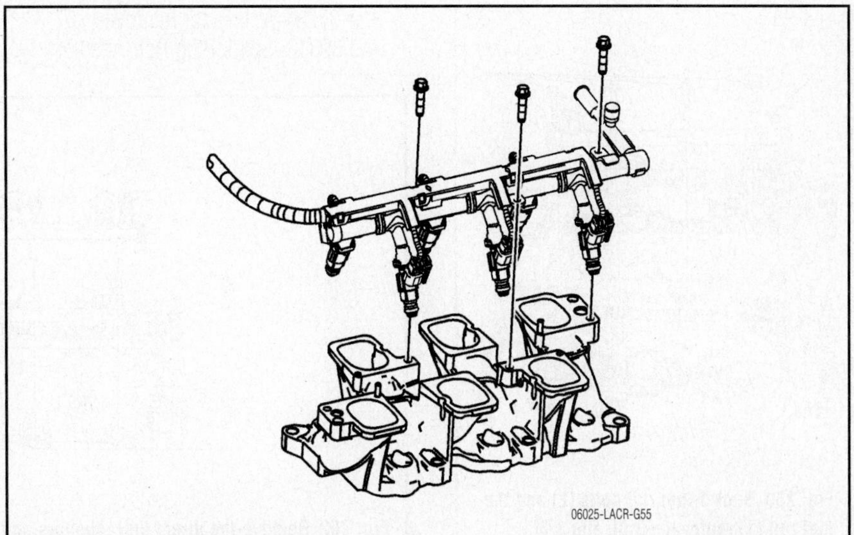
06025-LACR-G55

Fig. 257 Fuel rail removal—3.6L engine—2008

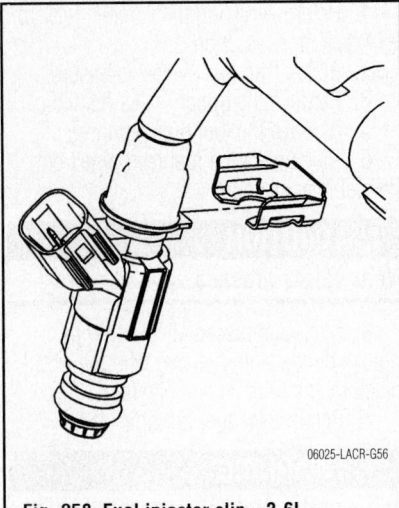

Fig. 258 Fuel injector clip—3.6L engine—2008

To install:

14. Install NEW fuel injector seals.

15. Install the fuel injector.

16. Install the fuel injector retainer clip.

17. Install the fuel injector electrical connector.

18. Engage the fuel injector electrical connector lock.

19. Install the fuel rail with the fuel injectors.

20. Install the fuel rail bolts. Tighten the fuel rail bolts to 89 inch lbs. (10 Nm).

21. Connect the fuel feed pipe to the fuel rail.

22. Install the fuel pipe retaining clip.

23. Install the upper intake manifold.

3.0L and 3.6L Engines—2010

See Figures 259 through 267.

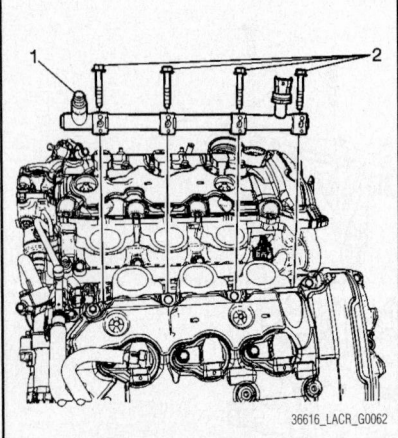

Fig. 259 Bank 1 fuel rail bolts (2) and the fuel rail (1) removal—3.0L and 3.6L engines (2010)

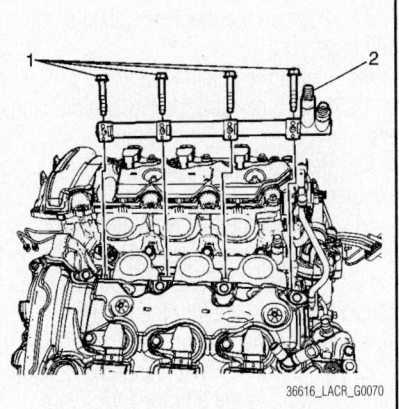

Fig. 260 Bank 2 fuel rail bolts (1) and the fuel rail (2) removal—3.0L and 3.6L engines (2010)

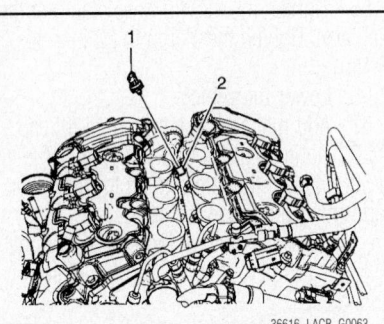

Fig. 261 Remove the fuel pressure sensor (1) from the fuel injection fuel rail (2)—3.0L and 3.6L engines (2010)

Special Tools:

- EN-47909: Injector Bore and Sleeve Cleaning Kit
- EN-48266: Injector Seal Installer and Sizer
- J 2619-01: Slide Hammer
- J-37281-A: Injector Remover
- J 39313: Spark Plug Port Adapter

1. Before servicing the vehicle, refer to the Precautions Section.

2. Relieve the high side fuel system pressure.

➡️ **The fuel injectors have an alignment feature, note the position of the injectors for installation.**

3. Remove the fuel pipe shield.

4. Remove the intake manifold. Refer to Intake Manifold, removal & installation.

5. Remove the high pressure fuel pipe. Discard the pipe.

6. Remove the fuel rail crossover pipe. Discard the pipe.

7. Remove the foam insulator from the fuel rails.

8. Disconnect the fuel pressure sensor electrical connector and cut the wire harness tie straps.

9. Remove the fuel rail bolts.

➡️ **To avoid fuel system contamination, clean the area where the sensor connects to the fuel line or fuel injection fuel rail before removing the sensor.**

✳️✳️ WARNING

Applying force to the plastic housing of the sensor will destroy the sensor. To tighten or loosen, only apply force to the attached hexagon fitting.

10. Using a 27mm socket, remove the fuel pressure sensor from the fuel injection fuel rail. Discard the fuel pressure sensor.

11. Allow any fuel to drain from the fuel rail and pressure sensor location.

12. Dry the sealing cone in the fuel rail and the area around the sensor joint with a lint free cloth.

13. Inspect the sealing cone in the fuel rail. The surface should be free of fuel, debris, and burrs.

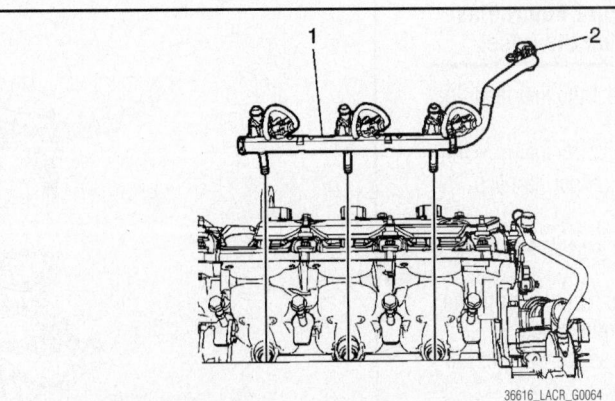

Fig. 262 Remove the direct fuel injectors and harness (1) as an assembly, and disconnect the electrical connector (2)—3.0L and 3.6L engines (2010)

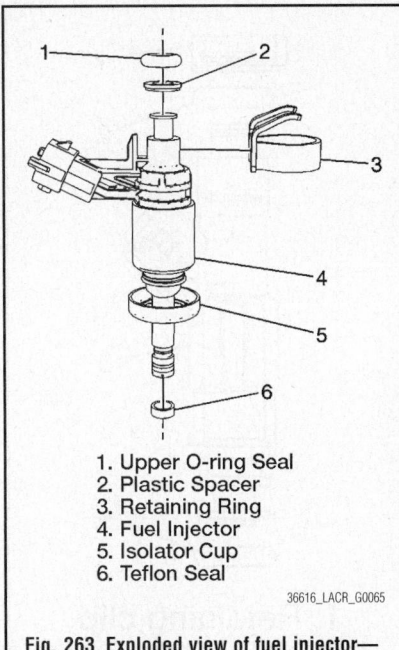

1. Upper O-ring Seal
2. Plastic Spacer
3. Retaining Ring
4. Fuel Injector
5. Isolator Cup
6. Teflon Seal

Fig. 263 Exploded view of fuel injector—3.0L and 3.6L engines (2010)

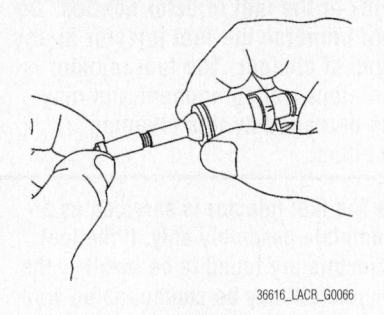

Fig. 264 Install a NEW Teflon® seal onto the EN 48266-1—3.0L and 3.6L engines (2010)

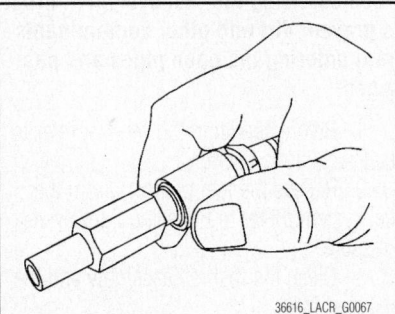

Fig. 265 Using the EN 48266-2, resize the Teflon seal—3.0L and 3.6L engines (2010)

Fig. 266 Install the rebuilt direct fuel injectors (1) to the cylinder heads—3.0L and 3.6L engines (2010)

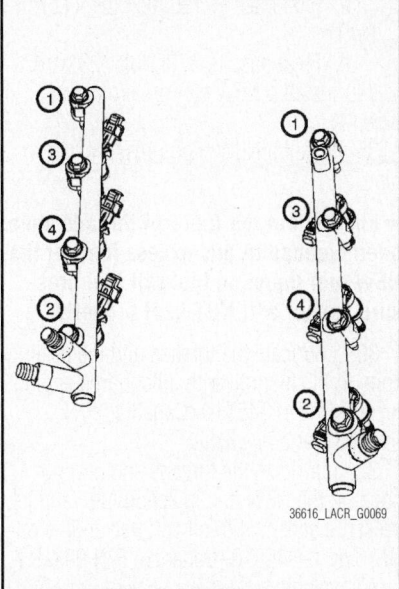

Fig. 267 Fuel rail bolt tightening sequence (bank 1 and bank 2)—3.0L and 3.6L engines (2010)

14. Remove and discard the direct fuel injector hold down clamps.

➡**The direct fuel injectors must be rebuilt whenever the injector has been released from the fuel rail or cylinder head.**

15. Once the fuel rail is removed, remove the fuel injectors and rebuild them.

16. Remove and discard the fuel injector retaining rings.

17. Remove the direct fuel injectors and harness as an assembly, and disconnect the electrical connector. If necessary, use the J 2619-01 slide hammer with the J-37281-A injector remover in order to remove the direct fuel injectors evenly.

18. Remove and discard the following components from the fuel injectors.
   a. Upper O-ring Seal
   b. Plastic Spacer
   c. Retaining Ring
   d. Isolator Cup
   e. Teflon® Seal

19. Inspect the fuel rail injector bores and clean with the J-39313 adapter, and EN-47909 cleaning kit, if required.

To install:

➡**Lubricate a NEW O-ring seal with silicon free engine oil GM P/N 12345610 (Canadian P/N 993193), or equivalent.**

Install the following NEW components to the fuel injectors.

- Upper O-ring Seal
- Plastic Spacer
- Retaining Ring
- Isolator Cup
- Teflon® Seal

20. From the EN-48266 Installer, position the EN 48266-1 to the injector tip.

➡**DO NOT lubricate the NEW Teflon® seal.**

21. Install a NEW Teflon® seal onto the EN 48266-1.

22. Pull the NEW Teflon® seal by hand over the EN 48266-1 and into the groove in the injector.

23. Remove the EN 48266-1 from the injector tip.

24. From the EN-48266 Installer, install the EN 48266-2 to the injector tip.

25. Using the EN 48266-2, resize the Teflon® seal. Install the EN 48266-2, until it bottoms out against the injector body, and rotate the EN 48266-2 while applying only moderate force 180 degrees in one direction and then 180 degrees back in the other direction.

26. Remove the EN 48266-2.

27. Install the direct fuel injectors and harness as an assembly and connect the electrical connector.

➡**The fuel injectors have an alignment feature and must be reinstalled as noted during removal.**

28. Install the rebuilt direct fuel injectors to the cylinder heads.

29. Install NEW direct injector hold down clamps to the injector.

30. On a new fuel rail, lubricate the fuel injector cups with silicon free engine oil GM P/N 12345610 (Canadian P/N 9931930), or equivalent.

31. Carefully place the fuel rail into position, placing the front into the fuel rail over the front injector and rotating the rear downward.

32. Install the 2 outer fuel rail bolts first, then the 2 inner bolts, and hand tighten.

33. Tighten the fuel rail bolts in the sequence shown.

a. First pass to 106 inch lbs. (12 Nm).

b. Final pass to 17 ft. lbs. (23 Nm).

34. Install a NEW fuel rail crossover pipe.

35. Install a NEW high pressure fuel pipe.

➡Ensure that the fuel rail threads have been cleaned of any excess fuel, or the NEW fuel injection fuel rail fuel pressure sensor will NOT seal properly.

36. Lubricate the threads and the sealing cone in the fuel rail with silicon free engine oil GM P/N 12345610 (Canadian P/N 993193), or equivalent.

37. Lubricate the threads and sealing cone on the NEW fuel injection fuel rail fuel pressure sensor with silicon free engine oil GM P/N 12345610 (Canadian P/N 993193), or equivalent.

38. Install the NEW fuel pressure sensor to the fuel injection fuel rail and hand tighten.

39. Remove the NEW fuel injection fuel rail fuel pressure sensor and re-lubricate.

40. Install the NEW fuel pressure sensor to the fuel injection fuel rail and tighten to 25 ft. lbs. (33 Nm).

41. Connect the fuel injector wiring harness electrical connector to the fuel injectors, fuel rail, and fuel pressure sensor.

➡If a fuel leak is evident at the fuel rail, the fuel rail will need to be replaced.

42. Inspect for fuel leaks using the following procedure:

a. Turn ON the ignition, with the engine OFF, for 2 seconds.

b. Turn OFF the ignition, for 10 seconds.

c. Turn ON the ignition, with the engine OFF.

d. Inspect for fuel leaks. Repair as needed.

43. Install the foam insulator to the fuel rails.

44. Install the intake manifold. Refer to Intake Manifold, removal & installation.

45. Install the fuel pipe shield.

46. Install the low side fuel pressure service port cap.

47. Install the fuel tank cap.

3.8L Engine

See Figures 268 and 269.

✳✳ WARNING

Use care in removing the fuel injectors in order to prevent damage to the fuel injector electrical connector

pins or the fuel injector nozzles. Do not immerse the fuel injector in any type of cleaner. The fuel injector is an electrical component and may be damaged by this cleaning method.

➡The fuel injector is serviced as a complete assembly only. If the fuel injectors are found to be leaking, the engine oil may be contaminated with fuel. Fuel injector O-rings should always be replaced whenever fuel injectors are serviced.

➡Cap the fittings and plug the holes when servicing the fuel system in order to prevent dirt and other contaminants from entering the open pipes and passages.

1. Before servicing the vehicle, refer to the Precautions Section.

2. Relieve the fuel pressure from the fuel system. Refer to Relieving Fuel System Pressure.

3. Clean the fuel rail assembly and the fuel feed pipe.

4. Disconnect the fuel feed pipe from the fuel rail.

5. Remove the spark plug wires from the fuel rail.

6. Disconnect and reposition the spark plug wires from the ignition control module.

7. Disconnect the fuel injector electrical connectors.

8. Remove the fuel rail hold-down nuts.

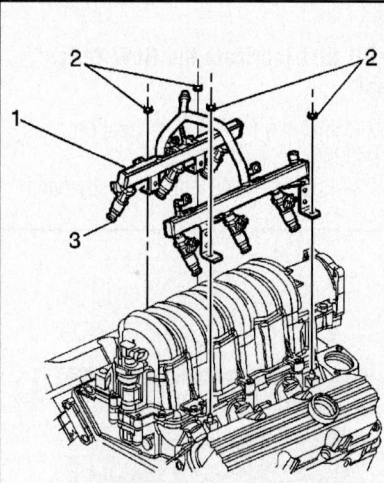

1. Fuel rail
2. Fuel rail hold-down nuts
3. Fuel injectors

36616_LACR_G0071

Fig. 268 Remove the fuel rail with the fuel injectors—3.8L engine

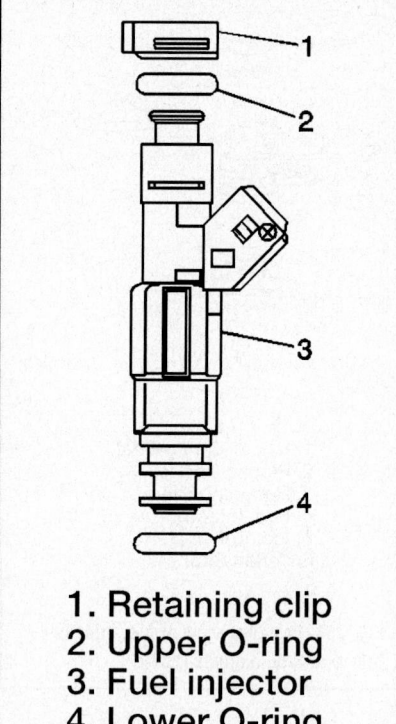

1. **Retaining clip**
2. **Upper O-ring**
3. **Fuel injector**
4. **Lower O-ring**

36616_LACR_G0072

Fig. 269 Exploded view of fuel injector—3.8L engine

9. Remove the fuel rail with the fuel injectors using equal force on both sides of the fuel rail.

10. Remove the fuel injector retaining clip.

11. Remove the fuel injector.

12. Remove the fuel injector upper O-ring.

13. Remove the fuel injector lower O-ring.

To install:

➡When ordering new fuel injectors, order the correct injector for the application being serviced. The fuel injector assembly (1) is stamped with a part number identification (2), a manufacturing date (3), a week code (1), and a production plant number (4).

14. The O-rings must be replaced on all components that are serviced.

15. Coat all new O-rings with clean engine oil before installing.

16. Install the fuel injector lower O-ring.

17. Install the fuel injector upper O-ring.

18. Install the fuel injector to the fuel rail.

19. Install the fuel injector retaining clip.

✳✳ CAUTION

In order to reduce the risk of fire and personal injury that may result from a fuel leak, always install the fuel injector O-rings in the proper position. If the upper and lower O-rings are different colors (black and brown), be sure to install the black O-ring in the upper position and the brown O-ring in the lower position on the fuel injector. The O-rings are the same size but are made of different materials.

20. Place the fuel rail with the fuel injectors on the intake manifold.

21. Seat the fuel injectors by HAND.

22. Install the fuel rail hold-down nuts and tighten to 89 inch lbs. (10 Nm).

23. Connect the fuel injector electrical connectors.

24. Reposition the spark plug wires to the fuel rail.

25. Connect the spark plug wires to the ignition control module.

26. Connect the fuel feed pipe to the fuel rail.

27. Tighten the fuel fill cap.

28. Connect the negative battery cable.

29. Inspect for fuel leaks using the following procedure:

    a. Turn ON the ignition, with the engine OFF, for 2 seconds.

    b. Turn OFF the ignition, for 10 seconds.

    c. Turn ON the ignition, with the engine OFF.

    d. Inspect for fuel leaks. Repair as needed.

30. Install the fuel injector sight shield.

5.3L Engine

See Figures 270 and 271.

➡ **An 8-digit identification number is located on the fuel rail. Refer to this identification number when servicing or when part replacement is required.**

1. Before servicing the vehicle, refer to the Precautions Section.

2. Remove the air cleaner outlet duct.

3. Relieve the fuel system pressure. Refer to Relieving Fuel System Pressure.

4. Remove the engine wiring harness bracket nut.

5. Disconnect the engine wiring harness electrical connector from the following:

    a. The Evaporative Emission (EVAP) purge solenoid.

    b. The alternator.

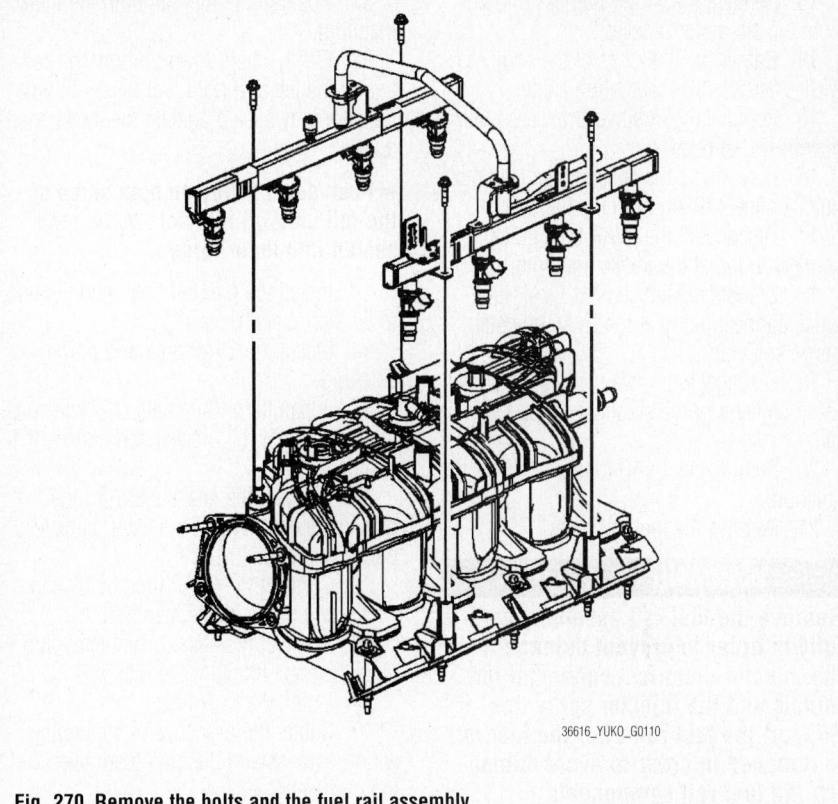

36616_YUKO_G0110

Fig. 270 Remove the bolts and the fuel rail assembly

    c. The Manifold Absolute Pressure (MAP) sensor.

6. Remove the Connector Position Assurance (CPA) retainer.

7. Disconnect the engine wiring harness electrical connector from the ignition coil main electrical connector.

8. Disconnect the engine wiring harness electrical connectors from the fuel injectors and perform the following:

    a. Mark the connectors to their corresponding injectors to ensure correct reassembly.

    b. Pull the CPA retainer on the connector up 1 click.

    c. Push in on the connector tab.

    d. Disconnect the fuel injector electrical connector.

9. Remove the CPA retainer.

10. Disconnect the engine wiring harness electrical connector from the electronic throttle control.

11. Remove the engine wiring harness clip from the alternator battery jumper cable and the ignition coil bracket stud.

12. Remove the negative battery cable stud from the right cylinder head and remove the negative battery cable terminal and engine wiring harness ground terminal.

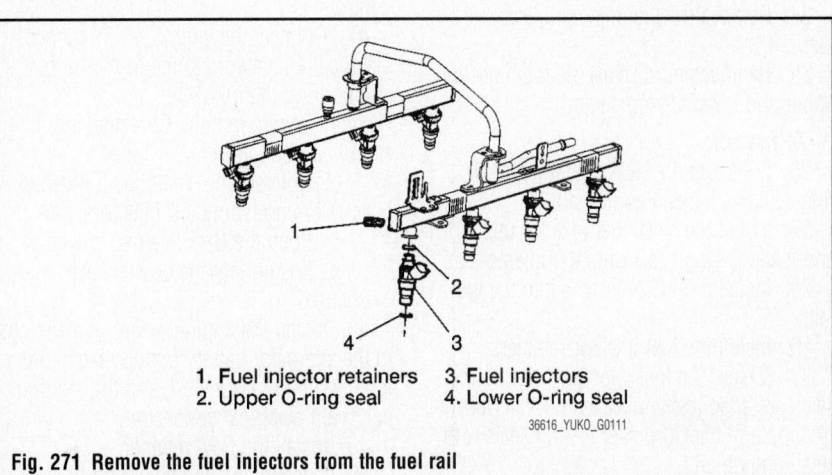

1. Fuel injector retainers   3. Fuel injectors
2. Upper O-ring seal   4. Lower O-ring seal

36616_YUKO_G0111

Fig. 271 Remove the fuel injectors from the fuel rail

13. Remove the wiring harness clip bolt from the alternator bracket.

14. Gather the branches of the engine wiring harness and reposition aside.

15. Remove the Positive Crankcase Ventilation (PCV) hose.

16. Disconnect the chassis fuel feed pipe quick connect fitting from the fuel rail.

17. Disconnect the EVAP tube quick connect fitting at the intake manifold.

18. Disconnect the chassis EVAP tube quick connect fitting at the EVAP canister purge solenoid.

19. Disengage the retainer securing the EVAP canister purge solenoid to the fuel rail.

20. Remove the EVAP tube and purge solenoid.

21. Remove the fuel rail bolts.

✳✳ WARNING

Remove the fuel rail assembly carefully in order to prevent damage to the injector electrical connector terminals and the injector spray tips. Support the fuel rail after the fuel rail is removed in order to avoid damaging the fuel rail components.

➡**Cap the fittings and plug the holes when servicing the fuel system in order to prevent dirt and other contaminants from entering open pipes and passages.**

➡**Before removal, clean the fuel rail with a spray type engine cleaner, such as GM X-30A or equivalent, if necessary. Follow the package instructions. Do not soak the fuel rail in liquid cleaning solvent.**

➡**Lift evenly on both sides of the fuel rail until all injectors are removed from their bores.**

22. Remove the fuel rail assembly.

23. Remove the fuel injector retainers.

24. Remove the fuel injectors from the fuel rail.

25. Remove and discard the fuel injector upper and lower O-ring seals.

To install:

26. Lubricate the NEW fuel injector O-ring seals with clean engine oil.

27. Install the NEW fuel injector upper and lower O-ring seals onto the injectors.

28. Install the fuel injectors into the fuel rails.

29. Install the fuel injector retainers.

30. Ensure the fuel injector lower O-ring seals are adequately lubricated, if not, lubricate the fuel injector lower O-ring seals with clean engine oil.

31. Position the fuel rail onto the intake manifold.

32. Firmly push down on both the centers of the left and right fuel rails, until the rails are fully seated against the intake manifold.

➡**Push down firmly on both sides of the rail until all injectors have been seated into their bores.**

33. Install the fuel rail bolts and tighten to 89 inch lbs. (10 Nm).

34. Install the EVAP tube and purge solenoid.

35. Install the EVAP canister purge solenoid to the fuel rail bracket and engage the retainer.

36. Connect the chassis EVAP tube quick connect fitting at the EVAP canister purge solenoid.

37. Connect the EVAP tube quick connect fitting at the intake manifold.

38. Connect the chassis fuel feed pipe quick connect fitting to the fuel rail.

39. Install the PCV hose.

40. Gather the branches of the engine wiring harness and position them over the top of the engine.

41. Position the engine wiring harness clip to the alternator bracket and install the clip bolt. Tighten the bolt to 80 inch lbs. (9 Nm).

42. Position the negative battery cable terminal and engine wiring harness ground terminal to the right cylinder head.

43. Install the negative battery cable stud to the cylinder head. Tighten the stud to 18 ft. lbs. (25 Nm).

44. Connect the engine wiring harness electrical connector to the ignition coil main electrical connector.

45. Install the CPA retainer.

46. Connect the engine wiring harness electrical connector to the electronic throttle control.

47. Connect the engine wiring harness electrical connectors to the fuel injectors and perform the following:

a. Ensure that the CPA retainer is pulled out 1 click.

b. Connect the electrical connectors to their corresponding injectors.

c. Push the CPA retainer in 1 click.

d. Ensure that the connector is secured.

48. Install the engine wiring harness clip to the alternator battery jumper cable, the ignition coil bracket stud, and the ignition coil main electrical connector.

49. Install the CPA retainer.

50. Connect the engine wiring harness

electrical connector to the MAP sensor, the alternator, and the EVAP purge solenoid.

51. Install the engine wiring harness bracket nut and tighten to 44 inch lbs. (5 Nm).

52. Connect the negative battery cable.

53. Use the following procedure in order to inspect for leaks:

a. Turn the ignition ON, with the engine OFF, for 2 seconds.

b. Turn the ignition OFF for 10 seconds.

c. Turn the ignition ON, with the engine OFF.

d. Inspect for leaks.

54. Install the air cleaner outlet duct.

FUEL TANK

REMOVAL & INSTALLATION

See Figure 272.

1. Before servicing the vehicle, refer to the Precautions Section.

2. Disconnect the negative battery cable.

➡**Cap the fittings and plug the holes when servicing the fuel system in order to prevent dirt and other contaminants from entering the open pipes and passages.**

➡**Always maintain cleanliness when servicing the fuel system components.**

3. Relieve the fuel system fuel pressure. Refer to Relieving Fuel System Pressure.

4. Drain the fuel tank.

5. Raise and support the vehicle.

6. Loosen the fuel filler hose clamp at the fuel tank.

7. Remove the fuel tank filler hose from the fuel tank.

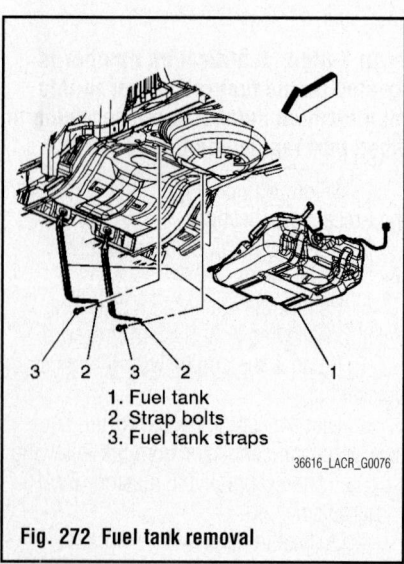

1. Fuel tank
2. Strap bolts
3. Fuel tank straps

36616_LACR_G0076

Fig. 272 Fuel tank removal

8. Disconnect the fuel feed, fuel return, and the Evaporative Emission (EVAP) pipes.

9. Support the exhaust system.

10. Remove the rubber exhaust pipe hangers in order to allow the exhaust system to drop slightly.

11. Separate the two halves of the EVAP fresh air hose at the splice.

12. Remove the fuel tank shield push pins.

13. Remove the fuel tank shield.

✳✳ WARNING

Do not bend the fuel tank straps as this may damage the straps.

14. Support the fuel tank with a suitable jack.

15. Remove the fuel tank strap bolts.

16. Using a suitable jack, lower the fuel tank.

17. Disconnect the fuel sender assembly electrical connectors.

18. Remove the fuel tank and place the tank in a suitable work area.

➡**Note the routing of the pipe assemblies and the retaining clips for installation.**

19. Disconnect and remove the fuel feed, fuel return, and EVAP pipe assemblies and the insulator clips from the fuel tank.

20. Remove the EVAP canister from the fuel tank.

21. Remove the insulator pads from the fuel tank.

➡**Note the location of the insulator pads for installation.**

To install:

22. Install the insulator pads to the fuel tank.

23. Install the EVAP canister to the fuel tank.

✳✳ WARNING

Do not attempt to straighten kinked nylon pipes. Replace any kinked nylon pipes in order to prevent damage to the vehicle. Do not attempt to repair sections of nylon pipes. Replace damaged nylon pipes. Replace the vapor pipes with original equipment or parts that meet GM specifications. Replace the vapor hoses with original equipment or parts meeting GM specifications. Use only reinforced fuel-resistant hose identified with the word Fluoroelastomer or GM 6163M on the hose.

24. Install and connect the fuel feed, fuel

return, and EVAP pipe assemblies and the insulator clips to the fuel tank as noted during removal.

25. Place the fuel tank on a suitable jack.

26. Raise the fuel tank to its original position.

➡**Use the correct fastener in the correct location. Replacement fasteners must be the correct part number for that application. Fasteners requiring replacement or fasteners requiring the use of thread locking compound or sealant are identified in the service procedure. Do not use paints, lubricants, or corrosion inhibitors on fasteners or fastener joint surfaces unless specified. These coatings affect fastener torque and joint clamping force and may damage the fastener. Use the correct tightening sequence and specifications when installing fasteners in order to avoid damage to parts and systems.**

27. Install the fuel tank strap bolts. Tighten the bolts to 35 ft. lbs. (48 Nm) on 2008–09 models and 15 ft. lbs. (20 Nm) on 2010 models.

28. Remove the jack from the fuel tank.

29. Position the fuel tank shield to the fuel tank.

30. Install the push pins that retain the fuel tank shield to the fuel tank.

31. Install the two parts of the EVAP fresh air hose at the splice.

32. Raise the exhaust system to the original position.

33. Install the exhaust system to the exhaust pipe hangers.

34. Connect the fuel feed, fuel return, and Evaporative Emission (EVAP) pipes.

35. Install the fuel tank filler hose to the fuel tank.

36. Fully seat the filler hose on the fuel tank port.

37. Ensure that the clamp is properly located on the tank port between the bead and the tank. Tighten the hose clamp to 22 inch lbs. (3 Nm).

38. Lower the vehicle.

39. Add fuel and install the fuel fill cap.

40. Connect the negative battery cable.

41. Inspect for fuel leaks using the following procedure:

a. Turn ON the ignition, with the engine OFF, for 2 seconds.

b. Turn OFF the ignition, for 10 seconds.

c. Turn ON the ignition, with the engine OFF.

d. Inspect for fuel leaks. Repair as needed.

IDLE SPEED

ADJUSTMENT

Idle speed is maintained by the Powertrain Control Module (PCM). No adjustment is necessary or possible.

THROTTLE BODY

REMOVAL & INSTALLATION

3.0L and 3.6L Engines
See Figure 273.

1. Before servicing the vehicle, refer to the Precautions Section.

2. Remove the air cleaner outlet duct.

3. Disconnect the engine wiring harness electrical connector from the Electronic Throttle Control (ETC).

4. Remove the throttle body bolts.

5. Remove the throttle body and gasket. Discard the gasket.

To install:

6. Clean the gasket mating surfaces.

7. Install a NEW gasket to the upper intake manifold.

8. Position the throttle body to the upper intake manifold.

9. Install the throttle body. Tighten the bolts to 89 inch lbs. (10 Nm).

10. Connect the engine wiring harness electrical connector to the ETC.

11. Install the air cleaner outlet duct.

12. Perform the Throttle Learn Procedure as follows:

a. Start and idle the engine in PARK for 3 minutes.

b. With a scan tool, monitor desired and actual RPM.

c. The ECM will start to learn the new idle cells and Desired RPM should start to decrease.

d. Turn the ignition OFF for 60 seconds.

e. Start and idle the engine in PARK for 3 minutes.

f. After the 3 minute run time, the engine should be idling at a normal RPM.

➡**During the drive cycle, the check engine light may come on with idle speed DTC's. If idle speed codes are set, clear codes so the ECM can continue to learn. If the engine idle speed has not been learned, the vehicle will need to be driven at speeds above 44 mph (70 km/h) with several decelerations and extended idles.**

g. After the drive cycle, the engine should be idling normally. If the engine

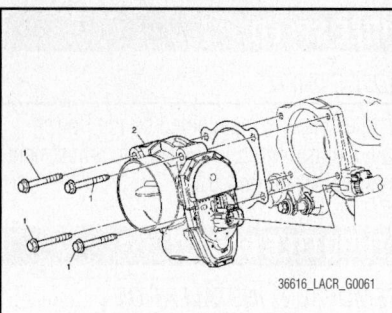

Fig. 273 Throttle body removal–3.0L and 3.6L engines

idle speed has not been learned, turn OFF the ignition for 60 seconds and repeat the throttle learn procedure.

h. Once the engine speed has returned to normal, clear any DTC's

3.8L Engine

1. Before servicing the vehicle, refer to the Precautions Section.
2. Turn the ignition OFF.
3. Partially drain the cooling system.
4. Remove the fuel injector sight shield.
5. Remove the air cleaner intake duct.
6. Disconnect the throttle body electrical connector.
7. Remove the throttle body nuts and the bolts.
8. Remove the throttle body assembly.
9. Clean the throttle body gasket mating surfaces.

To install:
10. Install the throttle body assembly.
11. Install the throttle body bolts and tighten to 89 inch lbs. (10 Nm).
12. Install the throttle body electrical connector.
13. Install the air cleaner intake duct.
14. Install the fuel injector sight shield.
15. Fill the cooling system.

5.3L Engine

See Figure 274.

❋❋ CAUTION

DO NOT place fingers in or around the throttle body plate. If the throttle body is energized, the throttle plate could move causing personal injury. Always disconnect the negative battery cable prior to servicing the throttle body.

➡ **DO NOT move the throttle plate while power is connected to the throttle body. This may cause fault codes to set.**

❋❋ WARNING

Handle the electronic throttle control components carefully. Use cleanliness in order to prevent damage. Do not drop the electronic throttle control components. Do not roughly handle the electronic throttle control components. Do not immerse the electronic throttle control components in cleaning solvents of any type.

❋❋ WARNING

DO NOT, for any reason, insert a screwdriver or other small hand tools into the throttle body to hold open the throttle plate, as the wedge inside the throttle body could be damaged.

1. Before servicing the vehicle, refer to the Precautions Section.
2. Disconnect and isolate the negative battery cable at the battery.
3. Remove the air cleaner outlet duct.
4. Disconnect the engine wiring harness electrical connector from the throttle body.
5. Remove the throttle body bolts and nuts.
6. Remove the throttle body.
7. Remove and discard the throttle body seal.

To install:
8. Install a NEW throttle body gasket.
9. Install the throttle body.
10. Install the throttle body bolts and nuts. Tighten the bolts and nuts to 89 inch lbs. (10 Nm).

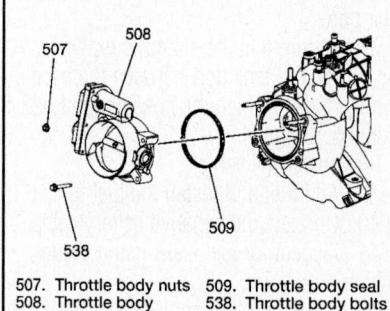

507. Throttle body nuts 509. Throttle body seal
508. Throttle body 538. Throttle body bolts

Fig. 274 Throttle body removal

11. Connect the engine wiring harness electrical connector to the throttle body.
12. Install the air cleaner outlet duct.
13. Perform the throttle learn procedure. Refer to Throttle Learn Procedure.

THROTTLE LEARN PROCEDURE

After the throttle body is cleaned or replaced, perform the RESET procedure.

After the ECM/PCM is flashed or replaced, perform the LEARN procedure.

1. Perform the following if the ECM/PCM is flashed or replaced.

➡ **Do NOT perform this procedure if DTC's are set. Refer to Diagnostic Trouble Codes.**

Start and idle the engine for 3 minutes.
2. With a scan tool, monitor the Desired Idle Speed and the actual Engine Speed.
3. The ECM will start to learn the new idle cells and the Desired Idle Speed should start to decrease.
4. Turn the ignition OFF for 60 seconds.
5. Start and idle the engine for 3 minutes.

➡ **During the drive cycle, the check engine light may come on with idle speed DTC's. If idle speed codes are set, clear the codes so the ECM can continue to learn.**

6. After the 3 minute run time, the engine should be idling normal. If the engine idle speed has not been learned, the vehicle will need to be driven at speeds above 44 mph (70 km/h) with several decelerations and extended idles.
7. After the drive cycle, the engine should be idling normally. If the engine idle speed has not been learned, turn OFF the ignition for 60 seconds and repeat Step 6.
8. Once the engine speed has returned to normal, clear any DTC's.

Throttle Reset Procedure

This procedure is to be performed after the throttle body is cleaned or replaced.

1. With the ignition ON and engine OFF, perform the Idle Learn Reset in Module Setup with a scan tool.
2. Start the engine and monitor the TB Idle Airflow Compensation parameter. The TB Idle Airflow Compensation value should equal 0 percent and the engine should be idling at a normal idle speed.
3. Clear any DTC's.

HEATING & AIR CONDITIONING SYSTEM

BLOWER MOTOR

REMOVAL & INSTALLATION

See Figures 275 and 276.

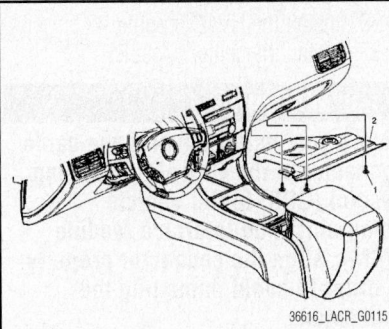

Fig. 275 Remove the right side instrument panel insulator

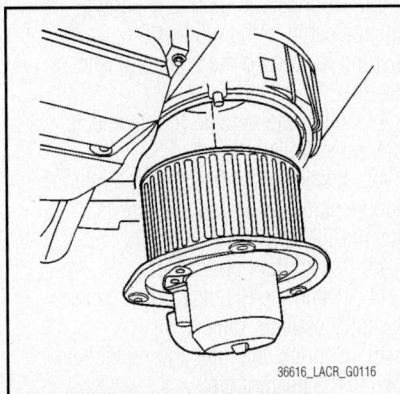

Fig. 276 Remove the blower motor

1. Before servicing the vehicle, refer to the Precautions Section.
2. Remove the right side instrument panel insulator.
3. Disconnect the blower motor electrical connector.
4. Remove the blower motor mounting screws.
5. Remove the blower motor.

To install:

6. Install the blower motor.
7. Install the blower motor screws and tighten to 13 inch lbs. (2 Nm).
8. Connect the blower motor electrical connector.
9. Install the right side instrument panel insulator.

HEATER CORE

REMOVAL & INSTALLATION

See Figures 277 and 278.

1. Before servicing the vehicle, refer to the Precautions Section.
2. Drain the coolant.
3. Position aside the heater hose inlet and outlet clamps at the heater core.
4. Disconnect the inlet and outlet heater hose from the heater core.
5. Remove the RH instrument panel closeout/insulator panel.
6. Remove the LH instrument panel closeout/insulator panel.
7. Remove the floor carpet.
8. Remove the center console, if equipped.
9. Remove the HVAC control.

➥**The Vehicle Communication Interface Module (VCIM) has a specific set of unique numbers that tie the module to each vehicle. These numbers, the 10-digit station identification and the 11-digit electronic serial number, are used by the National Cellular Network and OnStar® to identify the specific vehicle. Because these numbers are tied to the vehicle identification number of the vehicle, you must never exchange these parts with those of another vehicle.**

10. Remove the communication interface module screws.
11. Disconnect the mobile telephone antenna cable from the communication interface module by pulling outward on the square plastic housing.
12. Disconnect the electrical connectors.
13. Disconnect the navigation antenna coaxial antenna cable from the module.
14. Remove the communication interface module.
15. Remove the rear floor air outlet duct from the holes in the floor reinforcement.
16. Disconnect the rear floor air outlet duct from the heater core outlet cover.
17. Remove the rear floor air outlet duct.
18. Remove the heater core outlet cover screws.
19. Remove the heater core outlet cover heat stakes with a small chisel.
20. Remove the heater core outlet cover from the HVAC module assembly.
21. Remove the heater core cover screws.
22. Remove the heater core cover heat stakes with a small chisel.
23. Remove the heater core cover from the HVAC module assembly.

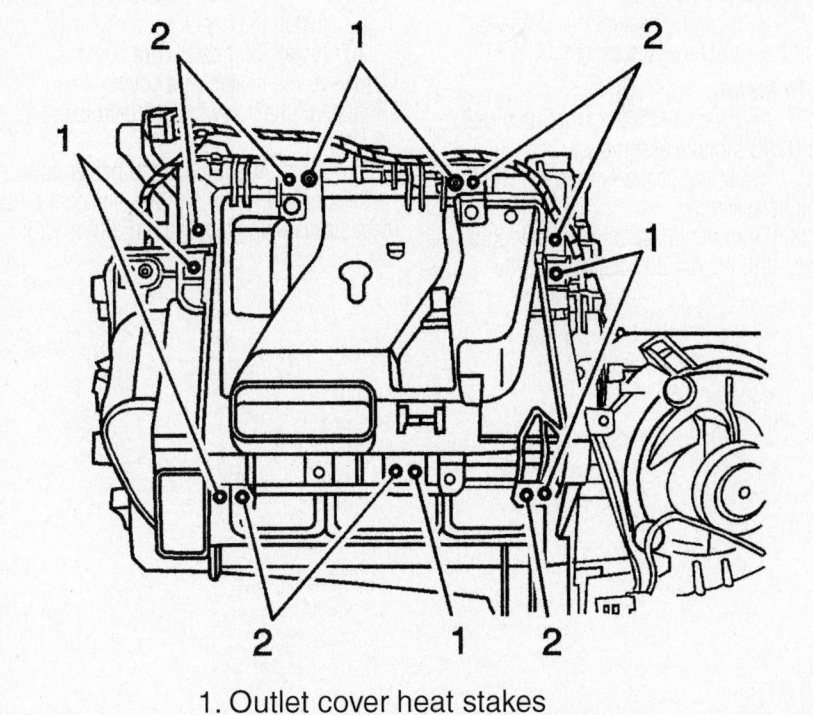

1. Outlet cover heat stakes
2. Heater core outlet cover screws

Fig. 277 HVAC core outlet side

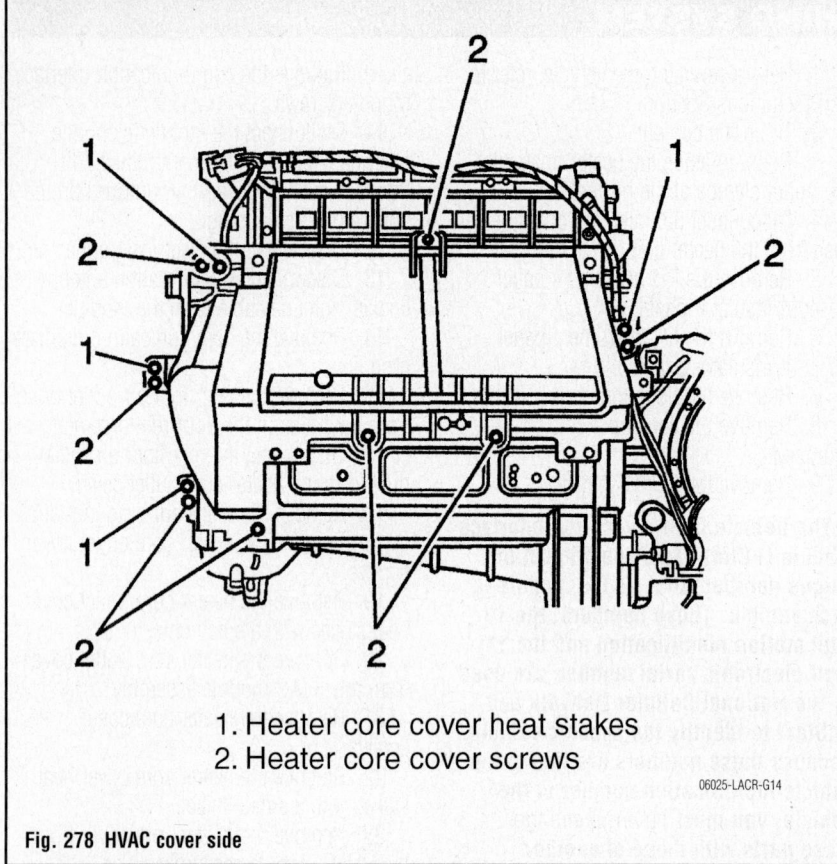

1. Heater core cover heat stakes
2. Heater core cover screws

06025-LACR-G14

Fig. 278 HVAC cover side

24. Remove the heater core from the HVAC module assembly.

25. Remove the heater core foam seal from the HVAC module assembly.

To install:

26. Install a new heater core foam seal to the HVAC module assembly.

27. Install the heater core to the HVAC module assembly.

28. From the inside of the heater core cover, drill the dimples adjacent to the heat stakes using a 7/32 inch (5.5mm) drill bit.

29. Install the heater core cover.

30. Install the heater core cover screws to the heater core cover. Tighten all the screws to 13 inch lbs. (2 Nm).

31. From the inside of the heater core outlet cover, drill the dimples adjacent to the heat stakes using a 7/32 inch (5.5mm) drill bit.

32. Install the heater core outlet cover.

33. Install the heater core outlet cover screws. Tighten the screws to 13 inch lbs. (2 Nm).

34. Connect the rear floor air outlet duct to the heater core outlet cover.

35. Install the rear floor air outlet duct to the holes in the floor reinforcement.

36. Install the HVAC module.

37. Install the center console.

✴✴ WARNING

Before you install the antenna cable connector of the Global Positioning System (GPS) to the Vehicle Communication Interface Module (VCM), align the connector properly in order to avoid damaging the connector.

38. Connect the navigation antenna coaxial cable to the module.

39. Connect the electrical connectors.

40. Connect the mobile telephone antenna cable to the module by pushing inward on the square plastic housing.

41. Align the module to the vehicle antenna module bracket.

42. Install the communication interface module screws. Tighten the screws to 18 inch lbs. (2 Nm).

43. Install the floor carpet.

44. Install the RH instrument panel closeout/insulator panel.

45. Connect the inlet and outlet heater hose to the heater core.

46. Reposition the heater hose inlet and outlet clamps to the heater core.

47. Refill the coolant with the proper type and amount of fluid.

STEERING

POWER RACK & PINION STEERING GEAR

REMOVAL & INSTALLATION

See Figures 279 through 281.

Special Tool:

• J-42640: Steering Column Anti-rotation Pin With wheels of the vehicle facing straight ahead, secure the steering wheel utilizing steering column anti-rotation pin, steering column lock, or a strap to prevent rotation. Locking of the steering column will prevent damage and a possible malfunction of the SIR system. The steering wheel must be secured in position before disconnecting the following components:

• The steering column
• The intermediate shaft(s)
• The steering gear

After disconnecting these components, do not rotate the steering wheel or move the front tires and wheels. Failure to follow this procedure may cause the SIR coil assembly to become un-centered and cause possible damage to the SIR coil. If you think the SIR coil has became un-centered, refer to Clockspring Centering.

1. Before servicing the vehicle, refer to the Precautions Section.

2. Insert the J-42640 pin into the steering column access hole in order to lock the steering column.

3. Raise and support the vehicle.

4. Place a drain pan under the vehicle.

5. Remove the tire and wheel assemblies.

6. Disconnect the snaps from the power steering heat shield.

7. Remove the power steering heat shield from the power steering gear.

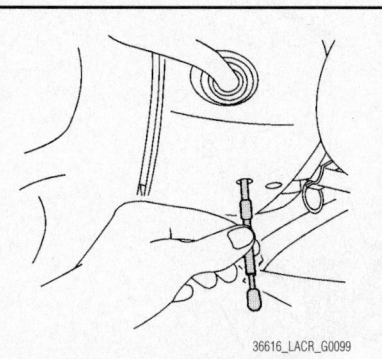

Fig. 279 Insert the J-42640 pin into the steering column access hole in order to lock the steering column

---

✳✳ WARNING

Failure to disconnect the intermediate shaft from the rack and pinion steering gear stub shaft can result in damage to the steering gear and/or intermediate shaft. This damage may cause loss of steering control which could result in an accident and possible personal injury.

8. Disconnect the intermediate steering shaft from the steering gear.

9. Disconnect both outer tie rod ends from the steering knuckles.

10. Disconnect the stabilizer shaft from the frame to allow bolt access.

11. Support the rear of the frame using jackstands.

➡**The power steering gear mounting bolts are different sizes. Note each bolt location for assembly.**

12. Remove the frame bolts from the rear of the frame.

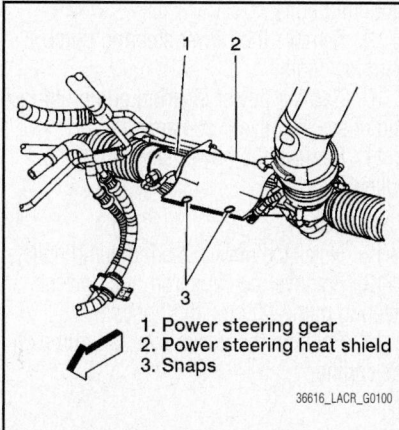

1. Power steering gear
2. Power steering heat shield
3. Snaps

36616_LACR_G0100

Fig. 280 Remove the power steering heat shield from the power steering gear

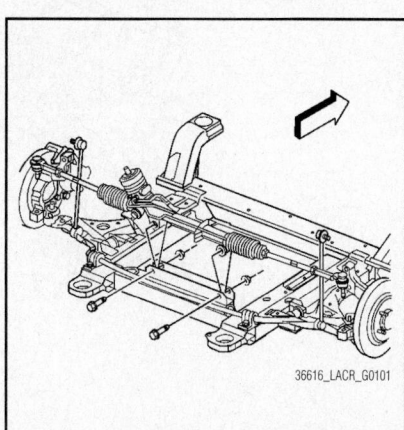

36616_LACR_G0101

Fig. 281 Remove the power steering gear

✳✳ WARNING

Do not lower the rear of the frame too far as damage to the engine components nearest to the cowl may result.

13. Lower the rear of the frame.

14. Disconnect the power steering pressure hose from the power steering gear.

15. Disconnect the power steering return hose from the power steering gear.

16. If applicable, disconnect the Magnasteer Variable Assist harness connector from the power steering gear assembly.

17. Remove the power steering gear mounting bolts and nuts.

18. Remove the power steering gear through the left wheel opening.

To install:

19. Install the power steering gear through the left wheel opening.

20. Install the power steering gear mounting bolts and nuts. Tighten both (M12) bolts to 42 ft. lbs. (60 Nm), plus 180°.

21. Inspect the threads on the power steering pressure hose and the power steering return hose.

22. Inspect the O-ring seals on the power steering hoses.

23. Replace the seals if damaged, lubricate the seals before installation.

24. Install the clamp that holds the power steering hoses to the power steering gear.

25. If applicable, connect the Magnasteer Variable Assist harness connector to the power steering gear assembly.

26. Connect the power steering pressure hose to the power steering gear.

27. Connect the power steering return hose to the power steering gear.

28. Raise the frame into position.

29. Install the rear frame bolts.

30. Remove the jackstands.

31. Connect the tie rod ends to the steering knuckles.

32. Connect the stabilizer shaft to the frame.

➡**During the installation of the intermediate steering shaft, ensure the steering shaft is seated before installing the pinch bolt. The 2 mating shafts may disengage if the pinch bolt is inserted into the coupling before the steering shaft installation.**

33. Connect the intermediate steering shaft to the steering gear.

34. Install the power steering heat shield to the steering gear.

35. Connect the snaps on the power steering heat shield.

36. Install the tire and wheel assemblies.

37. Remove the drain pan from under the vehicle.

38. Lower the vehicle.

39. Remove the J-42640 pin from the steering column.

40. Fill the power steering system with the proper type and amount of power steering fluid.

41. Bleed the power steering system. Refer to Power Steering System Bleeding.

42. Inspect the power steering system for leaks.

43. Perform a front end alignment.

POWER STEERING SYSTEM BLEEDING

Use clean, new power steering fluid type only. Hoses touching the frame, body, or engine may cause system noise. Verify that the hoses do not touch any other part of the vehicle.

Loose connections may not leak, but could allow air into the steering system. Verify that all hose connections are tight.

Power steering fluid level must be maintained throughout bleed procedure.

1. Before servicing the vehicle, refer to the Precautions Section.

2. Fill the pump reservoir with fluid to the minimum system level, FULL COLD level, or the middle of the hash mark on the cap stick fluid level indicator.

3. With hydro-boost only, the oil level will appear falsely high if the hydro-boost accumulator is not fully charged. Do not apply the brake pedal with the engine OFF. This will discharge the hydro-boost accumulator.

4. If equipped with hydro-boost, fully charge the hydro-boost accumulator using the following procedure:

   a. Start the engine.

   b. Firmly apply the brake pedal 10–15 times.

   c. Turn the engine OFF.

5. Raise the vehicle until the front wheels are off the ground.

6. With the key ON and engine OFF, turn the steering wheel from stop-to-stop 12 times.

7. Vehicles equipped with hydro-boost systems, or longer length power steering hoses, may require turns up to 15–20 stop-to-stops.

8. Verify the power steering fluid level per operating specification.

9. Start the engine.

10. Rotate the steering wheel from left to right. Check for sign of cavitation or fluid aeration (pump noise/whining).

11. Verify the fluid level. Repeat the bleed procedure, if necessary.

POWER STEERING PUMP

REMOVAL & INSTALLATION

3.6L Engine—2008

See Figure 282.

1. Before servicing the vehicle, refer to the Precautions Section.

2. Place a drain pan under the vehicle.

3. Remove the accessory drive belt. Refer to Accessory Drive Belts, removal & installation.

4. Turn the steering wheel to the right in order to allow clearance to remove the pump.

5. Raise and support the vehicle.

6. Remove the right front tire and wheel.

7. Disconnect the power steering pump inlet hose and pressure hose from the power steering pump.

8. Remove the power steering pump mounting bolts.

9. Remove the power steering pump from the engine.

10. Cap the power steering pump fittings and hoses to prevent contamination.

11. Remove the power steering pump pulley.

To install:

12. Install the power steering pump pulley.

13. Remove the caps from the power steering pump fittings and hoses.

14. Position the power steering pump on the engine.

15. Install the power steering pump mounting bolts. HAND TIGHTEN ONLY.

16. Tighten the front mounting bolt and then the rear to 37 ft. lbs. (50 Nm).

17. Clean the material from the power steering pressure hose and install a new seal.

18. Connect the power steering pressure hose to the power steering pump and tighten to 30 ft. lbs. (40 Nm).

19. Connect the power steering reservoir outlet hose to the power steering pump.

20. Install the right front tire and wheel.

21. Lower the vehicle.

22. Install the accessory drive belt. Refer to Accessory Drive Belts, removal & installation.

23. Remove the drain pan from under the vehicle.

24. Bleed the power steering system. Refer to Bleeding.

25. Inspect the system for leaks.

3.0L and 3.6L Engines—2010

See Figure 283.

1. Before servicing the vehicle, refer to the Precautions Section.

2. Place drain pans under the vehicle.

3. Remove as much power steering fluid from the power steering fluid reservoir as possible.

4. Remove the right front tire and wheel assembly.

5. Remove the accessory drive belt. Refer to Accessory Drive Belts, removal & installation.

6. Disconnect the power steering fluid reservoir outlet hose from the power steering pump.

7. Disconnect the power steering gear inlet hose from the power steering pump.

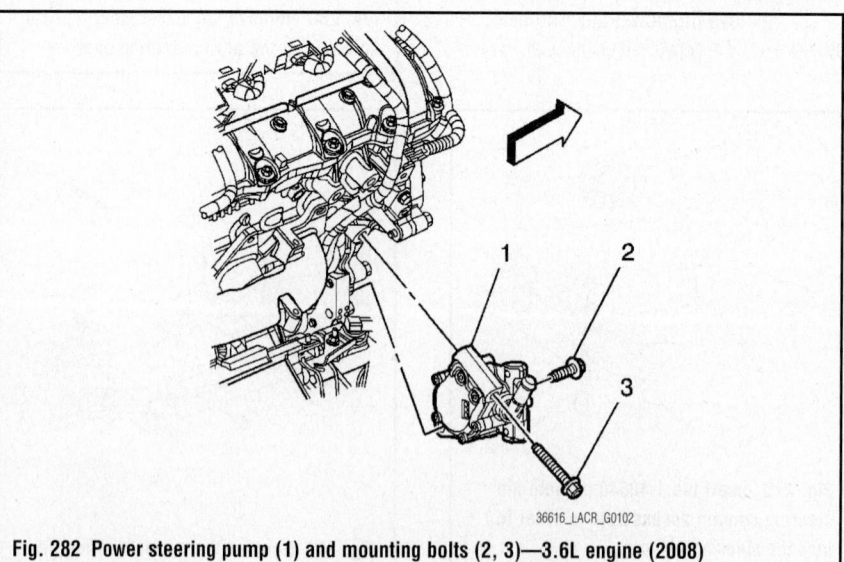

Fig. 282 Power steering pump (1) and mounting bolts (2, 3)—3.6L engine (2008)

36616_LACR_G0102

➡**Note the routing of the hoses for installation.**

8. Raise and safely support the vehicle.

9. Remove the right front tire and wheel assembly.

10. Remove the power steering pump bolts.

11. Remove the power steering pump through the right front wheel well opening.

12. Remove the power steering pump pulley.

To install:

13. Installation is the reverse of the removal procedure.

14. Install a NEW power steering gear inlet hose fitting seal. Tighten the hose fitting bolt to 28 ft. lbs. (38 Nm).

15. Tighten the power steering pump bolts to 16 ft. lbs. (22 Nm).

16. Fill and bleed the power steering system. Refer to Bleeding.

17. Clean any excess power steering fluid from the vehicle.

18. Inspect the system for leaks.

3.8L Engine

See Figure 284.

1. Before servicing the vehicle, refer to the Precautions Section.

2. Remove the accessory drive belt. Refer to Accessory Drive Belts, removal & installation.

3. Raise and support the vehicle.

4. Remove the tire and wheel assembly.

5. Disconnect the power steering pressure hose and return from the power steering pump.

6. Disconnect the harness connector - from the power steering pump.

7. Remove the power steering mounting bolts from the power steering pump.

8. Remove the power steering pump from the engine.

9. Remove the power steering pump pulley from the power steering pump.

10. Remove the power steering pump reservoir from the power steering pump.

To install:

11. Install the power steering pump reservoir to the power steering pump.

12. Install the power steering pump pulley to the power steering pump.

13. Position the power steering pump to the engine.

14. Install the power steering pump mounting bolts and tighten to 18 ft. lbs. (25 Nm).

15. Connect the power steering pressure hose to the power steering pump.

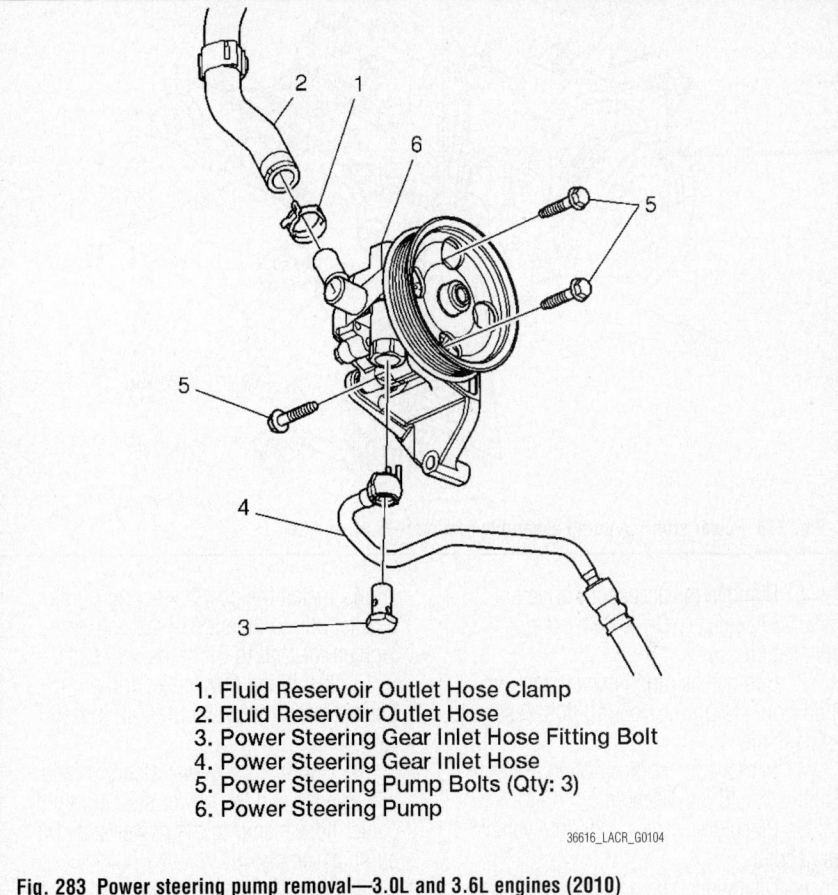

1. Fluid Reservoir Outlet Hose Clamp
2. Fluid Reservoir Outlet Hose
3. Power Steering Gear Inlet Hose Fitting Bolt
4. Power Steering Gear Inlet Hose
5. Power Steering Pump Bolts (Qty: 3)
6. Power Steering Pump

36616_LACR_G0104

Fig. 283 Power steering pump removal—3.0L and 3.6L engines (2010)

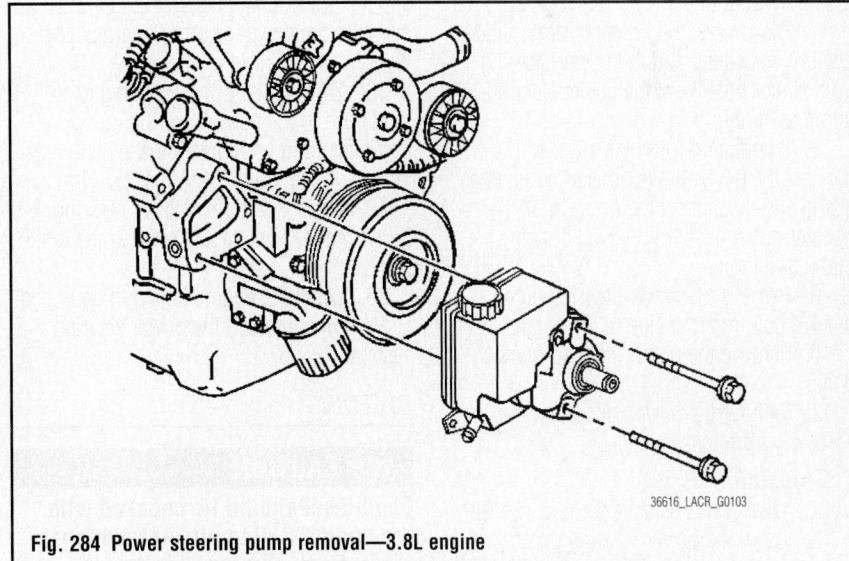

36616_LACR_G0103

Fig. 284 Power steering pump removal—3.8L engine

16. Install the harness connector to the power steering pump.

17. Install the accessory drive belt. Refer to Accessory Drive Belts, removal & installation.

18. Fill the power steering system with fluid.

19. Bleed the power steering system. Refer to Bleeding.

20. Operate the power steering system and inspect for power steering system leaks.

5.3L Engine

See Figure 285.

1. Before servicing the vehicle, refer to the Precautions Section.

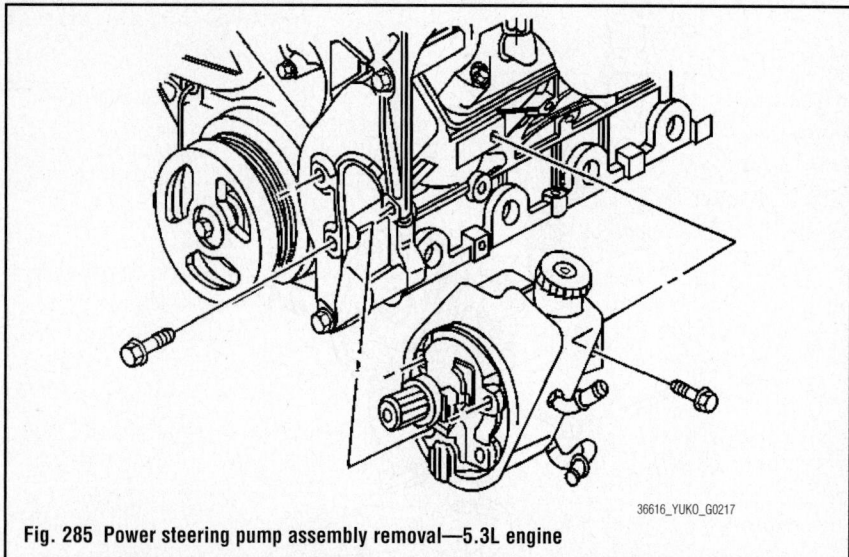

Fig. 285 Power steering pump assembly removal—5.3L engine

36616_YUKO_G0217

2. Remove the accessory drive belt. Refer to Accessory Drive Belts, removal & installation.

3. Remove as much power steering fluid from the power steering fluid reservoir as possible.

4. Remove the engine shield. Refer to Engine Shield Replacement.

5. Place drain pans under the vehicle as needed.

6. Disconnect the power steering gear inlet hose from the power steering pump assembly from underneath the vehicle.

7. Disconnect the power steering fluid cooler hose clamp and the power steering fluid cooler hose from the power steering pump assembly.

8. If equipped with hydro-boost, disconnect the power brake booster outlet hose clamp and disconnect the power brake booster outlet hose from power steering pump assembly.

9. Remove the power steering pump bracket bolt from the side of the engine.

10. Remove the power steering pump bolts.

11. Remove the power steering pump assembly from the vehicle.

To install:

12. Install all transferable parts, as needed.

13. Install the power steering pump assembly to the vehicle.

➡ **Start all the bolts by hand before finalizing each torque.**

14. Install the power steering pump bracket bolt to the side of the engine. Tighten the bolt to 37 ft. lbs. (50 Nm).

15. Install the power steering pump bolts. Tighten the bolts to 37 ft. lbs. (50 Nm).

16. Connect the power steering fluid cooler hose and the power steering fluid cooler hose clamp to the power steering pump assembly.

17. If equipped with hydro-boost, connect the power brake booster outlet hose and the power brake booster outlet hose clamp to the power steering pump assembly.

18. Connect the power steering gear inlet hose to the power steering pump assembly from underneath the vehicle. Tighten the fitting to 24 ft. lbs. (32 Nm).

19. Clean any excess power steering fluid from the vehicle and remove the drain pans.

20. Install the engine shield, if equipped.

21. Fill and bleed the power steering system.

BLEEDING

✳✳ CAUTION

Fluid level should be checked with the engine OFF to prevent personal injury from moving parts and to assure an accurate fluid level reading.

✳✳ WARNING

If the air is not purged from the power steering system correctly, pump failure could result.

Use clean, new power steering fluid type only. Hoses touching the frame, body, or engine may cause system noise. Verify that the hoses do not touch any other part of the vehicle.

Loose connections may not leak, but could allow air into the steering system. Verify that all hose connections are tight.

Power steering fluid level must be maintained throughout bleed procedure.

1. Before servicing the vehicle, refer to the Precautions Section.

2. Fill the pump reservoir with fluid to the minimum system level, FULL COLD level, or the middle of the hash mark on the cap stick fluid level indicator.

3. With hydro-boost only, the oil level will appear falsely high if the hydro-boost accumulator is not fully charged. Do not apply the brake pedal with the engine OFF. This will discharge the hydro-boost accumulator.

4. If equipped with hydro-boost, fully charge the hydro-boost accumulator using the following procedure:
   a. Start the engine.
   b. Firmly apply the brake pedal 10–15 times.
   c. Turn the engine OFF.

5. Raise the vehicle until the front wheels are off the ground.

6. With the key ON and engine OFF, turn the steering wheel from stop-to-stop 12 times.

7. Vehicles equipped with hydro-boost systems, or longer length power steering hoses, may require turns up to 15–20 stop-to-stops.

8. Verify the power steering fluid level per operating specification.

9. Start the engine.

10. Rotate the steering wheel from left to right. Check for sign of cavitation or fluid aeration (pump noise/whining).

11. Verify the fluid level. Repeat the bleed procedure, if necessary.

SUSPENSION **FRONT SUSPENSION**

CONTROL LINKS

REMOVAL & INSTALLATION

See Figure 286.

1. Before servicing the vehicle, refer to the Precautions Section.
2. Raise and safely support the vehicle.
3. Remove the tire and wheel assembly.
4. Remove the stabilizer control link bolt and nut.
5. Remove the stabilizer control link from the vehicle.

To install:

6. Install the control link into the vehicle.
7. Install the control link bolt and nut. Tighten the nut to 17 ft. lbs. (23 Nm).
8. Install the tire and wheel assembly.
9. Lower the vehicle.

LOWER BALL JOINT

REMOVAL & INSTALLATION

2008–09 Vehicles

See Figures 287 and 288.

1. Before servicing the vehicle, refer to the Precautions Section.
2. Raise and support the vehicle.
3. Remove the tire and wheel.
4. Drill a pilot hole through the rivets attaching the lower ball joint to the lower control arm.
5. Drill the remainder of the rivets.
6. Use a hammer and a chisel in order to remove the remainder of the rivet heads.

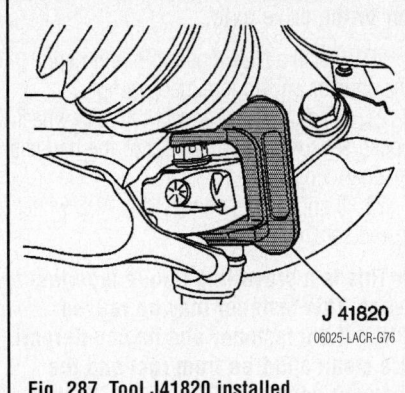

Fig. 287 Tool J41820 installed

06025-LACR-G76

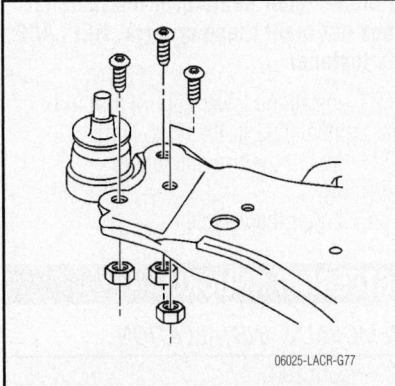

06025-LACR-G77

Fig. 288 Install the NEW ball stud bolts facing down, away from the ball stud

7. Remove the cotter pin from the ball stud.
8. Loosen the ball stud nut.
9. Install a tool such as J 41820 over the ball stud and lower control arm.
10. Rotate the ball stud nut counterclockwise in order to separate the ball stud from the steering knuckle.

11. Remove the tool.
12. Remove the ball stud nut.
13. Remove the ball stud from the lower control arm.

To install:

14. Install the ball stud to the lower control arm.
15. Install the NEW ball stud bolts facing down, away from the ball stud.
16. Install the NEW ball stud nuts. Tighten the NEW ball stud nuts to 50 ft. lbs. (68 Nm).
17. Install the ball stud to the steering knuckle.
18. Install the ball stud castle nut. Tighten the nut to 15 ft. lbs. (20 Nm), plus an additional 120°.
19. Install a new cotter pin and bend the ends.
20. Install the tire and wheels.
21. Lower the vehicle.
22. Check the wheel alignment.

2010 Vehicles

The ball joint is an integral part of the control arm, if defective, replace the control arm. Refer to Lower Control Arm, removal & installation.

LOWER CONTROL ARM

REMOVAL & INSTALLATION

See Figure 289.

Special Tool:

• J 41820: Ball Joint/Stud Separator
1. Before servicing the vehicle, refer to the Precautions Section.

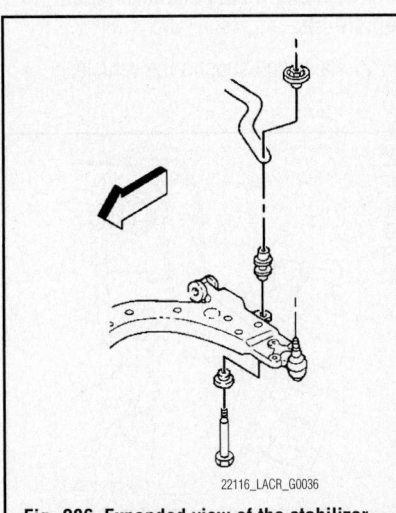

22116_LACR_G0036

Fig. 286 Expanded view of the stabilizer control link components

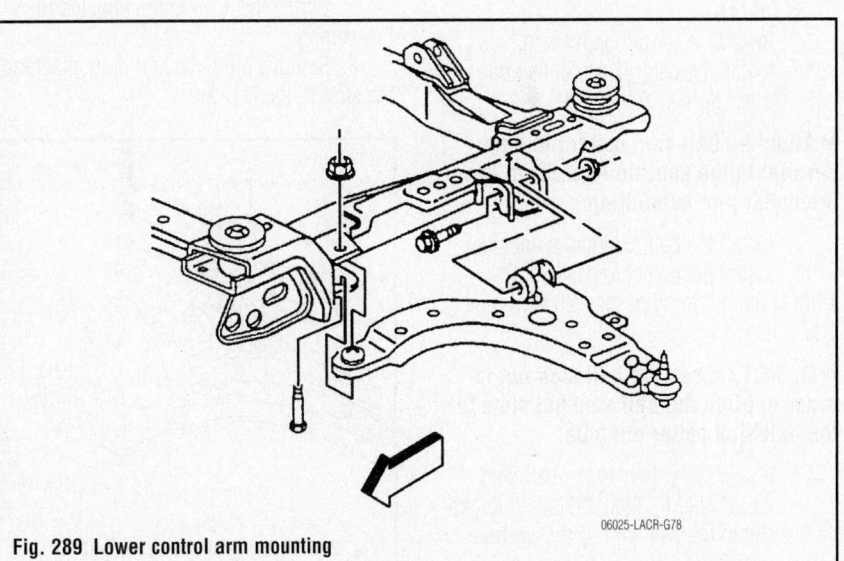

06025-LACR-G78

Fig. 289 Lower control arm mounting

✳✳ WARNING

Use only the recommended tools for separating the ball joint from the knuckle. Do NOT hammer or pry the ball joint from the knuckle. Failure to use the recommended tools may cause damage to the ball joint and seal.

➡Use the ignition key in order to unlock the steering column.

2. Turn the steering wheel in order to move the front of the applicable wheel to the outboard most position.

➡Use ONLY a frame-contact type vehicle lift or a floor jack at the recommended lift points. Do NOT use a suspension-contact type vehicle lift. Do NOT lift the vehicle by the lower control arms.

3. Raise and support the vehicle.
4. Remove the tire and wheel assembly.
5. If applicable, disconnect the ABS wheel speed sensor connector.
6. If applicable, disconnect the ABS wheel speed sensor jumper harness from the harness retainer clips.
7. Remove the cotter pin from the ball stud.
8. Loosen the ball stud nut.
9. Install tool J 41820 over the ball stud and lower control arm.
10. Rotate the ball stud nut counterclockwise in order to separate the ball stud from the steering knuckle.
11. Remove the tool.
12. Remove the ball stud nut.
13. Remove the lower control arm bolts and nuts.
14. Remove the lower control arm.

To install:

15. Install the lower control arm.
16. Install the control arm bolts and nuts. Do not tighten at this time.

➡Align the ball stud cotter pin hole parallel to the knuckle in order to ease the cotter pin installation.

17. Install the ball stud to the knuckle.
18. Install the ball stud castle nut. Tighten the nut to 15 ft. lbs. (20 Nm) plus 120°.

➡Do NOT loosen the ball stud nut in order to align the ball stud nut slots to the ball stud cotter pin hole.

19. If necessary, tighten the ball stud castle nut in order to align the ball stud castle nut slot to the ball stud cotter pin hole.

➡If applicable, ensure that the cotter pin ends do NOT contact the ABS wheel speed sensor, the ABS sensor connector or the drive axle.

20. Install a NEW cotter pin and bend the ends as shown in either example.
21. If applicable, connect the ABS wheel speed sensor jumper harness to the harness retainer clips.
22. If applicable, connect the ABS wheel speed sensor connector.

➡This is a prevailing torque type fastener. This fastener may be reused ONLY if the fastener and its counterpart are clean and free from rust and the fastener develops 27 inch lbs. (3 Nm) of torque against its counterpart prior to the fastener seating. If the fastener does not meet these criteria, REPLACE the fastener.

23. Install the lower control arm nuts and tighten to 92 ft. lbs. (125 Nm).
24. Install the tire and wheel assembly.
25. Lower the vehicle.

STEERING KNUCKLE

REMOVAL & INSTALLATION

See Figure 290.

1. Before servicing the vehicle, refer to the Precautions Section.
2. Raise and support the vehicle.
3. Remove the bearing/hub assembly. Refer to Wheel Hub and Bearing (sealed unit), removal & installation.
4. Disconnect the front lower control arm ball stud.
5. Disconnect the outer tie rod end from the steering knuckle.
6. Scribe the strut to the knuckle for reassembly.
7. Remove the bolts and nuts attaching the strut to the knuckle.

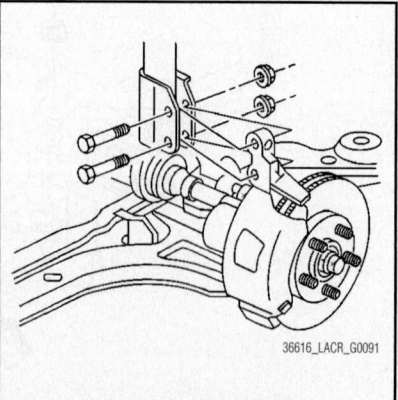

Fig. 290 Steering knuckle removal

8. Remove the steering knuckle from the vehicle.

To install:

9. Install the steering knuckle to the vehicle.
10. Install the through bolts and nuts attaching the strut to the knuckle. Tighten the through bolts and nuts to 89 ft. lbs. (120 Nm).

➡Align the matchmarks of strut-to-steering knuckle scribed during removal.

11. Connect the outer tie rod to the steering knuckle.
12. Connect the front lower control arm ball stud to the knuckle.
13. Install the front wheel halfshaft bearing. Refer to Wheel Hub and Bearing (sealed unit), removal & installation.
14. Lower the vehicle.
15. Inspect the front wheel alignment and adjust if necessary.

STRUT

REMOVAL & INSTALLATION

See Figures 291 and 292.

✳✳ WARNING

Care should be taken to avoid chipping or scratching the coating when handling the suspension coil spring. Damage to the coating can cause premature failure.

1. Before servicing the vehicle, refer to the Precautions Section.

➡Lift the vehicle using ONLY a frame-contact vehicle lift. Do NOT lift the vehicle using a suspension-contact vehicle lift.

2. Raise and support the vehicle.

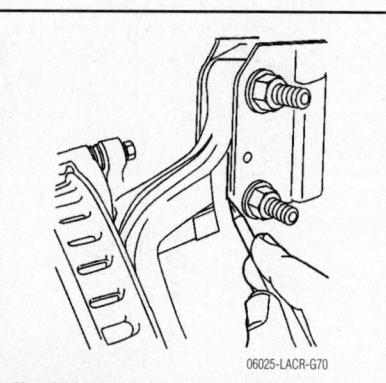

Fig. 291 Matchmark the strut to the knuckle

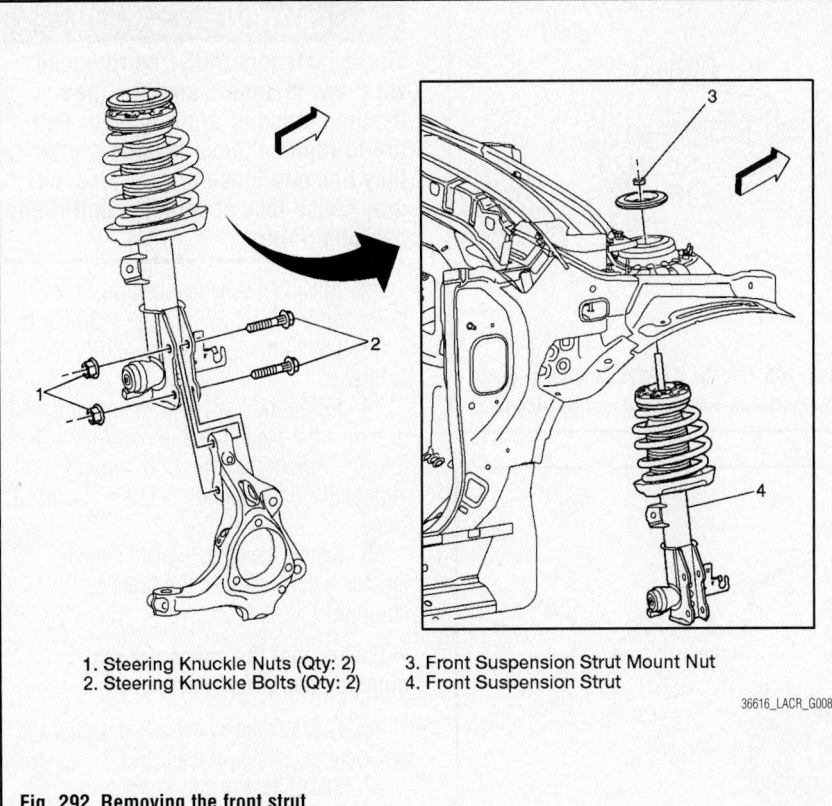

1. Steering Knuckle Nuts (Qty: 2)
2. Steering Knuckle Bolts (Qty: 2)
3. Front Suspension Strut Mount Nut
4. Front Suspension Strut

36616_LACR_G0089

Fig. 292 Removing the front strut

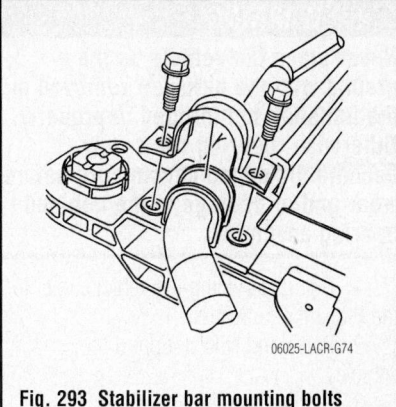

06025-LACR-G74

Fig. 293 Stabilizer bar mounting bolts

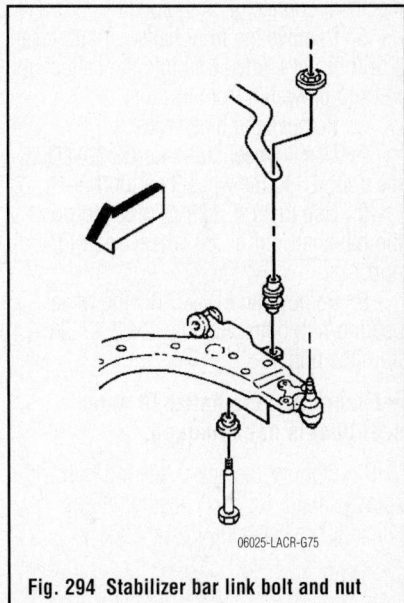

06025-LACR-G75

Fig. 294 Stabilizer bar link bolt and nut

3. Remove the tire and wheel assembly.

4. Support the lower control arm with a suitable jack stand.

5. Disconnect the wheel speed sensor electrical connector at the wheel speed sensor bracket.

6. Matchmark the strut to the knuckle.

7. Remove the stabilizer shaft link from the front strut. Refer to Control Links, removal & installation.

8. Remove the front strut nuts from the bolts.

9. Remove the wheel speed sensor bracket from the strut.

10. Remove the brake hose, connector, and clip from the strut.

11. Remove the strut-to-steering knuckle nuts and bolts.

12. Separate the front strut from the knuckle.

13. Remove the upper strut nut from the strut.

14. Remove the front strut assembly from the vehicle.

To install:

15. Install the front strut assembly.

16. Install the strut upper mounting nut and tighten to 33 ft. lbs. (45 Nm).

17. Install the strut lower bolts and nuts.

18. Align the strut to the marks on the knuckle. Tighten the strut lower bolts/nuts to 63 ft. lbs. (85 Nm), plus 60°.

19. Reconnect the wheel speed sensor electrical connector at the wheel speed sensor bracket.

20. Install the brake hose, connector, and clip to the strut.

21. Install the stabilizer shaft link. Refer to Control Links, removal & installation.

22. Remove the support from the lower control arm.

23. Install the front tire and wheel assembly.

24. Lower the vehicle.

25. Check the front end alignment specifications.

STABILIZER BAR

REMOVAL & INSTALLATION

See Figures 293 and 294.

1. Before servicing the vehicle, refer to the Precautions Section.

2. Raise and support the vehicle.

3. Remove the tire and wheel assembly.

4. Remove the left and right side stabilizer bar insulator clamp bolts.

5. Remove the left and right side stabilizer bar insulator clamp.

6. Remove the left and right side stabilizer bar insulators from the stabilizer bar.

7. Remove the stabilizer bar control link bolt and nut.

8. Remove the stabilizer bar from the vehicle.

To install:

9. Install the stabilizer bar into the vehicle.

10. Install the control link bolt and nut. Tighten the control link nut to 17 ft. lbs. (23 Nm).

11. Install the left and right side stabilizer bar insulators to the stabilizer bar.

12. Install the left and right side stabilizer bar insulator clamps.

13. Install the left and right side stabilizer bar insulator clamp bolts. Tighten the bolts to 31 ft. lbs. (42 Nm).

14. Install the tire and wheel assembly.

15. Lower the vehicle.

WHEEL HUB & BEARING

REMOVAL & INSTALLATION

See Figures 295 and 296.

Special Tool:
• J 42129: Wheel Hub Remover

Never place the vehicle on the ground with the halfshaft removed or the halfshaft nut torqued improperly. Otherwise, bearing seals may become dislodged causing premature wear and/or damage to the hub and bearing assembly.

1. Before servicing the vehicle, refer to the Precautions Section.

2. Raise and safely support the vehicle.

3. Remove the tire and wheel.

4. Disconnect the wheel speed sensor electrical connector, if equipped.

5. Remove the front halfshaft nut. Insert a drift or flat-bladed tool into the caliper and rotor to prevent it from turning.

6. Remove the brake rotor.

7. Use 3 wheel nuts in order to attach the J 42129 to the wheel bearing/hub.

8. Use the J 42129 in order to push the halfshaft out of the wheel bearing/hub.

9. Remove and DISCARD the wheel bearing/hub bolts. Remove the J 42129 from the hub.

➡ **Ensure that the halfshaft outer seal/boot is not damaged.**

10. Remove the wheel bearing/hub and splash shield. Note the position of the shield for reinstallation.

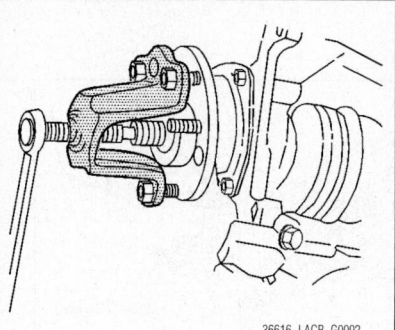

Fig. 295 Use the J 42129 in order to push the halfshaft out of the wheel bearing/hub

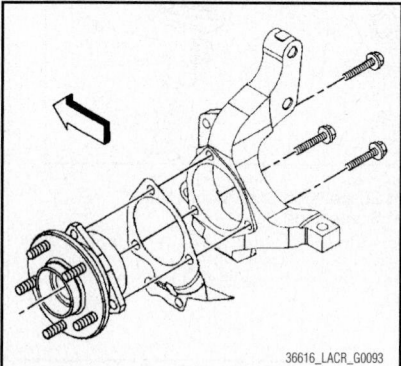

Fig. 296 Removing the wheel hub and bearing

To install:

11. Install the wheel bearing/hub with the splash shield.

These fasteners MUST be replaced with new fasteners anytime they become loose or are removed. Failure to replace these fasteners after they become loose or are removed may cause loss of vehicle control and personal injury.

12. Install NEW wheel bearing/hub bolts and tighten to 96 ft. lbs. (130 Nm).

13. Install the brake rotor and caliper.

14. Install the front halfshaft nut. Insert a drift on a flat-bladed tool into caliper and rotor to prevent the rotor from turning. Tighten the halfshaft nut to 118 ft. lbs. (160 Nm).

15. Install the wheel speed sensor electrical connector to the bracket, if equipped.

➡ **Ensure that the connector clip engages the bracket properly.**

16. Connect the wheel speed sensor electrical connector, if equipped.

17. Install the tire and wheel.

18. Lower the vehicle.

ADJUSTMENT

The wheel bearings are sealed at the factory and do not require any adjustment or maintenance.

SUSPENSION

COIL SPRING

REMOVAL & INSTALLATION

AWD Vehicles

See Figures 297 and 298.

To prevent personal injury and/or component damage, use the proper tools to support the lower control arm when removing the coil spring. The coil spring is under extreme pressure and can become a projectile should the spring separate from the lower control arm before all of the tension is relieved.

1. Before servicing the vehicle, refer to the Precautions Section.

2. Raise and support the vehicle.

3. Remove the rear tire and wheel.

4. Remove the rear stabilizer shaft link from the lower control arm. Refer to Stabilizer Shaft Control Links, removal & installation.

5. Remove the rear brake caliper and move it to one side. Refer to Brake Caliper, removal & installation.

6. Remove the rear wheel bearing and hub. Refer to Wheel Hub and Bearing (sealed unit), removal & installation.

7. Support the lower control arm with a suitable jack stand.

8. Remove the bolt from the adjust link to the rear wheel hub bracket.

9. Remove the bolt from the shock absorber to the rear wheel hub bracket.

10. Slowly lower the support from the rear suspension.

11. Remove the rear spring from the vehicle.

REAR SUSPENSION

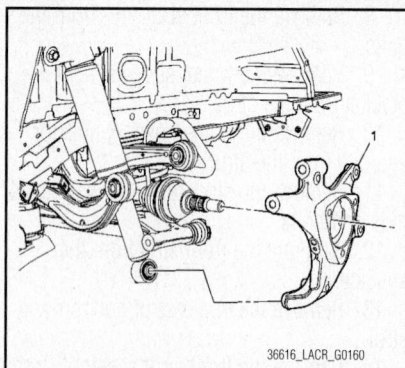

Fig. 297 Removing the rear wheel hub bracket (1)—AWD vehicles

To install:

12. Position the rear spring into the vehicle with the upper and lower spring insulators.

13. Support the lower control arm with a suitable jack stand.

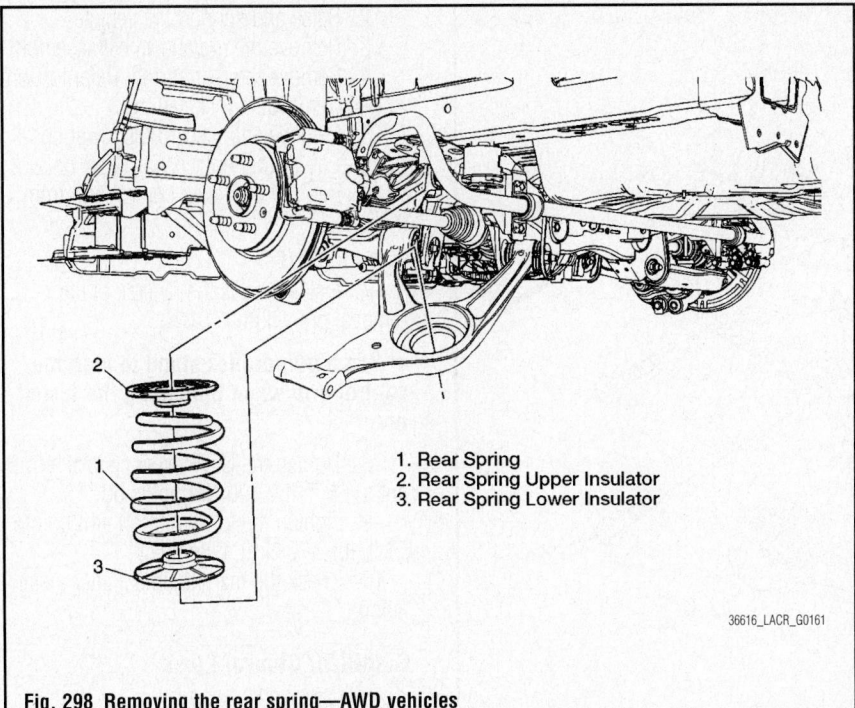

1. Rear Spring
2. Rear Spring Upper Insulator
3. Rear Spring Lower Insulator

36616_LACR_G0161

Fig. 298 Removing the rear spring—AWD vehicles

14. Raise the lower control arm into place with a suitable jack stand.
15. Install the shock absorber. Refer to Shock Absorber, removal & installation.
16. Install the rear wheel hub bracket, wheel bearing, and hub. Refer to Wheel Hub and Bearing (sealed unit), removal & installation.
17. Install the rear brake caliper. Refer to Brake Caliper, removal & installation.
18. Install the rear stabilizer shaft link to the lower control arm. Refer to Stabilizer Shaft Control Links, removal & installation.
19. Install the rear tire and wheel.
20. Lower the vehicle.

FWD Vehicles

See Figure 299.

> **✳✳ CAUTION**
>
> **To prevent personal injury and/or component damage, use the proper tools to support the lower control arm when removing the coil spring. The coil spring is under extreme pressure and can become a projectile should the spring separate from the lower control arm before all of the tension is relieved.**

1. Before servicing the vehicle, refer to the Precautions Section.
2. Raise and support the vehicle.
3. Remove the rear tire and wheel.
4. Remove the rear brake caliper and move it to one side. Refer to Brake Caliper, removal & installation.
5. Support the lower control arm with a suitable jack stand.
6. Disconnect the lower control arm from the rear wheel hub bracket. Refer to Lower Control Arm, removal & installation.
7. Remove the bolt from the shock absorber to the rear wheel hub bracket.

8. Slowly lower the support from the rear suspension.
9. Remove the rear spring from the vehicle.

To install:

10. Position the rear spring into the vehicle with the upper and lower spring insulators.
11. Raise the lower control arm into place with a suitable jack stand.
12. Install the shock absorber. Refer to Shock Absorber, removal & installation.
13. Install the rear wheel bearing, and hub. Refer to Wheel Hub and Bearing (sealed unit), removal & installation.
14. Install the rear brake caliper. Refer to Brake Caliper, removal & installation.
15. Install the rear tire and wheel.
16. Lower the vehicle.

CONTROL ARMS/LINKS

REMOVAL & INSTALLATION

Lower Control Arm

AWD Vehicles

See Figure 300.

1. Before servicing the vehicle, refer to the Precautions Section.
2. Raise and support the vehicle.
3. Remove the tire and wheel assembly.
4. Remove the rear spring. Refer to Coil Spring, removal & installation.

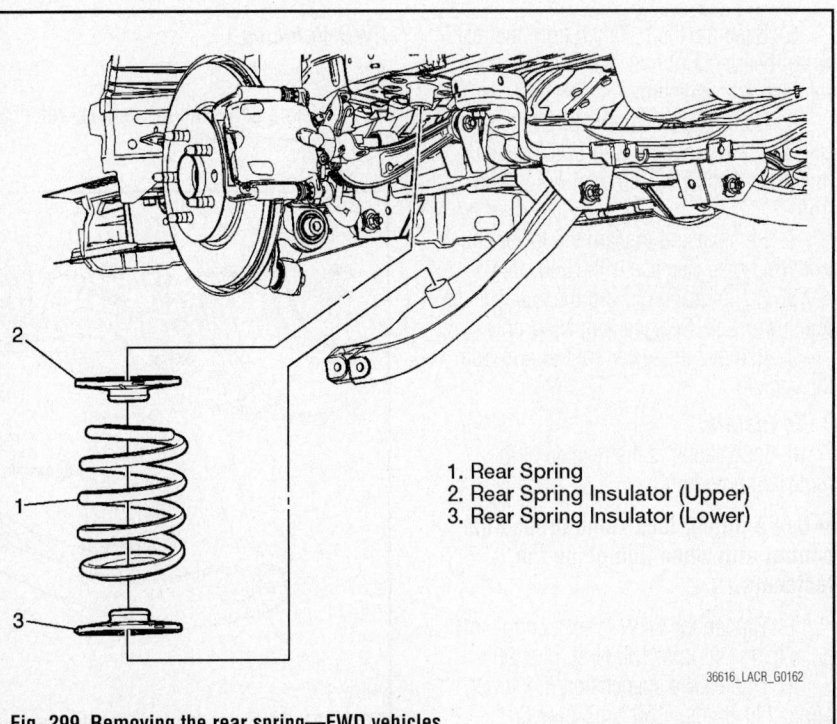

1. Rear Spring
2. Rear Spring Insulator (Upper)
3. Rear Spring Insulator (Lower)

36616_LACR_G0162

Fig. 299 Removing the rear spring—FWD vehicles

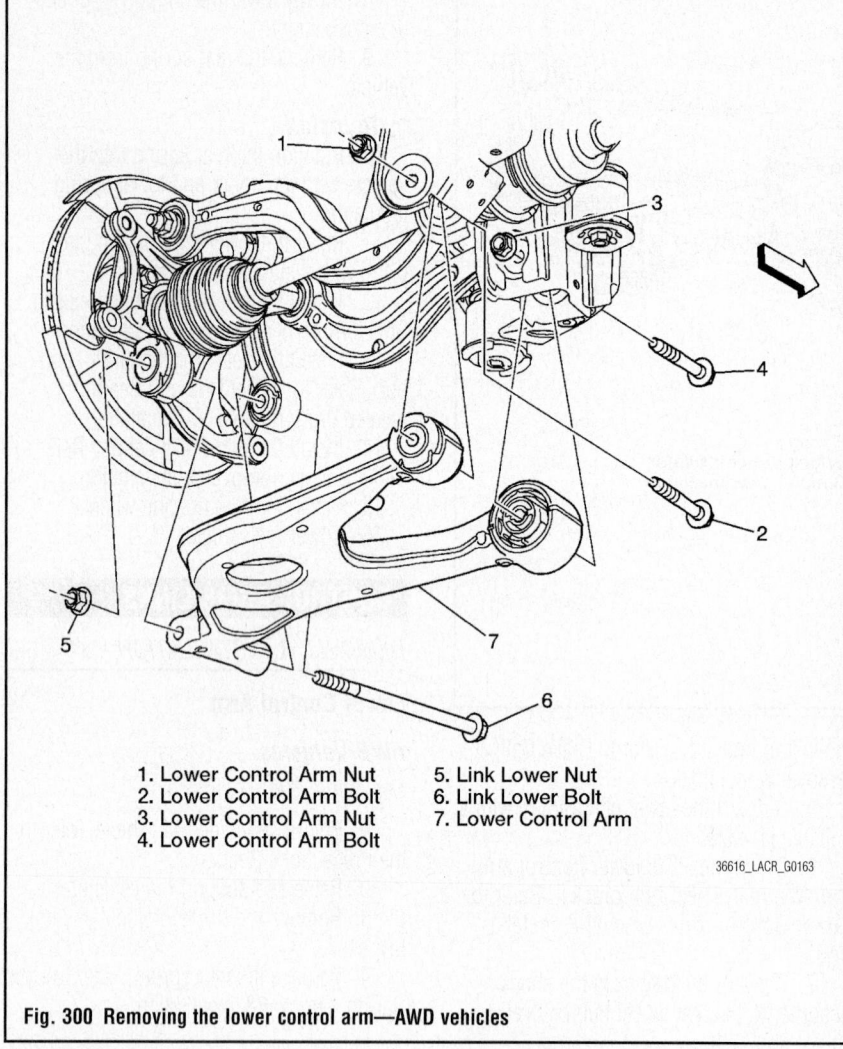

1. Lower Control Arm Nut
2. Lower Control Arm Bolt
3. Lower Control Arm Nut
4. Lower Control Arm Bolt
5. Link Lower Nut
6. Link Lower Bolt
7. Lower Control Arm

36616_LACR_G0163

Fig. 300 Removing the lower control arm—AWD vehicles

5. Separate the halfshaft from the rear wheel bearing and hub. Refer to Halfshafts, removal & installation.

6. Remove the shock absorber lower bolt at the rear wheel hub bracket. Refer to Shock Absorber, removal & installation.

7. Remove and discard the lower control arm bolts. Replace with NEW only.

8. Remove and discard the suspension link lower bolt. Replace with NEW only.

9. Remove the lower control arm from the vehicle.

To install:

10. Installation is the reverse of the removal procedure.

➡**Use a proper jack stand to load the control arm when tightening the fasteners.**

11. Tighten the NEW lower control arm bolts to 111 ft. lbs. (150 Nm), plus 90°.

12. Tighten the suspension link lower nut to 111 ft. lbs. (150 Nm), plus 60 °.

2. Raise and support the vehicle.

3. Remove the tire and wheel assembly.

4. Remove the rear spring. Refer to Coil Spring, removal & installation.

5. Remove and discard the lower control arm bolt/nut. Replace with NEW only.

6. Remove the lower control arm from the vehicle.

To install:

7. Installation is the reverse of the removal procedure.

➡**Use a proper jack stand to load the control arm when tightening the fasteners.**

8. Tighten the NEW lower control arm nut to 66 ft. lbs. (90 Nm), plus 60°.

9. Tighten the lower control arm bolt to 51 ft. lbs. (70 Nm), plus 90 °.

10. Check the rear alignment after installation.

Stabilizer Control Links

See Figures 302 and 303.

1. Before servicing the vehicle, refer to the Precautions Section.

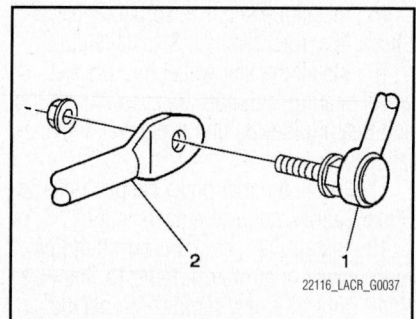

22116_LACR_G0037

Fig. 302 Remove the nut from the control link and the stabilizer shaft

FWD Vehicles

See Figure 301.

1. Before servicing the vehicle, refer to the Precautions Section.

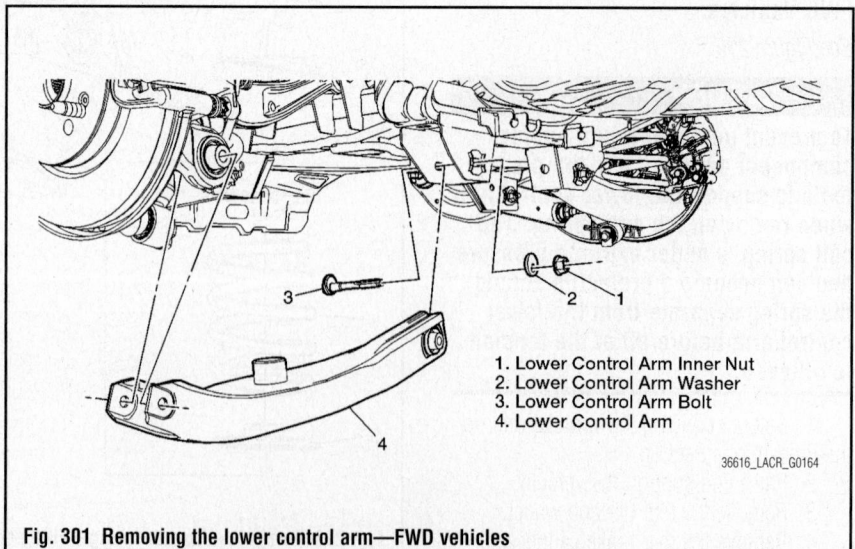

1. Lower Control Arm Inner Nut
2. Lower Control Arm Washer
3. Lower Control Arm Bolt
4. Lower Control Arm

36616_LACR_G0164

Fig. 301 Removing the lower control arm—FWD vehicles

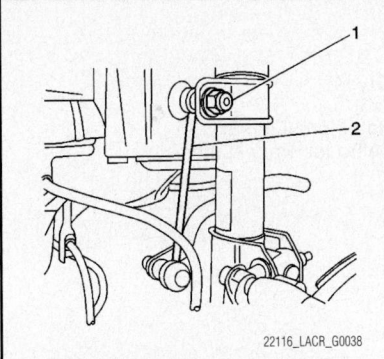

Fig. 303 Remove the nut (1) from the control link (2) and the strut

2. Raise and support the vehicle.

3. Remove the nut from the control link and the stabilizer shaft.

4. Remove the nut from the control link and the strut.

5. Remove the control link from the vehicle.

To install:

6. Install the control link to the vehicle.

7. Connect the control link to the stabilizer shaft.

8. Install the nut to the control link and the stabilizer shaft. Tighten the nut to 37 ft. lbs. (50 Nm).

9. Connect the control link to the strut.

10. Install the nut to the control link and the strut. Tighten the nut to 38 ft. lbs. (52 Nm).

11. Lower the vehicle.

Upper Control Arm

AWD Vehicles

See Figure 304.

1. Before servicing the vehicle, refer to the Precautions Section.

2. Raise and suitably support the vehicle.

3. Remove the rear tire and wheel assembly.

4. Using a proper jack stand, support the lower control arm and the rear wheel bracket.

5. Remove the bolt from the upper control to the lower control arm.

6. Remove the cable harness clips from the control arm.

7. Remove the upper control arm from the vehicle.

To install:

8. Installation is the reverse of the removal procedure.

9. Tighten the upper control arm inner nut to 111 ft. lbs. (150 Nm).

10. Verify the rear wheel alignment.

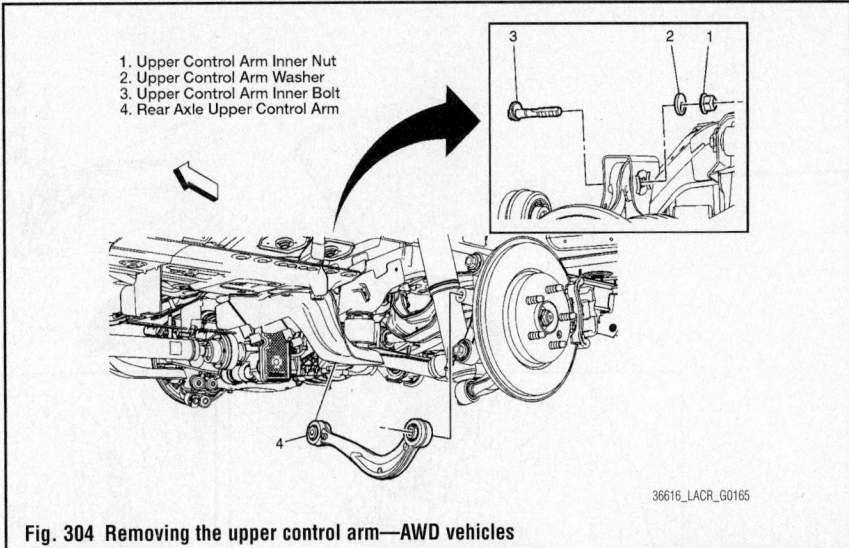

1. Upper Control Arm Inner Nut
2. Upper Control Arm Washer
3. Upper Control Arm Inner Bolt
4. Rear Axle Upper Control Arm

Fig. 304 Removing the upper control arm—AWD vehicles

FWD Vehicles

See Figure 305.

1. Before servicing the vehicle, refer to the Precautions Section.

2. Raise and suitably support the vehicle.

3. Remove the rear tire and wheel assembly.

4. Remove the control arm nuts and bolts.

5. Remove the upper control arm from the vehicle.

To install:

6. Installation is the reverse of the removal procedure.

7. Tighten the upper control arm nut (inboard) to 111 ft. lbs. (150 Nm).

8. Tighten the upper control arm nut (outboard) to 85 ft. lbs. (115 Nm).

9. Verify the rear wheel alignment.

SHOCK ABSORBER

REMOVAL & INSTALLATION

AWD Vehicles

See Figures 306 and 307.

1. Before servicing the vehicle, refer to the Precautions Section.

2. Raise and support the vehicle.

3. Remove the rear tire and wheel assembly.

4. Remove the rear wheelhouse panel liner from the vehicle.

5. Unclip the exhaust shield retainer.

6. Remove the upper body shock absorber bolts.

7. Remove any electrical connectors, if equipped.

8. Remove the lower shock absorber bolt and discard.

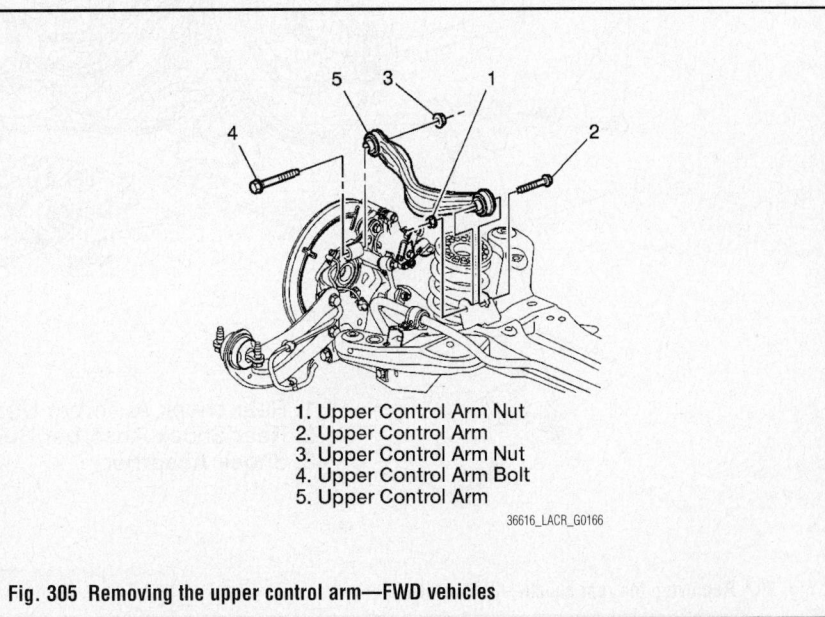

1. Upper Control Arm Nut
2. Upper Control Arm
3. Upper Control Arm Nut
4. Upper Control Arm Bolt
5. Upper Control Arm

Fig. 305 Removing the upper control arm—FWD vehicles

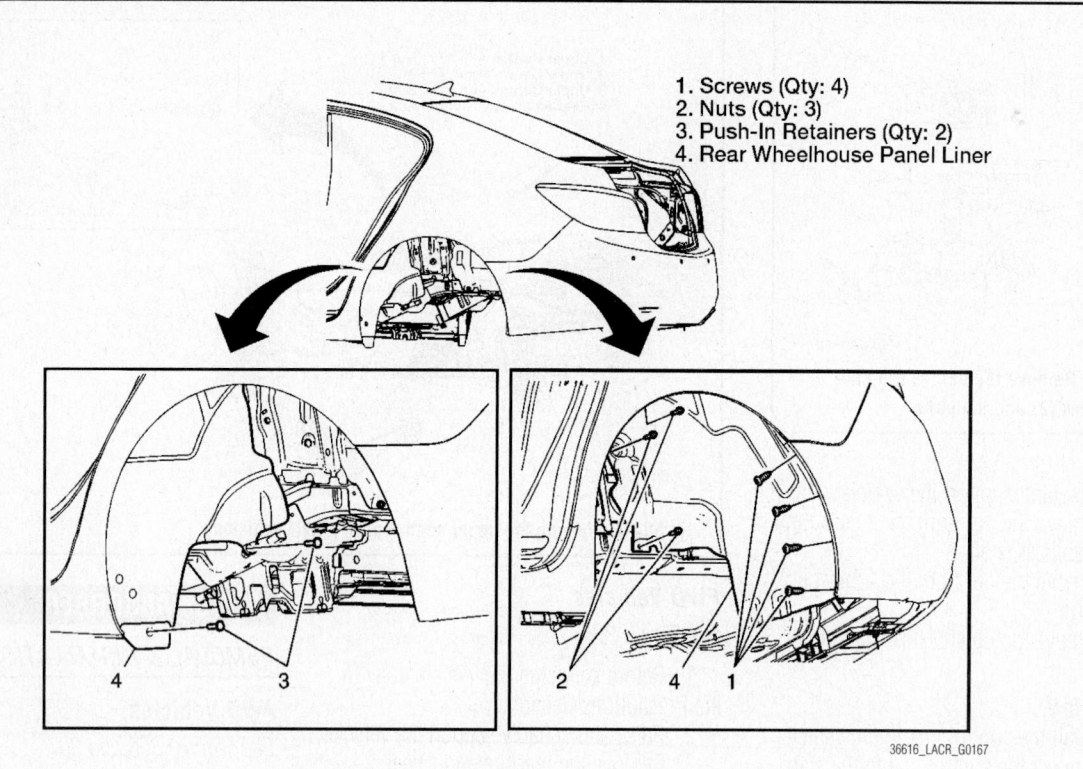

1. Screws (Qty: 4)
2. Nuts (Qty: 3)
3. Push-In Retainers (Qty: 2)
4. Rear Wheelhouse Panel Liner
4
3
2
4
1
36616_LACR_G0167

Fig. 306 Remove the rear wheelhouse panel liner

1
3
2
1. Rear shock Absorber Upper Body Bolts (Qty: 2)
2. Rear Shock Absorber Bolt
3. Shock Absorber
36616_LACR_G0168

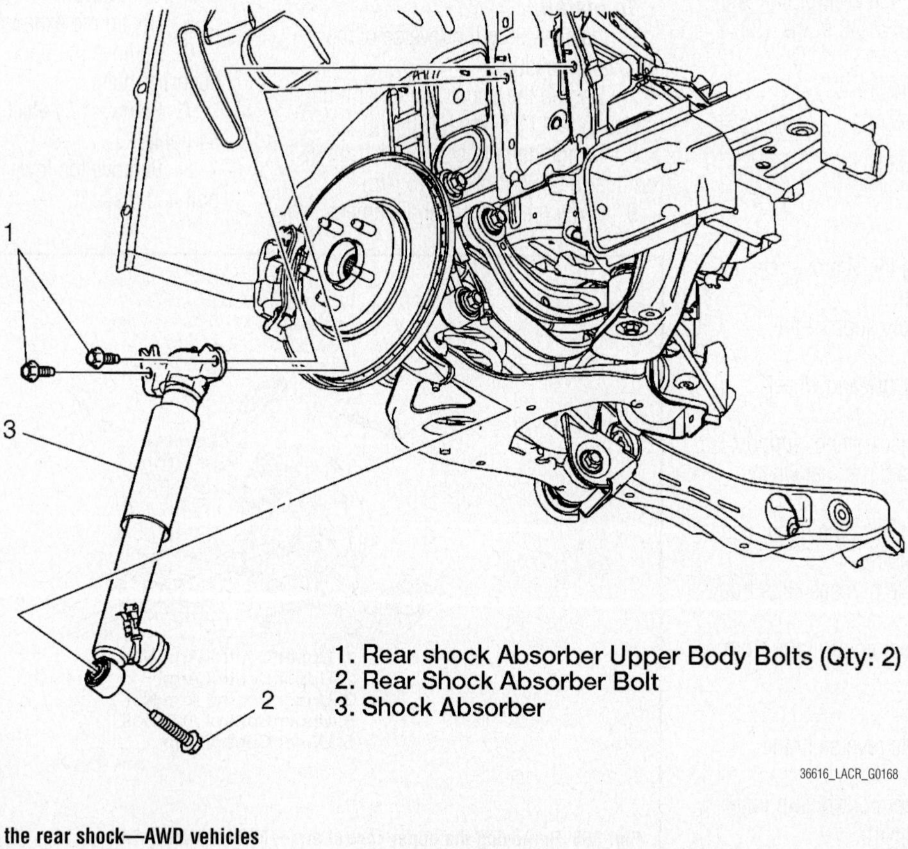

Fig. 307 Removing the rear shock—AWD vehicles

9. Remove the rear shock absorber from the vehicle.

To install:

10. Installation is the reverse of the removal procedure.

11. Tighten a NEW lower shock absorber bolt to 111 ft. lbs. (150 Nm), plus 60°, plus another 15°.

12. Tighten the upper shock absorber bolts to 81 ft. lbs. (110 Nm).

13. Tighten the wheelhouse panel liner screws to 27 inch lbs. (3 Nm).

14. Tighten the wheelhouse panel liner nuts to 15 inch lbs. (2 Nm).

FWD Vehicles

See Figures 306 and 308.

1. Before servicing the vehicle, refer to the Precautions Section.

2. Raise and support the vehicle.

3. Remove the rear tire and wheel assembly.

4. Remove the rear wheelhouse panel liner from the vehicle.

5. Unclip the exhaust shield retainer.

6. Remove the upper body shock absorber bolts.

7. Remove any electrical connectors, if equipped.

8. Remove the lower shock absorber bolt and discard.

9. Remove the rear shock absorber from the vehicle.

To install:

10. Installation is the reverse of the removal procedure.

➡**Apply thread-locker to the bolts.**

11. Tighten the NEW upper body shock absorber bolts to 74 ft. lbs. (100 Nm).

12. Tighten a NEW lower shock absorber bolt to 110 ft. lbs. (150 Nm), plus 70°.

13. Tighten the shock absorber nut to 15 ft. lbs. (20 Nm).

14. Tighten the wheelhouse panel liner screws to 27 inch lbs. (3 Nm).

15. Tighten the wheelhouse panel liner nuts to 15 inch lbs. (2 Nm).

STABILIZER BAR

REMOVAL & INSTALLATION

See Figures 309 and 310.

1. Before servicing the vehicle, refer to the Precautions Section.

2. Raise and support the vehicle.

3. Remove the tires and wheels.

4. Remove the left and right control link lower nuts from the control links.

5. Remove the clamp bolts from the stabilizer bar.

6. Remove the stabilizer bar from the support.

7. Remove the control link nut from the control link and the strut.

To install:

8. Install the stabilizer shaft to the support.

9. Install the stabilizer shaft clamps and bolts. Do not tighten the bolts at this time.

10. Install the right and left control link nuts to the control links. Tighten the control link nuts to 33 ft. lbs. (45 Nm). Tighten the stabilizer shaft insulator bracket nuts to 38 ft. lbs. (51 Nm).

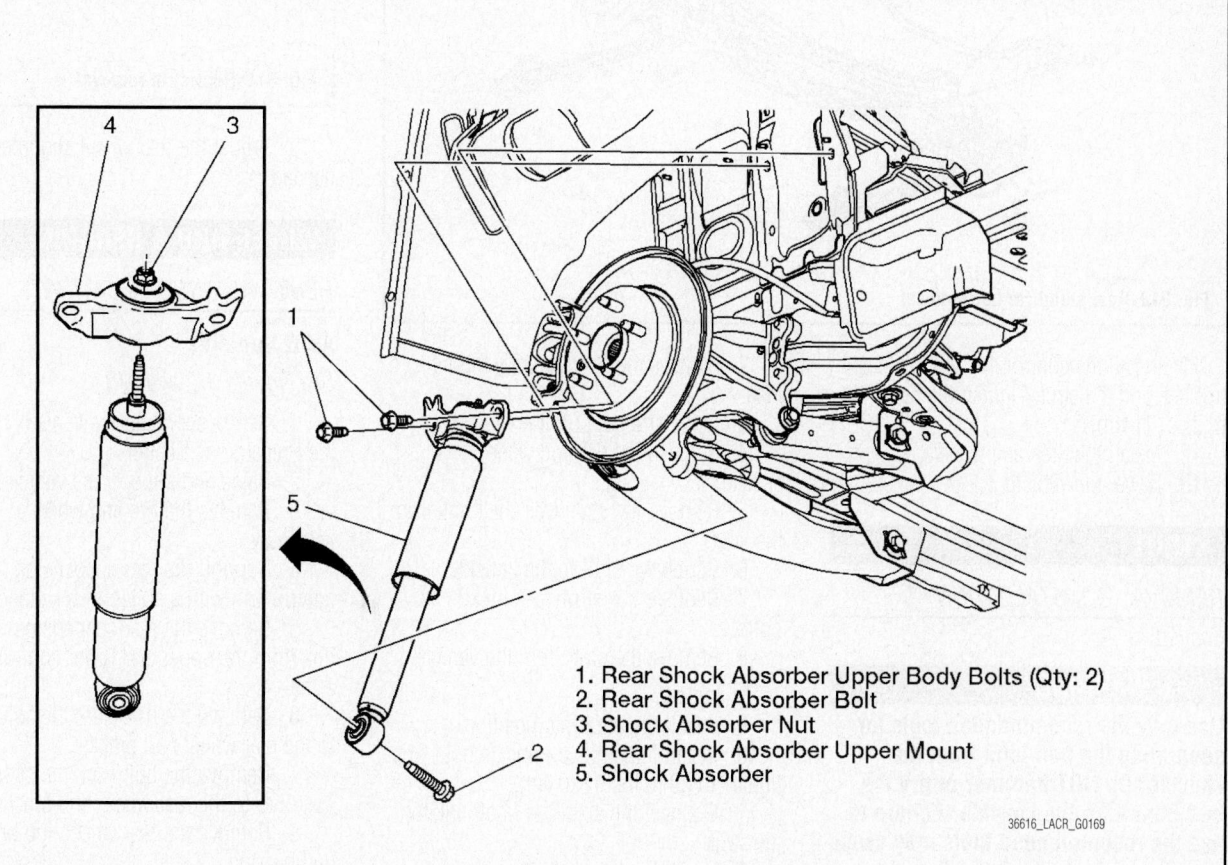

1. Rear Shock Absorber Upper Body Bolts (Qty: 2)
2. Rear Shock Absorber Bolt
3. Shock Absorber Nut
4. Rear Shock Absorber Upper Mount
5. Shock Absorber

36616_LACR_G0169

Fig. 308 Removing the rear shock—FWD vehicles

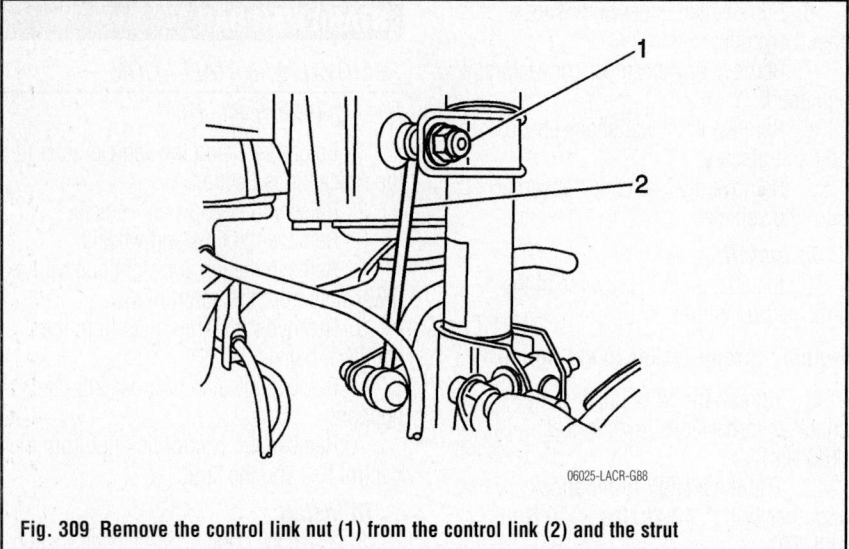

Fig. 309 Remove the control link nut (1) from the control link (2) and the strut

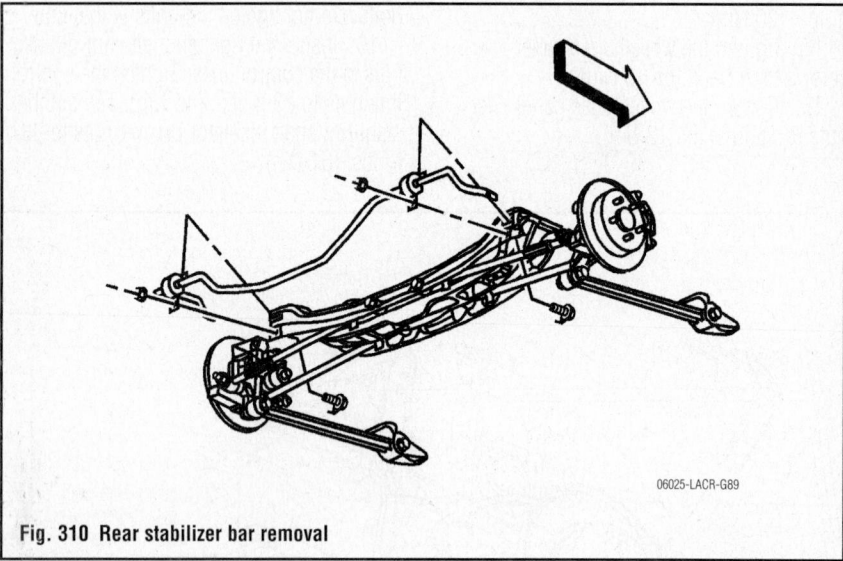

Fig. 310 Rear stabilizer bar removal

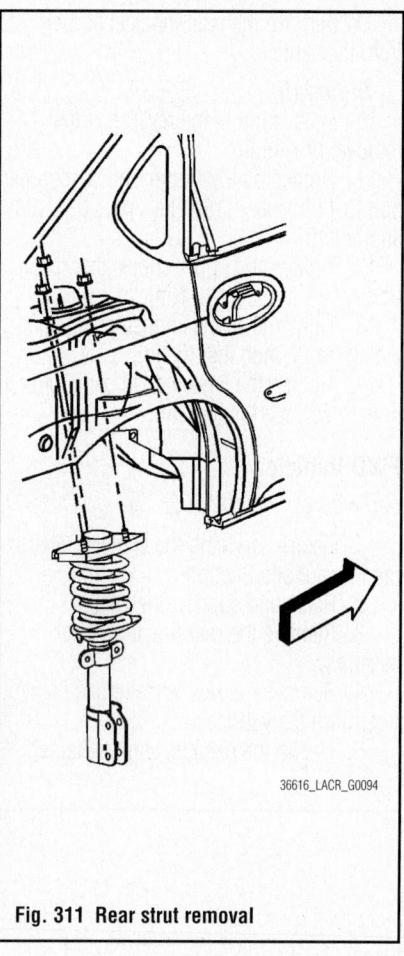

Fig. 311 Rear strut removal

11. Install the control link nut to the control link and the strut. Tighten the nut to 38 ft. lbs. (51 Nm).
12. Install the tires and wheels.
13. Lower the vehicle.

STRUT

REMOVAL & INSTALLATION

See Figure 311.

✳✳ WARNING

Use only the recommended tools for separating the ball joint from the knuckle. Do NOT hammer or pry the ball joint from the knuckle. Failure to use the recommended tools may cause damage to the ball joint and seal.

1. Before servicing the vehicle, refer to the Precautions Section.

2. Remove the strut-to-body mount nuts.
3. Raise and support the vehicle.
4. Remove the tire and wheel assembly.
5. Remove the stabilizer shaft link from the strut.
6. Scribe the strut to the knuckle.
7. Remove the strut-to-knuckle bolts.
8. Remove the strut from the vehicle.

To install:

9. Install the strut into position.
10. Install the strut-to-knuckle bolts and tighten to 89 ft. lbs. (120 Nm).
11. Connect the stabilizer shaft link to the strut.
12. Install the tire and wheel.
13. Install the strut-to-body mount nuts and tighten to 33 ft. lbs. (45 Nm).
14. Lower the vehicle.

15. Adjust the rear wheel alignment as needed.

WHEEL HUB & BEARING

REMOVAL & INSTALLATION

AWD Vehicles

See Figures 312 and 313.

1. Before servicing the vehicle, refer to the Precautions Section.
2. Raise and support the vehicle.
3. Remove the tire and wheel assembly.
4. Support the rear suspension lower control arm with a suitable jack stand.
5. Remove the rear suspension link from the upper and lower control arms.
6. Remove the bolt from the adjust link to the rear wheel hub bracket.
7. Remove the bolt from the shock absorber to the rear wheel hub bracket.
8. Remove the rear wheel hub bracket and bearing.

To install:

9. Installation is the reverse of the removal procedure.

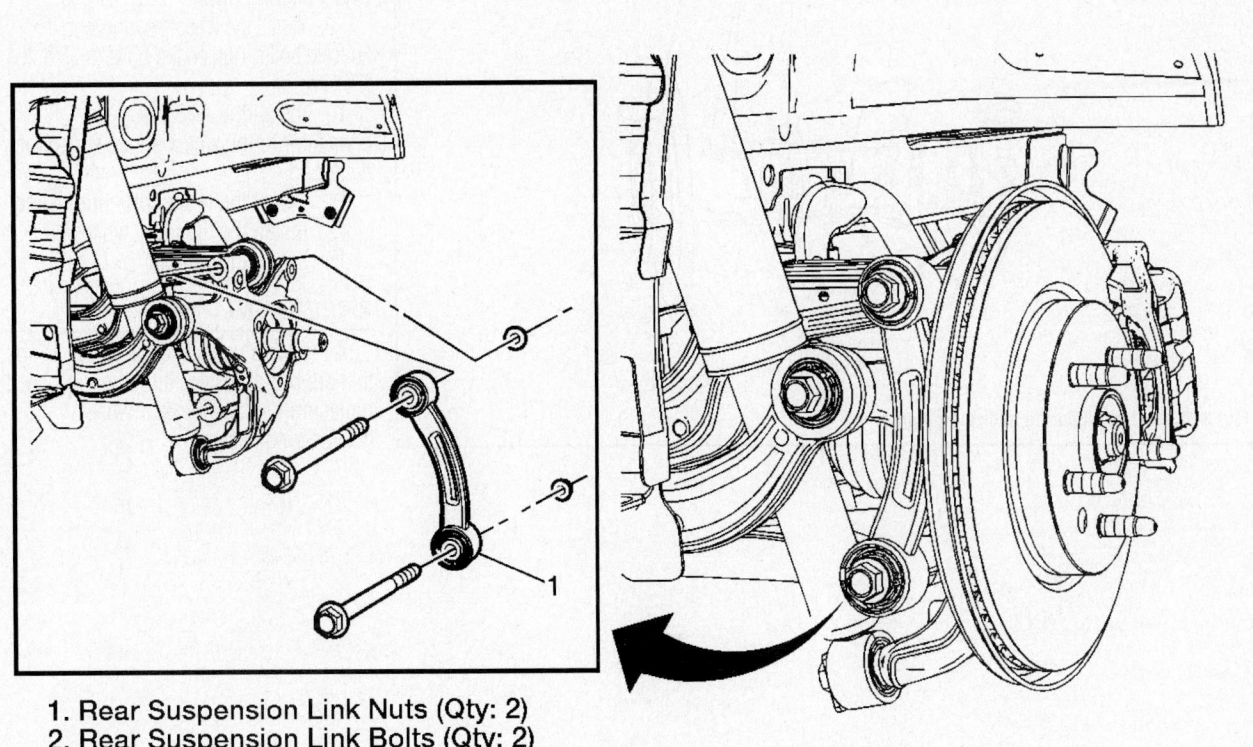

1. Rear Suspension Link Nuts (Qty: 2)
2. Rear Suspension Link Bolts (Qty: 2)
3. Rear Suspension Link

36616_LACR_G0167

Fig. 312 Removing the rear suspension link—AWD vehicles

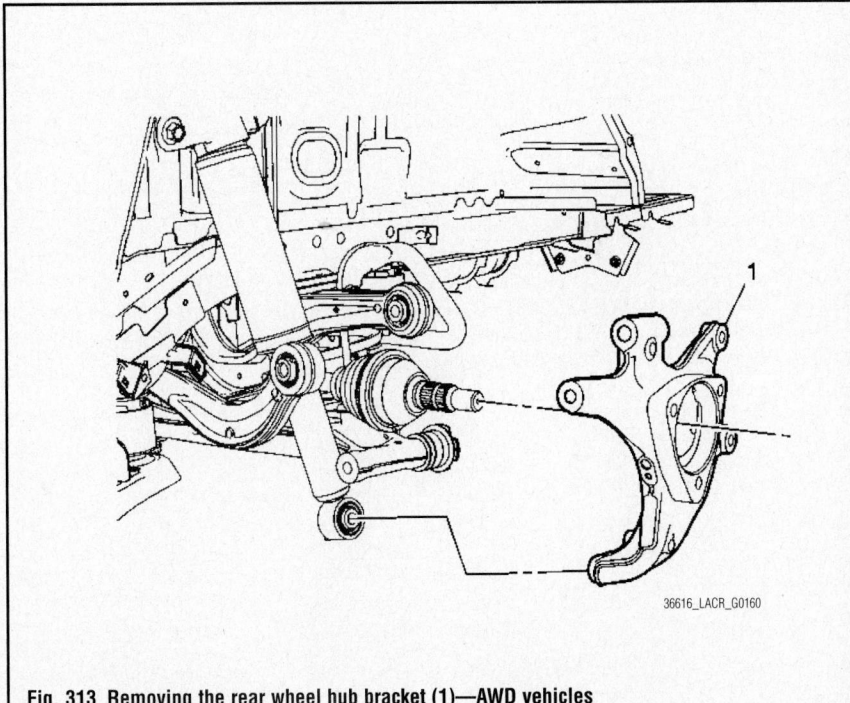

36616_LACR_G0160

Fig. 313 Removing the rear wheel hub bracket (1)—AWD vehicles

10. Tighten the rear suspension link nuts to 85 ft. lbs. (115 Nm), plus 90°.
11. Verify the rear wheel alignment.

FWD Vehicles

See Figure 314.

➡The wheel bearing in the rear wheel hub is integrated into one unit. The hub is non-serviceable. If the hub/bearing is damaged, replace the complete hub and bearing assembly.

1. Before servicing the vehicle, refer to the Precautions Section.
2. Raise and suitably support the vehicle.
3. Remove the tires and wheels.
4. Remove the brake rotor.
5. Remove the ABS electrical connector from the wheel speed sensor, if equipped.
6. Remove the mounting bolts from the rear bearing/hub.
7. Remove the wheel bearing/hub and the backing plate.

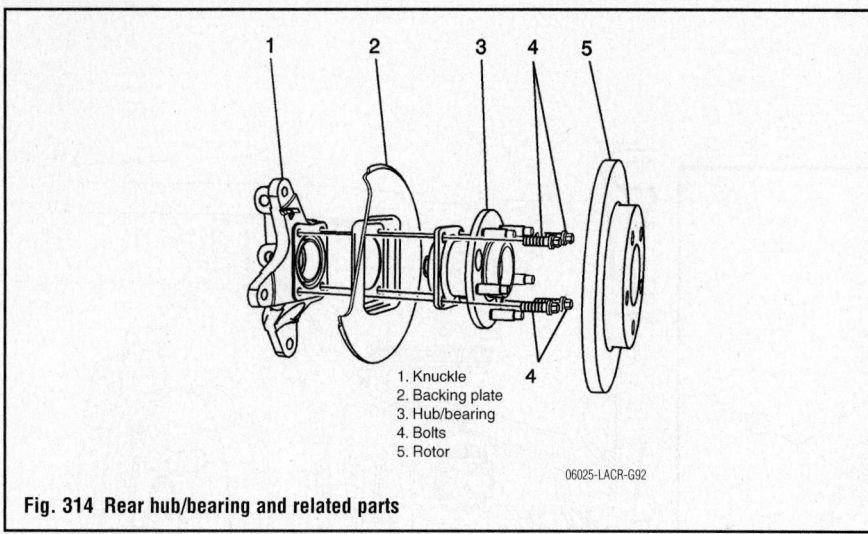

1. Knuckle
2. Backing plate
3. Hub/bearing
4. Bolts
5. Rotor

06025-LACR-G92

Fig. 314 Rear hub/bearing and related parts

To install:

8. Install the backing plate and the wheel bearing hub.

9. Install the wheel bearing/hub to knuckle bolts. Tighten the bolts to 55 ft. lbs. (75 Nm).

10. Install the ABS electrical connector to the wheel speed sensor, if equipped.

11. Install the brake rotor and caliper.

12. Install the tires and wheels.

13. Lower the vehicle.

ADJUSTMENT

All models use sealed wheel bearings that are pre-adjusted. If the bearing needs replacing, replace the rear wheel hub/bearing assembly.

SATURN

Astra

SPECIFICATIONS AND MAINTENANCE CHARTS

ENGINE AND VEHICLE IDENTIFICATION

			Engine						Model Year	
Code ①	Liters (cc)	Cu. In.	Cyl.	Fuel Sys.	Engine Type	Eng. Mfg.		Code ②	Year	
A	1.8 (1796)	109	4	SFI/VVT	DOHC	③		8	2008	
								9	2009	

1: Opel Austria GmbH

SFI/VVT: Sequential Fuel Injection with Variable Valve Timing

① 8th position of VIN

② 10th position of VIN

③ Opel Austria GmbH

36616_ASTR_C0001

GENERAL ENGINE SPECIFICATIONS

All measurements are given in inches.

Year	Model	Engine Displacement Liters	Engine Series VIN	Net Horsepower @ rpm	Net Torque @ rpm (ft. lbs.)	Bore x Stroke (in.)	Com-pression Ratio	Oil Pressure @ rpm
2008	Astra	1.8	1	138@6300	125@3800	3.17x3.47	10.5:1	50-80@1000
2009	Astra	1.8	1	138@6300	125@3800	3.17x3.47	10.5:1	50-80@1000
2010	Astra	1.8	1	138@6300	125@3800	3.17x3.47	10.5:1	50-80@1000

36616_ASTR_C0002

GASOLINE ENGINE TUNE-UP SPECIFICATIONS

Year	Engine Displacement Liters	Engine VIN	Spark Plug Gap (in.)	Ignition Timing (deg) AT	Fuel Pump (psi)	Idle Speed (rpm) AT	Valve Clearance (in.)	
							In.	Ex.
2008	1.8	1	0.035	①	50-60	②	.008-.011	.010-.014
2009	1.8	1	0.035	①	50-60	②	.008-.011	.010-.014
2010	1.8	1	0.035	①	50-60	②	.008-.011	.010-.014

NOTE: The Vehicle Emission Control Information label often reflects specification changes made during production.

The label figures must be used if they differ from those in this chart.

① Ignition timing is preset and cannot be adjusted

② Idle speed is maintained by the PCM

36616_ASTR_C0003

CAPACITIES

Year	Model	Engine Displacement Liters	Engine VIN	Engine Oil with Filter (qts.)	Transaxle (pts.) * A/T	Transaxle (pts.) * M/T	Transfer Case (pts.)	Drive Axle Rear (pts.)	Fuel Tank (gal.)	Cooling System (qts.)
2008	Astra	1.8	1	4.8	15.2	3.4	NA	NA	11.9	①
2009	Astra	1.8	1	4.8	15.2	3.4	NA	NA	11.9	①
2010	Astra	1.8	1	4.8	15.2	3.4	NA	NA	11.9	①

NOTE: All capacities are approximate. Add fluid gradually and check to be sure a proper fluid level is obtained.

NA: Not available

* Dry fill.

① Manual Transaxle: 7.3 Quarts

  Automatic Transaxle: 6.2 Quarts

36616_ASTR_C0004

VALVE SPECIFICATIONS

Year	Engine Displacement Liters	Engine ID/VIN	Seat Angle (deg.)	Face Angle (deg.)	Spring Test Pressure (lbs. @ in.)	Spring Installed Height (in.)	Stem-to-Guide Clearance (in.) Intake	Stem-to-Guide Clearance (in.) Exhaust	Stem Diameter (in.) Intake	Stem Diameter (in.) Exhaust
2008	1.8	T	46	45	NA	1.740	0.0012-0.0024	0.0020-0.0032	0.1951-0.1957	0.1943-0.1949
2009	1.8	T	46	45	NA	1.740	0.0012-0.0024	0.0020-0.0032	0.1951-0.1957	0.1943-0.1949
2010	1.8	T	46	45	NA	1.740	0.0012-0.0024	0.0020-0.0032	0.1951-0.1957	0.1943-0.1949

36616_ASTR_C0007

CAMSHAFT AND BEARING SPECIFICATIONS CHART

All measurements are given in inches.

Year	Engine Displ. Liters	Engine ID/VIN	Journal Dia.	Brg. Oil Clearance	Shaft End-play	Runout	Journal Bore	Lobe Height Intake	Lobe Height Exhaust
2008	1.8	1	NS	NS	NS	NS	NS	0.3267	0.3661
2009	1.8	1	NS	NS	NS	NS	NS	0.3267	0.3661
2010	1.8	1	NS	NS	NS	NS	NS	0.3267	0.3661

NS: Manufacturer does not supply information.

36616_ASTR_C0005

CRANKSHAFT AND CONNECTING ROD SPECIFICATIONS
All measurements are given in inches.

Year	Engine Displacement Liters	Engine VIN	Crankshaft				Connecting Rod		
			Main Brg. Journal Dia.	Main Brg. Oil Clearance	Shaft End-play	Thrust on No.	Journal Diameter	Oil Clearance	Side Clearance
2008	1.8	1	2.1646-2.1649	0.0008-0.0025	0.0039-0.0080	3	NA NA	NA NA	NA NA
2009	1.8	1	2.1646-2.1649	0.0008-0.0025	0.0039-0.0080	3	NA NA	NA NA	NA NA
2010	1.8	1	2.1646-2.1649	0.0008-0.0025	0.0039-0.0080	3	NA NA	NA NA	NA NA

NA: Not Available

36616_ASTR_C0006

PISTON AND RING SPECIFICATIONS
All measurements are given in inches.

Year	Engine Displ. Liters	Engine ID/VIN	Piston Clearance	Ring Gap			Ring Side Clearance		
				Top Compression	Bottom Compression	Oil Control	Top Compression	Bottom Compression	Oil Control
2008	1.8	T	NA	0.008-0.016	0.016-0.024	0.010-0.030	0.0015-0.0031	0.0012-0.0028	0.0012-0.0051
2009	1.8	T	NA	0.008-0.016	0.016-0.024	0.010-0.030	0.0015-0.0031	0.0012-0.0028	0.0012-0.0051
2010	1.8	T	NA	0.008-0.016	0.016-0.024	0.010-0.030	0.0015-0.0031	0.0012-0.0028	0.0012-0.0051

36616_ASTR_C0008

TORQUE SPECIFICATIONS
All readings in ft. lbs.

Year	Engine Displacement Liters	Engine VIN	Cylinder Head Bolts	Main Bearing Bolts	Rod Bearing Bolts	Crankshaft Damper Bolts	Flywheel Bolts	Manifold		Spark Plugs	Oil Pan Drain Plug
								Intake	Exhaust		
2008	1.8	T	①	②	③	④	⑤	15	15	18	18
2009	1.8	T	①	②	③	④	⑤	15	15	18	18
2010	1.8	T	①	②	③	④	⑤	15	15	18	18

① 1st pass: 18 ft. lbs.
   2nd pass: Plus 90 degrees
   3rd pass: Plus 90 degrees
   4th pass: Plus 90 degrees
   5th pass: Plus 45 degrees
② 1st pass: 37 ft. lbs.
   2nd pass: plus 45 degrees
   3rd pass: plus 15 degrees

③ 1st pass: 26 ft. lbs.
   2nd pass: plus 45 degrees
   3rd pass: plus 15 degrees
④ 1st pass: 70 ft. lbs.
   2nd pass: 45 ft. lbs.
   3rd pass: 15 ft. lbs.
⑤ 1st pass: 26 ft. lbs.
   2nd pass: 30 ft. lbs.
   3rd pass: 15 ft. lbs.

36616_ASTR_C0009

WHEEL ALIGNMENT

Year	All Models		Caster Range (+/-Deg.)	Caster Preferred Setting (Deg.)	Camber Range (+/-Deg.)	Camber Preferred Setting (Deg.)	Toe-in (Deg.)
2008	XE/XR	Front	0.75	4.00	0.75	-0.40	0.20+/-0.15
		Rear	NA	NA	0.75	-0.125	0.20+/-0.50
	ZQ8	Front	0.75	2.70	0.75	-0.50	0.20+/-0.15
		Rear	NA	NA	0.75	-1.25	0.15+/-0.50
2009	XE/XR	Front	0.75	4.00	0.75	-0.40	0.20+/-0.15
		Rear	NA	NA	0.75	-0.125	0.20+/-0.50
	ZQ8	Front	0.75	4.00	0.75	-0.50	0.20+/-0.15
		Rear	NA	NA	0.75	-1.25	0.15+/-0.50
2010	XE/XR	Front	0.75	4.00	0.75	-0.40	0.20+/-0.15
		Rear	NA	NA	0.75	-0.125	0.20+/-0.50
	ZQ8	Front	0.75	4.00	0.75	-0.50	0.20+/-0.15
		Rear	NA	NA	0.75	-1.25	0.15+/-0.50

NA: Not Applicable

36616_ASTR_C0010

TIRE, WHEEL AND BALL JOINT SPECIFICATIONS

Year	Model	OEM Tires Standard	OEM Tires Optional	Tire Pressures (psi) Front	Tire Pressures (psi) Rear	Wheel Size	Ball Joint Inspection	Lug Nut Torque (ft. lbs.)
2008	All	P225/45R17	None	①	①	17	②	81
2009	All	P225/45R17	None	①	①	17	②	81
2010	All	P225/45R17	None	①	①	17	②	81

OEM: Original Equipment Manufacturer

PSI: Pounds Per Square Inch

STD: Standard

OPT: Optional

① A tire and loading Information label is attached to the vehicle's center pillar (B-pillar), below the driver's door latch.

② Horizontal and vertical play, unloaded: 0.125 in. max.

36616_ASTR_C0012

BRAKE SPECIFICATIONS

All measurements in inches unless noted

Year	Model		Brake Disc Original Thickness	Brake Disc Minimum Thickness	Brake Disc Maximum Runout	Minimum Lining Thickness	Brake Caliper Bracket Bolts (ft. lbs.)	Brake Caliper Mounting Bolts (ft. lbs.)
2008	All	F	0.984	0.867	0.005	0.079	74	20
		R	3.543	3.149	0.005	0.079	74	18
2009	All	F	0.984	0.867	0.005	0.079	74	20
		R	3.543	3.149	0.005	0.079	74	18
2010	All	F	0.984	0.867	0.005	0.079	74	20
		R	3.543	3.149	0.005	0.079	74	18

36616_ASTR_C0011

MAINTENANCE I AND II SERVICE SCHEDULES
Saturn Astra

When the CHANGE ENGINE OIL light appears, certain services and inspections are required. Services are described below. Generally, it is recommended that the first service be Maintenance I, second service be Maintenance II, and that services are then alternated from Maintenance I and Maintenance II thereafter. In some cases, Maintenance II may be required more often. Required services are described as Maintenance I and Maintenance II.

The first service of a vehicle should be Maintance I, and the second service should be Maintenance II.

Alternate between the 2 services thereafter. However, in some cases, Maintenance II may be required more often.

Maintenance I: Use Maintenance I if the CHANGE ENGINE OIL light comes on within 10 months since the vehicle was purcahses or, if Maintenance II was performed.

Maintenance II: Use Maintenance II if the previous service performed was Maintenance I. Always used Maintenance II whenever the CHANGE ENGINE OIL light comes on 10 months or more since the last service, or, if the CHANGE ENGINE OIL light has not come on at all for one year.

Service	Maintenance I	Maintenance II
Change engine oil and filter. Reset oil life system.	✓	✓
Visually check for any leaks or damage. A fluid loss in the vehicle system could indicate a problem. Inspect, repair and add fluid to the system, if necessary.	✓	✓
Inspect engine air cleaner filter. If necessary, replace filter.	—	✓
Rotate tires and check inflation pressures and wear.	✓	✓
Visually inspect brake lines and hoses for proper hook-up, binding, leaks, cracks, chafing, etc. Inspect the disc brake pads for wear and the rotors for surface condition. Inspect the drum brake lings for wear or cracks. Inspect other brake parts, including drums, wheel cylinders, calipers, parking brake, etc. Inspect parking brake adjustment.	✓	✓
Check engine coolant and windshield washer fluid levels and add fluid as needed.	✓	✓
Inspect the suspension and steering components. Inspect the front and rear suspension systems and steering system for damaged, loose, or missing parts, or signs of wear. Inspect the power steering lines and the hoses for proper hook-up, binding, leaks, cracks, chafing, etc.	—	✓
Inspect the coolant hoses and replace the hoses if they are crackes, swollen or deteriorated. Inspect all pipes, fittings and clamps; replace with OEM parts as needed. To help ensure proper operation, a pressure test of the cooling system and pressure cap, and cleaning the outside of the radiator and A/C condesnser is recommended at least once a year.	—	✓
Inspect wiper blades for wear or cracking		✓
Inspect restraint system components.	—	✓
Lubricate all key lock cylinders, latch assemblies and hinges		✓
Inspect the transmission and transaxle fluid level and add fluid as needed.	—	✓
Replace passenger compartment air filter.		✓
Inspect throttle system	—	✓

Reset the oil life system:

1. Display OIL LIFE RESET on the DIC.

2. Press and hold the ENTER button for at least one second. An ACKNOWLEDGED display message will appear for three seconds or until the next button is pressed. This will tell you the system has been reset.

3. Turn the key to OFF.

If the Change Oil Soon message comes back on when you start your vehicle, the system has not reset; repeat.

36616_ASTR_C0013

ADDITIONAL MAINTENANCE SERVICES
Saturn Astra

TO BE SERVICED	TYPE OF SERVICE	VEHICLE MILEAGE INTERVAL (x1000)					
		25	50	75	100	125	150
Air cleaner filter	R		✓		✓		✓
Accessory drive belt	I						✓
Auto. Trans. Fluid ①	R		✓		✓		✓
Cooling system hoses and clamps	S/I						✓
Transfer case fluid	R		✓		✓		✓
Throttle body	I	✓	✓	✓	✓	✓	✓
Engine coolant	R						✓
Fuel system	I	✓	✓	✓	✓	✓	✓
Exhaust system & heat shields	S/I	✓	✓	✓	✓	✓	✓
Spark plugs	R				✓		

R: Replace

S/I: Inspect and service, if necessary

① Replace if any of the following condition are met:

Heavy city traffic where the outside temperature regularly reaches 90oF (32oC) or higher.

Hilly or mountainous terrain

Frequent trailer towing

Taxi, police or delivery service

Otherwise, change every 100,000 miles

36616_ASTR_C0014

PRECAUTIONS

Before servicing any vehicle, please be sure to read all of the following precautions, which deal with personal safety, prevention of component damage, and important points to take into consideration when servicing a motor vehicle:

• Never open, service or drain the radiator or cooling system when the engine is hot; serious burns can occur from the steam and hot coolant.

• Observe all applicable safety precautions when working around fuel. Whenever servicing the fuel system, always work in a well-ventilated area. Do not allow fuel spray or vapors to come in contact with a spark, open flame, or excessive heat (a hot drop light, for example). Keep a dry chemical fire extinguisher near the work area. Always keep fuel in a container specifically designed for fuel storage; also, always properly seal fuel containers to avoid the possibility of fire or explosion. Refer to the additional fuel system precautions later in this section.

• Fuel injection systems often remain pressurized, even after the engine has been turned **OFF**. The fuel system pressure must be relieved before disconnecting any fuel lines. Failure to do so may result in fire and/or personal injury.

• Brake fluid often contains polyglycol ethers and polyglycols. Avoid contact with the eyes and wash your hands thoroughly after handling brake fluid. If you do get brake fluid in your eyes, flush your eyes with clean, running water for 15 minutes. If eye irritation persists, or if you have taken brake fluid internally, IMMEDIATELY seek medical assistance.

• The EPA warns that prolonged contact with used engine oil may cause a number of skin disorders, including cancer. You should make every effort to minimize your exposure to used engine oil. Protective gloves should be worn when changing oil. Wash your hands and any other exposed skin areas as soon as possible after exposure to used engine oil. Soap and water, or waterless hand cleaner should be used.

• All new vehicles are now equipped with an air bag system, often referred to as a Supplemental Restraint System (SRS) or Supplemental Inflatable Restraint (SIR) system. The system must be disabled before performing service on or around system components, steering column, instrument panel components, wiring and sensors. Failure to follow safety and disabling procedures could result in accidental air bag deployment, possible personal injury and unnecessary system repairs.

• Always wear safety goggles when working with, or around, the air bag system. When carrying a non-deployed air bag, be sure the bag and trim cover are pointed away from your body. When placing a non-deployed air bag on a work surface, always face the bag and trim cover upward, away from the surface. This will reduce the motion of the module if it is accidentally deployed. Refer to the additional air bag system precautions later in this section.

• Clean, high quality brake fluid from a sealed container is essential to the safe and proper operation of the brake system. You should always buy the correct type of brake fluid for your vehicle. If the brake fluid becomes contaminated, completely flush the system with new fluid. Never reuse any brake fluid. Any brake fluid that is removed from the system should be discarded. Also, do not allow any brake fluid to come in contact with a painted surface; it will damage the paint.

• Never operate the engine without the proper amount and type of engine oil; doing so WILL result in severe engine damage.

• Timing belt maintenance is extremely important. Many models utilize an interference-type, non-freewheeling engine. If the timing belt breaks, the valves in the cylinder head may strike the pistons, causing potentially serious (also time-consuming and expensive) engine damage. Refer to the maintenance interval charts for the recommended replacement interval for the timing belt, and to the timing belt section for belt replacement and inspection.

• Disconnecting the negative battery cable on some vehicles may interfere with the functions of the on-board computer system(s) and may require the computer to undergo a relearning process once the negative battery cable is reconnected.

• When servicing drum brakes, only disassemble and assemble one side at a time, leaving the remaining side intact for reference.

• Only an MVAC-trained, EPA-certified automotive technician should service the air conditioning system or its components.

BRAKES

GENERAL INFORMATION

PRECAUTIONS

• Certain components within the ABS system are not intended to be serviced or repaired individually.

• Do not use rubber hoses or other parts not specifically specified for and ABS system. When using repair kits, replace all parts included in the kit. Partial or incorrect repair may lead to functional problems and require the replacement of components.

• Lubricate rubber parts with clean, fresh brake fluid to ease assembly. Do not use shop air to clean parts; damage to rubber components may result.

• Use only DOT 3 brake fluid from an unopened container.

• If any hydraulic component or line is removed or replaced, it may be necessary to bleed the entire system.

• A clean repair area is essential. Always clean the reservoir and cap thoroughly before removing the cap. The slightest amount of dirt in the fluid may plug an orifice and impair the system function. Perform repairs after components have been thoroughly cleaned; use only denatured alcohol to clean components. Do not allow ABS components to come into contact with any substance containing mineral oil; this includes used shop rags.

• The Anti-Lock control unit is a microprocessor similar to other computer units in the vehicle. Ensure that the ignition switch is **OFF** before removing or installing controller harnesses. Avoid static electricity discharge at or near the controller.

ANTI-LOCK BRAKE SYSTEM (ABS)

• If any arc welding is to be done on the vehicle, the control unit should be unplugged before welding operations begin.

WHEEL SPEED SENSORS

REMOVAL & INSTALLATION

Front Wheel Speed Sensor

See Figure 1.

1. Remove the front wheel.
2. Remove the brake rotor. Refer to Front Brake Rotor Removal & Installation.

a. Remove the wheel sensor wiring harness in the retaining clip (1).

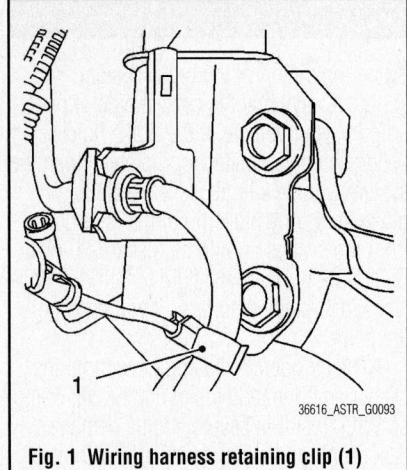

Fig. 1 Wiring harness retaining clip (1)

3. Disconnect the wiring harness connector for wheel sensor.

4. Remove the wheel speed sensor.

To install:

5. Install the wheel speed sensor.

6. Route the wiring harness.

   a. Secure the wheel sensor wiring harness in the retaining clip.

   b. Connect the wheel sensor wiring harness.

7. Install the brake rotor. Refer to Front Brake Rotor Removal & Installation.

8. Install the front wheel.

Rear Wheel Speed Sensor

See Figure 2.

1. Remove the rear wheel.

2. Disconnect the wheel sensor wiring harness (1).

3. Remove the wheel speed sensor.

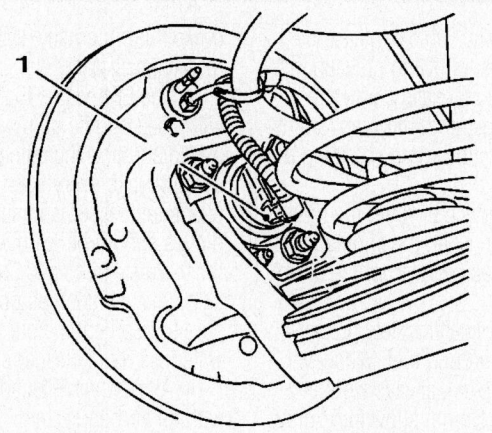

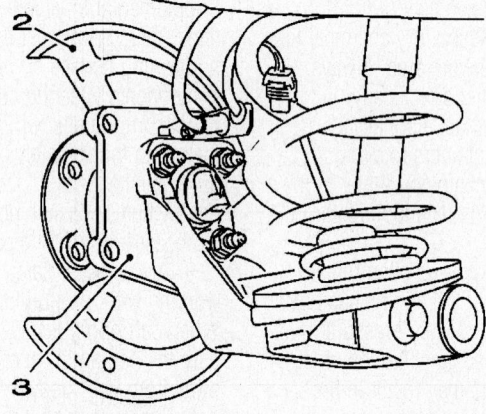

Fig. 2 Wheel sensor wiring harness (1)

To install:

4. Install the wheel speed sensor.

5. Route the wiring harness.

   a. Connect the wheel sensor wiring harness.

6. Install the rear wheel.

BRAKES
BLEEDING THE BRAKE SYSTEM

BLEEDING PROCEDURE

BLEEDING PROCEDURE

Special Service Tools:
- J 29532 Diaphragm Pressure Bleeder
- J 44894-A Brake Bleeder Adapter

❊ WARNING

Refer to Brake Fluid Irritant Warning in this section.

❊ CAUTION

When adding fluid to the brake fluid reservoir or to the clutch fluid reservoir, use only Super DOT-4 or equivalent DOT-4 brake fluid from a clean, sealed container. This polyglycol brake fluid is hygroscopic and absorbs moisture. Do not use fluid from an open container that may be contaminated with water. Improper or contaminated fluid could result in damage to the system components.

❊ CAUTION

Avoid spilling brake fluid onto painted surfaces, electrical connections, wiring, or cables. Brake fluid will damage painted surfaces and cause corrosion to electrical components. If any brake fluid comes in contact with painted surfaces, immediately flush the area with water. If any brake fluid comes in contact with electrical connections, wiring, or cables, use a clean shop cloth to wipe away the fluid.

1. Place a clean shop cloth beneath the brake master cylinder to catch brake fluid spills.

2. With the ignition OFF and the brakes cool, apply the brakes 3-5 times, or until the brake pedal becomes firm, in order to deplete the brake booster power reserve.

3. If you have performed a brake master cylinder bench bleeding on this vehicle, or if you disconnected the brake pipes from the master cylinder, or if you have disconnected the brake pipes from the proportioning valve assembly or the brake modulator assembly, you must perform the following steps to bleed air at the ports of the hydraulic component:

   a. Ensure that the brake master cylinder reservoir is full to the maximum-fill level. If necessary, add GM Vehicle Care Brake and Clutch Fluid Super DOT-4,

GM P/N 88958860 (Canadian P/N 88901244), or equivalent DOT-4 brake fluid from a clean, sealed container.

If removal of the reservoir cap and diaphragm is necessary, clean the outside of the reservoir on and around the cap prior to removal.

a. With the brake pipes installed securely to the master cylinder, proportioning valve assembly, or brake modulator assembly, loosen and separate one of the brake pipes from the port of the component.

For the proportioning valve assembly or the brake modulator assembly, perform these steps in the sequence of system flow; begin with the fluid feed pipes from the master cylinder.

a. Allow a small amount of brake fluid to gravity bleed from the open port of the component.

b. Connect the brake pipe to the component and tighten securely.

c. Have an assistant slowly press the brake pedal fully and maintain steady pressure on the pedal.

d. Loosen the same brake pipe to purge air from the open port of the component.

e. Tighten the brake pipe, then have the assistant slowly release the brake pedal.

f. Wait 15 seconds, then repeat steps 3.3-3.7 until all air is purged from the same port of the component.

g. With the brake pipe installed securely to the master cylinder, proportioning valve assembly, or brake modulator assembly, after all air has been purged from the first port of the component that was bled, loosen and separate the next brake pipe from the component, then repeat steps 3.3-3.8, until each of the ports on the component has been bled.

h. After completing the final component port bleeding procedure, ensure that each of the brake pipe-to-component fittings are properly tightened.

4. Fill the brake master cylinder reservoir to the maximum-fill level with GM Vehicle Care Brake and Clutch Fluid Super DOT-4, GM P/N 88958860 (Canadian P/N 88901244), or equivalent DOT-4 brake fluid from a clean, sealed container.

5. Clean the outside of the reservoir on and around the reservoir cap prior to removing the cap and diaphragm.

6. Install the J 44894-A to the brake master cylinder reservoir.

7. Check the brake fluid level in the J 29532 , or equivalent. Add GM Vehicle Care Brake and Clutch Fluid Super DOT-4, GM

P/N 88958860 (Canadian P/N 88901244), or equivalent DOT-4 brake fluid from a clean, sealed container as necessary to bring the level to approximately the half-full point.

8. Connect the J 29532 , or equivalent, to the J 44894-A .

9. Charge the J 29532 , or equivalent, air tank to 175-205 kPa (25-30 psi).

10. Open the J 29532 , or equivalent, fluid tank valve to allow pressurized brake fluid to enter the brake system.

11. Wait approximately 30 seconds, then inspect the entire hydraulic brake system in order to ensure that there are no existing external brake fluid leaks.

Any brake fluid leaks identified require repair prior to completing this procedure.

12. Install a proper box-end wrench onto the RIGHT REAR wheel hydraulic circuit bleeder valve.

13. Install a transparent hose over the end of the bleeder valve.

14. Submerge the open end of the transparent hose into a transparent container partially filled with GM Vehicle Care Brake and Clutch Fluid Super DOT-4, GM P/N 88958860 (Canadian P/N 88901244), or equivalent DOT-4 brake fluid from a clean, sealed container.

15. Loosen the bleeder valve to purge air from the wheel hydraulic circuit. Allow fluid to flow until air bubbles stop flowing from the bleeder, then tighten the bleeder valve.

16. With the right rear wheel hydraulic circuit bleeder valve tightened securely, after all air has been purged from the right rear hydraulic circuit, install a proper box-end wrench onto the LEFT FRONT wheel hydraulic circuit bleeder valve.

17. Install a transparent hose over the end of the bleeder valve, then repeat steps 13-14.

18. With the left front wheel hydraulic circuit bleeder valve tightened securely, after all air has been purged from the left front hydraulic circuit, install a proper box-end wrench onto the LEFT REAR wheel hydraulic circuit bleeder valve.

19. Install a transparent hose over the end of the bleeder valve, then repeat steps 13-14.

20. With the left rear wheel hydraulic circuit bleeder valve tightened securely, after all air has been purged from the left rear hydraulic circuit, install a proper box-end wrench onto the RIGHT FRONT wheel hydraulic circuit bleeder valve.

21. Install a transparent hose over the end of the bleeder valve, then repeat steps 13-14.

22. After completing the final wheel hydraulic circuit bleeding procedure, ensure

that each of the 4 wheel hydraulic circuit bleeder valves are properly tightened.

23. Close the J 29532 , or equivalent, fluid tank valve, then disconnect the J 29532 , or equivalent, from the J 44894-A .

24. Remove the J 44894-A from the brake master cylinder reservoir.

25. Fill the brake master cylinder reservoir to the maximum-fill level with GM Vehicle Care Brake and Clutch Fluid Super DOT-4, GM P/N 88958860 (Canadian P/N 88901244), or equivalent DOT-4 brake fluid from a clean, sealed container.

26. Slowly press and release the brake pedal. Observe the feel of the brake pedal.

27. If the brake pedal feels spongy perform the following steps:

a. Inspect the brake system for external leaks. Refer to Brake System External Leak Inspection.

b. If equipped with antilock brakes, using a scan tool, perform the antilock brake system automated bleeding procedure to remove any air that may have been trapped in the BPMV. Refer to Antilock Brake System Automated Bleed Procedure.

28. Turn the ignition key ON, with the engine OFF. Check to see if the brake system warning lamp remains illuminated.

➡**DO NOT allow the vehicle to be driven until the diagnosis and repair has been completed and verified.**

BLEEDING THE ABS SYSTEM

For vehicles equipped with MK60/MK70, bleed the brake system. Refer to Bleeding the Hydraulic Brake System.

• For vehicles equipped with MK60/MK70, apply the parking brake.

• For vehicles equipped with MK60/MK70, connect the Tech 2 and switch on:

1. Select menu "Vehicle Diagnoses"
2. Select model year
3. Select vehicle "Astra"
4. Select "MK70 / ABS MK60 ESP"
5. Switch on ignition and confirm by pressing the button
6. Select "Additional Functions"
7. Follow further instructions of Tech 2
8. For vehicles equipped with MK60/MK70, follow the instructions of the Tech 2.
9. Disconnect the Tech 2.

❄❄ **CAUTION**

Repeat bleeding brake system if brake pedal is not hard.

For vehicles equipped with MK60/MK70, bleed the brake system. Refer to Bleeding the Hydraulic Brake System.

❊❊ CAUTION

Dust and dirt accumulating on brake parts during normal use may contain asbestos fibers from production or aftermarket brake linings. Breathing excessive concentrations of asbestos fibers can cause serious bodily harm. Exercise care when servicing brake parts. Do not sand or grind brake lining unless equipment used is designed to contain the dust residue. Do not clean brake parts with compressed air or by dry brushing. Cleaning should be done by dampening the brake components with a fine mist of water, then wiping the brake components clean with a dampened cloth. Dispose of cloth and all residue containing asbestos fibers in an impermeable container with the appropriate label. Follow practices prescribed by the Occupational Safety and Health Administration (OSHA) and the Environmental Protection Agency (EPA) for the handling, processing, and disposing of dust or debris that may contain asbestos fibers.

BRAKE CALIPER

REMOVAL & INSTALLATION

See Figure 3.

1. Raise and support the vehicle.
2. Remove the front wheels.
3. Remove the banjo bolt (1) from the brake caliper.
4. Remove the front brake pads. Refer to Front Disc Brake Pads Removal & Installation.
5. Remove the brake carrier (2) from the steering knuckle.

To install:

➡Clean the thread and insert the bolts with the locking compound.

6. Install the brake carrier to the steering knuckle.
7. Tighten the brake carrier to steering knuckle bolt to 74 ft. lbs. (100 Nm).
8. Install the front brake pads. Refer to Front Disc Brake Pads Removal & Installation.

❊❊ WARNING

Ensure that the brake hose is not twisted.

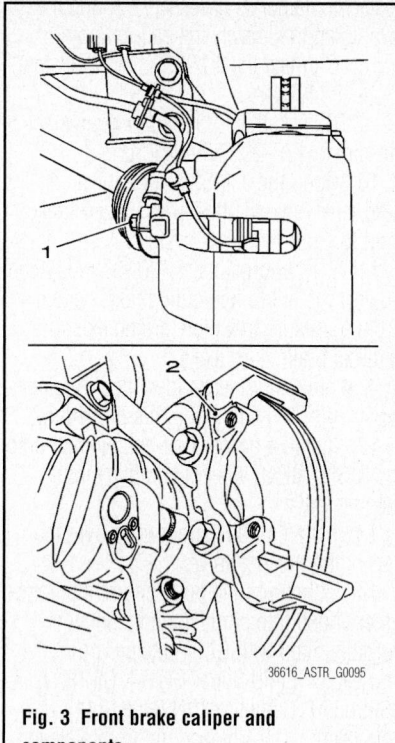

Fig. 3 Front brake caliper and components

9. Install the brake hose to the brake caliper with new seal rings.
10. Tighten the brake hose to brake caliper banjo bolt to 30 ft. lbs. (40 Nm).
11. Install the front wheels. Lower the vehicle.
12. Bleed the brake system and check for leaks. Refer to Bleeding the Hydraulic Brake System.
13. Pump the brake pedal repeatedly.
14. Refill the brake fluid to the MAX mark.

DISC BRAKE PADS

REMOVAL & INSTALLATION

See Figures 4 through 8.

➡Brake pads on an axle must be replaced as a set.

1. Raise and support the vehicle.
2. Remove the 2 front wheels.
3. Remove the brake lining sensor (1) from the inner brake lining if equipped.
4. Remove the retaining spring (2) out of the brake caliper with a screwdriver and remove.
5. Remove the dust caps (3) from the protective sleeves for the caliber guide bolts (4).
6. Remove the guide bolts for the brake caliper.

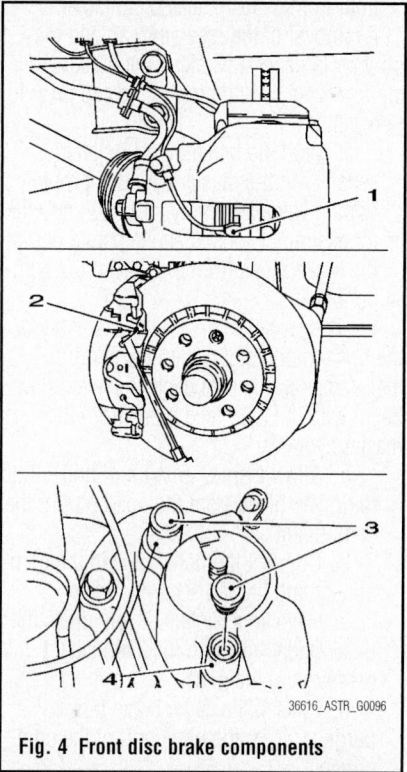

Fig. 4 Front disc brake components

❊❊ WARNING

Support the brake caliper with heavy mechanic wire, or equivalent, whenever it is separated from its mount and the hydraulic flexible brake hose is still connected. Failure to support the caliper in this manner will cause the flexible brake hose to bear the weight of the caliper, which may cause damage to the brake hose and in turn may cause a brake fluid leak.

7. Remove the brake caliper from the brake carrier.
8. Remove the outer brake pad (2) from the brake caliper.

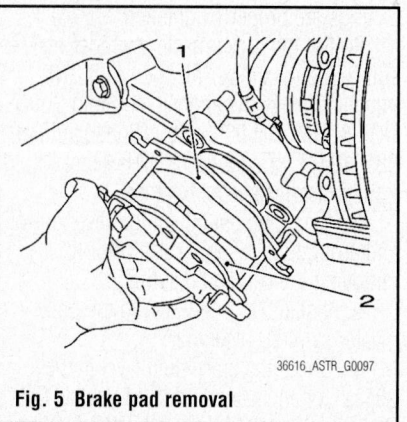

Fig. 5 Brake pad removal

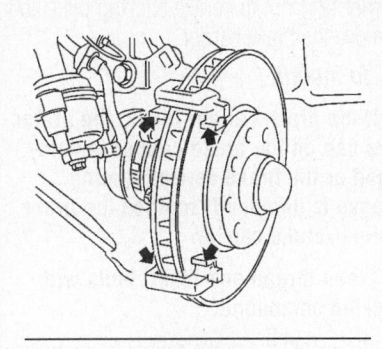

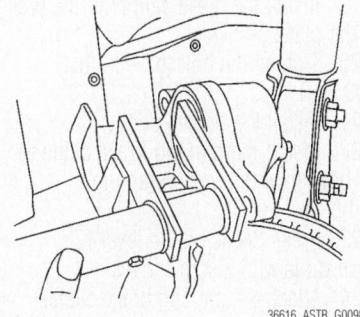

Fig. 6 Brake pad guides and piston compression

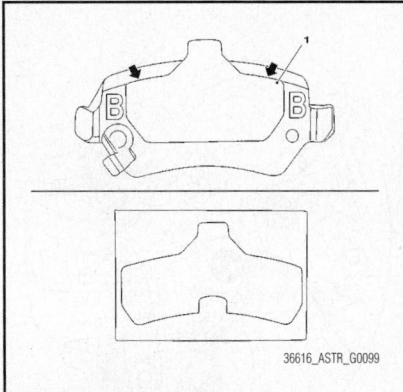

Fig. 7 Anti-squeal shims

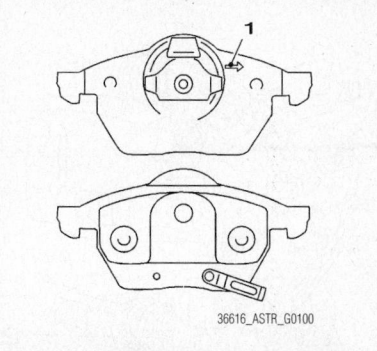

Fig. 8 Directional arrows indicate proper brake pad placement

9. Remove the inner brake pad (1) with the retaining clamp from the pistons.

10. Inspect the brake pads for wear.

11. Clean the guides in the brake carrier with a soft metal brush.

12. Coat the guides with anti-squeak compound.

➡Brake fluid level rises in brake fluid reservoir. If necessary, siphon out brake fluid with siphon bottle. If the brake caliper is leaking or the protective cap on the brake caliper is damaged, overhaul brake.

13. Compress the caliper pistons with a suitable piston compressing tool.

To install:

14. Replace the anti-squeal shims when replacing brake pads.

15. Press the inner brake lining into piston with the retaining clamp.

✳✳ WARNING
When installing the brake linings, ensure that the arrows (1) on the rear face of the lining point in the direction of rotation of the brake disc when the vehicle is travelling forwards.

16. Insert the outer brake lining in the brake caliper.

✳✳ CAUTION
Ensure that the brake hose is not twisted.

17. Place the brake caliper on the brake carrier with the brake linings.

18. Install the brake caliper to the brake carrier.

19. Tighten the brake caliper guide bolts to 20 ft. lbs. (28 Nm).

20. Install the dust caps to the guide bolts.

21. Install the retaining spring to the brake caliper.

22. Install the brake lining sensor to the inner brake lining, if equipped.

23. Install 2 front wheels.

24. Actuate the brake pedal repeatedly.

25. Lower the vehicle.

26. Refill the brake fluid to the MAX mark.

BRAKES

✳✳ CAUTION
Dust and dirt accumulating on brake parts during normal use may contain asbestos fibers from production or aftermarket brake linings. Breathing excessive concentrations of asbestos fibers can cause serious bodily harm. Exercise care when servicing brake parts. Do not sand or grind brake lining unless equipment used is designed to contain the dust residue. Do not clean brake parts with compressed air or by dry brushing. Cleaning should be done by dampening the brake components with a fine mist of water, then wiping the brake components clean with a dampened cloth. Dispose of cloth and all residue containing asbestos fibers in an impermeable container with the appropriate label. Follow practices prescribed by the Occupational Safety and Health Administration (OSHA) and the Environmental Protection Agency (EPA) for the handling, processing, and disposing of dust or debris that may contain asbestos fibers.

BRAKE CALIPER

REMOVAL & INSTALLATION
See Figures 9 through 13.

Special Service Tools:
• KM-6007 Resetting Tool
• KM-6007-30 Adaptor

➡The brake pads must be removed to remove the brake caliper of the rear wheel brake.

REAR DISC BRAKES

1. Release the parking brake cable.

a. Release the parking brake lever.

b. Remove the parking brake bellows.

c. Release the parking brake cable by unthreading the adjusting nut.

2. Top up the brake fluid the reservoir to the MAX marking and seal.

➡Mark the position in relation to center of wheel.

3. Remove the appropriate rear wheel.

4. Release the brake caliper.

5. Remove the parking brake cable.

a. Push down the brake caliper actuation lever with a screwdriver and remove the parking brake cable.

b. Pull off the locking plate (3).

c. Draw the parking brake cable out of the mounting on the brake caliper.

6. Unthread 1 screw (1).

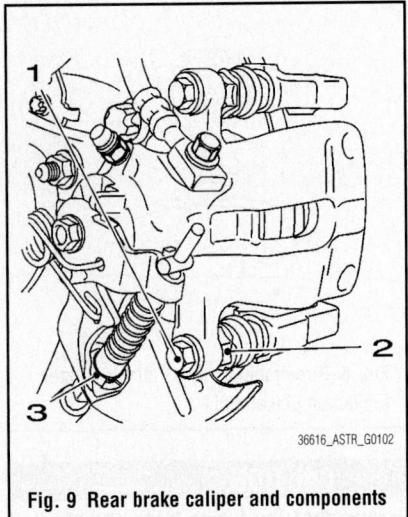

Fig. 9 Rear brake caliper and components

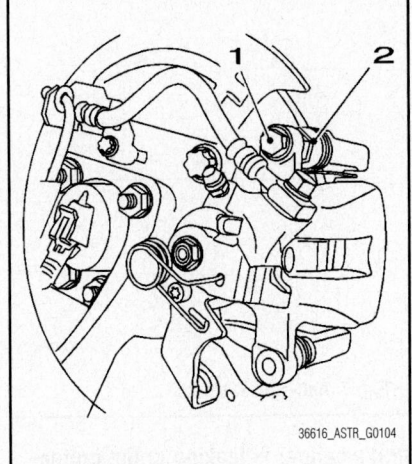

Fig. 11 Caliper bolt removal

7. Hold against the hexagon of the guide pin (2).

8. Fold the brake caliper upwards.

9. Unthread the brake piston.

10. Turn the brake piston back with KM-6007 (1) and KM-6007-30 (2).

11. Turn the piston back to stop.

12. Thread the piston outwards again until the next cut-out in the brake piston is aligned with the opening on the brake caliper (arrows).

➡️**The brake caliper must be completely removed from the brake carrier before mounting the brake pads.**

13. Remove the brake caliper from the brake support.

    a. Unthread the bolt (1).

    b. Hold against the hexagon of the guide pin (2).

14. Remove the brake caliper from the brake carrier.

15. Suspend the brake caliper from the rear spring with a suitable wire.

16. Remove the brake pads and the guide plates.

17. Remove the brake hose (1) from the brake caliper.

18. Remove the bolts (3) for the brake

carrier (2) from the brake backing plate and remove the brake carrier.

To install:

➡️**If the brake caliper leaks, the protective cap on the brake caliper is damaged or the brake carrier sealing sleeve is damaged, replace the brake caliper/brake carrier.**

➡️**Clean thread and insert bolts with locking compound.**

19. Install the brake caliper to the brake carrier plate.

20. Tighten the bolt to 74 ft. lbs. (100 Nm).

21. Install the brake pads.

22. Install the parking brake cable to the bracket with a new retaining clamp (3).

23. Press the actuating lever (2) downwards with a screwdriver.

24. Attach the parking brake cable.

25. Install the brake hose (1) to the brake caliper with new seal rings.

26. Tighten to 30 ft. lbs. (40 Nm).

27. Install the rear wheel.

28. Lower the vehicle.

29. Bleed the brake system and check for leaks. Refer to Hydraulic Brake System Bleeding.

30. Actuate the brake pedal repeatedly.

31. Top up the brake fluid to the MAX mark.

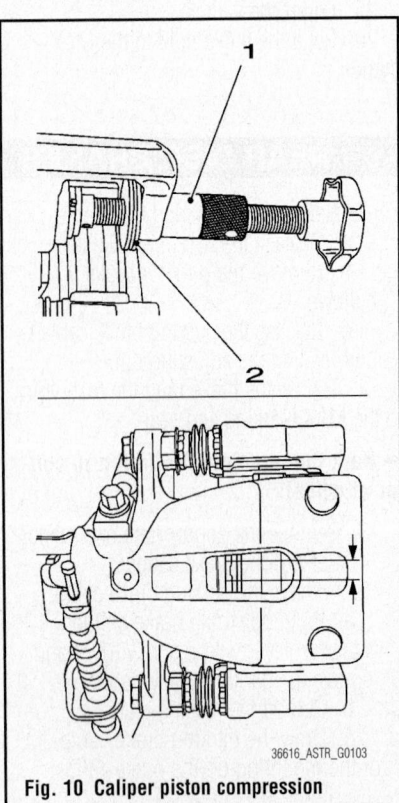

Fig. 10 Caliper piston compression

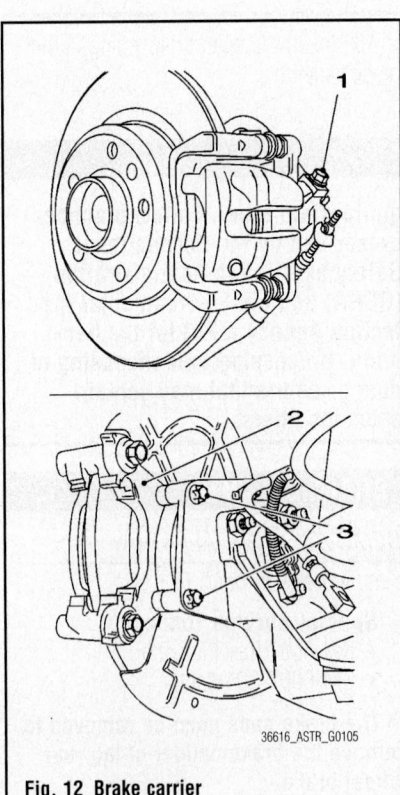

Fig. 12 Brake carrier

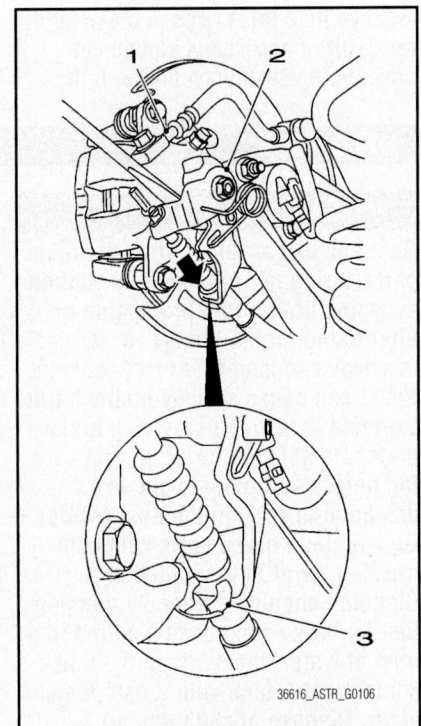

Fig. 13 Carrier plate and parking brake cable

32. Adjust the parking brake. Refer to Parking Brake Adjustment.

DISC BRAKE PADS

REMOVAL & INSTALLATION

See Figures 13,14 through 19.

Special Service Tools:
- KM-6007 Resetting Tool
- KM-6007-30 Adaptor

➡**Brake pads on one axle must be replaced as a set.**

1. Raise and support the vehicle.
   a. Release the parking brake cable.
   b. Release the parking brake lever.
   c. Remove the cover of the diagnostic connection.
   d. Remove the parking brake bellows.
   e. Release the parking brake cable by unscrewing the adjusting nut.

➡**Ensure that dust sleeve between actuating lever and brake caliper is not damaged.**

2. Remove the rear wheels.
3. Remove the parking brake cable from the brake caliper.
   a. Press the brake caliper actuating lever (1) downwards in the direction of

the arrow using a screwdriver (2) and remove the parking brake cable.
   b. Remove the retention clip (3) and pull the parking brake cable (4) out of the bracket.
4. Remove the brake pads from the brake caliper.
   a. Remove the bolt (1) from the brake caliper.
   b. Fold the brake caliper upwards.

➡**Brake fluid level increases in brake fluid reservoir. Remove brake fluid with siphon bottle if necessary.**

➡**Ensure that the collar (arrow) of KM-6007-30 points towards the hand wheel or hexagonal section of KM-6007 .**

5. Unthread the brake piston.
6. Position KM-6007 (2) on brake caliper with KM-6007-30 (1).
7. Push KM-6007-30 over KM-6007 .
8. Unthread the brake piston as far as the stop - then pull it out of the brake caliper until the next cutout (3) in the brake piston is flush with the opening on the brake caliper.

➡**The brake caliper must be completely removed from the brake carrier before mounting the brake pads.**

   a. Remove the brake caliper from the brake support.

   b. Remove the upper bolt from the brake caliper.
   c. Remove the brake caliper from the brake carrier.
   d. Suspend it from the rear spring with a suitable wire.
9. Remove the brake pads and the guide plates (1).

To install:

➡**Ensure that the residues of adhesive on the brake pad surfaces are removed and the surfaces cleaned afterwards.**

10. Clean the guides for the brake pads in the top and bottom of the brake carrier (2) and contact surfaces with the brake pads on the brake piston (1) and the opposing surfaces (arrows). Clean the threads in the brake caliper.

❊❊ WARNING

Replace brake caliper and/or brake carrier if the brake caliper is leaking, protective cap on piston is damaged or sealing sleeve on the brake carrier is damaged. Refer to Rear Brake Caliper Replacement.

11. Inspect the brake discs for wear. Refer to Brake Rotor Surface and Wear Inspection.

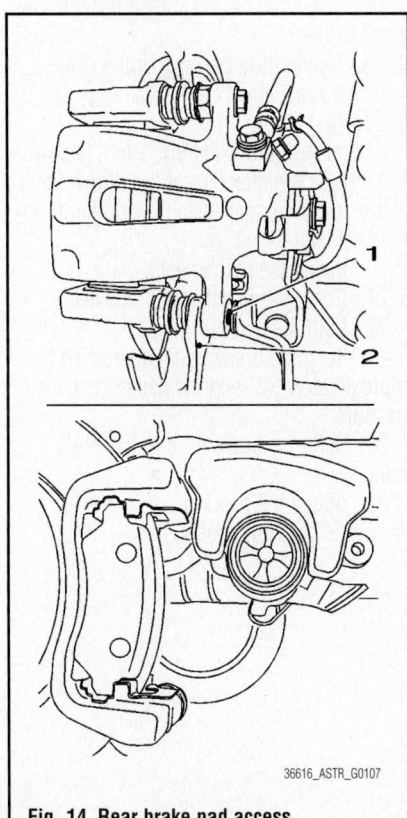

36616_ASTR_G0107

Fig. 14 Rear brake pad access

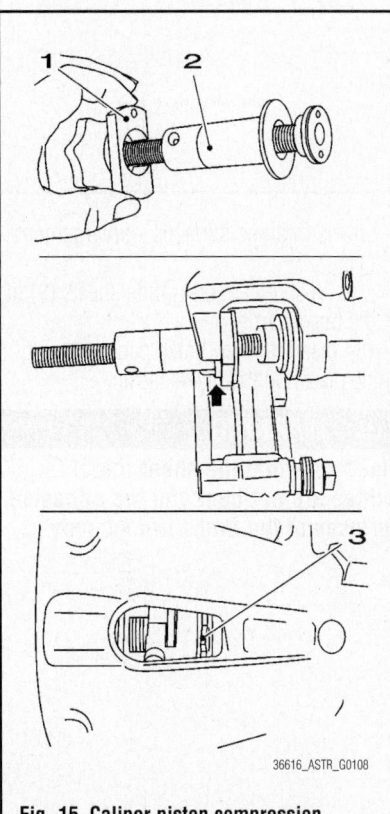
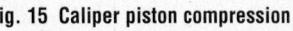

36616_ASTR_G0108

Fig. 15 Caliper piston compression

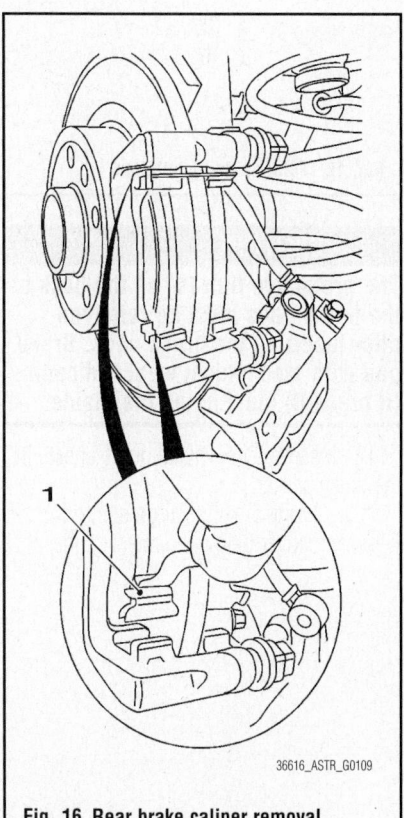

36616_ASTR_G0109

Fig. 16 Rear brake caliper removal

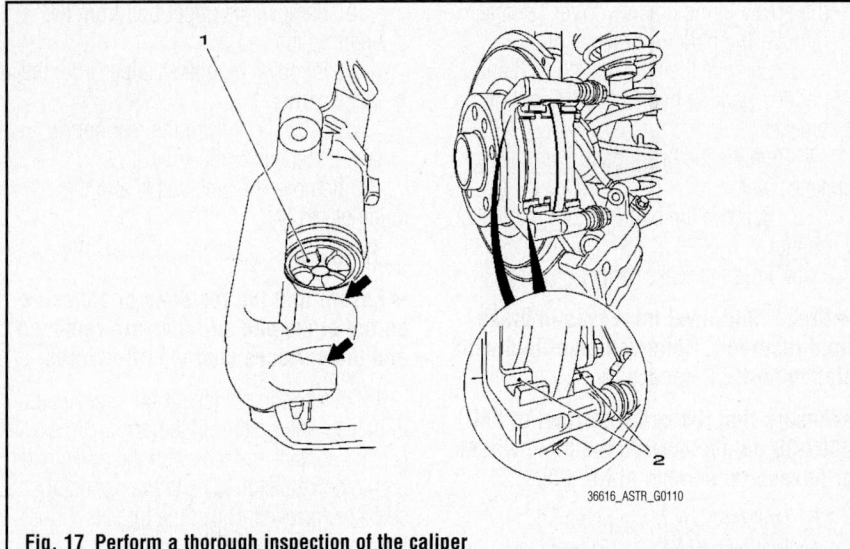

Fig. 17 Perform a thorough inspection of the caliper

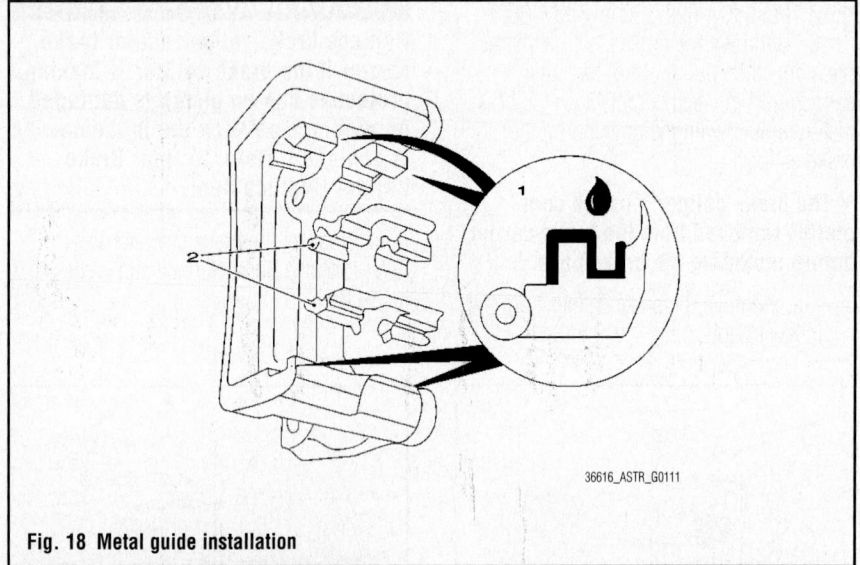

Fig. 18 Metal guide installation

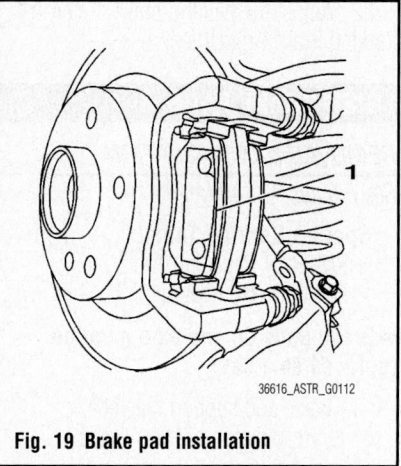

Fig. 19 Brake pad installation

※※ CAUTION

The protective film (1) on the back of the brake pads must be removed after inserting the brake pads. Brake pad with mechanical wear indicator (if present) must be on the inside.

12. Insert the new metal guide sheets in the brake carrier.
   a. Apply the special grease to the brake carrier below the metal guide sheets (marked surfaces - enlargement (1).
   b. Insert the metal guide sheets (2) in the brake carrier.
13. Insert the new brake pads in the guide plates on the brake carrier.

※※ WARNING

Make sure that the sheet metal guides are not bent and the adhesive surfaces of the brake linings only

contact the brake caliper after they have been correctly positioned.

14. Install the brake caliper to the brake carrier.
15. Place the brake caliper on the brake carrier.
16. Slide the brake caliper exactly in the direction of the arrow, from back to front, on the brake carrier.
17. Install the brake caliper bolts to the brake carrier.
   a. Clean the thread and insert the new bolts with the locking compound.
18. Tighten the bolts to 18 ft. lbs. (25 Nm).
19. Install the parking brake cable to the brake caliper.
   a. Install the parking brake cable to the bracket with the retaining clip (2).
   b. Press the actuating lever (1) downwards in the direction of the arrow using a screwdriver and install the parking brake cable.
20. Install the rear wheels.
21. Pump the brake pedal repeatedly.
22. Start the engine.
23. Keep the brake pedal depressed for approximately 30 seconds using medium pressure.
24. Refill the brake fluid to the MAX mark.
25. Adjust the parking park. Refer to Parking Brake Adjustment.

BRAKES

PARKING BRAKE

PARKING BRAKE CABLES

ADJUSTMENT
See Figure 20.

1. Raise and support the vehicle.
2. Remove the cover of the diagnostic connection.
3. Remove the parking brake lever (2) from the front floor console and lift upwards.
4. Release the adjusting nut (3) completely by turning it backwards.
5. Position the parking brake lever (1) to position "0" (released).

➡**To adjust the play on the parking brake at the brake caliper: ensure that each time the brake is activated, the brake pedal returns to the original position (fully relieved of stress).**

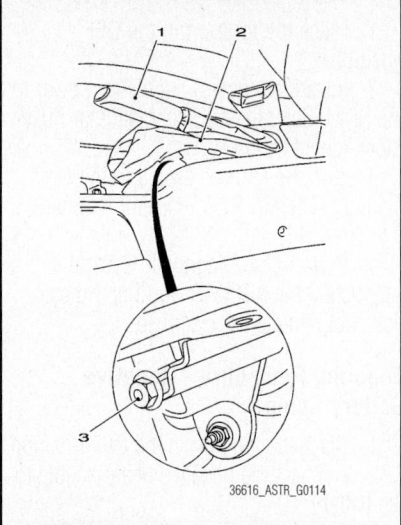

36616_ASTR_G0114

Fig. 20 Diagnostic connection cover and cable adjuster

6. Depress the brake pedal fully at least 5 times.
7. Pull the parking brake lever 5 times to the stop and release again.
8. Pull the parking brake lever (1) to the 2nd notch.

➡**The braking effect must be equal on both wheels.**

9. Turn the adjusting nut on the parking brake lever until the rear wheels can only be turned with difficulty.

➡**The wheels must be fixed at the 3rd notch.**

10. Pull the parking brake lever to the 3rd notch.
11. Install the parking brake lever bellows to the front floor console.
12. Install the cover of the diagnostic connection.

CHASSIS ELECTRICAL

AIR BAG (SUPPLEMENTAL RESTRAINT SYSTEM)

GENERAL INFORMATION

✳✳ CAUTION

These vehicles are equipped with an air bag system. The system must be disarmed before performing service on, or around, system components, the steering column, instrument panel components, wiring and sensors. Failure to follow the safety precautions and the disarming procedure could result in accidental air bag deployment, possible injury and unnecessary system repairs.

SERVICE PRECAUTIONS

Disconnect and isolate the battery negative cable before beginning any airbag system component diagnosis, testing, removal, or installation procedures. Allow system capacitor to discharge for two minutes before beginning any component service. This will disable the airbag system. Failure to disable the airbag system may result in accidental airbag deployment, personal injury, or death.

Do not place an intact undeployed airbag face down on a solid surface. The airbag will propel into the air if accidentally deployed and may result in personal injury or death.

When carrying or handling an undeployed airbag, the trim side (face) of the airbag should be pointing towards the body to minimize possibility of injury if accidental deployment occurs. Failure to do this may result in personal injury or death.

Replace airbag system components with OEM replacement parts. Substitute parts may appear interchangeable, but internal differences may result in inferior occupant protection. Failure to do so may result in occupant personal injury or death.

Wear safety glasses, rubber gloves, and long sleeved clothing when cleaning powder residue from vehicle after an airbag deployment. Powder residue emitted from a deployed airbag can cause skin irritation. Flush affected area with cool water if irritation is experienced. If nasal or throat irritation is experienced, exit the vehicle for fresh air until the irritation ceases. If irritation continues, see a physician.

Do not use a replacement airbag that is not in the original packaging. This may result in improper deployment, personal injury, or death.

The factory installed fasteners, screws and bolts used to fasten airbag components have a special coating and are specifically designed for the airbag system. Do not use substitute fasteners. Use only original equipment fasteners listed in the parts catalog when fastener replacement is required.

During, and following, any child restraint anchor service, due to impact event or vehicle repair, carefully inspect all mounting hardware, tether straps, and anchors for proper installation, operation, or damage. If a child restraint anchor is found damaged in any way, the anchor must be replaced. Failure to do this may result in personal injury or death.

Deployed and non-deployed airbags may or may not have live pyrotechnic material within the airbag inflator.

Do not dispose of driver/passenger/curtain airbags or seat belt tensioners unless you are sure of complete deployment. Refer to the Hazardous Substance Control System for proper disposal.

Dispose of deployed airbags and tensioners consistent with state, provincial, local, and federal regulations.

After any airbag component testing or service, do not connect the battery negative cable. Personal injury or death may result if the system test is not performed first.

If the vehicle is equipped with the Occupant Classification System (OCS), do not connect the battery negative cable before performing the OCS Verification Test using the scan tool and the appropriate diagnostic information. Personal injury or death may result if the system test is not performed properly.

Never replace both the Occupant Restraint Controller (ORC) and the Occupant Classification Module (OCM) at the same time. If both require replacement, replace one, then perform the Airbag System test before replacing the other.

Both the ORC and the OCM store

Occupant Classification System (OCS) calibration data, which they transfer to one another when one of them is replaced. If both are replaced at the same time, an irreversible fault will be set in both modules and the OCS may malfunction and cause personal injury or death.

If equipped with OCS, the Seat Weight Sensor is a sensitive, calibrated unit and must be handled carefully. Do not drop or handle roughly. If dropped or damaged, replace with another sensor. Failure to do so may result in occupant injury or death.

If equipped with OCS, the front passenger seat must be handled carefully as well. When removing the seat, be careful when setting on floor not to drop. If dropped, the sensor may be inoperative, could result in occupant injury, or possibly death.

If equipped with OCS, when the passenger front seat is on the floor, no one should sit in the front passenger seat. This uneven force may damage the sensing ability of the seat weight sensors. If sat on and damaged, the sensor may be inoperative, could result in occupant injury, or possibly death.

DISARMING THE SYSTEM

Disabling Procedure - Air Bag Fuse

1. Turn the steering wheel so that the vehicles wheels are pointing straight ahead.
2. Place the ignition in the OFF position.

➡️ **The SDM may have more than one fused power input. To ensure there is no unwanted SIR deployment, personal injury, or unnecessary SIR system repairs, remove all fuses supplying power to the SDM. With all SDM fuses removed and the ignition switch in the ON position, the AIR BAG warning indicator illuminates. This is normal operation, and does not indicate a SIR system malfunction.**

3. Locate and remove the fuse(s) supplying power to the SDM. Refer to SIR Schematics or Fuse Block Identification Views.
4. Wait 1 minute before working on the system.

Disabling Procedure - Negative Battery Cable

1. Turn the steering wheel so that the vehicles wheels are pointing straight ahead.
2. Place the ignition in the OFF position.
3. Disconnect the negative battery cable from the battery.
4. Wait 1 minute before working on system.

ARMING THE SYSTEM

Enabling Procedure - Air Bag Fuse

1. Place the ignition in the OFF position.
2. Install the fuse(s) supplying power to the SDM. Refer to SIR Schematics or Fuse Block Identification Views.
3. Turn the ignition switch to the ON position. The AIR BAG indicator will flash then turn OFF.
4. Perform the Diagnostic System Check - Vehicle if the AIR BAG warning indicator does not operate as described.

Enabling Procedure - Negative Battery Cable

1. Place the ignition in the OFF position.
2. Connect the negative battery cable to the battery.
3. Turn the ignition switch to the ON position. The AIR BAG indicator will flash then turn OFF.
4. Perform the Diagnostic System Check - Vehicle if the AIR BAG warning indicator does not operate as described.

STEERING WHEEL COIL MODULE

See Figure 21.

1. Install the steering wheel coil module.
   a. Connect the wiring harness connector.
   b. Insert the steering wheel coil module.
   c. Install the wiring harness clamp.

2. Tighten the 3 bolts to 11 ft. lbs. (15 Nm).
3. Install the turn signal switch paneling.
   a. Insert the lower paneling.
4. Tighten the 3 bolts to 11 ft. lbs. (15 Nm).
5. Insert the upper paneling.
6. Tighten the 3 bolts to 11 ft. lbs. (15 Nm).
7. Install the 2 panels.

> ✳✳ **WARNING**
>
> **Ensure that the marks on the steering wheel and the steering shaft align.**

➡️ **Clean the thread and fit the new bolt with the locking compound.**

8. Install the steering wheel to the steering shaft.
   a. Install the steering wheel to the steering column.
9. Tighten the bolt to 22 ft. lbs (30 Nm).
10. Connect the wiring harness connector for the signal horn/Infotainment.
11. Install the driver side airbag.
   a. Connect and latch the wiring harness connector.
   b. Install the 2 clips.
12. Perform the readiness inspection.
13. Connect the battery.

Control Module References

See Figure 22.

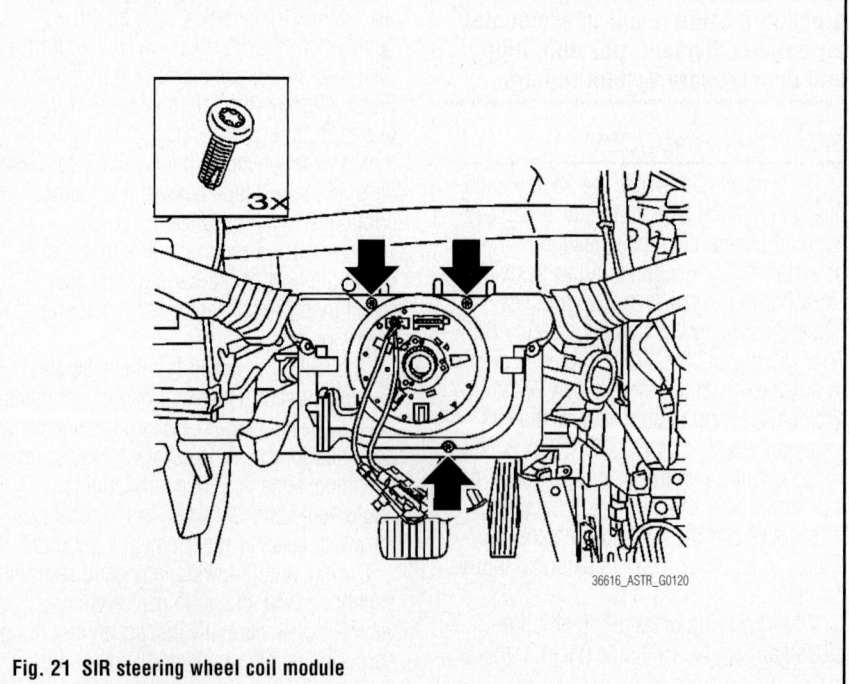

Fig. 21 SIR steering wheel coil module

36616_ASTR_G0120

Control Module	Schematic	Repair Instruction	Programming and Setup
Communication Interface Module Scan Tool Information	OnStar Schematics	Communication Interface Module Replacement	Communication Interface Module Programming and Setup
Driver Information Display Scan Tool Information (DIS)	Driver Information System Schematics	Driver Information Display Replacement	Driver Information Center Programming and Setup
Electronic Brake Control Module Scan Tool Information (ABS/TC/ESP)	Antilock Brake System Schematics	Electronic Brake Control Module Replacement	Electronic Brake Control Module Programming and Setup
Engine Control Module Scan Tool Information	Engine Controls Schematics	Engine Control Module Replacement	Engine Control Module Programming and Setup
Front Compartment Fuse Block Scan Tool Information (UEC)	Body Control System Schematics	Underhood Electrical Center or Junction Block Replacement	Front Compartment Fuse Block Programming and Setup
Heated Seat Control Module	Heated/Cooled Seat Schematics	Driver or Passenger Seat Cushion Heater Replacement	Heated Seat Control Module Programming and Setup
HVAC Control Module	HVAC Schematics	Heater and Air Conditioning Control Replacement	This device requires no programming or setup.
Inflatable Restraint Passenger Presence System	SIR Schematics	Inflatable Restraint Passenger Presence System Replacement - Front	Passenger Presence System Programming and Setup
Inflatable Restraint Sensing and Diagnostic Module Scan Tool Information (SDM)	SIR Schematics	Inflatable Restraint Sensing and Diagnostic Module Replacement	Inflatable Restraint Sensing and Diagnostic Module Programming and Setup
Instrument Cluster Scan Tool Information	Instrument Cluster Schematics	Instrument Cluster Replacement	Instrument Cluster Programming and Setup
Power Steering Control Module Scan Tool Information (EHPS)	Power Steering Schematics	Power Steering Pump Replacement	Power Steering Control Module Programming and Setup
Radio Scan Tool Information (EHU)	Radio/Navigation System Schematics	Radio Replacement	Radio Programming and Setup
Rear Body Fuse Block Scan Tool Information (REC)	Body Control System Schematics	Rear Electrical Center or Junction Block Replacement	Rear Body Fuse Block Programming and Setup
Sunroof	Sunroof Schematics	Power Sunroof Motor Replacement	Sunroof Control Module Programming and Setup
Steering Column Control Module Scan Tool Information (CIM)	Body Control System Schematics	Steering Column Control Module Replacement	Steering Column Control Module Programming and Setup
Tire Pressure Indicator Receiver Scan Tool Information	Tire Pressure Monitoring System Schematics	Tire Pressure Indicator Receiver Replacement	Tire Pressure Indicator Receiver Programming and Setup
Transmission Control Module Scan Tool Information Transmission Control Module	Automatic Transmission Controls Schematics	Transmission Control Module Replacement	Transmission Control Module Programming and Setup

36616_ASTR_G0088

Fig. 22 Control Module References

DRIVE TRAIN

AUTOMATIC TRANSAXLE ASSEMBLY

REMOVAL & INSTALLATION

See Figures 23 through 37.

Special Service Tools:
- DT-47648 /DT-47648-2/DT-47648-3/ DT-47648-5 Left/DT-47648-5 Right Transaxle Holder
- KM-904 Base Frame
- KM-911
- KM-924 Blanking Plugs
- KM-6001-A Engine Mount
- KM-6388 Bracket

➡ **In order to ensure that the drive unit is correctly aligned when the bolts for the left engine damping block are slackened, the drive unit must be** aligned with the front axle body using KM-6001-A . Instructions for attaching KM-6001-A are given in the following.

1. Remove the battery and the battery tray.
2. Remove the front exhaust pipe, catalytic converter and center silencer.
3. Install KM-6001-A to the front axle body.
   a. Release the 2 bolts (arrows) for the adjusting rails on KM-6001-A (1).

➡ **Two pins (2 and 5) must sit in the guide holes of the front axle body.**

   b. Insert the KM-6001-A as shown.
4. Tighten the 2 bolts for the adjustment rails.

➡ **The guide pins must sit in the support bearings free of play.**

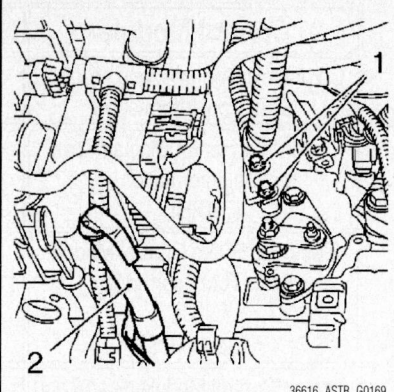

Fig. 24 Selector cable bracket and dipstick

5. Twist the front support bearing (4) as far up the stop on the guide pin of the front engine mount.

➡ **The guide pins must sit in the support bearings free of play.**

6. Twist up the rear support bearing (3) as far as the stop on the guide pin of the rear engine damping block bracket.
7. Release and disconnect the wiring harness connector for the selector lever position switch (2).
   a. Open the lock in the direction of the arrow.
8. Release and disconnect the wiring harness connector (3) for the transaxle wiring harness.
   a. Open the lock in the direction of the arrow.
9. Disconnect the selector cable from the counter hold.
   a. Open the retaining clamp (1).
   b. Remove the selector cable (4) from the selector lever.

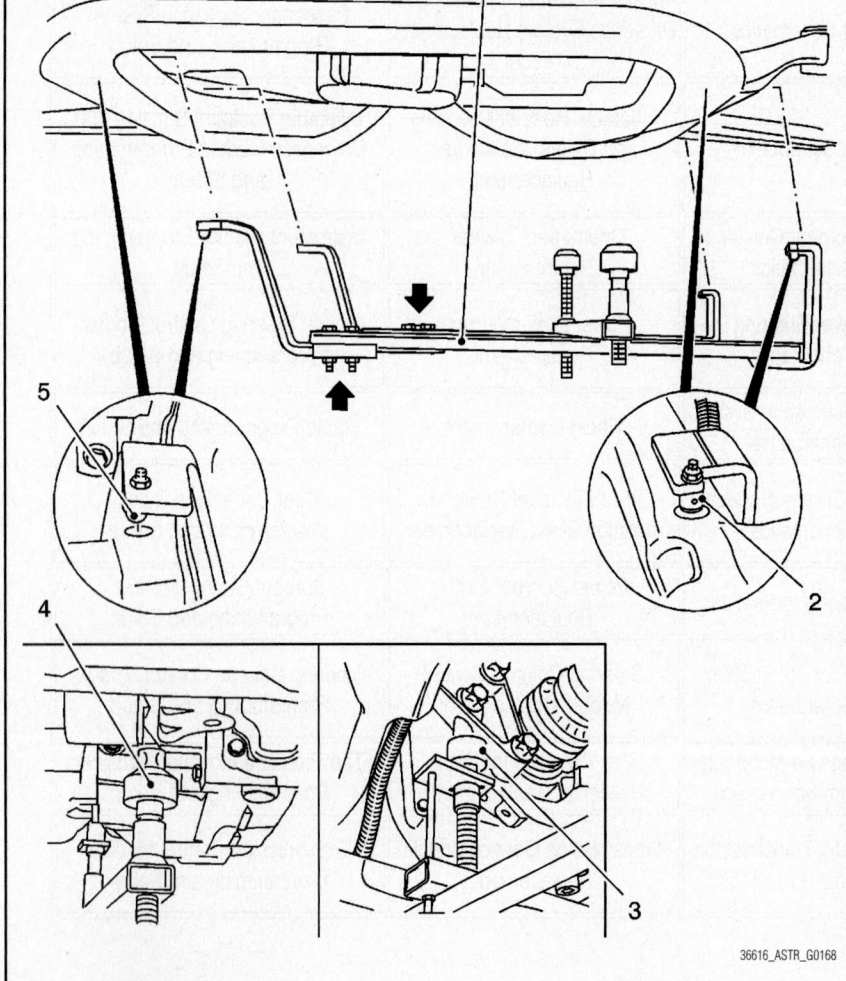

Fig. 23 KM 6001 A installation

Fig. 25 Transaxle top bolts

10. Remove the selector cable bracket.
   a. Remove the 2 bolts (1).
11. Remove the fluid filler tube (2) with the dipstick.
   a. Remove the nut.
12. Release the transaxle at the top.
   a. Remove the 3 bolts (1).

➡**KM-6001-A remains on the front axle body and may not be moved.**

13. Remove the front sub-frame.
➡**Place a drain pan underneath - transaxle fluid escapes. Halfshafts remain in the wheel hubs.**
14. Install the halfshafts to the underbody.
15. Remove the 2 halfshafts from the transaxle. Refer to Halfshaft Removal & Installation.
16. Seal the 2 apertures in the transaxle with the plugs.
17. Remove the converter from the drive disc.
   a. Remove the 2 sealing plugs.
   b. Lock the drive disc with KM-911 (2).

➡**Turn the drive disc by a further 120 degrees each time.**

   c. Remove the 3 bolts (1).

➡**Place a drain pan underneath - transaxle fluid escapes. Note the allocation of the fluid cooler lines.**

18. Remove the 2 fluid cooler lines (1) from the transaxle.
   a. Remove the 2 retaining clamps (2).
   b. Seal the apertures in the transaxle with KM-924 .
19. Remove the front engine damping block.
   a. Remove 2 bolts (3).
20. Remove the wiring harness bracket.
   a. Remove the bolt (1).
21. Remove the rear engine mount.
   a. Remove the 3 bolts (2).
22. Remove the transaxle venting hose from the transaxle.

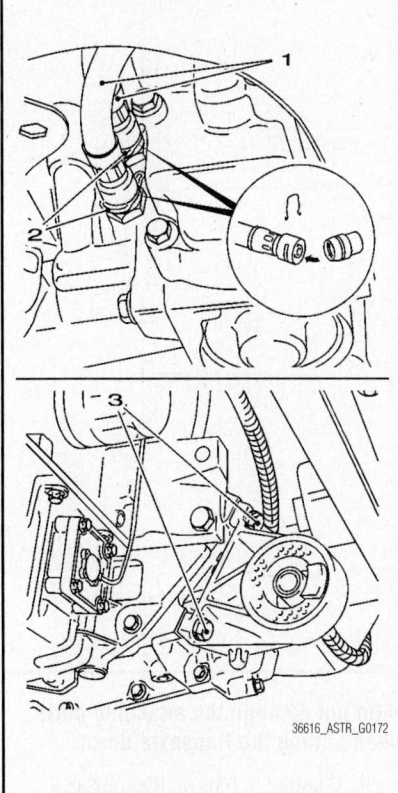

Fig. 27 Transaxle fluid cooler lines

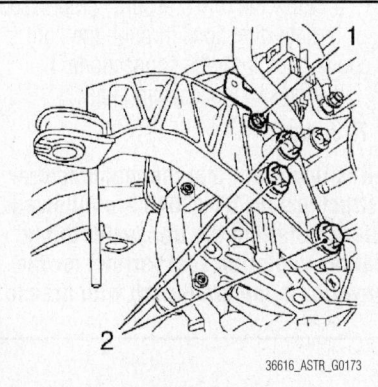

Fig. 28 Rear engine mount

23. Remove the left engine mount from the engine mount bracket.
   a. Remove the 3 bolts (1).

➡**Do not damage the wiring harnesses and attaching parts.**

24. Lower the engine and the transaxle with MKM-883-1 approximately 2 inches.
25. Remove the transaxle from the oil pan.
   a. Remove the 3 M10 bolts (1).
   b. Remove the M10 bolt connection (2).
26. Position the transaxle holder DT-47648 on KM-904 and pre-install as shown in the illustration.
   a. Converter housing support.
   • Position on the base plate: 2
   • Component: DT-47648 DT-47648-2 (4)
   b. Transaxle housing support
   • Position on base plate: 14
   • Component: DT-47648 DT-47648-3 (2)
   c. Support with rear the transaxle swivel arm.
   • Position on base plate: A
   • Component: DT-47648 DT-47648-5 Left (1)
   d. Support with the front transaxle swivel arm
   • Position on base plate: F
   • Component: DT-47648 DT-47648-5 Right (3)

➡**It is important that the manufacturer instructions for transaxle holder DT-47648 are followed.**

➡**Before placing in position slacken all bolt connections of the swivel arms and supports as far as the base plate. Adjust the supports for the converter housing and transaxle housing using the spindles until they are as low as possible.**

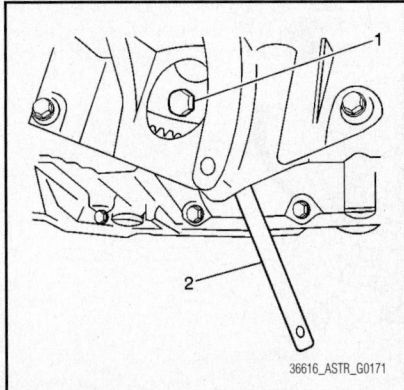

Fig. 26 Torque converter bolts

Fig. 29 Left engine mount

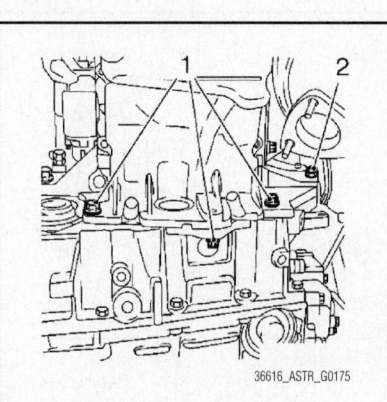

Fig. 30 Transaxle-to-oil pan bolts

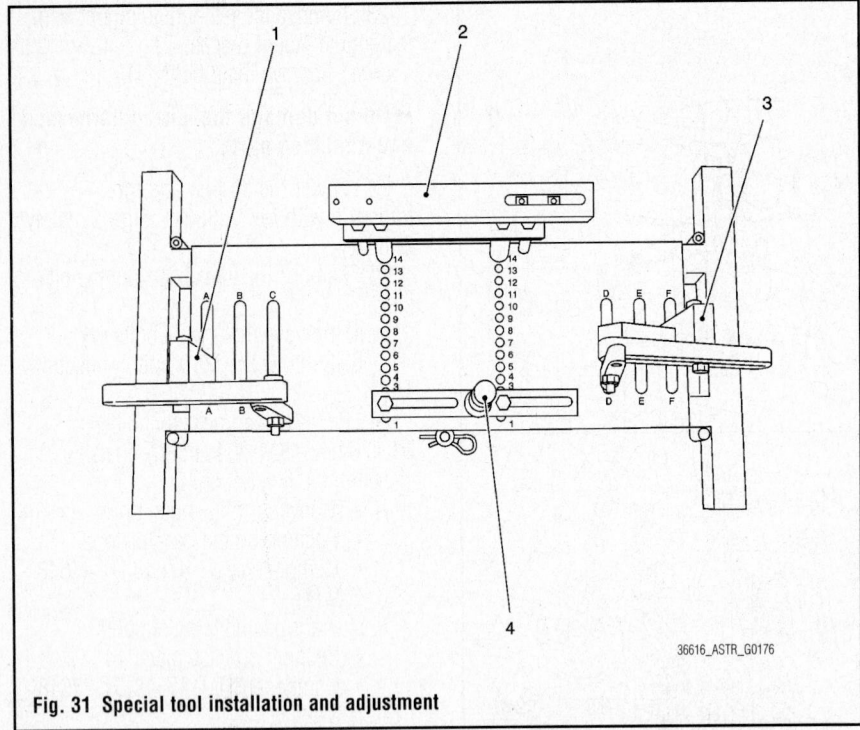

Fig. 31 Special tool installation and adjustment

27. Install the transaxle holder DT-47648 to the transaxle.

a. Align the transaxle holder DT-47648 under the transaxle.

b. Install the 2 swivel arms (1) to the transaxle.

➡️**Align the swivel arms so that as little leverage as possible is created.**

c. Tighten the bolt connections of the swivel arms, starting from the transaxle and going as far as the base plate.

d. Position the supports for the converter housing and the transaxle housing on the transaxle.

e. Twist up the spindles (2).

f. Tighten the bolt connections for the supports.

28. Secure the torque converter so it does not fall out.

➡️**Do not damage the attaching parts when putting the transaxle down.**

29. If required, remove the transaxle from the transaxle holder DT-47648 .

30. When replacing the transaxle:

a. Blow the low-pressure compressed air in both directions through the fluid cooler lines from the connections.

b. Transfer the attaching parts.

To install:

➡️**It is important that the manufacturer instructions for DT-47648 are followed. Before installing the transaxle, thinly coat the centering seat (arrow) for the converter in the crankshaft with grease.**

When replacing the transaxle, ensure that the two guide bushings (1) sit in the engine flange.

31. If required, install the transaxle to the transaxle holder DT-47648 .

32. Inspect the converter centering journal (3) for fretting.

33. Measure the torque converter installation depth in the transaxle.

a. Measure with measuring device (1).

b. Distance: approximately 12 mm

34. Coat the centering seat (arrow) for the torque converter in the crankshaft with grease.

35. Check the correct seating of the 2 guide bushes (1) in the engine flange.

36. Remove KM-6388 .

37. Raise the transaxle with the hydraulic jack and the transaxle holder DT-47648 and align it.

➡️**Ensure it is perfectly seated. Do not damage wiring harnesses and attaching parts.**

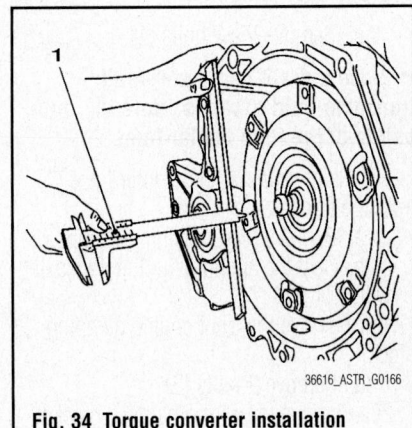

Fig. 34 Torque converter installation

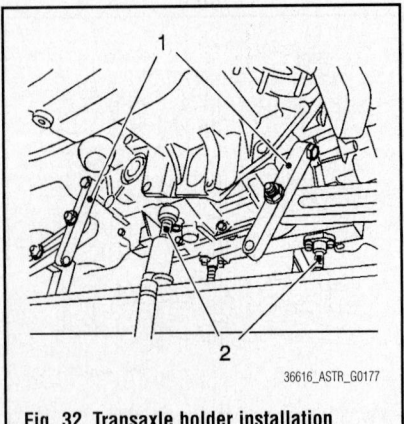

Fig. 32 Transaxle holder installation

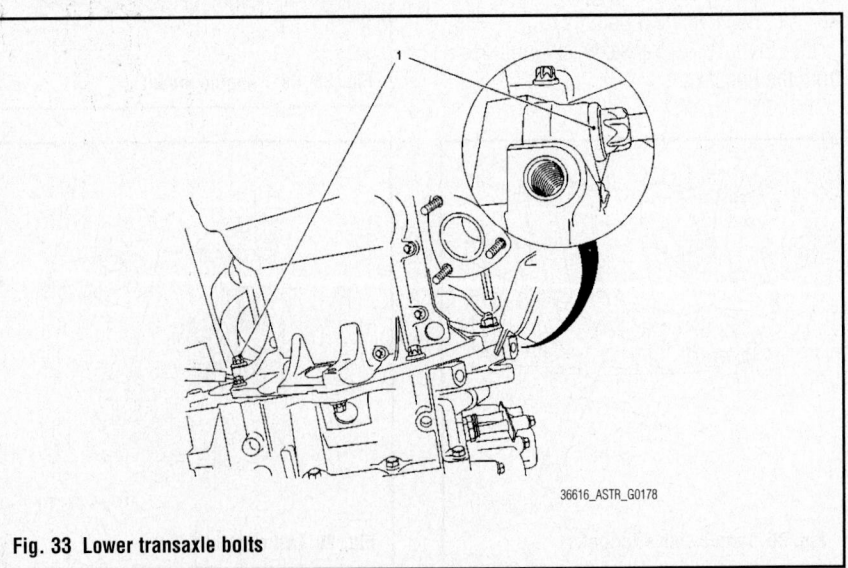

Fig. 33 Lower transaxle bolts

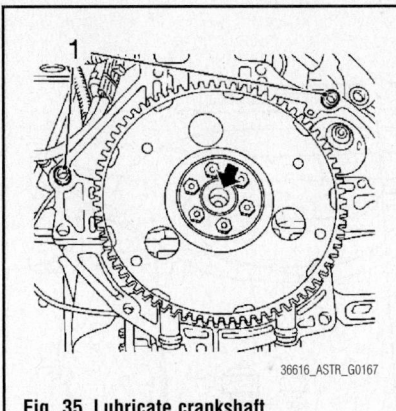

Fig. 35 Lubricate crankshaft

38. Position the transaxle evenly on the engine.

39. Fasten the transaxle to the engine with 2 bolts.

40. Tighten the 2 M12 bolts (1) to 44 ft. lbs. (60 Nm).

41. Remove the transaxle holder DT-47648 from the transaxle.

 a. Remove the 2 bolts.

 b. Lower the hydraulic jack with the transaxle holder DT-47648 and pull out.

42. Fasten the transaxle at the bottom.

 a. Install the transaxle on fluid sump.

43. Tighten the 3 M10 bolts to 30 ft. lbs. (40 Nm).

 a. Tighten the bolt connection (2).

44. Tighten bolt connection to 30 ft. lbs. (40 Nm).

45. Install the converter to the drive disc.

➡**Insert the bolts with locking compound. Turn drive disc by a further 120 degrees each time.**

46. Tighten 3 bolts (1).

 a. Stage 1: Tighten 3 bolts evenly to 15 ft. lbs. (20 Nm).

 b. Stage 2: Tighten 3 bolts to 33 ft. lbs. (45 Nm) plus 20 degrees, plus 25 degrees.

47. Remove KM-911 .

48. Install the 2 covers to the transaxle.

49. Install the engine mount to the transaxle at the front.

50. Tighten the 2 bolts (1) 59 ft. lbs. (80 Nm).

51. Install the engine mount to the transaxle at the front.

52. Tighten the 2 bolts (1) 59ft. lbs. (80 Nm).

53. Install the rear engine damping block to the transaxle.

54. Tighten the 3 bolts (2) 59 ft. lbs. (80 Nm).

55. Install the wiring harness bracket.

56. Tighten the bolt (1).

57. Install the halfshafts into the transaxle. Refer to Halfshaft Removal & Installation.

58. Install the oil cooler lines to the transaxle.

➡**Fluid cooler lines must be heard to engage.**

59. Use 2 NEW O-rings (1).

60. Raise the engine and the transaxle with MKM-883-1 and align.

61. Install the left engine mount to the engine mount bracket.

➡**Do not tighten the 3 bolts yet.**

62. Install the 3 bolts (1).

➡**When installing the front axle body, ensure that the support bearings with KM-6001-A sit properly in the guide pin of the front engine damping block and the rear engine damping block bracket. If necessary: correct installation position of engine and transaxle using MKM-883-1 .**

➡**Do not yet install front exhaust pipe, catalytic converter, center muffler, battery support and battery.**

63. Install front sub-frame.

64. Fasten the left engine mount.

65. Tighten the 3 bolts (1) to 40 ft. lbs. (55 Nm).

66. Secure the transaxle at the top.

67. Tighten the 3 bolts (1) to 44 ft. lbs. (60 Nm).

68. Install the selector cable bracket.

69. Tighten the 2 bolts (1) to 15 ft. lbs. (20 Nm).

➡**Use new seal ring.**

70. Install the fluid filler tube (2) with dipstick.

71. Tighten the nut.

72. Connect the transaxle venting hose to the transaxle.

73. Install the selector actuation cable.

 a. Install to the selector actuation cable bracket.

 b. Install to the actuation lever.

74. Connect and lock the wiring harness connector for the transaxle wiring harness.

75. Connect and lock the selector lever position switch wiring harness connector.

76. Adjust the range selector cable.

77. Install the battery tray and battery.

78. Remove KM-6001-A .

79. Install the front exhaust pipe, catalytic converter and center silencer.

80. Inspect the transaxle fluid level. Refer to Transaxle Fluid Check.

81. For programming procedures, refer to Control Module References in this section.

MANUAL TRANSAXLE ASSEMBLY

REMOVAL & INSTALLATION

See Figures 38 through 46.

Special Service Tools:
- KM-569-A Plug Remover
- KM-6001-A Engine Mount
- MKM-883-1 Engine Bridge
- DT-47648 Transaxle Holder
- KM-904 Base Frame

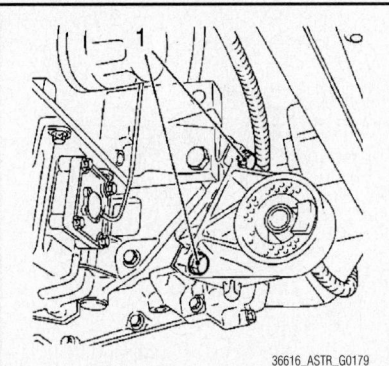

Fig. 36 Engine mount installation

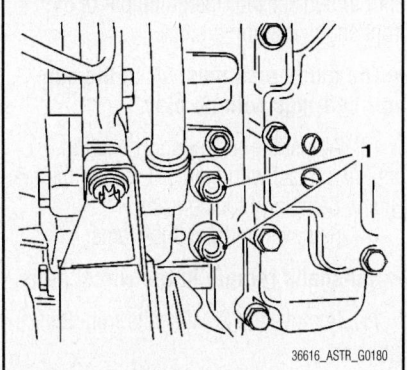

Fig. 37 Cooler line installation

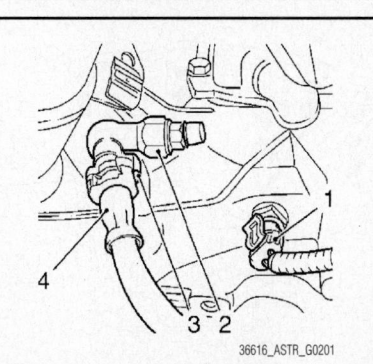

Fig. 38 Backup lamp switch and components

➡️**If the transaxle is replaced, the following parts must be transferred:**

- Connection piece for clutch actuation.
- Engine damping block bracket.
- Shift Bowden cable bracket.

1. Remove the battery tray.
2. Place a drain pan underneath.
3. Disconnect the wiring harness connector, backup lamp switch (1).
4. Remove the clutch pressure hose (4) from the connection piece (2).
    a. Open the retaining clamp (3).
    b. Remove the clutch pressure hose.
    c. Close the retaining clamp.
5. Remove the selector lever link (1) from the transaxle cover (2).
    a. Press in the retaining spring (arrow) of the hollow pin.
    b. Lever out roll pin with KM-569-A .
6. Release the transaxle at the top.
7. Remove the 4 bolts (arrows).
8. Attach KM-6001-A to the front subframe.
9. Remove the 2 bolts (arrows) for the adjustment rails on KM-6001-A (1).

➡️**Two journals (2) and (5) must sit flush in the guide holes of the front sub-frame.**

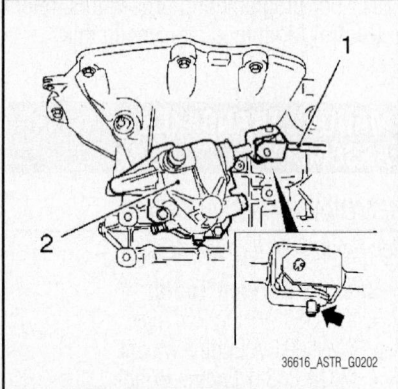

Fig. 39 Selector lever link

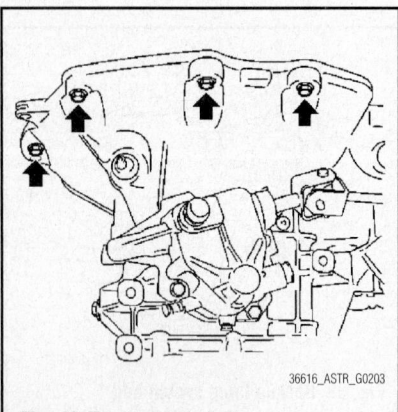

Fig. 40 Top transaxle bolts

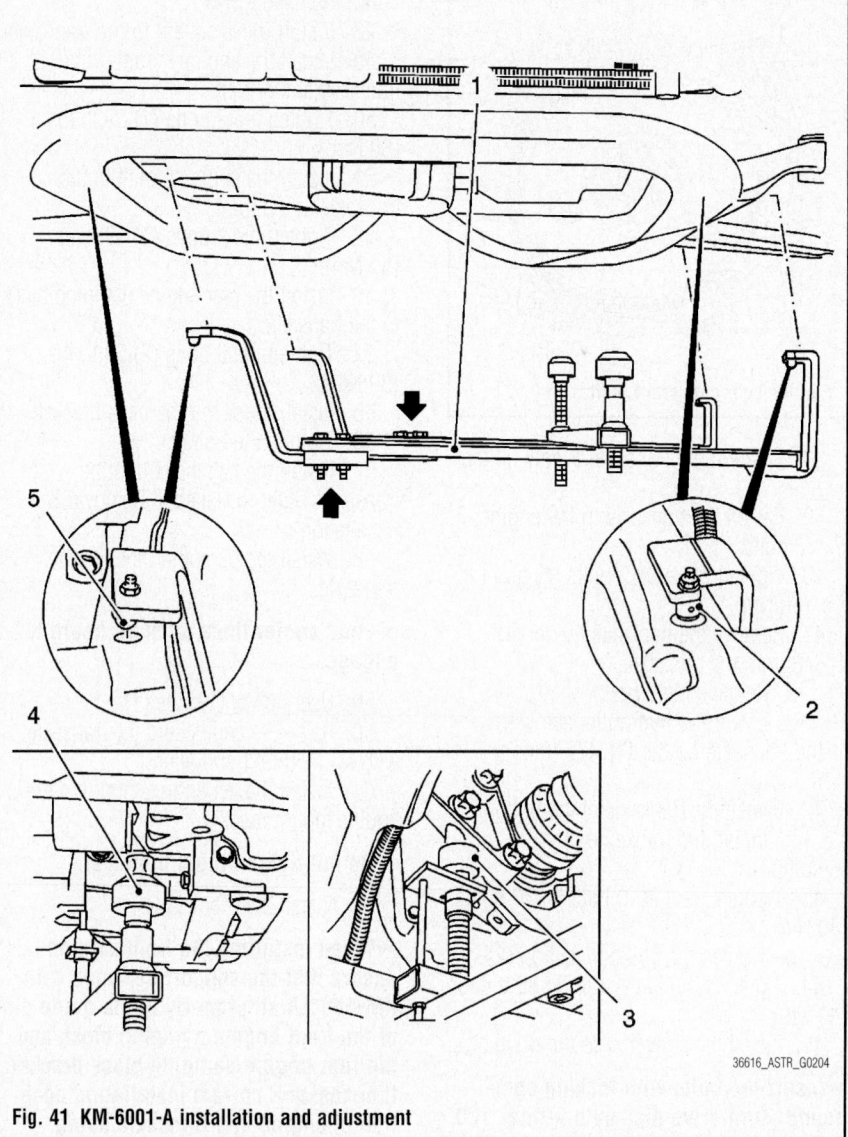

Fig. 41 KM-6001-A installation and adjustment

10. Insert KM-6001-A as shown.
11. Tighten the 2 bolts for the adjustment rails.

➡️**The guide pins must sit in the support bearings with no play.**

12. Adjust the front support bearing (4) until in contact with the guide pin of the front engine damping block.

➡️**The guide pins must sit in the support bearings with no play.**

13. Adjust the rear support bearing (3) until in contact with the guide pin of the rear engine damping block bracket.
14. Remove the front sub-frame.

➡️**Halfshafts remain in the wheel hubs.**

15. Remove the 2 halfshafts from the transaxle.
    a. Attach the halfshafts to the vehicle underbody.
    b. Seal the 2 openings for the 2 halfshafts with a plug.

➡️**Do not damage wiring harnesses and attaching parts.**

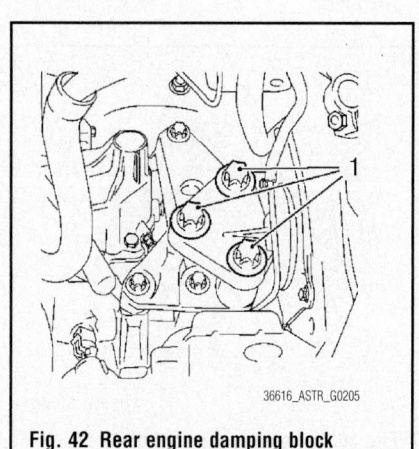

Fig. 42 Rear engine damping block

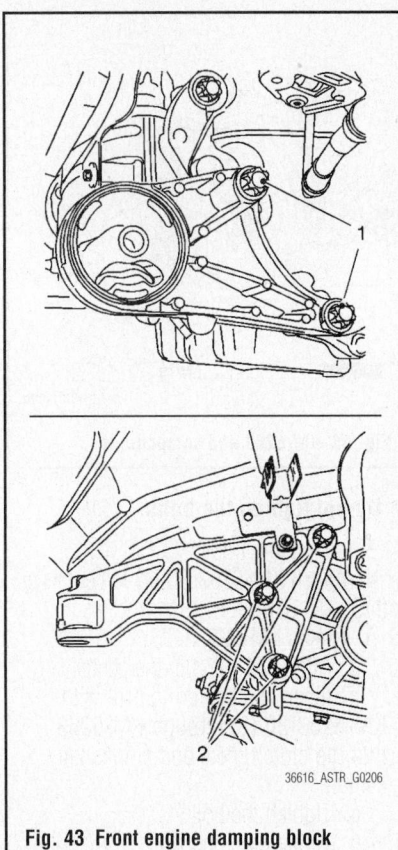

Fig. 43 Front engine damping block

16. Remove the transaxle from the left engine damping block.

17. Remove the 3 bolts (1).

18. Lower the engine and transaxle on the left-hand side.

a. Use MKM-883-1.

19. Remove the front engine damping block bracket.

a. Remove the 2 bolts (1).

20. Remove the rear engine damping block bracket.

a. Remove the 3 bolts (2).

21. Place the transaxle holder DT-47648 on KM-904 and pre-install as shown in the illustration:

22. DT-47648 (4)

a. Position on Base Plate-2

b. Designation-Clutch housing support

23. DT-47648 (2)

a. Position on Base Plate-14

b. Designation-Transaxle housing support

24. DT-47648 (1)

a. Position on Base Plate-A

b. Designation-Support with rear transaxle swivel arm

25. DT-47648 (3)

a. Position on Base Plate-F

b. Designation-Support with rear transaxle swivel arm

➡**It is essential to follow the manufacturer's instructions for transaxle holder DT-47648 .**

➡**Before placing in position, slacken all bolt connections of the swivel arms and supports as far as the base plate. Adjust the supports using the spindles until they are as low as possible.**

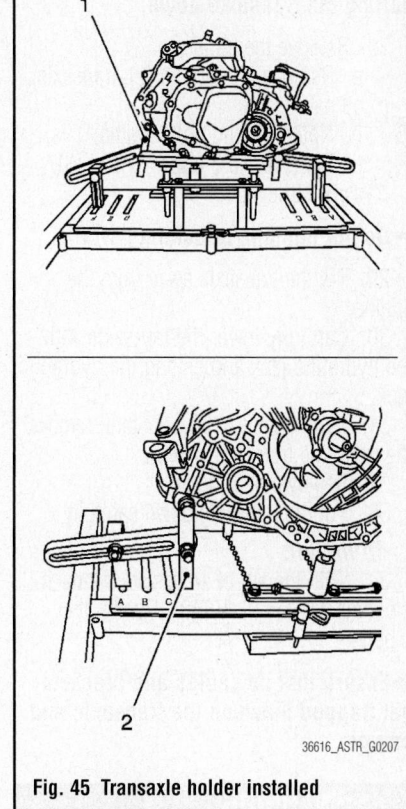

Fig. 45 Transaxle holder installed

26. Attach the transaxle holder DT-47648 to the transaxle.

a. Place the transaxle holder DT-47648 with supports in position under the transaxle.

b. Tighten the bolt connections of the supports

c. Attach the swivel arm (1) and (2) to the transaxle.

➡**Align the swivel arms so that as little leverage as possible is created.**

27. Tighten the bolt connections of the swivel arms starting from the transaxle and going as far as the base plate

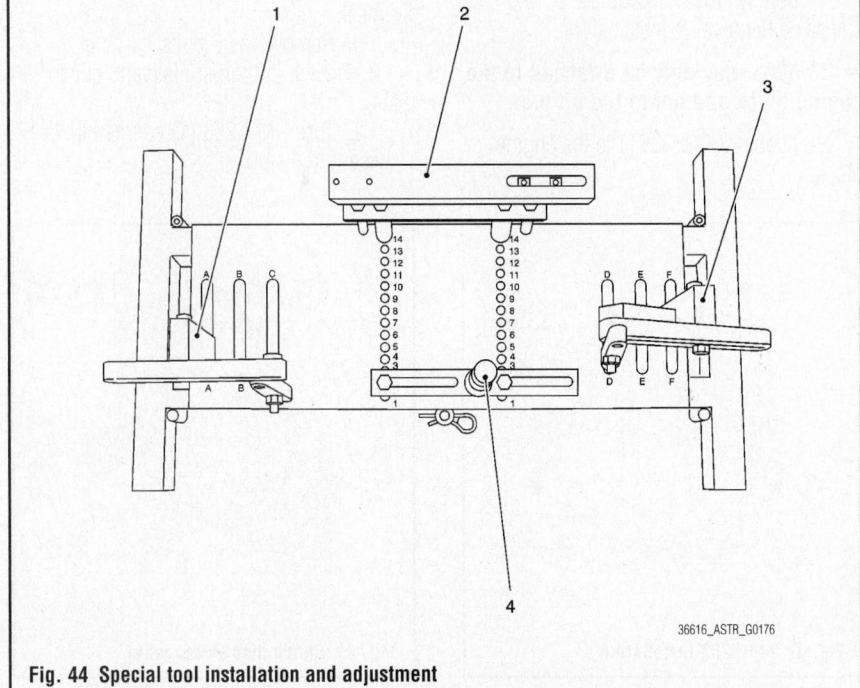

Fig. 44 Special tool installation and adjustment

Fig. 46 Transaxle removal

➡**Do not damage attaching parts when putting the transaxle down.**

28. Remove the transaxle.

a. Remove the 3 bolts (2), transaxle to oil pan.

b. Note differing bolt lengths.

c. Remove the 3 bolts (1) and (3), transaxle to cylinder block.

➡**Do not damage attaching parts.**

29. Pry the transaxle away from the engine.

30. Carefully lower the transaxle with the hydraulic jack and extend the hydraulic jack.

31. With the aid of an assistant, remove the transaxle from DT-47648 .

32. Remove the 2 bolts.

33. Put the transaxle down carefully.

To install:

34. With the aid of an assistant, attach the transaxle to DT-47648 . Tighten the 2 bolts.

➡**Ensure that no cables and brackets get trapped between the transaxle and engine.**

✳✳ WARNING

Ensure that the transaxle is seated correctly.

35. Install the transaxle with DT-47648

36. Raise the transaxle and align it.

37. Place the transaxle so that it is in even contact with the engine.

38. Install the transaxle.

39. Install the wiring harness bracket with the front bolt.

40. Tighten the 3 transaxle to cylinder block bolts (1) and (3) to 44 ft. lbs. (60 Nm).

41. Tighten the 2 transaxle to oil pan bolts (2) to 30 ft. lbs. (40 Nm).

42. Remove the transaxle holder DT-47648 from the transaxle.

a. Remove the 2 bolts.

b. Lower and extend the hydraulic jack.

✳✳ WARNING

Do not damage wiring harnesses and attaching parts.

43. Raise the engine and transaxle on the left hand side.

44. Raise with MKM-883-1 .

➡**Do not tighten bolts yet.**

45. Attach the transaxle to left hand engine damping block.

46. Tighten the 3 bolts (1) to 59 ft. lbs. (80 Nm).

47. Install the front engine damping block bracket.

48. Tighten the 2 bolts (1) to 59 ft. lbs. (80 Nm).

49. Install the rear engine damping block bracket.

50. Tighten the 3 bolts (2) to 59 ft. lbs. (80 Nm).

51. Install the 2 halfshafts to the transaxle. Refer to Wheel Drive Shaft Replacement.

➡**Do not detach MKM-883-1 yet.**

52. Install the front sub-frame.

CLUTCH

REMOVAL & INSTALLATION

See Figures 47 through 53.

Special Service Tools:
- KM-6263 Remover/Installer

➡**When performing this procedure, note the following:**

- To prevent damage to the spring fangs of the thrust plate use KM-6263 to remove and install the thrust plate.
- Note the different lengths of the brackets for attaching KM-6263 to the lower engine block.
- Thrust plate and clutch disc for vehicles with self-adjusting clutch (SAC) are only available in the aftermarket as a set.

1. Remove the transaxle. Refer to Transaxle Removal & Installation.

➡**KM-6263 may only be attached to the engine block and not to the oil pan.**

2. Attach KM-6263 (1) to the engine block.

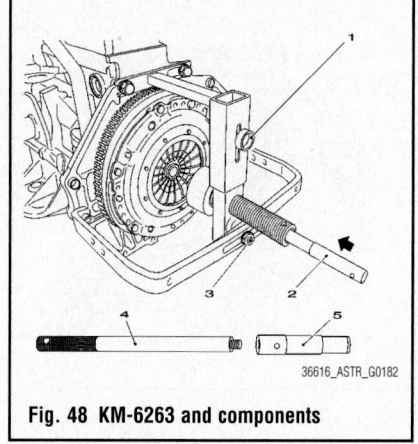

Fig. 48 KM-6263 and components

➡ **Do not tighten the bolts.**

3. Install the 4 bolts.

4. Attach KM-6263-30 (4) to centering drift (5) KM-6263-21.

5. Fasten KM-6263 .

a. Align KM-6263 in the center.

b. Insert the centering drift with KM-6263-30 (2) through KM-6263 into the clutch plate and crankshaft center.

c. Tighten the bolt (1).

d. Tighten the bolt (3).

e. Tighten the 4 bolts KM-6263 on the engine block.

6. Relieve stress on the clutch disc.

a. Move KM-6263 (1) so that it rests against the spring tangs of the thrust plate.

b. Turn KM-6263 clockwise to the stop.

7. Remove the thrust plate from the flywheel.

a. Remove the 6 bolts.

8. Detach the thrust plate and clutch plate.

a. Turn KM-6263 (1) counterclockwise to the stop.

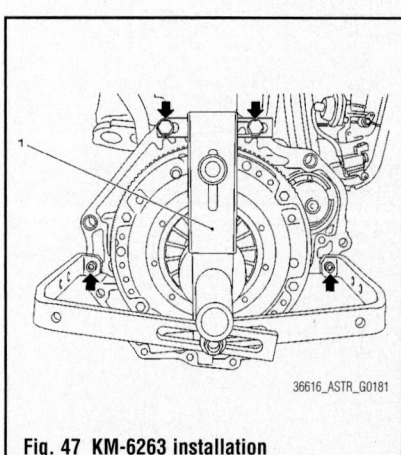

Fig. 47 KM-6263 installation

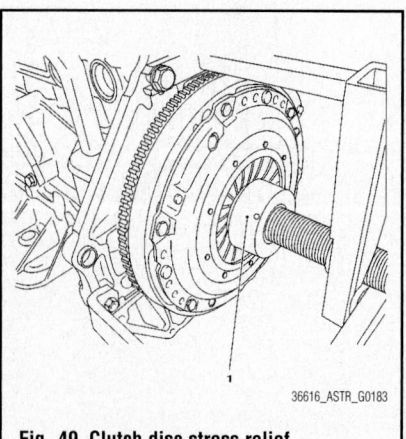

Fig. 49 Clutch disc stress relief

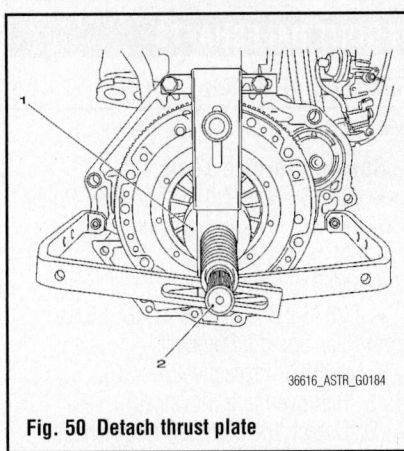
Fig. 50 Detach thrust plate

b. Remove the centering drift with KM-6263-30 (2).

✳✳ WARNING

Clutch plates contaminated by foreign bodies (oil, cleaning agent etc.) must be replaced. Check clutch disc for damage and friction rust in the hub profile and replace if necessary. Do not clean thrust plate and clutch disc with a high pressure cleaner or component washing machine.

9. Inspect the thrust plate and clutch disc for wear, replace if necessary.
10. Inspect the clutch plate for wear.
11. Inspect the projection of the lining at the clutch lining rivets. The clutch plate must be replaced if the lining projection is less than 0.5 mm (0.020 in). Also, press the

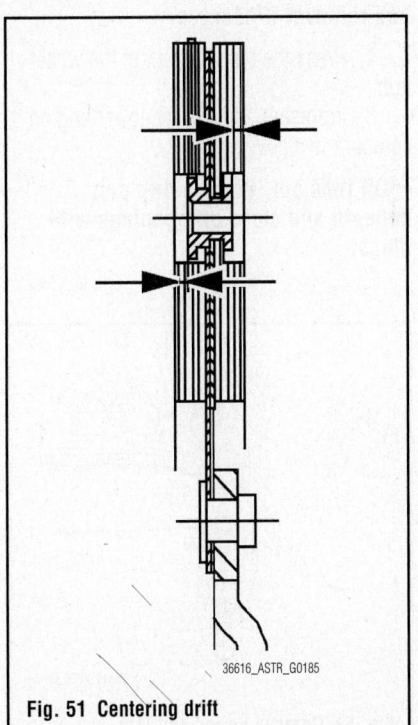
Fig. 51 Centering drift

clutch plate onto the transaxle input shaft and check for ease of movement.

To install:

➡**Lettering transaxle side faces the transaxle.**

12. Install the clutch disc and thrust plate to the flywheel.
13. Center the thrust plate and clutch plate with center drift and KM-6263-30 (1).

➡**Do not tighten the bolts.**

14. Install 6 new bolts.
15. Install the thrust plate to flywheel.
16. Turn KM-6263 (1) to align clutch.
17. Install the 6 bolts. Tighten the bolts crosswise.
18. Tighten the M7 bolt to 11 ft. lbs. (15 Nm).
19. Remove KM-6263 (1) from the engine block.
   a. Turn KM-6263 (3) counterclockwise to the stop.
   b. Install the centering drift and KM-6263-30 (2)
   c. Remove the 4 bolts KM-6263 on engine block.
20. Install the transaxle. Refer to Transaxle Removal & Installation.

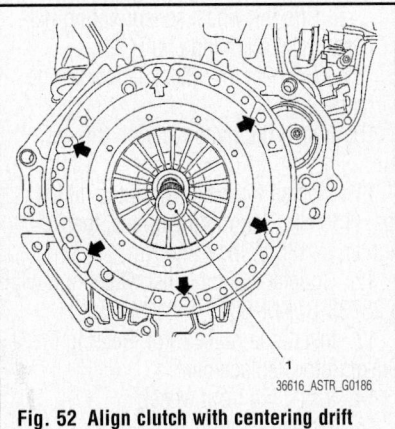
Fig. 52 Align clutch with centering drift

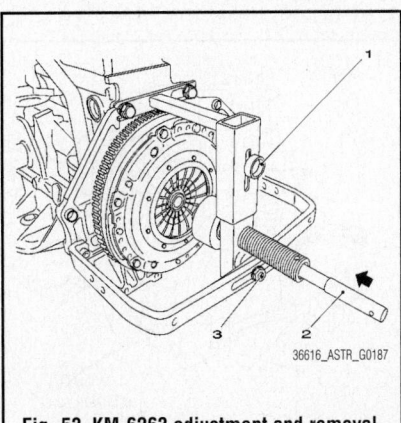
Fig. 53 KM-6263 adjustment and removal

BLEEDING

Special Service Tools:
• J 35555 Metal Mityvac
• J 43485 Power Steering Bleeder Adapter
1. Verify that all the lines and fittings are dry and secure.
2. Clean the dirt and grease from the reservoir cap in order to ensure that no foreign substances enter the system.
3. Remove the reservoir cap.
4. Fill the reservoir to the proper level with the required fluid.
5. Attach the J 43485 to the J 35555 , or equivalent.

➡**Brake fluid will deteriorate the rubber on the J 43485 . Use a clean shop cloth to wipe away the fluid after each use.**

6. Place and hold the adapter on the reservoir filler neck to ensure a tight fit. In some cases, the adapter will fit into the reservoir opening.
7. Apply a vacuum of 51-68 kPa (15-20 hg) on the gauge.
8. Hold vacuum for approximately 1 minute,
9. Slowly relieve vacuum and remove the J 43485 from the reservoir.
10. Refill the reservoir to the proper level.
11. Repeat steps 6-10.
12. If needed, refill the reservoir and continue to pull a vacuum until no more bubbles can be seen in the reservoir or until the fluid level no longer drops.

✳✳ WARNING

The vehicle will move if started in gear before the Actuator Cylinder is refilled and operational. Start the vehicle the first time in neutral to help prevent personal injury from vehicle movement and see if the transaxle will shift easily into gear.

13. Pump the clutch pedal until firm to refill actuator cylinder.
14. Add additional fluid if needed.

➡**The clutch and braking systems are integrated into one reservoir. The brake may be soft when first applying.**

15. Pump brake pedal until firm.
16. Add additional fluid if needed.
17. Test drive the vehicle to ensure proper operation of clutch and brake systems.

FRONT AXLE HUB, BEARING & SEAL

REMOVAL & INSTALLATION
See Figures 54 through 56.

Special Service Tools:
• J 28733-B /KM-6610 and KM-956-1 Front/Rear Spindle Remover

1. Remove the front wheel.
2. Remove the brake rotor.
3. Remove the nut from the halfshaft.
4. Counter-hold against the wheel hub with holding wrench J 28733-B /KM-6610 and KM-956-1.

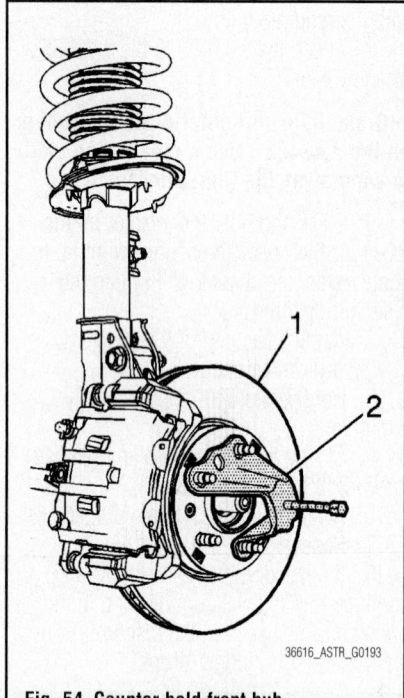

Fig. 54 Counter hold front hub

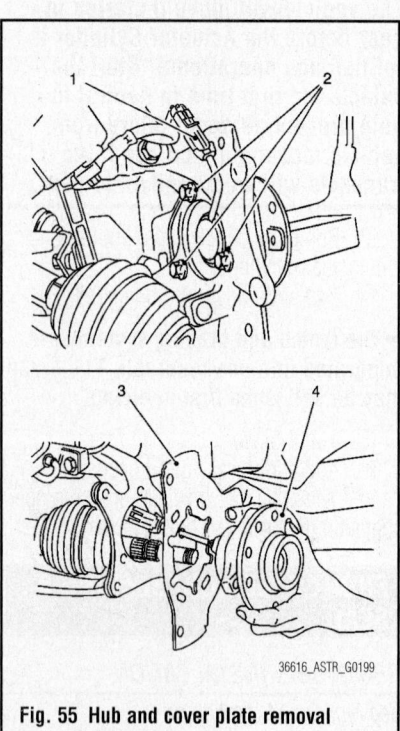

Fig. 55 Hub and cover plate removal

5. Disconnect the wiring harness connector (1) for wheel sensor.

➡**Pay attention to installation position of wheel bearing unit and cover plate.**

6. Remove the wheel bearing unit.
   a. Detach the 3 bolts (2).
   b. Pull the wheel bearing unit (4) with the cover plate (3) from the steering knuckle and halfshaft.

To install
   • Note installation position.
   • Clean thread and insert bolts with locking compound.
7. Install the wheel bearing unit.
   a. Place the cover plate on the wheel bearing unit.
   b. Slide the wheel bearing unit with the cover plate onto the halfshaft and place onto steering knuckle.
   c. Install the 3 new bolts.
8. Tighten the bolts to 67 ft. lbs. (90 Nm) plus 30 degrees plus 15 degrees.

➡**Ensure that wiring harness is correctly attached in all brackets and clips in order to prevent damage to wiring harness.**

9. Route the wiring harness.
   a. Clip the wheel sensor wiring harness in the retaining clip (1).
   b. Connect the wheel sensor wiring harness.
10. Install the halfshaft with the new nut.
11. Tighten the halfshaft nut to 111 ft. lbs. (150 Nm), undo 45 degrees, then tighten to 185 ft. lbs. (250 Nm)
12. Counter-hold against wheel hub with J 28733-B /KM-6610 and KM-956-1.
13. Install the brake rotor. Refer to Front Brake Rotor Replacement.
14. Install the front wheel.
15. Tighten the front wheel bolts to 81 ft. lbs. (110 Nm).

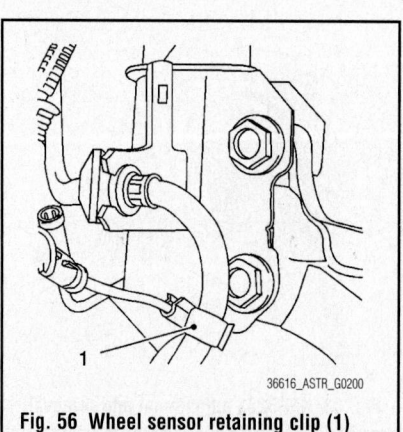

Fig. 56 Wheel sensor retaining clip (1)

FRONT HALFSHAFTS

REMOVAL & INSTALLATION

See Figures 54, 57 through 61.

Special Service Tools:
• KM-161-B /KM-161-2 Bearing Puller
• KM-313 Sliding Hammer
• KM-6003 Remover
• KM-915 Spreader
• J 28733-B /KM-956-1, KM-6610 Front/Rear Spindle Remover
• MK-6332 Protective Sleeve

1. Remove the front wheel(s).
2. Detach the halfshaft from wheel hub.
   a. Remove the nut (2) from the halfshaft.
   b. Counter hold at the front wheel hub with J 28733-B KM-6610 (1).
3. Press the tie rod out of the steering knuckle using the KM-161-B (1) together with the hook KM-161-B KM-161-2.
4. Detach the swing arm (1) from the spring strut support tube.
5. Counter hold at the flattened areas with a open-ended wrench.
6. Remove the guide joint from the steering knuckle.
   a. Remove the bolt.
   b. Spread the steering knuckle with KM-915 (2).
   c. Pull the guide joint out of the steering knuckle.

➡**During this process, draw the steering knuckle outwards, use the wheel hub remover if necessary.**

7. Press the halfshaft out of the wheel hub.
8. If present, remove the lower engine compartment cover.

➡**Oil runs out. Place a drip pan beneath and close off openings with plugs.**

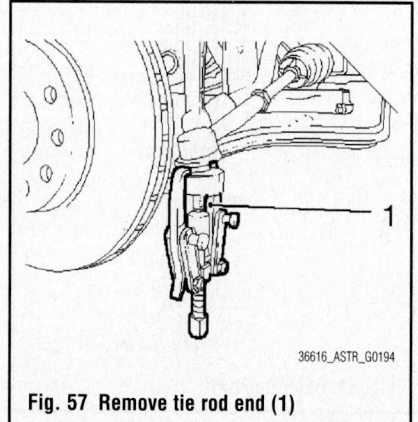

Fig. 57 Remove tie rod end (1)

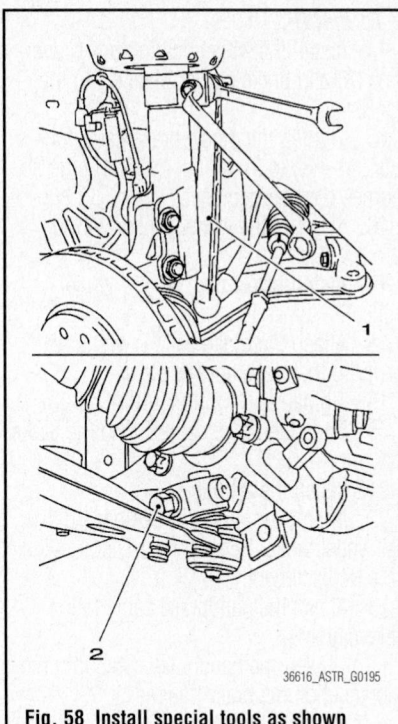

Fig. 58 Install special tools as shown

9. Remove the halfshaft from transaxle and knock off the intermediate shaft.

   a. Halfshaft, left.
- U18 XER
- KM-313 (1) and KM-6003 (2).

   b. Halfshaft, right
- U18 XER
- KM-313 (1) and KM-6003 (2).

➥**Do not put it on top of the boots.**

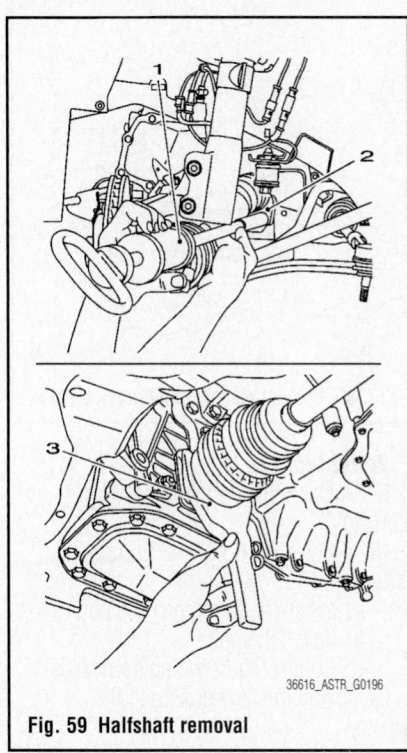

Fig. 59 Halfshaft removal

10. Take care when handling the halfshaft.

To install:

11. Replace the retaining ring (1) at the halfshaft.

12. Use the MK-6332 in order to avoid damaging the transaxle seal ring.

13. If the splines on the halfshaft (1) has passed through the MK-6332 (2), pull the MK-6332 (2) downwards, arrow, and remove it. Do not engage the halfshaft (1) yet.

14. Insert the halfshaft (1) into the transaxle.

15. Coat the splines and bearing points with transaxle fluid.

   a. Insert the MK-6332 (2) into the transaxle.

   b. Insert the halfshaft (1) into the MK-6332 (2) on the transaxle.

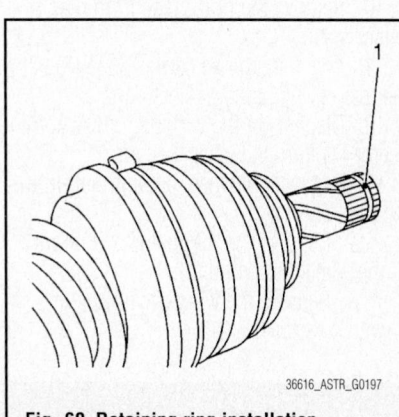

Fig. 60 Retaining ring installation

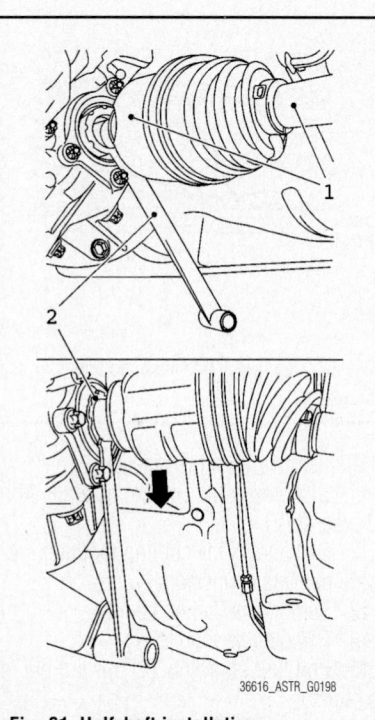

Fig. 61 Halfshaft installation

16. Insert the halfshaft into wheel hub.

17. Attach the guide joint to the steering knuckle.

18. Use NEW nuts.

19. Tighten the nuts to 37 ft. lbs. (50 Nm).

20. Attach the swing arm to spring strut support tube.

21. Use NEW nuts.

22. Tighten the nuts to 40 ft. lbs. (55 Nm).

23. Counter hold at the flattened areas with open-ended wrench.

24. Attach the tie rod end to the steering knuckle.

25. Release at the hex.

26. Tighten the new nut of tie rod end 22 ft. lbs. (30 Nm) plus 90 degrees, plus 15 degrees.

27. Attach the halfshaft to the wheel hub.

28. Tighten to 111 ft. lbs. (150 Nm), undo 45 degrees, then tighten to 185 ft. lbs. (250 Nm).

29. Use the NEW nuts.

30. Counter hold against the wheel hub with J 28733-B and extension J 28733-B KM-956-1.

31. Install the front wheel.

32. Tighten to 81 ft. lbs. (110 Nm).

33. Inspect the transaxle fluid level and adjust as required.

34. If present, install the lower engine compartment cover.

REAR HUB, BEARING & SEAL

REMOVAL & INSTALLATION

See Figures 62 and 63.

1. Release the handbrake.

2. Detach the boot of handbrake lever (2).

3. Slacken the handbrake cable by turning back the adjusting nut (3).

4. Remove the rear wheel.

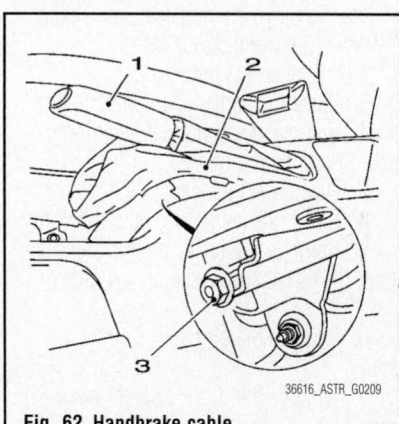

Fig. 62 Handbrake cable

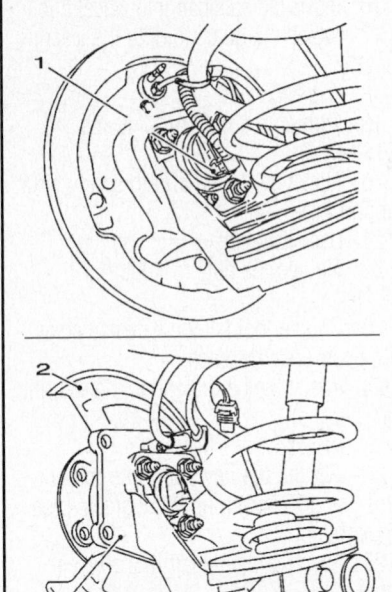

Fig. 63 Rear bearing and cover plate

5. In the vehicles with disc brakes, detach the handbrake cable from the brake caliper.

a. Push down the operating lever at the brake caliper using a screwdriver.

b. Remove the handbrake cable.

c. Detach the retaining clip.

d. Pull the handbrake cable out of the bracket.

➡ **If it is not possible to pull the brake caliper with brake carrier and installed brake pads from brake disc because of brake disc wear, for example: remove the brake pads from rear wheel brake, refer to Rear Disc Brake Pads Replacement .**

6. Detach the brake caliper with brake carrier from the brake backing plate.

7. Remove the 2 brake carrier bolts from the brake carrier plate.

8. Pull the brake caliper with brake carrier from the brake disc.

9. Suspend the brake caliper and brake carrier from the rear spring using suitable wire.

10. Remove the brake disc from rear wheel brake.

11. Attach the brake carrier plate (3) to the rear spring using cable straps.

12. Disconnect the wiring harness connector (1) from the wheel sensor.

13. Remove the wheel bearing unit from the rear axle.

a. Remove the 4 nuts (arrows) from the wheel bearing unit.

b. Remove the wheel bearing unit with cover plate (2).

To install:

14. Install the wheel bearing unit, cover plate (3) and brake carrier plate (2) to the rear axle.

15. Tighten the 4 new brake carrier plate nuts (arrows) to 37 ft. lbs. (50 Nm) plus 30 degrees plus 15 degrees.

16. Connect the wheel sensor wiring harness (1).

17. Install brake disc of rear wheel brake.

18. Attach the brake caliper with brake carrier to the brake anchor plate.

19. Tighten to 74 ft. lbs. (100 Nm).

20. Slide the brake caliper onto the brake disc.

21. Install the 2 bolts.

22. If removed, install brake pads of the rear wheel brake. Refer to Rear Disc Brake Pads Replacement.

23. Attach the handbrake cable to the brake caliper.

a. Insert the handbrake cable into the bracket on the brake caliper.

b. Attach the retaining clip to the handbrake cable.

c. Push down the operating lever at the brake caliper using a screwdriver.

d. Install the handbrake cable.

24. Install the rear wheel.

25. Tighten to 81 ft. lbs. (110 Nm).

ENGINE COOLING

ENGINE COOLING FAN

REMOVAL & INSTALLATION

See Figures 64 through 67.

✳ WARNING

Refer to Battery Disconnect Warning in this section.

1. Open the hood.

2. Disconnect the battery.

a. Remove the negative connection from the ground terminal.

b. Loosen the nut.

3. Raise the vehicle by its full height.

4. Remove the compressor wiring harness from the fan housing.

5. Disconnect the cable tie.

6. Lower the vehicle by its full height.

7. Remove the air cleaner assembly. Refer to Air Cleaner Assembly Replacement.

8. Remove the air cleaner outlet resonator.

9. Remove the upper radiator hose (1) from the fan housing.

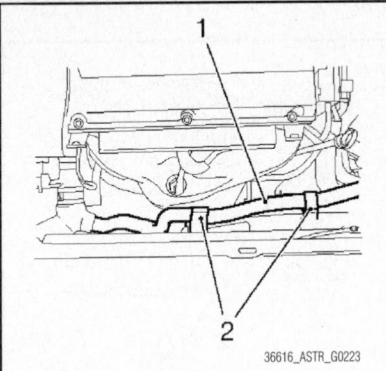

Fig. 64 Upper radiator hose (1) and bracket (2)

10. Remove from the bracket (2).

11. Disconnect the coolant hose (1) from the bracket (2).

12. Disconnect the cooling module wiring harness connector (1).

13. Remove the fan housing.

14. Remove the 2 bolts (1).

15. Pull the 2 brackets (2) upward out of the radiator.

16. Lift the fan housing up and off.

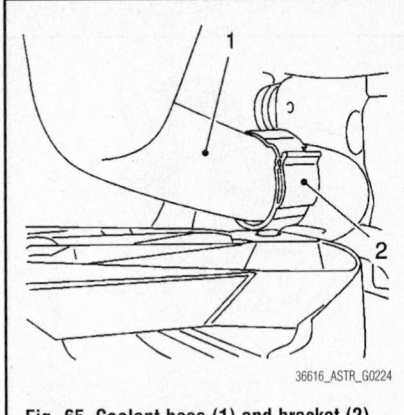

Fig. 65 Coolant hose (1) and bracket (2)

To install:

17. Install the fan motor in the fan housing.

18. Tighten the 3 bolts to 26 inch lbs. (3 Nm).

a. Install the wiring harness connector.

b. Install the bolt.

c. Connect the 2 wiring harnesses.

19. Install the fan housing to the radiator.

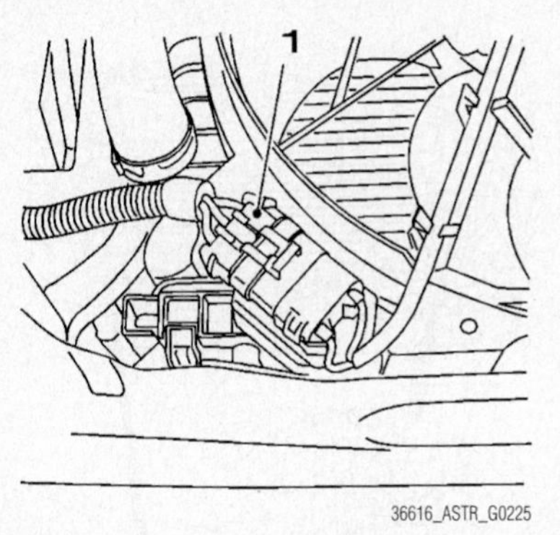

Fig. 66 Cooling module connector (1)

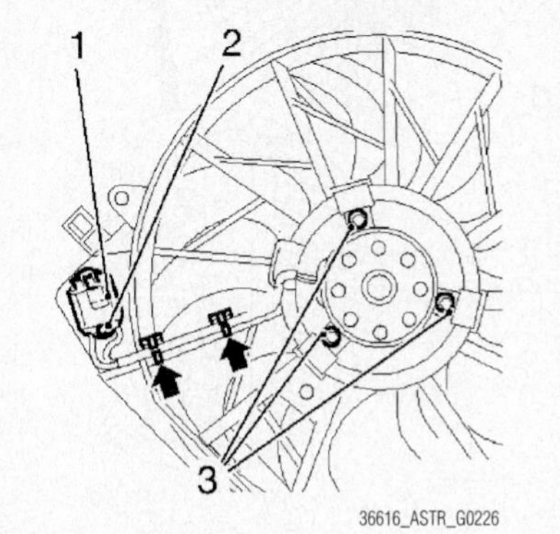

Fig. 67 Cooling fan removal

20. Tighten the 2 bolts to 44 inch lbs. (5 Nm).
21. Connect the cooling module wiring harness connector.
22. Install the 3 coolant hoses.
23. Install the air cleaner outlet resonator. Refer to Air Cleaner Inlet Duct Replacement.
24. Install the air cleaner assembly. Refer to Air Cleaner Assembly Replacement.
25. Raise the vehicle by its full height.
26. Install the compressor wiring harness to the fan housing.
27. Connect the cable ties.
28. Lower the vehicle by its full height.
29. Connect the battery.
30. Tighten the nut 44 inch lbs.(5 Nm).
31. Close the hood.

RADIATOR

REMOVAL & INSTALLATION

See Figures 68 through 76.

1. Open the hood.
2. Disconnect the battery.
3. Remove the upper grille.
   a. Remove the 4 body-bound rivets (1).
   b. Remove from the front fascia from above.
   c. Remove the 6 clips.
4. Remove the front fascia at the top.
   a. Remove the 2 bolts (1).
   b. Remove the 2 body-bound rivets (2).
   c. Disconnect the wiring harness connector.
5. Raise the vehicle by half its height.
6. Remove the front fascia.
   a. Remove the 6 body-bound rivets (2).
   b. Remove the 4 bolts (1).
7. Raise the vehicle by half its height.
8. Drain the coolant.
   a. Place a drain pan underneath.
   b. Install the suitable hose to the drain connection (2).
   c. Open the coolant drain screw (1).
   d. Drain the coolant.
   e. Close the coolant drain screw.
9. Disconnect the cooling module wiring harness connector (1).
10. Place a drain pan underneath.
11. Remove the 2 radiator hoses from the radiator.
12. Remove 2 clamps.
13. Lower the vehicle by its full height.
14. Remove the coolant hose from the radiator.
    a. Release the clamp.
    b. Remove the coolant hose.

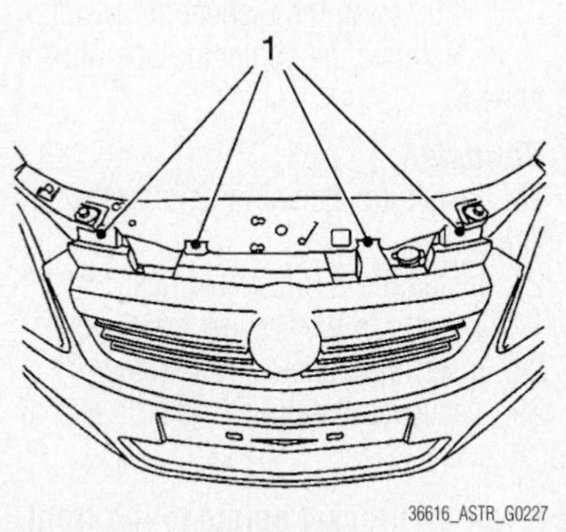

Fig. 68 Front grille removal

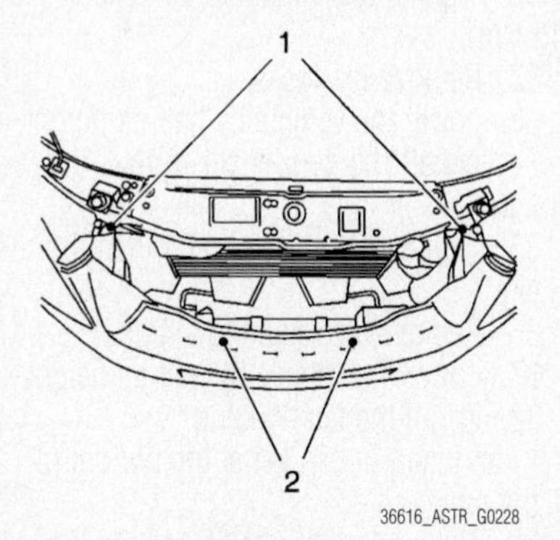

Fig. 69 Front fascia removal

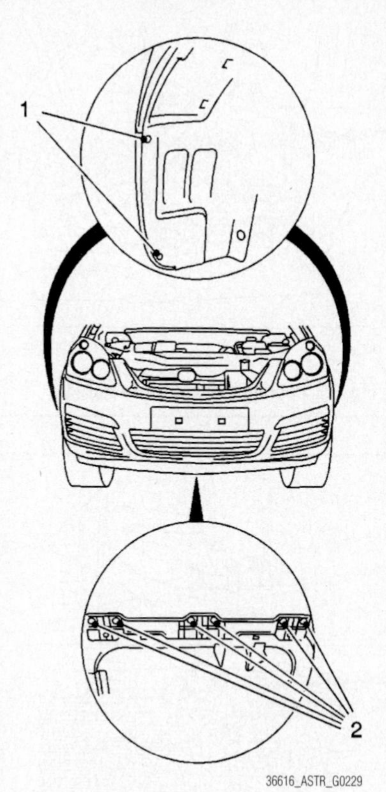

Fig. 70 Body rivets and bolts

15. Remove the 2 coolant hoses.
    a. Remove the radiator hose (top) from the bracket.
    b. Remove the coolant hose from the fan housing.
16. For vehicles equipped with an automatic transaxle:
    a. Remove the lower oil cooling line (2) with the connecting hose from the oil cooler.
    b. Remove the banjo bolt.
    c. Remove the upper oil cooling line (1) with the connecting hose from the oil cooler.
    d. Remove the banjo bolt.
17. Remove the fan housing from the radiator.
    a. Remove the 2 bolts (1).
    b. Pull the 2 brackets (2) upward out of the radiator.
18. Secure the radiator to the upper brackets (1).
19. Remove the condenser from the radiator.
    a. Secure the condenser to the upper front with the retaining straps (1).
    b. Remove the 4 bolts (2, 3).
20. Raise the vehicle by its full height.

➡Inspect the installation position.

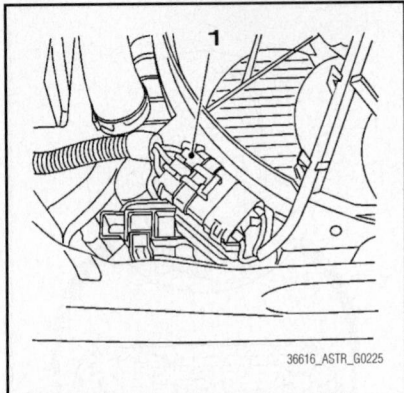

Fig. 71 Cooling module connector (1)

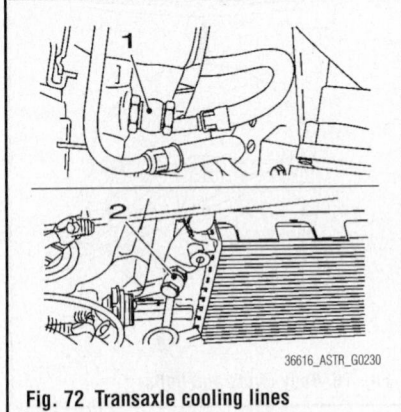

Fig. 72 Transaxle cooling lines

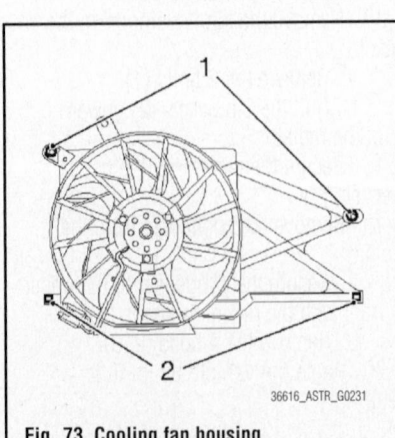

Fig. 73 Cooling fan housing

21. Remove the lower radiator bracket (1) from the front axle body.
22. Remove the 4 bolts.
23. Lower the radiator down and out.
24. Remove the fuses from the upper holders.
25. Push the condenser forward.

➡ **These operations must only be performed if the component is being replaced.**

   a. Remove the attached parts from the radiator.
   b. Remove the 2 rubber bearings.

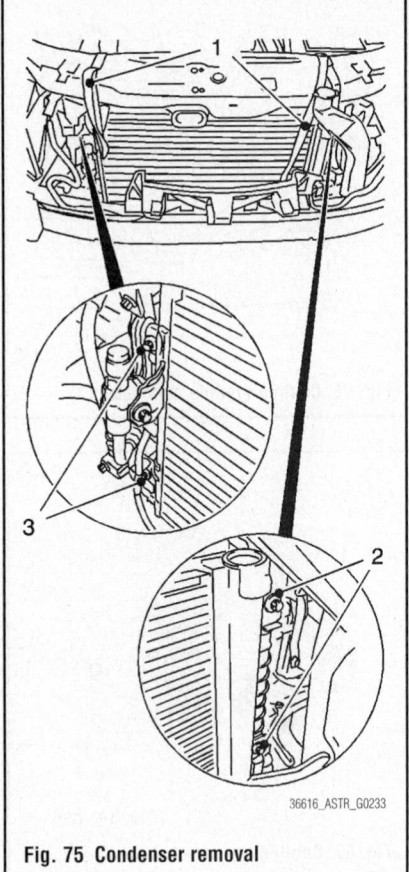

Fig. 74 Upper radiator brackets

   c. Pull away the 6 sheet metal nuts.
   d. Remove the coolant temperature sensor.

To install:
26. Install the attaching parts to the radiator.
27. Install the 2 rubber bushes.
   a. Push on the 6 sheet metal nuts.
28. Insert the radiator from below.
29. Secure to the upper radiator with a suitable tool.

➡ **Arrow on bracket points to the front of the vehicle.**

30. Install the lower radiator bracket.
31. Tighten the 4 bolts to 11 ft. lbs. (15 Nm).
32. Remove the fuses.
33. Lower the vehicle by half its height.
34. Install the condenser to the radiator.
35. Tighten the 4 bolts to 44 inch lbs. (5 Nm).
36. Remove the retaining straps.
37. Lower the vehicle by half its height.
38. Install the fan housing.
   a. Insert in bracket at the bottom of the radiator.
39. Tighten the 2 bolts to 44 inch lbs. (5 Nm).

40. Install the 2 radiator hoses into the bracket.
41. Install the NEW cable tie.
42. Install the expansion tank coolant hose to the radiator.
   a. Install the coolant hose.
43. Raise the vehicle by its full height.
44. Install the lower oil cooling line with the connecting hose on the oil cooler using NEW seal rings.
45. Tighten the bolt to 18 ft. lbs. (25 Nm).
46. Install the upper oil cooling line with the connecting hose on the oil cooler using NEW seal rings.

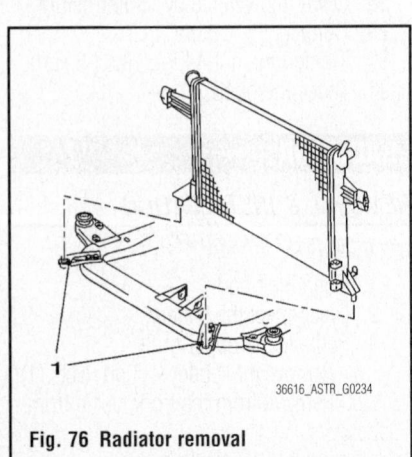

Fig. 76 Radiator removal

47. Tighten the bolt to 18 ft. lbs.
(25 Nm).
48. Install the 2 coolant hoses to the radiator.
49. Install the 2 clamps.
50. Connect the fan wiring harness connector.
51. Lower the vehicle by half its height.
52. Install the front fascia.
   a. Connect the 2 wiring harness connectors.
   b. Install the front fascia on the side.
53. Install the front paneling at bottom.
54. Install the 6 body-bound rivets.
55. Tighten the 4 bolts to 22 inch lbs.
(2.5 Nm).
56. Lower the vehicle by half its height.
57. Install the fascia at top.
58. Fasten the 2 body-bound rivets.
59. Tighten the 2 bolts to 22 inch lbs.
(2.5 Nm).
60. Install the radiator grille.
   a. Install the 6x bolts.
   b. Install the 4 body-bound rivets.
61. Fill and bleed the cooling system. Refer to Cooling System Draining and Filling.
62. Connect the battery.

THERMOSTAT

REMOVAL & INSTALLATION

See Figures 77 and 78.

1. Open the hood.
2. Disconnect the battery.
3. Raise the vehicle by its full height.
4. Place a drain pan underneath.
5. Drain the coolant.
   a. Place a drain pan underneath.
   b. Install the suitable hose to the drain connection (2).
   c. Open the coolant drain screw (1).
   d. Drain the coolant.
   e. Close the coolant drain screw.

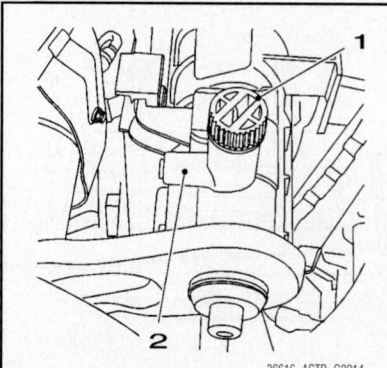

Fig. 77 Engine coolant drain

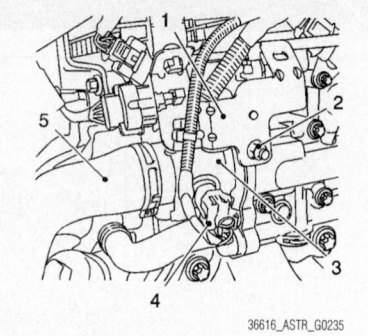

36616_ASTR_G0235

Fig. 78 Thermostat housing and components

6. Lower the vehicle by its full height.
7. Remove the wiring harness bracket (1) from the thermostat housing.
8. Remove the nut (2).
9. Disconnect the thermostat wiring harness connector (4).
10. Remove the upper radiator hose (5) from the coolant discharge port.
11. Release the clamp.
12. Remove the thermostat housing (3).
13. Remove the 4 bolts.

To install:
14. Clean the sealing surface.
15. Install the thermostat.
16. Replace the gasket.
17. Tighten the 4 bolts to 70 inch lbs.
(8 Nm).
18. Install the upper radiator hose to the coolant discharge port.
19. Fasten the clamp.
20. Install the wiring harness bracket to the thermostat housing.
21. Tighten the nut to 44 inch lbs.
(5 Nm).
22. Connect the thermostat wiring harness connector.
23. Fill and bleed the cooling system. Refer to Cooling System Draining and Filling.
24. Connect the battery.

WATER PUMP

REMOVAL & INSTALLATION

See Figures 79 and 80.

1. Remove the air cleaner assembly.
2. Remove the water pump strap disc (1).
   a. Remove the 3 bolts (2).
   b. Counter hold against the bolt of the vibration damper.
3. Raise the vehicle by its full height.
4. Remove the drive belt.

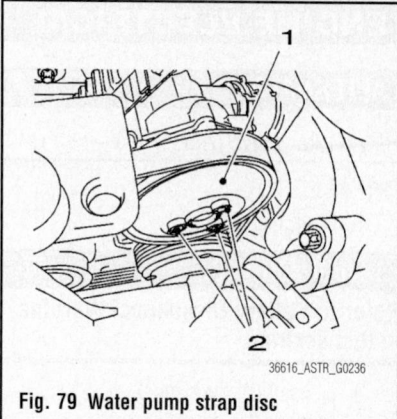

36616_ASTR_G0236

Fig. 79 Water pump strap disc

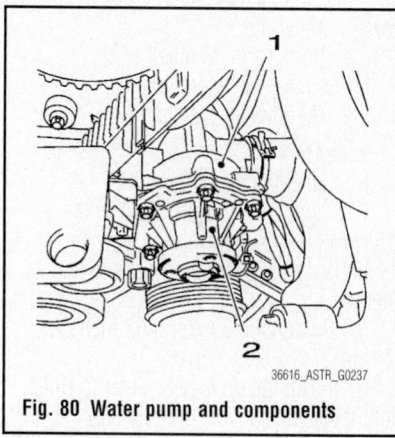

36616_ASTR_G0237

Fig. 80 Water pump and components

5. Drain the coolant.
   a. Place a drain pan underneath.
   b. Install the suitable hose to the drain connection (2).
   c. Open the coolant drain screw (1).
   d. Drain the coolant.
   e. Close the coolant drain screw.
6. Remove the water pump (2) from the pump module (1).
   a. Remove the 5 bolts.
   b. Remove the water pump.
7. Clean the sealing surfaces.
8. Clean the threads.

To install:
9. Install the water pump using NEW bolts.
10. Tighten the 5 bolts to 70 inch lbs.
(8 Nm).
11. Install the water pump strap disc.
   a. Use NEW bolts.
12. Raise the vehicle.
13. Install the drive belt.
14. Lower the vehicle.
15. Install the water pump belt pulley.
16. Tighten the 3 bolts to 15 ft. lbs.
(20 Nm).
17. Fill and bleed the cooling system. Refer to Cooling System Draining and Filling.
18. Install the air cleaner assembly.

ENGINE ELECTRICAL

CHARGING SYSTEM

ALTERNATOR

REMOVAL & INSTALLATION

See Figure 81.

1. Open the hood.

❋❋ WARNING

Refer to Battery Disconnect Warning in this section.

2. Disconnect the battery.
3. Remove the drive belt.
4. Disconnect the alternator from the power supply.
   a. Remove the 2 nuts (1, 2).
5. Remove the alternator.
   a. Remove the 2 bolts (3, 4).

To install

6. Install the alternator.
7. Tighten the 2 bolts to 25 ft. lbs. (35 Nm).
8. Install the wiring harness to the alternator.
9. Tighten the 2 nuts to 62 inch lbs. (7 Nm).
10. Install the drive belt. Refer to Drive Belt Replacement.
11. Connect the battery.

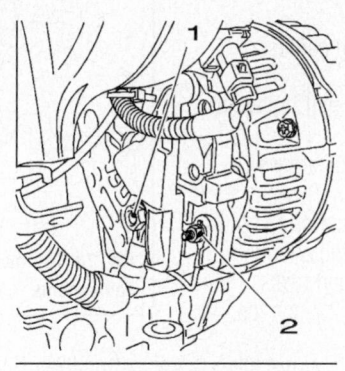
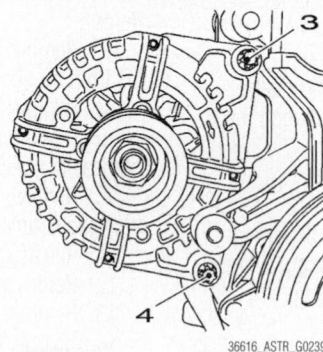

36616_ASTR_G0239

Fig. 81 Alternator location and components

ENGINE ELECTRICAL

IGNITION SYSTEM

FIRING ORDER

See Figure 82.

The engine firing order is 1 - 3 - 4 - 2.

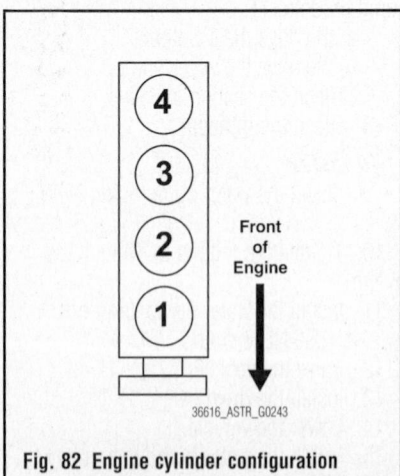

36616_ASTR_G0243

Fig. 82 Engine cylinder configuration

IGNITION COIL MODULE

REMOVAL & INSTALLATION

See Figures 83 through 85.

Special Service Tools:
• KM-6009 Remover/Installer

1. Remove the engine wiring trough (1) from the cylinder head.
2. Position the wiring trough to one side.
3. Disconnect the DIS-ignition module wiring harness connector (2).
4. Remove the DIS ignition module.

➡ **Note the arrow on the cover.**

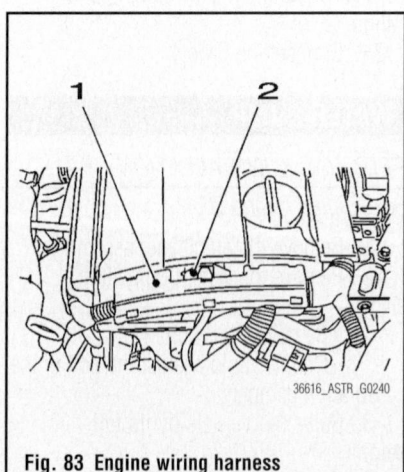

36616_ASTR_G0240

Fig. 83 Engine wiring harness

5. Remove the cover of the DIS ignition module in the direction of the arrow.
6. Remove the 2 bolts.
7. Remove from the spark plugs using KM-6009(1).

To install:

➡ **When installing a new DIS-ignition module it is not necessary to replace the gaskets.**

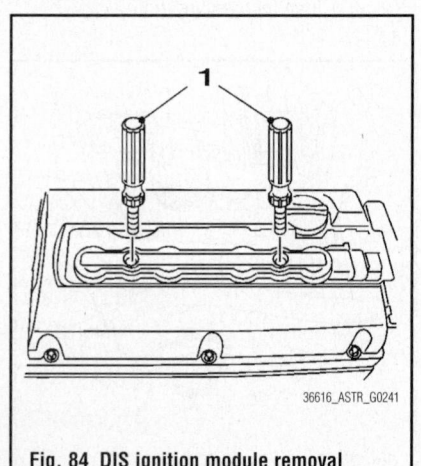

36616_ASTR_G0241

Fig. 84 DIS ignition module removal

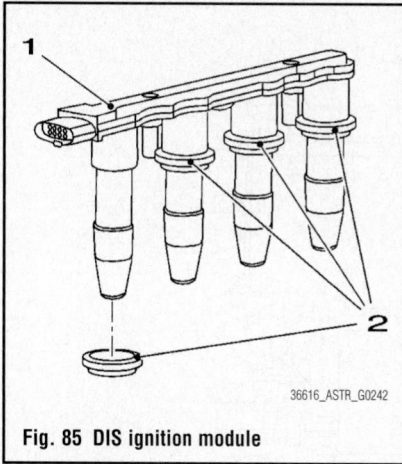

Fig. 85 DIS ignition module

8. Install the DIS ignition module (1) with KM-6009 .

9. Replace the gaskets (2).

10. Tighten the 2 bolts to 71 inch lbs. (8 Nm).

11. Install the DIS ignition module cover.

12. Connect the DIS-ignition module wiring harness connector.

13. Connect the engine wiring trough to cylinder head.

IGNITION TIMING

ADJUSTMENT

The ignition timing is controlled by the Engine Control Module (ECM), and there are no adjustments available.

SPARK PLUGS

REMOVAL & INSTALLATION

See Figures 83 through 86.

Special Service Tools:
- KM-6009 Remover/Installer

1. Remove the engine wiring trough (1) from the cylinder head.

2. Position the wiring trough to one side.

3. Disconnect the DIS-ignition module wiring harness connector (2).

4. Remove the DIS ignition module.

➡**Note the arrow on the cover.**

5. Remove the cover of the DIS ignition module in the direction of the arrow.

6. Remove the 2 bolts.

7. Remove from the spark plugs using KM-6009(1).

8. Remove the spark plugs.

To install:

9. Install the spark plugs.

➡**When installing a new DIS-ignition module it is not necessary to replace the gaskets.**

10. Install the DIS ignition module (1) with KM-6009 .

11. Replace the gaskets (2).

12. Tighten the 2 bolts to 71 inch lbs. (8 Nm).

13. Install the DIS ignition module cover.

14. Connect the DIS-ignition module wiring harness connector.

15. Connect the engine wiring trough to cylinder head.

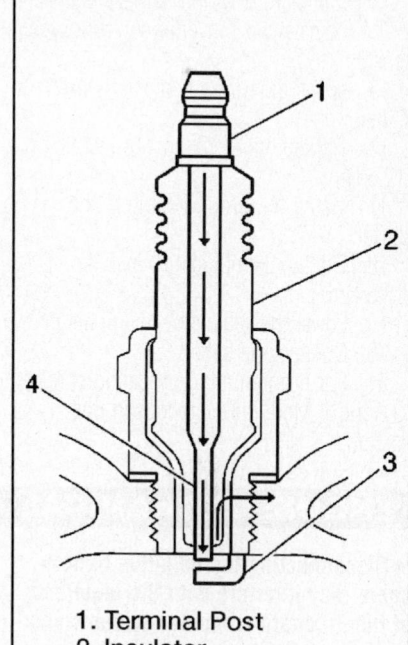

1. Terminal Post
2. Insulator
3. Positive Electrode
4. Negative Electrode

Fig. 86 Spark plug components

ENGINE ELECTRICAL

STARTING SYSTEM

STARTER

REMOVAL & INSTALLATION

See Figures 87 through 89.

❋❋ WARNING

Refer to Battery Disconnect Warning in this section.

1. Disconnect the battery.

2. Raise the vehicle by its full height.

3. Remove the ground cable (1) from starter.

4. Remove the nut.

5. Remove the 2 positive cable (2) starter.

6. Remove the 2 nuts.

7. Remove the intake manifold bracket (2).

   a. Disconnect the wiring harness connector of the catalytic converter control oxygen sensor.

   b. Disconnect the wiring harness connector (1) from the bracket.

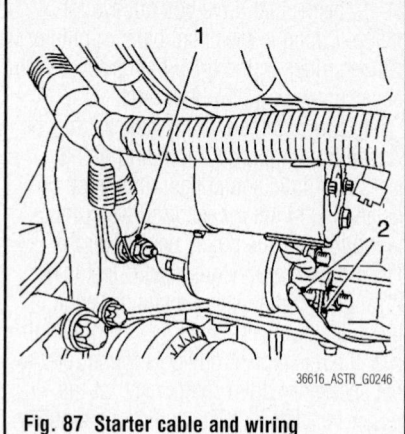

Fig. 87 Starter cable and wiring

   c. Remove the 2 bolts (3).

8. Remove the starter.

   a. Remove the 2 bolts (1, 2).

To install:

9. Install the starter.

10. Tighten the 2 bolts to 18 ft. lbs. (25 Nm).

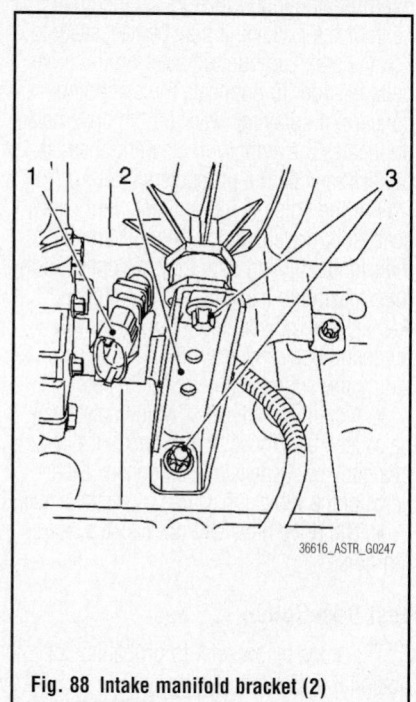

Fig. 88 Intake manifold bracket (2)

11. Install the intake manifold bracket.

12. Tighten the 2 bolts to 70 inch lbs. (8 Nm).

13. Install the wiring harness connector into the bracket.

14. Connect the wiring harness connector for the catalytic converter control oxygen sensor.

15. Install the wiring harness to the starter.

16. Tighten the 2 nuts to 110 inch lbs. (12.5 Nm).

17. Install the ground cable to the starter.

18. Tighten the nut to 110 inch lbs. (12.5 Nm).

19. Lower the vehicle by its full height.

20. Connect the battery.

21. For programming procedures, refer to Control Module References in this section.

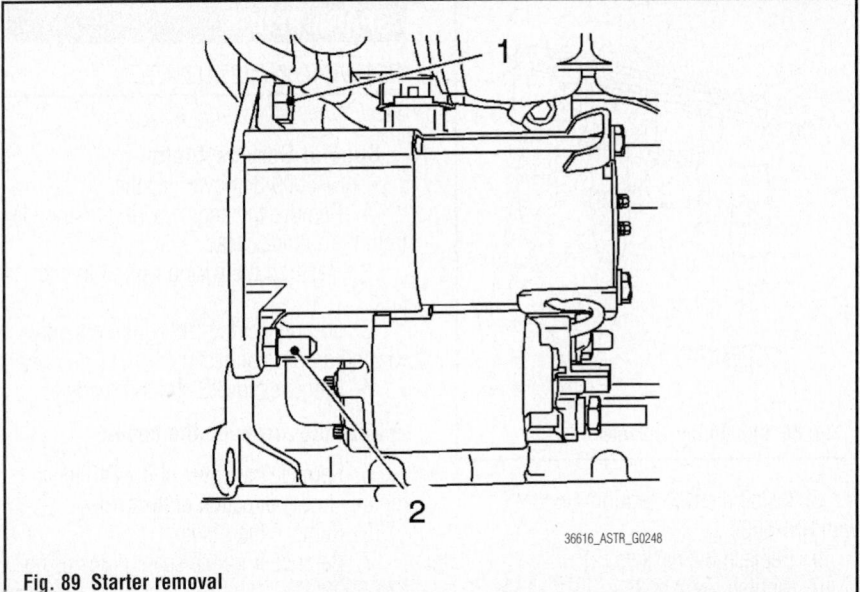

Fig. 89 Starter removal

ENGINE MECHANICAL

➡**Disconnecting the negative battery cable may interfere with the functions of the on board computer systems and may require the computer to undergo a relearning process, once the negative battery cable is reconnected.**

ACCESSORY DRIVE BELTS

INSPECTION

Diagnostic Aids

• A chirping or squeal noise may be intermittent due to moisture on the drive belts or the pulleys. It may be necessary to spray a small amount of water on the drive belts in order to duplicate the customers concern. If spraying water on the drive belt duplicates the symptom, cleaning the belt pulleys may be the probable solution.

• If the noise is intermittent, verify the accessory drive components by varying their loads making sure they are operated to their maximum capacity. An overcharged A/C system, power steering system with a pinched hose or wrong fluid, or a generator failing are suggested items to inspect.

• A chirping, squeal or whine noise may be caused by a loose or improper installation of a body or suspension component. Other items of the vehicle may also cause the noise.

• The drive belts will not cause a whining noise.

Test Description

The steps below refer to probability of potential noise concerns.

1. The noise may not be engine related. This step is to verify that the engine is making the noise. If the engine is not making the noise do not proceed further with this table.

2. The noise may be an internal engine noise. Removing the drive belts one at a time and operating the engine for a brief period will verify the noise is related to the drive belt. When removing the drive belt the water pump may not be operating and the engine may overheat. Also DTCs may set when the engine is operating with the drive belts removed.

3. Inspect all drive belt pulleys for pilling. Pilling is the small balls or pills or it can be strings in the drive belt grooves from the accumulation of rubber dust.

4. Misalignment of the pulleys may be caused from improper mounting of the accessory drive component, incorrect installation of the accessory drive component pulley, or the pulley bent inward or outward from a previous repair. Test for a misaligned pulley using a straight edge in the pulley grooves across two or three pulleys. If a misaligned pulley is found refer to that accessory drive component for the proper installation procedure for that pulley.

5. Inspecting of the fasteners can eliminate the possibility that a wrong bolt, nut, spacer, or washer was installed.

6. Inspecting the pulleys for being bent should include inspecting for a dent or other damage to the pulleys that would prevent the drive belt from not seating properly in all of the pulley grooves or on the

smooth surface of a pulley when the back side of the belt is used to drive the pulley.

7. This test is to verify that the drive belt tensioner operates properly. If the drive belt tensioner is not operating properly, proper belt tension may not be achieved to keep the drive belt from slipping which could cause a squeal noise.

8. This test is to verify that the drive belt is not too long, which would prevent the drive belt tensioner from working properly. Also if an incorrect length drive belt was installed, it may not be routed properly and may be turning an accessory drive component in the wrong direction.

9. Misalignment of the pulleys may be caused from improper mounting of the accessory drive component, incorrect installation of the accessory drive component pulley, or the pulley bent inward or outward from a previous repair. Test for a misaligned pulley using a straight edge in the pulley grooves across two or three pulleys. If a misaligned pulley is found refer to that accessory drive component for the proper installation procedure for that pulley.

10. This test is to verify that the pulleys are the correct diameter or width. Using a known good vehicle compare the pulley sizes.

11. Replacing the drive belt when it is not damaged or there is not excessive pilling will only be a temporary repair.

ADJUSTMENT

The drive belt tension is controlled by a self-adjusting tensioner. No adjustments are available.

REMOVAL & INSTALLATION

See Figure 90.

Special Service Tools:
- KM-6349 Fixing Rod
1. Raise the vehicle by its full height.
2. Remove the lower engine cover and the right engine splash shield.
3. Apply tension to the drive belt tensioner in the direction of the arrow at the projection (1) and lock with KM-6349 (2).
4. Remove the drive belt.

To install:
5. Install the drive belt.
   a. Apply tension to the tensioner at the projection counterclockwise in the direction of the arrow.
   b. Remove the KM-6349 .
   c. Allow the tensioner to slide back slowly.
6. Install the lower engine cover and the right engine splash shield.
7. Lower the vehicle by its full height.

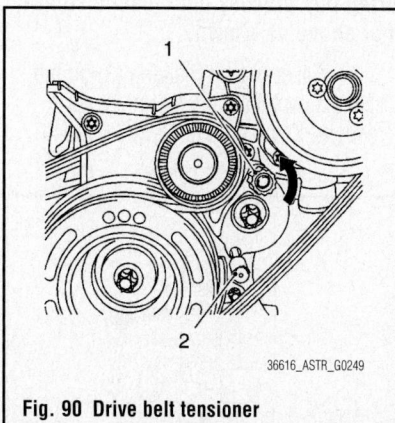

Fig. 90 Drive belt tensioner

CAMSHAFT AND VALVE LIFTERS

REMOVAL & INSTALLATION

See Figures 91 through 97.

Special Service Tools:
- KM-422 Installer
- KM-845 Suction Device
- KM-6361 Feeler Gage Set
- KM-6628 Locking Tool
1. Remove the rear timing belt cover. Refer to Timing Belt Rear Cover Removal & Installation.
2. Remove KM-6628 .
3. Counter hold at hexagon of camshafts.
4. Remove the 1st camshaft bearing support.
   a. Remove the 4 bolts.
Note removal sequence 1-4.

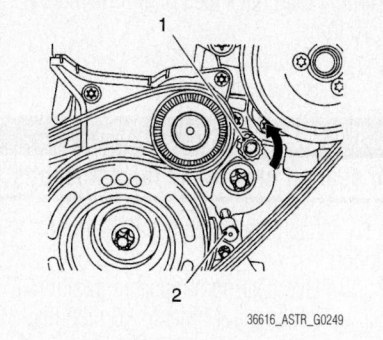

Fig. 91 Camshaft support removal sequence

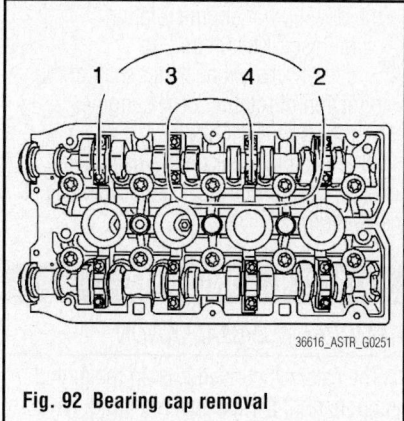

Fig. 92 Bearing cap removal

5. Release the bearing support by striking it gently with a plastic hammer.

➡ **Mark camshaft bearing caps before removal.**

6. Remove the exhaust camshaft.
   a. Detach the camshaft bearing caps 2-5 working from outside to inside in a spiral in steps of 1/2 up to 1 turn.
   b. Remove the camshaft bearing cover from the cylinder head and take out the camshaft.
7. Remove the intake camshaft.
   a. Detach the camshaft bearing caps 2-5 working from outside to inside in a spiral in steps of 1/2 up to 1 turn.
   b. Remove the camshaft bearing cover from the cylinder head and take out the camshaft.
8. Detach the seal rings from the camshafts.

To install:
9. Insert the 16 cup tappets with KM-845.
10. Lightly coat sliding surfaces with oil.
11. Install the intake camshaft.
   a. Coat with MoS 2 lubricating paste.
Note the identification marking on the camshaft bearing cover.
   a. Insert the camshaft.
   b. Install the camshaft bearing cover.

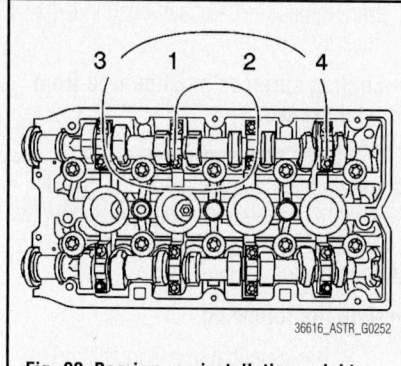

Fig. 93 Bearing cap installation—right side

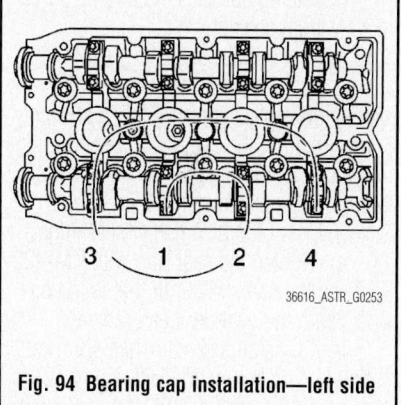

Fig. 94 Bearing cap installation—left side

   c. Tighten the camshaft bearing caps 2-5 in a spiral from the inside to the outside.
12. Tighten the camshaft bearing caps to 70 inch lbs. (8 Nm).
13. Install the exhaust camshaft.
   a. Coat with MoS 2 lubricating paste.
Note the identification marking on the camshaft bearing cover.
   a. Insert the camshaft.
   b. Install the camshaft bearing cover.
   c. Tighten the camshaft bearing caps 2-5 in a spiral from the inside to the outside.

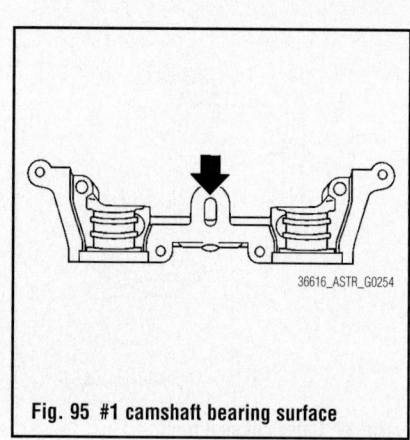

Fig. 95 #1 camshaft bearing surface

14. Tighten the camshaft bearing caps 70 inch lbs. (8 Nm).

➥**Sealing surfaces must be free from oil and grease.**

15. Clean sealing surfaces of the 1st camshaft bearing support and the cylinder head with a suitable tool, e.g. plastic wedge.

16. Clean oil duct (arrow) from any sealant residue.

➥**Note the following:**

- It is essential to ensure that no sealant is applied outside the marked sealing areas.
- The grooves (1) adjacent to the sealing surfaces must remain free from sealant.

17. Apply surface sealant (green) to sealing surfaces (arrows) of the 1st camshaft bearing support thinly and evenly.

18. Position the camshaft bearing bridge on the cylinder block and tighten the bolts hand tight, approximately 18 inch lbs. (2 Nm). Install the 2 camshaft seal rings.

a. Tighten the seal ring with KM-422 (4) on the camshaft until this is in contact with the cylinder head (arrow).

b. To install, use camshaft sprocket bolt (1) in conjunction with shims (2)

with a total thickness of approximately 10 mm.

c. Remove KM-422 .
d. Remove the bolt.

19. Attach the 1st camshaft bearing support.

20. Place bearing support in position.

21. Tighten the 4 bolts to 70 inch lbs. (8 Nm).

Note installation sequence 1-4.

22. Insert KM-6628.

a. Turn the intake camshaft against the direction of engine rotation

b. Insert KM-6628 .

c. Turn the exhaust camshaft in the direction of rotation of the engine.

d. Insert KM-6628 .

23. Install the rear timing belt cover. Refer to Timing Belt Rear Cover Removal & Installation.

CATALYTIC CONVERTER

REMOVAL & INSTALLATION

The catalytic converter is an integrated component of the exhaust manifold. Refer to Exhaust Manifold Removal & Installation.

CRANKSHAFT FRONT SEAL

REMOVAL & INSTALLATION
See Figures 98 through 106.

Special Service Tools:
- KM-6333 Fixing Rod
- MK-6340 Locking Tool
- KM-6351 Assembly Sleeves
- KM-6625 Flywheel Locking Device
- KM-J-45000 Remover

1. Disconnect the battery.
2. Loosen the nut.
3. Remove the air cleaner housing.

4. Remove the timing belt upper cover. Refer to Timing Belt Front Cover Removal & Installation.

5. Raise the vehicle by its full height.
6. Remove the drive belt tensioner.
7. Lower the vehicle by its full height.
8. Set the engine to Top Dead Center.
9. Set the torsional vibration damper in the direction of engine rotation to "1st cylinder TDC" (mark 1).

10. Recognizable from the lettering "Right" (arrow).

11. Prepare the right half of MK-6340 for use on the U 18 XER engine.

a. Detach the front panel (1) from MK-6340 .

b. Remove the 2 bolts (2).

12. Insert MK-6340 in the camshaft adjuster.

a. Insert MK-6340 (1, 2) in the camshaft adjuster as shown.

➥**The spot-type marking (4) on the intake camshaft adjuster does not correspond to the groove of MK-6340 during this process but must be somewhat above as shown.**

b. The spot type marking (3) on the exhaust camshaft adjuster must correspond to the groove on MK-6340 .

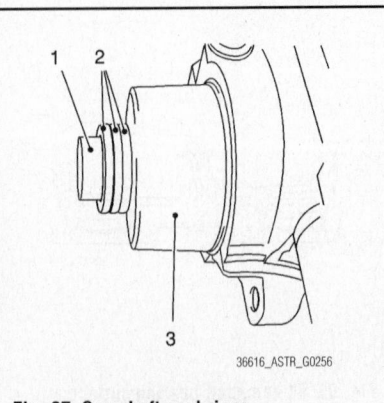
Fig. 96 Bearing bridge sealing areas

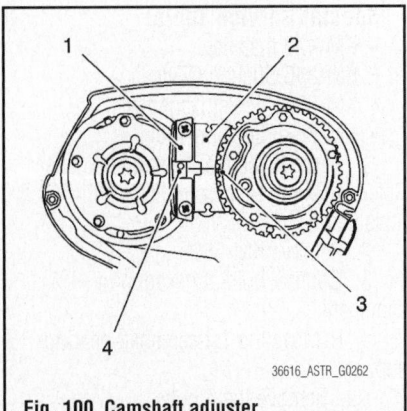
Fig. 99 Special service tool MK-6340

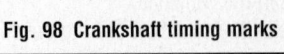
Fig. 97 Camshaft seal rings

Fig. 98 Crankshaft timing marks

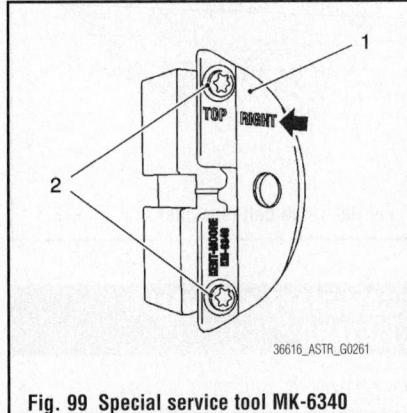
Fig. 100 Camshaft adjuster

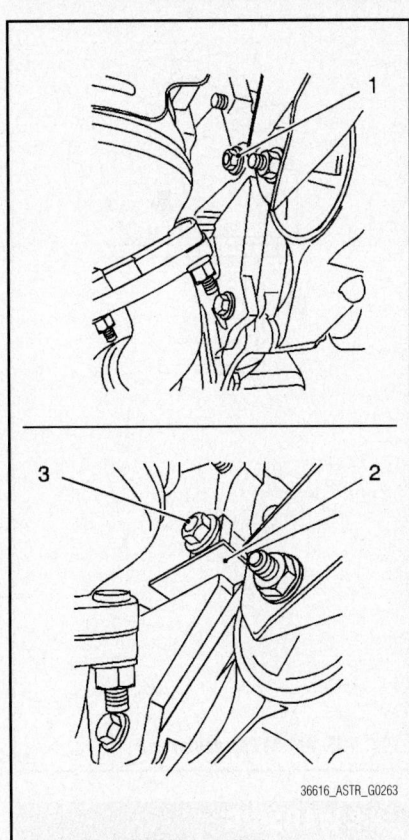

36616_ASTR_G0263

Fig. 101 KM-6625 installation

13. Raise the vehicle by its full height.
14. Hold the crankshaft.
15. Attach KM-6625 .
   a. Remove the threaded connection (1).
   b. Insert KM-6625 (2).
   c. Tighten the threaded connection (3).
16. Remove the torsional vibration damper (1).
   a. Remove the bolt (2).
17. Remove the front drive belt cover (bottom) (3).
   a. Remove the 4 bolts (4).
18. Lower the vehicle by its full height.
19. Block the timing belt tensioner.

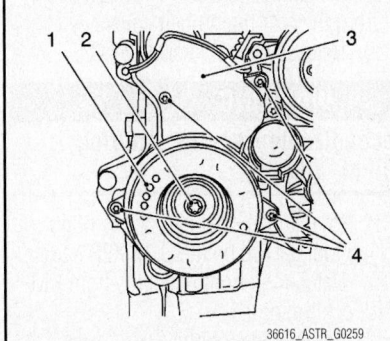

36616_ASTR_G0259

Fig. 102 Torsional vibration damper removal

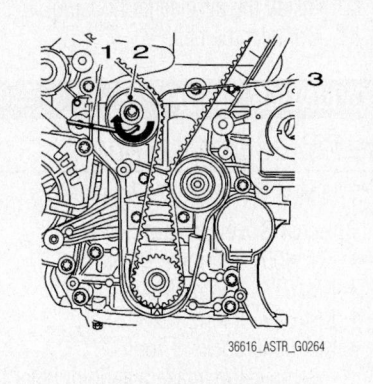

36616_ASTR_G0264

Fig. 103 Timing belt tensioner

20. Apply tension to the timing belt tensioner (2) in the direction of the arrow, using an Allen key (1). Fix using KM-6333 (3).
21. Mark the timing belt direction of rotation.
22. Remove the timing belt.
23. Raise the vehicle by its full height.

✴✴ **WARNING**

Do not damage sealing surfaces.

24. Remove the timing belt drive gear.
25. Remove the crankshaft seal ring (front) with KM-J-45000 .

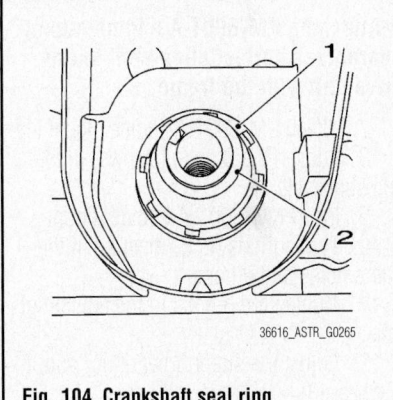

36616_ASTR_G0265

Fig. 104 Crankshaft seal ring

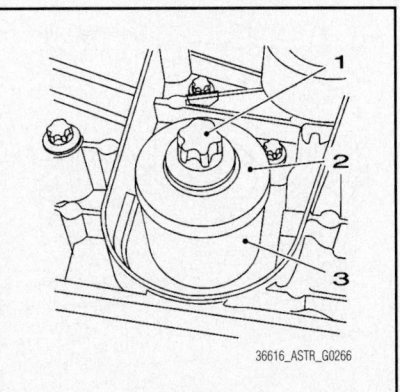

36616_ASTR_G0266

Fig. 105 Crankshaft seal ring installation

To install:
26. Insert the front crankshaft seal ring (1).
27. Clean the sealing surfaces.
28. Slide the protective sleeve of KM-6351 (2) onto the crankshaft journal.
29. Slide the seal ring over the protective sleeve on the crankshaft journal.
30. Press in the front crankshaft seal ring.
31. Remove the protective sleeve and press the seal ring into the pump housing with KM-6351 (3).
32. Use the bolt (1) and washer (2) of the crankshaft drive gear.
33. Install the timing belt drive gear.
34. Lower the vehicle by its full height.

✴✴ **WARNING**

Threading the timing belt through the engine mount support is only permissible in conjunction with the assembly tool supplied with new toothed belts as otherwise it is possible to damage the timing belt at this stage by kinking it.

35. Insert the timing belt.
36. Insert the drive belt (1) in the enclosed assembly tool (2)
   a. If the timing belt has been used, observe direction of rotation.
37. Guide the timing belt through the engine mount support with the assembly tool.
38. Remove the assembly tool.

➡ **Observe direction of rotation.**

39. Position the timing belt.
   a. Position the timing belt on the intake camshaft adjuster.

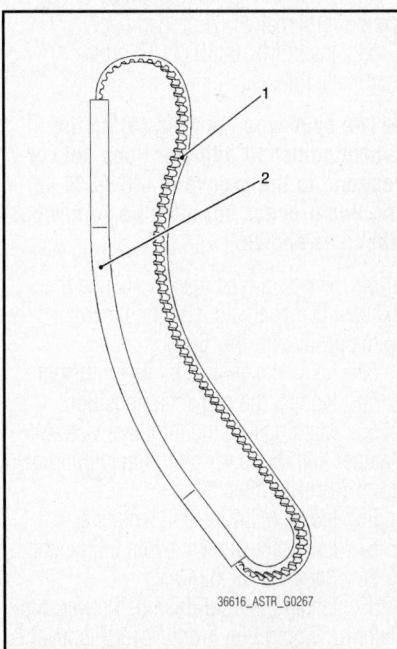

36616_ASTR_G0267

Fig. 106 Timing belt with assembly tool

b. Position the timing belt on the exhaust camshaft adjuster.

c. Guide the drive belt past the tension roller and place on the drive belt drive gear.

d. Apply tension to the timing belt tension roller and remove KM-6333.

40. Release tension on the timing belt tensioner.

a. Apply preliminary tension clockwise to the timing belt tension roller.

b. Remove KM-6333.

c. The timing belt tension pulley automatically moves to the correct position.

41. Raise vehicle by its full height.

42. Install the front timing belt cover (lower).

43. Tighten the 4 bolts to 53 inch lbs. (6 Nm).

➡ **New bolt must be coated with thread locking compound (red).**

44. Install the torsional vibration balancer.

a. Use a NEW bolt.

45. Tighten the bolt to 70 ft. lbs. (95 Nm) plus 30 degrees, plus 15 degrees.

46. Remove KM-6625.

a. Detach the threaded connection.

b. Tighten the bolted connection.

c. Use NEW nuts.

47. Lower the vehicle by its full height.

48. Remove the MK-6340.

49. Inspect the timing.

➡ **Note marking, camshaft sprockets.**

50. Turn the crankshaft 720 degrees in the direction of engine rotation by the bolt on the torsional vibration damper.

51. Insert MK-6340 (1, 2) in the camshaft adjuster as shown.

➡ **The spot-type marking (4) on the intake camshaft adjuster does not correspond to the groove of MK-6340 during this process but must be somewhat above as shown.**

52. The spot type marking (3) on the exhaust camshaft adjuster must correspond to the groove on MK-6340.

53. Raise the vehicle by its full height.

54. Inspect the crankshaft position.

55. Markings on the torsional vibration damper and the lower part of the timing belt cover (arrows) must align.

56. Install the drive belt tensioner.

57. Lower the vehicle by its full height.

58. Remove MK-6340.

59. Install the front drive belt cover (top). Refer to Timing Belt Front Cover Removal & Installation.

60. Install the air cleaner housing.

61. Connect the battery.

CYLINDER HEAD

REMOVAL & INSTALLATION

See Figures 107 through 118.

Special Service Tools:
- KM-6001-A Engine Mount
- KM-6173 Engine Mount Adapter
- KM-6333 Fixing Rod
- KM-6340 Locking Tool

1. Remove the intake manifold. Refer to Intake Manifold Replacement.

2. Remove the exhaust manifold. Refer to Exhaust Manifold Replacement.

3. Set the engine to "TDC".

4. Set the torsional vibration damper in the direction of engine rotation to cylinder 1, Top Dead Center (mark 1).

5. Remove the front lower timing belt cover. Refer to Timing Belt Front Cover Removal & Installation.

6. Insert KM-6173 adapter (3).

a. Loosen the 4 bolts (arrows) and hand-tighten.

b. Align KM-6173 adapter at frame.

c. Position the support bearing (1).

d. Journal (2) must sit in the mount at the cylinder block.

e. Tighten the 4 bolts.

➡ **Attaching KM-6001-A engine mount guarantees perfect alignment of the drive unit with the frame.**

7. Attach KM-6001-A engine mount (1).

8. Loosen the 3 bolts (arrows) in the adjusting rails.

9. Insert KM-6001-A engine mount.

10. The journals (2, 5) must sit in the guide holes of the frame.

11. Tighten the 3 bolts in the adjusting rails.

12. Adjust the support bearings, front (4) and rear (3).

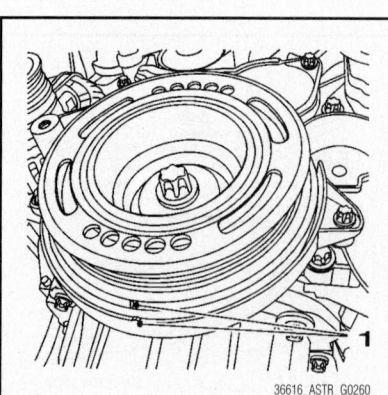

Fig. 107 Crankshaft timing marks (1)

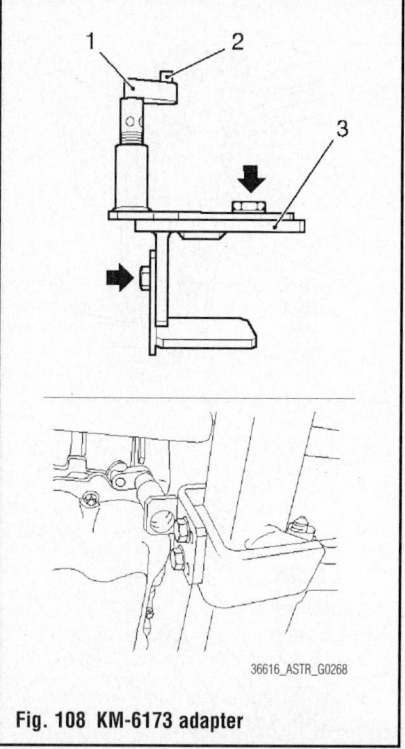

Fig. 108 KM-6173 adapter

⁑ **WARNING**

The guide journals must be seated free from play in the support bearings.

---

13. Raise the support bearings up to the stop on the guide journals.

14. Lower the vehicle by its full height.

15. Remove the engine damping block, right hand side.

a. Remove the 6 bolts (1).

16. Remove the engine damping block support (1).

a. Remove the 3 bolts (2).

17. Remove the front top front timing belt cover. Refer to Timing Belt Front Cover Removal & Installation.

18. Remove the front center timing belt cover. Refer to Timing Belt Front Cover Removal & Installation.

19. Disconnect the wiring trough cover (1) from the rear timing belt cover.

20. Release with a screwdriver (2).

⁑ **WARNING**

Recognizable from the lettering "Right" (arrow)

---

21. Prepare the right half of KM-6340 locking tool for use on the U 18 XER engine.

22. Detach the front panel (1) from KM-6340 locking tool.

23. Remove the 2 bolts (2).

24. Insert KM-6340 locking tool (1, 2) in the camshaft adjuster as shown.

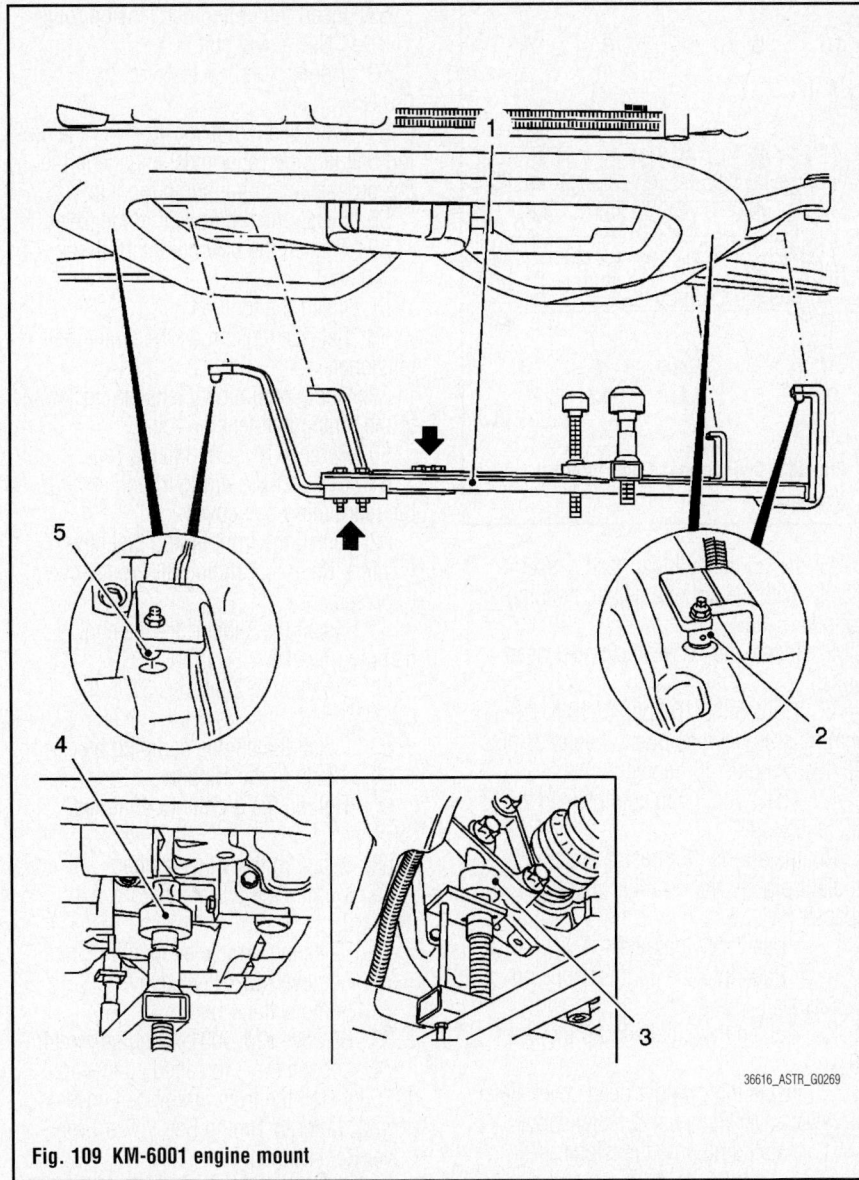

Fig. 109 KM-6001 engine mount

➡**The spot-type marking (4) on the intake camshaft adjuster does not correspond to the groove of KM-6340 locking tool during this process but must be somewhat above as shown.**

25. The spot type marking (3) on the exhaust camshaft adjuster must correspond to the groove on KM-6340 locking tool .

26. Block the timing belt tensioner.

27. Apply tension to the timing belt tensioner (2) in the direction of the arrow, using an Allen key (1). Fix using KM-6333 (3).

28. Mark the timing belt direction of rotation.

29. Remove the timing belt.

30. Remove the timing belt guide roller.

31. Remove the bolt.

32. Remove the timing belt tensioner (1) and bolt (2).

33. Remove the coolant pipe (1) between the thermostat housing and the oil filter housing adapter.

Fig. 112 Release wiring as shown

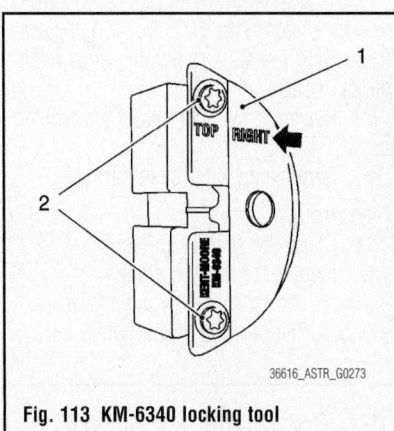

Fig. 113 KM-6340 locking tool

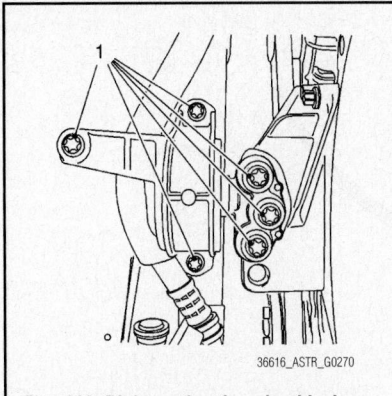

Fig. 110 Right engine damping block

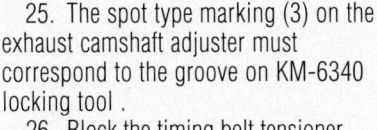
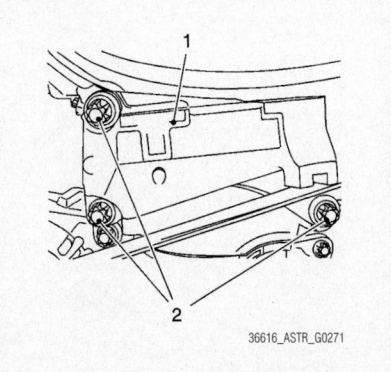

Fig. 111 Engine damping block support

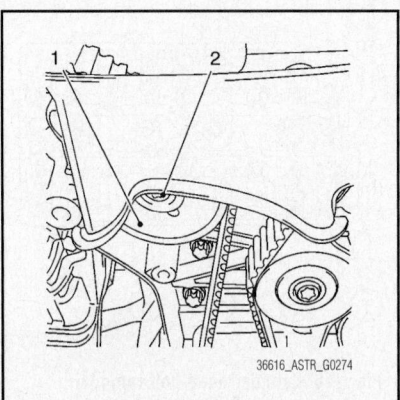

Fig. 114 Timing belt tensioner and bolt

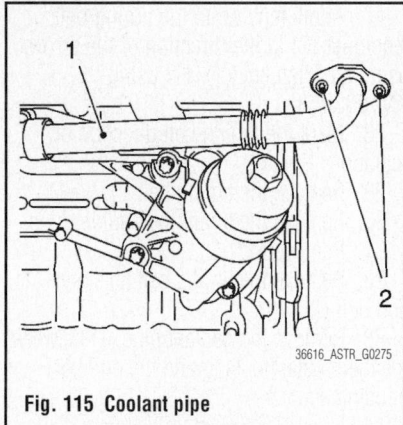

Fig. 115 Coolant pipe

a. Remove the 2 bolts (2).

b. Remove the oil filter housing adapter.

34. Detach the 3 coolant hoses from coolant flange.

35. Remove the 3 clamps.

✳✳ WARNING

Remove the cylinder head only when the engine is cold (room temperature).

36. Remove the valve cover. Refer to Valve Cover Removal & Installation.

37. Remove the 10 cylinder head bolts.

a. Unfasten the 10 bolts (90 degrees).

b. Unfasten the 10 bolts (180 degrees).

38. With the aid of a helper, remove the cylinder head.

39. Place the cylinder head on suitable base.

40. Remove cylinder head gasket.

To install:

41. Clean the sealing surfaces.

42. Inspect for plane surface.

a. Cylinder block, cylinder head

b. Straight-edge, feeler gauge

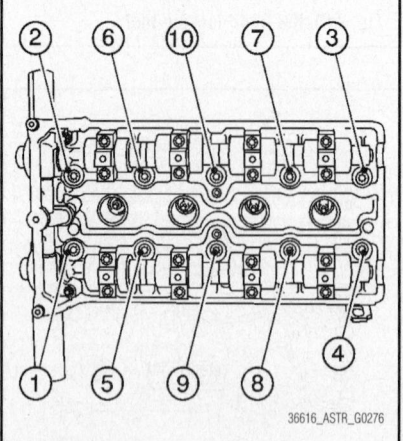

Fig. 116 Cylinder head bolt removal sequence

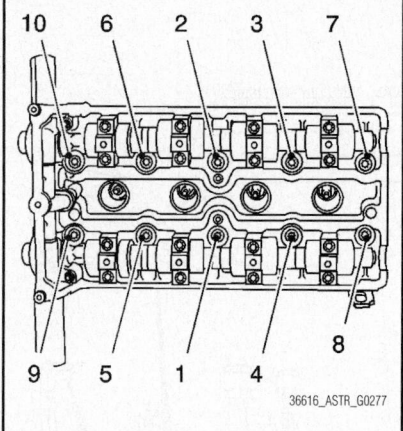

Fig. 117 Cylinder head bolt torque sequence

43. Install the cylinder head gasket.

44. With the aid of a helper, position the cylinder head.

45. Install the 10 NEW cylinder head bolts.

46. Tighten the 10 bolts to 18 ft. lbs. (25 Nm) plus 90 degrees plus 90 degrees plus 90 degrees plus 45 degrees.

47. Attach the 3 coolant hoses to the coolant flange.

48. Install the thermostat housing coolant pipe to the oil filter housing adapter.

a. Use 2 new gaskets.

b. Push into the oil filter housing adapter.

49. Tighten the 2 bolts to 80 inch lbs. (9 Nm).

50. Install the cylinder head cover. Refer to Valve Cover Removal & Installation.

51. Install timing belt tensioner.

52. Insert the timing belt tension roller.

a. Use a new bolt.

53. Tighten the bolt to 15 ft. lbs. (20 Nm).

54. Released leg of spring (1) of the timing belt tension roller must engage in the cut-out (arrow) of the pump module.

55. Install the timing belt guide roller.

56. Tighten the new bolt to 18 ft. lbs. (25 Nm).

57. Insert the toothed belt.

58. Release tension on the timing belt tensioner.

59. Apply preliminary tension clockwise to the timing belt tension roller.

60. Remove KM-6333 fixing rod .

61. Connect the wiring trough cover to the rear timing belt cover.

62. Install the front timing belt cover (center). Refer to Timing Belt Front Cover Replacement.

63. Install the support for the engine damping block.

64. Tighten the 3 bolts to 37 ft. lbs. (50 Nm).

65. Install the engine damping block.

66. Attach to the support.

67. Tighten the 3 bolts to 40 ft. lbs. (55 Nm).

68. Attach to the side member.

69. Tighten the 3 bolts to 25 ft. lbs. (35 Nm).

70. Raise the vehicle by its full height.

71. Remove KM-6173 adapter .

72. Remove the 4 bolts.

73. Remove KM-6001-A engine mount .

74. Loosen the 3 threaded connections.

75. Install the front timing belt cover (lower). Refer to Timing Belt Lower Front Cover Replacement.

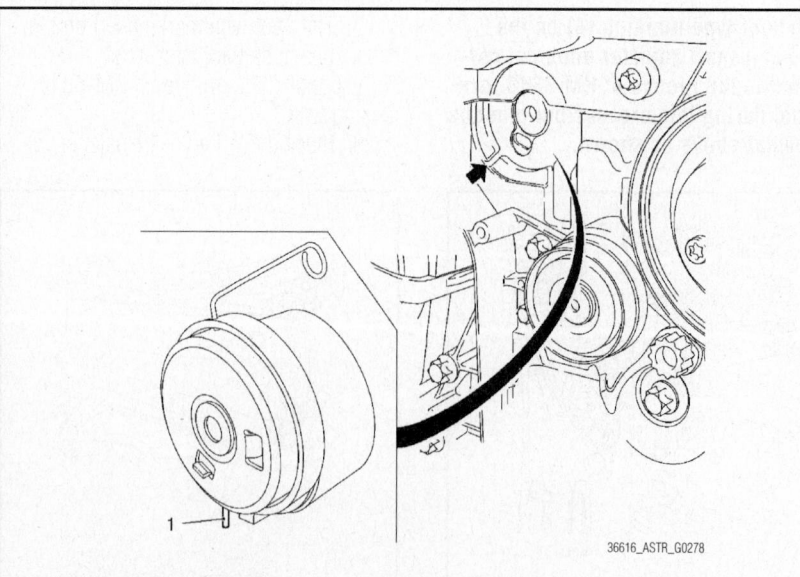

Fig. 118 Timing belt tensioner

76. Lower the vehicle by its full height.

77. Inspect the position of the camshaft sprockets.

Note marking, camshaft sprockets.

78. Turn the crankshaft 720 degrees in the direction of engine rotation by the bolt on the torsional vibration damper.

79. Insert KM-6340 locking tool into the camshaft timing gears.

80. Raise the vehicle by its full height.

81. Inspect the crankshaft position.

✳✳ WARNING

Markings on the torsional vibration damper and the lower part of the toothed belt cover (arrows) must align.

82. Lower the vehicle by its full height.

83. Install the exhaust manifold. Refer to Exhaust Manifold Replacement.

84. Install the intake manifold. Refer to Intake Manifold Replacement.

85. Inspect and correct the engine oil level.

86. Connect the battery.

87. Fill and bleed the cooling system. Refer to Cooling System Draining and Filling.

ENGINE ASSEMBLY

REMOVAL & INSTALLATION

See Figures 119 through 155.

Special Service Tools:

- J 37088-A Fuel Line Disconnect Tool Set
- KM-161-B Bearing Puller
- KM-468 Holding Bar
- KM-807 Closure Plugs
- KM-904 Base Frame
- KM-915 Spreader
- KM-6001-A Engine Mount
- KM-6042
- KM-6173

- KM-6390 Centering Equipment
- KM-J-34730-91 Pressure Tester

1. Disconnect and remove the battery. Refer to Battery Disconnect Warning in the Precautions section.

2. Remove the battery support (1).

3. Disconnect the 2 coolant hoses (3).

4. Remove the wiring harness (4) from the battery support.

5. Remove the 2 cable ties.

6. Remove the 3 bolts (2).

7. Remove the radiator grille.

   a. Remove the 4 body-bound rivets (1).

   b. Disconnect from the front panel from above.

   c. Disconnect the 6 clips.

8. Evacuate the HVAC system. Refer to Refrigerant Recovery and Recharging.

9. Remove the steering column interim spindle.

   a. Move the steering wheel to the straight-ahead position.

   b. Remove the ignition key and engage the steering lock.

   c. Remove the bolt (1).

10. Remove the coolant expansion tank (1).

   a. Pull out of the bracket in the direction of the arrow.

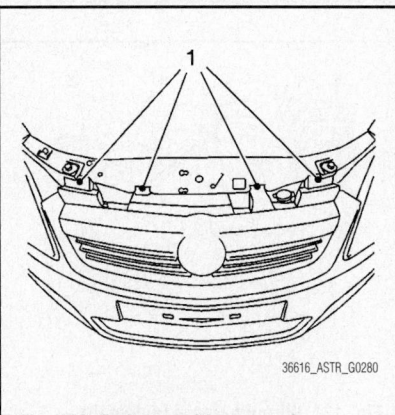

Fig. 120 Radiator grille removal

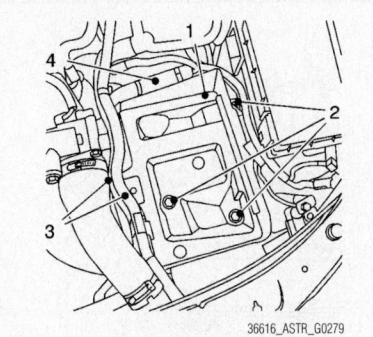

Fig. 119 Battery retaining plate and coolant hoses

Fig. 121 Steering column interim spindle

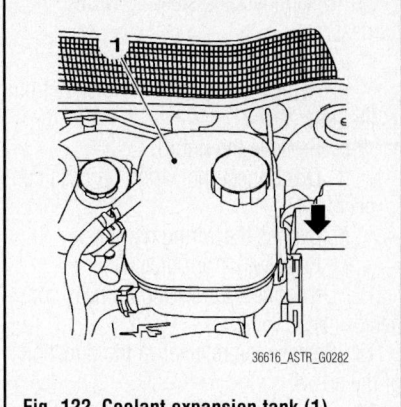

Fig. 122 Coolant expansion tank (1)

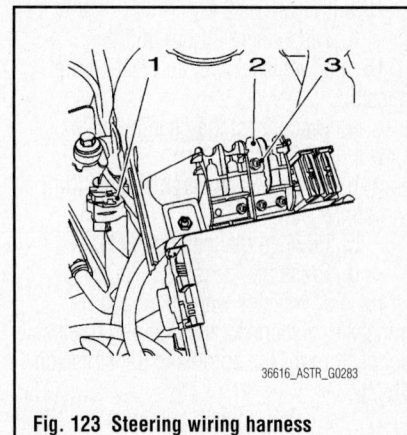

Fig. 123 Steering wiring harness

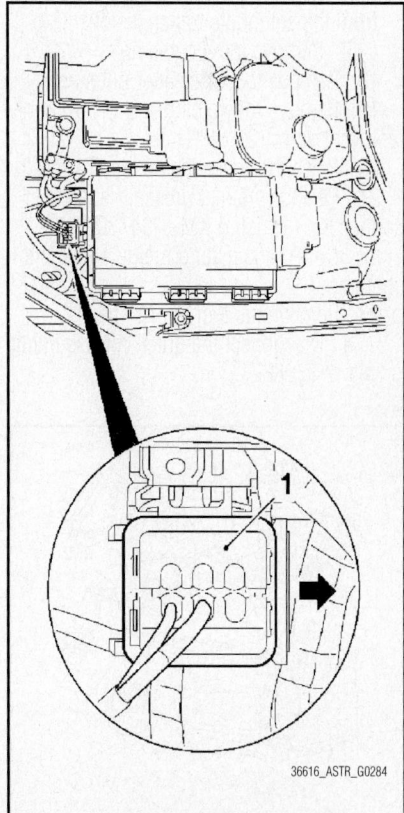

Fig. 124 Wiring harness connector

11. Disconnect the steering wiring harness.

   a. Remove the fuse carrier cover.

   b. Remove the positive cable (2) from the fuse carrier.

   c. Remove the nut (3).

   d. Disconnect the wiring harness connector (1).

   e. Expose the wiring harness.

   f. Remove 2 from bracket.

12. Disconnect the wiring harness connector (1).

13. Release the retainer in the direction of the arrow.

14. For vehicles with manual transaxle:

   a. Disconnect the 2 gearshift cables (1) with KM-6042 (2).

   b. Disconnect 2 from guide.

15. For vehicles with automatic transmission:

   a. Disconnect the gearshift cable (3) with KM-6042 (4).

   b. Remove the gearshift cable from counter stay.

   c. Remove the metal clip (1).

   d. Press the locks (2).

16. For vehicles with automatic transaxle, disconnect the 2 wiring harness connectors for the automatic transmission (1, 2).

17. For vehicles with automatic transaxle:

   a. Remove the wiring harness (2) from the automatic transmission.

   b. Remove the 4 cable ties.

18. Remove the air cleaner housing.

19. Remove the venting line (1) from the tank vent valve (2).

20. Place the collecting basin underneath.

21. Release the fuel pressure at the test connection (1) using KM-J-34730-91 .

22. Collect the exiting fuel in a suitable container.

23. Remove the fuel return line (1).

   a. Disconnect the quick-release fitting with J 37088-A .

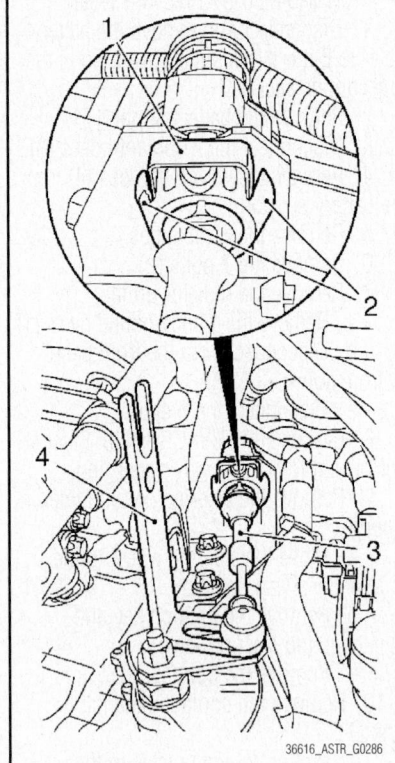

36616_ASTR_G0286

Fig. 126 Shift cable (automatic transaxle)

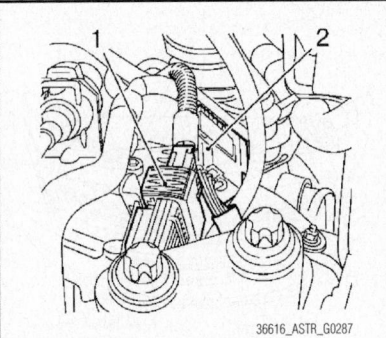

36616_ASTR_G0287

Fig. 127 Wiring harness (automatic transaxle- 1)

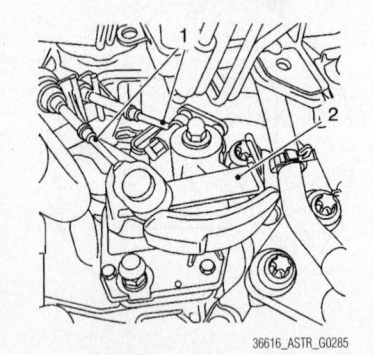

36616_ASTR_G0285

Fig. 125 Shift cable (manual transaxle)

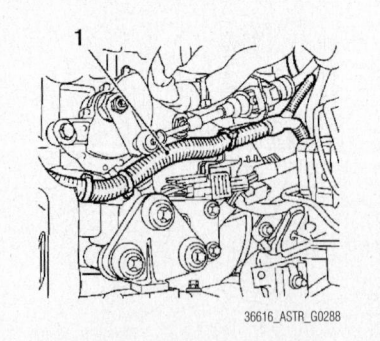

36616_ASTR_G0288

Fig. 128 Wiring harness (automatic transaxle - 2)

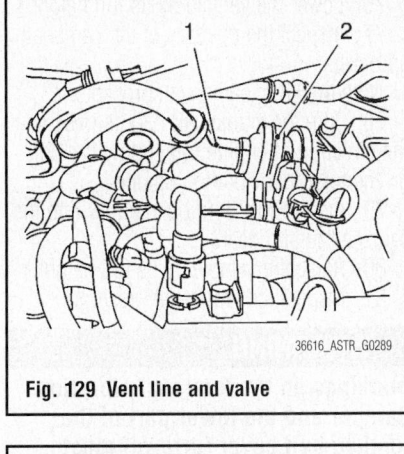

36616_ASTR_G0289

Fig. 129 Vent line and valve

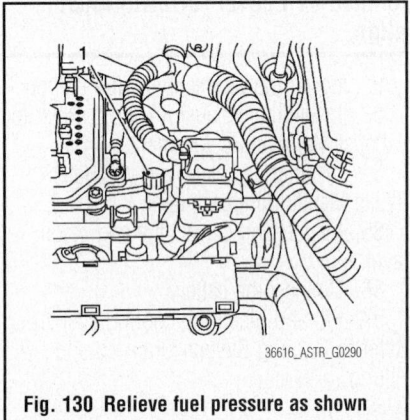

36616_ASTR_G0290

Fig. 130 Relieve fuel pressure as shown

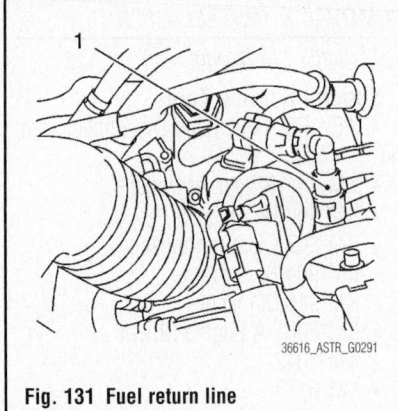

36616_ASTR_G0291

Fig. 131 Fuel return line

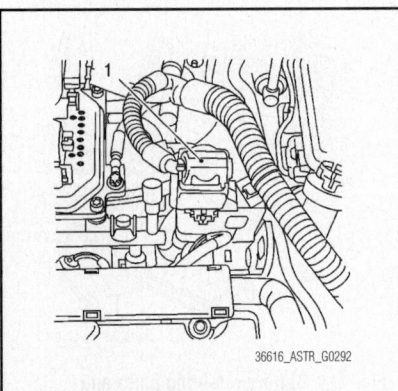

36616_ASTR_G0292

Fig. 132 Engine wiring harness connector

b. Seal the fuel line and the fuel rail with KM-807 .

24. Disconnect the wiring harness connector (1).

25. Remove the engine management wiring harness.

   a. Remove the ground cable (2) from the engine control unit.

   b. Remove the bolt.

   c. Disconnect the wiring harness connector (1).

   d. Disconnect 3 from bracket.

26. Remove the brake servo vacuum line (1) from the intake manifold.

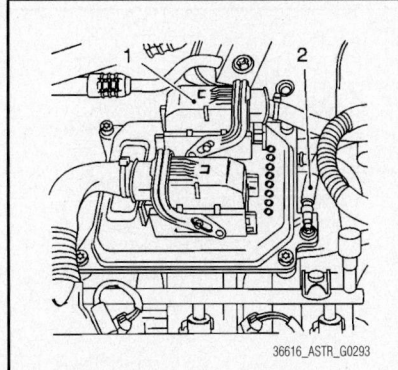

Fig. 133 Engine wiring harness

a. Disconnect the quick-release fitting.

27. For vehicles with manual transaxle:

   a. Remove the pressure hose, hydraulic clutch actuation (2).

   b. Disconnect the retaining clamp (1) with a screwdriver.

   c. Pull away the pressure hose.

   d. Bend the clip together a little and insert back into the connecting piece.

28. For vehicles with manual transmission:

   a. Disconnect the wiring harness connector, reverse gear switch (1).

29. Remove the front panel at the top.

   a. Remove the 2 bolts (1).

   b. Remove the 2 body-bound rivets (2).

   c. Disconnect the wiring harness connector.

30. Loosen the front wheels.

31. Raise the vehicle by half its height.

32. With the aid of an assistant, remove the front paneling.

   a. Remove the 6 body-bound rivets (2).

   b. Remove the 4 bolts (1).

➡**Push the front paneling upward at the side and pull out of the bracket.**

33. Remove the front paneling.

   a. Remove the front paneling from the bracket.

   b. Disconnect the 4 clips.

   c. Disconnect the outside temperature sensor.

34. Remove the front wheels.

➡**Use the wrench (1) to hold against flat surface.**

35. Remove the swing arm (2) from the spring strut support tube.
Remove the 2 nuts.

36. Remove the tie rods from the steering knuckle with KM-161-B (3).

37. Remove the 2 nuts.

38. Remove the guide joints from the steering knuckle.

   a. Remove the 2 screw connections.

   b. Expand the steering knuckle bolts with KM-915 (4).

   c. Pull the guide joints out of steering knuckle.

39. Remove the wheel arch inner paneling, left side.

40. Remove the body-bound rivet.

41. Disconnect the cooling module wiring harness connector (3).

   a. Disconnect the wiring harness.

   b. Disconnect the cable tie.

Fig. 134 Brake servo line

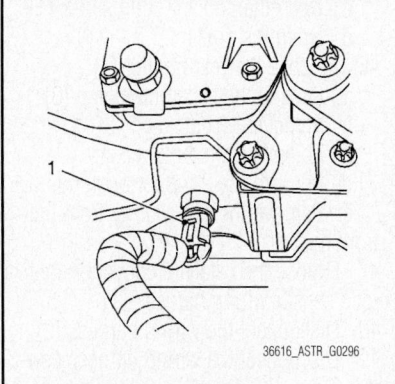

Fig. 136 Reverse lamp switch

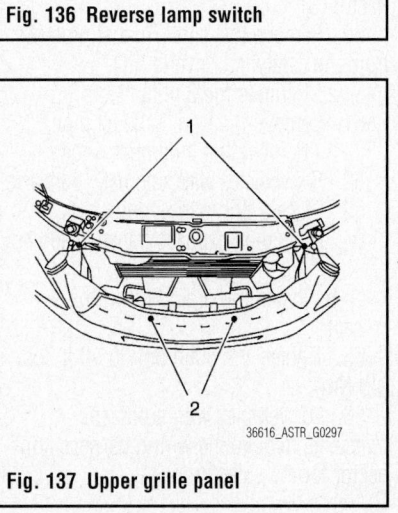

Fig. 135 Clutch hydraulic hose (manual transaxle)

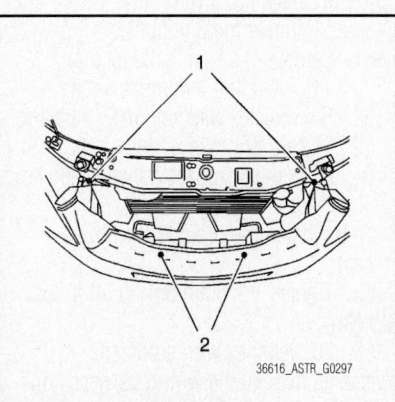

Fig. 137 Upper grille panel

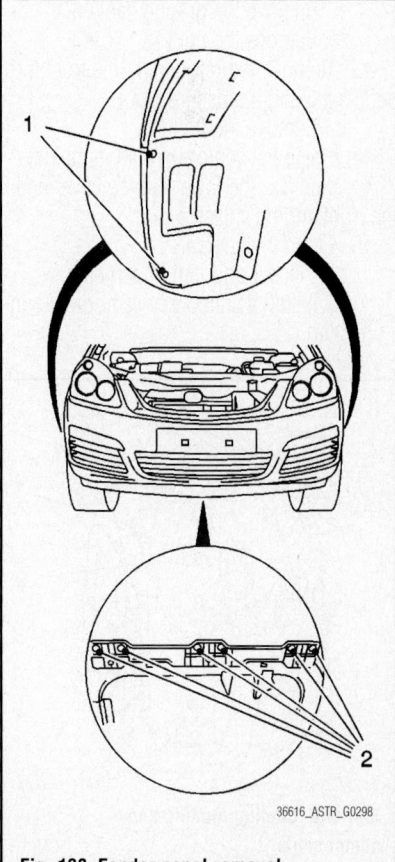

Fig. 138 Fender panel removal

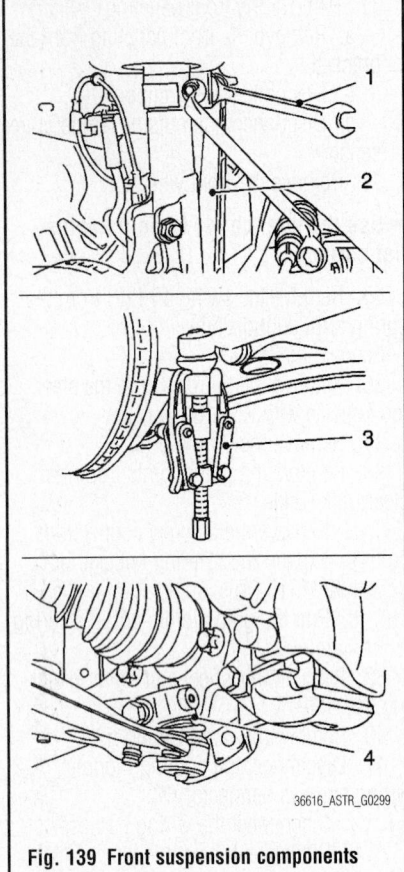

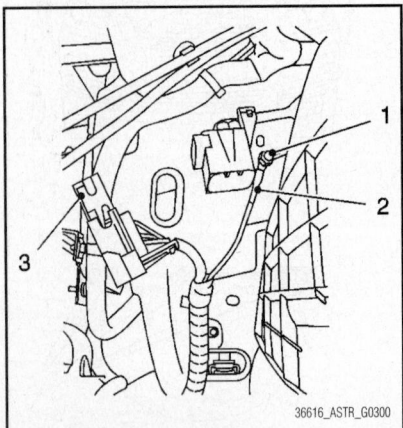

Fig. 139 Front suspension components

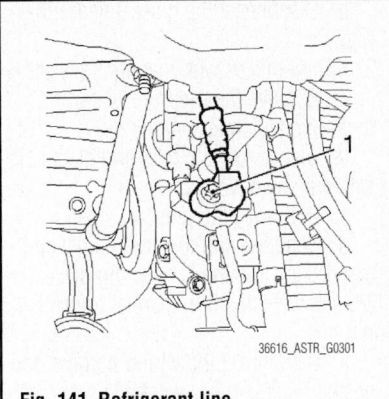

Fig. 141 Refrigerant line

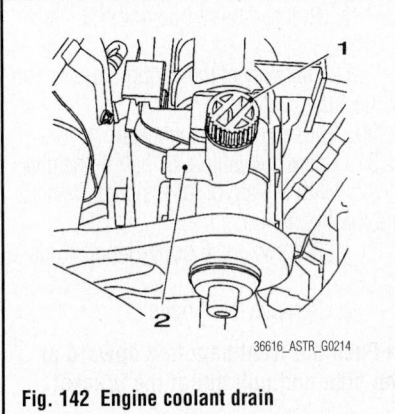
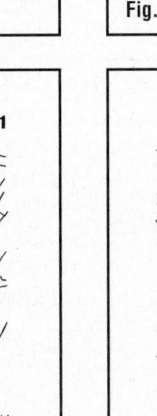

Fig. 142 Engine coolant drain

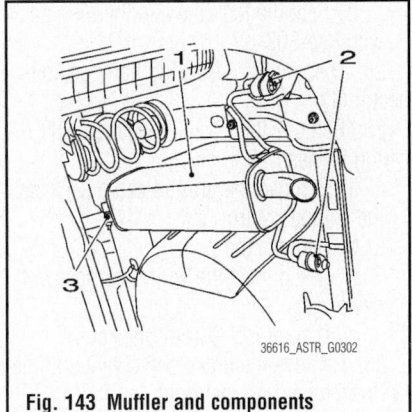

Fig. 143 Muffler and components

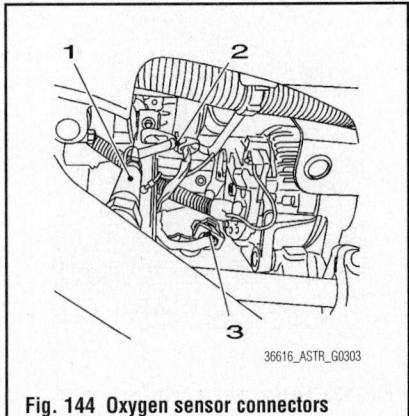

Fig. 144 Oxygen sensor connectors

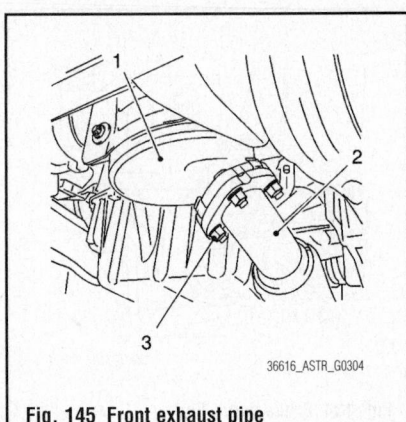

Fig. 145 Front exhaust pipe

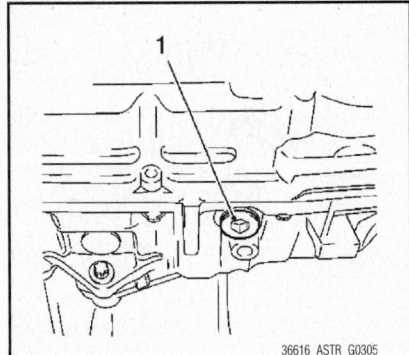

Fig. 146 Automatic transaxle drain plug

Fig. 140 Cooling module and components

  c. Remove the ground cable (2).
  d. Remove the nut (1).
42. Remove the refrigerant line from the condenser (high pressure side).
  a. Remove the bolt (1).
43. Raise the vehicle by half its height.
44. Remove the lower engine cover and the right engine splash guard.
45. Drain the coolant.
  a. Place a drip pan underneath.
  b. Install a suitable hose to drain connection (2).

  c. Open the coolant drain screw (1).
  d. Drain the coolant.
46. Remove the rear muffler (1).
  a. Loosen the fastening clamp (3).
  b. Remove the nut.
  c. Remove from the bracket.
  d. Remove the 2 rubber bushings (2).
  e. Remove the end muffler from the front muffler.
47. Expose the catalytic converter control oxygen sensor wiring harness (1).
48. Disconnect the wiring harness (2).
49. Disconnect the wiring harness connector (3).
50. Remove the front exhaust pipe (2) from the catalytic converter (1).
  a. Remove the 3 nuts (3).
51. Remove the front exhaust pipe.
  a. Remove the 4 damper rings.
52. For vehicles with automatic transaxle:
53. Place a drip pan underneath.
54. Drain the automatic transmission fluid.
  a. Remove drain bolt (1).
  b. Install the drain bolt with a new seal.
55. Tighten the drain bolt to 30 ft. lbs. (40 Nm).
56. For vehicles with automatic transaxle, remove the wiring harness connector for the selector lever

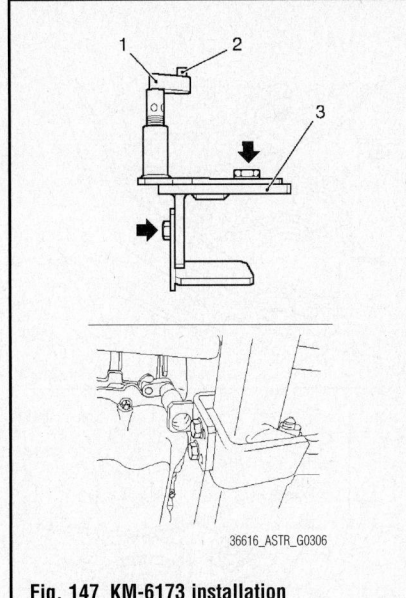

Fig. 147 KM-6173 installation

57. Insert KM-6173 (3).
 a. Loosen the 4 bolts (arrows) and hand-tighten.
 b. Align KM-6173 at the frame.
 c. Wind up the support bearing (1).
 d. The journal (2) must sit in the mount at the cylinder block.
 e. Tighten the 4 bolts.

➡**Installing KM-6001-A guarantees perfect alignment of the drive unit with the frame.**

58. Install KM-6001-A (1).
 a. Loosen the 3 bolts (arrows) in the adjusting rails.
 b. Insert KM-6001-A .
 c. The journals (2, 5) must sit in the guide holes of the frame.
 d. Tighten the 3 bolts in the adjusting rails.
 e. Adjust the support bearings, front (4, 3).

❋❋ **WARNING**

The guide journals must be seated free from play in the support bearings.

 f. Raise the support bearings up to the stop on the guide journals.
59. Lower the vehicle by its full height.
60. Disconnect the refrigerant line (low pressure side).

➡**Mark the assignment using colored markings.**

61. Remove the coolant hoses (1) from the heater core.
 a. Place the collecting basin underneath.

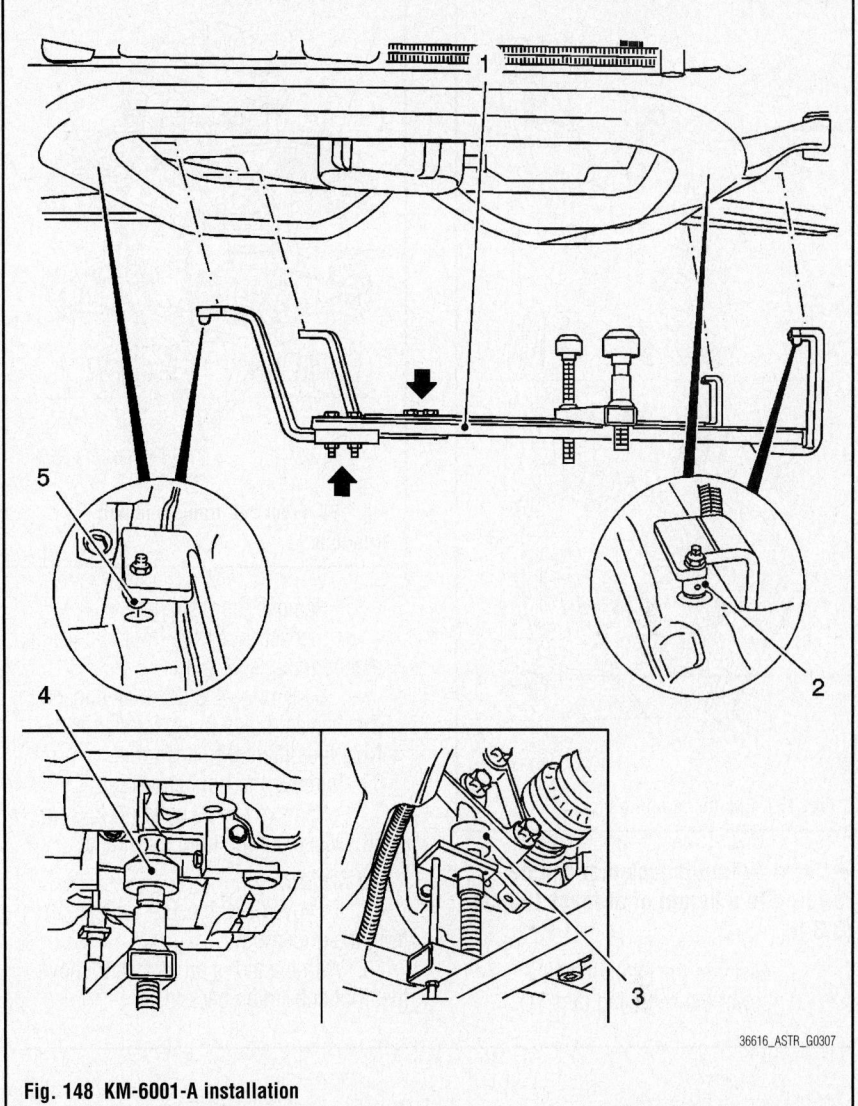

Fig. 148 KM-6001-A installation

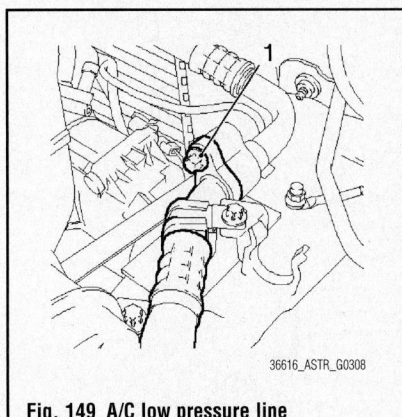

Fig. 149 A/C low pressure line

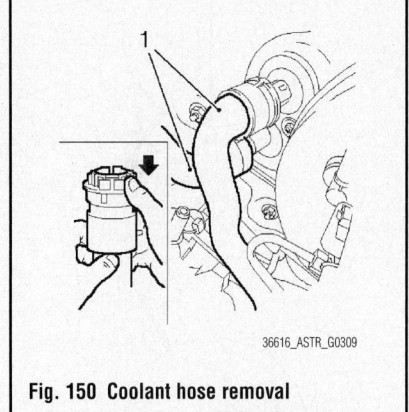

Fig. 150 Coolant hose removal

 b. Release the 2 quick-release fittings in the direction of the arrow.
 c. Pull off the 2 coolant hoses.
62. Remove the right engine damping block from the engine damping block bracket.

 a. Remove the 3 bolts (1).
63. Remove the left engine damping block from the engine damping block bracket.
 a. Remove the 3 bolts (2).
64. Install KM-904 with KM-6390 .

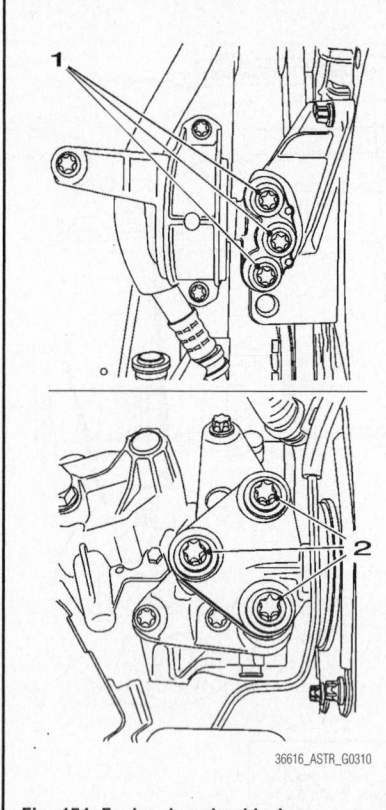

Fig. 151 Engine damping blocks

➡**Use a hydraulic jack that can be lowered to a height of at least 100 cm (3.3 ft).**

  a. Attach to the hydraulic lifter.
  b. Lower the centering pins (1).

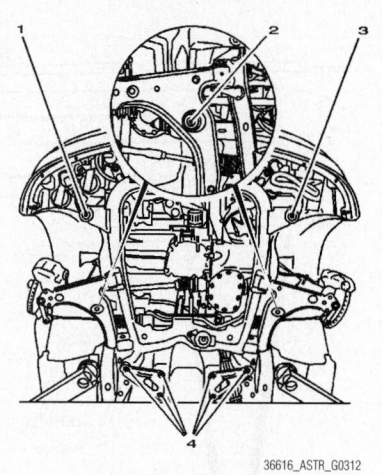

Fig. 153 Front sub-frame and bolt locations

  c. Remove the 2 splines.
  d. Inspect under the front sub-frame, ensure there is no play.
  e. Centering pins (2) must engage in the relevant holes in the frame.
Note the different bolt lengths.
65. Remove the front sub-frame.
  a. Remove the 10 bolts (1, 2, 3, 4).
66. Move out the front sub-frame.

To install:
67. Remove the 2 closure caps (1, 2) from the underbody.
68. With the aid of an assistant, move the front sub-frame back in.

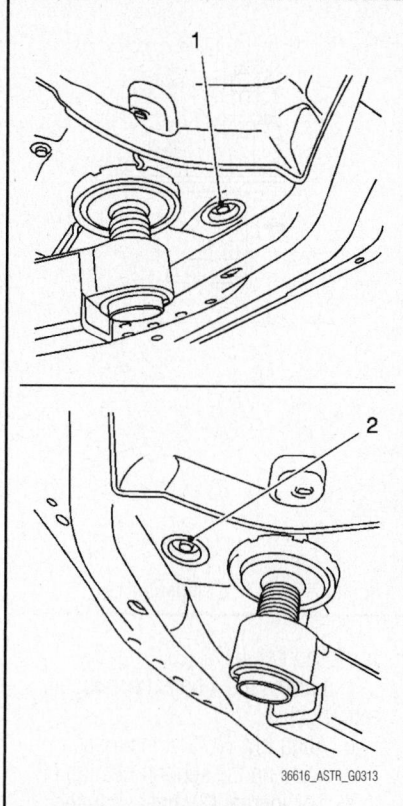

Fig. 154 Underbody closure caps

69. Install the front sub-frame.
70. Tighten 10 NEW bolts to 67 ft. lbs. (90 Nm) plus 45 degrees, plus 15 degrees.
71. Remove KM-904 with KM-6390 .
  a. Lower the hydraulic lifter.
  b. Remove the KM-904 and the KM-6100 from the hydraulic jack.
72. Install the 2 covers in the underbody.
73. Lower the vehicle by its full height.
74. Install the right engine damping block to the engine damping block adapter.
75. Tighten the 3 bolts to 41 ft. lbs. (55 Nm).
76. Install the left engine damping block to the engine damping block adapter.
77. Tighten the 3 bolts to 41 ft. lbs. (55 Nm).

➡**It is imperative to adhere to the following assembly order.**

78. Install the cooling hoses to the heater core.
  a. Slide the 2 quick release fitting locking mechanisms in the direction of the arrow as far as they will go.
  b. Plastic rings (green) will be covered.

➡**Pay attention to the colored markings.**

  c. Install the 2 quick release fittings onto the heater core connecting piece (1) as far as they will go.

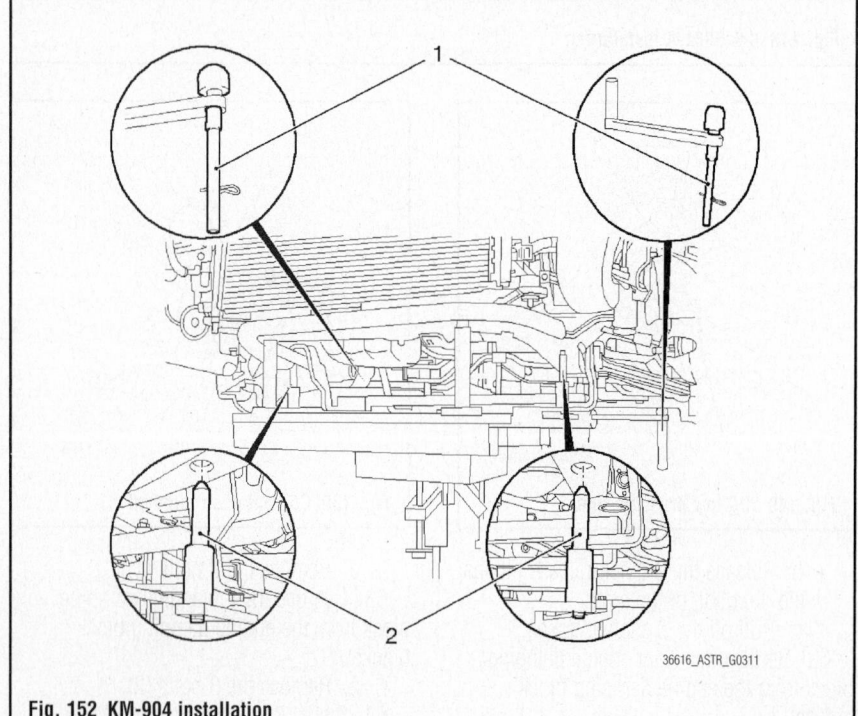

Fig. 152 KM-904 installation

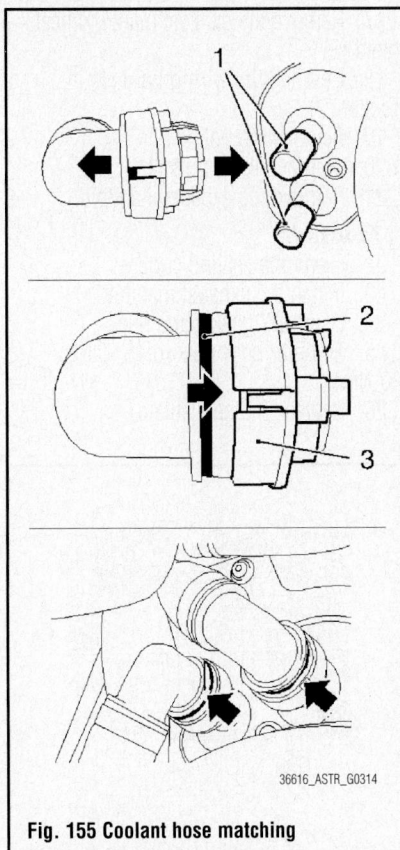

Fig. 155 Coolant hose matching

d. Slide the 2 quick release fitting locking mechanisms (3) in the direction of the arrow as far as they will go.

e. Plastic rings (green) must be visible.

f. Ensure the quick release fittings are correctly seated and that the plastic rings (arrows) are visible.

79. Connect the low pressure refrigerant line.

80. Tighten the bolt to 15 ft. lbs. (20 Nm).

81. Raise the vehicle by its full height.

82. Remove KM-6173.

83. Remove the 4 bolts.

84. Remove KM-6001-A .

85. For vehicles with automatic transaxle:

a. Install the wiring harness connector for the selector lever.

86. With the aid of an assistant, insert the front exhaust pipe with the front muffler.

87. Install the 4 damper rings.

88. Install the front exhaust pipe to the catalytic converter.

a. Use a new gasket.

b. Use new nuts.

89. Tighten the bolt to 15 ft. lbs. (20 Nm).

90. Install the rear muffler.

a. Install the rear muffler to the front muffler.

b. Install the 2 damper rings.

91. Align the exhaust system.

92. Connect the exhaust system.

93. Tighten the screwed joint to 37 ft. lbs. (50 Nm).

94. Connect the wiring harness connector for the catalytic converter control oxygen sensor.

95. Install the wiring harness.

96. Lower the vehicle by half its height.

97. Insert the 2 axle shafts into the wheel hub.

a. Insert the guiding joint into the steering knuckle.

b. Use new nuts.

98. Tighten the 2 nuts to 67 ft. lbs. (90 Nm) plus 75 degrees plus 15 degrees.

99. Counter hold at the wheel hub with KM-468 .

100. Install the 2 guide joints to the steering knuckle using new nuts.

101. Tighten the 2 screwed joints to 37 ft. lbs. (50 Nm).

102. Install the 2 tie rods to the steering knuckle using new nuts.

103. Tighten the 2 nuts to 22 ft. lbs. (30 Nm) plus 90 degrees plus 15 degrees.

➡**Use the wrench to counter hold against a flat surface.**

104. Install the 2 swing arms to the spring strut support tube using new nuts.

105. Tighten the 2 nuts to 41 ft. lbs. (55 Nm).

106. Install the lower engine cover and the right engine splash guard.

107. Connect the cooling module wiring harness connector.

108. Install the ground cable.

109. Tighten the nut to 44 inch lbs. (5 Nm).

a. Install the wiring harness connector.

b. Install the 2 wiring harnesses.

110. Install the wheel arch inner paneling, left side.

111. Install the body-bound rivet.

112. Lower the vehicle by half its height.

113. With the aid of an assistant, install the front paneling.

a. Connect the 2 wiring harness connectors.

b. Install the front paneling on the side.

c. Install the 2 body-bound rivets.

114. Raise the vehicle by half its height.

115. Install the front paneling at the bottom.

116. Install the 6 body-bound rivets.

117. Tighten the 4 bolts to 22 inch lbs. (2.5 Nm).

118. Lower the vehicle by half its height.

119. Install the 2 front wheels.

120. Tighten the 10 bolts to 81 ft. lbs. (110 Nm).

121. For vehicles with manual transaxle, connect the wiring harness connector, reverse the gear switch.

122. For vehicles with manual transaxle, install the connection, hydraulic clutch actuation.

123. Install the brake force amplifier vacuum line.

124. Connect the quick release fitting.

125. Install the engine management wiring harness.

a. Connect the 2 wiring harness connectors.

b. Connect 3 in bracket.

c. Install the negative cable to the engine control unit.

126. Tighten the bolt to 44 inch lbs. (5 Nm).

127. Install the fuel supply line to the fuel rail.

a. Connect the quick release fitting.

b. Connect into the bracket.

c. Remove the 2 KM-807 .

128. Install the venting line to the tank vent valve.

129. For vehicles with manual transaxle:

a. Install the 2 shift cables.

b. Connect 2 to the ball head.

c. Connect 2 in guide.

130. For vehicles with automatic transaxle:

a. Connect the 2 wiring harness connectors for the automatic transmission.

131. For vehicles with automatic transaxle:

a. Install the gearshift cable.

b. Install the metal clip.

c. Install in the gearshift cable.

132. Install the steering wiring harness.

133. Install the positive cable to the fuse carrier.

134. Tighten the nut to 44 inch lbs. (5 Nm).

a. Install the wiring harness connector.

b. Connect in the 2 wiring harnesses.

135. Install the coolant expansion tank.

136. Install the retaining clip.

137. Connect the wiring harness connector to the engine compartment electronics module.

138. For vehicles with manual transaxle:

a. Bleed the hydraulic clutch actuator. Refer to Hydraulic Clutch System Bleeding

139. For vehicles with automatic transaxle:

a. Install the wiring harness to the automatic transmission.

b. Install the 5 cable ties.

140. Install the battery holder.

a. Tighten the 3 bolts to 11 ft. lbs. (15 Nm).

141. Connect in the bracket for the coolant hose.

142. Connect on the 2 wiring harness.

143. Tighten the bolt to 44 inch lbs. (5 Nm).

144. Install the battery.

145. Charge the HVAC system. Refer to Refrigerant Recovery and Recharging.

146. Install the radiator grille.

147. Install the steering intermediate spindle to the steering gear.

148. Coat the bolt with the screw locking compound (red) and insert.

149. Tighten the bolt to 17 ft. lbs. (24 Nm).

150. Connect the battery.

151. Install the wiring harness connector.

152. Fill and bleed the cooling system.

153. Install air cleaner housing.

154. For programming procedures, Refer to Control Module References under Precautions.

155. For vehicles with automatic transmission:

156. Pour in the transmission oil retained.

157. Inspect and correct transmission fluid level. Refer to Transmission Fluid Check.

EXHAUST MANIFOLD

REMOVAL & INSTALLATION

See Figures 156 through 162.

❊❊ WARNING

Refer to Battery Disconnect Warning in the Preface section.

1. Disconnect the battery.

2. Remove the front Heated Oxygen Sensor (HO2S). Refer to Heated Oxygen Sensor Removal & Installation.

3. Remove the intake air duct.

4. Remove the oil dipstick guide tube.

5. Raise the vehicle by its full height.

6. Release the wiring harness connector, oxygen sensor of the catalytic converter control (1).

a. Disconnect the wiring harness connector (3).

b. Disconnect the wiring harness (2) from the bracket.

7. Remove the front exhaust pipe (2) from the catalytic converter (1).

8. Remove the heat shield from the catalytic converter.

a. Remove the 2 bolts.

9. Remove the exhaust system.

10. Remove the 6 damper rings.

11. Remove the catalytic converter from the catalytic converter bracket (1).

a. Remove the 2 bolts (3, 4).

12. Remove the bracket for the catalytic converter (1) from the cylinder block.

a. Remove the 2 bolts (2, 5).

13. If equipped with air conditioning, remove the drive belt. Refer to Drive Belt Removal & Installation.

14. If equipped with air conditioning, remove the compressor. Refer to Air Conditioning Compressor Removal & Installation.

a. Remove the 3 bolts (1).

b. Set aside.

15. Lower the vehicle by its full height.

16. Remove the 2 engine transport shackles (1).

a. Remove the 2 bolts (2).

17. Remove the exhaust manifold heat shield (3).

18. Remove the wiring harness bracket (2).

19. Remove the bolt (1).

20. Remove the 9 nuts (1).

21. Remove the exhaust manifold.

To install:

22. Clean the sealing surface.

23. Install the exhaust manifold.

24. Use NEW gasket and nuts.

25. Tighten the 9 nuts to 15 ft. lbs. (20 Nm).

26. Replace the heat shield.

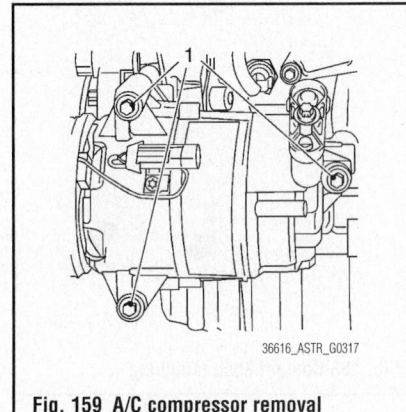

Fig. 159 A/C compressor removal

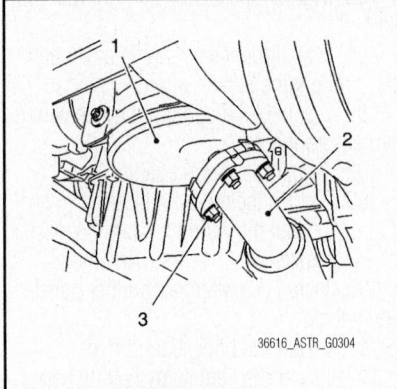

Fig. 157 Front exhaust pipe

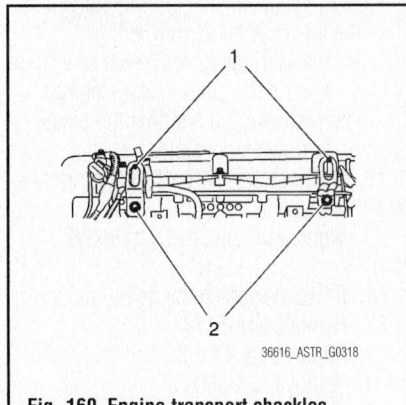

Fig. 160 Engine transport shackles

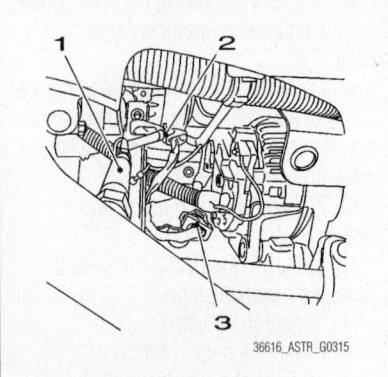

Fig. 156 Oxygen sensor plug

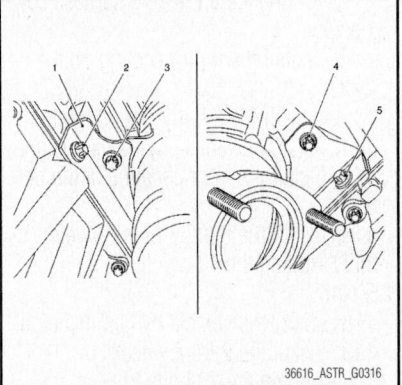

Fig. 158 Catalytic converter and bracket

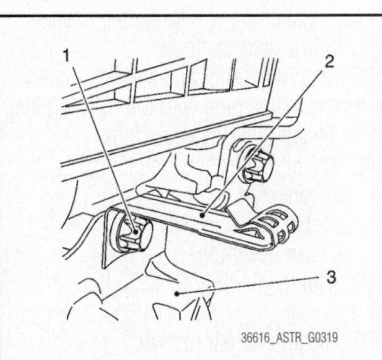

Fig. 161 Exhaust manifold heat shield and bracket

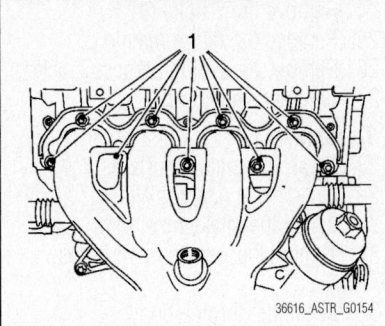

Fig. 162 Exhaust manifold and fastener locations (1)

27. Install the wiring harness bracket of the oxygen sensor mixture regulator.
28. Tighten the bolt to 11 ft. lbs. (15 Nm).
29. Raise the vehicle by its full height.
30. If equipped with air conditioning, install the compressor. Refer to Air Conditioning Compressor Removal & Installation.
31. Tighten the 3 bolts to 16 ft. lbs. (22 Nm).
32. In vehicles with air conditioning, install the drive belt. Refer to Drive Belt Replacement.
33. Install the catalytic converter bracket.
34. Install to the cylinder block.
35. Tighten the 2 bolts to 15 ft. lbs. (20 Nm).
36. Install the catalytic converter to the bracket.
37. Tighten the 2 bolts to 15 ft. lbs. Nm).
38. Install the heat shield to the catalytic converter.
39. Tighten the 2 bolts to 70 inch lbs. (8 Nm).
40. Install the exhaust system.
41. Install the 6 damper rings.
42. Install the front exhaust pipe to the catalytic converter.
43. Tighten the 3 new nuts to 15 ft. lbs. (20 Nm).
44. Install the catalytic converter control oxygen sensor wiring harness.
    a. Connect the wiring harness connector.
    b. Install the wiring harness into the bracket.
45. Install the oil dipstick guide tube. Refer to Oil Level Indicator and Tube Replacement.
46. Clean the 2 threads.
47. Install the 2 engine transport shackles.
48. Tighten the 2 bolts to 15 ft. lbs. (20 Nm).
49. Install the bracket, wiring harness for the mixture regulator oxygen sensor to the

cylinder head together with the exhaust manifold heat shield.
50. Tighten the bolt to 18 ft. lbs. (25 Nm).
51. Install the mixture regulator oxygen sensor. Refer to Heated Oxygen Sensor 1 Replacement.
52. Install the intake air duct.
53. Install the air cleaner assembly.
54. Connect the battery.
55. Inspect and correct the engine oil level.

INTAKE MANIFOLD

REMOVAL & INSTALLATION
See Figures 77, 163 through 173.

Special Service Tools:
• J 37088-A Fuel Line Disconnect Tool Set
• KM-807 Closure Plugs
• KM-J-34730-91 Pressure Tester

✳✳ WARNING

Refer to Battery Disconnect Warning in the Preface section.

1. Disconnect the battery.
2. Raise the vehicle by its full height.
3. Drain the coolant.
    a. Place a drip pan underneath.
    b. Connect a suitable hose to the drain connection (2).
    c. Open the coolant drain screw (1).
    d. Drain the coolant.
    e. Close coolant drain screw.
4. Remove the intake manifold support (2).
5. Disconnect the wiring harness connector of the catalytic converter control oxygen sensor.
6. Remove the wiring harness connector (1) from the bracket.
7. Remove the 2 bolts (3).
8. Remove the wiring harness from the intake manifold.

9. Lower the vehicle by its full height.
10. Remove the air cleaner housing.
11. Disconnect the tank vent valve from the intake manifold.
    a. Disconnect the wiring harness connector (2).
    b. Disconnect the rubber mounting (3) from the bracket.
    c. Disconnect the line (1) from the intake manifold.
    d. Set the tank vent valve aside.
12. Place a drip pan underneath.
13. Release the fuel pressure at the test connection (1) using KM-J-34730-91 .

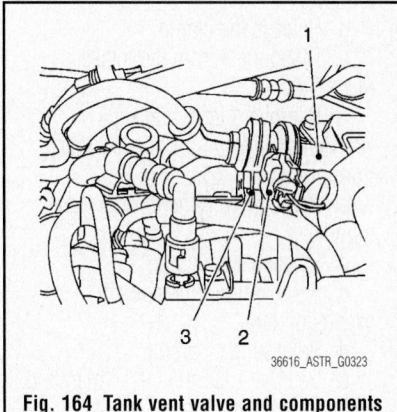

Fig. 164 Tank vent valve and components

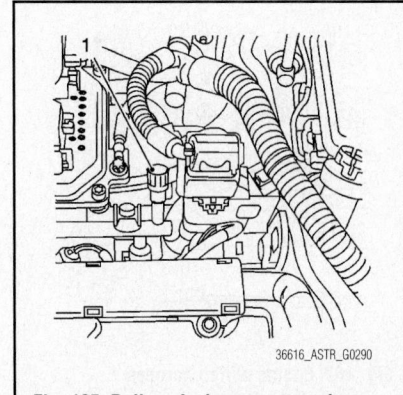

Fig. 165 Relieve fuel pressure as shown

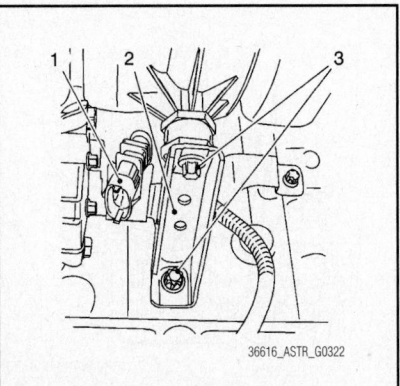

Fig. 163 Intake manifold support

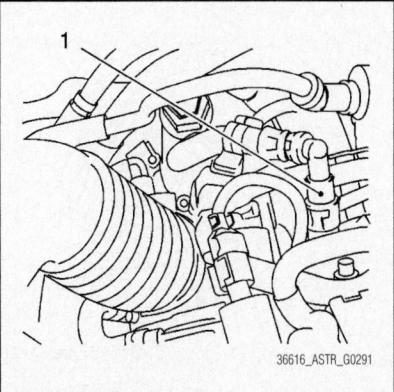

Fig. 166 Fuel return line

14. Collect the exiting fuel in a suitable container.

15. Remove the fuel return line (1).

   a. Disconnect the quick-release fitting with J 37088-A .

   b. Seal the fuel line and the fuel rail with KM-807 .

16. Disconnect the wiring harness connector (1).

17. Remove the supply line, fuel/air mixture preheating (1).

   a. Disconnect from thermostat housing.

   b. Disconnect the quick-release fitting.

   c. Disconnect from the throttle valve module.

   d. Release the clamp.

   e. Disconnect from the intake manifold.

   f. Remove 4 from bracket.

18. Remove the return line, fuel/air mixture preheating (2).

   a. Remove from the throttle valve module.

   b. Release the clamp.

   c. Remove from the coolant expansion tank.

   d. Release the clamp.

   e. Remove from the intake manifold.

   f. Remove the 3 brackets.

19. Disconnect the 2 wiring harness connectors.

   a. Wiring harness connector, vacuum unit change-over valves (1)

   b. Wiring harness connector, change-over valves for solenoid valve (2)

20. Disconnect the wiring harness bracket (1) from the engine transport shackle.

21. Remove the bolt (2).

22. Remove the brake servo vacuum line (1) from the intake manifold.

   a. Disconnect the quick-release fitting.

23. Remove the throttle body.

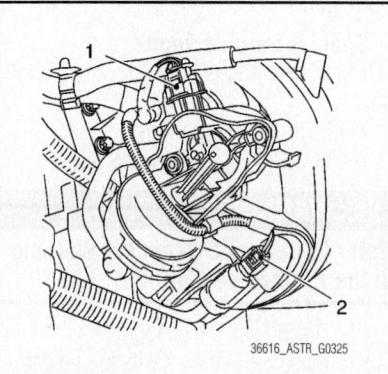

Fig. 169 Vacuum unit change-over valves

24. Remove the 7 bolts (1).

25. Remove the intake manifold.

26. Remove the wiring harness bracket.

27. Remove the fuel rail.

To install:

28. Clean the sealing surfaces.

29. Insert the 4 new gaskets.

30. Install the intake manifold.

31. Tighten the 7 bolts to 16 ft. lbs. (20 Nm).

32. Install the throttle body.

33. Tighten the 4 bolts to 80 inch lbs. (9 Nm).

34. Install the brake servo vacuum line to the intake manifold.

35. Connect the quick release fitting.

36. Install the wiring harness bracket to the engine transport shackle.

37. Tighten the bolt to 44 inch lbs. (5 Nm).

38. Connect the 2 wiring harness connectors.

   a. Vacuum unit change-over valves

   b. Solenoid valve for change-over valves

39. Install the return line, fuel/air mixture preheating.

   a. Connect the throttle body.

   b. Fasten the clamp.

   c. Connect the coolant expansion tank.

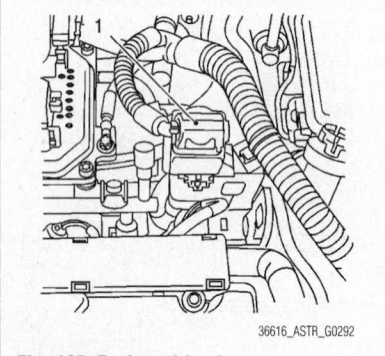

Fig. 167 Engine wiring harness connector (1)

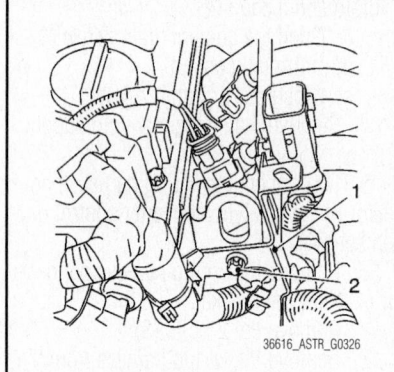

Fig. 170 Wiring harness bracket

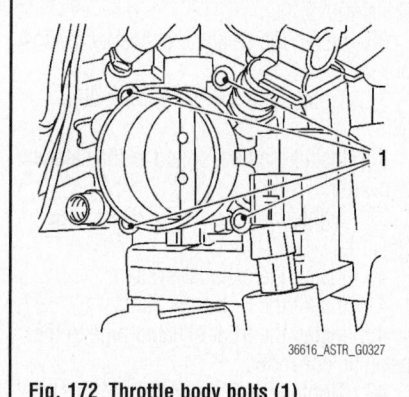

Fig. 172 Throttle body bolts (1)

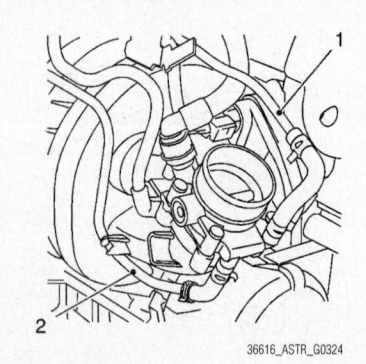

Fig. 168 Fuel supply line

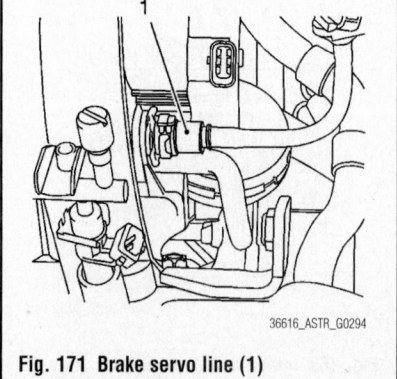

Fig. 171 Brake servo line (1)

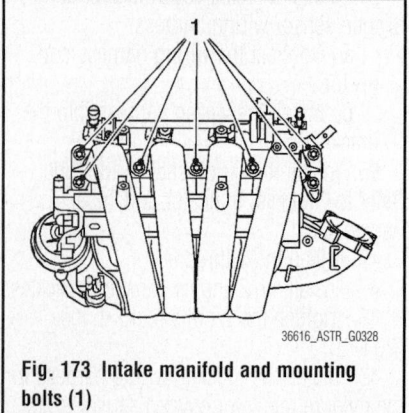

Fig. 173 Intake manifold and mounting bolts (1)

d. Fasten the clamp.

e. Install the intake manifold.

f. Install the 3 brackets.

40. Install the supply line, fuel/air mixture preheating.

a. Connect to the thermostat housing.

b. Connect the quick release fitting.

c. Install the throttle body.

d. Fasten the clamp.

e. Connect the 4 brackets.

41. Install the engine management wiring harness.

42. Connect the 7 wiring harness connectors.

a. Air mass flow meter

b. Throttle body

c. Valve, intake camshaft adjustment

d. Four injector valves

e. Clip on the 2 wiring harness brackets.

43. Install the engine control module. Refer to Engine Control Module Replacement.

44. Install the engine vent hose.

45. Connect the 2 quick-release fittings.

46. Clip the wiring harness to the cylinder head.

47. Install the fuel supply line to the fuel rail.

48. Remove KM-807.

49. Connect the quick release fitting.

50. Install into the bracket.

51. Connect the tank vent valve to the intake manifold.

a. Connect the line to the intake manifold.

b. Connect the rubber mounting to the bracket.

52. Install the wiring harness connector.

53. Install the air cleaner housing. Refer to Air Cleaner Assembly Replacement.

54. Raise the vehicle by its full height.

55. Install the wiring harness to the intake manifold.

56. Install the intake manifold support.

57. Tighten the 2 bolts to 71 inch lbs. (8 Nm).

58. Connect the wiring harness connector into the bracket.

59. Connect the wiring harness connector for the catalytic converter control oxygen sensor.

60. Lower the vehicle by its full height.

61. Fill and bleed the cooling system. Refer to Cooling System Draining and Filling.

62. Connect the battery.

OIL PAN

REMOVAL & INSTALLATION

See Figures 174 through 178.

⁂ **WARNING**

Refer to Battery Disconnect Warning in the Preface section.

1. Disconnect the battery.

2. Drain the engine oil.

3. Replace the seal ring.

4. Tighten the oil drain bolt.

5. Tighten the bolt to 10 ft. lbs. (14 Nm).

6. Lower the vehicle by its full height.

7. Remove the oil level indicator and tube. Refer to Oil Level Indicator and Tube Replacement.

8. Raise the vehicle by its full height.

9. Remove the lower engine cover and the right engine splash guard.

10. Remove the front Heated Oxygen Sensor (HO2S). Refer to Heated Oxygen Sensor Removal & Installation.

11. Remove the oil dipstick guide tube.

12. Raise the vehicle by its full height.

13. Release the wiring harness connector, oxygen sensor of the catalytic converter control (1).

a. Disconnect the wiring harness connector (3).

b. Disconnect the wiring harness (2) from the bracket.

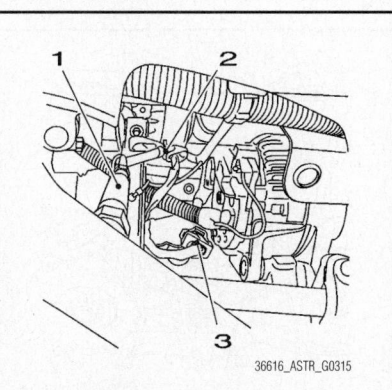

Fig. 174 Oxygen sensor plug

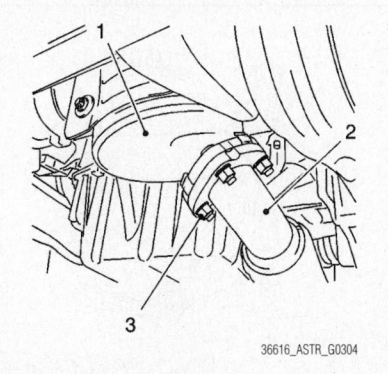

Fig. 175 Front exhaust pipe

14. Remove the front exhaust pipe (2) from the catalytic converter (1).

15. Remove the heat shield from the catalytic converter.

a. Remove the 2 bolts.

16. Remove the exhaust system.

17. Remove the 6 damper rings.

18. Disconnect the oil level sensor wiring harness connector.

19. Loosen the oil pan.

20. Remove the 3 bolts (arrows) from the transmission.

21. Remove the 13 bolts (arrows) from the engine block.

22. Remove the oil pan evenly all the way around with a suitable tool.

To install:

23. Clean the sealing surfaces.

24. Apply an approximately 3.5 mm (0.14 in) thick bead of oil pan sealant to the joints (arrows).

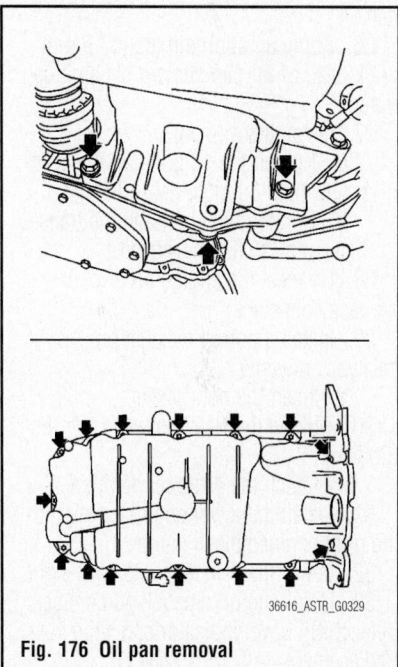

Fig. 176 Oil pan removal

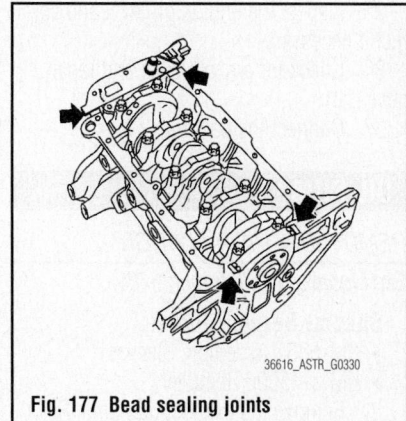

Fig. 177 Bead sealing joints

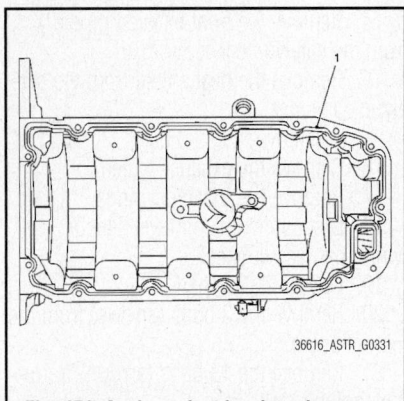

Fig. 178 Apply sealant bead as shown

⁂ **WARNING**

The assembly time including torque check must take no longer than 10 minutes.

25. Apply the oil pan sealant to the oil pan.

26. Apply an approximately 3.5 mm thick bead of oil pan sealant (1) as illustrated.

27. Install the oil pan.

a. Tighten the 13 bolts on the cylinder block to 89 inch lbs. (10 Nm).

b. Tighten the 3 bolts on the transmission to 30 ft. lbs. (40 Nm).

28. Connect the engine oil level wiring harness connector.

29. Install the front exhaust pipe to the catalytic converter.

a. Insert the new gasket.

30. Tighten the NEW nuts to 15 ft. lbs. (20 Nm).

a. Attach the 4 rubber dampers.

31. Install the lower engine cover and the right engine splash guard.

32. Lower the vehicle by its full height.

33. Install the oil dipstick guide tube. Refer to Oil Level Indicator and Tube Replacement

34. Refill the engine oil.

35. Inspect the engine oil level and correct if necessary.

36. Check for any oil leaks and repair if necessary.

37. Connect the battery.

OIL PUMP

REMOVAL & INSTALLATION

See Figures 77,179 through 185.

Special Service Tools:
• KM-6351 Assembly Sleeves
• KM-J-45000 Remover

1. Remove the exhaust manifold. Refer to Exhaust Manifold Removal & Installation.

2. Remove the oil pan. Refer to Oil Pan Removal & Installation.

3. Remove alternator. Refer to Alternator Removal & Installation.

4. Remove the engine damping block, right side. Refer to Engine Mount Removal & Installation - Right Side.

5. Remove the engine damping block support from the cylinder block.

6. Drain the coolant.

a. Place a drain pan underneath.

b. Install the suitable hose to the drain connection (2).

c. Open the coolant drain screw (1).

d. Drain the coolant.

e. Close the coolant drain screw.

7. Remove the timing belt tensioner (1).

8. Remove the bolt (2).

9. Raise the vehicle by its full height.

10. Remove the coolant hose from the coolant pump.

11. Release the clamp.

12. Detach the coolant pipe (2) from the pump module.

a. Remove the 2 bolts (1).

b. Push the coolant pipe into the oil pump housing adapter.

c. Detach the coolant pipe (3) from the pump module.

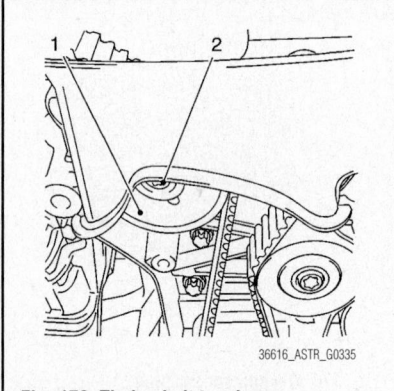

Fig. 179 Timing belt tensioner

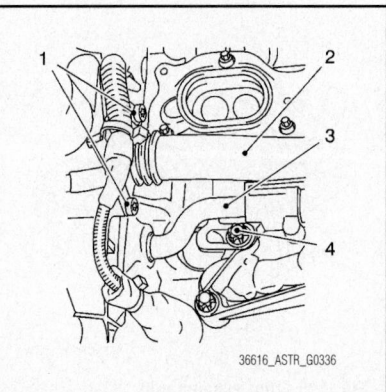

Fig. 180 Coolant pipe and pump module

d. Detach the coolant pipe from the oil filter housing adapter.

e. Remove the bolt (4).

f. Push the coolant pipe into the oil filter housing adapter.

13. Remove the timing belt drive gear. Note different screw lengths.

14. Remove the pump module.

a. Remove the 8 bolts (1, 2).

b. Remove the gasket.

15. Replace the 4 coolant pipe seal rings.

a. Remove the 2 coolant pipes from the oil filter housing adapter.

b. Insert the 2 coolant pipes in the oil filter housing adapter.

16. Clean the sealing surface.

⁂ **WARNING**

Do not damage the sealing surfaces.

17. Remove the crankshaft seal ring (front) with KM-J-45000 .

18. Remove the oil pump cover (1).

19. Remove the 6 bolts (2).

To install:

20. Clean the sealing surface.

21. Install the oil pump cover.

22. Tighten the 6 bolts to 71 inch lbs. (8 Nm).

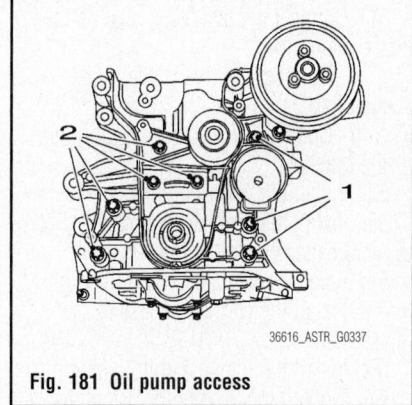

Fig. 181 Oil pump access

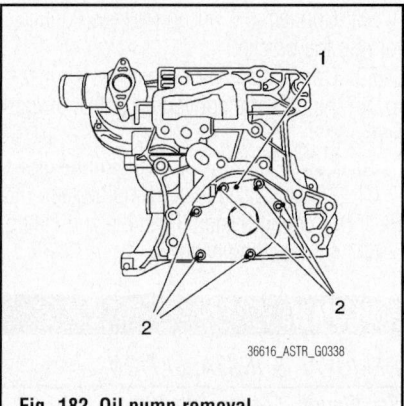

Fig. 182 Oil pump removal

Note different screw lengths.

23. Install the pump module.
  a. Replace the gasket.
24. Tighten the 8 bolts to 15 ft. lbs. (20 Nm).
25. Insert the timing belt drive gear.
26. Install the coolant pipe to the coolant module.
  a. Pull the coolant pipe out of the oil filter housing adapter.
27. Tighten the bolt to 80 inch lbs. (9 Nm).
28. Install the coolant pipe to the coolant module.
29. Pull the coolant pipe out of the oil pump housing adapter.
30. Tighten the 2 bolts to 80 inch lbs. (9 Nm).
31. Insert the front crankshaft seal ring (1).
32. Clean the sealing surfaces.
33. Slide the protective sleeve of KM-6351 (2) onto the crankshaft journal.
34. Slide the seal ring over the protective sleeve on the crankshaft journal.
35. Press in the front crankshaft seal ring.
36. Remove the protective sleeve and press the seal ring into the pump housing with KM-6351 (3).
37. Use the bolt (1) and washer (2) of the crankshaft drive gear.
38. Install the timing belt drive gear.
39. Lower the vehicle by its full height.

Threading the timing belt through the engine mount support is only permissible in conjunction with the assembly tool supplied with new toothed belts as otherwise it is possible to damage the timing belt at this stage by kinking it.

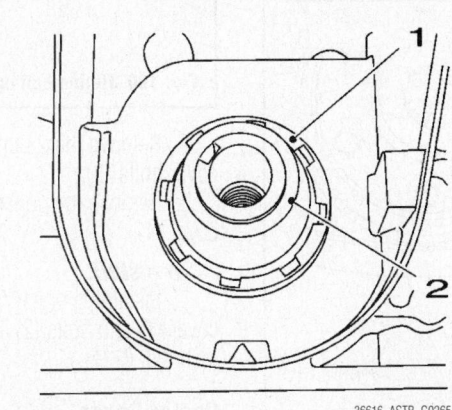

Fig. 183 Crankshaft seal ring

40. Insert the timing belt.
41. Insert the drive belt (1) in the enclosed assembly tool (2)
  a. If the timing belt has been used, observe direction of rotation.
42. Guide the timing belt through the engine mount support with the assembly tool.
43. Remove the assembly tool.

➡**Observe direction of rotation.**

44. Position the timing belt.
  a. Position the timing belt on the intake camshaft adjuster.
  b. Position the timing belt on the exhaust camshaft adjuster.
  c. Guide the drive belt past the tension roller and place on the drive belt drive gear.
  d. Apply tension to the timing belt tension roller and remove KM-6333.
45. Release tension on the timing belt tensioner.
  a. Apply preliminary tension clockwise to the timing belt tension roller.
  b. Remove KM-6333.
  c. The timing belt tension pulley automatically moves to the correct position.
46. Raise vehicle by its full height.
47. Install the front timing belt cover (lower).
48. Tighten the 4 bolts to 53 inch lbs. (6 Nm).

➡**New bolt must be coated with thread locking compound (red).**

49. Install the torsional vibration balancer.
  a. Use a NEW bolt.
50. Tighten the bolt to 70 ft. lbs. (95 Nm) plus 30 degrees, plus 15 degrees.
51. Remove KM-6625.
  a. Detach the threaded connection.
  b. Tighten the bolted connection.
  c. Use NEW nuts.
52. Lower the vehicle by its full height.

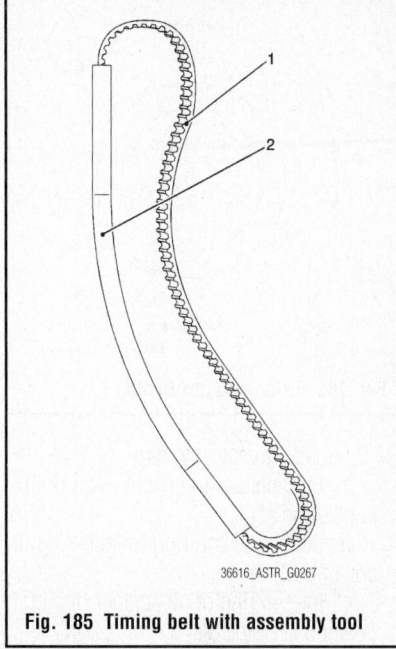

36616_ASTR_G0267

Fig. 185 Timing belt with assembly tool

53. Remove the MK-6340.
54. Inspect the timing.

➡**Note marking, camshaft sprockets.**

55. Turn the crankshaft 720 degrees in the direction of engine rotation by the bolt on the torsional vibration damper.
56. Insert MK-6340 (1, 2) in the camshaft adjuster as shown.

➡**The spot-type marking (4) on the intake camshaft adjuster does not correspond to the groove of MK-6340 during this process but must be somewhat above as shown.**

57. The spot type marking (3) on the exhaust camshaft adjuster must correspond to the groove on MK-6340.
58. Raise the vehicle by its full height.
59. Inspect the crankshaft position.
60. Markings on the torsional vibration damper and the lower part of the timing belt cover (arrows) must align.
61. Install the drive belt tensioner.
62. Lower the vehicle by its full height.
63. Remove MK-6340.
64. Install the front drive belt cover (top). Refer to Timing Belt Front Cover Removal & Installation.
65. Install the air cleaner housing.
66. Connect the battery

PISTON AND RING

POSITIONING

See Figure 186.

1. Insert into the pistons with piston ring wrench and "TOP" pointing upwards.

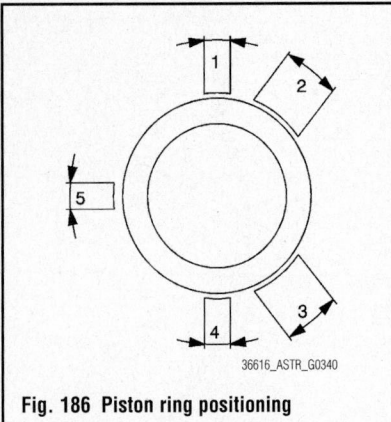

Fig. 186 Piston ring positioning

2. Set the piston ring gap.

a. First piston ring (right-hand ring) in position (1)

b. Second piston ring (minute ring) in position (2)

c. Interim ring of oil scraper ring in position (3), steel band rings of oil scraper ring in position (4 and/or 5)

REAR MAIN SEAL

REMOVAL & INSTALLATION

See Figures 187 through 189.

Special Service Tools:
- KM-328-B Remover
- KM-6624 Remover
- KM-6623 Installer

1. Remove the transaxle. Refer to Automatic or Manual Transaxle Removal & Installation.

2. Remove the flexplate or flywheel. Refer to Flexplate or Flywheel Removal & Installation.

3. Remove the encoder (1) from the crankshaft.

4. Disconnect the crankshaft pulse pick-up (2) from the pulse pick-up bracket.

5. Remove the bolt (1).

6. Remove the plastic ring on the pulse pick-up bracket (3).

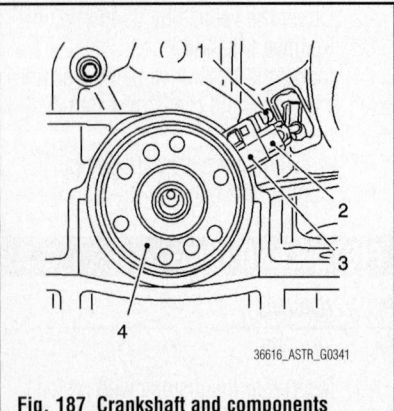

Fig. 187 Crankshaft and components

- Only make a hole at the 5 o'clock and 7 o'clock positions (1), as these are the only areas where there is a cavity behind the seal ring.
- The diameter of the hole must not exceed 2 mm. If the diameter of the hole exceeds 2 mm, the bolt of KM-6624 remover will not be able to grip.

7. Using a suitable tool, such as a scribe (2), make a hole in the seal ring. Position the scribe at the outer edge of the seal ring.

8. Remove the seal ring.

a. Attach KM-6624 remover (1) to the seal ring and tighten the bolt.

b. Attach KM-328-B remover (2) to KM-6624 remover (1).

c. Using KM-328-B remover (2) and KM-6624 remover (1), tap the seal ring out.

To install:

9. Position the new seal ring.

a. Position the seal ring in such a way that the pulse pick-up bracket is over the corresponding cut-out on the cylinder block.

b. Slide the seal ring over the crankshaft. Push, until the seal ring is flush and sits evenly in the cylinder block.

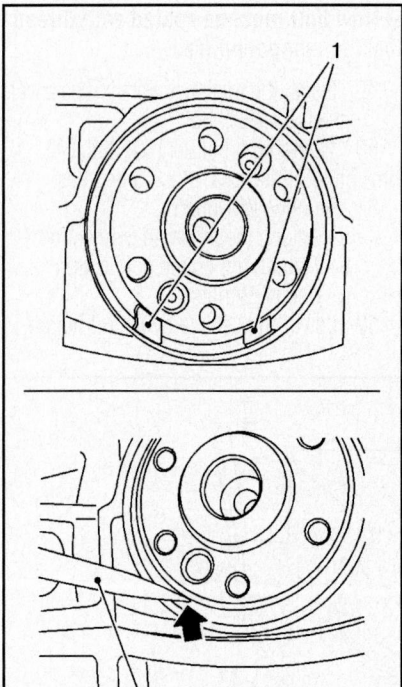

Fig. 188 Crankshaft rear main seal removal

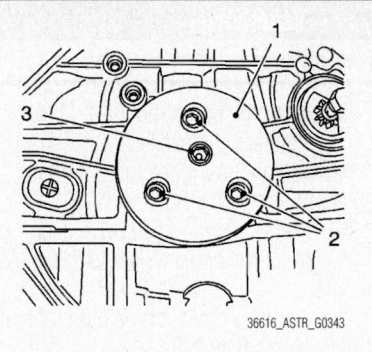

Fig. 189 Crankshaft rear main seal installation

10. Using the KM-6623 installer , install the seal ring (1).

a. Tighten the 3 bolts (2).

b. Press the seal ring all the way in.

c. Install the bolt (3).

11. Remove the KM-6623 installer .

12. Remove the 3 bolts.

13. Install the crankshaft pulse pick-up to the pulse pick-up bracket. Tighten the bolt to 44 inch lbs. (5 Nm).

14. Place the encoder on the crankshaft.

TIMING BELT FRONT COVER

REMOVAL & INSTALLATION

Upper Cover

See Figure 190.

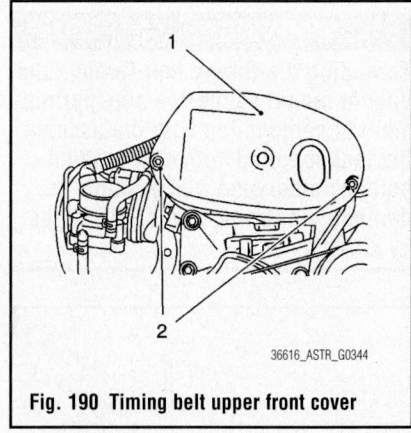

Fig. 190 Timing belt upper front cover

1. Remove the 2 upper front timing belt cover bolts (2).

2. Remove the upper front timing belt cover (1).

To install:

3. Install the upper front timing belt cover (1) and bolts (2) and tighten to 53 inch lbs. (6 Nm).

Center Cover

See Figure 191.

Fig. 191 Timing belt center front cover (1)

Fig. 193 Crankshaft timing marks

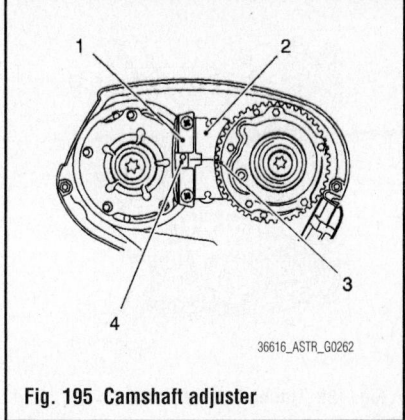

Fig. 195 Camshaft adjuster

1. Unclip the center front timing belt cover from the rear timing belt cover at 2 locations.
2. Remove the center front timing belt cover (1).

To install:

3. Install the center front timing belt cover (1) by clipping to the rear timing belt cover at 2 locations.

Lower Cover

See Figure 192.

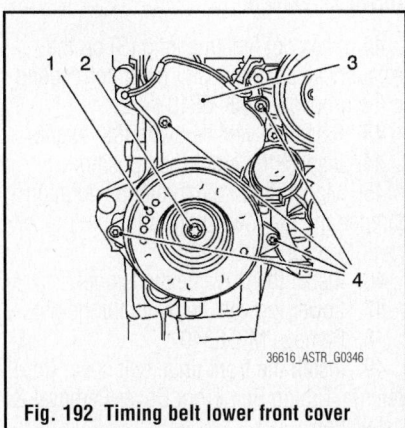

Fig. 192 Timing belt lower front cover

1. Remove the 4 lower front timing belt cover bolts (4).
2. Remove the lower front timing belt cover (3).

To install:

3. Install the lower front timing belt cover (3) and bolts (4) and tighten to 53 inch lbs. (6 Nm).

TIMING BELT AND SPROCKETS

REMOVAL & INSTALLATION

See Figures 193 through 201.

Special Service Tools:
- KM-6333 Fixing Rod
- KM-6340 Locking Tool
- KM-6628 Locking Tool

1. Disconnect the battery.
2. Loosen the nut.
3. Remove the air cleaner housing.
4. Remove the timing belt upper cover. Refer to Timing Belt Front Cover Removal & Installation.
5. Raise the vehicle by its full height.
6. Remove the drive belt tensioner.
7. Lower the vehicle by its full height.
8. Set the engine to Top Dead Center.
9. Set the torsional vibration damper in the direction of engine rotation to "1st cylinder TDC" (mark 1).
10. Recognizable from the lettering "Right" (arrow).
11. Prepare the right half of MK-6340 for use on the U 18 XER engine.
    a. Detach the front panel (1) from MK-6340 .
    b. Remove the 2 bolts (2).
12. Insert MK-6340 in the camshaft adjuster.
    a. Insert MK-6340 (1, 2) in the camshaft adjuster as shown.

➡**The spot-type marking (4) on the intake camshaft adjuster does not correspond to the groove of MK-6340 during this process but must be somewhat above as shown.**

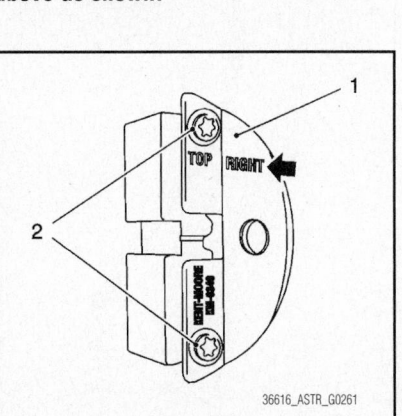

Fig. 194 Special service tool MK-6340

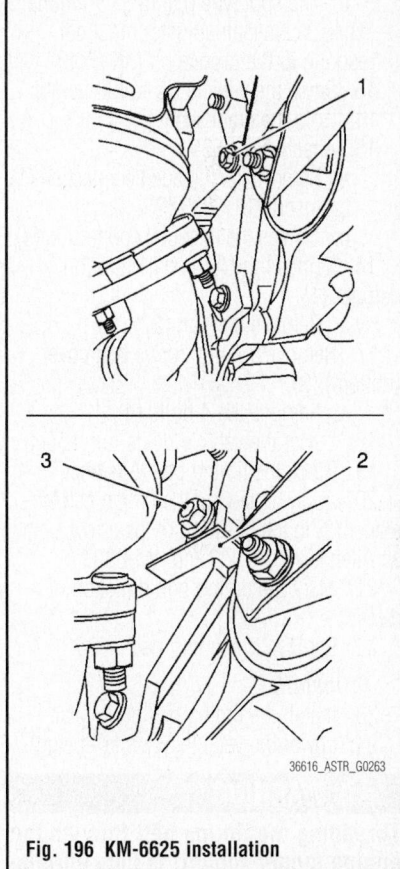

Fig. 196 KM-6625 installation

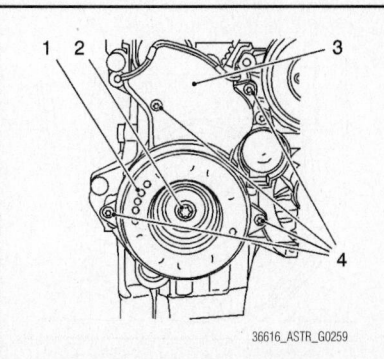

Fig. 197 Torsional vibration damper removal

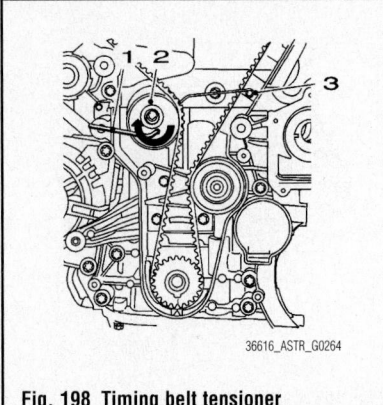

Fig. 198 Timing belt tensioner

b. The spot type marking (3) on the exhaust camshaft adjuster must correspond to the groove on MK-6340 .

13. Raise the vehicle by its full height.
14. Hold the crankshaft.
15. Attach KM-6625 .
   a. Remove the threaded connection (1).
   b. Insert KM-6625 (2).
   c. Tighten the threaded connection (3).
16. Remove the torsional vibration damper (1).
   a. Remove the bolt (2).
17. Remove the front drive belt cover (bottom) (3).
   a. Remove the 4 bolts (4).
18. Lower the vehicle by its full height.
19. Block the timing belt tensioner.
20. Apply tension to the timing belt tensioner (2) in the direction of the arrow, using an Allen key (1). Fix using KM-6333 (3).
21. Mark the timing belt direction of rotation.
22. Remove the timing belt.

To install:
23. Install the timing belt drive gear.
24. Lower the vehicle by its full height.

✳✳ WARNING

Threading the timing belt through the engine mount support is only permissible in conjunction with the assembly tool supplied with new toothed belts as otherwise it is possible to damage the timing belt at this stage by kinking it.

25. Insert the timing belt.
26. Insert the drive belt (1) in the enclosed assembly tool (2)
   a. If the timing belt has been used, observe direction of rotation.
27. Guide the timing belt through the engine mount support with the assembly tool.
28. Remove the assembly tool.

➡ Observe direction of rotation.

29. Position the timing belt.
   a. Position the timing belt on the intake camshaft adjuster.
   b. Position the timing belt on the exhaust camshaft adjuster.
   c. Guide the drive belt past the tension roller and place on the drive belt drive gear.
   d. Apply tension to the timing belt tension roller and remove KM-6333 .
30. Release tension on the timing belt tensioner.
   a. Apply preliminary tension clockwise to the timing belt tension roller.
   b. Remove KM-6333 .
   c. The timing belt tension pulley automatically moves to the correct position.
31. Raise vehicle by its full height.
32. Install the front timing belt cover (lower).

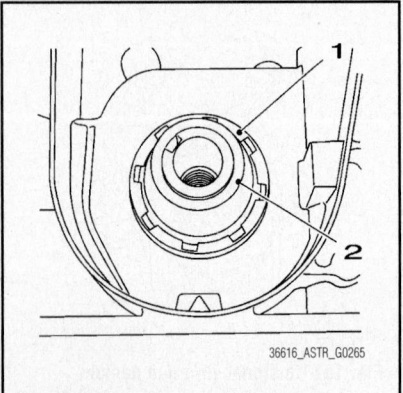

Fig. 199 Crankshaft seal ring

33. Tighten the 4 bolts to 53 inch lbs. (6 Nm).

➡ New bolt must be coated with thread locking compound (red).

34. Install the torsional vibration balancer.
   a. Use a NEW bolt.
35. Tighten the bolt to 70 ft. lbs. (95 Nm) plus 30 degrees, plus 15 degrees.
36. Remove KM-6625 .
   a. Detach the threaded connection.
   b. Tighten the bolted connection.
   c. Use NEW nuts.
37. Lower the vehicle by its full height.
38. Remove the MK-6340.
39. Inspect the timing.

➡ Note marking, camshaft sprockets.

40. Turn the crankshaft 720 degrees in the direction of engine rotation by the bolt on the torsional vibration damper.
41. Insert MK-6340 (1, 2) in the camshaft adjuster as shown.

➡ The spot-type marking (4) on the intake camshaft adjuster does not correspond to the groove of MK-6340 during this process but must be somewhat above as shown.

42. The spot type marking (3) on the exhaust camshaft adjuster must correspond to the groove on MK-6340 .
43. Raise the vehicle by its full height.
44. Inspect the crankshaft position.
45. Markings on the torsional vibration damper and the lower part of the timing belt cover (arrows) must align.
46. Install the drive belt tensioner.
47. Lower the vehicle by its full height.
48. Remove MK-6340 .
49. Install the front drive belt cover (top). Refer to Timing Belt Front Cover Removal & Installation.
50. Install the air cleaner housing.
51. Connect the battery.

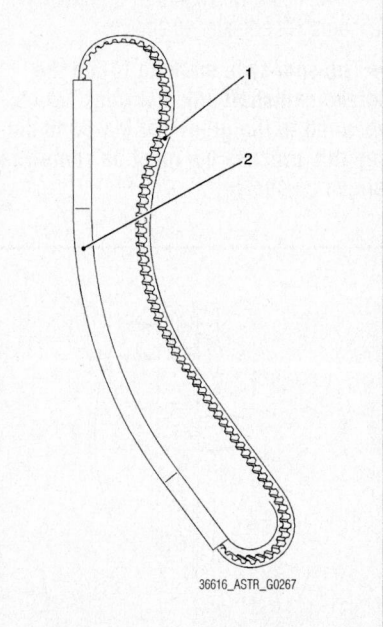

Fig. 200 Timing belt with assembly tool

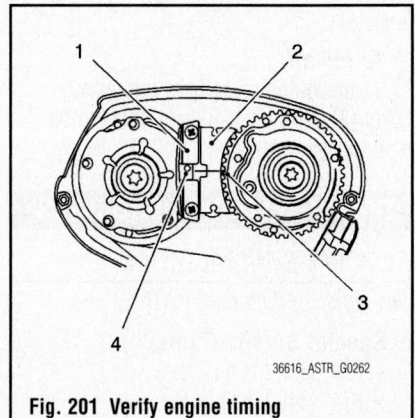

Fig. 201 Verify engine timing

TORSIONAL VIBRATION DAMPER

REMOVAL & INSTALLATION

See Figure 202.

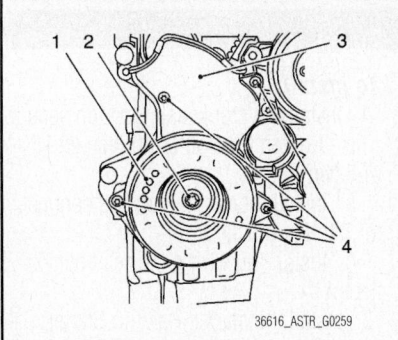

Fig. 202 Torsional vibration damper removal

1. Disconnect the battery. Refer to Battery Disconnect Warning in the Precautions section..
2. Raise the vehicle by its full height.
3. Remove the drive belt. Refer to Drive Belt Removal & Installation.
4. Lower the vehicle by its full height.
5. Set the engine to Top Dead Center.
   a. Remove the bolt (2).
6. Remove the torsional vibration damper (1).

To install:

7. Clean the sealing surfaces.
8. Install the torsional vibration damper (1).
9. Install the bolt (2).
10. Use a NEW bolt.
11. Tighten the bolt to 70 ft. lbs. (95 Nm) plus 30 degrees, plus 15 degrees.
12. Install the drive belt. Refer to Drive Belt Removal & Installation.
13. Disconnect battery.
14. Refer to Control Module References under Precautions.

VALVE LASH

ADJUSTMENT

See Figures 203 through 206.

Prescribed Valve Lash:
• Intake: 0.008–0.011 in. (0.21–0.29mm)
• Exhaust: 0.010–0.014 in. (0.27–0.35 mm)

1. Disconnect the battery.
2. Remove the air cleaner housing.
3. Remove the front timing belt cover (top). Refer to Timing Belt Upper Front Cover Removal & Installation.

4. Remove the valve cover. Refer to Valve Cover Removal & Installation.
5. Raise the vehicle by its full height.
6. Remove the drive belt tensioner.
7. Set the engine to TDC.
8. Turn the crankshaft in the direction of engine rotation by the bolt of the torsional vibration damper to cylinder 1 TDC of combustion stroke.
9. Cams at the intake side of cylinder number 2 (1) and the exhaust side of cylinder number 3 (2) are on top and tilted slightly towards the inside to the same extent.
10. Inspect valve lash.
11. Inspect the 4 valves and record the results.
12. Turn the engine over in increments of 90 degrees, and repeat the procedure until all valve clearances have been accurately measured and recorded.
13. If valve adjustment is required, remove the camshafts as required. Refer to camshaft Removal & Installation.

➡**Mark the camshaft bearing caps before removing them.**

14. Remove the intake camshaft.
   a. Detach camshaft bearing caps 2-5 working from outside to inside in a spiral in steps of 1/2 up to 1 turn.
15. Note the marking on the camshaft bearing cover with stamped numbers from 1 to 0 (there is a dot at bottom left before each number to avoid mistakes)

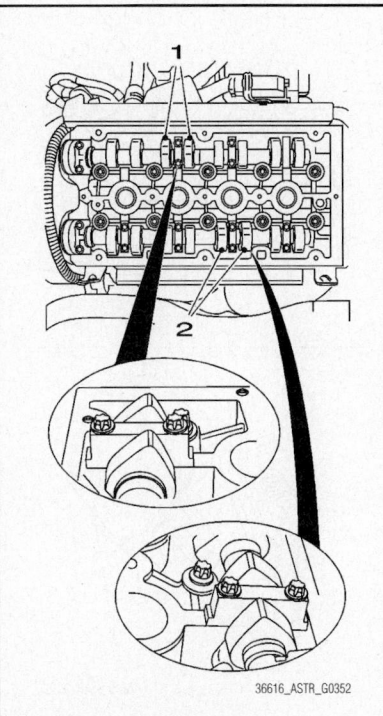

Fig. 203 Camshaft positioning

➡**Mark the camshaft bearing caps before removing them.**

16. Remove the exhaust camshaft.
   a. Detach camshaft bearing caps 2-5 working from outside to inside in a spiral in steps of 1/2 up to 1 turn.
Note the marking on the camshaft bearing cover with stamped numbers from 1 to 0 (there is a dot at bottom left before each number to avoid mistakes).
17. Remove the camshaft bearing cover from the cylinder head and take out the camshaft.
18. Remove the cup tappets.

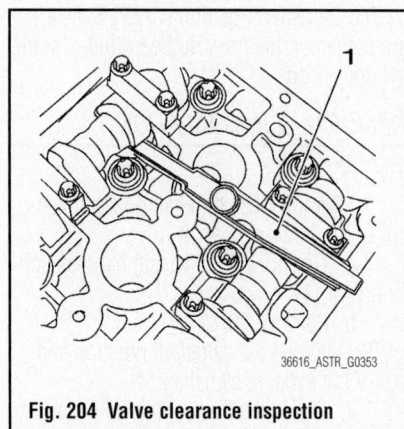

Fig. 204 Valve clearance inspection

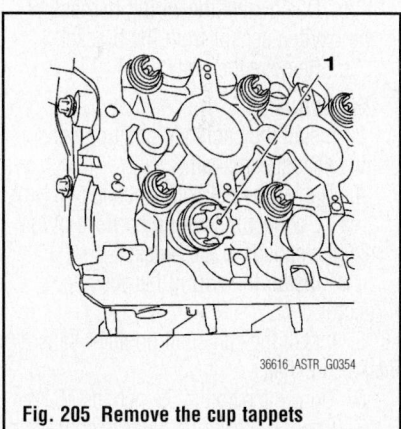

Fig. 205 Remove the cup tappets

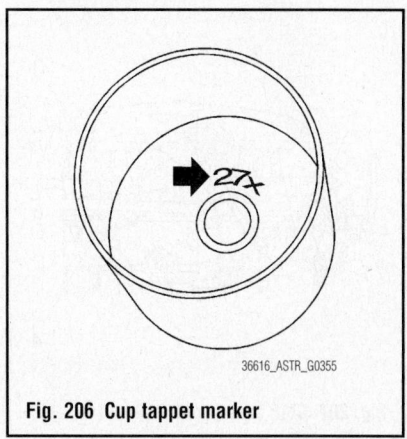

Fig. 206 Cup tappet marker

19. Determine cup tappet size.
Example of determining the size of a cup tappet, intake side:
- Dimension of fitted cup tappet 0.126" (3.20mm - Identification number 20)

- Measurement between cams and cup tappets + 0.31mm = 3.51 mm
- Required value, valve lash, intake side: 0.010" (0.25 mm)
- Note the identification number (arrow) is on the inside of the cup tappet.

- Nominal dimension of the new cup tappet 0.129" (3.265mm - Identification number 27x)
- Use a replacement cup tappet with this dimension or one that is nearest to it.

ENGINE PERFORMANCE & EMISSION CONTROLS

CAMSHAFT POSITION (CMP) SENSOR

LOCATION
See Figure 207.

The Camshaft Position (CMP) Sensors are located at the front outboard sides of the cylinder head.

REMOVAL & INSTALLATION
See Figure 207.

1. Remove the camshaft position sensor of the intake camshaft (2).
   a. Disconnect the wiring harness connector (1).
   b. Remove the bolt.
2. Remove the camshaft position sensor of the exhaust camshaft (4).
   a. Disconnect the wiring harness connector (3).
   b. Disconnect the wiring harness of the oxygen sensor from the bracket.
   c. Remove the bolt.

To install:
3. Install the camshaft position sensor of the exhaust camshaft.
4. Tighten the bolt to 53 inch lbs. (6 Nm).
   a. Connect the wiring harness of the oxygen sensor to the bracket.
   b. Install the wiring harness connector.
5. Install the camshaft position sensor, intake camshaft.
6. Tighten the bolt to 53 inch lbs. (6 Nm).
7. Connect the wiring harness connector.

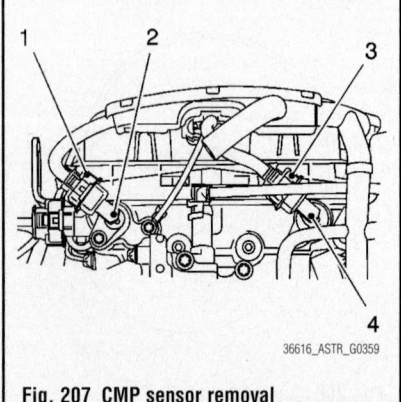

Fig. 207 CMP sensor removal

36616_ASTR_G0359

CRANKSHAFT POSITION (CKP) SENSOR

LOCATION
See Figure 208.

The Crankshaft Position (CKP) Sensor is located on the right-hand side of the engine block, behind the starter motor assembly.

REMOVAL & INSTALLATION
See Figure 208.

1. Disconnect the battery. Refer to Battery Disconnect Warning in the Precautions section.
2. Remove the starter. Refer to Starter Removal & Installation.
3. Remove the crankshaft position sensor.
   a. Disconnect the wiring harness connector (1).
   b. Disconnect the crankshaft position sensor (2) from the bracket.
   c. Remove the bolt (3).

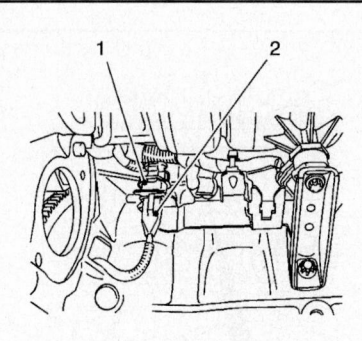

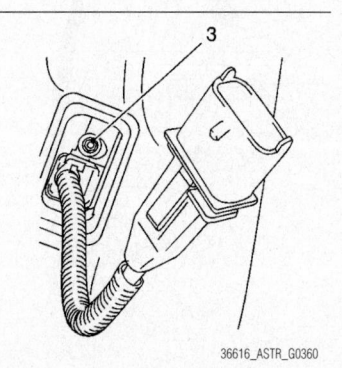

Fig. 208 CKP sensor and connector

36616_ASTR_G0360

To install:
4. Install the crankshaft position sensor.
   a. Tighten the bolt to 40 inch lbs. (4.5 Nm).
   b. Install the wiring harness connector into the bracket.
   c. Install the wiring harness connector.
5. Install the starter. Refer to Starter Removal & Installation.

ENGINE CONTROL MODULE (ECM)

REMOVAL & INSTALLATION
See Figure 209.

✳✳ WARNING

When returning a replaced control unit, do not clear the fault memory.

✳✳ WARNING

The security code must be reset using Tech 2 when replacing or interchanging the engine control module (before removal).

1. Read out control unit data with a Tech 2. Refer to Diagnostic System Check - Vehicle.
2. Disconnect the battery. Refer to Battery Disconnect Warning in the Precautions section.

✳✳ WARNING

The battery must not be disconnected until all consumers (e.g. fan) have ceased operation. However, a minimum waiting time of 30 seconds must be observed.

3. Disconnect the battery.
4. Remove the wiring harness from the engine control module (ECM).
   a. Disconnect the 2 wiring harness connectors (1).
5. Remove the ground cable (2) from the ECM.
   a. Remove the bolt.
6. Remove the ECM.
   a. Remove the 4 bolts (3).

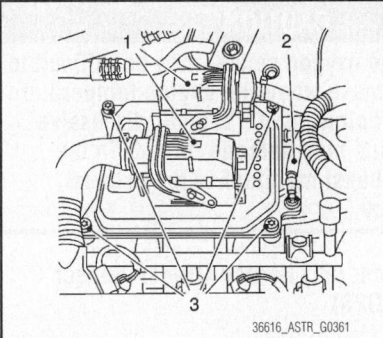

Fig. 209 Engine Control Module and components

To install:

7. Install the ECM.

8. Tighten the 4 bolts to 71 inch lbs. (8 Nm).

9. Install the ground cable to the ECM.

10. Tighten the bolt to 71 inch lbs. (8 Nm).

11. Install the wiring harness to the ECM.

12. Connect the 2 wiring harness connectors.

13. Connect the battery.

14. Tighten the nut to 44 inch lbs. (5 Nm).

15. Upload the control unit data with Tech 2. Refer to Diagnostic System Check.

RESET

1. Upload the control unit data with Tech 2. Refer to Diagnostic System Check.

Control Module References

See Figure 210.

Service Programming System (SPS)

Review the information below to ensure proper programming protocol.

Important:

• DO NOT program a control module unless you are directed by a service procedure or you are directed by a General Motors Corporation service bulletin. Programming a control module at any other time will not permanently correct the customer concern.

• It is essential that the Tech†2, MDI and the TIS terminal are all equipped with the latest software before performing service programming.

• Due to the time requirements of programming a controller, it is recommended that an external power source be used to maintain system voltage. Stable battery voltage is critical during programming. Any fluctuation, spiking, over voltage or loss of

Control Module	Schematic	Repair Instruction	Programming and Setup
Communication Interface Module Scan Tool Information	OnStar Schematics	Communication Interface Module Replacement	Communication Interface Module Programming and Setup
Driver Information Display Scan Tool Information (DIS)	Driver Information System Schematics	Driver Information Display Replacement	Driver Information Center Programming and Setup
Electronic Brake Control Module Scan Tool Information (ABS/TC/ESP)	Antilock Brake System Schematics	Electronic Brake Control Module Replacement	Electronic Brake Control Module Programming and Setup
Engine Control Module Scan Tool Information	Engine Controls Schematics	Engine Control Module Replacement	Engine Control Module Programming and Setup
Front Compartment Fuse Block Scan Tool Information (UEC)	Body Control System Schematics	Underhood Electrical Center or Junction Block Replacement	Front Compartment Fuse Block Programming and Setup
Heated Seat Control Module	Heated/Cooled Seat Schematics	Driver or Passenger Seat Cushion Heater Replacement	Heated Seat Control Module Programming and Setup
HVAC Control Module	HVAC Schematics	Heater and Air Conditioning Control Replacement	This device requires no programming or setup.
Inflatable Restraint Passenger Presence System	SIR Schematics	Inflatable Restraint Passenger Presence System Replacement - Front	Passenger Presence System Programming and Setup
Inflatable Restraint Sensing and Diagnostic Module Scan Tool Information (SDM)	SIR Schematics	Inflatable Restraint Sensing and Diagnostic Module Replacement	Inflatable Restraint Sensing and Diagnostic Module Programming and Setup
Instrument Cluster Scan Tool Information	Instrument Cluster Schematics	Instrument Cluster Replacement	Instrument Cluster Programming and Setup
Power Steering Control Module Scan Tool Information (EHPS)	Power Steering Schematics	Power Steering Pump Replacement	Power Steering Control Module Programming and Setup
Radio Scan Tool Information (EHU)	Radio/Navigation System Schematics	Radio Replacement	Radio Programming and Setup
Rear Body Fuse Block Scan Tool Information (REC)	Body Control System Schematics	Rear Electrical Center or Junction Block Replacement	Rear Body Fuse Block Programming and Setup
Sunroof	Sunroof Schematics	Power Sunroof Motor Replacement	Sunroof Control Module Programming and Setup
Steering Column Control Module Scan Tool Information (CIM)	Body Control System Schematics	Steering Column Control Module Replacement	Steering Column Control Module Programming and Setup
Tire Pressure Indicator Receiver Scan Tool Information	Tire Pressure Monitoring System Schematics	Tire Pressure Indicator Receiver Replacement	Tire Pressure Indicator Receiver Programming and Setup
Transmission Control Module Scan Tool Information Transmission Control Module	Automatic Transmission Controls Schematics	Transmission Control Module Replacement	Transmission Control Module Programming and Setup

36616_ASTR_G0088

Fig. 210 Control Module References

voltage will interrupt programming. To ensure trouble-free programming, GM recommends using one of the following external power sources:

a. A Midtronics PSC charger

b. A fully charged 12V jumper or booster pack disconnected from the AC voltage supply

• Some modules will require additional programming/setup events performed before or after programming.

• Some vehicles may require the use of a CANDi or MDI module for programming.

• Review the appropriate service information for these procedures.

• DTCs may set during programming. Clear DTCs after programming is complete.

• Clearing powertrain DTCs will set the Inspection/Maintenance (I/M) system status indicators to NO.

Ensure the following conditions are met before programming a control module:

1. Vehicle system voltage:

• There is not a charging system concern. All charging system concerns must be repaired before programming a control module.

• Battery voltage is greater than 12 volts but less than 16†volts. The battery must be fully charged before programming the control module.

- Turn OFF or disable any system that may put a load on the vehicles battery, such as the following components:
  a. Twilight sentinel
  b. Interior lights
  c. Daytime running lights (DRL)— Applying the parking brake, on most vehicles, disables the DRL system
  d. Heating, ventilation, and air conditioning (HVAC) systems
  e. Engine cooling fans, radio, etc.

2. The ignition switch must be in the proper position. SPS prompts you to turn ON the ignition, with the engine OFF. DO NOT change the position of the ignition switch during the programming procedure, unless instructed to do so.

3. Make certain all tool connections are secure, including the following components and circuits:
  a. Tech 2
  b. The RS-232 communication cable port
  c. The connection at the data link connector (DLC)
  d. The voltage supply circuits
  e. MDI

ENGINE COOLANT TEMPERATURE (ECT) SENSOR

LOCATION

See Figure 211.

Refer to component locations.
Refer to the accompanying illustration.

REMOVAL & INSTALLATION

See Figure 211.

1. Drain the coolant.
  a. Place a drain pan underneath.
  b. Install a suitable hose to the drain connection (2).
  c. Open the coolant drain screw (1).
  d. Drain the coolant.

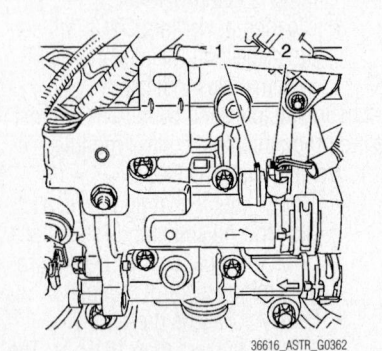

Fig. 211 ECT sensor removal

e. Close the coolant drain screw.
f. Lower the vehicle by its full height.

2. Remove the coolant temperature sensor.
  a. Disconnect the wiring harness connector (2).
  b. Disconnect the retaining clamp (1).

To install:

3. Install the coolant temperature sensor.
  a. Lock the retaining clamp.
  b. Install the wiring harness connector.

4. Fill and bleed the cooling system.

HEATED OXYGEN (HO2S) SENSOR

LOCATION

See Figures 212 and 213.

The front (#1) HO2S is located in the exhaust manifold.

The rear (#2) HO2S is located in the exhaust pipe, downstream of the catalytic converter.

REMOVAL & INSTALLATION

Special Service Tools:
- KM-6179 Oxygen Sensor Wrench Remover/Installer

✳✳ WARNING

Caution: The heated oxygen sensors each use a permanently attached pigtail and connector. Do not remove the pigtail from the heated oxygen sensor. Damage or removal of the pigtail or the connector affects proper operation of the heated oxygen sensor. Handle the oxygen sensor carefully. Do not drop the oxygen sensor. Keep the in-line connector and the louvered end free of grease, dirt, or other contaminants. Do not use cleaning solvents of any type. Do not repair the wiring, the connector, or the terminals. Replace the oxygen sensor if the pigtail wiring, the terminals, or the connector is damaged. Proper oxygen sensor operation requires an external air reference. This external air reference is obtained by way of the oxygen sensor signal and heater wires. Any attempt to repair the wires, the connectors, or the terminals results in the obstruction of the air reference and degrades the oxygen sensor performance. A dropped oxygen sensor is a bad oxygen sensor.

✳✳ CAUTION

The oxygen sensor may be difficult to remove when the engine temperature is below 48∞C (120∞F). Excessive force may damage threads in the exhaust manifold or the exhaust pipe.

Front (#1) Heated Oxygen Sensor (HO2S)

See Figure 212.

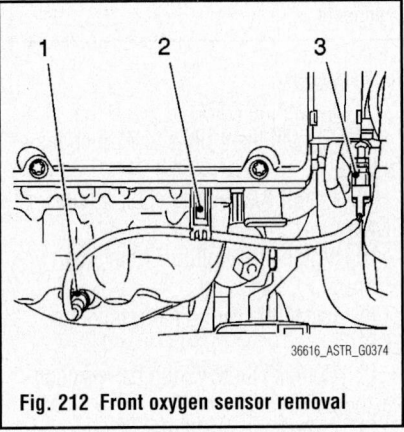

Fig. 212 Front oxygen sensor removal

1. Disconnect the battery. Refer to Battery Disconnect Warning in the Precautions section.

2. Remove the oxygen sensor (1).
  a. Disconnect the wiring harness connector (3).
  b. Disconnect the wiring harness (2) from bracket.

To install:

3. Install the oxygen sensor (1).

4. Tighten the oxygen sensor to 30 ft. lbs. (40 Nm).

5. Connect the wiring harness into the bracket.

6. Install the wiring harness connector.

7. Connect the battery.

Rear (#2) Heated Oxygen Sensor (HO2S)

See Figure 213.

1. Disconnect the oxygen sensor wiring harness connector (3).

2. Disconnect the wiring harness (2).

3. Remove the oxygen sensor (1) from the front exhaust pipe.

To install:

✳✳ CAUTION

When re-using the oxygen sensor, coat the thread of the oxygen sensor with assembly paste (white).

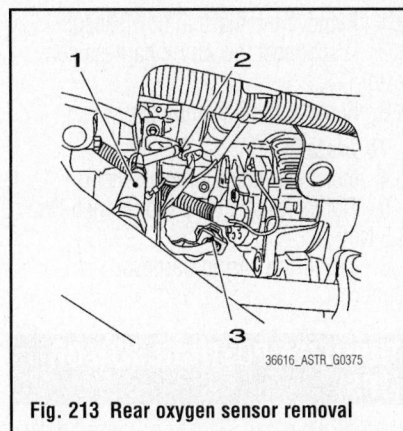

Fig. 213 Rear oxygen sensor removal

4. Install the oxygen sensor 2 in the front exhaust pipe using SA9603E /KM-6179.
5. Tighten to 30 ft. lbs. (40 Nm).
6. Connect the wiring harness connector for the oxygen sensor.
7. Install the wiring harness.

INTAKE AIR TEMPERATURE (IAT) SENSOR

LOCATION
See Figure 214.

REMOVAL & INSTALLATION
See Figure 215.

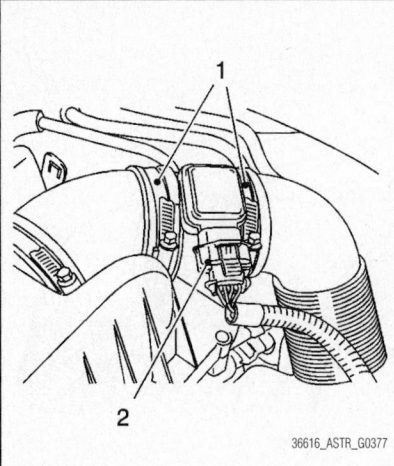

Fig. 215 Intake Air Temperature (IAT) Sensor

1. Remove the intake air temperature sensor.
2. Disconnect the wiring harness connector (2).
3. Remove the 2 clamps (1).

To install:

4. Install the intake air temperature sensor.
5. Tighten the 2 clamps to 31 inch lbs. (3.5 Nm).
6. Install the wiring harness connector.

KNOCK SENSOR (KS)

LOCATION

The Knock Sensor (KS) is located on the left-hand side of the engine block, just below the intake manifold.

REMOVAL & INSTALLATION
See Figures 216 and 217.

1. Disconnect the battery. Refer to Battery Disconnect Warning in the Precautions section.
2. Raise the vehicle by its full height.
3. Remove the intake manifold support (2).
4. Disconnect the wiring harness connector of the catalytic converter control oxygen sensor.
  a. Disconnect the wiring harness connector (1) from the bracket.
  b. Remove the 2 bolts (3).

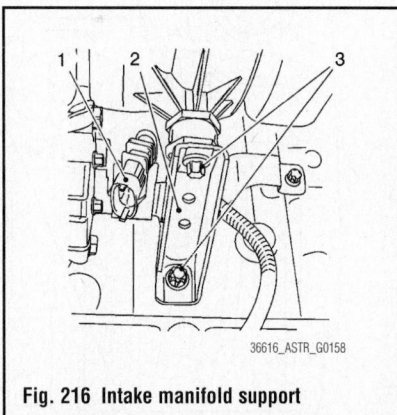

Fig. 216 Intake manifold support

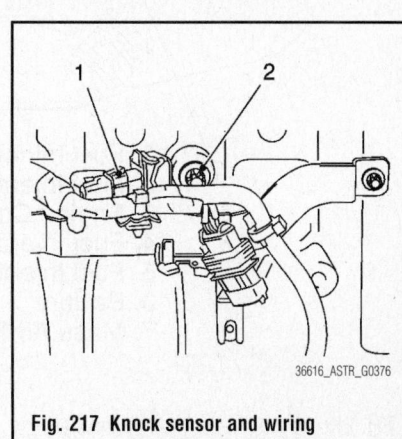

Fig. 217 Knock sensor and wiring

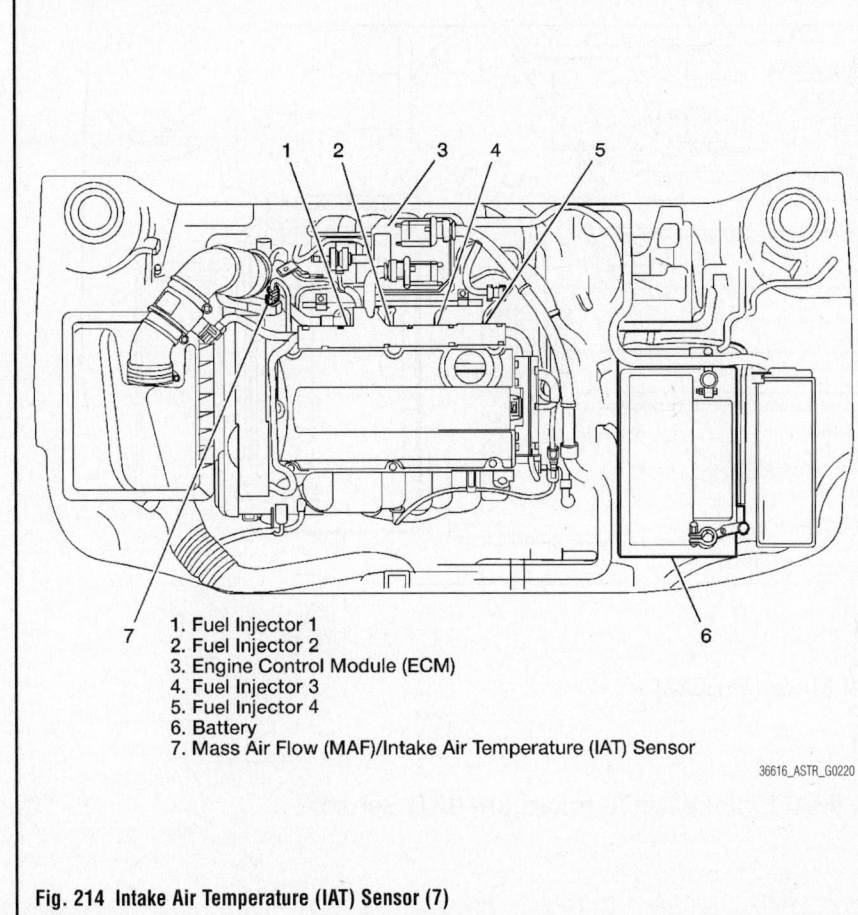

1. Fuel Injector 1
2. Fuel Injector 2
3. Engine Control Module (ECM)
4. Fuel Injector 3
5. Fuel Injector 4
6. Battery
7. Mass Air Flow (MAF)/Intake Air Temperature (IAT) Sensor

Fig. 214 Intake Air Temperature (IAT) Sensor (7)

5. Disconnect the knock sensor wiring harness connector (1).

6. Remove the knock sensor.

To install:

7. Install the knock sensor.

8. Tighten the bolt to 15 ft. lbs. (20 Nm).

9. Install the wiring harness connector.

10. Install the intake manifold support.

11. Tighten the 2 bolts to 71 inch lbs. (8 Nm).

12. Install the wiring harness connector into the bracket.

13. Connect the wiring harness connector for the catalytic converter control oxygen sensor.

14. Lower the vehicle by its full height.

15. Connect the battery.

MASS AIR FLOW (MAF) SENSOR

LOCATION

See Figure 218.

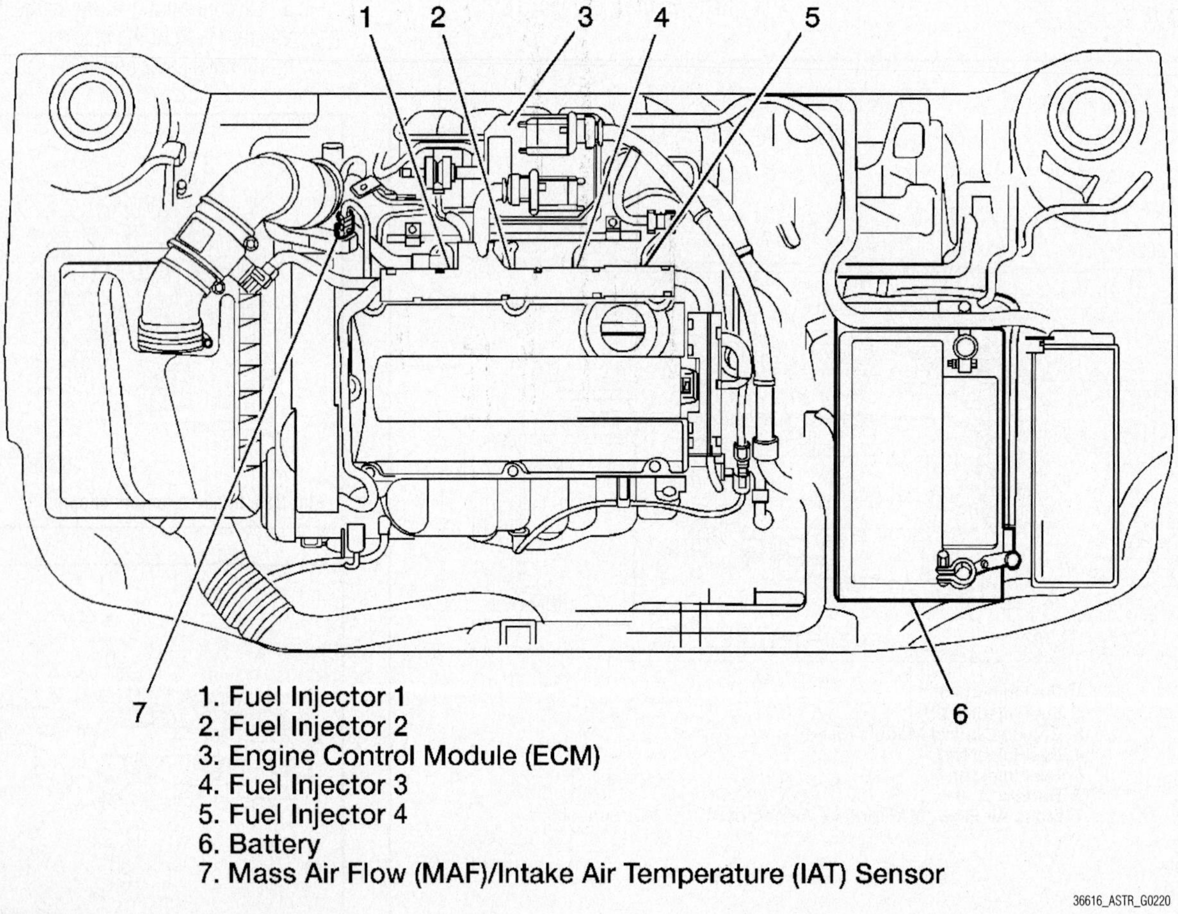

REMOVAL & INSTALLATION

See Figure 219.

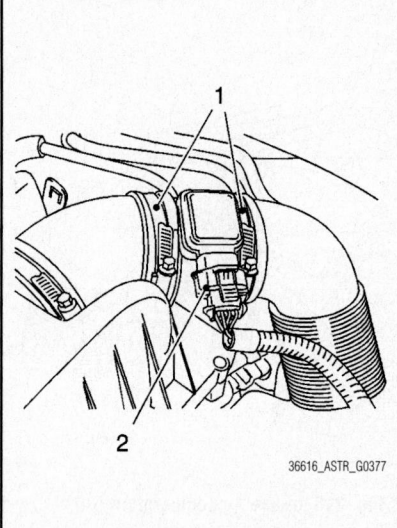

36616_ASTR_G0377

Fig. 219 Mass Air Flow (MAF) Sensor

---

1. Remove the mass airflow sensor.

2. Disconnect the wiring harness connector (2).

3. Remove the 2 clamps (1).

To install:

4. Install the mass airflow sensor.

5. Tighten the 2 clamps to 31 inch lbs. (3.5 Nm).

6. Install the wiring harness connector.

THROTTLE POSITION SENSOR (TPS)

LOCATION

The Throttle Position Sensor is integrated with the throttle body assembly. Refer to Throttle Body Location.

REMOVAL & INSTALLATION

Refer to Throttle Body Removal & Installation.

---

1. Fuel Injector 1
2. Fuel Injector 2
3. Engine Control Module (ECM)
4. Fuel Injector 3
5. Fuel Injector 4
6. Battery
7. Mass Air Flow (MAF)/Intake Air Temperature (IAT) Sensor

36616_ASTR_G0220

Fig. 218 Mass Air Flow (MAF) Sensor (7)

FUEL SYSTEM SERVICE PRECAUTIONS

Safety is the most important factor when performing not only fuel system maintenance but any type of maintenance. Failure to conduct maintenance and repairs in a safe manner may result in serious personal injury or death. Maintenance and testing of the vehicle's fuel system components can be accomplished safely and effectively by adhering to the following rules and guidelines.

• To avoid the possibility of fire and personal injury, always disconnect the negative battery cable unless the repair or test procedure requires that battery voltage be applied.

• Always relieve the fuel system pressure prior to disconnecting any fuel system component (injector, fuel rail, pressure regulator, etc.), fitting or fuel line connection. Exercise extreme caution whenever relieving fuel system pressure to avoid exposing skin, face and eyes to fuel spray. Please be advised that fuel under pressure may penetrate the skin or any part of the body that it contacts.

• Always place a shop towel or cloth around the fitting or connection prior to loosening to absorb any excess fuel due to spillage. Ensure that all fuel spillage (should it occur) is quickly removed from engine surfaces. Ensure that all fuel soaked cloths or towels are deposited into a suitable waste container.

• Always keep a dry chemical (Class B) fire extinguisher near the work area.

• Do not allow fuel spray or fuel vapors to come into contact with a spark or open flame.

• Always use a back-up wrench when loosening and tightening fuel line connection fittings. This will prevent unnecessary stress and torsion to fuel line piping.

• Always replace worn fuel fitting O-rings with new Do not substitute fuel hose or equivalent where fuel pipe is installed.

Before servicing the vehicle, make sure to also refer to the precautions in the beginning of this section as well.

RELIEVING FUEL SYSTEM PRESSURE

❊❊ WARNING

Remove the fuel tank cap and relieve the fuel system pressure before servicing the fuel system in order to reduce the risk of personal injury. After you relieve the fuel system

pressure, a small amount of fuel may be released when servicing the fuel lines, the fuel injection pump, or the connections. In order to reduce the risk of personal injury, cover the fuel system components with a shop towel before disconnection. This will catch any fuel that may leak out. Place the towel in an approved container when the disconnection is complete.

FUEL TANK PUMP MODULE

REMOVAL & INSTALLATION
See Figures 220 through 222.

➡Note the following:

• The fuel tank must be drained with a suitable, commercially-available fuel removal unit and suction hose - follow safety regulations and national legislation. The fuel tank is fitted with a refill limit float valve. This is located on the filler neck in the fuel tank. To prevent damaging the refill limit float valve, a suitable suction hose must be used.

• In the presence of fuel vapors or escaping fuel - observe safety regulations and national legislation. Store drained fuel in a suitable, sealable container.

• The electric fuel pump is a fixed component of the fuel tank fuel pump module and therefore cannot be replaced individually. If in need

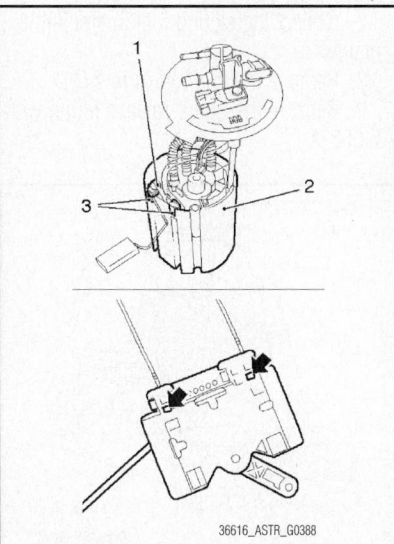

Fig. 220 Fuel level sending unit and components

of service, the entire fuel tank fuel pump module must be replaced.

❊❊ WARNING

In order to reduce the risk of fire and personal injury that may result from a fuel leak, always replace the fuel sender gasket when reinstalling the fuel sender assembly.

1. Remove the fuel tank. Refer to Fuel Tank Removal & Installation.

❊❊ WARNING

Do not pull on the shaft of the fuel tank sensor.

2. Remove the fuel tank sensor (1).
   a. Release the 2 retainers (3).
   b. Carefully pull from the guide upward.

➡**The wire connectors are to be pulled out carefully for disassembling of the connection wires.**

3. The cable connectors is to be depressed by a blunt rod-shaped article.
4. Disconnect the 2 wires.

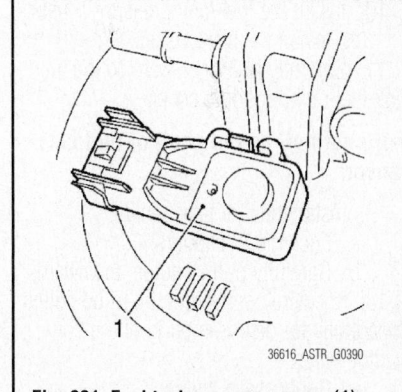

Fig. 221 Fuel tank pressure sensor (1)

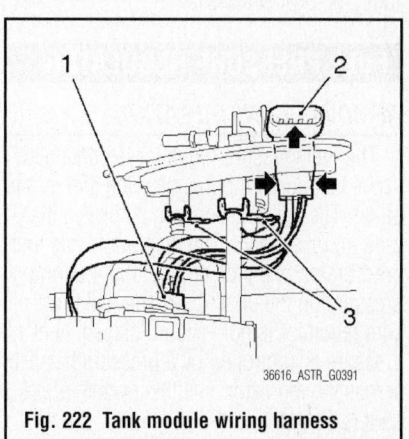

Fig. 222 Tank module wiring harness

5. Depress the 2 snap-on tongue (arrows) of the cable connectors.

6. Remove the fuel tank pressure sensor (1).

a. Carefully pull upward from the fuel tank fuel pump module cover.

7. Remove the wiring harness of the fuel pump.

a. Remove the wiring harness connector of the fuel pump (1).

b. Remove the 2 ground cables (3).

c. Remove the wiring harness connector of the fuel tank fuel pump module (3).

8. Release the 2 retainers and pull upward (arrows) from the fuel tank fuel pump module cover.

To install:

9. Install the wiring harness to the fuel pump.

a. Install the new gasket.

b. Install the wiring harness connector to the fuel tank fuel pump module (3).

➡ **The 2 retainers must be locked.**

c. Pull downward to fuel tank fuel pump module cover.

d. Connect the 2 ground cables.

e. Connect the wiring harness connector to the fuel pump.

10. Install the fuel tank pressure sensor.

a. Install the new gasket.

11. Carefully pull downward to the fuel tank fuel pump module cover.

➡ **Do not pull on the shaft of fuel tank sensor.**

12. Install the fuel tank sensor.

a. Lock the 2 retainers.

b. Carefully pull in guide downward.

13. The wire connectors are to be pulled in carefully for disassembling of the connection wires.

a. Connect the 2 wires.

14. Install the fuel tank. Refer to Fuel Tank Removal & Installation.

FUEL PRESSURE REGULATOR

REMOVAL & INSTALLATION

The fuel pressure regulator is contained in the fuel pump module near the fuel pump outlet. The fuel pressure regulator is a diaphragm relief valve. The diaphragm has fuel pressure on one side and regulator spring pressure on the other side. The fuel pressure regulator is not vacuum biased. Fuel pressure is controlled by a pressure balance across the regulator. The fuel system pressure is constant.

FUEL RAIL & INJECTORS

REMOVAL & INSTALLATION

See Figures 223 through 226.

Special Service Tools:

- J 34730-1A /KM-J-34730-91 Fuel Pressure Gage
- KM-807 Closure Plugs
- J 37088-A Fuel Line Disconnect Tool Set

1. Disconnect the battery. Refer to Battery Disconnect Warning in the Precautions section.

2. Remove the engine venting pipe (1).

a. Remove the wiring (2) from the cylinder head cover.

b. Disconnect the 2 quick-release fittings.

3. Remove the engine management wiring harness.

4. Disconnect the 9 wiring harness connectors.

- Engine control module
- Air mass flow meter
- Tank vent valve
- Throttle valve module
- Valve, intake camshaft adjustment
- Four injector valves

a. Remove the 2 wiring harness brackets.

b. Put the wiring harness to the side.

5. Place a drain pan underneath.

❊❊ WARNING

Refer to Gasoline/Gasoline Vapors Warning in the Preface section.

6. Release the fuel pressure via the test connection (1) using J 34730-1A / KM-J-34730-91.

7. Collect the exiting fuel in a suitable container.

8. Remove the fuel return line (1).

9. Remove the quick-release fitting with J 37088-A .

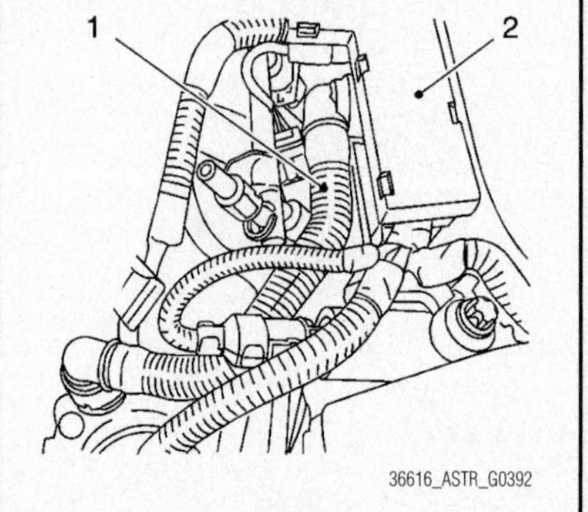

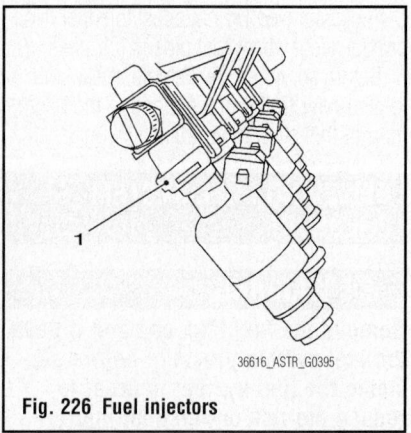

Fig. 223 Engine venting pipe and wiring

10. Seal the fuel line and the fuel rail with KM-807 .

11. Remove the fuel rail (2).

12. Remove the 2 bolts (1).

13. Remove the injectors.

a. Remove the 4 retaining clamps (1).

b. Pull out the 4 injectors.

To install:

❊❊ WARNING

Inspect the installation position and ensure correct fitting.

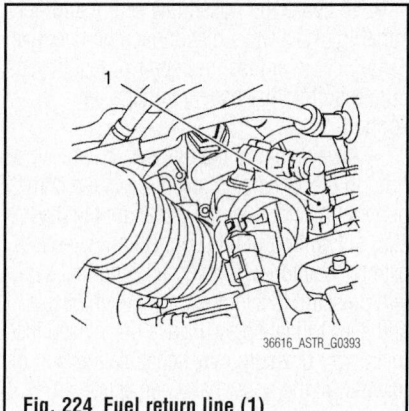

Fig. 224 Fuel return line (1)

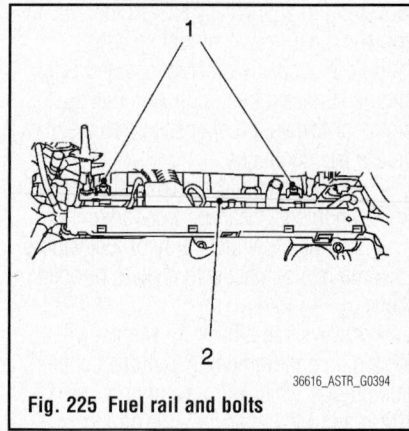

Fig. 225 Fuel rail and bolts

Fig. 226 Fuel injectors

14. Install the 4 injectors to the fuel rail.

　a. Install the 4 new seal rings.

　b. Coat the seal ring with silicone grease (white).

　c. Install the 4 injection valves.

　d. Install the 4 retaining clamps.

15. Install the fuel rail.

16. Tighten the 2 bolts to 71 inch lbs. (8 Nm).

17. Install the fuel supply line to the fuel rail.

　a. Remove the 2 KM-807 .

　b. Connect the quick release fitting.

　c. Connect into the bracket.

18. Install the engine management wiring harness.

　a. Connect the 9 wiring harness connectors.

　• Engine control unit

　• Air mass flow meter

　• Tank vent valve

　• Throttle valve module

　• Intake camshaft actuator

　• Four injectors

19. Install the 2 wiring harness brackets.

20. Install the engine vent hose.

　a. Connect the 2 quick-release fittings.

　b. Connect the wiring harness to the cylinder head.

21. Connect the battery.

FUEL TANK

REMOVAL & INSTALLATION

See Figures 227 through 233.

Special Service Tools:
• KM-796-A Fuel Line Separator

❊❊ WARNING

Gasoline or gasoline vapors are highly flammable. A fire could occur if an ignition source is present. Never drain or store gasoline or diesel fuel in an open container, due to the possibility of fire or explosion. Have a dry chemical (Class B) fire extinguisher nearby.

❊❊ WARNING

Wear safety glasses when using compressed air, as flying dirt particles may cause eye injury.

• The fuel tank must be drained with a suitable, commercially-available fuel removal unit and suction hose - follow safety regulations and national legislation. The fuel tank is fitted with a refill limit float valve. This is located on the filler neck in the fuel tank. To prevent damaging the refill limit float valve, a suitable suction hose must be used.

• In the presence of fuel vapors or escaping fuel - observe safety regulations and national legislation. Store drained fuel in a suitable, sealable container.

1. Disconnect the battery. Refer to Battery Disconnect Warning in the Precautions section.

2. Loosen the nuts on the right rear wheel.

3. Raise the vehicle halfway.

4. Remove the right rear wheel.

5. Remove the wheel housing inner paneling, right rear.

　a. Remove the 2 nuts (1).

　b. Remove the 2 bolts (2).

6. Remove the wiring harness from the pressure sensor (atmospheric pressure) (1).

　a. Remove the wiring harness connector (2).

　b. Remove the 3 cable ties (3).

7. Raise the vehicle halfway.

8. Remove the complete exhaust system.

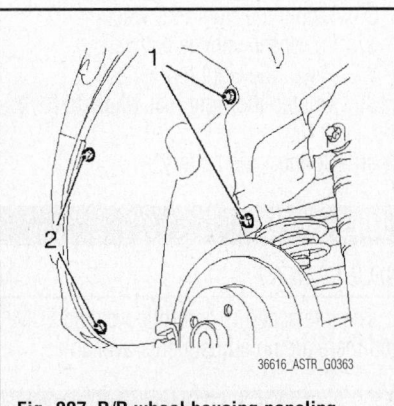

Fig. 227 R/R wheel housing paneling

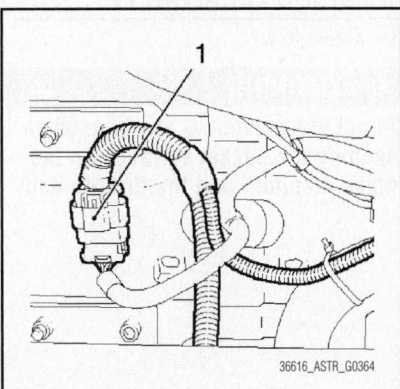

Fig. 228 Fuel tank pump module

9. Remove the wiring harness connector of the fuel tank fuel pump module (1).

10. Remove the vent hose (3) from the vent pipe (1).

　a. Disconnect the quick-release fitting (2) using KM-796-A.

11. Remove the fuel filler tube from the fuel tank.

　a. Release the clamp (1).

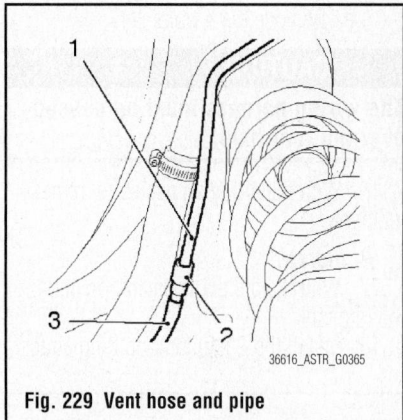

Fig. 229 Vent hose and pipe

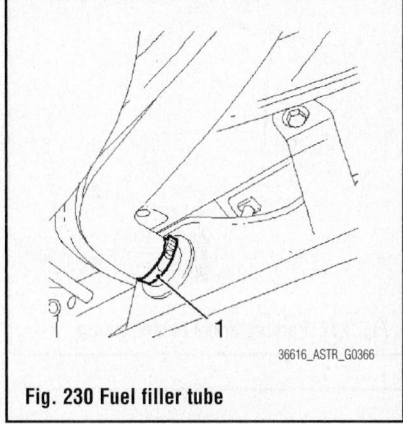

Fig. 230 Fuel filler tube

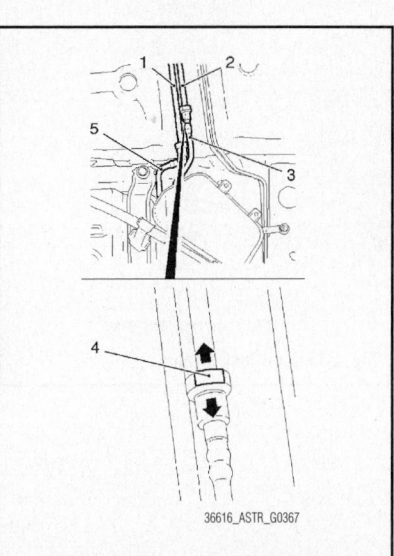

Fig. 231 Fuel lines with quick-release fittings

12. Remove the rear fuel lines (3, 5) from the middle fuel lines (1, 2).
    a. Disconnect the 2 quick-release fittings.
    b. Press release (4).
13. Remove the parking brake cable from the bracket (1) in 7 places.
14. Retract the jack.
15. Remove the 2 fuel tank holding straps.
    a. Remove the 4 bolts (1).

⁂ CAUTION

The wiring harness must be passed over the rear axle.

16. With the aid of an assistant, remove fuel tank.

To install:

17. With the aid an assistant, position the fuel tank.
18. Install the 2 fuel tank holding straps.

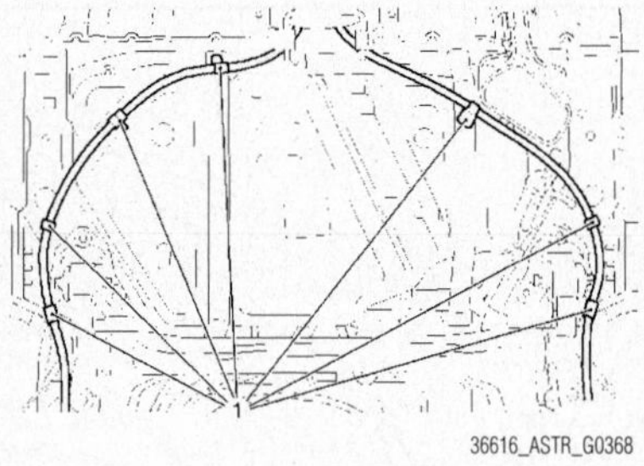

Fig. 232 Parking brake cable routing

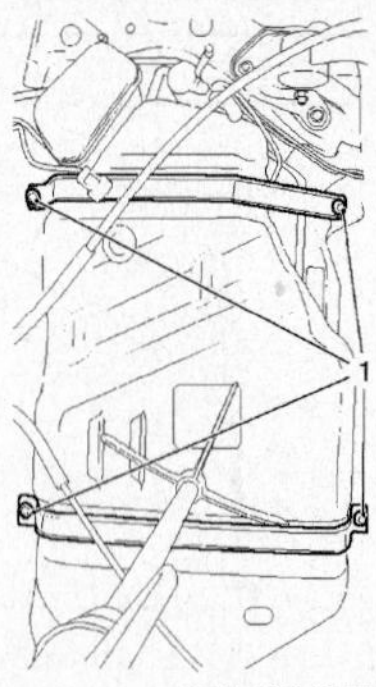

Fig. 233 Fuel tank straps

19. Tighten the 4 fuel tank holding strap bolts to 17 ft. lbs. (23 Nm).
20. Extend the jack.
21. Install the parking brake cable to the bracket in 7 places.
22. Connect the rear fuel lines to the middle fuel lines.
23. Connect the 2 quick-release fittings.
24. Install the fuel filler tube to the fuel tank.
25. Tighten the fuel filler tube to fuel tank clamp to 31 inch lbs. (3.5 Nm).
26. Install the vent hose to the vent pipe.
27. Connect the quick-release fittings.
28. Connect the wiring harness connector of the fuel tank fuel pump module.
29. Install the complete exhaust system. Refer to Exhaust System Replacement.
30. Connect the wiring harness of the pressure sensor (atmospheric pressure) to the fuel filler tube.
31. Install the 3 cable ties.
32. Lower the vehicle halfway.
33. Install the wiring harness of the pressure sensor (atmospheric pressure).
    a. Install the wiring harness connector.
    b. Install the 3 cable ties.
34. Install the wheel housing inner paneling, right rear.
35. Tighten the 2 wheel housing inner paneling nuts to 22 inch lbs. (2.5 Nm).
36. Mount the right rear wheel.
37. Lower the vehicle halfway.
38. Install the right rear wheel.
39. Tighten the right rear wheel to 81 ft. lbs. (110 Nm).
40. Connect the battery.

IDLE SPEED

ADJUSTMENT

The idle speed is controlled by the ECM, and there are no adjustments available.

THROTTLE BODY

REMOVAL & INSTALLATION

See Figure 234.

⁂ WARNING

Do not use solvent of any type when cleaning the gasket surfaces on the intake manifold and the throttle body assembly, as damage to the gasket surfaces and throttle body assembly may result.

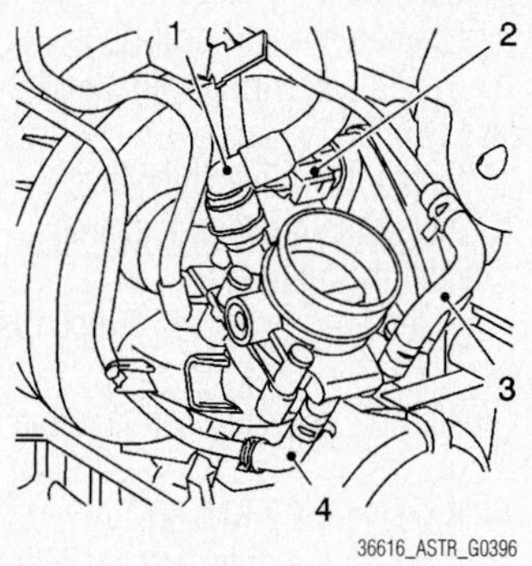

Fig. 234 Throttle body and components

Use care in cleaning the gasket surfaces on the intake manifold and the throttle body assembly, as sharp tools may damage the gasket surfaces.

⁂ CAUTION

Do not use any solvent that contains Methyl Ethyl Ketone (MEK). This solvent may damage fuel system components.

1. Remove the air cleaner assembly.
2. Disconnect the wiring harness connector (2).
3. Remove the engine venting pipe (1).
4. Disconnect the quick-release fitting.
5. Place the a drain pan underneath.
6. Remove the 2 coolant hoses (3, 4).
    a. Disconnect the 2 coolant hoses.
    b. Remove the 2 clamps.
7. Remove the 4 bolts, and remove the throttle valve assembly.

To install:

8. Install the throttle valve assembly.
    a. Use a NEW gasket.
9. Tighten the 4 bolts to 71 inch lbs. (8 Nm).
10. Install the 2 coolant hoses.
11. Install the 2 clamps.
12. Install the wiring harness connector.
13. Install the engine venting hose.
14. Connect the quick release fitting.
15. Install the air cleaner assembly.

HEATING & AIR CONDITIONING SYSTEM

BLOWER MOTOR

REMOVAL & INSTALLATION

See Figures 235 and 236.

1. Remove the instrument panel (I/P) compartment.
   a. Remove the 4 bolts (1).
   b. Disconnect the wiring harness connector.

2. Remove the passenger side lower foot well trim.
3. Remove the bolt (3).
4. Remove the air duct.
5. Remove the body-bound rivet (2).
6. Remove the blower motor (2).
   a. Disconnect the 2 wiring harness connectors (1) from series resistor.
   b. Remove the 5 bolts.

To install:

7. Install the blower motor.
   a. Connect the clip.
8. Tighten the 5 bolts to 63 inch lbs. (6 Nm).
   a. Connect the 2 wiring harness connectors.
9. Install the air duct.
10. Install the body-bound rivet.
11. Install the lower right foot well trim.
12. Tighten the bolt - pivot and lock.
13. Install the I/P compartment.
14. Connect the wiring harness connector.
15. Tighten the 4 bolts to 35 inch lbs. (4 Nm).

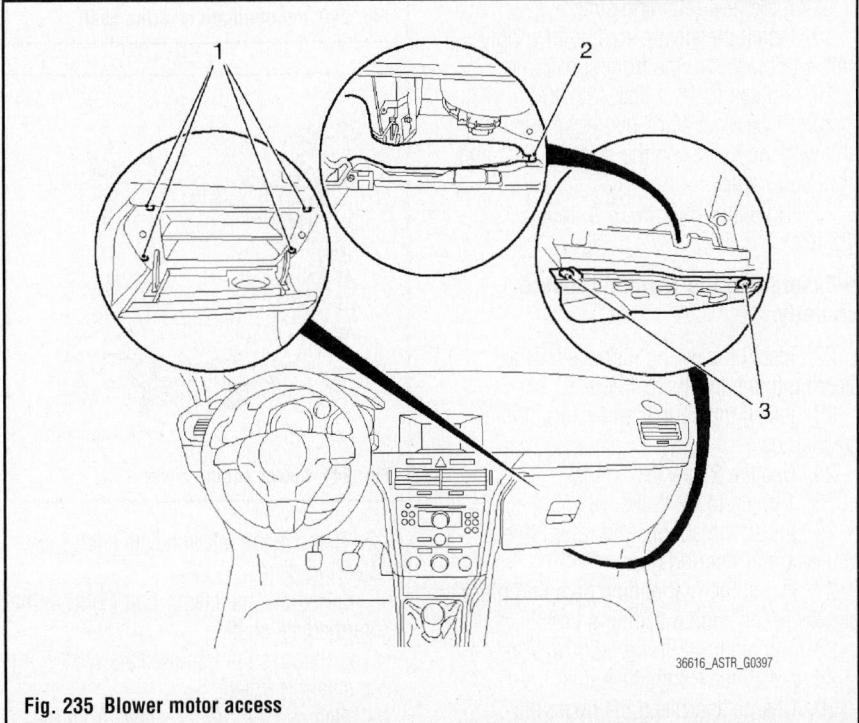

Fig. 235 Blower motor access

36616_ASTR_G0397

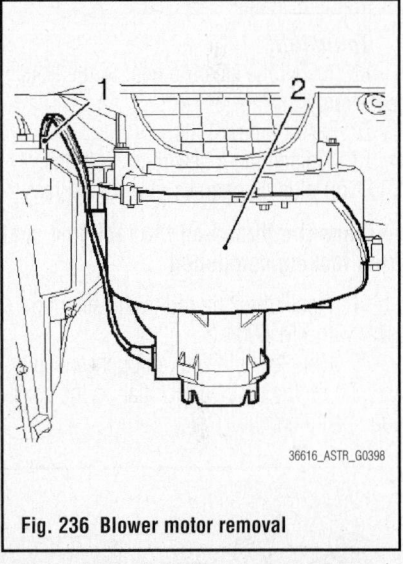

36616_ASTR_G0398

Fig. 236 Blower motor removal

STEERING

POWER RACK & PINION STEERING GEAR

REMOVAL & INSTALLATION

TRW

See Figures 237 through 239.

Special Service Tools:
- KM-6004-2 Tie Rod Wrench
- J 22610 Keystone Clamp Pliers

1. Remove the front sub-frame.
2. Remove the engine damping block bracket (1) at the rear of the engine damping block.
3. Remove the holder (2).
4. Place a drain pan under the power steering line connections and remove the supply line (3) and return line (4) from the steering gear.

5. Note and record the wiring routing.
6. Disconnect the wiring harness for the steering from the front sub-frame.

7. Remove the electro-hydraulic supply unit from the front sub-frame.
   a. Remove the 3 nuts (1, 2) from the steering gear and the front sub-frame.

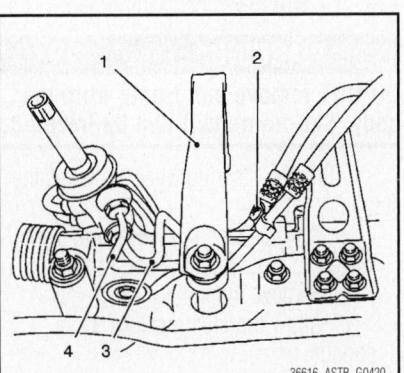

36616_ASTR_G0420

Fig. 237 Sub-frame and components

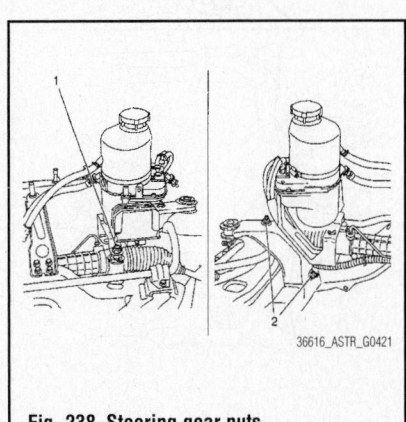

36616_ASTR_G0421

Fig. 238 Steering gear nuts

b. Remove the electro-hydraulic supply unit with supply and return line from the steering gear and the front sub-frame.

8. Remove the tie rods on both sides of the steering gear.

a. Remove the 2 retaining straps (1, 2).

b. Remove the 2 boots from the steering gear.

c. Remove the 2 tie rods (4) from the steering gear with KM-6004-2 .

9. Counter hold with an open-ended wrench on the toothed rack flat on the steering shaft side.

10. Remove the steering gear from the front sub-frame.

a. Remove the 2 nuts (2) from the front sub-frame.

b. Remove the 2 bolts.

c. Remove the steering gear from the front sub-frame.

To install:

11. Install the steering gear to the front sub-frame.

12. Insert 2 new bolts.

13. Tighten the 2 new nuts 33 ft. lbs. (45 Nm) plus 45 degrees plus 15 degrees.

➡️**Clean the thread on the rack and coat with locking compound.**

14. Install the 2 tie rod to the steering gear with KM-6004-2 .

15. Counter hold with an open-ended wrench on the toothed rack flat on the steering shaft side.

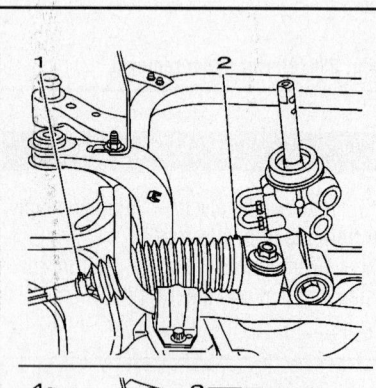

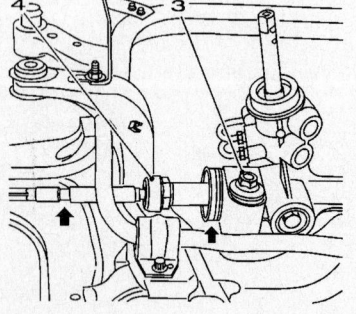

Fig. 239 Restraining straps and tie rods

16. Tighten to 66 ft. lbs. (90 Nm).
• Ensure that the boot sits in the grooves of the tie rod and the steering gear.
• Ensure that the boot sits in the grooves of the tie rod.

17. Install the 2 boots to the steering gear.

a. Place the 2 boots on the steering gear.

b. Install the 2 new retaining clamps to the steering gear with J 22610 .

c. Install the 2 boots to the tie rod using the new retaining strap.

18. Install the electro-hydraulic supply unit with bracket to the front sub-frame.

19. Tighten to 16 ft. lbs. (22 Nm).

20. Place the electro-hydraulic supply unit with the holder on the steering gear and front sub-frame.

21. Tighten 3 nuts to 16 ft. lbs. (22 Nm).

➡️**Ensure that the wiring is routed properly.**

22. Install the wiring harness for the steering to the front sub-frame.

23. Install the supply and return line to steering gear.

24. Use the 2 new seal rings.

25. Tighten to 22 ft. lbs. (30 Nm).

26. Install the supply and return line holder to the steering gear.

27. Install the rear engine damping block bracket to the engine damping block.

28. Tighten to 41 ft. lbs. (55 Nm).

29. Install the front sub-frame.

30. Charge and bleed the hydraulic system.

31. Perform a front wheel alignment. Refer to Wheel Alignment Specifications.

ZF

See Figures 240 through 249.

Special Service Tools:
• KM-6004-2 Tie Rod Wrench
• J 22610 Keystone Clamp Pliers

❊✳ **WARNING**

DO NOT remove sub-frame from the body. Sub-frame will just be lowered.

1. Turn the steering wheel as far as the stop.

a. Turn the steering wheel and front wheels to the straight-ahead position.

b. Remove the ignition key.

c. Allow the steering lock to engage.

➡️**The bolt is accessible from the passenger compartment.**

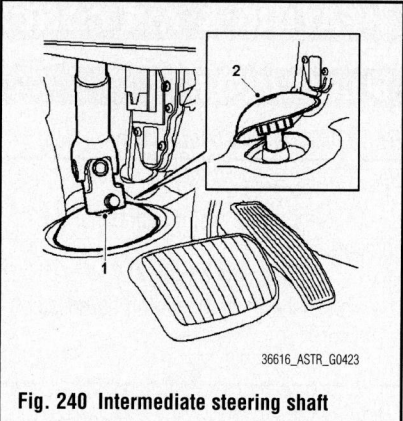

Fig. 240 Intermediate steering shaft

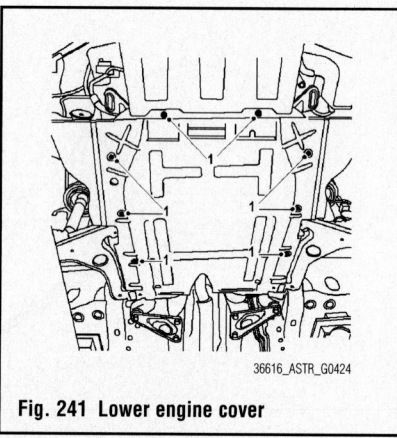

Fig. 241 Lower engine cover

2. Remove the intermediate shaft from the steering gear.

a. Remove the clamp bolt (1) from the intermediate shaft.

b. Remove the intermediate shaft from the steering wheel.

3. Remove the rubber sleeve from the steering gear (2).

➡️**Mark the position relative to the wheel hub.**

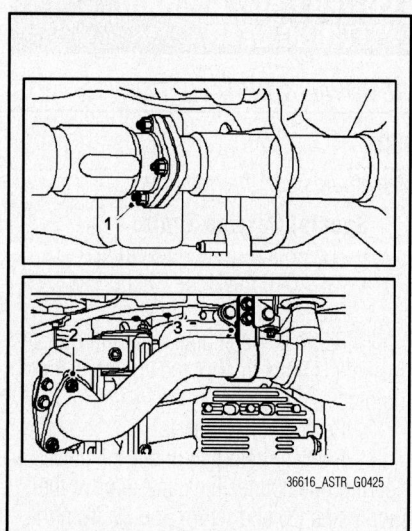

Fig. 242 Front exhaust pipe

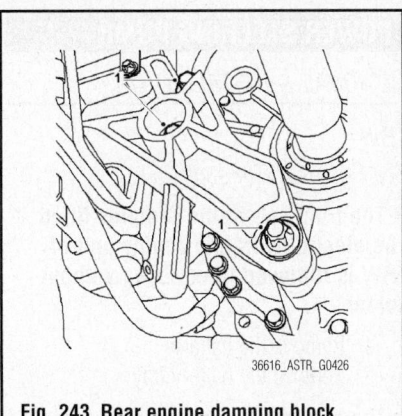

Fig. 243 Rear engine damping block

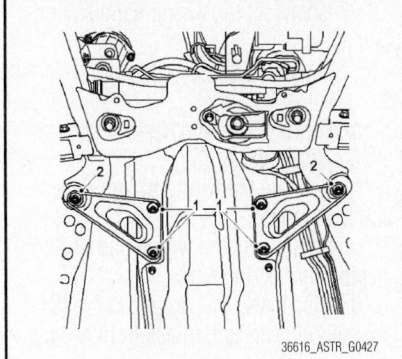

Fig. 244 Triangular plates

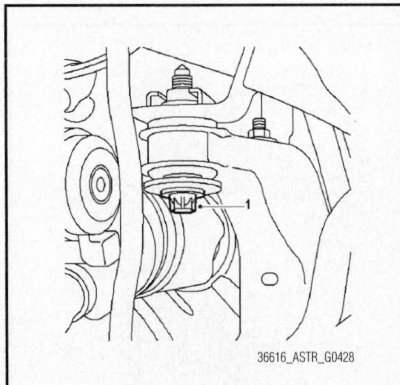

Fig. 245 Axle housing bolts

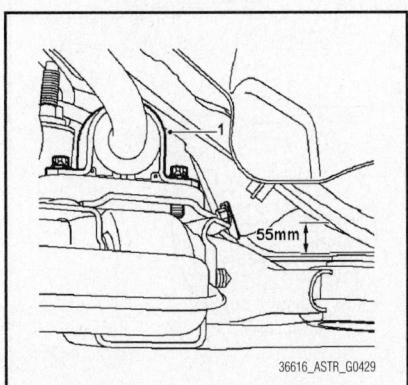

Fig. 246 Lower sub-frame as shown

4. Remove the 2 front wheels.
5. Release the 2 tie rod ends.
6. Remove the lower engine compartment cover.
7. Remove the front exhaust pipe.

   a. Remove the 3 nuts for connecting the front pipe to the particle filter/rear catalytic converter (1).
   b. Remove the 3 nuts for connecting the pipe to the front catalytic converter (2).
   c. Remove the bracket from the oil pan (3).
   d. Remove the exhaust pipe.
8. Remove the rear engine damping block from the transmission.
   a. Remove the 3 bolts (1).
9. Place the vehicle jack in a position under the front sub-frame.

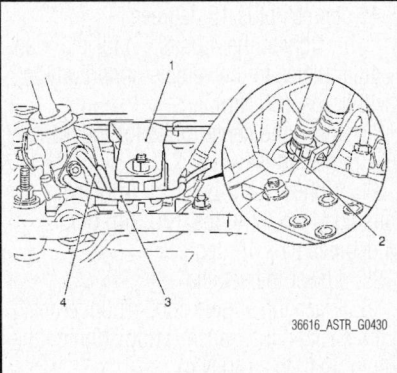

Fig. 247 Rear engine damping block

10. Remove the triangular plate.
   a. Remove the 6 bolts (1, 2).
11. Remove the center 2 bolts from the axle housing (1).

12. Lower the sub-frame.
13. Remove the engine damping block bracket (1) at the rear of the engine damping block.
14. Remove the rear engine damping block (2).
15. Remove the bolt connection.
16. Remove the supply line (3) and return line (4) from the steering gear.
17. Remove the electro-hydraulic supply unit from the front sub-frame.
   a. Release the 2 wiring harness connectors (1, 2) and remove from the electro-hydraulic supply unit.
   b. Remove the 3 nuts (3, 4) from the steering gear and the front sub-frame.
   c. Remove the electro-hydraulic supply unit with supply and return line from the steering gear and the front sub-frame.
18. Remove the tie rods on both sides of the steering gear.
   a. Remove the 2 retaining straps (1, 2).
   b. Remove the 2 boots from the steering gear.
   c. Remove the 2 tie rods (4) from the steering gear with KM-6004-2 .
19. Remove the steering gear from the front axle body.
   a. Remove the 2 nuts (2) from the front axle body.

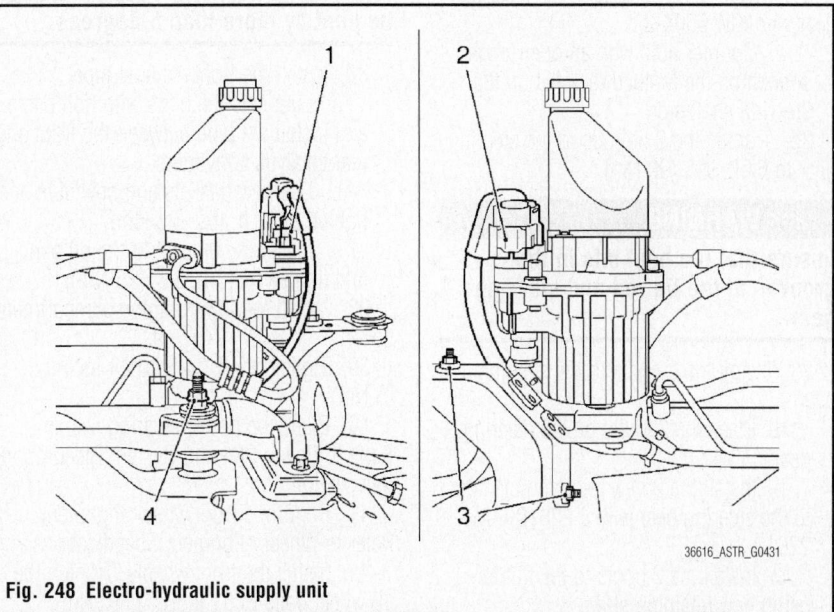

Fig. 248 Electro-hydraulic supply unit

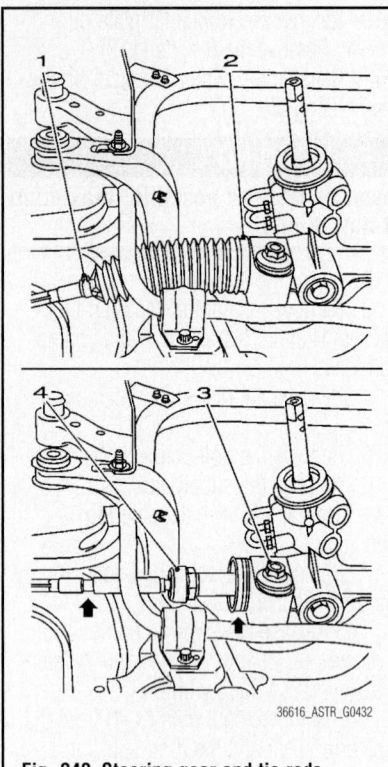

Fig. 249 Steering gear and tie rods

b. Remove the 2 bolts.

c. Remove the steering gear.

To install:

20. Install the steering gear to the front sub-frame.

   a. Insert the 2 new bolts.

   b. Tighten the 2 new nuts to 33 ft. lbs. (45 Nm) plus 45 degrees plus 15 degrees.

➡**Clean the thread on the rack and coat with locking compound.**

21. Install the 2 tie rods to the steering gear with KM-6004-2 .

   a. Counter hold with an open-ended wrench on the toothed rack flat on the steering shaft side.

22. Tighten the 2 tie rods to the steering gear to 67 ft. lbs. (90 Nm).

✳✳ WARNING

Ensure that the boot sits in the grooves of the tie rod and steering gear.

23. Install the 2 boots to the steering gear.

   a. Place the 2 boots on the steering gear.

   b. Install the 2 new retaining clamps to the steering gear with J 22610 /KMJ-22610.

   c. Install the 2 boots to the tie rod using new retaining strap.

24. Install the electro-hydraulic supply unit with bracket to the front sub-frame and tighten to 16 ft. lbs. (22 Nm).

25. Place the electro-hydraulic supply unit with the holder on the steering gear and front sub-frame. Tighten the 3 nuts.

26. Connect the 2 wiring harness connectors to the electro-hydraulic supply unit.

27. Install the supply and return line to the steering gear and tighten to 12 ft. lbs. (16 Nm).

28. Use the 2 new seal rings.

29. Install the supply and return line holder to the steering gear.

30. Install the rear engine damping block bracket to the engine damping block and tighten to 40 ft. lbs. (55 Nm).

31. Install the bolts for the front sub-frame.

32. Install the triangular plates, insert the following new bolts and leave loose.

   a. Tighten the 2 bolts (2) for the front axle housing to 67 ft. lbs. (90 Nm) plus 45 degrees plus 15 degrees.

   b. Tighten the 4 bolts (1) for the triangular plates to the vehicle underbody to 48 ft. lbs. (65 Nm).

33. Insert the center bolts for the front sub-frame and leave slack.

34. Tighten the 2 bolts for front axle housing (1) to 67 ft. lbs. (90 Nm) plus 45 degrees plus 15 degrees .

35. Lower the vehicle.

36. Place the engine support underneath, at the back on the transmission. Tighten the bolt to 59 ft. lbs. (80 Nm).

✳✳ WARNING

The flexible part of the pipe must not be bent by more than 5 degrees.

37. Install the front exhaust pipe.

   a. Lubricate the bolts with bolt paste and install the pipe between the front and rear catalytic converters.

   b. Use new gaskets and new nuts and tighten to 18 ft. lbs. (25 Nm).

   c. Install the bracket to the oil pan and tighten to 18 ft. lbs. (25 Nm).

38. Install the lower engine compartment cover.

39. Tighten the 8 bolts to 44 inch lbs. (5 Nm).

40. Bleed the power steering system. Refer to Power Steering System Bleeding in this section.

41. Perform a front wheel alignment. Refer to Wheel Alignment Specifications.

42. Install the front wheels. Tighten the 10 wheel bolts to 81 ft. lbs. (110 Nm).

POWER STEERING PUMP

REMOVAL & INSTALLATION

TRW

See Figures 250 through 254.

➡**The front sub-frame remains fitted. The electro-hydraulic supply unit of TRW is removed from above without holder.**

1. Remove the battery.

2. Remove the battery tray.

➡**The cooling system remains sealed.**

3. Reposition the surge tank.

4. Disconnect the wiring harness connector.

5. Disconnect the steering wiring harness.

   a. Disconnect the cover from the positive distribution.

   b. Remove the wiring harness from the fixing (1).

   c. Disconnect the wiring harness connector for steering (2).

   d. Disconnect the ground cable (3) for steering wiring harness from ground pole terminal.

   e. Expose wiring harness for steering underneath.

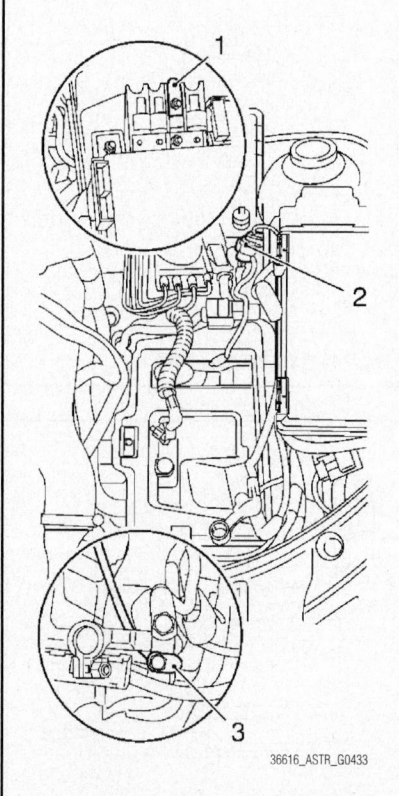

Fig. 250 Wiring harness and ground cable

Note wiring routing.

a. Remove the cable ties.

b. Release the wiring harness from the holder.

6. Remove the air cleaner housing with the air intake hose.

7. Remove the air cleaner assembly.

8. Remove the bleed hose from the tank bleed valve.

a. Disconnect the quick-acting closure.

b. Release from the holder.

9. Remove the right engine splash shield.

10. Disconnect the wiring harness for the steering from the front sub-frame.

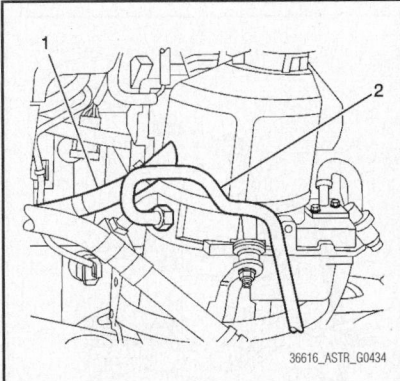

Fig. 251 Supply and return lines

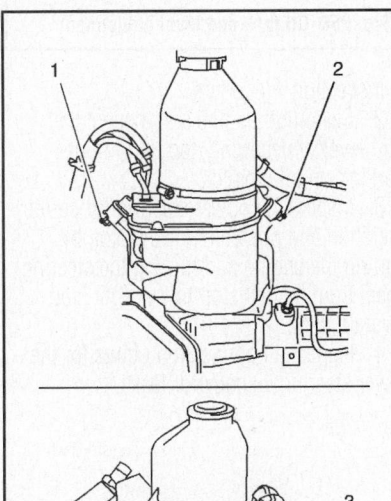
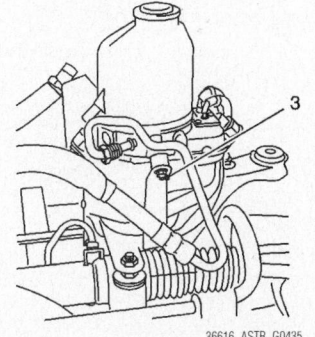

Fig. 252 Electro-hydraulic supply unit removal

11. Remove the return (1) and supply line (2) from the electro-hydraulic supply unit.

12. Remove the 3 nuts (1-3) from the holder.

➡**Remove the electro-hydraulic supply unit upwards.**

13. Remove the electro-hydraulic supply unit from the holder.

To install:

14. Tighten the retaining nut to 22 ft. lbs. (30 Nm).

15. Install the right engine splash shield.

16. Connect the steering wiring harness.

a. Position the steering wiring harness.

b. Attach the cable ties.

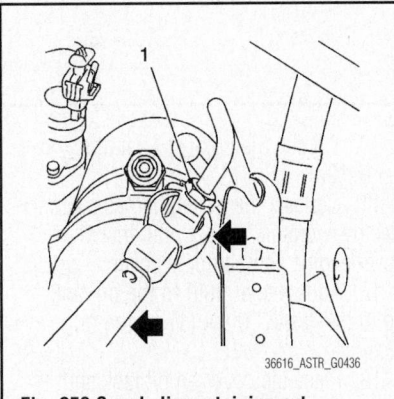

Fig. 253 Supply line retaining nut

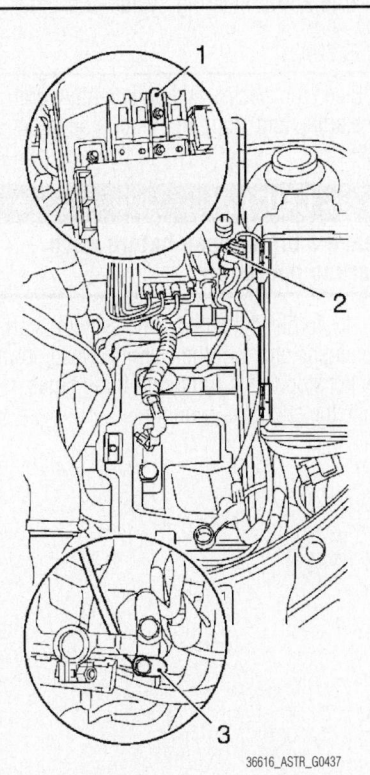

Fig. 254 Power steering wiring harness

c. Clip the wiring harness into the brackets.

d. Detach the cover from the positive distribution.

e. Attach the wiring harness to fixing (1).

f. Connect the wiring harness connector for steering (2).

g. Attach the ground cable (3) for the steering wiring harness to the ground pole terminal.

17. Attach the coolant surge tank to the holder.

18. Install the battery tray. Refer to Battery Tray Replacement.

✳✳ WARNING

Do not connect the battery ground at this point.

19. Install the battery.

20. Fit the bleed hose to the tank bleed valve.

a. Connect the quick-acting closure.

b. Clip into the bracket.

21. Install the air cleaner housing.

22. Connect the battery ground terminal.

23. Fill the power steering.

24. Charge and bleed the hydraulic system. Refer to Power Steering System Bleeding.

ZF

See Figures 255 through 258.

➡**The front axle body remains fitted. The electro-hydraulic supply unit of ZF is removed from above with the holder.**

1. Pump the hydraulic fluid out of the electro-hydraulic supply unit.

2. Disconnect the wiring harness from the electro-hydraulic supply unit.

a. Unlatch and disconnect the wiring harness connector (3).

b. Release the primary lock (1) from the wiring harness connector.

c. Compress the secondary lock and separate the wiring harness connector (2).

3. Remove the lower engine compartment cover.

4. Remove the supply and return line from the electro-hydraulic supply unit.

a. Remove the bolt (1).

5. Remove the electro-hydraulic supply unit with bracket from the front axle body.

a. Remove the 3 nuts.

To install:

6. Place the electro-hydraulic supply unit with bracket on the front axle body.

7. Install the electro-hydraulic supply unit to front axle body.

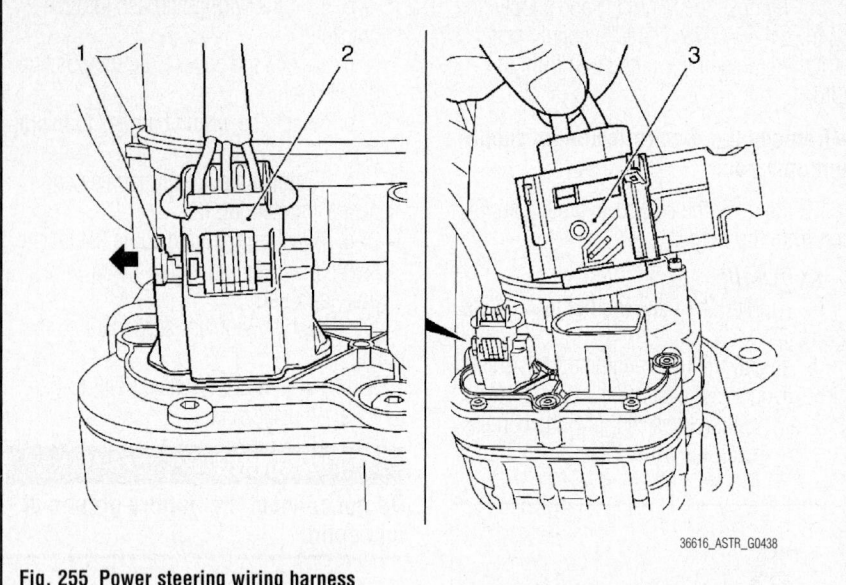

Fig. 255 Power steering wiring harness

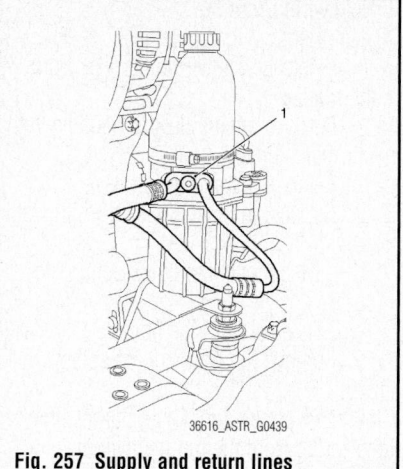

Fig. 257 Supply and return lines

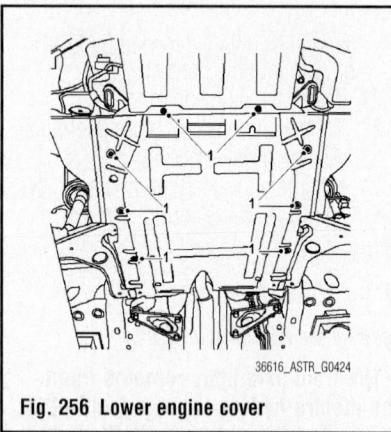

Fig. 256 Lower engine cover

10. Tighten the bolt (1) 12 ft. lbs. (16 Nm).

11. Connect the wiring harness with the electro-hydraulic supply unit. Install the lower engine compartment cover.

12. Add special fluid to the oil tank up to the "MAX" mark (1) on the oil dipstick.

13. Place the cover on oil tank and close.

14. Bleed the power steering system. Refer to Power Steering System Bleeding.

BLEEDING

Bleed the electro-hydraulic supply unit by starting and stopping the engine three times.

❊❊ CAUTION

Leave a brief pause before each starting operation.

1. To bleed the hydraulic system, start the engine and turn the steering wheel from the left stop to the right stop three times, while the engine is running.

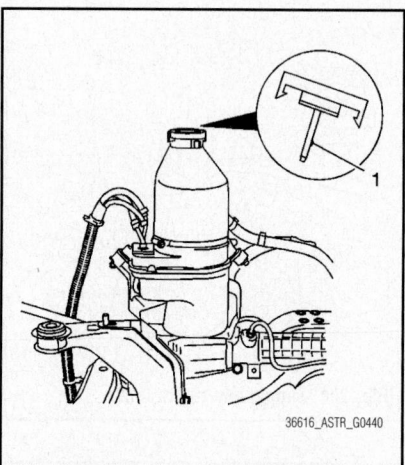

Fig. 258 Oil tank and level adjustment

8. Tighten the 3 nuts to 16 ft. lbs. (22 Nm).

❊❊ WARNING

Do not attach the bracket for electro-hydraulic supply unit at this time.

9. Install the pressure and return lines to the electro-hydraulic supply unit with the new seal rings.

Inspection Procedure

2. Switch off engine and inspect the fluid level; if necessary top up to upper marking on oil dipstick.

3. Inspect the power steering for correct operation and possible noise factor, by starting the engine and turning the steering wheel from the left stop to the right stop several times.

4. Inspect all connection points for the power steering visually for leaks.

SUSPENSION | **FRONT SUSPENSION**

LOWER BALL JOINT

REMOVAL & INSTALLATION

See Figures 259 and 260.

1. Remove the lower control arm. Refer to Lower Control Arm Removal & Installation.
2. Using a 5mm drill bit, drill through the 3 rivets in the center.
3. Start drilling the 3 rivet heads (1).
   a. Carefully remove the 3 rivet heads with a flat chisel.
   b. Remove remains of rivets.
   c. Remove the guide joint.
4. Coat the holes with corrosion protection material.

To install:

➡**The new guide joint is screwed to the control arm - use special bolts and nuts from "Service" area.**

5. Install the guide joint to control arm.
6. Tighten the 3 screwed connections (1) to 26 ft. lbs. (35 Nm).
7. Install the lower control arm. Refer to Lower Control Arm Removal & Installation.

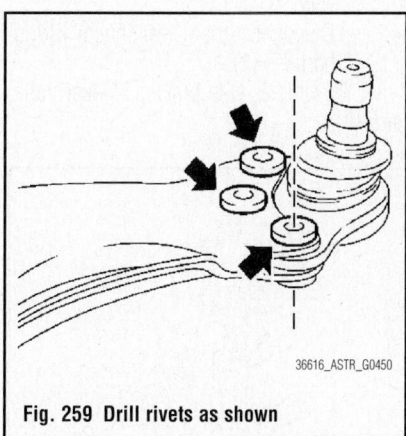

Fig. 259 Drill rivets as shown

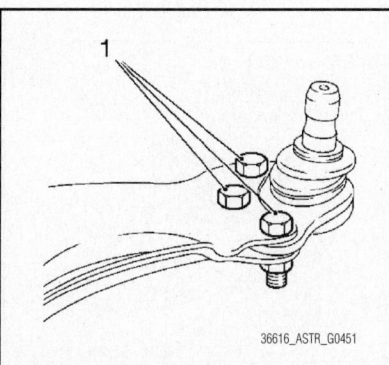

Fig. 260 Install replacement bolts as shown

LOWER CONTROL ARM

REMOVAL & INSTALLATION

See Figure 261.

1. Raise and support the vehicle.
2. Remove the wheel.

❋❋ WARNING

Do not pry in such a way that the ball joint seal is contacted. Damage to the seal may result.

3. Remove the ball stud to steering knuckle pinch bolt and nut (1).
4. Separate the ball stud from the steering knuckle (2).
5. Remove the lower control arm to frame bolts (3).
6. Remove the lower control arm from the frame.

To install:

➡**Only tighten bolted connection loosely. The bolted lower control arm connection to the front sub-frame is tightened at vehicle trim height.**

7. Install the lower control arm to front sub-frame.
   a. Install the 2 new bolts.
   b. Install the 2 new nuts.

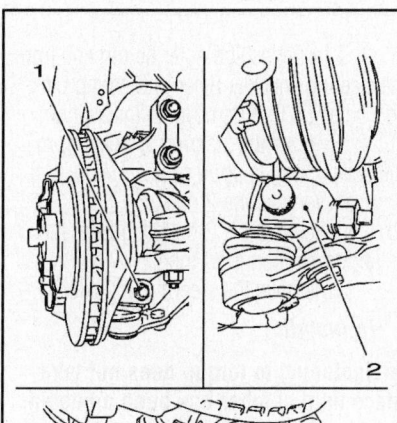

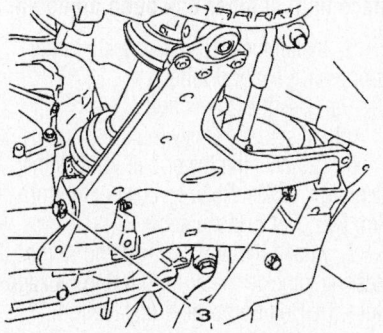

Fig. 261 Lower control arm removal

8. Install the lower control arm to the steering knuckle.
   a. Insert the guide joint into the steering knuckle.
   b. Install the bolted connection.

➡**Use NEW nuts.**

9. Tighten to 37 ft. lbs. (50 Nm).
10. Install the wheel.
11. Lower the vehicle.

➡**The vehicle must be standing on wheels, inspection stand or pit.**

12. Tighten the 2 bolted connections, lower control arm to the front sub-frame.
13. Load both front seats with 70 kg (154 lb).
14. Tighten the 2 new screw connections for the lower control arm on front sub-frame 67 ft. lbs. (90 Nm) plus 75 degrees, plus 15 degrees.
15. Road test the vehicle in order to test for leads or pulls.
16. If necessary, perform a front wheel alignment. Refer to Wheel Alignment Specifications.

STABILIZER BAR

REMOVAL & INSTALLATION

See Figures 262 and 263.

1. Remove the front sub-frame.
2. Remove the Stabilizer Bar link (1) from stabilizer on both sides.
3. Counter hold at the two flattened areas with the open-ended wrench.

➡**Note installation position of rubber insulators.**

4. Remove the right and left retaining brackets (2) with the rubber insulators from the front sub-frame.
5. Remove the stabilizer (3).

To install:

❋❋ WARNING

Stabilizers on vehicles must only be replaced in the assembly with the stabilizer insulators and clamps. Stabilizer insulators must never be greased or oiled.

➡**Note the installation position of the rubber insulator - the slot, must point forwards, in direction of travel.**

6. Install the stabilizer to the front sub-frame.
   a. Position the stabilizer on the front sub-frame.

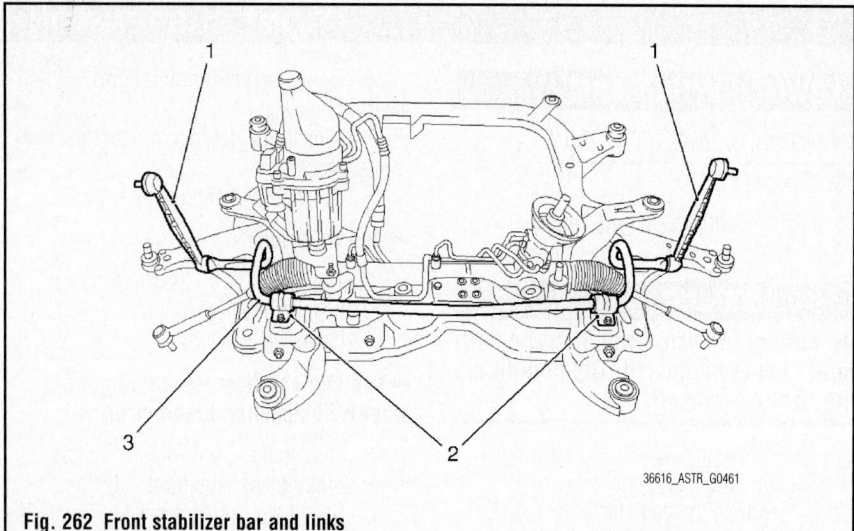

Fig. 262 Front stabilizer bar and links

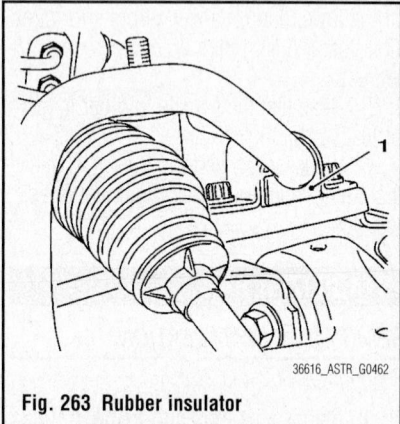

Fig. 263 Rubber insulator

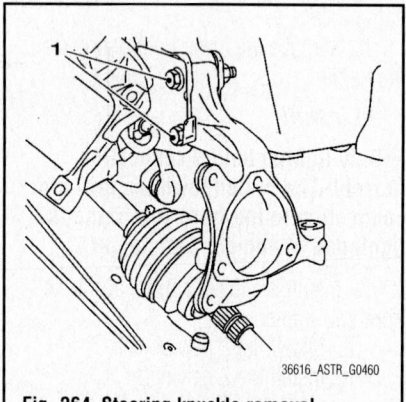

Fig. 264 Steering knuckle removal

b. Install the rubber insulator (1) to the stabilizer.

c. Install the retaining bracket.

d. Install the retaining bracket to the front sub-frame.

7. Tighten the bolts to 15 ft. lbs. (20 Nm).

8. Install the Stabilizer Bar link to the stabilizer on both sides.

9. Tighten the nuts to 48 ft. lbs. (65 Nm).

a. Use the 2 new nuts.

b. Counter hold at the two flattened areas with the open-ended wrench.

10. Install the front sub-frame.

STEERING KNUCKLE

REMOVAL & INSTALLATION

See Figure 264.

1. Remove the front wheel bearing and hub. Refer to Front Wheel Bearing and Hub Removal & Installation.

2. Disconnect the lower ball joint and separate the steering knuckle from the lower control arm. Refer to Lower Control Arm Removal & Installation.

3. Disconnect the outer tie rod end from the steering knuckle. Refer to Steering Linkage Outer Tie Rod Removal & Installation.

4. Remove the steering knuckle from the spring strut support tube.

a. Remove the 2 nuts.

b. Remove the 2 bolts (1) from the spring strut support tube.

c. Remove the steering knuckle.

To install:

➡**Tightening to torque does not take place until camber has been adjusted.**

5. Install the steering knuckle to the spring strut support tube.

a. Use the 2 new bolts.

b. Install the 2 new nuts.

6. Connect the lower ball joint to the steering knuckle. Refer to Lower Control Arm Removal & Installation.

7. Attach the outer tie rod end to the steering knuckle. Refer to Steering Linkage Outer Tie Rod Removal & Installation.

8. Install the front wheel bearing and hub. Refer to Front Wheel Bearing and Hub Removal & Installation.

9. Adjust the camber.

10. Tighten the 2 screwed joint, spring strut support tube to the steering knuckle, in 3 stages.

Tighten

11. Tighten the 2 spring strut support tube to steering knuckle bolted connections to 37 ft. lbs. (50 Nm).

12. Tighten the 2 new spring strut support tube to steering knuckle screwed joint to 62 ft. lbs. (85 Nm).

13. Tighten the 2 new spring strut support tube to steering knuckle screw connection an additional 75 degrees plus 15 degrees.

14. Perform a front wheel alignment. Refer to Wheel Alignment Specifications.

STRUT ASSEMBLY

REMOVAL & INSTALLATION

See Figures 265 through 269.

Special Service Tools:

• KM-6384 Assembly Clamp

1. Remove the front wheel.

2. Detach the wiring harness from the spring strut.

a. In vehicles without brake pad wear indicator (I):

• Push lock mechanism (1) downward.

• Disconnect the wheel sensor wiring harness (2).

3. In vehicles with brake pad wear indicator (II):

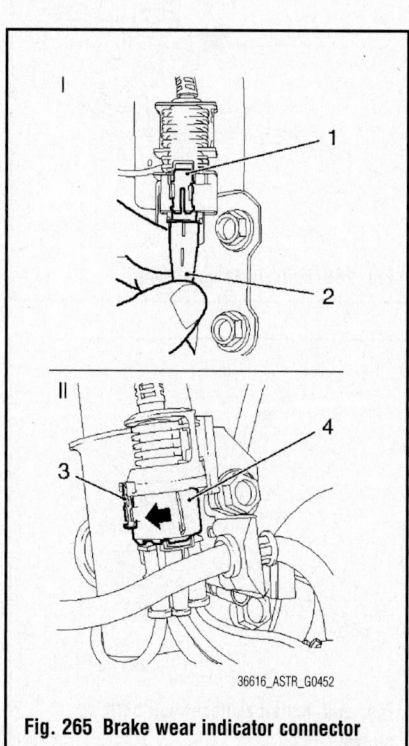

Fig. 265 Brake wear indicator connector

- Slide the primary lock mechanism (3) downward.
- Twist the secondary lock mechanism (4) in direction of arrow.
- Disconnect the brake pad wear indicator wiring harness connector from the wiring harness.
- Disconnect the wheel sensor wiring harness connector from the wiring harness.

4. Clip in spring strut wiring harness.
5. Remove the brake hose from the spring strut support tube.
    a. Remove the retaining clip (1).
    b. Pull the brake hose (2) out of bracket.
6. Remove the swing arm (1) from spring strut support tube.
7. Counter hold at the two flattened areas with open-ended wrench.
8. Remove the steering knuckle from the string strut.
    a. Remove the 2 bolted connections (2).
    b. Tilt the steering knuckle towards the outside.
    c. Before removing retaining ring, hold spring strut.

➡**The retaining ring cannot be removed without being destroyed and must be replaced during installation.**

9. Remove the retaining ring (1).
10. Remove the strut assembly.

To install:
11. Install the spring strut to wheel housing.
    a. Replace the spring strut in wheel housing.
    b. Install the new retaining ring (1) with the KM-6384 (2).
    c. Install both halves of retaining ring by hand.
    d. Compress the halves of retaining ring together with KM-6384 .

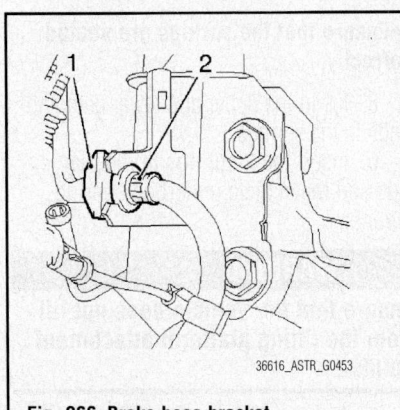

Fig. 266 Brake hose bracket

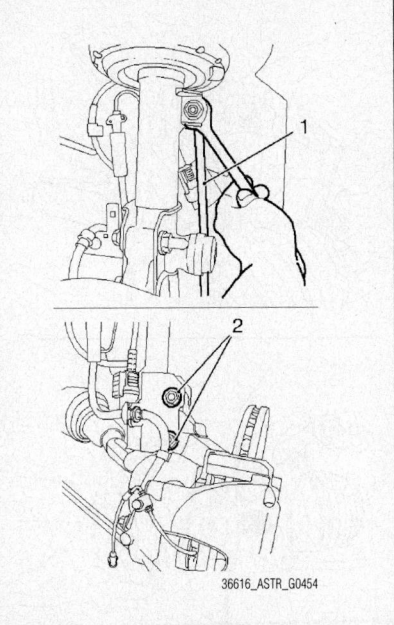

36616_ASTR_G0454

Fig. 267 Steering knuckle bolt connections

➡**Insert the bolts from front. Tightening to torque does not take place until camber has been adjusted.**

12. Install the spring strut to the steering knuckle.
    a. Insert 2 new screwed joints
    b. Use the 2 new bolts.
    c. Use the 2 new nuts.
13. Install the swing arm to the spring strut support tube.
14. Tighten to 41 ft. lbs. (55 Nm).
    a. Use the new nuts.
    b. Counter hold at the two flattened areas with open-ended wrench.

➡**Pay attention to correct hose routing.**

15. Install the brake hose to the spring strut support tube bracket.
    a. Insert the brake hose in the bracket.

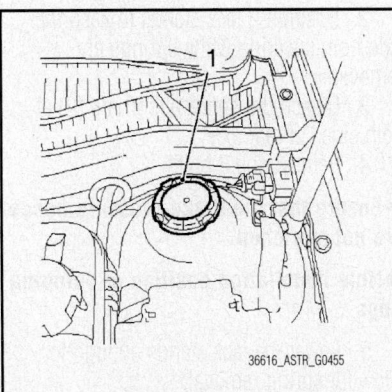

36616_ASTR_G0455

Fig. 268 Strut retaining ring

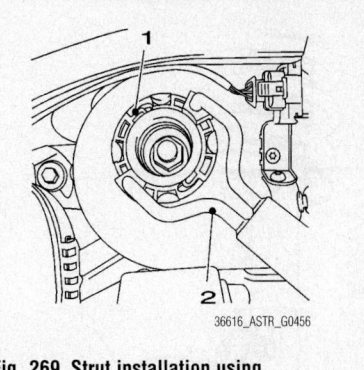

36616_ASTR_G0456

Fig. 269 Strut installation using KM-6384 (2)

    b. Secure the brake hose using the retaining clip.
16. Connect the wiring harness to the spring strut.
    a. Clip in the wiring harness to the spring strut
17. In vehicles without brake pad wear indicator:
    a. Connect the wheel sensor wiring harness.
    b. Slide the lock mechanism upward.
18. In vehicles with brake pad wear indicator:
    a. Connect the brake pad wear indicator wiring harness connector to the wiring harness.
    b. Connect the wheel sensor wiring harness connector to the wiring harness.
    c. Twist the secondary lock mechanism (4) in direction of arrow.
    d. Slide the primary lock mechanism (3) upward.
19. Install the front wheel.
20. Tighten to 81 ft. lbs. (110 Nm).
21. Tighten the 2 screwed joint, spring strut support tube to steering knuckle, in 3 stages.
Tighten
    a. Tighten the 2 bolted connections to 37 ft. lbs. (50 Nm).
    b. Tighten the 2 new screwed joints to 67 ft. lbs. (85 Nm).
    c. Tighten the 2 new screw connections to 75 degrees plus 15 degrees.
22. Perform a front wheel alignment. Refer to Wheel Alignment Specifications.

WHEEL BEARING & HUB

REMOVAL & INSTALLATION
See Figures 270 through 272.

Special Service Tools:
- J 28733-B /KM-6610 and KM-956-1 Front/Rear Spindle Remover

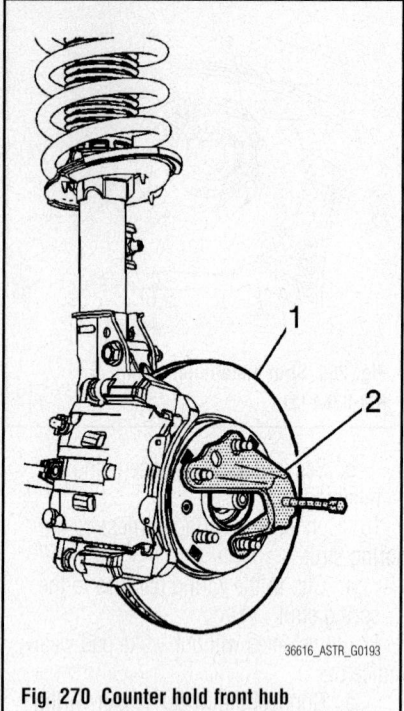

Fig. 270 Counter hold front hub

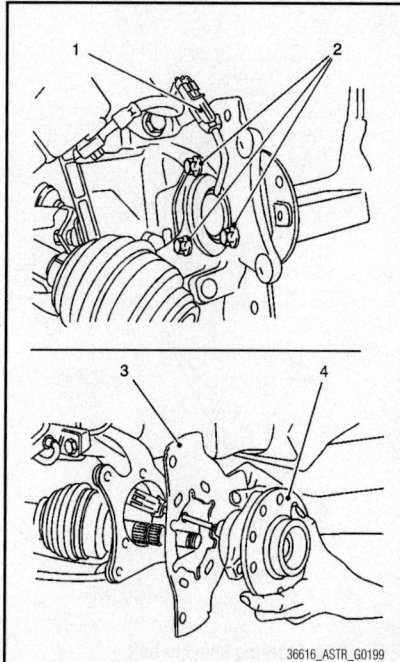

Fig. 271 Hub and cover plate removal

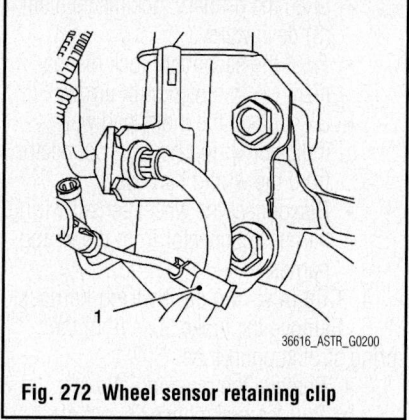

Fig. 272 Wheel sensor retaining clip

1. Remove the front wheel.
2. Remove the brake rotor.
3. Remove the nut from the halfshaft.
4. Counter-hold against the wheel hub with holding wrench J 28733-B /KM-6610 and KM-956-1.
5. Disconnect the wiring harness connector (1) for wheel sensor.

➡**Pay attention to installation position of wheel bearing unit and cover plate.**

6. Remove the wheel bearing unit.
   a. Detach the 3 bolts (2).
   b. Pull the wheel bearing unit (4)

with the cover plate (3) from the steering knuckle and halfshaft.

To install:
   • Note installation position.
   • Clean thread and insert bolts with locking compound.
7. Install the wheel bearing unit.
   a. Place the cover plate on the wheel bearing unit.
   b. Slide the wheel bearing unit with the cover plate onto the halfshaft and place onto steering knuckle.
   c. Install the 3 new bolts.

8. Tighten the bolts to 67 ft. lbs. (90 Nm) plus 30 degrees plus 15 degrees.

➡**Ensure that wiring harness is correctly attached in all brackets and clips in order to prevent damage to wiring harness.**

9. Route the wiring harness.
   a. Clip the wheel sensor wiring harness in the retaining clip (1).
   b. Connect the wheel sensor wiring harness.
10. Install the halfshaft with the new nut.
11. Tighten the halfshaft nut to 111 ft. lbs. (150 Nm), undo 45 degrees, then tighten to 185 ft. lbs. (250 Nm)
12. Counter-hold against wheel hub with J 28733-B /KM-6610 and KM-956-1.
13. Install the brake rotor. Refer to Front Brake Rotor Replacement.
14. Install the front wheel.
15. Tighten the front wheel bolts to 81 ft. lbs. (110 Nm).

SUSPENSION

COIL SPRING

REMOVAL & INSTALLATION

See Figures 273 and 274.

✳✳ WARNING

Only replace springs in pairs. When replacing the springs, the springs which correspond to the vehicle version and equipment level available from aftermarket must be used. When lifting at the jacking points on the vehicle, take care that all rear axle bolts and the contact points for the centering device remain accessible.

1. Remove the rear wheels.

➡**Ensure that the vehicle does not lift from the lifting platform attachment points.**

2. Position 2 jack stands to keep the axle from lowering while springs are removed.
3. Detach the shock absorbers (2) at both sides of rear axle.
4. Remove the 2 bolts.

➡**Ensure that the brake pressure hoses are not stretched.**

➡**Note installation position of damping rings.**

5. Lower the jack stands enough to allow for spring removal.
6. Remove the 2 springs with damping rings at top and bottom.

REAR SUSPENSION

7. Detach the 4 damping rings from the springs.

To install:

➡**Ensure that the springs are seated correctly.**

8. Insert the upper and lower damping rings in the springs.
9. Insert the 2 springs in the rear axle and the vehicle underbody spring mounts.

✳✳ WARNING

Ensure that the vehicle does not lift from the lifting platform attachment points.

10. Attach the shock absorbers (3) to rear axle at both sides.

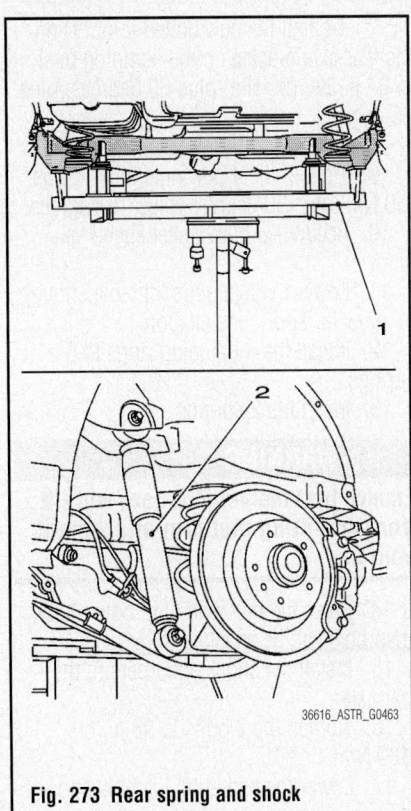

Fig. 273 Rear spring and shock

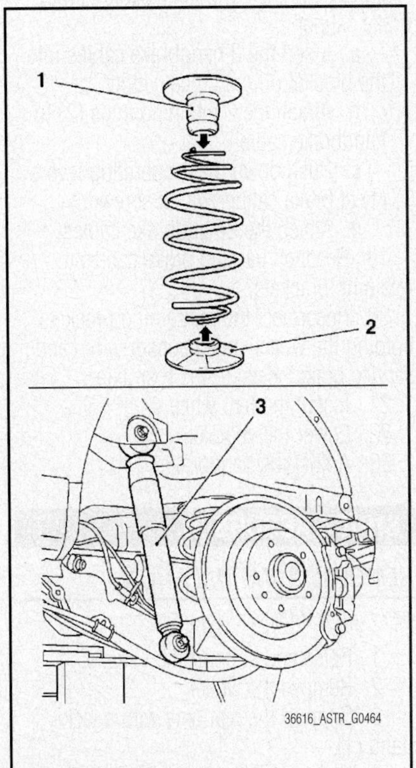

Fig. 274 Rear spring assembly

11. Raise the rear axle using jack stands until the rear shock absorbers can be installed.

12. Tighten the 2 bolts to 96 ft. lbs. (130 Nm).

13. Lower the jack stands and remove.
14. Install the rear wheels.
15. Tighten to 81 ft. lbs. (110 Nm).

REAR AXLE

REMOVAL & INSTALLATION

Removal

See Figures 275 through 278.

1. Ensure the vehicle is in park or gear.
2. Release the handbrake.
3. Detach the boot of the handbrake lever (2).
4. Slacken the handbrake cable by turning back the adjusting nut (3).
5. Raise and support the vehicle.
6. Remove the rear wheels.
7. Push down the 2 operating levers (1) at the brake caliper with a screwdriver.
8. Detach the 2 handbrake cables from operating levers.
9. Remove the 2 retaining clips (2).
10. Detach the 2 handbrake cables from brake caliper.
11. Separate the handbrake cables from the restraining clips along the axle.

➡**The brake system remains closed and the brake linings installed.**

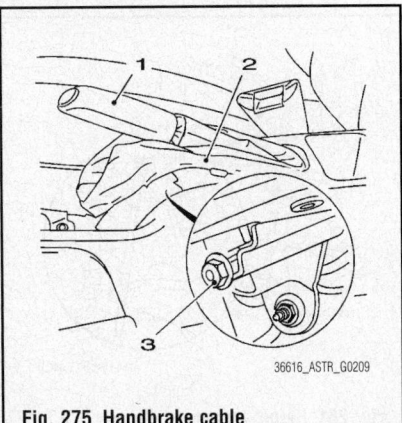

Fig. 275 Handbrake cable

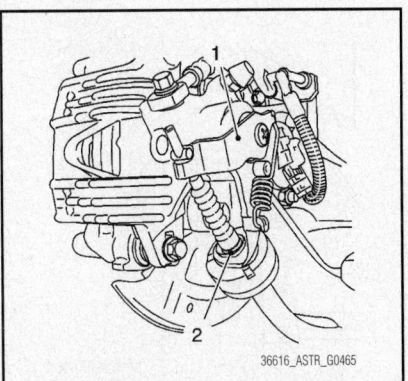

Fig. 276 Handbrake operating levers

12. Disconnect the restraining brackets holding the wheel speed sensor wires and service brake hoses to the rear axle.
13. Disconnect both wheel speed sensors.
14. Place a hydraulic lift table under the rear axle.

✳✳ WARNING

Ensure that the vehicle does not lift from the lifting platform attachment points.

15. Raise the hydraulic lift table.
16. Remove the 2 shock absorbers from the rear axle.
17. Remove the 2 bolts.
18. Lower the hydraulic lift table enough to allow for spring removal.

➡**Note installation position of damping rings.**

19. Remove the 2 springs.
20. Remove the 4 damping rings.
21. Separate both brake/hub assemblies from the axle by removing the bolts (1) and suspend hub/brake assembly in the wheel wells.
22. Mark all body to bracket bolt locations on both rear axle bushing brackets.

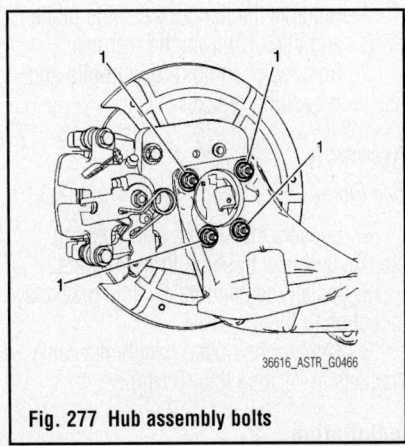

Fig. 277 Hub assembly bolts

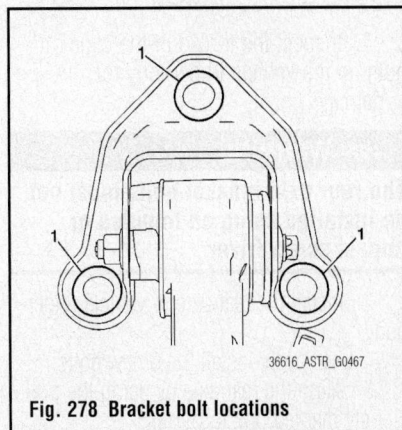

Fig. 278 Bracket bolt locations

✳✳ WARNING

The bolts must not be removed from the rear axle bracket using an impulse or impact screwdriver.

23. Make sure the hydraulic lift table is supporting the rear axle.

24. Remove the 6 bolts from the vehicle underbody.

25. Lower the rear axle with the hydraulic lift table.

Disassembly

See Figure 279.

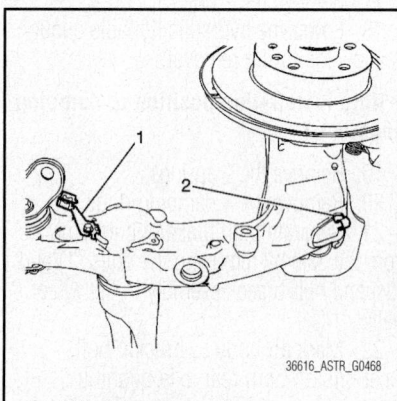

Fig. 279 Axle disassembly

1. Remove the handbrake cable brackets (1) and clips (2) from the rear axle.

2. Remove bushing through bolts and rear axle bushing bracket.

Assembly

See Figure 279.

1. Loosely install rear axle bushing bracket and new bushing through bolts.

2. Install the handbrake cable brackets and clips to the rear axle.

3. Tighten the bolted handbrake cable brackets to 71 inch lbs. (8 Nm).

Installation

See Figures 277, 276, 280 through 282.

1. Inspect the thread of the cage nuts on the vehicle underbody for damage.

✳✳ WARNING

The rear axle bracket bolts must not be installed using an impulse or impact screwdriver.

2. Install the rear axle to vehicle underbody.

   a. Loosely install the 6 new bolts.

3. Align the rear axle by using the previously marked bolt locations.

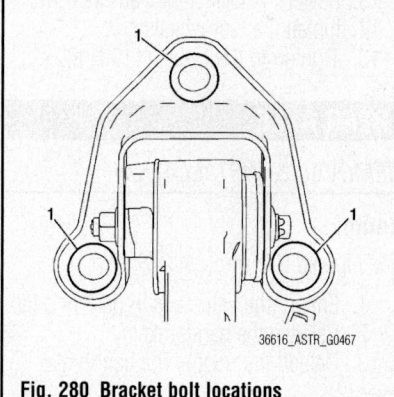

Fig. 280 Bracket bolt locations

4. Tighten the 6 new bolts on the rear axle bracket on the vehicle underbody.

5. Tighten the rear axle bracket bolts on the vehicle underbody to 67 ft. lbs. (90 Nm), plus 30 degrees, plus 15 degrees.

6. Raise the rear axle with hydraulic lift table until a distance of l=173±10 mm is achieved between the spring mounts at the rear axle and the spring mounts at the vehicle underbody.

✳✳ CAUTION

Distance has to be adjusted on both sides.

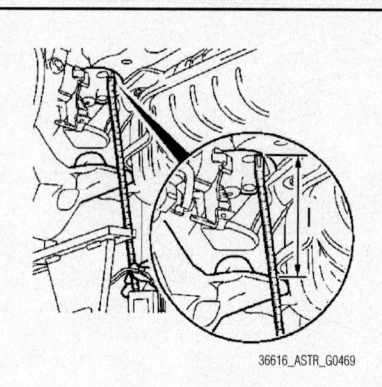

Fig. 281 Height measurement

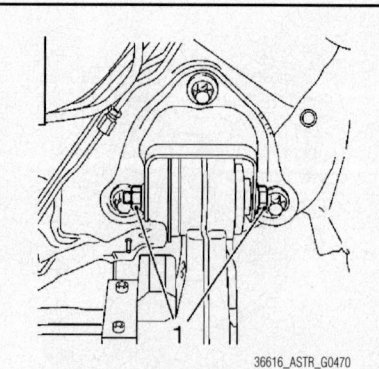

Fig. 282 Rear axle bushing

7. Tighten the new bolted joint (1) on the rear axle bracket on the damping bush to 67 ft. lbs. (90 Nm) plus 60 degrees, plus 15 degrees.

8. Install the hub/rotor/brake assemblies.

9. Tighten the 4 new nuts to 37 ft. lbs. (50 Nm) plus 30 degrees, plus 15 degrees.

10. Reconnect both wheel speed sensors.

11. Lower the hydraulic lift table enough to allow for spring installation.

12. Install the 4 damping rings to the springs.

13. Insert the 2 springs

✳✳ WARNING

Ensure that the vehicle does not lift from the lifting platform attachment points.

14. Raise the rear axle until both shock absorbers can be attached to rear axle.

15. Install the shock absorbers to the rear axle.

16. Tighten the 2 bolts to 96 ft. lbs. (130 Nm).

17. Lower the hydraulic lift table and remove.

18. Attach the handbrake cable to the brake caliper.

   a. Insert the 2 handbrake cables into the bracket on the brake caliper.

   b. Attach the 2 retaining clips (2) to handbrake cable.

   c. Push down the 2 operating levers (1) at brake caliper with a screwdriver.

   d. Attach the 2 handbrake cables.

19. Reattach parking brake cables to retaining brackets.

20. Reconnect the restraining brackets holding the wheel speed sensor wires and service brake hoses to the rear axle.

21. Install the rear wheels.

22. Lower the vehicle.

23. Adjust the handbrake.

SHOCK ABSORBER

REMOVAL & INSTALLATION

See Figure 283.

1. Raise and support the vehicle.

2. Remove the wheel.

3. Support the rear axle with a jack stand (1).

4. In the vehicles with CDC chassis, disconnect the proportional valve wiring harness connector.

5. Remove the upper and lower shock bolts.

6. Remove the shock (2) from the vehicle.

3. Slacken the handbrake cable by turning back the adjusting nut (3).

4. Remove the rear wheel.

5. In the vehicles with disc brakes, detach the handbrake cable from the brake caliper.

    a. Push down the operating lever at the brake caliper using a screwdriver.

    b. Remove the handbrake cable.

    c. Detach the retaining clip.

    d. Pull the handbrake cable out of the bracket.

➡**If it is not possible to pull the brake caliper with brake carrier and installed brake pads from brake disc because of brake disc wear, for example: remove the brake pads from rear wheel brake, refer to Rear Disc Brake Pads Replacement .**

6. Detach the brake caliper with brake carrier from the brake backing plate.

7. Remove the 2 brake carrier bolts from the brake carrier plate.

8. Pull the brake caliper with brake carrier from the brake disc.

9. Suspend the brake caliper and brake carrier from the rear spring using suitable wire.

10. Remove the brake disc from rear wheel brake.

11. Attach the brake carrier plate (3) to the rear spring using cable straps.

12. Disconnect the wiring harness connector (1) from the wheel sensor.

13. Remove the wheel bearing unit from the rear axle.

    a. Remove the 4 nuts (arrows) from the wheel bearing unit.

    b. Remove the wheel bearing unit with cover plate (2).

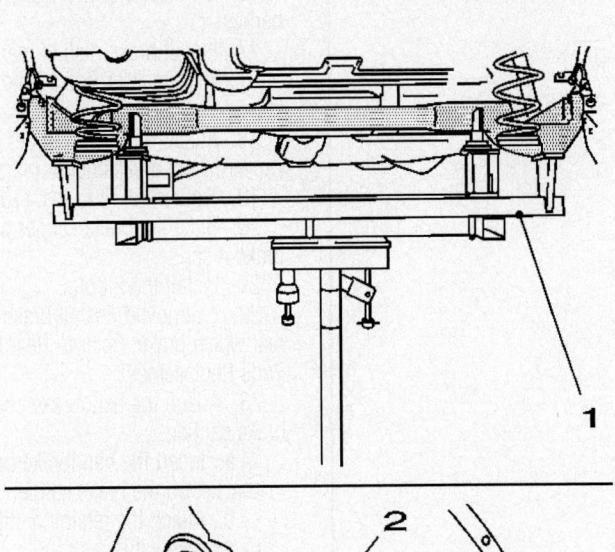

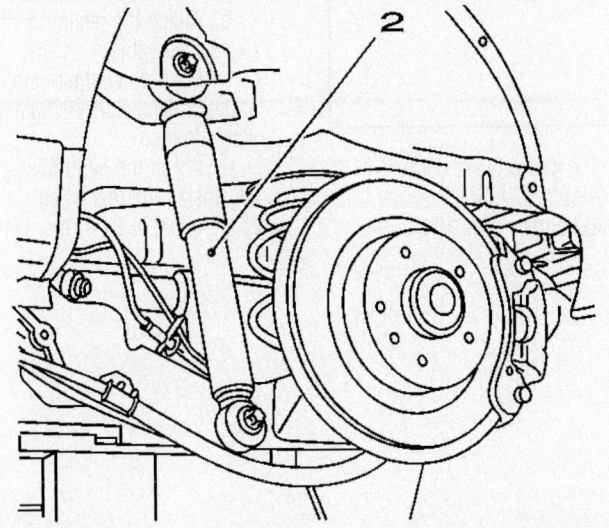

36616_ASTR_G0463

Fig. 283 Rear spring and shock

To install:

7. Position the shock absorber to the vehicle.

8. Install the upper shock bolt.

9. Tighten to 67 ft. lbs. (90 Nm).

10. Install the lower shock bolt.

11. Tighten to 96 ft. lbs. (130 Nm).

12. Remove the jack stand.

13. In the vehicles with CDC chassis, connect the proportional valve wiring harness connector.

14. Install the wheel.

15. Lower the vehicle.

WHEEL HUB & BEARING

REMOVAL & INSTALLATION

See Figures 284 and 285.

1. Release the handbrake.

2. Detach the boot of handbrake lever (2).

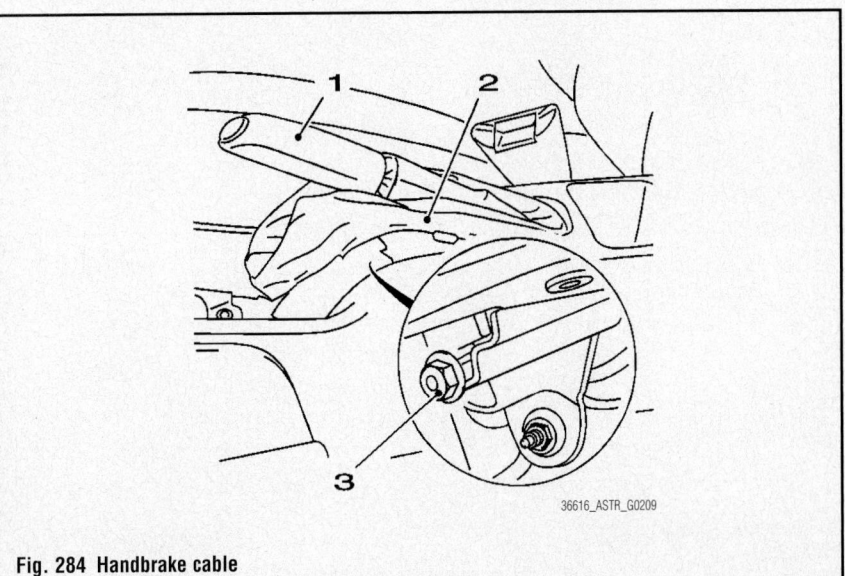

36616_ASTR_G0209

Fig. 284 Handbrake cable

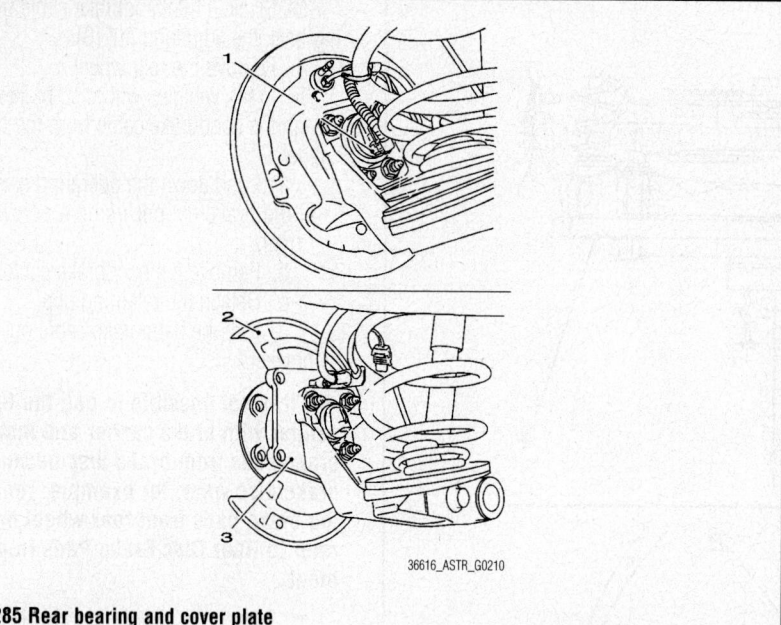

36616_ASTR_G0210

Fig. 285 Rear bearing and cover plate

To install:

14. Install the wheel bearing unit, cover plate (3) and brake carrier plate (2) to the rear axle.

15. Tighten the 4 new brake carrier plate nuts (arrows) to 37 ft. lbs. (50 Nm) plus 30 degrees plus 15 degrees.

16. Connect the wheel sensor wiring harness (1).

17. Install brake disc of rear wheel brake. Refer to Rear Brake Rotor Replacement.

18. Attach the brake caliper with brake carrier to the brake anchor plate.

19. Tighten to 74 ft. lbs. (100 Nm).

20. Slide the brake caliper onto the brake disc.

21. Install the 2 bolts.

22. If removed, install brake pads of the rear wheel brake. Refer to Rear Disc Brake Pads Replacement.

23. Attach the handbrake cable to the brake caliper.

   a. Insert the handbrake cable into the bracket on the brake caliper.

   b. Attach the retaining clip to the handbrake cable.

   c. Push down the operating lever at the brake caliper using a screwdriver.

   d. Install the handbrake cable.

24. Install the rear wheel.

25. Tighten to 81 ft. lbs. (110 Nm).

SPECIFICATIONS AND MAINTENANCE CHARTS

ENGINE AND VEHICLE IDENTIFICATION

	Engine							Model Year	
Code ①	Liters (cc)	Cu. In.	Cyl.	Fuel Sys.	Engine Type	Eng. Mfg.		Code ②	Year
5	2.4 (2398)	146	4	MFI	DOHC	Saturn		8	2008
N	3.5 (3499)	214	6	SFI	DOHC	Saturn		9	2009
7	3.6 (3598)	217	6	SFI	DOHC	Saturn			

MFI: Multi-point Fuel Injection

SFI: Sequential Fuel Injection

DOHC: Double Overhead Camshafts

SOHC: Single Overhead Camshaft

① 8th digit of VIN

② 10th digit of VIN

36616_AURA_C0001

GENERAL ENGINE SPECIFICATIONS

Year	Model	Engine Displacement Liters (cc)	Engine ID/VIN	Fuel System Type	Net Horsepower @ rpm	Net Torque @ rpm (ft. lbs.)	Bore x Stroke (in.)	Com-pression Ratio	Oil Pressure @ rpm
2008	Aura	2.4 (2398)	5	MFI	169@6400	160@4500	3.47x3.86	10.0:1	50-80@1000
		3.5 (3499)	N	SFI	224@5800	220@4000	3.90x2.99	9.8:1	30-45@1850
		3.6 (3598)	7	SFI	252@6300	251@3200	3.70x3.37	10.2:1	20@2000
2009	Aura	2.4 (2398)	5	MFI	169@6400	160@4500	3.47x3.86	10.0:1	50-80@1000
		3.6 (3598)	7	SFI	252@6300	251@3200	3.70x3.37	10.2:1	20@2000

MFI: Multi-port Fuel Injection

SFI: Sequential Fuel Injection

36616_AURA_C0002

ENGINE TUNE-UP SPECIFICATIONS

Year	Engine Displacement Liters	Engine ID/VIN	Spark Plug Gap (in.)	Ignition Timing (deg.) MT	Ignition Timing (deg.) AT	Fuel Pump (psi) ①	Idle Speed (rpm) MT ②	Idle Speed (rpm) AT ②	Valve Clearance In.	Valve Clearance Ex.
2008	2.4	5	0.037-0.043	③	③	50-60	④	④	HYD	HYD
	3.5	N	0.040	③	③	56-62	④	④	HYD	HYD
	3.6	7	0.043	③	③	56-62	④	④	HYD	HYD
2009	2.4	5	0.037-0.043	③	③	50-60	④	④	HYD	HYD
	3.6	7	0.043	③	③	56-62	④	④	HYD	HYD

HYD: Hydraulic

① Pressure measured at idle

② Idle speed measured with manual transmission in Neutral; automatic transmission in D (drive)

③ Engines equipped with Distributorless Ignition System (DIS). Ignition timing is not adjustable

④ Refer to the Vehicle Emission Control Information label

36616_AURA_C0003

CAPACITIES

Year	Model	Engine Displacement Liters	Engine ID/VIN	Engine Oil with Filter (qts.)	Transaxle (qts.) Auto.	Fuel Tank (gal.)	Cooling System (qts.)
2008	Aura	2.4	5	5.0	①	16.3	7.5
		3.5	N	4.0	①	16.3	9.7
		3.6	7	5.5	②	16.3	9.7
2009	Aura	2.4	5	5.0	①	16.3	7.5
		3.6	7	5.5	②	16.3	9.7

NOTE: All capacities are approximate. Add fluid gradually and ensure a proper fluid level is obtained.

① 4 speed: Bottom pan: 7 qts., Overhaul: 9.5 qts.

② 6 speed: Fluid change: 5.3-7.4 qts., Overhaul: 7.4-9.5 qts.

36616_AURA_C0004

FLUID SPECIFICATIONS

Year	Model	Engine Displacement Liters (VIN)	Engine Oil	Auto. Trans.	Drive Axle	Power Steering Fluid	Brake Master Cylinder
2008	Aura	2.4 (5)	5W-30	①	—	Power Steering Fluid	DOT 3
		3.5 (N)	5W-30	①	—	Power Steering Fluid	DOT 3
		3.6 (7)	5W-30	①	—	Power Steering Fluid	DOT 3
2009	Aura	2.4 (5)	5W-30	①	—	Power Steering Fluid	DOT 3
		3.6 (7)	5W-30	①	—	Power Steering Fluid	DOT 3

DOT: Department Of Transpotation

① DEXRON®-VI Automatic Transmission Fluid

36616_AURA_C0011

VALVE SPECIFICATIONS

Year	Engine Displ. Liters	Engine ID/VIN	Seat Angle (deg.)	Face Angle (deg.)	Spring Test Pressure (lbs. @ in.)	Spring Free-Length (in.)	Stem-to-Guide Clearance (in.)		Stem Diameter (in.)	
							Intake	Exhaust	Intake	Exhaust
2008	2.4	5	46	45	①	NA	0.0012	0.0020	0.2344	0.2337
					②		0.0022	0.0026	0.2355	0.2343
	3.5	N	46	45	③	2.08	0.0009	0.0009	NA	NA
					④		0.0025	0.0025		
	3.6	7	⑤	44.25	⑥	1.6555-	0.0010	0.0014	0.2344	0.2341
					⑦	1.766	0.0026	0.0030	0.2352	0.2348
2009	2.4	5	46	45	①	NA	0.0012	0.0020	0.2344	0.2337
					②		0.0022	0.0026	0.2355	0.2343
	3.6	7	⑤	44.25	⑥	1.6555-	0.0010	0.0014	0.2344	0.2341
					⑦	1.766	0.0026	0.0030	0.2352	0.2348

NA: Not available

① Valve spring load closed: 252-575 N @ 22.5mm
② Valve spring load open: 245-271 N @32mm
③ Valve spring load closed: 321-359 N @ 43.2mm
④ Valve spring load open: 979-1067 N @32mm
⑤ Valve seat angle - seating surface: 45
   Valve seat angle - relief surface: 30
   Valve seat angle - undercut surface: 60
⑥ Valve spring load closed: 247-273 N @ 56-61 lb.
⑦ Valve spring load open: 598-662 N @ 134-149 lb.

36616_AURA_C0006

CAMSHAFT AND BEARING SPECIFICATIONS CHART
All measurements are given in inches.

Year	Engine Displacement Liters	Engine ID/VIN	Journal Dia.	Journal dia. Front	Shaft End-play	Thrust Surface	Journal Bore	Lobe Height Intake	Exhaust
2008	2.4	5	1.0604-1.0614	NA	0.0016-0.0057	0.8268-0.8252	NA	NA	NA
	3.5	N	2.024-2.0250	NA	NA	NA	NA	0.2727	0.2727
	3.6	7	1.0605-1.0614	1.3754-1.3764	0.0018-0.0085	NA	0.0016-0.0033	1.6687-1.6805	1.6703-1.6821
2009	2.4	5	1.0604-1.0614	NA	0.0016-0.0057	0.8268-0.8252	NA	NA	NA
	3.6	7	1.0605-1.0614	1.3754-1.3764	0.0018-0.0085	NA	0.0016-0.0033	1.6687-1.6805	1.6703-1.6821

NA: Not Available

36616_AURA_C0007

CRANKSHAFT AND CONNECTING ROD SPECIFICATIONS

All measurements are given in inches.

Year	Engine Displacement Liters	Engine ID/VIN	Crankshaft				Connecting Rod		
			Main Brg. Journal Dia.	Main Brg. Oil Clearance	Shaft End-play	Thrust on No.	Journal Diameter	Oil Clearance	Side Clearance
2008	2.4	5	2.2045-2.2050	0.0012 0.0026	0.0012-0.0150	2	2.0519-2.0525	0.0011-0.0029	0.0028-0.0146
	3.5	N	2.840-2.841	①	0.0024-0.0083	3	2.3750-2.3760	0.0007-0.0170	0.008-0.009
	3.6	7	2.6768-2.6775	0.0004-0.0024	0.0039-0.0130	3	2.2044-2.2050	0.0004-0.0028	0.0374-0.0140
2009	2.4	5	2.2045-2.2050	0.0012 0.0026	0.0012-0.0150	2	2.0519-2.0525	0.0011-0.0029	0.0028-0.0146
	3.6	7	2.6768-2.6775	0.0004-0.0024	0.0039-0.0130	3	2.2044-2.2050	0.0004-0.0028	0.0374-0.0140

NA: Not available

① Except # 3: 0.0008-0.0025 in.

  # 3: 0.0012-0.0030 in.

36616_AURA_C0005

PISTON AND RING SPECIFICATIONS

All measurements are given in inches.

Year	Engine Displacement Liters	Engine ID/VIN	Piston Clearance	Ring Gap			Ring Side Clearance	
				Top Compression	Bottom Compression	Oil Control	Top Compression	Bottom Compression
2008	2.4	5	0.0004-0.0016	0.006-0.012	0.0080 0.0180	0.0060 0.0020	0.0015-0.0031	0.0012-0.0030
	3.5	N	0.0011-0.0110	0.007-0.015	0.019-0.029	0.010 0.029	0.0010-0.0030	0.0020-0.0030
	3.6	7	0.0010-0.0021	0.0059-0.0118	0.0110-0.0189	0.0059-0.0236	0.0012-0.0026	0.0006-0.0024
2009	2.4	5	0.0004-0.0016	0.006-0.012	0.0080 0.0180	0.0060 0.0020	0.0015-0.0031	0.0012-0.0030
	3.6	7	0.0010-0.0021	0.0059-0.0118	0.0110-0.0189	0.0059-0.0236	0.0012-0.0026	0.0006-0.0024

36616_AURA_C0008

TORQUE SPECIFICATIONS
All readings in ft. lbs.

Year	Engine Displacement Liters	Engine ID/VIN	Cylinder Head Bolts	Main Bearing Bolts	Rod Bearing Bolts	Crankshaft Balancer Bolts	Flywheel Bolts	Manifold		Spark Plugs	Oil Pan Drain Plug
								Intake	Exhaust		
2008	2.4	5	①	②	③	④	⑤	⑥	⑦	15	18
	3.5	N	⑧	⑨	⑩	⑪	52	⑫	15	11	18
	3.6	7	⑬	⑭	⑮	⑯	⑰	⑱	15	13	18
2009	2.4	5	①	②	③	④	⑤	⑥	⑦	15	18
	3.6	7	⑬	⑭	⑮	⑯	⑰	⑱	15	13	18

① Step 1: 22 ft. lbs.
   Step 2: 155 degrees

② 15 ft. lbs. Plus 70 degrees

③ 18 ft. lbs. Plus 100 degrees

④ 74 ft. lbs. Plus 125 degrees

⑤ Flexplate specification: 39 ft. lbs. Plus 25 degrees

⑥ Intake manifold to head nut and bolt: 89 inch lbs.
   Intake manifold to head stud: 53 inch lbs.

⑦ Exhaust manifold to head nut: 124 inch lbs.
   Exhaust manifold to head stud: 89 inch lbs.

⑧ Step 1: 44 ft. lbs.
   Step 2: 140 degrees

⑨ Step 1: 37 ft. lbs.
   Step 2: 77 degrees

⑩ 18 ft. lbs. Plus 110 degrees

⑪ Step 1: Old bolt 92 ft. lbs. Then remove bolt
   Step 2: Install a new bolt and tighten to 92 ft. lbs.
   Step 3: tighten an additional 130 degrees

⑫ Lower manifold center ; Step 1; 62 in. lbs.
   Step 2: 115 in. lbs.
   Lower manifold corner: Step 1: 62 in. lbs.
   Step 2: 18 ft. lbs. lbs.
   Upper manifold: 18 ft. lbs.

⑬ M8 bolt Step 1: 11 ft. lbs.
   Step 2: 75 degrees
   M11 bolt Step 1: 22 ft. lbs.
   Step 2: 150 degrees

⑭ Inner Step 1: 15 ft. lbs.
   Step 2: 80 degrees
   Outer Step 1: 10 ft. lbs.
   Step 2: 110 degrees
   Side Step 1:22 ft. lbs
   Step 2: 60 degrees

⑮ Step 1: 22 ft. lbs.
   Step 2: back off to zero
   Step 3: 18 ft. lbs
   Step 4: 110 degrees

⑯ 74 ft. lbs. Plus 150 degrees

⑰ Flywheel specification: 22 ft. lbs. Plus 45 degrees

⑱ Upper manifold: 17 ft. lbs.
   Tuning valve bolt: 89 inch lbs.

36616_AURA_C0009

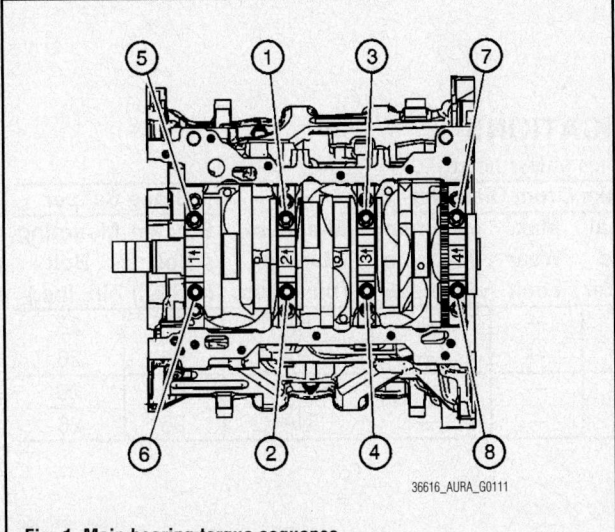

36616_AURA_G0111

Fig. 1 Main bearing torque sequence

WHEEL ALIGNMENT

Year	Model		Caster Range (+/-Deg.)	Caster Preferred Setting (Deg.)	Camber Range (+/-Deg.)	Camber Preferred Setting (Deg.)	Toe-in (in.)
2008	Aura	F	0.75	2.90	0.75	①	0.20 +/- 0.20
		R	—	—	0.60	0.80	0.20 +/- 0.20
2009	Aura	F	0.75	2.90	0.75	①	0.20 +/- 0.20
		R	—	—	0.60	0.80	0.20 +/- 0.20

① Left: 1.00 degrees

  Right: 0.70 degrees

36616_AURA_C0010

TIRE, WHEEL AND BALL JOINT SPECIFICATIONS

Year	Model	OEM Tires Standard	OEM Tires Optional	Tire Pressures (psi) Front	Tire Pressures (psi) Rear	Wheel Size	Ball Joint Inspection	Lug Nut (ft. lbs.)
2008	Aura	①	①	①	①	①	①	100
2009	Aura	①	①	①	①	①	①	100

OEM: Original Equipment Manufacturer

PSI: Pounds Per Square Inch

STD: Standard

OPT: Optional

NS: Not specified by manufacturer

① For tire size and information, check the label located inside the glove compartment door.

36616_AURA_C0012

BRAKE SPECIFICATIONS

All measurements in inches unless noted

Year	Model		Brake Disc Original Thickness	Brake Disc Minimum Thickness	Brake Disc Maximum Runout	Brake Drum Diameter Original Inside Diameter	Brake Drum Diameter Max. Wear Limit	Brake Drum Diameter Maximum Machine Diameter	Minimum Lining Thickness	Brake Caliper Bracket Bolt (ft. lbs.)	Brake Caliper Mounting Bolt (ft. lbs.)
2008	Aura	F	1.023	0.898	0.002	—	—	—	NA	96	26
		R	0.551	0.465	0.002	—	—	—	NA	96	26
2009	Aura	F	1.023	0.898	0.002	—	—	—	NA	96	26
		R	0.551	0.465	0.002	—	—	—	NA	96	26

F: Front

R: Rear

36616_AURA_C0013

MAINTENANCE I AND II SERVICE SCHEDULES
Saturn Aura

When the CHANGE ENGINE OIL light appears, certain services and inspections are required.

Required services are described as Maintenance I and Maintenance II.

The first service on a vehicle should be Maintenance I, and the second service should be Maintenance II.

Alternate between the 2 thereafter. However, in some cases, Maintenance II may be required more often.

Maintenance I: Use Maintenance I if the CHANGE ENGINE OIL light comes on within 10 months since vehicle was purchased or, if Maintenance II was performed.

Maintenance II: Use Maintenance II if the previous service performed was Maintenance I. Always use Maintenance II whenever the CHANGE ENGINE OIL light comes on 10 months or more since the last service, or, if the CHANGE ENGINE OIL light has not come on at all for one year.

Service	I	II
Change the engine oil and filter. Reset the oil life system.	✓	✓
Visually inspect the vehicle for leaks or damage. A fluid loss in the vehicle system could indicate a problem. Inspected, repair and add fluid to the system if necessary.	✓	✓
Inspect the engine air cleaner filter. If necessary, replace the filter.		✓
Rotate the tires. Inspect the tire inflation pressures and the tire wear.	✓	✓
Visually inspect the brake lines and hoses for proper hook-up, binding, leaks, cracks, chafing, etc. Inspect the disc brake pads for wear and the rotors for surface condition. Inspect the drum brake linings for wear or cracks. Inspect other brake parts, including drums, wheel cylinders, calipers, parking brake, etc. Inspect the parking brake adjustment.	✓	✓
Inspect the engine coolant and the windshield washer fluid levels. Add fluid as needed.	✓	✓
Perform any needed additional services.	✓	✓
Inspect the suspension and steering components. Inspect the front and rear suspension and the steering system for damaged, loose or missing parts, or signs of wear. Inspect the power steering lines and the hoses for proper hook-up, binding, leaks, cracks, chafing, etc.	--	✓
Visually inspect the coolant hoses and replace the hoses if they are cracked, swollen or deteriorated. Inspect all pipes, fittings and clamps; replace with GM parts as needed. To help ensure proper operation, a pressure test of the cooling system and pressure cap and cleaning the outside of the radiator and air conditioning condenser is recommended at least once a year.	--	✓
Inspect the wiper blades for wear or cracking. Clean the windshield and wiper blades, if contaminated. Replace wiper blades that are worn or damaged.	--	✓
Inspect the restraint system components. Ensure the safety belt reminder light and all the belts, buckles, latch plates, retractors and anchorages are working properly. Look for any other loose or damaged safety belt system parts. If you see anything that might keep a safety belt system from working correctly, repair or replaced the damaged part. Replace torn or frayed safety belts, refer to Operational and Functional Checks in Seat Belts. Inspect for any opened or broken air bag coverings, and repair or replace as needed. The air bag system does require regular maintenance.	--	✓
Lubricate the body components. Lubricate all key lock cylinders, hood latch assemblies, secondary latches, pivots, spring anchor and release pawl, hood and door hinges, rear folding seats and liftgate hinges. Frequent lubrication may be required when exposed to a corrosive environment, refer to Fluid and Lubricant Recommendations . Applying dielectric silicone grease GM P/N 12345579 (Canadian P/N 1974984) or equivalent on weatherstrip with a clean cloth.	--	✓
Inspect the transaxle fluid level and add fluid as needed (3.6L engine only).	--	✓
Replace the passenger compartment air filter.		✓
Inspect the throttle system. Inspect the throttle system for interference or binding and for damaged or missing parts. Replace the parts as needed. Replace any components that have high effort or excessive wear. Do not lubricate the accelerator or the cruise control cables.	--	✓

To reset the CHANGE ENGINE OIL LIGHT:

1. Turn the ignition switch to RUN with the engine OFF.
2. Fully press and release the accelerator pedal three times within five seconds.

If the messafe is not displayed, the system is reset.

If the CHANGE ENGINE OIL SOON message comes back on when the vehicle is started, the system has not reset; repeat.

ADDITIONAL MAINTENANCE SERVICES
Saturn Aura

TO BE SERVICED	TYPE OF SERVICE	VEHICLE MILEAGE INTERVAL (x1000)					
		25	50	75	100	125	150
Air cleaner filter	R		✓		✓		✓
Accessory drive belt	I						✓
Auto. Trans. Fluid ①	R		✓		✓		✓
Cooling system hoses and clamps	S/I						✓
Engine coolant ②	R						✓
Fuel system	I	✓	✓	✓	✓	✓	✓
Exhaust system & heat shields	S/I	✓	✓	✓	✓	✓	✓
Spark plugs	R				✓		

R: Replace   S/I: Inspect and service, if necessary

① Replace if any of the following conditions are met:

    Heavy city traffic where the outside temperature regularly reaches 32°C (90°F) or higher

    Hilly or mountainous terrain

    Frequent trailer towing

    Taxi, police or delivery service

    Otherwise, change every 100,000 miles

② Drain, flush, and refill cooling system. This service should be performed by the dealer/retailer.

    Clean radiator, condenser, pressure cap, and filler neck. Pressure test the cooling system and pressure cap.

36616_AURA_C0015

PRECAUTIONS

Before servicing any vehicle, please be sure to read all of the following precautions, which deal with personal safety, prevention of component damage, and important points to take into consideration when servicing a motor vehicle:

• Never open, service or drain the radiator or cooling system when the engine is hot; serious burns can occur from the steam and hot coolant.

• Observe all applicable safety precautions when working around fuel. Whenever servicing the fuel system, always work in a well-ventilated area. Do not allow fuel spray or vapors to come in contact with a spark, open flame, or excessive heat (a hot drop light, for example). Keep a dry chemical fire extinguisher near the work area. Always keep fuel in a container specifically designed for fuel storage; also, always properly seal fuel containers to avoid the possibility of fire or explosion. Refer to the additional fuel system precautions later in this section.

• Fuel injection systems often remain pressurized, even after the engine has been turned **OFF**. The fuel system pressure must be relieved before disconnecting any fuel lines. Failure to do so may result in fire and/or personal injury.

• Brake fluid often contains polyglycol ethers and polyglycols. Avoid contact with the eyes and wash your hands thoroughly after handling brake fluid. If you do get brake fluid in your eyes, flush your eyes with clean, running water for 15 minutes. If eye irritation persists, or if you have taken brake fluid internally, IMMEDIATELY seek medical assistance.

• The EPA warns that prolonged contact with used engine oil may cause a number of skin disorders, including cancer. You should make every effort to minimize your exposure to used engine oil. Protective gloves should be worn when changing oil. Wash your hands and any other exposed skin areas as soon as possible after exposure to used engine oil. Soap and water, or waterless hand cleaner should be used.

• All new vehicles are now equipped with an air bag system, often referred to as a Supplemental Restraint System (SRS) or Supplemental Inflatable Restraint (SIR) system. The system must be disabled before performing service on or around system components, steering column, instrument panel components, wiring and sensors. Failure to follow safety and disabling procedures could result in accidental air bag deployment, possible personal injury and unnecessary system repairs.

• Always wear safety goggles when working with, or around, the air bag system. When carrying a non-deployed air bag, be sure the bag and trim cover are pointed away from your body. When placing a non-deployed air bag on a work surface, always face the bag and trim cover upward, away from the surface. This will reduce the motion of the module if it is accidentally deployed. Refer to the additional air bag system precautions later in this section.

• Clean, high quality brake fluid from a sealed container is essential to the safe and proper operation of the brake system. You should always buy the correct type of brake fluid for your vehicle. If the brake fluid becomes contaminated, completely flush the system with new fluid. Never reuse any brake fluid. Any brake fluid that is removed from the system should be discarded. Also, do not allow any brake fluid to come in contact with a painted surface; it will damage the paint.

• Never operate the engine without the proper amount and type of engine oil; doing so WILL result in severe engine damage.

• Timing belt maintenance is extremely important. Many models utilize an interference-type, non-freewheeling engine. If the timing belt breaks, the valves in the cylinder head may strike the pistons, causing potentially serious (also time-consuming and expensive) engine damage. Refer to the maintenance interval charts for the recommended replacement interval for the timing belt, and to the timing belt section for belt replacement and inspection.

• Disconnecting the negative battery cable on some vehicles may interfere with the functions of the on-board computer system(s) and may require the computer to undergo a relearning process once the negative battery cable is reconnected.

• When servicing drum brakes, only disassemble and assemble one side at a time, leaving the remaining side intact for reference.

• Only an MVAC-trained, EPA-certified automotive technician should service the air conditioning system or its components.

BRAKES

ANTI-LOCK BRAKE SYSTEM (ABS)

GENERAL INFORMATION

PRECAUTIONS

• Certain components within the ABS system are not intended to be serviced or repaired individually.

• Do not use rubber hoses or other parts not specifically specified for and ABS system. When using repair kits, replace all parts included in the kit. Partial or incorrect repair may lead to functional problems and require the replacement of components.

• Lubricate rubber parts with clean, fresh brake fluid to ease assembly. Do not use shop air to clean parts; damage to rubber components may result.

• Use only DOT 3 brake fluid from an unopened container.

• If any hydraulic component or line is removed or replaced, it may be necessary to bleed the entire system.

• A clean repair area is essential. Always clean the reservoir and cap thoroughly before removing the cap. The slightest amount of dirt in the fluid may plug an orifice and impair the system function. Perform repairs after components have been thoroughly cleaned; use only denatured alcohol to clean components. Do not allow ABS components to come into contact with any substance containing mineral oil; this includes used shop rags.

• The Anti-Lock control unit is a microprocessor similar to other computer units in the vehicle. Ensure that the ignition switch is **OFF** before removing or installing controller harnesses. Avoid static electricity discharge at or near the controller.

• If any arc welding is to be done on the vehicle, the control unit should be unplugged before welding operations begin.

BLEEDING PROCEDURE

BLEEDING PROCEDURE

1. Place a clean shop cloth beneath the brake master cylinder to catch brake fluid spills.

2. With the ignition OFF and the brakes cool, apply the brakes 3–5 times, or until the brake pedal effort increases significantly, in order to deplete the brake booster power reserve.

3. If you have performed a brake master cylinder bench bleeding on this vehicle, or if you disconnected the brake pipes from the master cylinder, or if you have disconnected the brake pipes from the proportioning valve assembly or the brake modulator assembly, you must perform the following steps to bleed air at the ports of the hydraulic component.

   a. Ensure that the brake master cylinder reservoir is full to the maximum-fill level.

   If removal of the reservoir cap and diaphragm is necessary, clean the outside of the reservoir on and around the cap prior to removal.

   b. With the brake pipes installed securely to the master cylinder, proportioning valve assembly, or brake modulator assembly, loosen and separate one of the brake pipes from the port of the component.

   For the proportioning valve assembly or the brake modulator assembly, perform these steps in the sequence of system flow; begin with the fluid feed pipes from the master cylinder.

   c. Allow a small amount of brake fluid to gravity bleed from the open port of the component.

   d. Connect the brake pipe to the component and tighten securely.

   e. Have an assistant slowly press the brake pedal fully and maintain steady pressure on the pedal.

   f. Loosen the same brake pipe to purge air from the open port of the component.

   g. Tighten the brake pipe, then have the assistant slowly release the brake pedal.

   h. Wait 15 seconds, then repeat the steps until all air is purged from the same port of the component.

   i. With the brake pipe installed securely to the master cylinder, proportioning valve assembly, or brake modulator assembly, after all air has been purged from the first port of the component that was bled, loosen and separate the next brake pipe from the component, until each of the ports on the component has been bled.

   j. After completing the final component port bleeding procedure, ensure that each of the brake pipe-to-component fittings are properly tightened.

4. Fill the brake master cylinder reservoir. Make sure that the brake master cylinder reservoir remains at least half-full during this bleeding procedure. Add fluid as needed to maintain the proper level.

Clean the outside of the reservoir on and around the reservoir cap prior to removing the cap and diaphragm.

5. Install a box-end wrench onto the right rear wheel hydraulic circuit bleeder valve.

6. Install a transparent hose over the end of the bleeder valve.

7. Submerge the open end of the transparent hose into a transparent container partially filled with brake fluid from a clean, sealed brake fluid container.

8. Have an assistant slowly press the brake pedal fully and maintain steady pressure on the pedal.

9. Loosen the bleeder valve to purge air from the wheel hydraulic circuit.

10. Tighten the bleeder valve, then have the assistant slowly release the brake pedal.

11. Wait 15 seconds, then repeat steps 8-10 until all air is purged from the same wheel hydraulic circuit.

12. With the right rear wheel hydraulic circuit bleeder valve tightened securely, after all air has been purged from the right rear hydraulic circuit, install a proper box-end wrench onto the left front wheel hydraulic circuit bleeder valve.

13. Install a transparent hose over the end of the bleeder valve and perform the same procedure used to bleed the right rear.

14. Bleed the left rear and front right in the same manner.

15. Fill the brake master cylinder reservoir to the maximum-fill level with brake fluid from a clean, sealed brake fluid container.

16. Slowly press and release the brake pedal. Observe the feel of the brake pedal.

17. If the brake pedal feels spongy, repeat the bleeding procedure again. If the brake pedal still feels spongy after repeating the bleeding procedure check for leaks in the system and pressure test the system to purge trapped air.

18. Turn the ignition key ON, with the engine OFF. Check to see if the brake system warning lamp remains illuminated.

➡**DO NOT allow the vehicle to be driven until it is diagnosed and repaired.**

❊ CAUTION

Dust and dirt accumulating on brake parts during normal use may contain asbestos fibers from production or aftermarket brake linings. Breathing excessive concentrations of asbestos fibers can cause serious bodily harm. Exercise care when servicing brake parts. Do not sand or grind brake lining unless equipment used is designed to contain the dust residue. Do not clean brake parts with compressed air or by dry brushing. Cleaning should be done by dampening the brake components with a fine mist of water, then wiping the brake components clean with a dampened cloth. Dispose of cloth and all residue containing asbestos fibers in an impermeable container with the appropriate label. Follow practices prescribed by the Occupational Safety and Health Administration (OSHA) and the Environmental Protection Agency (EPA) for the handling, processing, and disposing of dust or debris that may contain asbestos fibers.

BRAKE CALIPER

REMOVAL & INSTALLATION
See Figure 2.

1. Empty the master cylinder reservoir until it is half full.

2. Raise and support the vehicle.

3. Remove the tire and wheel assembly.

4. Install and firmly hand tighten 2 wheel nuts to opposite wheel studs in order to retain the rotor to the hub.

5. Install a large C-clamp over the body of the brake caliper with the C-clamp ends against the rear of the caliper body and against the outer brake pad.

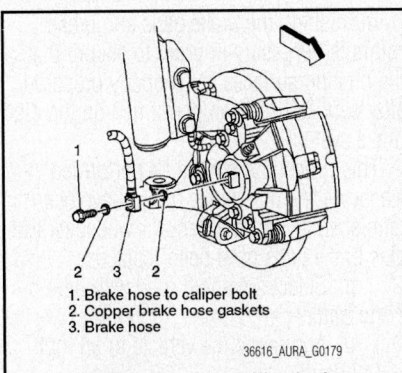

1. Brake hose to caliper bolt
2. Copper brake hose gaskets
3. Brake hose

36616_AURA_G0179

Fig. 2 Removing and installing brake hose and gaskets

6. Tighten the C-clamp until the caliper piston is compressed into the caliper bore enough to allow the caliper to slide past the brake rotor.

7. Remove the C-clamp from the caliper.

8. Remove the brake hose-to-caliper bolt from the brake caliper.

9. Remove the brake hose from the brake caliper.

10. Remove and discard the 2 copper brake hose gaskets. These gaskets may be stuck to the brake caliper and/or the brake hose end.

11. Cap or plug the opening in the brake caliper and the brake hose to prevent fluid loss and contamination.

12. Remove the brake caliper guide pin bolts.

13. Remove the brake caliper from the caliper bracket.

14. Inspect the brake caliper guide pins for freedom of movement, and inspect the condition of the guide pin boots. Move the guide pins inboard and outboard within the bracket bores, without disengaging the slides from the boots, and observe the following:

- Restricted caliper guide pin movement
- Looseness in the brake caliper mounting bracket
- Seized or binding caliper guide pins
- Split or torn boots

15. If any of the conditions listed are found, the brake caliper guide pins and/or boots require replacement.

To install:

16. Install the brake caliper to the brake caliper bracket.

17. Install the brake caliper guide pin bolts and tighten to 26 ft. lbs. (35 Nm).

18. Remove the caps or plugs from the brake caliper opening and the brake hose.

➡**Do not reuse the copper brake hose gaskets.**

19. Install NEW copper brake hose gaskets to the brake hose-to-caliper bolt and to the brake hose.

20. Install the brake hose and the brake hose-to-brake caliper bolt to the brake caliper. Tighten to 37 ft. lbs. (50 Nm).

21. Bleed the hydraulic brake system.

22. Remove the wheel nuts retaining the brake rotor to the wheel hub.

23. Install the tire and wheel assembly.

24. Lower the vehicle.

25. With the engine OFF, gradually apply the brake pedal to approximately ⅔ of its travel distance.

26. Slowly release the brake pedal.

27. Wait 15 seconds, then repeat the last 2 steps until a firm brake pedal is obtained.

28. Fill the master cylinder reservoir to the proper level.

DISC BRAKE PADS

REMOVAL & INSTALLATION

See Figures 3 through 5.

1. Empty the master cylinder reservoir until it is half full.

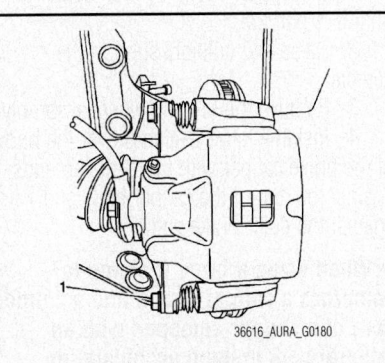

36616_AURA_G0180

Fig. 3 Locating the brake caliper lower guide pin bolt

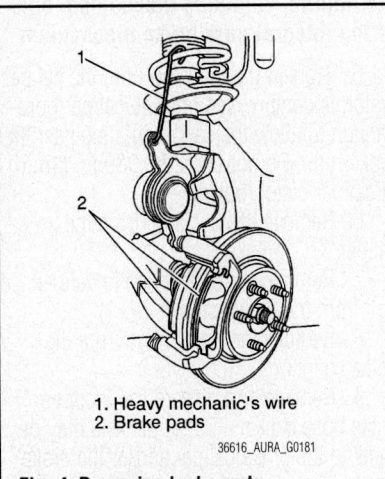

1. Heavy mechanic's wire
2. Brake pads

36616_AURA_G0181

Fig. 4 Removing brake pads

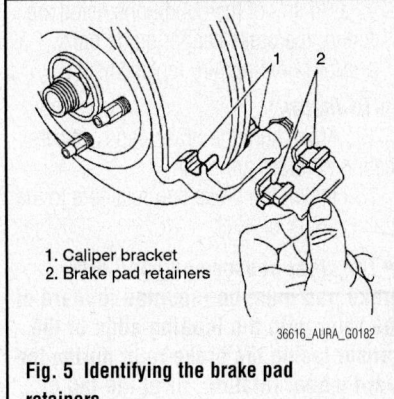

1. Caliper bracket
2. Brake pad retainers

36616_AURA_G0182

Fig. 5 Identifying the brake pad retainers

2. Raise and support the vehicle.

3. Remove the tire and wheel assembly.

4. Install and firmly hand tighten 2 wheel nuts to opposite wheel studs in order to retain the rotor to the hub.

5. Remove the brake caliper lower guide pin bolt.

➡**Support the brake caliper with heavy mechanic wire, or equivalent, whenever it is separated from its mount and the hydraulic flexible brake hose is still connected. Failure to support the caliper in this manner will cause the flexible brake hose to bear the weight of the caliper, which may cause damage to the brake hose and in turn may cause a brake fluid leak.**

6. Without disconnecting the hydraulic brake flexible hose, pivot the caliper upward and secure the caliper with heavy mechanics wire, or equivalent.

7. Remove the brake pads from the caliper mounting bracket.

8. Push the disc brake caliper piston into the caliper bore using an old inner disc brake pad and a disc brake piston installation tool.

9. Remove the brake pad retainers from the caliper bracket.

10. Thoroughly clean the brake pad hardware mating surfaces of the caliper bracket, of any debris and corrosion.

11. Inspect the brake caliper guide pins for freedom of movement, and inspect the condition of the guide pin boots. Move the guide pins inboard and outboard within the bracket bores, without disengaging the slides from the boots, and observe for the following:

- Restricted caliper guide pin movement
- Looseness in the brake caliper mounting bracket
- Seized or binding caliper guide pins
- Split or torn boots

a. If any of the conditions listed are found, the brake caliper guide pins and/or boots require replacement.

To install:

12. Make sure the brake pad hardware mating surfaces are clean.

13. Install the brake pad retainers to the brake caliper bracket.

➡**The wear sensor equipped disc brake pad must be mounted inboard of the rotor with the leading edge of the sensor facing the brake rotor during forward wheel rotation, or at the top of the pad when installed in vehicle position.**

14. Install the brake pads to the caliper bracket.

15. Remove the support, and rotate the brake caliper into position over the disc brake pads and to the caliper mounting bracket.

16. Install the lower brake caliper guide pin bolt. Tighten to 26 ft. lbs. (35 Nm).

17. Remove the wheel nuts retaining the brake rotor to the hub.

18. Install the tire and wheel assembly. Lower the vehicle.

19. With the engine OFF, gradually apply the brake pedal to approximately ⅔ of its travel distance.

20. Slowly release the brake pedal.

21. Wait 15 seconds, then repeat the last 2 steps until a firm brake pedal is obtained

22. Fill the master cylinder reservoir to the proper level.

23. Burnish the brake pad and rotor.

✳✳ CAUTION

Road test a vehicle under safe conditions and while obeying all traffic laws. Do not attempt any maneuvers that could jeopardize vehicle control. Failure to adhere to these precautions could lead to serious personal injury and vehicle damage.

Burnishing the brake pads and brake rotors is necessary in order to ensure that the braking surfaces are properly prepared after service has been performed on the disc brake system.

This procedure should be performed whenever the disc brake rotors have been refinished or replaced, and/or whenever the disc brake pads have been replaced.

a. Select a smooth road with little or no traffic.

b. Accelerate the vehicle to 30 mph (48 km/h).

➡**Use care to avoid overheating the brakes while performing this step.**

c. Using moderate to firm pressure, apply the brakes to bring the vehicle to a stop. Do not allow the brakes to lock.

d. Repeat the previous 2 steps until approximately 20 stops have been completed. Allow sufficient cooling periods between stops in order to properly burnish the brake pads and rotors.

BRAKES   REAR DISC BRAKES

✳✳ CAUTION

Dust and dirt accumulating on brake parts during normal use may contain asbestos fibers from production or aftermarket brake linings. Breathing excessive concentrations of asbestos fibers can cause serious bodily harm. Exercise care when servicing brake parts. Do not sand or grind brake lining unless equipment used is designed to contain the dust residue. Do not clean brake parts with compressed air or by dry brushing. Cleaning should be done by dampening the brake components with a fine mist of water, then wiping the brake components clean with a dampened cloth. Dispose of cloth and all residue containing asbestos fibers in an impermeable container with the appropriate label. Follow practices prescribed by the Occupational Safety and Health Administration (OSHA) and the Environmental Protection Agency (EPA) for the handling, processing, and disposing of dust or debris that may contain asbestos fibers.

BRAKE CALIPER

REMOVAL & INSTALLATION

See Figures 6 through 8.

1. Empty the master cylinder reservoir until it is half full.

2. Raise and suitably support the vehicle.

3. Remove the tire and wheel assembly.

4. Install a large C-clamp over the body of the brake caliper with the C-clamp ends against the rear of the caliper body and against the outer brake pad.

➡**When using a large C-clamp to compress a caliper piston into a caliper bore of a caliper equipped with an integral park brake mechanism, do not exceed more than 0.039 in. (1mm) of piston travel. Exceeding this amount of piston travel will cause damage to the internal adjusting mechanism and/or the integral park brake mechanism.**

5. Tighten the C-clamp until the caliper piston is compressed into the caliper bore enough to allow the caliper to slide past the brake rotor. Do not exceed 0.039 in. (1mm) of caliper piston travel.

6. Remove the C-clamp from the caliper.

7. Remove the brake hose to caliper bolt from the brake caliper.

8. Remove the brake hose from the brake caliper.

9. Remove and discard the 2 copper brake hose gaskets. These gaskets may be stuck to the brake caliper and/or the brake hose end.

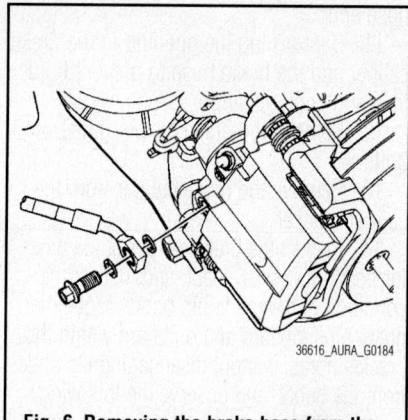

36616_AURA_G0184

Fig. 6 Removing the brake hose from the caliper

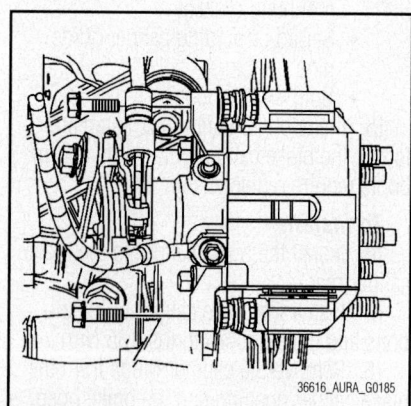

36616_AURA_G0185

Fig. 7 Locating the 2 brake caliper pin bolts

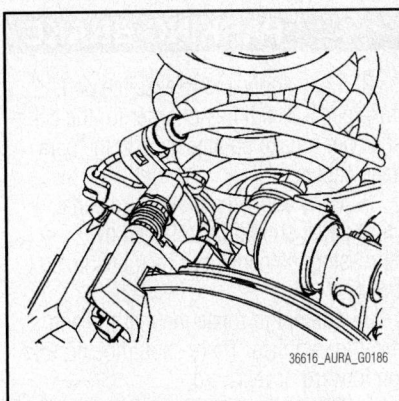

Fig. 8 Identifying the park brake cable

10. Cap or plug the opening in the brake caliper and the brake hose to prevent fluid loss and contamination.

11. Remove the 2 brake caliper pin bolts.

12. Remove the park brake cable from the caliper.

13. Remove the brake caliper from the brake caliper bracket.

To install:

14. Inspect the caliper slide boots for cuts, tears, or deterioration. If damaged, replace the slides and boots.

15. Install the brake caliper to the brake caliper bracket.

16. Install the 2 brake caliper pin bolts. Tighten the bolts to 26 ft. lbs. (35 Nm).

17. Install the park brake cable to the caliper.

18. Remove the caps or plugs from the brake caliper opening and the brake hose.

➡**DO NOT reuse the copper brake hose gaskets.**

19. Install NEW copper brake hose gaskets to the brake hose-to-caliper bolt and to the brake hose.

20. Install the brake hose and the brake hose-to-caliper bolt to the brake caliper. Tighten the bolts to 37 ft. lbs. (50 Nm).

21. Bleed the hydraulic brake system.

22. With the engine OFF, gradually apply the brake pedal to approximately ⅔ of its travel distance.

23. Slowly release the brake pedal.

24. Wait 15 seconds, then repeat the last 2 steps until a firm brake pedal is obtained.

25. Fill the master cylinder reservoir to the proper level.

26. Install the tire and wheel assembly.

27. Lower the vehicle.

28. Apply and release the park brake lever 4 times.

DISC BRAKE PADS

REMOVAL & INSTALLATION

See Figures 9 and 10.

1. Empty the master cylinder reservoir until it is half full.

2. Raise and suitably support the vehicle.

3. Remove the tire and wheel assembly.

4. Install a large C-clamp over the body of the brake caliper with the C-clamp ends against the rear of the caliper body and against the outer brake pad. Do not exceed 0.039 in. (1mm) of caliper piston travel.

➡**When using a large C-clamp to compress a caliper piston into a caliper bore of a caliper equipped with an integral park brake mechanism, donot exceed more than 0.039 in. (1mm) of piston travel. Exceeding this amount of piston travel will cause damage to the internal adjusting mechanism and/or the integral park brake mechanism.**

5. Tighten the C-clamp until the caliper piston is compressed into the caliper bore enough to allow the caliper to slide past the brake rotor.

6. Remove the C-clamp from the caliper.

7. Remove the lower brake caliper guide pin bolt.

➡**Support the brake caliper with heavy mechanic wire, or equivalent, whenever it is separated from its mount and the hydraulic flexible brake hose is still connected. Failure to support the caliper in this manner will cause the flexible brake hose to bear the weight of the caliper, which may cause damage to the brake hose and in turn may cause a brake fluid leak.**

8. Pivot the brake caliper upward from the caliper bracket and support the caliper out of the way with heavy mechanic's wire; ensure that there is no tension on the

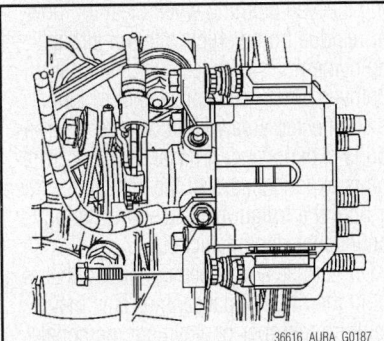

Fig. 9 Locating the lower brake caliper guide pin bolt

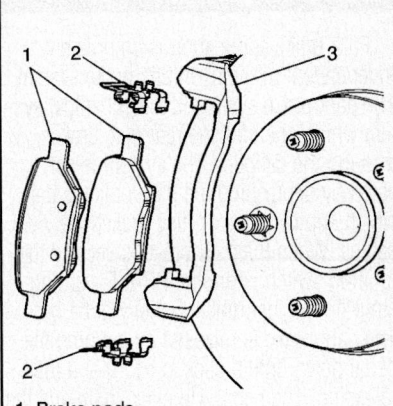

1. Brake pads
2. Brake pad retainers
3. Brake caliper mounting bracket

Fig. 10 Removing and installing the rear brake pad

hydraulic brake flexible hose. Do NOT disconnect the hydraulic brake flexible hose from the caliper.

9. Remove the brake pads from the brake caliper mounting bracket.

10. Remove and the brake pad retainers from the brake caliper mounting bracket.

To install:

➡**Do not attempt to clean away any corrosion. If damaged or corroded replace the necessary components.**

11. Inspect the brake caliper piston boot for deterioration, replace if damaged.

12. Use a piston installation tool in order to twist the brake caliper piston into the brake caliper bore.

13. Install the brake pad retainers to the brake caliper mounting bracket.

14. Install the brake pads to the brake caliper mounting bracket.

15. Pivot the brake caliper downward, over the brake pads and into the caliper bracket.

16. Install the brake caliper guide pin bolt to the brake caliper guide pin. Tighten the bolts to 26 ft. lbs. (35 Nm).

17. Install the tire and wheel assembly.

18. Lower the vehicle.

19. With the engine OFF, gradually apply the brake pedal to approximately ⅔ of its travel distance.

20. Slowly release the brake pedal.

21. Wait 15 seconds, then repeat the last 2 steps until a firm brake pedal is obtained

22. Fill the master cylinder reservoir to the proper level.

23. Apply and release the park brake lever 4 times.

24. Burnish the pads and rotors.

BRAKES

PARKING BRAKE

Park brake application is completely independent of the hydraulic brake system. The park brake system is a mechanical system which operates the rear disc brakes through the calipers. The system is activated by depressing the park brake pedal, which applies the rear disc brakes via cables. When the park brake is set and the ignition switch is on, the BRAKE warning lamp on the instrument panel will be on. The park brake is released by pushing the pedal down until a click is heard and then releasing. The pedal will click again and the BRAKE lamp in the instrument panel will go out when the park brake system is fully released.

PARKING BRAKE CABLES

ADJUSTMENT

➡This vehicle utilizes a self-tensioning, or self-adjusting park brake cable system. The park brake system does not require adjustment under normal operating conditions. The tension on

the park brake cables can be disabled and enabled when necessary during service of the disc brake and/or the park brake system.

1. Apply and fully release the park brake several times. Verify that the park brake pedal releases completely.
2. Turn ON the ignition. Verify the red BRAKE warning lamp is not illuminated.
3. If the red BRAKE warning lamp is illuminated, check that the park brake pedal is in the fully released position and against the stop or that there is no slack in the cables.
4. If the red BRAKE warning lamp remained illuminated and there were no other visible causes.
5. Turn OFF the ignition.
6. Raise and support the vehicle.
7. With the park brake pedal fully released, check the park brake levers on the rear calipers. The levers should be against the stops on the caliper housings. If the levers are not against the stops, binding may exist.

8. Fully apply and release the park brake pedal 3–5 times in order for the cable tensioner to take up any slack in the park brake cables.
9. Fully apply the park brake pedal, a firm pedal should be obtained by depressing the pedal less than one full stroke.
10. Attempt to rotate the rear tire and wheel assemblies. There should be no rotation forward or rearward.
11. Fully release the park brake pedal.
12. Verify the park brake is released by rotating the rear tire and wheel assemblies. The rear tire and wheel assemblies should rotate freely and exhibit no brake drag.
13. Lower the vehicle.

PARKING BRAKE SHOES

REMOVAL & INSTALLATION

The rear disc brake pads serve as the parking brakes. Refer to the procedures under Rear Disc Brakes.

CHASSIS ELECTRICAL

AIR BAG (SUPPLEMENTAL RESTRAINT SYSTEM)

GENERAL INFORMATION

✳✳ CAUTION

These vehicles are equipped with an air bag system. The system must be disarmed before performing service on, or around, system components, the steering column, instrument panel components, wiring and sensors. Failure to follow the safety precautions and the disarming procedure could result in accidental air bag deployment, possible injury and unnecessary system repairs.

SERVICE PRECAUTIONS

Disconnect and isolate the battery negative cable before beginning any airbag system component diagnosis, testing, removal, or installation procedures. Allow system capacitor to discharge for two minutes before beginning any component service. This will disable the airbag system. Failure to disable the airbag system may result in accidental airbag deployment, personal injury, or death.

Do not place an intact undeployed airbag face down on a solid surface. The airbag will propel into the air if accidentally

deployed and may result in personal injury or death.

When carrying or handling an undeployed airbag, the trim side (face) of the airbag should be pointing towards the body to minimize possibility of injury if accidental deployment occurs. Failure to do this may result in personal injury or death.

Replace airbag system components with OEM replacement parts. Substitute parts may appear interchangeable, but internal differences may result in inferior occupant protection. Failure to do so may result in occupant personal injury or death.

Wear safety glasses, rubber gloves, and long sleeved clothing when cleaning powder residue from vehicle after an airbag deployment. Powder residue emitted from a deployed airbag can cause skin irritation. Flush affected area with cool water if irritation is experienced. If nasal or throat irritation is experienced, exit the vehicle for fresh air until the irritation ceases. If irritation continues, see a physician.

Do not use a replacement airbag that is not in the original packaging. This may result in improper deployment, personal injury, or death.

The factory installed fasteners, screws and bolts used to fasten airbag components

have a special coating and are specifically designed for the airbag system. Do not use substitute fasteners. Use only original equipment fasteners listed in the parts catalog when fastener replacement is required.

During, and following, any child restraint anchor service, due to impact event or vehicle repair, carefully inspect all mounting hardware, tether straps, and anchors for proper installation, operation, or damage. If a child restraint anchor is found damaged in any way, the anchor must be replaced. Failure to do this may result in personal injury or death.

Deployed and non-deployed airbags may or may not have live pyrotechnic material within the airbag inflator.

Do not dispose of driver/passenger/curtain airbags or seat belt tensioners unless you are sure of complete deployment. Refer to the Hazardous Substance Control System for proper disposal.

Dispose of deployed airbags and tensioners consistent with state, provincial, local, and federal regulations.

After any airbag component testing or service, do not connect the battery negative cable. Personal injury or death may result if the system test is not performed first.

If the vehicle is equipped with the Occupant Classification System (OCS), do not connect the battery negative cable before performing the OCS Verification Test using the scan tool and the appropriate diagnostic information. Personal injury or death may result if the system test is not performed properly.

Never replace both the Occupant Restraint Controller (ORC) and the Occupant Classification Module (OCM) at the same time. If both require replacement, replace one, then perform the Airbag System test before replacing the other.

Both the ORC and the OCM store Occupant Classification System (OCS) calibration data, which they transfer to one another when one of them is replaced. If both are replaced at the same time, an irreversible fault will be set in both modules and the OCS may malfunction and cause personal injury or death.

If equipped with OCS, the Seat Weight Sensor is a sensitive, calibrated unit and must be handled carefully. Do not drop or handle roughly. If dropped or damaged, replace with another sensor. Failure to do so may result in occupant injury or death.

If equipped with OCS, the front passenger seat must be handled carefully as well. When removing the seat, be careful when setting on floor not to drop. If dropped, the sensor may be inoperative, could result in occupant injury, or possibly death.

If equipped with OCS, when the passenger front seat is on the floor, no one should sit in the front passenger seat. This uneven force may damage the sensing ability of the seat weight sensors. If sat on and damaged, the sensor may be inoperative, could result in occupant injury, or possibly death.

DISARMING THE SYSTEM

1. Turn the steering wheel so that the vehicles wheels are pointing straight ahead.
2. Place the ignition in the OFF position.

➡ The SDM may have more than one fused power input. To ensure there is no unwanted SIR deployment, personal injury, or unnecessary SIR system repairs, remove all fuses supplying power to the SDM. With all SDM fuses removed and the ignition switch in the ON position, the AIR BAG warning indicator illuminates. This is normal operation, and does not indicate a SIR system malfunction.

3. Locate and remove the fuse(s) supplying power to the SDM.
4. Wait 1 minute before working on the system.

ARMING THE SYSTEM

1. Place the ignition in the OFF position.
2. Install the fuse(s) supplying power to the SDM.
3. Turn the ignition switch to the ON position. The AIR BAG indicator will flash then turn OFF.

DRIVE TRAIN

AUTOMATIC TRANSAXLE ASSEMBLY

REMOVAL & INSTALLATION

4T45-E Transaxle

2.4L Engine

See Figure 11.

1. Remove the battery tray.
2. Disconnect the air cleaner outlet duct.
3. Disconnect the transaxle wiring harness from the transaxle and the Park Neutral Position (PNP) switch.
4. Remove the radiator outlet pipe.
5. Disconnect the transaxle shift control cable terminal from the transaxle manual shift lever pin.
6. Remove the retainer from the transaxle shift control cable.
7. Press the locking tabs inward in order to release the transaxle shift control cable from the cable bracket.
8. Remove the shift cable bracket.
9. Remove the transaxle wiring harness from the retainer on the transaxle.
10. Remove the upper transaxle to engine studs and bolts.
11. Install the engine support fixture.
12. Remove the left transmission mount.
13. Secure the radiator and condenser to the vehicle structure and the engine in order to prepare for frame removal.

14. Raise the vehicle.
15. Remove the front wheels and tires.
16. Remove the bolts from the transaxle brace.
17. Remove the transaxle brace.
18. Remove the starter.
19. Mark the relationship of the flywheel to the torque converter for reassembly.
20. Use the flywheel holding tool to prevent the crankshaft from rotating.
21. Remove the torque converter to flywheel bolts.
22. Remove the nut holding the transaxle cooler line retainer to the transaxle.
23. Disconnect the transaxle cooler lines from the transaxle.
24. Disconnect the Vehicle Speed Sensor (VSS) wiring harness from the sensor.
25. Remove the intermediate shaft to steering gear pinch bolt. Discard the bolt.
26. Disconnect the intermediate shaft from the steering gear.
27. Disconnect the tie rods from the steering knuckle.
28. Disconnect the stabilizer shaft links from the stabilizer shaft.
29. Disconnect the ball joints from the steering knuckles.
30. Remove the frame as follows;
    a. Install the engine support fixture.
    b. Support the radiator and condenser from above using the condenser tabs on each side.

c. Remove the tire and wheel assemblies.
d. Remove the front fender liner.
e. Remove the engine splash shield.
f. Remove the lower ball joints from the steering knuckles.
g. Remove the tie rod ends from the steering knuckles.
h. Remove both stabilizer links from the stabilizer bar.
i. Separate the steering gear from the intermediate shaft.
j. Remove the front transmission mount bolt from the frame.
k. Remove the rear transmission mount bracket fasteners from the frame.
l. Lower the vehicle until the frame contacts the engine support stand.
m. Remove the reinforcement bolts.
n. Remove the front frame bolts.
o. Remove the rear frame bolts.
p. Remove the frame reinforcements.
q. Raise the vehicle off of the frame.

31. Disconnect the wheel drive shafts from the transaxle. Secure the wheel drive shafts out of the way.
32. Support the transaxle with a suitable jack.
33. Remove the lower transaxle to engine bolts.
34. Separate the engine and the transaxle.
35. Remove the transaxle from the vehicle.

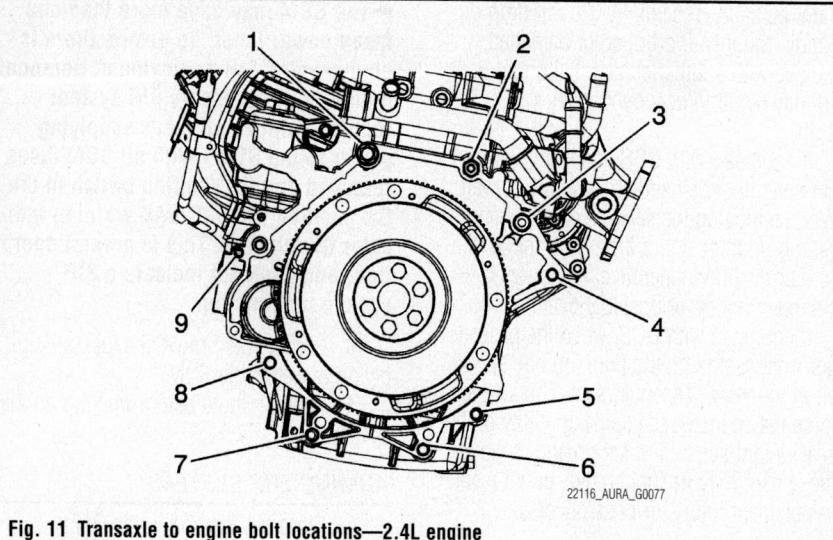

Fig. 11 Transaxle to engine bolt locations—2.4L engine

To install:

36. Position the transaxle in the vehicle.

37. Install the lower transaxle to engine bolts and tighten to 55 ft. lbs. (75 Nm).

38. Install the wheel drive shafts to the transaxle.

39. Lubricate the transaxle cooler pipes before inserting into seals.

40. Connect the transaxle cooler pipes to the transaxle.

41. Install the transaxle cooler pipes retainer nut and tighten to 62 inch lbs. (7 Nm).

42. Install the torque converter to flywheel bolts and tighten to 44 ft. lbs. (60 Nm).

43. Install the starter.

44. Install the frame as follows:

   a. Lower the vehicle on to the frame.

   b. Install the frame reinforcements.

   c. Install the front frame bolts and hand tighten only.

   d. Install the reinforcement bolts and hand tighten only.

   e. Install the rear frame bolts. Tighten to 74 ft. lbs. (100 Nm) , plus an additional 90 degrees.

   f. Tighten the front frame bolts. Tighten to 74 ft. lbs. (100 Nm) , plus an additional 90 degrees.

   g. Install the cradle support bolts. Tighten to 74 ft. lbs. (100 Nm).

   h. Raise the vehicle.

   i. Install the rear transmission mount bracket fasteners. Tighten the transaxle mount to transmission bolts to 66 ft. lbs. (90 Nm) and the transaxle to mount bracket through bolt to 66 ft. lbs. (90 Nm).

   j. Install the front transmission mount bracket bolt. Tighten the transaxle mount to transmission bolts to 66 ft. lbs. (90 Nm) and the transaxle to mount bracket through bolt to 66 ft. lbs. (90 Nm).

   k. Install the power steering gear mounting bolts.

   l. Connect the steering gear to the intermediate shaft.

   m. Install both stabilizer links to the stabilizer bar. Tighten the stabilizer link nut to 48 ft. lbs. (65 Nm).

   n. Install the tie rod ends to the steering knuckles.

   o. Install the lower ball joints to the steering knuckles. Tighten the ball stud to steering knuckle pinch nut to 37 ft. lbs. (50 Nm). Reverse the nut ¾ of a turn. Tighten to 37 ft. lbs. (50 Nm) plus an additional 60 degrees.

   p. Install the front fender liner.

   q. Install the engine splash shield. Remove the engine support fixture.

45. Connect the intermediate shaft to the steering gear shaft.

46. Install the new steering gear pinch bolt to the intermediate shaft Tighten the steering gear pinch bolt to 36 ft. lbs. (49 Nm).

47. Tighten the torque converter bolts to 37 ft. lbs. (50 Nm)

48. Connect the ball joints to the steering knuckles.

49. Connect the stabilizer shaft links to the stabilizer shaft.

50. Connect the tie rods to the steering knuckle.

51. Connect the wiring harness to the VSS.

52. Install the transaxle brace.

53. Install the transaxle brace bolts. Tighten to 39 ft. lbs. (53 Nm)

54. Install the front splash shields.

55. Install the catalytic converters.

56. Install the front wheel and tire assemblies.

57. Lower the vehicle.

58. Install the left transaxle mount.

59. Install the upper transaxle to engine bolts and studs. Tighten to 55 ft. lbs. (75 Nm)

60. Untie the radiator, air conditioning condenser, and fan module assembly.

61. Remove the engine support fixture.

62. Install the radiator outlet pipe.

63. Connect the transaxle wiring harness to the main transaxle electrical connector, and the PNP switch.

64. Install the shift cable bracket.

65. Install the transaxle shift control cable to the cable bracket.

66. Install the retainer to the transaxle shift control cable.

67. Connect the transaxle shift control cable terminal to the transaxle manual shift lever pin.

68. Install the battery tray.

69. Connect the air cleaner outlet duct.

70. Add automatic transmission fluid (ATF) and verify the proper fluid level of the transaxle.

71. Prime the auxiliary fluid pump.

➡**It is recommended that Transmission Adaptive Pressure (TAP) information be reset. Reset the TAP values using a scan tool will erase all learned values in all cells. As a result, the ECM, PCM, or TCM will need to relearn TAP values. Transmission performance may be affected as new TAP values are learned.**

72. Reset the TAP values by selecting the following:

- Scan tool
- Special functions
- Transmission output controls
- Reset transmission adapts

73. Road test the vehicle.

3.5L Engine

See Figure 12.

1. Remove the air cleaner outlet duct.

2. Disconnect the negative battery cable. Refer

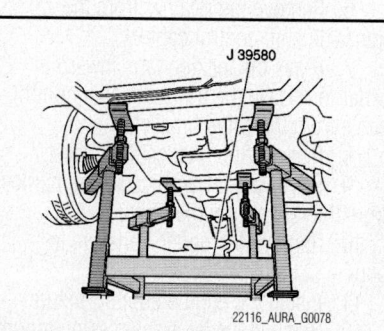

Fig. 12 Lower the vehicle until the frame contacts the engine support stand—3.5L engine

3. Disconnect the transaxle wiring harness from the transaxle and the Park Neutral Position (PNP) switch.

4. Remove the shift cable bracket front bolt and shift cable from the lever.

5. Remove the transmission wiring harness from the retainer on the transmission.

6. Disconnect bank 2, Oxygen Sensor (O2S) sensor 1 electrical connector.

7. Remove the left exhaust manifold heat shield.

8. Remove the exhaust manifold heat shield.

9. Remove the front exhaust pipe nuts.

10. Remove the upper transmission to engine bolts and stud.

11. Install the engine support fixture.

12. Support the radiator and condenser from above using the condenser tabs on each side.

13. Raise the vehicle.

14. Remove the front wheels and tires.

15. Disconnect the bank 2, O2S sensor 2 electrical connector.

16. Remove the left catalytic converter to right catalytic converter nuts.

17. Remove the left catalytic converter.

18. Remove the steering gear intermediate shaft.

➡ **It is only necessary to remove the control arms from the frame if the frame is being replaced.**

19. Remove the frame as follows:

a. Support the radiator and condenser from above.

b. Raise the vehicle on a hoist.

20. Remove the front fender liner.

a. Remove the engine splash shield.

b. Remove the lower ball joints from the steering knuckles.

c. Remove the tie rod ends from the steering knuckles.

d. Remove both stabilizer links from the stabilizer bar.

e. Remove the power steering gear mounting bolts and secure the gear out of the way using mechanic's wire, being sure not to overextend the intermediate shaft.

f. Remove the engine mount fasteners from the frame.

g. Remove the front transmission mount bolt from the frame.

h. Remove the left transmission mount fasteners from the frame.

i. Remove the rear transmission mount bracket fasteners from the frame.

j. Remove the brake lines from the retainers on the frame.

k. Remove the power steering outlet pipe/hose from the frame. .

l. Remove the rear catalytic converter.

m. Lower the vehicle until the frame contacts the engine support stand.

n. Remove the reinforcement bolts.

o. Remove the front frame bolts.

p. Remove the rear frame bolts.

q. Remove the frame reinforcements.

r. Raise the vehicle off of the frame.

21. Disconnect the wheel drive shafts from the transaxle.

22. Remove the 3 bolts from the transmission brace near the right axle shaft.

23. Remove the oil pan to bellhousing bolts and bracket.

24. Remove the flywheel inspection cover.

25. Remove the starter.

26. Mark the relationship of the flywheel to the torque converter for reassembly.

27. Remove the torque converter to flywheel bolts.

28. Remove the transmission oil cooler lines by removing the nut holding the bracket to the transaxle case.

29. Disconnect the Vehicle Speed Sensor (VSS) wiring harness from the sensor.

30. Disconnect the rear Heated Oxygen Sensor (HO2S) harness from the rear transmission mount.

31. Remove the remaining (rear) bolt from the shift cable bracket.

32. Remove the front transmission mount bracket from the transmission.

33. Use a transmission jack in order to support the transmission.

34. Remove the remaining bellhousing bolts and separate the transmission from the engine.

35. Lower the transmission with the transmission jack far enough to remove the transmission.

To install:

36. Position the transaxle in the vehicle.

37. Install the lower transmission to engine bolts and tighten to 66 ft. lbs. (90 Nm).

38. Install the front transmission mount bracket to the transmission.

39. Install the wheel drive shafts to the transaxle.

40. Connect the wiring harness to the VSS.

41. Install the torque converter to flywheel bolts and tighten to 46 ft. lbs. (62 Nm).

42. Install the starter.

43. Install the flywheel inspection cover bolts and tighten to 89 inch lbs. (10 Nm).

44. Connect the transaxle oil cooler pipes to the transaxle. Tighten the pipes to 70 inch lbs. (8 Nm).

45. Install the oil pan to bellhousing bracket and bolts. Tighten the bolts to 53 ft. lbs. (72 Nm).

46. Install the 3 bolts to the transmission brace at the final drive area and tighten.

47. Remove the transmission jack.

48. Install the frame as follows:

a. Lower the vehicle on to the frame.

b. Install the frame reinforcements.

c. Install the front frame bolts and hand tighten only.

d. Install the reinforcement bolts and hand tighten only.

e. Tighten the rear frame bolts. Tighten to 74 ft. lbs. (100 Nm) , plus an additional 90 degrees.

f. Tighten the front frame bolts. Tighten to 74 ft. lbs. (100 Nm) , plus an additional 90 degrees.

g. Install the reinforcement bolts. Tighten to 74 ft. lbs. (100 Nm).

h. Raise the vehicle.

i. Install the power steering outlet pipe/hose to the frame.

j. Install the brake lines to the retainers on the frame.

k. Install the rear transmission mount bracket fasteners. Tighten the transaxle mount to transmission bolts to 37 ft. lbs. (50 Nm) and the transaxle to mount bracket through bolt to 66 ft. lbs. (90 Nm).

l. Install the left transmission mount fasteners to the frame. Tighten the transmission mount nuts to 37 ft. lb. (50 Nm).

m. Install the front transmission mount bracket bolt. Tighten the transaxle mount to transmission bolts to 66 ft. lbs. (90 Nm) and the transaxle to mount bracket through bolt to 66 ft. lbs. (90 Nm).

n. Install the engine mount fasteners to the frame. Tighten the nuts/bolts to 37 ft. lbs. (50 Nm).

o. Install the power steering gear mounting fasteners.

p. Install both stabilizer links to the stabilizer bar. Tighten to 48 ft. lbs. (65 Nm) plus an additional 180 degrees.

q. Install the tie rod ends to the steering knuckles.

r. Install the lower ball joints to the steering knuckles. Tighten the ball stud to steering knuckle pinch nut to 37 ft. lbs. (50 Nm). Reverse the nut ¾ of a turn. Tighten to 37 ft. lbs. (50 Nm) plus an additional 60 degrees.

s. Install the rear catalytic converter.

t. Install the front fender liner.

u. Install the engine splash shield.

v. Lower the vehicle.

w. Remove the temporary radiator and condenser support.

x. Remove the engine support fixture.

49. Install the engine splash shields.

50. Install the front wheels and tires.

51. Lower the vehicle.

52. Remove the radiator and condenser support and the engine support fixture.

53. Install the upper transmission to engine bolts and stud and tighten to 66 ft. lbs. (90 Nm).

54. Install the shift cable bracket and shift cable to the lever.

55. Install the remaining components in the reverse order of removal.

56. Connect bank 2, O2 sensor 2 electrical connector.

57. Connect the negative battery cable.

58. Add automatic transmission fluid (ATF) and verify the proper fluid level of the transaxle.

➡**It is recommended that Transmission Adaptive Pressure (TAP) information be reset. Reset the TAP values using a scan tool will erase all learned values in all cells. As a result, the ECM, PCM, or TCM will need to relearn TAP values. Transmission performance may be affected as new TAP values are learned.**

59. Reset the TAP values by selecting the following:
- Scan tool
- Special functions
- Transmission output controls
- Reset transmission adapts

60. Road test the vehicle.

6T70/6T75 Transaxle

3.6L Engine

See Figure 13.

1. Remove the battery tray.

2. Remove the transmission range select lever cable and bracket.

3. Drain the transmission fluid.

4. Remove the wire harness retainer from the control valve body cover stud.

5. Disconnect the control valve body Transmission Control Module (TCM) electrical connector.

6. Remove the transmission fluid cooler pipe retainer nut.

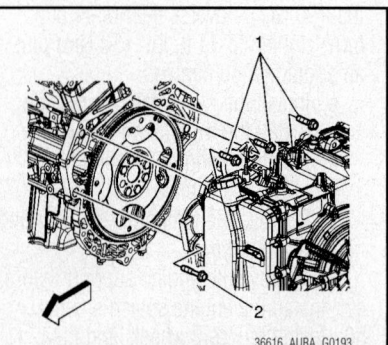

Fig. 13 Locating the upper transmission to engine bolts (1)

36616_AURA_G0193

7. Remove the transmission fluid cooler inlet hose and seal from the transmission.

8. Plug and/or cap the hose and transmission to prevent contamination.

9. Remove the transmission fluid cooler pipe retainer nut.

10. Remove the transmission fluid cooler outlet hose and seal from the transmission.

11. Plug and/or cap the hose and transmission to prevent contamination.

12. Disconnect both pipes from the retainer.

13. Remove the upper transmission to engine bolts.

14. Remove the frame as follows:
  a. Install the engine support fixture.
  b. Support the radiator and condenser from above.
  c. Raise the vehicle on a hoist.
  d. Remove the tire and wheel assemblies.
  e. Remove the front fender liner.
  f. Remove the engine splash shield.
  g. Remove the lower ball joints from the steering knuckles.
  h. Remove the tie rod ends from the steering knuckles.
  i. Remove both stabilizer links from the stabilizer bar.
  j. Remove the power steering gear mounting bolts and secure the gear out of the way using mechanic's wire or equivalent, being sure not to overextend the intermediate shaft.
  k. Remove the engine mount fasteners from the frame.
  l. Remove the front transmission mount bolt from the frame.
  m. Remove the left transmission mount fasteners from the frame.
  n. Remove the rear transmission mount bracket fasteners from the frame.
  o. Remove the brake lines from the retainers on the frame.
  p. Remove the power steering outlet pipe/hose from the frame.
  q. Remove the rear catalytic converter.
  r. Lower the vehicle until the frame contacts the engine support fixture.
  s. Remove the reinforcement bolts.
  t. Remove the front frame bolts.
  u. Remove the rear frame bolts.
  v. Remove the frame reinforcements.
  w. Raise the vehicle off of the frame.

15. Disconnect the wheel drive shafts from the transmission.

16. Remove the intermediate drive shaft.

17. Remove the front transmission mount from the transmission.

18. Remove the starter.

19. Mark the relationship of the flywheel to the torque converter for reassembly.

20. Remove the torque converter to flywheel bolts.

21. Use a transmission jack in order to support the transmission.

22. Remove the flywheel inspection cover bolts.

23. Remove the flywheel inspection cover.

24. Remove the remaining transmission bolts.

➡**Ensure the torque converter remains securely in place on the transmission input shaft while separating and removing the transmission.**

25. Separate the transmission from the engine.

26. Lower the transmission with the transmission jack far enough to remove the transmission.

To install:

27. Raise the transmission with the transmission jack and position the transmission to the engine.

28. Install the transmission bolts to 55 ft. lbs. (75 Nm).

29. Install the flywheel inspection cover and bolts. Tighten the bolts to 55 ft. lbs. (75 Nm).

30. Remove the transmission jack.

31. Install the torque converter to flywheel bolts. Tighten the bolts to 46 ft. lbs. (62 Nm).

32. Install the starter.

33. Install the front transmission mount to the transmission. Tighten the nut to 66 ft. lbs. (90 Nm) and the bolts to 37 ft. lbs. (50 Nm).

34. Install the rear transmission mount to the transmission. Tighten the transaxle mount to transmission bolts to 37 ft. lbs. (50 Nm) and the transaxle to mount bracket through bolt to 66 ft. lbs. (90 Nm).

35. Install the transmission brace.

36. Install the transmission brace bolts. Tighten the bolts to 37 ft. lbs. (50 Nm)

37. Install the intermediate drive shaft.

38. Install the wheel drive shafts to transmission.

39. Install the frame as follows:
  a. Lower the vehicle on to the frame.
  b. Install the frame reinforcements.
  c. Install the front frame bolts and hand tighten only.
  d. Install the reinforcement bolts and hand tighten only.
  e. Tighten the rear frame bolts. Tighten to 74 ft. lbs. (100 Nm) , plus an additional 90 degrees.
  f. Tighten the front frame bolts. Tighten to 74 ft. lbs. (100 Nm) , plus an additional 90 degrees.
  g. Install the reinforcement bolts. Tighten to 74 ft. lbs. (100 Nm).

h. Raise the vehicle.

i. Install the power steering outlet pipe/hose to the frame.

j. Install the brake lines to the retainers on the frame.

k. Install the rear transmission mount bracket fasteners. Tighten the transaxle mount to transmission bolts to 37 ft. lbs. (50 Nm) and the transaxle to mount bracket through bolt to 66 ft. lbs. (90 Nm).

l. Install the left transmission mount fasteners to the frame. Tighten the transaxle mount to transmission bolts to 66 ft. lbs. (90 Nm) and the transaxle to mount bracket through bolt to 66 ft. lbs. (90 Nm).

m. Install the front transmission mount bracket bolt. Tighten the transaxle mount to transmission bolts to 66 ft. lbs. (90 Nm) and the transaxle to mount bracket through bolt to 66 ft. lbs. (90 Nm).

n. Install the engine mount fasteners to the frame. Tighten the nuts/bolts to 38 ft. lbs. (50 Nm).

o. Install the power steering gear mounting fasteners.

p. Install both stabilizer links to the stabilizer bar. Tighten to 48 ft. lbs. (65 Nm) plus an additional 180 degrees.

q. Install the tie rod ends to the steering knuckles.

r. Install the lower ball joints to the steering knuckles. Tighten the ball stud to steering knuckle pinch nut to 37 ft. lbs. (50 Nm). Reverse the nut ¾ of a turn. Tighten to 37 ft. lbs. (50 Nm) plus an additional 60 degrees.

s. Install the rear catalytic converter.

t. Install the front fender liner.

u. Install the engine splash shield.

v. Lower the vehicle.

w. Remove the temporary radiator and condenser support.

x. Remove the engine support fixture.

40. Install the upper transmission to engine bolt. Tighten the bolts to 55 ft. lbs. (75 Nm).

41. Install the transmission fluid cooler outlet and inlet hoses and seal to the transmission.

42. Install the transmission fluid cooler pipe retainer nut. Tighten to 16 ft. lbs. (22 Nm).

43. Install the remaining components in the reverse order of removal.

44. Fill the transmission with fluid.

➡**It is recommended that Transmission Adaptive Pressure (TAP) information be reset. Reset the TAP values using a scan tool will erase all learned values in all cells. As a result, the ECM, PCM, or TCM will need to relearn TAP val-**

ues. Transmission performance may be affected as new TAP values are learned.

45. Reset the TAP values by selecting the following:
- Scan tool
- Special functions
- Transmission output controls
- Reset transmission adapts

46. Road test the vehicle.

FRONT AXLE SHAFT, BEARING & SEAL

REMOVAL & INSTALLATION

1. Remove the halfshaft.
2. Remove the intermediate shaft bolts and the shaft.

➡**Use care when removing the intermediate drive shaft from the transmission as not to damage the seal.**

To install:

3. Installation is the reverse of removal. Tighten the intermediate shaft bolts to 44 ft. lbs. (60 Nm).

➡**A seal protector such as J-44394 must be installed into the differential output shaft seal prior to removing and installing the intermediate shaft. Failure to install the tool as indicated may cause the splines of the intermediate shaft to cut the differential output seal.**

FRONT HALFSHAFTS

REMOVAL & INSTALLATION

See Figure 14.

✷✷ CAUTION

To prevent personal injury and/or component damage, do not allow the weight of the vehicle to load the front wheels, or attempt to operate the vehicle, when the wheel drive shaft(s) or wheel drive shaft nut(s) are removed. To do so may cause the inner bearing race to separate, resulting in damage to brake and suspension components and loss of vehicle control.

➡**Wheel drive shaft boots, seals and clamps should be protected from sharp objects any time service is performed on or near the wheel drive shaft(s). Damage to the boot(s), the seal(s) or the clamp(s) may cause lubricant to leak from the joint and lead to increased noise and possible failure of the wheel drive shaft.**

1. Raise and suitably support the vehicle.
2. Remove the wheel and the tire.
3. Insert a brass drift or punch between the brake rotor cooling fins and the brake caliper mounting bracket.
4. Using the appropriate size socket and breaker bar, loosen the wheel drive shaft nut.

➡**Do NOT re-use the wheel drive shaft nut. Discard the nut and replace with a NEW one.**

5. Remove the front wheel drive shaft nut from the wheel drive shaft.
6. Using the hub spindle remover (J 42129), separate the brake rotor and wheel bearing/hub assembly.
7. Remove the outer tie rod assembly from the steering knuckle.
8. Remove the ball joint from the steering knuckle.

➡**A seal protector such as J-44394 must be installed into the differential output shaft seal prior to removing and installing the wheel drive shaft. Failure to install the tool as indicated may cause the splines of the wheel drive shaft to cut the differential output seal.**

9. Using the slide hammer (J 2619-01), the axle shaft remover extension (J 29794), and the axle shaft remover (J 33008-A), remove the wheel drive shaft from the vehicle.

To install:

➡**A seal protector such as J-44394 must be installed into the differential output shaft seal prior to removing and installing the wheel drive shaft. Failure to install the tool as indicated may cause the splines of the wheel drive shaft to cut the differential output seal.**

10. Install a seal protector such as J-44394 into the differential output shaft seal.

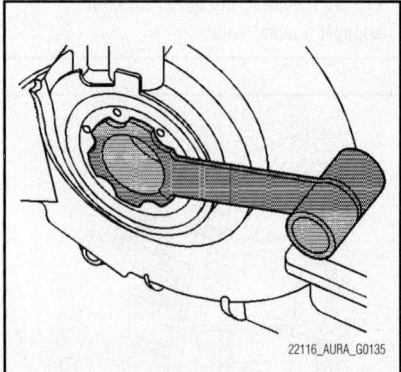

22116_AURA_G0135

Fig. 14 A seal protector such as J-44394 must be installed into the differential output shaft seal prior to removing and installing the wheel drive shaft

➤In order to prevent lubricant leaks, use care when installing the wheel drive shaft to the differential. Do not damage the oil seal. Replace the oil seal if it becomes nicked, distorted, or otherwise damaged.

11. Carefully install the wheel drive shaft into the differential until the splines are past the seal protector.

12. Carefully remove the seal protector from the differential output shaft seal.

13. Carefully continue installing the wheel drive shaft into the differential until the retaining ring is fully seated.

14. Verify the front wheel drive shaft retaining ring is properly seated by grasping the inner housing and pull the inner housing outward.

15. Install the front wheel drive shaft into the front wheel bearing/hub.

16. Install the ball joint to the steering knuckle.

17. Install the outer tie rod assembly to the steering knuckle.

18. Install the NEW wheel drive shaft nut on the wheel drive shaft.

19. Insert a drift or punch into the cooling fin of the brake rotor caliper and against the brake caliper mounting bracket.

20. Using a torque wrench and the appropriate size socket, tighten the wheel drive shaft nut to 159 ft. lbs. (215 Nm).

21. Install the wheel and the tire.

22. Lower the vehicle.

23. Inspect the transaxle fluid level.

ENGINE COOLING

ENGINE FAN

REMOVAL & INSTALLATION

See Figures 15 and 16.

1. Drain and recycle the engine coolant.

2. Remove the air cleaner outlet air duct on the 2.4L engine.

3. Remove the air cleaner inlet air duct on the 3.5L and 3.6L engines

4. Remove the upper radiator air deflector.

5. Remove the transmission oil cooler pipes from the radiator.

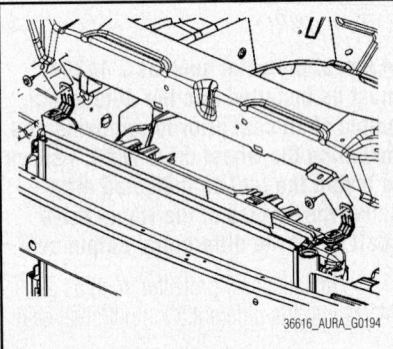

Fig. 15 Locating the upper radiator support bracket bolts

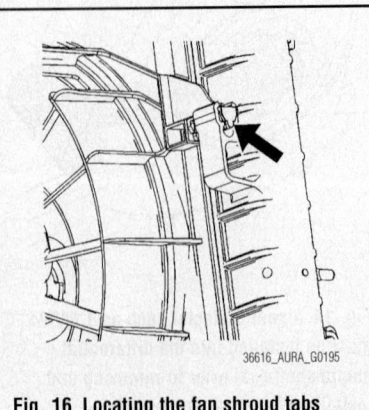

Fig. 16 Locating the fan shroud tabs

6. Loop a rope around each of the upper 2 tabs of the condenser and tie a rope around the upper tie bar.

7. Remove the upper radiator support bracket bolts.

8. Remove the upper radiator support brackets.

9. Pry upward on the fan shroud tabs at the radiator clips to release the fan shroud from the radiator.

10. Remove the lower radiator air deflector.

11. Lower the vehicle.

12. Remove the radiator inlet hose from the radiator.

13. Remove the radiator outlet hose from the radiator.

14. Disconnect the cooling fan wire harness connectors.

15. Remove the A/C compressor and condenser hose assembly.

16. Raise the vehicle.

17. Remove the lower radiator support bracket bolts.

18. Remove the lower radiator support brackets.

19. Remove the transmission oil cooler pipe clip from the fan shroud.

20. Remove the fan assembly.

To install:

21. Install the fan shroud assembly.

22. Install the transmission oil cooler pipes to the radiator.

23. Install the transmission oil cooler pipe clip to the fan shroud.

24. Install the lower radiator support brackets.

25. Install the lower radiator support bracket bolts and tighten to 44 ft. lbs. (60 Nm).

26. Install the cooling fan wire harness connectors.

27. Install the radiator outlet hose to the radiator.

28. Install the lower radiator air deflector.

29. Lower the vehicle.

30. Snap fan shroud tabs into the radiator clips.

31. Remove the rope attached to the condenser and upper tie bar.

32. Install the upper radiator support brackets.

33. Install the upper radiator support bracket bolts and tighten to 89 inch lbs. (10 Nm).

34. Install the radiator inlet hose to the radiator.

35. Install the A/C compressor and condenser hose assembly.

36. Install the upper radiator air deflector.

37. Install the air duct.

38. Fill the cooling system.

39. Inspect the transmission fluid level.

RADIATOR

REMOVAL & INSTALLATION

2.4L Engine

See Figures 17 and 18.

1. Remove the cooling fan and shroud assembly.

2. Remove and discard the condenser mounting bolts.

3. Push upward on the condenser and downward on the radiator to unsnap the condenser mounting tabs from the radiator clips.

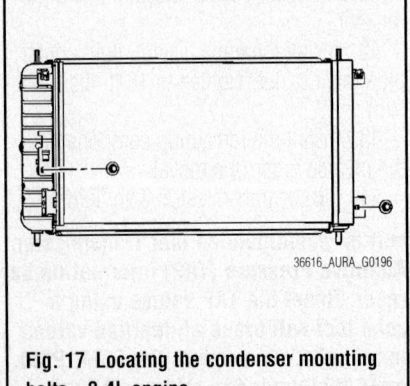

Fig. 17 Locating the condenser mounting bolts—2.4L engine

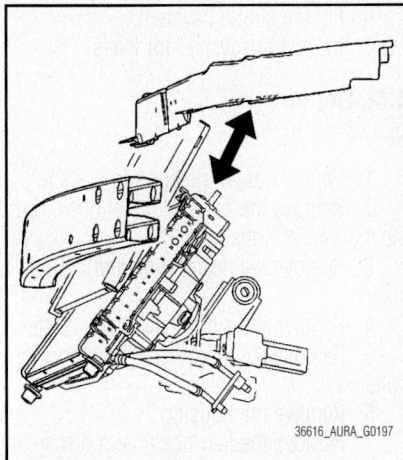

Fig. 18 Removing the radiator from the vehicle

4. Remove and discard the condenser mounting nuts from the radiator.

5. Remove the radiator from the vehicle.

To install:

6. Install the radiator to the vehicle.

7. Push upward on the radiator and downward on the condenser to snap the condenser mounting tabs into the radiator clips.

8. Install new condenser mounting nut to the radiator and tighten the nut to 53 inch lbs. (6 Nm).

9. Install new condenser mounting bolts and tighten to 53 inch lbs. (6 Nm).

10. Install the cooling fan and shroud assembly.

3.6L Engine

See Figures 19 through 22.

1. Drain and recycle the engine coolant.

2. Loop a rope around each of the upper 2 tabs of the condenser and tie the rope around the upper tie bar.

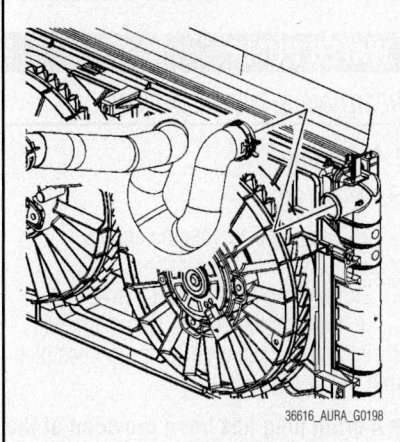

Fig. 19 Removing the radiator inlet hose from the radiator—3.6L engine

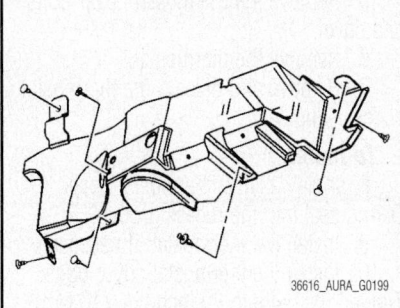

Fig. 20 Locating the right engine splash shield retainers

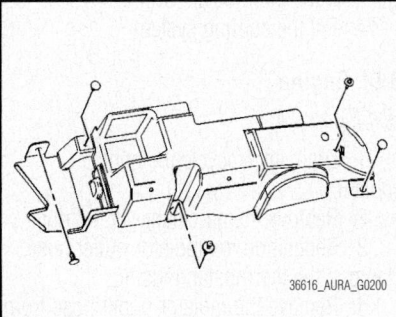

Fig. 21 Locating the left engine splash shield retainers

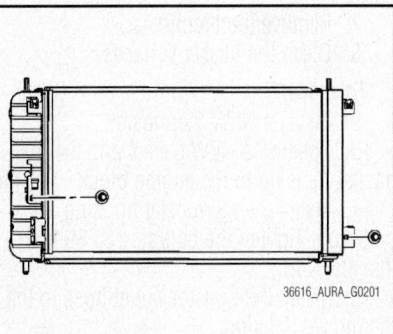

Fig. 22 Locating the condenser mounting bolts

3. Remove the upper radiator support brackets.

4. Reposition the radiator inlet hose clamp at the radiator.

5. Remove the radiator inlet hose from the radiator.

6. Remove the front air dam.

7. Remove the right engine splash shield retainers.

8. Remove the right engine splash shield.

9. Remove the left engine splash shield retainers.

10. Remove the left engine splash shield.

11. Reposition the radiator outlet hose clamp at the radiator.

12. Remove the radiator outlet hose from the radiator.

13. Remove the transmission oil cooler pipes from the transmission.

14. Remove the lower radiator support bracket bolts.

15. Remove the lower radiator support brackets.

16. Remove the radiator lower mounts.

17. Remove and discard the condenser mounting bolts from the radiator.

18. Push upward on the radiator and downward on the condenser to unsnap the condenser mounting tabs from the radiator clips.

19. Remove and discard the condenser mounting nuts from the radiator.

20. Remove the radiator air side seals.

21. Remove the radiator and cooling fan shroud assembly from the vehicle.

22. Pry upward on the fan shroud tabs at the radiator clips.

23. Remove the cooling fan and shroud assembly from the radiator.

To install:

24. Install the cooling fan and shroud assembly to the radiator.

25. Snap the fan shroud tabs into the radiator clips.

26. Install the radiator and cooling fan shroud assembly to the vehicle.

27. Install the radiator air side seals onto the condenser mounting tabs on the radiator.

➡The bolt retaining the condenser to the radiator end tank is a special length and should be the ONLY bolt used upon reinstallation. The use of a longer bolt will damage the radiator end tank.

➡Replace the condenser mounting bolts and nuts.

28. Install the condenser mounting nuts to the radiator.

29. Insert the condenser mounting tabs into the radiator clips.

30. Install the condenser to the radiator bolts and tighten to 53 inch lbs. (6 Nm).

31. Bend the radiator air side seals and insert the seals into the channel of the intake air splash shields.

➡The radiator air side seals must be in the proper position for proper air flow.

➡Replace the radiator lower mounts as a pair or vibration may result.

32. Install the radiator lower mounts.

33. Install the lower radiator support brackets and tighten the bolts to 44 ft. lbs. (60 Nm).
34. Install the transmission oil cooler pipes to the transmission.
35. Install the radiator outlet hose to the radiator.
36. Reposition the radiator outlet hose clamp at the radiator.

➡**Engine splash shields must be properly installed or reduced A/C and engine cooling system performance could occur.**

37. Install the left engine splash shield.
38. Install the left engine splash shield retainers.
39. Install the right engine splash shield.
40. Install the right engine splash shield retainers.
41. Install the front air dam.
42. Lower the vehicle.
43. Install the radiator inlet hose to the radiator.
44. Reposition the radiator inlet hose clamp at the radiator.
45. Remove the rope attached to the condenser and upper tie bar.
46. Install the upper radiator support brackets.
47. Fill the coolant.
48. Inspect the transmission fluid level.

THERMOSTAT

REMOVAL & INSTALLATION

2.4L Engine

See Figure 23.

1. Drain the cooling system.
2. Reposition the radiator outlet hose clamp at the thermostat cover.
3. Remove the radiator outlet hose from the thermostat cover.
4. Remove the battery tray.

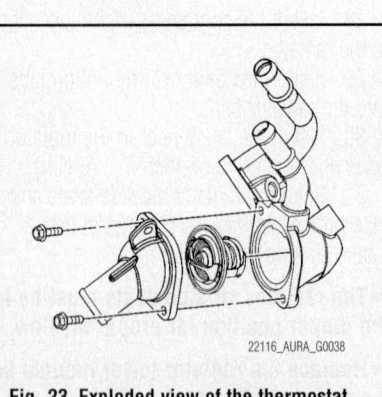

Fig. 23 Exploded view of the thermostat housing assembly—2.4L engine

5. Remove the thermostat cover bolts and cover.
6. Remove the thermostat.
7. Remove and discard the thermostat cover o-ring seal.

To install:

8. Install a NEW thermostat cover O-ring seal into the recess groove.
9. Install the thermostat, if necessary.
10. Install the thermostat cover bolts. Tighten the bolts to 89 inch lbs. (10 Nm).
11. Install the battery tray.
12. Install the radiator outlet hose to the thermostat cover.
13. Position the radiator outlet hose clamp at the thermostat cover.
14. Fill the cooling system.

3.5L Engine

See Figure 24.

1. Drain and recycle the engine coolant.
2. Remove the air cleaner outlet duct.
3. Reposition the radiator outlet hose clamp at the thermostat housing.
4. Remove the radiator outlet hose from the thermostat housing.
5. Remove the thermostat housing bolt/stud.
6. Remove the thermostat housing and gasket.
7. Remove the thermostat.
8. Clean the gasket surfaces.

To install:

9. Install a NEW thermostat.
10. Position a NEW gasket and the thermostat housing to the engine block.
11. Install the thermostat housing bolt/stud. Tighten the bolt/stud to 89 inch lbs. (10 Nm).
12. Install the radiator outlet hose to the thermostat housing.
13. Position the radiator outlet hose clamp at the thermostat housing.
14. Install the air cleaner outlet duct.

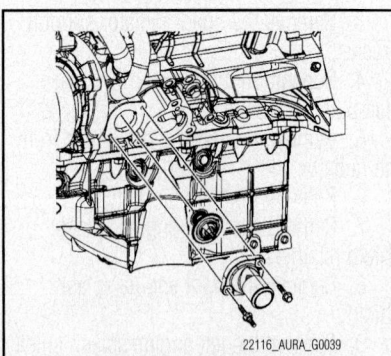

Fig. 24 Exploded view of the thermostat housing assembly—3.5L engine

15. Fill the cooling system.
16. Inspect the system for leaks

3.6L Engine

See Figure 25.

1. Partially drain the cooling system.
2. Remove the radiator outlet hose from the thermostat housing.
3. Remove the heater inlet and outlet hoses.
4. Remove the surge tank outlet hose.
5. Remove the thermostat housing bolts.
6. Remove the housing.
7. Remove the thermostat and discard the thermostat gasket.

To install:

8. Install the thermostat with a NEW thermostat gasket.
9. Install the thermostat housing bolts. Tighten the bolts to 89 inch lbs. (10 Nm).
10. Install the surge tank outlet hose.
11. Install the heater inlet and outlet hoses.
12. Install the radiator outlet hose to the thermostat housing.
13. Fill the cooling system.

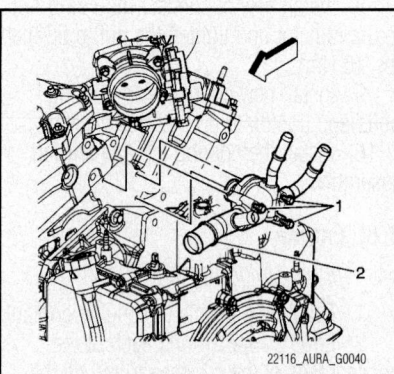

Fig. 25 Exploded view of the thermostat housing assembly—3.6L engine

WATER PUMP

REMOVAL & INSTALLATION

2.4L Engine

See Figure 26.

1. Drain and recycle the engine coolant.
2. Remove the thermostat housing.
3. Remove the engine splash shield.
4. Remove the water pump access plate from the front cover.

➡**A drain plug has been provided at the bottom of the water pump assembly for additional coolant drainage from the engine block and water pump.**

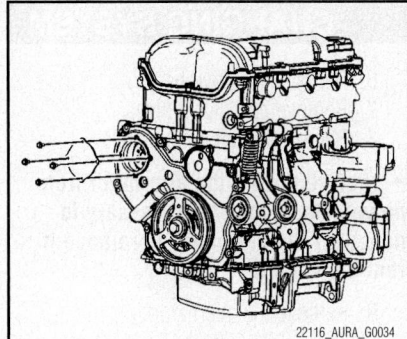

Fig. 26 Removing the thermostat housing—2.4L engine

5. Drain the coolant from the water pump using the plug at the bottom of the pump.

➡**The water pump holding tool supports the sprocket and chain during water pump service. The tool must be used or the balance shaft must be re-timed.**

6. Install a water pump holding tool such as J 43651 into position.

7. Tighten the bolts on the water pump holding tool into the threads on the water pump sprocket. Install the access cover bolts that were removed earlier to secure the water pump holding tool to the front cover assembly.

8. Remove the 3 inner water pump sprocket to water pump blots.

➡**Be sure to remove both water pump bolts from the front of the engine block.**

9. Remove the 2 water pump bolts.

10. Remove the rear 2 water pump bolts.

11. Remove the water pump.

12. Remove and discard the water pump O-ring seal.

To install:

➡**Prior to installing the water pump, read the entire procedure. This will help avoid balance shaft chain re-timing and ensure proper sealing.**

13. Install a NEW water pump O-ring seal.

➡**A guide pin can be created to aid in water pump alignment. Use a M6 m x 6 mm stud. Thread the pin into the water pump sprocket.**

14. Using the guide pin, align the pin with the water pump holding tool.

15. Position the water pump against the engine block and hand tighten the water pump bolts.

16. Install the inner water pump sprocket bolts. After 2 are snug, remove the guide

pin and install the 3rd bolt. Tighten the water pump bolts to 18 ft. lbs. (25 Nm).

17. Tighten the water pump sprocket bolts last to 89 inch lbs. (10 Nm).

18. Remove the water pump holding tool.

19. Install the water pump access plate and bolts and tighten to 89 inch lbs. (10 Nm).

20. Install the engine splash shield.

21. Install the thermostat housing.

3.5L Engine

See Figure 27.

1. Drain and recycle the engine coolant.

2. Loosen the water pump pulley bolts.

3. Remove the drive belt.

4. Remove the water pump pulley bolts and pulley.

5. Remove the water pump bolts.

6. Remove the water pump and gasket.

7. Clean the water pump mating surfaces.

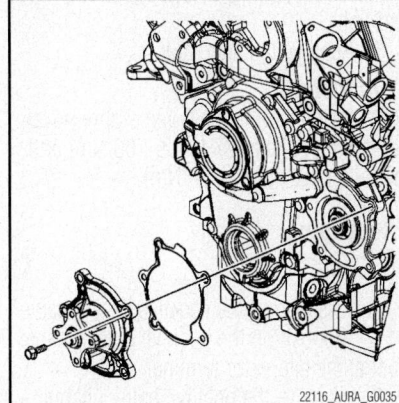

Fig. 27 Exploded view of the water pump assembly—3.5L engine

To install:

8. Position a NEW water pump gasket and the water pump to the engine front cover.

9. Install the water pump bolts and tighten to 18 ft. lbs. (25 Nm).

10. Install the water pump pulley and bolts.

11. Install the drive belt.

12. Tighten the water pump bolts to 18 ft. lbs. (25 Nm).

13. Fill the cooling system.

14. Inspect for leaks.

3.6L Engine

See Figures 28 and 29.

1. Drain and recycle the engine coolant.

2. Remove the drive belt, as outlined in the Engine Mechanical Section.

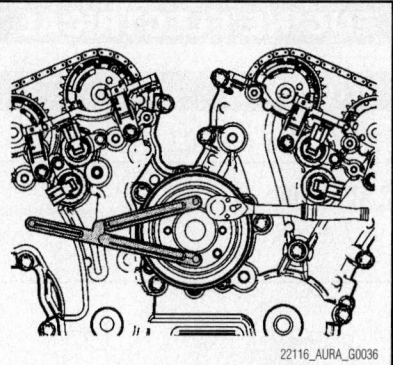

Fig. 28 Use the a water pump pulley holding tool such as EN 46104 in order to retain the water pump pulley—3.6L engine

3. Use a water pump pulley holding tool such as EN 46104 in order to retain the water pump pulley.

4. Remove the water pump pulley bolts.

5. Remove the water pump pulley.

6. Remove the water pump bolts.

7. Remove the water pump.

8. Remove and DISCARD the water pump seal.

9. Carefully clean the water pump sealing surfaces.

To install:

10. Install a NEW water pump seal.

11. Install the water pump.

12. Install the water pump bolts and tighten to 89 inch lbs. (10 Nm).

13. Install the water pump pulley and the water pump pulley bolts.

14. Use the water pump pulley holding tool such as EN 46104 in order to retain the water pump pulley.

15. Install and tighten the water pump pulley bolts to 89 inch lbs. (10 Nm).

16. Install the drive belt.

17. Fill the cooling system.

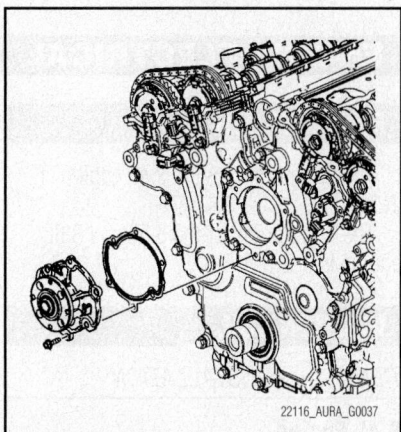

Fig. 29 Exploded view of the water pump assembly—3.6L engine

ENGINE ELECTRICAL | **CHARGING SYSTEM**

ALTERNATOR

REMOVAL & INSTALLATION

2.4L Engine

See Figure 30.

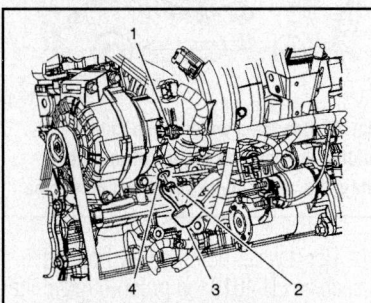

1. Generator electrical connector
2. Engine harness terminal lead to generator nut
3. Rubber boot
4. Engine harness terminal

36616_AURA_G0204

Fig. 30 Disconnecting the generator

1. Disconnect the negative battery cable.
2. Remove the drive belt.
3. Remove the generator electrical connector.
4. Reposition the rubber boot.
5. Remove the engine harness terminal lead to generator nut.
6. Remove the engine harness terminal from the generator stud.
7. Remove the generator fasteners.
8. Remove the generator.

To install:

9. Installation is the reverse of removal, tighten the bolts to 37 ft. lbs. (50 Nm) and the nuts to 22 ft. lbs. (30 Nm).

3.5L Engine

See Figure 31.

22116_AURA_G0006

Fig. 31 Alternator mounting—3.5L engine

1. Disconnect the negative battery cable.
2. Remove the drive belt.
3. Remove the alternator electrical connections.
4. Remove the alternator mounting nuts and bolts.
5. Remove the alternator.

To install:

6. Installation is the reverse of removal, tighten the bolts to 37 ft. lbs. (50 Nm) and the nuts to 22 ft. lbs. (30 Nm).

3.6L Engine

See Figure 32.

1. Disconnect the negative battery cable.
2. Reposition the positive battery cable boot at the alternator terminal.
3. Remove the positive battery cable nut at the alternator.
4. Remove the positive battery cable terminal from the alternator.
5. Disconnect the engine harness electrical connector from the alternator.

6. Remove the drive belt.
7. Remove the idler pulley.
8. Remove the alternator bolts.

➡ **When removing the alternator from the vehicle, it may be necessary to maneuver the alternator to remove it from the vehicle.**

9. Remove the alternator.

To install:

10. Install the alternator.
11. Loosely install the alternator bolts.
12. Install the idler pulley. Tighten the bolts to 43 ft. lbs. (58 Nm).
13. Tighten the generator bolts to 37 ft. lbs. (50 Nm).
14. Install the drive belt.
15. Connect the engine harness electrical connector to the alternator.
16. Install the positive battery cable terminal to the alternator.
17. Install the positive battery cable nut at the alternator. Tighten to 15 ft. lbs. (20 Nm).
18. Position the positive battery cable boot at the alternator terminal.
19. Connect the negative battery cable.

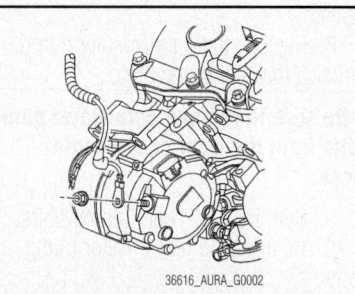

36616_AURA_G0002

Fig. 32 Connecting the electrical harness electrical connector to the alternator— 3.6L engine

ENGINE ELECTRICAL | **IGNITION SYSTEM**

FIRING ORDER

The firing order for the 2.4L engine is 1-3-4-2.
The firing order for the 3.5L and 3.6L engine is 1-2-3-4-5-6.

IGNITION COIL

REMOVAL & INSTALLATION

2.4L Engine

See Figure 33.

1. Remove the intake manifold cover.

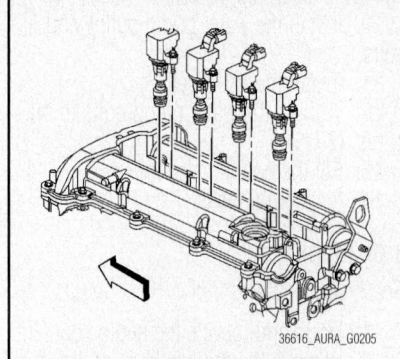

36616_AURA_G0205

Fig. 33 Removing the ignition coils

2. Disconnect the engine wiring harness electrical connectors from the ignition coil.
3. Remove the ignition coil bolt(s).
4. Remove the ignition coil(s).

To install:

5. Installation is the reverse of removal. Tighten the coil bolts to 89 inch lbs. (10 Nm).

3.5L Engine

1. Remove the intake manifold cover.
2. Disconnect the engine wiring harness electrical connector from the Manifold Absolute Pressure (MAP) sensor.

3. Disconnect the engine wiring harness electrical connector from the ignition coil.

4. Reposition the brake booster vacuum hose clamp at the upper intake manifold.

5. Remove the brake booster vacuum hose from the upper intake manifold.

6. Remove the left side spark plug wires from the ignition coils.

7. Remove the right side spark plug wires from the ignition coils.

8. Remove the Heated Oxygen Sensor (HO2S) electrical connector rosebud clip from the ignition coil bracket.

9. Remove the ignition coil bolts and nuts.

10. Remove the ignition coil.

To install:

11. Install the ignition coil.

12. Install the ignition coil bolts and nuts and tighten to 18 ft. lbs. (25 Nm).

13. Install the HO2S electrical connector rosebud clip to the ignition coil bracket.

14. Install the right side spark plug wires to the ignition coils.

15. Install the left side spark plug wires to the ignition coils.

16. Install the brake booster vacuum hose to the upper intake manifold.

17. Position the brake booster vacuum hose clamp at the upper intake manifold.

18. Connect the engine wiring harness electrical connector to the ignition coil.

19. Connect the engine wiring harness electrical connector to the MAP sensor.

20. Install the intake manifold cover.

3.6L Engine

Bank 1

See Figure 34.

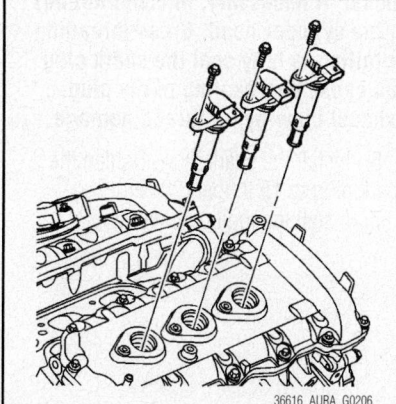

Fig. 34 Removing the ignition coils—3.6L engine (Bank 1)

1. Remove the fuel injector sight shield.

2. Disconnect the engine wiring harness electrical connector(s) from the ignition coil(s).

3. If removing the number 5 cylinder ignition coil, remove the Evaporative Emission (EVAP) canister purge tube.

4. If removing the number one ignition coil, remove the canister purge solenoid.

5. Remove the ignition coil bolt(s).

6. Remove the ignition coil(s).

To install:

7. Install the ignition coil(s).

8. Install the ignition coil bolt(s) and tighten to 89 inch lbs. (10 Nm).

9. If the number 5 cylinder ignition coil was removed, install the EVAP canister purge tube.

10. If the number one ignition coil was removed, install the canister purge solenoid.

11. Connect the engine wiring harness electrical connector(s) to the ignition coil(s).

12. Install the fuel injector sight shield.

Bank 2

See Figure 35.

Fig. 35 Removing the ignition coils—3.6L engine (Bank 2)

1. Remove the fuel injector sight shield.

2. Disconnect the engine wiring harness electrical connector(s) from the ignition coil(s).

3. Remove the ignition coil bolt(s).

4. Remove the ignition coil(s).

To install:

To install, reverse the removal procedure. Tighten the ignition coil bolts to 89 inch lbs. (10 Nm).

IGNITION TIMING

ADJUSTMENT

The ignition timing is controlled by the Powertrain Control Module (PCM). No adjustment is necessary or possible.

SPARK PLUGS

REMOVAL & INSTALLATION

2.4L Engine

See Figure 36.

✳✳ WARNING

This engine has aluminum cylinder heads. Do not remove the spark plugs from a hot engine, allow it to cool first. Removing the spark plugs from a hot engine may cause spark plug thread damage or cylinder head damage.

1. Remove the intake manifold cover.

2. Disconnect the engine wiring harness electrical connectors from the ignition coil.

3. Remove the ignition coil bolt(s).

4. Remove the ignition coil(s).

➡ Make sure that any water and or debris is blown out of the spark plug holes prior to removing the spark plugs.

5. Remove the spark plugs using a ⅝ inch spark plug socket.

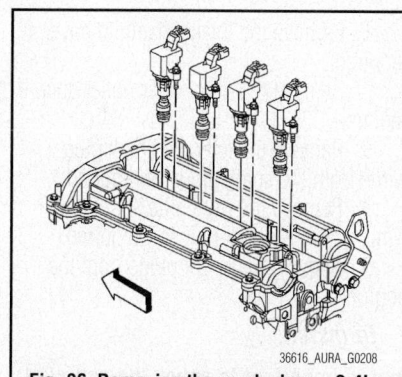

Fig. 36 Removing the spark plugs—2.4L engine

To install:

6. Installation is the reverse of removal. Tighten the spark plugs to 15 ft. lbs. (20 Nm) and the coil bolts to 89 inch lbs. (10 Nm).

3.5L Engine

See Figure 37.

➡ Allow the engine to cool before removing the spark plugs. Attempting to remove the spark plugs from a hot engine can cause the spark plugs to seize. This can damage the cylinder head threads.

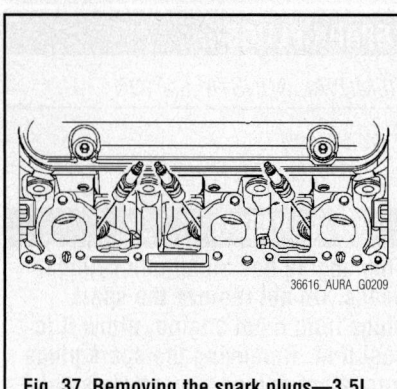

Fig. 37 Removing the spark plugs—3.5L engine

➡Clean the spark plug recess area before removing the spark plug. Failure to do so can result in engine damage due to dirt or foreign material entering the cylinder head, or in contamination of the cylinder head threads. Contaminated threads may prevent proper seating of the new spark plug.

➡Use only the spark plugs specified for use in the vehicle. Do not install spark plugs that are either hotter or colder than those specified for the vehicle. Installing spark plugs of another type can severely damage the engine.

1. Remove the intake manifold cover, if required.
2. Remove the air cleaner outlet duct, if required.
3. Remove the left side spark plug wires from the spark plugs, if required.
4. Remove the right side spark plug wires from the spark plugs, if required.
5. Remove the spark plugs from the engine.

To install:

➡It is important to check the gap of all new and reconditioned spark plugs before installation. Pre-set gaps may have changed during handling. Use a round wire feeler gauge to be sure of an accurate check, particularly on used plugs. Installing plugs with the wrong gap can cause poor engine performance and may even damage the engine.

➡Be sure plug threads smoothly into cylinder head and is fully seated. Use a thread chaser if necessary to clean threads in cylinder head. Cross-threading or failing to fully seat spark plug can cause overheating of plug, exhaust blow-by, or thread damage. Follow the recommended torque specifications carefully. Over or under-tightening can also cause severe damage to engine or spark plug.

6. Gap the NEW spark plugs to 0.040 inch.
7. Install the NEW spark plugs and tighten to 15 ft. lbs. (20 Nm).
8. Install the right side spark plug wires to the spark plugs, if required.
9. Install the left side spark plug wires to the spark plugs, if required.
10. Install the air cleaner outlet duct, if required.
11. Install the intake manifold cover, if required.

3.6L Engine

See Figure 38.

1. Remove the ignition coil(s).

❊❊ CAUTION

Wear safety glasses when using compressed air in order to prevent eye injury.

➡Clean the spark plug recess area before removing the spark plug. Failure to do so could result in engine damage because of dirt or foreign material entering the cylinder head, or by the contamination of the cylinder head threads. The contaminated threads may prevent the proper seating of the new plug. Use a thread chaser to clean the threads of any contamination.

2. Use compressed air in order to remove debris from the spark plug cavity.

➡Allow the engine to cool before removing the spark plugs. Attempting to remove the spark plugs from a hot engine may cause the plug threads to seize, causing damage to cylinder head threads.

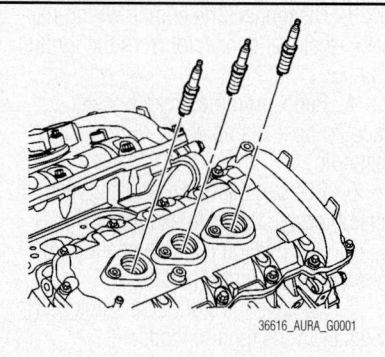

Fig. 38 Removing and installing spark plugs—3.6L engine

3. Remove the spark plug(s).

To install:

➡Use only the spark plugs specified for use in the vehicle. Do not install spark plugs that are either hotter or colder than those specified for the vehicle. Installing spark plugs of another type can severely damage the engine.

➡Check the gap of all new and reconditioned spark plugs before installation. The pre-set gaps may have changed during handling. Use a round feeler gage to ensure an accurate check. Installing the spark plugs with the wrong gap can cause poor engine performance and may even damage the engine.

4. Ensure that the spark plug is equivalent to the spark plug gap of 0.0433 inch.
5. Be sure that the spark plug threads smoothly into the cylinder head and the spark plug is fully seated.

➡Be sure that the spark plug threads smoothly into the cylinder head and the spark plug is fully seated. Use a thread chaser, if necessary, to clean threads in the cylinder head. Cross-threading or failing to fully seat the spark plug can cause overheating of the plug, exhaust blow-by, or thread damage.

6. Install the spark plug. Tighten the spark plug to 15 ft. lbs. (20 Nm).
7. Install the ignition coil(s).

ENGINE ELECTRICAL   **STARTING SYSTEM**

STARTER

REMOVAL & INSTALLATION

2.4L Engine (LAT)

See Figures 39 through 41.

1. Disconnect the negative battery cable.
2. Raise and support the vehicle.
3. Disconnect the engine wiring harness electrical connector from the generator control module coolant pump.

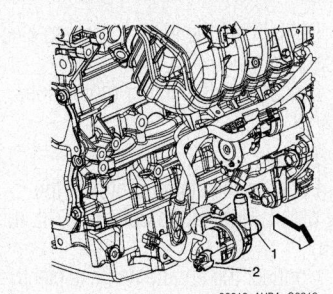

Fig. 39 Disconnecting the engine wiring harness electrical connector from the generator coolant pump—2.4L engine (LAT)

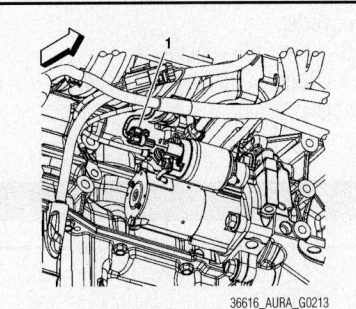

Fig. 40 Disconnecting the engine wiring harness electrical connector (1) from the starter—2.4L (LAT)

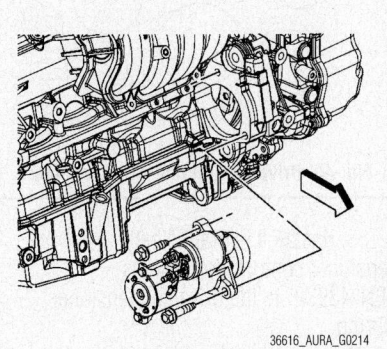

Fig. 41 Removing the starter—2.4L (LAT)

4. Remove the generator control module coolant pump bolt.
5. Remove the generator control module coolant pump (with the hoses attached) from the oil pan.
6. Reposition and secure the generator control module coolant pump (with the hoses attached) out of the way.
7. Disconnect the engine wiring harness electrical connector from the starter.
8. Remove the positive battery cable to starter motor nut.
9. Remove the positive battery cable lead from the starter motor.
10. Remove the starter motor bolts and starter.

To install:

11. Install the starter motor and bolts. Tighten to 39 ft. lbs. (53 Nm).
12. Install the positive battery cable lead to the starter motor.
13. Install the positive battery cable to starter motor nut. Tighten the nut to 89 inch lbs. (10 Nm).
14. Connect the engine wiring harness electrical connector to the starter.
15. Unsecure the generator control module coolant pump.
16. Position the generator control module coolant pump (with the hoses attached) to the oil pan. Ensure the anti-rotation tab is inserted into the hole in the oil pan.
17. Install the generator control module coolant pump bolt. Tighten the bolt to 16 ft. lbs. (22 Nm).
18. Connect the engine wiring harness electrical connector to the generator control module coolant pump.
19. Lower the vehicle.
20. Connect the negative battery cable.

2.4L Engine

See Figure 42.

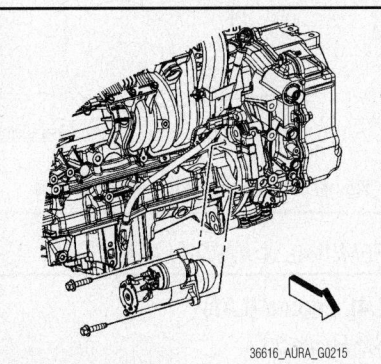

Fig. 42 Removing the starter motor—2.4L engine

1. Disconnect the negative battery cable.
2. Raise and support the vehicle.
3. Remove the "S" terminal connector from the starter solenoid.
4. Remove the engine harness lead from the starter.
5. Remove the positive battery cable nut from the starter solenoid.
6. Remove the positive battery cable and engine harness terminal from the starter solenoid.
7. Remove the starter motor bolts.
8. Remove the starter motor.

To install:

9. Install the starter motor.
10. Install the starter motor bolts and tighten to 30 ft. lbs. (40 Nm).
11. Install the engine harness terminal and positive battery cable to the starter solenoid.
12. Install the positive battery cable nut to the starter solenoid and tighten to 89 inch lbs. (10 Nm).
13. Install the engine harness lead to the starter.
14. Install the "S" terminal connector to the starter solenoid.
15. Lower the vehicle.
16. Connect the negative battery cable.

3.5L Engine

See Figures 43 and 44.

1. Disconnect the negative battery cable.
2. Raise the vehicle.
3. Remove the flywheel inspection cover bolts.
4. Remove the flywheel inspection cover.
5. Remove the electrical connections from the starter motor.

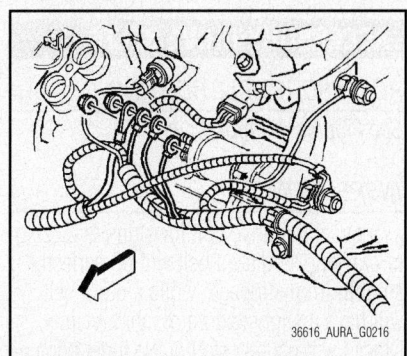

Fig. 43 Removing the electrical connections from the starter motor

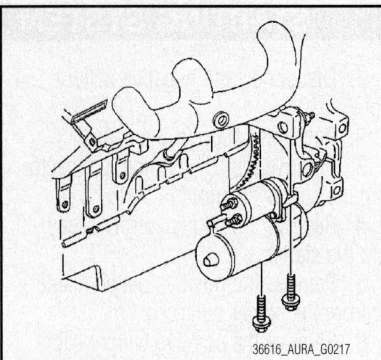

Fig. 44 Removing the starter motor—3.5L engine

6. Remove the starter motor mounting bolts.

7. Remove the starter motor.

To install:

➡**Before installing the starter motor to the engine, tighten the nut next to the cap on the solenoid BAT terminal. If this terminal is not tight in the solenoid cap, the cap may be damaged during installation of electrical connections and cause the starter motor to fail later.**

8. Install the starter motor to the engine. Tighten the bolts to 30 ft. lbs. (40 Nm).

9. Install the electrical connection to the battery terminal on the solenoid. Tighten to 13 ft. lbs. (17 Nm).

10. Install the electrical connections to the S terminal on the solenoid. Tighten the S terminal nut to 27 inch lbs. (3 Nm).

11. Install the flywheel inspection cover and bolts. Tighten the flywheel inspection cover bolts to 89 inch lbs. (10 Nm).

12. Lower the vehicle.

13. Connect the negative battery cable

3.6L Engine

See Figures 45 and 46.

1. Disconnect the negative battery cable.

2. Raise the vehicle.

3. Remove the front left side catalytic converter.

4. Remove the knock sensor Bank 2.

5. Remove the starter solenoid BAT terminal nut.

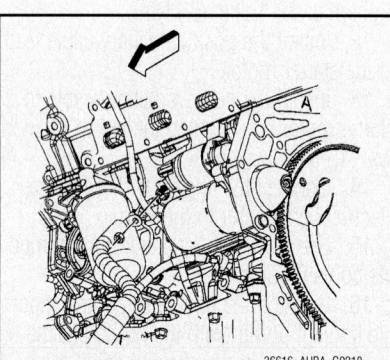

Fig. 45 Removing the starter solenoid BAT terminal nut—3.6L engine

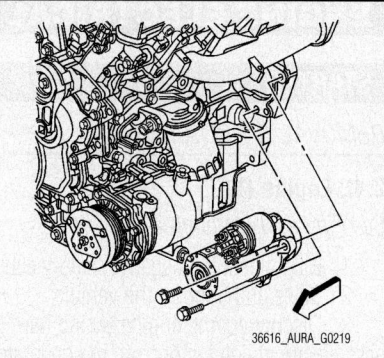

Fig. 46 Removing the starter motor—3.6L engine

6. Disconnect the engine harness electrical connector.

7. Disconnect the starter motor bolts and starter.

To install:

8. Position the starter motor in the engine block. Tighten the bolts to 37 ft. lbs. (50 Nm).

9. Connect the engine harness electrical connector to the starter.

10. Install the starter solenoid BAT terminal nut. Tighten the nut to 115 inch lbs. (13 Nm).

11. Install the knock sensor Bank 2.

12. Install the front catalytic converter.

13. Lower the vehicle.

14. Connect the negative battery cable.

ENGINE MECHANICAL

➡**Disconnecting the negative battery cable may interfere with the functions of the on board computer systems and may require the computer to undergo a relearning process, once the negative battery cable is reconnected.**

ACCESSORY DRIVE BELTS

ACCESSORY BELT ROUTING

See Figures 47 through 49.

INSPECTION

Inspect the drive belt for signs of glazing or cracking. A glazed belt will be perfectly smooth from slippage, while a good belt will have a slight texture of fabric visible. Cracks will usually start at the inner edge of the belt and run outward. All worn or damaged drive belts should be replaced immediately.

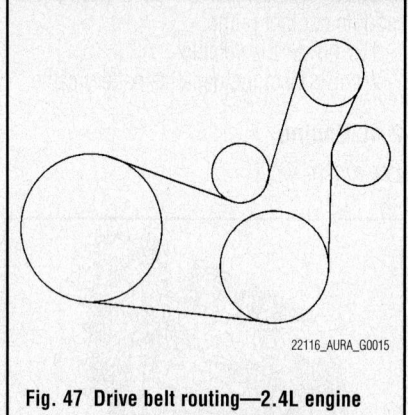

Fig. 47 Drive belt routing—2.4L engine

REMOVAL & INSTALLATION

2.4L Engine (LAT)

See Figure 50.

1. Remove the right engine splash shield.

2. Remove the air cleaner assembly.

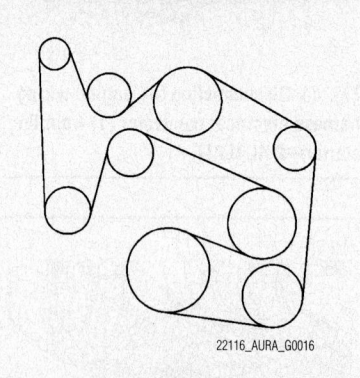

Fig. 48 Drive belt routing—3.5L engine

3. Install a hydraulic belt tensioner compressor such as (EN-48932) to the drive belt tensioner spring.

4. Compress the drive belt tensioner spring fully using the hydraulic belt tensioner compressor.

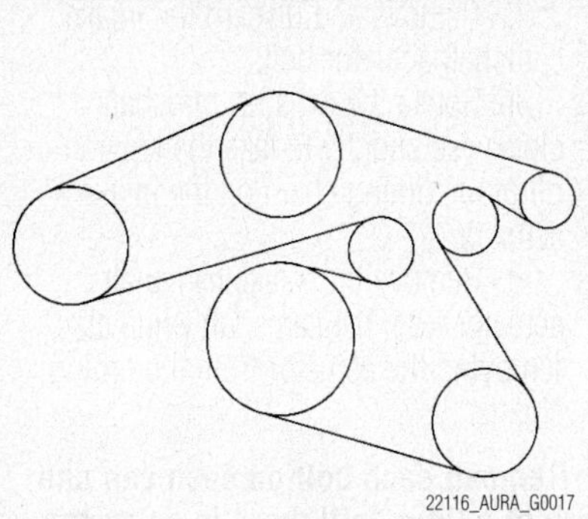

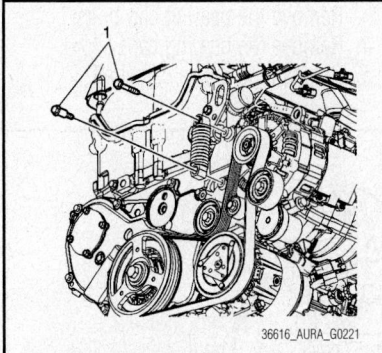

Fig. 49 Drive belt routing—3.6L engine

Fig. 50 Removing the tensioner spring bolts from the tensioner

5. Remove the tensioner spring bolts from the tensioner.

6. Remove the tensioner spring from the tensioner.

7. Remove the drive belt from under the middle idler pulley.

8. Remove the drive belt from the vehicle.

To install:

9. Install and position the drive belt around all of the pulleys except for the middle idler pulley.

10. Install the tensioner spring on the tensioner.

11. Install the tensioner spring bolts to the tensioner. Tighten the bolts to 16 ft. lbs. (22 Nm).

12. Install the drive belt under the middle idler pulley.

13. Loosen the forcing bolt on the hydraulic belt tensioner and remove from the drive belt tensioner spring.

14. Install and position the drive belt around all of the pulleys except for the middle idler pulley.

15. Ensure that the drive belt tensioner idler is fully seated against the drive belt.

16. Install the air cleaner assembly.

17. Install the right engine splash shield.

2.4L Engine

See Figures 47 and 51.

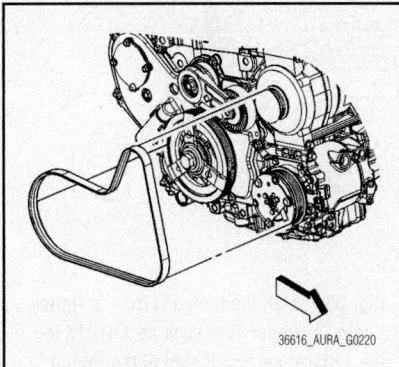

Fig. 51 Removing the drive belt—2.4L engine

1. Remove the right engine splash shield.

2. Remove the air cleaner assembly.

3. Install a hydraulic belt tensioner compressor such as Accessory Belt Tensioner Unloader (J44811) to the drive belt tensioner.

4. Using the tool, rotate the tensioner counterclockwise in order to release the tensioner from the drive belt.

5. Remove the drive belt from the vehicle.

6. Slowly rotate the tool and the tensioner clockwise in order to allow the tensioner to rest.

7. Remove the tool from the drive belt tensioner.

To install:

8. Install and position the drive belt around all of the pulleys except for the drive belt tensioner.

9. Install the tool to the drive belt tensioner.

10. Using the tool, rotate the tensioner counterclockwise.

11. Position the drive belt under the tensioner pulley.

12. Using the tool, rotate the tensioner clockwise in order to seat the tensioner pulley onto the drive belt.

13. Install the air cleaner assembly.

14. Install the right side engine splash shield.

3.5L Engine

See Figures 48 and 52.

1. Remove the air cleaner assembly.

2. Remove the engine mount snubber bracket.

3. Rotate the drive belt tensioner clockwise to release the drive belt tension.

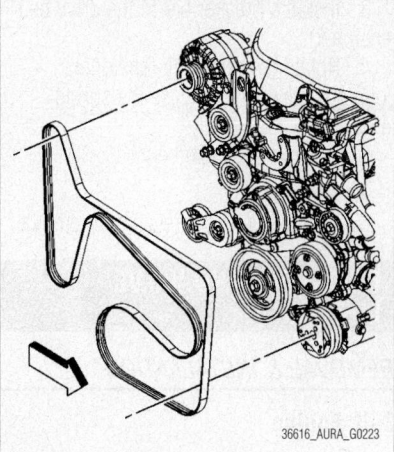

Fig. 52 Removing the drive belt—3.5L engine

4. Slide the drive belt off the belt idler pulley.

5. Slowly release the drive belt tensioner.

6. Remove the drive belt from the accessory drive pulleys.

To install:

7. Install the drive belt to the crankshaft pulley, the tensioner and the generator.

8. Rotate the drive belt tensioner clockwise.

9. Install the drive belt to the idler pulley.

➡**Ensure the drive belt is properly aligned and seated into the grooves of the accessory drive pulley.**

10. Slowly release the drive belt tensioner.

11. Install the engine mount snubber bracket.

12. Install the air cleaner assembly.

3.6L Engine

See Figures 49 and 53.

1. Remove the air cleaner assembly.

2. Remove the engine mount snubber.

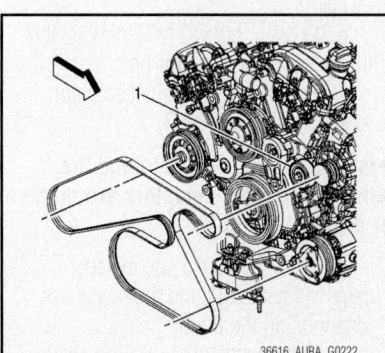

Fig. 53 Removing the drive belt—3.6L engine

3. Install a breaker bar to the drive belt tensioner.

4. Rotate the drive belt tensioner counterclockwise to release the spring tension.

5. Remove the drive belt.

To install:

6. Installation is the reverse of removal.

CAMSHAFT AND VALVE LIFTERS

REMOVAL & INSTALLATION

2.4L Engine

Intake

See Figures 54 through 56.

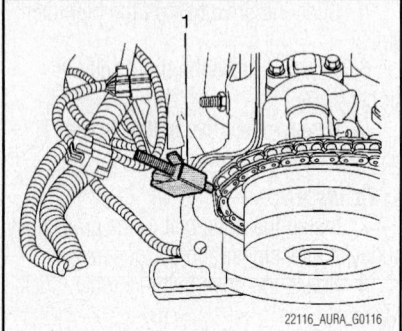

Fig. 54 Make sure that the tips of a Timing Chain Tensioner Tool such as J 44217 (1) are fully engaged into the timing chain—2.4L engine

1. Remove the intake camshaft position actuator as follows:

  a. Remove the camshaft cover.

  b. Remove the spark plugs.

  c. Rotate the crankshaft clockwise and install the camshaft actuator retainer (EN-48953).

  d. Install the camshaft actuator retainer bolts and tighten to 89 inch lbs. (10 Nm).

  e. Loosen, but DO NOT remove the intake camshaft actuator bolt.

  f. Remove the camshaft actuator locking tool (EN-48953).

➡**Ensure the timing chain and the camshaft position actuators are marked for proper assembly.**

  g. Mark the intake and exhaust camshaft actuators and the respective locations on the timing chain.

  h. Remove the upper timing chain guide bolts and guide.

  i. Remove the timing chain tensioner.

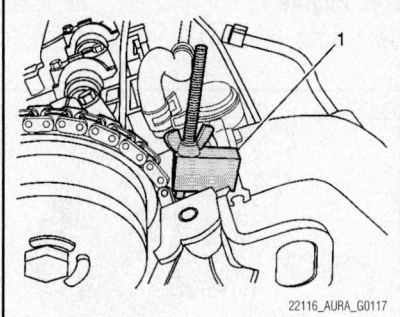

Fig. 55 Install the tools (1) from a Timing Chain Tensioner Tool such as J 44217 to the exhaust camshaft side of the timing chain assembly in order to retain the timing chain—2.4L engine

➡**The intake camshaft actuator should not rotate during the removal or installation.**

➡**Ensure the tips of the timing chain tensioner tool are fully engaged into the timing chain. The retention tool rod can be used on the back side of the chain to ensure the teeth from the retention tool are engaged.**

  j. Install the timing chain retention tool (EN-48749) to the intake side of the timing chain.

  k. Install the timing chain retention tool (EN-48749) to the exhaust side of the timing chain.

l. Remove and discard the intake camshaft actuator bolt.

  m. Rotate the exhaust camshaft clockwise slightly to take the tension off of the timing chain on the intake actuator.

  n. Remove the intake camshaft actuator from the camshaft while also removing the actuator from the timing chain.

➡**Remove each bolt on each cap one turn at a time until there is no spring tension pushing on the camshaft.**

2. Mark the bearing caps to ensure they are installed in the original position.

3. Remove the bearing cap bolts.

4. Remove the bearing caps.

5. Remove the intake camshaft.

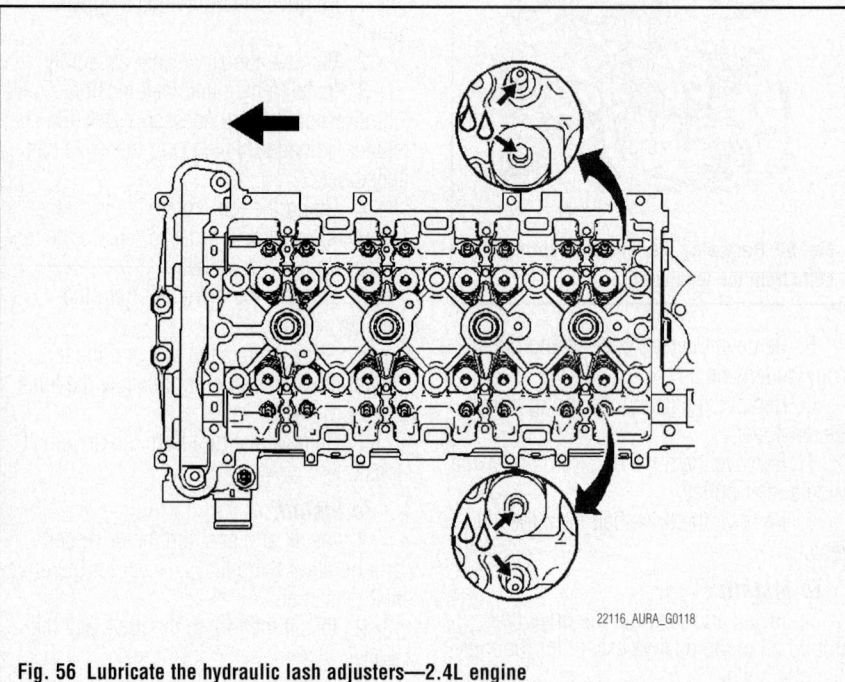

Fig. 56 Lubricate the hydraulic lash adjusters—2.4L engine

➡**Keep all of the roller followers and hydraulic adjusters in order so that they can be reinstalled in their respective locations.**

6. Remove the camshaft roller followers.

7. Remove the hydraulic element lash adjusters.

To install:

8. Install the hydraulic element lash adjusters into their bores in the cylinder head.

9. Lubricate the hydraulic lash adjusters with molylube.

10. Lubricate the valve tips with GM molylube.

→ **Used roller followers MUST be returned to their original position on the camshaft. If the camshaft is being replaced, the roller followers actuated by the camshaft must also be replaced.**

11. Position the camshaft roller followers on the tip of the valve stem and on the lash adjuster. Lubricate the roller followers with molylube.

12. Install the intake camshaft and lubricate with molylube.

13. Install the camshaft bearing caps. Hand tighten the cap bolts.

14. Tighten the bearing cap bolts in increments of 3 turns until they are seated to 89 inch lbs. (10 Nm).

15. Install the intake camshaft position actuator as follows:

→ **Ensure that the alignment mark made previously on the exhaust camshaft actuator is still aligned properly with the mark on the timing chain.**

a. Install the timing chain onto the intake camshaft actuator.

b. Align the intake camshaft actuator alignment mark made previously with the timing chain mark and install the actuator onto the camshaft rotating the exhaust camshaft clockwise, if required.

c. Install a NEW intake camshaft actuator bolt until snug.

d. Remove the timing chain retention tool from the intake side of the timing chain.

→ **Ensure that the alignment mark previously on the intake camshaft actuator is still aligned properly with the timing chain. If the mark made previously on the intake camshaft actuator is not aligned properly, refer to replacement procedure.**

e. Remove the timing chain retention tool from the exhaust side of the timing chain.

→ **Failure to reset the tensioner will allow the tensioner to over extend limiting the timing chain life.**

f. Reset and install the timing chain tensioner.

g. Install the camshaft actuator retainer (EN-48953) Camshaft Actuator Locking Tool.

h. Install the camshaft actuator retainer bolts and tighten to 89 inch lbs. (10 Nm).

i. Tighten the NEW camshaft actuator bolt to 22 ft. lbs. (30 Nm) plus an additional 100 degrees.

→ **You must have the Camshaft Actuator Locking Tool (EN-48953) installed to perform this procedure.**

j. To release the tensioner apply a counterclockwise rotational torque to the crankshaft balancer bolt of 33 ft. lbs. (45 Nm).

k. Remove the camshaft actuator retainer.

l. Install the upper timing chain guide and bolts and tighten to 89 inch lbs. (10 Nm).

m. Install the spark plugs.

n. Install the camshaft cover.

Exhaust

See Figures 54 through 56.

1. Remove the exhaust camshaft position actuator as follows:

a. Remove the camshaft cover.

b. Remove the spark plugs.

c. Rotate the crankshaft clockwise and install the camshaft actuator retainer.

d. Install the camshaft actuator retainer bolts and tighten to 89 inch lbs. (10 Nm).

e. Loosen, but do NOT remove the exhaust camshaft actuator bolt.

f. Clean the timing chain and gears with solvent.

→ **Ensure that the timing chain and the camshaft position actuators are marked for proper assembly.**

g. Mark the intake and exhaust camshaft actuators and the respective locations on the timing chain.

h. Remove the upper timing chain guide bolts and guide.

i. Remove the timing chain tensioner.

→ **The camshaft actuators should not rotate during the removal or installation.**

→ **Ensure the tips of the timing chain tensioner are fully engaged into the timing chain. The retention tool rod can be used on the back side of the chain to ensue the teeth from the retention tool are engaged.**

j. Install the timing chain retention tool (EN-48749) to the exhaust side of the timing chain.

→ **Remove each bolt on each cap one turn at a time until there is no spring tension pushing on the camshaft.**

2. Mark the bearing caps to ensure they are installed in the original position.

3. Remove the bearing cap bolts.

4. Remove the bearing caps.

5. Remove the exhaust camshaft.

→ **Keep all of the roller followers and hydraulic adjusters in order so that they can be reinstalled in their respective locations.**

6. Remove the camshaft roller followers.

7. Remove the hydraulic element lash adjusters.

To install:

8. Install the hydraulic element lash adjusters into their bores in the cylinder head.

9. Lubricate the hydraulic lash adjusters with molylube.

10. Lubricate the valve tips with GM molylube.

→ **Used roller followers MUST be returned to their original position on the camshaft. If the camshaft is being replaced, the roller followers actuated by the camshaft must also be replaced.**

11. Position the camshaft roller followers on the tip of the valve stem and on the lash adjuster. Lubricate the roller followers with molylube.

12. Install the exhaust camshaft and lubricate with molylube.

13. Install the camshaft bearing caps. Hand tighten the cap bolts.

14. Tighten the bearing cap bolts in increments of 3 turns until they are seated to 89 inch lbs. (10 Nm).

15. Install the exhaust camshaft position actuator as follows:

→ **Ensure that the alignment mark made previously on the intake camshaft actuator is still aligned properly with the mark on the timing chain.**

→ **The exhaust camshaft may need to be rotated clockwise to fully set the camshaft actuator.**

a. Install the timing chain onto the exhaust camshaft actuator.

b. Align the intake camshaft actuator alignment mark made previously with the timing chain mark and install the actuator onto the camshaft.

c. Install a NEW exhaust camshaft actuator bolt until snug.

→ **Ensure that the alignment mark previously on the exhaust camshaft actuator is still aligned properly with the timing chain. If the mark made previously on the intake camshaft actuator is not aligned properly, refer to CAMSHAFT TIMING CHAIN.**

d. Remove the tool from the exhaust camshaft side of the timing chain assembly.

➡️**Failure to reset the tensioner will allow the tensioner to over extend limiting the timing chain life.**

e. Reset and install the timing chain tensioner.

f. Install the intake camshaft actuator retainer.

g. Install the camshaft actuator retainer bolts and tighten to 89 inch lbs. (10 Nm).

h. Tighten the NEW camshaft actuator bolt to 22 ft. lbs. (30 Nm) plus an additional 100 degrees.

➡️**You must have the Camshaft Actuator Locking Tool (EN-48953) installed to perform this procedure.**

i. To release the tensioner apply a counterclockwise rotational torque to the crankshaft balancer bolt of 33 ft. lbs. (45 Nm).

j. Remove the Camshaft Actuator Retainer (EN-48953).

k. Install the upper timing chain guide and bolts and tighten to 89 inch lbs. (10 Nm).

l. Install the camshaft cover.

m. Install the spark plugs.

3.5L Engine

See Figures 57 through 59.

1. Remove the camshaft position sensor bolt.
2. Remove the camshaft position sensor.
3. Remove the camshaft thrust plate screws.
4. Remove the camshaft thrust plate.

➡️**All camshaft journals are the same diameter, so care must be used in removing or installing the camshaft**

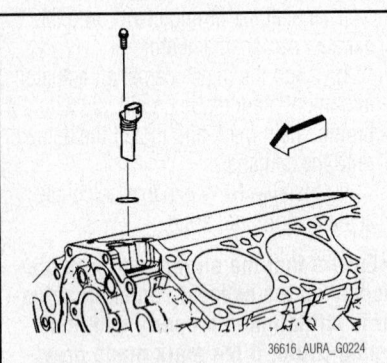

Fig. 57 Removing the Camshaft Position Sensor (CMP) bolt—3.5L engine

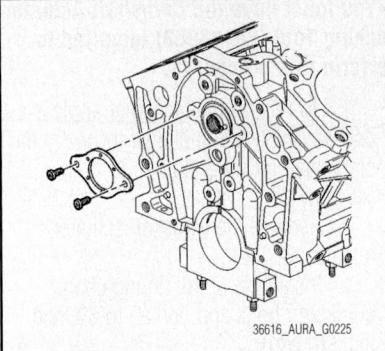

Fig. 58 Removing the camshaft thrust plate—3.5L engine

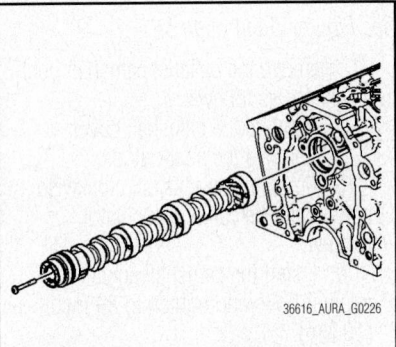

Fig. 59 Removing the camshaft—3.5L engine

to avoid damage to the camshaft bearings.

5. Install a camshaft sprocket bolt into the camshaft. Tighten finger tight only.
6. Carefully rotate and remove the camshaft from the engine block.

To install:

7. Coat the camshaft journals with clean engine oil.
8. Coat the camshaft lobes with prelube.
9. Install a camshaft sprocket bolt into the camshaft. Tighten finger tight only.
10. Carefully rotate the camshaft while installing the camshaft into the camshaft bearings.
11. Install the camshaft thrust plate.
12. Install the camshaft thrust plate screws. Tighten to 89 inch lbs. (10 Nm).
13. Install the camshaft position sensor.
14. Install the camshaft position sensor bolt. Tighten to 89 inch lbs. (10 Nm).

3.6L Engine

Right Side

See Figures 60 through 65.

1. Remove the lower intake manifold.
2. Remove the camshaft cover.
3. Remove the camshaft sensors.

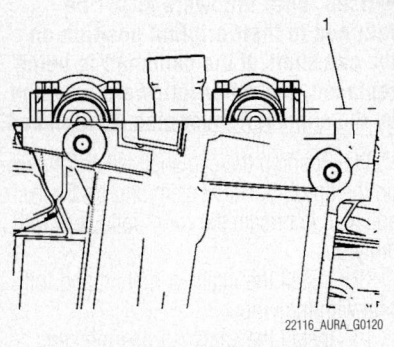

Fig. 60 Rotate the crankshaft with a camshaft rotation socket such as EN 46111 until the camshafts are in a neutral (low tension) position. The camshaft flats will be parallel with the camshaft cover rail (1)–Right side 3.6L engine

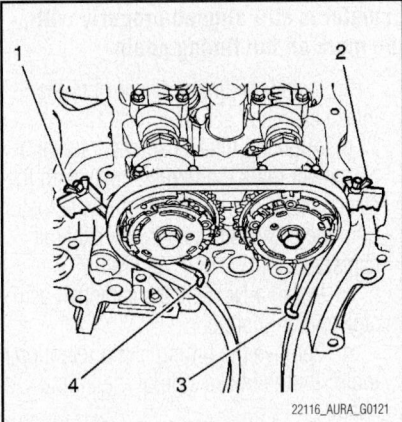

Fig. 61 Make sure that the tips of a timing chain tensioner tool such as EN 46108 are fully engaged into the timing chain (3 and 4). Install a timing chain tensioner tool such as EN 46108 (1 and 2) in order to retain the timing chain–Rights side 3.6L engine

4. Remove the intake camshaft position actuator solenoid.
5. Remove the crankshaft balancer.
6. Rotate the crankshaft with a camshaft rotation socket such as EN 46111 until the camshafts are in a neutral (low tension) position. The camshaft flats will be parallel with the camshaft cover rail.

➡️**Use an open-end wrench at the camshaft hex to prevent camshaft/engine rotation.**

➡️**DO NOT remove the camshaft position actuator bolt at this time.**

7. Loosen the camshaft position actuator bolt.

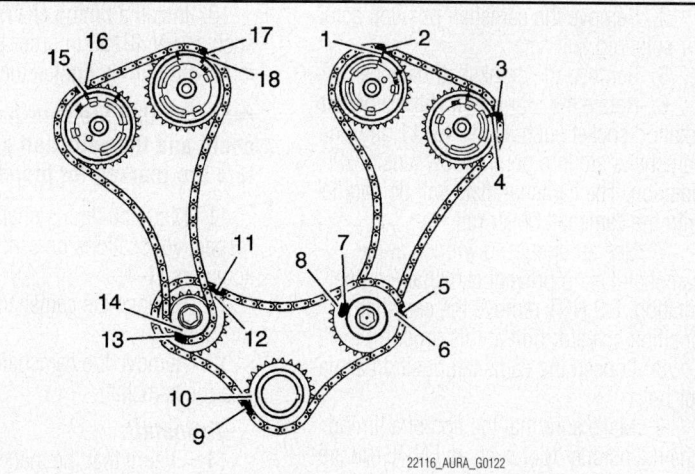

Fig. 62 Mark the timing chain and the respective locations on camshaft position actuators (15-18)–Right side 3.6L engine

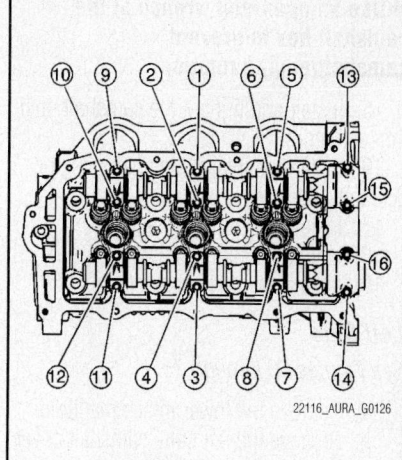

Fig. 65 Right side camshaft bearing caps torque sequence—3.6L engine

8. Make sure that the tips of a timing chain tensioner tool such as EN 46108 are fully engaged into the timing chain.

9. Install a timing chain tensioner tool such as EN 46108 in order to retain the timing chain. Firmly tighten the tool nuts.

➡**Ensure that the camshaft timing chain and the camshaft position actuators are marked for proper assembly.**

10. Mark the timing chain and the respective locations on camshaft position actuators (15-18).

11. Remove the camshaft position actuator bolt.

12. Remove the camshaft bearing caps and the camshaft.

To install:

➡**Make sure that the marks on the camshaft position actuators and the timing chain (15-18) are aligned.**

➡**DO NOT tighten the camshaft position actuator bolt at this time.**

13. Locate the camshafts to the cylinder head and assemble the camshaft actuators to the camshafts.

14. Install the camshafts and the camshaft bearing caps as follows:

a. Ensure that the camshaft sealing rings are in place in the camshaft grooves. Camshaft sealing rings must be in place below the surface of the camshaft journal in order to avoid being pinched between the cylinder head and the camshaft caps.

b. Apply a liberal amount of lubricant to the camshaft journals and the right cylinder head camshaft carriers.

c. Place the right intake and right exhaust camshafts in position in the right cylinder head.

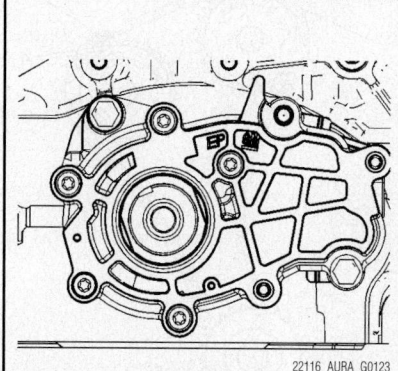

Fig. 63 Ensure that the crankshaft is in the stage one timing drive assembly position using a crankshaft rotation socket such as EN 46111–Right side 3.6L engine

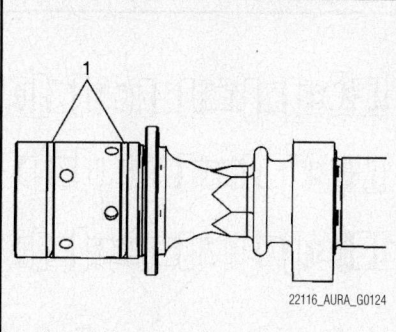

Fig. 64 Ensure that the camshaft sealing rings (1) are in place in the camshaft grooves. Camshaft sealing rings must be in place below the surface of the camshaft journal in order to avoid being pinched between the cylinder head and the camshaft caps–Right side 3.6L engine

d. Position the camshaft lobes in a neutral position with the flats on the back of the camshafts up and parallel with the right cylinder head camshaft cover rail.

e. Observe the markings on the right cylinder head camshaft bearing caps. Each bearing cap is marked in order to identify its location. The markings have the following meanings:

- The raised feature must always be oriented toward the center of the cylinder head.
- The I indicates the intake camshaft
- The E indicates the exhaust camshaft
- The number 1, 3, 5 indicates the cylinder position from the front of the engine

f. Apply a liberal amount of lubricant to the camshaft bearing caps.

g. Install the camshaft bearing thrust caps in the first journal of the right cylinder head.

h. Install the remaining bearing caps with their orientation mark toward the center of the cylinder head.

i. Hand start all the camshaft bearing cap bolts.

j. Tighten the camshaft bearing cap bolts in the sequence shown to 89 inch lbs. (10 Nm).

k. Loosen the center intake camshaft bearing cap bolts (1, 2) and the center exhaust camshaft bearing cap bolts (3, 4). Retighten the center camshaft bearing cap bolts (1, 2, 3, and 4) to 89 inch lbs. (10 Nm).

l. Remove the timing chain retention tool.

m. Install the crankshaft balancer.

→**Use an open-end wrench at the camshaft hex to prevent camshaft/engine rotation.**

15. Install and tighten the camshaft position actuators.

16. Install the intake camshaft position actuator solenoid.

17. Install the camshaft sensors.

18. Install the camshaft cover.

19. Install the lower intake manifold.

Left Side

See Figures 66 through 71.

1. Remove the lower intake manifold.

2. Remove the left bank camshaft cover.

3. Remove the camshaft sensors.

Fig. 66 Rotate the crankshaft with a camshaft rotation socket such as EN 46111 until the camshafts are in a neutral (low tension) position. The camshaft flats will be parallel with the camshaft cover rail (1)—3.6L engine

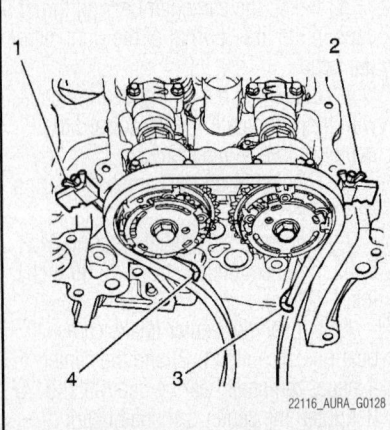

Fig. 67 Install a timing chain tensioner tool such as EN 46108 (1 and 2) in order to retain the timing chain—left side 3.6L engine

4. Remove the camshaft position actuator solenoid.

5. Remove the crankshaft balancer.

6. Rotate the crankshaft with camshaft rotation socket such as EN 46111 until the camshafts are in a neutral (low tension) position. The camshaft flats will be parallel with the camshaft cover rail.

7. Use an open-end wrench at the camshaft hex to prevent camshaft/engine rotation. DO NOT remove the camshaft position actuator bolt at this time.

8. Loosen the camshaft position actuator bolt.

9. Make sure that the tips of a timing chain tensioner tool such as EN 46108 are fully engaged into the timing chain.

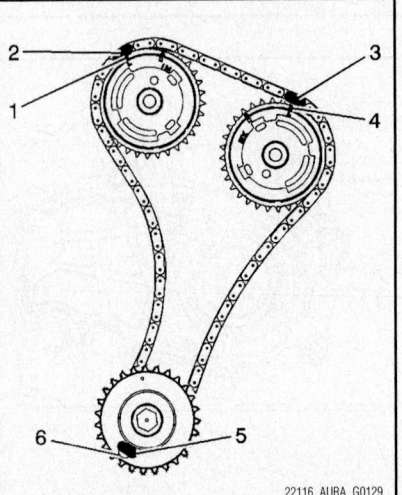

Fig. 68 Install a timing chain tensioner tool such as EN 46108 (1 and 2) in order to retain the timing chain—Left side 3.6L engine

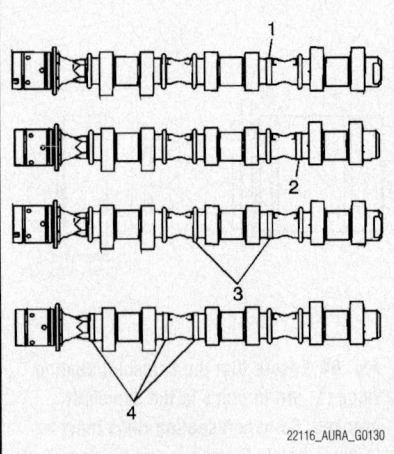

Fig. 69 Select the proper camshaft for the particular installation location—Left side 3.6L engine

10. Install a timing chain tensioner tool such as EN 46108 in order to retain the timing chain. Firmly tighten the tool nuts.

→**Ensure that the camshaft timing chain and the camshaft position actuators are marked for proper assembly.**

11. Mark the timing chain and the respective locations on camshaft position actuators (1-4).

12. Remove the camshaft position actuator bolt.

13. Remove the camshaft bearing caps and the camshaft.

To install:

14. Ensure that the marks on the camshaft position actuator and the timing chain (1-4) are aligned. DO NOT tighten the camshaft position actuator bolt at this time

15. Locate the camshafts to the cylinder head and assemble the camshaft actuators to the camshafts.

16. Install the camshafts and the camshaft bearing caps as follows:

   a. Ensure that the crankshaft is in the stage one timing drive assembly position using a crankshaft rotation socket such as EN 46111 .

   b. Ensure that the camshaft sealing rings are in place in the camshaft grooves. Camshaft sealing rings must be in place below the surface of the camshaft journal in order to avoid being pinched between the cylinder head and the camshaft caps.

   c. Apply a liberal amount of lubricant to the camshaft journals and the right cylinder head camshaft carriers.

   d. Place the left intake and left exhaust camshafts in position in the left cylinder head.

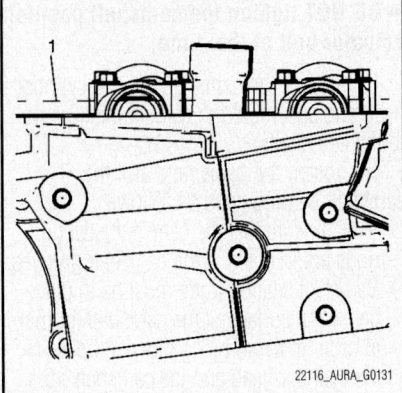

Fig. 70 Position the camshaft lobes in a neutral position with the flats on the back of the camshafts up and parallel with the left cylinder head camshaft cover rail (1)—left side 3.6L engine

e. Position the camshaft lobes in a neutral position with the flats on the back of the camshafts up and parallel with the right cylinder head camshaft cover rail.

f. Observe the markings on the left cylinder head camshaft bearing caps. Each bearing cap is marked in order to identify its location. The markings have the following meanings:

- The raised feature must always be oriented toward the center of the cylinder head.
- The I indicates the intake camshaft
- The E indicates the exhaust camshaft
- The number 2, 4, 6 indicates the cylinder position from the front of the engine

g. Apply a liberal amount of lubricant to the camshaft bearing caps.

h. Install the camshaft bearing thrust caps in the first journal of the left cylinder head.

i. Install the remaining bearing caps with their orientation mark toward the center of the cylinder head.

j. Hand start all the camshaft bearing cap bolts.

k. Tighten the camshaft bearing cap bolts in the sequence shown to 89 inch lbs. (10 Nm).

l. Loosen the center intake camshaft bearing cap bolts (1, 2) and the center exhaust camshaft bearing cap bolts (3, 4). Retighten the center camshaft bearing cap bolts (1, 2, 3, and 4) to 89 inch lbs. (10 Nm).

m. Remove the timing chain retention tool.

n. Install the crankshaft balancer.

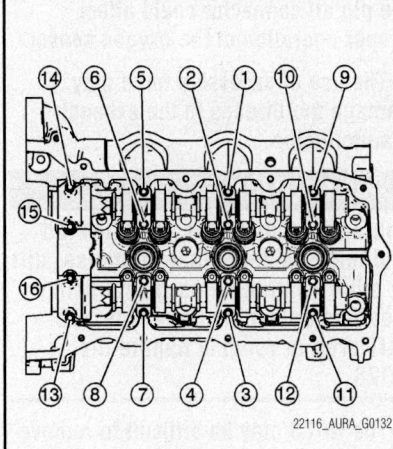

Fig. 71 Left side camshaft bearing caps torque sequence—3.6L engine

➡**Use an open-end wrench at the camshaft hex to prevent camshaft/ engine rotation.**

17. Install and tighten the camshaft position actuators.
18. Install the intake camshaft position actuator solenoid.
19. Install the camshaft sensors.
20. Install the camshaft cover.
21. Install the lower intake manifold.

CATALYTIC CONVERTER

REMOVAL & INSTALLATION

2.4L Engine (LAT)

See Figure 72.

❊❊ **WARNING**

In order to avoid being burned, do not service the exhaust system while it is still hot. Service the system when it is cool.

1. Remove the heated oxygen sensor.
2. Remove the catalytic converter to exhaust manifold nuts.
3. Remove the catalytic converter to muffler nuts.
4. Separate the exhaust pipe from the catalytic converter studs.
5. Position and support the exhaust pipe out of the way.
6. Remove the catalytic converter and gasket.

To install:

7. Install the catalytic converter along with a NEW gasket to the exhaust manifold.
8. Position and join the exhaust pipe to the catalytic converter studs.
9. Install the catalytic converter to muffler nuts and tighten to 13 ft. lbs. (17 Nm).

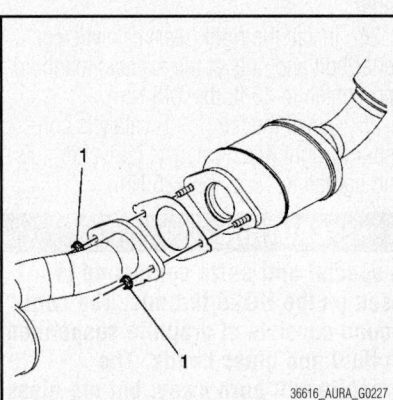

Fig. 72 Removing the catalytic converter and gasket—2.4L engine (LAT)

10. Install the catalytic converter to exhaust manifold nuts and tighten to 37 ft. lbs. (50 Nm).
11. Install the heated oxygen sensor.

3.5L Engine

❊❊ **WARNING**

In order to avoid being burned, do not service the exhaust system while it is still hot. Service the system when it is cool.

Left Side

See Figures 73 through 76.

➡**The oxygen sensor uses a permanently attached pigtail and connector. Do not remove the pigtail from the oxygen sensor. Damage to or removal of the pigtail connector could affect proper operation of the oxygen sensor.**

➡**The use of excessive force may damage the threads in the exhaust manifold/ pipe.**

❊❊ **CAUTION**

The in-line connector and louvered end must be kept clear of grease, dirt or other contaminants. Avoid using cleaning solvents of any type. DO NOT drop or roughly handle the HO2S.

❊❊ **CAUTION**

The HO2S may be difficult to remove when the engine temperature is less than 120°F (48°C).

1. Remove the air cleaner assembly.
2. Remove the Connector Position Assurance (CPA) retainer.
3. Disconnect the engine wiring harness electrical connector from the Heated Oxygen Sensor (HO2S) electrical connector.

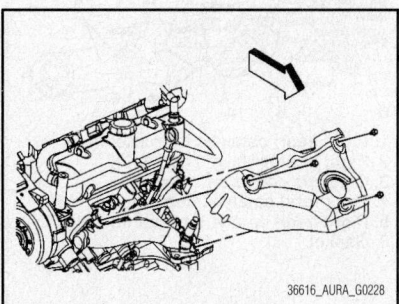

Fig. 73 Removing the exhaust manifold heat shield—3.5L engine

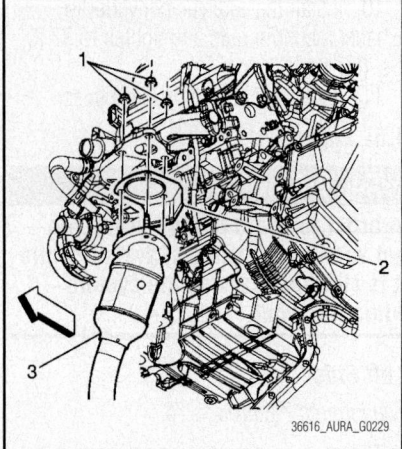

Fig. 74 Removing the left (front) catalytic converter nuts

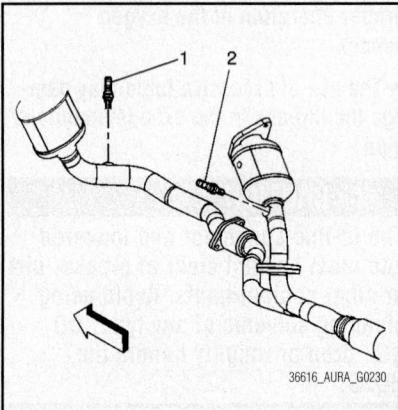

Fig. 75 Removing the lower right and left HO2S (1, 2)—3.5L engine

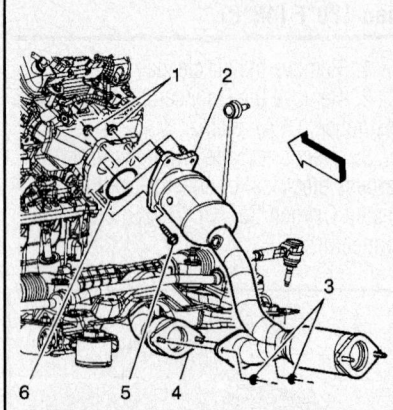

1. Right (rear) catalytic converter nuts
2. Right (rear) catalytic converter
3. Catalytic converter nuts
4. Left (front) catalytic converter
5. Right (rear) catalytic converter bolt
6. Gasket

Fig. 76 Removing the catalytic converter—3.5L engine (left side)

4. Remove the HO2S electrical connector rosebud clip from the oil level indicator tube tab.

5. Remove the exhaust manifold heat shield bolts and shield.

6. Remove the left (front) catalytic converter nuts at the exhaust manifold.

7. Remove the muffler assembly.

8. Remove the lower right HO2S electrical connector CPA retainer.

9. Disconnect the rear HO2S electrical connector from the engine wiring harness electrical connector.

10. Remove the lower left HO2S CPA retainer.

11. Disconnect the front engine wiring harness electrical connector from the HO2S electrical connector.

12. Remove the lower right and left HO2S using the heated oxygen sensor wrench (J 39194-B).

13. Remove the left (front) catalytic converter to right (rear) catalytic converter nuts.

14. Remove the right (rear) catalytic converter bolt and nuts at the exhaust manifold.

15. Remove and discard the gasket.

16. Remove the right (rear) catalytic converter.

17. Remove the left (front) catalytic converter.

18. Remove and discard the left (front) catalytic converter to manifold gasket.

19. Inspect the catalytic converter-to-exhaust manifold flange. The standard and service limit for the converter to manifold flange warpage is 0.028 inch (0.7 mm).

To install:

20. Install a NEW gasket to the left (front) catalytic converter studs.

21. Install the left (front) catalytic converter.

22. Install a NEW gasket to the right (rear) catalytic converter studs.

23. Install the right (rear) catalytic converter.

24. Install the right (rear) catalytic converter bolt and nuts at the exhaust manifold and tighten to 33 ft. lbs. (45 Nm).

25. Install the left (front) catalytic converter to right (rear) catalytic converter nuts and tighten to 18 ft. lbs. (25 Nm).

✳✳ CAUTION

A special anti-seize compound is used on the HO2S threads. The compound consists of graphite suspended in fluid and glass beads. The graphite will burn away, but the glass beads will remain, making the sensor easier to remove. New or service sensors will already have the com-

pound applied to the threads. If a sensor is removed from an engine and is to be reinstalled, the threads must have anti-seize compound applied before the reinstallation.

26. If reinstalling the old HO2S, coat the threads with anti-seize compound GM P/N 12377953 or equivalent.

27. Install the lower right and left HO2S and tighten to 31 ft. lbs. (42 Nm).

28. Connect the front engine wiring harness electrical connector to the HO2S electrical connector.

29. Install the lower left HO2S CPA retainer.

30. Connect the rear HO2S electrical connector to the engine wiring harness electrical connector.

31. Install the lower right HO2S electrical connector CPA retainer.

32. Remove the muffler assembly.

33. Install the left (front) catalytic converter nuts at the exhaust manifold and tighten to 33 ft. lbs. (45 Nm).

34. Remove the exhaust manifold heat shield bolts and shield and tighten to 89 inch lbs. (10 Nm).

35. Connect the engine wiring harness electrical connector to the HO2S electrical connector.

36. Install the CPA retainer.

37. Install the HO2S electrical connector rosebud clip to the oil level indicator tube tab.

38. Install the air cleaner assembly.

Right Side

See Figure 77.

➡ The oxygen sensor uses a permanently attached pigtail and connector. Do not remove the pigtail from the oxygen sensor. Damage to or removal of the pigtail connector could affect proper operation of the oxygen sensor.

➡ The use of excessive force may damage the threads in the exhaust manifold/pipe.

✳✳ CAUTION

The in-line connector and louvered end must be kept clear of grease, dirt or other contaminants. Avoid using cleaning solvents of any type. DO NOT drop or roughly handle the HO2S.

➡ The HO2S may be difficult to remove when the engine temperature is less than 120°F (48D°C).

1. Remove the muffler assembly.
2. Remove the rear stabilizer shaft.

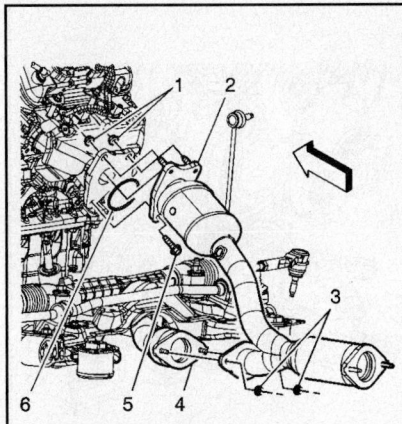

1. Right (rear) catalytic converter nuts
2. Right (rear) catalytic converter
3. Catalytic converter nuts
4. Left (front) catalytic converter
5. Right (rear) catalytic converter bolt
6. Gasket

36616_AURA_G0232

Fig. 77 Removing the catalytic converter—3.5L engine (right side)

3. Remove the Connector Position Assurance (CPA) retainer.

4. Disconnect the lower right heated oxygen sensor (HO2S) electrical connector from the engine wiring harness electrical connector.

5. Remove the lower right HO2S using the heated oxygen sensor wrench.

6. Remove the left (front) catalytic converter to right (rear) catalytic converter nuts.

7. Remove the right (rear) catalytic converter bolt and nuts at the exhaust manifold.

8. Remove the right catalytic converter.

9. Remove and discard the gasket.

10. Inspect the catalytic converter-to-exhaust manifold flange. The standard and service limit for the converter to manifold flange warpage is 0.028 inch (0.7 mm).

To install:

11. Install a NEW gasket to the catalytic converter.

12. Install the right (rear) catalytic converter.

13. Install the right (rear) catalytic converter bolt (5) and nuts (1) at the exhaust manifold and tighten to 33 ft. lbs. (45 Nm).

14. Install the left (front) catalytic converter to right (rear) catalytic converter nuts and tighten to 18 ft. lbs. (25 Nm).

✸✸ CAUTION

A special anti-seize compound is used on the HO2S threads. The compound consists of graphite suspended in fluid and glass beads. The graphite will burn away, but the glass beads will remain, making the sensor

easier to remove. New or service sensors will already have the compound applied to the threads. If a sensor is removed from an engine and is to be reinstalled, the threads must have anti-seize compound applied before the reinstallation.

15. If reinstalling the old HO2S, coat the threads with anti-seize compound GM P/N 12377953 or equivalent.

16. Install the lower right HO2S using the heated oxygen sensor wrench. Tighten to 31 ft. lbs. (42 Nm).

17. Connect the lower right HO2S electrical connector to the engine wiring harness electrical connector.

18. Install the CPA retainer.

19. Install the rear stabilizer shaft.

20. Install the muffler assembly.

3.6L Engine

Left Side

See Figure 78.

1. Remove the exhaust manifold heat shield.

2. Remove the left catalytic converter to exhaust manifold nuts.

3. Raise and support the vehicle.

4. Disconnect the bank 2 sensor 2 heated oxygen sensor (HO2S) electrical connector from the engine wiring harness electrical connector.

5. Remove the left catalytic converter to right catalytic converter nuts.

6. Remove the left catalytic converter from the vehicle.

7. Discard the catalytic converter to exhaust manifold gasket.

8. Discard the left catalytic converter to right catalytic converter gasket.

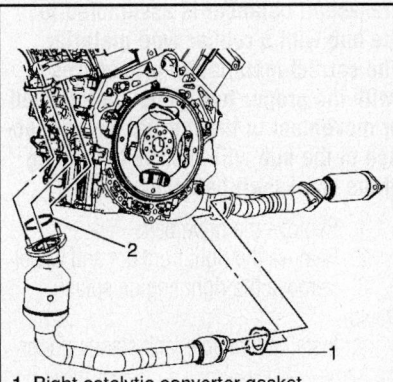

1. Right catalytic converter gasket
2. Catalytic converter to exhaust manifold gasket

36616_AURA_G0233

Fig. 78 Removing the catalytic converter—3.6L engine (left side)

To install:

9. Install a NEW catalytic converter seal onto the catalytic converter.

10. Install the catalytic converter to the vehicle.

11. Install a NEW left catalytic converter to right catalytic converter gasket.

12. Install the left catalytic converter to right catalytic converter nuts and tighten to 18 ft. lbs. (25 Nm).

13. Connect the bank 2 sensor 2 HO2S electrical connector to the engine wiring harness electrical connector.

14. Install the left catalytic converter to exhaust manifold nuts and tighten to 33 ft. lbs. (45 Nm).

15. Install the exhaust manifold heat shield.

16. Lower the vehicle and inspect for exhaust leaks.

Right Side

See Figure 79.

1. Remove the exhaust manifold heat shield.

2. Remove the catalytic converter to exhaust manifold nuts.

3. Remove the bank 1 sensor 2 heated oxygen sensor (HO2S).

4. Remove the left catalytic converter to right catalytic converter nuts.

5. Remove the exhaust pipe to right catalytic converter nuts.

6. Remove the catalytic converter from the vehicle.

7. Remove and discard the catalytic converter to exhaust manifold gasket.

8. Remove and discard the left catalytic converter to right catalytic converter gasket.

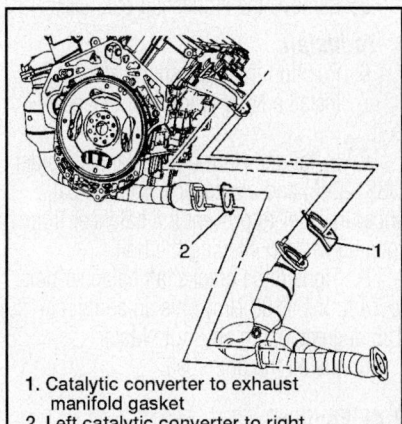

1. Catalytic converter to exhaust manifold gasket
2. Left catalytic converter to right catalytic converter gasket

36616_AURA_G0234

Fig. 79 Removing the catalytic converter—3.6L engine (right side)

To install:

9. Install a NEW catalytic converter to exhaust manifold gasket onto the catalytic converter.

10. Install the catalytic converter to the vehicle.

11. Install a NEW left catalytic converter to right catalytic converter gasket between the converters.

CRANKSHAFT DAMPER

REMOVAL & INSTALLATION

2.4L Engine (LAT)

See Figure 80.

Fig. 80 Removing the crankshaft balancer—2.4L engine (LAT)

1. Remove the drive belt.
2. Install the Harmonic Balancer Holder (J38122-A), and a breaker bar to the balancer in order to prevent the balancer from rotating when loosening the balancer bolt.
3. Remove the tool and breaker bar.
4. Remove and discard the crankshaft balancer bolt.
5. Remove the crankshaft balancer.

To install:

6. Position the crankshaft balancer.
7. Install a NEW crankshaft balancer bolt.
8. Install the Harmonic Balancer Holder (J38122-A) and a breaker bar to the balancer in order to prevent the balancer from rotating while tightening the bolt.
9. Tighten the crankshaft balancer bolt to 74 ft. lbs. (100 Nm) plus an additional 125 degrees using an Angle Meter.
10. Install the drive belt.

2.4L Engine

See Figure 81.

1. Remove the drive belt.
2. Remove the engine splash shield.

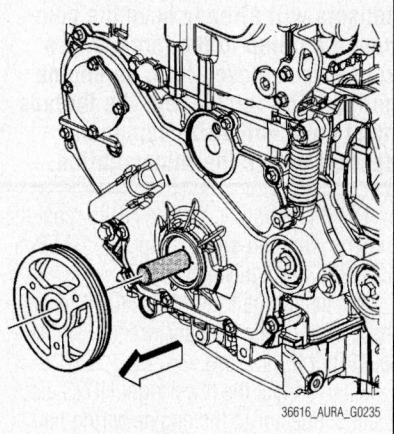

Fig. 81 Removing the crankshaft balancer—2.4L engine

3. Install a crankshaft holding tool and a breaker bar to the balancer in order to prevent the balancer from rotating when loosening the balancer bolt.
4. Remove and discard the crankshaft balancer bolt.
5. Remove the crankshaft balancer.

To install:

6. Position the crankshaft balancer.
7. Install a NEW crankshaft balancer bolt.
8. Install the holding tool and a breaker bar to the balancer in order to prevent the balancer from rotating while tightening the bolt.
9. Tighten the crankshaft balancer bolt to 74 ft. lbs. (100 Nm) plus an additional 125 degrees.
10. Install the engine splash shield.
11. Install the drive belt.

3.5L Engine

See Figure 82.

➡The inertial weight section of the crankshaft balancer is assembled to the hub with a rubber type material. The correct installation procedures (with the proper tool) must be followed or movement of the inertial weight section of the hub will destroy the tuning of the crankshaft balancer.

1. Remove the drive belt.
2. Remove the right front tire and wheel.
3. Remove the right engine splash shield.
4. Install adjustable jack stands under the frame.
5. Loosen the left frame bolts and remove the right side frame bolts.
6. Using the jack stands, lower the right side of the frame to access the crankshaft balancer.
7. Remove the torque converter covers.

Fig. 82 Removing the crankshaft balancer—3.5L engine

8. Install the a suitable holding tool to the flywheel to prevent flywheel rotation.
9. Remove the crankshaft balancer bolt and the washer.
10. Remove the crankshaft balancer.

To install:

➡The inertial weight section of the crankshaft balancer is assembled to the hub with a rubber type material. The correct installation procedures (with the proper tool) must be followed or movement of the inertial weight section of the hub will destroy the tuning of the crankshaft balancer.

11. Apply sealant to the keyway of the crankshaft balancer.
12. Place the crankshaft balancer into position over the key in the crankshaft.

➡Do NOT use a power-assisted tool with the special tool in order to remove or install this component. You cannot properly control the alignment of this component using a power-assisted tool, and this can damage the component.

13. Install a balancer and crankshaft sprocket installer onto the crankshaft.
14. Rotate the hex nut on the tool in order to install the crankshaft balancer onto the crankshaft.
15. Remove the tool from the crankshaft.
16. Install the crankshaft balancer washer and the bolt.
17. Install the used crankshaft balancer bolt, tighten to 92 ft. lbs. (125 Nm).
18. Remove the used crankshaft balancer bolt.
19. Install the NEW crankshaft balancer bolt, tighten to 92 ft. lbs. (125 Nm) plus an additional 130 degrees.

20. Remove the tool from the flywheel.
21. Install the torque converter covers.
22. Raise the frame to the original position.
23. Install and tighten the right and left side frame bolts to 74 ft. lbs. (100 Nm) plus an additional 90 degrees.
24. Install the right engine splash shield.
25. Install the right front tire and wheel.
26. Lower the vehicle.
27. Install the drive belt.

3.6L Engine

See Figures 83 and 84.

1. Remove the drive belt.
2. Install the engine support fixture.
3. Remove the engine mount strut bracket.
4. Remove the engine mount.
5. Remove the starter.

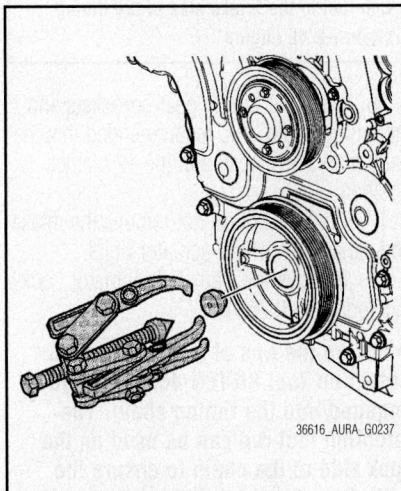

Fig. 83 Removing the crankshaft balancer—3.6L engine

Fig. 84 Use the tool, nut, bearing and washer to install the crankshaft balancer—3.6L engine

6. Install a flywheel holding tool through the starter mounting hole.
7. Using engine support fixture, lower engine approximately two inches.
8. Remove the crankshaft balancer bolt.
9. Install a crankshaft button tool such as J 38416-2 in the nose of the crankshaft.
10. Install crankshaft balancer remover tool such as J 41816 in order to remove the crankshaft balancer.
11. Tighten the center bolt of the crankshaft balancer remover tool in order to pull the crankshaft balancer off of the crankshaft.
12. Remove the crankshaft balancer remover tool from the crankshaft balancer.

To install:

➡**The crankshaft balancer remover tool must be installed onto the flywheel.**

13. Use the tool , nut, bearing and washer to install the crankshaft balancer.

➡**Do not lubricate the crankshaft front oil seal or crankshaft balancer sealing surfaces. The crankshaft balancer is installed into a dry seal.**

14. Apply lubricant to the inside of the crankshaft balancer hub bore.
15. Place the crankshaft balancer in position on the crankshaft.
16. Thread the tool in the crankshaft. Ensure you engage at least 10 threads of the tool before pressing the crankshaft balancer in place.
17. Push the crankshaft balancer into position by tightening the nut on the tool until the large washer bottoms out on the crankshaft end.
18. Remove the tool.
19. Install the crankshaft balancer bolt.
20. Tighten the crankshaft balancer bolt and tighten to 74 ft. lbs. (100 Nm) plus an additional 150 degrees.
21. Remove the flywheel holding tool.
22. Install the starter.
23. Using engine support fixture, raise the engine into position.
24. Install the engine mount.
25. Install the engine mount strut bracket.
26. Install the drive belt.

CRANKSHAFT FRONT SEAL

REMOVAL & INSTALLATION

2.4L Engine

See Figure 85.

1. Remove the crankshaft damper.
2. Use a flat-bladed tool to remove the seal from the front cover.

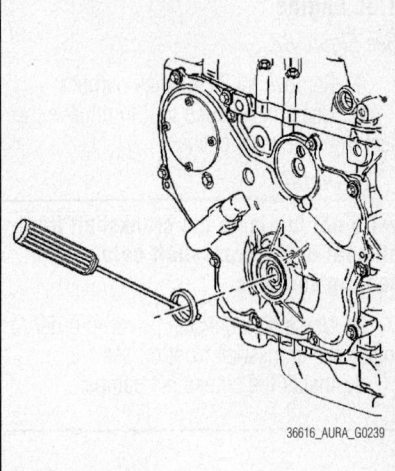

Fig. 85 Removing the crankshaft front oil seal—2.4L engine

To install:

3. Use a suitable seal driver in order to install the crankshaft front oil seal to the engine front cover.
4. Install the crankshaft damper.

3.5L Engine

See Figure 86.

1. Remove the crankshaft damper.
2. Remove the crankshaft key from the keyway.
3. Use a flat-bladed tool to remove the seal from the front cover.

To install:

4. Use a suitable seal driver in order to install the crankshaft front oil seal to the engine front cover.
5. Install the crankshaft key from the keyway.
6. Install the crankshaft damper.

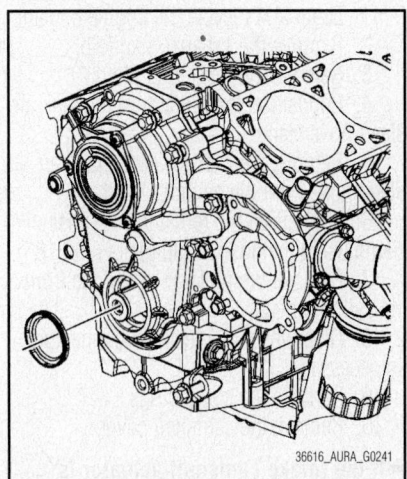

Fig. 86 Removing the crankshaft front seal—3.5L engine

3.6L Engine

See Figure 87.

1. Remove the crankshaft damper.
2. Use a flat-bladed tool to remove the seal from the front cover.

To install:

➡ **Do not lubricate the crankshaft front oil seal or the crankshaft balancer sealing surfaces.**

3. Use a suitable seal driver in order to install the crankshaft front oil seal.
4. Install the crankshaft damper.

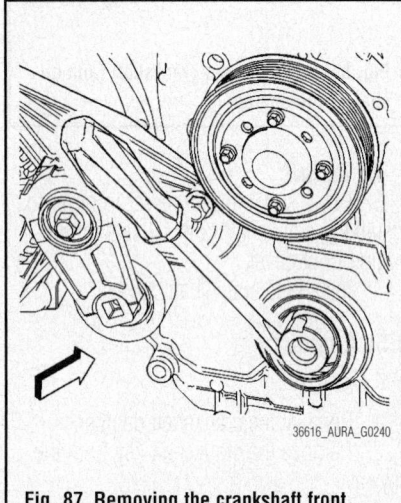

Fig. 87 Removing the crankshaft front seal—3.6L engine

CYLINDER HEAD

REMOVAL & INSTALLATION

2.4L Engine

See Figures 88 through 94.

1. Drain and recycle the engine coolant.
2. Remove the exhaust manifold.
3. Remove the intake manifold.
4. Reposition the radiator surge tank air bleed hose clamp.
5. Remove the radiator surge tank air bleed hose from the cylinder head.
6. Reposition the radiator inlet hose clamp using the hose clamp pliers (J 38185).
7. Remove the radiator inlet hose from the cylinder head.
8. Disconnect all electrical connectors as necessary.
9. Remove the spark plugs.
10. Remove the camshaft cover.

➡ **If the intake camshaft actuator is moving independently of the camshaft, this means the camshaft is not locked to the actuator. Rotate the camshaft**

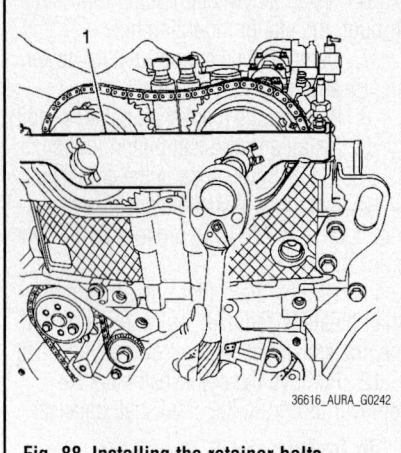

Fig. 88 Installing the retainer bolts

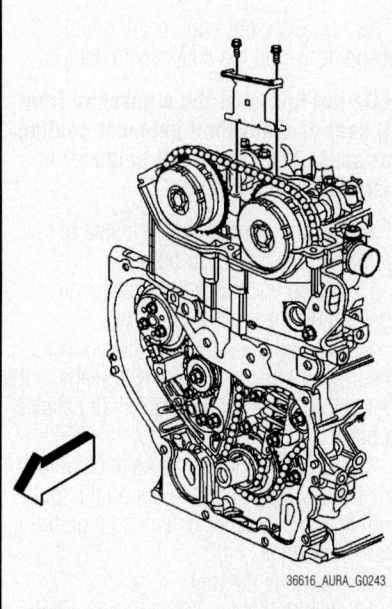

Fig. 89 Removing the upper timing chain guide bolts and guide—2.4L engine

counter-clockwise while the holing tool is installed and this will lock the camshaft to the actuator.

11. Rotate the crankshaft clockwise to install the Camshaft Actuator Retaining Tool (EN-48953).
12. Install the Camshaft Actuator Locking Tool (EN-48953).
13. Install the camshaft actuator retainer bolts and tighten to 89 inch lbs. (10 Nm).
14. Remove the upper timing chain guide bolts and guide.
15. Clean the timing chain and gears with solvent.

➡ **Ensure the timing chain and the camshaft position actuators are marked for proper assembly.**

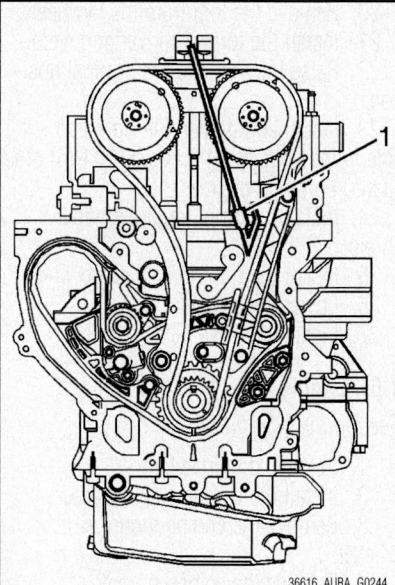

Fig. 90 Installing the Timing Chain Retention tool to the intake side of the timing chain—2.4L engine

16. Mark the timing gear sprockets and the timing chain. It is recommended that the paint marks are located in the 12 o'clock position.
17. Loosen, but do not remove the intake and exhaust camshaft actuator bolts.
18. Remove the Camshaft Actuator Locking Tool (EN-48953).

➡ **Ensure the tips of the Timing Chain Retention Tool Kit (EN-48749) are fully engaged into the timing chain. The retention tool rod can be used on the back side of the chain to ensure the teeth from the retention tool are engaged.**

19. Install the Timing Chain Retention Tool (EN-48749) to the intake side of the timing chain.
20. Remove the timing chain tensioner.

➡ **The intake camshaft and actuator should not rotate during the removal or installation.**

21. Install the Timing Chain Retention Tool (EN-48749) to the exhaust side of the timing chain.
22. Remove and discard the exhaust camshaft actuator bolt.
23. Remove the exhaust cam actuator from the exhaust camshaft while also removing the actuator from the chain.
24. Remove and discard the intake camshaft actuator bolt.
25. Remove the intake camshaft actuator from the camshaft while also removing the actuator from the timing chain.

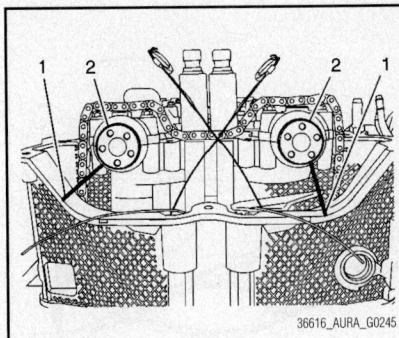

Fig. 91 Marking the cylinder head—2.4L engine

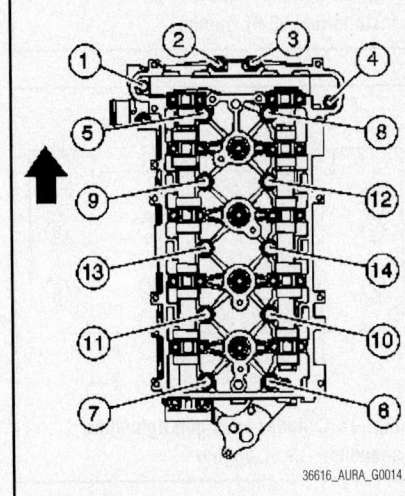

Fig. 92 Cylinder head bolt removal sequence

26. Mark the cylinder head in relationship to the camshaft actuator notch is on the camshaft.

27. Remove the fixed timing chain guide access plug.

28. Remove the upper fixed timing chain guide bolt.

➡ **The threaded rod from the timing chain retention tool can be used to help feed the rubber band around the chain guides.**

29. Install the rubber band around the top of the timing chain guides in order to pull the guides together.

30. Remove the cylinder head bolts in the sequence shown. Discard the bolts.

31. Remove the cylinder head.

32. Remove the cylinder head gasket.

33. Clean all of the gasket surfaces.

34. Use the following steps when cleaning the cylinder head and cylinder block surfaces:

    a. Use a razor blade gasket scraper to clean the cylinder head and cylinder

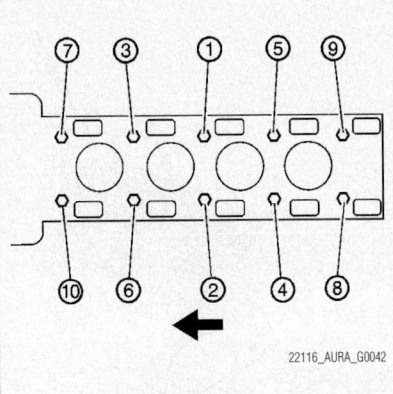

Fig. 93 Cylinder head bolt tightening sequence—2.4L engine

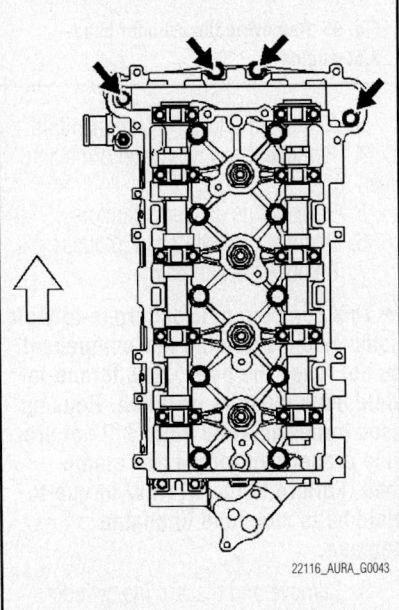

Fig. 94 Location of the front cylinder head bolts—2.4L engine

block gasket surfaces. Do not scratch or gouge either surface.

➡ **DO NOT use any other method or technique to clean these gasket surfaces.**

    b. Use a NEW razor blade on the cylinder head and a NEW blade on the cylinder block.

➡ **Be careful not to gouge or scratch the gasket surfaces. DO NOT gouge or scrape the combustion chamber surfaces. The feel of the gasket surface is important, not the appearance. There will be indentations from the gasket left in the cylinder head after all of the gasket material is removed. These small indentations will be filled in by the NEW gasket.**

    c. Hold the razor blade as parallel to the gasket surface as possible.

35. Clean the old sealer/lube and any dirt from around the bolt holes.

➡ **DO NOT use a tap to clean the cylinder head bolt holes.**

36. Clean the bolt holes with a nylon bristle brush.

37. When cleaning the cylinder head bolt holes use suitable commercial spray liquid solvent and compressed air from an extended-tip blow gun in order to reach the bottom of the holes.

38. If replacing the cylinder head, transfer all parts as necessary.

To install:

➡ **DO NOT use any sealing material.**

39. Install the cylinder head gasket.

40. Install the cylinder head.

41. Install NEW cylinder head bolts.

42. Install and tighten the cylinder head bolts in the sequence shown in 2 steps to 22 ft. lbs. (30 Nm) plus an additional 155 degrees.

43. Install the NEW front cylinder head bolts and tighten to 26 ft. lbs. (35 Nm).

44. Ensure the cylinder head and the camshaft are correctly aligned.

45. Remove the rubber band from around the top of the upper timing chain guides.

46. Install the fixed guide bolt into the cylinder head and tighten to 106 inch lbs. (12 Nm).

47. Apply sealant compound to the thread and install the timing chain guide bolt access hole plug.

48. Install the fixed timing chain guide access plug and tighten the plug to 59 ft. lbs. (90 Nm).

➡ **Ensure that the alignment mark made previously on the intake camshaft actuator is still aligned properly with the mark on the timing chain. If the mark made previously on the intake camshaft actuator is not aligned properly, refer to CAMSHAFT TIMING CHAIN, SPROCKET, AND TENSIONER.**

49. Install the timing chain onto the intake camshaft actuator.

50. Align the intake camshaft actuator alignment mark made previously with the timing chain mark and install the actuator onto the camshaft.

51. Install a NEW intake camshaft actuator bolt until snug.

52. Remove the Timing Chain Retention Tool (EN-48749) from the intake side of the timing chain.

➡Ensure that the alignment mark made previously on the exhaust camshaft actuator is still aligned properly with the mark on the timing chain. The exhaust cam may have to be rotated clockwise to install the exhaust actuator.

53. Install the timing chain onto the exhaust camshaft actuator.

54. Align the exhaust camshaft actuator alignment mark made previously with the timing chain mark and install the actuator onto the camshaft.

55. Install a NEW exhaust camshaft actuator bolt until snug.

56. Remove the Timing Chain Retention Tool (EN-48749) from the exhaust side of the timing chain.

➡Failure to reset the chain tensioner will put excess tension on the chain, limiting the chains life.

57. Reset and install the timing chain tensioner.

58. Install the Camshaft Actuator Locking Tool (EN-48953) to the actuators.

59. Install the camshaft actuator locking tool bolts and tighten to 89 inch lbs. (10 Nm).

60. Tighten the ENW camshaft actuator bolt to 22 ft. lbs. (30 Nm), plus an additional 100 degrees using the Angle Meter (J 45059).

61. Release the tensioner by applying a counterclockwise rotational torque of 33 ft. lbs. (45 Nm) to the harmonic balancer bolt.

62. Remove the Camshaft Actuator Locking tool.

63. Install the upper timing chain guide bolts and guide. Tighten the bolts to 89 inch lbs. (10 Nm).

64. Install the camshaft cover.

65. Install the spark plugs.

66. Connect all necessary electrical connectors.

67. Install the radiator inlet hose to the cylinder head.

68. Position the radiator inlet hose clamp.

69. Install the radiator surge tank air bleed hose to the cylinder head.

70. Position the radiator surge tank air bleed hose clamp.

71. Install the exhaust manifold.

72. Install the intake manifold.

73. Fill the cooling system

3.5L Engine

Right Side

See Figures 95 through 97.

1. Drain the engine oil.
2. Lower the vehicle.

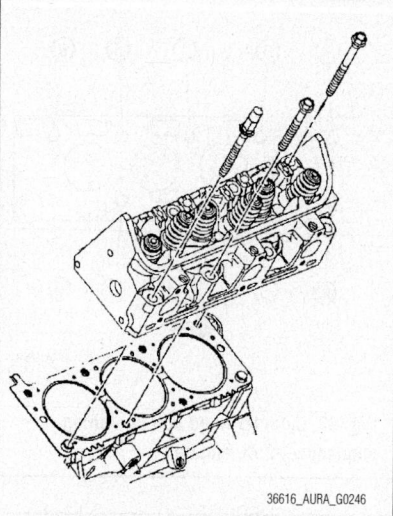

Fig. 95 Removing the cylinder head—3.5L engine

3. Remove the lower intake manifold.
4. Remove the valve rocker arms and push rods.
5. Remove the exhaust manifold.
6. Remove the right spark plugs.
7. Remove the alternator.

➡ This component uses torque-to-yield bolts. When servicing this component do not reuse the bolts, New torque-to-yield bolts must be installed. Reusing used torque-to-yield bolts will not provide proper bolt torque and clamp load. Failure to install NEW torque-to-yield bolts may lead to engine damage.

8. Remove and discard the cylinder head bolts.
9. Remove the cylinder head.
10. Remove and discard the cylinder head gasket.
11. Remove the cylinder locator dowel pins, if necessary.
12. Clean and inspect the cylinder head.

To install:

➡Head gaskets are specific for right hand and left hand applications, and also must be installed with the correct side facing up. Note the markings (1) on the head gaskets for proper installation. Failure to do so may lead to engine damage.

13. Install the cylinder head locator dowel pins, if necessary.
14. Inspect the cylinder head locator dowel pins for proper installation.
15. Install the cylinder head gasket.
16. Install the cylinder head and bolts.

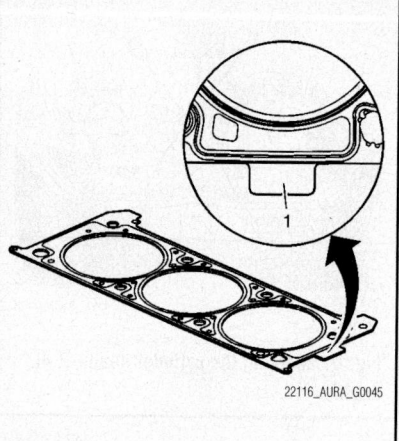

Fig. 96 Cylinder head gasket installation—3.5L engine

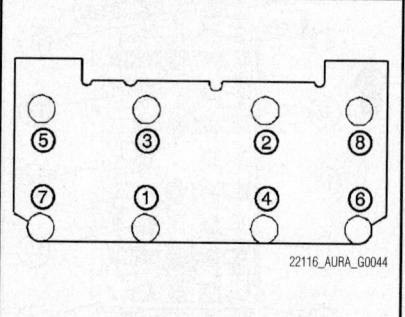

Fig. 97 Cylinder head bolt tightening sequence—3.5L engine

➡This component uses torque-to-yield bolts. When servicing this component do not reuse the bolts, New torque-to-yield bolts must be installed. Reusing used torque-to-yield bolts will not provide proper bolt torque and clamp load. Failure to install NEW torque-to-yield bolts may lead to engine damage.

17. Install the NEW small hex cylinder head bolts (5 and 8).

18. Install the NEW large hex cylinder head bolts (1, 2, 3, 4, 6 and 7).

19. Tighten the NEW cylinder head bolts using the following 2 steps:

   a. Step 1: in sequence to 44 ft. lbs. (60Nm).

   b. Step 2: in sequence an additional 140 degrees.

20. Install the alternator.
21. Install the right spark plugs.
22. Install the exhaust manifold.
23. Install the valve rocker arms and push rods.
24. Install the lower intake manifold.
25. Fill the engine with oil.
26. Inspect for leaks.

Left Side

See Figure 98.

1. Drain the engine oil.
2. Lower the vehicle.
3. Remove the lower intake manifold.
4. Remove the valve rocker arms and pushrods.
5. Remove the exhaust manifold.
6. Remove the oil level indicator tube.
7. Remove the left spark plugs.

➡ **This component uses torque-to-yield bolts. When servicing this component do not reuse the bolts, New torque-to-yield bolts must be installed. Reusing used torque-to-yield bolts will not provide proper bolt torque and clamp load. Failure to install NEW torque-to-yield bolts may lead to engine damage.**

8. Remove and discard the cylinder head bolts.
9. Remove the cylinder head.
10. Remove and discard the cylinder head gasket.
11. Remove the cylinder head locator dowel pins, if necessary.
12. Clean and inspect the cylinder head.

To install:

➡ **Head gaskets are specific for right hand and left hand applications, and also must be installed with the correct side facing up. Note the markings (1) on the head gaskets for proper installation. Failure to do so may lead to engine damage.**

13. Install the cylinder head locator dowel pins, if necessary.
14. Inspect the cylinder head locator dowel pins for proper installation.
15. Install the cylinder head gasket.
16. Install the cylinder head and bolts.

➡ **This component uses torque-to-yield bolts. When servicing this component do not reuse the bolts, New torque-to-yield bolts must be installed. Reusing**

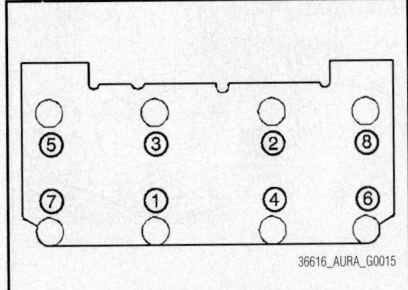

Fig. 98 Left side cylinder head bolt tightening sequence—3.5L engine

used torque-to-yield bolts will not provide proper bolt torque and clamp load. Failure to install NEW torque-to-yield bolts may lead to engine damage.

17. Install the NEW small hex cylinder head bolts (5 and 8).
18. Install the NEW large hex cylinder head bolts (1, 2, 3, 4, 6 and 7).
19. Tighten the NEW cylinder head bolts using the following 2 steps:
  a. Step 1: in sequence to 44 ft. lbs. (60Nm).
  b. Step 2: in sequence an additional 140 degrees.
20. Install the left spark plugs.
21. Install the oil level indicator tube.
22. Install the exhaust manifold.
23. Install the valve rocker arms and pushrods.
24. Install the lower intake manifold. Fill the engine with oil.
25. Inspect for leaks

3.6L Engine

Right Side

See Figure 99.

1. Remove the hood.
2. Remove the right bank secondary timing chain.
3. With the aid of an assistant, remove the cylinder head with the exhaust manifold.
4. Remove and discard the cylinder head gasket.
5. Clean and inspect the cylinder head and the engine block sealing surfaces.

To install:

6. Install a NEW cylinder head gasket.
7. With the aid of an assistant, carefully install the cylinder head with the exhaust manifold to the engine. Ensure the cylinder

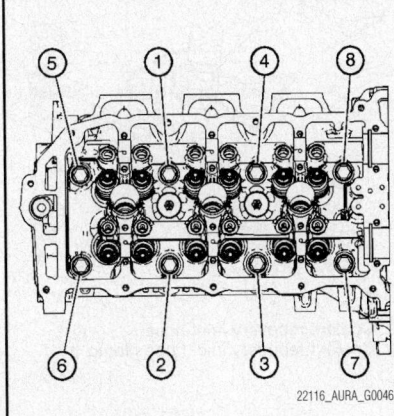

Fig. 99 Right side cylinder head bolt tightening sequence—3.6L engine

head locating pins are securely mounted in the cylinder block deck face.

8. Install a NEW right cylinder head gasket using the deck face locating pins for retention.
9. Align the right cylinder head with the deck face locating pins.
10. Place the right cylinder head in position on the deck face.

➡ **DO NOT allow oil on the cylinder head bolt bosses or DO NOT reuse the old M11 cylinder head bolts.**

11. Tighten the NEW M11 cylinder head bolts using the following 2 steps:
  a. Step 1: in sequence to 22ft. lbs. (30Nm).
  b. Step 2: in sequence an additional 150 degrees.
12. Install and tighten the NEW M8 cylinder head bolt using the following 2 steps:
  a. Step 1: first pass to 11 ft. lbs. (15 Nm).
  b. Step 2: second pass an additional 75 degrees.
13. Install the right bank secondary timing chain.
14. Install the hood.

Left Side

1. Remove the left bank secondary timing chain.
2. Remove the oil level indicator.
3. Disconnect the coolant temperature sensor electrical connector.
4. Remove the wiring harness ground from the cylinder head.
5. Remove the catalytic converter.
6. Remove the cylinder head with the exhaust manifold.
7. Remove and discard the left cylinder head gasket.
8. Clean and inspect the cylinder head and the engine block sealing surfaces.

To install:

9. Install a NEW cylinder head gasket.
10. Carefully install the cylinder head with the exhaust manifold to the engine.
11. Install the catalytic converter to the exhaust manifold.
12. Connect the wiring harness electrical connector located at the side of the cylinder head.
13. Install the wiring harness ground to the cylinder head.
14. Install the coolant temperature sensor electrical connector.
15. Install the oil level indicator.
16. Install the left bank secondary timing chain.

ENGINE ASSEMBLY

REMOVAL & INSTALLATION

2.4L Engine

See Figures 100 through 107.

1. Relieve the fuel system pressure.
2. Remove the air cleaner assembly.
3. Disconnect the fuel feed pipe quick connect fitting at the fuel rail.
4. Disconnect the Evaporative Emission (EVAP) line quick connect fitting from the EVAP purge solenoid.
5. Remove the fuel feed pipe clip from the fuel line bracket.
6. Remove the transaxle shift cable clip from the fuel line bracket.
7. Remove the battery tray.

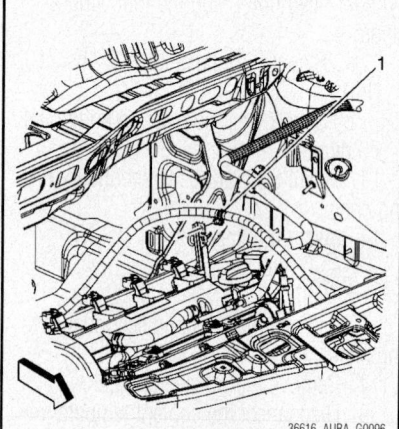

Fig. 100 Removing the transaxle shift cable clip (1) from the fuel line bracket—2.4L engine

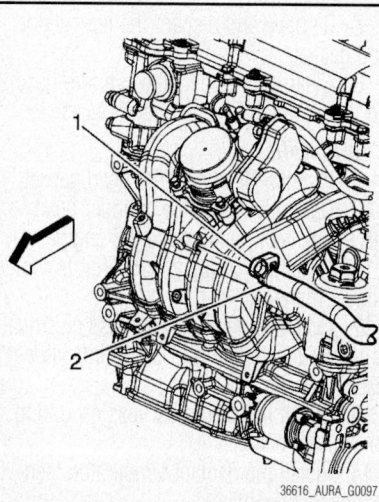

Fig. 101 Locating the vacuum brake booster hose on the intake manifold—2.4L engine

8. Reposition the vacuum brake booster hose clamp at the intake manifold.
9. Remove the vacuum brake booster hose from the intake manifold. Reposition the brake booster hose out of the way.
10. Remove the coolant recovery inlet hose clamp at the cylinder head.
11. Remove the coolant recovery inlet pipe clip from the fuel rail.
12. Remove the coolant recovery inlet hose from the cylinder head. Reposition the hose/pipe out of the way.
13. Reposition the radiator inlet hose clamp.
14. Remove the radiator inlet hose from the cylinder head.
15. Remove the radiator outlet hose.
16. Reposition the heater inlet hose clamp at the thermostat housing.
17. Remove the heater inlet hose from the thermostat housing.
18. Reposition the coolant recovery reservoir/heater inlet hose clamp at the thermostat housing.
19. Remove the coolant recovery reservoir/heater inlet hose from the thermostat housing.
20. Raise and support the vehicle.
21. Drain the engine oil.
22. Unbolt the A/C compressor and reposition out of the way.
23. Remove the positive battery cable to starter motor nut.
24. Remove the positive battery cable lead from the starter motor.
25. Remove the positive battery cable from in between the starter and the engine. Reposition the positive battery cable out of the way.

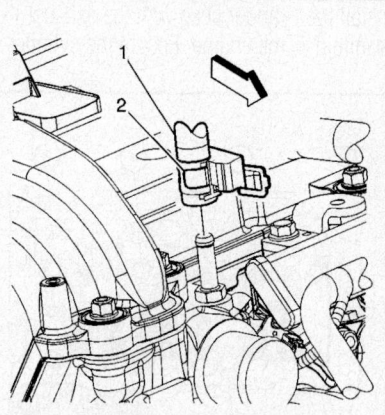

1. Coolant recovery inlet hose
2. Coolant recovery inlet hose clamp

Fig. 102 Removing the coolant recovery inlet hose from the cylinder head—2.4L engine

26. Disconnect the generator electrical connector.
27. Reposition the engine harness boot.
28. Remove the generator nut.
29. Remove the engine harness lead from the generator.
30. Lower the vehicle.
31. Remove the transaxle shift cable from the range select lever.
32. Release the shift control cable retaining clip and remove the cable from the shift control cable bracket.

➡**The radiator/condenser/fan assembly will stay in the vehicle during engine removal.**

33. Using long tie straps, secure the radiator/condenser/fan assembly to the radiator support.
34. Raise the vehicle.
35. Remove the front wheels and tires.
36. Remove the front fender liners.

➡**A piece of hardwood should be used between the transaxle and the engine cradle. This wood will support the engine when the left side engine mounts bolts are removed.**

37. Install a piece of hardwood 1 x 2 x 4 between the transaxle and the engine cradle.
38. Drain the transaxle fluid.
39. Remove the transaxle oil cooler line to transaxle nut.
40. Remove the transaxle oil cooler lines from the transaxle.
41. Remove the catalytic converter.

➡**Secure the steering wheel in the straight forward position before separating the intermediate shaft from the steering gear, or damage to the SIR coil will occur.**

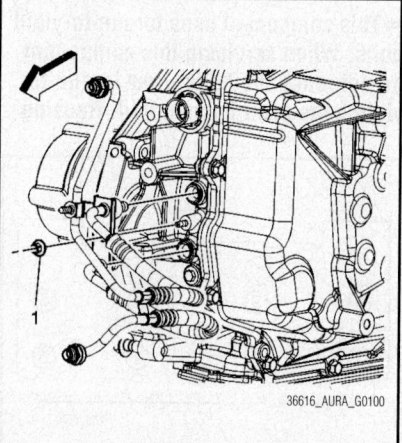

Fig. 103 Locating the transaxle oil cooler line to transaxle nut (1)—2.4L engine

42. Remove the intermediate to steering gear pinch bolt and disconnect the intermediate shaft from the steering gear. Discard the pinch bolt.

43. Remove and discard both outer tie rod to steering knuckle nuts.

➡**Hold the ball stud to prevent turning during removal of the nut.**

44. Separate the tie rods from the steering knuckles.

45. Remove the stabilizer link to stabilizer shaft nuts and disconnect the stabilizer links from the stabilizer shaft.

46. Remove and discard both of the lower control arm ball stud cotter pins.

47. Loosen the ball stud nuts until the nuts are level with the top of the ball stud.

48. Separate the lower control arms from the steering knuckles.

49. Remove the ball stud nuts.

50. Remove the wheel drive shafts.

51. Lower the vehicle.

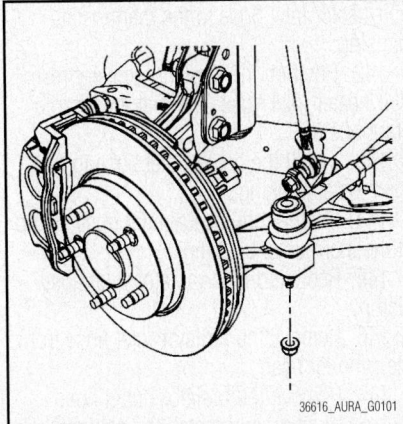

Fig. 104 Locating the outer tie rod to steering knuckle nuts—2.4L engine

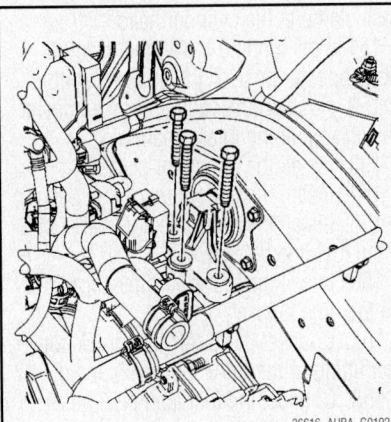

Fig. 105 Locating the transaxle mount to transaxle bolts—2.4L engine

52. Remove the engine mount to bracket bolts.

53. Remove the transaxle mount to transaxle bolts.

54. Raise the vehicle.

➡**During the powertrain removal support the vehicle body by placing a jack at the rear of the vehicle.**

55. Position a engine support table under the powertrain assembly.

➡**Blocks of wood can be used between the front of the cradle and the oil pan to table in order to level the powertrain during the removal.**

56. With the table positioned, fully raise the table to contact with the powertrain assembly.

57. Remove the cradle to body bolts. Discard the bolts.

➡**When lowering the engine/transaxle assembly, verify all brake lines, shifter cables and other components are free during removal.**

58. Lower the engine table and raise the body on the hoist until the engine/transaxle and cradle are free from the vehicle.

59. Disconnect the engine wiring harness electrical connector from the throttle actuator.

60. Disconnect the engine wiring harness electrical connector from the fuel injector wiring harness electrical connector.

61. Remove the engine wiring harness clip from the oil level indicator tube bracket.

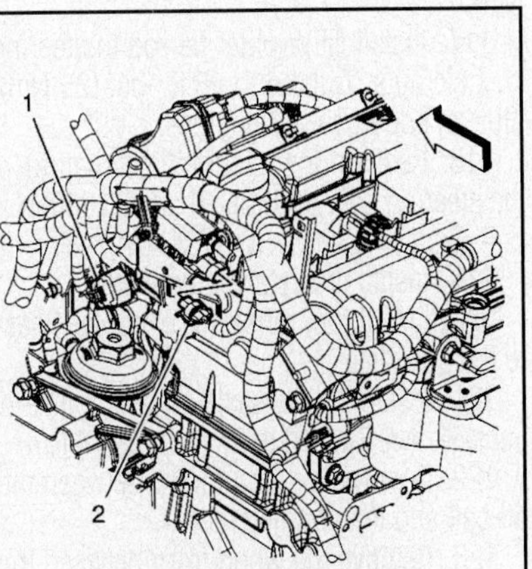

1. Engine wiring harness electrical connector to intake CMP sensor
2. Engine wiring harness electrical connector to EVAP emission canister purge solenoid valve

Fig. 106 Locating the CMP and EVAP emission canister purge solenoid valve electrical connectors—2.4L engine

62. Disconnect the engine wiring harness electrical connectors from the ignition coils.

63. Disconnect the engine wiring harness electrical connectors from the camshaft actuators.

64. Disconnect the engine wiring harness electrical connector from the Crankshaft Position (CKP) sensor.

65. Disconnect the engine wiring harness electrical connector from the oil pressure sensor.

66. Disconnect the engine wiring harness electrical connector from the knock sensor.

67. Disconnect the engine wiring harness electrical connector from the intake Camshaft Position (CMP) sensor.

68. Disconnect the engine wiring harness electrical connector from the EVAP emission canister purge solenoid valve.

69. Disconnect the engine wiring harness electrical connector from the exhaust CMP sensor.

70. Disconnect the engine wiring harness electrical connector) from the Engine Coolant Temperature (ECT) sensor.

71. Disconnect the engine wiring harness electrical connector from the Heated Oxygen Sensor (HO2S) electrical connector.

72. Remove the engine wiring harness clip from the stud.

73. Remove the engine wiring harness ground bolt and reposition the ground terminal from the engine.

74. Gather all branches of the engine wiring harness and reposition the harness out of the way.

75. Remove the starter motor bolts and starter.

76. Remove the torque converter to flexplate bolts.

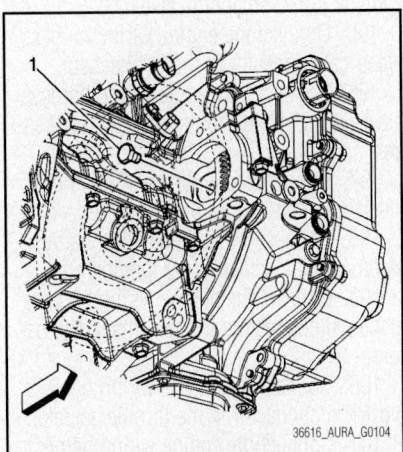

Fig. 107 Removing the torque converter to flexplate bolts (1)—2.4L engine

77. Install a suitable lifting devise to the engine.

78. Remove the transaxle bolts from the engine.

79. Separate the engine from the transaxle.

80. Install the engine to a suitable engine stand.

To install:

81. Install a suitable lifting devise to the engine.

82. Using the lifting devise, position and install the engine to the transaxle.

83. Install the transaxle bolts to the engine and tighten to 55 ft. lbs. (75 Nm).

84. Install the torque converter to flex-plate bolts and tighten to 44 ft. lbs. (60 Nm).

85. Remove the engine lifting devise.

86. Install the starter motor and bolts. Tighten to 39 ft. lbs. (53 Nm).

87. Gather all branches of the engine wiring harness and position the harness to the engine.

88. Position the engine wiring harness ground terminal to the engine and install the engine wiring harness ground bolt and tighten the bolts to 15 ft. lbs. (20 Nm).

89. Connect the engine wiring harness electrical connector to the ECT sensor.

90. Connect the engine wiring harness electrical connector to the HO2S electrical connector.

91. Install the engine wiring harness clip to the stud.

92. Connect the engine wiring harness electrical connector to the exhaust CMP sensor.

93. Connect the engine wiring harness electrical connector to the intake CMP sensor.

94. Connect the engine wiring harness electrical connector to the EVAP emission canister purge solenoid valve.

95. Connect the engine wiring harness electrical connector to the CKP sensor.

96. Connect the engine wiring harness electrical connector to the oil pressure sensor.

97. Connect the engine wiring harness electrical connector to the knock sensor.

98. Connect the engine wiring harness electrical connectors to the ignition coils.

99. Connect the engine wiring harness electrical connectors to the camshaft actuators.

100. Connect the engine wiring harness electrical connector to the throttle actuator.

101. Connect the engine wiring harness electrical connector to the fuel injector wiring harness electrical connector .

102. Install the engine wiring harness clip to the oil level indicator tube bracket.

103. Position the powertrain and support table under the vehicle.

104. Raise the powertrain into position under the vehicle.

105. With the table positioned, if required, lower the vehicle over the powertrain.

106. Align the lower radiator pins with the cradle. Ensure all hoses and electrical harnesses are correctly routed and free from the loading path of the powertrain.

107. Install the NEW cradle to body bolts and tighten to 114 ft. lbs. (155 Nm).

108. Lower the vehicle.

109. Install the transaxle mount to transaxle bolts. Tighten to 41 ft. lbs. (55 Nm).

➡ **The engine mount to bracket bolts must be hand started. Do not pry the engine mount to align the holes.**

110. Install the engine mount to bracket bolts and tighten to 37 ft. lbs. (50 Nm).

111. Install the wheel drive shafts.

112. Install the control arm ball studs into the steering knuckles.

113. Install the ball stud nuts and tighten to 30 ft. lbs. (40 Nm).

114. Continue to tighten the nuts only enough to align the castle nut slots with the ball stud, install NEW cotter pins.

115. Connect the stabilizer links to the stabilizer shaft and install the stabilizer link to stabilizer shaft nuts. Tighten to 48 ft. lbs. (65 Nm).

116. Connect the outer tie rods to the steering knuckles. Tighten to 30 ft. lbs. (40 Nm).

117. Install NEW outer tie rod to steering knuckle nuts. Tighten to 48 ft. lbs. (25 Nm) plus an additional 90 degrees.

118. Position the intermediate shaft to the steering gear and install a NEW pinch bolt. Tighten to 25 ft. lbs. (34 Nm).

119. Install the catalytic converter.

120. Install the transaxle oil cooler lines to the transaxle.

121. Install the transaxle oil cooler line to transaxle nut. Tighten to 27 inch lbs. (4 Nm).

122. Remove the wood from between the oil pan and the engine cradle.

123. Remove the wood from between the transaxle and the engine cradle.

124. Install the front fender liners.

125. Install the front wheels and tires.

126. Lower the vehicle.

127. Unsecure and position the radiator/condenser/fan assembly.

128. Install the shift control cable to the shift control cable bracket and engage the shift control cable retaining clip.

129. Install the transaxle shift cable to the range select lever.

130. Raise and support the vehicle.

131. Install the engine harness lead to the generator.

132. Install the generator nut and tighten to 15 ft. lbs. (20 Nm).

133. Seat the engine harness boot.

134. Connect the generator electrical connector.

135. Position and install the positive battery cable between the starter and the engine.

136. Install the positive battery cable lead to the starter motor.

137. Install the positive battery cable to starter motor nut. Tighten the nut to 80 inch lbs. (9 Nm).

138. Position the A/C compressor and install the bolts. Tighten to 16 ft. lbs. (22 Nm).

139. Connect the engine wiring harness electrical connector to the A/C compressor.

140. Lower the vehicle.

141. Install the coolant recovery reservoir/heater inlet hose to the thermostat housing.

142. Position the coolant recovery reservoir/heater inlet hose clamp at the thermostat housing.

143. Install the heater inlet hose to the thermostat housing.

144. Position the heater inlet hose clamp at the thermostat housing.

145. Reposition the radiator inlet hose clamp.

146. Remove the radiator inlet hose from the cylinder head.

147. Remove the radiator outlet hose.

148. Position and install the coolant recovery inlet hose to the cylinder head.

149. Install the coolant recovery inlet pipe clip to the fuel rail.

150. Install the coolant recovery inlet hose clamp at the cylinder head.

151. Position and install the vacuum brake booster hose to the intake manifold.

152. Position the vacuum brake booster hose clamp at the intake manifold.

153. Install the alternator starter.

154. Install the battery tray.

155. Install the transaxle shift cable clip to the fuel line bracket.

156. Install the fuel feed pipe clip (2) to the fuel line bracket.

157. Connect the EVAP line quick connect fitting to the EVAP purge solenoid.

158. Connect the fuel feed pipe quick connect fitting at the fuel rail.

159. Install the air cleaner assembly.

160. Fill the transaxle with fluid.

161. Refill the engine with oil.

162. Start the engine and allow the engine to run, inspect for leaks. Correct as necessary.

3.5L Engine

See Figures 108 through 111.

1. Disconnect the negative battery cable.
2. Remove the intake manifold cover.
3. Drain the cooling system.
4. Drain the engine oil.
5. Remove the air cleaner assembly.
6. Remove the hood.
7. Remove the engine mount strut.
8. Remove the drive belt.
9. Disconnect the front Knock Sensor (KS).
10. Disconnect the rear Knock Sensor (KS).
11. Disconnect the Camshaft Position (CMP) sensor, Crankshaft Position (CKP) sensor and the oil control valves.
12. Disconnect the Manifold Absolute Pressure (MAP) sensor.
13. Disconnect the Evaporative Emission (EVAP) canister purge solenoid.
14. Disconnect the front and rear ignition coils.
15. Disconnect the A/C compressor.
16. Disconnect the coolant temperature sensor.
17. Disconnect the following electrical connectors:
    a. The Heated Oxygen Sensor (HO2S)
    b. The Exhaust Gas Recirculation (EGR) valve
    c. The electronic throttle control
    d. The body wiring harness-to-engine harness
18. Raise and support the vehicle.
19. Remove the catalytic converters.

20. Remove the engine wiring harness grounds from the transaxle.
21. Remove the engine mount lower bolts.
22. Remove the torque converter covers.
23. Remove the starter motor.
24. Remove the Air Conditioning (A/C) compressor. DO NOT discharge the A/C system. Support the compressor.
25. Remove the torque converter bolts.
26. Remove the engine mount bracket.
27. Remove the transaxle to oil pan brace bolts and brace.
28. Remove the lower transaxle-to-engine bolt and the stud.
29. Remove the radiator outlet hose from the engine.
30. Lower the vehicle and support the transaxle.

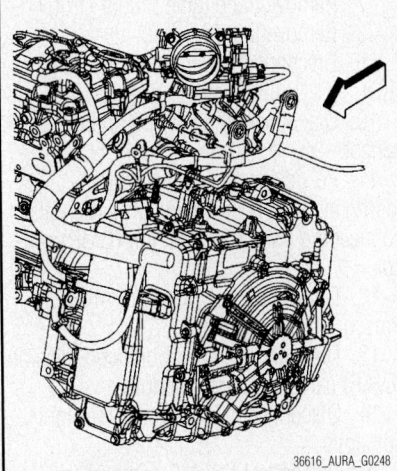

36616_AURA_G0248

Fig. 109 Disconnecting the engine wiring harness grounds from the transaxle—3.5L engine

31. Remove the heater outlet and inlet hoses from the engine.
32. Remove the vacuum hoses from the upper intake manifold.
33. Remove the brake booster vacuum hose from the upper intake manifold.
34. Remove the fuel lines from the fuel rail.
35. Remove the radiator inlet hose from the engine.
36. Install the engine lifting device to the engine.
37. Remove the upper transaxle-to-engine bolts and the stud.
38. Remove the engine from the vehicle.
39. Remove the flywheel.
40. Install the engine to the engine stand.

To install:

41. Remove the engine from the engine stand.
42. Install the flywheel.
43. Install the engine to the vehicle.
44. Install the upper transaxle-to-engine bolts and the stud. Tighten the bolts and the stud to 55 ft. lbs. (75 Nm).
45. Remove the engine lifting device.
46. Install the radiator inlet hose to the engine.
47. Install the fuel lines to the fuel rail.
48. Install the brake booster vacuum hose to the upper intake manifold.
49. Install the vacuum hoses to the upper intake manifold.
50. Install the heater inlet and outlet hoses to the engine.
51. Raise the vehicle and remove the transaxle support.
52. Install the radiator outlet hose to the engine.
53. Install the lower transaxle-to-engine

36616_AURA_G0247

Fig. 108 Removing the Knock Sensors (1, 2)

36616_AURA_G0249

Fig. 110 Removing the transaxle to oil pan brace bolts and brace—3.5L engine

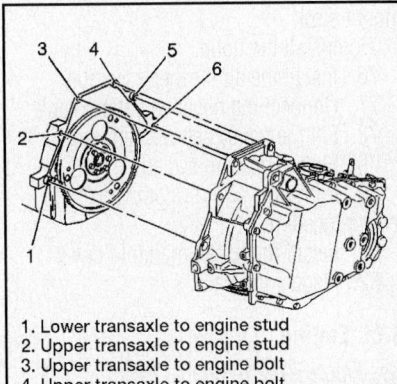

1. Lower transaxle to engine stud
2. Upper transaxle to engine stud
3. Upper transaxle to engine bolt
4. Upper transaxle to engine bolt
5. Upper transaxle to engine bolt
6. Lower transaxle to engine bolt

36616_AURA_G0250

Fig. 111 Disconnecting the engine—3.5L engine

bolt and the stud. Tighten the bolts and the stud to 55 ft. lbs. (75 Nm).

54. Position the transaxle to oil pan brace and install the bolts. Tighten the bolts to 37 ft. lbs. (50 Nm).

55. Install the engine mount bracket.

56. Install the torque converter bolts.

57. Install the A/C compressor.

58. Install the starter motor.

59. Install the torque converter covers.

60. Install the engine mount lower bolts. Tighten the bolts to 38 ft. lbs. (50 Nm).

61. Install the engine wiring harness grounds to the transaxle.

62. Install the engine wiring harness ground nut to the transaxle stud. Tighten the nut to 26 ft. lbs. (35 Nm).

63. Install the catalytic converters.

64. Lower the vehicle.

65. Connect the following electrical connectors:

- The body wiring harness—to — engine harness
- The electronic throttle control
- The Exhaust Gas Recirculation (EGR) valve
- the heated oxygen sensor (HO2S)

66. Connect the coolant temperature sensor.

67. Connect the A/C compressor.

68. Connect the front and rear ignition coils.

69. Connect the Evaporative Emission (EVAP) canister purge solenoid.

70. Connect the Manifold Absolute Pressure (MAP) sensor.

71. Connect the Camshaft Position (CMP) sensor, Crankshaft Position (CKP) sensor and the oil control valves.

72. Connect the rear Knock Sensor (KS).

73. Connect the front Knock Sensor (KS).

74. Install the drive belt and engine mount strut.

75. Install the hood.

76. Install the air cleaner assembly.

77. Connect the negative battery cable.

78. Fill the crankcase with engine oil.

79. Fill the cooling system.

80. Perform a CKP system variation learn procedure.

81. Install the intake manifold cover.

82. Inspect for leaks.

3.6L Engine

See Figures 112 through 115.

1. Disconnect the negative battery cable.

2. Remove the intake manifold cover.

3. Drain the cooling system.

4. Drain the engine oil.

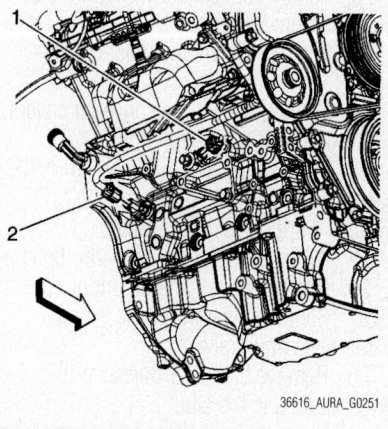

Fig. 112 Disconnecting the Knock Sensors (1, 2)—3.6L engine

5. Remove the air cleaner assembly.

6. Remove the hood.

7. Remove the engine mount strut.

8. Remove the drive belt.

9. Disconnect the front Knock Sensor (KS).

10. Disconnect the rear KS and the crank sensor.

11. Re-position the plastic wire loom/shield on each valve cover, then disconnect the Camshaft Position (CMP) sensor.

12. Disconnect the Manifold Absolute Pressure (MAP) sensor.

13. Disconnect the Evaporative Emission (EVAP) canister purge solenoid.

14. Disconnect the front and rear ignition coils.

15. Disconnect the A/C compressor.

16. Disconnect the coolant temperature sensor, Heated Oxygen Sensor (HO2S), Exhaust Gas Recirculation (EGR) valve, electronic throttle control and body wiring harness-to-engine harness.

17. Raise and support the vehicle.

18. Remove the catalytic converters.

19. Remove the engine wiring harness grounds from the transaxle.

20. Remove the engine mount lower bolts.

21. Remove the torque converter covers.

22. Remove the starter motor.

23. Remove the Air Conditioning (A/C) compressor. DO NOT discharge the A/C system. Support the compressor.

24. Remove the power steering pump and position aside.

25. Remove the torque converter bolts.

26. Remove the engine mount bracket.

27. Remove the transaxle to oil pan brace bolts and brace.

28. Remove the lower transaxle-to-engine bolt and the stud.

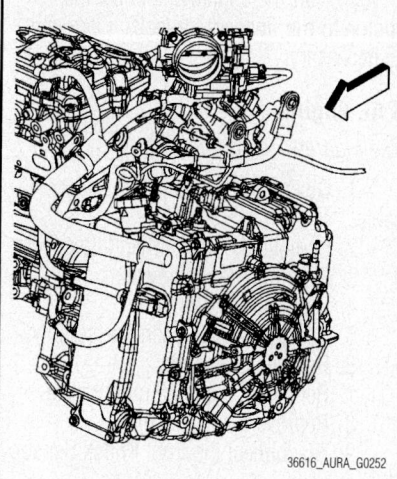

Fig. 113 Removing the engine wiring harness grounds from the transaxle—3.6L engine

Fig. 114 Removing the transaxle to oil pan brace bolts and brace—3.6L engine

29. Remove the radiator outlet hose from the engine.

30. Lower the vehicle and support the transaxle.

31. Remove the engine coolant thermostat housing from the engine.

32. Remove the vacuum hoses from the upper intake manifold.

33. Remove the brake booster vacuum hose from the upper intake manifold.

34. Remove the fuel lines from the fuel rail.

35. Remove the battery ground from the rear of engine.

36. Remove the radiator inlet hose from the engine.

37. Install the engine lifting device to the engine.

38. Remove the upper transaxle-to-engine bolts and the stud.

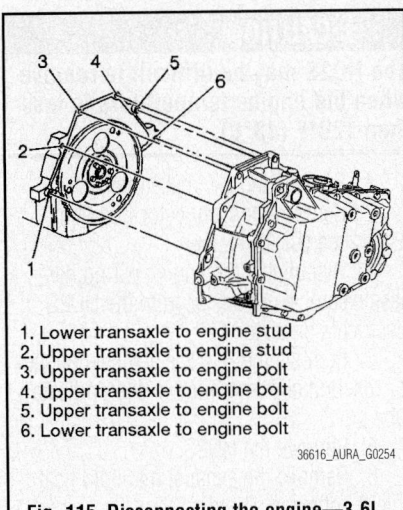

1. Lower transaxle to engine stud
2. Upper transaxle to engine stud
3. Upper transaxle to engine bolt
4. Upper transaxle to engine bolt
5. Upper transaxle to engine bolt
6. Lower transaxle to engine bolt

36616_AURA_G0254

Fig. 115 Disconnecting the engine—3.6L engine

39. Remove the engine from the vehicle.
40. Remove the flywheel.
41. Install the engine to the engine stand.

To install:
42. Remove the engine from the engine stand.
43. Install the flywheel. Install the engine to the vehicle.
44. Install the upper transaxle-to-engine bolts and the stud. Tighten to 55 ft. lbs. (75 Nm).
45. Remove the engine lifting device.
46. Install the radiator inlet hose to the engine.
47. Install the battery ground to the rear of engine. Install the fuel lines to the fuel rail.
48. Install the brake booster vacuum hose to the upper intake manifold.
49. Install the vacuum hoses to the upper intake manifold.
50. Install the engine coolant thermostat housing to the engine.
51. Raise the vehicle and remove the transaxle support.
52. Install the radiator outlet hose to the engine.
53. Install the lower transaxle-to-engine bolt and the stud. Tighten to 55 ft. lbs. (75 Nm).
54. Position the transaxle to oil pan brace and install the bolts. Tighten to 37 ft. lbs. (50 Nm).
55. Install the engine mount bracket.
56. Install the torque converter bolts.
57. Install the power steering pump.
58. Install the A/C compressor.
59. Install the starter motor.
60. Install the torque converter covers.
61. Install the engine mount lower bolts. Tighten to 38 ft. lbs. (50 Nm).

62. Install the engine wiring harness grounds to the transaxle.
63. Install the engine wiring harness ground nut to the transaxle stud. Tighten to 26 ft. lbs. (35 Nm).
64. Install the remaining components in the reverse order of removal.
65. Fill the crankcase with engine oil.
66. Fill cooling system.
67. Perform a CKP system variation learn procedure.
68. install the intake manifold cover.
69. Inspect for leaks.

EXHAUST MANIFOLD

REMOVAL & INSTALLATION

2.4L Engine

See Figure 116.

1. Remove the exhaust manifold heat shield.
2. Remove the Heated Oxygen Sensor (HO2S).
3. Remove and discard the exhaust manifold to cylinder head retaining nuts.
4. Remove the exhaust manifold.
5. Clean all of the sealing surfaces.

To install:
6. Install new exhaust manifold studs. Tighten the studs to 89 inch lbs. (10 Nm).
7. Install the exhaust manifold gasket.
8. Install the exhaust manifold to the cylinder head.
9. Install the NEW exhaust manifold to cylinder head retaining nuts finger tight.
10. Tighten the NEW exhaust manifold to cylinder head retaining nuts in the sequence shown. Tighten the nuts a second time to 124 inch lbs. (14 Nm).
11. Coat the threads of the oxygen sensor with anti-seize GM P/N 12397953 or equivalent.
12. Install the oxygen sensor to 31 ft. lbs. (42 Nm).

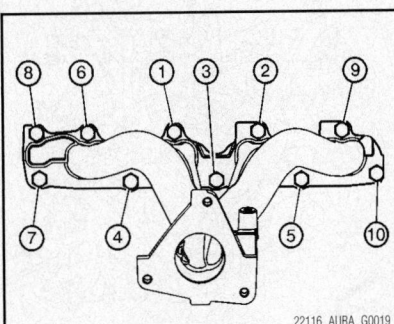

22116_AURA_G0019

Fig. 116 Exhaust manifold torque sequence—2.4L engine

13. Install the exhaust manifold heat shield. Tighten the bolts to 16 ft. lbs. (22 Nm).

3.5L Engine

Right Side

See Figures 117 through 119.

➡The oxygen sensor uses a permanently attached pigtail and connector. Do not remove the pigtail from the oxygen sensor. Damage to or removal of the pigtail connector could affect proper operation of the oxygen sensor.

➡The use of excessive force may damage the threads in the exhaust manifold/pipe.

> ✳✳ **CAUTION**
>
> The in-line connector and louvered end must be kept clear of grease, dirt or other contaminants. Avoid using cleaning solvents of any type. DO NOT drop or roughly handle the heated oxygen sensor (HO2S).

> ✳✳ **CAUTION**
>
> The HO2S may be difficult to remove when the engine temperature is less than 120°F (48°C).

1. Remove the generator.
2. Remove the Connector Position Assurance (CPA) retainer.
3. Disconnect the engine wiring harness electrical connector from the HO2S electrical connector.
4. Remove the HO2S electrical connector rosebud clip from the ignition coil bracket.

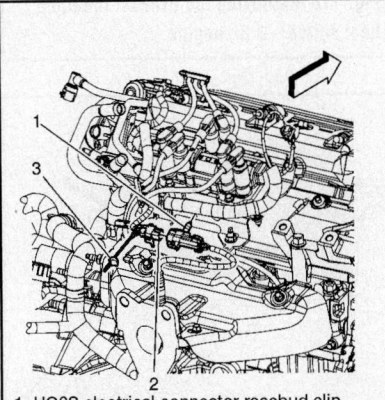

1. HO2S electrical connector rosebud clip
2. Engine wiring harness electrical connector
3. Connector Position Assurance (CPA) retainer

36616_AURA_G0255

Fig. 117 Disconnecting the electrical connectors—3.5L engine

5. Remove the Heated Oxygen Sensor (HO2S).

6. Remove the exhaust manifold heat shield bolts and shield.

7. Remove the upper exhaust manifold bolts.

8. Remove the right catalytic converter.

9. Remove the lower exhaust manifold bolts.

10. Remove the exhaust manifold.

11. Remove and discard the exhaust manifold gasket.

To install:

12. Install a NEW exhaust manifold gasket onto the cylinder head studs.

13. Install the exhaust manifold.

14. Install the exhaust manifold bolts and tighten to 15 ft. lbs. (20 Nm).

15. Install the right catalytic converter.

16. Install the exhaust manifold heat shield and bolts and tighten to 89 inch lbs. (10 Nm).

➡A special anti-seize compound is used on the HO2S threads. The compound consists of graphite suspended

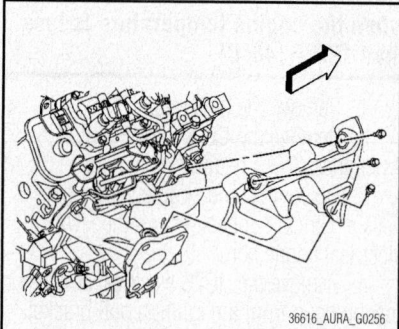

Fig. 118 Removing the exhaust manifold heat shield—3.5L engine

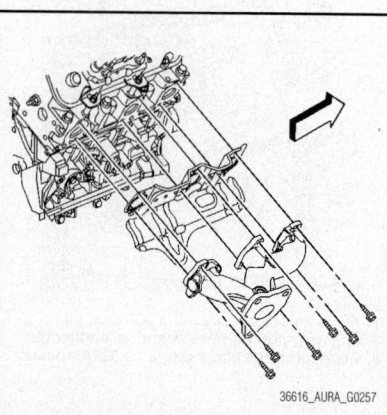

Fig. 119 Removing the exhaust manifold (right side)—3.5L engine

in fluid and glass beads. The graphite will burn away, but the glass beads will remain, making the sensor easier to remove. New or service sensors will already have the compound applied to the threads. If a sensor is removed from an engine and is to be reinstalled, the threads must have anti-seize compound applied before the reinstallation.

17. Coat the threads of the HO2S with anti-seize compound GM P/N 12377953 or equivalent, if necessary.

18. Install the HO2S and tighten to 31 ft. lbs. (42 Nm).

19. Connect the engine wiring harness electrical connector to the HO2S electrical connector.

20. Install the CPA retainer.

21. Install the HO2S electrical connector rosebud clip to the ignition coil bracket.

22. Install the generator.

Left Side

See Figures 120 through 122.

➡The oxygen sensor uses a permanently attached pigtail and connector. Do not remove the pigtail from the oxygen sensor. Damage to or removal of the pigtail connector could affect proper operation of the oxygen sensor.

➡The use of excessive force may damage the threads in the exhaust manifold/pipe.

✴✴ CAUTION

The in-line connector and louvered end must be kept clear of grease, dirt or other contaminants. Avoid using cleaning solvents of any type. DO NOT drop or roughly handle the heated oxygen sensor (HO2S).

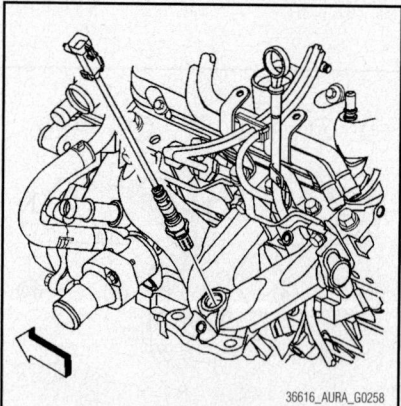

Fig. 120 Removing the HO2S— 3.5L engine

✴✴ CAUTION

The HO2S may be difficult to remove when the engine temperature is less than 120°F (48°C).

1. Remove the air intake duct.

2. Remove the Connector Position Assurance (CPA) retainer.

3. Disconnect the engine wiring harness electrical connector from the HO2S electrical connector.

4. Remove the HO2S electrical connector rosebud clip from the oil level indicator tube tab.

5. Remove the HO2S.

6. Remove the exhaust manifold heat shield bolts and shield.

7. Remove the upper exhaust manifold bolts.

8. Raise and support the vehicle.

9. Remove the left catalytic converter.

10. Remove the lower exhaust manifold bolts.

11. Remove the exhaust manifold.

12. Remove and discard the exhaust manifold gasket.

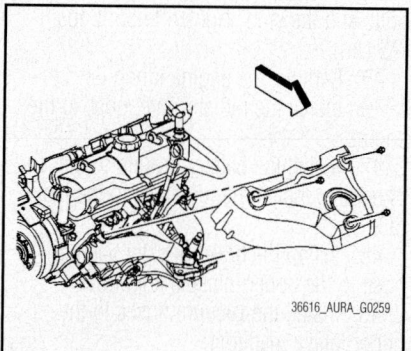

Fig. 121 Removing the exhaust manifold heat shield (left side)—3.5L engine

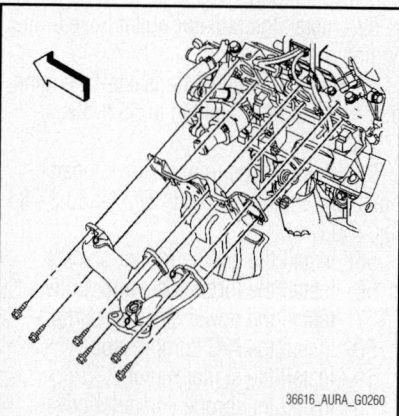

Fig. 122 Removing the exhaust manifold (left side)—3.5L engine

To install:

13. Install a NEW exhaust manifold gasket onto the cylinder head studs.
14. Install the exhaust manifold.
15. Install the exhaust manifold bolts and tighten to 15 ft. lbs. (20 Nm).
16. Install the left catalytic converter.
17. Lower the vehicle.
18. Install the exhaust manifold heat shield and bolts and tighten to 89 inch lbs. (10 Nm).

✳✳ CAUTION

A special anti-seize compound is used on the HO2S threads. The compound consists of graphite suspended in fluid and glass beads. The graphite will burn away, but the glass beads will remain, making the sensor easier to remove. New or service sensors will already have the compound applied to the threads. If a sensor is removed from an engine and is to be reinstalled, the threads must have anti-seize compound applied before the reinstallation.

19. Coat the threads of the HO2S with anti-seize compound GM P/N 12377953 or equivalent, if necessary.
20. Install the HO2S and tighten to 31 ft. lbs. (42 Nm).
21. Connect the engine wiring harness electrical connector to the HO2S electrical connector.
22. Install the HO2S electrical connector rosebud clip to the oil level indicator tube tab.
23. Install the CPA retainer.
24. Install the air intake duct.

3.6L Engine

Right Side

See Figures 123 through 125.

1. Remove the catalytic converter.
2. Remove the exhaust manifold lower bolts.
3. Lower the vehicle half way.
4. Remove the exhaust manifold upper bolts.
5. Remove the exhaust manifold.
6. Remove and discard the exhaust manifold gasket.

To install:

7. Install one upper exhaust manifold bolt to the exhaust manifold.
8. Place the NEW exhaust manifold gasket onto the bolt.
9. Position and install the exhaust manifold (with gasket) to the cylinder head.

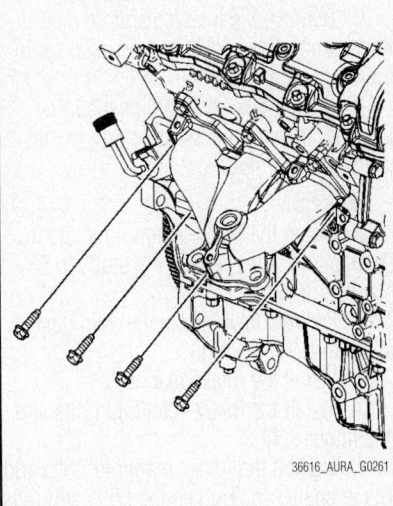

36616_AURA_G0261

Fig. 123 Removing the exhaust manifold lower bolts (right side)—3.6L engine

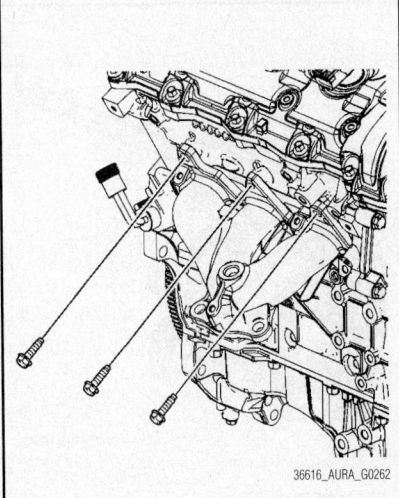

36616_AURA_G0262

Fig. 124 Removing the exhaust manifold upper bolts (right side)—3.6L engine

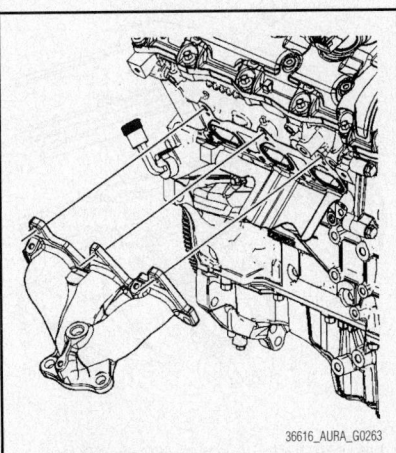

36616_AURA_G0263

Fig. 125 Removing the exhaust manifold

10. Loosely install the remaining upper exhaust manifold bolts.
11. Raise and support the vehicle.
12. Loosely install the lower exhaust manifold bolts.
13. Tighten the exhaust manifold bolts to 15 ft. lbs. (20 Nm).
14. Install the catalytic converter.

Left Side

See Figures 126 and 127.

1. Remove the exhaust manifold heat shield.
2. Remove the oil level indicator.
3. Remove the catalytic converter to exhaust manifold nuts.
4. Remove the exhaust manifold bolts.
5. Remove the exhaust manifold and gasket. Discard the gasket.

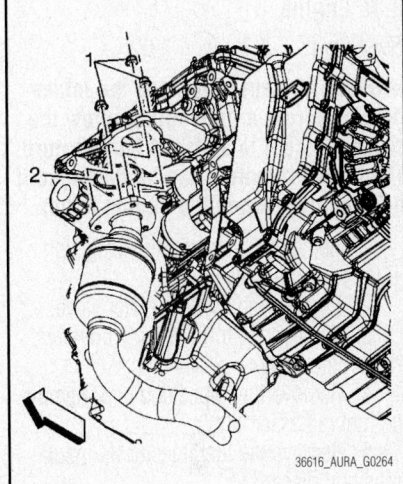

36616_AURA_G0264

Fig. 126 Removing the catalytic converter to exhaust manifold nuts (left side)—3.6L engine

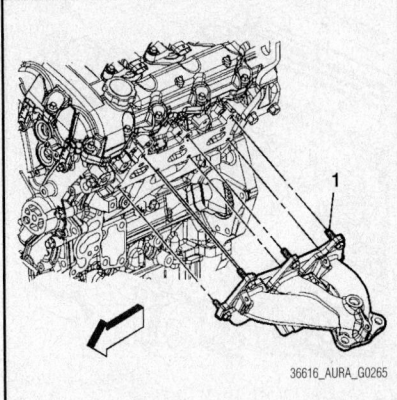

36616_AURA_G0265

Fig. 127 Removing the exhaust manifold (left side)—3.6L engine

To install:

6. Install one exhaust manifold bolt to the exhaust manifold.

7. Install the NEW exhaust manifold gasket onto the cylinder head and bolt.

8. Install the exhaust manifold (with gasket) to the catalytic converter and the cylinder head.

9. Install the remaining exhaust manifold bolts and tighten to 15 ft. lbs. (20 Nm).

10. Install the catalytic converter to exhaust manifold nuts and tighten to 33 ft. lbs. (45 Nm).

11. Install the oil level indicator.

12. Install the exhaust manifold heat shield.

13. Inspect for exhaust leaks.

INTAKE MANIFOLD

REMOVAL & INSTALLATION

2.4L Engine

See Figures 128 through 133.

➡**Never attempt to remove the intake manifold from a hot engine, allow the engine to cool to ambient temperature. The intake manifold can be damaged if it is removed when the engine is hot.**

1. Remove the evaporative emission (EVAP) canister valve tube .

2. Remove the EVAP canister valve.

3. Remove the throttle body bolts and the throttle body.

4. Remove fuel pipes and clip. Remove the fuel rail assembly.

5. Remove the fuel injector tip insulations and discard.

6. Remove the intake manifold retaining nuts and bolts.

7. Removing the intake manifold.

8. Remove the intake manifold gasket, if necessary. The gasket can be used again if it is not damaged.

9. If the intake manifold needs to be replaced, transfer the throttle body to the new intake manifold.

To install:

10. Install the intake manifold studs in the manifold face. Tighten the studs to 53 inch lbs. (6 Nm).

11. Install a new intake manifold gasket on the intake manifold.

12. Install the intake manifold.

13. Install the intake manifold bolts and nuts finger tight.

14. Tighten the intake manifold bolts and nuts in sequence. Tighten the bolts and nuts to 89 inch lbs. (10 Nm).

15. Lubricate NEW fuel injector tip insulators with engine oil.

16. Install NEW fuel injector tip insulators.

17. Lubricate the fuel injector oil rings with engine oil.

18. Install the fuel rail assembly.

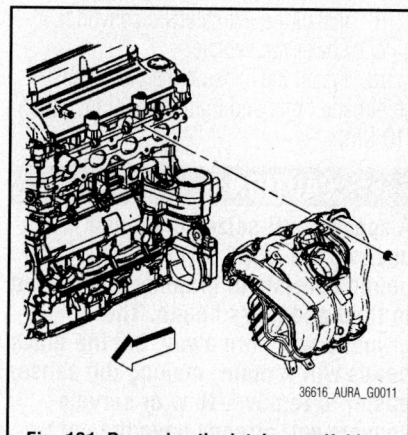

Fig. 131 Removing the intake manifold

Fig. 129 Removing the fuel rail assembly

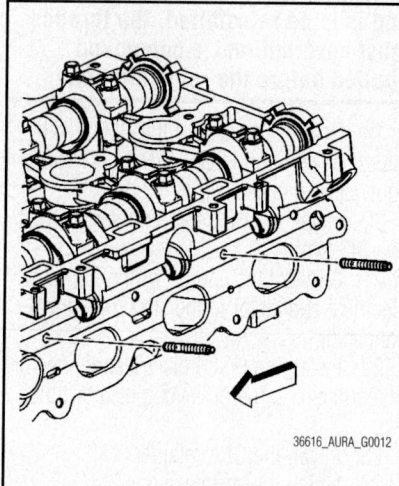

Fig. 132 Installing the intake manifold studs

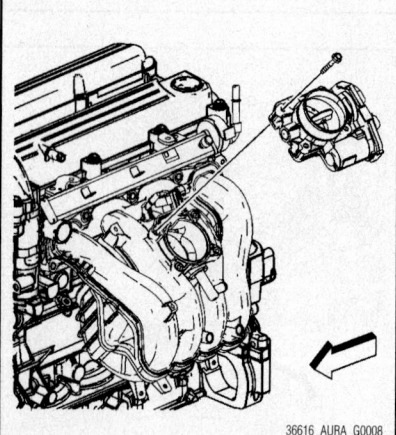

Fig. 128 Removing the throttle body—2.4L engine

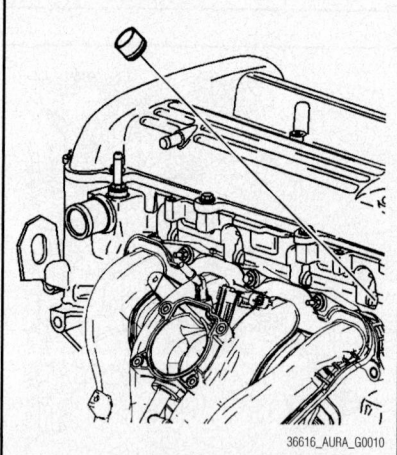

Fig. 130 Removing the fuel injector tip insulators

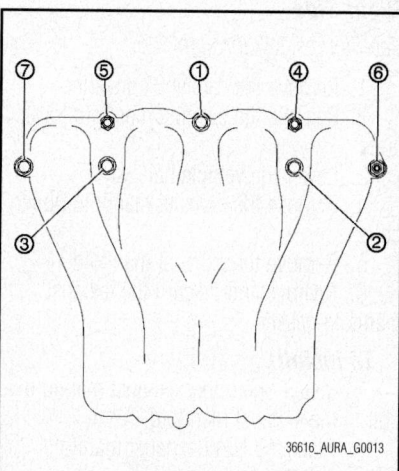

Fig. 133 Identifying intake manifold tightening sequence

19. Install the fuel rail stud. Tighten the stud to 89 inch lbs. (10 Nm).

20. Install a new throttle body gasket.

21. Install the throttle body. Tighten the bolts to 89 inch lbs. (10 Nm).

22. Install the EVAP canister valve. Tighten the EVAP canister valve to 16 ft. lbs. (22 Nm).

23. Install the EVAP canister valve tube.

3.5L Engine

Upper

See Figures 134 through 138.

1. Remove the intake manifold cover.

2. Disconnect the fuel feed pipe quick connect fitting from the fuel rail.

3. Disconnect the Evaporative Emission (EVAP) pipe quick connect fitting from the purge solenoid.

4. Remove the fuel line clip from the Manifold Absolute Pressure (MAP) sensor bracket.

5. Reposition the fuel/EVAP lines out of the way.

6. Drain and recycle the engine coolant.

7. Remove the air cleaner outlet duct.

8. Remove the Positive Crankcase Ventilation (PCV) fresh air tube from the rocker cover.

9. Remove the PCV foul air tube quick connect fitting from the rocker cover.

10. Remove the PCV foul air tube from the intake manifold.

11. Reposition the brake booster vacuum hose clamp at the intake manifold.

12. Remove the brake booster vacuum hose from the intake manifold.

13. Reposition the radiator surge tank inlet hose clamp.

14. Remove the radiator surge tank inlet hose from the inlet pipe.

15. Remove the radiator surge tank inlet pipe bolts.

16. Remove the radiator surge tank inlet pipe.

17. Remove and discard the O-ring seal.

18. Disconnect the engine wiring harness electrical connector from the MAP sensor.

19. Disconnect the engine wiring harness electrical connector from the EVAP canister purge solenoid.

20. Disconnect the engine wiring harness electrical connector from the electronic throttle control (ETC).

21. Disconnect the left side spark plug wires from the spark plugs.

22. Disconnect the left side spark plug wires from the ignition coil.

23. Disengage the spark plug wire retainer clips from the heater inlet and outlet pipe bracket and the MAP sensor bracket.

24. Remove the left side spark plug wires.

25. Remove the heater inlet and outlet pipe nuts from the throttle body studs.

26. Reposition the heater inlet and outlet hose clamps from the pipes.

27. Remove the heater inlet and outlet hoses from the heater inlet and outlet pipes.

28. Remove the heater inlet and outlet pipe bracket from the throttle body studs. Reposition the inlet and outlet pipe out of the way.

29. Remove the ignition coil bracket bolts.

30. Remove the alternator rear brace upper nut.

31. Remove the alternator through bolt.

32. Remove the alternator rear brace.

33. Remove the upper intake manifold bolts and stud.

34. Separate and remove the upper intake manifold from the lower intake manifold.

35. Remove the upper to lower intake manifold gaskets.

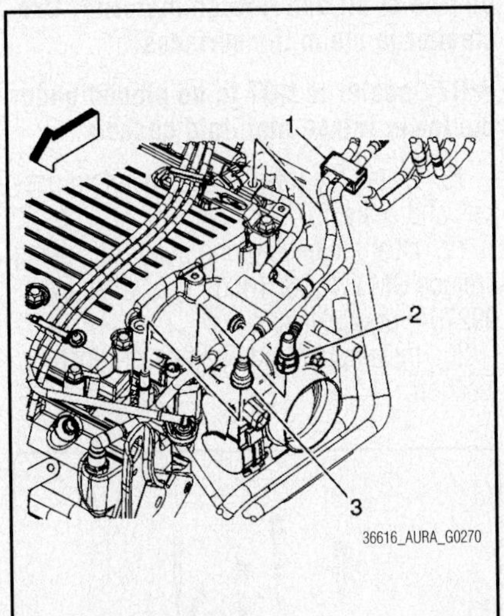

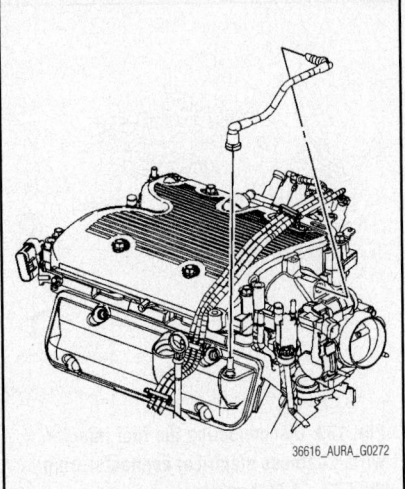

Fig. 134 Disconnecting the fuel and EVAP lines—3.5L engine

Fig. 136 Removing the PCV foul air tube—3.5L engine

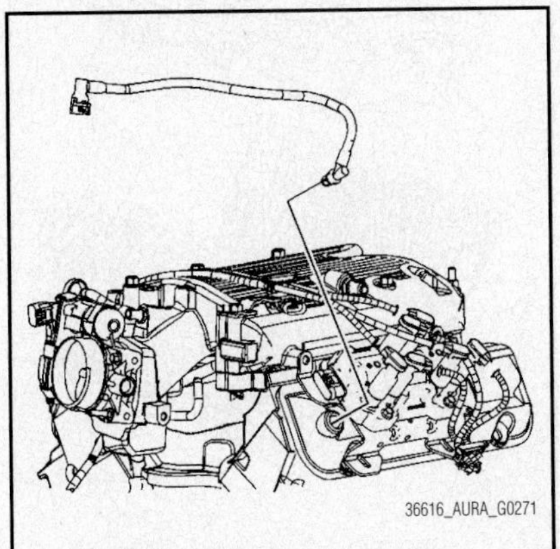

Fig. 135 Removing the PCV fresh air tube—3.5L engine

Fig. 137 Removing the ignition coil bracket bolts (1)—3.5L engine

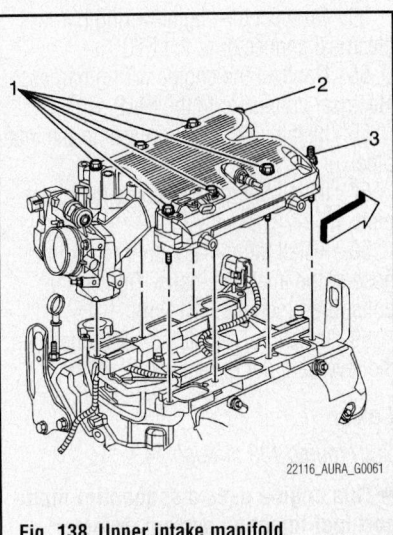

Fig. 138 Upper intake manifold mounting—3.5L engine

To install:

36. Install the NEW upper to lower intake manifold gaskets.

37. Install the upper intake manifold onto the lower intake manifold.

38. Apply threadlock to the upper intake manifold bolts/stud threads.

39. Install the upper intake manifold bolts and stud and tighten to 18 ft. lbs. (25 Nm).

40. Place the alternator rear brace onto the stud.

41. Install the alternator through bolt until snug.

42. Install the alternator rear brace upper nut until snug.

43. Tighten the alternator through bolt to 37 ft. lbs. (50 Nm) and the rear brace upper nut to 18 ft. lbs. (25 Nm).

44. Install the ignition coil bracket bolts and tighten to 18 ft. lbs. (25 Nm).

45. Position the inlet and outlet pipe and install the heater inlet and outlet pipe bracket to the throttle body studs.

46. Install the heater inlet and outlet hoses to the heater inlet and outlet pipes.

47. Position the heater inlet and outlet hose clamps to the pipes.

48. Install the heater inlet and outlet pipe nuts to the throttle body studs. Tighten the nuts to 89 inch lbs. (10 Nm).

49. Install the left side spark plug wires.

50. Connect the left side spark plug wires to the spark plugs.

51. Connect the left side spark plug wires to the ignition coil.

52. Engage the spark plug wire retainer clips to the heater inlet and outlet pipe bracket and the MAP sensor bracket.

53. Connect the engine wiring harness electrical connector to the EVAP canister purge solenoid.

54. Connect the engine wiring harness electrical connector to the ETC.

55. Connect the engine wiring harness electrical connector to the MAP sensor.

56. Install a NEW O-ring seal to the inlet pipe.

57. Install the radiator surge tank inlet pipe.

58. Install the radiator surge tank inlet hose to the inlet pipe bolts. Tighten the bolts to 89 inch lbs. (10 Nm).

59. Install the remaining components in the reverse order of removal.

Lower

See Figures 139 through 143.

➡This engine uses a sequential multi-port fuel injection system. Injector wiring harness connectors must be connected to their appropriate fuel injector or exhaust emissions and engine performance may be seriously affected.

1. Remove the upper intake manifold.
2. Remove the valve rocker arm covers.
3. Remove the coolant crossover pipe.
4. Disconnect the fuel injector wiring harness electrical connector from the Engine Coolant Temperature (ECT) sensor.
5. Disconnect the engine wiring harness electrical connector from the fuel injector inline electrical connector.
6. Disconnect the fuel injector wiring harness electrical connector from the Camshaft Position (CMP) sensor.
7. Remove the fuel injector wiring harness connector bracket bolt from the intake manifold.
8. Remove the fuel rail bolts and rail.
9. Remove the lower intake manifold bolts.

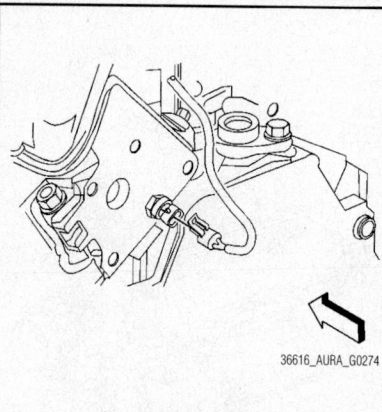

36616_AURA_G0274

Fig. 139 Disconnecting the fuel injector wiring harness electrical connector from the ECT—3.5L engine

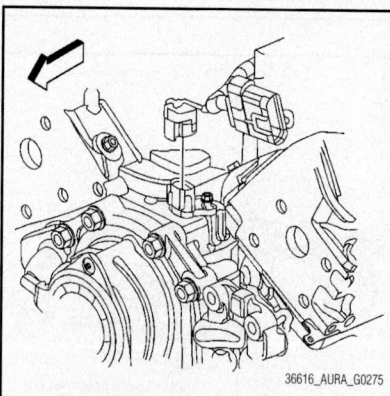

36616_AURA_G0275

Fig. 140 Disconnecting the fuel injector wiring harness electrical connector from the CMP—3.5L engine

10. Remove the lower intake manifold.
11. Loosen the rocker arm bolts.

➡Place the valve train components in a rack in order to ensure that the components are installed in the same location from which they were removed.

12. Remove the rocker arms.
13. Remove the push rods. The intake push rods measure 5.81 inch (147.51 mm). The exhaust push rods measure 6.1 inch (154.87 mm).
14. Remove the lower intake manifold gaskets and seals.
15. Clean the lower intake manifold gasket mating surfaces on the cylinder heads and engine block.
16. Clean the gasket and seal surfaces on the lower intake manifold with degreaser.
17. Remove all the loose room temperature vulcanizing (RTV) sealer.

To install:

➡All gasket–mating surfaces need to be free of oil and foreign material. Use cleaner to clean the surfaces.

➡RTV sealer is NOT to be placed under the lower intake manifold gaskets.

18. Install the lower intake manifold gaskets and seals.
19. Coat the ends of the push rods using prelube GM P/N 36616501 (Canadian P/N 992704) or equivalent.
20. Install push rods in their original location.

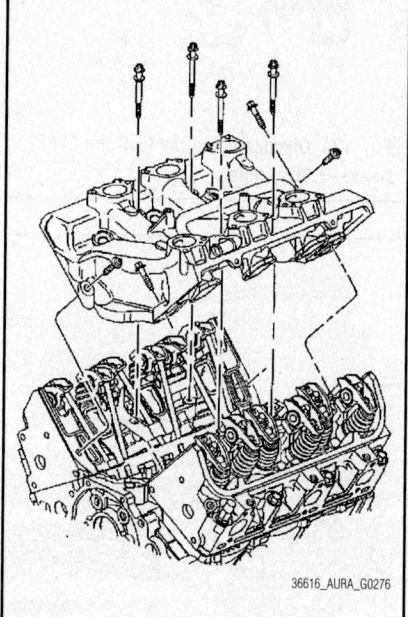

36616_AURA_G0276

Fig. 141 Removing the lower intake manifold—3.5L engine

- The intake pushrods are identified with yellow stripes.
- The exhaust pushrods are identified with green stripes.

21. Coat the rocker arm friction surfaces using prelube GM P/N 36616501 (Canadian P/N 992704) or equivalent.

➡**Shims (P/N 88894006) may be required under the valve rocker arm pedestals if reconditioning has been performed on the cylinder head or its components.**

22. Install the rocker arms in their original locations.

23. Install the rocker arm bolts. Tighten the bolts to 25 ft. lbs. (34 Nm).

24. With the NEW gaskets and seals in place, apply a small drop, 0.31–0.39 in. (8–10mm) of RTV sealer to the 4 corners of the intake manifold to block joints (1).

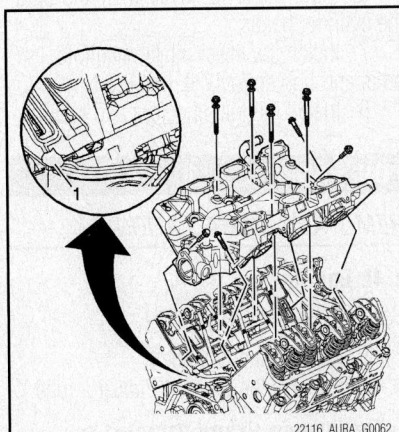

Fig. 142 Apply a small drop, 0.31–0.39 in. (8–10mm) of RTV sealer to the 4 corners of the intake manifold to block joints (1)—3.5L engine

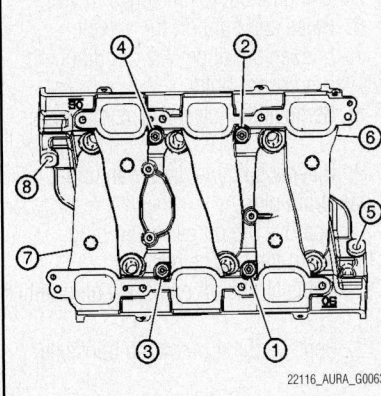

Fig. 143 Lower intake manifold torque sequence—3.5L engine

➡**Maximum gasket performance is achieved when using new fasteners, which contain a thread-locking patch. If the fasteners are not replaced, a thread locking chemical must be applied to the fastener threads. Failure to replace the fasteners or apply a thread-locking chemical MAY reduce gasket sealing capability.**

➡**Failure to tighten vertical bolts before the diagonal bolts may cause an oil leak.**

25. Apply sealer to the lower intake manifold bolt threads.

26. Install the lower intake manifold bolts and tighten the lower intake manifold bolts in the sequence as follows:

    a. Bolts 1, 2, 3, 4 to 12 ft. lbs. (16 Nm).

      b. Bolts 5, 8 to 18 ft. lbs. (25 Nm).

      c. Bolts 6, 7 to 18 ft. lbs. (25 Nm).

27. Inspect the fuel rail, fuel injectors for damage and replace as necessary.

28. Lubricate with clean engine oil and install NEW injector lower O-rings seals onto the injectors.

29. Install the injector nozzles into the lower intake manifold injector bores.

30. Press on the injector rail using the palms of both hands until the injectors are fully seated.

31. Install the fuel injector rail bolts and tighten to 89 inch lbs. (10 Nm).

32. Position the fuel injector wiring harness electrical connector bracket to the intake manifold and install the bolt. Tighten to 10 ft. lbs. (14 Nm).

33. Connect the fuel injector wiring harness electrical connector to the CMP sensor.

34. Connect the engine wiring harness electrical connector to the fuel injector inline electrical connector.

35. Connect the fuel injector wiring harness electrical connector to the ECT sensor.

36. Install the coolant crossover pipe.

37. Install the valve rocker arm covers.

38. Install the upper intake manifold.

3.6L Engine

Upper

See Figures 144 through 147.

1. Remove the fuel injector sight shield.

2. Remove the air cleaner outlet duct.

3. Disconnect the fuel feed line quick connect fitting from the fuel rail.

4. Remove the fuel feed pipe line nut and remove the fuel feed line clip from the stud.

5. Reposition the fuel feed line out of the way.

6. Remove the coolant air bleed hose/pipe clip bolt from the upper intake manifold.

7. Reposition the coolant air bleed hose clamp at the water outlet.

8. Remove the coolant air bleed hose from the water outlet.

9. Remove the coolant air bleed hose/pipe clip from the upper intake manifold stud and reposition out of the way.

10. Reposition the brake booster vacuum hose clamp at the upper intake manifold.

11. Remove the brake booster vacuum hose from the upper intake manifold.

12. Disconnect the engine wiring harness electrical connector from the Manifold Absolute Pressure (MAP) sensor.

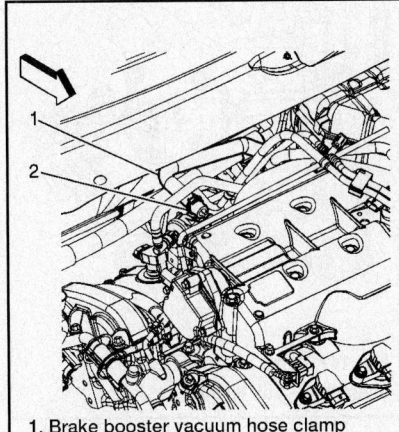

1. Brake booster vacuum hose clamp
2. Brake booster vacuum hose

Fig. 144 Removing the brake booster vacuum hose from the upper intake manifold—3.6L engine

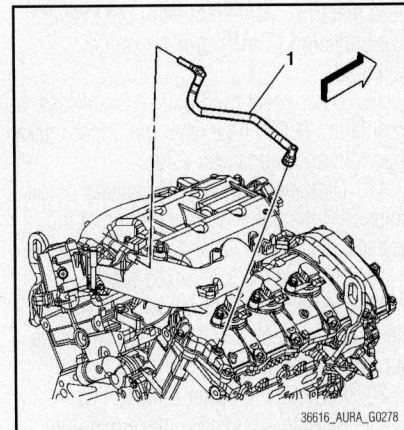

Fig. 145 Disconnecting the PCV tube—3.6L engine

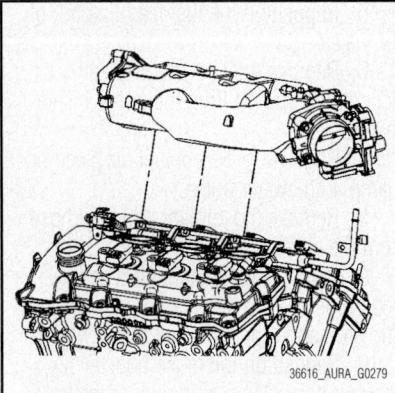

36616_AURA_G0279

Fig. 146 Removing the upper intake manifold—3.6L engine

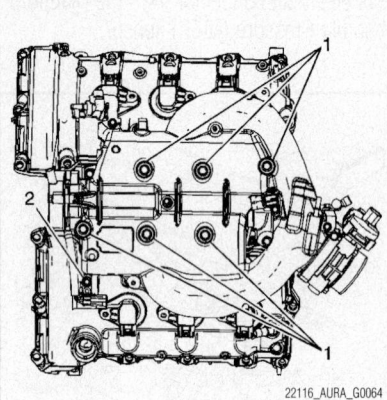

22116_AURA_G0064

Fig. 147 Upper intake manifold mounting—3.6L engine

13. Disconnect the engine wiring harness electrical connector from the electronic throttle control (ETC).

14. Disconnect the engine wiring harness electrical connector from the intake manifold tuning valve.

15. Disconnect the engine wiring harness electrical connector from the Evaporative Emission (EVAP) canister purge solenoid.

16. Disconnect the Positive Crankcase Ventilation (PCV) tube from the upper intake manifold and reposition aside.

17. Disconnect the EVAP canister purge solenoid tube quick connect fitting at the upper intake manifold and reposition aside.

18. Remove the fuel rail to bracket bolt.

19. Remove the fuel rail wiring harness electrical connector bolt and reposition the harness out of the way.

20. Remove the upper intake bolts.

21. Remove the upper intake manifold and gaskets. Discard gaskets.

22. Clean the gasket mating surfaces.

To install:

23. Place NEW upper intake manifold gaskets onto the lower intake manifold.

24. Place the upper intake manifold onto the lower intake manifold.

25. Install the upper intake bolts and tighten to 17 ft. lbs. (23 Nm).

26. Position the fuel rail wiring harness and install the fuel rail wiring harness electrical connector bolt Tighten to 89 inch lbs. (10 Nm).

27. Install the fuel rail to bracket bolt. Tighten to 89 inch lbs. (10 Nm).

28. Position and install the EVAP canister purge solenoid tube quick connect fitting to the upper intake manifold.

29. Position and install the PCV tube to the upper intake manifold.

30. Connect the engine wiring harness electrical connector to the EVAP canister purge solenoid.

31. Connect the engine wiring harness electrical connector to the intake manifold tuning valve.

32. Connect the engine wiring harness electrical connector to the ETC.

33. Connect the engine wiring harness electrical connector to the MAP sensor.

34. Install the brake booster vacuum hose to the upper intake manifold.

35. Position the brake booster vacuum hose clamp at the upper intake manifold.

36. Position and install the coolant air bleed hose/pipe clip to the upper intake manifold stud.

37. Install the coolant air bleed hose to the water outlet.

38. Position the coolant air bleed hose clamp at the water outlet.

39. Install the coolant air bleed hose/pipe clip bolt to the upper intake manifold. Tighten to 89 inch lbs. (10 Nm).

40. Position the fuel feed line and install the fuel feed line clip to the stud. Install the fuel feed line nut. Tighten to 89 inch lbs. (10 Nm).

41. Connect the fuel feed line quick connect fitting to the fuel rail.

42. Install the air cleaner outlet duct.

43. Install the fuel injector sight shield.

Lower

See Figure 148.

1. Remove the fuel injectors and fuel rail.

2. Remove the lower intake manifold bolts.

3. Remove the lower intake manifold and gasket. Discard the gasket.

4. Clean and inspect the intake manifold and mating surfaces.

36616_AURA_G0280

Fig. 148 Removing the lower intake manifold—3.6L engine

To install:

5. Place a NEW lower intake manifold gasket onto the cylinder heads.

6. Place the lower intake manifold onto the cylinder heads.

7. Install the lower intake manifold bolts and tighten to 17 ft. lbs. (23 Nm).

8. Install the fuel injectors and fuel rail.

OIL PAN

REMOVAL & INSTALLATION

2.4L Engine

See Figures 149 through 151.

1. Remove the drive belt.

2. Remove the oil level indicator tube.

➡**The support fixture bar must be installed to provide enough access to remove and properly tighten the oil pan bolts.**

3. Install the engine support fixture.

4. Remove engine mount.

5. Using the engine support fixture, raise the engine approximately 3 inches.

6. Raise and support the vehicle.

7. Loosen the upper Air Conditioning (A/C) compressor bolts.

8. Remove the lower A/C compressor bolt.

9. Place a suitable drain pan under the oil pan drain plug.

10. Remove the oil pan drain plug.

11. Drain the engine oil.

12. Reinstall the oil pan drain plug until snug.

13. Remove the 4 oil pan to transaxle bolts.

14. Remove the oil pan bolts.

15. Remove the oil pan.

16. Remove any old oil pan sealant.

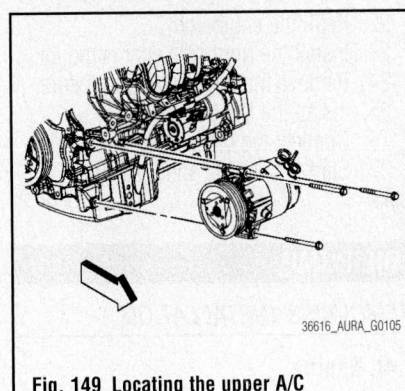

Fig. 149 Locating the upper A/C compressor bolts

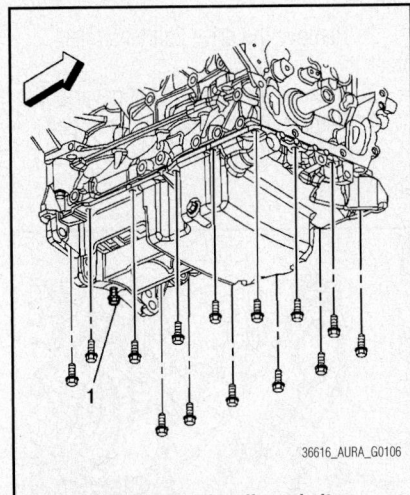

Fig. 150 Removing the oil pan bolts

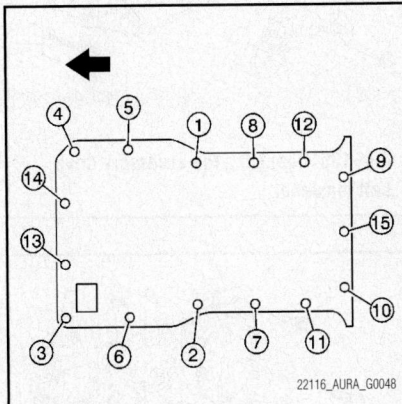

Fig. 151 Oil pan bolt tightening sequence—2.4L engine

To install:

17. Ensure that the oil pan and the sealing surface on the lower crankcase are free of all oil and debris. Apply a 2 mm bead of sealant around the perimeter of the oil pan and the oil suction port opening. DO NOT over apply the sealant. More than a 2 mm bead is not required.

18. Install the oil pan.

19. Install the oil pan bolts and hand tighten.

20. Install the 4 oil pan to transaxle bolts. Tighten the bolts to 55 ft. lbs. (75 Nm).

21. Tighten the oil pan bolts in the sequence shown to 18 ft. lbs. (25 Nm).

22. Lower the vehicle.

23. Using the engine support fixture, lower the engine.

24. Install the engine mount.

25. Remove the engine support fixture.

26. Install the oil level indicator tube.

27. Install the drive belt.

28. Fill the engine oil to the proper level.

3.5L Engine

See Figure 152.

➡ **The vehicle is equipped with an automatic transaxle to oil pan lower brace. The brace boss on the transaxle may interfere with the oil pan removal.**

1. Disconnect the negative battery cable.

2. Remove the drive belt.

3. Remove the air cleaner inlet duct.

4. Install the engine support fixture.

5. Raise and support the vehicle.

6. Place a suitable drain pan under the oil pan drain plug.

7. Remove the oil pan drain plug and drain the engine oil from the crankcase.

8. Reinstall the oil pan drain plug and tighten to 19 ft. lbs. (26 Nm).

9. Remove the right front splash shield.

10. Remove the starter.

11. Remove the oil filter adapter.

12. Remove the Air Conditioning (A/C) compressor bolts/nut and position the compressor aside.

13. Remove the catalytic converters.

14. Remove the engine mount bracket bolts and bracket.

15. Remove the transaxle brace bolts and remove the brace.

16. Remove the transaxle to oil pan brace bolts and brace.

17. Remove the flexplate to torque converter bolts.

18. Lower the vehicle.

19. Remove the engine harness ground nut from the transaxle stud.

20. Remove the engine wiring harness ground and the negative battery cable ground from the transaxle stud.

21. Remove the engine wiring harness clip nut from the transaxle stud.

22. Remove the engine wiring harness clip from the transaxle stud.

23. Remove the engine wiring harness clips from the oil pan.

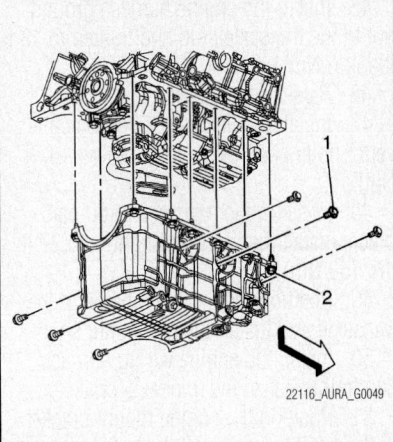

Fig. 152 Refer to the text for the oil pan bolt tightening torques for bolts 1 and 2—3.5L engine

24. Loosen, DO NOT REMOVE the transaxle studs and bolts.

25. Using the engine support fixture, raise the engine and transaxle slightly.

26. Raise and support the vehicle.

27. Remove the oil pan bolts.

28. Separate the engine and transaxle approximately ½ in. (13 mm).

29. Ensure that when removing the oil pan, the pan clears the boss on the transaxle.

30. Remove the oil pan.

31. Remove and discard the oil pan gasket.

32. Clean the oil pan sealing surfaces.

To install:

33. Apply sealer to both sides of the front cover/block mating area.

34. Apply sealer to both sides of the crankcase rear main bearing cap. Press the sealer into the gap using a putty knife.

35. Install a NEW oil pan gasket.

36. Install the oil pan.

37. Install the oil pan bolts. Tighten bolts (1) to 37 ft. lbs. (50 Nm) and bolts (2) to 18 ft. lbs. (25 Nm).

38. Lower the vehicle.

39. Using the engine support fixture, lower the engine and transaxle.

40. Tighten the transaxle studs and bolts to 55 ft. lbs. (75 Nm).

41. Install the engine wiring harness clips to the oil pan.

42. Install the engine wiring harness clip to the transaxle stud.

43. Install the engine wiring harness clip nut to the transaxle stud and tighten to 18 ft. lbs. (25 Nm).

44. Install the negative battery cable ground and the engine wiring harness ground to the transaxle stud.

45. Install the engine harness ground nut to the transaxle stud and tighten to 18 ft. lbs. (25 Nm).

46. Raise and support the vehicle.

47. Install the flexplate to torque converter bolts and tighten to 46 ft. lbs. (62 Nm).

48. Position the transaxle to oil pan brace, install the bolts and tighten to 37 ft. lbs. (50 Nm).

49. Position the transaxle brace to the transaxle and install the bolts until snug.

50. Install the engine wiring harness clip to the rear of the transaxle brace.

51. Position the engine mount bracket to the engine and install the bolts until snug.

52. Tighten the engine mount bracket upper bolt to 66 ft. lbs. (90 Nm).

53. Tighten the engine mount bracket lower bolts to 37 ft. lbs. (50 Nm).

54. Tighten the transaxle brace bolts to 53 ft. lbs. (72 Nm).

55. Install the catalytic converters.

56. Install the A/C compressor and bolts. Tighten the bolts to 37 ft. lbs. (50 Nm).

57. Install the oil filter adapter.

58. Install the starter.

59. Install the right front splash shield.

60. Tighten the oil pan drain plug to 19 ft. lbs. (26 Nm).

61. Lower the vehicle.

62. Remove the engine support fixture.

63. Install the air cleaner inlet duct.

64. Install the drive belt.

65. Fill the crankcase with oil.

66. Connect the negative battery cable.

67. Start the vehicle and inspect for leaks.

3.6L Engine

See Figures 153 and 154.

1. Disconnect the battery negative cable.

2. Remove the front cover.

3. Install the engine support fixture.

4. Raise the engine using the support fixture until the oil pan will clear.

5. Raise and support the vehicle.

6. Drain the engine oil and remove the oil filter.

7. Remove the catalytic converter.

8. Remove the Air Conditioning (A/C) compressor.

9. Remove the transmission bellhousing bolts.

10. Remove the oil pan bolts.

11. Remove the oil pan.

12. Clean the oil pan and the engine block gasket surface.

To install:

13. Install the 0.315 in. (8mm) guides from the a guide pin set such as EN 46109 into the center oil pan rail bolt hole on each side of the engine block.

14. Place a 0.118 in. (3mm) bead of RTV sealant on the block pan rail and the crankshaft rear oil seal housing.

15. Position the oil pan onto the block.

16. Remove guide pin set guides from the engine block.

17. Loosely install the oil pan bolts.

18. Tighten the oil pan bolts in sequence shown as follows:

    a. 8mm bolts 1 through 11 to 17 ft. lbs. (23 Nm).

    b. 6mm bolts 12 and 13 to 89 inch lbs. (10 Nm).

19. Install the Air Conditioning (A/C) compressor.

20. Install the catalytic converter.

21. Lower the vehicle.

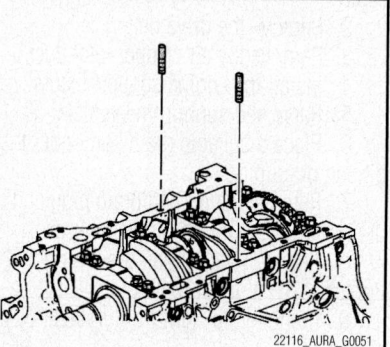

Fig. 153 Install the 0.315 in. (8mm) guides from the a guide pin set such as EN 46109 into the center oil pan rail bolt hole on each side of the engine block—3.6L engine

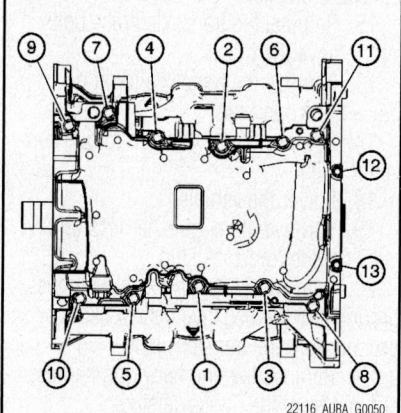

Fig. 154 Oil pan bolt tightening sequence—3.6L engine

22. Refill the engine oil.

23. Install the right side engine mount.

24. Remove the engine support fixture.

25. Install the front cover.

26. Connect the battery negative cable.

27. Start the vehicle and inspect for leaks.

OIL PUMP

REMOVAL & INSTALLATION

2.4L Engine

See Figures 155 through 158.

1. Remove the accessory drive belt tensioner.

2. Remove the drive belt tensioner bracket.

3. Remove the engine front cover bolts.

4. Remove the long water pump bolt.

5. Remove the engine front cover and gaskets.

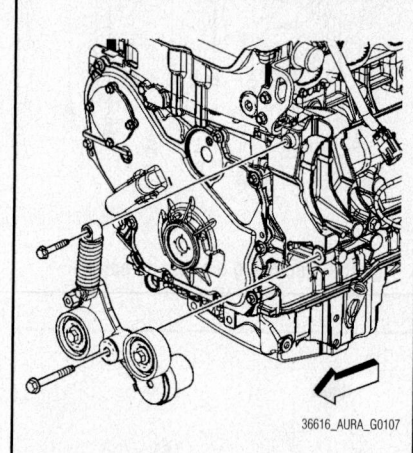

Fig. 155 Removing the accessory drive belt tensioner

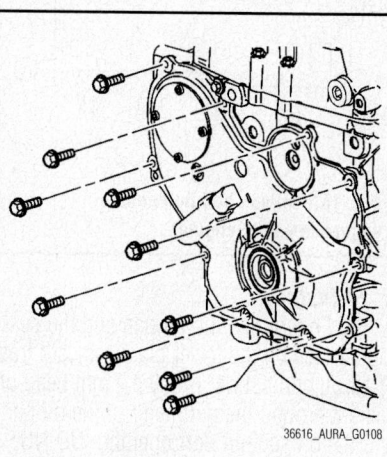

Fig. 156 Removing the drive belt tensioner

6. Remove the crankshaft front cover oil seal with an appropriate tool.

7. Remove the oil pump.

To install:

8. Install the oil pump.

9. Install the engine front cover with a new gasket.

➡Use the correct fastener in the correct location. Replacement fasteners must be the correct part number for that application. Fasteners requiring replacement or fasteners requiring the use of thread locking compound or sealant are identified in the service procedure. Do not use paints, lubricants, or corrosion inhibitors on fasteners or fastener joint surfaces unless specified. These coatings affect fastener torque and joint clamping force and may damage the fastener. Use the correct tightening sequence and specifications when installing fasteners in order to avoid damage to parts and systems.

10. Install the long water pump bolt and tighten to 18 ft. lbs. (25 Nm).

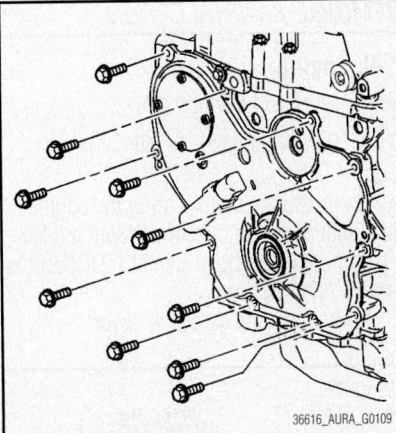

Fig. 157 Removing the engine front cover bolts

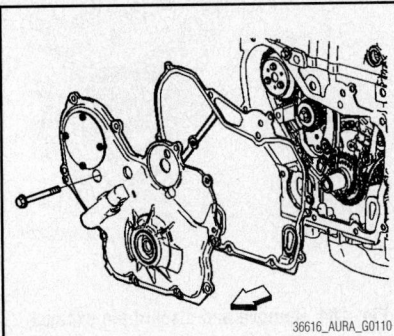

Fig. 158 Removing the long water pump bolt

11. Install the engine front cover bolts and tighten to 18 ft. lbs. (25 Nm).

12. Install the drive belt tensioner bracket and tighten to 33 ft. lbs. (45 Nm).

13. Install the accessory drive belt tensioner and tighten to 33 ft. lbs. (45 Nm).

3.5L Engine

See Figure 159.

1. Remove the oil pan.
2. Remove the oil pump bolt.
3. Remove the oil pump and the oil pump drive shaft.

To install:

➡Use the correct fastener in the correct location. Replacement fasteners must be the correct part number for that application. Fasteners requiring replacement or fasteners requiring the use of thread locking compound or sealant are identified in the service procedure. Do not use paints, lubricants, or corrosion inhibitors on fasteners or fastener joint surfaces unless specified. These coatings affect fastener torque and joint clamping force and may damage the fastener. Use the correct tightening sequence and specifications when installing fasteners in order to avoid damage to parts and systems.

➡Do NOT reuse the oil pump driveshaft retainer. During assembly install a NEW oil pump driveshaft retainer.

4. Install the oil pump drive shaft and the oil pump.

5. Install the oil pump bolt attaching the oil pump to the rear crankshaft bearing cap and tighten to 30 ft. lbs. (41 Nm).

6. Install the oil pan

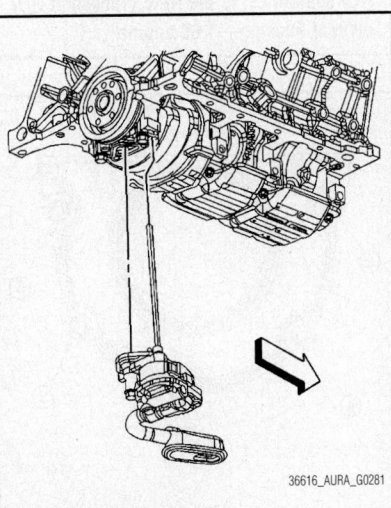

Fig. 159 Removing the oil pump—3.5L engine

3.6L Engine

See Figure 160.

1. Remove the primary timing chain.
2. Remove the oil pump bolts and the oil pump.

To install:

3. Align the oil pump alternator with the crankshaft flats and install the oil pump to the engine block.

4. Align the pump body with the mounting holes in the cylinder block.

5. Install the oil pump bolts and tighten to 17 ft. lbs. (23 Nm).

6. Install the primary timing chain.

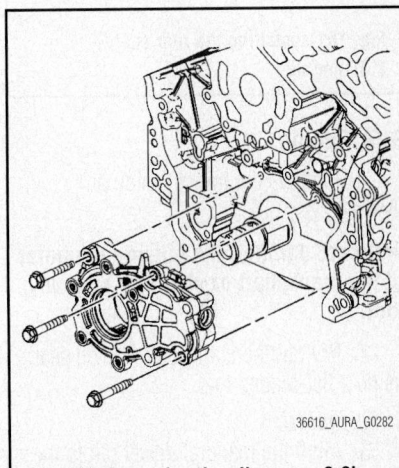

Fig. 160 Removing the oil pump—3.6L engine

PISTON AND RING

POSITIONING

A dot showing proper piston orientation is located on the top of the piston.

REAR MAIN SEAL

REMOVAL & INSTALLATION

2.4L Engine

See Figure 161.

1. Remove the transmission and flywheel.

➡Do not damage the outside diameter of the crankshaft or chamber with any tool.

2. Pry out the crankshaft rear oil seal using a flat-bladed tool.

To install:

3. Using a seal installer such as J 42067, install a NEW crankshaft real oil seal.

4. Install the flywheel and transmission

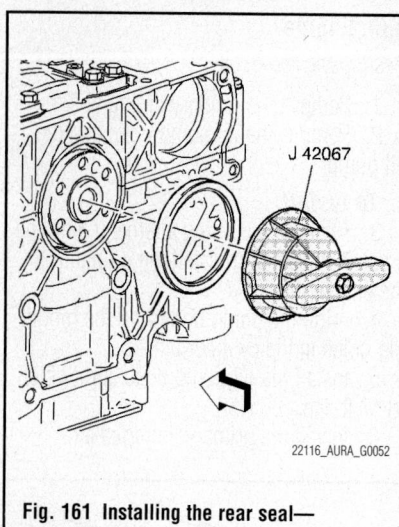

Fig. 161 Installing the rear seal—2.4L engine

3.5L Engine

1. Remove the transmission and flywheel.

➡**Do not damage the outside diameter of the crankshaft or chamber with any tool.**

2. Pry out the crankshaft rear oil seal using a flat-bladed tool.

To install:

3. Align the mandrel dowel pin to the dowel pin hole in the crankshaft

4. Using a large flat blade screwdriver, tighten the two mandrel screws to the crankshaft, ensuring the mandrel is snug to the crankshaft hub.

➡**The seal will only fit one way onto the mandrel, and if properly installed, will center on a step that protrudes from the center of the mandrel.**

5. Install the rear main seal, with the protective nylon sleeve attached, onto the mandrel.

➡**Before installing the outer drive drum, bearing, washer, and drive nut onto the threaded shaft, apply a small amount of the extreme pressure lubricant, provided in the tool kit.**

6. Install the outer drive drum onto the mandrel.

7. Install the bearing, washer, and the drive nut onto the threaded shaft.

8. Using a wrench, turn the drive nut on the mandrel, which will push the seal into the engine block.

9. Turn the wrench until the drive drum is snug and flush against the engine block.

10. Loosen and remove the drive nut, washer, bearing and drive drum. Discard the nylon plastic seal protector.

11. Verify that the seal has seated properly

12. Use a flat blade screwdriver to remove the two attachment screws from the mandrel and remove the mandrel from the crankshaft hub.

13. Install the flywheel and transmission.

14. Inspect for proper fluid levels.

15. Inspect for leaks.

3.6L Engine

See Figures 162 and 163.

1. Remove the oil pan. Remove the engine flywheel.

2. Remove the crankshaft rear oil seal housing bolts.

3. Use the pry points located at the edge of the crankshaft rear oil seal housing to separate the RTV sealant

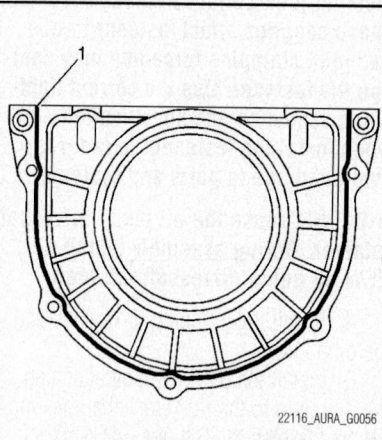

Fig. 162 Place a 0.118 in. (3mm) bead of RTV sealant (1) to the NEW crankshaft rear oil seal housing—3.6L engine

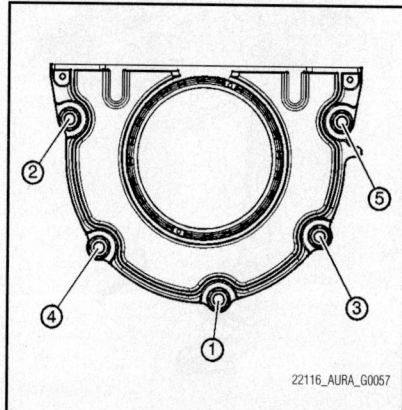

Fig. 163 Crankshaft rear oil seal housing bolt tightening sequence—3.6L engine

4. Remove and discard the crankshaft rear oil seal housing.

To install:

5. Using a guide pin set such as EN 46109, install the 0.236 in. (6mm) guides from the tool into the 2 crankshaft rear oil seal housing corner bolt holes of the engine block.

6. Install crankshaft rear oil seal installation tool such as EN 47839 and handle onto the rear of the crankshaft flange.

7. Place a 0.118 in. (3mm) bead of RTV sealant to the NEW crankshaft rear oil seal housing.

8. Install the crankshaft rear oil seal housing to the engine block

9. Remove the guides from the block.

10. Install the crankshaft rear oil seal housing bolts, tighten to 89 inch lbs. (10 Nm) in the sequence illustrated.

11. Remove the guide pin set.

12. Install the oil pan.

13. Install the engine flywheel.

TIMING CHAIN, SPROCKETS, FRONT COVER AND SEAL

REMOVAL & INSTALLATION

2.4L Engine

See Figures 164 through 174.

1. Remove the No. 1 cylinder spark plug.

2. Rotate the crankshaft in the engine rotational direction clockwise, until the No. 1 piston is at Top Dead Center (TDC) on the compression stroke.

3. Remove the camshaft cover.

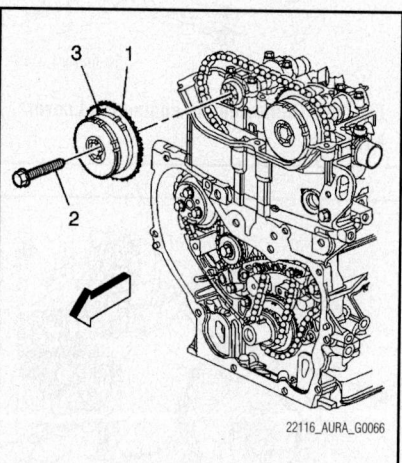

Fig. 164 Remove and discard the exhaust camshaft actuator bolt (2). Remove the exhaust camshaft actuator (1, 3) from the camshaft and timing chain—2.4L engine

4. Remove the engine front cover as follows:

   a. Remove the drive belt tensioner.

   b. Remove the crankshaft balancer.

   c. Install the engine support fixture.

   d. Remove the engine mount to bracket bolts.

   e. Remove the engine mount to side rail nuts.

   f. Remove the engine mount from the engine compartment.

   g. Remove the engine mount bracket to engine bolts.

   h. Remove the engine mount bracket.

   i. Remove the engine front cover to water pump bolt.

   j. Raise and suitably support the vehicle.

   k. Remove the engine front cover bolts.

   l. Remove the engine front cover.

   m. Remove and discard the engine front cover gasket.

5. Remove the upper timing chain guide bolts and guide.

➥**The timing chain tensioner must be removed to unload chain tension before the timing chain is removed. If it is not, the timing chain will become cocked and it will be difficult to remove.**

6. Remove the timing chain tensioner.

7. Install a 24 mm wrench on the hex on the exhaust camshaft in order to hold the camshaft.

8. Remove and discard the exhaust camshaft actuator bolt.

9. Remove the exhaust camshaft actuator from the camshaft and timing chain.

10. Remove the timing chain tensioner guide bolt and guide.

11. Remove the fixed timing chain guide access plug.

12. Remove the fixed timing chain guide bolts and guide.

13. Install a 24 mm wrench on the hex on the intake camshaft in order to hold the camshaft.

14. Remove and discard the intake camshaft actuator bolt.

15. Remove the intake camshaft actuator, and the timing chain through the top of the cylinder head.

16. Remove the timing chain crankshaft sprocket.

17. If replacing the balance shaft timing chain and sprocket, perform the following:

   a. Remove the balance shaft drive chain tensioner bolts and tensioner.

   b. Remove the adjustable balance shaft chain guide bolt and guide.

   c. Remove the small balance shaft drive chain guide bolts and guide.

   d. Remove the upper balance shaft drive chain guide bolts and guide.

➥**It may ease removal of the balance shaft drive chain to get all the slack in the chain between the crankshaft and water pump sprockets.**

18. Remove the balance shaft drive chain.

19. Remove the balance shaft drive sprocket .

To install:

20. If replacing the balance shaft timing chain, perform the following:

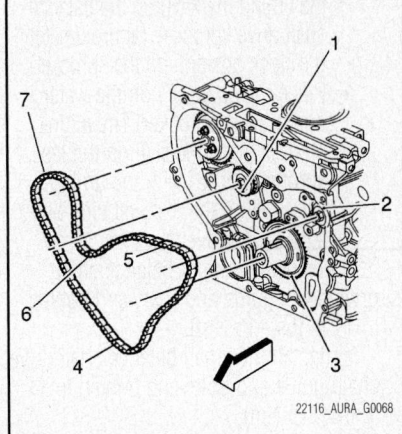

Fig. 166 Balance shaft drive chain components—2.4L engine

   a. Install the balance shaft drive sprocket.

➥**If the balance shafts are not properly timed to the engine, the engine may vibrate or make noise.**

   b. Install the balance shaft drive chain with the colored link lined up with the marks on the balance shaft sprockets and the balance shaft drive sprocket. There are 3 colored links on the chain. Two are chrome and 1 is copper.

   c. Use the following steps in order to line up the links with the sprockets:

   • Place the copper link (5) so that it lines up with the timing mark (2) on the intake side balance shaft sprocket.

   • Working clockwise around the chain, place the chrome link (4) in line with

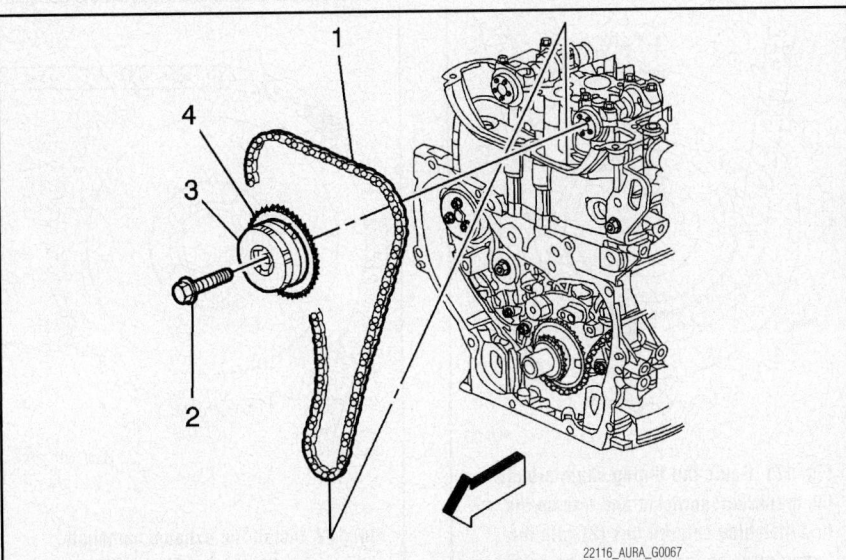

Fig. 165 Remove and discard the intake camshaft actuator bolt (2). Remove the intake camshaft actuator (3), and the timing chain through the top of the cylinder head—2.4L engine

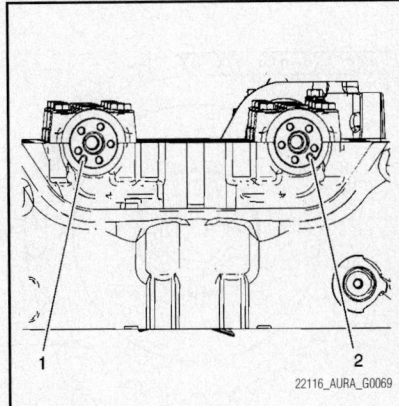

Fig. 167 Ensure the intake camshaft notch is in the 5 o'clock position (2) and the exhaust camshaft notch is in the 7 o'clock position (1). The number 1 piston should be at top dead center (TDC), crankshaft key at 12 o'clock—2.4L engine

the timing mark (3) on the balance shaft drive sprocket. (approximately 6 o'clock position on the sprocket).

• Place the chain (7) on the water pump drive sprocket. The alignment is not critical Align the last chrome link (6) with the timing mark (1) on the exhaust side balance shaft drive sprocket.

d. Install the upper balance shaft drive chain guide and bolts and tighten to 11 ft. lbs. (15 Nm).

e. Install the small balance shaft drive chain guide and bolts and tighten to 11 ft. lbs. (15 Nm).

21. Install the adjustable balance shaft

chain guide and bolt and tighten to 89 inch lbs. (10 Nm).

22. Reset the timing chain tensioner by performing the following:

a. Rotate the tensioner plunger 90 degrees in its bore and compress the plunger

b. Rotate the tensioner back to the original 12 o'clock position and insert a paper clip through the hole in the plunger body and into the hose in the tensioner plunger.

c. Install the balance shaft drive chain tensioner and bolt and tighten to 89 inch lbs. (10 Nm).

d. Remove the paper clip from the balance shaft drive chain tensioner.

23. Ensure the intake camshaft notch is in the 5 o'clock position (2) and the exhaust camshaft notch is in the 7 o'clock position (1). The number 1 piston should be at top dead center (TDC), crankshaft key at 12 o'clock.

24. Install the timing chain drive sprocket to the crankshaft with the timing mark in the 5 o'clock position and the front of the sprocket facing out.

➡**There are 3 colored links on the timing chain. Two links are of matching color, and 1 link is of a unique color. Use the following procedure to line up the links with the actuators. Orient the chain so that the colored links are visible. Always use new actuator bolts.**

25. Assemble the intake camshaft actuator into the timing chain with the timing mark lined up with the uniquely colored link.

26. Lower the timing chain through the opening in the cylinder head. Use care to ensure that the chain goes around both sides of the cylinder block bosses (1, 2).

27. Install the intake camshaft actuator onto the intake camshaft while aligning the dowel pin into the camshaft slot.

28. Hand tighten the new intake camshaft actuator bolt.

29. Route the timing chain around the crankshaft sprocket and line up the first matching colored link (2) with the timing mark on the crankshaft sprocket, in approximately the 5 o'clock position.

30. Rotate the crankshaft clockwise to remove all chain slack. Do not rotate the intake camshaft.

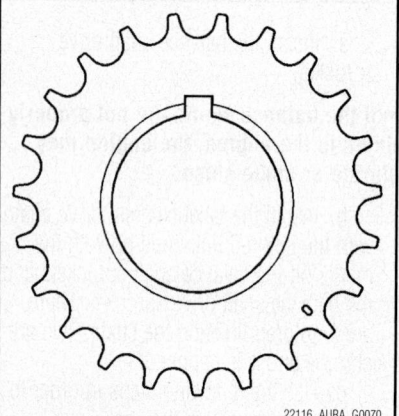

22116_AURA_G0070

Fig. 168 Install the timing chain drive sprocket to the crankshaft with the timing mark in the 5 o'clock position and the front of the sprocket facing out—2.4L engine

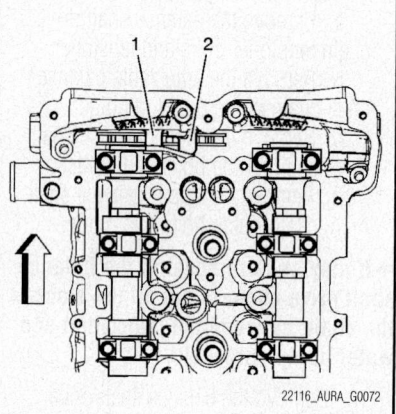

22116_AURA_G0072

Fig. 170 Lower the timing chain through the opening in the cylinder head. Use care to ensure that the chain goes around both sides of the cylinder block bosses (1, 2)—2.4L engine

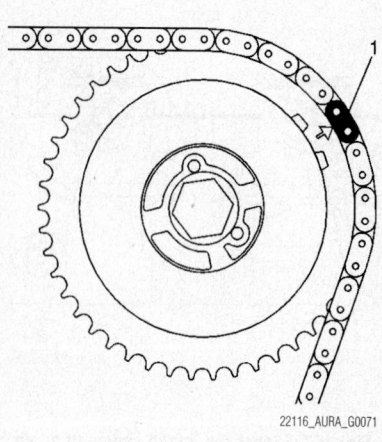

22116_AURA_G0071

Fig. 169 Assemble the intake camshaft actuator into the timing chain with the timing mark lined up with the uniquely colored link (1)—2.4L engine

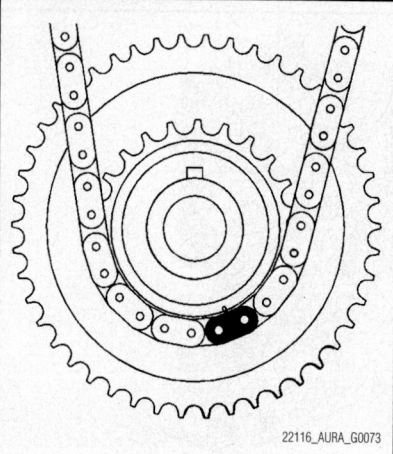

22116_AURA_G0073

Fig. 171 Route the timing chain around the crankshaft sprocket and line up the first matching colored link (2) with the timing mark on the crankshaft sprocket, in approximately the 5 o'clock position—2.4L engine

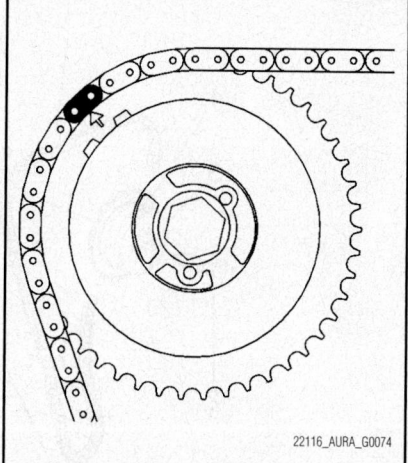

22116_AURA_G0074

Fig. 172 Install the exhaust camshaft actuator into the timing chain with the timing mark lined up with the second matching colored link—2.4L engine

31. Install the adjustable timing chain guide down through the opening in the cylinder head and install the adjustable timing chain bolt and tighten to 89 inch lbs. (10 Nm).

➡**Always install NEW actuator bolts.**

32. Install the exhaust camshaft actuator into the timing chain with the timing mark lined up with the second matching colored link.

33. Install the exhaust camshaft actuator onto the exhaust camshaft, aligning the dowel pin into the camshaft slot.

34. Using a 23 mm open end wrench, rotate the exhaust camshaft approximately 45 degrees until the dowel pin in the camshaft actuator goes into the camshaft slot.

35. When the actuator seats on the cam, tighten the new exhaust camshaft actuator bolt hand tight.

36. Verify that all of the colored links and the appropriate timing marks are still aligned. If they are not aligned, repeat the portion of the procedure necessary to align the timing marks

37. Install the fixed timing chain guide and bolts and tighten to 106 inch lbs. (12 Nm).

38. Install the upper timing chain guide and bolts and tighten to 89 inch lbs. (10 Nm).

39. Reset the timing chain tensioner by performing the following:

    a. Remove the snap ring.

    b. Remove the piston assembly from the body of the timing chain tensioner.

    c. Install tensioner tool J 45027-2 (2) into a vise.

    d. Install the notch end of the piston assembly into the tool.

    e. Using the J 45027-1 handle (1), turn the ratchet cylinder into the piston.

    f. Reinstall the piston assembly into the body of the tensioner.

    g. Install the snap ring.

40. Inspect the timing chain tensioner seal for damage. If damaged, replace the seal.

41. Inspect to ensure all dirt and debris is removed from the timing chain tensioner threaded hole in the cylinder head.

➡**Ensure the timing chain tensioner seal is centered throughout the torque procedure to eliminate the possibility of an oil leak.**

42. Install the timing chain tensioner assembly.

43. Tighten the timing chain tensioner to 55 ft. lbs. (75 Nm).

➡**The timing chain tensioner is released by compressing it 2 mm**

(0.079 in), which will release the locking mechanism in the ratchet.

44. To release the timing chain tensioner, use a suitable tool with a rubber tip on the end. Feed the tool down through the cam drive chest to rest on the cam chain. Then give a sharp jolt diagonally downwards to release the tensioner.

45. Using a 23 mm wrench, engage the hex on the intake camshaft, and using a torque wrench, tighten the camshaft actuator bolt.

46. Tighten the intake camshaft position actuator bolt to 22 ft. lbs. (30 Nm), plus an additional 100 degrees.

47. Using a 23 mm wrench, engage the hex on the exhaust camshaft, and using a torque wrench, tighten the camshaft actuator bolt.

48. Tighten the exhaust camshaft position actuator bolt to 22 ft. lbs. (30 Nm), plus an additional 100 degrees.

49. Install the timing chain oiling nozzle and bolt and tighten to 89 inch lbs. (10 Nm).

50. Apply sealant compound to the thread of the timing chain guide bolt access hole plug.

51. Install the timing chain guide bolt access hole plug and tighten to 66 ft. lbs. lbs. (90 Nm).

52. Install the engine front cover as follows:

    a. Install a NEW engine front cover gasket to the dowel pins.

    b. Install the engine front cover.

    c. Install the engine front cover bolts and tighten to 18 ft. lbs. (25 Nm).

    d. Lower the vehicle.

    e. Install the engine front cover to water pump bolt and tighten to 18 ft. lbs. (25 Nm).

    f. Position the engine mount bracket to the engine.

    g. Install the engine mount bracket bolts in the following locations:

- The long bolts in the forward and lower rear holes
- The short bolt in the upper rear hole

    h. Tighten the engine mount bracket bolts to 74 ft. lbs. (100 Nm) in the following sequence:

- Upper left
- Lower left
- Right

    i. Install the engine mount to the engine compartment.

    j. Install the engine mount to side rail nuts and tighten to 74 ft. lbs. (100 Nm)

    k. Install the engine mount to bracket bolts.

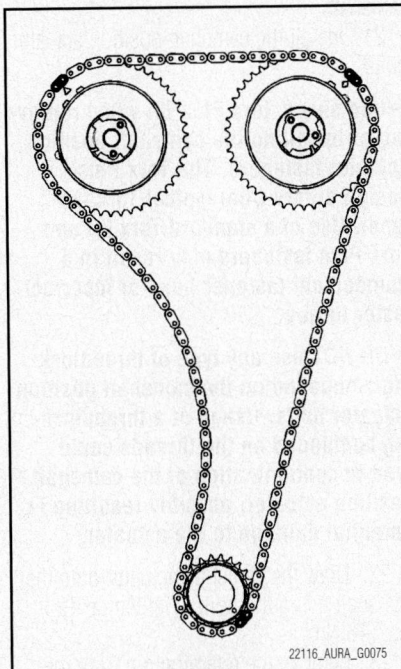

22116_AURA_G0075

Fig. 173 Verify that all of the colored links and the appropriate timing marks are still aligned. If they are not aligned, repeat the portion of the procedure necessary to align the timing marks—2.4L engine

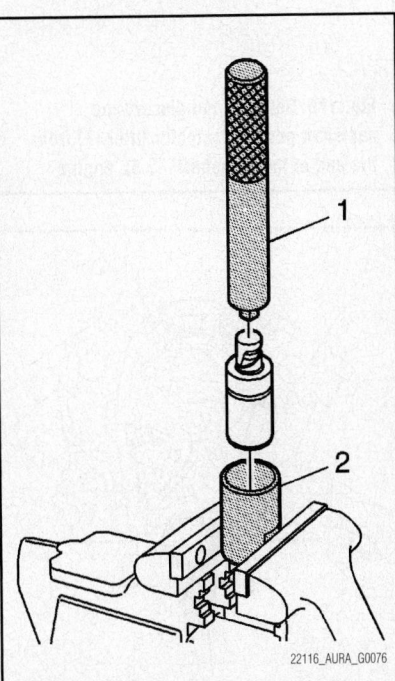

22116_AURA_G0076

Fig. 174 Install tensioner tool J 45027-2 (2) into a vise, Install the notch end of the piston assembly into the tool and using the J 45027-1 handle (1), turn the ratchet cylinder into the piston—2.4L engine

l. Tighten the engine mount to bracket bolts to 37 ft. lbs. (50 Nm) in the following sequence.
- Middle
- Rear
- Front

m. Remove the engine support fixture.

n. Install the crankshaft balancer.

o. Install the drive belt tensioner.

53. Install the camshaft cover.

54. Install the No. 1 cylinder spark plug.

3.5L Engine

See Figures 175 through 177.

1. Remove the engine front cover as follows:

a. Drain the cooling system.

b. Remove the drive belt tensioner.

c. Remove the oil pan.

d. Remove the crankshaft balancer.

e. Remove the crankshaft position actuator magnet.

f. Remove the thermostat housing.

g. Remove the water pump.

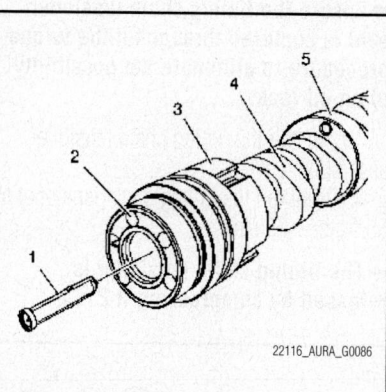

1. **Crankshaft timing mark**
2. **Timing chain tensioner bottom timing mark**
3. **Camshaft position actuator gear timing mark**
4. **Timing chain tensioner top timing mark**

22116_AURA_G0085

Fig. 175 Align the crankshaft timing mark(1) to the timing mark on the bottom of the timing chain tensioner (2).Align the timing mark on the camshaft position actuator gear (4) with the timing mark on top of the timing chain tensioner (3)—3.5L engine

h. Remove the engine front cover bolts.

i. Remove the engine front cover.

j. Remove the engine front cover gasket.

2. Align the crankshaft timing mark (1) to the timing mark on the bottom of the timing chain tensioner (2). Refer to the illustration for mark locations.

3. Align the timing mark on the camshaft position actuator gear (4) with the timing mark on top of the timing chain tensioner (3). Refer to the illustration for mark locations.

4. Remove the camshaft position actuator bolts.

5. Remove the timing chain, camshaft position actuator, and crankshaft sprockets.

6. Remove the timing chain tensioner bolts.

7. Remove the timing chain tensioner.

8. Remove the crankshaft sprocket.

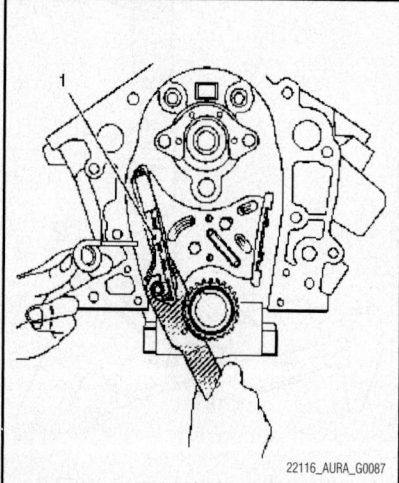

Fig. 176 Remove and discard the camshaft position actuator filter (1) from the end of the camshaft—3.5L engine

22116_AURA_G0086

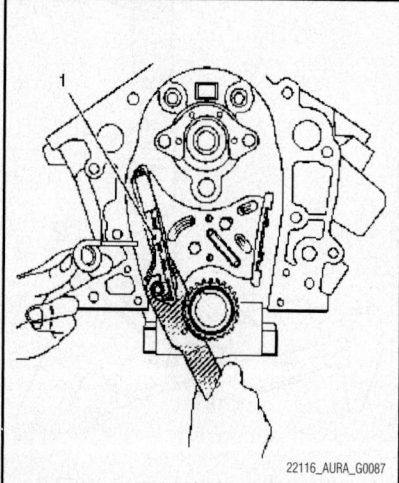

Fig. 177 Use tensioner compressor EN-47719 fully collapse the tensioner, and place he tensioner retaining pin into the retaining hole (1)—3.5L engine

22116_AURA_G0087

9. Remove the timing chain dampener bolts.

10. Remove the timing chain dampener.

11. Remove and discard the camshaft position actuator filter from the end of the camshaft.

➡**Always install a NEW camshaft position actuator filter anytime the camshaft actuator is removed.**

To install:

12. Install a NEW the camshaft position actuator filter to the end of the camshaft.

13. Install the crankshaft sprocket.

14. Apply prelube to the crankshaft sprocket thrust surface.

15. Install the timing chain tensioner. Tighten the bolts to 15 ft. lbs. (21 Nm).

16. Use tensioner compressor EN-47719 , fully collapse the tensioner, and place he tensioner retaining pin into the retaining hole.

17. Align the crankshaft timing mark to the timing mark on the bottom of the timing chain tensioner.

18. Hold the camshaft sprocket with the timing chain hanging down and install the timing chain to the crankshaft gear.

19. Align the timing mark on the camshaft position actuator gear with the timing mark on top of the timing chain tensioner.

20. Align the dowel in the camshaft position actuator with the dowel hole in the camshaft.

21. Install the camshaft position actuator bolts.

➡**Use only a Torx Plus Bit when removing or installing the camshaft position actuator fasteners. The Torx Plus design differs from typical Torx fastener. Use of a standard Torx bit on Torx Plus fasteners may result in a rounded out fastener head or incorrect faster torque.**

➡**DO NOT use any type of threadlocking compound on the camshaft position actuator bolts. Usage of a threadlocking compound on the threads could lead to contamination of the camshaft position actuator, possibly resulting in potential damage to the actuator.**

22. Draw the camshaft actuator onto the camshaft using the bolts. Tighten op 12 ft. lbs. (16 Nm).

23. Remove the retaining pin from the timing chain tensioner in order to make the tensioner active.

24. Coat the crankshaft and camshaft sprockets with clean engine oil.

25. Install the engine front cover as follows:

a. Install the engine front cover gasket.

b. Install the engine front cover.

c. Apply sealant to the bolts in the locations pointed out in the illustration.

d. Install the engine front cover bolts. Tighten to 18 ft. lbs. (25 Nm).

e. Install the water pump.

f. Install the thermostat housing.

g. Install the crankshaft position actuator magnet.

h. Install the crankshaft balancer.

i. Install the oil pan. Install the drive belt tensioner.

j. Fill the cooling system.

3.6L Engine

See Figures 178 through 204.

1. Remove the spark plugs in order to ease crankshaft/engine rotation.

2. Remove the engine front cover as follows:

a. Remove the lower intake manifold.

b. Remove the camshaft covers.

c. Drain the engine coolant.

d. Remove the drive belt tensioner.

e. Remove the water pump.

f. Remove the power steering pump and position aside.

g. Remove the Camshaft Position sensors (CMP).

h. Remove the camshaft position actuator valves from the front cover.

i. Remove the camshaft position actuator solenoid valves from the front cover.

j. Remove the alternator.

k. Remove the crankshaft balancer. Clean the front cover of the components first before installing a support fixture.

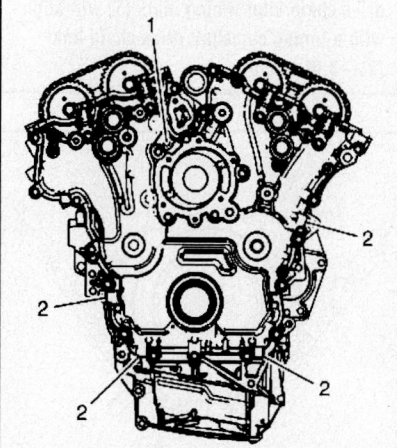

Fig. 178 Loosely install a 10 x 1.5 mm bolt in the "jackscrew" hole (1). Using the pry points (2) located at the edge of the front cover and the "jackscrew", shear the RTV sealant—3.6L engine

l. Insert a block of hard wood between the frame and engine before using the support fixture. Lower the engine onto the block of wood.

m. Install the engine support fixture.

n. Remove the lift hook and strut mount bracket from the front cover.

➡ **There are a total of 22 M8 bolts that must be removed and 3 optional M12 bolts that may need to be removed before the front cover will separate from the engine block.**

o. Remove the engine front cover bolts that hold the engine front cover deadener into position.

p. Remove the engine front cover deadener.

q. Remove the remaining front cover bolts.

➡ **Do not use the jackscrew hole without first removing all engine front cover bolts. Failure to remove all engine front cover bolts before using the jackscrew hole could result in damage to components.**

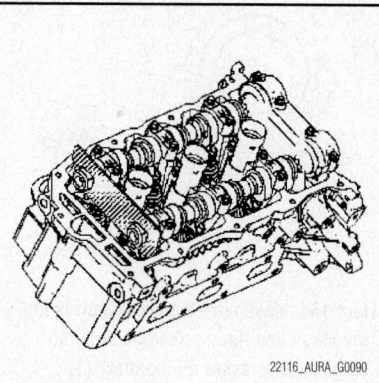

Fig. 179 Install a camshaft locking tool to the right camshafts—3.6L engine

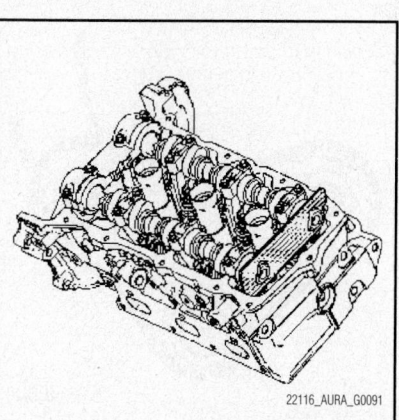

Fig. 180 Install a camshaft locking tool to the left camshafts—3.6L engine

➡ **Do not pry between the engine front cover and the camshaft position sensors or the camshaft position actuators in order to separate the RTV. Use the pry points and a bolt in the jackscrew hole in order to remove the engine front cover. Damage to the camshaft position sensors or the camshaft position actuators are used to pry against in order to remove the engine front cover.**

r. Loosely install a 10 x 1.5mm bolt in the "jackscrew" hole (1).

s. Using the pry points (2) located at the edge of the front cover and the "jackscrew", separate the room temperature vulcanizing RTV sealant.

t. Remove the engine front cover.

3. Using the crankshaft rotational socket EN 46111, rotate the crankshaft until the left cylinder head camshafts align with the a camshaft locking tool and the

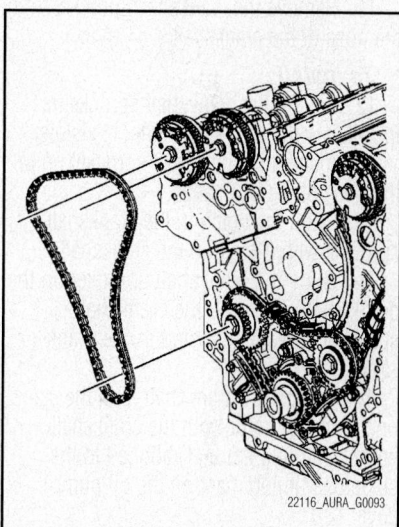

Fig. 181 Secondary camshaft drive chain—3.6L engine

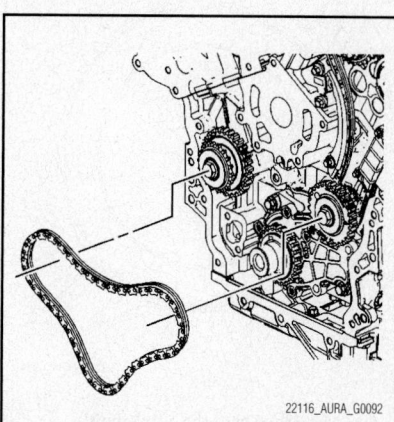

Fig. 182 Primary camshaft drive chain—3.6L engine

right cylinder head camshafts align with the a camshaft locking tool

    a. Install a camshaft locking tool to the right camshafts.

    b. Install a camshaft locking tool to the left camshafts.

4. Remove the right bank secondary camshaft drive chain tensioner.

5. Remove the right bank secondary camshaft drive chain shoe.

6. Remove the right bank secondary camshaft drive chain guide.

7. Remove the right secondary camshaft drive chain from the right camshaft position actuators and the right camshaft intermediate drive chain idler sprocket.

8. Remove the primary camshaft drive chain tensioner.

9. Remove the primary camshaft drive chain upper guide.

10. Remove the primary camshaft timing chain.

11. Remove the crankshaft sprocket from the nose of the crankshaft.

To install:

12. Ensure the crankshaft sprocket is installed with the timing mark (1) visible.

13. Install the crankshaft sprocket on to the nose of the crankshaft.

14. Align the notch in the crankshaft sprocket with the pin in the crankshaft.

15. Slide the crankshaft sprocket on the crankshaft nose until the crankshaft sprocket contacts the step in the crankshaft.

16. Ensure the crankshaft is in the stage one timing position with the crankshaft sprocket timing mark (1) aligned to the stage one timing mark on the oil pump cover (2).

17. Install the primary camshaft timing chain as follows:

    a. Install the primary camshaft drive chain.

    b. Wrap the primary camshaft drive chain around the large sprockets of each camshaft intermediate drive chain idler and the crankshaft sprocket.

    c. The left camshaft intermediate drive chain idler timing mark (1) will align with a timing camshaft drive chain link (2).

    d. The right camshaft intermediate drive chain idler timing mark (2) will align with a timing camshaft drive chain link (1).

    e. The crankshaft sprocket timing mark (2) will align with a timing camshaft drive chain link (1).

    f. Ensure all the timing marks (2, 3, 6) are properly aligned with the timing camshaft drive chain links (1, 4, 5).

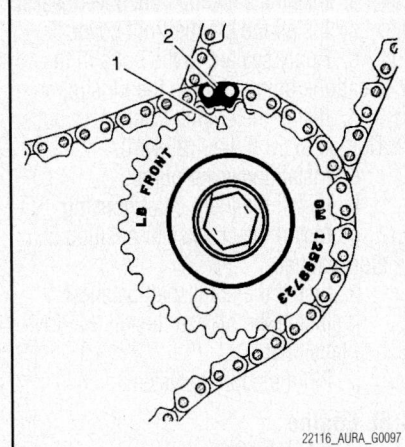

Fig. 186 The left camshaft intermediate drive chain idler timing mark (1) will align with a timing camshaft drive chain link (2)—3.6L engine

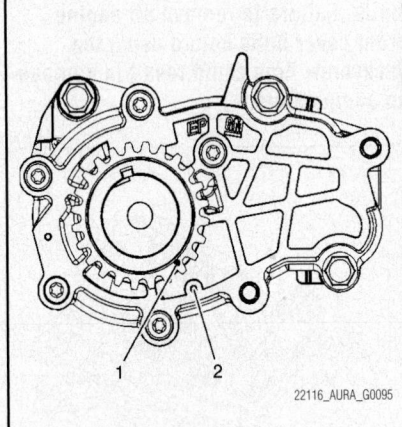

Fig. 184 Make sure the crankshaft is in the stage one timing position with the crankshaft sprocket timing mark (1) aligned to the stage one timing mark on the oil pump cover (2)—3.6L engine

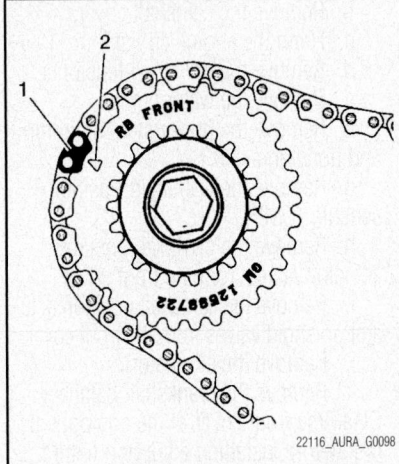

Fig. 187 The left camshaft intermediate drive chain idler timing mark (1) will align with a timing camshaft drive chain link (2)—3.6L engine

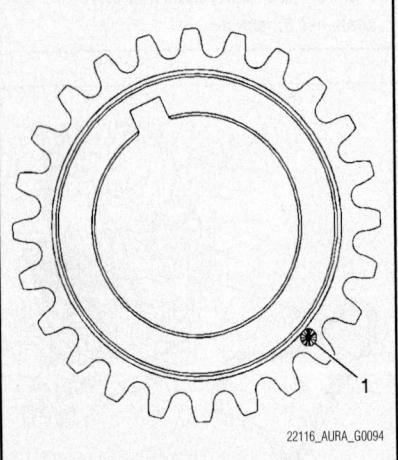

Fig. 183 Make sure the crankshaft sprocket is installed with the timing mark (1) visible—3.6L engine

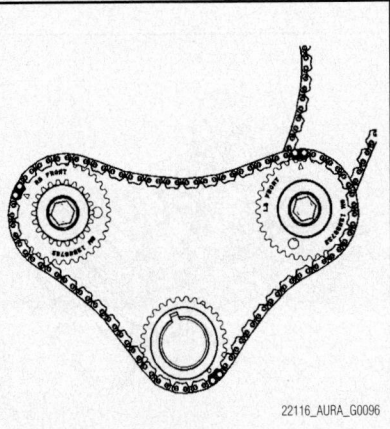

Fig. 185 Install the primary camshaft drive chain—3.6L engine

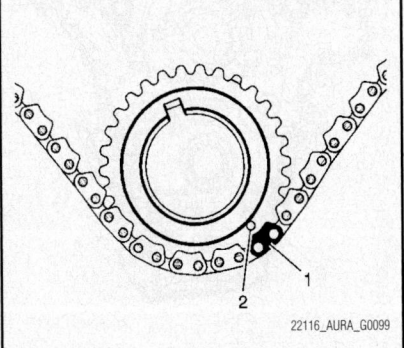

Fig. 188 The right camshaft intermediate drive chain idler timing mark (2) will align with a timing camshaft drive chain link (1)—3.6L engine

18. Install the primary upper camshaft drive chain guide. Tighten the bolts to 17 ft. lbs. (23 Nm).

19. Install the primary camshaft drive chain tensioner as follows:

a. Using the tensioner tool J 45027 , reset the primary camshaft drive chain tensioner plunger.

b. Install the plunger into the primary camshaft drive chain tensioner body.

c. Compress the plunger into the body and lock the primary camshaft drive chain tensioner by inserting the paper clip into the access hole in the side of the primary camshaft drive chain tensioner body.

d. Slowly release pressure on the primary camshaft drive chain tensioner. The primary camshaft drive chain tensioner should remain compressed.

e. Install a NEW primary camshaft drive chain tensioner gasket to the primary camshaft drive chain tensioner.

f. Install the primary camshaft drive chain tensioner bolts through the primary camshaft drive chain tensioner and gasket.

g. Ensure the primary camshaft drive chain tsensioner mounting surface on the engine block does not have any burrs or defects that would degrade the sealing of the NEW primary camshaft drive chain tensioner gasket.

h. Place the primary camshaft drive chain tensioner into position and loosely install the bolts to the block.

i. Verify the proper placement of the primary camshaft drive chain tensioner gasket tab.

j. Tighten the tensioner bolts in two stages. First tighten to 44 inch lbs. (5 Nm) and then to 17 ft. lbs. (23 Nm).

k. Release the primary camshaft drive chain tensioner by pulling out the paper clip and unlocking the tensioner plunger.

l. Verify the primary and left secondary camshaft drive chain timing mark alignments (1-12).

m. Remove the camshaft holding tool from the rear of the left camshafts.

n. Rotate the crankshaft and crankshaft sprocket from the stage 1 alignment position (1) to the stage 2 alignment position (2), 115 crankshaft degrees, in order to install the right secondary camshaft drive chain components.

o. Install the camshaft holding tool onto the rear of the left camshafts.

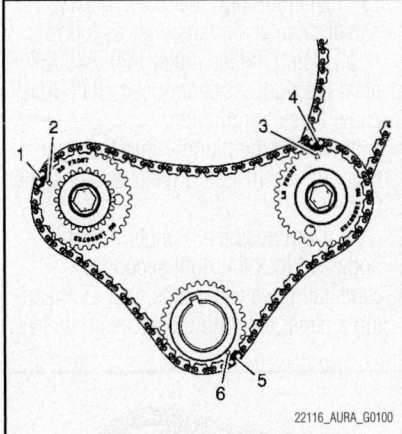

Fig. 189 Ensure all the timing marks (2, 3, 6) are properly aligned with the timing camshaft drive chain links (1, 4, 5)—3.6L engine

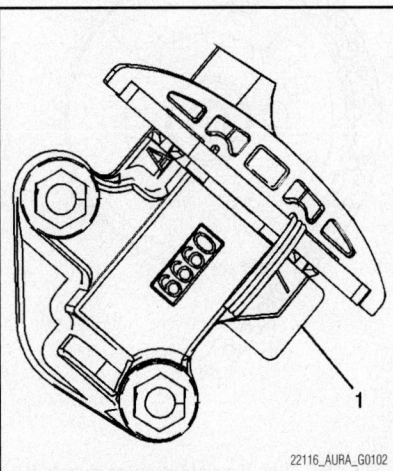

Fig. 191 Verify the proper placement of the primary camshaft drive chain tensioner gasket tab (1)—3.6L engine

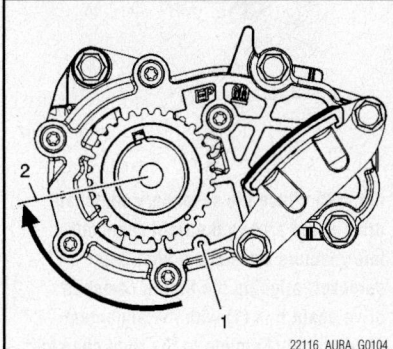

Fig. 193 Rotate the crankshaft and crankshaft sprocket from the stage 1 alignment position (1) to the stage 2 alignment position (2), 115 crankshaft degrees, in order to install the right secondary camshaft drive chain components—3.6L engine

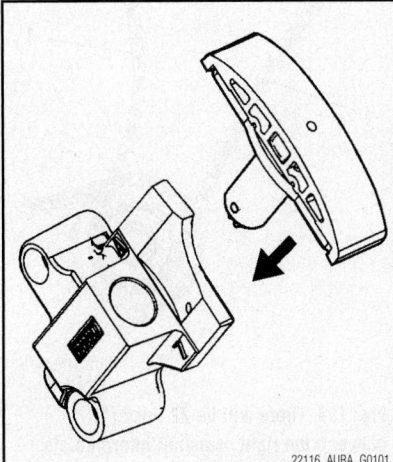

Fig. 190 Using the tensioner tool J 45027, reset the primary camshaft drive chain tensioner plunger—3.6L engine

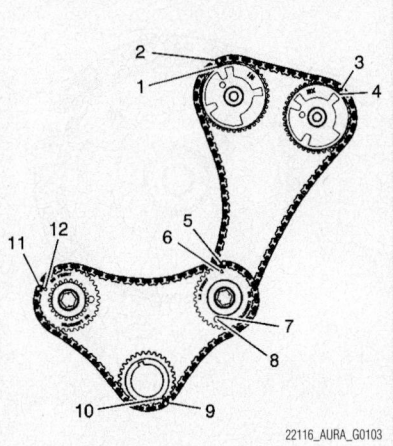

Fig. 192 Verify the primary and left secondary camshaft drive chain timing mark alignments (1-12)—3.6L engine

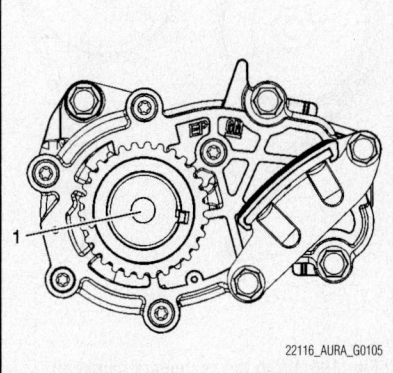

Fig. 194 Ensure that the crankshaft is in the stage 2 timing drive assembly position (1)—3.6L engine

p. Install the camshaft holding tool onto the rear of the right camshafts

20. Install the right bank secondary camshaft drive chain as follows:

a. Ensure that the crankshaft is in the stage 2 timing drive assembly position (1).

b. Install the right secondary camshaft drive chain.

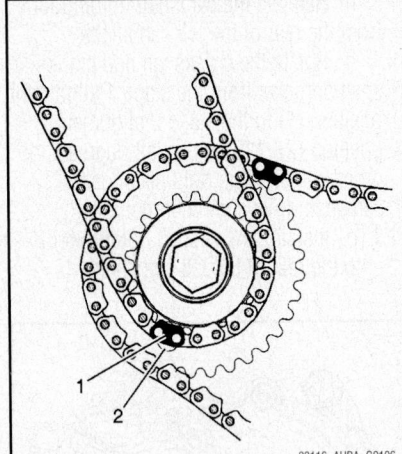

Fig. 195 Place the secondary camshaft drive chain around the right camshaft intermediate drive chain idler outer sprocket, aligning the timing camshaft drive chain link (1) with the alignment access hole (2) made in the right camshaft intermediate drive chain idler inner sprocket—3.6L engine

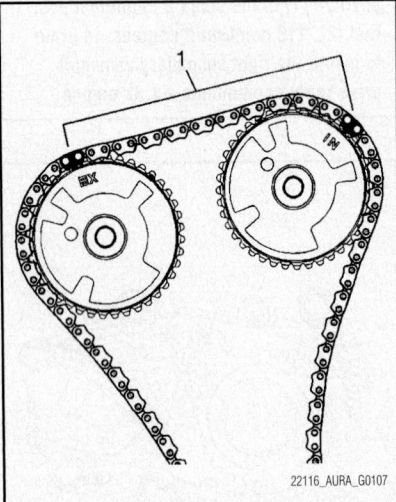

Fig. 196 Wrap the secondary camshaft drive chain around both right actuator drive sprockets. Ensure there are 10 links (1) between the timing camshaft drive chain links for the camshaft position actuator sprockets—3.6L engine

c. Place the secondary camshaft drive chain around the right camshaft intermediate drive chain idler outer sprocket, aligning the timing camshaft drive chain link (1) with the alignment access hole (2) made in the right camshaft intermediate drive chain idler inner sprocket.

d. Wrap the secondary camshaft drive chain around both right actuator drive sprockets. Ensure there are 10 links (1) between the timing camshaft drive chain links for the camshaft position actuator sprockets.

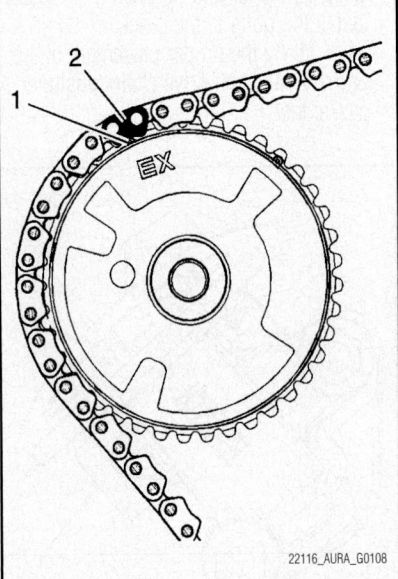

Fig. 197 Align the right exhaust camshaft position actuator sprocket alignment triangle mark (1) with the timing camshaft drive chain link (2)—3.6L engine

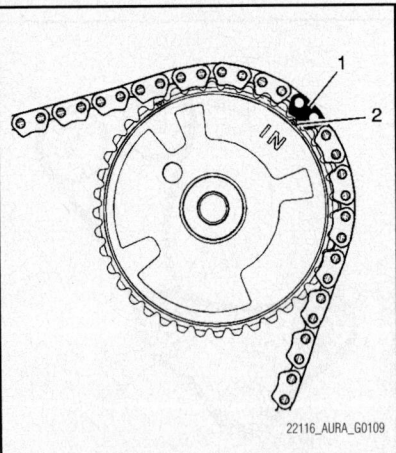

Fig. 198 Align the right intake camshaft position actuator sprocket alignment triangle mark (2) with the timing camshaft drive chain link (1)—3.6L engine

e. Align the right exhaust camshaft position actuator sprocket alignment triangle mark (1) with the timing camshaft drive chain link (2).

f. Align the right intake camshaft position actuator sprocket alignment triangle mark (2) with the timing camshaft drive chain link (1).

g. There will be 22 links (1) between the right camshaft intermediate drive chain idler timing camshaft drive chain link and each right camshaft position actuator sprocket timing camshaft drive chain link.

21. Install the right bank secondary camshaft drive chain guide. Tighten the bolts to 17 ft. lbs. (23 Nm).

22. Install the right bank secondary camshaft drive chain shoe. Tighten the bolts to 17 ft. lbs. (23 Nm).

23. Install the right bank secondary camshaft drive chain tensioner as follows:

a. Using the tensioner tool J 45027 , reset the right secondary camshaft drive chain tensioner plunger.

b. Install the plunger into the right secondary camshaft drive chain tensioner body.

c. Compress the plunger into the body and lock the right secondary camshaft drive chain tensioner by inserting a paper clip into the access hole in

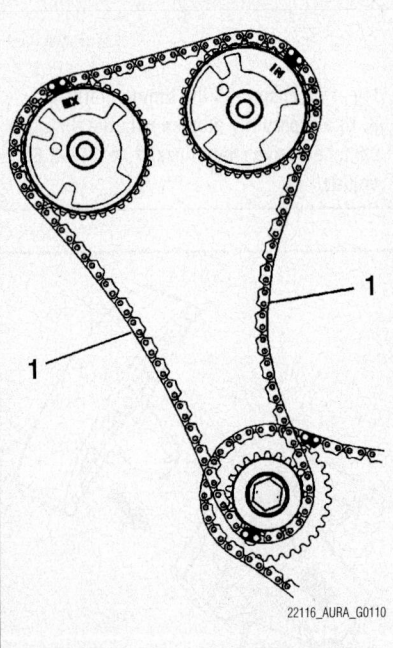

Fig. 199 There will be 22 links (1) between the right camshaft intermediate drive chain idler timing camshaft drive chain link and each right camshaft position actuator sprocket timing camshaft drive chain link—3.6L engine

the side of the right secondary camshaft drive chain tensioner body.

d. Slowly release pressure on the right secondary camshaft drive chain tensioner. The right secondary camshaft drive chain tensioner should remain compressed.

e. Install a NEW right secondary camshaft drive chain tensioner gasket to the right secondary camshaft drive chain tensioner.

f. Install the right secondary camshaft drive chain tensioner bolts through the right secondary camshaft drive chain tensioner and gasket.

g. Ensure the right secondary camshaft drive chain tensioner mounting surface on the right cylinder head does not have any burrs or defects that would degrade the sealing of the NEW right secondary camshaft drive chain tensioner gasket.

h. Place the right secondary camshaft drive chain tensioner into position and loosely install the bolts to the block.

i. Verify the proper placement of the right secondary camshaft drive chain tensioner gasket tab.

j. Tighten the tensioner bolts in two stages. First tighten to 44 inch lbs. (5 Nm) and then to 17 ft. lbs. (23 Nm).

k. Release the right camshaft drive chain tensioner by pulling out the paper clip and unlocking the tensioner plunger.

l. Ensure that all timing chain tensioners are completely released. A timing chain tensioner that is not properly released can lead to serious engine damage.

m. Verify all primary and secondary camshaft drive chain timing mark alignments (1-18).

24. Install the spark plugs.

25. Install the engine front cove as follows:

a. Install the 8mm (0.315 in) guide from a guide pin set such as EN 46109 into the cylinder block positions as shown.

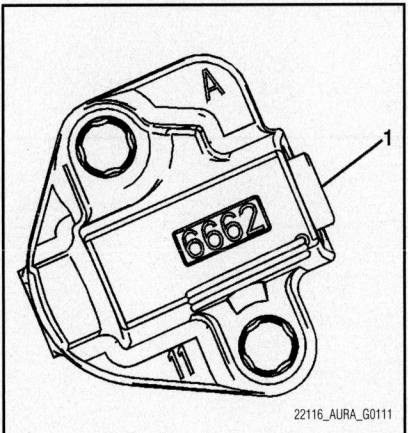

Fig. 200 Verify the proper placement of the right secondary camshaft drive chain tensioner gasket tab (1)—3.6L engine

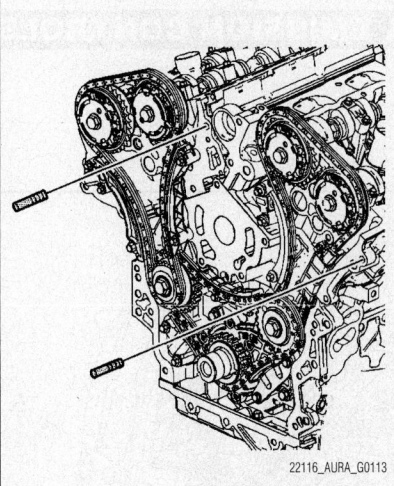

Fig. 202 Install the 8 mm (0.315 in) guide from a guide pin set such as EN 46109 into the cylinder block positions—3.6L engine

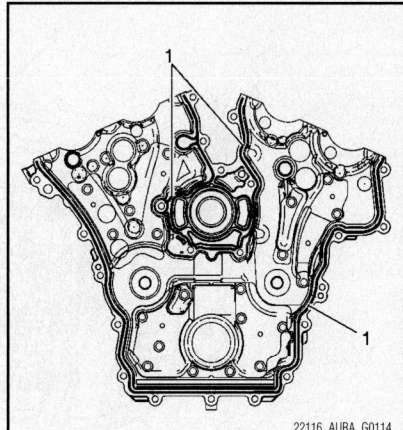

Fig. 203 Place a 3 mm (0.118 in) bead of RTV sealant, on the engine front cover at points indicated by (1)—3.6L engine

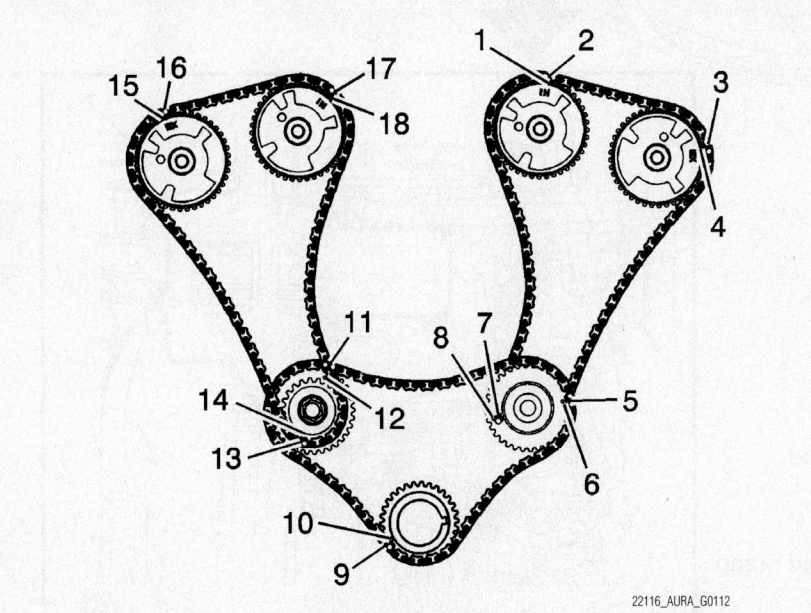

Fig. 201 Verify all primary and secondary camshaft drive chain timing mark alignments (1-18)—3.6L engine

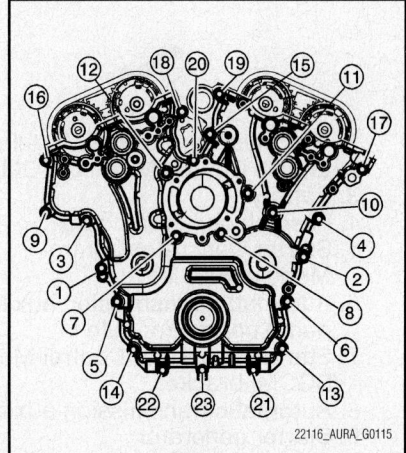

Fig. 204 Front cover fastener torque sequence—3.6L engine

b. Install the engine front cover to cylinder block seal.

c. Place a 3mm (0.118 in) bead of RTV sealant, on the engine front cover at points indicated by (1).

d. Place the engine front cover onto the guide pin set and slide into position.

e. Remove the guide pin set from the cylinder block.

f. Hand start all the front cover bolts.

g. Tighten the engine front cover bolts in the sequence show to 17 ft. lbs. (23 Nm).

h. Install the engine oil pan.

i. Install the engine coolant thermostat housing.

j. Reinstall the engine support fixture.

k. Remove the engine mount bracket.

l. Install the camshaft position actuator solenoid valves to the front cover.

m. Install the camshaft position actuator valves to the front cover.

n. Install the crankshaft balancer.

o. Install the power steering pump and position aside.

p. Install the water pump.

q. Install the drive belt tensioner.

r. Install the camshaft covers.

s. Install the lower intake manifold.

t. Refill the engine coolant.

VALVE LASH

ADJUSTMENT

All engines utilize hydraulic lash adjusters; no adjustment is necessary.

ENGINE PERFORMANCE & EMISSION CONTROLS

COMPONENT LOCATIONS

See Figures 205 through 226.

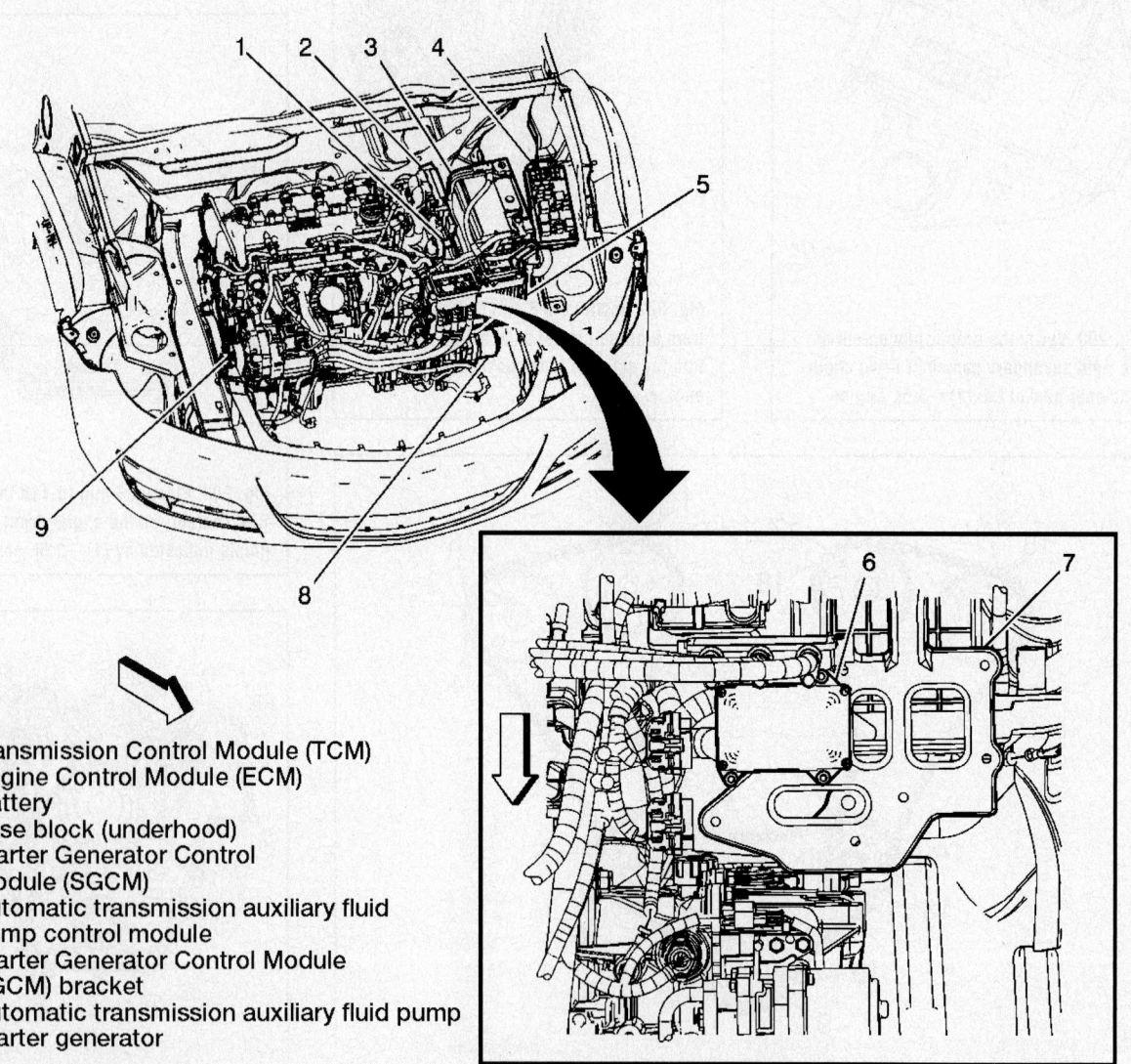

1. Transmission Control Module (TCM)
2. Engine Control Module (ECM)
3. Battery
4. Fuse block (underhood)
5. Starter Generator Control Module (SGCM)
6. Automatic transmission auxiliary fluid pump control module
7. Starter Generator Control Module (SGCM) bracket
8. Automatic transmission auxiliary fluid pump
9. Starter generator

36616_AURA_G0044

Fig. 205 Front of engine compartment 1 of 2—2.4L engine (LAT)

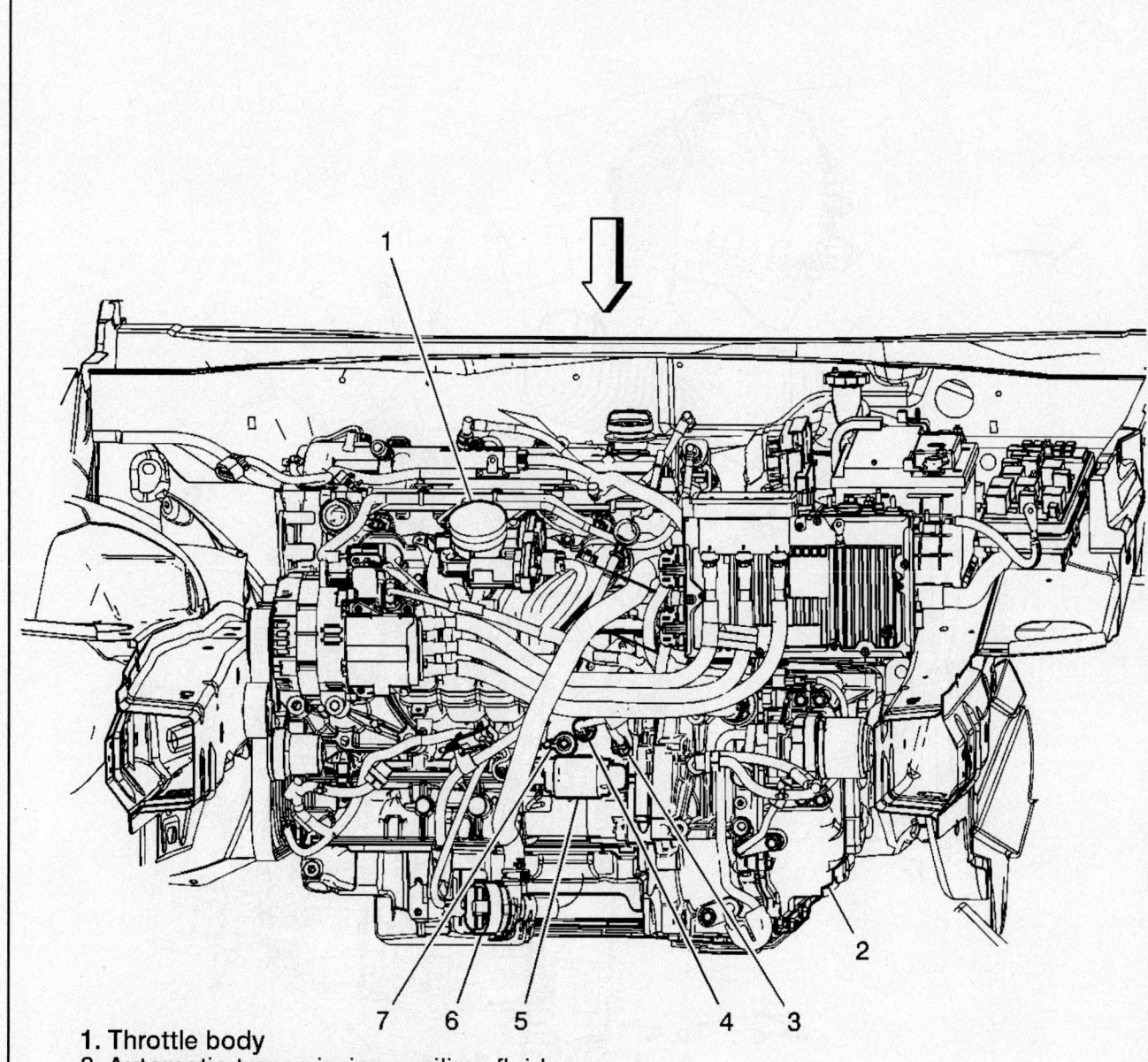

1. Throttle body
2. Automatic transmission auxiliary fluid pump
3. Crankshaft Position (CKP) sensor
4. Engine Oil Pressure (EOP) switch
5. Starter motor
6. Starter Generator Control Module (SGCM) coolant pump
7. Knock Sensor (KS)

36616_AURA_G0045

Fig. 206 Front of engine compartment 2 of 2—2.4L engine (LAT)

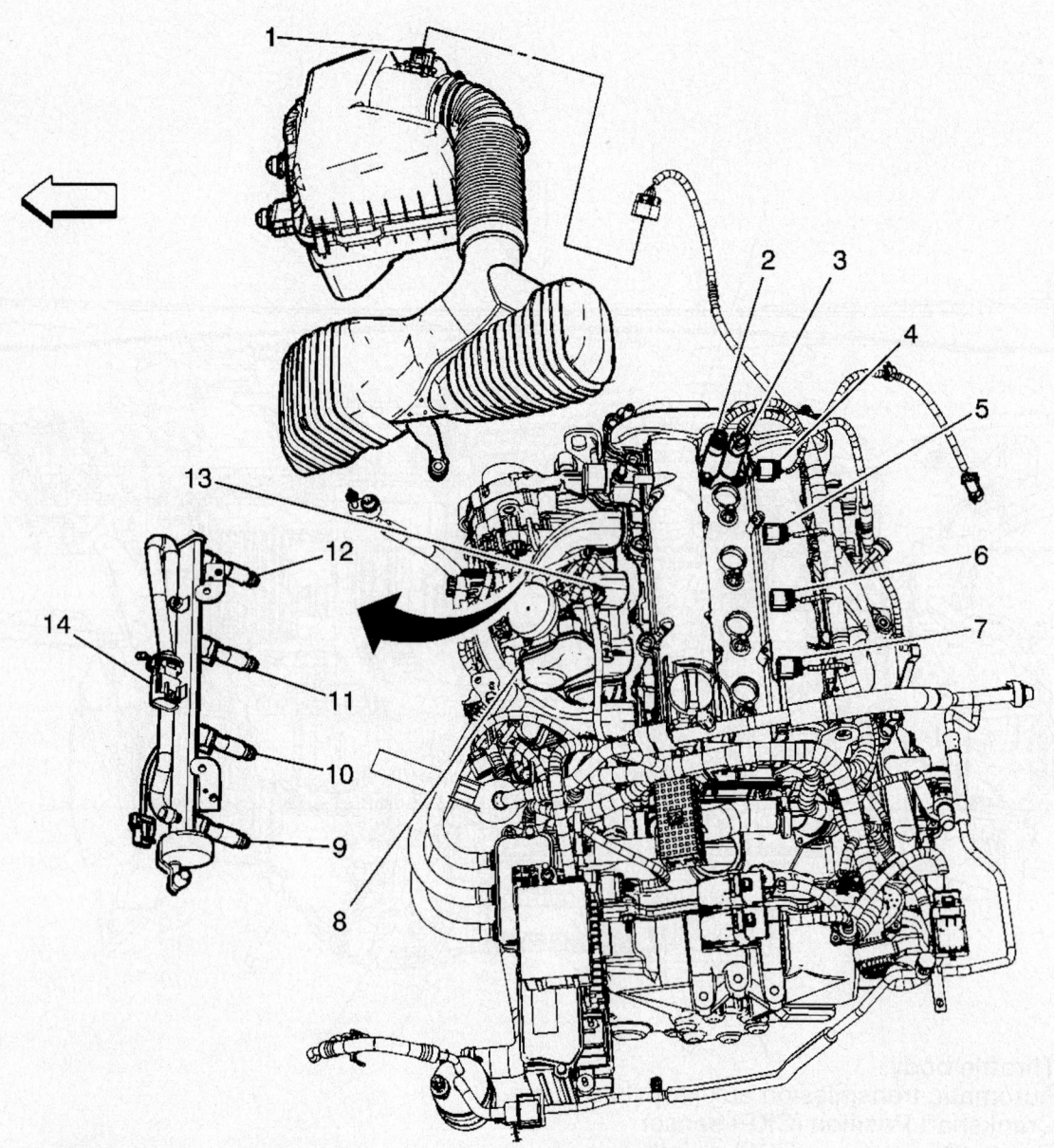

1. Mass Air Flow (MAF)/Intake Air Temperature (IAT) sensor
2. Camshaft Position (CMP) actuator solenoid valve – intake
3. Camshaft Position (CMP) actuator solenoid valve – exhaust
4. Ignition coil 1
5. Ignition coil 2
6. Ignition coil 3
7. Ignition coil 4
8. Throttle body
9. Fuel injector 4
10. Fuel injector 3
11. Fuel injector 2
12. Fuel injector 1
13. Manifold Absolute Pressure (MAP) sensor
14. X130

36616_AURA_G0046

Fig. 207 Top of engine components—2.4L engine (LAT)

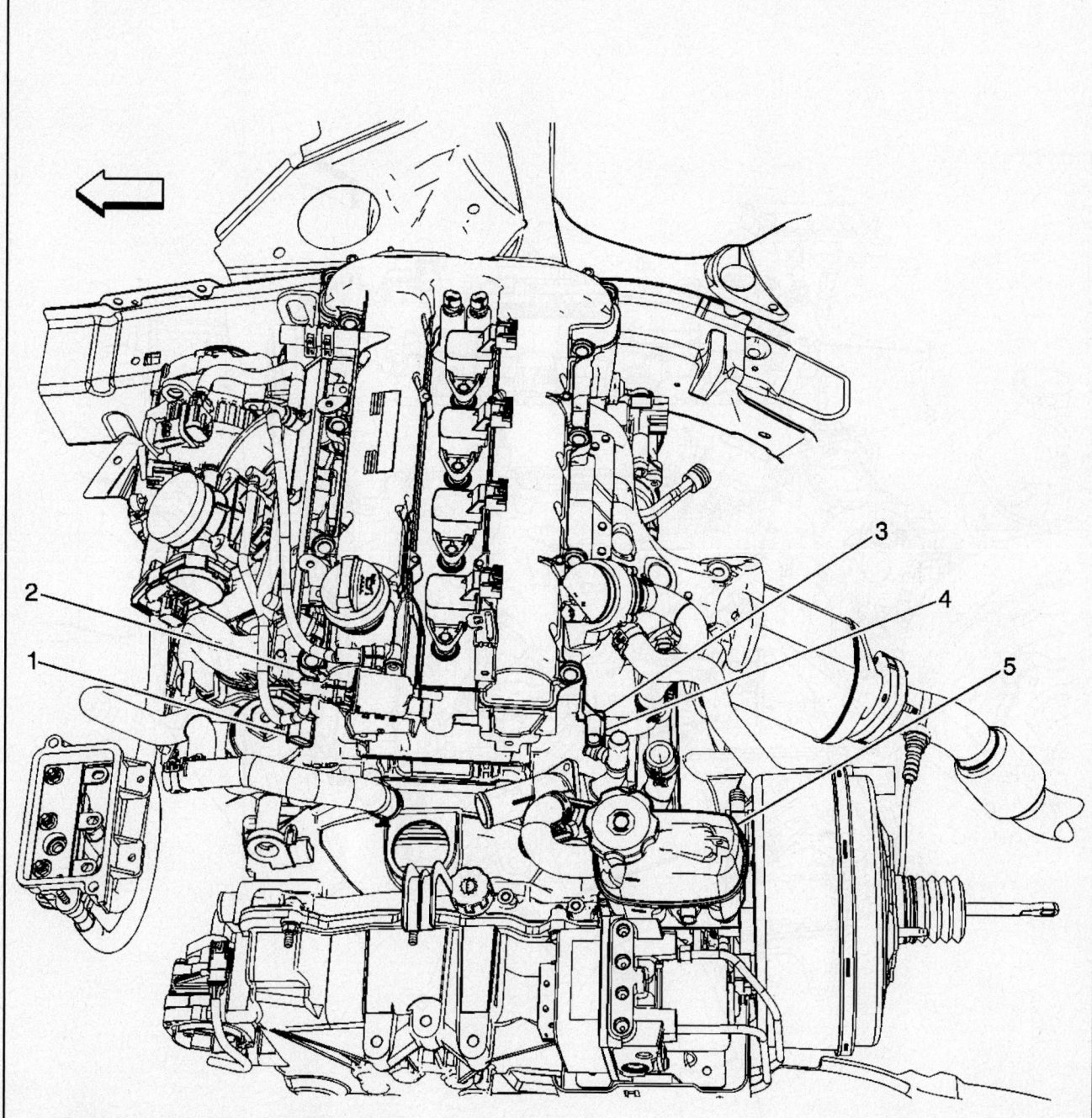

1. Camshaft Position (CMP) sensor - intake
2. G106
3. G110
4. Camshaft Position (CMP) sensor - exhaust
5. Master cylinder

36616_AURA_G0047

Fig. 208 Left side of engine compartment—2.4L engine (LAT)

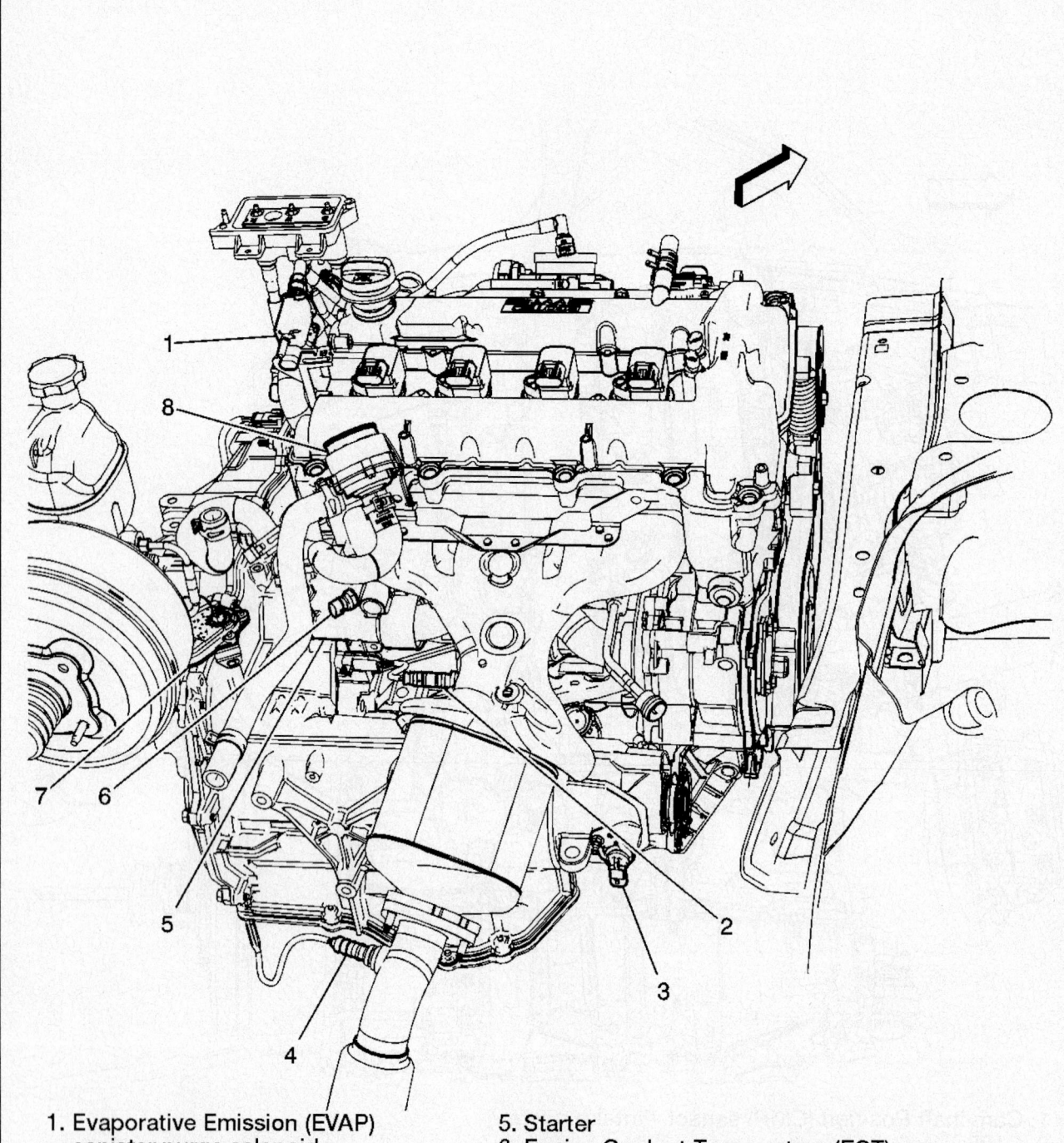

1. Evaporative Emission (EVAP) canister purge solenoid
2. Heated Oxygen Sensor (HO2S) 1
3. Vehicle Speed Sensor (VSS)
4. Heated Oxygen Sensor (HO2S) 2
5. Starter
6. Engine Coolant Temperature (ECT) sensor
7. Park/Neutral Position (PNP) switch
8. Heater coolant pump

36616_AURA_G0048

Fig. 209 Rear of engine components—2.4L engine (LAT)

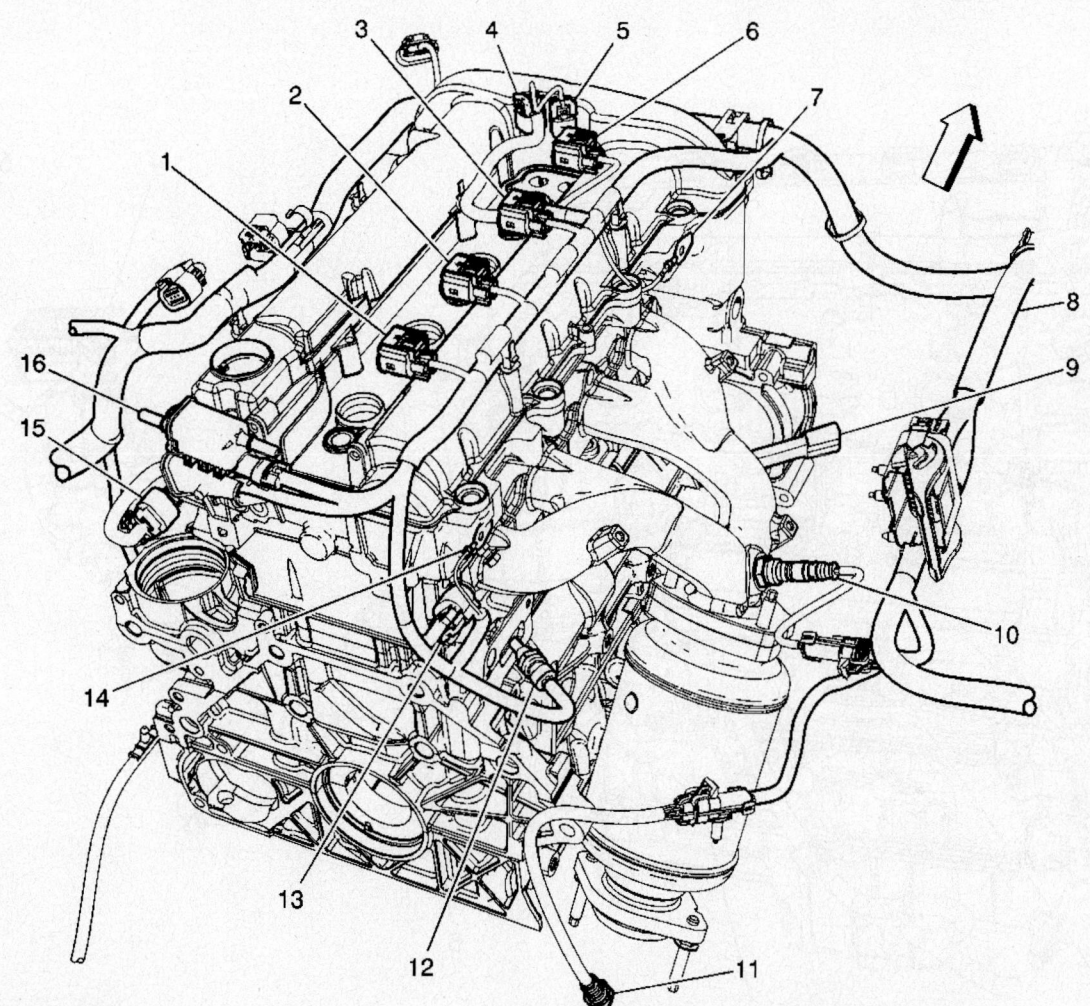

1. Ignition Coil 4
2. Ignition Coil 3
3. Ignition Coil 2
4. Camshaft Position (CMP) Actuator Solenoid - Intake
5. Camshaft Position (CMP) Actuator Solenoid - Exhaust
6. Ignition Coil 1
7. G107
8. Engine harness
9. Engine block heater connector
10. Heated Oxygen Sensor (HO2S) 1
11. Heated Oxygen Sensor (HO2S) 2
12. Engine Coolant Temperature (ECT) sensor
13. Camshaft Position (CMP) Sensor 2 (Exhaust)
14. G110
15. Camshaft Position (CMP) sensor 1 (Intake)
16. Evaporative Emission (EVAP) canister purge solenoid

36616_AURA_G0062

Fig. 210 Top of engine compartment components—2.4L engine (LE5)

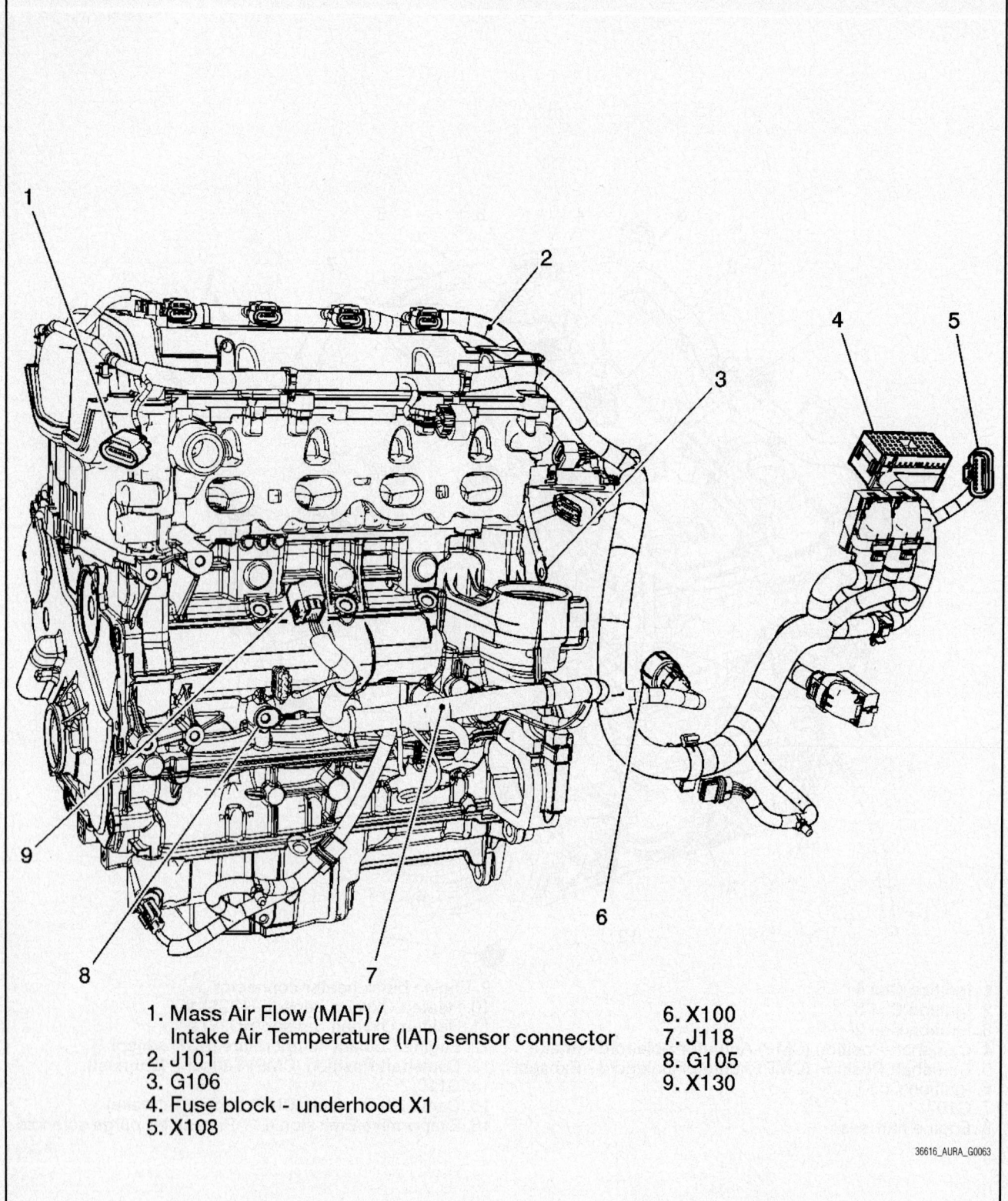

1. Mass Air Flow (MAF) /
   Intake Air Temperature (IAT) sensor connector
2. J101
3. G106
4. Fuse block - underhood X1
5. X108

6. X100
7. J118
8. G105
9. X130

36616_AURA_G0063

Fig. 211 Front of the engine components 1 of 2—2.4L engine (LE5)

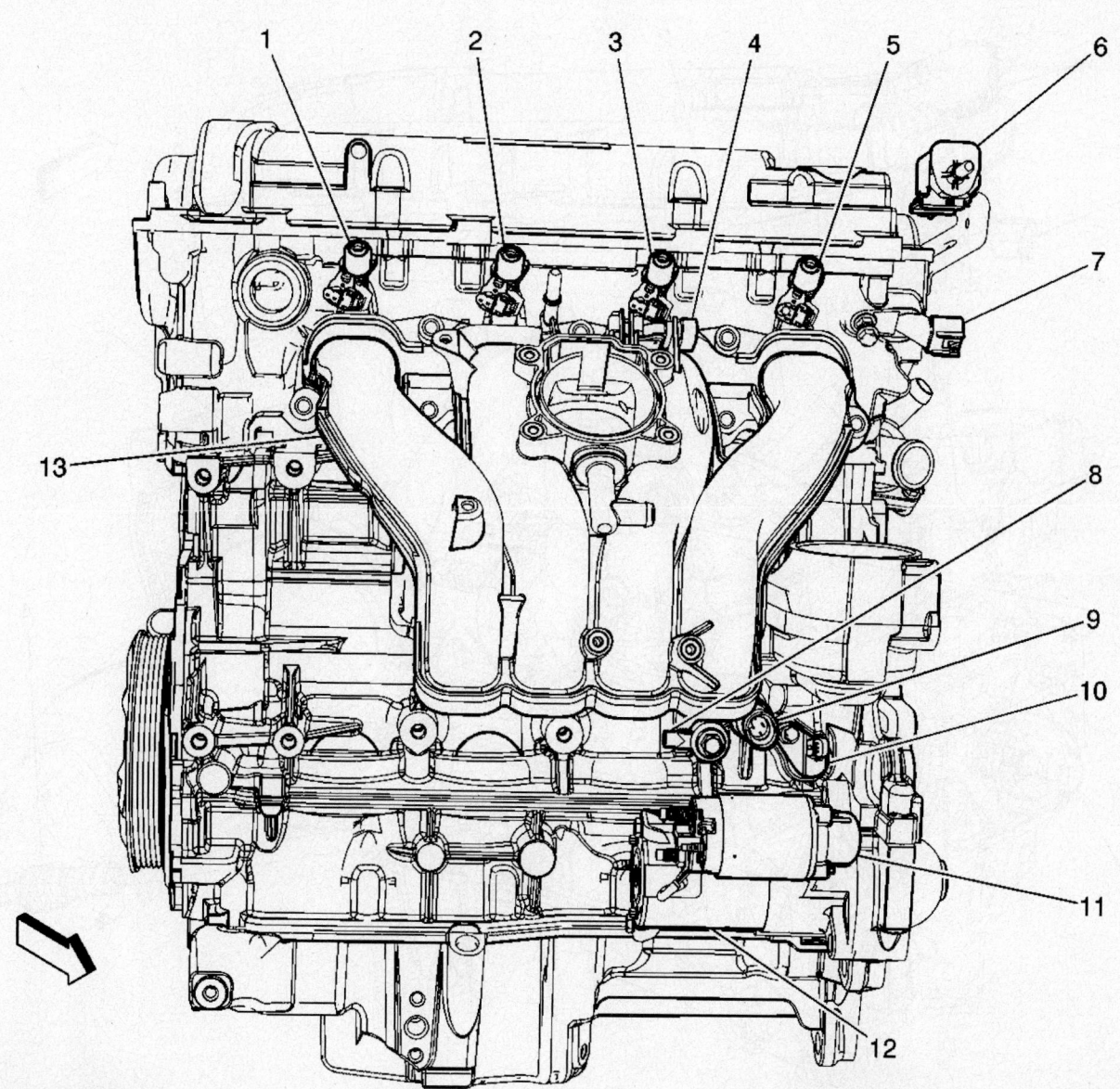

1. Fuel Injector 1
2. Fuel Injector 2
3. Fuel Injector 3
4. Manifold Absolute Pressure (MAP) sensor
5. Fuel Injector 4
6. Evaporative Emission (EVAP) canister purge solenoid valve
7. Camshaft Position (CMP) sensor - intake

8. Knock Sensor (KS)
9. Engine Oil Pressure (EOP) switch
10. Crankshaft Position (CKP) sensor
11. Starter solenoid
12. Starter motor
13. Intake manifold

36616_AURA_G0064

Fig. 212 Front of the engine components 2 of 2—2.4L engine (LE5)

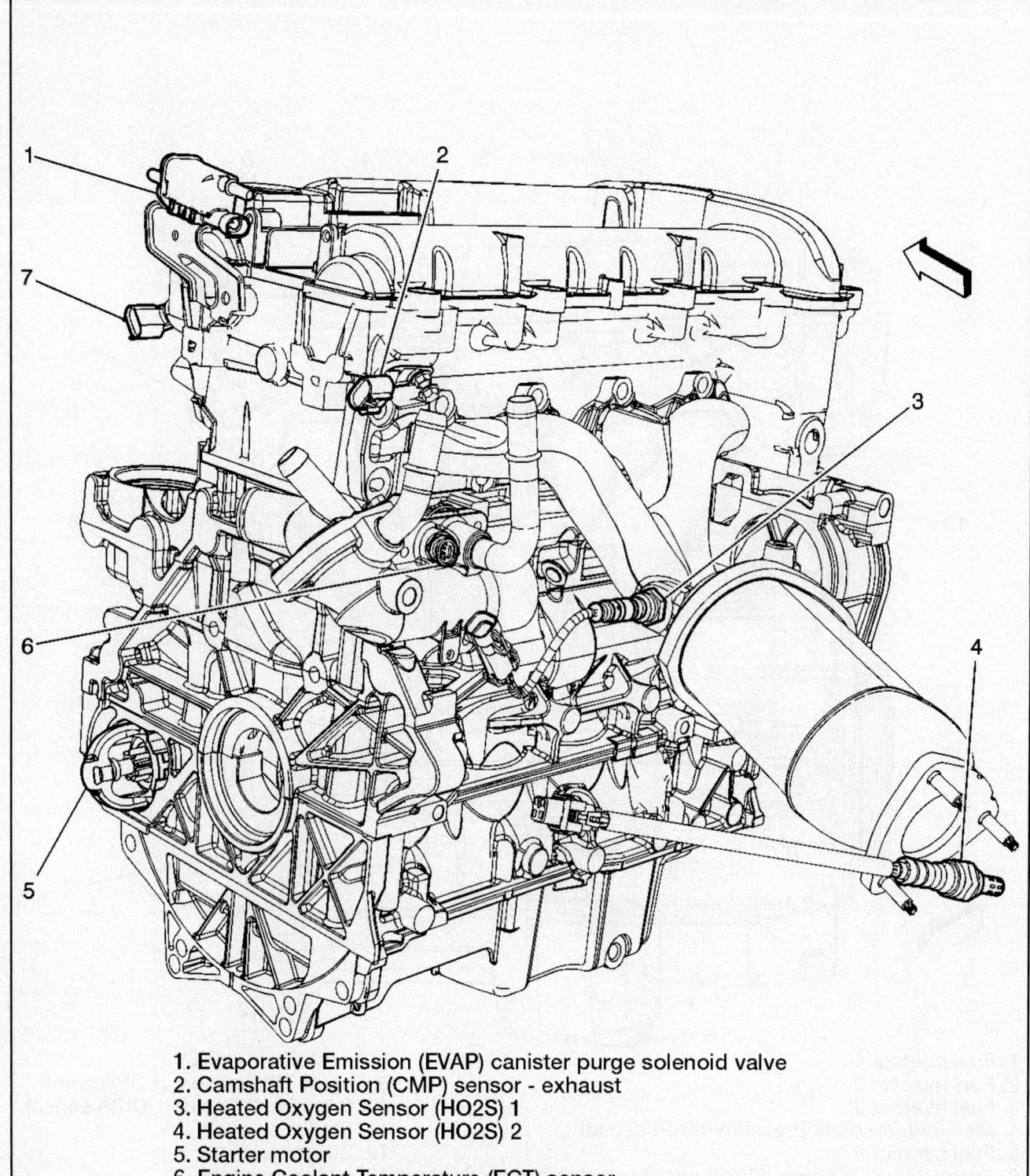

1. Evaporative Emission (EVAP) canister purge solenoid valve
2. Camshaft Position (CMP) sensor - exhaust
3. Heated Oxygen Sensor (HO2S) 1
4. Heated Oxygen Sensor (HO2S) 2
5. Starter motor
6. Engine Coolant Temperature (ECT) sensor
7. Camshaft Position (CMP) sensor - intake

36616_AURA_G0065

Fig. 213 Rear of engine components—2.4L engine (LE5)

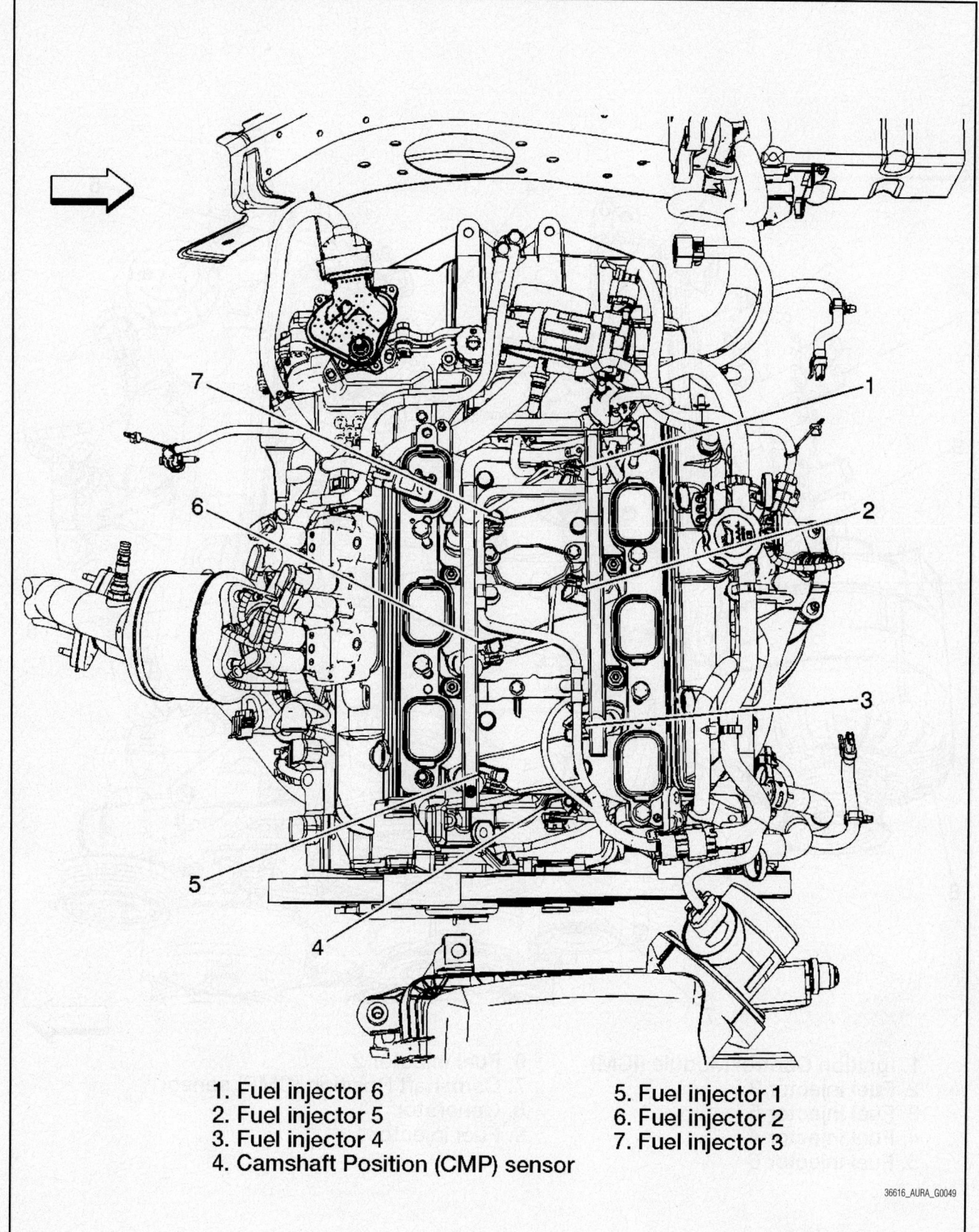

1. Fuel injector 6
2. Fuel injector 5
3. Fuel injector 4
4. Camshaft Position (CMP) sensor
5. Fuel injector 1
6. Fuel injector 2
7. Fuel injector 3

36616_AURA_G0049

Fig. 214 Top of engine components 1 of 2—3.5L engine

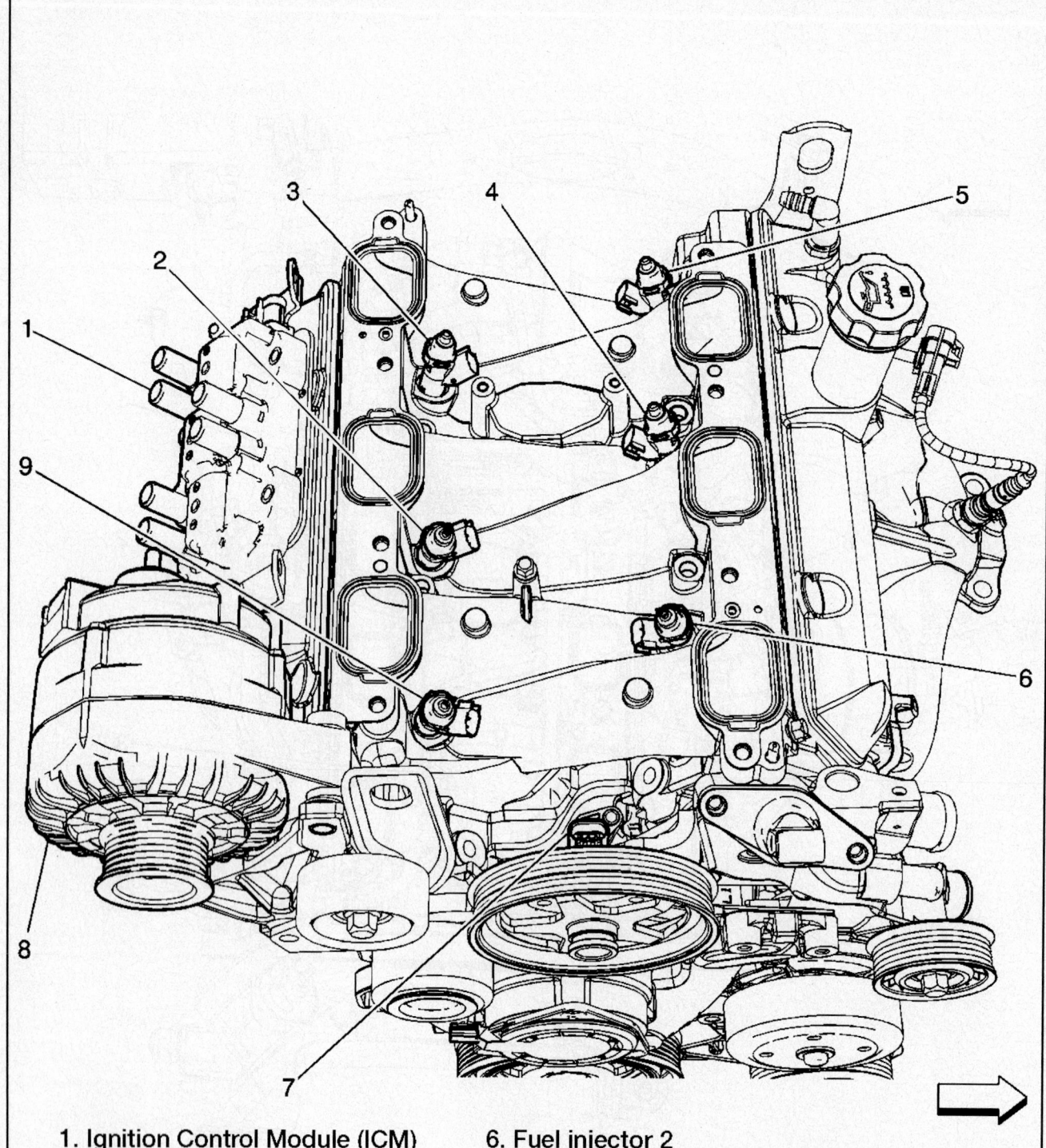

1. Ignition Control Module (ICM)
2. Fuel injector 3
3. Fuel injector 5
4. Fuel injector 4
5. Fuel injector 6
6. Fuel injector 2
7. Camshaft Position (CMP) sensor
8. Generator
9. Fuel injector 1

36616_AURA_G0050

Fig. 215 Top of engine components 2 of 2—3.5L engine

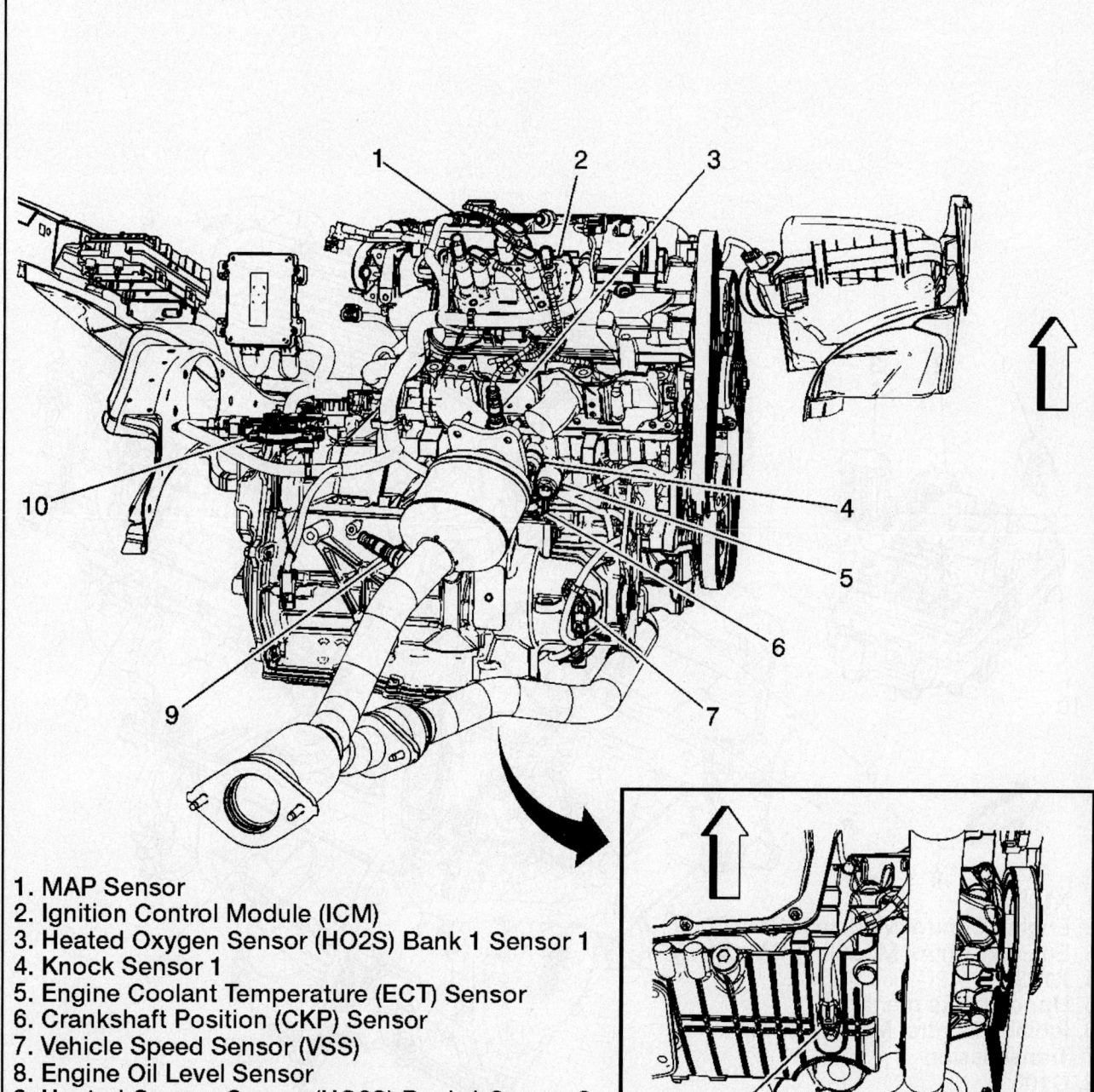

1. MAP Sensor
2. Ignition Control Module (ICM)
3. Heated Oxygen Sensor (HO2S) Bank 1 Sensor 1
4. Knock Sensor 1
5. Engine Coolant Temperature (ECT) Sensor
6. Crankshaft Position (CKP) Sensor
7. Vehicle Speed Sensor (VSS)
8. Engine Oil Level Sensor
9. Heated Oxygen Sensor (HO2S) Bank 1 Sensor 2
10. Park/Neutral Position (PNP) Switch

36616_AURA_G0051

Fig. 216 Rear of engine components 1 of 3—3.5L engine

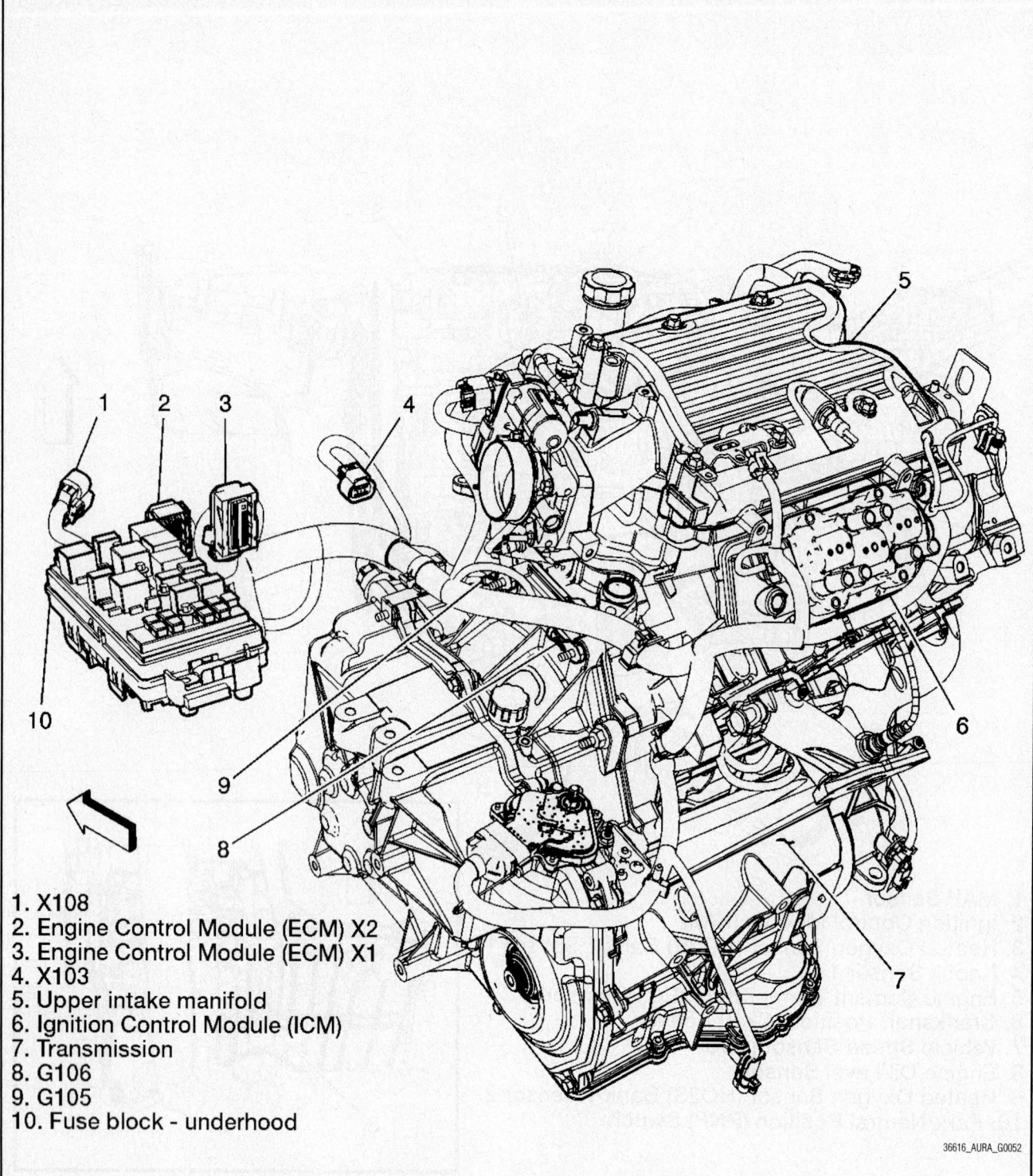

1. X108
2. Engine Control Module (ECM) X2
3. Engine Control Module (ECM) X1
4. X103
5. Upper intake manifold
6. Ignition Control Module (ICM)
7. Transmission
8. G106
9. G105
10. Fuse block - underhood

36616_AURA_G0052

Fig. 217 Rear of engine components 2 of 3—3.5L engine

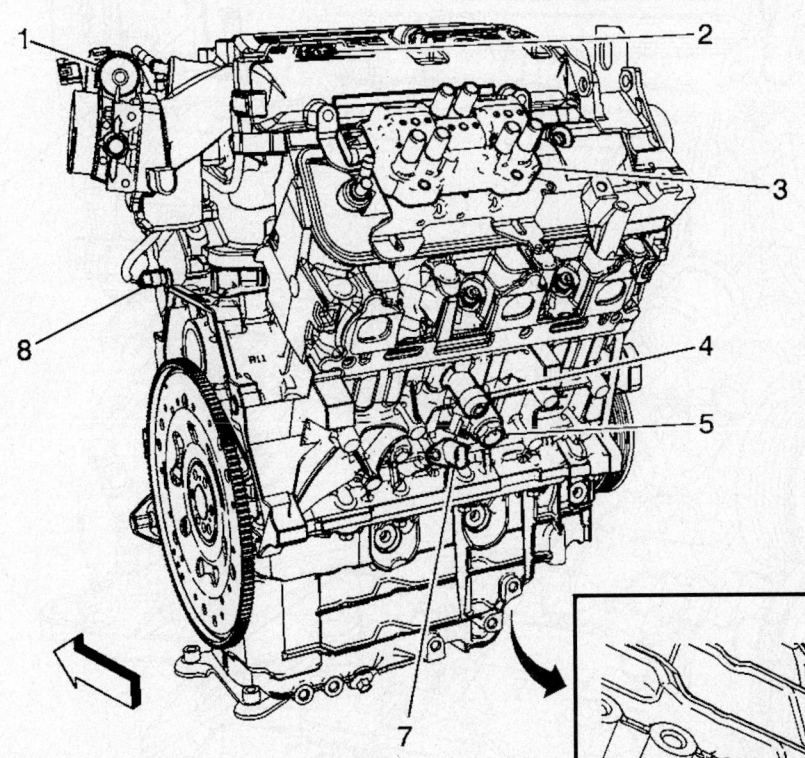

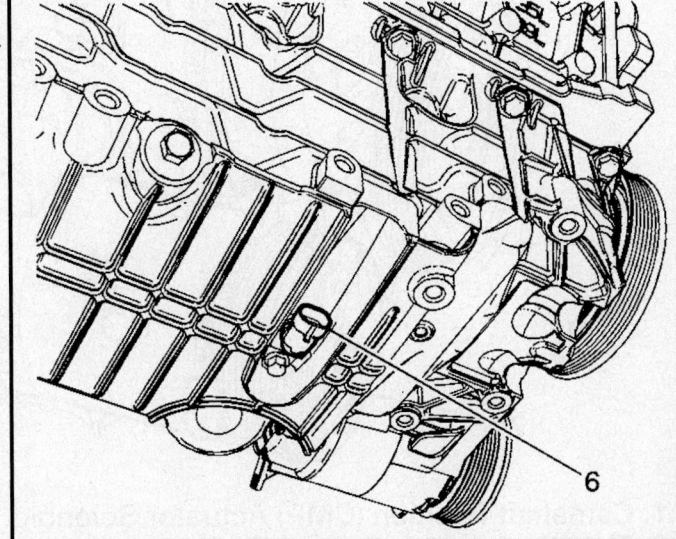

1. Throttle Actuator Control (TAC) Module
2. Manifold Absolute Pressure (MAP) Sensor
3. Ignition Control Module (ICM)
4. Knock Sensor (KS) 2
5. Engine block heater
6. Engine oil level Sensor
7. Crankshaft Position (CKP) Sensor
8. Engine Coolant Temperature (ECT) Sensor

36616_AURA_G0053

Fig. 218 Rear of engine components 3 of 3—3.5L engine

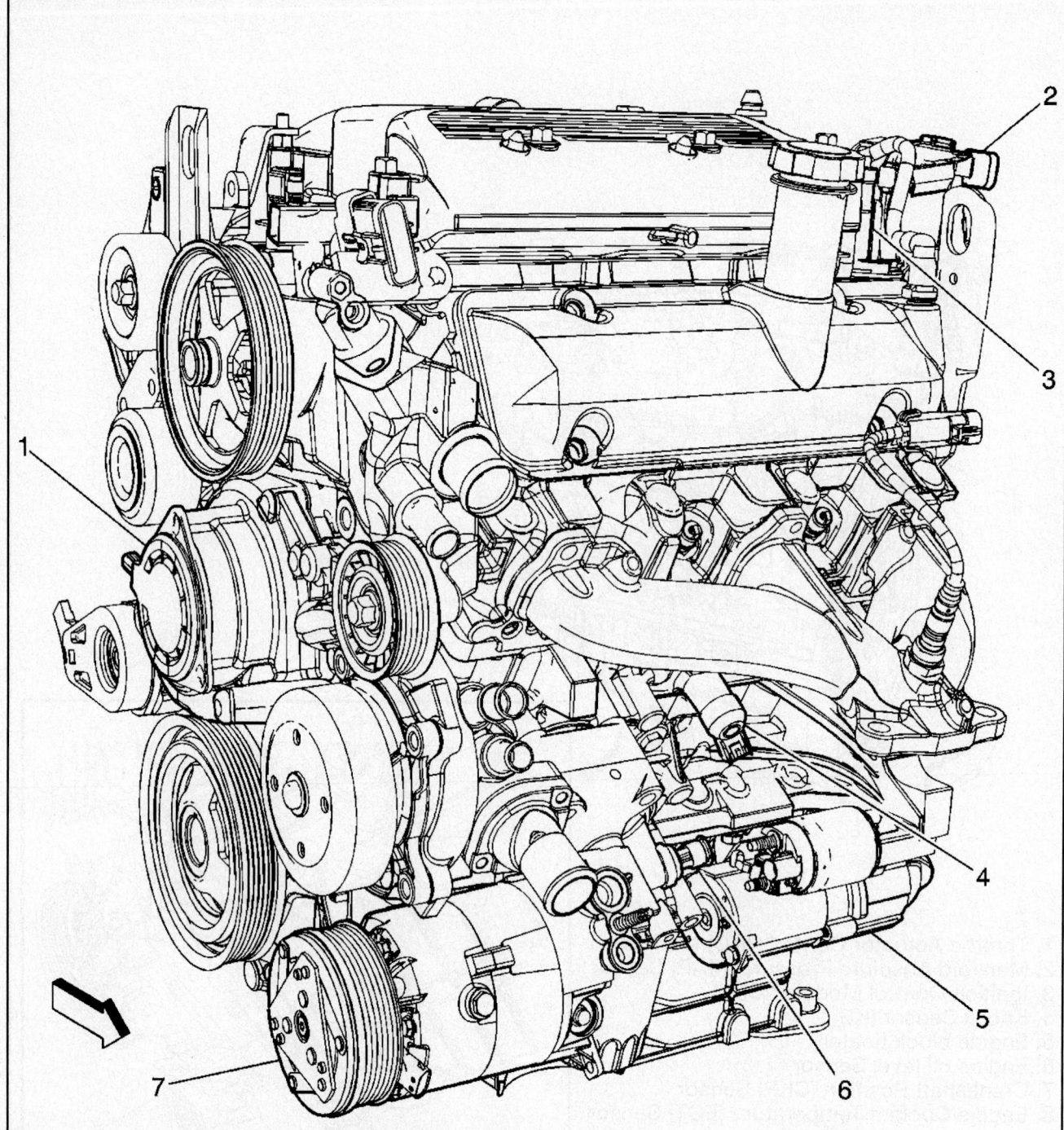

1. Camshaft Position (CMP) Actuator Solenoid
2. Throttle Actuator Control (TAC) Module
3. Evaporative Emission (EVAP) Canister Purge Solenoid
4. Knock Sensor (KS) 1
5. Starter motor
6. Engine Oil Pressure (EOP) Sensor
7. A/C compressor clutch

36616_AURA_G0054

Fig. 219 Front of the engine components 1 of 2—3.5L engine

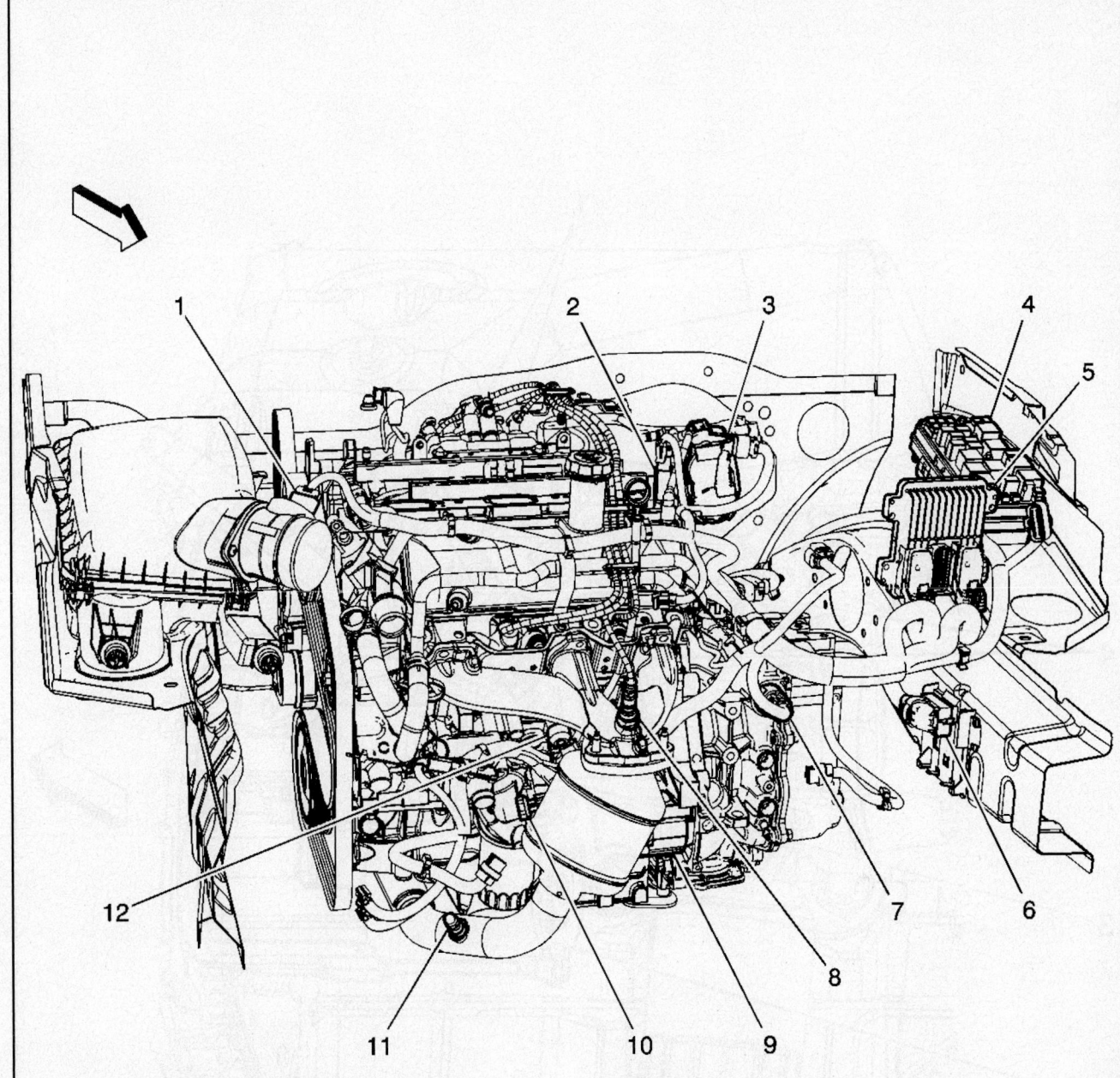

1. MAF/IAT Sensor
2. Evaporative Emission (EVAP)
   canister purge solenoid valve
3. Throttle Actuator Control (TAC) module
4. Fuse block - underhood
5. Engine Control Module (ECM)
6. Transmission Control Module (TCM)

7. X100
8. Heated Oxygen Sensor (HO2S)
   Bank 2 Sensor 1
9. Starter
10. Engine Oil Pressure (EOP) Sensor
11. Heated Oxygen Sensor (HO2S)
    Bank 2 Sensor 2
12. Knock Sensor 2

36616_AURA_G0055

Fig. 220 Front of the engine components 2 of 2—3.5L engine

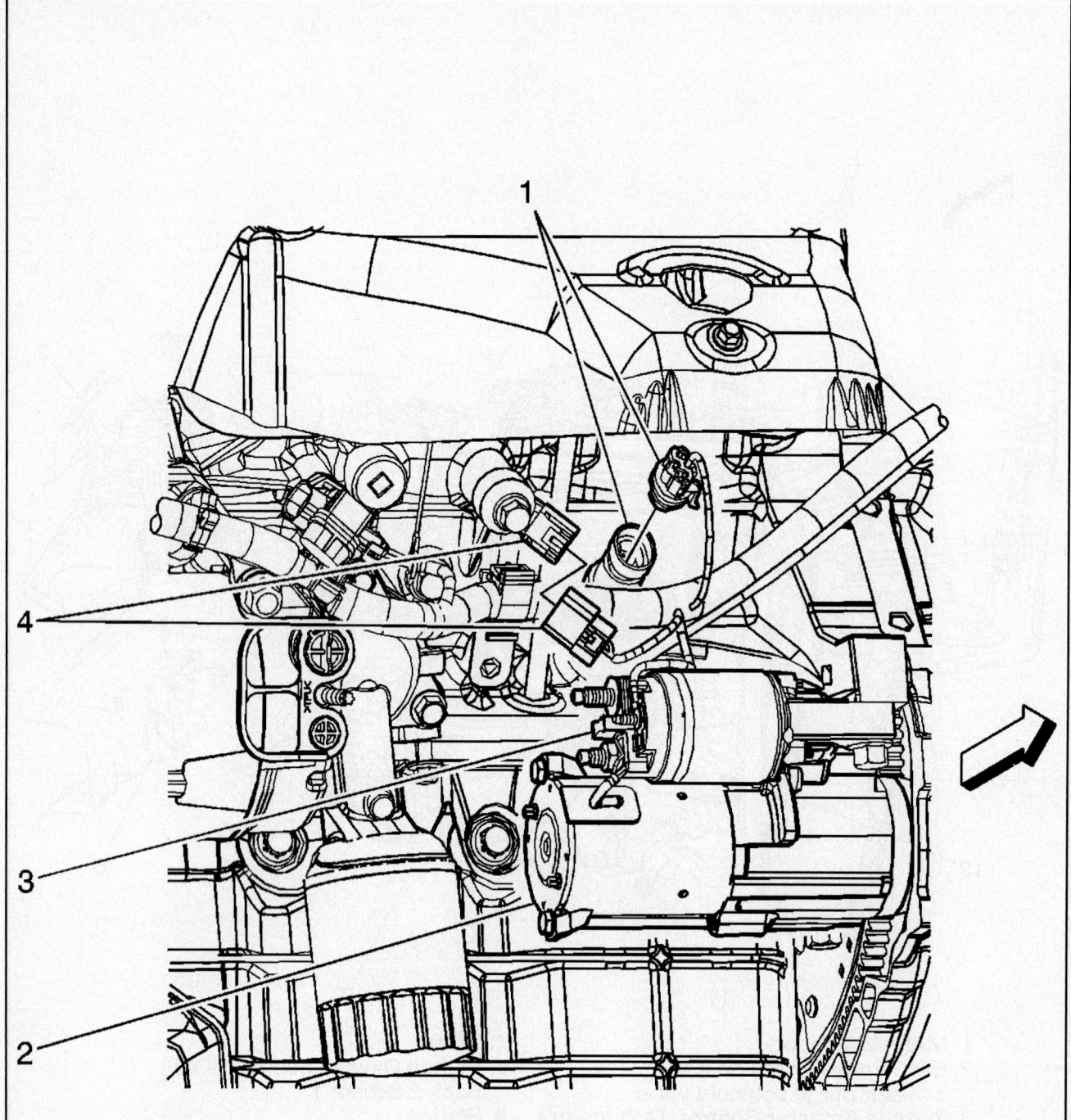

1. Engine Oil Pressure (EOP) Sensor
2. Starter
3. Starter solenoid
4. Knock Sensor (KS) 2

36616_AURA_G0056

Fig. 221 Left of engine components—3.5L engine

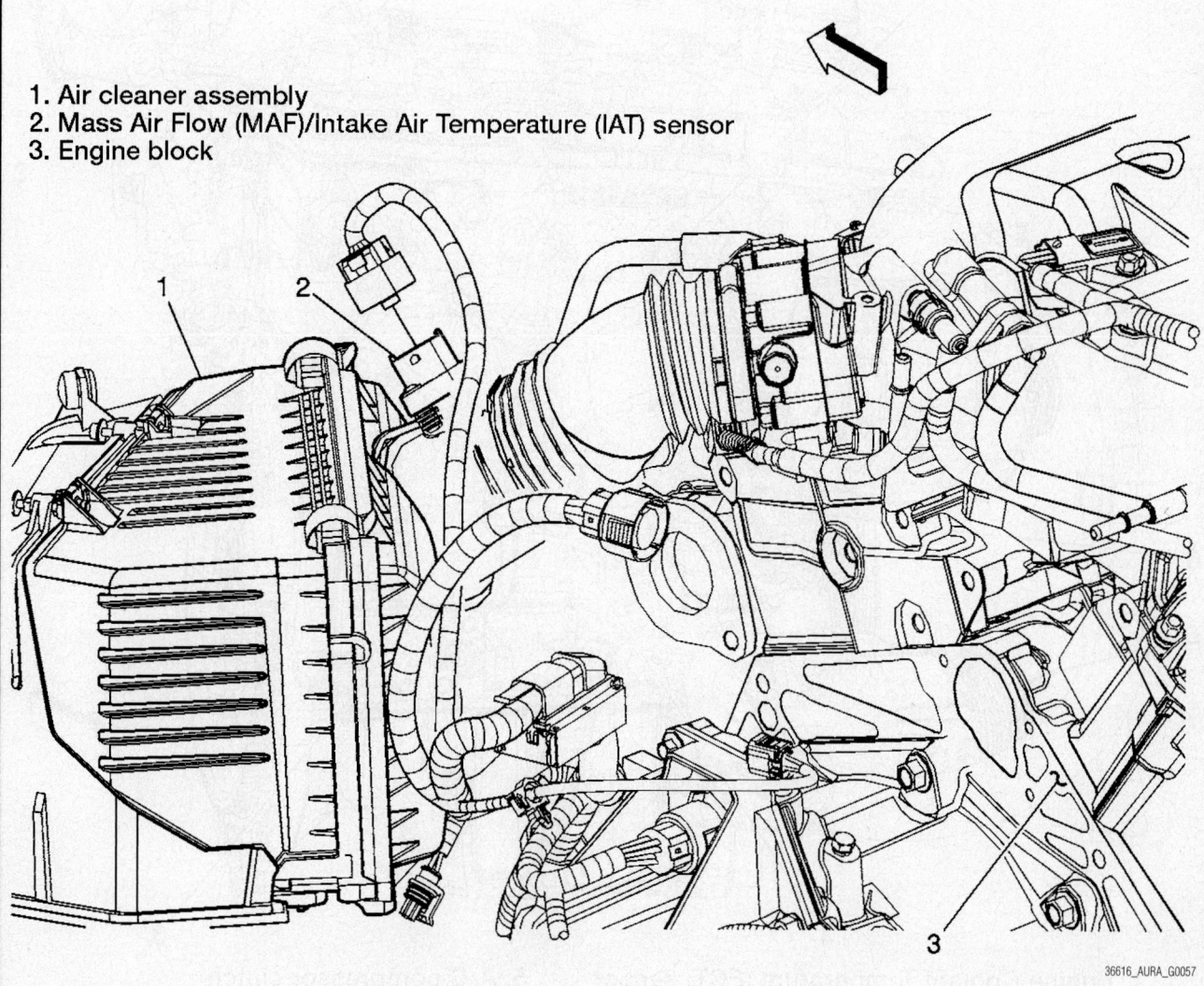

1. Air cleaner assembly
2. Mass Air Flow (MAF)/Intake Air Temperature (IAT) sensor
3. Engine block

36616_AURA_G0057

Fig. 222 Front of engine compartment components 1 of 3—3.6L engine

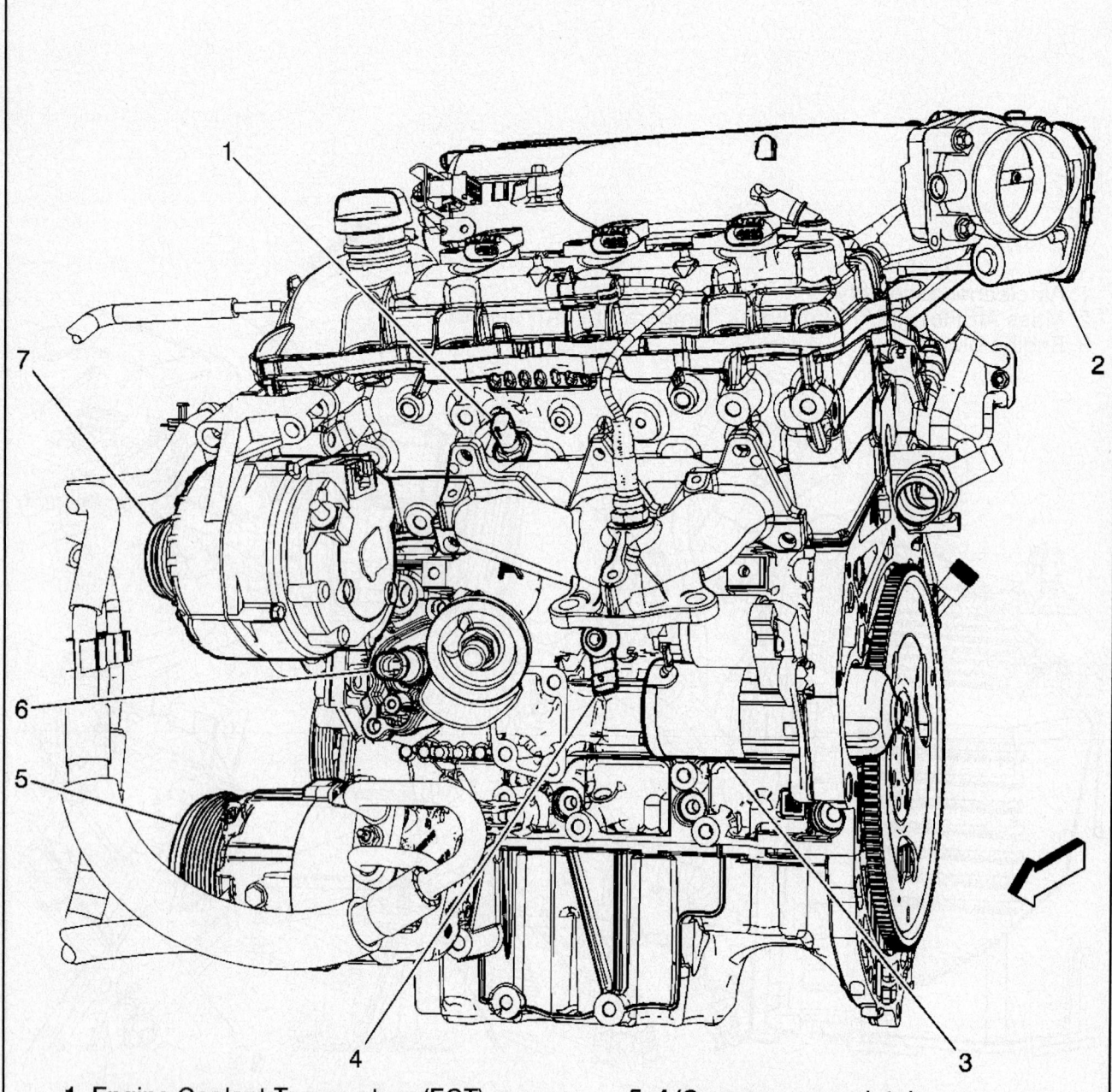

1. Engine Coolant Temperature (ECT) sensor
2. Throttle Actuator Control (TAC) module
3. Starter motor
4. Knock Sensor (KS) 2
5. A/C compressor clutch
6. Engine Oil Pressure (EOP) Switch
7. Generator

36616_AURA_G0058

Fig. 223 Front of engine compartment components 2 of 3—3.6L engine

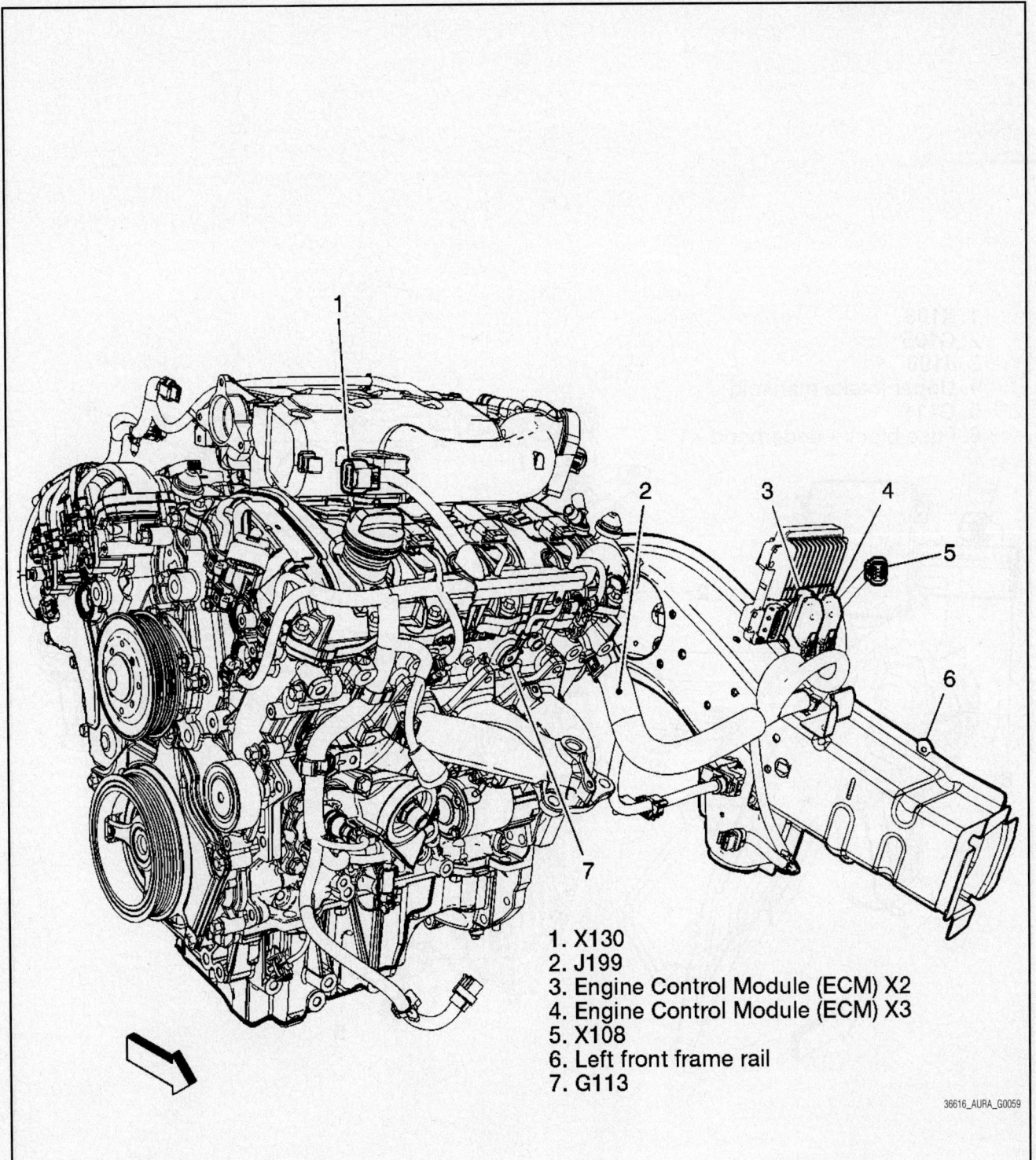

1. X130
2. J199
3. Engine Control Module (ECM) X2
4. Engine Control Module (ECM) X3
5. X108
6. Left front frame rail
7. G113

36616_AURA_G0059

Fig. 224 Front of engine compartment components 3 of 3—3.6L engine

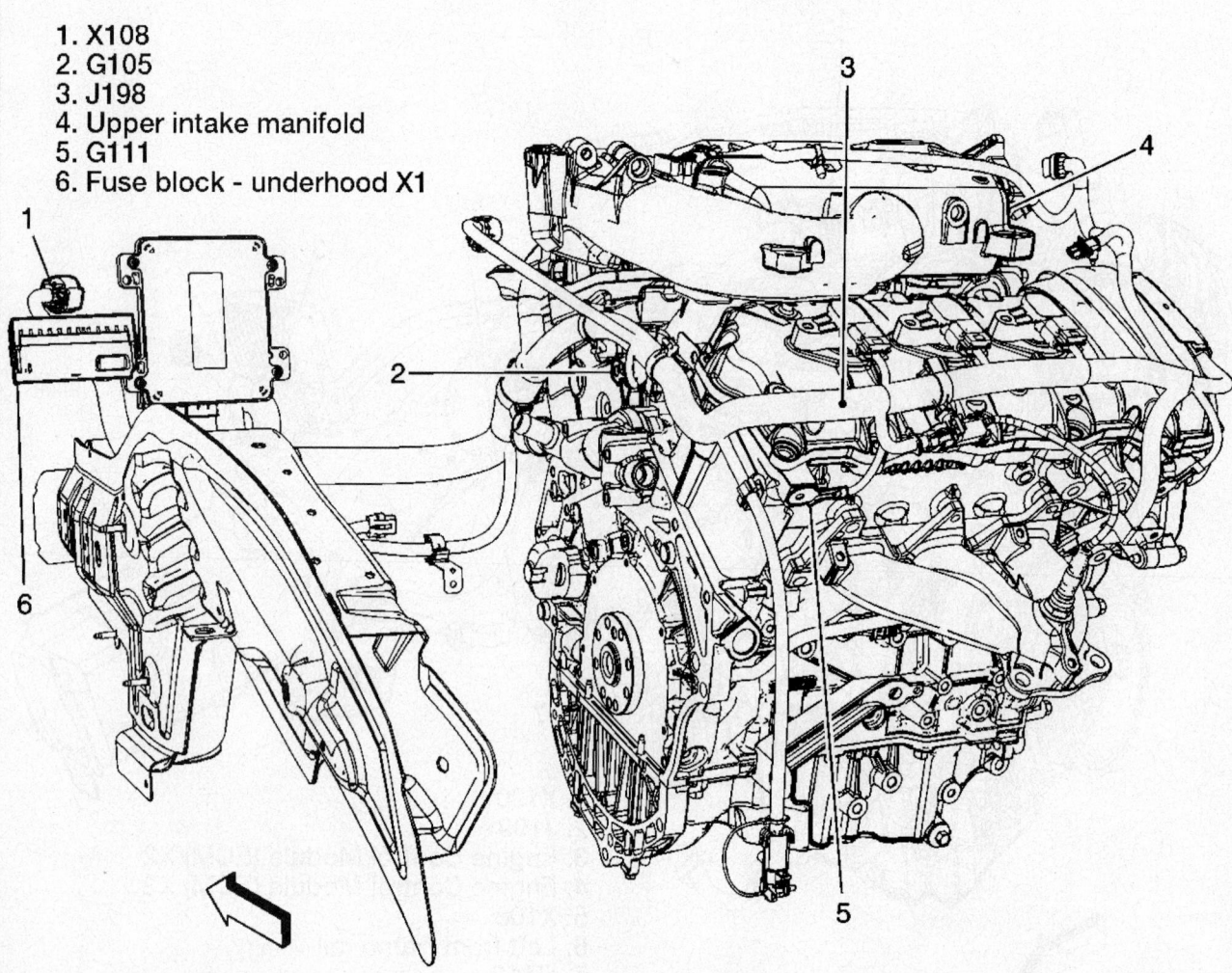

1. X108
2. G105
3. J198
4. Upper intake manifold
5. G111
6. Fuse block - underhood X1

36616_AURA_G0060

Fig. 225 Rear of engine components 1 of 2—3.6L engine

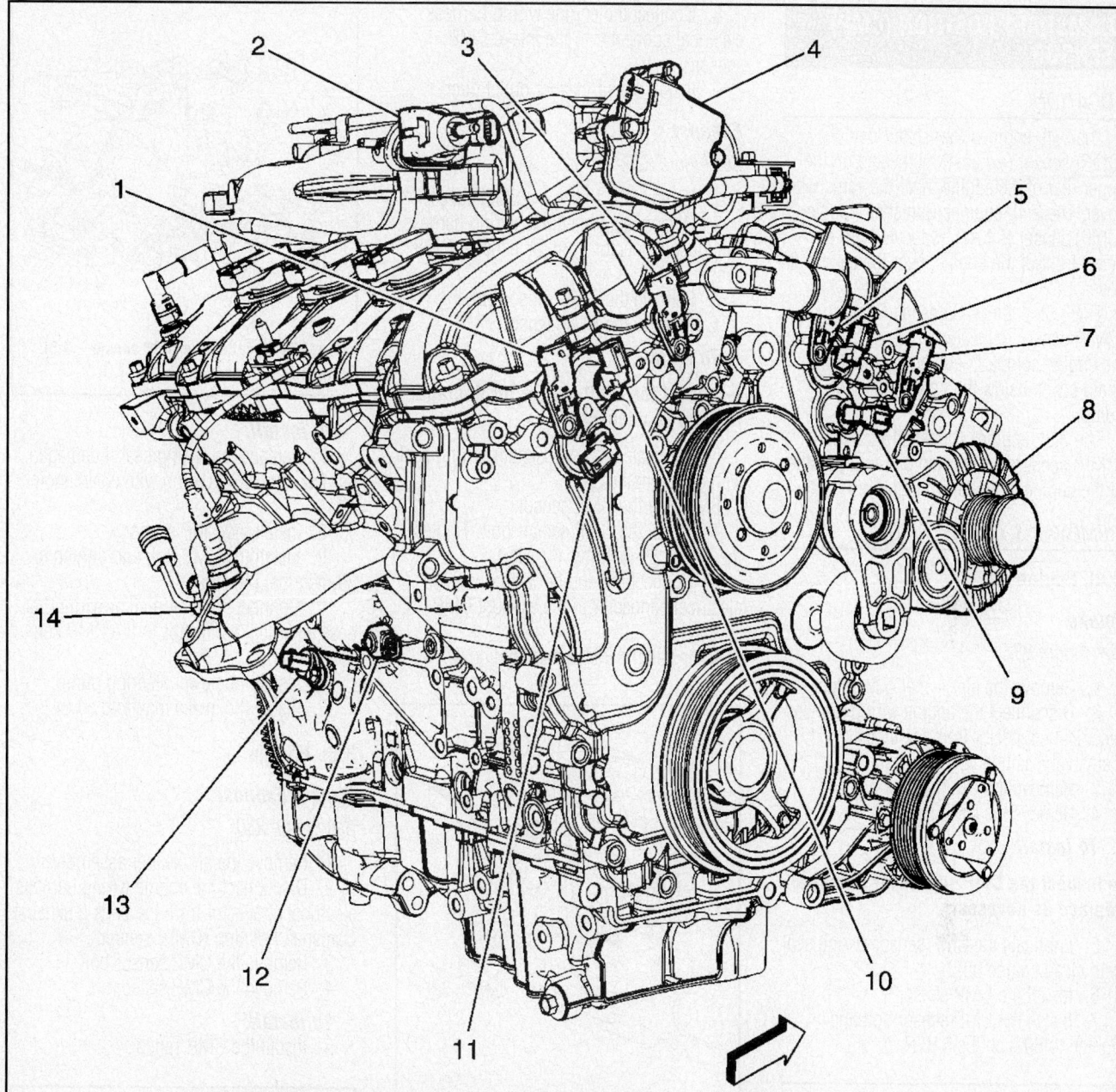

1. Camshaft Position (CMP) sensor - Bank 1 exhaust
2. Evaporative Emission (EVAP) canister purge solenoid valve
3. Camshaft Position (CMP) sensor - Bank 1 entake
4. Intake Manifold Tuning (IMT) solenoid valve
5. Camshaft Position (CMP) sensor - Bank 2 intake
6. Camshaft Position (CMP) actuator solenoid valve - Bank 2 intake
7. Camshaft Position (CMP) sensor - Bank 2 exhaust
8. Generator
9. Camshaft Position (CMP) actuator solenoid valve - Bank 2 exhaust
10. Camshaft Position (CMP) actuator solenoid valve - Bank 1 intake
11. Camshaft Position (CMP) actuator solenoid valve - Bank 1 exhaust
12. Knock Sensor (KS) 2
13. Crankshaft Position (CKP) sensor
14. Engine block heater

36616_AURA_G0061

Fig. 226 Rear of engine components 2 of 2—3.6L engine

CAMSHAFT POSITION (CMP) SENSOR

LOCATION

The 2.4L engines Camshaft Position (CMP) sensor (exhaust), is located on the upper rear of the engine, near the camshaft cover. The 2.4L engines Camshaft Position (CMP) sensor (intake), is located on the upper front of the engine, near the camshaft cover.

The 3.5L engines Camshaft Position (CMP) sensor is located in the right side of the engine compartment, above the timing chain cover, below the power steering pump.

The 3.6L engines Camshaft Position (CMP) sensors are located on the right side of the engine, near the front and rear.

REMOVAL & INSTALLATION

2.4L Engine

Intake

See Figure 227.

1. Remove the air cleaner outlet duct.
2. Disconnect the engine wiring harness electrical connector from the intake Camshaft Position (CMP) sensor.
3. Remove the CMP sensor bolt.
4. Remove the CMP sensor.

To install:

➡**Inspect the CMP sensor for damage, replace as necessary.**

5. Lubricate the CMP sensor O-ring seal with clean engine oil.
6. Install the CMP sensor.
7. Install the CMP sensor bolt and tighten to 89 inch lbs. (10 Nm).

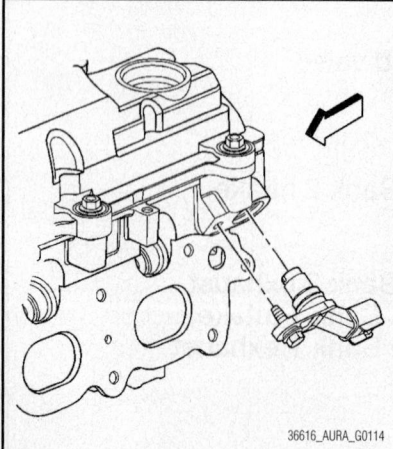

Fig. 227 Removing and installing the CMP sensor (intake)

8. Connect the engine wiring harness electrical connector to the intake CMP sensor.
9. Install the air cleaner outlet duct.

Exhaust

See Figure 228.

1. Remove the intake manifold cover.
2. Disconnect the engine wiring harness electrical connector from the exhaust CMP sensor.
3. Remove the CMP sensor bolt.
4. Remove the CMP sensor.

To install:

➡**Inspect the CMP sensor for damage, replace as necessary.**

5. Lubricate the CMP sensor O-ring seal with clean engine oil.
6. Install the CMP sensor.
7. Install the CMP sensor bolt. Tighten the bolt to 89 inch lbs. (10 Nm).
8. Connect the engine wiring harness electrical connector to the exhaust CMP sensor.
9. Install the intake manifold cover.

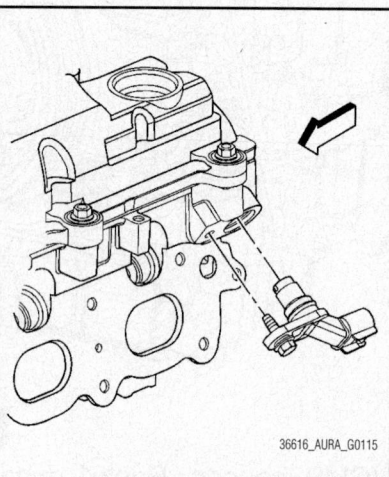

Fig. 228 Removing and installing the CMP sensor (exhaust)

3.5L Engine

See Figure 229.

1. Remove the intake manifold cover.
2. Remove the power steering pump.
3. Disconnect the fuel injector wiring harness electrical connector from the CMP sensor.
4. Remove the CMP sensor bolt.
5. Remove the CMP sensor.
6. Inspect the sensor O-ring for wear, cracks, or leakage if the sensor is not being replaced.

Fig. 229 Locating the CMP sensor—3.5L engine

To install:

7. Replace the O-ring seal if damaged, lubricate the NEW O-ring with clean engine oil.
8. Install the CMP sensor.
9. Install the CMP bolt and tighten to 89 inch lbs. (10 Nm).
10. Connect the fuel injector wiring harness electrical connector to the CMP sensor.
11. Install the power steering pump.
12. Install the intake manifold cover.

3.6L Engine

Bank 2 Exhaust

See Figure 230.

1. Remove the air cleaner assembly.
2. Disconnect the engine wiring harness electrical connector from the bank 2 exhaust Camshaft Position (CMP) sensor.
3. Remove the CMP sensor bolt.
4. Remove the CMP sensor.

To install:

5. Install the CMP sensor.

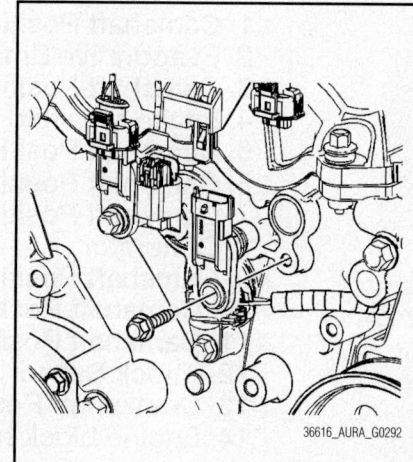

Fig. 230 Removing and installing the CMP sensor (bank 2 exhaust)—3.6L

6. Install the CMP sensor bolt and tighten to 89 inch lbs. (10 Nm).

7. Connect the engine wiring harness electrical connector to the bank 2 exhaust CMP sensor.

8. Install the air cleaner assembly.

Bank 1 Exhaust

See Figure 231.

1. Remove the air cleaner assembly.

2. Disconnect the engine wiring harness electrical connector from the bank 1 exhaust Camshaft Position (CMP) sensor.

3. Remove the CMP sensor bolt.

4. Remove the CMP sensor.

To install:

5. Install the CMP sensor.

6. Install the CMP sensor bolt and tighten to 89 inch lbs. (10 Nm).

7. Connect the engine wiring harness electrical connector to the bank 1 exhaust CMP sensor.

8. Install the air cleaner assembly.

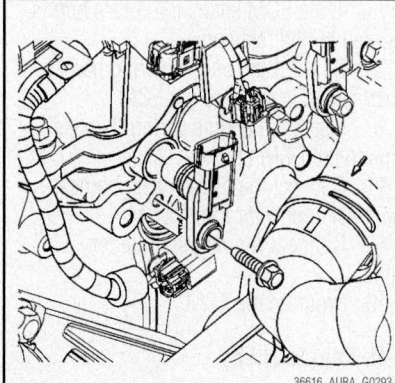

Fig. 231 Removing and installing the CMP sensor (bank 1 exhaust)—3.6L

Bank 2 Intake

See Figure 232.

1. Remove the air cleaner assembly.

2. Disconnect the engine wiring harness electrical connector from the bank 2 intake Camshaft position (CMP) sensor.

3. Remove the CMP sensor bolt.

4. Remove the CMP sensor.

To install:

5. Install the CMP sensor.

6. Install the CMP sensor bolt. Tighten the bolt to 89 inch lbs. (10 Nm).

7. Connect the engine wiring harness electrical connector to the bank 2 intake CMP sensor.

8. Install the air cleaner assembly.

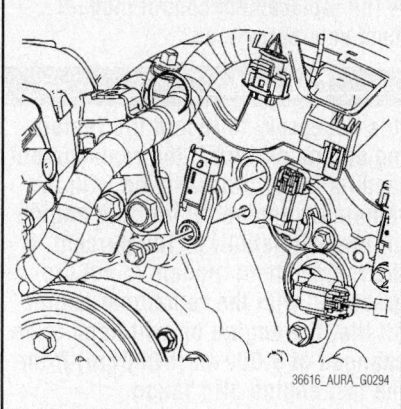

Fig. 232 Removing and installing the CMP sensor (bank 2 intake)—3.6L

Bank 1 Intake

See Figure 233.

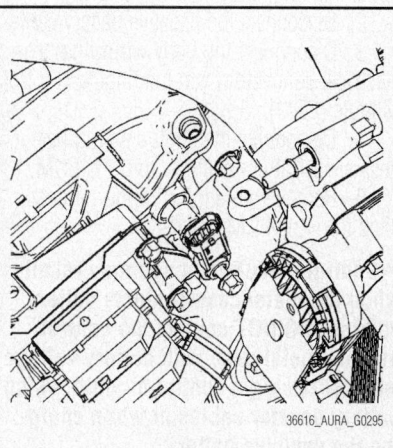

Fig. 233 Removing and installing the CMP sensor (bank 1 intake)—3.6L

1. Remove the air cleaner assembly.

2. Disconnect the engine wiring harness electrical connector from the bank 1 intake Camshaft position (CMP) sensor.

3. Remove the CMP sensor bolt.

4. Remove the CMP sensor.

To install:

5. Install the CMP sensor.

6. Install the CMP sensor bolt. Tighten the bolt to 89 inch lbs. (10 Nm).

7. Connect the engine wiring harness electrical connector to the bank 1 intake CMP sensor.

8. Install the air cleaner assembly.

CRANKSHAFT POSITION (CKP) SENSOR

LOCATION

For the 2.4L and 3.6L engines the Crankshaft Position (CKP) sensor is located on the right side of the engine, at the end of the crankshaft, behind the harmonic balancer.

For the 3.5L engine, the Crankshaft Position (CKP) sensor is located at the rear side of the engine, on the left side of the engine block.

REMOVAL & INSTALLATION

2.4L Engine

See Figure 234.

1. Remove the starter motor.

2. Disconnect the engine wiring harness electrical connector from the Crankshaft Position (CKP) sensor.

3. Remove the CKP sensor bolt and sensor.

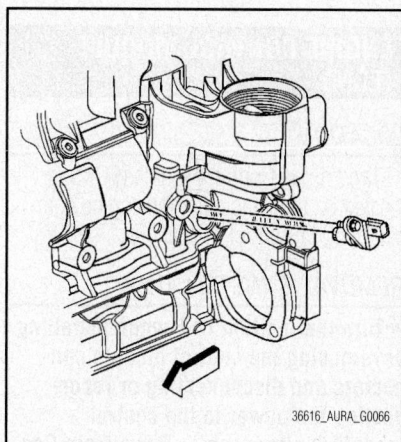

Fig. 234 Removing and installing the CKP sensor—2.4L engine

To install:

4. Lubricate the CKP sensor O-ring seal with clean engine oil.

5. Install the CKP sensor.

6. Install the CKP sensor bolt and tighten to 89 inch lbs. (10 Nm).

3.5L Engine

See Figure 235.

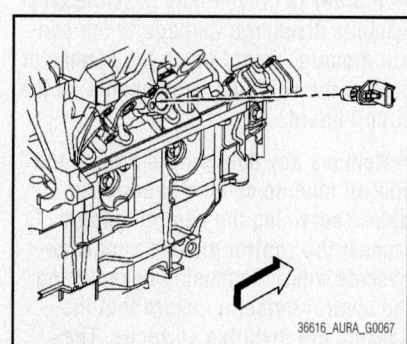

Fig. 235 Removing and installing the CKP sensor—3.5L engine

1. Raise and support the vehicle.

2. Disconnect the engine wiring harness electrical connector from the Crankshaft Position (CKP) sensor.

3. Remove the CKP sensor stud.

4. Remove the CKP sensor.

To install:

5. Lubricate the CKP sensor O-ring with clean engine oil .

6. Install the CKP sensor.

7. Install the CKP sensor stud.

8. Tighten the CKP sensor stud to 89 inch lbs. (10 Nm).

9. Connect the engine wiring harness electrical connector to the CKP sensor.

10. Lower the vehicle.

11. Perform the CKP system variation learn procedure.

ENGINE CONTROL MODULE (ECM)

LOCATION

The Engine Control Module (ECM) is located on the left side of the engine compartment, in front of the battery.

REMOVAL & INSTALLATION

➡️**Turn the ignition OFF when installing or removing the control module connectors and disconnecting or reconnecting the power to the control module (battery cable, Powertrain Control Module (PCM)/Engine Control Module (ECM)/Transaxle Control Module (TCM) pigtail, control module fuse, jumper cables, etc.) in order to prevent internal control module damage.**

➡️**Control module damage may result when the metal case contacts battery voltage. DO NOT contact the control module metal case with battery voltage when servicing a control module, using battery booster cables, or when charging the vehicle battery.**

➡️**In order to prevent any possible electrostatic discharge damage to the control module, do not touch the connector pins or the soldered components on the circuit board.**

➡️**Remove any debris from around the control module connector surfaces before servicing the control module. Inspect the control module connector gaskets when diagnosing or replacing the control module. Ensure that the gaskets are installed correctly. The gaskets prevent contaminant intrusion into the control module**

➡️The replacement control module must be programmed.

✴️ CAUTION

It is necessary to record the remaining engine oil life. If the replacement module is not programmed with the remaining engine oil life, the engine oil life will default to 100 percent. If the replacement module is not programmed with the remaining engine oil life, the engine oil will need to be changed at 3,000 mi (5 000 km) from the last engine oil change.

2.4L Engine (LAT)

See Figures 236 and 237.

1. Using a scan tool, retrieve the percentage of remaining engine oil. Record the remaining engine oil life.

2. Disconnect the negative battery cable.

3. Disconnect the body wiring harness electrical connector from the Engine Control Module (ECM).

4. Disconnect the engine wiring harness electrical connectors from the ECM.

5. Remove the engine wiring harness clips from the ECM bracket.

➡️Control module damage may result when the metal case contacts battery voltage. DO NOT contact the control module metal case with battery voltage when servicing a control module, using battery booster cables or when charging the vehicles battery.

6. Gently lift the ECM retainers up, disengaging the retainers from the ECM.

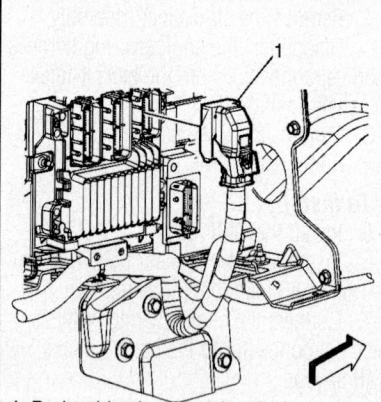

1. Body wiring harness electrical connector

36616_AURA_G0082

Fig. 236 Disconnecting the body wiring harness electrical connector from the Engine Control Module (ECM)—2.4L engine

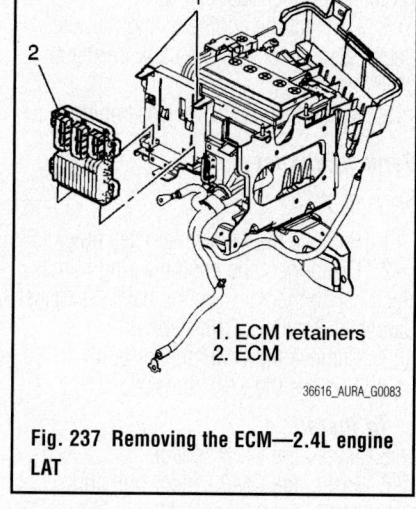

1. ECM retainers
2. ECM

36616_AURA_G0083

Fig. 237 Removing the ECM—2.4L engine LAT

7. Tilt the ECM towards the engine and remove the ECM from the bracket.

To install:

8. Set the ECM into the bottom of the bracket and push the ECM towards the battery until the ECM snaps into place and is secured by the retainers

9. Connect the engine wiring harness electrical connectors to the ECM.

10. Install the engine wiring harness clips to the ECM bracket.

11. Connect the body wiring harness electrical connector to the ECM.

12. Connect the negative battery cable.

13. Program the ECM.

2.4L Engine (LE5)

See Figure 238.

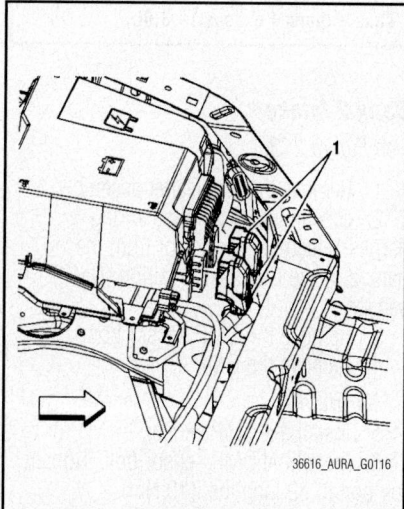

36616_AURA_G0116

Fig. 238 Disconnecting the engine wiring harness electrical connectors (1) from the ECM

1. Using a scan tool, retrieve the percentage of remaining engine oil. Record the remaining engine oil life.

2. Disconnect the negative battery cable.

3. Slide the lever locks to the up position in order to release the engine wiring harness electrical connectors.

4. Disconnect the engine wiring harness electrical connectors from the Engine Control Module (ECM).

5. Release the retaining tab located in the battery tray using a small screwdriver or other suitable tool.

6. Remove the ECM by lifting upward after releasing the tab.

To install:

7. Slide the ECM into the bracket on the battery tray.

8. Push down on the ECM until the retaining tab snaps into place.

9. Connect the engine wiring harness electrical connectors to the ECM.

10. Slide the lever locks to the down position in order to engage the engine wiring harness electrical connectors.

11. Connect the negative battery cable.

12. If a NEW ECM was installed, program the ECM.

3.5L Engine

See Figure 239.

1. Using a scan tool, retrieve the percentage of remaining engine oil. Record the remaining engine oil life.

2. Disconnect the negative battery cable.

3. Slide the lever locks to the up position in order to release the engine wiring harness electrical connectors.

4. Disconnect the engine wiring harness electrical connectors from the Engine Control Module (ECM).

5. Release the retaining tab located in the battery tray using a small screwdriver or other suitable tool.

6. Remove the ECM by lifting upward after releasing the tab.

To install:

7. Slide the ECM into the bracket on the battery tray.

8. Push down on the ECM until the retaining tab snaps into place.

9. Connect the engine wiring harness electrical connectors to the ECM.

10. Slide the lever locks to the down position in order to engage the engine wiring harness electrical connectors.

11. Connect the negative battery cable.

12. If a NEW ECM was installed, program the ECM.

3.6L Engine

See Figure 240.

1. Using a scan tool, retrieve the percentage of remaining engine oil. Record the remaining engine oil life.

2. Record the preset radio stations.

3. Turn the ignition OFF.

4. Disconnect the negative battery cable.

5. Lift and gently pull the ECM up and out of the retainer on the battery tray.

6. Disconnect the engine wiring harness electrical connectors from the ECM.

7. Disconnect the body wiring harness electrical connector from the ECM.

To install:

8. Connect the engine wiring harness electrical connectors (1) to the ECM.

9. Connect the body wiring harness electrical connector (2) to the ECM.

10. Position the ECM above the retainer in the battery tray and slide the ECM down into the retainer.

11. Connect the negative battery cable.

12. Reset the clock and preset radio stations.

13. If a NEW ECM was installed, the ECM must be programmed.

ENGINE COOLANT TEMPERATURE (ECT) SENSOR

LOCATION

The Engine Coolant Temperature (ECT) sensor for the 2.4L engine is located on the rear of the engine, below the Camshaft Position (CMP) exhaust sensor.

The Engine Coolant Temperature (ECT) sensor for the 3.5L engine is mounted in the rear cylinder head, below the coolant reservoir.

The Engine Coolant Temperature (ECT) sensor for the 3.6L engine is located on the left side of the front cylinder head, below the throttle actuator control module.

REMOVAL & INSTALLATION

2.4L Engine

See Figure 241.

➡**Use care when handling the coolant sensor. Damage to the coolant sensor will affect the operation of the fuel system.**

1. Drain the cooling system.

2. Disconnect the engine wiring harness electrical connector from the Engine Coolant Temperature (ECT) sensor.

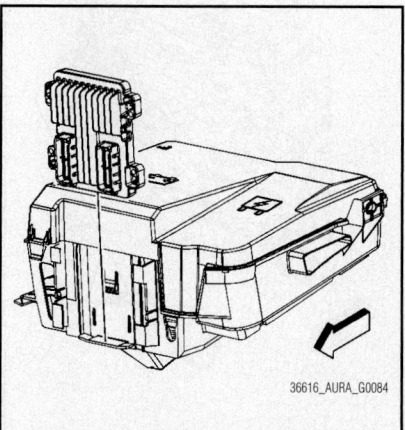

36616_AURA_G0084

Fig. 239 Removing the ECM—3.5L engine

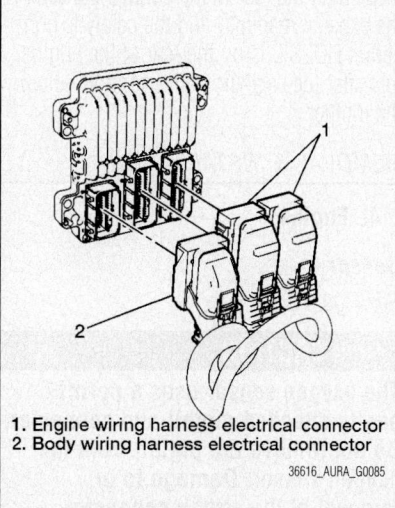

1. Engine wiring harness electrical connector
2. Body wiring harness electrical connector

36616_AURA_G0085

Fig. 240 Disconnecting the ECM— 3.6L engine

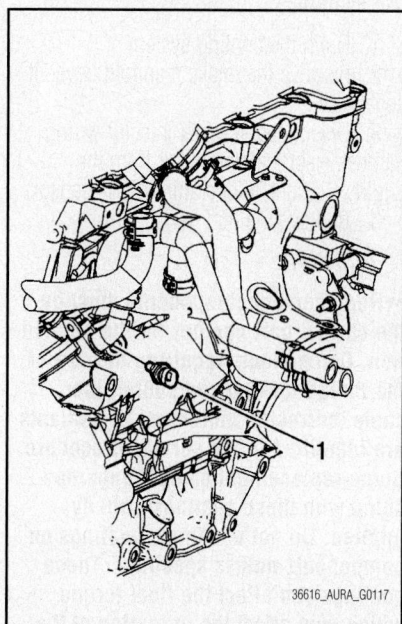

36616_AURA_G0117

Fig. 241 Removing and installing the ECT sensor (1) from the thermostat housing

3. Remove the ECT sensor from the thermostat housing.

To install:

➡ **Replacement components must be the correct part number for the application. Components requiring the use of the thread locking compound, lubricants, corrosion inhibitors, or sealants are identified in the service procedure. Some replacement components may come with these coatings already applied. Do not use these coatings on components unless specified. These coatings can affect the final torque, which may affect the operation of the component. Use the correct torque specification when installing components in order to avoid damage.**

➡ **Use care when handling the coolant sensor. Damage to the coolant sensor will affect the operation of the fuel control system.**

4. If reinstalling the original sensor, or if installing a NEW sensor without a sealer, coat the threads with sealant.

5. Install the ECT sensor to the thermostat housing.

6. Connect the engine wiring harness electrical connector to the ECT sensor.

7. Fill the cooling system.

3.5L Engine

➡ **Use care when handling the coolant sensor. Damage to the coolant sensor will affect the operation of the fuel control system.**

1. Drain the cooling system.

2. Remove the intake manifold cover, if necessary.

3. Disconnect the fuel injector wiring harness electrical connector from the Engine Coolant Temperature (ECT) sensor.

4. Remove the ECT sensor.

To install:

➡ **Replacement components must be the correct part number for the application. Components requiring the use of the thread locking compound, lubricants, corrosion inhibitors, or sealants are identified in the service procedure. Some replacement components may come with these coatings already applied. Do not use these coatings on components unless specified. These coatings can affect the final torque, which may affect the operation of the component. Use the correct torque specification when installing components in order to avoid damage.**

5. Coat the threads of the ECT sensor with sealer GM P/N 13246004 (Canadian P/N 10953480) or equivalent.

6. Install the ECT sensor and tighten to 15 ft. lbs. (20 Nm).

7. Connect the fuel injector wiring harness electrical connector to the ECT sensor.

8. Install the intake manifold cover, if necessary.

9. Fill the cooling system.

3.6L Engine

1. Disconnect the engine wiring harness electrical connector from the Engine Coolant Temperature (ECT) sensor.

2. Remove the ECT sensor.

To install:

3. Install the ECT sensor and tighten to 16 ft. lbs. (22 Nm).

4. Connect the engine wiring harness electrical connector to the ECT sensor.

HEATED OXYGEN (HO2S) SENSOR

LOCATION

For the 3.5L and 3.6L engines, the Heated Oxygen Sensor (HO2S) is located in the center of the rear exhaust manifold (bank 1, sensor 1). In the rear of the engine compartment after the catalytic convertor (bank 1, sensor 2). In the front of the engine compartment, on the exhaust manifold (bank 2, sensor 1). In the lower front of the engine compartment, after the catalytic convertor (bank 2, sensor 2).

For the 2.4L engine, the HO2S 1 is located on the rear of the engine, between the exhaust manifold and the catalytic convertor. HO2S 2 is on the rear of the engine, just after the catalytic convertor and before the muffler.

REMOVAL & INSTALLATION

2.4L Engine

Sensor 1

See Figure 242.

❋❋ CAUTION

The oxygen sensor uses a permanently attached pigtail and connector. Do not remove the pigtail from the oxygen sensor. Damage to or removal of the pigtail connector could affect proper operation of the oxygen sensor.

❋❋ CAUTION

The use of excessive force may damage the threads in the exhaust manifold/pipe.

➡ **The in-line connector and louvered end must be kept clear of grease, dirt or other contaminants. Avoid using cleaning solvents of any type. DO NOT drop or roughly handle the heated oxygen sensor (HO2S).**

➡ **The HO2S may be difficult to remove when the engine temperature is less than 120°F (48°C).**

1. Remove the Connector Position Assurance (CPA) retainer.

2. Disconnect the engine wiring harness electrical connector from the HO2S electrical connector.

3. Remove the HO2S connector clip from the thermostat housing tab.

4. Remove the HO2S.

To install:

➡ **A special anti-seize compound is used on the heated oxygen sensor threads. The compound consists of a liquid graphite and glass beads. The graphite will burn away, but the glass beads will remain, making the sensor easier to remove. New or service replacement sensors will have the compound applied to the threads. If a sensor is removed and is to be reinstalled, the threads must have an anti-seize compound applied prior to installation.**

5. If necessary, coat the threads of the HO2S with anti-seize compound GM P/N 12377953 or equivalent.

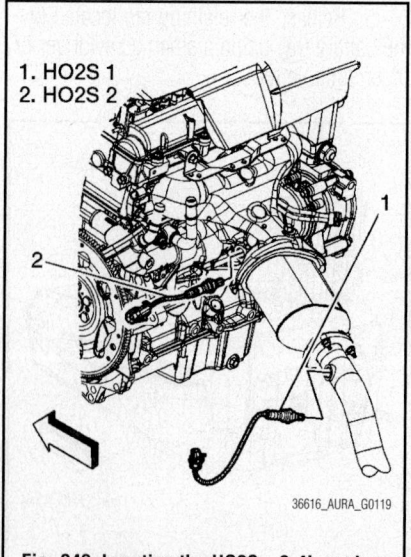

1. HO2S 1
2. HO2S 2

36616_AURA_G0119

Fig. 242 Locating the HO2S—2.4L engine

6. Install the HO2S and tighten to 31 ft. lbs. (42 Nm).

7. Install the HO2S connector clip to the thermostat housing tab.

8. Connect the engine wiring harness electrical connector to the HO2S electrical connector.

9. Install the CPA retainer.

Sensor 2

See Figure 242.

➡ **The oxygen sensor uses a permanently attached pigtail and connector. Do not remove the pigtail from the oxygen sensor. Damage to or removal of the pigtail connector could affect proper operation of the oxygen sensor.**

➡ **The use of excessive force may damage the threads in the exhaust manifold/pipe.**

✳✳ CAUTION

The in-line connector and louvered end must be kept clear of grease, dirt or other contaminants. Avoid using cleaning solvents of any type. DO NOT drop or roughly handle the heated oxygen sensor (HO2S).

➡ **The HO2S may be difficult to remove when the engine temperature is less than 120°F (48°C).**

1. Raise and suitably support the vehicle.

2. Remove the Connector Position Assurance (CPA) retainer.

3. Disconnect the HO2S electrical connector (2) from the engine wiring harness electrical connector.

4. Remove the HO2S.

To install:

➡ **A special anti-seize compound is used on the heated oxygen sensor threads. The compound consists of a liquid graphite and glass beads. The graphite will burn away, but the glass beads will remain, making the sensor easier to remove. New or service replacement sensors will have the compound applied to the threads. If a sensor is removed and is to be reinstalled, the threads must have an anti-seize compound applied prior to installation.**

5. If necessary, coat the threads of the HO2S with anti-seize compound GM P/N 12377953 or equivalent.

6. Install the HO2S and tighten to 31 ft. lbs. (42 Nm).

7. Connect the HO2S electrical connector to the engine wiring harness electrical connector.

8. Install the CPA retainer.

9. Lower the vehicle.

3.5L Engine

Bank 1 Sensor 1

See Figure 243.

➡ **When replacing the HO2S perform the following resistance learned value to avoid possible HO2S failure:**

- A code clear with a scan tool, regardless of whether or not a DTC is set
- HO2S heater resistance learn reset with a scan tool, where available

1. Remove the intake manifold cover.

2. Remove the Connector Position Assurance (CPA) retainer.

3. Disconnect the engine wiring harness electrical connector from the Heated Oxygen Sensor (HO2S) electrical connector.

4. Remove the HO2S electrical connector rosebud clip from the ignition coil bracket.

➡ **The HO2S may be difficult to remove when the engine temperature is less than 120°F (48°C).**

5. Remove the HO2S using the Heated Oxygen Sensor Wrench (J39194-B).

To install:

➡ **A special anti-seize compound is used on the heated oxygen sensor threads. The compound consists of** a liquid graphite and glass beads. The graphite will burn away, but the glass beads will remain, making the sensor easier to remove. New or service replacement sensors will have the compound applied to the threads. If a sensor is removed and is to be reinstalled, the threads must have an anti-seize compound applied prior to installation.

6. Coat the threads of the HO2S with anti-seize compound GM P/N 12377953 or equivalent.

7. Install the HO2S and tighten to 31 ft. lbs. (42 Nm).

8. Connect the HO2S electrical connector to the engine wiring harness electrical connector.

9. Install the CPA retainer.

10. Install the HO2S electrical connector rosebud clip to the ignition coil bracket.

11. Install the intake manifold cover.

Bank 1 Sensor 2

See Figure 244.

➡ **The HO2S may be difficult to remove when the engine temperature is less than 120°F (48°C).**

1. Raise and suitably support the vehicle.

2. Remove the Connector Position Assurance (CPA) retainer.

3. Disconnect the HO2S electrical connector from the engine wiring harness electrical connector.

4. Remove the HO2S.

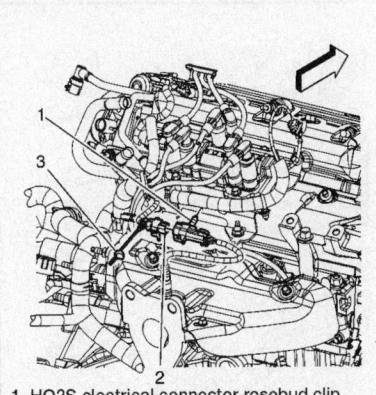

1. HO2S electrical connector rosebud clip
2. Engine wiring harness electrical connector
3. Connector Position Assurance (CPA) retainer

36616_AURA_G0068

Fig. 243 Removing and installing the HO2S (bank 1 sensor 1)—3.5L engine

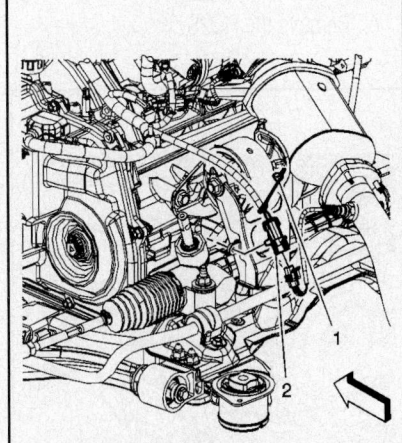

1. Connector Position Assurance (CPA) retainer
2. Heated Oxygen Sensor (HO2S) electrical connector

36616_AURA_G0069

Fig. 244 Removing and installing HO2S (bank 1 sensor 2)—3.5L engine

To install:

➡A special anti-seize compound is used on the heated oxygen sensor threads. The compound consists of a liquid graphite and glass beads. The graphite will burn away, but the glass beads will remain, making the sensor easier to remove. New or service replacement sensors will have the compound applied to the threads. If a sensor is removed and is to be reinstalled, the threads must have an anti-seize compound applied prior to installation.

5. Coat the threads of the HO2S with anti-seize compound GM P/N 12377953 or equivalent.
6. Install the HO2S and tighten to 31 ft. lbs. (42 Nm).
7. Connect the HO2S electrical connector to the engine wiring harness electrical connector.
8. Install the CPA retainer.
9. Lower the vehicle.

Bank 2 Sensor 1

See Figure 245.

1. Remove the Connector Position Assurance (CPA) retainer.
2. Disconnect the engine wiring harness electrical connector from the Heated Oxygen Sensor (HO2S) electrical connector.
3. Remove the HO2S rosebud clip from the oil level indicator tube tab.

➡The HO2S may be difficult to remove when the engine temperature is less than 120°F (48°C).

4. Remove the HO2S.

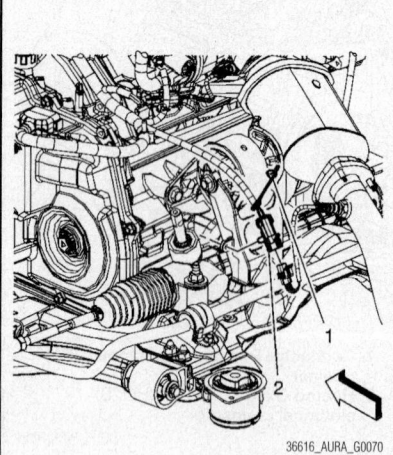

36616_AURA_G0070

Fig. 245 Removing and installing the HO2S (bank 2 sensor 1)—3.5L engine

---

To install:

➡A special anti-seize compound is used on the heated oxygen sensor threads. The compound consists of a liquid graphite and glass beads. The graphite will burn away, but the glass beads will remain, making the sensor easier to remove. New or service replacement sensors will have the compound applied to the threads. If a sensor is removed and is to be reinstalled, the threads must have an anti-seize compound applied prior to installation.

5. Coat the threads of the HO2S with anti-seize compound GM P/N 12377953 or equivalent.
6. Install the HO2S and tighten to 31 ft. lbs. (42 Nm).
7. Connect the HO2S electrical connector to the engine wiring harness electrical connector.
8. Install the CPA retainer.
9. Install the HO2S rosebud clip to the oil level indicator tube tab.

Bank 2 Sensor 2

See Figure 246.

➡The HO2S may be difficult to remove when the engine temperature is less than 120°F (48°C).

1. Raise and suitably support the vehicle.
2. Remove the Connector Position Assurance (CPA) retainer.
3. Disconnect the HO2S electrical connector from the engine wiring harness electrical connector.
4. Remove the HO2S.

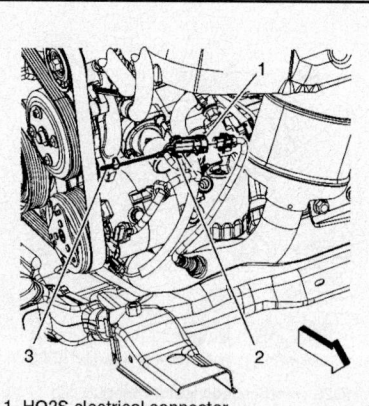

1. HO2S electrical connector
2. Engine wiring harness electrical connector
3. Connector Position Assurance (CPA) retainer

36616_AURA_G0071

Fig. 246 Removing and installing the HO2S (bank 2 sensor 2)—3.5L engine

---

To install:

➡A special anti-seize compound is used on the heated oxygen sensor threads. The compound consists of a liquid graphite and glass beads. The graphite will burn away, but the glass beads will remain, making the sensor easier to remove. New or service replacement sensors will have the compound applied to the threads. If a sensor is removed and is to be reinstalled, the threads must have an anti-seize compound applied prior to installation.

5. Coat the threads of the HO2S with anti-seize compound GM P/N 12377953 or equivalent.
6. Install the HO2S and tighten to 31 ft. lbs. (42 Nm).
7. Connect the HO2S electrical connector to the engine wiring harness electrical connector.
8. Install the CPA retainer.
9. Lower the vehicle.

3.6L Engine

Bank 1 Sensor 1

See Figure 247.

1. Remove the fuel injector sight shield by performing the following steps.
   a. Remove the oil fill cap.
   b. Grasp the cover by the upper left and the lower right corners and lift up, disengaging the cover grommets from the ball studs.

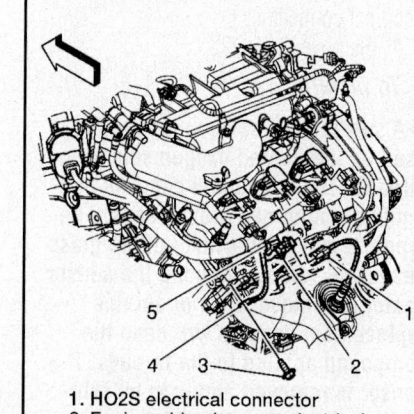

1. HO2S electrical connector
2. Engine wiring harness electrical connector
3. Bolt
4. HO2S electrical connector clip
5. Connector Position Assurance (CPA) retainer

36616_AURA_G0072

Fig. 247 Removing and installing HO2S (bank 1 sensor 1)—3.6L engine

c. If necessary, lift upward on front of cover, then reach under center of cover disengaging the cover grommet for the ball stud.

2. Remove the engine wiring harness Heated Oxygen Sensor (HO2S) electrical connector clip from the engine harness.

3. Remove the Connector Position Assurance (CPA) retainer from the HO2S electrical connection.

4. Disconnect the engine wiring harness electrical connector (2) from the HO2S electrical connector.

5. Raise and support the vehicle to an appropriate height to reach the HO2S.

6. Remove the HO2S from the exhaust manifold.

To install:

➡**A special anti-seize compound is used on the heated oxygen sensor threads. The compound consists of a liquid graphite and glass beads. The graphite will burn away, but the glass beads will remain, making the sensor easier to remove. New or service replacement sensors will have the compound applied to the threads. If a sensor is removed and is to be reinstalled, the threads must have an anti-seize compound applied prior to installation.**

7. If reinstalling the old sensor, coat the threads with anti-seize compound GM P/N 12377953, or equivalent.

8. Install the HO2S to the exhaust manifold and tighten to 31 ft. lbs. (42 Nm).

9. Lower the vehicle.

10. Connect the engine wiring harness electrical connector to the HO2S electrical connector.

11. Install the engine wiring harness HO2S electrical connector clip to the engine harness.

12. Install the CPA retainer to the HO2S electrical connection.

13. Install the fuel injector sight shield.

a. If necessary, place the cover into position over the ball stud. Press down near the center of the cover, engaging the cover to the ball stud.

b. Place the cover into position over the ball studs. Press down near the upper left and the lower right corners, engaging the cover to the ball studs.

c. Install the oil fill cap.

Bank 1 Sensor 2

See Figure 248.

1. Raise and support the vehicle.
2. Remove the Connector Position

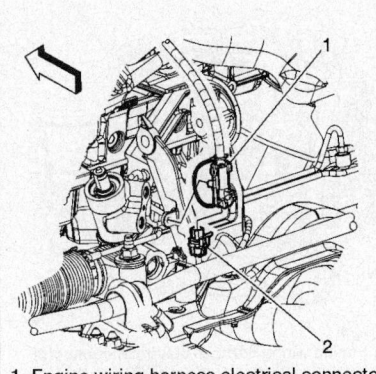

1. Engine wiring harness electrical connector
2. Heated Oxygen Sensor (HO2S) electrical connector

36616_AURA_G0073

Fig. 248 Removing and installing HO2S (bank 1 sensor 2)—3.6L engine

Assurance (CPA) retainer from the HO2S electrical connection.

3. Disconnect the heated oxygen sensor (HO2S) electrical connector from the engine wiring harness electrical connector.

4. Remove the bank 1 sensor 2 HO2S from the catalytic converter.

To install:

➡**A special anti-seize compound is used on the heated oxygen sensor threads. The compound consists of a liquid graphite and glass beads. The graphite will burn away, but the glass beads will remain, making the sensor easier to remove. New or service replacement sensors will have the compound applied to the threads. If a sensor is removed and is to be reinstalled, the threads must have an anti-seize compound applied prior to installation.**

5. If reinstalling the old sensor, coat the threads with anti-seize compound GM P/N 12377953, or equivalent.

6. Install the bank 1 sensor 2 HO2S to the catalytic converter and tighten to 31 ft. lbs. (42 Nm).

7. Connect the HO2S electrical connector to the engine wiring harness electrical connector.

8. Install the CPA retainer to the HO2S electrical connection.

9. Lower the vehicle.

Bank 2 Sensor 1

See Figure 249.

1. Remove the fuel injector sight shield by performing the following:

a. Remove the oil fill cap.

b. Grasp the cover by the upper left

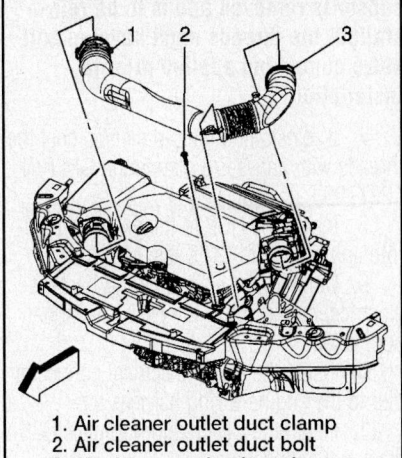

1. Air cleaner outlet duct clamp
2. Air cleaner outlet duct bolt
3. Air cleaner outlet duct clamp

36616_AURA_G0074

Fig. 249 Removing the air cleaner outlet duct

and the lower right corners and lift up, disengaging the cover grommets from the ball studs.

c. If necessary, lift upward on front of cover, then reach under center of cover disengaging the cover grommet for the ball stud.

2. Remove the air cleaner outlet duct by performing the following:

a. Disconnect the Positive Crankcase Ventilation (PCV) fresh air tube fitting from the air cleaner outlet duct.

b. Reposition the tube out of the way.

c. Loosen the air cleaner outlet duct clamps at the Mass Air Flow (MAF)/Intake Air Temperature (IAT) sensor and throttle body.

d. Remove the air cleaner outlet duct bolt.

e. Remove the air cleaner outlet duct.

3. Remove the Connector Position Assurance (CPA) retainer from the HO2S electrical connection.

4. Disconnect the engine wiring harness electrical connector from the Heated Oxygen Sensor (HO2S) electrical connector.

5. Remove the HO2S electrical connector clip from the engine wiring harness tab.

6. Remove the HO2S from the exhaust manifold.

To install:

➡**A special anti-seize compound is used on the heated oxygen sensor threads. The compound consists of a liquid graphite and glass beads. The graphite will burn away, but the glass beads will remain, making the sensor easier to remove. New or service replacement sensors will have the compound applied to the threads. If a** sensor is removed and is to be rein-stalled, the threads must have an anti-seize compound applied prior to installation.

7. If reinstalling the old sensor, coat the threads with anti-seize compound GM P/N 12377953, or equivalent.

8. Install the HO2 to the exhaust mani-fold and tighten to 31 ft. lbs. (42 Nm).

9. Connect the engine wiring harness electrical connector to the HO2S electrical connector.

10. Install the HO2S electrical connector clip to the engine wiring harness tab.

11. Install the CPA retainer to the HO2S electrical connection.

12. Install the air cleaner outlet duct by performing the following:

   a. Position and install the air cleaner outlet duct to the MAF/IAT sensor and the throttle body.

   b. Install the air cleaner outlet duct bolt and tighten to 89 inch lbs. (10 Nm).

   c. Tighten the air cleaner outlet duct clamps at the MAF/IAT sensor and throttle body to 35 inch lbs. (4 Nm).

   d. Position the PCV tube.

   e. Connect the PCV fresh air tube quick connect fitting to the air cleaner outlet duct.

13. Install the fuel injector sight shield by performing the following:

   a. If necessary, place the cover into position over the ball stud. Press down near the center of the cover, engaging the cover to the ball stud.

   b. Place the cover into position over the ball studs. Press down near the upper left and the lower right corners, engaging the cover to the ball studs.

   c. Install the oil fill cap.

Bank 2 Sensor 2

See Figure 250.

1. Raise and support the vehicle.

2. Remove the Connector Position Assurance (CPA) retainer from the HO2S electrical connection.

3. Disconnect the Heated Oxygen Sensor (HO2S) electrical connector from the engine wiring harness electrical connector

4. Remove the bank 2 sensor 2 HO2S from the catalytic converter.

To install:

➡A special anti-seize compound is used on the heated oxygen sensor threads. The compound consists of a liquid graphite and glass beads. The graphite will burn away, but the glass

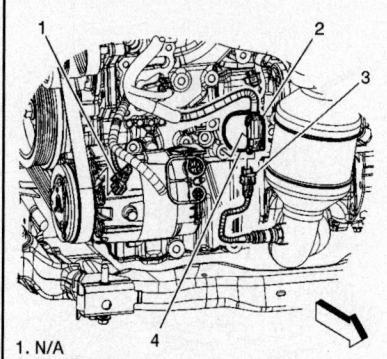

1. N/A
2. Engine wiring harness electrical connector
3. Heated Oxygen Sensor (HO2S) electrical connector
4. Connector Position Assurance (CPA) retainer

36616_AURA_G0075

Fig. 250 Removing and installing HO2S (bank 2 sensor 2)—3.6L engine

beads will remain, making the sensor easier to remove. New or service replacement sensors will have the compound applied to the threads. If a sensor is removed and is to be rein-stalled, the threads must have an anti-seize compound applied prior to installation.

5. If reinstalling the old sensor, coat the threads with anti-seize compound GM P/N 12377953, or equivalent.

6. Install the bank 2 sensor 2 HO2S to the catalytic converter and tighten to 31 ft. lbs. (42 Nm).

7. Connect the HO2S electrical connec-tor to the engine wiring harness electrical connector.

8. Install the CPA retainer to the HO2S electrical connection.

9. Lower the vehicle.

INTAKE AIR TEMPERATURE (IAT) SENSOR

LOCATION

The Intake Air Temperature (IAT)/Mass Air Flow (MAF) sensor is located on the top right side of the engine, at the air cleaner.

REMOVAL & INSTALLATION

2.4L Engine

See Figure 251.

1. Disconnect the engine wiring har-ness electrical connector from the Mass Air Flow (MAF)/Intake Air Temperature (IAT) sensor.

2. Remove the MAF/IAT sensor screws.

3. Remove the MAF/IAT sensor.

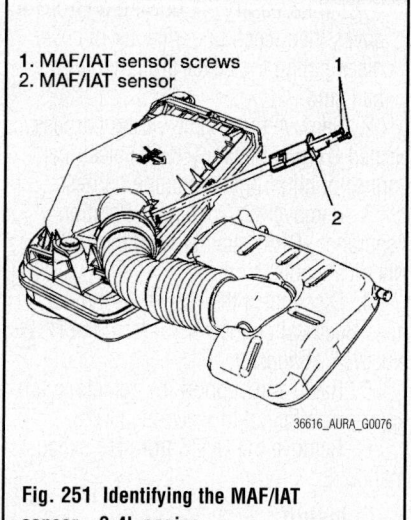

1. MAF/IAT sensor screws
2. MAF/IAT sensor

36616_AURA_G0076

Fig. 251 Identifying the MAF/IAT sensor—2.4L engine

To install:

4. Install the MAF/IAT sensor.

5. Install the MAF/IAT sensor screws and tighten to 5 inch lbs. (0.6 Nm).

6. Connect the engine wiring harness electrical connector to the MAF/IAT sensor.

3.5L Engine

See Figure 252.

1. Remove the air cleaner outlet duct.

   a. Remove the intake manifold cover.

   b. Disconnect the Positive Crankcase Ventilation (PCV) fresh air tube quick connect fitting from the air cleaner outlet duct.

   c. Reposition the tube out of the way.

   d. Loosen the air cleaner outlet duct clamps at the Mass Air Flow (MAF)/Intake Air Temperature (IAT) sen-sor and throttle body.

   e. Remove the air cleaner outlet duct bolt.

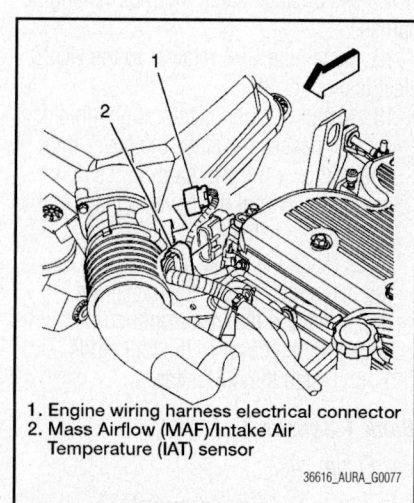

1. Engine wiring harness electrical connector
2. Mass Airflow (MAF)/Intake Air Temperature (IAT) sensor

36616_AURA_G0077

Fig. 252 Identifying MAF/IAT sensor

f. Remove the air cleaner outlet duct spacer and insulator, if required.

g. Remove the air cleaner outlet duct.

2. Disconnect the engine wiring harness electrical connector (1) from the mass airflow (MAF)/intake air temperature (IAT) sensor.

3. Remove the MAF/IAT sensor screws.

4. Remove the MAF/IAT sensor.

5. Remove and discard the MAF/IAT sensor seal.

To install:

6. Install a NEW MAF/IAT sensor seal.

7. Install the MAF/IAT sensor. Tighten the screws to 44 inch lbs. (5 Nm).

8. Connect the engine wiring harness electrical connector to the MAF/IAT sensor.

9. Install the air cleaner outlet duct.

a. Position and install the air cleaner outlet duct to the MAF/IAT sensor and the throttle body.

b. Position the air cleaner outlet duct insulator and spacer, if required.

c. Install the air cleaner outlet duct bolt and tighten to 89 inch lbs. (10 Nm).

d. Tighten the air cleaner outlet duct clamps at the MAF/IAT sensor and throttle body to 35 inch lbs. (4 Nm).

e. Position the PCV tube.

f. Connect the PCV fresh air tube quick connect fitting to the air cleaner outlet duct.

g. Install the intake manifold cover.

KNOCK SENSOR (KS)

LOCATION

For the 2.4L engine, the Knock Sensor (KS) is located on the front of the engine, below the intake manifold.

For the 3.5L and 3.6L engine, the Knock Sensor (KS) 1 is located on the front of the engine, above the starter. The KS 2 is located on the rear of the engine, below the exhaust manifold, above the transaxle.

REMOVAL & INSTALLATION

2.4L Engine

1. Disconnect the negative battery cable.

2. Raise and support the vehicle.

3. Disconnect the engine wiring harness electrical connector from the Knock Sensor (KS) pigtail electrical connector.

4. Remove the knock sensor electrical connector pigtail clip from the oil level indicator tube bracket.

5. Remove the KS bolt.

6. Remove the KS.

To install:

→**Rotate the pigtail 90 degrees from vertical before securing the fastener.**

7. Install the KS.

8. Install the KS bolt and tighten to 18 ft. lbs. (25 Nm).

9. Install the KS electrical connector pigtail clip to the oil level indicator tube bracket.

10. Connect the engine wiring harness electrical connector to the KS pigtail electrical connector.

11. Lower the vehicle.

12. Connect the negative battery cable.

3.5L Engine

Bank 1

See Figure 253.

1. Raise and support the vehicle.

2. Disconnect the engine wiring harness electrical connector from the knock senor.

3. Remove the knock sensor bolt and sensor.

To install:

4. Position the KS to the engine block and install the KS bolt. Tighten the bolt to 18 ft. lbs. (25 Nm).

5. Connect the engine wiring harness electrical connector to the KS.

6. Lower the vehicle.

1. Engine wiring harness electrical connector
2. Knock Sensor (KS)

36616_AURA_G0078

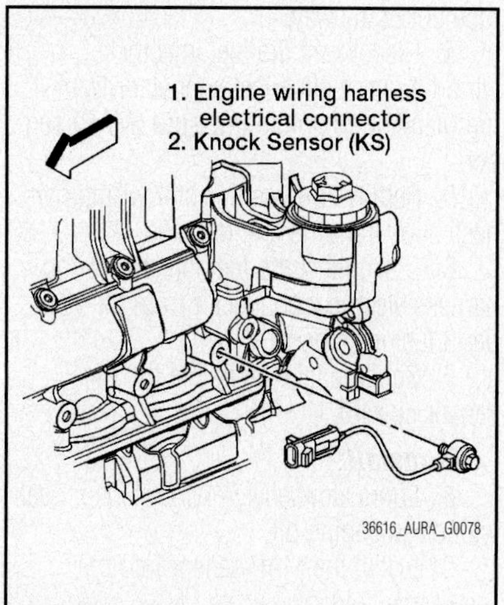

Fig. 253 Locating the KS bank 2—3.5L engine

Bank 2

See Figure 254.

1. Raise and support the vehicle.

2. Disconnect the engine wiring

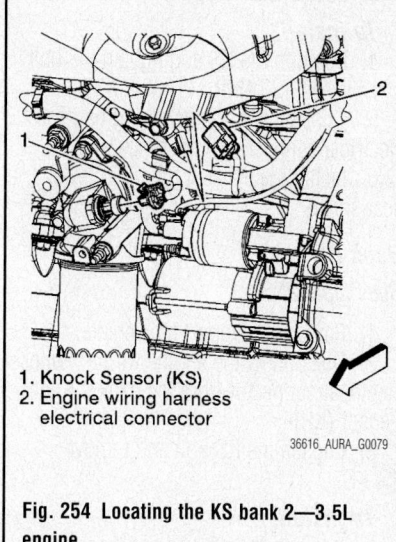

1. Knock Sensor (KS)
2. Engine wiring harness electrical connector

36616_AURA_G0079

Fig. 254 Locating the KS bank 2—3.5L engine

harness electrical connector from the Knock Sensor (KS).

3. Remove the KS bolt and sensor.

To install:

4. Position the KS to the engine block and install the KS bolt. Tighten the bolt to 18 ft. lbs. (25 Nm).

5. Connect the engine wiring harness electrical connector to the KS.

6. Lower the vehicle.

3.6L Engine

Bank 1

See Figure 255.

1. Remove the exhaust manifold lower heat shield.

2. Disconnect the engine wiring harness electrical connector from the bank 1 Knock Sensor (KS).

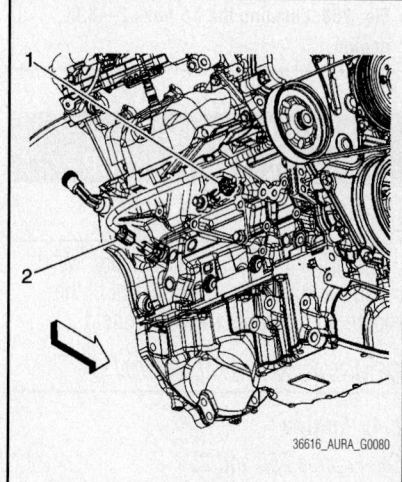

36616_AURA_G0080

Fig. 255 Locating the KS bank 1—3.6L engine

3. Loosen the KS bolt and remove the KS.

To install:

4. Position the KS and tighten the bolt to 17 ft. lbs. (23 Nm).

5. Connect the engine wiring harness electrical connector to the bank 1 KS.

6. Install the exhaust manifold lower heat shield.

Bank 2

See Figure 256.

1. Raise and support the vehicle.

2. Disconnect the engine wiring harness electrical connector from the bank 2 Knock Sensor (KS).

3. Loosen the KS bolt and remove the KS.

To install:

4. Position the KS and tighten the bolt to 17 ft. lbs. (23 Nm).

5. Connect the engine wiring harness electrical connector to the bank 2 KS.

6. Lower the vehicle.

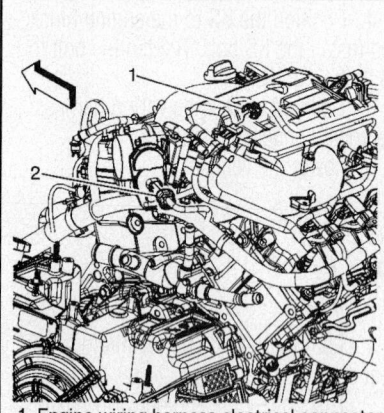

1. Engine wiring harness electrical connector
2. Manifold Absolute Pressure (MAP) sensor

36616_AURA_G0081

Fig. 256 Locating the KS bank 2—3.6L engine

MANIFOLD ABSOLUTE PRESSURE (MAP) SENSOR

LOCATION

The Manifold Absolute Pressure (MAP) sensor is located on the top front of the engine, in the upper intake manifold.

REMOVAL & INSTALLATION

2.4L Engine

See Figures 257 and 258.

1. Remove the air cleaner outlet duct.
2. Disconnect the Evaporative Emission

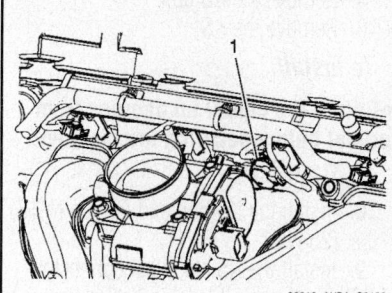

36616_AURA_G0120

Fig. 257 Disconnecting the fuel injector wiring harness electrical connector (1) from the MAP sensor—2.4L engine

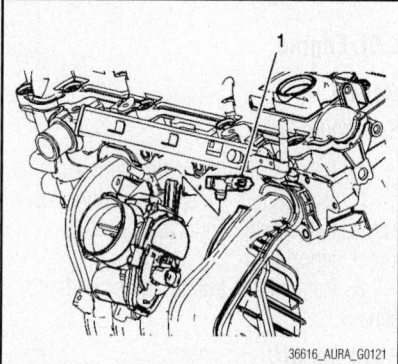

36616_AURA_G0121

Fig. 258 Removing and installing the MAP sensor (1)—2.4L engine

(EVAP) canister purge tube from the intake manifold.

3. Reposition the EVAP canister purge tube out of the way.

4. Disconnect the fuel injector wiring harness electrical connector from the Manifold Absolute Pressure (MAP) sensor.

5. Remove the fuel injector wiring harness clips from the fuel rail tabs.

6. Disconnect the fuel injector wiring harness electrical connector from the number 3 fuel injector.

7. Squeeze tabs and slide the MAP sensor upward.

To install:

8. Lubricate the NEW MAP sensor seal with clean engine oil.

9. Install the MAP sensor into the intake manifold.

10. Connect the fuel injector wiring harness electrical connector to the number 3 fuel injector.

11. Install the fuel injector wiring harness clips to the fuel rail tabs.

12. Connect the fuel injector wiring harness electrical connector to the MAP sensor.

13. Position the EVAP canister purge tube out of the way.

14. Connect the EVAP canister purge tube to the intake manifold.

15. Install the air cleaner outlet duct.

3.5L Engine

1. Remove the intake manifold cover.

2. Disconnect the engine wiring harness electrical connector from the Manifold Absolute Pressure (MAP) sensor.

3. Remove the spark plug wire clip from the MAP sensor bracket, if necessary.

4. Remove the upper intake manifold bolt.

5. Remove the MAP sensor bracket.

6. Remove the MAP sensor and seal from the upper intake manifold. Discard the seal.

To install:

7. Lubricate the NEW MAP sensor seal with clean engine oil.

8. Install the MAP sensor into the upper intake manifold.

9. Place the MAP sensor bracket into position.

10. Install the upper intake manifold bolt. Tighten the bolt to 18 ft. lbs. (25 Nm).

11. Install the spark plug wire clip to the MAP sensor bracket, if necessary.

12. Connect the engine wiring harness electrical connector to the MAP sensor.

13. Install the intake manifold cover.

3.6L Engine

See Figure 259.

1. Remove the fuel injector sight shield.

    a. Remove the oil fill cap.

    b. Grasp the cover by the upper left

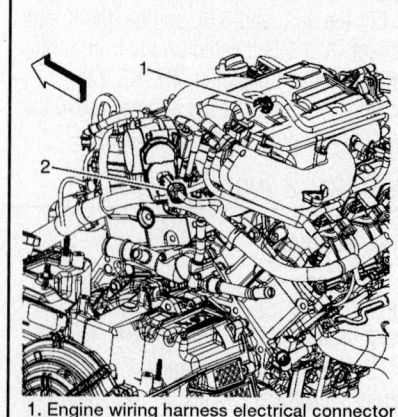

1. Engine wiring harness electrical connector
2. Manifold Absolute Pressure (MAP) sensor

36616_AURA_G0081

Fig. 259 Locating the MAP sensor—3.6L engine

and the lower right corners and lift up, disengaging the cover grommets from the ball studs.

c. If necessary, lift upward on the front of the cover, then reach under the center of the cover disengaging the cover grommet for the ball stud.

2. Disconnect the engine wiring harness electrical connector from the Manifold Absolute Pressure (MAP) sensor.

3. Remove the MAP sensor bolt and sensor.

To install:

4. Lubricate the MAP sensor O-ring seal with clean engine oil.

5. Install the MAP sensor and bolt. Tighten the bolt to 89 inch lbs. (10 Nm).

6. Connect the engine wiring harness electrical connector to the MAP sensor.

7. Install the fuel injector sight shield.

a. If necessary, place the cover into position over the ball stud. Press down near the center of the cover, engaging the cover to the ball stud.

8. Place the cover into position over the ball studs. Press down near the upper left and the lower right corners, engaging the cover to the ball studs.

9. Install the oil fill cap.

MASS AIR FLOW (MAF) SENSOR

LOCATION

For information on the Mass Air Flow (MAF) sensor, refer to Intake Air Temperature (IAT) Sensor in this section.

REMOVAL & INSTALLATION

For information on the Mass Air Flow (MAF) sensor, refer to Intake Air Temperature (IAT) Sensor in this section.

VEHICLE SPEED SENSOR (VSS)

LOCATION

The Vehicle Speed Sensor (VSS) is located on the transmission.

REMOVAL & INSTALLATION

Automatic Transaxle 4T45-E

See Figure 260.

✳✳ CAUTION

Ensure that the vehicle is properly supported and squarely positioned. To help avoid personal injury when a vehicle is on a hoist, provide additional support for the vehicle on the opposite end from which the components are being removed.

1. Position the vehicle on a hoist and raise the vehicle.

2. Disconnect the Vehicle Speed Sensor (VSS) electrical connector.

3. Remove the VSS electrical harness retainer from the VSS stud.

4. Remove the VSS stud.

5. Remove the output VSS from the transmission case.

✳✳ CAUTION

Inspect the O-ring for damage and replace if necessary.

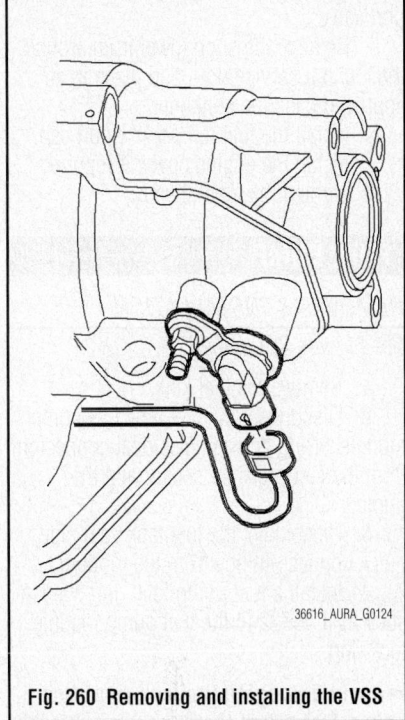

Fig. 260 Removing and installing the VSS

6. Remove the O-ring from the VSS.

To install:

7. Install the O-ring onto the VSS.

8. Install the output VSS into the transmission case.

9. Install the VSS stud and tighten to 106 inch lbs. (12 Nm).

10. Install the VSS electrical harness retainer to the VSS stud.

11. Connect the VSS electrical connector.

12. Lower the vehicle.

FUEL

GASOLINE FUEL INJECTION SYSTEM

FUEL SYSTEM SERVICE PRECAUTIONS

Safety is the most important factor when performing not only fuel system maintenance but any type of maintenance. Failure to conduct maintenance and repairs in a safe manner may result in serious personal injury or death. Maintenance and testing of the vehicle's fuel system components can be accomplished safely and effectively by adhering to the following rules and guidelines.

• To avoid the possibility of fire and personal injury, always disconnect the negative battery cable unless the repair or test procedure requires that battery voltage be applied.

• Always relieve the fuel system pressure prior to disconnecting any fuel system component (injector, fuel rail, pressure reg-

ulator, etc.), fitting or fuel line connection. Exercise extreme caution whenever relieving fuel system pressure to avoid exposing skin, face and eyes to fuel spray. Please be advised that fuel under pressure may penetrate the skin or any part of the body that it contacts.

• Always place a shop towel or cloth around the fitting or connection prior to loosening to absorb any excess fuel due to spillage. Ensure that all fuel spillage (should it occur) is quickly removed from engine surfaces. Ensure that all fuel soaked cloths or towels are deposited into a suitable waste container.

• Always keep a dry chemical (Class B) fire extinguisher near the work area.

• Do not allow fuel spray or fuel vapors to come into contact with a spark or open flame.

• Always use a back-up wrench when loosening and tightening fuel line connection fittings. This will prevent unnecessary stress and torsion to fuel line piping.

• Always replace worn fuel fitting O-rings with new. Do not substitute fuel hose or equivalent where fuel pipe is installed.

Before servicing the vehicle, make sure to also refer to the precautions in the beginning of this section as well.

RELIEVING FUEL SYSTEM PRESSURE

1. Loosen the fuel fill cap in order to relieve the fuel tank vapor pressure.

2. Remove the engine cover, if required.

3. Remove the fuel rail service port cap.

4. Wrap a shop towel around the fuel rail service port and using a small flat

bladed tool, depress (open) the fuel rail test port valve.

5. Remove the shop towel from around the fuel rail service port, and place in an approved gasoline container.

6. Install the fuel rail service port cap.

7. Install the engine cover, if required.

8. Tighten the fuel fill cap.

FUEL PUMP

REMOVAL & INSTALLATION

See Figures 261 and 262.

1. Remove the fuel tank.

2. Disconnect the fuel tank fuel pump module wiring harness electrical connectors from the fuel pressure sensor and the pump.

3. Disconnect the fuel tank vent pipe quick connect fittings from the module.

4. Install a fuel pump lock ring wrench such as J 45722 to the fuel pump module lock ring.

➡**Avoid damaging the lock ring. Use only a fuel pump lock ring wrench such as J 45722 to prevent damage to the lock ring.**

➡**Do Not handle the fuel sender assembly by the fuel pipes. The amount of leverage generated by handling the fuel pipes could damage the joints.**

➡**Do NOT use impact tools. Significant force will be required to release the lock ring. The use of a hammer and screwdriver is not recommended. Secure the fuel tank in order to prevent fuel tank rotation.**

5. Using a fuel pump lock ring wrench such as J 45722 and a long breaker-bar,

rotate the lock ring in a counterclockwise direction in order to unlock the lock ring.

6. Remove the fuel pump lock ring wrench such as J 45722 from the fuel pump module lock ring.

7. Lift the fuel pump module up slightly in order to disconnect the fuel tank vent pipe quick connect fitting from the pump cover.

8. Raise the fuel pump up from the fuel tank. Tilt the pump in order to allow the fuel level sensor arm and float to clear the pump opening.

9. Remove the fuel pump.

10. Remove and discard the fuel pump module seal.

11. Clean the fuel pump sealing surfaces.

To install:

✳✳ CAUTION

Drain the fuel from the fuel sender assembly into an approved container in order to reduce the risk of fire and personal injury. Never store the fuel in an open container.

➡**Some lock rings were manufactured with "DO NOT REUSE" stamped into them. These lock rings may be reused if they are not damaged or warped. Inspect the lock ring for damage due to improper removal or installation procedures. If damage is found, install a NEW fuel pump module. Inspect the lock ring for flatness as best as possible. If the lock ring is warped, replace the fuel pump module.**

12. Clean any contamination from the male pipe ends of the fuel pump.

13. Place a NEW fuel tank pump seal onto the fuel tank.

14. Insert the fuel pump into the fuel tank allowing the sensor arm and float to clear the module opening.

15. Lower the pump down into the fuel tank until the fuel tank vent pipe quick connect fitting can be connected.

16. Connect the fuel tank vent pipe quick connect fitting at the pump cover.

17. Press the fuel tank pump downward.

18. Install the pump lock ring wrench such as J 45722 to the fuel pump module lock ring.

➡**Ensure that the lock ring is installed with the correct side facing upward. A correctly installed lock ring will only turn in a clockwise direction.**

19. Using the pump lock ring wrench such as J 45722 and a long breaker-bar, rotate the lock ring in a clockwise direction in order the lock the lock ring.

20. Remove the pump lock ring wrench from the fuel pump module lock ring.

21. Connect the fuel tank vent pipe quick connect fittings to the pump.

22. Connect the fuel tank fuel pump module wiring harness electrical connectors to the fuel pressure sensor and the pump.

23. Install the fuel tank

FUEL RAIL & INJECTORS

REMOVAL & INSTALLATION

2.4L Engine

See Figure 263.

1. Disconnect the negative battery cable.

2. Relieve the fuel system pressure.

3. Remove the air cleaner outlet duct.

4. Disconnect the fuel feed line quick connect fitting from the fuel rail

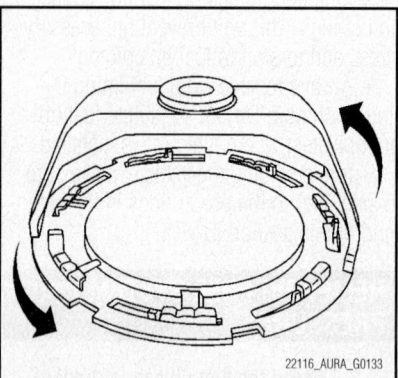

22116_AURA_G0133

Fig. 261 Install a fuel pump lock ring wrench such as J 45722 to the fuel pump module lock ring

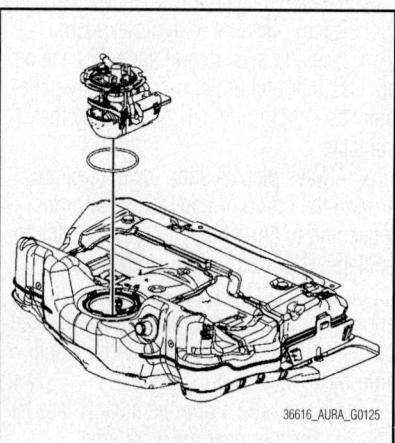

36616_AURA_G0125

Fig. 262 Removing the fuel pump module and seal

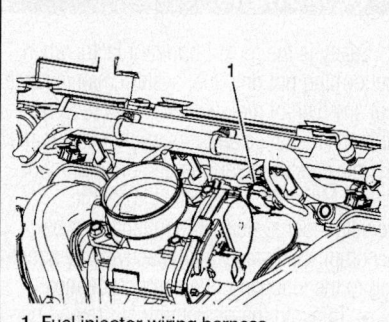

1. Fuel injector wiring harness

36616_AURA_G0018

Fig. 263 Disconnecting the fuel injector wiring harness from the MAP sensor—2.4L engine

5. Disconnect the engine wiring harness electrical connector from the fuel injector wiring harness electrical connector.

6. Disconnect the fuel injector wiring harness electrical from the Manifold Absolute Pressure (MAP) sensor.

7. Remove the engine wiring harness clips from the fuel rail tabs.

8. Remove the fuel rail bolts.

➡**Use care when removing the fuel rail assembly in order to prevent damage to the fuel injector spray tips.**

9. Pull the fuel rail back and upward in order to release the fuel injectors from the cylinder head ports.

10. Remove the fuel rail.

➡**The fuel injector tip insulators may be located on the injector or may still be located in the cylinder head. Either way, ensure that all 4 injector tip insulators are removed and discarded.**

11. Remove and discard the fuel injector tip insulators.

12. Disconnect the fuel injector wiring harness electrical connectors from the fuel injectors.

13. Remove the fuel injector wiring harness clips from the fuel rail.

14. Remove the fuel injector wiring harness from the fuel rail.

➡**Use care in removing the fuel injectors in order to prevent damage to the fuel injector electrical connector pins or the fuel injector nozzles. Do not immerse the fuel injector in any type of cleaner. The fuel injector is an electrical component and may be damaged by this cleaning method.**

➡**If the fuel injectors are found to be leaking, the engine oil may be contaminated with fuel.**

15. Remove the fuel injector retainer.

16. Remove the fuel injector from the fuel rail.

17. Remove the fuel injector upper O-ring.

18. Remove the fuel injector lower O-ring.

To install:

➡**The fuel injector assembly is stamped with a part number identification. Be sure to use the correct part number when ordering replacement fuel injectors.**

19. Lubricate the NEW fuel injector O-rings with clean engine oil.

20. Install the NEW fuel injector O-rings.

21. Install the fuel injector to the fuel rail.

22. Install the fuel injector retainer.

23. Install the fuel injector wiring harness clips to the fuel rail.

24. Connect the fuel injector wiring harness electrical connectors to the fuel injectors.

25. Lubricate the NEW fuel injector tip insulators with clean engine oil.

26. Install the NEW fuel injector tip insulators to the cylinder head.

27. With the fuel injectors positioned downward, lower the fuel injectors into the cylinder head ports.

28. Carefully push down on the fuel rail in order to insert the injectors into the cylinder head ports.

29. Install the fuel rail bolts. Tighten the bolts to 89 inch lbs. (10 Nm).

30. Install the engine wiring harness clips to the fuel rail tabs.

31. Connect the fuel injector wiring harness electrical to the MAP sensor.

32. Connect the engine wiring harness electrical connector to the fuel injector wiring harness electrical connector.

33. Connect the fuel feed line quick connect fitting to the fuel rail.

34. Install the air cleaner outlet duct.

35. Connect the negative battery cable.

36. Inspect for fuel leaks using the following procedure:

    a. Turn ON the ignition, with the engine OFF for 2 seconds.

    b. Turn OFF the ignition for 10 seconds

    c. Turn ON the ignition

    d. Inspect for fuel leaks.

3.5L Engine

See Figure 264.

> **✳✳ CAUTION**
>
> **In order to reduce the risk of fire and personal injury that may result from a fuel leak, always install the fuel injector O-rings in the proper position. If the upper and lower O-rings are different colors (black and brown), be sure to install the black O-ring in the upper position and the brown O-ring in the lower position on the fuel injector. The O-rings are the same size but are made of different materials.**

➡**Cap the fittings and plug the holes when servicing the fuel system in order to prevent dirt and other contaminants from entering the open pipes and passages.**

➡**An 8-digit identification number is stamped on the fuel rail. Refer to this number if servicing or part replacement is required.**

1. Disconnect the fuel feed pipe quick connect fitting from the fuel rail.

2. Remove the upper intake manifold.

3. Disconnect the fuel injector wiring harness electrical connector from the Engine Coolant Temperature (ECT) sensor.

4. Disconnect the fuel injector wiring harness electrical connector from the Camshaft Position (CMP) sensor.

5. Remove the fuel injector wiring harness electrical connector bracket bolt from the intake manifold.

6. Remove the fuel rail bolts.

7. Remove the fuel rail.

8. Remove the fuel injector O-ring seal from the spray tip end of each injector, if the fuel rail was removed for other purposes.

9. Disconnect the fuel injector wiring harness electrical connectors from the fuel injectors.

10. Remove the fuel injector wiring harness retainers from the fuel rail.

11. Remove the fuel injector wiring harness.

12. Remove the fuel injector retainers.

13. Remove the fuel injectors.

14. Remove the fuel injector upper and lower O-ring seals.

To install:

15. Lubricate the NEW injector O-ring seals with clean engine oil.

16. Install the NEW fuel injector upper and lower O-ring seals.

17. Install the fuel injectors.

18. Install the fuel injector retainers.

19. Position the fuel injector wiring harness.

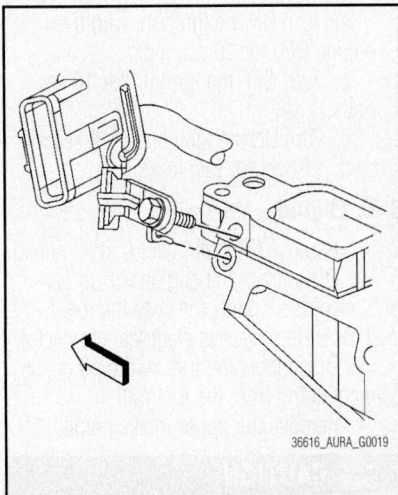

36616_AURA_G0019

Fig. 264 Removing the fuel injector wiring harness electrical connector bracket bolt from the intake manifold—3.5L engine

20. Install the fuel injector wiring harness retainers to the fuel rail.

21. Connect the fuel injector wiring harness electrical connectors to the fuel injectors.

➥Use care when servicing the fuel system components, especially the fuel injector electrical connectors, the fuel injector tips, and the injector O-rings. Plug the inlet and the outlet ports of the fuel rail in order to prevent contamination. Do not use compressed air to clean the fuel rail assembly as this may damage the fuel rail components. Do not immerse the fuel rail assembly in a solvent bath in order to prevent damage to the fuel rail assembly.

22. Install NEW fuel injector O-ring seals onto the spray tip end of each injector, if the fuel rail was removed for other purposes.

23. Install the fuel rail.

24. Install the fuel rail bolts. Tighten the bolts to 89 inch lbs. (10 Nm).

25. Align the bracket pin to the hole in the lower intake manifold.

26. Install the fuel injector wiring harness electrical connector bracket bolt to the intake manifold. Tighten the bolt to 10 ft. lbs. (14 Nm).

27. Connect the fuel injector wiring harness electrical connector to the CMP sensor.

28. Connect the fuel injector wiring harness electrical connector to the ECT sensor.

29. Install the upper intake manifold.

30. Connect the fuel feed pipe quick connect fitting to the fuel rail.

31. Connect the negative battery cable. Refer

32. Tighten the fuel fill cap.

33. Inspect for fuel leaks using the following procedure:

a. Turn ON the ignition, with the engine OFF for 10 seconds.

b. Turn OFF the ignition for 10 seconds.

c. Turn ON the ignition for 10 seconds.

d. Inspect for fuel leaks.

3.6L Engine

1. Remove the fuel injector sight shield.

2. Disconnect the engine wiring harness electrical connector from the fuel injector wiring harness electrical connector.

3. Disconnect the fuel feed pipe quick connect fitting from the fuel rail.

4. Remove the upper intake manifold.

✳ CAUTION

Wear safety glasses while using the compressed air to avoid eye injury.

5. Use compressed air in order to remove any debris from the around the area where the fuel injectors enter the lower intake manifold.

6. Remove the fuel rail bolts.

➥Remove the fuel rail assembly carefully in order to prevent damage to the injector electrical connector terminals and the injector spray tips. Support the fuel rail after the fuel rail is removed in order to avoid damaging the fuel rail components. Cap the fittings and plug the holes when servicing the fuel system in order to prevent dirt and other contaminants from entering open pipes and passages.

7. Remove the fuel rail with fuel injectors from the lower intake manifold.

8. Lift up the fuel injector electrical connector retainer.

9. Push in the fuel injector electrical connector tab in order to disconnect the connector from the injector.

10. Remove the fuel injector retainer clip.

11. Remove the fuel injector.

12. Remove and discard the fuel injector seals.

To install:

13. Install NEW fuel injector seals.

14. Install the fuel injector.

15. Install the fuel injector retainer clip.

16. Install the fuel injector electrical connector.

17. Push down on the fuel injector electrical connector retainer, securing the electrical connector.

18. Install the fuel rail with fuel injectors to the lower intake manifold. Tighten the bolts to 89 inch lbs. (10 Nm).

19. Install the upper intake manifold.

20. Connect the fuel feed pipe quick connect fitting to the fuel rail.

21. Connect the engine wiring harness electrical connector to the fuel injector wiring harness electrical connector.

22. Inspect for fuel leaks using the following procedure:

a. Turn ON the ignition, with the engine OFF for 10 seconds.

b. Turn OFF the ignition for 10 seconds.

c. Turn ON the ignition for 10 seconds.

d. Inspect for fuel leaks.

23. Install the fuel injector sight shield.

FUEL TANK

REMOVAL & INSTALLATION

See Figures 265 through 268.

➥Clean the fuel and Evaporative Emission (EVAP) connections and surrounding areas prior to disconnecting the lines in order the avoid possible system contamination.

1. Relieve the fuel system pressure.

2. Drain the fuel tank.

3. Raise and support the vehicle.

4. Disconnect the fuel tank fuel pump module wiring harness electrical connector from body wiring harness electrical connector.

5. Remove the body wiring harness electrical connector clip from the EVAP canister.

6. Disconnect the body wiring harness electrical connector from the rear Antilock

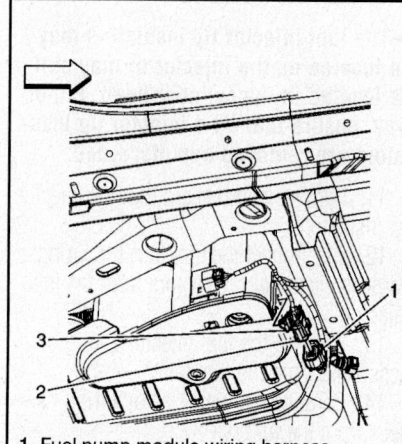

1. Fuel pump module wiring harness electrical connector
2. Body wiring harness electrical connector
3. Body wiring harness electrical connector clip

36616_AURA_G0127

Fig. 265 Disconnecting the fuel pump module wiring harness electrical connector

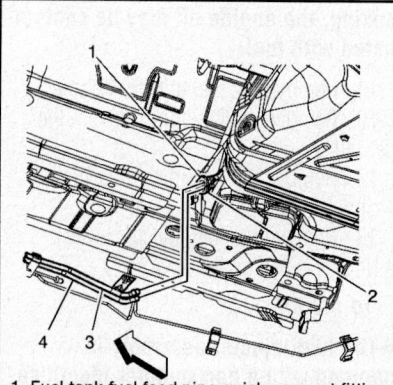

1. Fuel tank fuel feed pipe quick connect fitting
2. Fuel tank EVAP pipe quick connect fitting
3. Chassis fuel feed pipe
4. Chassis EVAP pipe

36616_AURA_G0128

Fig. 266 Disconnecting quick connect fittings

Brake System (ABS) wiring harness electrical connector.

7. Remove the rear ABS wiring harness electrical connector clip from the EVAP canister.

8. Disconnect the fuel tank fuel feed pipe quick connect fitting from the chassis fuel feed pipe.

9. Disconnect the fuel tank EVAP pipe quick connect fitting from the chassis EVAP pipe.

10. Cap the chassis fuel and EVAP pipes in order to prevent possible fuel and/or EVAP system contamination.

11. Loosen the fuel fill pipe hose clamp at the fuel tank.

12. Separate the fuel fill pipe hose from the fuel tank.

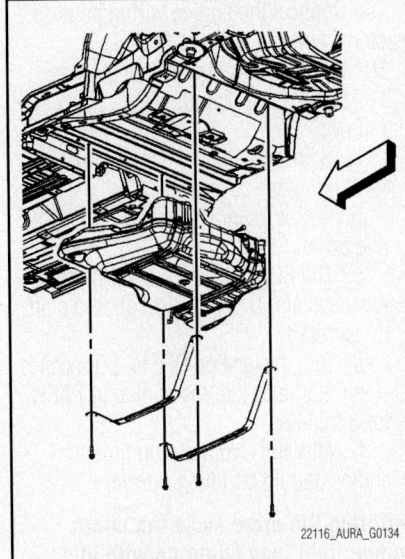

Fig. 267 Fuel tank mounting

22116_AURA_G0134

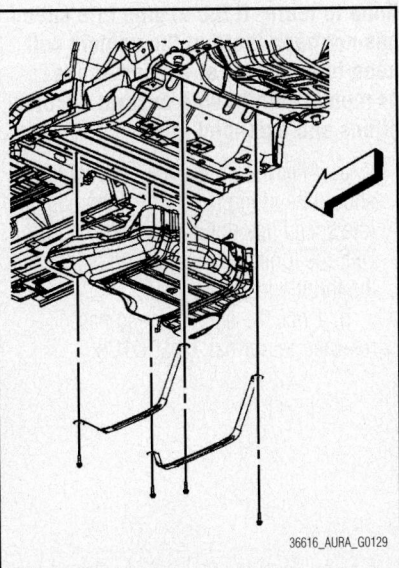

Fig. 268 Removing the fuel tank straps

36616_AURA_G0129

13. Disconnect the fuel tank fill EVAP emission pipe quick connect fitting from the fuel tank vent pipe.

14. Place a jackstand under the muffler assembly.

15. With the aid of an assistant, separate the muffler insulators from the underbody hangers.

16. Slowly lower the muffler assembly allowing it to rest on the jackstand. If this is not possible, remove the muffler assembly.

17. Have assistants support either side of the fuel tank.

18. Place a suitable adjustable jack under the fuel tank, and have the assistants rest the fuel tank on the adjustable jack.

19. Remove fuel tank strap bolts and straps.

20. If applicable, in order to clear the muffler assembly, slowly lower the right side of the fuel tank.

21. Once the tank is clear of the right frame rail, lower the fuel tank down and remove forward toward the right side of the vehicle.

To install:

22. Have assistants support either side of the fuel tank.

23. If applicable, begin to install the right side of the fuel tank over the muffler assembly.

24. If applicable, raise the right side of the fuel tank into position inboard of the right frame rail. Use care in feeding the fuel feed, EVAP line wiring harness over the muffler assembly.

25. If applicable and the muffler assembly was removed, have assistants raise the fuel tank into position.

26. Install fuel tank straps and bolts. Tighten the bolts to 15 ft. lbs. (20 Nm).

27. Raise the muffler assembly into position if applicable, otherwise install the muffler assembly.

28. With the aid of an assistant, install the muffler insulators to the underbody hangers.

29. Remove the jackstand from under the muffler assembly.

30. Install the fuel fill pipe hose to the fuel tank.

31. Connect the fuel tank fill EVAP emission pipe quick connect fitting to the fuel tank vent pipe.

32. Tighten the fuel fill pipe hose clamp at the fuel tank to 35 inch lbs. (4 Nm).

33. Remove the caps from the fuel and EVAP pipes.

34. Connect the fuel tank EVAP pipe quick connect fitting to the chassis EVAP pipe.

35. Connect the fuel tank fuel feed pipe quick connect fitting to the chassis fuel feed pipe.

36. Install the rear ABS wiring harness electrical connector clip to the EVAP canister.

37. Connect the body wiring harness electrical connector to the rear ABS wiring harness electrical connector.

38. Install the body wiring harness electrical connector clip to the underbody.

39. Connect the fuel tank fuel pump module wiring harness electrical connector to the body wiring harness electrical connector.

40. Lower the vehicle.

41. Refill the fuel tank.

42. Tighten the fuel fill cap.

43. Inspect for fuel leaks using the following procedure:

   a. Turn ON the ignition, with the engine OFF for 10 seconds.

   b. Turn OFF the ignition for 10 seconds.

   c. Turn ON the ignition, with the engine OFF.

   d. Inspect for fuel leaks.

IDLE SPEED

ADJUSTMENT

Idle speed is maintained by the Powertrain Control Module (PCM). No adjustment is necessary or possible.

THROTTLE BODY

REMOVAL & INSTALLATION

2.4L Engine

See Figure 269.

➡**Do not use solvent of any type when cleaning the gasket surfaces on the intake manifold and the throttle body assembly, as damage to the gasket surfaces and throttle body assembly may result. Use care in cleaning the gasket surfaces on the intake manifold and the throttle body assembly, as sharp tools may damage the gasket surfaces.**

➡**Do not use any solvent that contains Methyl Ethyl Ketone (MEK). This solvent may damage fuel system components.**

➡**DO NOT prop open the throttle blade with the ignition key in the ON position as it may set a Diagnostic Trouble Code (DTC).**

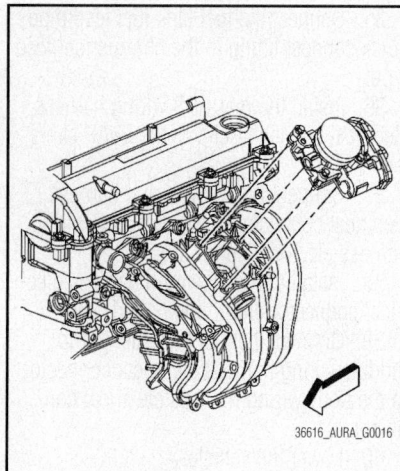

Fig. 269 Removing and installing the throttle body—2.4L engine

1. Remove the air cleaner outlet duct.
2. Disconnect the engine wiring harness electrical connector from the Electronic Throttle Control (ETC).
3. Remove the throttle body bolts.
4. Remove the throttle body.
5. Inspect the throttle body gasket, and replace if necessary.

To install:

6. Install the throttle body. Tighten the bolts to 89 inch lbs. (10 Nm).
7. Connect the engine wiring harness electrical connector to the ETC.
8. Install the air cleaner outlet duct.

3.5L Engine

➡Do not use solvent of any type when cleaning the gasket surfaces on the intake manifold and the throttle body assembly, as damage to the gasket surfaces and throttle body assembly may result. Use care in cleaning the gasket surfaces on the intake manifold and the throttle body assembly, as sharp tools may damage the gasket surfaces.

1. Remove the intake manifold cover.
2. Remove the air cleaner outlet duct.
3. Disconnect the engine wiring harness electrical connector from the Electronic Throttle Control (ETC).

4. Remove the heater inlet and outlet pipe nuts.
5. Remove the heater inlet and outlet pipe bracket from the throttle body studs. Reposition the pipes aside.
6. Remove the throttle body bolts and nuts.
7. Remove the throttle body.
8. Remove and discard the throttle body gasket.

To install:

9. Clean the gasket mating surfaces.
10. Install a new gasket.
11. Install the throttle body. Tighten the bolts and nuts to 89 inch lbs. (10 Nm).
12. Reposition the heater inlet and outlet pipes and install the pipe bracket to the throttle body studs. Tighten the nuts to 89 inch lbs. (10 Nm).
13. Connect the engine wiring harness electrical connector to the ETC.
14. Install the air cleaner outlet duct.
15. Install the intake manifold cover.
16. Perform the Throttle Learn Procedure as follows:
    a. Start and idle the engine in PARK for 3 minutes.
    b. With a scan tool, monitor desired and actual RPM.
    c. The ECM will start to learn the new idle cells and Desired RPM should start to decrease.
    d. Turn the ignition OFF for 60 seconds.
    e. Start and idle the engine in PARK for 3 minutes.
    f. After the 3 minute run time the engine should be idling normal.

➡During the drive cycle the check engine light may come on with idle speed DTCs. If idle speed codes are set, clear codes so the ECM can continue to learn. If the engine idle speed has not been learned the vehicle will need to be driven at speeds above 44 mph (70 km/h) with several decelerations and extended idles.

    a. After the drive cycle, the engine should be idling normally. If the engine idle speed has not been learned, turn OFF the ignition for 60 seconds repeat the throttle learn procedure.

    b. Once the engine speed has returned to normal, clear DTCs.

3.6L Engine

1. Remove the air cleaner outlet duct.
2. Disconnect the engine wiring harness electrical connector from the Electronic Throttle Control (ETC).
3. Remove the throttle body bolts.
4. Remove the throttle body and gasket. Discard the gasket.

To install:

5. Clean the gasket mating surfaces.
6. Install a new gasket to the upper intake manifold.
7. Position the throttle body to the upper intake manifold.
8. Install the throttle body. Tighten the bolts to 89 inch lbs. (10 Nm).
9. Connect the engine wiring harness electrical connector to the ETC.
10. Install the air cleaner outlet duct.
11. Perform the Throttle Learn Procedure as follows:
    a. Start and idle the engine in PARK for 3 minutes.
    b. With a scan tool, monitor desired and actual RPM.
    c. The ECM will start to learn the new idle cells and Desired RPM should start to decrease.
    d. Turn the ignition OFF for 60 seconds.
    e. Start and idle the engine in PARK for 3 minutes.
    f. After the 3 minute run time the engine should be idling normal.

➡During the drive cycle the check engine light may come on with idle speed DTCs. If idle speed codes are set, clear codes so the ECM can continue to learn. If the engine idle speed has not been learned the vehicle will need to be driven at speeds above 44 mph (70 km/h) with several decelerations and extended idles.

    a. After the drive cycle, the engine should be idling normally. If the engine idle speed has not been learned, turn OFF the ignition for 60 seconds repeat the throttle learn procedure.
    b. Once the engine speed has returned to normal, clear DTCs.

HEATING & AIR CONDITIONING SYSTEM

BLOWER MOTOR

REMOVAL & INSTALLATION

See Figures 270 and 271.

1. Remove the right closeout panel.
2. Remove the blower motor wire harness connector.

➡ **Cut through the case as straight as possible because the motor cup must be replaced. In order to prevent damage to the component, do not cut any deeper than necessary to remove the motor cup.**

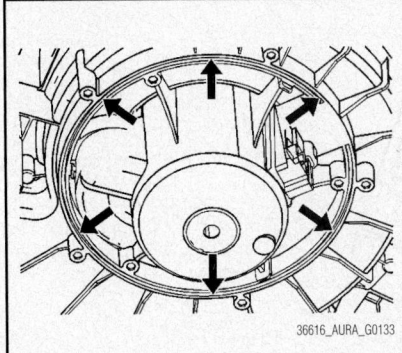

Fig. 270 Cutting out the blower motor

3. Cut out the blower motor using a utility knife in the narrow groove of the lower case.
4. Remove the blower motor.
5. Remove the blower motor nuts.
6. Remove the blower motor from the blower motor cup.

To install:

7. Install the new blower motor to the blower motor cup.
8. Install the blower motor nuts. Tighten to 21 inch lbs. (2.4 Nm).
9. Install the motor blower seal to the blower motor service ring.
10. Install the blower motor.
11. Install the blower motor attachment ring.
12. Install the blower motor screws. Tighten the screws to 13 inch lbs. (1.5 Nm).
13. Install the blower motor wire harness connector.
14. Install the right closeout panel.

HEATER CORE

REMOVAL & INSTALLATION

See Figures 272 through 282.

1. Disable the SIR system, as outlined in the Chassis Electrical Section.

2. Remove the HVAC module assembly as follows:
   a. Remove the Air Conditioner (A/C) lines from the thermal expansion valve
   b. Recover the refrigerant.
   c. Remove the surge tank from the surge tank bracket.
   d. Remove the suction line from the dash clip.
   e. Remove the liquid line from the dash clip.
   f. Remove the liquid line and suction line nut from the thermal expansion valve (TXV).
   g. Remove the suction line from the TXV.
   h. Remove the liquid line from the TXV.
   i. Remove the TXV screws.
   j. Remove the TXV.

➡ **Cap all A/C components immediately to prevent system contamination.**

   k. Remove and discard the sealing washers.
   l. Remove the heater hose from the heater core.
   m. Instrument panel (I/P) assembly by removing the following:
   - Windshield garnish molding
   - Instrument panel upper trim panel

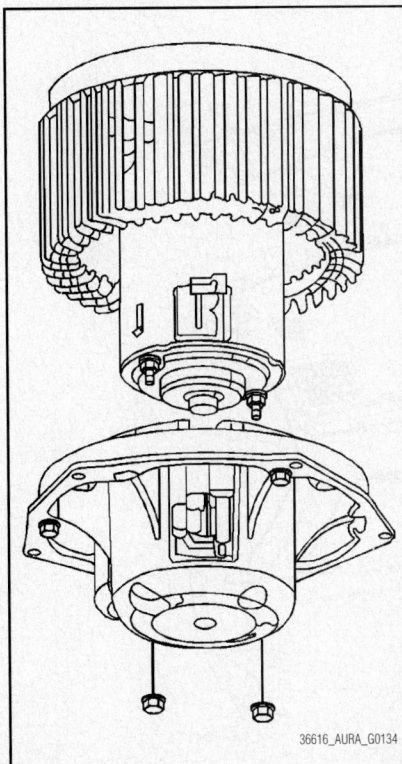

Fig. 271 Removing the blower motor from the cup

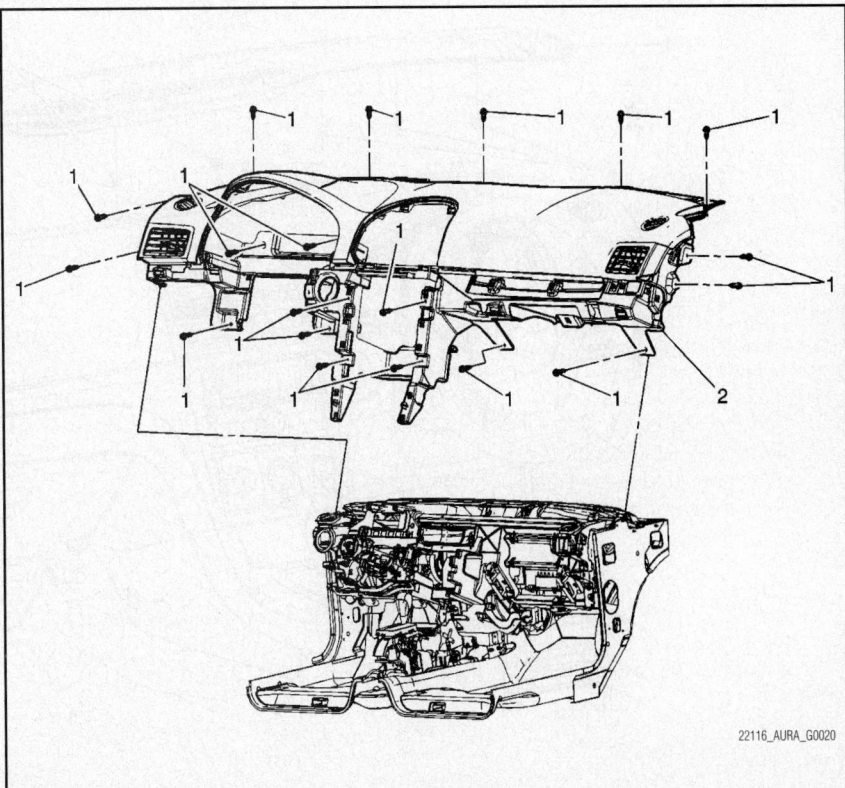

Fig. 272 Exploded view of the instrument panel assembly (2) and retainers (1)

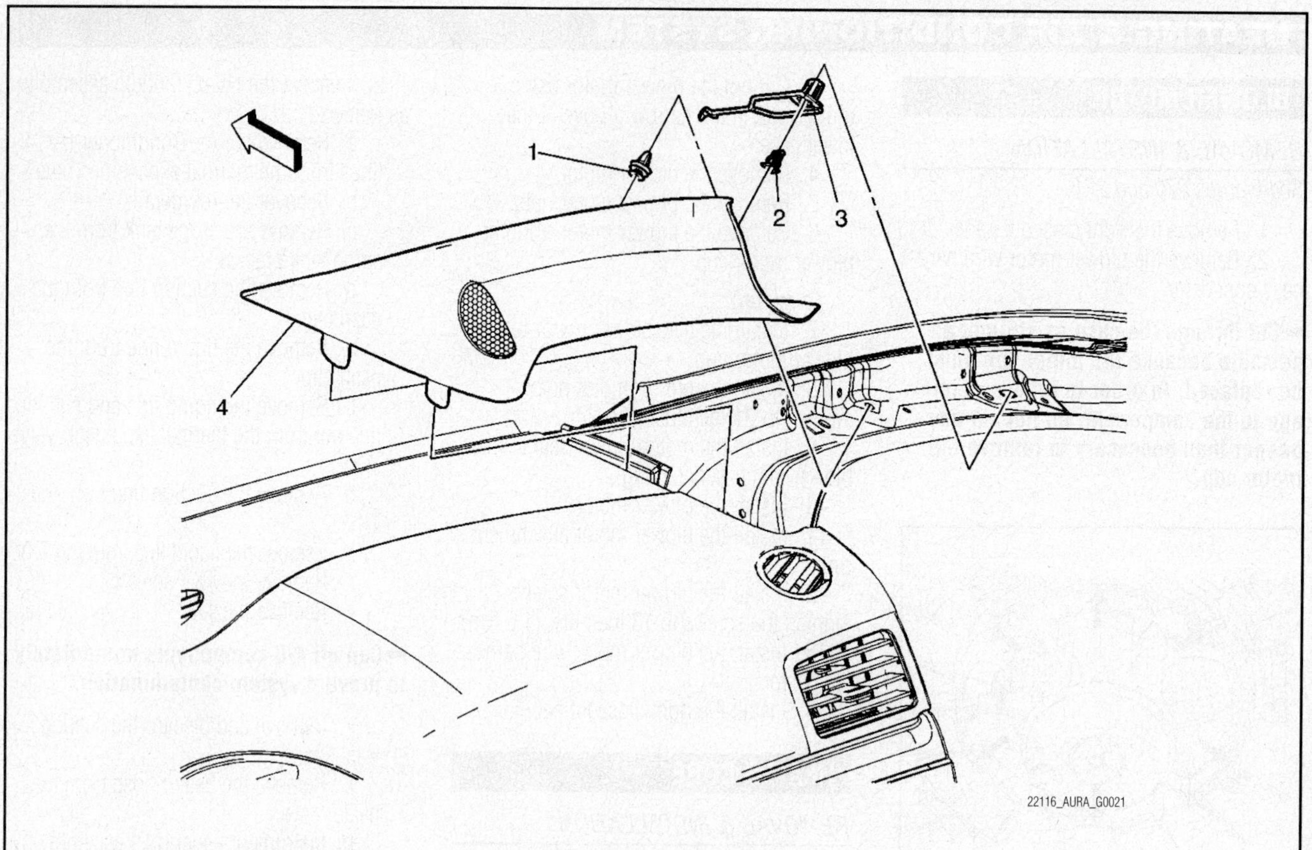
1
2
3
4
22116_AURA_G0021

Fig. 273 Exploded view of the windshield garnish molding (4) and related components

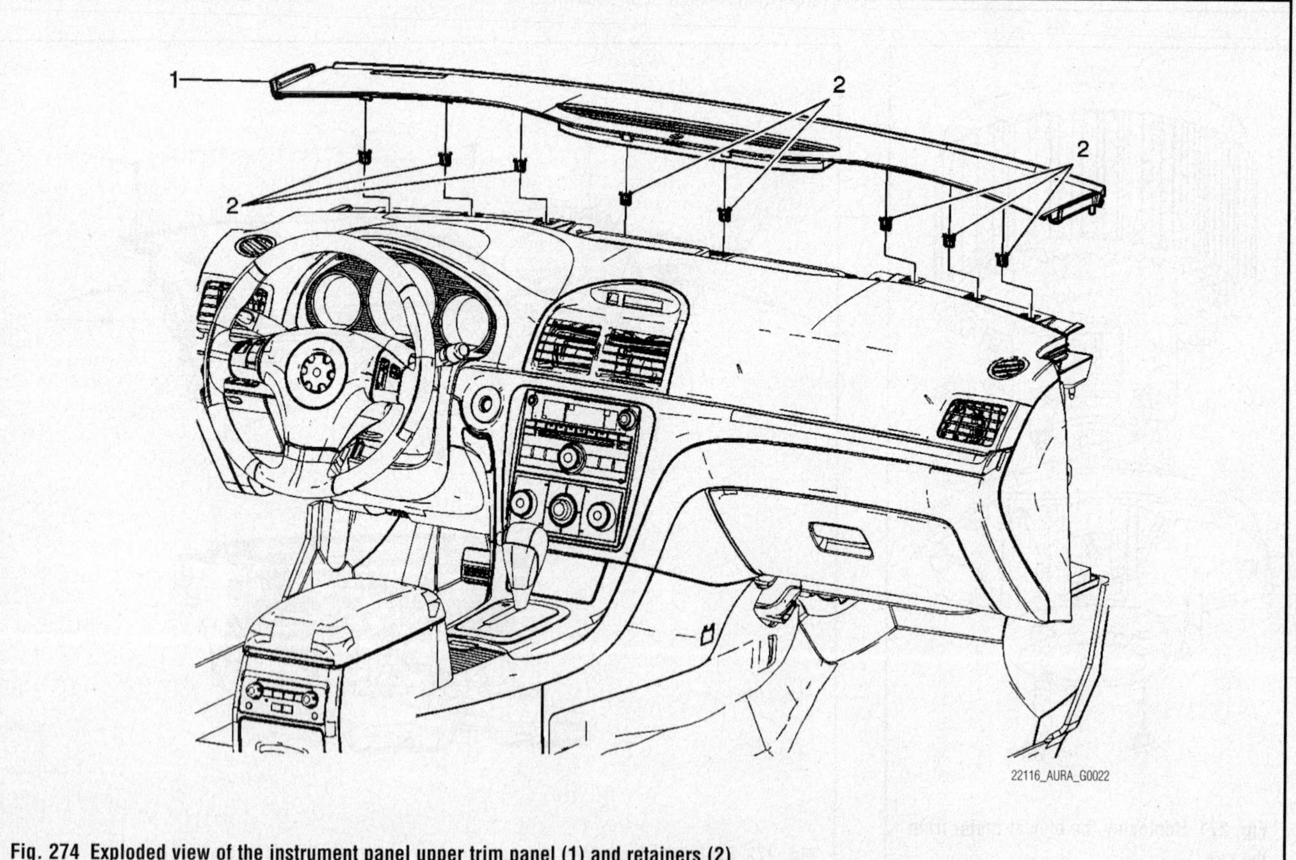
1
2
2
2
22116_AURA_G0022

Fig. 274 Exploded view of the instrument panel upper trim panel (1) and retainers (2)

1
2
2
2
1
2
22116_AURA_G0023

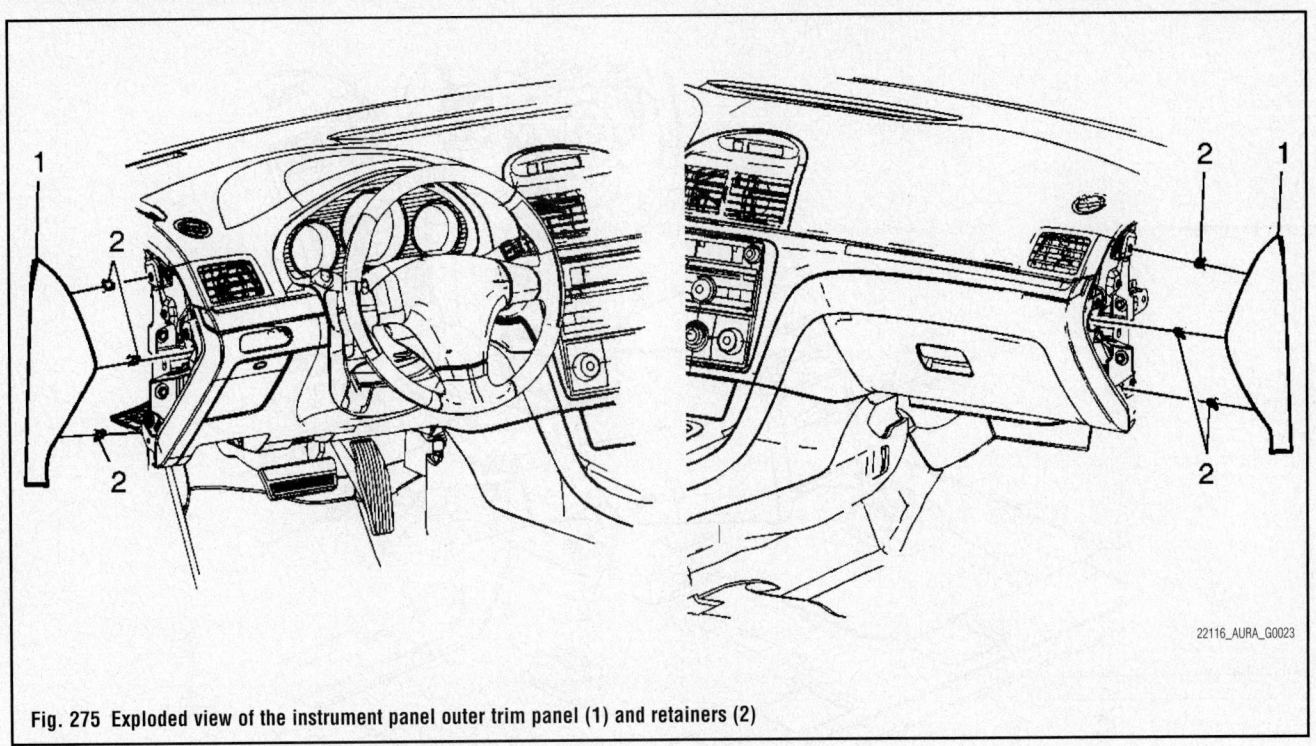

Fig. 275 Exploded view of the instrument panel outer trim panel (1) and retainers (2)

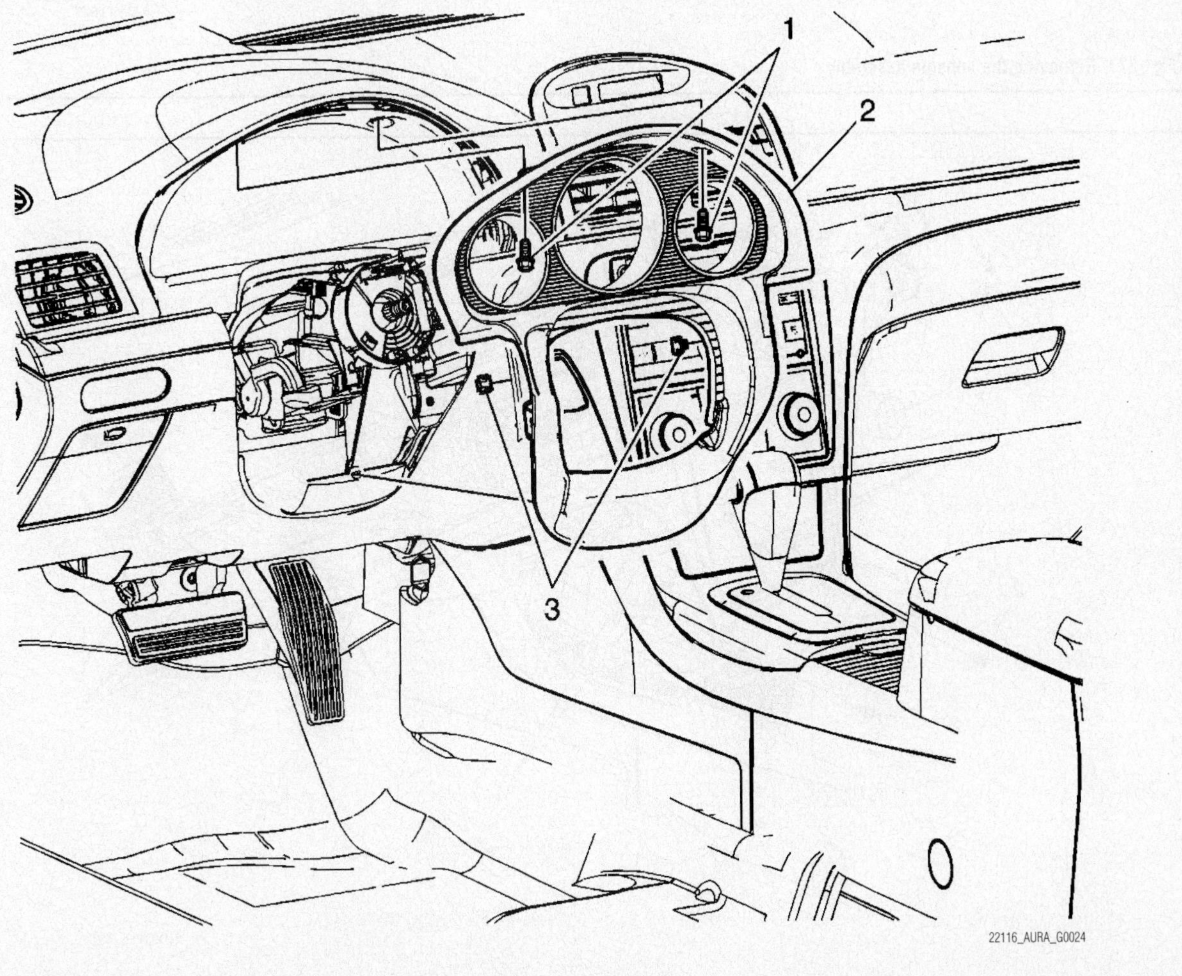

1
2
3
22116_AURA_G0024

Fig. 276 Exploded view of the instrument panel cluster trim plate bezel (2) and retainers (1)

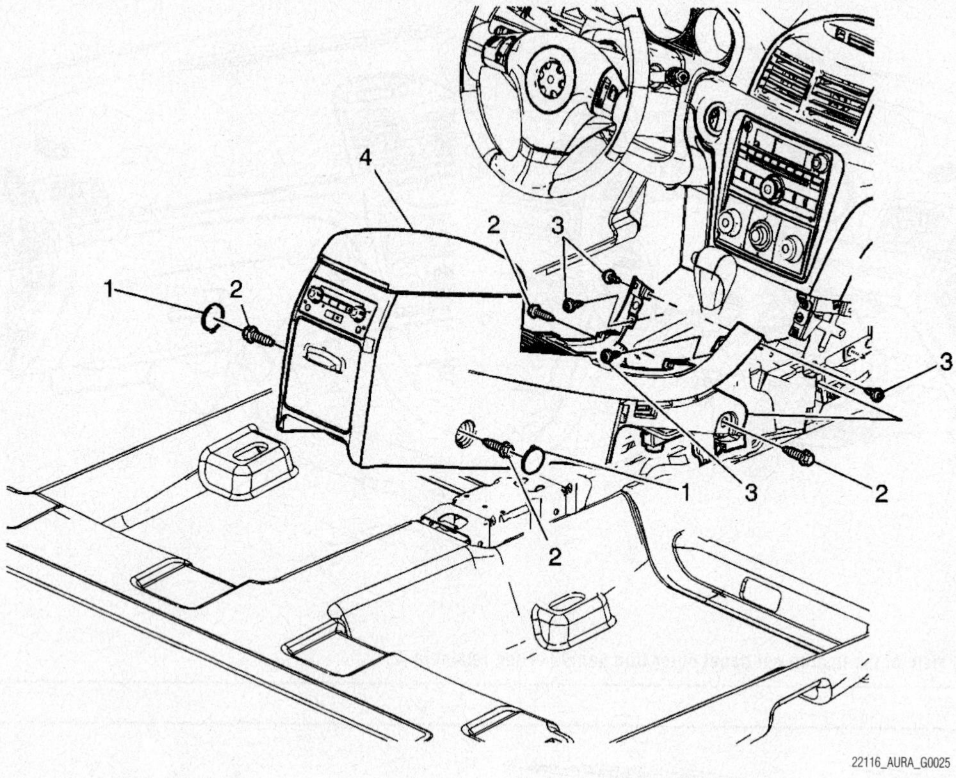

Fig. 277 Removing the console assembly

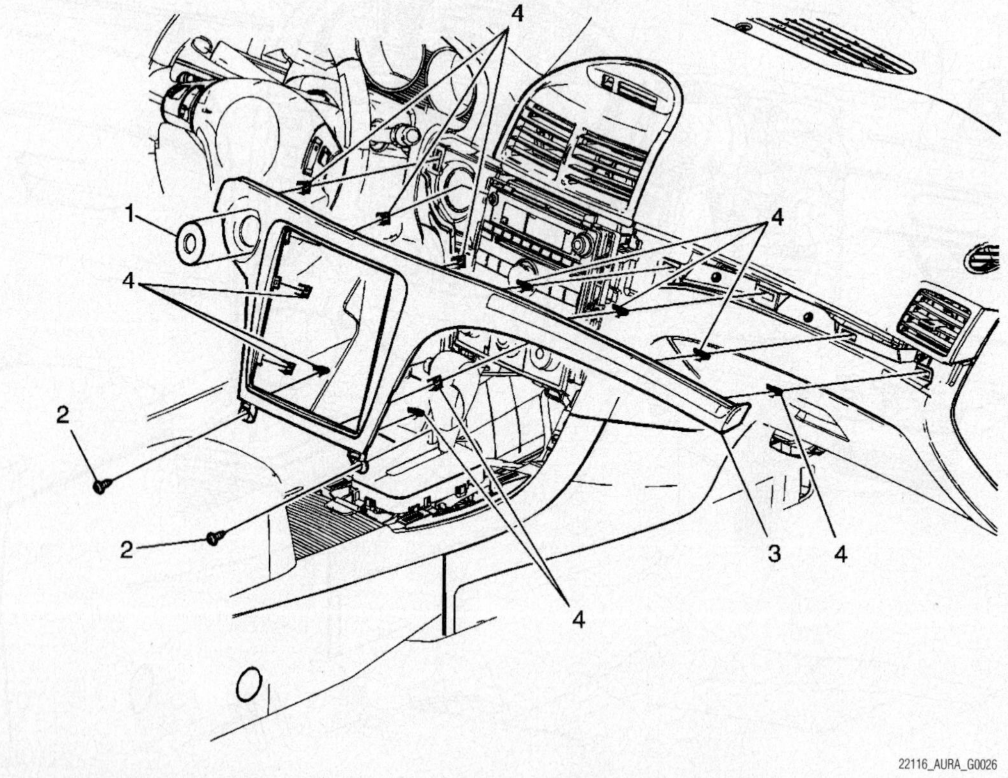

Fig. 278 Exploded view of the instrument panel center molding assembly

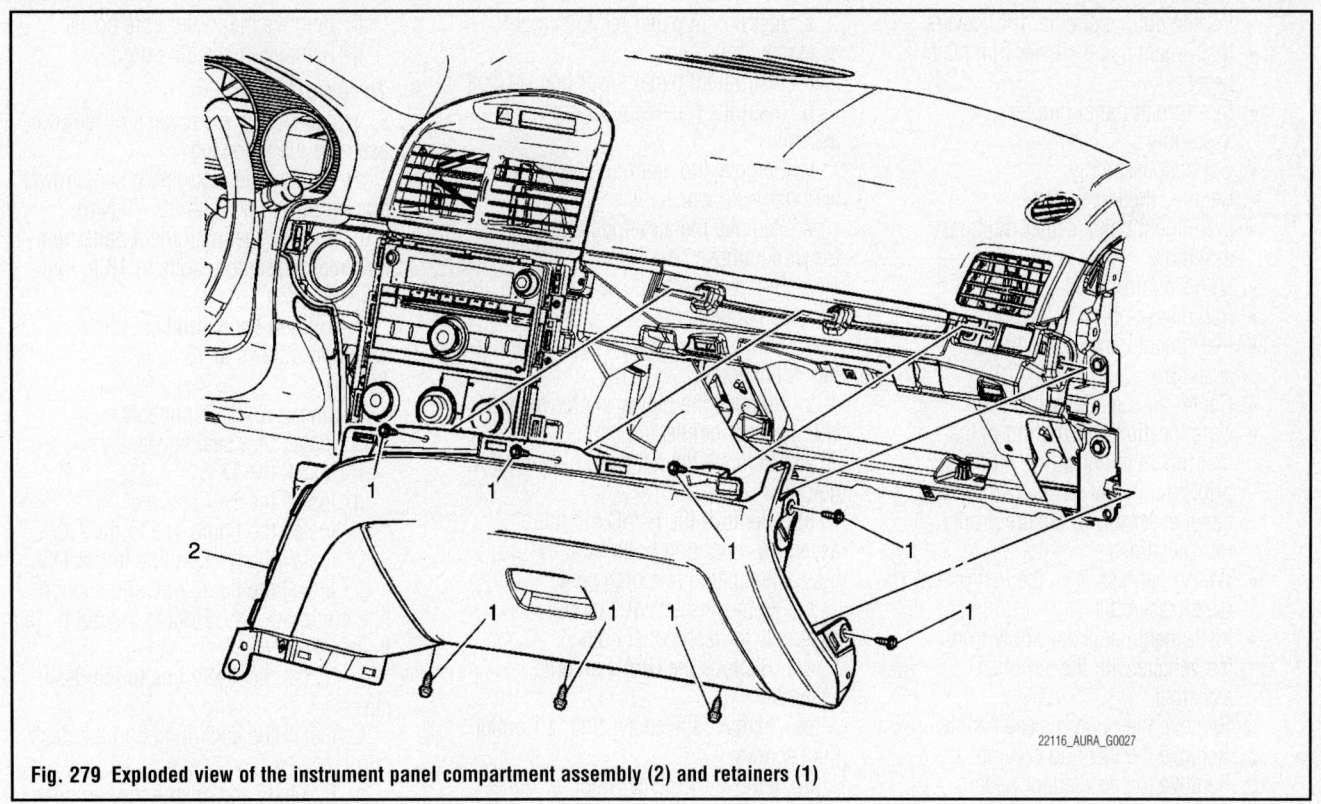

Fig. 279 Exploded view of the instrument panel compartment assembly (2) and retainers (1)

22116_AURA_G0027

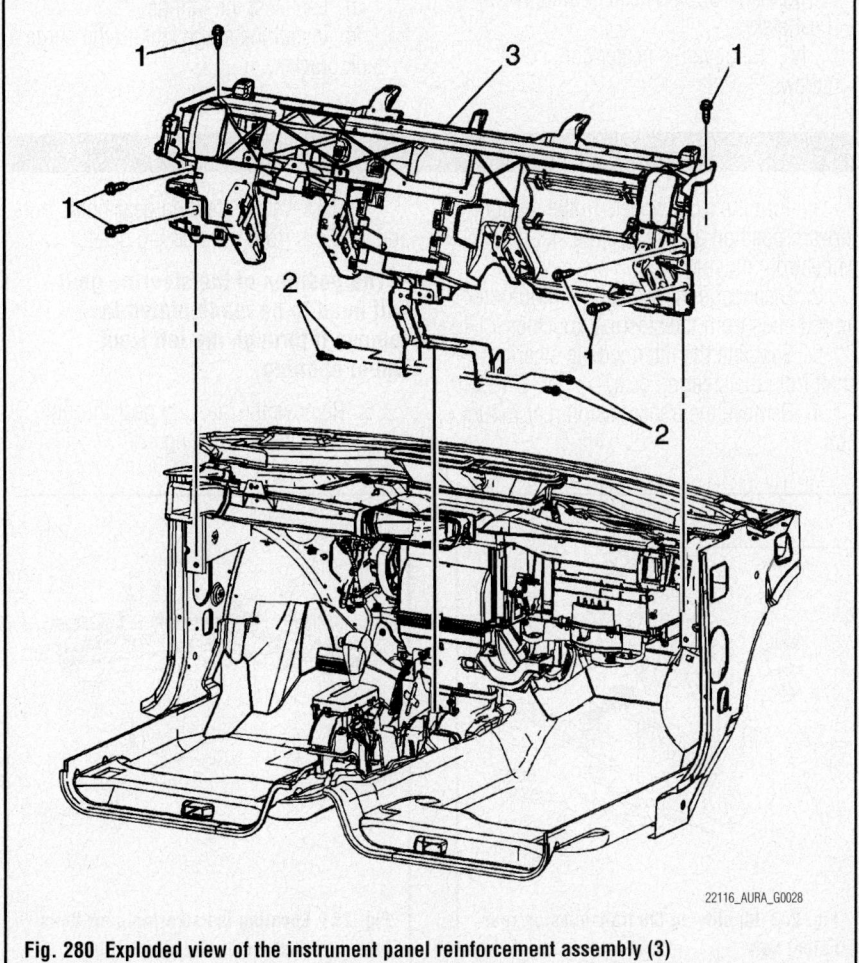

22116_AURA_G0028

Fig. 280 Exploded view of the instrument panel reinforcement assembly (3)

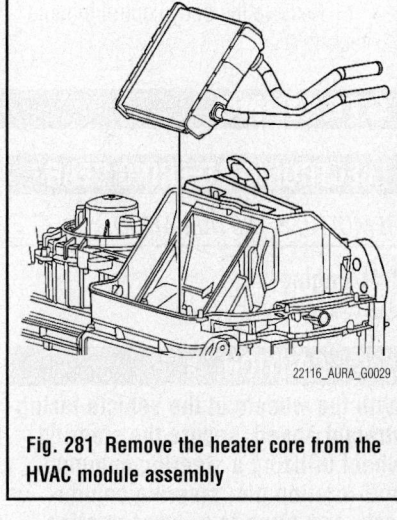

22116_AURA_G0029

Fig. 281 Remove the heater core from the HVAC module assembly

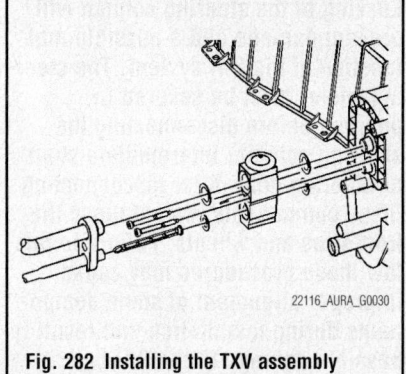

22116_AURA_G0030

Fig. 282 Installing the TXV assembly

- Instrument panel outer trim covers
- Instrument panel cluster trim plate bezel
- Instrument panel cluster assembly
- Console assembly
- Remove the knee bolster
- Instrument panel center molding assembly
- HVAC control module
- Radio assembly
- Instrument panel compartment assembly
- Center air outlet assembly
- Note location and routing of the instrument panel wiring harness prior to removal of the instrument panel assembly to ensure proper reinstallation
- Wiring harness from the instrument panel assembly
- Instrument panel assembly from the vehicle with the aid of an assistant

n. Remove the hood release handle

o. Remove the steering column.

p. Remove the accelerator pedal assembly.

q. Remove the brake pedal assembly.

r. Remove the body control module bracket.

s. Instrument panel reinforcement assembly bolt

t. Instrument panel lower bracket bolt

u. Instrument panel reinforcement assembly

v. Remove the recirculation actuator wire harness connector.

w. Remove the air temperature actuator wire harness connector.

x. Remove the mode actuator wire harness connector.

y. Remove the blower motor wire harness connector.

z. Remove the blower motor resistor wire harness connector.

aa. Remove the left hand side window defogger outlet duct.

bb. Remove the HVAC module assembly mounting bolts from the instrument panel reinforcement.

cc. Remove the HVAC module assembly to dash panel bolts.

dd. Remove the HVAC module assembly.

ee. Remove the center floor air outlet duct screws.

ff. Remove the center floor air outlet duct.

gg. Drill out the heater core cover heat stakes.

hh. Remove the heater core cover screws.

ii. Remove the heater core cover.

jj. Remove the heater core.

To install:

3. Installation is the reverse of removal, please note the following:

a. Tighten the instrument panel lower bracket bolt to 80 inch lbs. (9 Nm).

b. Tighten the instrument panel reinforcement assembly bolts to 18 ft. lbs. (25 Nm).

c. Tighten the instrument panel assembly screws to 18 inch lbs. (2 Nm).

d. Uncap A/C components.

e. Install new sealing washers.

f. Install the TXV.

g. Install the TXV screws.

h. Install the liquid line to the TXV.

i. Install the suction line to the TXV.

j. Install the liquid line and suction line nut to the TXV. Tighten the nut to 15 ft. lbs. (20 Nm).

k. Install the liquid line to the dash clip.

l. Install the suction line to the dash clip.

m. Evacuate and charge the refrigerant system.

n. Leak test the fittings.

o. Install the surge tank to the surge tank bracket.

STEERING

ELECTRONIC STEERING GEAR

REMOVAL & INSTALLATION

2.4L Engine

See Figures 283 and 284.

✸✸ CAUTION

With the wheels of the vehicle facing straight ahead, secure the steering wheel utilizing a steering column anti-rotation pin, steering column lock, or a strap to prevent rotation. Locking of the steering column will prevent damage and a possible malfunction of the SIR system. The steering wheel must be secured in position before disconnecting the steering column, intermediate shaft or steering gear. After disconnecting these components, do not move the front tires and wheels. Failure to follow these procedures may cause improper alignment of some components during installation and result in possible damage to the SIR coil.

1. Turn the front wheels to the straight forward position and secure the steering wheel from moving.

2. Disengage the rack and pinion outer tie rod ends from the steering knuckles.

3. Separate the intermediate steering shaft from the steering gear.

4. Remove the transmission rear mount bolt.

5. Remove the steering gear bolts, nuts, and washers from the steering gear.

➡**The position of the steering gear will need to be manipulated to remove it through the left front wheel opening.**

6. Remove the steering gear through the left front wheel opening.

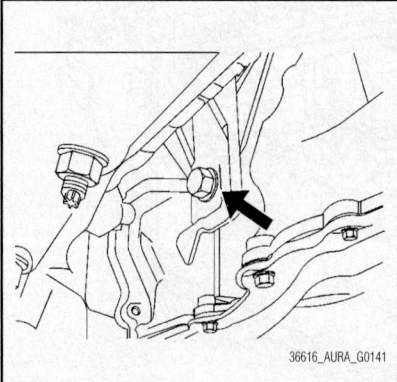

Fig. 283 Identifying the transmission rear mount bolt

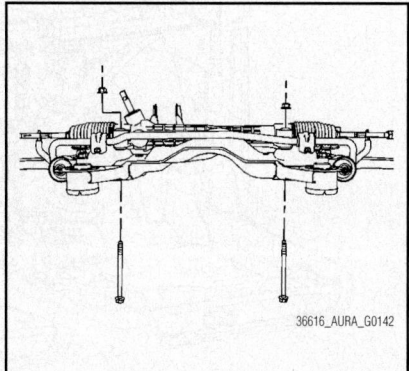

Fig. 284 Locating the steering gear bolts, nuts and washers on the steering gear

To install:

7. Install the steering gear through the left front wheel opening.

➡**Start all of the bolts and nuts by hand before finalizing any torques.**

8. Install the steering gear bolts, nuts, and washers to the steering gear. Tighten the bolts and nuts to 52 ft. lbs. (70 Nm) plus an additional 90 degrees.

9. Install the transmission rear mount bolt. Tighten to 66 ft. lbs. (90 Nm).

10. Connect the intermediate steering shaft to the steering column. Install a NEW bolt and tighten to 36 ft. lbs. (49 Nm) for models with electronic steering or 46 ft. lbs. (62 Nm) for models with hydraulic steering.

11. Connect the intermediate steering shaft to the steering gear. Tighten a new bolt to 36 ft. lbs. (49 Nm).

12. Install the rack and pinion outer tie rod ends to the steering knuckles.

13. Adjust the front toe.

POWER STEERING PUMP

REMOVAL & INSTALLATION

3.5L Engine

See Figures 285 and 286.

1. Remove the drive belt.

2. Use a power steering pulley remover/installer such as SA9162C to remove the power steering pump pulley.

3. Remove the drive belt idler pulley

4. Remove as much power steering fluid from the power steering fluid reservoir as possible.

5. Place drain pans under the vehicle as needed.

6. Remove the engine lift bracket bolt and bracket.

7. Remove the power steering gear inlet hose.

➡**Discard the and install a NEW power steering gear inlet hose O-ring seal prior to installation of the hose.**

8. Remove the power steering reservoir inlet hose.

9. Remove the power steering pump bolt and pump.

To install:

10. Installation is the reverse of removal:

a. Tighten the pump bolts to 18 ft. lbs. (25 Nm).

b. Install a new inlet hose O-ring seal

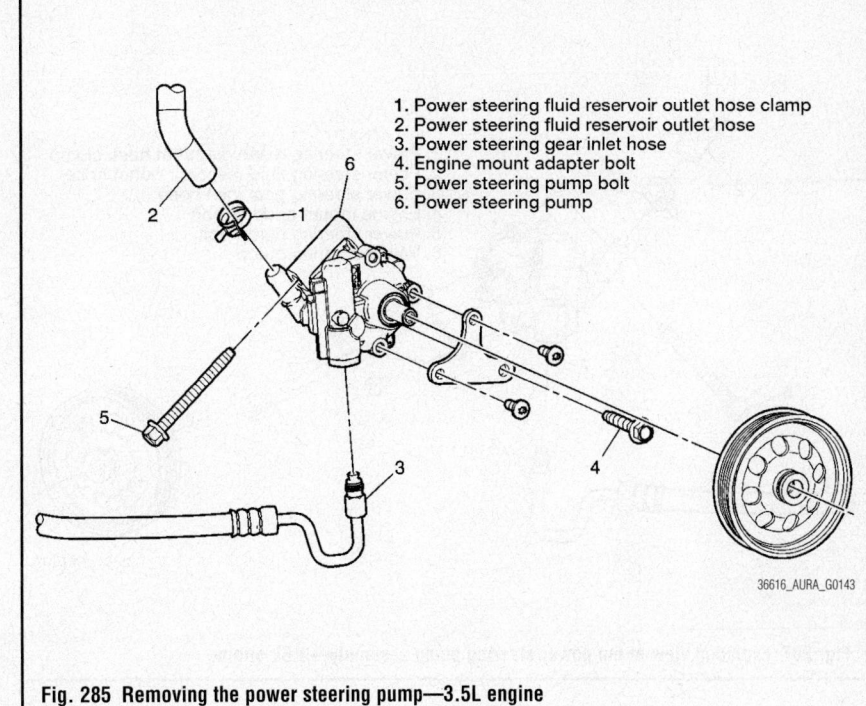

1. Power steering fluid reservoir outlet hose clamp
2. Power steering fluid reservoir outlet hose
3. Power steering gear inlet hose
4. Engine mount adapter bolt
5. Power steering pump bolt
6. Power steering pump

Fig. 285 Removing the power steering pump—3.5L engine

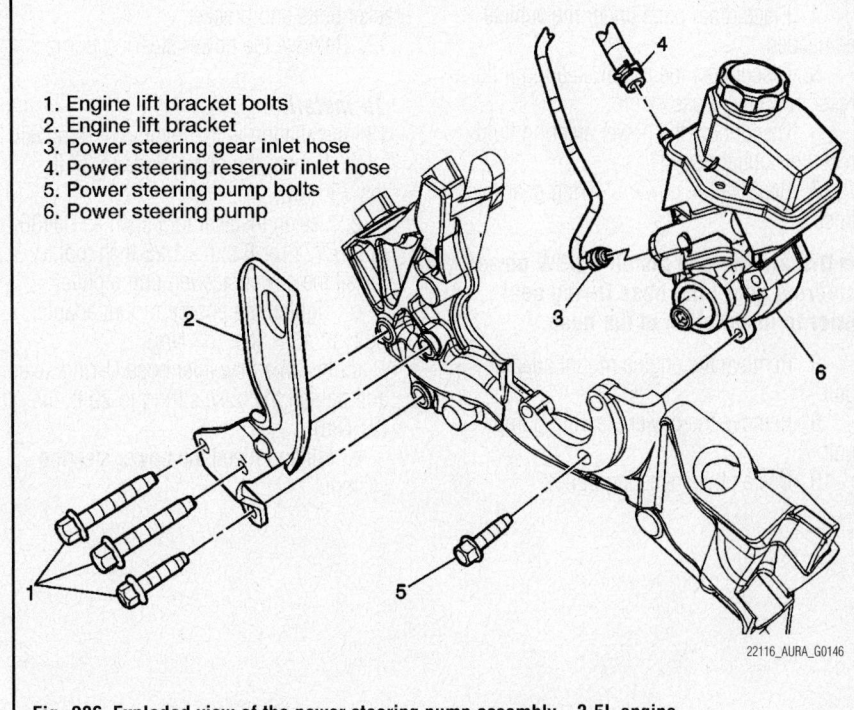

1. Engine lift bracket bolts
2. Engine lift bracket
3. Power steering gear inlet hose
4. Power steering reservoir inlet hose
5. Power steering pump bolts
6. Power steering pump

Fig. 286 Exploded view of the power steering pump assembly—3.5L engine

and tighten the hose sitting to 20 ft. lbs. (27 Nm).

c. Tighten the engine lift bracket bolts to 37 ft. lbs. (50 Nm).

d. Use a power steering pulley remover/installer such as SA9162C to install the power steering pump pulley.

e. Fill and bleed the power steering system.

3.6L Engine

See Figure 287.

1. Remove the drive belt.

2. Remove the right front tire and wheel assembly.

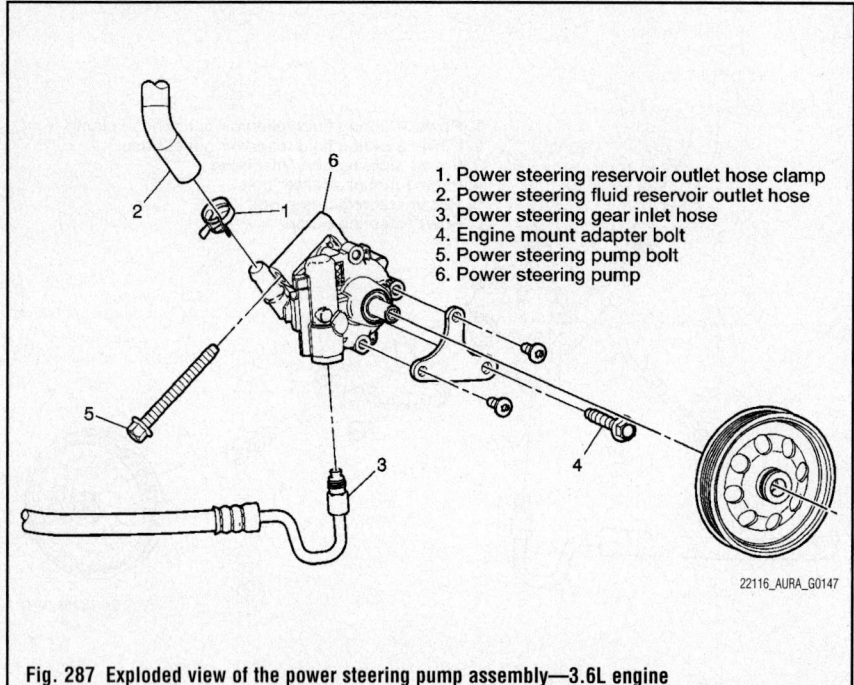

1. Power steering reservoir outlet hose clamp
2. Power steering fluid reservoir outlet hose
3. Power steering gear inlet hose
4. Engine mount adapter bolt
5. Power steering pump bolt
6. Power steering pump

22116_AURA_G0147

Fig. 287 Exploded view of the power steering pump assembly—3.6L engine

3. Remove as much power steering fluid from the remote power steering fluid reservoir as possible.

4. Place drain pans under the vehicle as needed.

5. Disconnect the power steering fluid reservoir outlet hose clamp.

6. Disconnect the power steering fluid reservoir outlet hose.

7. Remove the power steering gear inlet hose.

➡**Discard the and install a NEW power steering gear inlet hose O-ring seal prior to installation of the hose.**

8. Remove the engine mount adapter bolt.

9. Remove the power steering pump bolt

10. Use a power steering pulley remover/installer such as SA9162C to remove the power steering pump pulley.

11. Remove the engine mount adapter bracket bolts and bracket.

12. Remove the power steering pump.

To install:

13. Installation is the reverse of removal:
   a. Tighten the pump bolts to 37 ft. lbs. (50 Nm).
   b. Use an installer tool such as CJ138 or OTC7771or 8 mm x 1.25 inch tool to install the power steering pump pulley.
   c. Tighten the engine mount adapter bolts to 43 ft. lbs. (58 Nm).
   d. Install a new inlet hose O-ring seal and tighten the hose sitting to 20 ft. lbs. (27 Nm).
   e. Fill and bleed the power steering system.

BLEEDING

➡**Use clean, new power steering fluid only. Hoses touching the frame, body or engine may cause system noise. Verify that the hoses do not touch any other part of the vehicle. Loose connections may not leak, but could allow air into the steering system. Verify that all hoses connections are tight.**

➡**Power steering fluid level must be maintained throughout bleed procedure.**

1. Fill pump reservoir with fluid to minimum system level, FULL COLD level, or middle of hash mark on cap stick fluid level indicator.

➡**With hydro-boost only, the oil level will appear falsely high if the hydro-boost accumulator is not fully charged. Do not apply the brake pedal with the engine OFF. This will discharge the hydro-boost accumulator.**

2. If equipped with hydro-boost, fully charge the hydro-boost accumulator, start the engine, firmly apply the brake pedal 10-15 times and turn the engine off.

3. Raise the vehicle until the front wheels are off the ground.

4. Key on engine OFF, turn the steering wheel from stop to stop 12 times.

5. Vehicles equipped with hydro-boost systems or longer length power steering hoses may require turns up to 15 to 20 stop to stops.

6. Verify power steering fluid level per operating specification.

7. Start the engine. Rotate steering wheel from left to right. Check for sign of cavitation or fluid aeration (pump noise/whining).

8. Verify the fluid level. Repeat the bleed procedure, if necessary.

SUSPENSION　　　　　　　　　　　　　**FRONT SUSPENSION**

LOWER BALL JOINT

REMOVAL & INSTALLATION

The ball joint is an integral part of the control arm, if defective replace the control arm.

LOWER CONTROL ARM

REMOVAL & INSTALLATION

See Figures 288 through 290.

1. Raise and support the vehicle.
2. Remove the tire and wheel.
3. Remove the front lower control arm busing to frame bolt and nut.
4. Remove the rear lower control arm busing to frame bolts and nuts.
5. Prior to removal, note the orientation of the lower control arm ball stud to steering knuckle pinch bolt and remove the pinch bolt and discard.
6. Separate the ball stud from the steering knuckle.

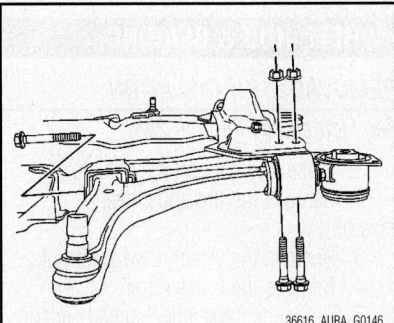

Fig. 288 Locating the lower control arm bushing to frame bolts and nuts

7. Remove the control arm from the vehicle.
8. Remove the rear lower control arm bushing.

To install:

9. Install the rear lower control arm bushing.
10. Using LOCTITE® 234 or equivalent on the bolt threads, install the lower control arm to busing bolt.
11. Hold the rear busing inner sleeve when tightening the rear bushings to the control arm bolt. Tighten the bolt to 32 ft. lbs. (44Nm).
12. Position the lower control arm to the frame assembly and steering knuckle.
13. Note the previous orientation and install the new ball stud to the steering knuckle pinch bolt. Hand tighten only.
14. Install the front busing to frame bolt and nut. Hand tighten only.
15. Install the rear busing to frame bolts and nuts.

   a. Tighten the ball stud to steering knuckle pinch nut to 37 ft. lbs. (50 Nm). Reverse the nut¾ of a turn. Tighten to 37 ft. lbs. (50 Nm). Rotate an additional 30 degrees.

   b. Tighten the nuts and the bolts with the front suspension loaded by using the proper jackstand.

   c. Tighten the front bushing to frame bolt to 37 ft. lbs. (50 Nm). Rotate an additional 90 degrees.

   d. Tighten the rear bushing to frame nuts to 37 ft. lbs. (50 Nm). Rotate an additional 90 degrees.

16. Install the tire and wheel.
17. Lower the vehicle.

STABILIZER BAR

REMOVAL & INSTALLATION

See Figure 291.

1. Raise and support the vehicle.
2. Remove the front tire and wheel assemblies.
3. Disconnect the stabilizer links from the stabilizer shaft.
4. Using a suitable jack stand, support the rear of the frame assembly.
5. Remove the frame support to body bolts.
6. Remove the rear frame assembly mounting bolts.
7. Lower the rear of the cradle in order to gain clearance to the stabilizer shaft.
8. Remove the stabilizer bar clamps and insulators.
9. Remove the stabilizer shaft through the opening between the frame and body.

To install:

10. Position the stabilizer shaft to the frame.
11. Install the stabilizer bar clamps and insulators. Tighten the clamps and bolts to 18 ft. lbs. (25 Nm).
12. Raise the rear of the cradle and install the cradle bolts. Tighten the rear frame bolts. Tighten to 74 ft. lbs. (100 Nm).
13. Remove the jack stand.
14. Connect the stabilizer link to the stabilizer bar. Tighten the link nuts to 48 ft. lbs. (65 Nm).
15. Install the front tire and wheel assemblies.
16. Lower the vehicle.

Fig. 289 Removing the pinch bolt

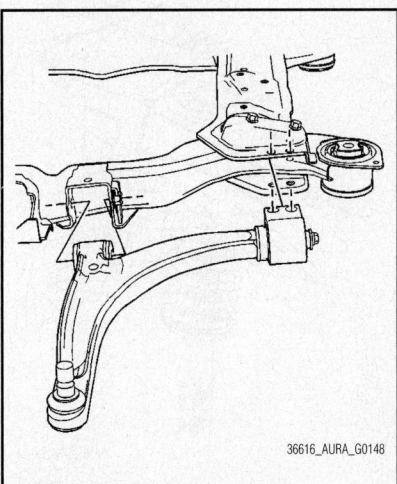

Fig. 290 Removing the control arm

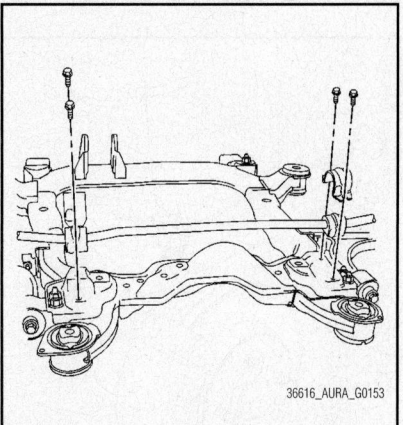

Fig. 291 Removing the stabilizer bar clamps and insulators

STEERING KNUCKLE

REMOVAL & INSTALLATION

See Figures 292 and 293.

1. Raise and support the vehicle.
2. Remove the wheel bearing/hub.
3. Remove the outer tie rod to knuckle nut.
4. Remove the lower control arm.
5. Remove the strut to steering knuckle nuts and bolts.
6. Remove the steering knuckle from the vehicle.

To install:

7. Install the steering knuckle to the strut assembly and if applicable the ABS harness bracket. Tighten the bolts and nuts to 89 ft. lbs. (120 Nm).
8. Guide the axle through the steering knuckle.
9. Install the lower control arm.
10. Install the outer tie rod to the steering knuckle. Tighten the nut to 15 ft. lbs. (20 Nm). Rotate the nut an additional 180 degrees. Verify the torque to 37 ft. lbs. (50 Nm).
11. Install the wheel bearing, brake rotor, brake caliper and front wheels.

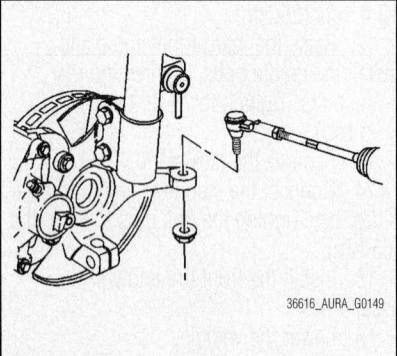

Fig. 292 Removing the lower control arm

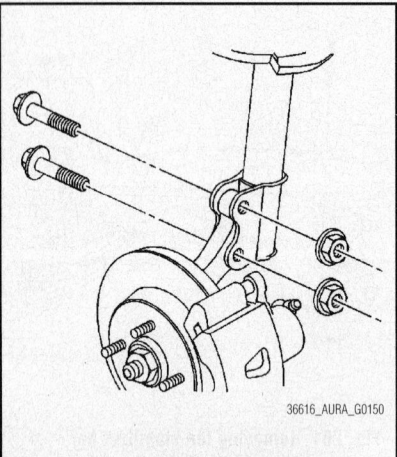

Fig. 293 Removing the steering knuckle

12. Lower the vehicle.
13. Road test the vehicle in order to verify alignment. If a lead or pull is present realign.

STRUT

REMOVAL & INSTALLATION

See Figures 294 and 295.

1. Raise and support the vehicle.
2. Remove the front wheel.
3. Disconnect the stabilizer link from the strut.
4. Remove the strut to steering knuckle nuts.
5. If applicable, reposition the wheel speed sensor/ABS harness and bracket.
6. Remove the strut to steering knuckle bolts.
7. Remove the upper strut cap to body nuts.

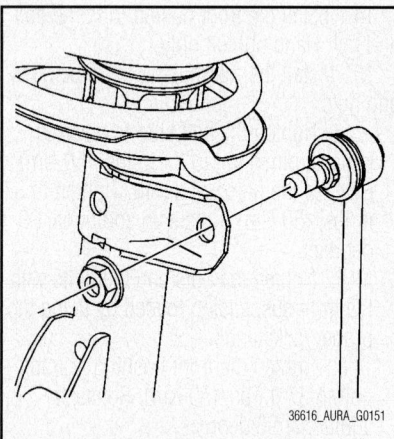

Fig. 294 Disconnecting the stabilizer link from the strut

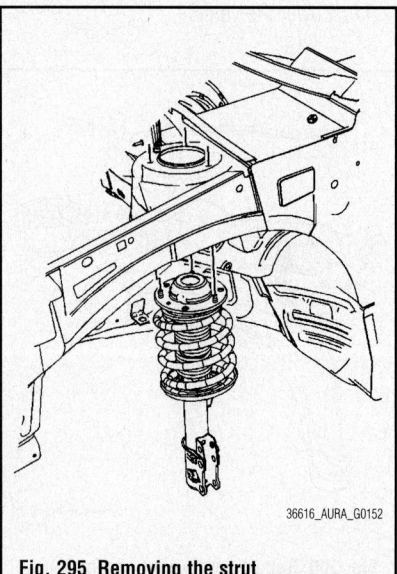

Fig. 295 Removing the strut

➡ **In order to prevent damage to the CV joint boot, place a shop towel over the CV joint.**

8. Remove the strut from the vehicle.

To install:

➡ **It may be necessary to rotate the upper strut mount cover guide to match the hole in the strut tower.**

9. Position the strut to the vehicles strut tower, using the alignment pin as a guide.
10. Install the upper strut cap to body nuts. Tighten to 18 ft. lbs. (25 Nm).
11. Install the strut to steering knuckle bolts leaving the nuts off.
12. If applicable, place the wheel speed sensor harness and bracket to the bolt end.
13. Install the strut to steering knuckle nuts and tighten to 89 ft. lbs. (120 Nm).
14. Connect the stabilizer link to the strut. Tighten to 48 ft. lbs. (65 Nm).
15. Install the front wheel.
16. Lower the vehicle.
17. Road test the vehicle and check the alignment.

WHEEL HUB & BEARING

REMOVAL & INSTALLATION

See Figures 296 through 298.

1. Raise and support the vehicle.
2. Remove the tire and wheel assembly.
3. Remove the wheel drive shaft nut.
4. Remove the brake rotor.
5. Disconnect the wheel speed sensor electrical connector.
6. Remove the wheel speed sensor electrical connector from the mounting bracket by depressing the locking tabs.

➡ **Avoid tool contact to the outer CV boot seal when removing the wheel**

Fig. 296 Removing the drive shaft nut

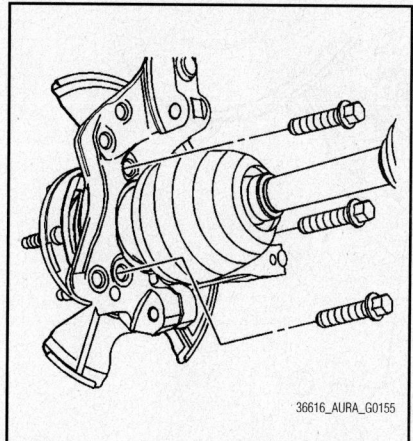

Fig. 297 Identifying the hub and bearing assembly bolts

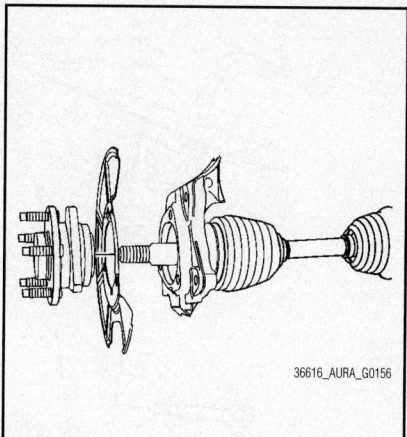

Fig. 298 Removing the hub and bearing from the steering knuckle

bearing mounting bolts. Failure to observe this notice may result in damage to the CV boot.

7. Remove the 3 hub and bearing assembly bolts.

8. Install the wheel hub remover to the hub and bearing assembly in order to remove the hub and bearing assembly from the wheel drive shaft.

9. Remove the hub and bearing assembly from the steering knuckle.

To install:

10. Install the hub and bearing assembly to the steering knuckle.

➡ This is a self-retaining fastener joint that does not require thread locking compounds. Do not attempt to clean the threads with a standard tap. If a standard tap is used, damage to the joint threads will occur.

➡ Use the correct fastener in the correct location. Replacement fasteners must be the correct part number for that application. Fasteners requiring replacement or fasteners requiring the use of thread locking compound or sealant are identified in the service procedure. Do not use paints, lubri-

cants, or corrosion inhibitors on fasteners or fastener joint surfaces unless specified. These coatings affect fastener torque and joint clamping force and may damage the fastener. Use the correct tightening sequence and specifications when installing fasteners in order to avoid damage to parts and systems.

11. Install the 3 hub and bearing assembly bolts. Tighten the hub and bearing assembly bolts to 85 ft. lbs. (115 Nm).

12. Install the wheel speed sensor connector into the bracket until the locking tab clicks into place.

13. Connect the electrical connector to the wheel speed sensor.

14. Install the axle nut to the wheel drive shaft, hand tighten the wheel drive shaft nut.

15. Install the brake rotor.

16. Install the wheel drive shaft nut to the wheel drive shaft.

17. Use a screw driver or similar tool to stop the rotation of the brake rotor. Tighten the wheel drive shaft nut 159 ft. lb. (215 Nm).

18. Install the tire and wheel assemblies.

ADJUSTMENT

The wheel bearing are sealed at the factory and do not require any adjustment or maintenance.

SUSPENSION

REAR SUSPENSION

COIL SPRING

REMOVAL & INSTALLATION

See Figures 299 and 300.

1. Raise and support the vehicle.

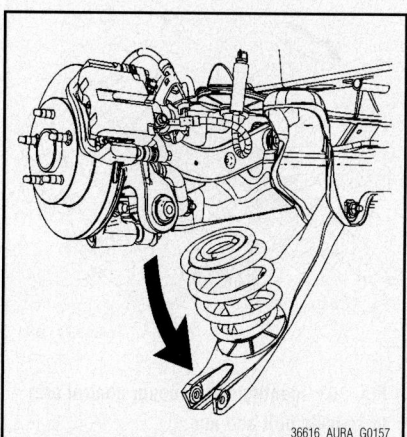

Fig. 299 Lowering the lower control arm with the coil spring

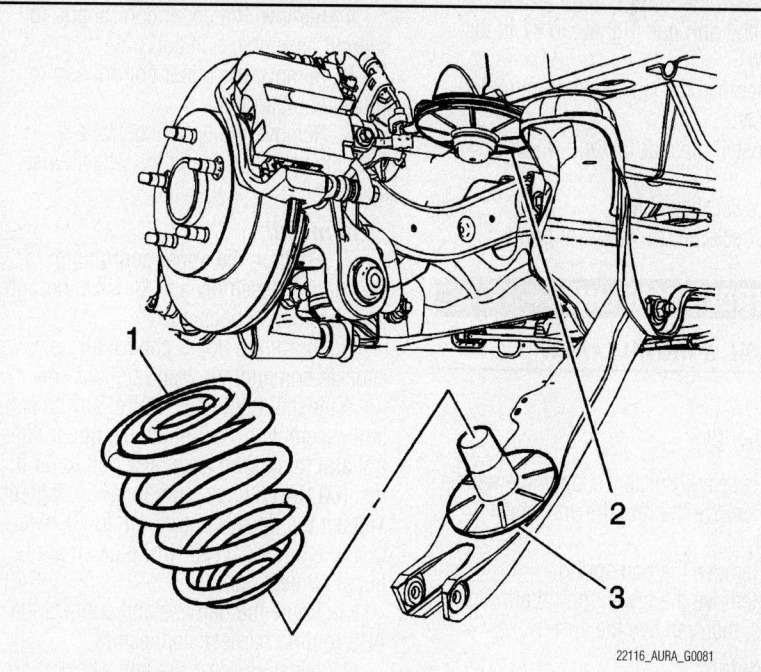

Fig. 300 Rear spring mounting (1)–Aura

2. Remove the rear tire and wheel assembly.

3. Using a suitable jack stand, support the lower control arm.

4. Remove the lower control arm to knuckle bolt and nut.

⁂ CAUTION

To prevent personal injury and/or component damage, use the proper tools to support the lower control arm when removing the coil spring. The coil spring is under extreme pressure and can become a projectile should the spring separate from the lower control arm before all of the tension is relieved.

5. Use the jackstand to swing the lower control arm downward with the coil spring attached.

6. Remove the coil spring from the lower control arm.

7. Inspect the coil spring upper and lower insulators for damage, replace as necessary.

To install:

➡ **Be sure that the coil spring upper and lower insulators are properly seated prior to installation of the coil spring.**

8. Position the coil spring onto the lower control arm.

9. Use the jack stand to raise the lower control arm upward into position.

10. Install the lower control arm to knuckle bolt and nut. Tighten to 81 ft. lbs. (110 Nm).

11. Remove the jack stand from under the vehicle.

12. Install the rear tire and wheel assembly.

13. Lower the vehicle.

14. Check the rear wheel alignment.

CONTROL ARMS/LINKS

REMOVAL & INSTALLATION

Lower

See Figure 301.

1. Raise and suitably support the vehicle.

2. Remove the rear tire and wheel assembly.

3. Remove the coil spring.

4. Remove the lower control arm bolts and nuts, then remove the arm.

To install:

5. Installation is the reverse of removal. Tighten the bolt/nut to 81 ft. lbs. (110 Nm).

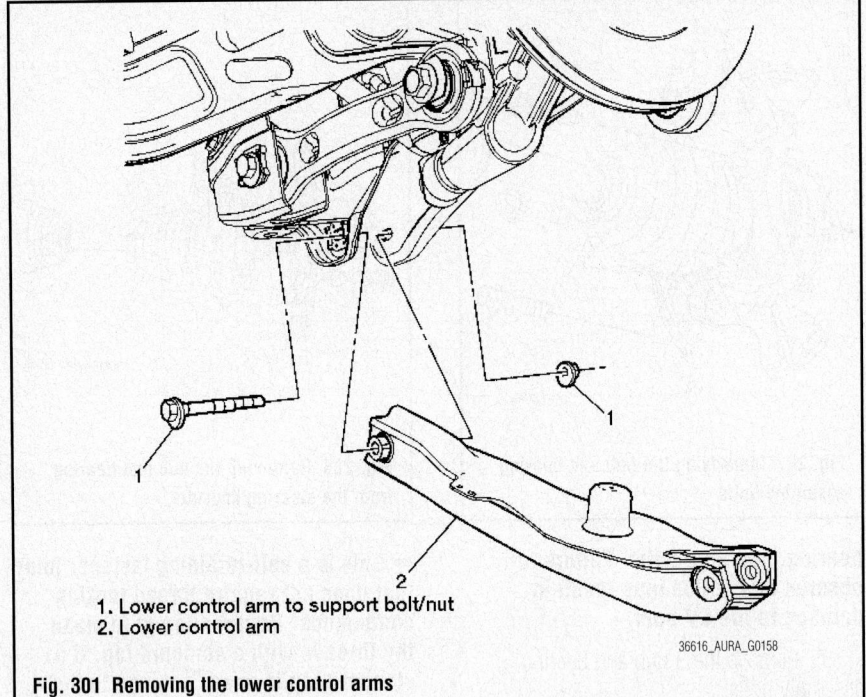

1. Lower control arm to support bolt/nut
2. Lower control arm

36616_AURA_G0158

Fig. 301 Removing the lower control arms

6. Inspect the wheel alignment and adjust as needed.

Upper

See Figures 302 and 303.

1. Raise and support the vehicle.

2. Remove the rear tire and wheel assembly.

3. Disconnect the ABS routing harness connectors and position the harness aside.

4. Remove the upper control arm to support assembly bolt and nut.

5. Remove the upper control arm to knuckle bolt and nut.

6. Remove the upper control arm from the vehicle through the wheelhouse opening.

To install:

7. Position the upper control arm to the support assembly and knuckle through the wheelhouse opening.

8. Install the upper control arm o knuckle bolt and nut. Hand tighten only.

9. Install the upper control arm to support assembly bolt. Tighten the upper control arm to support assembly bolt to 44 ft. lbs. (60 Nm) plus an additional 60 degrees. Tighten the upper control arm to knuckle bolt to 81 ft. lbs. (110 Nm) plus an additional 70 degrees.

10. Route the harness and connect the ABS routing harness connectors.

11. Install the rear tire and wheel assembly.

12. Lower the vehicle.

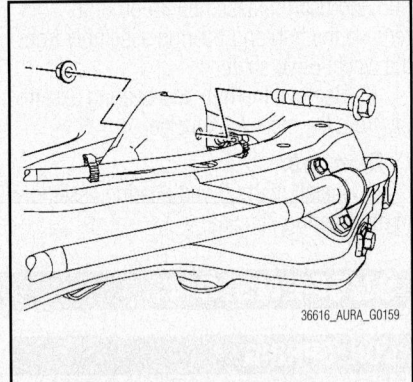

36616_AURA_G0159

Fig. 302 Identifying the upper control arm to support assembly bolt and nut

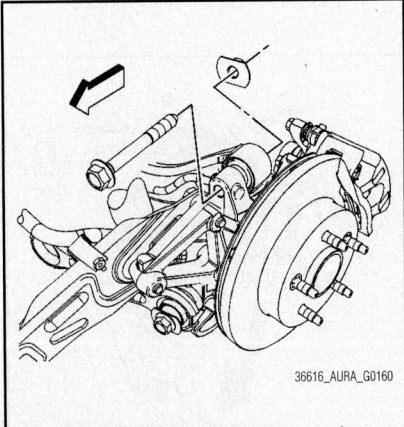

36616_AURA_G0160

Fig. 303 Identifying the upper control arm to knuckle bolt and nut

Trailing Arms

See Figures 304 through 306.

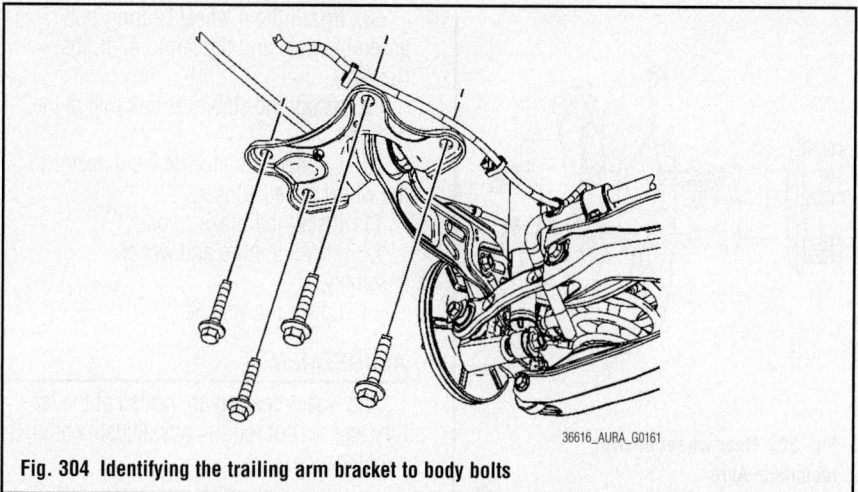

Fig. 304 Identifying the trailing arm bracket to body bolts

1. Raise and support the vehicle.
2. Remove the rear tire and wheel assembly.
3. Remove the 4 trailing arm bracket to body bolts.

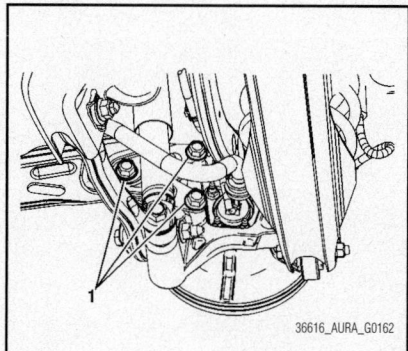

Fig. 305 Locating the trailing arm to knuckle bolts (1)

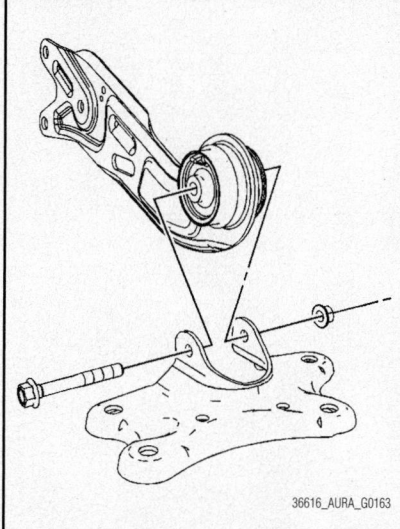

Fig. 306 Removing the trailing arm to bracket bolt and nut

4. Remove the rear parking brake cable from the trailing arm.
5. Remove the 3 trailing arm to knuckle through bolts.
6. Disconnect the park brake cable routing clip from the trailing arm bracket.
7. Remove the trailing arm and bracket as an assembly from the vehicle.
8. Place the trailing arm and bracket as an assembly on a work bench.
9. Remove the trailing arm to bracket bolt and nut.
10. Separate the trailing arm bracket from the trailing arm.

To install:

11. Position the trailing arm to the bracket, install the bolt and nut. Tighten the trailing arm to bracket through bolt and nut to 44 ft. lbs. (60 Nm) plus an additional 60 degrees.
12. Position the trailing arm to the vehicle.
13. Connect the park brake cable routing clip to the trailing arm bracket.
14. Install the 3 trailing arm to knuckle bolts. Tighten to 133 ft. lbs. (180 Nm).
15. Install the rear parking brake cable routing bolt to the trailing arm. Tighten to 89 inch lbs. (10 Nm).
16. Install the trailing arm bracket to body bolts. Tighten to 66 ft. lbs. (90 Nm) plus an additional 30 degrees and then a further 15 degrees.
17. Install the rear tire and wheel assembly.
18. Lower the vehicle.

SHOCK ABSORBER

REMOVAL & INSTALLATION
See Figures 307 and 308.

1. Raise and support the vehicle.
2. Remove the tire and wheel.

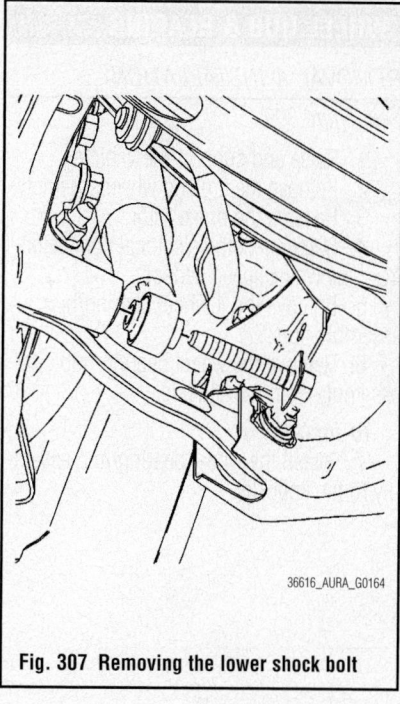

Fig. 307 Removing the lower shock bolt

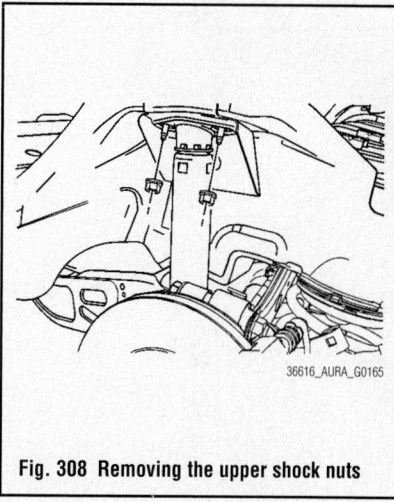

Fig. 308 Removing the upper shock nuts

3. Using a suitable jack stand, raise the rear knuckle to remove spring tension.
4. Remove the lower shock bolt.
5. Remove the upper shock nuts.
6. Remove the shock from the vehicle.

To install:

7. Place the shock in the vehicle.
8. Install the shock absorber to body nuts. Tighten to 18 ft. lbs. (25 Nm).
9. Install the shock absorber to knuckle bolt. Tighten to 133 ft. lbs. (180 Nm).
10. Remove the jack stand from the rear knuckle.
11. Install the tire and wheel.
12. Lower the vehicle.

WHEEL HUB & BEARING

REMOVAL & INSTALLATION

See Figure 309.

1. Raise and support the vehicle.
2. Remove the tire and wheel assembly.
3. Remove the brake rotor.
4. Disconnect the electrical connector from the wheel speed sensor.
5. Remove the 4 wheel bearing/hub assembly nuts.
6. Remove the wheel bearing/hub assembly from the knuckle.

To install:

7. Install the wheel bearing/hub assembly to the knuckle.

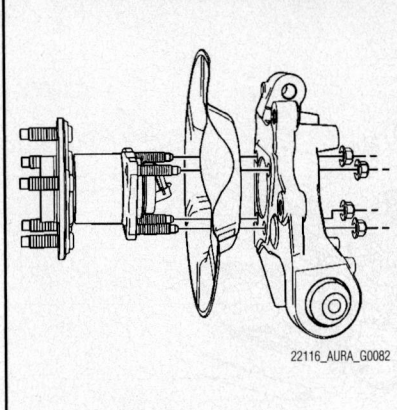

22116_AURA_G0082

Fig. 309 Rear wheel bearing mounting–Aura

8. Install the 4 wheel bearing/hub assembly nuts and tighten to 47 ft. lbs. (63 Nm).
9. Install the stabilizer link bolt at the knuckle.
10. Connect the electrical connector to the wheel speed sensor.
11. Install the brake rotor.
12. Install the tire and wheel assembly.
13. Lower the vehicle.

ADJUSTMENT

The wheel bearing are sealed at the factory and do not require any adjustment or maintenance.

SATURN

5

Aura Hybrid

SPECIFICATIONS AND MAINTENANCE CHARTS

ENGINE AND VEHICLE IDENTIFICATION

		Engine					Model Year	
Code ①	Liters (cc)	Cu. In.	Cyl.	Fuel Sys.	Engine Type	Eng. Mfg.	Code ②	Year
5	2.4 (2398)	145	4	MFI/Hybrid	NA	Saturn	9	2009

① 8th digit of VIN

② 10th digit of VIN

36616_AURH_C0001

GENERAL ENGINE SPECIFICATIONS

Year	Model	Engine Displacement Liters (cc)	Engine ID/VIN	Fuel System Type	Net Horsepower @ rpm	Net Torque @ rpm (ft. lbs.)	Bore x Stroke (in.)	Com- pression Ratio	Oil Pressure @ rpm
2009	Aura	2.4 (2398)	NA	MFI/Hybrid	164@6400	159@5000	3.47x3.86	10.0:1	50-80@1000

MFI: Multi-port Fuel Injection

36616_AURH_C0002

ENGINE TUNE-UP SPECIFICATIONS

Year	Engine Displacement Liters	Engine ID/VIN	Spark Plug Gap (in.)	Ignition Timing (deg.) MT	Ignition Timing (deg.) AT	Fuel Pump (psi) ①	Idle Speed (rpm) MT ②	Idle Speed (rpm) AT ②	Valve Clearance In.	Valve Clearance Ex.
2009	2.4	5	0.037-0.043	③	③	50-60	④	④	HYD	HYD

HYD: Hydraulic

① Pressure measured at idle

② Idle speed measured with manual transmission in Neutral; automatic transmission in D (drive)

③ Engines equipped with Distributorless Ignition System (DIS). Ignition timing is not adjustable

④ Refer to the Vehicle Emission Control Information label

36616_AURH_C0003

CAPACITIES

Year	Model	Engine Displacement Liters	Engine ID/VIN	Engine Oil with Filter (qts.)	Transaxle (qts.)		Fuel Tank (gal.)	Cooling System (gts.)
					Manual	Auto.		
2009	Aura	2.4	5	5.0	—	7.0	16.3	8.1

NOTE: All capacities are approximate. Add fluid gradually and ensure a proper fluid level is obtained.

36616_AURH_C0004

FLUID SPECIFICATIONS

Year	Model	Engine Displacement Liters (VIN)	Engine Oil	Auto. Trans.	Drive Axle	Power Steering Fluid	Brake Master Cylinder
2009	Aura	2.4 (5)	5W-30	①	—	Power Steering Fluid	DOT 3

DOT: Department Of Transpotation

① DEXRON®-VI Automatic Transmission Fluid

36616_AURH_C0011

VALVE SPECIFICATIONS

Year	Engine Displ. Liters	Engine ID/VIN	Seat Angle (deg.)	Face Angle (deg.)	Spring Test Pressure (lbs. @ in.)	Spring Free- Length (in.)	Stem-to-Guide Clearance (in.)		Stem Diameter (in.)	
							Intake	Exhaust	Intake	Exhaust
2009	2.4	5	46	45	①	NA	0.0012	0.0020	0.2344	0.2337
					②		0.0022	0.0026	0.2355	0.2343

NA: Not available

① Valve spring load closed: 252-575 N @ 22.5mm

② Valve spring load open: 245-271 N @32mm

36616_AURH_C0006

CAMSHAFT AND BEARING SPECIFICATIONS CHART

All measurements are given in inches.

Year	Engine Displacement Liters	Engine ID/VIN	Journal Dia.	Journal dia. Front	Shaft End-play	Thrust Surface	Journal Bore	Lobe Height Intake	Lobe Height Exhaust
2009	2.4	5	1.0604-1.0614	NA	0.0016-0.0057	0.8268-0.8252	NA	NA	NA

NA: Not Available

36616_AURH_C0007

CRANKSHAFT AND CONNECTING ROD SPECIFICATIONS

All measurements are given in inches.

Year	Engine Displacement Liters	Engine ID/VIN	Crankshaft Main Brg. Journal Dia.	Main Brg. Oil Clearance	Shaft End-play	Thrust on No.	Connecting Rod Journal Diameter	Oil Clearance	Side Clearance
2009	2.4	5	2.2045-2.2050	0.0012 0.0026	0.0012-0.0150	2	2.0519-2.0525	0.0011-0.0029	0.0028-0.0146

NA: Not available

36616_AURH_C0005

PISTON AND RING SPECIFICATIONS

All measurements are given in inches.

Year	Engine Displacement Liters	Engine ID/VIN	Piston Clearance	Ring Gap Top Compression	Ring Gap Bottom Compression	Oil Control	Ring Side Clearance Top Compression	Ring Side Clearance Bottom Compression
2009	2.4	5	0.0004-0.0016	0.006-0.012	0.0080 0.0180	0.0060 0.0020	0.0015-0.0031	0.0012-0.0030

36616_AURH_C0008

TORQUE SPECIFICATIONS
All readings in ft. lbs.

Year	Engine Displacement Liters	Engine ID/VIN	Cylinder Head Bolts	Main Bearing Bolts	Rod Bearing Bolts	Crankshaft Balancer Bolts	Flywheel Bolts	Manifold		Spark Plugs	Oil Pan Drain Plug
								Intake	Exhaust		
2009	2.4	5	①	②	③	④	⑤	⑥	⑦	15	18

① Step 1: 22 ft. lbs.

   Step 2: 155 degrees

② 15 ft. lbs. Plus 70 degrees

③ 18 ft. lbs. Plus 100 degrees

④ 74 ft. lbs. Plus 125 degrees

⑤ Flexplate specification: 39 ft. lbs. Plus 25 degrees

⑥ Intake manifold to head nut and bolt: 89 inch lbs.

   Intake manifold to head stud: 53 inch lbs.

⑦ Exhaust manifold to head nut: 124 inch lbs.

   Exhaust manifold to head stud: 89 inch lbs.

36616_AURH_C0009

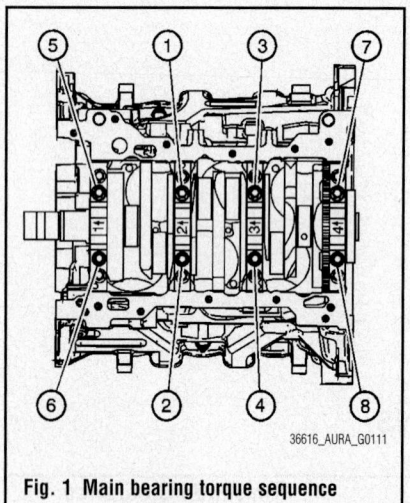

36616_AURA_G0111

Fig. 1 Main bearing torque sequence

WHEEL ALIGNMENT

Year	Model		Caster		Camber		Toe-in (in.)
			Range (+/-Deg.)	Preferred Setting (Deg.)	Range (+/-Deg.)	Preferred Setting (Deg.)	
2009	Aura	F	0.75	2.90	0.75	①	0.20 +/- 0.20
		R	—	—	0.60	0.80	0.20 +/- 0.20

① Left: 1.00 degrees

  Right: 0.70 degrees

36616_AURH_C0010

TIRE, WHEEL AND BALL JOINT SPECIFICATIONS

Year	Model	OEM Tires		Tire Pressures (psi)		Wheel Size	Ball Joint Inspection	Lug Nut (ft. lbs.)
		Standard	Optional	Front	Rear			
2009	Aura	①	①	①	①	①	①	100

OEM: Original Equipment Manufacturer

PSI: Pounds Per Square Inch

STD: Standard

OPT: Optional

NS: Not specified by manufacturer

① For tire size and information, check the label located inside the glove compartment door.

36616_AURH_C0012

BRAKE SPECIFICATIONS

All measurements in inches unless noted

Year	Model		Brake Disc			Brake Drum Diameter			Minimum Lining Thickness	Brake Caliper	
			Original Thickness	Minimum Thickness	Maximum Runout	Original Inside Diameter	Max. Wear Limit	Maximum Machine Diameter		Bracket Bolt (ft. lbs.)	Mounting Bolt (ft. lbs.)
2009	Aura	F	1.023	0.898	0.002	—	—	—	NA	96	26
		R	0.551	0.465	0.002	—	—	—	NA	96	26

F: Front

R: Rear

36616_AURH_C0013

MAINTENANCE I AND II SERVICE SCHEDULES
2009 Saturn Aura Hybrid

When the CHANGE ENGINE OIL light appears, certain services and inspections are required.

Required services are described as Maintenance I and Maintenance II.

The first service on a vehicle should be Maintenance I, and the second service should be Maintenance II.

Alternate between the 2 thereafter. However, in some cases, Maintenance II may be required more often.

Maintenance I: Use Maintenance I if the CHANGE ENGINE OIL light comes on within 10 months since vehicle was purchased or, if Maintenance II was performed.

Maintenance II: Use Maintenance II if the previous service performed was Maintenance I. Always use Maintenance II whenever the CHANGE ENGINE OIL light comes on 10 months or more since the last service, or, if the CHANGE ENGINE OIL light has not come on at all for one year.

Service	I	II
Change the engine oil and filter. Reset the oil life system.	✓	✓
Visually inspect the vehicle for leaks or damage. A fluid loss in the vehicle system could indicate a problem. Inspected, repair and add fluid to the system if necessary.	✓	✓
Inspect the engine air cleaner filter. If necessary, replace the filter.		✓
Rotate the tires. Inspect the tire inflation pressures and the tire wear.	✓	✓
Visually inspect the brake lines and hoses for proper hook-up, binding, leaks, cracks, chafing, etc. Inspect the disc brake pads for wear and the rotors for surface condition. Inspect the drum brake linings for wear or cracks. Inspect other brake parts, including drums, wheel cylinders, calipers, parking brake, etc. Inspect the parking brake adjustment.	✓	✓
Inspect the engine coolant and the windshield washer fluid levels. Add fluid as needed.	✓	✓
Perform any needed additional services.	✓	✓
Inspect the suspension and steering components. Inspect the front and rear suspension and the steering system for damaged, loose or missing parts, or signs of wear. Inspect the power steering lines and the hoses for proper hook-up, binding, leaks, cracks, chafing, etc.	--	✓
Visually inspect the coolant hoses and replace the hoses if they are cracked, swollen or deteriorated. Inspect all pipes, fittings and clamps; replace with GM parts as needed. To help ensure proper operation, a pressure test of the cooling system and pressure cap and cleaning the outside of the radiator and air conditioning condenser is recommended at least once a year.	--	✓
Inspect the wiper blades for wear or cracking. Clean the windshield and wiper blades, if contaminated. Replace wiper blades that are worn or damaged.	--	✓
Inspect the restraint system components. Ensure the safety belt reminder light and all the belts, buckles, latch plates, retractors and anchorages are working properly. Look for any other loose or damaged safety belt system parts. If you see anything that might keep a safety belt system from working correctly, repair or replaced the damaged part. Replace torn or frayed safety belts, refer to Operational and Functional Checks in Seat Belts. Inspect for any opened or broken air bag coverings, and repair or replace as needed. The air bag system does require regular maintenance.	--	✓
Lubricate the body components. Lubricate all key lock cylinders, hood latch assemblies, secondary latches, pivots, spring anchor and release pawl, hood and door hinges, rear folding seats and liftgate hinges. Frequent lubrication may be required when exposed to a corrosive environment, refer to Fluid and Lubricant Recommendations . Applying dielectric silicone grease GM P/N 12345579 (Canadian P/N 1974984) or equivalent on the weatherstrips with a clean cloth.	--	✓
Replace the passenger compartment air filter.	--	✓
Inspect the throttle system. Inspect the throttle system for interference or binding and for damaged or missing parts. Replace the parts as needed. Replace any components that have high effort or excessive wear. Do not lubricate the accelerator or the cruise control cables.	--	✓

To reset the CHANGE ENGINE OIL LIGHT:

1. Turn the ignition switch to RUN with the engine OFF.

2. Fully press and release the accelerator pedal three times within five seconds.

If the messafe is not displayed, the system is reset.

If the CHANGE ENGINE OIL SOON message comes back on when the vehicle is started, the system has not reset; repeat.

ADDITIONAL MAINTENANCE SERVICES
2009 Saturn Aura Hybrid

TO BE SERVICED	TYPE OF SERVICE	VEHICLE MILEAGE INTERVAL (x1000)					
		25	50	75	100	125	150
Air cleaner filter	R		✓		✓		✓
Accessory drive belt	I						✓
Auto. Trans. Fluid ①	R		✓		✓		✓
Cooling system hoses and clamps	S/I						✓
Engine coolant ②	R						✓
Fuel system	I	✓	✓	✓	✓	✓	✓
Exhaust system & heat shields	S/I	✓	✓	✓	✓	✓	✓
Spark plugs	R				✓		

R: Replace   S/I: Inspect and service, if necessary

① Replace if any of the following conditions are met:

Heavy city traffic where the outside temperature regularly reaches 32°C (90°F) or higher

Hilly or mountainous terrain

Frequent trailer towing

Taxi, police or delivery service

Otherwise, change every 100,000 miles

② Drain, flush, and refill cooling system. This service should be performed by the dealer/retailer.

Clean radiator, condenser, pressure cap, and filler neck. Pressure test the cooling system and pressure cap.

36616_AURH_C0015

PRECAUTIONS

Before servicing any vehicle, please be sure to read all of the following precautions, which deal with personal safety, prevention of component damage, and important points to take into consideration when servicing a motor vehicle:

• Never open, service or drain the radiator or cooling system when the engine is hot; serious burns can occur from the steam and hot coolant.

• Observe all applicable safety precautions when working around fuel. Whenever servicing the fuel system, always work in a well-ventilated area. Do not allow fuel spray or vapors to come in contact with a spark, open flame, or excessive heat (a hot drop light, for example). Keep a dry chemical fire extinguisher near the work area. Always keep fuel in a container specifically designed for fuel storage; also, always properly seal fuel containers to avoid the possibility of fire or explosion. Refer to the additional fuel system precautions later in this section.

• Fuel injection systems often remain pressurized, even after the engine has been turned **OFF**. The fuel system pressure must be relieved before disconnecting any fuel lines. Failure to do so may result in fire and/or personal injury.

• Brake fluid often contains polyglycol ethers and polyglycols. Avoid contact with the eyes and wash your hands thoroughly after handling brake fluid. If you do get brake fluid in your eyes, flush your eyes with clean, running water for 15 minutes. If eye irritation persists, or if you have taken brake fluid internally, IMMEDIATELY seek medical assistance.

• The EPA warns that prolonged contact with used engine oil may cause a number of skin disorders, including cancer. You should make every effort to minimize your exposure to used engine oil. Protective gloves should be worn when changing oil. Wash your hands and any other exposed skin areas as soon as possible after exposure to used engine oil. Soap and water, or waterless hand cleaner should be used.

• All new vehicles are now equipped with an air bag system, often referred to as a Supplemental Restraint System (SRS) or Supplemental Inflatable Restraint (SIR) system. The system must be disabled before performing service on or around system components, steering column, instrument panel components, wiring and sensors. Failure to follow safety and disabling procedures could result in accidental air bag deployment, possible personal injury and unnecessary system repairs.

• Always wear safety goggles when working with, or around, the air bag system. When carrying a non-deployed air bag, be sure the bag and trim cover are pointed away from your body. When placing a non-deployed air bag on a work surface, always face the bag and trim cover upward, away from the surface. This will reduce the motion of the module if it is accidentally deployed. Refer to the additional air bag system precautions later in this section.

• Clean, high quality brake fluid from a sealed container is essential to the safe and proper operation of the brake system. You should always buy the correct type of brake fluid for your vehicle. If the brake fluid becomes contaminated, completely flush the system with new fluid. Never reuse any brake fluid. Any brake fluid that is removed from the system should be discarded. Also, do not allow any brake fluid to come in contact with a painted surface; it will damage the paint.

• Never operate the engine without the proper amount and type of engine oil; doing so WILL result in severe engine damage.

• Timing belt maintenance is extremely important. Many models utilize an interference-type, non-freewheeling engine. If the timing belt breaks, the valves in the cylinder head may strike the pistons, causing potentially serious (also time-consuming and expensive) engine damage. Refer to the maintenance interval charts for the recommended replacement interval for the timing belt, and to the timing belt section for belt replacement and inspection.

• Disconnecting the negative battery cable on some vehicles may interfere with the functions of the on-board computer system(s) and may require the computer to undergo a relearning process once the negative battery cable is reconnected.

• When servicing drum brakes, only disassemble and assemble one side at a time, leaving the remaining side intact for reference.

• Only an MVAC-trained, EPA-certified automotive technician should service the air conditioning system or its components.

BRAKES   ANTI-LOCK BRAKE SYSTEM (ABS)

GENERAL INFORMATION

PRECAUTIONS

• Certain components within the ABS system are not intended to be serviced or repaired individually.

• Do not use rubber hoses or other parts not specifically specified for and ABS system. When using repair kits, replace all parts included in the kit. Partial or incorrect repair may lead to functional problems and require the replacement of components.

• Lubricate rubber parts with clean, fresh brake fluid to ease assembly. Do not use shop air to clean parts; damage to rubber components may result.

• Use only DOT 3 brake fluid from an unopened container.

• If any hydraulic component or line is removed or replaced, it may be necessary to bleed the entire system.

• A clean repair area is essential. Always clean the reservoir and cap thoroughly before removing the cap. The slightest amount of dirt in the fluid may plug an orifice and impair the system function. Perform repairs after components have been thoroughly cleaned; use only denatured alcohol to clean components. Do not allow ABS components to come into contact with any substance containing mineral oil; this includes used shop rags.

• The Anti-Lock control unit is a microprocessor similar to other computer units in the vehicle. Ensure that the ignition switch is **OFF** before removing or installing controller harnesses. Avoid static electricity discharge at or near the controller.

• If any arc welding is to be done on the vehicle, the control unit should be unplugged before welding operations begin.

BLEEDING PROCEDURE

BRAKE LINE BLEEDING

1. Place a clean shop cloth beneath the brake master cylinder to catch brake fluid spills.

2. With the ignition OFF and the brakes cool, apply the brakes 3–5 times, or until the brake pedal effort increases significantly, in order to deplete the brake booster power reserve.

3. If you have performed a brake master cylinder bench bleeding on this vehicle, or if you disconnected the brake pipes from the master cylinder, or if you have disconnected the brake pipes from the proportioning valve assembly or the brake modulator assembly, you must perform the following steps to bleed air at the ports of the hydraulic component.

   a. Ensure that the brake master cylinder reservoir is full to the maximum-fill level.

   If removal of the reservoir cap and diaphragm is necessary, clean the outside of the reservoir on and around the cap prior to removal.

   b. With the brake pipes installed securely to the master cylinder, proportioning valve assembly, or brake modulator assembly, loosen and separate one of the brake pipes from the port of the component.

   For the proportioning valve assembly or the brake modulator assembly, perform these steps in the sequence of system flow; begin with the fluid feed pipes from the master cylinder.

   c. Allow a small amount of brake fluid to gravity bleed from the open port of the component.

   d. Connect the brake pipe to the component and tighten securely.

   e. Have an assistant slowly press the brake pedal fully and maintain steady pressure on the pedal.

   f. Loosen the same brake pipe to purge air from the open port of the component.

   g. Tighten the brake pipe, then have the assistant slowly release the brake pedal.

   h. Wait 15 seconds, then repeat the steps until all air is purged from the same port of the component.

   i. With the brake pipe installed securely to the master cylinder, proportioning valve assembly, or brake modulator assembly, after all air has been purged from the first port of the component that was bled, loosen and separate the next brake pipe from the component, until each of the ports on the component has been bled.

   j. After completing the final component port bleeding procedure, ensure that each of the brake pipe-to-component fittings are properly tightened.

4. Fill the brake master cylinder reservoir. Make sure that the brake master cylinder reservoir remains at least half-full during this bleeding procedure. Add fluid as needed to maintain the proper level.

Clean the outside of the reservoir on and around the reservoir cap prior to removing the cap and diaphragm.

5. Install a box-end wrench onto the right rear wheel hydraulic circuit bleeder valve.

6. Install a transparent hose over the end of the bleeder valve.

7. Submerge the open end of the transparent hose into a transparent container partially filled with brake fluid from a clean, sealed brake fluid container.

8. Have an assistant slowly press the brake pedal fully and maintain steady pressure on the pedal.

9. Loosen the bleeder valve to purge air from the wheel hydraulic circuit.

10. Tighten the bleeder valve, then have the assistant slowly release the brake pedal.

11. Wait 15 seconds, then repeat steps 8-10 until all air is purged from the same wheel hydraulic circuit.

12. With the right rear wheel hydraulic circuit bleeder valve tightened securely, after all air has been purged from the right rear hydraulic circuit, install a proper box-end wrench onto the left front wheel hydraulic circuit bleeder valve.

13. Install a transparent hose over the end of the bleeder valve and perform the same procedure used to bleed the right rear.

14. Bleed the left rear and front right in the same manner.

15. Fill the brake master cylinder reservoir to the maximum-fill level with brake fluid from a clean, sealed brake fluid container.

16. Slowly press and release the brake pedal. Observe the feel of the brake pedal.

17. If the brake pedal feels spongy, repeat the bleeding procedure again. If the brake pedal still feels spongy after repeating the bleeding procedure check for leaks in the system and pressure test the system to purge trapped air.

18. Turn the ignition key ON, with the engine OFF. Check to see if the brake system warning lamp remains illuminated.

➡**DO NOT allow the vehicle to be driven until it is diagnosed and repaired.**

BLEEDING THE ABS SYSTEM

✳✳ CAUTION

The Auto Bleed Procedure may be terminated at any time during the process by pressing the EXIT button. No further Scan Tool prompts pertaining to the Auto Bleed procedure will be given. After exiting the bleed procedure, relieve bleed pressure and disconnect bleed equipment per manufacturer's instructions. Failure to properly relieve pressure may result in spilled brake fluid causing damage to components and painted surfaces.

1. Raise the vehicle on a suitable support.

2. Remove all four tire and wheel assemblies.

3. Inspect the brake system for leaks and visual damage.

4. Repair or replace as needed.

5. Lower the vehicle.

6. Prepare the brake bleeding equipment and the vehicle for a pressure bleed of the base hydraulic brake system.

7. Inspect the battery state of charge.

8. Install a scan tool.

9. Turn ON the ignition, with the engine OFF.

10. With the scan tool, perform the following steps:

   a. Select Diagnostics

   b. Select the appropriate vehicle information

   c. Select Chassis

   d. Select Electronic Brake Control Module (EBCM)

   e. Select Special Functions

   f. Select Automated Bleed

✳✳ CAUTION

Dust and dirt accumulating on brake parts during normal use may contain asbestos fibers from production or aftermarket brake linings. Breathing excessive concentrations of asbestos fibers can cause serious bodily harm. Exercise care when servicing brake parts. Do not sand or grind brake lining unless equipment used is designed to contain the dust residue. Do not clean brake parts with compressed air or by dry brushing. Cleaning should be done by dampening the brake components with a fine mist of water, then wiping the brake components clean with a dampened cloth. Dispose of cloth and all residue containing asbestos fibers in an impermeable container with the appropriate label. Follow practices prescribed by the Occupational Safety and Health Administration (OSHA) and the Environmental Protection Agency (EPA) for the handling, processing, and disposing of dust or debris that may contain asbestos fibers.

BRAKE CALIPER

REMOVAL & INSTALLATION

See Figure 2.

1. Empty the master cylinder reservoir until it is half full.
2. Raise and support the vehicle.
3. Remove the tire and wheel assembly.
4. Install and firmly hand tighten 2 wheel nuts to opposite wheel studs in order to retain the rotor to the hub.
5. Install a large C-clamp over the body of the brake caliper with the C-clamp ends against the rear of the caliper body and against the outer brake pad.
6. Tighten the C-clamp until the caliper piston is compressed into the caliper bore enough to allow the caliper to slide past the brake rotor.
7. Remove the C-clamp from the caliper.
8. Remove the brake hose-to-caliper bolt from the brake caliper.
9. Remove the brake hose from the brake caliper.
10. Remove and discard the 2 copper brake hose gaskets. These gaskets may be stuck to the brake caliper and/or the brake hose end.

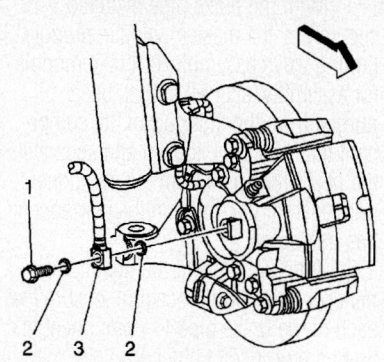

1. Brake hose to caliper bolt
2. Copper brake hose gaskets
3. Brake hose

36616_AURA_G0179

Fig. 2 Removing and installing brake hose and gaskets

11. Cap or plug the opening in the brake caliper and the brake hose to prevent fluid loss and contamination.
12. Remove the brake caliper guide pin bolts.
13. Remove the brake caliper from the caliper bracket.
14. Inspect the brake caliper guide pins for freedom of movement, and inspect the condition of the guide pin boots. Move the guide pins inboard and outboard within the bracket bores, without disengaging the slides from the boots, and observe the following:

- Restricted caliper guide pin movement
- Looseness in the brake caliper mounting bracket
- Seized or binding caliper guide pins
- Split or torn boots

15. If any of the conditions listed are found, the brake caliper guide pins and/or boots require replacement.

To install:

16. Install the brake caliper to the brake caliper bracket.
17. Install the brake caliper guide pin bolts and tighten to 26 ft. lbs. (35 Nm).
18. Remove the caps or plugs from the brake caliper opening and the brake hose.

➡**Do not reuse the copper brake hose gaskets.**

19. Install NEW copper brake hose gaskets to the brake hose-to-caliper bolt and to the brake hose.
20. Install the brake hose and the brake hose-to-brake caliper bolt to the brake caliper. Tighten to 37 ft. lbs. (50 Nm).

21. Bleed the hydraulic brake system.
22. Remove the wheel nuts retaining the brake rotor to the wheel hub.
23. Install the tire and wheel assembly.
24. Lower the vehicle.
25. With the engine OFF, gradually apply the brake pedal to approximately ⅔ of its travel distance.
26. Slowly release the brake pedal.
27. Wait 15 seconds, then repeat the last 2 steps until a firm brake pedal is obtained.
28. Fill the master cylinder reservoir to the proper level.

DISC BRAKE PADS

REMOVAL & INSTALLATION

See Figures 3 through 5.

1. Empty the master cylinder reservoir until it is half full.
2. Raise and support the vehicle.
3. Remove the tire and wheel assembly.
4. Install and firmly hand tighten 2 wheel nuts to opposite wheel studs in order to retain the rotor to the hub.
5. Remove the brake caliper lower guide pin bolt.

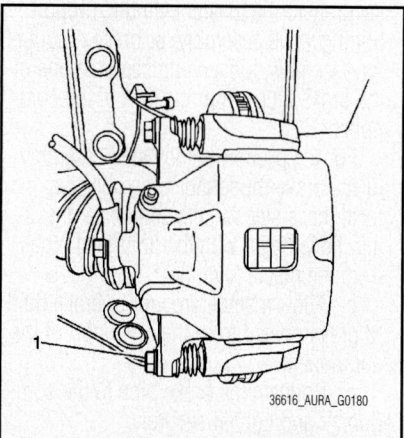

36616_AURA_G0180

Fig. 3 Locating the brake caliper lower guide pin bolt (1)

➡**Support the brake caliper with heavy mechanic wire, or equivalent, whenever it is separated from its mount and the hydraulic flexible brake hose is still connected. Failure to support the caliper in this manner will cause the flexible brake hose to bear the weight of the caliper, which may cause damage to the brake hose and in turn may cause a brake fluid leak.**

6. Without disconnecting the hydraulic brake flexible hose, pivot the caliper upward

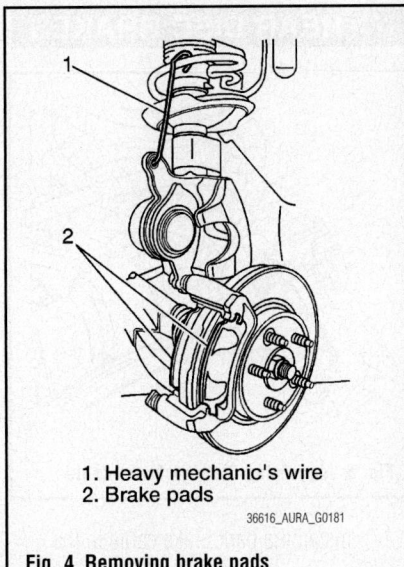

1. Heavy mechanic's wire
2. Brake pads

36616_AURA_G0181

Fig. 4 Removing brake pads

and secure the caliper with heavy mechanics wire, or equivalent.

7. Remove the brake pads from the caliper mounting bracket.

8. Push the disc brake caliper piston into the caliper bore using an old inner disc brake pad and a disc brake piston installation tool.

9. Remove the brake pad retainers from the caliper bracket.

10. Thoroughly clean the brake pad hardware mating surfaces of the caliper bracket, of any debris and corrosion.

11. Inspect the brake caliper guide pins for freedom of movement, and inspect the condition of the guide pin boots. Move the guide pins inboard and outboard within the bracket bores, without disengaging the slides from the boots, and observe for the following:

- Restricted caliper guide pin movement
- Looseness in the brake caliper mounting bracket
- Seized or binding caliper guide pins

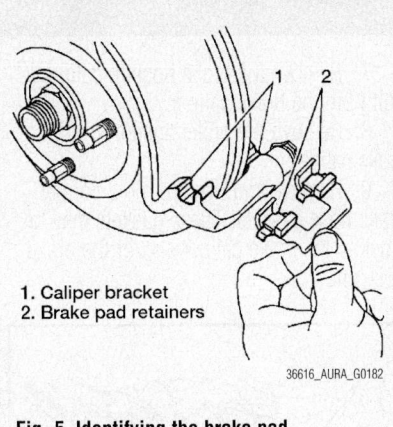

1. Caliper bracket
2. Brake pad retainers

36616_AURA_G0182

Fig. 5 Identifying the brake pad retainers

- Split or torn boots

a. If any of the conditions listed are found, the brake caliper guide pins and/or boots require replacement.

To install:

12. Make sure the brake pad hardware mating surfaces are clean.

13. Install the brake pad retainers to the brake caliper bracket.

➡**The wear sensor equipped disc brake pad must be mounted inboard of the rotor with the leading edge of the sensor facing the brake rotor during forward wheel rotation, or at the top of the pad when installed in vehicle position.**

14. Install the brake pads to the caliper bracket.

15. Remove the support, and rotate the brake caliper into position over the disc brake pads and to the caliper mounting bracket.

16. Install the lower brake caliper guide pin bolt. Tighten to 26 ft. lbs. (35 Nm).

17. Remove the wheel nuts retaining the brake rotor to the hub.

18. Install the tire and wheel assembly. Lower the vehicle.

19. With the engine OFF, gradually apply the brake pedal to approximately ⅔ of its travel distance.

20. Slowly release the brake pedal.

21. Wait 15 seconds, then repeat the last 2 steps until a firm brake pedal is obtained

22. Fill the master cylinder reservoir to the proper level.

23. Burnish the brake pad and rotor.

✳✳ CAUTION

Road test a vehicle under safe conditions and while obeying all traffic laws. Do not attempt any maneuvers that could jeopardize vehicle control. Failure to adhere to these precautions could lead to serious personal injury and vehicle damage.

Burnishing the brake pads and brake rotors is necessary in order to ensure that the braking surfaces are properly prepared after service has been performed on the disc brake system.

This procedure should be performed whenever the disc brake rotors have been refinished or replaced, and/or whenever the disc brake pads have been replaced.

a. Select a smooth road with little or no traffic.

b. Accelerate the vehicle to 30 mph (48 km/h).

➡**Use care to avoid overheating the brakes while performing this step.**

c. Using moderate to firm pressure, apply the brakes to bring the vehicle to a stop. Do not allow the brakes to lock.

d. Repeat the previous 2 steps until approximately 20 stops have been completed. Allow sufficient cooling periods between stops in order to properly burnish the brake pads and rotors.

✳✳ CAUTION

Dust and dirt accumulating on brake parts during normal use may contain asbestos fibers from production or aftermarket brake linings. Breathing excessive concentrations of asbestos fibers can cause serious bodily harm. Exercise care when servicing brake parts. Do not sand or grind brake lining unless equipment used is designed to contain the dust residue. Do not clean brake parts with compressed air or by dry brushing. Cleaning should be done by dampening the brake components with a fine mist of water, then wiping the brake components clean with a dampened cloth. Dispose of cloth and all residue containing asbestos fibers in an impermeable container with the appropriate label. Follow practices prescribed by the Occupational Safety and Health Administration (OSHA) and the Environmental Protection Agency (EPA) for the handling, processing, and disposing of dust or debris that may contain asbestos fibers.

BRAKE CALIPER

REMOVAL & INSTALLATION

See Figures 6 through 8.

1. Empty the master cylinder reservoir until it is half full.
2. Raise and suitably support the vehicle.
3. Remove the tire and wheel assembly.
4. Install a large C-clamp over the body of the brake caliper with the C-clamp ends against the rear of the caliper body and against the outer brake pad.

➡When using a large C-clamp to compress a caliper piston into a caliper bore of a caliper equipped with an integral park brake mechanism, do not exceed more than 0.039 in. (1mm) of piston travel. Exceeding this amount of piston travel will cause damage to the internal adjusting mechanism and/or the integral park brake mechanism.

5. Tighten the C-clamp until the caliper piston is compressed into the caliper bore enough to allow the caliper to slide past the brake rotor. Do not exceed 0.039 in. (1mm) of caliper piston travel.
6. Remove the C-clamp from the caliper.

7. Remove the brake hose to caliper bolt from the brake caliper.
8. Remove the brake hose from the brake caliper.
9. Remove and discard the 2 copper brake hose gaskets. These gaskets may be stuck to the brake caliper and/or the brake hose end.

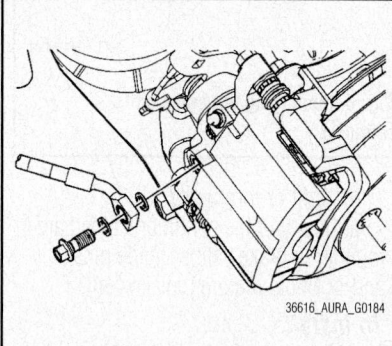

Fig. 6 Removing the brake hose from the caliper

10. Cap or plug the opening in the brake caliper and the brake hose to prevent fluid loss and contamination.
11. Remove the 2 brake caliper pin bolts.

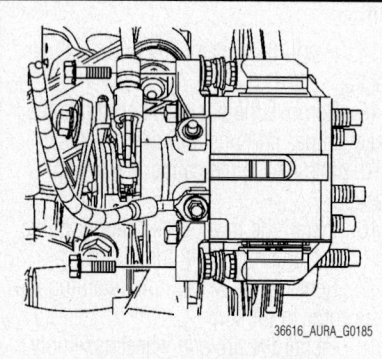

Fig. 7 Locating the 2 brake caliper pin bolts

12. Remove the park brake cable from the caliper.
13. Remove the brake caliper from the brake caliper bracket.

To install:

14. Inspect the caliper slide boots for cuts, tears, or deterioration. If damaged, replace the slides and boots.
15. Install the brake caliper to the brake caliper bracket.
16. Install the 2 brake caliper pin bolts. Tighten the bolts to 26 ft. lbs. (35 Nm).

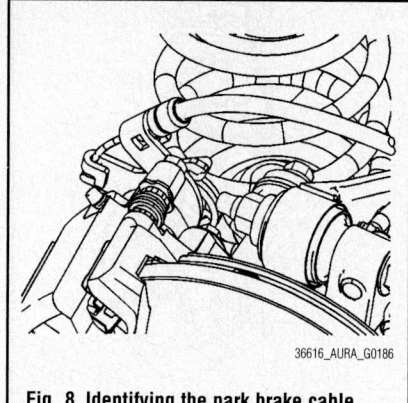

Fig. 8 Identifying the park brake cable

17. Install the park brake cable to the caliper.
18. Remove the caps or plugs from the brake caliper opening and the brake hose.

➡DO NOT reuse the copper brake hose gaskets.

19. Install NEW copper brake hose gaskets to the brake hose-to-caliper bolt and to the brake hose.
20. Install the brake hose and the brake hose-to-caliper bolt to the brake caliper. Tighten the bolts to 37 ft. lbs. (50 Nm).
21. Bleed the hydraulic brake system.
22. With the engine OFF, gradually apply the brake pedal to approximately ⅔ of its travel distance.
23. Slowly release the brake pedal.
24. Wait 15 seconds, then repeat the last 2 steps until a firm brake pedal is obtained.
25. Fill the master cylinder reservoir to the proper level.
26. Install the tire and wheel assembly.
27. Lower the vehicle.
28. Apply and release the park brake lever 4 times.

DISC BRAKE PADS

REMOVAL & INSTALLATION

See Figures 9 and 10.

1. Empty the master cylinder reservoir until it is half full.
2. Raise and suitably support the vehicle.
3. Remove the tire and wheel assembly.
4. Install a large C-clamp over the body of the brake caliper with the C-clamp ends against the rear of the caliper body and against the outer brake pad. Do not exceed 0.039 in. (1mm) of caliper piston travel.

➡When using a large C-clamp to compress a caliper piston into a caliper bore of a caliper equipped with an integral park brake mechanism, do not exceed more than 0.039 in. (1mm) of piston travel. Exceeding this amount of piston travel will cause damage to the internal adjusting mechanism and/or the integral park brake mechanism.

5. Tighten the C-clamp until the caliper piston is compressed into the caliper bore enough to allow the caliper to slide past the brake rotor.

6. Remove the C-clamp from the caliper.

7. Remove the lower brake caliper guide pin bolt.

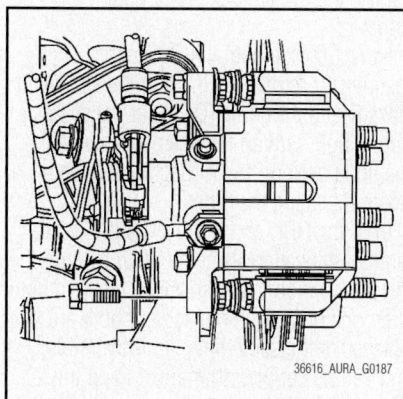

Fig. 9 Locating the lower brake caliper guide pin bolt

➡ **Support the brake caliper with heavy mechanic wire, or equivalent, when-**ever it is separated from its mount and the hydraulic flexible brake hose is still connected. Failure to support the caliper in this manner will cause the flexible brake hose to bear the weight of the caliper, which may cause damage to the brake hose and in turn may cause a brake fluid leak.

8. Pivot the brake caliper upward from the caliper bracket and support the caliper out of the way with heavy mechanic's wire; ensure that there is no tension on the hydraulic brake flexible hose. Do NOT disconnect the hydraulic brake flexible hose from the caliper.

9. Remove the brake pads from the brake caliper mounting bracket.

10. Remove and the brake pad retainers from the brake caliper mounting bracket.

To install:

➡**Do not attempt to clean away any corrosion. If damaged or corroded replace the necessary components.**

11. Inspect the brake caliper piston boot for deterioration, replace if damaged.

12. Use a piston installation tool in order to twist the brake caliper piston into the brake caliper bore.

13. Install the brake pad retainers to the brake caliper mounting bracket.

14. Install the brake pads to the brake caliper mounting bracket.

15. Pivot the brake caliper downward, over the brake pads and into the caliper bracket.

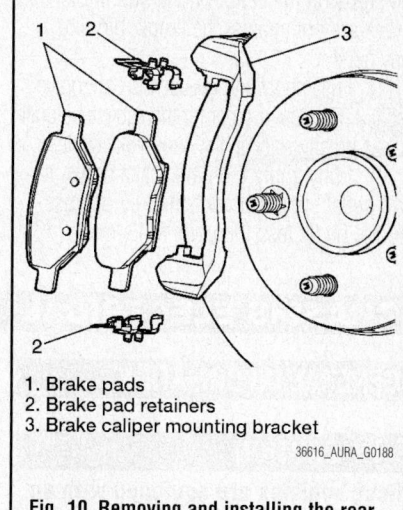

1. Brake pads
2. Brake pad retainers
3. Brake caliper mounting bracket

Fig. 10 Removing and installing the rear brake pad

16. Install the brake caliper guide pin bolt to the brake caliper guide pin. Tighten the bolts to 26 ft. lbs. (35 Nm).

17. Install the tire and wheel assembly.

18. Lower the vehicle.

19. With the engine OFF, gradually apply the brake pedal to approximately ⅔ of its travel distance.

20. Slowly release the brake pedal.

21. Wait 15 seconds, then repeat the last 2 steps until a firm brake pedal is obtained

22. Fill the master cylinder reservoir to the proper level.

23. Apply and release the park brake lever 4 times.

24. Burnish the pads and rotors.

BRAKES

PARKING BRAKE

Park brake application is completely independent of the hydraulic brake system. The park brake system is a mechanical system which operates the rear disc brakes through the calipers. The system is activated by depressing the park brake pedal, which applies the rear disc brakes via cables. When the park brake is set and the ignition switch is on, the BRAKE warning lamp on the instrument panel will be on. The park brake is released by pushing the pedal down until a click is heard and then releasing. The pedal will click again and the BRAKE lamp in the instrument panel will go out when the park brake system is fully released.

PARKING BRAKE CABLES

ADJUSTMENT

➡**This vehicle utilizes a self-tensioning, or self-adjusting park brake cable system. The park brake system does not require adjustment under normal operating conditions. The tension on the park brake cables can be disabled and enabled when necessary during service of the disc brake and/or the park brake system.**

1. Apply and fully release the park brake several times. Verify that the park brake pedal releases completely.

2. Turn ON the ignition. Verify the red BRAKE warning lamp is not illuminated.

3. If the red BRAKE warning lamp is illuminated, check that the park brake pedal is in the fully released position and against the stop or that there is no slack in the cables.

4. If the red BRAKE warning lamp remained illuminated and there were no other visible causes.

5. Turn OFF the ignition.

6. Raise and support the vehicle.

7. With the park brake pedal fully released, check the park brake levers on the rear calipers. The levers should be against

the stops on the caliper housings. If the levers are not against the stops, binding may exist.

8. Fully apply and release the park brake pedal 3–5 times in order for the cable tensioner to take up any slack in the park brake cables.

9. Fully apply the park brake pedal, a firm pedal should be obtained by depressing the pedal less than one full stroke.

10. Attempt to rotate the rear tire and wheel assemblies. There should be no rotation forward or rearward.

11. Fully release the park brake pedal.

12. Verify the park brake is released by rotating the rear tire and wheel assemblies. The rear tire and wheel assemblies should rotate freely and exhibit no brake drag.

13. Lower the vehicle.

PARKING BRAKE SHOES

REMOVAL & INSTALLATION

The rear disc brake pads serve as the parking brakes. Refer to the procedures under Rear Disc Brakes.

CHASSIS ELECTRICAL

GENERAL INFORMATION

✳✳ CAUTION

These vehicles are equipped with an air bag system. The system must be disarmed before performing service on, or around, system components, the steering column, instrument panel components, wiring and sensors. Failure to follow the safety precautions and the disarming procedure could result in accidental air bag deployment, possible injury and unnecessary system repairs.

SERVICE PRECAUTIONS

Disconnect and isolate the battery negative cable before beginning any airbag system component diagnosis, testing, removal, or installation procedures. Allow system capacitor to discharge for two minutes before beginning any component service. This will disable the airbag system. Failure to disable the airbag system may result in accidental airbag deployment, personal injury, or death.

Do not place an intact undeployed airbag face down on a solid surface. The airbag will propel into the air if accidentally deployed and may result in personal injury or death.

When carrying or handling an undeployed airbag, the trim side (face) of the airbag should be pointing towards the body to minimize possibility of injury if accidental deployment occurs. Failure to do this may result in personal injury or death.

Replace airbag system components with OEM replacement parts. Substitute parts may appear interchangeable, but internal differences may result in inferior occupant protection. Failure to do so may result in occupant personal injury or death.

Wear safety glasses, rubber gloves, and

AIR BAG (SUPPLEMENTAL RESTRAINT SYSTEM)

long sleeved clothing when cleaning powder residue from vehicle after an airbag deployment. Powder residue emitted from a deployed airbag can cause skin irritation. Flush affected area with cool water if irritation is experienced. If nasal or throat irritation is experienced, exit the vehicle for fresh air until the irritation ceases. If irritation continues, see a physician.

Do not use a replacement airbag that is not in the original packaging. This may result in improper deployment, personal injury, or death.

The factory installed fasteners, screws and bolts used to fasten airbag components have a special coating and are specifically designed for the airbag system. Do not use substitute fasteners. Use only original equipment fasteners listed in the parts catalog when fastener replacement is required.

During, and following, any child restraint anchor service, due to impact event or vehicle repair, carefully inspect all mounting hardware, tether straps, and anchors for proper installation, operation, or damage. If a child restraint anchor is found damaged in any way, the anchor must be replaced. Failure to do this may result in personal injury or death.

Deployed and non-deployed airbags may or may not have live pyrotechnic material within the airbag inflator.

Do not dispose of driver/passenger/curtain airbags or seat belt tensioners unless you are sure of complete deployment. Refer to the Hazardous Substance Control System for proper disposal.

Dispose of deployed airbags and tensioners consistent with state, provincial, local, and federal regulations.

After any airbag component testing or service, do not connect the battery negative cable. Personal injury or death may result if the system test is not performed first.

If the vehicle is equipped with the Occupant Classification System (OCS), do not

connect the battery negative cable before performing the OCS Verification Test using the scan tool and the appropriate diagnostic information. Personal injury or death may result if the system test is not performed properly.

Never replace both the Occupant Restraint Controller (ORC) and the Occupant Classification Module (OCM) at the same time. If both require replacement, replace one, then perform the Airbag System test before replacing the other.

Both the ORC and the OCM store Occupant Classification System (OCS) calibration data, which they transfer to one another when one of them is replaced. If both are replaced at the same time, an irreversible fault will be set in both modules and the OCS may malfunction and cause personal injury or death.

If equipped with OCS, the Seat Weight Sensor is a sensitive, calibrated unit and must be handled carefully. Do not drop or handle roughly. If dropped or damaged, replace with another sensor. Failure to do so may result in occupant injury or death.

If equipped with OCS, the front passenger seat must be handled carefully as well. When removing the seat, be careful when setting on floor not to drop. If dropped, the sensor may be inoperative, could result in occupant injury, or possibly death.

If equipped with OCS, when the passenger front seat is on the floor, no one should sit in the front passenger seat. This uneven force may damage the sensing ability of the seat weight sensors. If sat on and damaged, the sensor may be inoperative, could result in occupant injury, or possibly death.

DISARMING THE SYSTEM

1. Turn the steering wheel so that the vehicles wheels are pointing straight ahead.

2. Place the ignition in the OFF position.

➡**The SDM may have more than one fused power input. To ensure there is** no unwanted SIR deployment, personal injury, or unnecessary SIR system repairs, remove all fuses supplying power to the SDM. With all SDM fuses removed and the ignition switch in the ON position, the AIR BAG warning indicator illuminates. This is normal operation, and does not indicate a SIR system malfunction.

3. Locate and remove the fuse(s) supplying power to the SDM.
4. Wait 1 minute before working on the system.

ARMING THE SYSTEM

1. Place the ignition in the OFF position.
2. Install the fuse(s) supplying power to the SDM.
3. Turn the ignition switch to the ON position. The AIR BAG indicator will flash then turn OFF.

DRIVE TRAIN

AUTOMATIC TRANSAXLE ASSEMBLY

REMOVAL & INSTALLATION

See Figure 11.

1. Remove the battery tray.
2. Disconnect the air cleaner outlet duct.
3. Disconnect the transaxle wiring harness from the transaxle and the Park Neutral Position (PNP) switch.
4. Remove the radiator outlet pipe.
5. Disconnect the transaxle shift control cable terminal from the transaxle manual shift lever pin.
6. Remove the retainer from the transaxle shift control cable.
7. Press the locking tabs inward in order to release the transaxle shift control cable from the cable bracket.
8. Remove the shift cable bracket.
9. Remove the transaxle wiring harness from the retainer on the transaxle.
10. Remove the upper transaxle to engine studs and bolts.
11. Install the engine support fixture.
12. Remove the left transmission mount.
13. Secure the radiator and condenser to the vehicle structure and the engine in order to prepare for frame removal.
14. Raise the vehicle.
15. Remove the front wheels and tires.
16. Remove the bolts from the transaxle brace.
17. Remove the transaxle brace.
18. Remove the starter.
19. Mark the relationship of the flywheel to the torque converter for reassembly.
20. Use the flywheel holding tool to prevent the crankshaft from rotating.
21. Remove the torque converter to flywheel bolts.
22. Remove the nut holding the transaxle cooler line retainer to the transaxle.
23. Disconnect the transaxle cooler lines from the transaxle.
24. Disconnect the Vehicle Speed Sensor (VSS) wiring harness from the sensor.

25. Remove the intermediate shaft to steering gear pinch bolt. Discard the bolt.
26. Disconnect the intermediate shaft from the steering gear.
27. Disconnect the tie rods from the steering knuckle.
28. Disconnect the stabilizer shaft links from the stabilizer shaft.
29. Disconnect the ball joints from the steering knuckles.
30. Remove the frame as follows;
    a. Install the engine support fixture.
    b. Support the radiator and condenser from above using the condenser tabs on each side.
    c. Remove the tire and wheel assemblies.
    d. Remove the front fender liner.
    e. Remove the engine splash shield.
    f. Remove the lower ball joints from the steering knuckles.
    g. Remove the tie rod ends from the steering knuckles.
    h. Remove both stabilizer links from the stabilizer bar.

i. Separate the steering gear from the intermediate shaft.
    j. Remove the front transmission mount bolt from the frame.
    k. Remove the rear transmission mount bracket fasteners from the frame.
    l. Lower the vehicle until the frame contacts the engine support stand.
    m. Remove the reinforcement bolts.
    n. Remove the front frame bolts.
    o. Remove the rear frame bolts.
    p. Remove the frame reinforcements.
    q. Raise the vehicle off of the frame.
31. Disconnect the wheel drive shafts from the transaxle. Secure the wheel drive shafts out of the way.
32. Support the transaxle with a suitable jack.
33. Remove the lower transaxle to engine bolts.
34. Separate the engine and the transaxle.
35. Remove the transaxle from the vehicle.

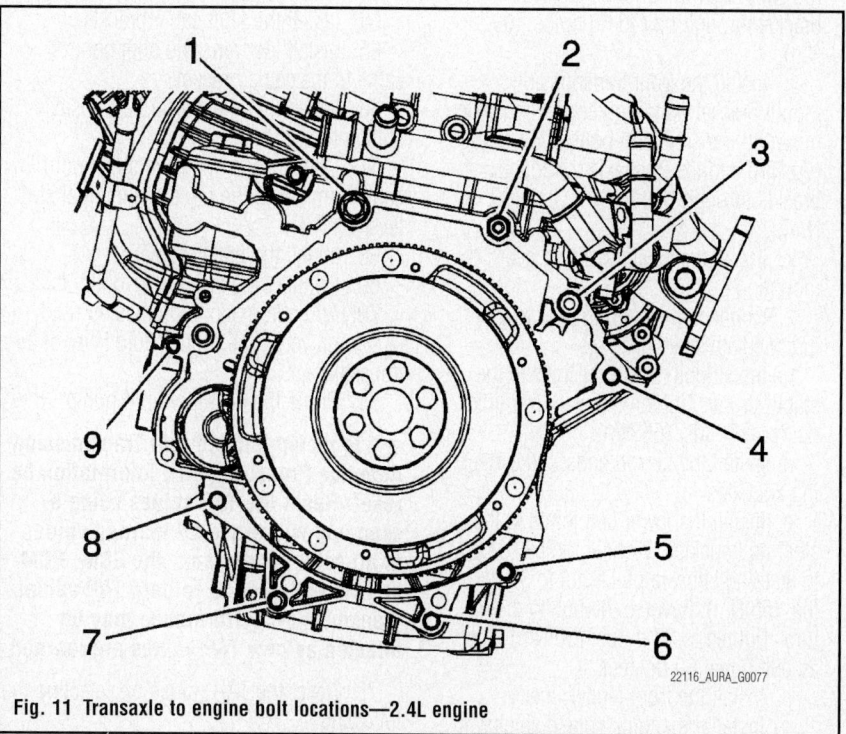

Fig. 11 Transaxle to engine bolt locations—2.4L engine

22116_AURA_G0077

To install:

36. Position the transaxle in the vehicle.

37. Install the lower transaxle to engine bolts and tighten to 55 ft. lbs. (75 Nm).

38. Install the wheel drive shafts to the transaxle.

39. Lubricate the transaxle cooler pipes before inserting into seals.

40. Connect the transaxle cooler pipes to the transaxle.

41. Install the transaxle cooler pipes retainer nut and tighten to 62 inch lbs. (7 Nm).

42. Install the torque converter to flywheel bolts and tighten to 44 ft. lbs. (60 Nm).

43. Install the starter.

44. Install the frame as follows:

   a. Lower the vehicle on to the frame.

   b. Install the frame reinforcements.

   c. Install the front frame bolts and hand tighten only.

   d. Install the reinforcement bolts and hand tighten only.

   e. Install the rear frame bolts. Tighten to 74 ft. lbs. (100 Nm), plus an additional 90 degrees.

   f. Tighten the front frame bolts. Tighten to 74 ft. lbs. (100 Nm), plus an additional 90 degrees.

   g. Install the cradle support bolts. Tighten to 74 ft. lbs. (100 Nm).

   h. Raise the vehicle.

   i. Install the rear transmission mount bracket fasteners. Tighten the transaxle mount to transmission bolts to 66 ft. lbs. (90 Nm) and the transaxle to mount bracket through bolt to 66 ft. lbs. (90 Nm).

   j. Install the front transmission mount bracket bolt. Tighten the transaxle mount to transmission bolts to 66 ft. lbs. (90 Nm) and the transaxle to mount bracket through bolt to 66 ft. lbs. (90 Nm).

   k. Install the power steering gear mounting bolts.

   l. Connect the steering gear to the intermediate shaft.

   m. Install both stabilizer links to the stabilizer bar. Tighten the stabilizer link nut to 48 ft. lbs. (65 Nm).

   n. Install the tie rod ends to the steering knuckles.

   o. Install the lower ball joints to the steering knuckles. Tighten the ball stud to steering knuckle pinch nut to 37 ft. lbs. (50 Nm). Reverse the nut ¾ of a turn. Tighten to 37 ft. lbs. (50 Nm) plus an additional 60 degrees.

   p. Install the front fender liner.

   q. Install the engine splash shield.

   r. Remove the engine support fixture.

45. Connect the intermediate shaft to the steering gear shaft.

46. Install the new steering gear pinch bolt to the intermediate shaft Tighten the steering gear pinch bolt to 36 ft. lbs. (49 Nm).

47. Tighten the torque converter bolts to 37 ft. lbs. (50 Nm)

48. Connect the ball joints to the steering knuckles.

49. Connect the stabilizer shaft links to the stabilizer shaft.

50. Connect the tie rods to the steering knuckle.

51. Connect the wiring harness to the VSS.

52. Install the transaxle brace.

53. Install the transaxle brace bolts. Tighten to 39 ft. lbs. (53 Nm)

54. Install the front splash shields.

55. Install the catalytic converters.

56. Install the front wheel and tire assemblies.

57. Lower the vehicle.

58. Install the left transaxle mount.

59. Install the upper transaxle to engine bolts and studs. Tighten to 55 ft. lbs. (75 Nm)

60. Untie the radiator, air conditioning condenser, and fan module assembly.

61. Remove the engine support fixture.

62. Install the radiator outlet pipe.

63. Connect the transaxle wiring harness to the main transaxle electrical connector, and the PNP switch.

64. Install the shift cable bracket.

65. Install the transaxle shift control cable to the cable bracket.

66. Install the retainer to the transaxle shift control cable.

67. Connect the transaxle shift control cable terminal to the transaxle manual shift lever pin.

68. Install the battery tray.

69. Connect the air cleaner outlet duct.

70. Add automatic transmission fluid (ATF) and verify the proper fluid level of the transaxle.

71. Prime the auxiliary fluid pump.

➡️It is recommended that Transmission Adaptive Pressure (TAP) information be reset. Reset the TAP values using a scan tool will erase all learned values in all cells. As a result, the ECM, PCM, or TCM will need to relearn TAP values. Transmission performance may be affected as new TAP values are learned.

72. Reset the TAP values by selecting the following:

- Scan tool
- Special functions
- Transmission output controls
- Reset transmission adapts

73. Road test the vehicle.

FRONT AXLE SHAFT, BEARING & SEAL

REMOVAL & INSTALLATION

See Figure 12.

✳✳ WARNING

To prevent personal injury and/or component damage, do not allow the weight of the vehicle to load the front wheels, or attempt to operate the vehicle, when the wheel drive shaft(s) or wheel drive shaft nut(s) are removed. To do so may cause the inner bearing race to separate, resulting in damage to brake and suspension components and loss of vehicle control.

✳✳ CAUTION

Wheel drive shaft boots, seals and clamps should be protected from sharp objects any time service is performed on or near the wheel drive shaft(s). Damage to the boot(s), the seal(s) or the clamp(s) may cause lubricant to leak from the joint and lead to increased noise and possible failure of the wheel drive shaft.

1. Raise and suitably support the vehicle.

2. Remove the wheel and the tire.

3. Insert a brass drift or punch between

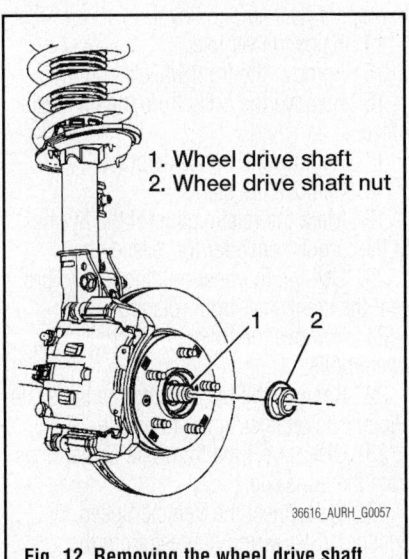

1. Wheel drive shaft
2. Wheel drive shaft nut

36616_AURH_G0057

Fig. 12 Removing the wheel drive shaft

the brake rotor cooling fins and the brake caliper mounting bracket.

4. Using the appropriate size socket and breaker bar, loosen the wheel drive shaft nut.

➡**DO NOT re-use the wheel drive shaft nut. Discard the nut and replace with NEW.**

5. Remove the wheel drive shaft nut from the wheel drive shaft.

6. Using the Hub Spindle Remover (J 42129), separate the brake rotor and wheel bearing/hub assembly.

7. Remove the outer tie rod assembly from the steering knuckle.

8. Remove the ball joint from the steering knuckle.

9. Using the Slide Hammer (J 2619-01), the Axle Shaft Remover Extension (J 29794), and the Axle Shaft Remover (J 33008-A), remove the wheel drive shaft from the vehicle.

To install:

✳✳ CAUTION

The Seal Protector (J-44394-A) must be installed into the differential output shaft seal prior to removing and installing the wheel drive shaft. Failure to install this tool as indicated may cause the splines of the wheel drive shaft to cut the differential output seal.

10. Install the Seal Protector (J-44394-A) into the differential output shaft seal.

➡**In order to prevent lubricant leaks, use care when installing the wheel drive shaft to the differential. Do not damage the oil seal. Replace the oil seal if it becomes nicked, distorted, or otherwise damaged.**

11. Carefully install the wheel drive shaft into the differential until the splines are past the seal protector.

12. Remove the seal protector from the differential output shaft seal.

13. Installing the wheel drive shaft into the differential until the retaining ring is fully seated.

14. Confirm that the front wheel drive shaft retaining ring is properly seated by holding the inner housing and pull the inner housing outward.

15. Install the front wheel drive shaft into the front wheel bearing/hub.

16. Install the ball joint to the steering knuckle.

17. Install the outer tie rod assembly to the steering knuckle.

18. Install the NEW wheel drive shaft nut on the wheel drive shaft

19. Insert a drift or punch into the cooling fin of the brake rotor caliper and against the brake caliper mounting bracket.

20. Using a torque wrench and the appropriate size socket, tighten the wheel drive shaft nut to 159 ft. lbs. (215 Nm).

21. Install the wheel and the tire.

22. Lower the vehicle.

23. Inspect the transaxle fluid level.

FRONT HALFSHAFTS

REMOVAL & INSTALLATION
See Figure 13.

✳✳ CAUTION

To prevent personal injury and/or component damage, do not allow the weight of the vehicle to load the front wheels, or attempt to operate the vehicle, when the wheel drive shaft(s) or wheel drive shaft nut(s) are removed. To do so may cause the inner bearing race to separate, resulting in damage to brake and suspension components and loss of vehicle control.

➡**Wheel drive shaft boots, seals and clamps should be protected from sharp objects any time service is performed on or near the wheel drive shaft(s). Damage to the boot(s), the seal(s) or the clamp(s) may cause lubricant to leak from the joint and lead to increased noise and possible failure of the wheel drive shaft.**

1. Raise and suitably support the vehicle.

2. Remove the wheel and the tire.

3. Insert a brass drift or punch between the brake rotor cooling fins and the brake caliper mounting bracket.

4. Using the appropriate size socket and breaker bar, loosen the wheel drive shaft nut.

➡**Do NOT re-use the wheel drive shaft nut. Discard the nut and replace with a NEW one.**

5. Remove the front wheel drive shaft nut from the wheel drive shaft.

6. Using the hub spindle remover (J 42129), separate the brake rotor and wheel bearing/hub assembly.

7. Remove the outer tie rod assembly from the steering knuckle.

8. Remove the ball joint from the steering knuckle.

➡**A seal protector such as J-44394 must be installed into the differential output shaft seal prior to removing and installing the wheel drive shaft. Failure to install the tool as indicated may cause the splines of the wheel drive shaft to cut the differential output seal.**

9. Using the slide hammer (J 2619-01), the axle shaft remover extension (J 29794), and the axle shaft remover (J 33008-A), remove the wheel drive shaft from the vehicle.

To install:

➡**A seal protector such as J-44394 must be installed into the differential output shaft seal prior to removing and installing the wheel drive shaft. Failure to install the tool as indicated may cause the splines of the wheel drive shaft to cut the differential output seal.**

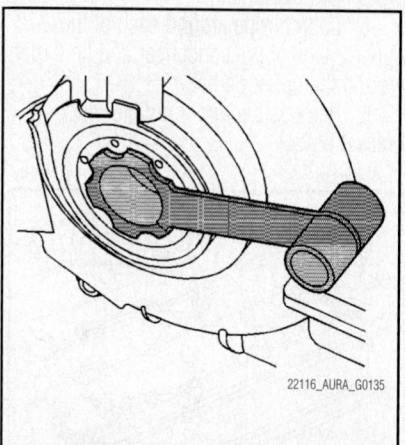

22116_AURA_G0135

Fig. 13 A seal protector such as J-44394 must be installed into the differential output shaft seal prior to removing and installing the wheel drive shaft

10. Install a seal protector such as J-44394 into the differential output shaft seal.

➡**In order to prevent lubricant leaks, use care when installing the wheel drive shaft to the differential. Do not damage the oil seal. Replace the oil seal if it becomes nicked, distorted, or otherwise damaged.**

11. Carefully install the wheel drive shaft into the differential until the splines are past the seal protector.

12. Carefully remove the seal protector from the differential output shaft seal.

13. Carefully continue installing the wheel drive shaft into the differential until the retaining ring is fully seated.

14. Verify the front wheel drive shaft

retaining ring is properly seated by grasping the inner housing and pull the inner housing outward.

15. Install the front wheel drive shaft into the front wheel bearing/hub.

16. Install the ball joint to the steering knuckle.

17. Install the outer tie rod assembly to the steering knuckle.

18. Install the NEW wheel drive shaft nut on the wheel drive shaft.

19. Insert a drift or punch into the cooling fin of the brake rotor caliper and against the brake caliper mounting bracket.

20. Using a torque wrench and the appropriate size socket, tighten the wheel drive shaft nut to 159 ft. lbs. (215 Nm).

21. Install the wheel and the tire.

22. Lower the vehicle.

23. Inspect the transaxle fluid level.

ENGINE COOLING

ENGINE FAN

REMOVAL & INSTALLATION

See Figures 14 and 15.

1. Drain and recycle the engine coolant.

2. Remove the air cleaner outlet air duct.

3. Remove the upper radiator air deflector.

4. Remove the transmission oil cooler pipes from the radiator.

5. Loop a rope around each of the upper 2 tabs of the condenser and tie a rope around the upper tie bar.

6. Remove the upper radiator support bracket bolts.

Fig. 14 Locating the upper radiator support bracket bolts

7. Remove the upper radiator support brackets.

8. Pry upward on the fan shroud tabs at the radiator clips to release the fan shroud from the radiator.

9. Remove the lower radiator air deflector.

10. Lower the vehicle.

11. Remove the radiator inlet hose from the radiator.

12. Remove the radiator outlet hose from the radiator.

13. Disconnect the cooling fan wire harness connectors.

14. Remove the A/C compressor and condenser hose assembly.

15. Raise the vehicle.

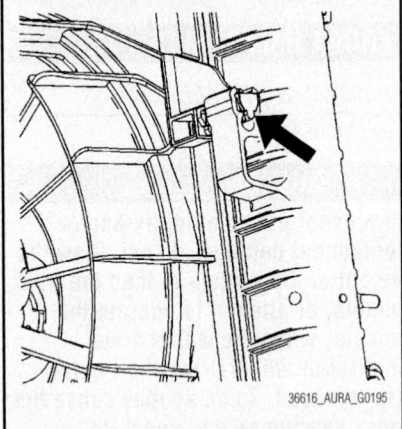

36616_AURA_G0195

Fig. 15 Locating the fan shroud tabs

16. Remove the lower radiator support bracket bolts.

17. Remove the lower radiator support brackets.

18. Remove the transmission oil cooler pipe clip from the fan shroud.

19. Remove the fan assembly.

To install:

20. Install the fan shroud assembly.

21. Install the transmission oil cooler pipes to the radiator.

22. Install the transmission oil cooler pipe clip to the fan shroud.

23. Install the lower radiator support brackets.

24. Install the lower radiator support bracket bolts and tighten to 44 ft. lbs. (60 Nm).

25. Install the cooling fan wire harness connectors.

26. Install the radiator outlet hose to the radiator.

27. Install the lower radiator air deflector.

28. Lower the vehicle.

29. Snap fan shroud tabs into the radiator clips.

30. Remove the rope attached to the condenser and upper tie bar.

31. Install the upper radiator support brackets.

32. Install the upper radiator support bracket bolts and tighten to 89 inch lbs. (10 Nm).

33. Install the A/C compressor and condenser hose assembly.

34. Install the upper radiator air deflector.

35. Install the air duct.

36. Fill the cooling system.

37. Inspect the transmission fluid level.

RADIATOR

REMOVAL & INSTALLATION

See Figures 16 through 20.

1. Drain and recycle the engine coolant.

2. Loop a rope around each of the upper 2 tabs of the condenser and tie the rope around the upper tie bar.

3. Remove the upper radiator support brackets.

4. Reposition the radiator inlet hose clamp at the radiator.

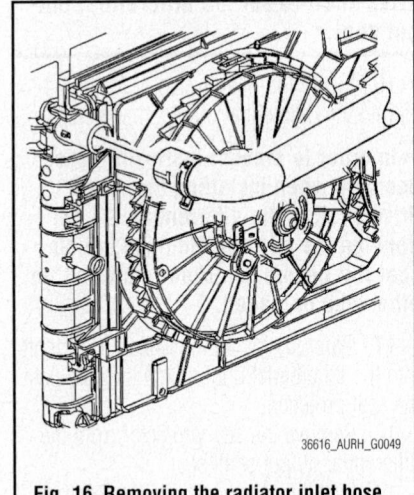

36616_AURH_G0049

Fig. 16 Removing the radiator inlet hose

5. Remove the radiator inlet hose from the radiator.

6. Remove the front air dam.

7. Remove the right engine splash shield retainers.

8. Remove the right engine splash shield.

9. Remove the left engine splash shield retainers.

10. Remove the left engine splash shield.

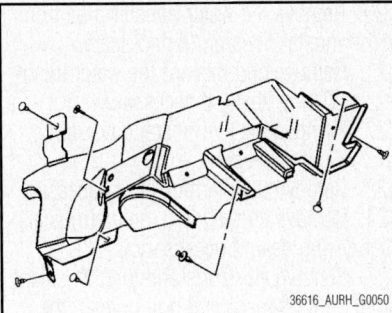

Fig. 17 Locating the right engine splash shield retainers

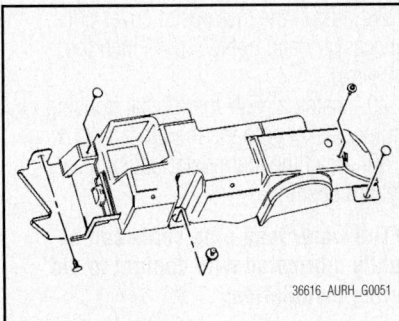

Fig. 18 Locating the left engine splash shield retainers

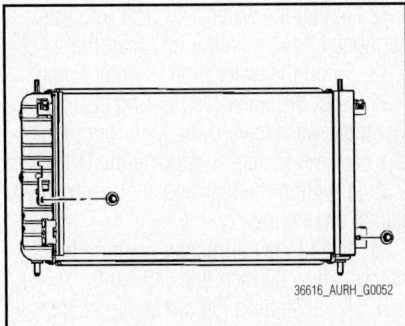

Fig. 19 Locating the condenser mounting bolts

11. Reposition the radiator outlet hose clamp at the radiator.

12. Remove the radiator outlet hose from the radiator.

13. Remove the transmission oil cooler pipes from the transmission.

14. Remove the lower radiator support bracket bolts.

15. Remove the lower radiator support brackets.

16. Remove the radiator lower mounts.

17. Remove and discard the condenser mounting bolts from the radiator.

18. Push upward on the radiator and downward on the condenser to unsnap the condenser mounting tabs from the radiator clips.

19. Remove and discard the condenser mounting nuts from the radiator.

20. Remove the radiator air side seals.

21. Remove the radiator and cooling fan shroud assembly from the vehicle.

22. Pry upward on the fan shroud tabs at the radiator clips.

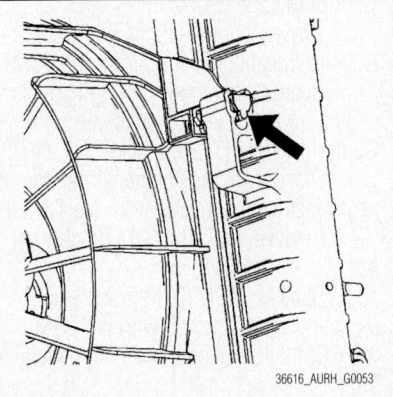

Fig. 20 Locating the fan shroud tabs and retainer clips

23. Remove the cooling fan and shroud assembly from the radiator.

To install:

24. Install the cooling fan and shroud assembly to the radiator.

25. Snap the fan shroud tabs into the radiator clips.

26. Install the radiator and cooling fan shroud assembly to the vehicle.

27. Install the radiator air side seals onto the condenser mounting tabs on the radiator.

➡**The bolt retaining the condenser to the radiator end tank is a special length and should be the ONLY bolt used upon reinstallation. The use of a longer bolt will damage the radiator end tank.**

➡**Replace the condenser mounting bolts and nuts.**

28. Install the condenser mounting nuts to the radiator.

29. Insert the condenser mounting tabs into the radiator clips.

30. Install the condenser to the radiator bolts and tighten to 53 inch lbs. (6 Nm).

31. Bend the radiator air side seals and insert the seals into the channel of the intake air splash shields.

➡**The radiator air side seals must be in the proper position for proper air flow.**

➡**Replace the radiator lower mounts as a pair or vibration may result.**

32. Install the radiator lower mounts.

33. Install the lower radiator support brackets and tighten the bolts to 44 ft. lbs. (60 Nm).

34. Install the transmission oil cooler pipes to the transmission.

35. Install the radiator outlet hose to the radiator.

36. Reposition the radiator outlet hose clamp at the radiator.

➡**Engine splash shields must be properly installed or reduced A/C and engine cooling system performance could occur.**

37. Install the left engine splash shield.

38. Install the left engine splash shield retainers.

39. Install the right engine splash shield.

40. Install the right engine splash shield retainers.

41. Install the front air dam.

42. Lower the vehicle.

43. Install the radiator inlet hose to the radiator.

44. Reposition the radiator inlet hose clamp at the radiator.

45. Remove the rope attached to the condenser and upper tie bar.

46. Install the upper radiator support brackets.

47. Fill the coolant.

48. Inspect the transmission fluid level.

THERMOSTAT

REMOVAL & INSTALLATION

See Figures 21 and 22.

1. Drain the cooling system.

➡**A drain has been provided at the bottom of the water pump for engine block coolant drainage.**

2. Drain the coolant from the engine block at the water pump drain. After the coolant has drained, tighten the drain bolt.

3. Lower the vehicle.

4. Remove the battery tray by performing the following:

a. Remove the battery.

b. Remove the Underhood Bussed Electrical Center (UBEC) cover.

c. Loosen the integral bolt on the positive battery cable lead and remove the lead from the UBEC.

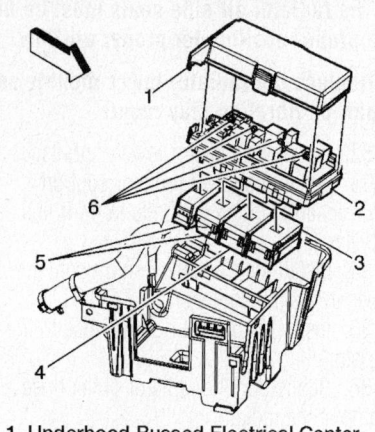

1. Underhood Bussed Electrical Center (UBEC) cover
2. Junction block
3. Engine wiring harness
4. Forward lamp wiring harness
5. Body wiring harness
6. Junction block bolts

36616_AURH_G0001

Fig. 21 Identifying Underhood Bussed Electrical Center

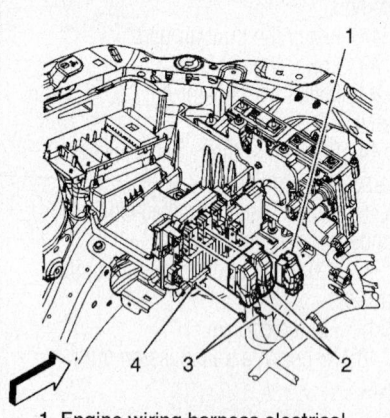

1. Engine wiring harness electrical connector (at the TCM)
2. Engine wiring harness electrical connector (at the ECM)
3. Engine wiring harness clips
4. ECM/TCM bracket

36616_AURH_G0002

Fig. 22 Locating the Engine Control Module (ECM) and Transmission Control Module (TCM)

d. Reposition the positive battery cable out of the way.

e. Loosen the integral bolt on the steering column harness package lead and remove the lead from the UBEC.

f. Loosen the junction block bolts, once loose, tap the bolts once in order to disengage the bolts from the electrical connectors.

g. Remove the junction block.

➡**Note the color and location of each electrical connector.**

h. Remove the engine wiring harness UBEC electrical connector from the UBEC bracket and secure out of the way.

i. Remove the forward lamp wiring harness UBEC electrical connector from the UBEC bracket and secure out of the way.

j. Remove the body wiring harness UBEC electrical connectors from the UBEC bracket and secure out of the way.

k. Disconnect the body wiring harness electrical connector from the Engine Control Module (ECM).

l. Disconnect the engine wiring harness electrical connectors from the ECM.

m. Remove the engine wiring harness clips from the ECM/Transmission Control Module (TCM) bracket.

n. Disconnect the engine wiring harness electrical connector from the TCM.

o. Remove the ECM/TCM bracket bolt.

p. Slide the ECM/TCM bracket up and remove the bracket (with the ECM and TCM still attached) from the battery tray.

q. Remove the battery tray bolts, nut, and battery tray.

5. Disconnect the engine wiring harness electrical connector from the Engine Coolant Temperature (ECT) sensor.

6. Remove the Heated Oxygen Sensor (HO2S) electrical connector rosebud clip from the thermostat housing.

7. Reposition the radiator outlet hose clamp at the thermostat cover.

8. Remove the radiator outlet hose from the thermostat cover.

9. Remove the exhaust heat shield bolts.

10. Remove the exhaust heat shield.

11. Remove the auxiliary heater water pump hose clip from the heater outlet hose.

12. Reposition the auxiliary heater water pump hose clamp at the thermostat housing.

13. Remove the auxiliary heater water pump hose from the thermostat housing.

14. Reposition the heater inlet hose clamp at the thermostat housing.

15. Remove the heater inlet hose from the thermostat housing.

16. Raise and support the vehicle.

17. Remove the ECT sensor, if necessary.

18. Remove the thermostat housing bolts.

➡**Twist the water transfer pipe while pulling in order to remove it from the water pump.**

19. Remove the thermostat from the vehicle.

20. Remove the water transfer pipe from the thermostat housing, if necessary.

21. Remove and discard the water transfer pipe O-ring seals, if necessary.

22. Remove the thermostat cover bolts and cover, if necessary.

23. Remove the thermostat, if necessary.

24. Remove and discard the thermostat cover O-ring seal, if necessary.

25. Remove all debris and thread sealant from the ECT sensor and bolt holes if the housing is being re-used.

To install:

26. Install a NEW thermostat cover O-ring seal into the recess groove.

27. Install the thermostat, if necessary.

28. Install the thermostat cover bolts, if necessary and tighten to 89 inch lbs. (10 Nm).

29. Install a NEW thermostat housing to engine gasket onto the thermostat housing.

30. Load the thermostat housing assembly into position

➡**The water feed pipe seals can be lightly lubricated with coolant to aid during installation.**

31. Install NEW O-ring seals onto the water feed pipe.

➡ **Lubricate the O-rings with coolant ONLY.**

32. Install the water feed pipe into the thermostat housing aligning locator tab.

33. Align the water pipe to water pump.

34. Seat the water feed O-ring seal by pushing inward toward the water pump. Take care not to tear or damage the O-ring.

35. Position the thermostat housing against the engine.

36. Install the thermostat housing bolts and tighten to 89 inch lbs. (10 Nm).

37. If reinstalling the old sensor, coat the threads with sealant.

38. Install the ECT sensor, if necessary and tighten the sensor to 15 ft. lbs. (20 Nm).

39. Lower the vehicle.

40. Install the heater inlet hose to the thermostat housing.

41. Position the heater inlet hose clamp at the thermostat housing.

42. Install the auxiliary heater water pump hose to the thermostat housing.

43. Position the auxiliary heater water pump hose clamp at the thermostat housing.

44. Install the auxiliary heater water pump hose clip to the heater outlet hose.

45. Install the exhaust heat shield.

46. Install the exhaust heat shield bolts and tighten the studs to 16 ft. lbs. (22 Nm).

47. Install the radiator outlet hose to the thermostat cover.

48. Position the radiator outlet hose clamp at the thermostat cover.

49. Connect the engine wiring harness electrical connector (1) to the ECT sensor.

50. Install the HO2S electrical connector rosebud clip to the thermostat housing.

51. Install the battery tray by performing the following:

52. Set the battery tray into position and install the, and nut. Tighten the bolts to 18 ft. lbs. (25 Nm).

   a. Slide the ECM/TCM bracket into position on the battery tray.

   b. Install the ECM/TCM bracket bolt and tighten to 71 inch lbs. (8 Nm).

   c. Connect the engine wiring harness electrical connector to the TCM.

   d. Connect the engine wiring harness electrical connectors to the ECM.

   e. Install the engine wiring harness clips to the ECM/TCM bracket.

   f. Connect the body wiring harness electrical connector to the ECM.

   g. Position the body wiring harness UBEC electrical connectors to the UBEC bracket and snap into place.

   h. Position the forward lamp wiring harness UBEC electrical connector to the UBEC bracket and snap into place.

   i. Position the engine wiring harness UBEC electrical connector to the UBEC bracket and snap into place.

   j. Install junction block.

   k. Tighten the junction block bolts until the bolts engage the electrical connectors, an audible click will be heard. Tighten the bolts to 35 inch lbs. (4 Nm).

   l. Position the steering column harness package lead to the UBEC and tighten the integral bolt.

   m. Tighten the bolt to 44 inch lbs. (5 Nm).

   n. Position the positive battery cable to the battery.

   o. Position positive battery cable lead to the UBEC and tighten the integral bolt. Tighten the bolt to 44 inch lbs. (5 Nm).

   p. Install the UBEC cover.

   q. Install the battery.

53. Verify the drain valves at the radiator and water pump are closed.

54. Lower the vehicle.

55. Fill the cooling system.

WATER PUMP

REMOVAL & INSTALLATION

See Figures 23 through 26.

1. Remove the thermostat housing.

2. Remove the engine splash shield.

3. Remove the water pump access plate from the front cover.

➡ **A drain plug has been provided at the bottom of the water pump assembly for additional coolant drainage from the engine block and water pump.**

4. Drain the coolant from the water pump using the plug at the bottom of the pump.

36616_AURH_G0054

Fig. 23 Locating the drain plug

➡ **The water pump holding tool supports the sprocket and chain during water pump service. The tool must be used or the balance shaft must be re-timed.**

5. Install a water pump holding tool such as J 43651 into position.

6. Tighten the bolts on the water pump holding tool into the threads on the water pump sprocket.

7. Install the access cover bolts that were removed earlier to secure the water pump holding tool to the front cover assembly.

8. Remove the 3 inner water pump sprocket to water pump blots.

➡ **Be sure to remove both water pump bolts from the front of the engine block.**

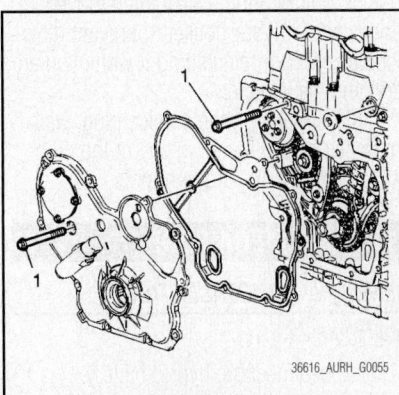

36616_AURH_G0055

Fig. 24 Locating the 2 water pump bolts

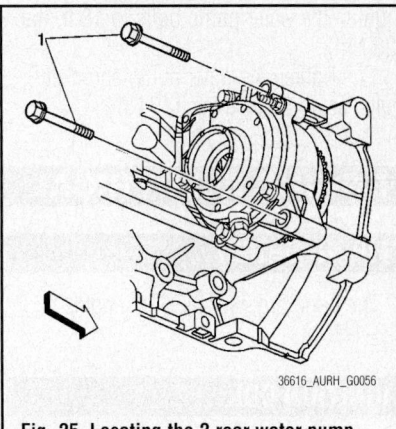

36616_AURH_G0056

Fig. 25 Locating the 2 rear water pump bolts

9. Remove the 2 water pump bolts.

10. Remove the rear 2 water pump bolts.

11. Remove the water pump.

12. Remove and discard the water pump O-ring seal.

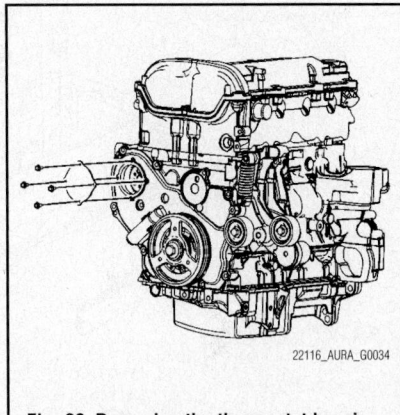

22116_AURA_G0034

Fig. 26 Removing the thermostat housing

To install:

➡ **Prior to installing the water pump, read the entire procedure. This will help avoid balance shaft chain re-timing and ensure proper sealing.**

13. Install a NEW water pump O-ring seal.

➡ **A guide pin can be created to aid in water pump alignment. Use a M6 m x 6 mm stud. Thread the pin into the water pump sprocket.**

14. Using the guide pin, align the pin with the water pump holding tool.

15. Position the water pump against the engine block and hand tighten the water pump bolts.

16. Install the inner water pump sprocket bolts. After 2 are snug, remove the guide pin and install the 3rd bolt.

Tighten the water pump bolts to 18 ft. lbs. (25 Nm).

17. Tighten the water pump sprocket bolts last to 89 inch lbs. (10 Nm).

electrical connectors from the ignition coil.

3. Remove the ignition coil bolt(s).
4. Remove the ignition coil(s).

To install:

5. Installation is the reverse of removal. Tighten the coil bolts to 89 inch lbs. (10 Nm).

18. Remove the water pump holding tool.

19. Install the water pump access plate and bolts and tighten to 89 inch lbs. (10 Nm).

20. Install the engine splash shield.

21. Install the thermostat housing.

ENGINE ELECTRICAL

FIRING ORDER

The firing order for the 2.4L engine is 1-3-4-2.

IGNITION COIL

REMOVAL & INSTALLATION

See Figure 27.

1. Remove the air cleaner outlet duct.
2. Disconnect the engine wiring harness

IGNITION TIMING

ADJUSTMENT

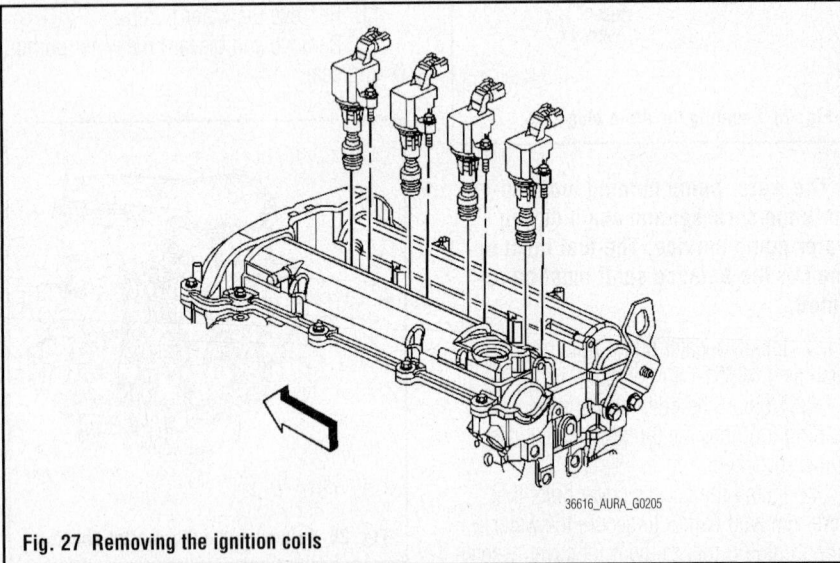

Fig. 27 Removing the ignition coils

36616_AURA_G0205

IGNITION SYSTEM

The ignition timing is controlled by the Powertrain Control Module (PCM). No adjustment is necessary or possible.

SPARK PLUGS

REMOVAL & INSTALLATION

See Figure 27.

➡ **This engine has aluminum cylinder heads. Do not remove the spark plugs from a hot engine, allow it to cool first. Removing the spark plugs from a hot engine may cause spark plug thread damage or cylinder head damage.**

1. Remove the air cleaner outlet duct.
2. Disconnect the engine wiring harness electrical connectors from the ignition coil.
3. Remove the ignition coil bolt(s).
4. Remove the ignition coil(s).

➡ **Make sure that any water and or debris is blown out of the spark plug holes prior to removing the spark plugs.**

5. Remove the spark plugs using a ⅝ inch spark plug socket.

To install:

6. Installation is the reverse of removal. Tighten the spark plugs to 15 ft. lbs. (20 Nm) and the coil bolts to 89 inch lbs. (10 Nm).

ENGINE ELECTRICAL

GENERAL INFORMATION

PRECAUTIONS

- The hybrid system operates at voltages up to 650 volts. Be sure to follow the instructions in this manual to handle the system correctly. Failure to do so may result in serious injury or electrocution. Engineer must undergo special training to be able to perform high-voltage system inspection and servicing.
- All high-voltage wire harness connectors are colored orange. The HV battery and other high-voltage components have "High Voltage" caution labels. Do not carelessly touch these wires and components.
- Before inspecting or servicing the high-voltage system, be sure to follow

safety measures, such as wearing insulated gloves and removing the service plug to prevent electrocution. Carry the removed service plug in your pocket to prevent other technicians from reinstalling it while you are servicing the vehicle.

- After removing the service plug, wait 5 minutes before touching any of the high-voltage connectors and terminals.

175 AMP MEGA FUSE

REMOVAL & INSTALLATION

See Figure 29.

1. Disconnect the hybrid battery.
2. Remove the 2 Connector Position Assurance (CPA) retainers.

HYBRID SYSTEM

✳✳ WARNING

To help avoid personal injury, additional precautions must be taken prior to working on the generator control module or the generator starter. After removing the 36V battery cables from the generator battery, remove both engine wiring harness connectors from the generator control module. Wait at least 5 minutes and then remove the generator control module cover. Verify voltage levels at all 36V, 12V, and 3-phase connections, are less than 3 volts using a DMM before proceeding.

3. Disconnect the 2 engine wiring har-

ness electrical connectors from the generator control module.

4. WAIT at least 5 minutes in order to allow the voltage stored in the generator control module to discharge.

5. Remove the generator control module bracket reinforcement bolt and nuts.

6. Remove the generator control module bracket reinforcement

7. Loosen the generator control module cover integral bolts and remove the cover.

8. The generator control module will have to be checked for voltage potential using a voltmeter. First, verify that the voltmeter works.

   a. Set the voltmeter to DC voltage.

   b. Measure the vehicle's 12V battery voltage.

   c. The meter should read greater than +12V DC.

9. Now, check the generator control module for voltage potential, in order to ensure that the module has been disabled.

   a. Measure from the 36V positive terminal to a known good chassis ground. The voltage should be less than 3V.

   b. Measure from the 12V positive terminal to a known good chassis ground. The voltage should be less than 3V.

   c. Measure from the ground terminal to know good chassis ground, checking for continuity.

❊❊ WARNING

To help avoid personal injury, always treat the 3-phase cable and connectors as if voltage is present and as if the surface of all parts of the cable is hot.

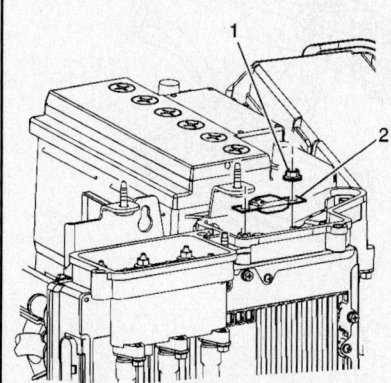

1. Battery positive cable fuse nut
2. Battery positive cable fuse

36616_AURH_G0022

Fig. 29 Removing the battery positive cable fuse from the generator control module

10. Verify that the generator control module 3-phase cables are disabled.

   a. Measure from each phase 1, 2, and 3 connection to a known good chassis ground. The voltage should be less than 3V.

   b. After verifying that there is no voltage present, the battery positive fuse can now be removed from the generator control module.

11. Remove the battery positive cable extension cable nut from the generator control module.

12. Carefully lift the extension cable off of the lug and position aside.

13. Remove the battery positive cable fuse nut.

14. Remove the battery positive cable fuse from the generator control module.

To install:

15. Install the battery positive cable fuse to the generator control module.

16. Loosely install the battery positive cable fuse nut.

17. Carefully install the extension cable to the lug.

18. Install the battery positive cable extension cable nut to the generator control module.

19. Tighten the fuse and the battery positive cable extension cable nuts. Tighten the nuts to 89 inch lbs. (10 Nm).

20. Place the generator control module cover on top of the generator control module and tighten the bolts. Tighten the bolts to 89 inch lbs. (10 Nm).

21. Install the generator control module bracket reinforcement.

22. Install the generator control module bracket reinforcement bolt and nuts. Tighten the bolt/nuts to 89 inch lbs. (10 Nm).

23. Connect the 2 engine wiring harness electrical connectors to the generator control module.

24. Install the 2 CPA retainers.

25. Connect the hybrid battery.

36V BATTERY INTERNAL CABLE

REMOVAL & INSTALLATION

See Figures 30 and 31.

1. Disconnect the generator battery.

2. Remove the 2 generator battery vent fan cover bolts.

3. Remove the 12 generator battery cover bolts.

4. Remove the generator battery cover.

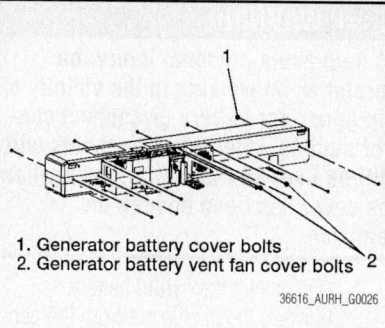

1. Generator battery cover bolts
2. Generator battery vent fan cover bolts

36616_AURH_G0026

Fig. 30 Removing the generator battery vent and cover bolts

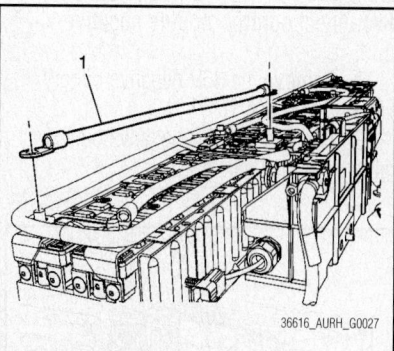

36616_AURH_G0027

Fig. 31 Removing the 36V battery internal cable

➡**Removing the interconnect cables will disable the 36 volts within the generator battery control module.**

5. Remove the generator battery terminal rubber cups.

6. Remove the generator battery cable nuts.

7. Remove the 36-Volt battery internal cable from the battery.

To install:

8. Install the 36-Volt battery internal cable to the battery.

9. Install the generator battery cable nuts and tighten to 71 inch lbs. (8 Nm).

10. Install the generator battery terminal rubber cups.

11. Install the generator battery cover.

12. Install the 12 generator battery cover bolts and tighten to 71 inch lbs. (8 Nm).

13. Install the 2 generator battery vent fan cover bolts and tighten to 71 inch lbs. (8 Nm).

14. Connect the generator battery.

36V BATTERY NEGATIVE CABLE

REMOVAL & INSTALLATION

See Figure 32.

✳✳ WARNING

To help avoid personal injury, be careful when working in the vicinity of the generator battery disconnect control module. Internal components will still be live, 36V potential, even when the cover has been opened or removed.

    1. Disconnect the hybrid battery.
    2. Remove the plastic nut from the generator battery disconnect control module negative stud.
    3. Remove the 36V negative battery cable lead from the generator battery disconnect control module negative stud.
    4. Remove the 36V negative battery cable ground nut.
    5. Remove the 36V negative battery cable from the vehicle.

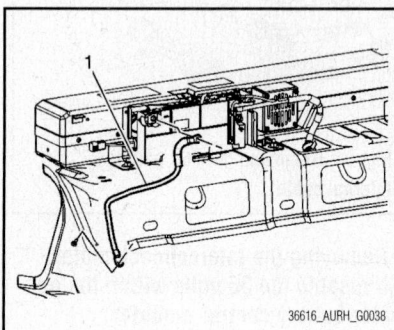

Fig. 32 Removing the 36V negative battery cable

To install:

    6. Install the 36V negative battery cable to the vehicle.
    7. Install the 36V negative battery cable ground nut. Tighten the nut to 80 inch lbs. (9 Nm).

➡**Position the plastic nut to the negative battery cable and ensure that the nipple is inserted to the terminal prior to installing the negative cable to the generator battery, Otherwise damage to the nut may occur.**

    8. Position the plastic nut to the 36V negative battery cable lead ensuring that the nipple on the plastic nut is inserted through the hole in the terminal.
    9. Install the 36V negative battery cable lead and nut to the generator battery disconnect module negative stud. Tighten the nut to 95 inch lbs. (10.7 Nm).
    10. Connect the hybrid battery.

36V BATTERY POSITIVE CABLE

REMOVAL & INSTALLATION

Passenger Compartment To Module
See Figure 33.

✳✳ WARNING

To help avoid personal injury, be careful when working in the vicinity of the generator battery disconnect control module. Internal components will still be live, 36V potential, even when the cover has been opened or removed.

    1. Disconnect the hybrid battery.
    2. Remove and discard the 36V positive battery cable lead nut.
    3. Remove the 36V positive battery cable lead nut.
    4. Remove the 36V positive battery cable leads.
    5. Remove the 36V positive battery cable retainer bolt.
    6. Raise and support the vehicle.
    7. Remove the 36V positive battery cable clip nut.
    8. Remove the 36V positive battery cable casting nuts.

    9. Carefully lower the 36V positive battery cable casting until the cable connector and 36V positive battery cable pigtail connector is accessible.
    10. Disconnect the 36V positive battery cable pigtail connector from the 36V positive battery cable casting by rotating the connector ring on the pigtail counterclockwise.
    11. Lower the vehicle.
    12. Remove the 36V positive battery cable pigtail connector.

To install:

    13. Install the 36Vpositive battery cable pigtail connector.
    14. Raise and suitably support the vehicle.
    15. Align the 36V positive battery cable pigtail connection keyway with the paint dot on the 36V positive battery cable casting. Once aligned, rotate the pigtail lock ring securing the connection.
    16. Carefully feed the 36V positive battery cable pigtail into the rear compartment panel until the 36V positive battery cable casting is seated onto the studs.
    17. Install the 36V positive battery cable casting nuts. Tighten the nuts to 80 inch lbs. (9 Nm).
    18. Install the 36V positive battery cable clip nut. Tighten the nuts to 80 inch lbs. (9 Nm).

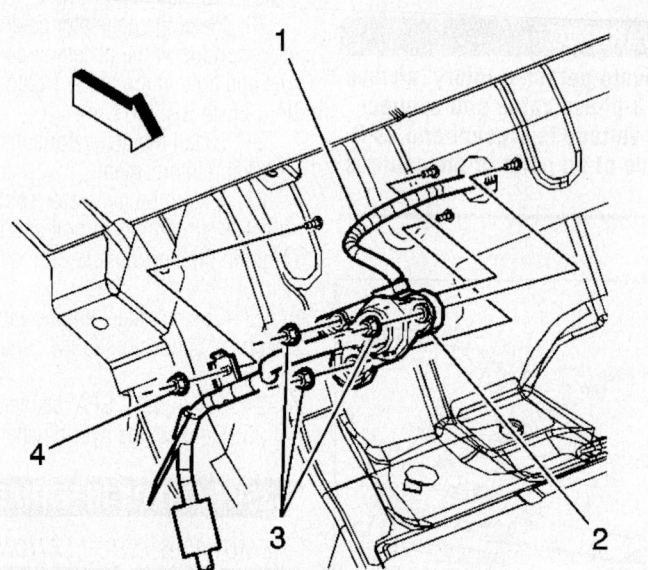

1. 36V positive battery cable pigtail connector
2. 36V positive battery cable casting
3. 36V positive battery cable nuts
4. 36V positive battery cable clip nut

Fig. 33 Locating the 36V positive battery cable clip nut, casting nuts, casting and pigtail connector

19. Lower the vehicle.
20. Position the 36V positive battery cable retainer to the fan cover.
21. Install the 36V positive battery cable retainer bolt. Tighten the bolt to 71 inch lbs. (8 Nm).
22. Install the 36V positive battery cable leads.
23. Install the 36V positive battery cable lead nut. Tighten the nut to 18 inch lbs. (9 Nm).
24. Install a NEW 36V positive battery cable lead nut. Start the nut finger tight, and then torque to the specification given. Tighten the nut to 11 ft. lbs. (15 Nm).
25. Connect the hybrid battery.

Engine to Passenger Compartment

See Figures 34 and 35.

1. Disconnect the hybrid battery.
2. Remove the fuel tank.
3. Remove the (12V) battery tray.
4. Remove the left rear frame bolts.
5. Remove the left rear frame reinforcement.
6. Lower the vehicle.
7. Disconnect the 2 Connector Position Assurance (CPA) retainers.
8. Disconnect the 2 engine wiring harness electrical connectors (2) from the generator control module.
9. WAIT at least 5 minutes in order to allow the voltage stored in the generator control module to discharge.

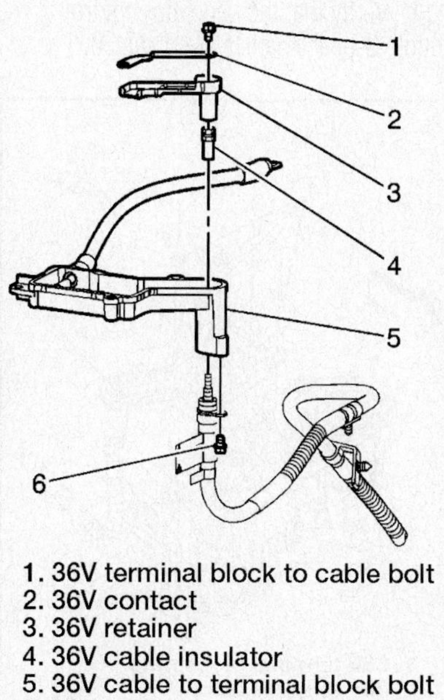

10. Remove the generator control module bracket reinforcement bolt and nuts.
11. Remove the generator control module bracket reinforcement.
12. Loosen the generator control module cover integral bolts and remove the cover.
13. The generator control module will have to be checked for voltage potential using a voltmeter. First, verify that the voltmeter works:
   a. Set the voltmeter to DC voltage.
   b. Measure the vehicle's 12V battery voltage.
   c. The meter should read greater than +12V DC.
14. Now, check the generator control module for voltage potential, in order to ensure that the module has been disabled.
   a. Measure from the 36V positive terminal to a known good chassis ground. The voltage should be less than 3V.
   b. Measure the 12V positive terminal to a known good chassis ground. The voltage should be less than 3 volts.
   c. Measure the ground terminal to a known good chassis ground, checking for continuity.

✷✷ WARNING

To help avoid personal injury, always treat the 3-phase cable and connectors as if voltage is present and as if the surface of all parts of the cable is hot.

15. Verify that the generator control module 3-phase cables are disabled.
   a. Measure from each phase 1, 2, and 3 connection to a known good chassis ground. The voltage should be less than 3V.

b. After verifying that there is no voltage present, the 12V and 36V positive battery cables can now be removed from the generator control module.
16. Remove the 36V terminal block nuts from the generator control module.
17. Lift up, and reposition the 36V terminal block. Discard the terminal block seal.
18. Remove the 36V terminal block to cable bolt.
19. Remove the 36V contact and retainer.
20. Remove the 36V cable insulator.
21. Remove the 36V cable to terminal block bolt.
22. Remove the 36V cable terminal block from the cable.
23. Remove the 36V positive battery cable clip from the side rail.
24. Raise and support the vehicle.
25. Remove the 36V positive battery cable clips from the side rail and the front of dash.
26. Remove the 36V positive battery cable clip nut.
27. Remove the 36V positive battery cable casting nuts.
28. Carefully lower the 36V positive battery cable casting until the cable connector and 36-volt positive battery cable pigtail connector is accessible.
29. Disconnect the 36V positive battery cable pigtail connector from the 36V positive battery cable casting by rotating the connector ring on the pigtail counterclockwise.
30. Have an assistant support the 36V positive battery cable.
31. Remove the 36V positive battery cable to underbody nuts.

1. 36V terminal block to cable bolt
2. 36V contact
3. 36V retainer
4. 36V cable insulator
5. 36V cable to terminal block bolt
6. 36V cable terminal block

36616_AURH_G0023

Fig. 34 Removing the 36V cable terminal block from the cable

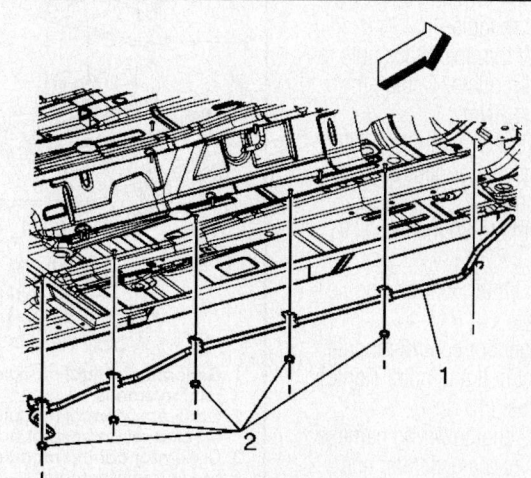

1. 36V positive battery cable
2. 36V positive battery cable to underbody nuts

36616_AURH_G0024

Fig. 35 Locating 36V positive battery cable to underbody nuts

32. Remove the 36V positive battery cable from the vehicle.

To install:

33. With the aid of an assistant, position the 36V positive battery cable to the vehicle.

34. Install the 36V positive battery cable to underbody nuts. Tighten the nuts to 80 inch lbs. (9 Nm).

35. Align the 36V positive battery cable pigtail connection keyway to the paint dot on the 36V positive battery cable casting. Once aligned, rotate the pigtail lock ring securing the connection.

36. Carefully feed the 36V positive battery cable pigtail into the rear compartment panel until the 36V positive battery cable casting is seated onto the studs.

37. Install the 36V positive battery cable casting nuts. Tighten the nuts to 80 inch lbs. (9 Nm).

38. Install the 36V positive battery cable clip nut. Tighten the nuts to 80 inch lbs. (9 Nm).

39. Install the 36V positive battery cable clips to the side rail and the front of dash.

40. Lower the vehicle.

41. Install the 36V positive battery cable clip to the side rail.

42. Install the 36V cable terminal block to the cable.

43. Install the 36V cable to the terminal block bolt. Tighten the bolt to 80 inch lbs. (9 Nm).

44. Install the 36V cable insulator.

45. Install the 36V retainer and contact.

46. Install the 36V terminal block to cable bolt. Tighten the bolt to 80 inch lbs. (9 Nm).

47. Place a NEW terminal block seal onto the generator control module.

48. Position the 36V terminal block to the generator control module.

49. Install the 36V terminal block nuts to the generator control module. Tighten the nuts to 89 inch lbs. (10 Nm).

50. Place the generator control module cover on top of the generator control module and tighten the bolts.

51. Tighten the nuts to 89 inch lbs. (10 Nm).

52. Install the generator control module bracket reinforcement.

53. Install the generator control module bracket reinforcement bolt and nuts. Tighten the nuts to 89 inch lbs. (10 Nm).

54. Connect the 2 engine wiring harness electrical connectors to the generator control module.

55. Connect the 2 CPA retainers.

56. Raise and suitably support the vehicle.

57. Install the left rear frame reinforcement.

58. Install the left rear frame bolts. Tighten the bolts to 74 ft. lbs. (100 Nm) plus an additional 90 degrees using the Angle Meter (J 45059) .

59. Install the (12V) battery tray.

60. Install the fuel tank.

61. Connect the hybrid battery.

BATTERY POSITIVE CABLE EXTENSION CABLE

REMOVAL & INSTALLATION

See Figures 36 through 38.

1. Disconnect the hybrid battery.
2. Remove the 2 Connector Position Assurance (CPA) retainers.

> ### ❊❊ WARNING
>
> **To help avoid personal injury, additional precautions must be taken prior to working on the generator control module or the generator starter. After removing the 36V battery cables from the generator battery, remove both engine wiring harness connectors from the generator control module.**

3. Wait at least 5 minutes and then remove the generator control module cover. Verify voltage levels at all 36V, 12V, and 3-phase connections, are less than 3 volts using a DMM before proceeding.

4. Disconnect the 2 engine wiring harness electrical connectors from the generator control module.

5. WAIT at least 5 minutes in order to

allow the voltage stored in the generator control module to discharge.

6. Remove the generator control module bracket reinforcement bolt and nuts.

7. Remove the generator control module bracket reinforcement.

8. Loosen the generator control module cover integral bolts and remove the cover.

9. The generator control module will have to be checked for voltage potential using a voltmeter. First, verify that the voltmeter works:

   a. Set the voltmeter to DC voltage.

   b. Measure the vehicle's 12V battery voltage.

   c. The meter should read greater than +12 volts DC.

10. Now, check the generator control module for voltage potential, in order to ensure that the module has been disabled.

   a. Measure from the 36V positive terminal to a known good chassis ground. The voltage should be less than 3 volts.

   b. Measure from the 12V positive terminal to a known good chassis ground. The voltage should be less than 3 volts.

   c. Measure from the ground terminal to known good chassis ground, checking for continuity.

> ### ❊❊ WARNING
>
> **To help avoid personal injury, always treat the 3-phase cable and connectors as if voltage is present and as if the surface of all parts of the cable is hot.**

11. Verify that the generator control module 3-phase cables are disabled.

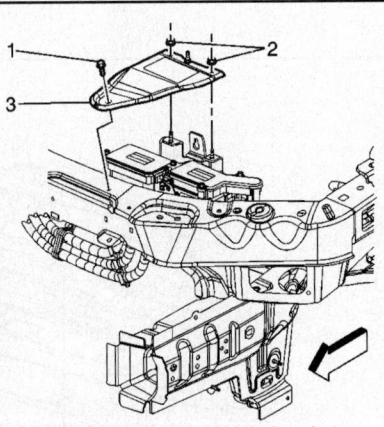

1. Generator control module bracket reinforcement
2. Generator control module bracket reinforcement nuts
3. Generator control module bracket reinforcement

36616_AURH_G0028

Fig. 36 Removing the generator control bracket reinforcement

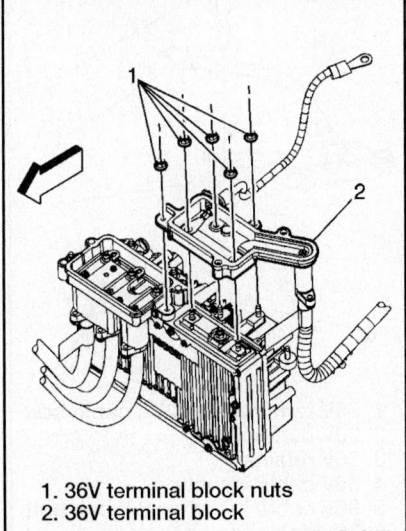

1. 36V terminal block nuts
2. 36V terminal block

36616_AURH_G0029

Fig. 37 Repositioning the 36V terminal block

a. Measure from each phase 1, 2, and 3 connection to a known good chassis ground. The voltage should be less than 3 volts.

b. After verifying that there is no voltage present, the battery positive fuse can now be removed from the generator control module.

12. Remove the 36V terminal block nuts from the generator control module.

13. Lift up, and reposition the 36V terminal block. Discard the terminal block seal.

14. Remove the battery positive cable extension cable bolt.

15. Disengage the two side retaining tabs on the positive battery cable, and open the cover.

16. Remove the battery positive cable extension cable nut.

17. Remove the battery positive cable extension cable lead from the positive battery cable.

18. Remove the battery positive cable extension cable from the vehicle.

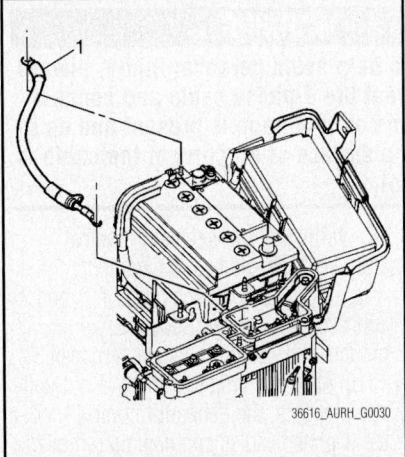

Fig. 38 Removing the battery positive cable extension cable (1)

To install:

19. Install the battery positive cable extension cable to the vehicle.

20. Install the battery positive cable extension cable lead to the positive battery cable.

21. Install the battery positive cable extension cable nut. Tighten the nut to 89 inch lbs. (10 Nm).

22. Close the positive battery cable cover.

23. Install the battery positive cable extension cable bolt. Tighten the bolt to 89 inch lbs. (10 Nm).

24. Place a NEW terminal block seal onto the generator control module.

25. Position the 36V terminal block to the generator control module.

26. Install the 36V terminal block nuts to the generator control module. Tighten the nuts to 89 inch lbs. (10 Nm).

27. Place the generator control module cover on top of the generator control module and tighten the bolts. Tighten the bolts to 89 inch lbs. (10 Nm).

28. Install the generator control module bracket reinforcement.

29. Install the generator control module bracket reinforcement bolt and nuts. Tighten the bolt/nuts to 89 inch lbs. (10 Nm).

30. Connect the 2 engine wiring harness electrical connectors to the generator control module.

31. Install the 2 CPA retainers.

32. Connect the hybrid battery.

GENERATOR AND STARTER

REMOVAL & INSTALLATION

See Figures 39 through 47.

1. Disconnect the hybrid battery.
2. Remove the drive belt tensioner.
3. Remove the radiator inlet hose.
4. Reposition the power brake booster vacuum hose clamp at the intake manifold.
5. Remove the power brake booster vacuum hose from the intake manifold.

6. Remove the power brake booster vacuum hose from the clamp on the generator control module coolant outlet hose.

7. Reposition the power brake booster vacuum hose out of the way.

❊❊ WARNING

To help avoid personal injury, additional precautions must be taken prior to working on the generator control module or the generator starter. After removing the 36V battery cables from the generator battery, remove both engine wiring harness connectors from the generator control module. Wait at least 5 minutes and then remove the generator control module cover. Verify voltage levels at all 36V, 12V, and 3-phase connections, are less than 3 volts using a DMM before proceeding.

8. Remove the 2 Connector Position Assurance (CPA) retainers.

9. Disconnect the 2 engine wiring harness electrical connectors from the generator control module.

10. WAIT at least 5 minutes in order to allow the voltage stored in the generator control module to discharge.

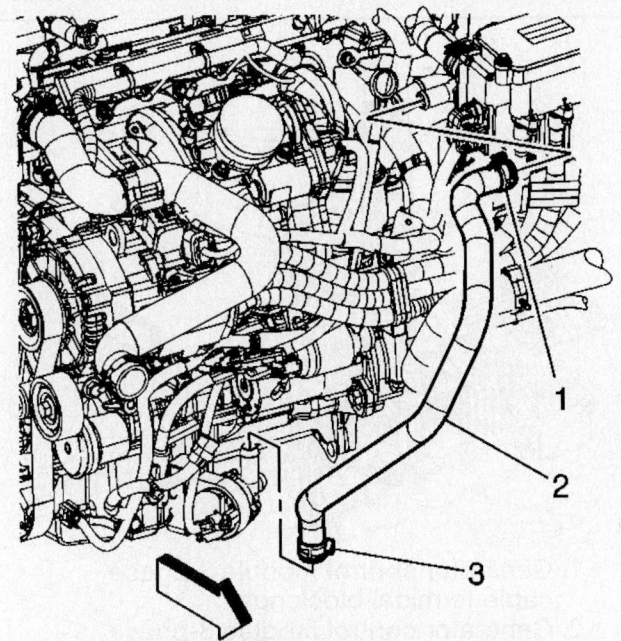

1. **Generator control module coolant inlet hose clamp**
2. **Generator control module coolant inlet hose**
3. **Hose clamp**

Fig. 39 Removing the generator control module coolant inlet hose

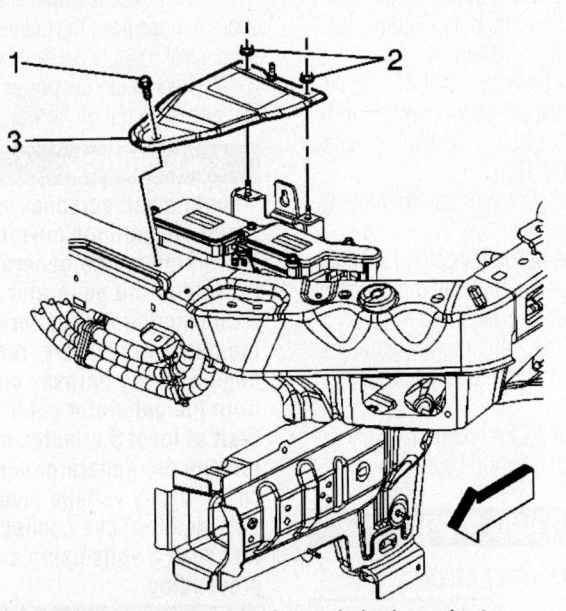

1. **Generator control module bracket reinforcement bolt**
2. **Generator control module bracket reinforcement nut**
3. **Generator control module bracket reinforcement**

36616_AURH_G0004

Fig. 40 Removing and installing the generator control module bracket reinforcement

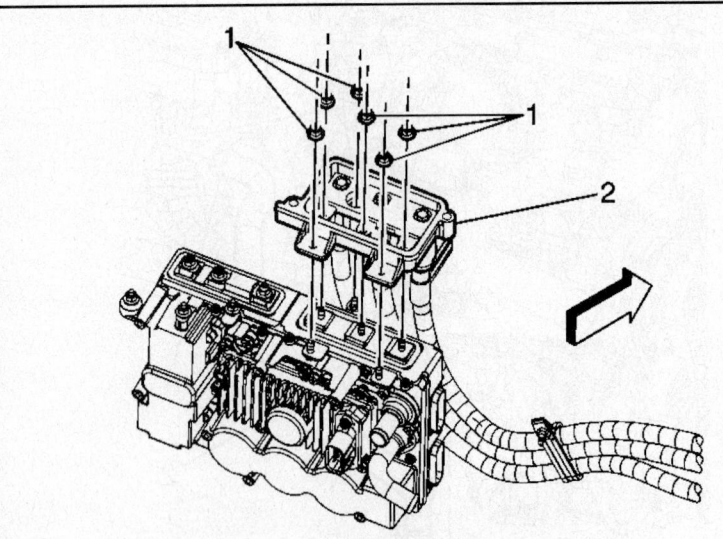

1. **Generator control module 3-phase cable terminal block nuts**
2. **Generator control module 3-phase cable terminal block**

36616_AURH_G0005

Fig. 41 Repositioning the generator control module 3-phase cable terminal block

11. Reposition the generator control module coolant inlet hose clamp at the generator control module using the Hose Clamp Pliers (J 38185) or equivalent.

12. Remove the generator control module coolant inlet hose from the generator control module.

13. Remove the generator control

module bracket reinforcement bolt and nuts.

14. Remove the generator control module bracket reinforcement.

15. Loosen the generator control module cover integral bolts and remove the cover.

16. The generator control module will have to be checked for voltage potential using a voltmeter. First verify that the voltmeter works. Set the voltmeter to DC voltage. Measure the vehicle 12V battery voltage. The meter should read greater than +12V DC.

17. Now, check the generator control module for voltage potential, in order to ensure that the module has been disabled.

   a. Measure from the 36V positive terminal to a known good chassis ground. The voltage should be less than 3 volts.

   b. Measure from the 12V positive terminal to a known good chassis ground. The voltage should be less than 3 volts.

   c. Measure the ground terminal to a know good chassis ground, checking for continuity.

❋❋ WARNING

To help avoid personal injury, always treat the 3-phase cable and connectors as if voltage is present and as if the surface of all parts of the cable is hot.

18. Verify that the generator control module 3-phase cables are disabled.

   a. Measure front each phase 1, 2, and 3 connection to a known good chassis ground. The voltage should be less than 3V.

   b. After verifying that there is not voltage presents, the generator control module 3-phase cables can now be removed from the generator control module.

19. Disconnect the engine wiring harness electrical connectors from the generator starter.

20. Reposition the wiring harness out of the way.

21. Remove the 36V terminal block nuts from the generator control module.

22. Lift up, and reposition the 36-volt terminal block, secure the block out of the way. Discard the terminal block seal.

23. Remove the Air Conditioning (A/C) condenser/evaporator tube clip from the front end upper tie bar reinforcement.

24. Reposition the A/C condenser/evaporator tube out of the way.

25. Remove the starter 3-phase cable clip bolt from the oil level indicator tube bracket.

26. Remove the upper generator starter bolt.

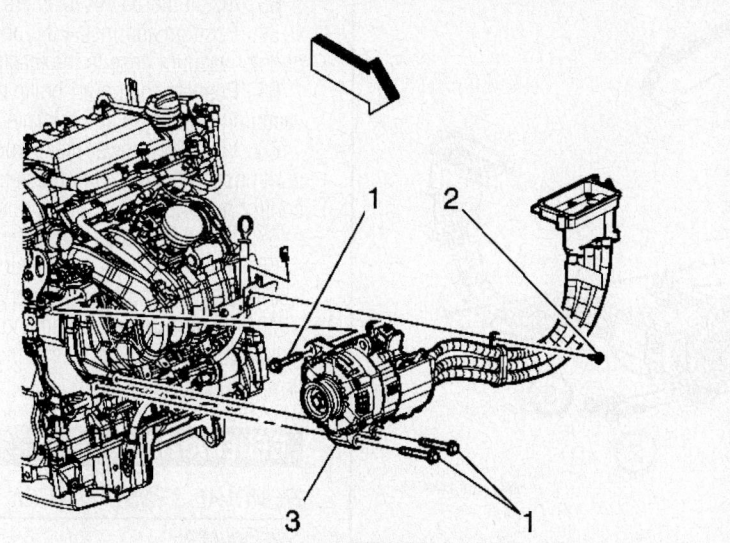

1. Upper generator starter bolt
2. Starter 3-phase cable clip bolt
3. Generator starter (with the generator control module 3-phase cables attached)

Fig. 42 Removing and installing the generator

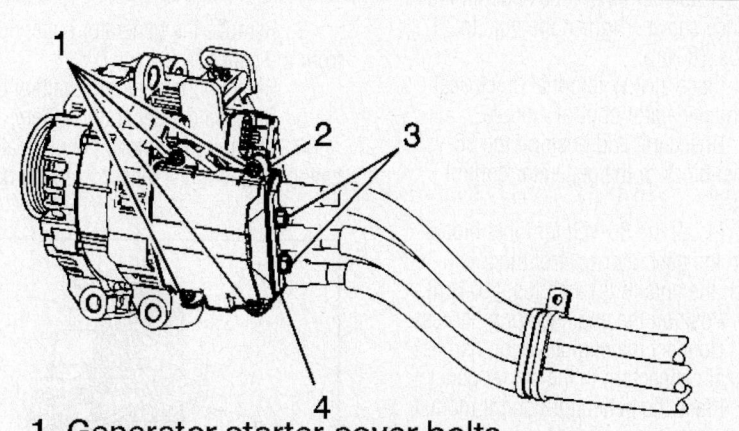

1. Generator starter cover bolts
2. Generator starter cover
3. Generator control module 3-phase cable bracket bolts
4. Generator control module 3-phase cable bracket

Fig. 43 Removing the generator control module 3-phase bracket

27. Raise and suitably support the vehicle.

28. Remove the 2 lower generator starter bolts.

29. Lower the vehicle.

30. Remove the generator starter (with the generator control module 3-phase cables attached) from the vehicle and place on a clean work surface.

31. Remove the generator starter cover bolts and cover.

32. Remove the generator control module 3-phase cable bracket bolts and bracket.

33. From inside the generator starter,

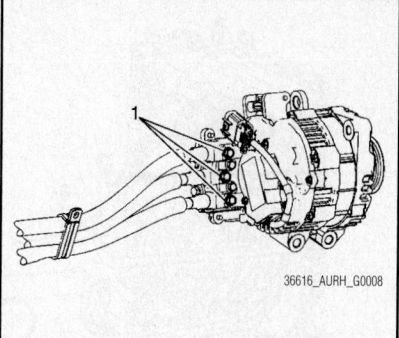

Fig. 44 Locating the rear generator control module 3-phase cable bolts (1)

remove the generator control module 3-phase cable to generator starter nuts.

34. Remove the rear generator control module 3-phase cable bolts.

35. Remove the generator control module 3-phase cable assembly from the generator starter.

To install:

36. Install the generator control module 3-phase cable assembly to the NEW generator starter.

37. Inside the generator starter, install the generator control module 3-phase cable to the studs and install the generator starter nuts. Tighten the nuts to 71 inch lbs. (8 Nm).

38. Install the generator control module 3-phase cable bracket and bolts. Tighten the bolts to 71 inch lbs. (8 Nm).

39. Install the generator starter cover and bolts. Tighten the bolts to 44 inch lbs. (5 Nm).

40. Install the rear generator control module 3-phase cable bolts. Tighten to 71 inch lbs. (8 Nm).

41. Position the generator starter (with the generator control module 3-phase cables attached) to the vehicle and install the upper bolt until snug.

42. Raise and suitably support the vehicle.

43. Install the 2 lower generator starter bolts until snug.

44. Install the generator starter 3-phase cable clip bolt to the oil level indicator tube bracket. Tighten the bolt to 89 inch lbs. (10 Nm).

45. Tighten the generator starter bolts in the sequence shown. Tighten the bolts to 43 ft. lbs. (58 Nm).

46. Position the A/C condenser/evaporator tube to the front end upper tie bar reinforcement.

47. Install the A/C condenser/evaporator tube clip to the front end upper tie bar reinforcement.

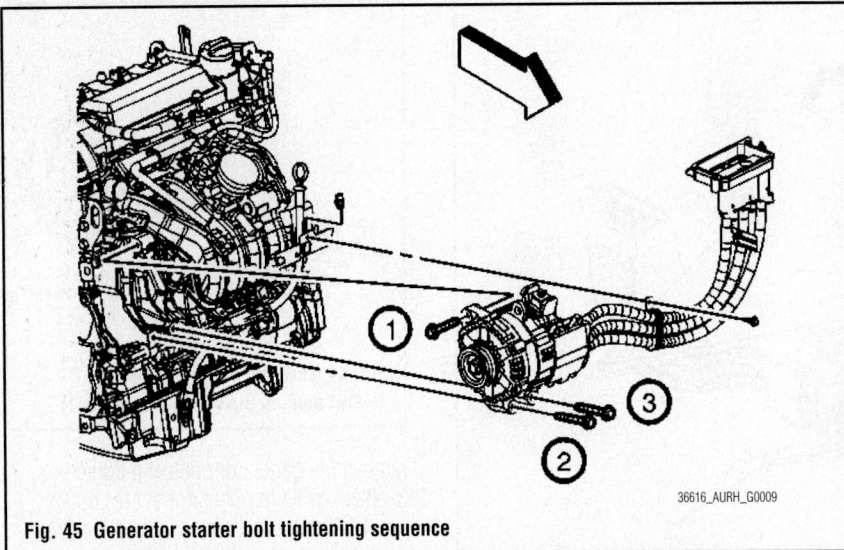

Fig. 45 Generator starter bolt tightening sequence

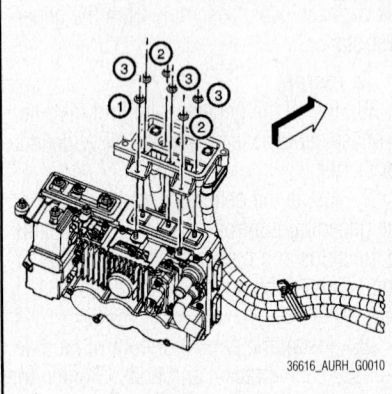

Fig. 46 Generator control module 3-phase cable terminal block nut tightening sequence

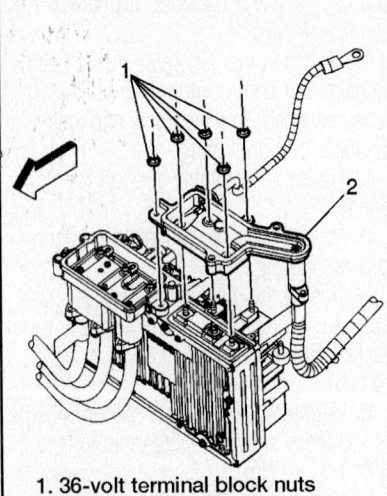

1. 36-volt terminal block nuts
2. 36-volt terminal block

Fig. 47 Positioning the 36-volt terminal block on the generator control module

48. Place a NEW terminal block seal onto the generator control module.

49. Install the generator control module 3-phase cable terminal block onto the generator control module.

50. Install the generator control module 3-phase cable terminal block nuts until snug.

51. Tighten the generator control module 3-phase cable terminal block nuts in the sequence shown. Tighten the nuts to 71 inch lbs. (8 Nm).

52. Place a NEW terminal block seal onto the generator control module.

53. Unsecure, and position the 36-volt terminal block to the generator control module.

54. Install the 36-volt terminal block nuts to the generator control module. Tighten the nuts to 89 inch lbs. (10 Nm).

55. Position the engine wiring harness.

56. Connect the engine wiring harness electrical connectors to the starter generator.

57. Place the generator control module cover on top of the generator control module and tighten the bolts. Tighten the bolts to 89 inch lbs. (10 Nm).

58. Install the generator control module bracket reinforcement.

59. Install the generator control module bracket reinforcement bolt and nuts. Tighten the bolt/nuts to 89 inch lbs. (10 Nm).

60. Install the generator control module coolant inlet hose to the generator control module.

61. Position the generator control module coolant inlet hose clamp at the generator control module using the Hose Clamp Pliers (J 38185) or equivalent.

62. Connect the 2 engine wiring harness electrical connectors to the generator control module.

63. Install the 2 CPA retainers.

64. Position and install the power brake booster vacuum hose to the intake manifold.

65. Position the power brake booster vacuum hose clamp at the intake manifold.

66. Install the power brake booster vacuum hose to the clamp to the generator control module coolant outlet hose.

67. Install the radiator inlet hose.

68. Install the drive belt tensioner.

69. Connect the hybrid battery.

70. Using a Tech 2, command an autostart in order to verify that the system is working properly.

GENERATOR BATTERY

REMOVAL & INSTALLATION

See Figure 48.

➡**If one battery requires replacement, the other batteries also are to be replaced.**

1. Remove the generator battery temperature sensor wiring harness.

2. Remove the generator battery cable nuts from the battery cable terminals.

➡ **Note original routing of battery cables to ensure proper installation.**

3. Remove the generator battery cables from the batteries.

4. Remove the generator battery bolts.

5. Remove the generator battery.

6. If required, remove the generator battery temperature sensor from the battery.

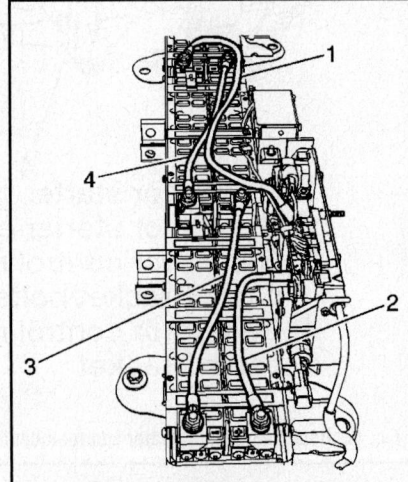

1. Generator battery cable nut
2. Generator battery cable nut
3. Generator battery cable nut
4. Generator battery cable nut

Fig. 48 Removing generator battery cable nuts

To install:

7. If required, install the generator battery temperature sensor to the battery.

8. Install the generator battery

9. Install the generator battery bolts. Tighten the bolts to 89 inch lbs. (10 Nm).

10. Install the generator battery cables to the batteries.

11. Install the generator battery cable nuts to the battery cable terminals. Tighten the nuts to 71 inch lbs. (8 Nm).

12. Install the generator battery temperature sensor wiring harness.

GENERATOR BATTERY CARRIER

REMOVAL & INSTALLATION

See Figure 49.

❊❊ WARNING

To help avoid personal injury, be careful when working in the vicinity of the generator battery disconnect control module. Internal components will still be live, 36V potential, even when the cover has been opened or removed.

1. Disconnect the hybrid battery.

2. Remove the plastic nut from the generator battery disconnect control module negative stud.

3. Remove the 36V negative battery cable lead from the generator battery disconnect control module negative stud.

4. Remove the generator battery fuse from the generator battery disconnect module negative stud.

5. Remove the 36V positive battery cable retainer bolt.

6. Remove and discard the 36V positive battery cable lead nut.

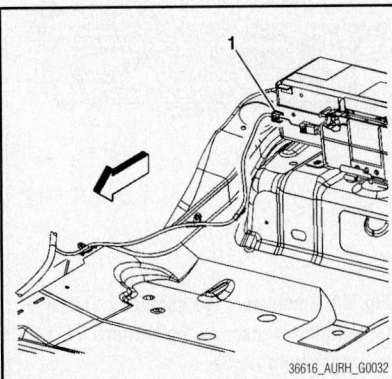

Fig. 49 Disconnecting the body wiring harness electrical connector from the generator battery disconnect control module pigtail

7. Remove the 36V positive battery cable lead nut.

8. Remove the 36V positive battery cable leads.

9. Secure the cables out of the way, ensuring that the cables CANNOT be reinstalled without your knowledge.

10. Disconnect the body wiring harness electrical connector from the generator battery disconnect control module pigtail.

11. Remove the generator battery carrier nuts.

12. With the aid of an assistant, lift the generator battery carrier up off of the studs, and rotate and position the carrier towards the rear of the vehicle.

13. With the aid of an assistant, remove the generator battery carrier out though the truck opening.

To install:

14. With the aid of an assistant, install the generator battery carrier in though the truck opening and rotate and position the carrier towards the front of the vehicle.

15. With the aid of an assistant, lift the generator battery carrier up onto the studs.

16. Install the generator battery carrier nuts. Tighten the nuts to 18 ft. lbs. (25 Nm).

17. Connect the body wiring harness electrical connector to the generator battery disconnect control module pigtail.

18. Install the 36V positive battery cable leads.

19. Install the 36V positive battery cable lead nut. Tighten the nut to 18 inch lbs. (9 Nm).

20. Install a NEW 36V positive battery cable lead nut. Start the nut finger tight, and then torque to the specification given. Tighten the nut to 11 ft. lbs. (15 Nm).

21. Position the 36V positive battery cable retainer to the fan cover.

22. Install the 36V positive battery cable retainer bolt. Tighten the bolt to 71 inch lbs. (8 Nm).

23. Install the generator battery fuse to the generator battery disconnect module negative stud.

➡**Position the plastic nut to the negative battery cable and ensure that the nipple is inserted to the terminal prior to installing the negative cable to the generator battery, Otherwise damage to the nut may occur.**

24. Position the plastic nut to the 36V negative battery cable lead ensuring that the nipple on the plastic nut is inserted through the hole in the terminal.

25. Install the 36V negative battery cable lead and nut to the generator battery dis-

connect module negative stud. Tighten the nut to 95 inch lbs. (10.7 Nm).

26. Connect the hybrid battery.

GENERATOR BATTERY TEMPERATURE SENSOR

REMOVAL & INSTALLATION

See Figure 50.

1. Remove the generator battery.

2. Remove the generator battery temperature sensor from the battery.

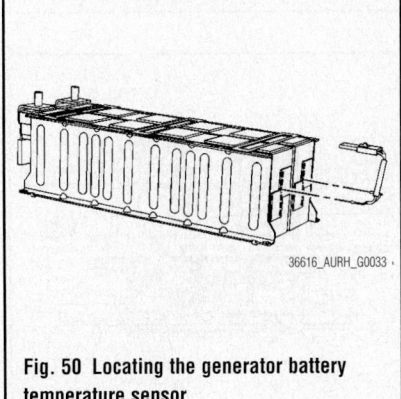

Fig. 50 Locating the generator battery temperature sensor

To install:

3. Install the generator battery temperature sensor to the battery.

4. Install the generator battery.

GENERATOR BATTERY TEMPERATURE SENSOR WIRING HARNESS

REMOVAL & INSTALLATION

See Figures 51 through 54.

1. Disconnect the generator battery.

2. Remove the 2 generator battery vent fan cover bolts.

3. Remove the 12 generator battery cover bolts.

4. Remove the generator battery cover.

➡**Removing the interconnect cables will disable the 36 volts within the generator battery control module.**

5. Remove the generator battery terminal covers.

6. Remove the generator battery cable nuts.

7. Remove the generator battery cable leads (1, 2, and 3) from the batteries.

8. Remove the 2 small temperature sensor wiring harness terminal leads located under the battery cable leads from the batteries.

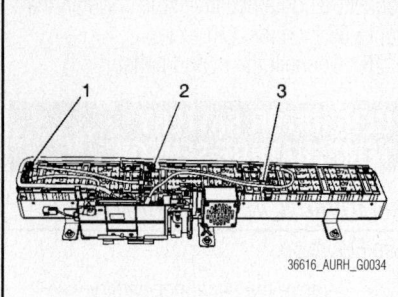

Fig. 51 Removing the generator battery cable leads

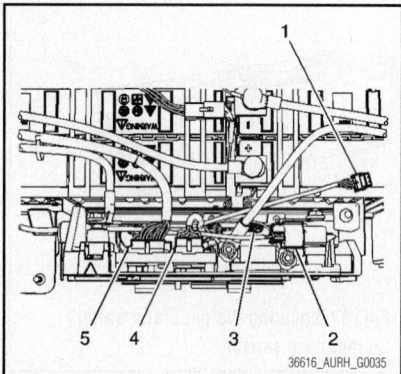

Fig. 52 Disconnecting generator battery temperature sensor wiring harness electrical connectors (2, 5)

9. Disconnect the generator battery temperature sensor wiring harness electrical connectors (2, 5) from the generator control module.

10. Disconnect the generator battery temperature sensor wiring harness electrical connectors from the battery temperature sensors.

11. Remove the generator battery terminal covers and nuts securing the generator battery cable leads.

12. Remove the generator battery cable leads from the batteries.

13. Remove the 2 small temperature sensor wiring harness terminal leads located under the battery cable leads from the batteries.

14. Cut the tie straps securing the battery cables to the generator battery temperature sensor wiring harness.

15. Unclip the wiring harness retainers.

16. Remove the generator battery temperature sensor wiring harness from the generator battery assembly.

To install:

17. Install the generator battery temperature sensor wiring harness to the generator battery assembly.

18. Clip the wiring harness retainers.

19. Install the 2 small temperature sensor wiring harness terminal leads to the batteries.

20. Install the generator battery cable leads (2 and 3) to the batteries.

21. Install the generator battery cable lead nuts and terminal covers. Tighten the nut to 71 inch lbs. (8 Nm).

22. Connect the generator battery temperature sensor wiring harness electrical connectors to the battery temperature sensors.

23. Install NEW tie straps in order to secure the battery cables to the generator battery temperature sensor wiring harness.

24. Connect the generator battery temperature sensor wiring harness electrical connectors (2, 5) to the generator control module.

25. Install the 2 small temperature sensor wiring harness terminal leads to the batteries.

26. Install the generator battery cable leads to the batteries.

27. Install the generator battery cable nuts. Tighten the nut to 71 inch lbs. (8 Nm).

28. Install the generator battery terminal covers.

29. Install the generator battery cover

30. Install the 12 generator battery cover bolts. Tighten the bolts to 71 inch lbs. (8 Nm).

31. Install the 2 generator battery vent fan cover bolts. Tighten the bolts to 71 inch lbs. (8 Nm).

32. Connect the generator battery.

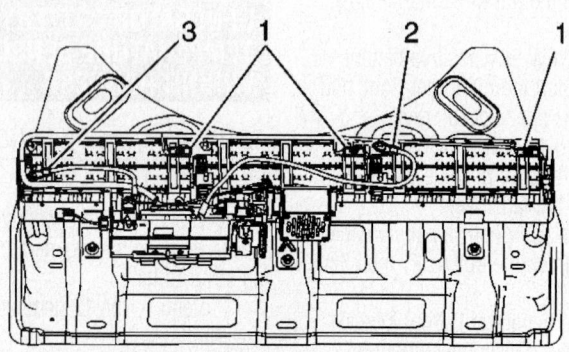

1. Generator battery temperature sensor wiring harness electrical connectors
2. Generator battery cable lead
3. Generator battery cable lead

Fig. 53 Disconnecting the generator battery cable leads

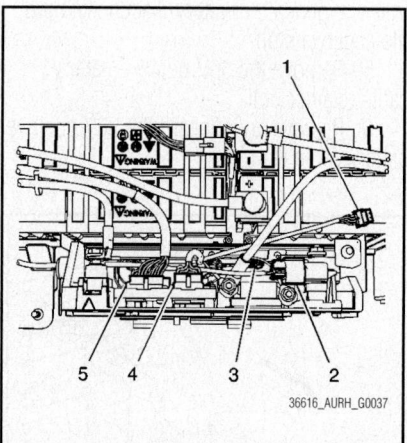

Fig. 54 Connecting the generator battery temperature sensor wiring harness electrical connectors (2, 5)

GENERATOR BATTERY DISCONNECT CONTROL MODULE

REMOVAL & INSTALLATION

See Figures 55 through 59.

✳✳ WARNING

To help avoid personal injury, be careful when working in the vicinity of the generator battery disconnect control module. Internal components will still be live, 36V potential, even when the cover has been opened or removed.

1. Disconnect the hybrid battery.
2. Remove the plastic nut from the generator battery disconnect control module negative stud.
3. Remove the 36V negative battery cable lead from the generator battery disconnect control module negative stud.
4. Remove the generator battery fuse from the generator battery disconnect module negative stud.
5. Remove and discard the 36V positive battery cable lead nut.

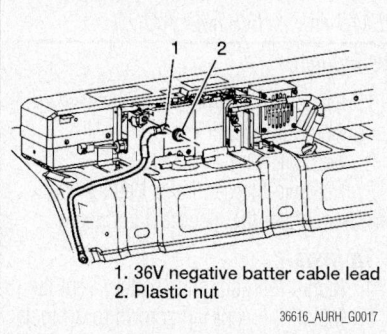

1. 36V negative batter cable lead
2. Plastic nut

36616_AURH_G0017

Fig. 55 Disconnecting 36V negative battery cable lead from the generator battery disconnect control module negative stud

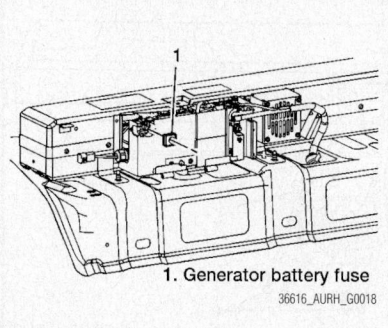

1. Generator battery fuse

36616_AURH_G0018

Fig. 56 Removing the generator battery fuse from the generator batter disconnect module negative stud

6. Remove the 36V positive battery cable lead nut.
7. Remove the 36V positive battery cable leads.
8. Secure the cables out of the way,

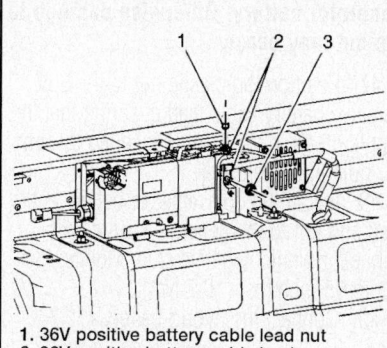

1. 36V positive battery cable lead nut
2. 36V positive battery cable leads
3. 36V positive battery cable lead nut

36616_AURH_G0019

Fig. 57 Removing the 36V positive battery cable lead

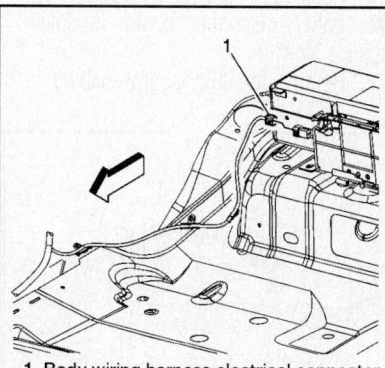

1. Body wiring harness electrical connector

36616_AURH_G0020

Fig. 58 Disconnecting the body wiring harness electrical connector from the generator battery disconnect control module pigtail

ensuring that the cables CANNOT be reinstalled without your knowledge.

9. Disconnect the body wiring harness electrical connector from the generator battery disconnect control module pigtail.
10. Remove the 2 generator battery vent fan cover bolts.
11. Remove the 12 generator battery cover bolts.
12. Remove the generator battery cover.

➡ **Removing the interconnect cables will disable the 36 volts within the generator battery control module.**

13. Remove the generator battery terminal covers.
14. Remove the generator battery cable nuts.
15. Remove the generator battery cable leads from the batteries.
16. Remove the 2 small temperature sensor wiring harness terminal leads located under the battery cable leads from the batteries.
17. Remove the generator battery control module nuts, and the battery cables from the studs.
18. Disconnect the wiring harness electrical connector from the vent fan electrical connector.
19. Disconnect the generator battery temperature sensor wiring harness electrical connectors from the generator control module.
20. Reposition the battery cables and the generator battery temperature sensor wiring harness out of the way.
21. Remove the generator battery disconnect control module pigtail clip from the side of the battery carrier.
22. Unclip the fan harness retainer from the battery.
23. Remove the 4 generator battery disconnect control module bolts.

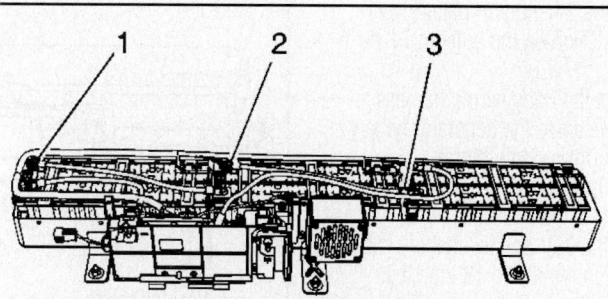

1. Generator battery cable lead
2. Generator battery cable lead
3. Generator battery cable lead

36616_AURH_G0021

Fig. 59 Removing the generator battery cable leads

24. Remove the generator battery disconnect control module.

To install:

25. Install the generator battery disconnect control module.

26. Install the 4 generator battery disconnect control module bolts. Tighten the bolts to 71 inch lb (8 Nm).

27. Clip the fan harness retainer to the battery.

28. Install the generator battery disconnect control module pigtail clip to the side of the battery carrier.

29. Position the generator battery temperature sensor wiring harness and the battery cables to the generator control module.

30. Connect the generator battery temperature sensor wiring harness electrical connectors to the generator control module.

31. Connect the wiring harness electrical connector to the vent fan electrical connector.

32. Ensure that the generator battery temperature sensor wiring harness terminals and installed on the generator battery control module studs.

33. Install the battery cable, and the generator battery control module nut to the stud. Tighten the nut to 71 inch lbs. (8 Nm).

34. Install the battery cable, and the generator battery control module nut to the stud. Tighten the nut to 71 inch lbs. (8 Nm).

35. Install the 2 small temperature sensor wiring harness terminal leads to the batteries.

36. Install the generator battery cable leads to the batteries.

37. Install the generator battery cable nuts. Tighten the nut to 71 inch lbs. (8 Nm).

38. Install the generator battery terminal covers.

39. Install the generator battery cover

40. Install the 12 generator battery cover bolts. Tighten the bolts to 71 inch lbs. (8 Nm).

41. Install the 2 generator battery vent fan cover bolts. Tighten the bolts to 71 inch lbs. (8 Nm).

42. Connect the body wiring harness electrical connector to the generator battery disconnect control module pigtail.

43. Install the 36V positive battery cable leads.

44. Install the 36V positive battery cable lead nut. Tighten the nut to 18 inch lbs. (9 Nm).

45. Install a NEW 36-volt positive battery cable lead nut. Start the nut finger tight, and then torque to the specification given. Tighten the nut to 11 ft. lbs. (15 Nm).

46. Install the generator battery fuse to

the generator battery disconnect module negative stud.

➡ **Position the plastic nut to the negative battery cable and ensure that the nipple is inserted to the terminal prior to installing the negative cable to the generator battery, Otherwise damage to the nut may occur.**

47. Position the plastic nut to the 36V negative battery cable lead ensuring that the nipple on the plastic nut is inserted through the hole in the terminal.

48. Install the 36V negative battery cable lead and nut to the generator battery disconnect module negative stud. Tighten the nut to 95 inch lbs. (10.7 Nm).

49. Connect the hybrid battery.

GENERATOR BATTERY FUSE

REMOVAL & INSTALLATION

See Figure 60.

1. Disconnect the hybrid battery.

2. Remove the plastic nut from the generator battery disconnect control module negative stud.

3. Remove the 36V negative battery

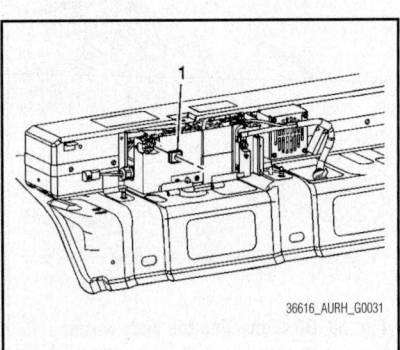

Fig. 60 Removing the generator battery fuse (1)

cable lead from the generator battery disconnect module negative stud.

4. Remove the generator battery fuse from the generator battery disconnect module negative stud.

To install:

5. Install the generator battery fuse to the generator battery disconnect module negative stud.

➡ **Position the plastic nut to the negative battery cable and ensure that the nipple is inserted to the terminal prior to installing the negative cable to the generator battery, Otherwise damage to the nut may occur.**

6. Position the plastic nut to the 36V negative battery cable lead ensuring that the nipple on the plastic nut is inserted through the hole in the terminal.

7. Install the 36V negative battery cable lead and nut to the generator battery disconnect module negative stud. Tighten the nut to 95 inch lbs. (10.7 Nm).

8. Connect the hybrid battery.

GENERATOR BATTERY VENT FAN

REMOVAL & INSTALLATION

See Figure 61.

1. Remove the hybrid battery service disconnect/connect cover.

2. Remove the fan screws.

3. Remove the generator battery vent fan. Disconnect the electrical connector.

To install:

4. Install the generator battery vent fan.

5. Install the vent fan screws to 80 inch lbs. (9 Nm).

6. Install the hybrid battery service disconnect/connect cover.

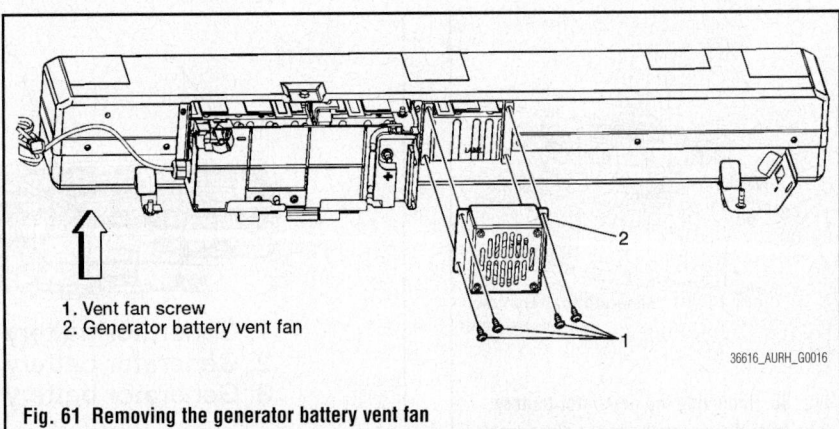

1. Vent fan screw
2. Generator battery vent fan

36616_AURH_G0016

Fig. 61 Removing the generator battery vent fan

GENERATOR CONTROL MODULE

REMOVAL & INSTALLATION

See Figures 62 through 64.

1. Disconnect the hybrid battery.
2. Drain the cooling system.
3. Remove the battery tray.
4. Reposition the power brake booster vacuum hose clamp at the intake manifold.
5. Reposition the power brake booster vacuum hose clamp at the intake manifold.
6. Remove the power brake booster vacuum hose from the intake manifold.
7. Remove the power brake booster vacuum hose from the clamp on the generator control module coolant outlet hose.
8. Reposition the power brake booster vacuum hose out of the way.

✷✷ WARNING

To help avoid personal injury, additional precautions must be taken prior to working on the generator control module or the generator starter. After removing the 36V battery cables from the generator battery, remove both engine wiring harness connectors from the generator control module. Wait at least 5 minutes and then remove the generator control module cover. Verify voltage levels at all 36V, 12V, and 3-phase connections, are less than 3 volts using a DMM before proceeding.

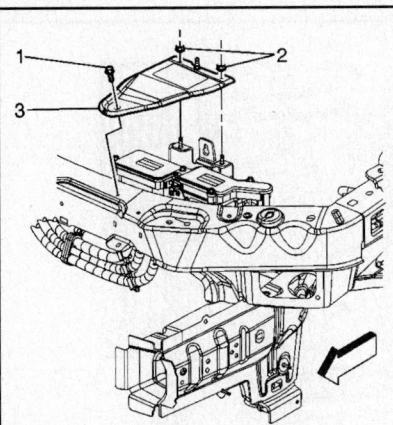

1. Generator control module bracket reinforcement bolt
2. Generator control module bracket reinforcement nuts
3. Generator control module bracket reinforcement

36616_AURH_G0012

Fig. 62 Removing the generator control module bracket reinforcement

9. Remove the 2 Connector Position Assurance (CPA) retainers.
10. Disconnect the 2 engine wiring harness electrical connectors from the generator control module.
11. WAIT at least 5 minutes in order to allow the voltage stored in the generator control module to discharge.
12. Remove the generator control module bracket reinforcement bolt and nuts.
13. Remove the generator control module bracket reinforcement.
14. Reposition the generator control module coolant inlet hose clamp at the generator control module using the Hose Clamp Pliers (J 38185) or equivalent.
15. Remove the generator control module coolant inlet hose from the generator control module.
16. Loosen the generator control module cover integral bolts and remove the cover.
17. The generator control module will have to be checked for voltage potential using a voltmeter. First verify that the voltmeter works:
   a. Set the voltmeter to DC voltage.
   b. Measure the vehicle 12V battery voltage.
   c. The meter should read greater than +12V DC.
18. Check the generator control module for voltage potential, in order to ensure that the module has been disabled.
   a. Measure from the 36V positive terminal to a known good chassis ground. The voltage should be less than 3V.
   b. Measure from the 12V positive terminal to a known good chassis ground. The voltage should be less than 3V.
   c. Measure from the ground terminal to a known good chassis ground, checking for continuity.

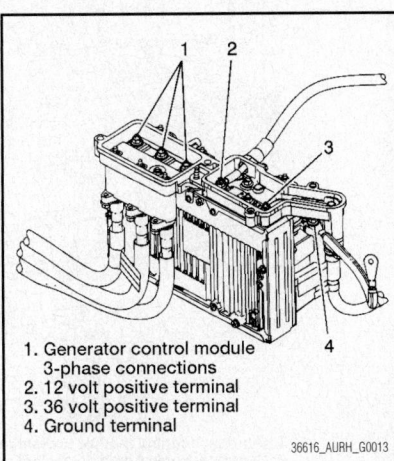

1. Generator control module 3-phase connections
2. 12 volt positive terminal
3. 36 volt positive terminal
4. Ground terminal

36616_AURH_G0013

Fig. 63 Checking generator control module

✷✷ WARNING

To help avoid personal injury, always treat the 3-phase cable and connectors as if voltage is present and as if the surface of all parts of the cable is hot.

19. Verify that the generator control module 3-phase cables are disabled.
   a. Measure from each phase 1, 2, and 3 connection to a known good ground. The voltage should be less than 3V.
   b. After verifying that there is no voltage present, the generator control module 3-phase cables can now be removed from the generator control module.
20. Remove the 36V terminal block nuts from the generator control module.
21. Lift up, and reposition the 36V terminal block, secure the block out of the way. Discard the terminal block seal.
22. Remove the generator control module 3-phase cable terminal block nuts from the generator control module.
23. Lift up, and reposition the generator control module 3-phase cable terminal block, secure the block out of the way. Discard the terminal block seal.
24. Disconnect the engine wiring harness electrical connector from the transaxle auxiliary pump module.
25. Remove the generator control module ground strap nut and strap from the module stud.
26. Remove the engine wiring harness clips from the battery tray bracket studs.
27. Remove the generator control module nuts.
28. Remove the generator control module (with bracket) from the vehicle.
29. Place the generator control module assembly on a clean work surface.
30. Remove the generator control module bracket to module bolts. Separate the generator control module from the bracket.
31. If replacing the generator control module. Remove the transaxle auxiliary pump control module.

To install:

32. If the generator control module was replaced. install the transaxle auxiliary pump control module.
33. Position the generator control module to the bracket, and install the generator control module bracket to module bolts. Tighten the bolts to 89 inch lbs. (10 Nm).
34. Install the generator control module (with bracket) to the vehicle.

35. Install the generator control module bracket nuts. Tighten the nuts to 89 inch lbs. (10 Nm).

36. Connect the engine wiring harness electrical connector to the transaxle auxiliary pump.

37. Place a NEW terminal block seal onto the generator control module.

38. Install the generator control module 3-phase cable terminal block onto the generator control module.

39. Install the generator control module 3-phase cable terminal block nuts until snug.

40. Tighten the generator control module 3-phase cable terminal block nuts in the sequence shown. Tighten the nuts to 71 inch lbs. (8 Nm).

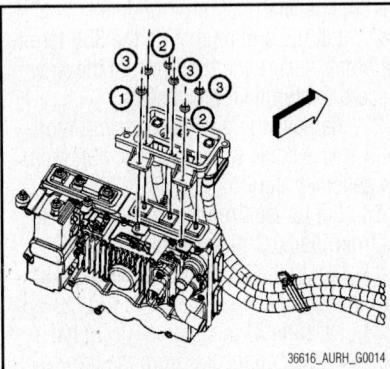

Fig. 64 Identifying generator control module 3-phase cable terminal block nut tightening sequence

41. Place a NEW terminal block seal onto the generator control module.

42. Unsecure, and position the 36V terminal block to the generator control module.

43. Install the 36V terminal block nuts to the generator control module. Tighten the nuts to 89 inch lbs. (10 Nm).

44. Place the generator control module cover on top of the generator control module and tighten bolts.

45. Tighten the bolts to 89 inch lbs. (10 Nm).

46. Install the generator control module coolant outlet hose to the generator control module.

47. Position the generator control module coolant outlet hose clamp at the generator control module using the Hose Clamp Pliers (J 38185) or equivalent.

48. Install the generator control module coolant inlet hose to the generator control module.

49. Position the generator control module coolant inlet hose clamp at the generator control module using the Hose Clamp Pliers (J 38185) or equivalent.

50. Install the generator control module bracket reinforcement.

51. Install the generator control module bracket reinforcement bolt and nuts. Tighten the bolt/nuts to 89 inch lbs. (10 Nm).

52. Connect the 2 engine wiring harness electrical connectors to the generator control module.

53. Install the 2 CPA retainers.

54. Position and install the power brake booster vacuum hose to the intake manifold.

55. Position the power brake booster vacuum hose clamp at the intake manifold.

56. Install the power brake booster vacuum hose to the clamp to the generator control module coolant outlet hose.

57. Install the battery tray.

58. Fill the cooling system.

59. Connect the hybrid battery.

60. If the generator control module was replaced, program the NEW module.

61. Using a Tech 2, command an autostart in order to verify that the system is working properly.

GENERATOR CONTROL MODULE COOLANT PUMP

REMOVAL & INSTALLATION
See Figure 65.

1. Drain the cooling system.
2. Raise and support the vehicle.
3. Remove the generator control module coolant pump bolt.

4. Remove the generator control module coolant pump.

   a. Using Hose Clamp Pliers (J 38185) reposition the generator coolant pump hose clamps.

   b. Remove the hoses from the generator control module coolant pump.

   c. Disconnect the electrical connection.

To install:
To install, reverse the removal procedures. Fill and check the cooling system.

HYBRID BATTERY

DISCONNECT PROCEDURE

✳✳ WARNING

To help avoid personal injury, always ensure the ignition switch is in the OFF position and the ignition key has been removed prior to working on any 36V components. After the key has been removed, disconnect the negative 12V battery cable and then open the generator battery disconnect control module cover. After waiting for at least 5 minutes, measure the voltage potential using a DMM between the following:

- 36V positive and negative battery cables
- 36V positive battery cable and vehicle ground
- 36V negative battery cable and vehicle ground

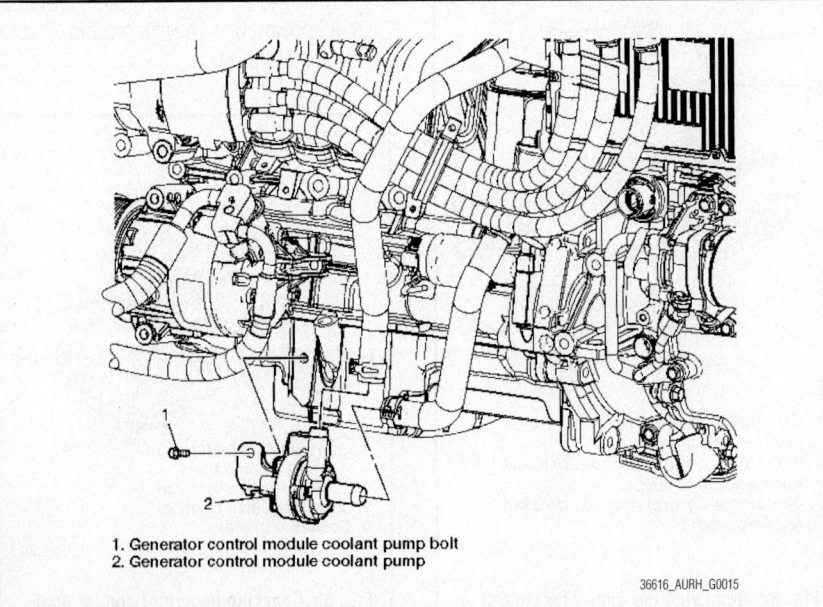

1. Generator control module coolant pump bolt
2. Generator control module coolant pump

Fig. 65 Locating the generator control module coolant pump

All measured voltage levels must be below 3V.

1. Remove the ignition key from the ignition switch. Secure the ignition key in order to ensure that the key CANNOT be reinstalled without your knowledge.

2. Disconnect the 12 volt negative battery cable.

3. Fold down both rear seat backs.

4. Carefully lift up on the load floor rear compartment cover at the retaining clip locations.

5. Tilt the load floor rear compartment cover towards the rear of the vehicle slightly, disengaging the tabs and remove the load floor rear compartment cover.

✳✳ WARNING

To help avoid personal injury, be careful when working in the vicinity of the generator battery disconnect control module. Internal components will still be live, 36V potential, even when the cover has been opened or removed.

6. Remove the generator battery disconnect control module cover bolt.

7. Open and slide the generator battery disconnect control module cover to the right, removing the cover.

8. WAIT at least 5 minutes in order to allow the generator control module capacitors to discharge.

➡ **Never assume the battery pack is disabled when the generator battery disconnect control module cover is opened.**

9. The generator battery will have to be checked for voltage potential using a voltmeter first, verify that the voltmeter works:

a. Set the voltmeter to DC voltage.

b. Measure the vehicle's 12V battery voltage (at 12V positive jumper location and negative battery cable).

c. The meter should read greater than +12V DC.

10. Now, check the generator battery for voltage potential in order to ensure that the generator battery has been disabled.

a. Measure from the positive stud to the negative stud. The voltage should be less than 3V.

b. Measure from the positive stud to

the vehicle chassis ground. The voltage should be less than 3V.

c. Measure from the negative stud to the vehicle chassis ground. The voltage should be less than 3V.

d. After verifying that there is no voltage present, the vehicle is now safe to work on.

CONNECT PROCEDURE

1. Install and close the generator battery disconnect control module cover.

2. Install the generator battery cover bolt. Tighten the bolt to 89 inch lbs. (10 Nm).

3. Tilt the load floor rear compartment cover towards the rear of the vehicle slightly in order to insert the tabs into the battery tray rear support.

4. Set the load floor rear compartment cover down ensuring that the retaining clips align to the proper locations, carefully push down securing the cover.

5. Return both rear seat backs to their proper positions.

6. Connect the 12V negative battery cable.

ENGINE MECHANICAL

➡**Disconnecting the negative battery cable may interfere with the functions of the on board computer systems and may require the computer to undergo a relearning process, once the negative battery cable is reconnected.**

ACCESSORY DRIVE BELTS

ACCESSORY BELT ROUTING

See Figure 66.

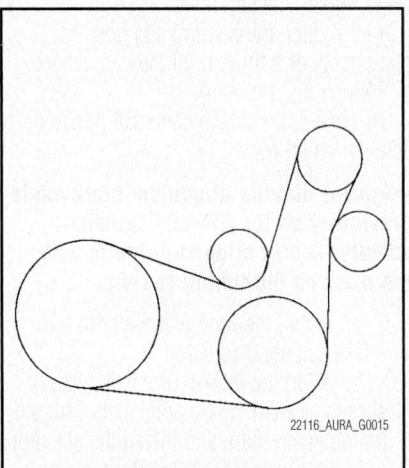

Fig. 66 Drive belt routing

INSPECTION

Inspect the drive belt for signs of glazing or cracking. A glazed belt will be perfectly smooth from slippage, while a good belt will have a slight texture of fabric visible. Cracks will usually start at the inner edge of the belt and run outward. All worn or damaged drive belts should be replaced immediately.

REMOVAL & INSTALLATION

See Figure 67.

1. Remove the right engine splash shield.

2. Remove the air cleaner assembly.

3. Install a hydraulic belt tensioner compressor such as (EN-48932) to the drive belt tensioner spring.

4. Compress the drive belt tensioner spring fully using the hydraulic belt tensioner compressor.

5. Remove the tensioner spring bolts from the tensioner.

6. Remove the tensioner spring from the tensioner.

7. Remove the drive belt from under the middle idler pulley.

8. Remove the drive belt from the vehicle.

To install:

9. Install and position the drive belt around all of the pulleys except for the middle idler pulley.

10. Install the tensioner spring on the tensioner.

11. Install the tensioner spring bolts to the tensioner. Tighten the bolts to 16 ft. lbs. (22 Nm).

12. Install the drive belt under the middle idler pulley.

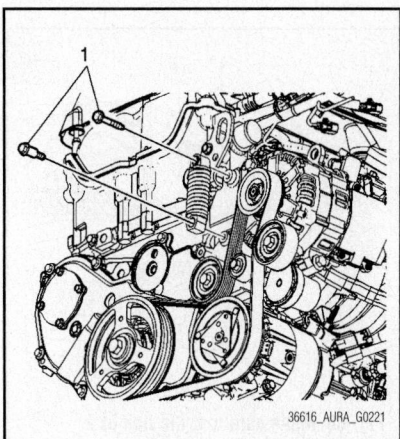

Fig. 67 Removing the tensioner spring bolts from the tensioner

13. Loosen the forcing bolt on the hydraulic belt tensioner and remove from the drive belt tensioner spring.

14. Install and position the drive belt around all of the pulleys except for the middle idler pulley.

15. Ensure that the drive belt tensioner idler is fully seated against the drive belt.

16. Install the air cleaner assembly.

17. Install the right engine splash shield.

CAMSHAFT AND VALVE LIFTERS

REMOVAL & INSTALLATION

Intake

See Figures 68 through 70.

1. Remove the intake camshaft position actuator as follows:

a. Remove the camshaft cover.

b. Remove the spark plugs.

c. Rotate the crankshaft clockwise and install the camshaft actuator retainer (EN-48953).

d. Install the camshaft actuator retainer bolts and tighten to 89 inch lbs. (10 Nm).

e. Loosen, but DO NOT remove the intake camshaft actuator bolt.

f. Remove the camshaft actuator locking tool (EN-48953).

g. Clean the timing chain and gears with solvent.

➥Ensure the timing chain and the camshaft position actuators are marked for proper assembly.

h. Mark the intake and exhaust camshaft actuators and the respective locations on the timing chain.

i. Remove the upper timing chain guide bolts and guide.

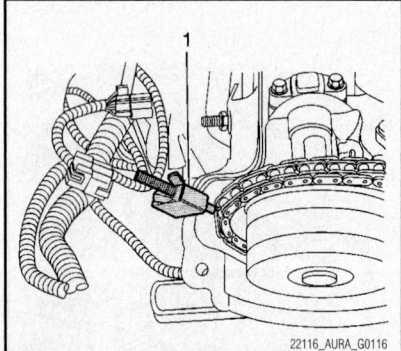

Fig. 68 Make sure that the tips of a Timing Chain Tensioner Tool such as J 44217 (1) are fully engaged into the timing chain—2.4L engine

j. Remove the timing chain tensioner.

➥The intake camshaft actuator should not rotate during the removal or installation.

➥Ensure the tips of the timing chain tensioner tool are fully engaged into the timing chain. The retention tool rod can be used on the back side of the chain to ensure the teeth from the retention tool are engaged.

k. Install the timing chain retention tool (EN-48749) to the intake side of the timing chain.

l. Install the timing chain retention tool (EN-48749) to the exhaust side of the timing chain.

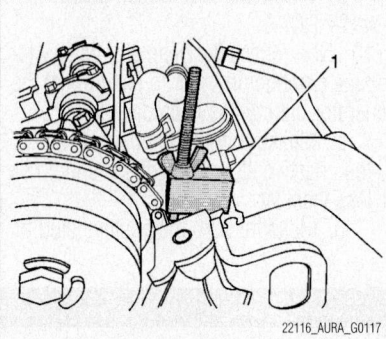

Fig. 69 Install the tools (1) from a Timing Chain Tensioner Tool such as J 44217 to the exhaust camshaft side of the timing chain assembly in order to retain the timing chain—2.4L engine

m. Remove and discard the intake camshaft actuator bolt.

n. Rotate the exhaust camshaft clockwise slightly to take the tension off of the timing chain on the intake actuator.

o. Remove the intake camshaft actuator from the camshaft while also removing the actuator from the timing chain.

➥Remove each bolt on each cap one turn at a time until there is no spring tension pushing on the camshaft.

2. Mark the bearing caps to ensure they are installed in the original position.

3. Remove the bearing cap bolts.

4. Remove the bearing caps.

5. Remove the intake camshaft.

➥Keep all of the roller followers and hydraulic adjusters in order so that they can be reinstalled in their respective locations.

6. Remove the camshaft roller followers.

7. Remove the hydraulic element lash adjusters.

To install:

8. Install the hydraulic element lash adjusters into their bores in the cylinder head.

9. Lubricate the hydraulic lash adjusters with molylube.

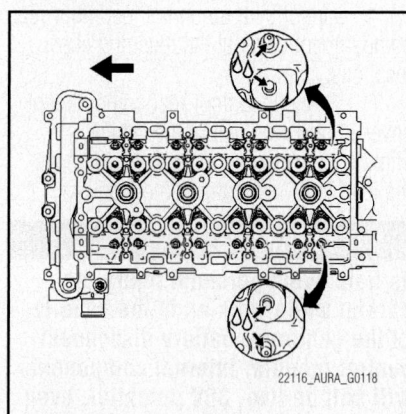

Fig. 70 Lubricate the hydraulic lash adjusters—2.4L engine

10. Lubricate the valve tips with GM molylube.

➥Used roller followers MUST be returned to their original position on the camshaft. If the camshaft is being replaced, the roller followers actuated by the camshaft must also be replaced.

11. Position the camshaft roller followers on the tip of the valve stem and on the lash adjuster. Lubricate the roller followers with molylube.

12. Install the intake camshaft and lubricate with molylube.

13. Install the camshaft bearing caps. Hand tighten the cap bolts.

14. Tighten the bearing cap bolts in increments of 3 turns until they are seated to 89 inch lbs. (10 Nm).

15. Install the intake camshaft position actuator as follows:

➥Ensure that the alignment mark made previously on the exhaust camshaft actuator is still aligned properly with the mark on the timing chain.

a. Install the timing chain onto the intake camshaft actuator.

b. Align the intake camshaft actuator alignment mark made previously with the timing chain mark and install the actuator onto the camshaft rotating the exhaust camshaft clockwise, if required.

c. Install a NEW intake camshaft actuator bolt until snug.

d. Remove the timing chain retention tool from the intake side of the timing chain.

➡**Ensure that the alignment mark previously on the intake camshaft actuator is still aligned properly with the timing chain. If the mark made previously on the intake camshaft actuator is not aligned properly, refer to replacement procedure.**

e. Remove the timing chain retention tool from the exhaust side of the timing chain.

➡**Failure to reset the tensioner will allow the tensioner to over extend limiting the timing chain life.**

f. Reset and install the timing chain tensioner.

g. Install the camshaft actuator retainer (EN-48953) Camshaft Actuator Locking Tool.

h. Install the camshaft actuator retainer bolts and tighten to 89 inch lbs. (10 Nm).

i. Tighten the NEW camshaft actuator bolt to 22 ft. lbs. (30 Nm) plus an additional 100 degrees.

➡**You must have the Camshaft Actuator Locking Tool (EN-48953) installed to perform this procedure.**

j. To release the tensioner apply a counterclockwise rotational torque to the crankshaft balancer bolt of 33 ft. lbs. (45 Nm).

k. Remove the camshaft actuator retainer.

l. Install the upper timing chain guide and bolts and tighten to 89 inch lbs. (10 Nm).

m. Install the spark plugs.

n. Install the camshaft cover.

Exhaust

See Figures 68 through 70.

1. Remove the exhaust camshaft position actuator as follows:
   a. Remove the camshaft cover.
   b. Remove the spark plugs.
   c. Rotate the crankshaft clockwise and install the camshaft actuator retainer.
   d. Install the camshaft actuator retainer bolts and tighten to 89 inch lbs. (10 Nm).
   e. Loosen, but do NOT remove the exhaust camshaft actuator bolt.

f. Clean the timing chain and gears with solvent.

➡**Ensure that the timing chain and the camshaft position actuators are marked for proper assembly.**

g. Mark the intake and exhaust camshaft actuators and the respective locations on the timing chain.

h. Remove the upper timing chain guide bolts and guide.

i. Remove the timing chain tensioner.

➡**The camshaft actuators should not rotate during the removal or installation.**

➡**Ensure the tips of the timing chain tensioner are fully engaged into the timing chain. The retention tool rod can be used on the back side of the chain to ensue the teeth from the retention tool are engaged.**

j. Install the timing chain retention tool (EN-48749) to the exhaust side of the timing chain.

➡**Remove each bolt on each cap one turn at a time until there is no spring tension pushing on the camshaft.**

2. Mark the bearing caps to ensure they are installed in the original position.

3. Remove the bearing cap bolts.

4. Remove the bearing caps.

5. Remove the exhaust camshaft.

➡**Keep all of the roller followers and hydraulic adjusters in order so that they can be reinstalled in their respective locations.**

6. Remove the camshaft roller followers.

7. Remove the hydraulic element lash adjusters.

To install:

8. Install the hydraulic element lash adjusters into their bores in the cylinder head.

9. Lubricate the hydraulic lash adjusters with molylube.

10. Lubricate the valve tips with GM molylube.

➡**Used roller followers MUST be returned to their original position on the camshaft. If the camshaft is being replaced, the roller followers actuated by the camshaft must also be replaced.**

11. Position the camshaft roller followers on the tip of the valve stem and on the lash

adjuster. Lubricate the roller followers with molylube.

12. Install the exhaust camshaft and lubricate with molylube.

13. Install the camshaft bearing caps. Hand tighten the cap bolts.

14. Tighten the bearing cap bolts in increments of 3 turns until they are seated to 89 inch lbs. (10 Nm).

15. Install the exhaust camshaft position actuator as follows:

➡**Ensure that the alignment mark made previously on the intake camshaft actuator is still aligned properly with the mark on the timing chain.**

➡**The exhaust camshaft may need to be rotated clockwise to fully set the camshaft actuator.**

a. Install the timing chain onto the exhaust camshaft actuator.

b. Align the intake camshaft actuator alignment mark made previously with the timing chain mark and install the actuator onto the camshaft.

c. Install a NEW exhaust camshaft actuator bolt until snug.

➡**Ensure that the alignment mark previously on the exhaust camshaft actuator is still aligned properly with the timing chain. If the mark made previously on the intake camshaft actuator is not aligned properly, refer to CAMSHAFT TIMING CHAIN.**

d. Remove the tool from the exhaust camshaft side of the timing chain assembly.

➡**Failure to reset the tensioner will allow the tensioner to over extend limiting the timing chain life.**

e. Reset and install the timing chain tensioner.

f. Install the intake camshaft actuator retainer.

g. Install the camshaft actuator retainer bolts and tighten to 89 inch lbs. (10 Nm).

h. Tighten the NEW camshaft actuator bolt to 22 ft. lbs. (30 Nm) plus an additional 100 degrees.

➡**You must have the Camshaft Actuator Locking Tool (EN-48953) installed to perform this procedure.**

i. To release the tensioner apply a counterclockwise rotational torque to the crankshaft balancer bolt of 33 ft. lbs. (45 Nm).

j. Remove the Camshaft Actuator Retainer (EN-48953).

k. Install the upper timing chain guide and bolts and tighten to 89 inch lbs. (10 Nm).

l. Install the camshaft cover.

m. Install the spark plugs.

CATALYTIC CONVERTER

REMOVAL & INSTALLATION

See Figure 71.

✳✳ WARNING

In order to avoid being burned, do not service the exhaust system while it is still hot. Service the system when it is cool.

1. Remove the heated oxygen sensor.

2. Remove the catalytic converter to exhaust manifold nuts.

3. Remove the catalytic converter to muffler nuts.

4. Separate the exhaust pipe from the catalytic converter studs.

5. Position and support the exhaust pipe out of the way.

6. Remove the catalytic converter and gasket.

To install:

7. Install the catalytic converter along with a NEW gasket to the exhaust manifold.

8. Position and join the exhaust pipe to the catalytic converter studs.

9. Install the catalytic converter to muffler nuts and tighten to 13 ft. lbs. (17 Nm).

10. Install the catalytic converter to exhaust manifold nuts and tighten to 37 ft. lbs. (50 Nm).

11. Install the heated oxygen sensor.

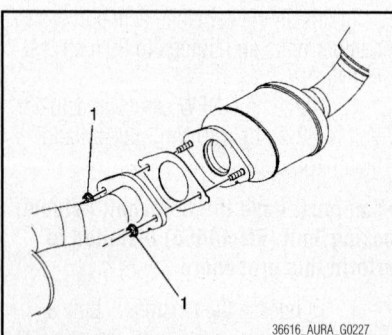

36616_AURA_G0227

Fig. 71 Removing the catalytic converter and gasket

CRANKSHAFT DAMPER

REMOVAL & INSTALLATION

See Figure 72.

1. Remove the drive belt.

2. Install the Harmonic Balancer Holder (J38122-A), and a breaker bar to the balancer in order to prevent the balancer from rotating when loosening the balancer bolt.

3. Remove the tool and breaker bar.

4. Remove and discard the crankshaft balancer bolt.

5. Remove the crankshaft balancer.

36616_AURA_G0238

Fig. 72 Removing the crankshaft balancer

To install:

6. Position the crankshaft balancer.

7. Install a NEW crankshaft balancer bolt.

8. Install the Harmonic Balancer Holder (J38122-A) and a breaker bar to the balancer in order to prevent the balancer from rotating while tightening the bolt.

9. Tighten the crankshaft balancer bolt to 74 ft. lbs. (100 Nm) plus an additional 125 degrees using an Angle Meter.

10. Install the drive belt.

CRANKSHAFT FRONT SEAL

REMOVAL & INSTALLATION

See Figure 73.

1. Remove the crankshaft damper.

2. Use a flat-bladed tool to remove the seal from the front cover.

To install:

3. Use a suitable seal driver in order to install the crankshaft front oil seal to the engine front cover.

4. Install the crankshaft damper.

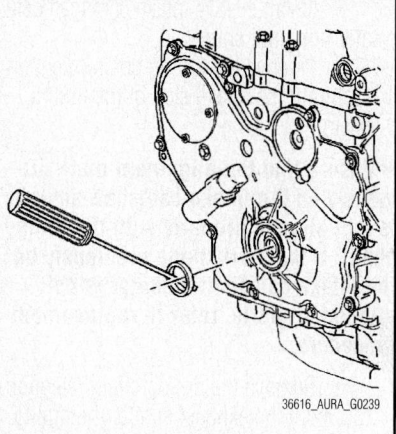

36616_AURA_G0239

Fig. 73 Removing the crankshaft front oil seal—2.4L engine

CYLINDER HEAD

REMOVAL & INSTALLATION

See Figures 74 through 80.

1. Drain and recycle the engine coolant.

2. Remove the exhaust manifold.

3. Remove the intake manifold.

4. Reposition the radiator surge tank air bleed hose clamp.

5. Remove the radiator surge tank air bleed hose from the cylinder head.

6. Reposition the radiator inlet hose clamp using the hose clamp pliers (J 38185).

7. Remove the radiator inlet hose from the cylinder head.

8. Disconnect all electrical connectors as necessary.

9. Remove the spark plugs.

10. Remove the camshaft cover.

➡️**If the intake camshaft actuator is moving independently of the camshaft, this means the camshaft is not locked to the actuator. Rotate the camshaft**

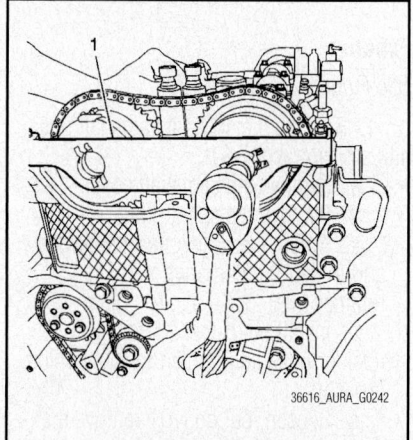

36616_AURA_G0242

Fig. 74 Installing the retainer bolts

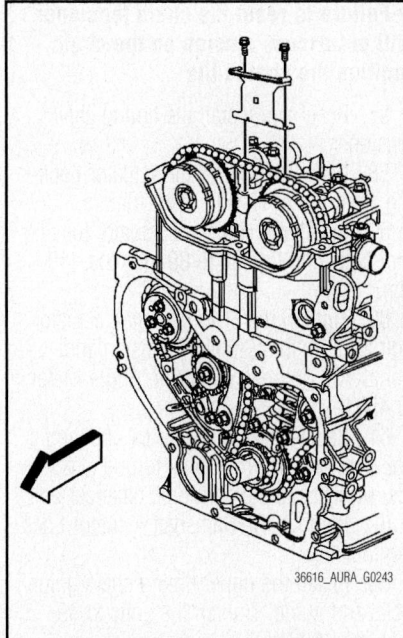

Fig. 75 Removing the upper timing chain guide bolts and guide—2.4L engine

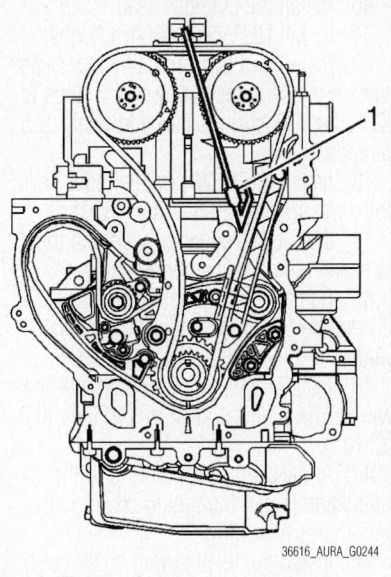

Fig. 76 Installing the Timing Chain Retention tool to the intake side of the timing chain

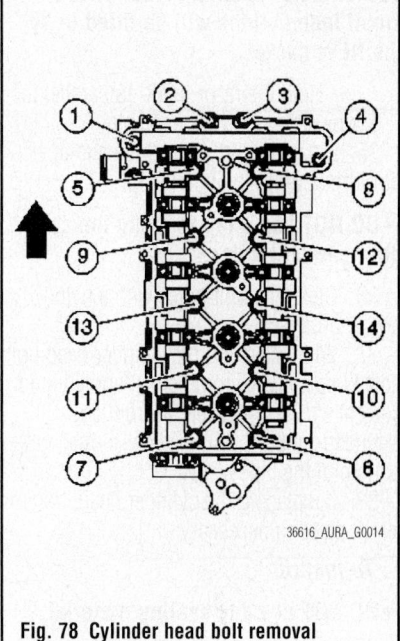

Fig. 78 Cylinder head bolt removal sequence

counter-clockwise while the holing tool is installed and this will lock the camshaft to the actuator.

11. Rotate the crankshaft clockwise to install the Camshaft Actuator Retaining Tool (EN-48953).

12. Install the Camshaft Actuator Locking Tool (EN-48953).

13. Install the camshaft actuator retainer bolts and tighten to 89 inch lbs. (10 Nm).

14. Remove the upper timing chain guide bolts and guide.

15. Clean the timing chain and gears with solvent.

➡️**Ensure the timing chain and the camshaft position actuators are marked for proper assembly.**

16. Mark the timing gear sprockets and the timing chain. It is recommended that the paint marks are located in the 12 o'clock position.

17. Loosen, but do not remove the intake and exhaust camshaft actuator bolts.

18. Remove the Camshaft Actuator Locking Tool (EN-48953).

➡️**Ensure the tips of the Timing Chain Retention Tool Kit (EN-48749) are fully engaged into the timing chain. The retention tool rod can be used on the back side of the chain to ensure the teeth from the retention tool are engaged.**

19. Install the Timing Chain Retention Tool (EN-48749) to the intake side of the timing chain.

20. Remove the timing chain tensioner.

➡️**The intake camshaft and actuator should not rotate during the removal or installation.**

21. Install the Timing Chain Retention Tool (EN-48749) to the exhaust side of the timing chain.

22. Remove and discard the exhaust camshaft actuator bolt.

23. Remove the exhaust cam actuator from the exhaust camshaft while also removing the actuator from the chain.

24. Remove and discard the intake camshaft actuator bolt.

25. Remove the intake camshaft actuator from the camshaft while also removing the actuator from the timing chain.

26. Mark the cylinder head in relationship to the camshaft actuator notch is on the camshaft.

27. Remove the fixed timing chain guide access plug.

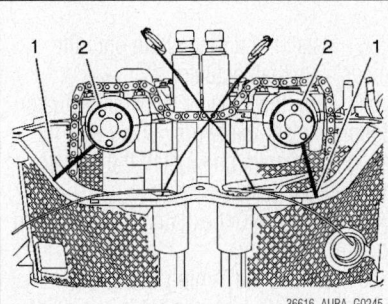

Fig. 77 Marking the cylinder head

28. Remove the upper fixed timing chain guide bolt.

➡️**The threaded rod from the timing chain retention tool can be used to help feed the rubber band around the chain guides.**

29. Install the rubber band around the top of the timing chain guides in order to pull the guides together.

30. Remove the cylinder head bolts in the sequence shown. Discard the bolts.

31. Remove the cylinder head.

32. Remove the cylinder head gasket.

33. Clean all of the gasket surfaces.

34. Use the following steps when cleaning the cylinder head and cylinder block surfaces:

   a. Use a razor blade gasket scraper to clean the cylinder head and cylinder block gasket surfaces. Do not scratch or gouge either surface.

➡️**DO NOT use any other method or technique to clean these gasket surfaces.**

   b. Use a NEW razor blade on the cylinder head and a NEW blade on the cylinder block.

➡️**Be careful not to gouge or scratch the gasket surfaces. DO NOT gouge or scrape the combustion chamber surfaces. The feel of the gasket surface is important, not the appearance. There will be indentations from the gasket left in the cylinder head after all of the** gasket material is removed. These small indentations will be filled in by the NEW gasket.

c. Hold the razor blade as parallel to the gasket surface as possible.

35. Clean the old sealer/lube and any dirt from around the bolt holes.

➡**DO NOT use a tap to clean the cylinder head bolt holes.**

36. Clean the bolt holes with a nylon bristle brush.

37. When cleaning the cylinder head bolt holes use suitable commercial spray liquid solvent and compressed air from an extended-tip blow gun in order to reach the bottom of the holes.

38. If replacing the cylinder head, transfer all parts as necessary.

To install:

➡**DO NOT use any sealing material.**

39. Install the cylinder head gasket.

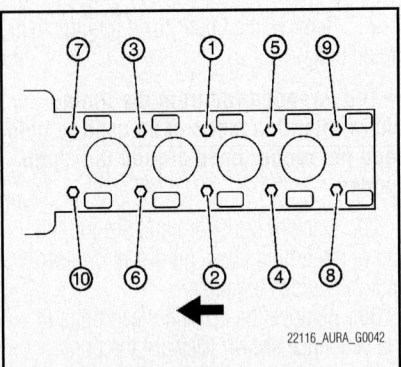

Fig. 79 Cylinder head bolt tightening sequence—2.4L engine

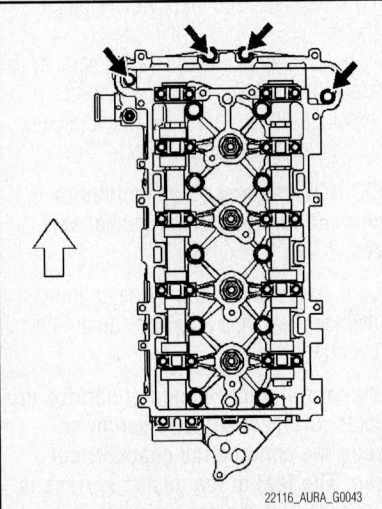

Fig. 80 Location of the front cylinder head bolts—2.4L engine

40. Install the cylinder head.
41. Install NEW cylinder head bolts.
42. Install and tighten the cylinder head bolts in the sequence shown in 2 steps to 22 ft. lbs. (30 Nm) plus an additional 155 degrees.
43. Install the NEW front cylinder head bolts and tighten to 26 ft. lbs. (35 Nm).
44. Ensure the cylinder head and the camshaft are correctly aligned.
45. Remove the rubber band from around the top of the upper timing chain guides.
46. Install the fixed guide bolt into the cylinder head and tighten to 106 inch lbs. (12 Nm).
47. Apply sealant compound to the thread and install the timing chain guide bolt access hole plug.
48. Install the fixed timing chain guide access plug and tighten the plug to 59 ft. lbs. (90 Nm).

➡**Ensure that the alignment mark made previously on the intake camshaft actuator is still aligned properly with the mark on the timing chain. If the mark made previously on the intake camshaft actuator is not aligned properly, refer to CAMSHAFT TIMING CHAIN, SPROCKET, AND TENSIONER.**

49. Install the timing chain onto the intake camshaft actuator.
50. Align the intake camshaft actuator alignment mark made previously with the timing chain mark and install the actuator onto the camshaft.
51. Install a NEW intake camshaft actuator bolt until snug.
52. Remove the Timing Chain Retention Tool (EN-48749) from the intake side of the timing chain.

➡**Ensure that the alignment mark made previously on the exhaust camshaft actuator is still aligned properly with the mark on the timing chain. The exhaust cam may have to be rotated clockwise to install the exhaust actuator.**

53. Install the timing chain onto the exhaust camshaft actuator.
54. Align the exhaust camshaft actuator alignment mark made previously with the timing chain mark and install the actuator onto the camshaft.
55. Install a NEW exhaust camshaft actuator bolt until snug.
56. Remove the Timing Chain Retention Tool (EN-48749) from the exhaust side of the timing chain.

➡**Failure to reset the chain tensioner will put excess tension on the chain, limiting the chains life.**

57. Reset and install the timing chain tensioner.
58. Install the Camshaft Actuator Locking Tool (EN-48953) to the actuators.
59. Install the camshaft actuator locking tool bolts and tighten to 89 inch lbs. (10 Nm).
60. Tighten the ENW camshaft actuator bolt to 22 ft. lbs. (30 Nm), plus an additional 100 degrees using the Angle Meter (J 45059).
61. Release the tensioner by applying a counterclockwise rotational torque of 33 ft. lbs. (45 Nm) to the harmonic balancer bolt.
62. Remove the Camshaft Actuator Locking tool.
63. Install the upper timing chain guide bolts and guide. Tighten the bolts to 89 inch lbs. (10 Nm).
64. Install the camshaft cover.
65. Install the spark plugs.
66. Connect all necessary electrical connectors.
67. Install the radiator inlet hose to the cylinder head.
68. Position the radiator inlet hose clamp.
69. Install the radiator surge tank air bleed hose to the cylinder head.
70. Position the radiator surge tank air bleed hose clamp.
71. Install the exhaust manifold.
72. Install the intake manifold.
73. Fill the cooling system

ENGINE ASSEMBLY

REMOVAL & INSTALLATION

See Figures 81 through 93.

1. Relieve the fuel system pressure.

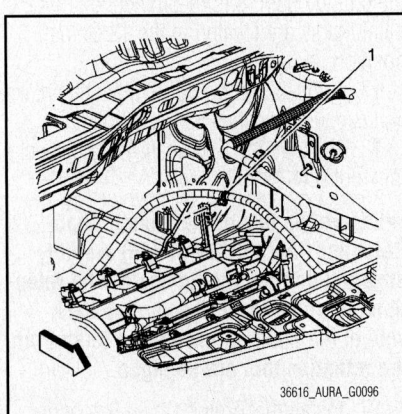

Fig. 81 Removing the transaxle shift cable clip (1) from the fuel line bracket

2. Remove the air cleaner assembly.

3. Disconnect the fuel feed pipe quick connect fitting at the fuel rail.

4. Disconnect the Evaporative Emission (EVAP) line quick connect fitting from the EVAP purge solenoid.

5. Remove the fuel feed pipe clip from the fuel line bracket.

6. Remove the transaxle shift cable clip from the fuel line bracket.

7. Remove the battery tray.

8. Remove the generator starter.

9. Reposition the vacuum brake booster hose clamp at the intake manifold.

10. Remove the vacuum brake booster hose from the intake manifold. Reposition the brake booster hose out of the way.

11. Remove the coolant recovery inlet hose clamp at the cylinder head.

12. Remove the coolant recovery inlet pipe clip from the fuel rail.

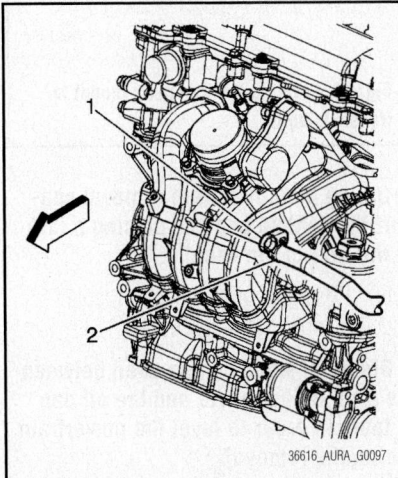

Fig. 82 Locating the vacuum brake booster hose on the intake manifold

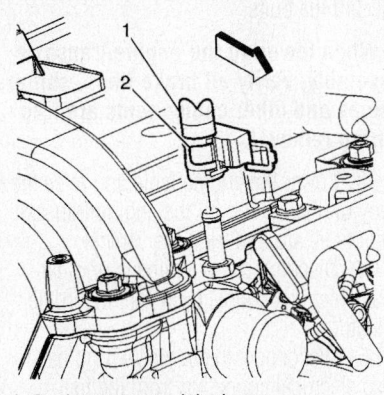

1. Coolant recovery inlet hose
2. Coolant recovery inlet hose clamp

36616_AURA_G0098

Fig. 83 Removing the coolant recovery inlet hose from the cylinder head

13. Remove the coolant recovery inlet hose from the cylinder head. Reposition the hose/pipe out of the way.

14. Reposition the radiator inlet hose clamp.

15. Remove the radiator inlet hose from the cylinder head.

16. Remove the radiator outlet hose.

17. Reposition the generator control module coolant hose clamp at the alternator control module.

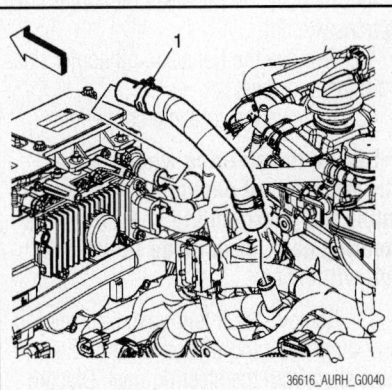

36616_AURH_G0040

Fig. 84 Removing the generator control module coolant hose (1) from the generator control module

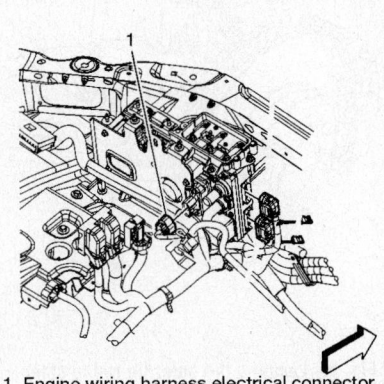

1. Engine wiring harness electrical connector

36616_AURH_G0041

Fig. 85 Disconnecting the engine wiring harness electrical connector from the transaxle module

18. Remove the generator control module coolant hose from the alternator control module.

19. Disconnect the engine wiring harness electrical connector from the transaxle auxiliary pump module.

20. Reposition the heater inlet hose clamp at the thermostat housing.

21. Remove the heater inlet hose from the thermostat housing.

22. Reposition the coolant recovery reservoir/heater inlet hose clamp at the thermostat housing.

23. Remove the coolant recovery reservoir/heater inlet hose from the thermostat housing.

24. Raise and support the vehicle.

25. Drain the engine oil.

26. Disconnect the engine wiring harness electrical connector from the alternator control module coolant pump.

27. Disconnect the engine wiring harness electrical connector from the Air Conditioning (A/C) compressor.

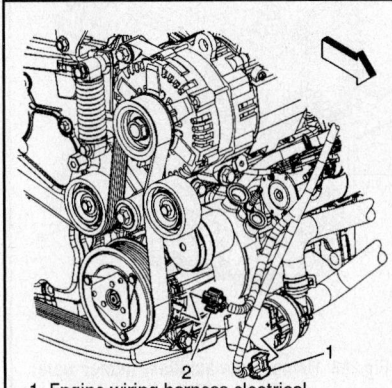

1. Engine wiring harness electrical connector to generator control module coolant pump
2. Engine wiring harness electrical connector to A/C compressor

36616_AURH_G0042

Fig. 86 Disconnecting the engine wiring harness electrical connectors

28. Remove the generator control module coolant pump bolt and pump.

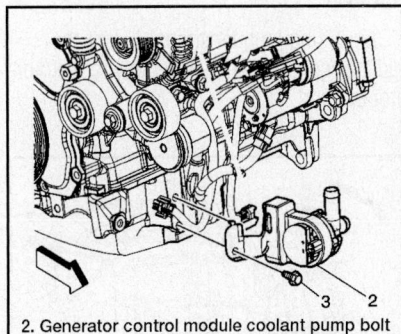

2. Generator control module coolant pump bolt
3. Generator control module coolant pump

36616_AURH_G0043

Fig. 87 Removing the generator control module coolant pump

29. Unbolt the A/C compressor and reposition out of the way.

30. Remove the positive battery cable to starter motor nut.

31. Remove the positive battery cable lead from the starter motor.

32. Remove the positive battery cable from in between the starter and the engine. Reposition the positive battery cable out of the way.

33. Disconnect the engine wiring harness electrical connector from the auxiliary heater water pump.

34. Remove the auxiliary heater water pump bolt and pump.

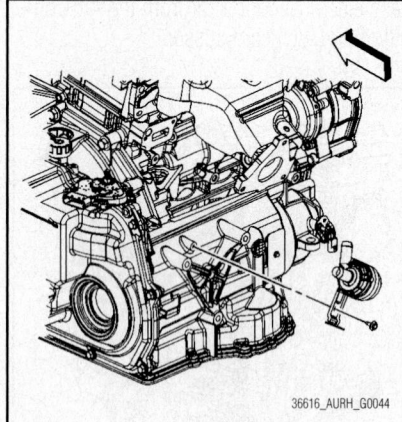

Fig. 88 Remove the auxiliary heater water pump

35. Lower the vehicle.

36. Remove the transaxle shift cable from the range select lever.

37. Release the shift control cable retaining clip and remove the cable from the shift control cable bracket.

➡ **The radiator/condenser/fan assembly will stay in the vehicle during engine removal.**

38. Using long tie straps, secure the radiator/condenser/fan assembly to the radiator support.

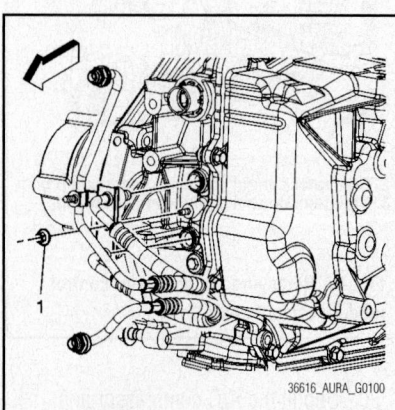

Fig. 89 Locating the transaxle oil cooler line to transaxle nut

39. Raise the vehicle.

40. Remove the front wheels and tires.

41. Remove the front fender liners.

➡ **A piece of hardwood should be used between the transaxle and the engine cradle. This wood will support the engine when the left side engine mounts bolts are removed.**

42. Install a piece of hardwood 1 x 2 x 4 between the transaxle and the engine cradle.

43. Drain the transaxle fluid.

44. Remove the transaxle oil cooler line to transaxle nut.

45. Remove the transaxle oil cooler lines from the transaxle.

46. Remove the catalytic converter.

➡ **Secure the steering wheel in the straight forward position before separating the intermediate shaft from the steering gear, or damage to the SIR coil will occur.**

47. Remove the intermediate to steering gear pinch bolt and disconnect the intermediate shaft from the steering gear. Discard the pinch bolt.

48. Remove and discard both outer tie rod to steering knuckle nuts.

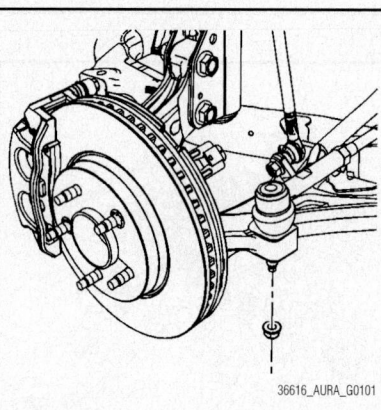

Fig. 90 Locating the outer tie rod to steering knuckle nuts

➡ **Hold the ball stud to prevent turning during removal of the nut.**

49. Separate the tie rods from the steering knuckles.

50. Remove the stabilizer link to stabilizer shaft nuts and disconnect the stabilizer links from the stabilizer shaft.

51. Remove and discard both of the lower control arm ball stud cotter pins.

52. Loosen the ball stud nuts until the nuts are level with the top of the ball stud.

53. Separate the lower control arms from the steering knuckles.

54. Remove the ball stud nuts.

55. Remove the wheel drive shafts.

56. Lower the vehicle.

57. Remove the engine mount to bracket bolts.

58. Remove the transaxle mount to transaxle bolts.

59. Raise the vehicle.

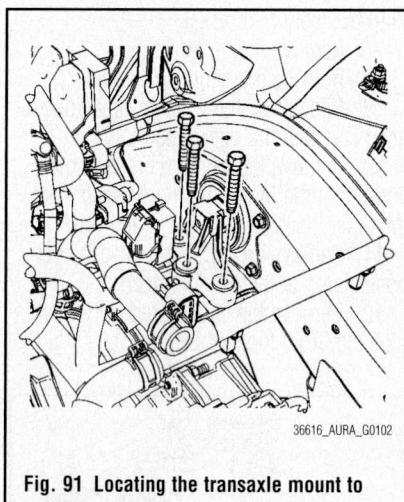

Fig. 91 Locating the transaxle mount to transaxle bolts

➡ **During the powertrain removal support the vehicle body by placing a jack at the rear of the vehicle.**

60. Position a engine support table under the powertrain assembly.

➡ **Blocks of wood can be used between the front of the cradle and the oil pan to table in order to level the powertrain during the removal.**

61. With the table positioned, fully raise the table to contact with the powertrain assembly.

62. Remove the cradle to body bolts. Discard the bolts.

➡ **When lowering the engine/transaxle assembly, verify all brake lines, shifter cables and other components are free during removal.**

63. Lower the engine table and raise the body on the hoist until the engine/transaxle and cradle are free from the vehicle.

64. Disconnect the engine wiring harness electrical connector from the throttle actuator.

65. Disconnect the engine wiring harness electrical connector from the fuel injector wiring harness electrical connector.

66. Remove the engine wiring harness clip from the oil level indicator tube bracket.

67. Disconnect the engine wiring harness electrical connectors from the ignition coils.

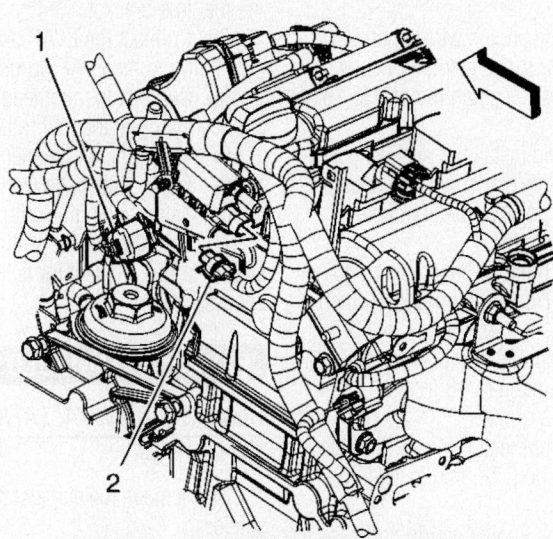

1. Engine wiring harness electrical connector to intake CMP sensor
2. Engine wiring harness electrical connector to EVAP emission canister purge solenoid valve

36616_AURA_G0103

Fig. 92 Locating the CMP and EVAP emission canister purge solenoid valve electrical connectors

68. Disconnect the engine wiring harness electrical connectors from the camshaft actuators.

69. Disconnect the engine wiring harness electrical connector from the Crankshaft Position (CKP) sensor.

70. Disconnect the engine wiring harness electrical connector from the oil pressure sensor.

71. Disconnect the engine wiring harness electrical connector from the knock sensor.

72. Disconnect the engine wiring harness electrical connector from the intake Camshaft Position (CMP) sensor.

73. Disconnect the engine wiring harness electrical connector from the EVAP emission canister purge solenoid valve.

74. Disconnect the engine wiring harness electrical connector from the exhaust CMP sensor.

75. Disconnect the engine wiring harness electrical connector) from the Engine Coolant Temperature (ECT) sensor.

76. Disconnect the engine wiring harness electrical connector from the Heated Oxygen Sensor (HO2S) electrical connector.

77. Remove the engine wiring harness clip from the stud.

78. Remove the engine wiring harness ground bolt and reposition the ground terminal from the engine.

79. Gather all branches of the engine wiring harness and reposition the harness out of the way.

80. Remove the starter motor bolts and starter.

81. Remove the torque converter to flexplate bolts.

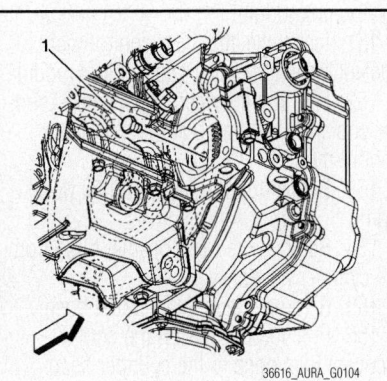

36616_AURA_G0104

Fig. 93 Removing the torque converter to flexplate bolts (1)

82. Install a suitable lifting devise to the engine.

83. Remove the transaxle bolts from the engine.

84. Separate the engine from the transaxle.

85. Install the engine to a suitable engine stand.

To install:

86. Install a suitable lifting devise to the engine.

87. Using the lifting devise, position and install the engine to the transaxle.

88. Install the transaxle bolts to the engine and tighten to 55 ft. lbs. (75 Nm).

89. Install the torque converter to flexplate bolts and tighten to 44 ft. lbs. (60 Nm).

90. Remove the engine lifting devise.

91. Install the starter motor and bolts. Tighten to 39 ft. lbs. (53 Nm).

92. Gather all branches of the engine wiring harness and position the harness to the engine.

93. Position the engine wiring harness ground terminal to the engine and install the engine wiring harness ground bolt and tighten the bolts to 15 ft. lbs. (20 Nm).

94. Connect the engine wiring harness electrical connector to the ECT sensor.

95. Connect the engine wiring harness electrical connector to the HO2S electrical connector.

96. Install the engine wiring harness clip to the stud.

97. Connect the engine wiring harness electrical connector to the exhaust CMP sensor.

98. Connect the engine wiring harness electrical connector to the intake CMP sensor.

99. Connect the engine wiring harness electrical connector to the EVAP emission canister purge solenoid valve.

100. Connect the engine wiring harness electrical connector to the CKP sensor.

101. Connect the engine wiring harness electrical connector to the oil pressure sensor.

102. Connect the engine wiring harness electrical connector to the knock sensor.

103. Connect the engine wiring harness electrical connectors to the ignition coils.

104. Connect the engine wiring harness electrical connectors to the camshaft actuators.

105. Connect the engine wiring harness electrical connector to the throttle actuator.

106. Connect the engine wiring harness electrical connector to the fuel injector wiring harness electrical connector .

107. Install the engine wiring harness clip to the oil level indicator tube bracket.

108. Position the powertrain and support table under the vehicle.

109. Raise the powertrain into position under the vehicle.

110. With the table positioned, if required, lower the vehicle over the powertrain.

111. Align the lower radiator pins with the cradle. Ensure all hoses and electrical harnesses are correctly routed and free from the loading path of the powertrain.

112. Install the NEW cradle to body bolts and tighten to 114 ft. lbs. (155 Nm).

113. Lower the vehicle.

114. Install the transaxle mount to transaxle bolts. Tighten to 41 ft. lbs. (55 Nm).

➡**The engine mount to bracket bolts must be hand started. Do not pry the engine mount to align the holes.**

115. Install the engine mount to bracket bolts and tighten to 37 ft. lbs. (50 Nm).

116. Install the wheel drive shafts.

117. Install the control arm ball studs into the steering knuckles.

118. Install the ball stud nuts and tighten to 30 ft. lbs. (40 Nm).

119. Continue to tighten the nuts only enough to align the castle nut slots with the ball stud, install NEW cotter pins.

120. Connect the stabilizer links to the stabilizer shaft and install the stabilizer link to stabilizer shaft nuts. Tighten to 48 ft. lbs. (65 Nm).

121. Connect the outer tie rods to the steering knuckles. Tighten to 30 ft. lbs. (40 Nm).

122. Install NEW outer tie rod to steering knuckle nuts. Tighten to 48 ft. lbs. (25 Nm) plus an additional 90 degrees.

123. Position the intermediate shaft to the steering gear and install a NEW pinch bolt. Tighten to 25 ft. lbs. (34 Nm).

124. Install the catalytic converter.

125. Install the transaxle oil cooler lines to the transaxle.

126. Install the transaxle oil cooler line to transaxle nut. Tighten to 27 inch lbs. (4 Nm).

127. Remove the wood from between the oil pan and the engine cradle.

128. Remove the wood from between the transaxle and the engine cradle.

129. Install the front fender liners.

130. Install the front wheels and tires.

131. Lower the vehicle.

132. Unsecure and position the radiator/condenser/fan assembly.

133. Install the shift control cable to the shift control cable bracket and engage the shift control cable retaining clip.

134. Install the transaxle shift cable to the range select lever.

135. Raise and support the vehicle.

136. Install the auxiliary heater water pump and bolt. Tighten the bolt to 80 inch lbs. (9 Nm).

137. Connect the engine wiring harness electrical connector to the auxiliary heater water pump and bolt. Tighten the bolt to 18 ft. lbs. (25 Nm).

138. Position and install the positive battery cable between the starter and the engine.

139. Install the positive battery cable lead to the starter motor.

140. Install the positive battery cable to starter motor nut. Tighten the nut to 80 inch lbs. (9 Nm).

141. Position the A/C compressor and install the bolts. Tighten to 16 ft. lbs. (22 Nm).

142. Install the alternator control module coolant pump and bolt. Tighten to 18 ft. lbs. (25 Nm).

143. Connect the engine wiring harness electrical connector to the alternator control module coolant pump.

144. Connect the engine wiring harness electrical connector to the A/C compressor.

145. Lower the vehicle.

146. Install the coolant recovery reservoir/heater inlet hose to the thermostat housing.

147. Position the coolant recovery reservoir/heater inlet hose clamp at the thermostat housing.

148. Install the heater inlet hose to the thermostat housing.

149. Position the heater inlet hose clamp at the thermostat housing.

150. Connect the engine wiring harness electrical connector to the transaxle auxiliary pump module.

151. Install the alternator control module coolant hose to the alternator control module.

152. Position the alternator control module coolant hose clamp at the alternator control module.

153. Reposition the radiator inlet hose clamp.

154. Remove the radiator inlet hose from the cylinder head.

155. Remove the radiator outlet hose.

156. Position and install the coolant recovery inlet hose to the cylinder head.

157. Install the coolant recovery inlet pipe clip to the fuel rail.

158. Install the coolant recovery inlet hose clamp at the cylinder head.

159. Position and install the vacuum brake booster hose to the intake manifold.

160. Position the vacuum brake booster hose clamp at the intake manifold.

161. Install the alternator starter.

162. Install the battery tray.

163. Install the transaxle shift cable clip to the fuel line bracket.

164. Install the fuel feed pipe clip (2) to the fuel line bracket.

165. Connect the EVAP line quick connect fitting to the EVAP purge solenoid.

166. Connect the fuel feed pipe quick connect fitting at the fuel rail.

167. Install the air cleaner assembly.

168. Fill the transaxle with fluid.

169. Refill the engine with oil.

170. Start the engine and allow the engine to run, inspect for leaks. Correct as necessary.

EXHAUST MANIFOLD

REMOVAL & INSTALLATION

See Figure 94.

1. Remove the exhaust manifold heat shield.

2. Remove the Heated Oxygen Sensor (HO2S).

3. Remove and discard the exhaust manifold to cylinder head retaining nuts.

4. Remove the exhaust manifold.

5. Clean all of the sealing surfaces.

To install:

6. Install new exhaust manifold studs. Tighten the studs to 89 inch lbs. (10 Nm).

7. Install the exhaust manifold gasket.

8. Install the exhaust manifold to the cylinder head.

9. Install the NEW exhaust manifold to cylinder head retaining nuts finger tight.

10. Tighten the NEW exhaust manifold to cylinder head retaining nuts in the sequence shown. Tighten the nuts a second time to 124 inch lbs. (14 Nm).

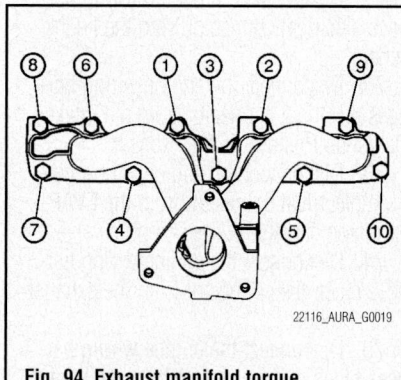

22116_AURA_G0019

Fig. 94 Exhaust manifold torque sequence—2.4L engine

11. Coat the threads of the oxygen sensor with anti-seize GM P/N 12397953 or equivalent.

12. Install the oxygen sensor to 31 ft. lbs. (42 Nm).

13. Install the exhaust manifold heat shield. Tighten the bolts to 16 ft. lbs. (22 Nm).

INTAKE MANIFOLD

REMOVAL & INSTALLATION

See Figures 95 and 96.

1. Remove the air cleaner outlet duct.
2. Remove the radiator inlet hose.
3. Disconnect the engine wiring harness electrical connector from the Throttle Actuator Control (TAC).
4. Disconnect the engine wiring harness electrical connector from the generator starter.
5. Disconnect the engine wiring harness electrical connector from the generator starter.
6. Remove the fuel injector wiring harness electrical connector retainer from the generator starter.
7. Disconnect the fuel injector wiring harness electrical connector from the engine wiring harness electrical connector.
8. Remove the engine wiring harness clips from the intake manifold.
9. Reposition the vacuum brake booster hose clamp at the intake manifold.
10. Remove the vacuum brake booster hose from the intake manifold.
11. Remove the throttle body.
12. Disconnect the engine wiring harness electrical connector from the Manifold Absolute Pressure (MAP) sensor.
13. Disconnect the Evaporative Emission (EVAP) canister purge tube from the intake manifold and the EVAP solenoid.
14. Remove the oil level indicator tube.

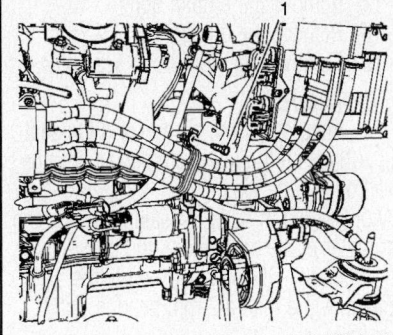

Fig. 96 Removing the 3-phase voltage cable bracket bolt (1) at the oil level indicator tube

15. Remove the fuel rail.
16. Remove the 3-phase voltage cable bracket bolt at the oil level indicator tube.
17. Remove the generator starter bolts.
18. Reposition and secure the generator starter out of the way.
19. Remove the intake manifold lower bolts.
20. Remove the intake manifold upper bolt and nuts.
21. Remove the intake manifold.

➡**The intake manifold gasket is reusable, only replace the gasket if damage has occurred.**

22. Remove and inspect the intake manifold gasket.

To install:

23. Install a NEW intake manifold gasket if necessary, otherwise install the old gasket.
24. Install the intake manifold.
25. Install the intake manifold upper bolt and nuts.
26. Install the intake manifold lower bolts. Tighten the bolts/nuts (1) to 89 inch lbs. (10 Nm).
27. Position the starter/generator to the bracket.
28. Install the starter/generator bolts until snug.
29. Tighten the starter generator bolts. Start with the front bolts then tighten the bottom bolts. Tighten the bolts to 43 ft. lbs. (58 Nm).
30. Install the 3-phase voltage cable bracket to the tie bar.
31. Install the 3-phase voltage cable bracket bolt at the oil level indicator tube. Tighten the bolt to 89 inch lbs. (10 Nm).
32. Install the fuel rail.
33. Install the oil level indicator tube.
34. Connect the EVAP canister purge tube to the intake manifold and the EVAP solenoid.
35. Connect the engine wiring harness electrical connector to the MAP sensor.
36. Install the throttle body.
37. Install the vacuum brake booster hose to the intake manifold.
38. Position the vacuum brake booster hose clamp at the intake manifold.
39. Install the engine wiring harness clips to the intake manifold.
40. Connect the fuel injector wiring harness electrical connector to the engine wiring harness electrical connector.
41. Install the fuel injector wiring harness electrical connector retainer to the generator starter.
42. Connect the engine wiring harness electrical connector to the generator starter.
43. Connect the engine wiring harness electrical connector to the generator starter.
44. Connect the engine wiring harness electrical connector to the TAC.
45. Install the radiator inlet hose.
46. Install the air cleaner outlet duct.

OIL PAN

REMOVAL & INSTALLATION

See Figures 97 through 99.

1. Remove the drive belt.
2. Remove the oil level indicator tube.

➡**The support fixture bar must be installed to provide enough access to remove and properly tighten the oil pan bolts.**

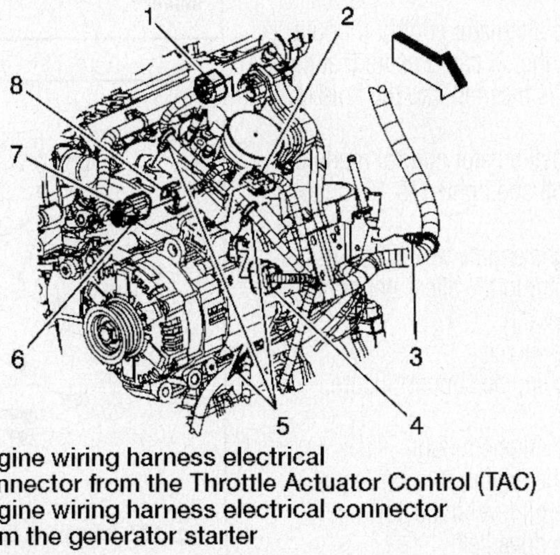

1. Engine wiring harness electrical connector from the Throttle Actuator Control (TAC)
2. Engine wiring harness electrical connector from the generator starter
3. NA
4. Engine wiring harness electrical connector from the generator starter
5. Engine wiring harness clips from the intake manifold
6. Fuel injector wiring harness electrical connector retainer
7. Fuel injector wiring harness electrical connector
8. Engine wiring harness electrical connector

36616_AURH_G0046

Fig. 95 Identifying engine wiring harness electrical connectors

3. Install the engine support fixture.

4. Remove engine mount.

5. Using the engine support fixture, raise the engine approximately 3 inches.

6. Raise and support the vehicle.

7. Loosen the upper Air Conditioning (A/C) compressor bolts.

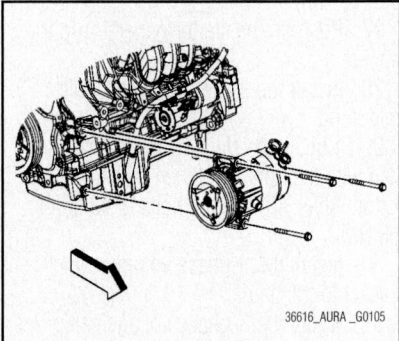

Fig. 97 Locating the upper A/C compressor bolts

8. Remove the lower A/C compressor bolt.

9. Place a suitable drain pan under the oil pan drain plug.

10. Remove the oil pan drain plug.

11. Drain the engine oil.

12. Reinstall the oil pan drain plug until snug.

13. Disconnect the engine wiring harness electrical connector from the alternator control module coolant pump.

14. Remove the alternator control module coolant pump bolt.

15. Remove the alternator control module coolant pump from the oil pan.

16. Remove the 4 oil pan to transaxle bolts.

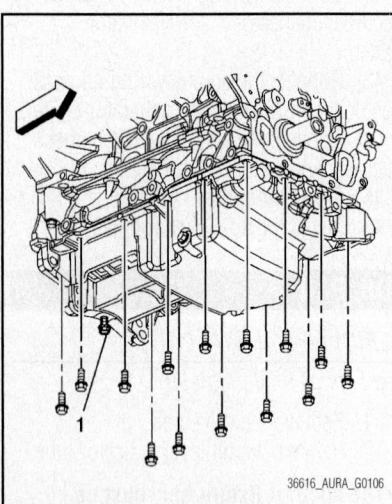

Fig. 98 Removing the oil pan bolts

17. Remove the oil pan bolts.

18. Remove the oil pan.

19. Remove any old oil pan sealant.

To install:

20. Ensure that the oil pan and the sealing surface on the lower crankcase are free of all oil and debris.

Apply a 2 mm bead of sealant around the perimeter of the oil pan and the oil suction port opening. DO NOT over apply the sealant. More than a 2 mm bead is not required.

21. Install the oil pan.

22. Install the oil pan bolts and hand tighten.

23. Install the 4 oil pan to transaxle bolts. Tighten the bolts to 55 ft. lbs. (75 Nm).

24. Tighten the oil pan bolts in the sequence shown to 18 ft. lbs. (25 Nm).

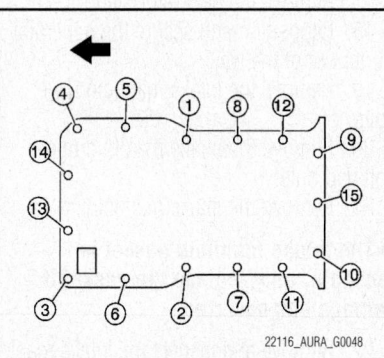

Fig. 99 Oil pan bolt tightening sequence—2.4L engine

25. Install the alternator control module coolant pump to the oil pan. Ensure that the anti-rotation tab is inserted into the hole in the oil pan.

26. Install the alternator control module coolant pump bolt and tighten to 18 ft. lbs. (25 Nm).

27. Connect the engine wiring harness electrical connector to the alternator control module coolant pump.

28. Lower the vehicle.

29. Using the engine support fixture, lower the engine.

30. Install the engine mount.

31. Remove the engine support fixture.

32. Install the oil level indicator tube.

33. Install the drive belt.

34. Fill the engine oil to the proper level.

OIL PUMP

REMOVAL & INSTALLATION

See Figures 100 through 103.

1. Remove the accessory drive belt tensioner.

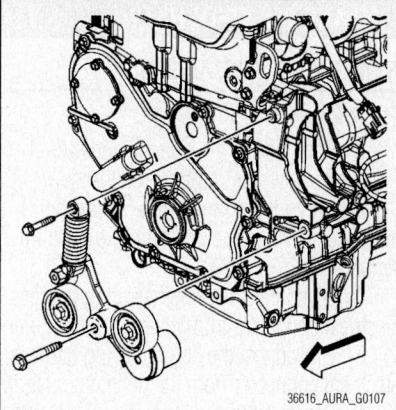

Fig. 100 Removing the accessory drive belt tensioner

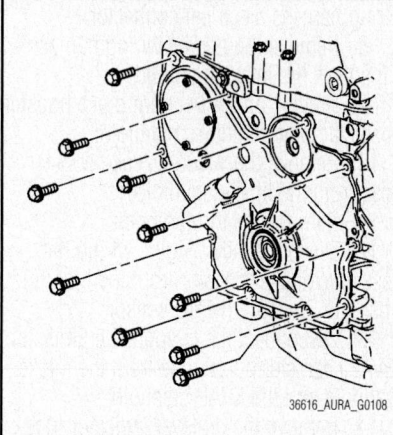

Fig. 101 Removing the drive belt tensioner

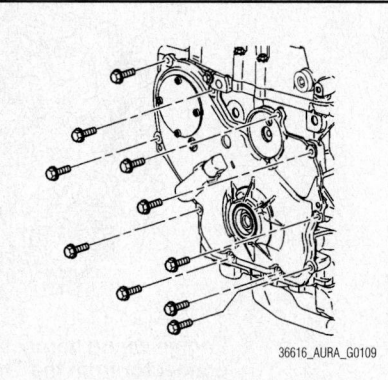

Fig. 102 Removing the engine front cover bolts

2. Remove the drive belt tensioner bracket.

3. Remove the engine front cover bolts.

4. Remove the long water pump bolt.

5. Remove the engine front cover and gaskets.

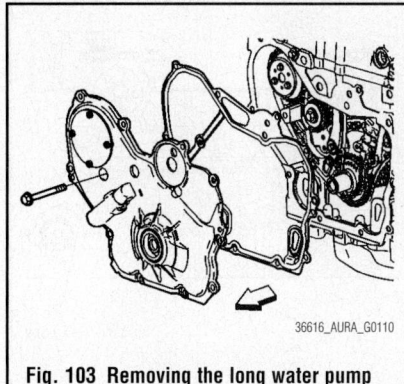

Fig. 103 Removing the long water pump bolt

6. Remove the crankshaft front cover oil seal with an appropriate tool.
7. Remove the oil pump.

To install:
8. Install the oil pump.
9. Install the engine front cover with a new gasket.

➡ Use the correct fastener in the correct location. Replacement fasteners must be the correct part number for that application. Fasteners requiring replacement or fasteners requiring the use of thread locking compound or sealant are identified in the service procedure. Do not use paints, lubricants, or corrosion inhibitors on fasteners or fastener joint surfaces unless specified. These coatings affect fastener torque and joint clamping force and may damage the fastener. Use the correct tightening sequence and specifications when installing fasteners in order to avoid damage to parts and systems.

10. Install the long water pump bolt and tighten to 18 ft. lbs. (25 Nm).
11. Install the engine front cover bolts and tighten to 18 ft. lbs. (25 Nm).
12. Install the drive belt tensioner bracket and tighten to 33 ft. lbs. (45 Nm).
13. Install the accessory drive belt tensioner and tighten to 33 ft. lbs. (45 Nm).

PISTON AND RING

POSITIONING

A dot showing proper piston orientation is located on the top of the piston.

REAR MAIN SEAL

REMOVAL & INSTALLATION
See Figure 104.

1. Remove the transmission and flywheel.

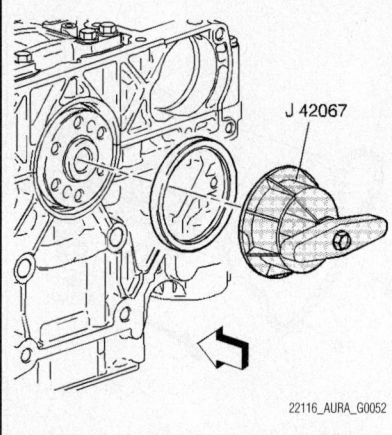

Fig. 104 Installing the rear seal—2.4L engine

➡ Do not damage the outside diameter of the crankshaft or chamber with any tool.

2. Pry out the crankshaft rear oil seal using a flat-bladed tool.

To install:
3. Using a seal installer such as J 42067, install a NEW crankshaft real oil seal.
4. Install the flywheel and transmission

TIMING CHAIN, SPROCKETS, FRONT COVER AND SEAL

REMOVAL & INSTALLATION
See Figures 105 through 115.

1. Remove the No. 1 cylinder spark plug.
2. Rotate the crankshaft in the engine

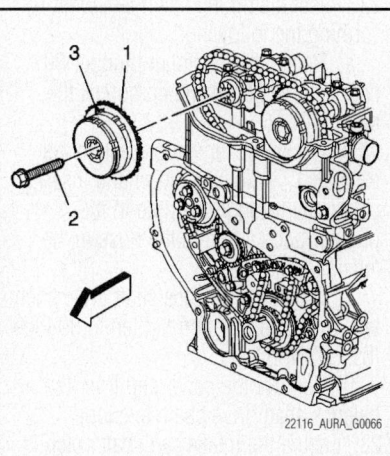

Fig. 105 Remove and discard the exhaust camshaft actuator bolt (2). Remove the exhaust camshaft actuator (1, 3) from the camshaft and timing chain—2.4L engine

rotational direction clockwise, until the No. 1 piston is at Top Dead Center (TDC) on the compression stroke.
3. Remove the camshaft cover.
4. Remove the engine front cover as follows:
   a. Remove the drive belt tensioner.
   b. Remove the crankshaft balancer.
   c. Install the engine support fixture.
   d. Remove the engine mount to bracket bolts.
   e. Remove the engine mount to side rail nuts.
   f. Remove the engine mount from the engine compartment.
   g. Remove the engine mount bracket to engine bolts.
   h. Remove the engine mount bracket.
   i. Remove the engine front cover to water pump bolt.
   j. Raise and suitably support the vehicle.
   k. Remove the engine front cover bolts.
   l. Remove the engine front cover.
   m. Remove and discard the engine front cover gasket.
5. Remove the upper timing chain guide bolts and guide.

➡ The timing chain tensioner must be removed to unload chain tension before the timing chain is removed. If it is not, the timing chain will become cocked and it will be difficult to remove.

6. Remove the timing chain tensioner.
7. Install a 24 mm wrench on the hex

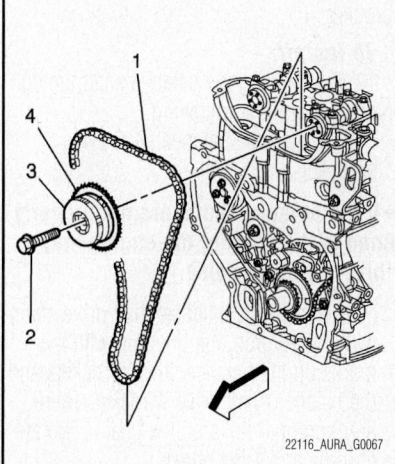

Fig. 106 Remove and discard the intake camshaft actuator bolt (2).
Remove the intake camshaft actuator (3), and the timing chain through the top of the cylinder head—2.4L engine

on the exhaust camshaft in order to hold the camshaft.

8. Remove and discard the exhaust camshaft actuator bolt.

9. Remove the exhaust camshaft actuator from the camshaft and timing chain.

10. Remove the timing chain tensioner guide bolt and guide.

11. Remove the fixed timing chain guide access plug.

12. Remove the fixed timing chain guide bolts and guide.

13. Install a 24 mm wrench on the hex on the intake camshaft in order to hold the camshaft.

14. Remove and discard the intake camshaft actuator bolt.

15. Remove the intake camshaft actuator, and the timing chain through the top of the cylinder head.

16. Remove the timing chain crankshaft sprocket.

17. If replacing the balance shaft timing chain and sprocket, perform the following:

a. Remove the balance shaft drive chain tensioner bolts and tensioner.

b. Remove the adjustable balance shaft chain guide bolt and guide.

c. Remove the small balance shaft drive chain guide bolts and guide.

d. Remove the upper balance shaft drive chain guide bolts and guide.

➡**It may ease removal of the balance shaft drive chain to get all the slack in the chain between the crankshaft and water pump sprockets.**

18. Remove the balance shaft drive chain.

19. Remove the balance shaft drive sprocket .

To install:

20. If replacing the balance shaft timing chain, perform the following:

a. Install the balance shaft drive sprocket.

➡**If the balance shafts are not properly timed to the engine, the engine may vibrate or make noise.**

b. Install the balance shaft drive chain with the colored link lined up with the marks on the balance shaft sprockets and the balance shaft drive sprocket. There are 3 colored links on the chain. Two are chrome and 1 is copper.

c. Use the following steps in order to line up the links with the sprockets:

- Place the copper link (5) so that it lines up with the timing mark (2) on the intake side balance shaft sprocket.

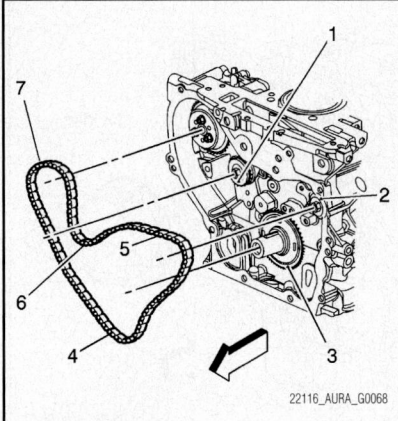

Fig. 107 Balance shaft drive chain components—2.4L engine

- Working clockwise around the chain, place the chrome link (4) in line with the timing mark (3) on the balance shaft drive sprocket. (approximately 6 o'clock position on the sprocket).

- Place the chain (7) on the water pump drive sprocket. The alignment is not critical

Align the last chrome link (6) with the timing mark (1) on the exhaust side balance shaft drive sprocket.

d. Install the upper balance shaft drive chain guide and bolts and tighten to 11 ft. lbs. (15 Nm).

e. Install the small balance shaft drive chain guide and bolts and tighten to 11 ft. lbs. (15 Nm).

21. Install the adjustable balance shaft chain guide and bolt and tighten to 89 inch lbs. (10 Nm).

22. Reset the timing chain tensioner by performing the following:

a. Rotate the tensioner plunger 90 degrees in its bore and compress the plunger

b. Rotate the tensioner back to the original 12 o'clock position and insert a paper clip through the hole in the plunger body and into the hose in the tensioner plunger.

c. Install the balance shaft drive chain tensioner and bolt and tighten to 89 inch lbs. (10 Nm).

d. Remove the paper clip from the balance shaft drive chain tensioner.

23. Ensure the intake camshaft notch is in the 5 o'clock position (2) and the exhaust camshaft notch is in the 7 o'clock position (1). The number 1 piston should be at top dead center (TDC), crankshaft key at 12 o'clock.

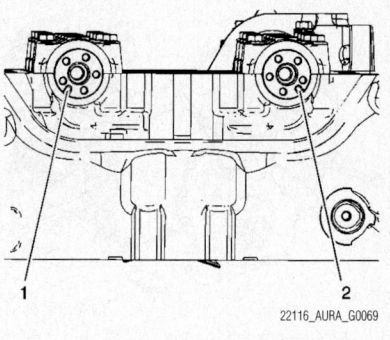

Fig. 108 Ensure the intake camshaft notch is in the 5 o'clock position (2) and the exhaust camshaft notch is in the 7 o'clock position (1). The number 1 piston should be at top dead center (TDC), crankshaft key at 12 o'clock—2.4L engine

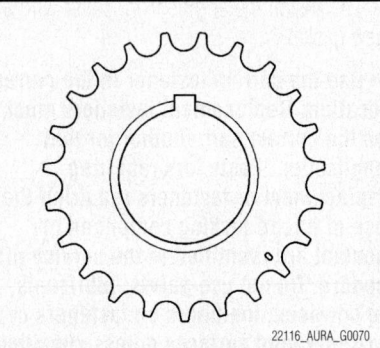

Fig. 109 Install the timing chain drive sprocket to the crankshaft with the timing mark in the 5 o'clock position and the front of the sprocket facing out—2.4L engine

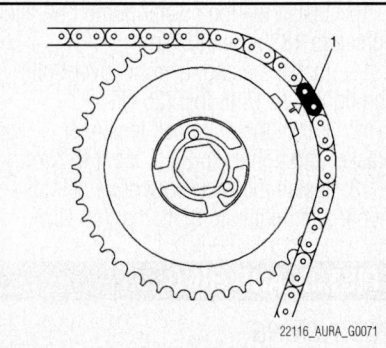

Fig. 110 Assemble the intake camshaft actuator into the timing chain with the timing mark lined up with the uniquely colored link (1)—2.4L engine

24. Install the timing chain drive sprocket to the crankshaft with the timing mark in the 5 o'clock position and the front of the sprocket facing out.

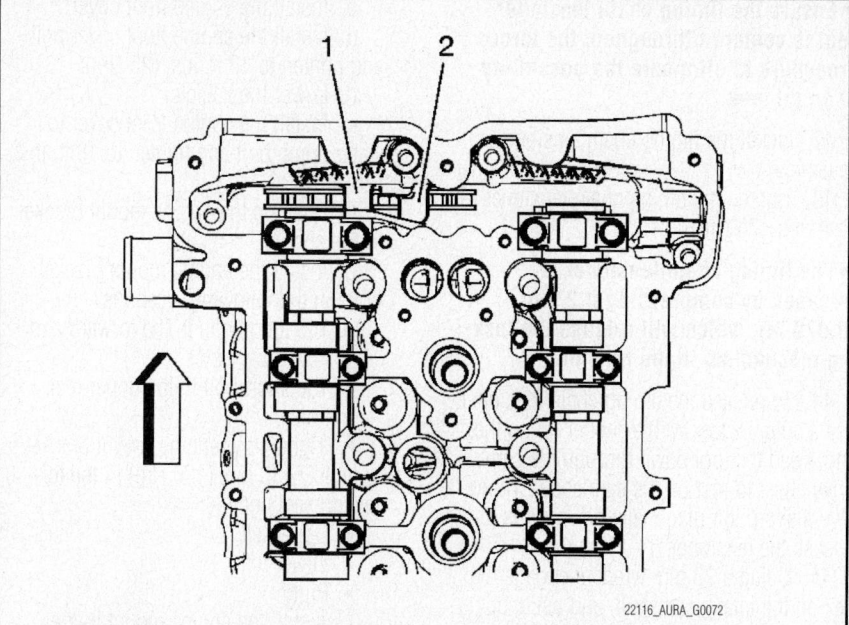

Fig. 111 Lower the timing chain through the opening in the cylinder head. Use care to ensure that the chain goes around both sides of the cylinder block bosses (1, 2)—2.4L engine

➡There are 3 colored links on the timing chain. Two links are of matching color, and 1 link is of a unique color. Use the following procedure to line up the links with the actuators. Orient the chain so that the colored links are visible. Always use new actuator bolts.

25. Assemble the intake camshaft actuator into the timing chain with the timing mark lined up with the uniquely colored link.

26. Lower the timing chain through the opening in the cylinder head. Use care to ensure that the chain goes around both sides of the cylinder block bosses (1, 2).

27. Install the intake camshaft actuator onto the intake camshaft while aligning the dowel pin into the camshaft slot.

28. Hand tighten the new intake camshaft actuator bolt.

29. Route the timing chain around the crankshaft sprocket and line up the first matching colored link (2) with the timing mark on the crankshaft sprocket, in approximately the 5 o'clock position.

30. Rotate the crankshaft clockwise to remove all chain slack. Do not rotate the intake camshaft.

31. Install the adjustable timing chain guide down through the opening in the cylinder head and install the adjustable timing chain bolt and tighten to 89 inch lbs. (10 Nm).

➡Always install NEW actuator bolts.

32. Install the exhaust camshaft actuator into the timing chain with the timing mark lined up with the second matching colored link.

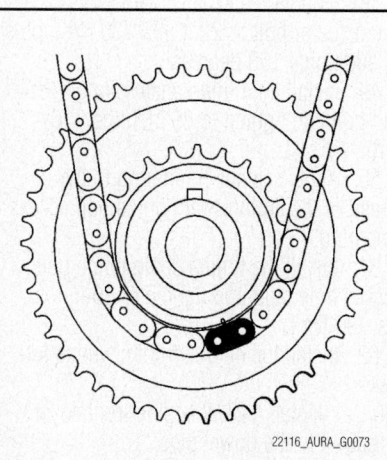

Fig. 112 Route the timing chain around the crankshaft sprocket and line up the first matching colored link (2) with the timing mark on the crankshaft sprocket, in approximately the 5 o'clock position—2.4L engine

33. Install the exhaust camshaft actuator onto the exhaust camshaft, aligning the dowel pin into the camshaft slot.

34. Using a 23 mm open end wrench, rotate the exhaust campshaft approximately 45 degrees until the dowel pin in the camshaft actuator goes into the camshaft slot.

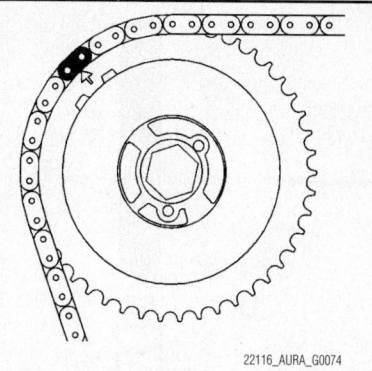

Fig. 113 Install the exhaust camshaft actuator into the timing chain with the timing mark lined up with the second matching colored link—2.4L engine

35. When the actuator seats on the cam, tighten the new exhaust camshaft actuator bolt hand tight.

36. Verify that all of the colored links and the appropriate timing marks are still aligned. If they are not aligned, repeat the portion of the procedure necessary to align the timing marks

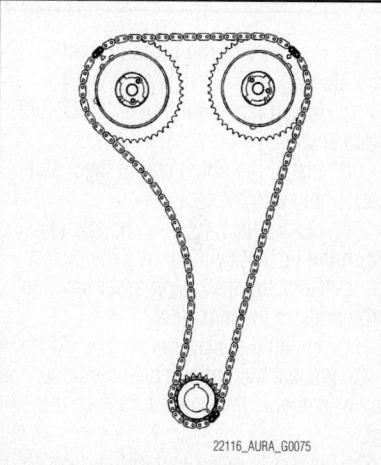

Fig. 114 Verify that all of the colored links and the appropriate timing marks are still aligned. If they are not aligned, repeat the portion of the procedure necessary to align the timing marks—2.4L engine

37. Install the fixed timing chain guide and bolts and tighten to 106 inch lbs. (12 Nm).

38. Install the upper timing chain guide and bolts and tighten to 89 inch lbs. (10 Nm).

39. Reset the timing chain tensioner by performing the following:
   a. Remove the snap ring.
   b. Remove the piston assembly

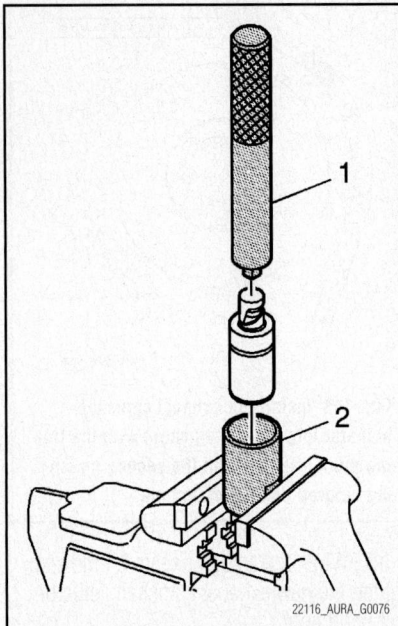

Fig. 115 Install tensioner tool J 45027-2 (2) into a vise, Install the notch end of the piston assembly into the tool and using the J 45027-1 handle (1), turn the ratchet cylinder into the piston— 2.4L engine

22116_AURA_G0076

from the body of the timing chain tensioner.

c. Install tensioner tool J 45027-2 (2) into a vise.

d. Install the notch end of the piston assembly into the tool.

e. Using the J 45027-1 handle (1), turn the ratchet cylinder into the piston.

f. Reinstall the piston assembly into the body of the tensioner.

g. Install the snap ring.

40. Inspect the timing chain tensioner seal for damage. If damaged, replace the seal.

41. Inspect to ensure all dirt and debris is removed from the timing chain tensioner threaded hole in the cylinder head.

➡Ensure the timing chain tensioner seal is centered throughout the torque procedure to eliminate the possibility of an oil leak.

42. Install the timing chain tensioner assembly.

43. Tighten the timing chain tensioner to 55 ft. lbs. (75 Nm).

➡The timing chain tensioner is released by compressing it 2 mm (0.079 in), which will release the locking mechanism in the ratchet.

44. To release the timing chain tensioner, use a suitable tool with a rubber tip on the end. Feed the tool down through the cam drive chest to rest on the cam chain. Then give a sharp jolt diagonally downwards to release the tensioner.

45. Using a 23 mm wrench, engage the hex on the intake camshaft, and using a torque wrench, tighten the camshaft actuator bolt.

46. Tighten the intake camshaft position actuator bolt to 22 ft. lbs. (30 Nm), plus an additional 100 degrees.

47. Using a 23 mm wrench, engage the hex on the exhaust camshaft, and using a torque wrench, tighten the camshaft actuator bolt.

48. Tighten the exhaust camshaft position actuator bolt to 22 ft. lbs. (30 Nm), plus an additional 100 degrees.

49. Install the timing chain oiling nozzle and bolt and tighten to 89 inch lbs. (10 Nm).

50. Apply sealant compound to the thread of the timing chain guide bolt access hole plug.

51. Install the timing chain guide bolt access hole plug and tighten to 66 ft. lbs. lbs. (90 Nm).

52. Install the engine front cover as follows:

   a. Install a NEW engine front cover gasket to the dowel pins.

b. Install the engine front cover.

c. Install the engine front cover bolts and tighten to 18 ft. lbs. (25 Nm).

d. Lower the vehicle.

e. Install the engine front cover to water pump bolt and tighten to 18 ft. lbs. (25 Nm).

f. Position the engine mount bracket to the engine.

g. Install the engine mount bracket bolts in the following locations:

- The long bolts in the forward and lower rear holes
- The short bolt in the upper rear hole

h. Tighten the engine mount bracket bolts to 74 ft. lbs. (100 Nm) in the following sequence.

- Upper left
- Lower left
- Right

i. Install the engine mount to the engine compartment.

j. Install the engine mount to side rail nuts and tighten to 74 ft. lbs. (100 Nm)

k. Install the engine mount to bracket bolts.

l. Tighten the engine mount to bracket bolts to 37 ft. lbs. (50 Nm) in the following sequence.

- Middle
- Rear
- Front

m. Remove the engine support fixture.

n. Install the crankshaft balancer.

o. Install the drive belt tensioner.

53. Install the camshaft cover.

54. Install the No. 1 cylinder spark plug.

VALVE LASH

ADJUSTMENT

These engines utilize hydraulic lash adjusters; no adjustment is necessary.

ENGINE PERFORMANCE & EMISSION CONTROLS

COMPONENT LOCATIONS

See Figures 116 through 120.

CAMSHAFT POSITION (CMP) SENSOR

LOCATION

The Camshaft Position (CMP) sensor (exhaust), is located on the upper rear of the engine, near the camshaft cover. The 2.4L engines Camshaft Position (CMP) sensor (intake), is located on the upper front of the engine, near the camshaft cover.

REMOVAL & INSTALLATION

Intake

See Figure 121.

1. Remove the air cleaner outlet duct.
2. Disconnect the engine wiring harness electrical connector from the intake Camshaft Position (CMP) sensor.
3. Remove the CMP sensor bolt.
4. Remove the CMP sensor.

To install:

→ **Inspect the CMP sensor for damage, replace as necessary.**

5. Lubricate the CMP sensor O-ring seal with clean engine oil.
6. Install the CMP sensor.

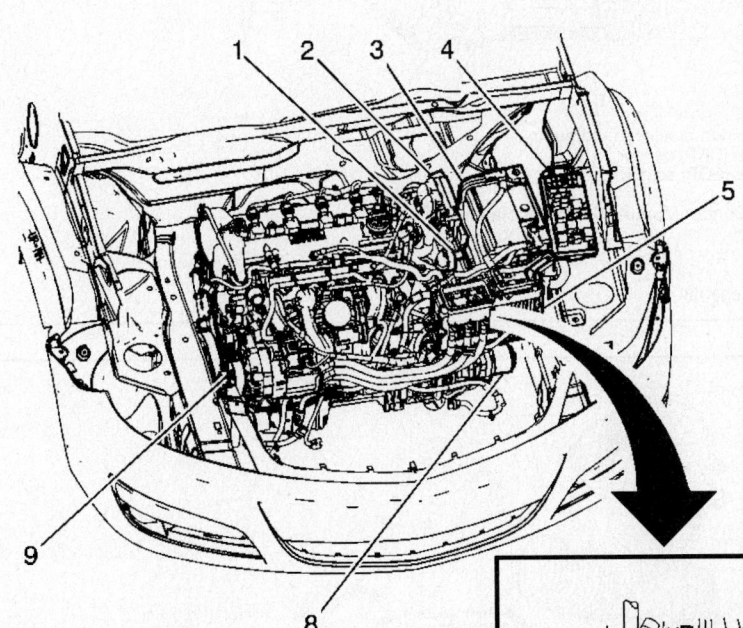

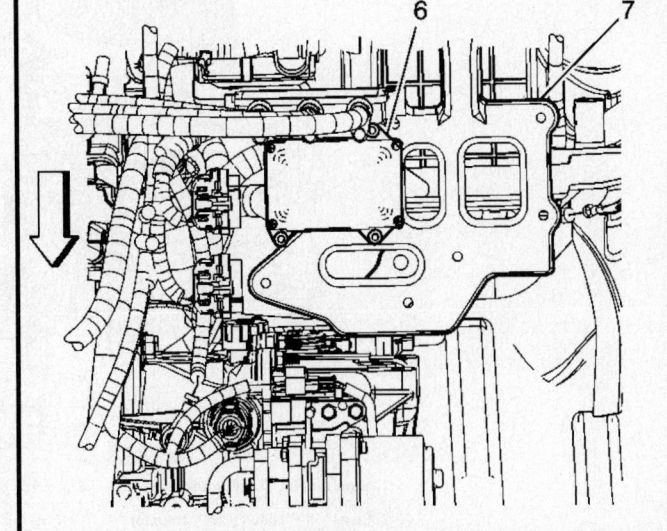

1. Transmission Control Module (TCM)
2. Engine Control Module (ECM)
3. Battery
4. Fuse block (underhood)
5. Starter Generator Control Module (SGCM)
6. Automatic transmission auxiliary fluid pump control module
7. Starter Generator Control Module (SGCM) bracket
8. Automatic transmission auxiliary fluid pump
9. Starter generator

36616_AURA_G0044

Fig. 116 Front of engine compartment 1 of 2—2.4L engine

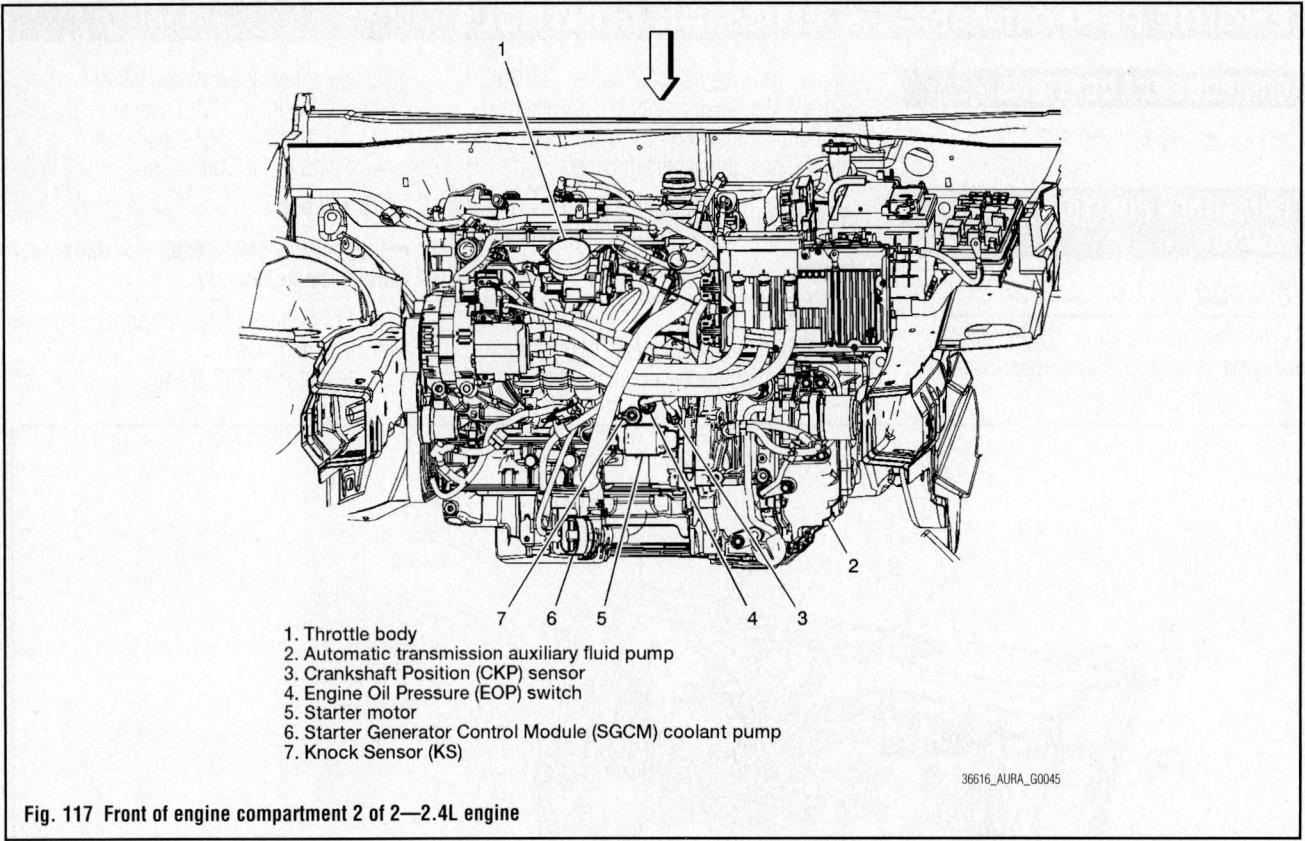

1. Throttle body
2. Automatic transmission auxiliary fluid pump
3. Crankshaft Position (CKP) sensor
4. Engine Oil Pressure (EOP) switch
5. Starter motor
6. Starter Generator Control Module (SGCM) coolant pump
7. Knock Sensor (KS)

36616_AURA_G0045

Fig. 117 Front of engine compartment 2 of 2—2.4L engine

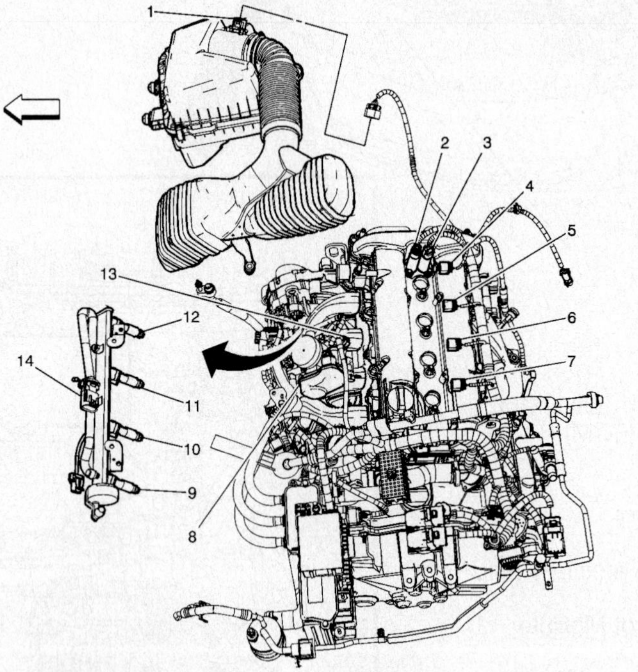

1. Mass Air Flow (MAF)/Intake Air
   Temperature (IAT) sensor
2. Camshaft Position (CMP) actuator
   solenoid valve – intake
3. Camshaft Position (CMP) actuator
   solenoid valve – exhaust
4. Ignition coil 1
5. Ignition coil 2
6. Ignition coil 3
7. Ignition coil 4

8. Throttle body
9. Fuel injector 4
10. Fuel injector 3
11. Fuel injector 2
12. Fuel injector 1
13. Manifold Absolute Pressure (MAP) sensor
14. X130

36616_AURA_G0046

Fig. 118 Top of engine components—2.4L engine

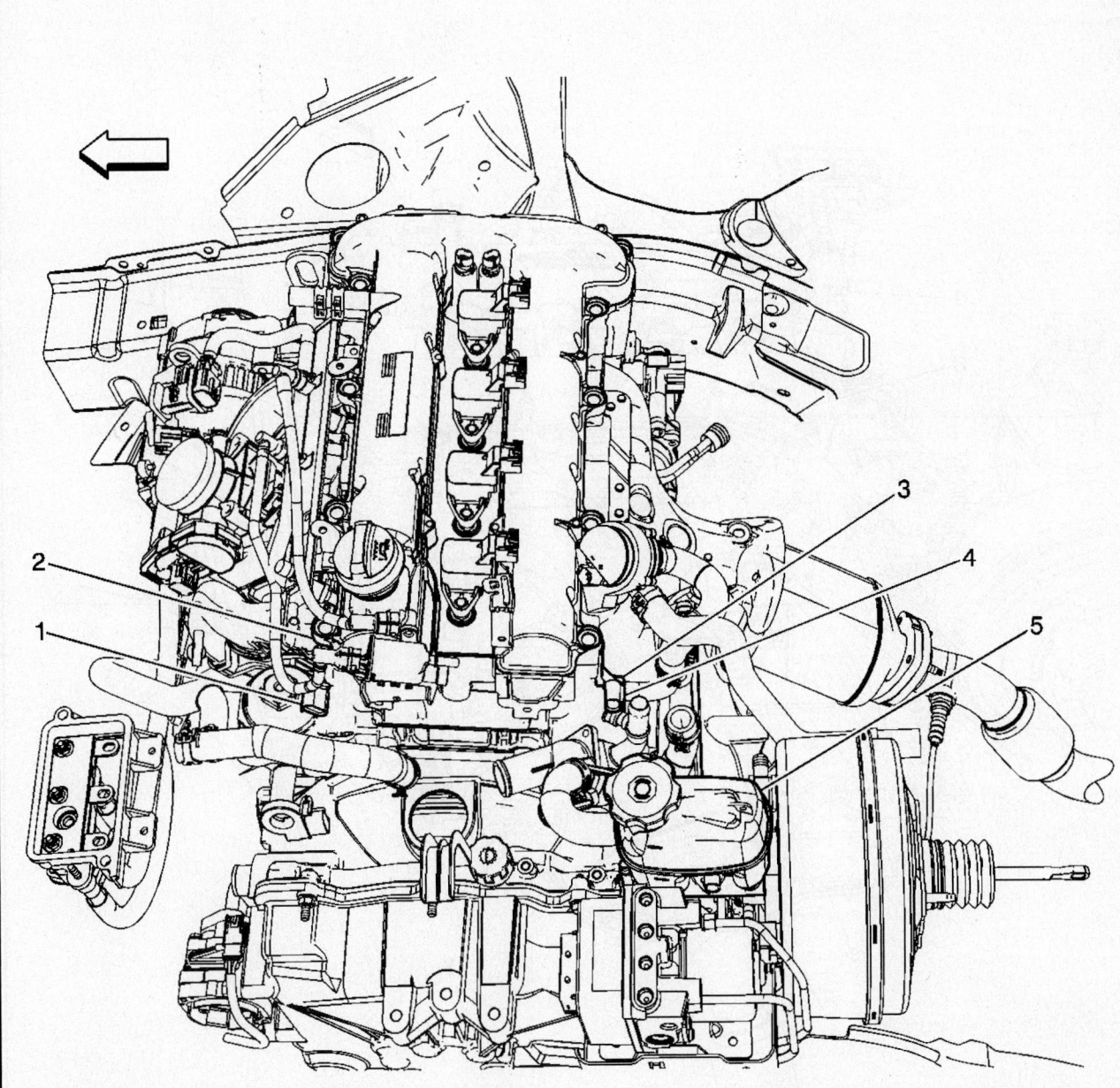

1. Camshaft Position (CMP) sensor - intake
2. G106
3. G110
4. Camshaft Position (CMP) sensor - exhaust
5. Master cylinder

36616_AURA_G0047

Fig. 119 Left side of engine compartment—2.4L engine

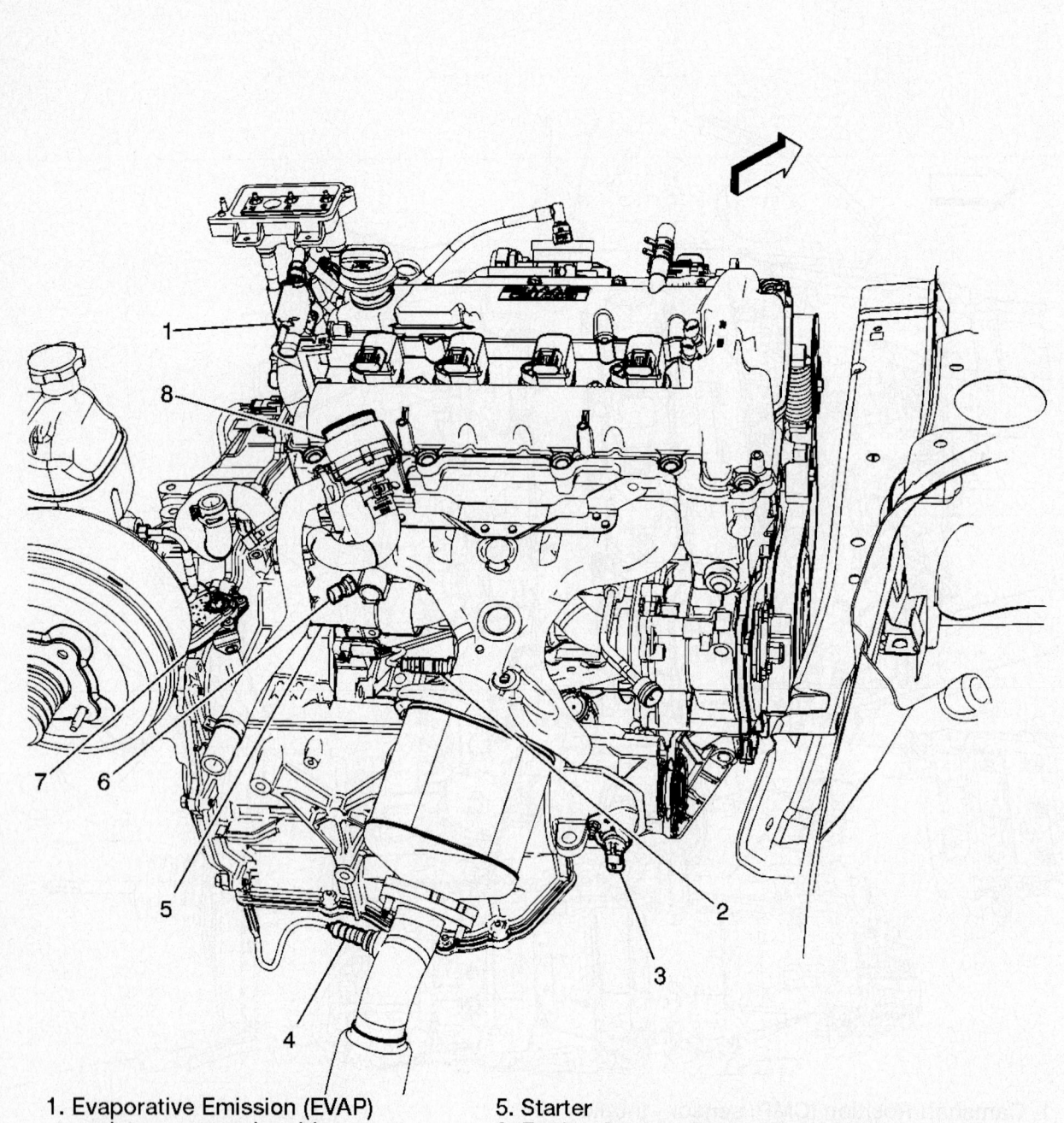

1. Evaporative Emission (EVAP)
   canister purge solenoid
2. Heated Oxygen Sensor (HO2S) 1
3. Vehicle Speed Sensor (VSS)
4. Heated Oxygen Sensor (HO2S) 2
5. Starter
6. Engine Coolant Temperature (ECT) sensor
7. Park/Neutral Position (PNP) switch
8. Heater coolant pump

36616_AURA_G0048

Fig. 120 Rear of engine components—2.4L engine

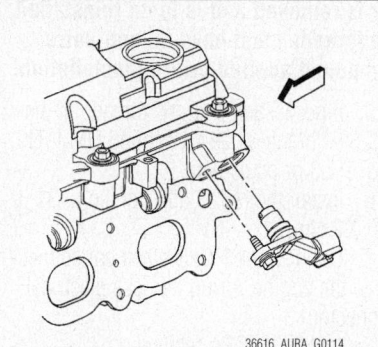

Fig. 121 Removing and installing the CMP sensor (intake)

7. Install the CMP sensor bolt and tighten to 89 inch lbs. (10 Nm).

8. Connect the engine wiring harness electrical connector to the intake CMP sensor.

9. Install the air cleaner outlet duct.

Exhaust

See Figure 122.

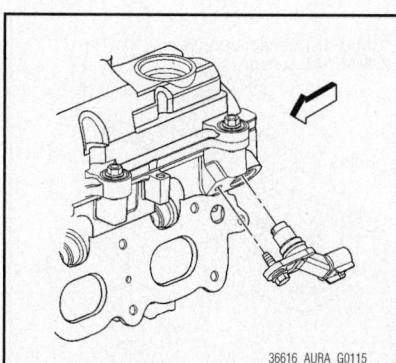

Fig. 122 Removing and installing the CMP sensor (exhaust)

1. Remove the intake manifold cover.

2. Disconnect the engine wiring harness electrical connector from the exhaust CMP sensor.

3. Remove the CMP sensor bolt.

4. Remove the CMP sensor.

To install:

➡ **Inspect the CMP sensor for damage, replace as necessary.**

5. Lubricate the CMP sensor O-ring seal with clean engine oil.

6. Install the CMP sensor.

7. Install the CMP sensor bolt. Tighten the bolt to 89 inch lbs. (10 Nm).

8. Connect the engine wiring harness electrical connector to the exhaust CMP sensor.

9. Install the intake manifold cover.

CRANKSHAFT POSITION (CKP) SENSOR

LOCATION

The engines the Crankshaft Position (CKP) sensor is located on the right side of the engine, at the end of the crankshaft, behind the harmonic balancer.

REMOVAL & INSTALLATION

See Figure 123.

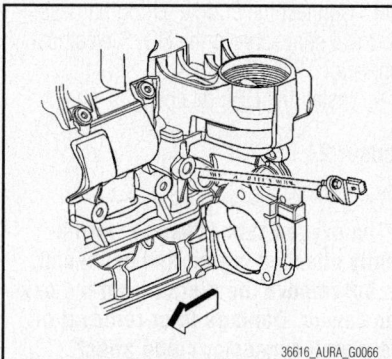

Fig. 123 Removing and installing the CKP sensor—2.4L engine

1. Remove the starter motor.

2. Disconnect the engine wiring harness electrical connector from the Crankshaft Position (CKP) sensor.

3. Remove the CKP sensor bolt and sensor.

To install:

4. Lubricate the CKP sensor O-ring seal with clean engine oil.

5. Install the CKP sensor.

6. Install the CKP sensor bolt and tighten to 89 inch lbs. (10 Nm).

ENGINE COOLANT TEMPERATURE (ECT) SENSOR

LOCATION

The Engine Coolant Temperature (ECT) sensor is located on the rear of the engine, below the Camshaft Position (CMP) exhaust sensor.

REMOVAL & INSTALLATION

See Figure 124.

➡ **Use care when handling the coolant sensor. Damage to the coolant sensor will affect the operation of the fuel system.**

1. Drain the cooling system.

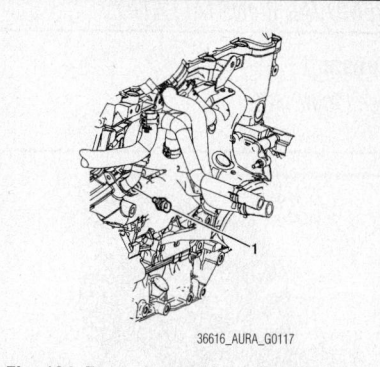

Fig. 124 Removing and installing the ECT sensor from the thermostat housing

2. Disconnect the engine wiring harness electrical connector from the Engine Coolant Temperature (ECT) sensor.

3. Remove the ECT sensor from the thermostat housing.

To install:

➡ **Replacement components must be the correct part number for the application. Components requiring the use of the thread locking compound, lubricants, corrosion inhibitors, or sealants are identified in the service procedure. Some replacement components may come with these coatings already applied. Do not use these coatings on components unless specified. These coatings can affect the final torque, which may affect the operation of the component. Use the correct torque specification when installing components in order to avoid damage.**

➡ **Use care when handling the coolant sensor. Damage to the coolant sensor will affect the operation of the fuel control system.**

4. If reinstalling the original sensor, or if installing a NEW sensor without a sealer, coat the threads with sealant.

5. Install the ECT sensor to the thermostat housing.

6. Connect the engine wiring harness electrical connector to the ECT sensor.

7. Fill the cooling system.

HEATED OXYGEN (HO2S) SENSOR

LOCATION

The HO2S 1 is located on the rear of the engine, between the exhaust manifold and the catalytic convertor. HO2S 2 is on the rear of the engine, just after the catalytic convertor and before the muffler.

REMOVAL & INSTALLATION

Sensor 1

See Figure 125.

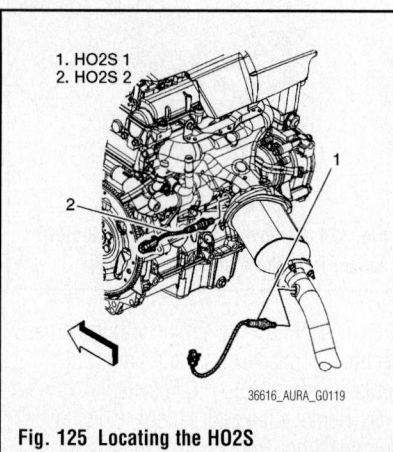

1. HO2S 1
2. HO2S 2

Fig. 125 Locating the HO2S

✳✳ CAUTION

The oxygen sensor uses a permanently attached pigtail and connector. Do not remove the pigtail from the oxygen sensor. Damage to or removal of the pigtail connector could affect proper operation of the oxygen sensor.

✳✳ CAUTION

The use of excessive force may damage the threads in the exhaust manifold/pipe.

➡The in-line connector and louvered end must be kept clear of grease, dirt or other contaminants. Avoid using cleaning solvents of any type. DO NOT drop or roughly handle the heated oxygen sensor (HO2S).

➡The HO2S may be difficult to remove when the engine temperature is less than 120°F (48°C).

1. Remove the Connector Position Assurance (CPA) retainer.
2. Disconnect the engine wiring harness electrical connector from the HO2S electrical connector.
3. Remove the HO2S connector clip from the thermostat housing tab.
4. Remove the HO2S.

To install:

➡A special anti-seize compound is used on the heated oxygen sensor threads. The compound consists of a liquid graphite and glass beads. The graphite will burn away, but the glass

beads will remain, making the sensor easier to remove. New or service replacement sensors will have the compound applied to the threads. If a sensor is removed and is to be reinstalled, the threads must have an anti-seize compound applied prior to installation.

5. If necessary, coat the threads of the HO2S with anti-seize compound GM P/N 12377953 or equivalent.
6. Install the HO2S and tighten to 31 ft. lbs. (42 Nm).
7. Install the HO2S connector clip to the thermostat housing tab.
8. Connect the engine wiring harness electrical connector to the HO2S electrical connector.
9. Install the CPA retainer.

Sensor 2

See Figure 125.

➡The oxygen sensor uses a permanently attached pigtail and connector. Do not remove the pigtail from the oxygen sensor. Damage to or removal of the pigtail connector could affect proper operation of the oxygen sensor.

➡The use of excessive force may damage the threads in the exhaust manifold/pipe.

✳✳ CAUTION

The in-line connector and louvered end must be kept clear of grease, dirt or other contaminants. Avoid using cleaning solvents of any type. DO NOT drop or roughly handle the heated oxygen sensor (HO2S).

➡The HO2S may be difficult to remove when the engine temperature is less than 120°F (48°C).

1. Raise and suitably support the vehicle.
2. Remove the Connector Position Assurance (CPA) retainer.
3. Disconnect the HO2S electrical connector (2) from the engine wiring harness electrical connector.
4. Remove the HO2S.

To install:

➡A special anti-seize compound is used on the heated oxygen sensor threads. The compound consists of a liquid graphite and glass beads. The graphite will burn away, but the glass beads will remain, making the sensor easier to remove. New or service replacement sensors will have the compound applied to the threads. If a sen-

sor is removed and is to be reinstalled, the threads must have an anti-seize compound applied prior to installation.

5. If necessary, coat the threads of the HO2S with anti-seize compound GM P/N 12377953 or equivalent.
6. Install the HO2S and tighten to 31 ft. lbs. (42 Nm).
7. Connect the HO2S electrical connector to the engine wiring harness electrical connector.
8. Install the CPA retainer.
9. Lower the vehicle.

INTAKE AIR TEMPERATURE (IAT) SENSOR

LOCATION

The Intake Air Temperature (IAT)/Mass Air Flow (MAF) sensor is located on the top right side of the engine, at the air cleaner.

REMOVAL & INSTALLATION

See Figure 126.

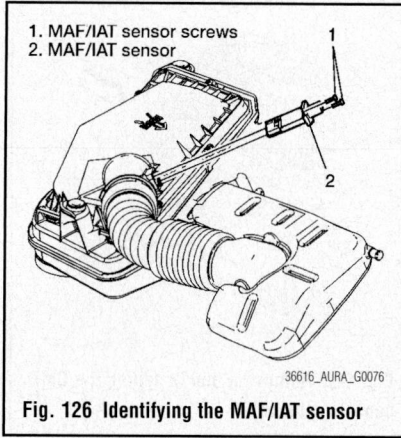

1. MAF/IAT sensor screws
2. MAF/IAT sensor

Fig. 126 Identifying the MAF/IAT sensor

1. Disconnect the engine wiring harness electrical connector from the Mass Air Flow (MAF)/Intake Air Temperature (IAT) sensor.
2. Remove the MAF/IAT sensor screws.
3. Remove the MAF/IAT sensor.

To install:

4. Install the MAF/IAT sensor.
5. Install the MAF/IAT sensor screws and tighten to 5 inch lbs. (0.6 Nm).
6. Connect the engine wiring harness electrical connector to the MAF/IAT sensor.

KNOCK SENSOR (KS)

LOCATION

The Knock Sensor (KS) is located on the front of the engine, below the intake manifold.

REMOVAL & INSTALLATION

See Figure 127.

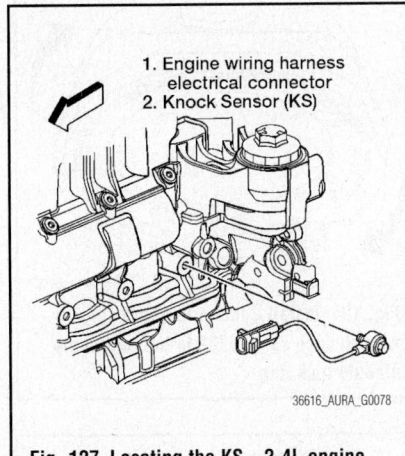

Fig. 127 Locating the KS—2.4L engine

1. Disconnect the negative battery cable.
2. Raise and support the vehicle.
3. Disconnect the engine wiring harness electrical connector from the Knock Sensor (KS) pigtail electrical connector.
4. Remove the knock sensor electrical connector pigtail clip from the oil level indicator tube bracket.
5. Remove the KS bolt.
6. Remove the KS.

To install:

➡Rotate the pigtail 90 degrees from vertical before securing the fastener.

7. Install the KS.
8. Install the KS bolt and tighten to 18 ft. lbs. (25 Nm).
9. Install the KS electrical connector pigtail clip to the oil level indicator tube bracket.
10. Connect the engine wiring harness electrical connector to the KS pigtail electrical connector.
11. Lower the vehicle.
12. Connect the negative battery cable.

MANIFOLD ABSOLUTE PRESSURE (MAP) SENSOR

LOCATION

The Manifold Absolute Pressure (MAP) sensor is located on the top front of the engine, in the upper intake manifold.

REMOVAL & INSTALLATION

See Figures 128 and 129.

1. Remove the air cleaner outlet duct.
2. Disconnect the Evaporative Emission (EVAP) canister purge tube from the intake manifold.

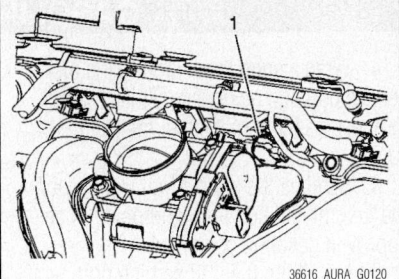

Fig. 128 Disconnecting the fuel injector wiring harness electrical connector (1) from the MAP sensor

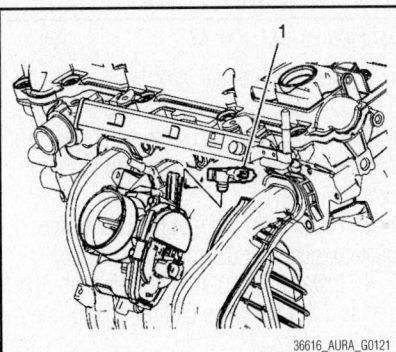

Fig. 129 Removing and installing the MAP sensor (1)

3. Reposition the EVAP canister purge tube out of the way.
4. Disconnect the fuel injector wiring harness electrical connector from the Manifold Absolute Pressure (MAP) sensor.
5. Remove the fuel injector wiring harness clips from the fuel rail tabs.
6. Disconnect the fuel injector wiring harness electrical connector from the number 3 fuel injector.
7. Squeeze tabs and slide the MAP sensor upward.

To install:

8. Lubricate the NEW MAP sensor seal with clean engine oil.
9. Install the MAP sensor into the intake manifold.
10. Connect the fuel injector wiring harness electrical connector to the number 3 fuel injector.
11. Install the fuel injector wiring harness clips to the fuel rail tabs.
12. Connect the fuel injector wiring harness electrical connector to the MAP sensor.
13. Position the EVAP canister purge tube out of the way.
14. Connect the EVAP canister purge tube to the intake manifold.
15. Install the air cleaner outlet duct.

VEHICLE SPEED SENSOR (VSS)

LOCATION

The Vehicle Speed Sensor (VSS) is located on the transmission.

REMOVAL & INSTALLATION

Automatic Transaxle 4T45-E

See Figure 130.

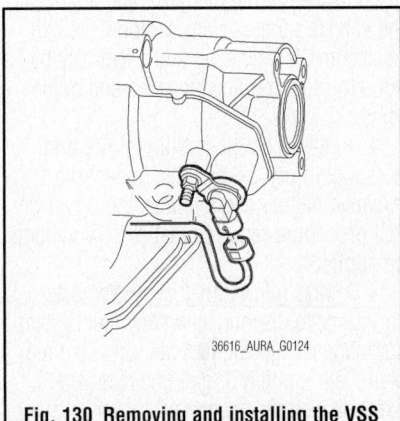

Fig. 130 Removing and installing the VSS

✳✳ CAUTION

Ensure that the vehicle is properly supported and squarely positioned. To help avoid personal injury when a vehicle is on a hoist, provide additional support for the vehicle on the opposite end from which the components are being removed.

1. Position the vehicle on a hoist and raise the vehicle.
2. Disconnect the Vehicle Speed Sensor (VSS) electrical connector.
3. Remove the VSS electrical harness retainer from the VSS stud.
4. Remove the VSS stud.
5. Remove the output VSS from the transmission case.

✳✳ CAUTION

Inspect the O-ring for damage and replace if necessary.

6. Remove the O-ring from the VSS.

To install:

7. Install the O-ring onto the VSS.
8. Install the output VSS into the transmission case.
9. Install the VSS stud and tighten to 106 inch lbs. (12 Nm).
10. Install the VSS electrical harness retainer to the VSS stud.
11. Connect the VSS electrical connector.
12. Lower the vehicle.

FUEL   **GASOLINE FUEL INJECTION SYSTEM**

FUEL SYSTEM SERVICE PRECAUTIONS

Safety is the most important factor when performing not only fuel system maintenance but any type of maintenance. Failure to conduct maintenance and repairs in a safe manner may result in serious personal injury or death. Maintenance and testing of the vehicle's fuel system components can be accomplished safely and effectively by adhering to the following rules and guidelines.

• To avoid the possibility of fire and personal injury, always disconnect the negative battery cable unless the repair or test procedure requires that battery voltage be applied.

• Always relieve the fuel system pressure prior to disconnecting any fuel system component (injector, fuel rail, pressure regulator, etc.), fitting or fuel line connection. Exercise extreme caution whenever relieving fuel system pressure to avoid exposing skin, face and eyes to fuel spray. Please be advised that fuel under pressure may penetrate the skin or any part of the body that it contacts.

• Always place a shop towel or cloth around the fitting or connection prior to loosening to absorb any excess fuel due to spillage. Ensure that all fuel spillage (should it occur) is quickly removed from engine surfaces. Ensure that all fuel soaked cloths or towels are deposited into a suitable waste container.

• Always keep a dry chemical (Class B) fire extinguisher near the work area.

• Do not allow fuel spray or fuel vapors to come into contact with a spark or open flame.

• Always use a back-up wrench when loosening and tightening fuel line connection fittings. This will prevent unnecessary stress and torsion to fuel line piping.

• Always replace worn fuel fitting O-rings with new. Do not substitute fuel hose or equivalent where fuel pipe is installed.

Before servicing the vehicle, make sure to also refer to the precautions in the beginning of this section as well.

RELIEVING FUEL SYSTEM PRESSURE

1. Loosen the fuel fill cap in order to relieve the fuel tank vapor pressure.
2. Remove the engine cover, if required.
3. Remove the fuel rail service port cap.

4. Wrap a shop towel around the fuel rail service port and using a small flat bladed tool, depress (open) the fuel rail test port valve.
5. Remove the shop towel from around the fuel rail service port, and place in an approved gasoline container.
6. Install the fuel rail service port cap.
7. Install the engine cover, if required.
8. Tighten the fuel fill cap.

FUEL PUMP

REMOVAL & INSTALLATION
See Figures 131 and 132.

1. Remove the fuel tank.
2. Disconnect the fuel tank fuel pump module wiring harness electrical connectors from the fuel pressure sensor and the pump.
3. Disconnect the fuel tank vent pipe quick connect fittings from the module.
4. Install a fuel pump lock ring wrench such as J 45722 to the fuel pump module lock ring.

➡**Avoid damaging the lock ring. Use only a fuel pump lock ring wrench such as J 45722 to prevent damage to the lock ring.**

➡**Do Not handle the fuel sender assembly by the fuel pipes. The amount of leverage generated by handling the fuel pipes could damage the joints.**

➡**Do NOT use impact tools. Significant force will be required to release the lock ring. The use of a hammer and screwdriver is not recommended. Secure the fuel tank in order to prevent fuel tank rotation.**

5. Using a fuel pump lock ring wrench such as J 45722 and a long breaker-bar, rotate the lock ring in a counterclockwise direction in order to unlock the lock ring.
6. Remove the fuel pump lock ring wrench such as J 45722 from the fuel pump module lock ring.
7. Lift the fuel pump module up slightly in order to disconnect the fuel tank vent pipe quick connect fitting from the pump cover.
8. Raise the fuel pump up from the fuel tank. Tilt the pump in order to allow the fuel level sensor arm and float to clear the pump opening.
9. Remove the fuel pump.
10. Remove and discard the fuel pump module seal.

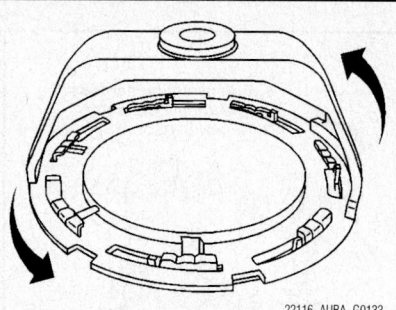

22116_AURA_G0133

Fig. 131 Install a fuel pump lock ring wrench such as J 45722 to the fuel pump module lock ring

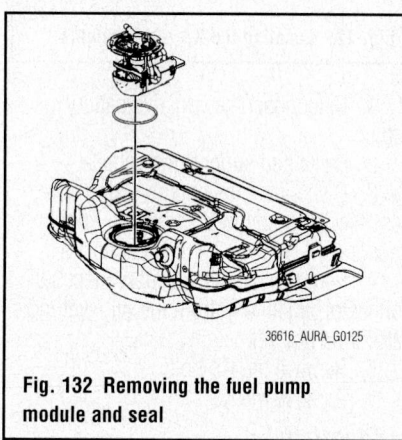

36616_AURA_G0125

Fig. 132 Removing the fuel pump module and seal

11. Clean the fuel pump sealing surfaces.

To install:

✳✳ CAUTION

Drain the fuel from the fuel sender assembly into an approved container in order to reduce the risk of fire and personal injury. Never store the fuel in an open container.

➡**Some lock rings were manufactured with "DO NOT REUSE" stamped into them. These lock rings may be reused if they are not damaged or warped. Inspect the lock ring for damage due to improper removal or installation procedures. If damage is found, install a NEW fuel pump module. Inspect the lock ring for flatness as best as possible. If the lock ring is warped, replace the fuel pump module.**

12. Clean any contamination from the male pipe ends of the fuel pump.
13. Place a NEW fuel tank pump seal onto the fuel tank.

14. Insert the fuel pump into the fuel tank allowing the sensor arm and float to clear the module opening.

15. Lower the pump down into the fuel tank until the fuel tank vent pipe quick connect fitting can be connected.

16. Connect the fuel tank vent pipe quick connect fitting at the pump cover.

17. Press the fuel tank pump downward.

18. Install the pump lock ring wrench such as J 45722 to the fuel pump module lock ring.

➡**Ensure that the lock ring is installed with the correct side facing upward. A correctly installed lock ring will only turn in a clockwise direction.**

19. Using the pump lock ring wrench such as J 45722 and a long breaker-bar, rotate the lock ring in a clockwise direction in order the lock the lock ring.

20. Remove the pump lock ring wrench from the fuel pump module lock ring.

21. Connect the fuel tank vent pipe quick connect fittings to the pump.

22. Connect the fuel tank fuel pump module wiring harness electrical connectors to the fuel pressure sensor and the pump.

23. Install the fuel tank

FUEL RAIL & INJECTORS

REMOVAL & INSTALLATION

See Figure 133.

1. Disconnect the negative battery cable.

2. Relieve the fuel system pressure.

3. Remove the air cleaner outlet duct.

4. Disconnect the fuel feed line quick connect fitting from the fuel rail

5. Disconnect the engine wiring harness electrical connector from the fuel injector wiring harness electrical connector.

6. Disconnect the fuel injector wiring harness electrical from the Manifold Absolute Pressure (MAP) sensor.

7. Remove the engine wiring harness clips from the fuel rail tabs.

8. Remove the fuel rail bolts.

➡**Use care when removing the fuel rail assembly in order to prevent damage to the fuel injector spray tips.**

9. Pull the fuel rail back and upward in order to release the fuel injectors from the cylinder head ports.

10. Remove the fuel rail.

➡**The fuel injector tip insulators may be located on the injector or may still be located in the cylinder head. Either**

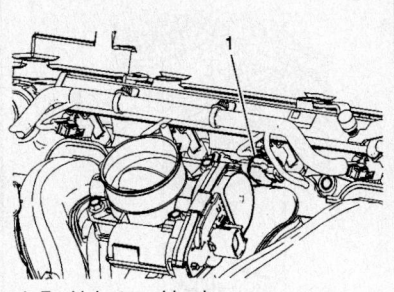

1. Fuel injector wiring harness

36616_AURA_G0018

Fig. 133 Disconnecting the fuel injector wiring harness from the MAP sensor

way, ensure that all 4 injector tip insulators are removed and discarded.**

11. Remove and discard the fuel injector tip insulators.

12. Disconnect the fuel injector wiring harness electrical connectors from the fuel injectors.

13. Remove the fuel injector wiring harness clips from the fuel rail.

14. Remove the fuel injector wiring harness from the fuel rail.

➡**Use care in removing the fuel injectors in order to prevent damage to the fuel injector electrical connector pins or the fuel injector nozzles. Do not immerse the fuel injector in any type of cleaner. The fuel injector is an electrical component and may be damaged by this cleaning method.**

➡**If the fuel injectors are found to be leaking, the engine oil may be contaminated with fuel.**

15. Remove the fuel injector retainer.

16. Remove the fuel injector from the fuel rail.

17. Remove the fuel injector upper O-ring.

18. Remove the fuel injector lower O-ring.

To install:

➡**The fuel injector assembly is stamped with a part number identification. Be sure to use the correct part number when ordering replacement fuel injectors.**

19. Lubricate the NEW fuel injector O-rings with clean engine oil.

20. Install the NEW fuel injector O-rings.

21. Install the fuel injector to the fuel rail.

22. Install the fuel injector retainer.

23. Install the fuel injector wiring harness clips to the fuel rail.

24. Connect the fuel injector wiring harness electrical connectors to the fuel injectors.

25. Lubricate the NEW fuel injector tip insulators with clean engine oil.

26. Install the NEW fuel injector tip insulators to the cylinder head.

27. With the fuel injectors positioned downward, lower the fuel injectors into the cylinder head ports.

28. Carefully push down on the fuel rail in order to insert the injectors into the cylinder head ports.

29. Install the fuel rail bolts. Tighten the bolts to 89 inch lbs. (10 Nm).

30. Install the engine wiring harness clips to the fuel rail tabs.

31. Connect the fuel injector wiring harness electrical to the MAP sensor.

32. Connect the engine wiring harness electrical connector to the fuel injector wiring harness electrical connector.

33. Connect the fuel feed line quick connect fitting to the fuel rail.

34. Install the air cleaner outlet duct.

35. Connect the negative battery cable.

36. Inspect for fuel leaks using the following procedure:

a. Turn ON the ignition, with the engine OFF for 2 seconds.

b. Turn OFF the ignition for 10 seconds

c. Turn ON the ignition

d. Inspect for fuel leaks.

FUEL TANK

REMOVAL & INSTALLATION

See Figures 134 through 137.

➡**Clean the fuel and Evaporative Emission (EVAP) connections and surround-**

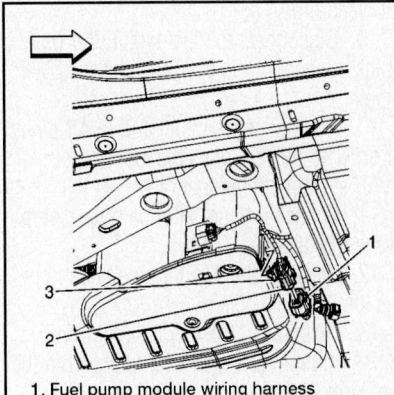

1. Fuel pump module wiring harness electrical connector
2. Body wiring harness electrical connector
3. Body wiring harness electrical connector clip

36616_AURA_G0127

Fig. 134 Disconnecting the fuel pump module wiring harness electrical connector

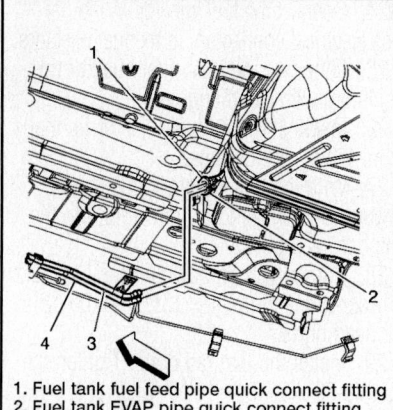

1. Fuel tank fuel feed pipe quick connect fitting
2. Fuel tank EVAP pipe quick connect fitting
3. Chassis fuel feed pipe
4. Chassis EVAP pipe

36616_AURA_G0128

Fig. 135 Disconnecting quick connect fittings

ing areas prior to disconnecting the lines in order the avoid possible system contamination.

1. Relieve the fuel system pressure.
2. Drain the fuel tank.
3. Raise and support the vehicle.
4. Disconnect the fuel tank fuel pump module wiring harness electrical connector from body wiring harness electrical connector.
5. Remove the body wiring harness electrical connector clip from the EVAP canister.
6. Disconnect the body wiring harness electrical connector from the rear Antilock Brake System (ABS) wiring harness electrical connector.
7. Remove the rear ABS wiring harness electrical connector clip from the EVAP canister.
8. Disconnect the fuel tank fuel feed pipe quick connect fitting from the chassis fuel feed pipe.
9. Disconnect the fuel tank EVAP pipe quick connect fitting from the chassis EVAP pipe.
10. Cap the chassis fuel and EVAP pipes in order to prevent possible fuel and/or EVAP system contamination.
11. Loosen the fuel fill pipe hose clamp at the fuel tank.
12. Separate the fuel fill pipe hose from the fuel tank.
13. Disconnect the fuel tank fill EVAP emission pipe quick connect fitting from the fuel tank vent pipe.
14. Place a jackstand under the muffler assembly.
15. With the aid of an assistant, separate the muffler insulators from the underbody hangers.
16. Slowly lower the muffler assembly

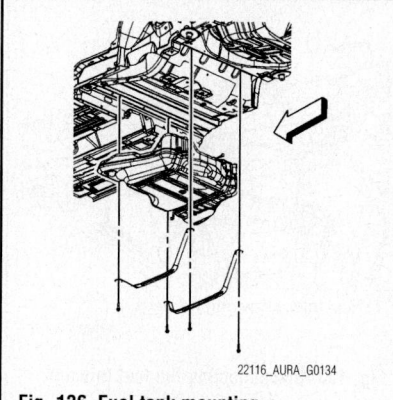

22116_AURA_G0134

Fig. 136 Fuel tank mounting

36616_AURA_G0129

Fig. 137 Removing the fuel tank straps

allowing it to rest on the jackstand. If this is not possible, remove the muffler assembly.

17. Have assistants support either side of the fuel tank.
18. Place a suitable adjustable jack under the fuel tank, and have the assistants rest the fuel tank on the adjustable jack.
19. Remove fuel tank strap bolts and straps.
20. If applicable, in order to clear the muffler assembly, slowly lower the right side of the fuel tank.
21. Once the tank is clear of the right frame rail, lower the fuel tank down and remove forward toward the right side of the vehicle.

To install:

22. Have assistants support either side of the fuel tank.
23. If applicable, begin to install the right side of the fuel tank over the muffler assembly.
24. If applicable, raise the right side of the fuel tank into position inboard of the right frame rail. Use care in feeding the fuel feed, EVAP line wiring harness over the muffler assembly.
25. If applicable and the muffler assembly was removed, have assistants raise the fuel tank into position.

26. Install fuel tank straps and bolts. Tighten the bolts to 15 ft. lbs. (20 Nm).
27. Raise the muffler assembly into position if applicable, otherwise install the muffler assembly.
28. With the aid of an assistant, install the muffler insulators to the underbody hangers.
29. Remove the jackstand from under the muffler assembly.
30. Install the fuel fill pipe hose to the fuel tank.
31. Connect the fuel tank fill EVAP emission pipe quick connect fitting to the fuel tank vent pipe.
32. Tighten the fuel fill pipe hose clamp at the fuel tank to 35 inch lbs. (4 Nm).
33. Remove the caps from the fuel and EVAP pipes.
34. Connect the fuel tank EVAP pipe quick connect fitting to the chassis EVAP pipe.
35. Connect the fuel tank fuel feed pipe quick connect fitting to the chassis fuel feed pipe.
36. Install the rear ABS wiring harness electrical connector clip to the EVAP canister.
37. Connect the body wiring harness electrical connector to the rear ABS wiring harness electrical connector.
38. Install the body wiring harness electrical connector clip to the underbody.
39. Connect the fuel tank fuel pump module wiring harness electrical connector to the body wiring harness electrical connector.
40. Lower the vehicle.
41. Refill the fuel tank.
42. Tighten the fuel fill cap.
43. Inspect for fuel leaks using the following procedure:
  a. Turn ON the ignition, with the engine OFF for 10 seconds.
  b. Turn OFF the ignition for 10 seconds.
  c. Turn ON the ignition, with the engine OFF.
  d. Inspect for fuel leaks.

IDLE SPEED

ADJUSTMENT

Idle speed is maintained by the Powertrain Control Module (PCM). No adjustment is necessary or possible.

THROTTLE BODY

REMOVAL & INSTALLATION

See Figure 138.

➡**Do not use solvent of any type when cleaning the gasket surfaces on the intake manifold and the throttle body**

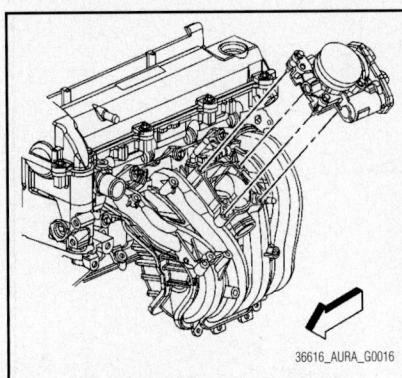

Fig. 138 Removing and installing the throttle body—2.4L engine

assembly, as damage to the gasket surfaces and throttle body assembly may result. Use care in cleaning the gasket surfaces on the intake manifold and the throttle body assembly, as sharp tools may damage the gasket surfaces.

➡Do not use any solvent that contains Methyl Ethyl Ketone (MEK). This solvent may damage fuel system components.

➡DO NOT prop open the throttle blade with the ignition key in the ON position as it may set a Diagnostic Trouble Code (DTC).

1. Remove the air cleaner outlet duct.
2. Disconnect the engine wiring harness electrical connector from the Electronic Throttle Control (ETC).
3. Remove the throttle body bolts.
4. Remove the throttle body.
5. Inspect the throttle body gasket, and replace if necessary.

To install:
6. Install the throttle body. Tighten the bolts to 89 inch lbs. (10 Nm).
7. Connect the engine wiring harness electrical connector to the ETC.
8. Install the air cleaner outlet duct.

HEATING & AIR CONDITIONING SYSTEM

BLOWER MOTOR

REMOVAL & INSTALLATION

See Figures 139 and 140.

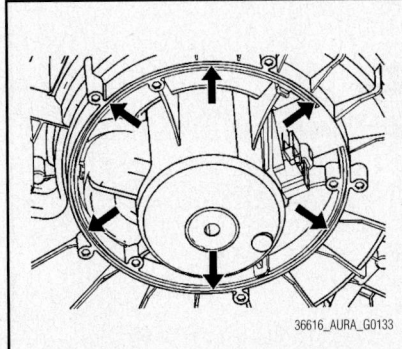

Fig. 139 Cutting out the blower motor

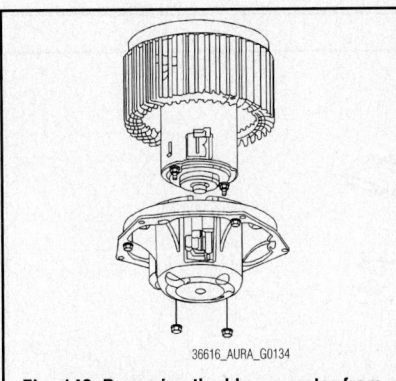

Fig. 140 Removing the blower motor from the cup

1. Remove the right closeout panel.
2. Remove the blower motor wire harness connector.

➡Cut through the case as straight as possible because the motor cup must be replaced. In order to prevent damage to the component, do not cut any deeper than necessary to remove the motor cup.

3. Cut out the blower motor using a utility knife in the narrow groove of the lower case.
4. Remove the blower motor.
5. Remove the blower motor nuts.
6. Remove the blower motor from the blower motor cup.

To install:
7. Install the new blower motor to the blower motor cup.
8. Install the blower motor nuts. Tighten to 21 inch lbs. (2.4 Nm).
9. Install the motor blower seal to the blower motor service ring.
10. Install the blower motor.
11. Install the blower motor attachment ring.
12. Install the blower motor screws. Tighten the screws to 13 inch lbs. (1.5 Nm).
13. Install the blower motor wire harness connector.
14. Install the right closeout panel.

HEATER CORE

REMOVAL & INSTALLATION

See Figures 141 through 151.

1. Disable the SIR system, as outlined in the Chassis Electrical Section..
2. Remove the HVAC module assembly as follows:
   a. Remove the air conditioner (A/C) lines from the thermal expansion valve
   b. Recover the refrigerant.
   c. Remove the surge tank from the surge tank bracket.
   d. Remove the suction line from the dash clip.
   e. Remove the liquid line from the dash clip.
   f. Remove the liquid line and suction line nut from the thermal expansion valve (TXV).
   g. Remove the suction line from the TXV.
   h. Remove the liquid line from the TXV.
   i. Remove the TXV screws.
   j. Remove the TXV.

➡Cap all A/C components immediately to prevent system contamination.

   k. Remove and discard the sealing washers.
   l. Remove the heater hose from the heater core.
   m. Instrument panel (I/P) assembly by removing the following:
   • Windshield garnish molding
   • Instrument panel upper trim panel
   • Instrument panel outer trim covers
   • Instrument panel cluster trim plate bezel
   • Instrument panel cluster assembly
   • Console assembly
   • Remove the knee bolster
   • Instrument panel center molding assembly
   • HVAC control module
   • Radio assembly
   • Instrument panel compartment assembly
   • Center air outlet assembly
   • Note location and routing of the instrument panel wiring harness prior to removal of the instrument panel assembly to ensure proper reinstallation
   • Wiring harness from the instrument panel assembly
   • Instrument panel assembly from the vehicle with the aid of an assistant

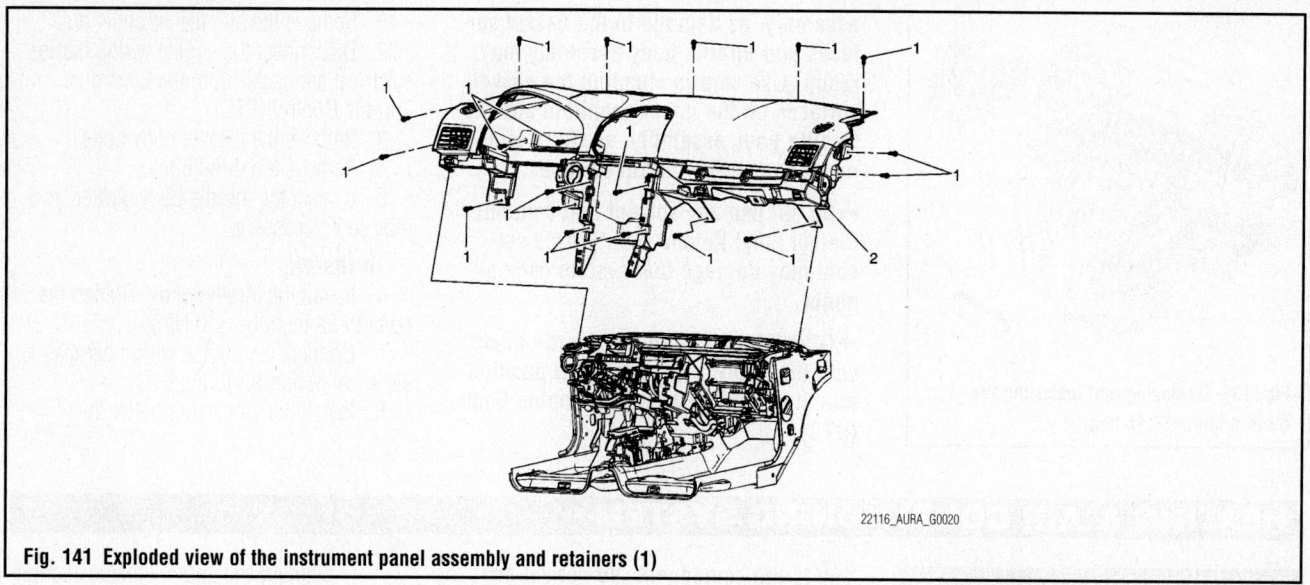

Fig. 141 Exploded view of the instrument panel assembly and retainers (1)

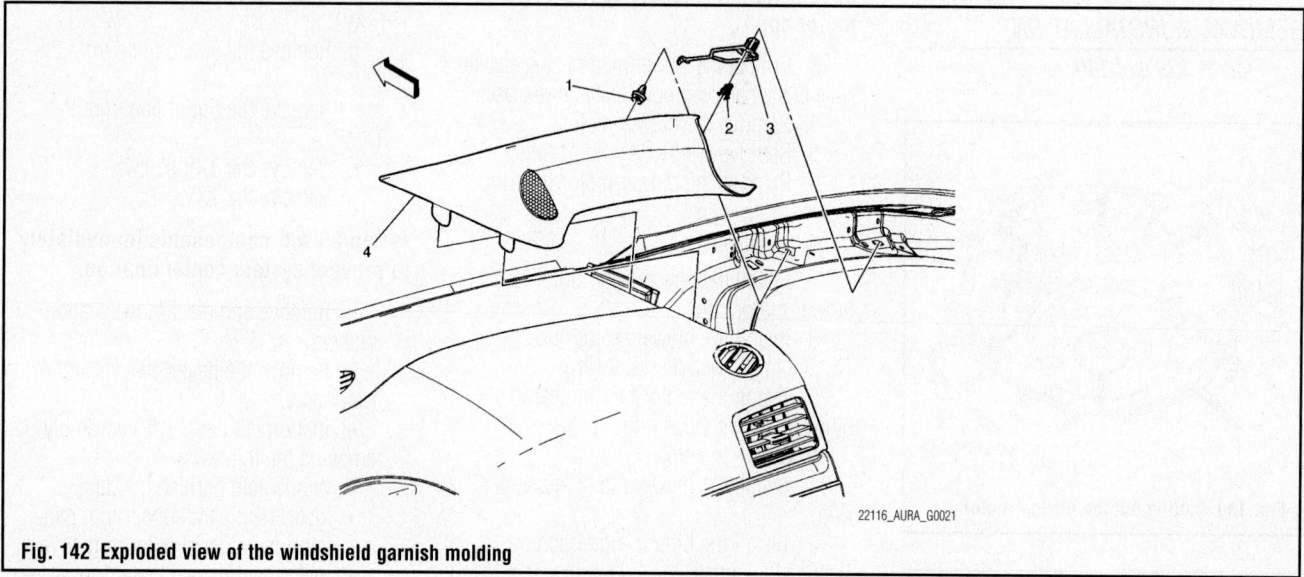

Fig. 142 Exploded view of the windshield garnish molding

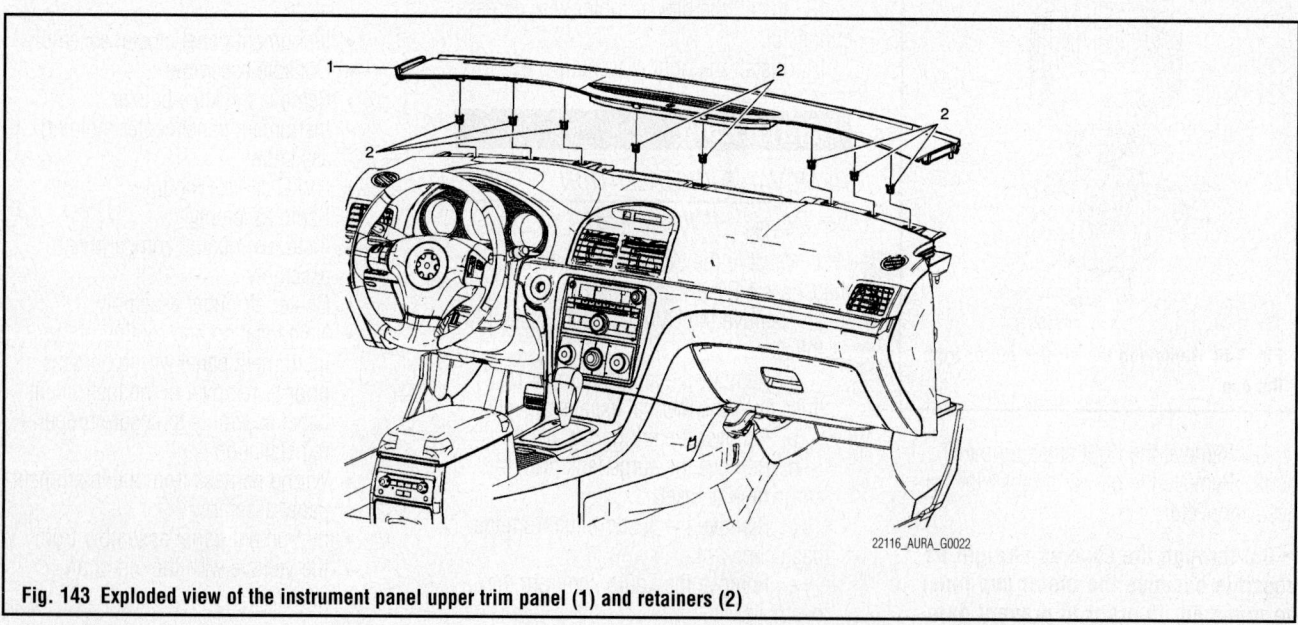

Fig. 143 Exploded view of the instrument panel upper trim panel (1) and retainers (2)

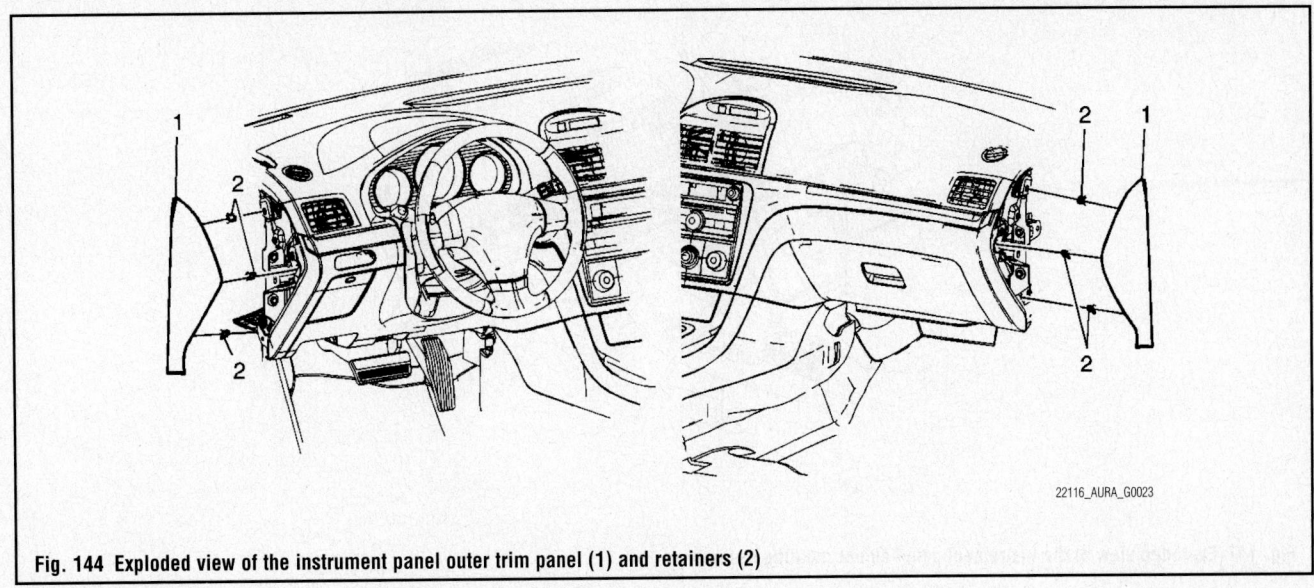

Fig. 144 Exploded view of the instrument panel outer trim panel (1) and retainers (2)

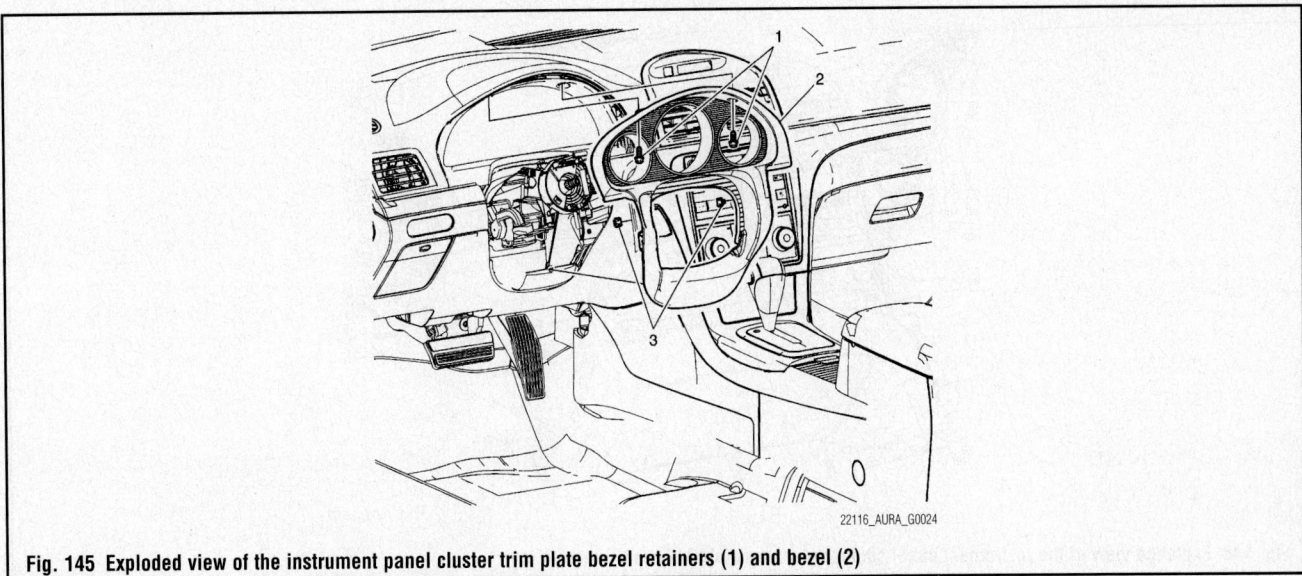

Fig. 145 Exploded view of the instrument panel cluster trim plate bezel retainers (1) and bezel (2)

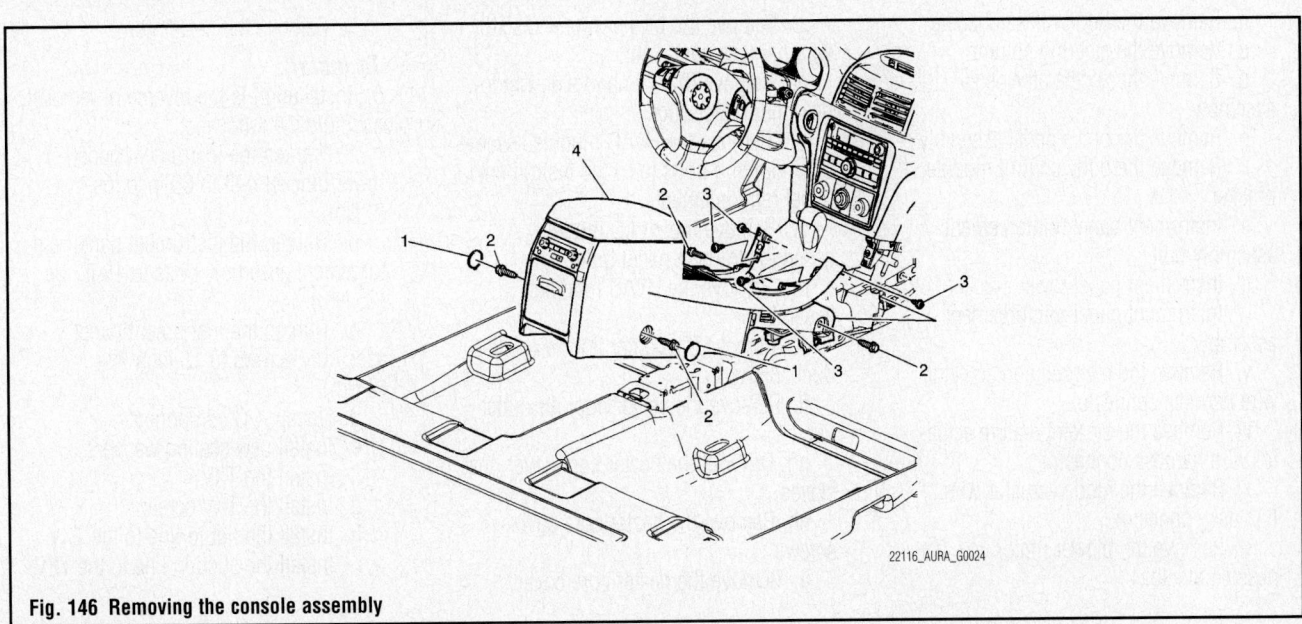

Fig. 146 Removing the console assembly

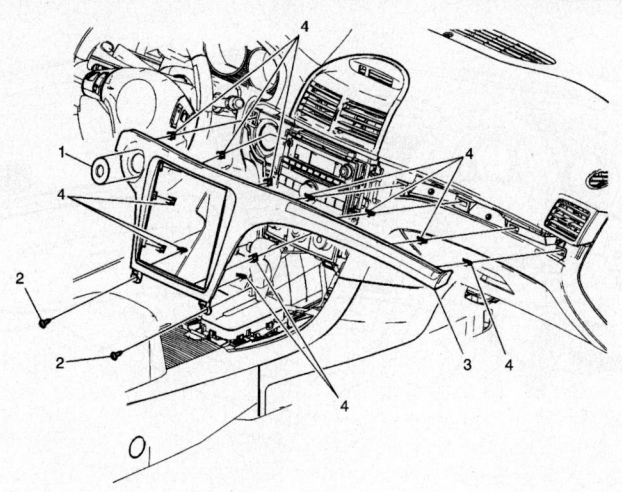

Fig. 147 Exploded view of the instrument panel center molding assembly

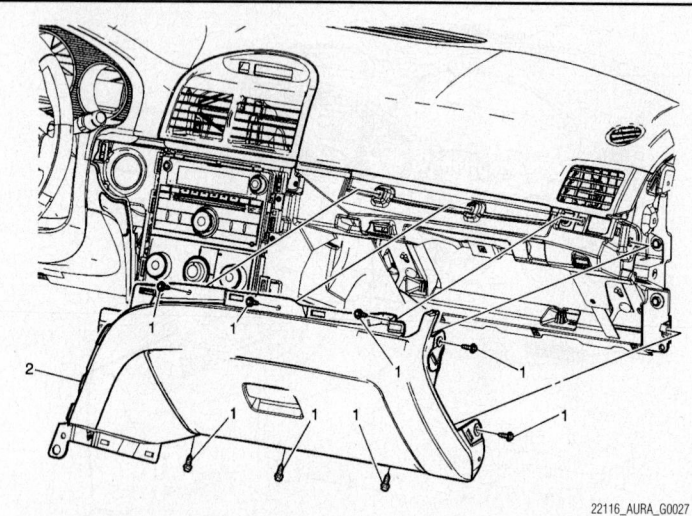

Fig. 148 Exploded view of the instrument panel compartment assembly (2) and retainers (1)

n. Remove the hood release handle

o. Remove the steering column.

p. Remove the accelerator pedal assembly.

q. Remove the brake pedal assembly.

r. Remove the body control module bracket.

s. Instrument panel reinforcement assembly bolt

t. Instrument panel lower bracket bolt

u. Instrument panel reinforcement assembly

v. Remove the recirculation actuator wire harness connector.

w. Remove the air temperature actuator wire harness connector.

x. Remove the mode actuator wire harness connector.

y. Remove the blower motor wire harness connector.

z. Remove the blower motor resistor wire harness connector.

aa. Remove the left hand side window defogger outlet duct.

bb. Remove the HVAC module assembly mounting bolts from the instrument panel reinforcement.

cc. Remove the HVAC module assembly to dash panel bolts.

dd. Remove the HVAC module assembly.

ee. Remove the center floor air outlet duct screws.

ff. Remove the center floor air outlet duct.

gg. Drill out the heater core cover heat stakes.

hh. Remove the heater core cover screws.

ii. Remove the heater core cover.

jj. Remove the heater core.

To install:

3. Installation is the reverse of removal, please note the following:

a. Tighten the instrument panel lower bracket bolt to 80 inch lbs. (9 Nm).

b. Tighten the instrument panel reinforcement assembly bolts to 18 ft. lbs. (25 Nm).

c. Tighten the instrument panel assembly screws to 18 inch lbs. (2 Nm).

d. Uncap A/C components.

e. Install new sealing washers.

f. Install the TXV.

g. Install the TXV screws.

h. Install the liquid line to the TXV.

i. Install the suction line to the TXV.

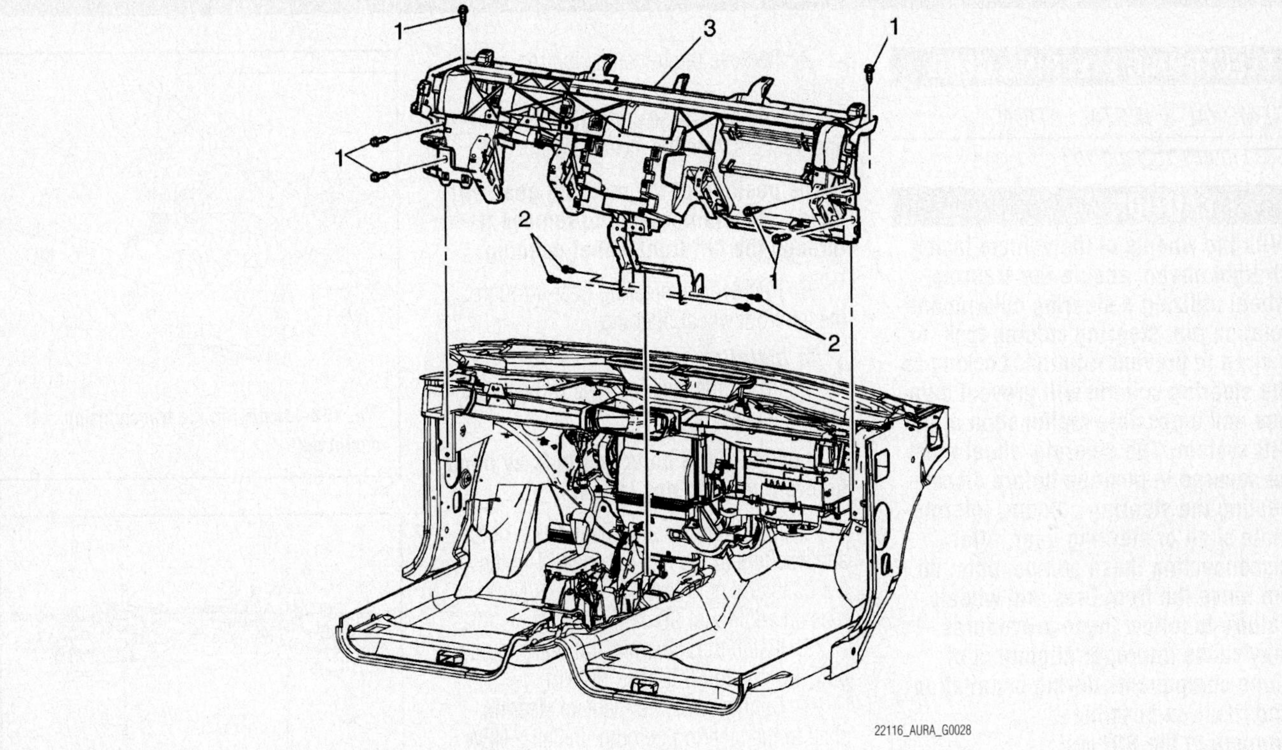

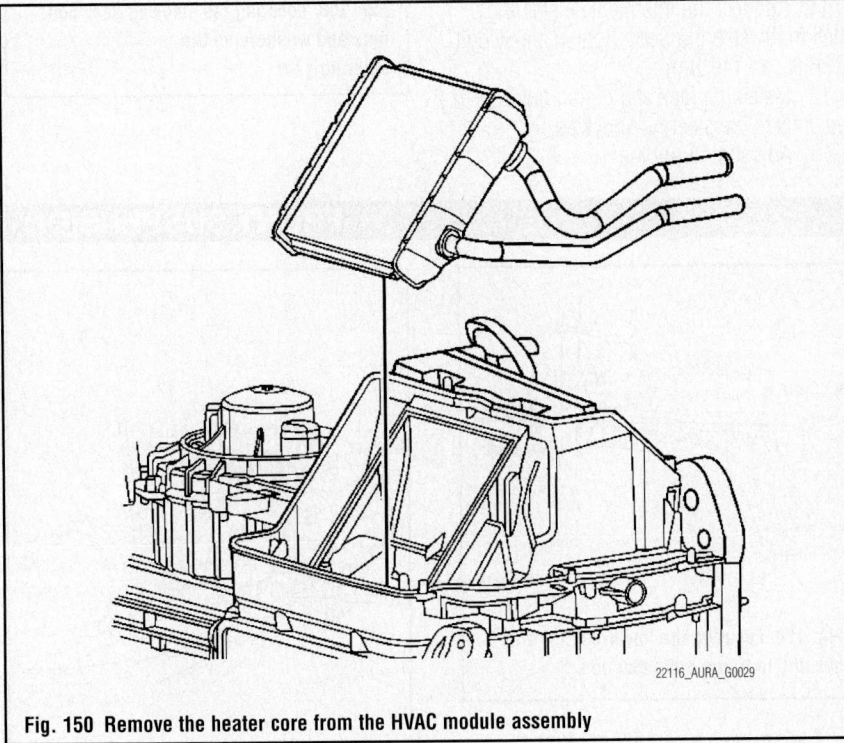

Fig. 149 Exploded view of the instrument panel reinforcement assembly (3)

22116_AURA_G0028

Fig. 150 Remove the heater core from the HVAC module assembly

22116_AURA_G0029

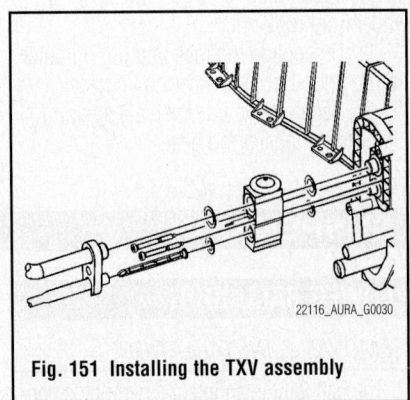

Fig. 151 Installing the TXV assembly

22116_AURA_G0030

j. Install the liquid line and suction line nut to the TXV. Tighten the nut to 15 ft. lbs. (20 Nm).

k. Install the liquid line to the dash clip.

l. Install the suction line to the dash clip.

m. Evacuate and charge the refrigerant system.

n. Leak test the fittings.

o. Install the surge tank to the surge tank bracket.

STEERING

ELECTRONIC STEERING GEAR

REMOVAL & INSTALLATION

See Figures 152 and 153.

✻✻ CAUTION

With the wheels of the vehicle facing straight ahead, secure the steering wheel utilizing a steering column anti-rotation pin, steering column lock, or a strap to prevent rotation. Locking of the steering column will prevent damage and a possible malfunction of the SIR system. The steering wheel must be secured in position before disconnecting the steering column, intermediate shaft or steering gear. After disconnecting these components, do not move the front tires and wheels. Failure to follow these procedures may cause improper alignment of some components during installation and result in possible damage to the SIR coil.

1. Turn the front wheels to the straight forward position and secure the steering wheel from moving.
2. Disengage the rack and pinion outer tie rod ends from the steering knuckles.
3. Separate the intermediate steering shaft from the steering gear.

4. Remove the transmission rear mount bolt.
5. Remove the steering gear bolts, nuts, and washers from the steering gear.

➡The position of the steering gear will need to be manipulated to remove it through the left front wheel opening.

6. Remove the steering gear through the left front wheel opening.

To install:

7. Install the steering gear through the left front wheel opening.

➡Start all of the bolts and nuts by hand before finalizing any torques.

8. Install the steering gear bolts, nuts, and washers to the steering gear. Tighten the bolts and nuts to 52 ft. lbs. (70 Nm) plus an additional 90 degrees.
9. Install the transmission rear mount bolt. Tighten to 66 ft. lbs. (90 Nm).
10. Connect the intermediate steering shaft to the steering column. Install a NEW bolt and tighten to 36 ft. lbs. (49 Nm) for models with electronic steering or 46 ft. lbs. (62 Nm) for models with hydraulic steering.
11. Connect the intermediate steering shaft to the steering gear. Tighten a new bolt to 36 ft. lbs. (49 Nm).
12. Install the rack and pinion outer tie rod ends to the steering knuckles.
13. Adjust the front toe.

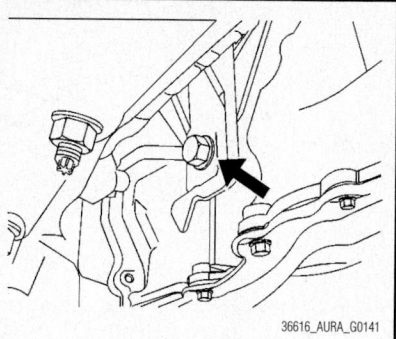

36616_AURA_G0141

Fig. 152 Identifying the transmission rear mount bolt

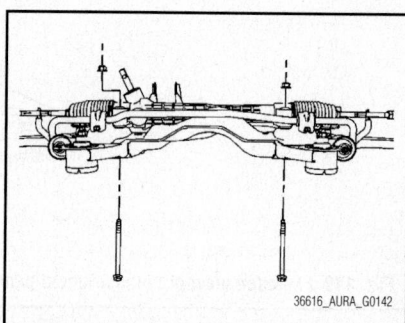

36616_AURA_G0142

Fig. 153 Locating the steering gear bolts, nuts and washers on the steering gear

SUSPENSION   FRONT SUSPENSION

LOWER BALL JOINT

REMOVAL & INSTALLATION

The ball joint is an integral part of the control arm, if defective replace the control arm.

LOWER CONTROL ARM

REMOVAL & INSTALLATION

See Figures 154 through 156.

1. Raise and support the vehicle.
2. Remove the tire and wheel.
3. Remove the front lower control arm busing to frame bolt and nut.
4. Remove the rear lower control arm busing to frame bolts and nuts.
5. Prior to removal, note the orientation of the lower control arm ball stud to steering knuckle pinch bolt and remove the pinch bolt and discard.
6. Separate the ball stud from the steering knuckle.

36616_AURA_G0146

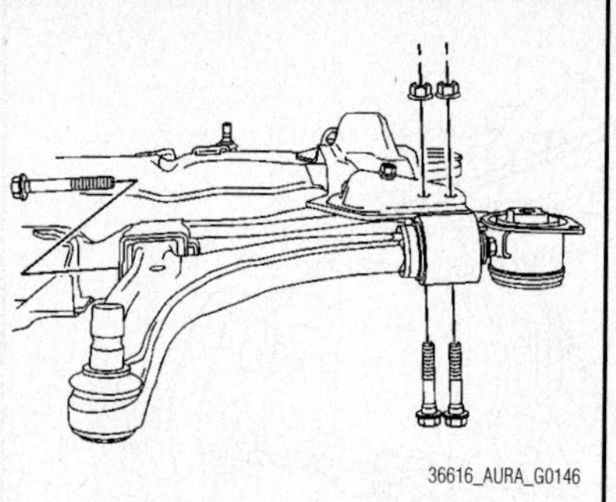

Fig. 154 Locating the lower control arm bushing to frame bolts and nuts

7. Remove the control arm from the vehicle.
8. Remove the rear lower control arm bushing.

To install:

9. Install the rear lower control arm bushing.

36616_AURA_G0147

Fig. 155 Removing the pinch bolt

10. Using LOCTITE® 234 or equivalent on the bolt threads, install the lower control arm to busing bolt.
11. Hold the rear busing inner sleeve

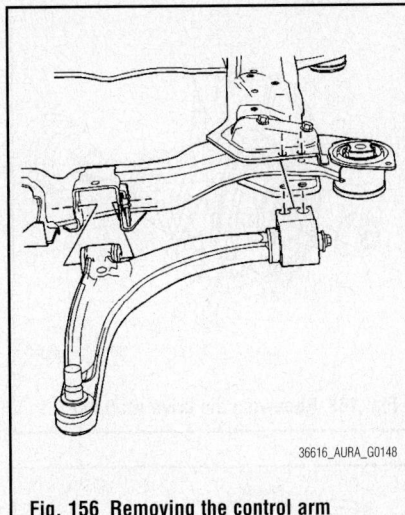

Fig. 156 Removing the control arm

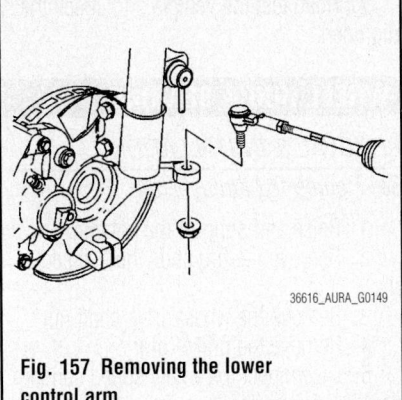

Fig. 157 Removing the lower control arm

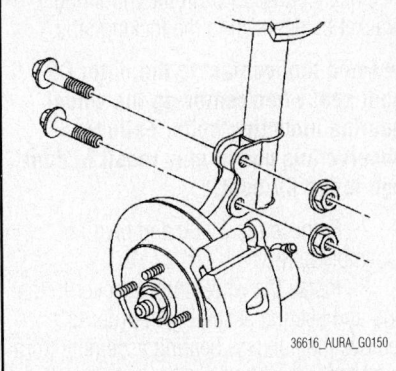

Fig. 158 Removing the steering knuckle

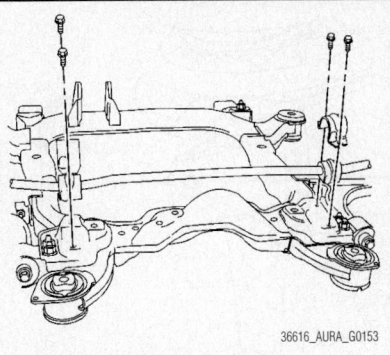

Fig. 159 Removing the stabilizer bar clamps and insulators

when tightening the rear bushings to the control arm bolt. Tighten the bolt to 32 ft. lbs. (44Nm).

12. Position the lower control arm to the frame assembly and steering knuckle.

13. Note the previous orientation and install the new ball stud to the steering knuckle pinch bolt. Hand tighten only.

14. Install the front busing to frame bolt and nut. Hand tighten only.

15. Install the rear busing to frame bolts and nuts.

   a. Tighten the ball stud to steering knuckle pinch nut to 37 ft. lbs. (50 Nm). Reverse the nut ¾ of a turn. Tighten to 37 ft. lbs. (50 Nm). Rotate an additional 30 degrees.

   b. Tighten the nuts and the bolts with the front suspension loaded by using the proper jackstand.

   c. Tighten the front bushing to frame bolt to 37 ft. lbs. (50 Nm). Rotate an additional 90 degrees.

   d. Tighten the rear bushing to frame nuts to 37 ft. lbs. (50 Nm). Rotate an additional 90 degrees.

16. Install the tire and wheel.

17. Lower the vehicle.

STEERING KNUCKLE

REMOVAL & INSTALLATION

See Figures 157 and 158.

1. Raise and support the vehicle.

2. Remove the wheel bearing/hub.

3. Remove the outer tie rod to knuckle nut.

4. Remove the lower control arm.

5. Remove the strut to steering knuckle nuts and bolts.

6. Remove the steering knuckle from the vehicle.

To install:

7. Install the steering knuckle to the strut assembly and if applicable the ABS harness bracket. Tighten the bolts and nuts to 89 ft. lbs. (120 Nm).

8. Guide the axle through the steering knuckle.

9. Install the lower control arm.

10. Install the outer tie rod to the steering knuckle. Tighten the nut to 15 ft. lbs. (20 Nm). Rotate the nut an additional 180 degrees. Verify the torque to 37 ft. lbs. (50 Nm).

11. Install the wheel bearing, brake rotor, brake caliper and front wheels.

12. Lower the vehicle.

13. Road test the vehicle in order to verify alignment. If a lead or pull is present re-align.

STABILIZER BAR

REMOVAL & INSTALLATION

See Figure 159.

1. Raise and support the vehicle.

2. Remove the front tire and wheel assemblies.

3. Disconnect the stabilizer links from the stabilizer shaft.

4. Using a suitable jack stand, support the rear of the frame assembly.

5. Remove the frame support to body bolts.

6. Remove the rear frame assembly mounting bolts.

7. Lower the rear of the cradle in order to gain clearance to the stabilizer shaft.

8. Remove the stabilizer bar clamps and insulators.

9. Remove the stabilizer shaft through the opening between the frame and body.

To install:

10. Position the stabilizer shaft to the frame.

11. Install the stabilizer bar clamps and insulators. Tighten the clamps and bolts to 18 ft. lbs. (25 Nm).

12. Raise the rear of the cradle and install the cradle bolts. Tighten the rear frame bolts. Tighten to 74 ft. lbs. (100 Nm).

13. Remove the jack stand.

14. Connect the stabilizer link to the stabilizer bar. Tighten the link nuts to 48 ft. lbs. (65 Nm).

15. Install the front tire and wheel assemblies.

16. Lower the vehicle.

STRUT

REMOVAL & INSTALLATION

See Figures 160 and 161.

1. Raise and support the vehicle.

2. Remove the front wheel.

3. Disconnect the stabilizer link from the strut.

4. Remove the strut to steering knuckle nuts.

5. If applicable, reposition the wheel speed sensor/ABS harness and bracket.

6. Remove the strut to steering knuckle bolts.

7. Remove the upper strut cap to body nuts.

➡In order to prevent damage to the CV joint boot, place a shop towel over the CV joint.

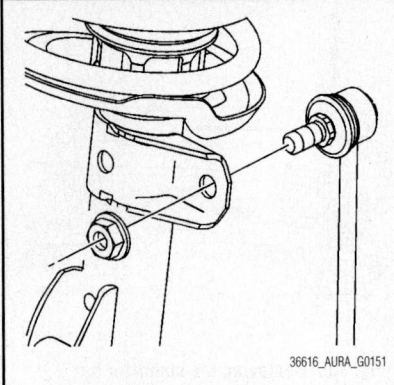

Fig. 160 Disconnecting the stabilizer link from the strut

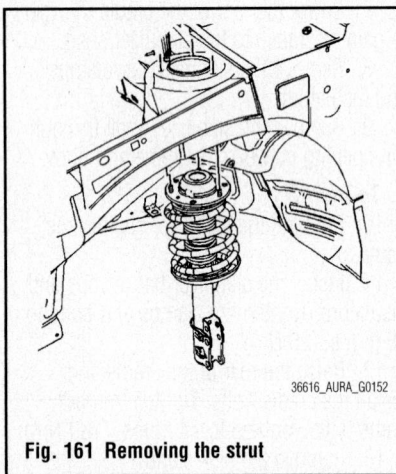

Fig. 161 Removing the strut

8. Remove the strut from the vehicle.

To install:

→**It may be necessary to rotate the upper strut mount cover guide to match the hole in the strut tower.**

9. Position the strut to the vehicles strut tower, using the alignment pin as a guide.

10. Install the upper strut cap to body nuts. Tighten to 18 ft. lbs. (25 Nm).

11. Install the strut to steering knuckle bolts leaving the nuts off.

12. If applicable, place the wheel speed sensor harness and bracket to the bolt end.

13. Install the strut to steering knuckle nuts and tighten to 89 ft. lbs. (120 Nm).

14. Connect the stabilizer link to the strut. Tighten to 48 ft. lbs. (65 Nm).

15. Install the front wheel.

16. Lower the vehicle.

17. Road test the vehicle and check the alignment.

WHEEL HUB & BEARING

REMOVAL & INSTALLATION

See Figures 162 through 164.

1. Raise and support the vehicle.

2. Remove the tire and wheel assembly.

3. Remove the wheel drive shaft nut.

4. Remove the brake rotor.

5. Disconnect the wheel speed sensor electrical connector.

6. Remove the wheel speed sensor electrical connector from the mounting bracket by depressing the locking tabs.

→**Avoid tool contact to the outer CV boot seal when removing the wheel bearing mounting bolts. Failure to observe this notice may result in damage to the CV boot.**

7. Remove the 3 hub and bearing assembly bolts.

8. Install the wheel hub remover to the hub and bearing assembly in order to remove the hub and bearing assembly from the wheel drive shaft.

9. Remove the hub and bearing assembly from the steering knuckle.

To install:

10. Install the hub and bearing assembly to the steering knuckle.

→ **This is a self-retaining fastener joint that does not require thread locking compounds. Do not attempt to clean the threads with a standard tap. If a standard tap is used, damage to the joint threads will occur.**

→ **Use the correct fastener in the correct location. Replacement fasteners must be the correct part number for that application. Fasteners requiring replacement or fasteners requiring the use of thread locking compound or sealant are identified in the service procedure. Do not use paints, lubricants, or corrosion inhibitors on fasteners or fastener joint surfaces unless specified. These coatings affect fastener torque and joint clamping force and may damage the fastener. Use the correct tightening sequence and speci-**

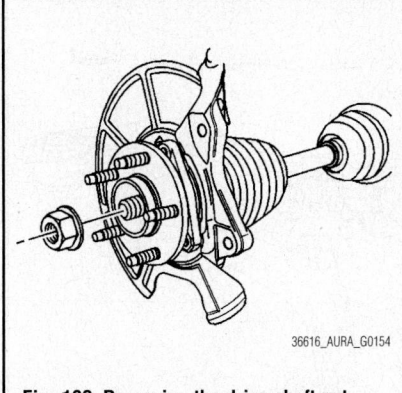

Fig. 162 Removing the drive shaft nut

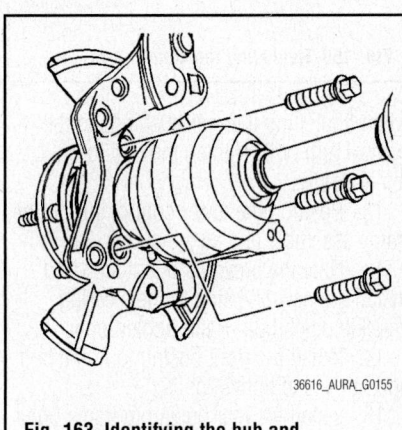

Fig. 163 Identifying the hub and bearing assembly bolts

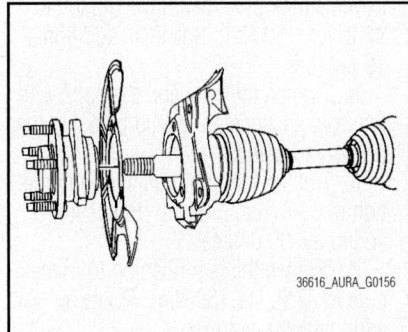

Fig. 164 Removing the hub and bearing from the steering knuckle

fications when installing fasteners in order to avoid damage to parts and systems.

11. Install the 3 hub and bearing assembly bolts. Tighten the hub and bearing assembly bolts to 85 ft. lbs. (115 Nm).

12. Install the wheel speed sensor con-

nector into the bracket until the locking tab clicks into place.

13. Connect the electrical connector to the wheel speed sensor.

14. Install the axle nut to the wheel drive shaft, hand tighten the wheel drive shaft nut.

15. Install the brake rotor.

16. Install the wheel drive shaft nut to the wheel drive shaft.

17. Use a screw driver or similar tool to stop the rotation of the brake rotor. Tighten the wheel drive shaft nut 159 ft. lbs. (215 Nm).

18. Install the tire and wheel assemblies.

ADJUSTMENT

The wheel bearing are sealed at the factory and do not require any adjustment or maintenance.

SUSPENSION

COIL SPRING

REMOVAL & INSTALLATION

See Figures 165 and 166.

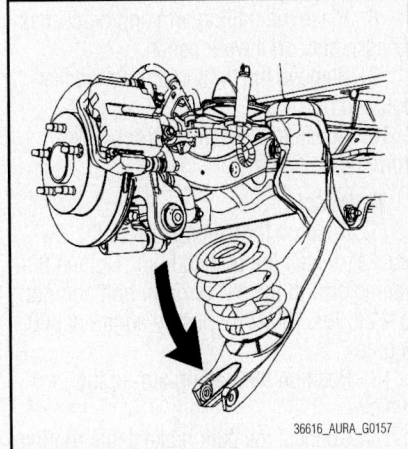

36616_AURA_G0157

Fig. 165 Lowering the lower control arm with the coil spring

1. Raise and support the vehicle.

2. Remove the rear tire and wheel assembly.

3. Using a suitable jack stand, support the lower control arm.

4. Remove the lower control arm to knuckle bolt and nut.

> ### ✳✳ CAUTION
>
> **To prevent personal injury and/or component damage, use the proper tools to support the lower control arm when removing the coil spring. The coil spring is under extreme pressure and can become a projectile should the spring separate from the lower control arm before all of the tension is relieved.**

5. Use the jackstand to swing the lower control arm downward with the coil spring attached.

6. Remove the coil spring from the lower control arm.

REAR SUSPENSION

7. Inspect the coil spring upper and lower insulators for damage, replace as necessary.

To install:

➡**Be sure that the coil spring upper and lower insulators are properly seated prior to installation of the coil spring.**

8. Position the coil spring onto the lower control arm.

9. Use the jack stand to raise the lower control arm upward into position.

10. Install the lower control arm to knuckle bolt and nut. Tighten to 81 ft. lbs. (110 Nm).

11. Remove the jack stand from under the vehicle.

12. Install the rear tire and wheel assembly.

13. Lower the vehicle.

14. Check the rear wheel alignment.

CONTROL ARMS/LINKS

REMOVAL & INSTALLATION

Lower

See Figure 167.

1. Raise and suitably support the vehicle.

2. Remove the rear tire and wheel assembly.

3. Remove the coil spring.

4. Remove the lower control arm bolts and nuts, then remove the arm.

To install:

5. Installation is the reverse of removal. Tighten the bolt/nut to 81 ft. lbs. (110 Nm).

6. Inspect the wheel alignment and adjust as needed.

Upper

See Figures 168 and 169.

1. Raise and support the vehicle.

2. Remove the rear tire and wheel assembly.

3. Disconnect the ABS routing harness connectors and position the harness aside.

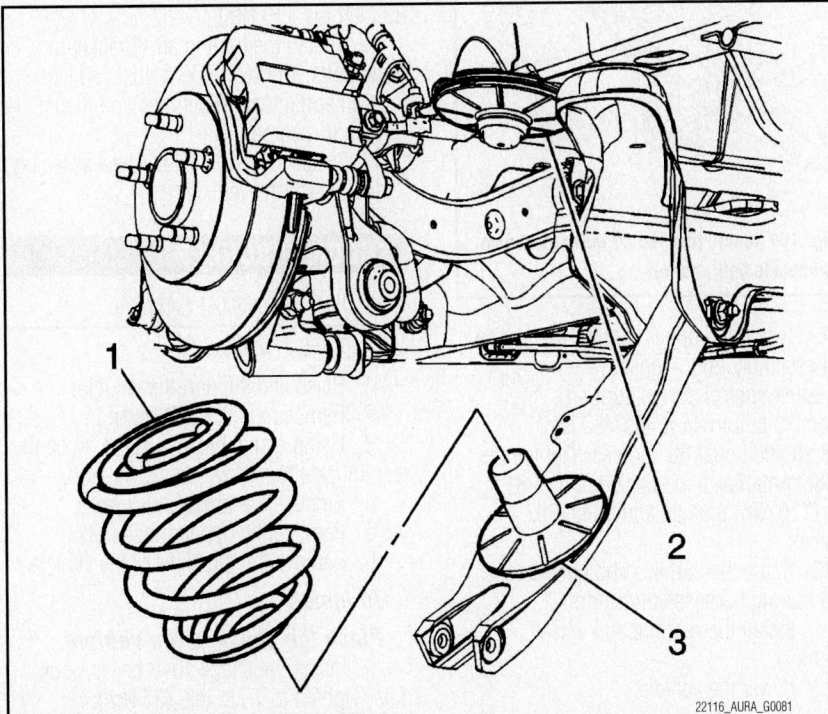

22116_AURA_G0081

Fig. 166 Rear spring (1) mounting –Aura

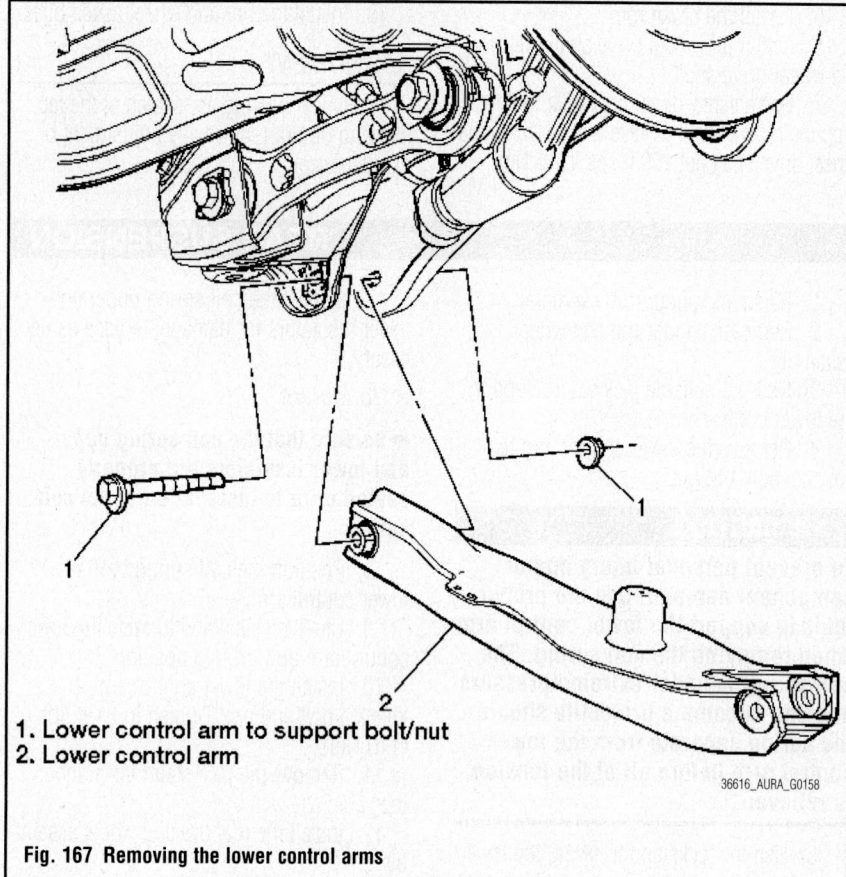

1. Lower control arm to support bolt/nut
2. Lower control arm

36616_AURA_G0158

Fig. 167 Removing the lower control arms

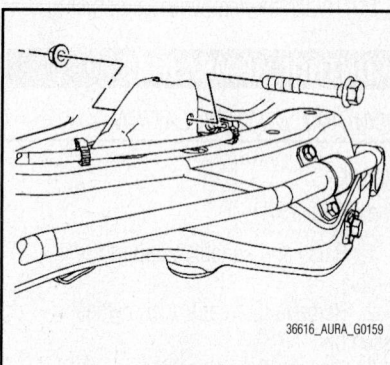

36616_AURA_G0159

Fig. 168 Identifying the upper control arm to support assembly bolt and nut

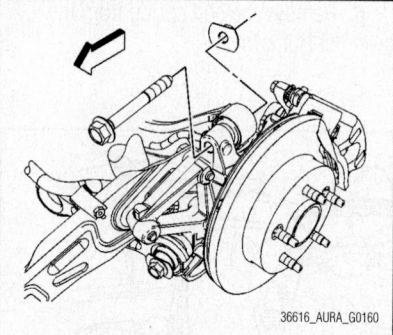

36616_AURA_G0160

Fig. 169 Identifying the upper control arm to knuckle bolt and nut

4. Remove the upper control arm to support assembly bolt and nut.
5. Remove the upper control arm to knuckle bolt and nut.
6. Remove the upper control arm from the vehicle through the wheelhouse opening.

To install:
7. Position the upper control arm to the support assembly and knuckle through the wheelhouse opening.
8. Install the upper control arm to knuckle bolt and nut. Hand tighten only.

9. Install the upper control arm to support assembly bolt. Tighten the upper control arm to support assembly bolt to 44 ft. lbs. (60 Nm) plus an additional 60 degrees. Tighten the upper control arm to knuckle bolt to 81 ft. lbs. (110 Nm) plus an additional 70 degrees.
10. Route the harness and connect the ABS routing harness connectors.
11. Install the rear tire and wheel assembly.
12. Lower the vehicle.

Trailing Arms

See Figures 170 through 172.

1. Raise and support the vehicle.
2. Remove the rear tire and wheel assembly.
3. Remove the 4 trailing arm bracket to body bolts.
4. Remove the rear parking brake cable from the trailing arm.
5. Remove the 3 trailing arm to knuckle through bolts.
6. Disconnect the park brake cable routing clip from the trailing arm bracket.
7. Remove the trailing arm and bracket as an assembly from the vehicle.
8. Place the trailing arm and bracket as an assembly on a work bench.
9. Remove the trailing arm to bracket bolt and nut.
10. Separate the trailing arm bracket from the trailing arm.

To install:
11. Position the trailing arm to the bracket, install the bolt and nut. Tighten the trailing arm to bracket through bolt and nut to 44 ft. lbs. (60 Nm) plus an additional 60 degrees.
12. Position the trailing arm to the vehicle.
13. Connect the park brake cable routing clip to the trailing arm bracket.
14. Install the 3 trailing arm to knuckle bolts. Tighten to 133 ft. lbs. (180 Nm).
15. Install the rear parking brake cable routing bolt to the trailing arm. Tighten to 89 inch lbs. (10 Nm).
16. Install the trailing arm bracket to body bolts. Tighten to 66 ft. lbs. (90 Nm) plus an additional 30 degrees and then a further 15 degrees.
17. Install the rear tire and wheel assembly.
18. Lower the vehicle.

SHOCK ABSORBER

REMOVAL & INSTALLATION

See Figures 173 and 174.

1. Raise and support the vehicle.
2. Remove the tire and wheel.
3. Using a suitable jack stand, raise the rear knuckle to remove spring tension.
4. Remove the lower shock bolt.
5. Remove the upper shock nuts.
6. Remove the shock from the vehicle.

To install:

Place the shock in the vehicle.
7. Install the shock absorber to body nuts. Tighten to 18 ft. lbs. (25 Nm).

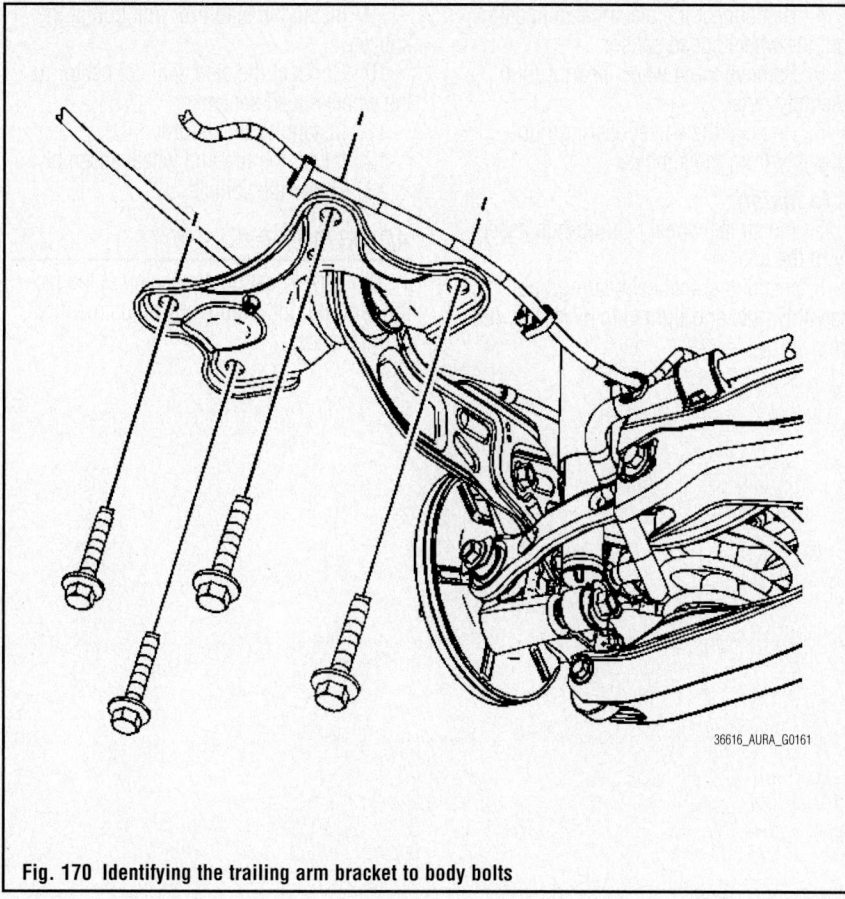

Fig. 170 Identifying the trailing arm bracket to body bolts

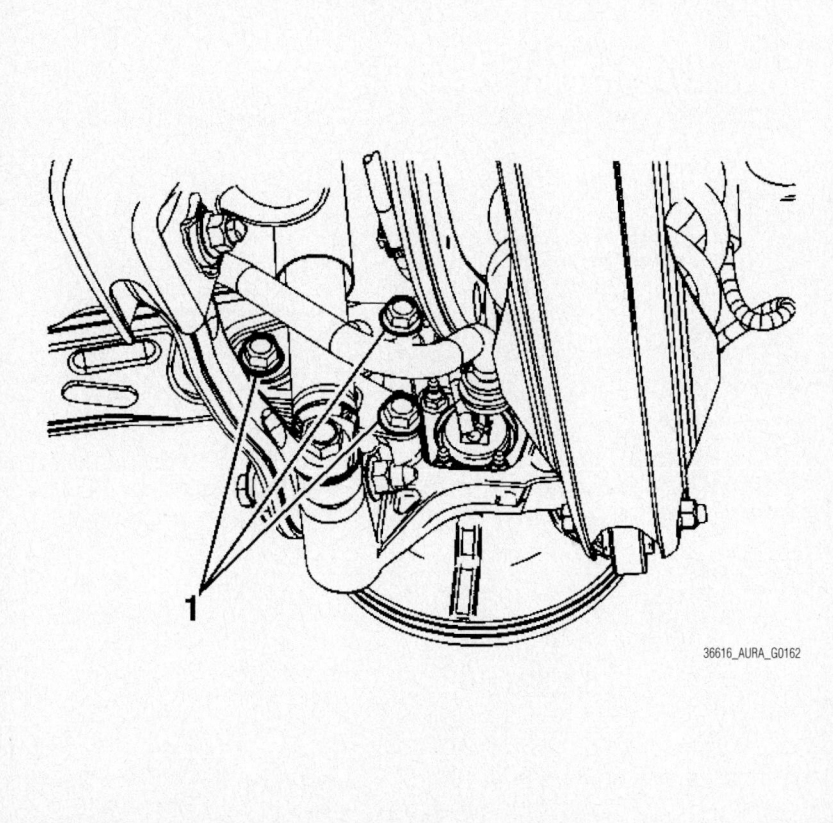

Fig. 171 Locating the trailing arm to knuckle bolts (1)

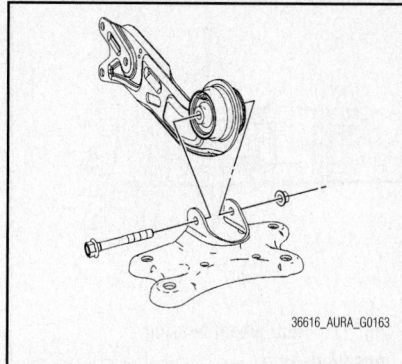

Fig. 172 Removing the trailing arm to bracket bolt and nut

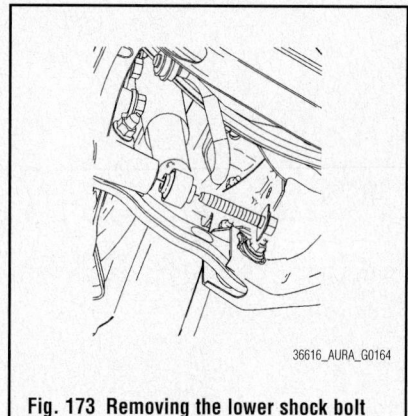

Fig. 173 Removing the lower shock bolt

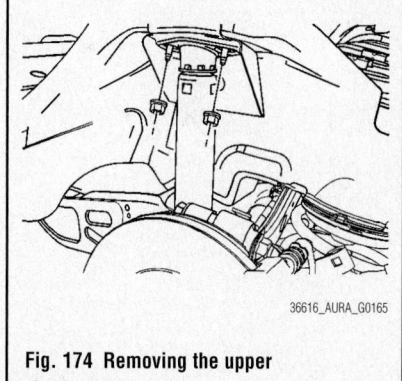

Fig. 174 Removing the upper shock nuts

8. Install the shock absorber to knuckle bolt. Tighten to 133 ft. lbs. (180 Nm).

9. Remove the jack stand from the rear knuckle.

10. Install the tire and wheel.

11. Lower the vehicle.

WHEEL HUB & BEARING

REMOVAL & INSTALLATION

See Figure 175.

1. Raise and support the vehicle.
2. Remove the tire and wheel assembly.
3. Remove the brake rotor.

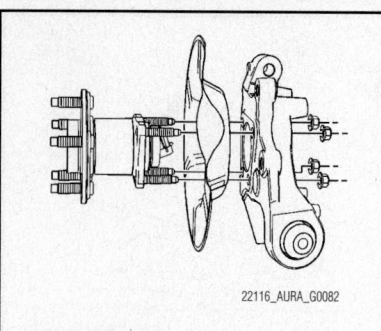

Fig. 175 Rear wheel bearing mounting—Aura

4. Disconnect the electrical connector from the wheel speed sensor.

5. Remove the 4 wheel bearing/hub assembly nuts.

6. Remove the wheel bearing/hub assembly from the knuckle.

To install:

7. Install the wheel bearing/hub assembly to the knuckle.

8. Install the 4 wheel bearing/hub assembly nuts and tighten to 47 ft. lbs. (63 Nm).

9. Install the stabilizer link bolt at the knuckle.

10. Connect the electrical connector to the wheel speed sensor.

11. Install the brake rotor.

12. Install the tire and wheel assembly.

13. Lower the vehicle.

ADJUSTMENT

The wheel bearing are sealed at the factory and do not require any adjustment or maintenance.

CADILLAC, CHEVROLET AND GMC

Avalanche • Escalade • Suburban • Tahoe • Yukon

SPECIFICATIONS AND MAINTENANCE CHARTS

ENGINE AND VEHICLE IDENTIFICATION

Code ①	Liters (cc)	Cu. In.	Cyl.	Fuel Sys.	Engine Type	Eng. Mfg.
C	4.8 (4,807)	293	8	SFI	OHV	GM
J	5.3 (5,328)	325	8	SFI	OHV	GM
3	5.3 (5,328)	325	8	SFI	OHV	GM
0	5.3 (5,328)	325	8	SFI	OHV	GM
5	6.0 (5,967)	364	8	SFI	OHV	GM
Y	6.0 (5,967)	364	8	SFI	OHV	GM
K	6.0 (5,967)	364	8	SFI	OHV	GM
8	6.2 (6,162)	376	8	SFI	OHV	GM

Model Year Code ②	Year
8	2008
9	2009

SFI: Sequential Fuel Injection

① 8th position of Vehicle Identification Number (VIN)

② 10th position of VIN

36616_YUKO_C0001

GENERAL ENGINE SPECIFICATIONS

All measurements are given in inches.

Year	Model	Engine Displacement Liters	Engine Series ID/VIN	Net Horsepower @ rpm	Net Torque @ rpm (ft. lbs.)	Bore x Stroke (in.)	Compression Ratio	Oil Pressure @ rpm
2008	Avalanche	5.3	0	320@5200	340@4200	3.78 x 3.62	9.95:1	18@2000
		5.3	3	320@5200	340@4200	3.78 x 3.62	9.95:1	18@2000
		5.3	J	310@5200	335@4400	3.78 x 3.62	9.95:1	18@2000
		6.0	Y	352@5400	382@4200	4.00 x 3.62	9.67:1	18@2000
	Escalade	6.2	8	403@5700	417@4300	4.07 x 3.62	10.5:1	18@2000
	Suburban	5.3	0	320@5200	340@4200	3.78 x 3.62	9.95:1	18@2000
		5.3	3	320@5200	340@4200	3.78 x 3.62	9.95:1	18@2000
		5.3	J	310@5200	335@4400	3.78 x 3.62	9.95:1	18@2000
		6.0	K	332@5100	367@4100	4.00 x 3.62	9.67:1	18@2000
		6.0	Y	352@5400	382@4200	4.00 x 3.62	9.67:1	18@2000
	Tahoe	4.8	C	295@5600	305@4800	3.78 x 3.27	9.08:1	18@2000
		5.3	0	320@5200	340@4200	3.78 x 3.62	9.95:1	18@2000
		5.3	J	310@5200	335@4400	3.78 x 3.62	9.95:1	18@2000
		6.0	5	332@5100	367@4100	4.00 x 3.62	10.7:1	42@2000
		6.2	8	403@5700	417@4300	4.07 x 3.62	10.5:1	18@2000
	Yukon	4.8	C	295@5600	305@4800	3.78 x 3.27	9.08:1	18@2000
		5.3	0	320@5200	340@4200	3.78 x 3.62	9.95:1	18@2000
		5.3	J	310@5200	335@4400	3.78 x 3.62	9.95:1	18@2000
		6.0	5	332@5100	367@4100	4.00 x 3.62	10.7:1	42@2000
	Yukon XL	5.3	0	320@5200	340@4200	3.78 x 3.62	9.95:1	18@2000
		5.3	3	320@5200	340@4200	3.78 x 3.62	9.95:1	18@2000
		5.3	J	310@5200	335@4400	3.78 x 3.62	9.95:1	18@2000
		6.0	K	332@5100	367@4100	4.00 x 3.62	9.67:1	18@2000
		6.0	Y	352@5400	382@4200	4.00 x 3.62	9.67:1	18@2000
	Yukon Denali	6.2	8	403@5700	417@4300	4.07 x 3.62	10.5:1	18@2000
2009	Avalanche	5.3	0	320@5200	340@4200	3.78 x 3.62	9.95:1	18@2000
		5.3	3	320@5200	340@4200	3.78 x 3.62	9.95:1	18@2000
		5.3	J	310@5200	335@4400	3.78 x 3.62	9.95:1	18@2000
		6.0	Y	352@5400	382@4200	4.00 x 3.62	9.67:1	18@2000
	Escalade	6.0	5	332@5100	367@4100	4.00 x 3.62	10.7:1	42@2000
		6.2	8	403@5700	417@4300	4.07 x 3.62	10.5:1	18@2000
	Suburban	5.3	0	320@5200	340@4200	3.78 x 3.62	9.95:1	18@2000
		5.3	3	320@5200	340@4200	3.78 x 3.62	9.95:1	18@2000
		5.3	J	310@5200	335@4400	3.78 x 3.62	9.95:1	18@2000
		6.0	K	332@5100	367@4100	4.00 x 3.62	9.67:1	18@2000
		6.0	Y	352@5400	382@4200	4.00 x 3.62	9.67:1	18@2000
	Tahoe	4.8	C	295@5600	305@4800	3.78 x 3.27	9.08:1	18@2000
		5.3	0	320@5200	340@4200	3.78 x 3.62	9.95:1	18@2000
		5.3	J	310@5200	335@4400	3.78 x 3.62	9.95:1	18@2000
		6.0	5	332@5100	367@4100	4.00 x 3.62	10.7:1	42@2000
		6.2	8	403@5700	417@4300	4.07 x 3.62	10.5:1	18@2000
	Yukon	4.8	C	295@5600	305@4800	3.78 x 3.27	9.08:1	18@2000
		5.3	0	320@5200	340@4200	3.78 x 3.62	9.95:1	18@2000
		5.3	J	310@5200	335@4400	3.78 x 3.62	9.95:1	18@2000
		6.0	5	332@5100	367@4100	4.00 x 3.62	10.7:1	42@2000
	Yukon XL	5.3	0	320@5200	340@4200	3.78 x 3.62	9.95:1	18@2000
		5.3	3	320@5200	340@4200	3.78 x 3.62	9.95:1	18@2000
		5.3	J	310@5200	335@4400	3.78 x 3.62	9.95:1	18@2000
		6.0	K	332@5100	367@4100	4.00 x 3.62	9.67:1	18@2000
		6.0	Y	352@5400	382@4200	4.00 x 3.62	9.67:1	18@2000
	Yukon Denali	6.2	8	403@5700	417@4300	4.07 x 3.62	10.5:1	18@2000

GASOLINE ENGINE TUNE-UP SPECIFICATIONS

Year	Engine Displacement Liters	Engine VIN	Spark Plug Gap (in.)	Ignition Timing (deg.)	Fuel Pump (psi)	Idle Speed (rpm)	Valve Lash Clearance	
							Intake	Exhaust
2008	4.8	C	0.040	①	50-60 ②	③	HYD	HYD
	5.3	0	0.040	①	50-60 ②	③	HYD	HYD
	5.3	J	0.040	①	50-60 ②	③	HYD	HYD
	5.3	3	0.040	①	50-60 ②	③	HYD	HYD
	6.0	5	0.040	①	50-60 ②	③	HYD	HYD
	6.0	Y	0.040	①	50-60 ②	③	HYD	HYD
	6.0	K	0.040	①	50-60 ②	③	HYD	HYD
	6.2	8	0.040	①	50-60 ②	③	HYD	HYD
2009	4.8	C	0.040	①	50-60 ②	③	HYD	HYD
	5.3	0	0.040	①	50-60 ②	③	HYD	HYD
	5.3	J	0.040	①	50-60 ②	③	HYD	HYD
	5.3	3	0.040	①	50-60 ②	③	HYD	HYD
	6.0	5	0.040	①	50-60 ②	③	HYD	HYD
	6.0	Y	0.040	①	50-60 ②	③	HYD	HYD
	6.0	K	0.040	①	50-60 ②	③	HYD	HYD
	6.2	8	0.040	①	50-60 ②	③	HYD	HYD

NOTE: The Vehicle Emission Control Information label often reflects specification changes made during production.

The label figures must be used if they differ from those in this chart.

HYD: Hydraulic

① Ignition timing is controlled by the PCM and is not adjustable

② With key ON and engine OFF

③ Idle speed is controlled by the PCM and is not adjustable

36616_YUKO_C0003

CAPACITIES

Year	Model	Engine Displacement Liters	Engine VIN	Engine Oil with Filter (qts.)	Transmission (pts.) Manual	Transmission (pts.) Auto. ①	Transfer Case (pts.)	Drive Axle Front (pts.)	Drive Axle Rear (pts.)	Fuel Tank (gal.)	Cooling System (qts.)
2008	Avalanche	5.3	0	6.0	NA	②	4.0	③	④	⑤	18.3
		5.3	3	6.0	NA	②	4.0	③	④	⑤	18.3
		5.3	J	6.0	NA	②	4.0	③	④	⑤	18.3
		6.0	Y	6.0	NA	②	4.0	③	④	⑤	⑥
	Escalade	6.2	8	6.0	NA	②	4.0	③	④	⑤	17.6
	Suburban	5.3	0	6.0	NA	②	4.0	③	④	⑤	18.3
		5.3	3	6.0	NA	②	4.0	③	④	⑤	18.3
		5.3	J	6.0	NA	②	4.0	③	④	⑤	18.3
		6.0	K	6.0	NA	②	4.0	③	④	⑤	⑥
		6.0	Y	6.0	NA	②	4.0	③	④	⑤	⑥
	Tahoe	4.8	C	6.0	NA	⑦	NA	NA	4.3	⑤	17.8
		5.3	0	6.0	NA	②	4.0	③	④	⑤	18.3
		5.3	J	6.0	NA	②	4.0	③	④	⑤	18.3
		6.0	5	6.0	NA	⑧	4.0	③	④	⑤	2.9
		6.2	8	6.0	NA	②	4.0	③	④	⑤	17.6
	Yukon	4.8	C	6.0	NA	⑦	NA	NA	4.3	⑤	17.8
		5.3	0	6.0	NA	②	4.0	③	④	⑤	18.3
		5.3	J	6.0	NA	②	4.0	③	④	⑤	18.3
		6.0	5	6.0	NA	⑧	4.0	③	④	⑤	2.9
	Yukon XL	5.3	0	6.0	NA	②	4.0	③	④	⑤	18.3
		5.3	3	6.0	NA	②	4.0	③	④	⑤	18.3
		5.3	J	6.0	NA	②	4.0	③	④	⑤	18.3
		6.0	K	6.0	NA	②	4.0	③	④	⑤	⑥
		6.0	Y	6.0	NA	②	4.0	③	④	⑤	⑥
	Yukon Denali	6.2	8	6.0	NA	②	4.0	③	④	⑤	17.6
2009	Avalanche	5.3	0	6.0	NA	②	4.0	③	④	⑤	18.3
		5.3	3	6.0	NA	②	4.0	③	④	⑤	18.3
		5.3	J	6.0	NA	②	4.0	③	④	⑤	18.3
		6.0	Y	6.0	NA	②	4.0	③	④	⑤	⑥
	Escalade	6.0	5	6.0	NA	⑧	4.0	③	④	⑤	2.9
		6.2	8	6.0	NA	②	4.0	③	④	⑤	17.6
	Suburban	5.3	0	6.0	NA	②	4.0	③	④	⑤	18.3
		5.3	3	6.0	NA	②	4.0	③	④	⑤	18.3
		5.3	J	6.0	NA	②	4.0	③	④	⑤	18.3
		6.0	K	6.0	NA	②	4.0	③	④	⑤	⑥
		6.0	Y	6.0	NA	②	4.0	③	④	⑤	⑥
	Tahoe	4.8	C	6.0	NA	⑦	NA	NA	4.3	⑤	17.8
		5.3	0	6.0	NA	②	4.0	③	④	⑤	18.3
		5.3	J	6.0	NA	②	4.0	③	④	⑤	18.3
		6.0	5	6.0	NA	⑧	4.0	③	④	⑤	2.9
		6.2	8	6.0	NA	②	4.0	③	④	⑤	17.6
	Yukon	4.8	C	6.0	NA	⑦	NA	NA	4.3	⑤	17.8
		5.3	0	6.0	NA	②	4.0	③	④	⑤	18.3
		5.3	J	6.0	NA	②	4.0	③	④	⑤	18.3
		6.0	5	6.0	NA	⑧	4.0	③	④	⑤	2.9

36616_YUKO_C0004

FLUID SPECIFICATIONS

Year	Model	Engine Displacement Liters	Engine VIN	Engine Oil	Auto. Trans.	Drive Axle Front	Drive Axle Rear	Power Steering Fluid	Brake Master Cylinder	Cooling System
2008	Avalanche	5.3	0	5W-30	Dexron VI	①	②	③	DOT-3	④
		5.3	3	5W-30	Dexron VI	①	②	③	DOT-3	④
		5.3	J	5W-30	Dexron VI	①	②	③	DOT-3	④
		6.0	Y	5W-30	Dexron VI	①	②	③	DOT-3	④
	Escalade	6.2	8	5W-30	Dexron VI	①	②	③	DOT-3	④
	Suburban	5.3	0	5W-30	Dexron VI	①	②	③	DOT-3	④
		5.3	3	5W-30	Dexron VI	①	②	③	DOT-3	④
		5.3	J	5W-30	Dexron VI	①	②	③	DOT-3	④
		6.0	K	5W-30	Dexron VI	①	②	③	DOT-3	④
		6.0	Y	5W-30	Dexron VI	①	②	③	DOT-3	④
	Tahoe	4.8	C	5W-30	Dexron VI	NA	②	③	DOT-3	④
		5.3	0	5W-30	Dexron VI	①	②	③	DOT-3	④
		5.3	J	5W-30	Dexron VI	①	②	③	DOT-3	④
		6.0	5	5W-30	Dexron VI	①	②	③	DOT-3	④
		6.2	8	5W-30	Dexron VI	①	②	③	DOT-3	④
	Yukon	4.8	C	5W-30	Dexron VI	NA	②	③	DOT-3	④
		5.3	0	5W-30	Dexron VI	①	②	③	DOT-3	④
		5.3	J	5W-30	Dexron VI	①	②	③	DOT-3	④
		6.0	5	5W-30	Dexron VI	①	②	③	DOT-3	④
	Yukon XL	5.3	0	5W-30	Dexron VI	①	②	③	DOT-3	④
		5.3	3	5W-30	Dexron VI	①	②	③	DOT-3	④
		5.3	J	5W-30	Dexron VI	①	②	③	DOT-3	④
		6.0	K	5W-30	Dexron VI	①	②	③	DOT-3	④
		6.0	Y	5W-30	Dexron VI	①	②	③	DOT-3	④
	Yukon Denali	6.2	8	5W-30	Dexron VI	①	②	③	DOT-3	④
2009	Avalanche	5.3	0	5W-30	Dexron VI	①	②	③	DOT-3	④
		5.3	3	5W-30	Dexron VI	①	②	③	DOT-3	④
		5.3	J	5W-30	Dexron VI	①	②	③	DOT-3	④
		6.0	Y	5W-30	Dexron VI	①	②	③	DOT-3	④
	Escalade	6.0	5	5W-30	Dexron VI	①	②	③	DOT-3	④
		6.2	8	5W-30	Dexron VI	①	②	③	DOT-3	④
	Suburban	5.3	0	5W-30	Dexron VI	①	②	③	DOT-3	④
		5.3	3	5W-30	Dexron VI	①	②	③	DOT-3	④
		5.3	J	5W-30	Dexron VI	①	②	③	DOT-3	④
		6.0	K	5W-30	Dexron VI	①	②	③	DOT-3	④
		6.0	Y	5W-30	Dexron VI	①	②	③	DOT-3	④
	Tahoe	4.8	C	5W-30	Dexron VI	NA	②	③	DOT-3	④
		5.3	0	5W-30	Dexron VI	①	②	③	DOT-3	④
		5.3	J	5W-30	Dexron VI	①	②	③	DOT-3	④
		6.0	5	5W-30	Dexron VI	①	②	③	DOT-3	④
		6.2	8	5W-30	Dexron VI	①	②	③	DOT-3	④
	Yukon	4.8	C	5W-30	Dexron VI	NA	②	③	DOT-3	④
		5.3	0	5W-30	Dexron VI	①	②	③	DOT-3	④
		5.3	J	5W-30	Dexron VI	①	②	③	DOT-3	④
		6.0	5	5W-30	Dexron VI	①	②	③	DOT-3	④

36616_YUKO_C0005

VALVE SPECIFICATIONS

Year	Engine Displacement Liters	Engine VIN	Seat Angle (deg.)	Face Angle (deg.)	Spring Test Pressure (lbs. @ in.)	Spring Installed Height (in.)	Stem-to-Guide Clearance (in.)		Stem Diameter (in.)	
							Intake	Exhaust	Intake	Exhaust
2008	4.8	C	46.0	45.0	220@1.32	1.80	0.0010-0.0026	0.0010-0.0026	0.3130-0.3140	0.3130-0.3140
	5.3	0	46.0	45.0	220@1.32	1.80	0.0010-0.0026	0.0010-0.0026	0.3130-0.3140	0.3130-0.3140
	5.3	J	46.0	45.0	220@1.32	1.80	0.0010-0.0026	0.0010-0.0026	0.3130-0.3140	0.3130-0.3140
	5.3	3	46.0	45.0	220@1.32	1.80	0.0010-0.0026	0.0010-0.0026	0.3130-0.3140	0.3130-0.3140
	6.0	5	46.0	45.0	220@1.32	1.80	0.0010-0.0026	0.0010-0.0026	0.3130-0.3140	0.3130-0.3140
	6.0	Y	46.0	45.0	220@1.32	1.80	0.0010-0.0026	0.0010-0.0026	0.3130-0.3140	0.3130-0.3140
	6.0	K	46.0	45.0	220@1.32	1.80	0.0010-0.0026	0.0010-0.0026	0.3130-0.3140	0.3130-0.3140
	6.2	8	46.0	45.0	220@1.32	1.80	0.0010-0.0026	0.0010-0.0026	0.3130-0.3140	0.3130-0.3140
2009	4.8	C	46.0	45.0	220@1.32	1.80	0.0010-0.0026	0.0010-0.0026	0.3130-0.3140	0.3130-0.3140
	5.3	0	46.0	45.0	220@1.32	1.80	0.0010-0.0026	0.0010-0.0026	0.3130-0.3140	0.3130-0.3140
	5.3	J	46.0	45.0	220@1.32	1.80	0.0010-0.0026	0.0010-0.0026	0.3130-0.3140	0.3130-0.3140
	5.3	3	46.0	45.0	220@1.32	1.80	0.0010-0.0026	0.0010-0.0026	0.3130-0.3140	0.3130-0.3140
	6.0	5	46.0	45.0	220@1.32	1.80	0.0010-0.0026	0.0010-0.0026	0.3130-0.3140	0.3130-0.3140
	6.0	Y	46.0	45.0	220@1.32	1.80	0.0010-0.0026	0.0010-0.0026	0.3130-0.3140	0.3130-0.3140
	6.0	K	46.0	45.0	220@1.32	1.80	0.0010-0.0026	0.0010-0.0026	0.3130-0.3140	0.3130-0.3140
	6.2	8	46.0	45.0	220@1.32	1.80	0.0010-0.0026	0.0010-0.0026	0.3130-0.3140	0.3130-0.3140

36616_YUKO_C0006

CAMSHAFT AND BEARING SPECIFICATIONS CHART
All measurements are given in inches.

Year	Engine Displ. Liters	Engine VIN	Journal Dia.	Brg. Oil Clearance	Shaft End-play	Runout	Journal Bore	Lobe Lift	
								Intake	Exhaust
2008	4.8	C	2.1640-2.1660	0.0009-0.0038	0.0010-0.0120	0.0020	①	0.2830	0.2830
	5.3	0	2.1640-2.1660	0.0009-0.0038	0.0010-0.0120	0.0020	①	②	②
	5.3	J	2.1640-2.1660	0.0009-0.0038	0.0010-0.0120	0.0020	①	②	②
	5.3	3	2.1640-2.1660	0.0009-0.0038	0.0010-0.0120	0.0020	①	②	②
	6.0	5	2.1650-2.1660	0.0002-0.0038	0.0010-0.0120	0.0020	①	③	④
	6.0	Y	2.1640-2.1660	0.0009-0.0038	0.0010-0.0120	0.0020	①	⑤	⑤
	6.0	K	2.1640-2.1660	0.0009-0.0038	0.0010-0.0120	0.0020	①	0.2740	0.2810
	6.2	8	2.1640-2.1660	0.0009-0.0038	0.0010-0.0120	0.0020	①	0.2940	0.2940
2009	4.8	C	2.1640-2.1660	0.0009-0.0038	0.0010-0.0120	0.0020	①	0.2830	0.2830
	5.3	0	2.1640-2.1660	0.0009-0.0038	0.0010-0.0120	0.0020	①	②	②
	5.3	J	2.1640-2.1660	0.0009-0.0038	0.0010-0.0120	0.0020	①	②	②
	5.3	3	2.1640-2.1660	0.0009-0.0038	0.0010-0.0120	0.0020	①	②	②
	6.0	5	2.1650-2.1660	0.0002-0.0038	0.0010-0.0120	0.0020	①	③	④
	6.0	Y	2.1640-2.1660	0.0009-0.0038	0.0010-0.0120	0.0020	①	⑤	⑤
	6.0	K	2.1640-2.1660	0.0009-0.0038	0.0010-0.0120	0.0020	①	0.2740	0.2810
	6.2	8	2.1640-2.1660	0.0009-0.0038	0.0010-0.0120	0.0020	①	0.2940	0.2940

① Cam Bearing Bore 1 and 5: 2.345-2.347 inches
  Bore 2 and 4: 2.325-2.327 inches
  Bore 3: 2.306-2.308 inches
② Active Fuel Management Cylinders: 0.2890 inch
  Non-active Fuel Management Cylinders: 0.2830 inch

③ Active Fuel Management Cylinders: 0.2830 inch
  Non-active Fuel Management Cylinders: 0.2790 inch
④ Active Fuel Management Cylinders: 0.2870 inch
  Non-active Fuel Management Cylinders: 0.2820 inch
⑤ Active Fuel Management Cylinders: 0.2990 inch
  Non-active Fuel Management Cylinders: 0.2940 inch

36616_YUKO_C0007

CRANKSHAFT AND CONNECTING ROD SPECIFICATIONS

All measurements are given in inches.

Year	Engine Displacement Liters	Engine VIN	Crankshaft				Connecting Rod		
			Main Brg. Journal Dia.	Main Brg. Oil Clearance	Shaft End-play	Thrust on No.	Journal Diameter	Oil Clearance	Side Clearance
2008	4.8	C	2.5580-2.5590	0.0008-0.0021	0.0015-0.0078	5	2.0991-2.0999	0.0009-0.0025	0.0043-0.0200
	5.3	0	2.5580-2.5590	0.0008-0.0021	0.0015-0.0078	5	2.0991-2.0999	0.0009-0.0025	0.0043-0.0200
	5.3	J	2.5580-2.5590	0.0008-0.0021	0.0015-0.0078	5	2.0991-2.0999	0.0009-0.0025	0.0043-0.0200
	5.3	3	2.5580-2.5590	0.0008-0.0021	0.0015-0.0078	5	2.0991-2.0999	0.0009-0.0025	0.0043-0.0200
	6.0	5	2.5580-2.5590	0.0008-0.0021	0.0015-0.0078	5	2.0991-2.0999	0.0009-0.0025	0.0043-0.0200
	6.0	Y	2.5580-2.5590	0.0008-0.0021	0.0015-0.0078	5	2.0991-2.0999	0.0009-0.0025	0.0043-0.0200
	6.0	K	2.5580-2.5590	0.0008-0.0021	0.0015-0.0078	5	2.0991-2.0999	0.0009-0.0025	0.0043-0.0200
	6.2	8	2.5580-2.5590	0.0008-0.0021	0.0015-0.0078	5	2.0991-2.0999	0.0009-0.0025	0.0043-0.0200
2009	4.8	C	2.5580-2.5590	0.0008-0.0021	0.0015-0.0078	5	2.0991-2.0999	0.0009-0.0025	0.0043-0.0200
	5.3	0	2.5580-2.5590	0.0008-0.0021	0.0015-0.0078	5	2.0991-2.0999	0.0009-0.0025	0.0043-0.0200
	5.3	J	2.5580-2.5590	0.0008-0.0021	0.0015-0.0078	5	2.0991-2.0999	0.0009-0.0025	0.0043-0.0200
	5.3	3	2.5580-2.5590	0.0008-0.0021	0.0015-0.0078	5	2.0991-2.0999	0.0009-0.0025	0.0043-0.0200
	6.0	5	2.5580-2.5590	0.0008-0.0021	0.0015-0.0078	5	2.0991-2.0999	0.0009-0.0025	0.0043-0.0200
	6.0	Y	2.5580-2.5590	0.0008-0.0021	0.0015-0.0078	5	2.0991-2.0999	0.0009-0.0025	0.0043-0.0200
	6.0	K	2.5580-2.5590	0.0008-0.0021	0.0015-0.0078	5	2.0991-2.0999	0.0009-0.0025	0.0043-0.0200
	6.2	8	2.5580-2.5590	0.0008-0.0021	0.0015-0.0078	5	2.0991-2.0999	0.0009-0.0025	0.0043-0.0200

36616_YUKO_C0008

PISTON AND RING SPECIFICATIONS
All measurements are given in inches.

Year	Engine Displ. Liters	Engine VIN	Piston Clearance	Ring Gap			Ring Side Clearance		
				Top Compression	Bottom Compression	Oil Control	Top Compression	Bottom Compression	Oil Control
2008	4.8	C	-0.0014-0.0006	0.0090-0.0196	0.0173-0.0300	0.0070-0.0320	0.0016-0.0034	0.0016-0.0031	0.0005-0.0078
	5.3	0	-0.0014-0.0006	0.0090-0.0196	0.0173-0.0300	0.0070-0.0320	0.0016-0.0034	0.0016-0.0031	0.0005-0.0078
	5.3	J	-0.0014-0.0006	0.0090-0.0196	0.0173-0.0300	0.0070-0.0320	0.0016-0.0034	0.0016-0.0031	0.0005-0.0078
	5.3	3	-0.0014-0.0006	0.0090-0.0196	0.0173-0.0300	0.0070-0.0320	0.0016-0.0034	0.0016-0.0031	0.0005-0.0078
	6.0	5	-0.0012-0.0008	0.0079-0.0181	0.0146-0.0295	0.0086-0.0331	0.0016-0.0033	0.0014-0.0031	0.0005-0.0079
	6.0	Y	-0.0012-0.0008	0.0079-0.0181	0.0146-0.0295	0.0086-0.0331	0.0016-0.0033	0.0014-0.0031	0.0005-0.0079
	6.0	K	-0.0012-0.0008	0.0079-0.0181	0.0146-0.0295	0.0086-0.0331	0.0016-0.0033	0.0014-0.0031	0.0005-0.0079
	6.2	8	-0.0019-0.0000	0.0067-0.0173	0.0126-0.0272	0.0086-0.0335	0.0012-0.0033	0.0016-0.0033	0.0005-0.0079
2009	4.8	C	-0.0014-0.0006	0.0090-0.0196	0.0173-0.0300	0.0070-0.0320	0.0016-0.0034	0.0016-0.0031	0.0005-0.0078
	5.3	0	-0.0014-0.0006	0.0090-0.0196	0.0173-0.0300	0.0070-0.0320	0.0016-0.0034	0.0016-0.0031	0.0005-0.0078
	5.3	J	-0.0014-0.0006	0.0090-0.0196	0.0173-0.0300	0.0070-0.0320	0.0016-0.0034	0.0016-0.0031	0.0005-0.0078
	5.3	3	-0.0014-0.0006	0.0090-0.0196	0.0173-0.0300	0.0070-0.0320	0.0016-0.0034	0.0016-0.0031	0.0005-0.0078
	6.0	5	-0.0012-0.0008	0.0079-0.0181	0.0146-0.0295	0.0086-0.0331	0.0016-0.0033	0.0014-0.0031	0.0005-0.0079
	6.0	Y	-0.0012-0.0008	0.0079-0.0181	0.0146-0.0295	0.0086-0.0331	0.0016-0.0033	0.0014-0.0031	0.0005-0.0079
	6.0	K	-0.0012-0.0008	0.0079-0.0181	0.0146-0.0295	0.0086-0.0331	0.0016-0.0033	0.0014-0.0031	0.0005-0.0079
	6.2	8	-0.0019-0.0000	0.0067-0.0173	0.0126-0.0272	0.0086-0.0335	0.0012-0.0033	0.0016-0.0033	0.0005-0.0079

36616_YUKO_C0009

TORQUE SPECIFICATIONS
All readings in ft. lbs.

Year	Engine Displacement Liters	Engine VIN	Cylinder Head Bolts	Main Bearing Bolts	Rod Bearing Bolts	Crankshaft Damper Bolts	Flywheel Bolts	Manifold		Spark Plugs	Oil Pan Drain Plug
								Intake	Exhaust		
2008	4.8	C	①	②	③	④	⑤	⑥	⑦	11	18
	5.3	0	①	②	③	④	⑤	⑥	⑦	11	18
	5.3	J	①	②	③	④	⑤	⑥	⑦	11	18
	5.3	3	①	②	③	④	⑤	⑥	⑦	11	18
	6.0	5	①	②	③	④	⑤	⑥	⑦	11	18
	6.0	Y	①	②	③	④	⑤	⑥	⑦	11	18
	6.0	K	①	②	③	④	⑤	⑥	⑦	11	18
	6.2	8	①	②	③	④	⑤	⑥	⑦	11	18
2009	4.8	C	①	②	③	④	⑤	⑥	⑦	11	18
	5.3	0	①	②	③	④	⑤	⑥	⑦	11	18
	5.3	J	①	②	③	④	⑤	⑥	⑦	11	18
	5.3	3	①	②	③	④	⑤	⑥	⑦	11	18
	6.0	5	①	②	③	④	⑤	⑥	⑦	11	18
	6.0	Y	①	②	③	④	⑤	⑥	⑦	11	18
	6.0	K	①	②	③	④	⑤	⑥	⑦	11	18
	6.2	8	①	②	③	④	⑤	⑥	⑦	11	18

① Refer to procedure for torque sequence and bolt identification
M11 bolts Step 1: 22 ft. lbs.
M11 bolts Step 2: 90 degrees
M11 bolts Step 3: 70 degrees
M8 bolts: 22 ft. lbs.

② Refer to procedure for torque sequence and bolt identification
M10 bolts Step 1: 15 ft. lbs.
M10 bolts Step 2: 80 degrees
M10 studs Step 1: 15 ft. lbs.
M10 studs Step 2: 51 degrees
M8 bolts: 18 ft. lbs.

③ Step 1: 15 ft. lbs.
Step 2: 85 degrees

④ Step 1: 110 ft. lbs.
Step 2: loosen 360 degrees
Step 3: 37 ft. lbs.
Step 4: 230 degrees

⑤ Step 1: 15 ft. lbs.
Step 2: 37 ft. lbs.
Step 3: 74 ft. lbs.

⑥ Refer to procedure for torque sequence and bolt identification
Step 1: 44 inch lbs.
Step 2: 89 inch lbs.

⑦ Bolts Step 1: 11 ft. lbs.
Bolts Step 2: 15 ft. lbs.
Heat shield bolts: 80 inch lbs.
Manifold studs: 15 ft. lbs.

36616_YUKO_C0010

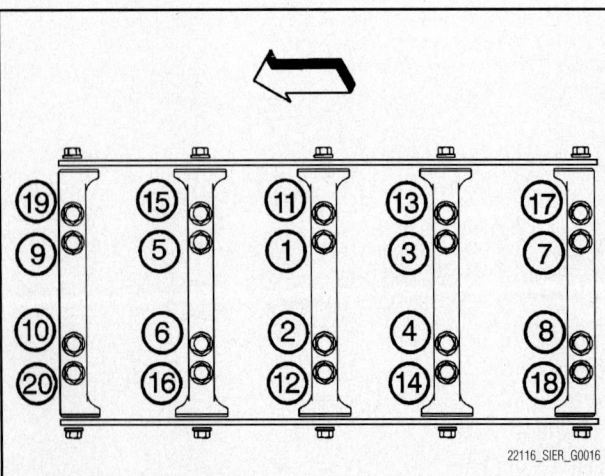

22116_SIER_G0016

Fig. 1 Main bearing torque sequence—4.8L, 5.3L, 6.0L, and 6.2L engines

WHEEL ALIGNMENT

Year	Series/Tire Descrip.①	Model		Caster Range (+/-Deg.)	Caster Preferred Setting (Deg.)	Camber Range (+/-Deg.)	Camber Preferred Setting (Deg.)	Toe-in (Deg.)
2008	C/K 1500 w/17 inch Bridgestone Tires w/QJP, QJM, QAN, and R5C	Avalanche/Tahoe/Suburban/ Yukon/Yukon XL	L	1.00	3.35	0.60	-0.10	+0.10+/-0.20
			R	1.00	3.45	0.60	-0.10	
	C/K 1500 w/17 inch Goodyear Tires w/QAS, QAN, and R4Y	Avalanche/Tahoe/Suburban/ Yukon/Yukon XL	L	1.00	3.20	0.60	-0.10	+0.10+/-0.20
			R	1.00	3.60	0.60	-0.10	
	C/K 1500 w/18 inch Tires w/QXK and Y91	Avalanche/Escalade/Tahoe/ Suburban/Yukon Denali/Yukon Denali XL	L	1.00	3.45	0.60	-0.10	+0.10+/-0.20
			R	1.00	3.35	0.60	-0.10	
	C/K 1500 w/18 inch Tires w/QXN and Z71, QXO and EXP	Avalanche/Escalade/Tahoe/ Suburban/Yukon/Yukon XL	L	1.00	3.30	0.60	-0.10	+0.10+/-0.20
			R	1.00	3.50	0.60	-0.10	
	C/K 1500 w/20 inch Bridgestone Tires w/QSS and R5C	Avalanche/Tahoe/Suburban/ Yukon/Yukon XL/Yukon Denali/Yukon Denali XL	L	1.00	3.55	0.60	-0.10	+0.10+/-0.20
			R	1.00	3.25	0.60	-0.10	
	C/K 1500 w/20 inch Goodyear Tires w/QSS and R4Y	Avalanche/Tahoe/Suburban/ Yukon/Yukon XL/Yukon Denali/Yukon Denali XL	L	1.00	3.50	0.60	-0.10	+0.10+/-0.20
			R	1.00	3.50	0.60	-0.10	
	C/K 1500 w/22 inch Tires w/QST	Escalade/Escalade ESV/Escalade EXT	L	1.00	3.30	0.60	-0.10	+0.10+/-0.20
			R	1.00	3.50	0.60	-0.10	
	C/K 2500 All Tires	Suburban/Yukon XL	L	1.00	3.50	0.60	+0.25	+0.10+/-0.20
			R	1.00	3.75	0.60	+0.25	
2009	C/K 1500 w/17 inch Bridgestone Tires w/QJP, QJM, QAN, and R5C	Avalanche/Tahoe/Suburban/ Yukon/Yukon XL	L	1.00	3.35	0.60	-0.10	+0.10+/-0.20
			R	1.00	3.45	0.60	-0.10	
	C/K 1500 w/17 inch Goodyear Tires w/QAS, QAN, and R4Y	Avalanche/Tahoe/Suburban/ Yukon/Yukon XL	L	1.00	3.20	0.60	-0.10	+0.10+/-0.20
			R	1.00	3.60	0.60	-0.10	
	C/K 1500 w/18 inch Tires w/QXK and Y91	Avalanche/Escalade/Tahoe/ Suburban/Yukon Denali/Yukon Denali XL	L	1.00	3.45	0.60	-0.10	+0.10+/-0.20
			R	1.00	3.35	0.60	-0.10	
	C/K 1500 w/18 inch Tires w/QXN and Z71, QXO and EXP	Avalanche/Escalade/Tahoe/ Suburban/Yukon/Yukon XL	L	1.00	3.30	0.60	-0.10	+0.10+/-0.20
			R	1.00	3.50	0.60	-0.10	
	C/K 1500 w/20 inch Bridgestone Tires w/QSS and R5C	Avalanche/Tahoe/Suburban/ Yukon/Yukon XL/Yukon Denali/Yukon Denali XL	L	1.00	3.55	0.60	-0.10	+0.10+/-0.20
			R	1.00	3.25	0.60	-0.10	
	C/K 1500 w/20 inch Goodyear Tires w/QSS and R4Y	Avalanche/Tahoe/Suburban/ Yukon/Yukon XL/Yukon Denali/Yukon Denali XL	L	1.00	3.50	0.60	-0.10	+0.10+/-0.20
			R	1.00	3.50	0.60	-0.10	
	C/K 1500 w/22 inch Tires w/QST	Escalade/Escalade ESV/Escalade EXT	L	1.00	3.30	0.60	-0.10	+0.10+/-0.20
			R	1.00	3.50	0.60	-0.10	
	C/K 2500 All Tires	Suburban/Yukon XL	L	1.00	3.50	0.60	+0.25	+0.10+/-0.20
			R	1.00	3.75	0.60	+0.25	

NOTE: Measurements are given for unladen vehicle: fuel, engine coolant, and fluid levels are full.

Spare tire, jack, hand tools, and mats are in designated positions.

① Tire/wheel size refers to OEM wheels only

TIRE, WHEEL AND BALL JOINT SPECIFICATIONS

| Year | Model | OEM Tires | | Tire Pressure (psi) | | Wheel Size | Ball Joint Inspection | Lug Nut Torque (ft. lbs.) |
		Standard	Optional	Front	Rear			
2008	Avalanche LS/LT	P265/70R17	NA	①	①	7.5 x 17	②	140
	Avalanche LTZ	P275/55R20	NA	①	①	8.5 x 20	②	140
	Escalade ESV/EXT	P265/65R18	P285/45R22	①	①	8.0 x 18 or 9.0 x 22	②	140
	Escalade Platinum	P285/45R22	NA	①	①	9.0 x 22	②	140
	Suburban 1LS/1LT (1500)	P265/70R17	NA	①	①	7.5 x 17	②	140
	Suburban 2LT (1500)	P265/70R17	P265/65R18	①	①	7.5 x 17 or 8.0 x 18	②	140
	Suburban LTZ (1500)	P275/55R20	NA	①	①	8.5 x 20	②	140
	Suburban LS 1LS (2500)	P265/70R17	NA	①	①	7.5 x 17	②	140
	Suburban LT 1LT (2500)	P265/70R17	P275/55R20	①	①	7.5 x 17 or 8.5 x 20	②	140
	Suburban LT 2LT (2500)	P265/70R17	NA	①	①	7.5 x 17	②	140
	Tahoe LS/LT/HY	P265/70R17	NA	①	①	7.5 x 17	②	140
	Tahoe LTZ	P275/55R20	NA	①	①	7.5 x 17	②	140
	Yukon/Yukon XL (1500)	P265/70R17	P275/55R20	①	①	7.5 x 17 or 8.5 x 20	②	140
	Yukon XL (2500)	LT245/75R16E	LT265/70R17E	①	①	6.5 x 16 or 7.5 x 17	②	140
	Yukon Denali	P275/55R20	P265/65R18	①	①	8.5 x 20 or 8.0 x 18	②	140
	Yukon Hybrid	P265/65R18	NA	①	①	8.0 x 18	②	140
2009	Avalanche LS/LT	P265/70R17	NA	①	①	7.5 x 17	②	140
	Avalanche LTZ	P275/55R20	NA	①	①	8.5 x 20	②	140
	Escalade ESV/EXT	P265/65R18	P285/45R22	①	①	8.0 x 18 or 9.0 x 22	②	140
	Escalade Platinum/Hybrid	P285/45R22	NA	①	①	9.0 x 22	②	140
	Suburban 1LS/1LT (1500)	P265/70R17	NA	①	①	7.5 x 17	②	140
	Suburban 2LT (1500)	P265/70R17	P265/65R18	①	①	7.5 x 17 or 8.0 x 18	②	140
	Suburban LTZ (1500)	P275/55R20	NA	①	①	8.5 x 20	②	140
	Suburban LS 1LS (2500)	P265/70R17	NA	①	①	7.5 x 17	②	140
	Suburban LT 1LT (2500)	P265/70R17	P275/55R20	①	①	7.5 x 17 or 8.5 x 20	②	140
	Suburban LT 2LT (2500)	P265/70R17	NA	①	①	7.5 x 17	②	140
	Tahoe LS/LT/HY	P265/70R17	NA	①	①	7.5 x 17	②	140
	Tahoe LTZ	P275/55R20	NA	①	①	7.5 x 17	②	140
	Yukon/Yukon XL (1500)	P265/70R17	P275/55R20	①	①	7.5 x 17 or 8.5 x 20	②	140
	Yukon XL (2500)	LT245/75R16E	LT265/70R17E	①	①	6.5 x 16 or 7.5 x 17	②	140
	Yukon Denali	P275/55R20	P265/65R18	①	①	8.5 x 20 or 8.0 x 18	②	140
	Yukon Hybrid	P265/65R18	NA	①	①	8.0 x 18	②	140

OEM: Original Equipment Manufacturer

PSI: Pounds Per Square Inch

NA: Not Applicable

① See the tire placard on the vehicle

② Lift or pry the suspension upward, then let it settle. The dial indicator reading should be no more than 0.079 inch of play on either the upper or lower ball joint.

36616_YUKO_C0012

BRAKE SPECIFICATIONS
All measurements in inches unless noted

Year	Model		Brake Disc Original Thickness	Brake Disc Minimum Thickness	Brake Disc Maximum Runout	Brake Drum Diameter Original Inside Diameter	Brake Drum Max. Wear Limit	Brake Drum Maximum Machine Diameter	Minimum Lining Thickness	Brake Caliper Bracket Bolts (ft. lbs.)	Brake Caliper Guide Pin Bolts (ft. lbs.)
2008	Avalanche	F	①	②	③	NA	NA	NA	0.030	④	⑤
		R	⑥	⑦	③	NA	NA	NA	0.030	⑧	⑨
	Escalade	F	①	②	③	NA	NA	NA	0.030	④	⑤
		R	⑥	⑦	③	NA	NA	NA	0.030	⑧	⑨
	Suburban	F	①	②	③	NA	NA	NA	0.030	④	⑤
		R	⑥	⑦	③	NA	NA	NA	0.030	⑧	⑨
	Tahoe	F	①	②	③	NA	NA	NA	0.030	④	⑤
		R	⑥	⑦	③	NA	NA	NA	0.030	⑧	⑨
	Yukon	F	①	②	③	NA	NA	NA	0.030	④	⑤
		R	⑥	⑦	③	NA	NA	NA	0.030	⑧	⑨
	Yukon XL	F	①	②	③	NA	NA	NA	0.030	④	⑤
		R	⑥	⑦	③	NA	NA	NA	0.030	⑧	⑨
	Yukon Denali	F	①	②	③	NA	NA	NA	0.030	④	⑤
		R	⑥	⑦	③	NA	NA	NA	0.030	⑧	⑨
2009	Avalanche	F	①	②	③	NA	NA	NA	0.030	④	⑤
		R	⑥	⑦	③	NA	NA	NA	0.030	⑧	⑨
	Escalade	F	①	②	③	NA	NA	NA	0.030	④	⑤
		R	⑥	⑦	③	NA	NA	NA	0.030	⑧	⑨
	Suburban	F	①	②	③	NA	NA	NA	0.030	④	⑤
		R	⑥	⑦	③	NA	NA	NA	0.030	⑧	⑨
	Tahoe	F	①	②	③	NA	NA	NA	0.030	④	⑤
		R	⑥	⑦	③	NA	NA	NA	0.030	⑧	⑨
	Yukon	F	①	②	③	NA	NA	NA	0.030	④	⑤
		R	⑥	⑦	③	NA	NA	NA	0.030	⑧	⑨
	Yukon XL	F	①	②	③	NA	NA	NA	0.030	④	⑤
		R	⑥	⑦	③	NA	NA	NA	0.030	⑧	⑨
	Yukon Denali	F	①	②	③	NA	NA	NA	0.030	④	⑤
		R	⑥	⑦	③	NA	NA	NA	0.030	⑧	⑨

NA: Not Applicable

F: Front

R: Rear

① JD9 (7,700 lbs.): 1.181 inches
   JH6 (9,900 lbs.): 1.496 inches

② JD9 (7,700 lbs.): 1.102 inches
   JH6 (9,900 lbs.): 1.457 inches

③ JD9 (7,700 lbs.): 0.002 inch
   JH6 (9,900 lbs.): 0.005 inch

④ (1500 Series): 148 ft. lbs.
   (2500 Series): 221 ft. lbs.

⑤ (1500 Series): 74 ft. lbs.
   (2500 Series): 80 ft. lbs.

⑥ JD9 (7,700 lbs.): 0.787 inch
   JH6 (9,900 lbs.): 1.181 inches

⑦ JD9 (7,700 lbs.): 0.7282 inch
   JH6 (9,900 lbs.): 1.102 inches

⑧ (1500 Series): 148 ft. lbs.
   (2500 Series): 148 ft. lbs.

⑨ (1500 Series): 28 ft. lbs.
   (2500 Series): 80 ft. lbs.

MAINTENANCE I AND II SERVICE SCHEDULES
AVALANCHE, ESCALADE, SUBURBAN, TAHOE, AND YUKON

When the CHANGE ENGINE OIL light appears, certain services and inspections are required.

Required services are described as Maintenance I and Maintenance II.

The first service of a vehicle should be Maintenance I, and the second service should be Maintenance II.

Alternate between the 2 services thereafter. However, in some cases, Maintenance II may be required more often.

Maintenance I: Use Maintenance I if the CHANGE ENGINE OIL light comes on within 10 months since the vehicle was purchased or, if Maintenance II was performed.

Maintenance II: Use Maintenance II if the previous service performed was Maintenance I. Always use Maintenance II whenever the CHANGE ENGINE OIL light comes on 10 months or more since the last service, or, if the CHANGE ENGINE OIL light has not come on at all for one year.

Service	Maintenance I	Maintenance II
Change the engine oil and filter. Reset the oil life system.	✓	✓
Visually inspect the vehicle for leaks or damage. A fluid loss in the vehicle system could indicate a problem. Inspect, repair, and add fluid to the system as necessary.	✓	✓
Inspect the engine air cleaner filter. If necessary, replace the filter.	—	✓
Rotate the tires. Inspect the tire inflation pressures and the tire wear.	✓	✓
Visually inspect the brake lines and hoses for proper hook-up, binding, leaks, cracks, chafing, etc. Inspect the disc brake pads for wear and the rotors for surface condition. Inspect other brake parts, including wheel cylinders, calipers, parking brake, etc. Inspect the parking brake adjustment.	✓	✓
Check the engine coolant and windshield washer fluid levels and add fluid as needed.	✓	✓
Inspect the suspension and steering components. Inspect the front and rear suspension and the steering system for damaged, loose or missing parts, or signs of wear. Inspect the power steering lines and the hoses for proper hook-up, binding, leaks, cracks, chafing, etc.	—	✓
Inspect the coolant hoses and replace the hoses if they are cracked, swollen, or deteriorated. Inspect all pipes, fittings, and clamps; replace with GM parts as needed. To help ensure proper operation, a pressure test of the cooling system and pressure cap. Cleaning the outside of the radiator and air conditioning condenser is recommended at least once a year.	—	✓
Inspect the wiper blades for wear or cracking.	—	✓
Inspect the restraint system components. Ensure that the safety belt reminder light and all the belts, buckles, latch plates, retractors, and anchorages are working properly. Look for any other loose or damaged safety belt system parts. If you see anything that might keep a safety belt system from working correctly, repair or replace the damaged part. Replace torn or frayed safety belts. Inspect for any opened or broken air bag coverings and repair or replace, as needed. The air bag system requires regular maintenance.	—	✓
Lubricate the body components. Lubricate all key lock cylinders, hood latch assemblies, secondary latches, pivots, spring anchor and release pawl, hood and door hinges, rear folding seats and liftgate hinges. Frequent lubrication may be required when exposed to a corrosive environment. Apply dielectric silicone grease GM P/N 12345579 (Canadian P/N 1974984), or equivalent, on the weatherstrips with a clean cloth.	✓	✓
Inspect the transmission fluid level and add fluid as needed.	—	✓
Inspect the throttle system for interference or binding and for damaged or missing parts. Replace the parts as needed. Replace any components that have high effort or excessive wear.	—	✓
Check transfer case fluid level and add fluid as needed.	—	✓
Replace passenger compartment air filter.	—	✓

To reset the CHANGE ENGINE OIL light:

1. Turn the ignition key to the ON/RUN position with the engine OFF.
2. Press and release the stem in the lower center of the instrument cluster until the OIL LIFE message is displayed.
3. Once the alternating OIL LIFE and RESET messages appear, press and hold the stem until several beeps sound.
    This confirms that the oil life system has been reset to 100 percent.
4. Turn the ignition key to the OFF position.
    If the CHANGE ENGINE OIL message comes back on when the vehicle is started, the engine oil life system has not been reset. Repeat the procedure.

ADDITIONAL MAINTENANCE SERVICES

AVALANCHE, ESCALADE, SUBURBAN, TAHOE, AND YUKON

TO BE SERVICED	TYPE OF SERVICE	VEHICLE MILEAGE INTERVAL (x1000)					
		25	50	75	100	125	150
Air cleaner filter	R		✓		✓		✓
Accessory drive belt	I						✓
Automatic transmission fluid ①	R				✓		
Engine coolant ②	R	Every 5 years or 150,000 miles					
Evaporative control system ③	I		✓		✓		✓
Fuel system (for damage or leaks)	I	✓	✓	✓	✓	✓	✓
Exhaust system	S/I	✓	✓	✓	✓	✓	✓
Spark plugs	R				✓		
Spark plug wires	I				✓		
Transfer case fluid (4WD models) ④	R		✓		✓		✓

R: Replace

S/I: Inspect and service, if necessary

FREQUENT OPERATION MAINTENANCE (SEVERE SERVICE)

If a vehicle is operated under any of the following conditions it is considered severe service:

- Extremely dusty areas

- 50% or more of the vehicle operation is in 90°F (32°C) or higher temperatures, or constant operation in temperatures below 32°F (0°C)

- Prolonged idling (vehicle operation in stop and go traffic)

- Frequent short running periods (engine does not warm to normal operating temperatures)

- Police, taxi, delivery usage, or trailer towing usage

- Driving in hilly or mountainous terrain

① Replace the fluid every 50,000 miles under Severe Service

② Drain, flush, and refill the cooling system. Inspect hoses. Clean the radiator, condenser, pressure cap, and filler neck. Pressure test the cooling system pressure cap.

③ Check all fuel and vapor lines and hoses for proper hook-up, routing, and condition. Check that the purge valve works properly, if equipped. Replace as needed.

④ Check the vent hose at transfer case for kinks and proper installation. Check to be sure the vent hose is unobstructed, clear, and free of debris. During any maintenance, if a power washer is used to clean mud & dirt from the underbody, avoid directly spraying the transfer case output seals.

High pressure water can overcome the seals and contaminate the transfer case fluid. Contaminated fluid will decrease the life of the transfer case; the fluid should be replaced. For Severe Service, replace the fluid every 25,000 miles.

36616_YUKO_C0015

PRECAUTIONS

Before servicing any vehicle, please be sure to read all of the following precautions, which deal with personal safety, prevention of component damage, and important points to take into consideration when servicing a motor vehicle:

• Never open, service or drain the radiator or cooling system when the engine is hot; serious burns can occur from the steam and hot coolant.

• Observe all applicable safety precautions when working around fuel. Whenever servicing the fuel system, always work in a well-ventilated area. Do not allow fuel spray or vapors to come in contact with a spark, open flame, or excessive heat (a hot drop light, for example). Keep a dry chemical fire extinguisher near the work area. Always keep fuel in a container specifically designed for fuel storage; also, always properly seal fuel containers to avoid the possibility of fire or explosion. Refer to the additional fuel system precautions later in this section.

• Fuel injection systems often remain pressurized, even after the engine has been turned **OFF**. The fuel system pressure must be relieved before disconnecting any fuel lines. Failure to do so may result in fire and/or personal injury.

• Brake fluid often contains polyglycol ethers and polyglycols. Avoid contact with the eyes and wash your hands thoroughly after handling brake fluid. If you do get brake fluid in your eyes, flush your eyes with clean, running water for 15 minutes. If eye irritation persists, or if you have taken

brake fluid internally, IMMEDIATELY seek medical assistance.

• The EPA warns that prolonged contact with used engine oil may cause a number of skin disorders, including cancer. You should make every effort to minimize your exposure to used engine oil. Protective gloves should be worn when changing oil. Wash your hands and any other exposed skin areas as soon as possible after exposure to used engine oil. Soap and water, or waterless hand cleaner should be used.

• All new vehicles are now equipped with an air bag system, often referred to as a Supplemental Restraint System (SRS) or Supplemental Inflatable Restraint (SIR) system. The system must be disabled before performing service on or around system components, steering column, instrument panel components, wiring and sensors. Failure to follow safety and disabling procedures could result in accidental air bag deployment, possible personal injury and unnecessary system repairs.

• Always wear safety goggles when working with, or around, the air bag system. When carrying a non-deployed air bag, be sure the bag and trim cover are pointed away from your body. When placing a non-deployed air bag on a work surface, always face the bag and trim cover upward, away from the surface. This will reduce the motion of the module if it is accidentally deployed. Refer to the additional air bag system precautions later in this section.

• Clean, high quality brake fluid from a sealed container is essential to the safe and

proper operation of the brake system. You should always buy the correct type of brake fluid for your vehicle. If the brake fluid becomes contaminated, completely flush the system with new fluid. Never reuse any brake fluid. Any brake fluid that is removed from the system should be discarded. Also, do not allow any brake fluid to come in contact with a painted surface; it will damage the paint.

• Never operate the engine without the proper amount and type of engine oil; doing so WILL result in severe engine damage.

• Timing belt maintenance is extremely important. Many models utilize an interference-type, non-freewheeling engine. If the timing belt breaks, the valves in the cylinder head may strike the pistons, causing potentially serious (also time-consuming and expensive) engine damage. Refer to the maintenance interval charts for the recommended replacement interval for the timing belt, and to the timing belt section for belt replacement and inspection.

• Disconnecting the negative battery cable on some vehicles may interfere with the functions of the on-board computer system(s) and may require the computer to undergo a relearning process once the negative battery cable is reconnected.

• When servicing drum brakes, only disassemble and assemble one side at a time, leaving the remaining side intact for reference.

• Only an MVAC-trained, EPA-certified automotive technician should service the air conditioning system or its components.

BRAKES

ANTI-LOCK BRAKE SYSTEM (ABS)

GENERAL INFORMATION

PRECAUTIONS

• Certain components within the ABS system are not intended to be serviced or repaired individually.

• Do not use rubber hoses or other parts not specifically specified for and ABS system. When using repair kits, replace all parts included in the kit. Partial or incorrect repair may lead to functional problems and require the replacement of components.

• Lubricate rubber parts with clean, fresh brake fluid to ease assembly. Do not use shop air to clean parts; damage to rubber components may result.

• Use only DOT 3 brake fluid from an unopened container.

• If any hydraulic component or line is removed or replaced, it may be necessary to bleed the entire system.

• A clean repair area is essential. Always clean the reservoir and cap thoroughly before removing the cap. The slightest amount of dirt in the fluid may plug an orifice and impair the system function. Perform repairs after components have been thoroughly cleaned; use only denatured alcohol to clean components. Do not allow ABS components to come into contact with any substance containing mineral oil; this includes used shop rags.

• The Anti-Lock control unit is a microprocessor similar to other computer units in the vehicle. Ensure that the ignition switch is **OFF** before removing or installing controller harnesses. Avoid static electricity discharge at or near the controller.

• If any arc welding is to be done on the vehicle, the control unit should be unplugged before welding operations begin.

WHEEL SPEED SENSORS

REMOVAL & INSTALLATION

Front

See Figures 2 and 3.

1. Before servicing the vehicle, refer to the Precautions Section.
2. Raise and safely support the vehicle.
3. Remove the tire and wheel assembly.
4. Remove the front brake rotor. Refer to Front Disc Brakes, Rotor, removal & installation.
5. Disconnect the Wheel Speed Sensor (WSS) electrical connector.

6. Release the WSS electrical connector clip and harness clip from the brake hose bracket.

7. Release the WSS harness clip from the steering knuckle bracket.

To install:

➡**Be sure to use new fasteners, as required.**

8. Position the sensor on its mounting.

9. Tighten the retaining bolt to 13 ft. lbs. (18 Nm).

10. Continue the installation in the reverse order of the removal procedure.

➡**Using the GM diagnostic scan tool, or equivalent, refer to the on-screen reprogramming directions and perform the diagnostic system check procedure.**

Rear

See Figure 4.

1. Before servicing the vehicle, refer to the Precautions Section.

2. Raise and safely support the vehicle.

3. Remove the tire and wheel assembly.

4. Disconnect the Wheel Speed Sensor (WSS) electrical connector.

5. Release the WSS electrical connector and sensor harness clips from the inboard frame rail.

6. Remove the WSS bolt.

7. Remove the WSS from the rear axle.

To install:

8. Install the WSS to the rear axle.

➡**Be sure to use new fasteners, as required.**

9. Install the WSS bolt and tighten to 80 inch lbs. (9 Nm).

10. Connect the WSS electrical connector.

11. Install the WSS electrical connector and sensor harness clips to the inboard frame rail.

➡**Using the GM diagnostic scan tool, or equivalent, refer to the on-screen reprogramming directions and perform the diagnostic system check procedure.**

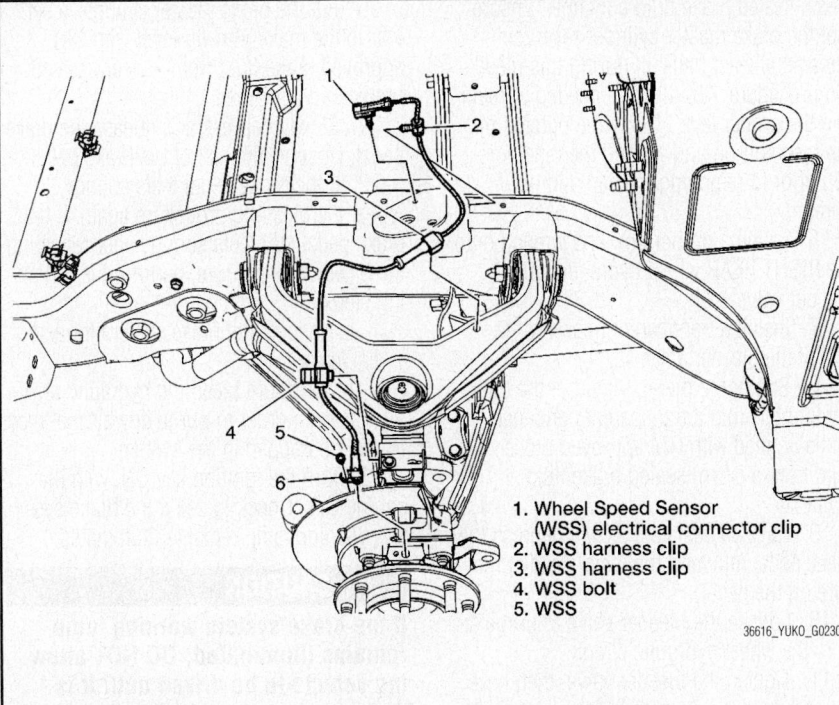

1. Wheel Speed Sensor (WSS) electrical connector clip
2. WSS harness clip
3. WSS harness clip
4. WSS bolt
5. WSS

36616_YUKO_G0230

Fig. 2 Front wheel speed sensor removal—vehicles less than 8,600 lbs. GVW

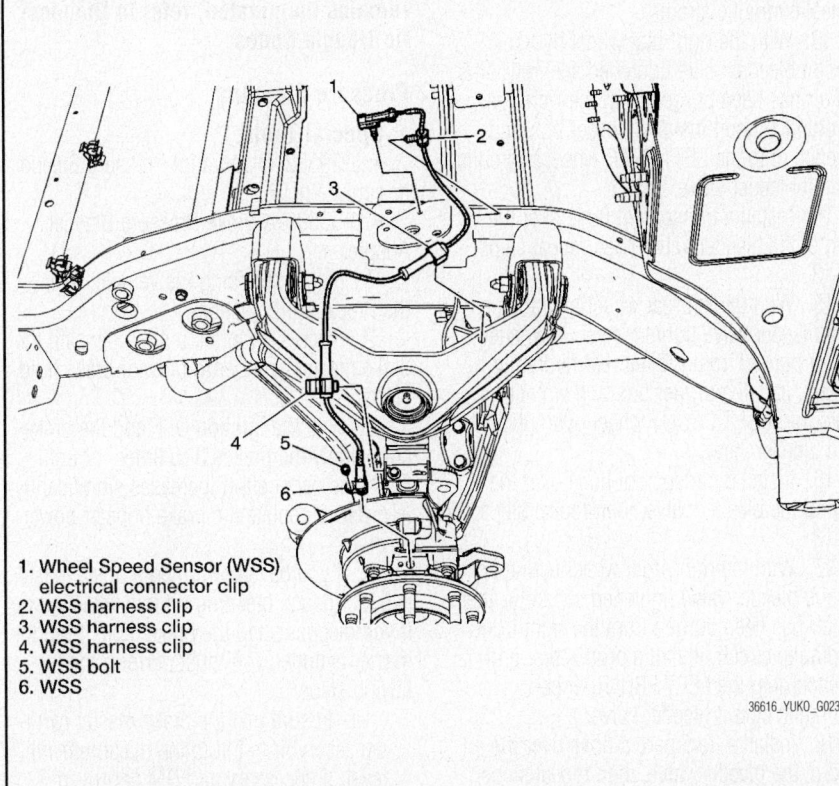

1. Wheel Speed Sensor (WSS) electrical connector clip
2. WSS harness clip
3. WSS harness clip
4. WSS harness clip
5. WSS bolt
6. WSS

36616_YUKO_G0231

Fig. 3 Front wheel speed sensor removal—vehicles equal to, or greater than, 8,600 lbs. GVW

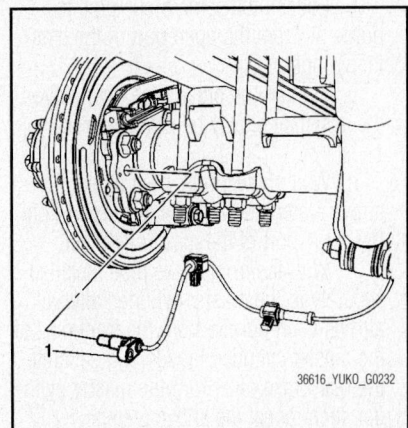

36616_YUKO_G0232

Fig. 4 Rear wheel speed sensor (1) removal

BRAKES   **BLEEDING THE BRAKE SYSTEM**

BLEEDING PROCEDURE

BLEEDING PROCEDURE

Manual Bleeding

1. Before servicing the vehicle, refer to the Precautions Section.

2. Place a clean shop cloth beneath the brake master cylinder to prevent brake fluid spills.

3. With the ignition OFF and the brakes cool, apply the brakes 3–5 times, or until the brake pedal effort increases significantly, in order to deplete the brake booster power reserve.

4. If you have performed a brake master cylinder bench bleeding on this vehicle, or if you disconnected the brake pipes from the master cylinder, you must perform the following steps:

a. Ensure that the brake master cylinder reservoir is full to the maximum-fill level. If necessary, add GM approved brake fluid from a clean, sealed brake fluid container. If removal of the reservoir cap and diaphragm is necessary, clean the outside of the reservoir on and around the cap prior to removal.

b. With the rear brake pipe installed securely to the master cylinder, loosen and separate the front brake pipe from the front port of the brake master cylinder.

c. Allow a small amount of brake fluid to gravity bleed from the open port of the master cylinder.

d. Reconnect the brake pipe to the master cylinder port and tighten securely.

e. Have an assistant slowly depress the brake pedal fully and maintain steady pressure on the pedal.

f. Loosen the same brake pipe to purge air from the open port of the master cylinder.

g. Tighten the brake pipe, then have the assistant slowly release the brake pedal.

h. Wait 15 seconds, then repeat the above 5 steps until all air is purged from the same port of the master cylinder.

i. With the front brake pipe installed securely to the master cylinder, after all air has been purged from the front port of the master cylinder, loosen and separate the rear brake pipe from the master cylinder, then repeat the above 6 steps.

j. After completing the final master cylinder port bleeding procedure, ensure

that both of the brake pipe-to-master cylinder fittings are properly tightened.

5. Fill the brake master cylinder reservoir with GM approved brake fluid from a clean, sealed brake fluid container. Ensure that the brake master cylinder reservoir remains at least half-full during this bleeding procedure. Add fluid as needed to maintain the proper level. Clean the outside of the reservoir on and around the reservoir cap prior to removing the cap and diaphragm.

6. Install a proper box-end wrench onto the RIGHT REAR wheel hydraulic circuit bleeder valve.

7. Install a transparent hose over the end of the bleeder valve.

8. Submerge the open end of the transparent hose into a transparent container partially filled with GM approved brake fluid from a clean, sealed brake fluid container.

9. Have an assistant slowly depress the brake pedal fully and maintain steady pressure on the pedal.

10. Loosen the bleeder valve to purge air from the wheel hydraulic circuit.

11. Tighten the bleeder valve, then have the assistant slowly release the brake pedal.

12. Wait 15 seconds, then repeat steps 9–11 until all air is purged from the same wheel hydraulic circuit.

13. With the right rear wheel hydraulic circuit bleeder valve tightened securely, after all air has been purged from the right rear hydraulic circuit install a proper box-end wrench onto the LEFT REAR wheel hydraulic circuit bleeder valve.

14. Install a transparent hose over the end of the bleeder valve, then repeat steps 9–13.

15. With the left rear wheel hydraulic circuit bleeder valve tightened securely, after all air purged from the left rear hydraulic circuit, install a proper box-end wrench onto the RIGHT FRONT wheel hydraulic circuit bleeder valve.

16. Install a transparent hose over the end of the bleeder valve, then repeat steps 9–13.

17. With the right front wheel hydraulic circuit bleeder valve tightened securely, after all air has been purged from the right front hydraulic circuit, install a proper box-end wrench onto the LEFT FRONT wheel hydraulic circuit bleeder valve.

18. Install a transparent hose over the end of the bleeder valve, then repeat steps 9–13.

19. After completing the final wheel hydraulic circuit bleeding procedure, ensure that each of the 4 wheel hydraulic circuit bleeder valves are properly tightened.

20. Fill the brake master cylinder reservoir to the maximum-fill level with GM approved brake fluid from a clean, sealed brake fluid container.

21. Slowly depress and release the brake pedal. Observe the feel of the brake pedal.

22. If the brake pedal feels spongy, repeat the bleeding procedure again. If the brake pedal still feels spongy after repeating the bleeding procedure, perform the following steps:

a. Inspect the brake system for external leaks.

b. Pressure bleed the hydraulic brake system in order to purge any air that may still be trapped in the system.

23. Turn the ignition key ON, with the engine OFF. Check to see if the brake system warning lamp remains illuminated.

❊❊ CAUTION

If the brake system warning lamp remains illuminated, DO NOT allow the vehicle to be driven until it is diagnosed and repaired.

➡ **If the brake system warning lamp remains illuminated, refer to Diagnostic Trouble Codes.**

Pressure Bleeding

Special Tools:
• J-29532: Diaphragm Pressure Bleeder, or equivalent
• J-35589-A Brake Pressure Bleeder Adapter

1. Before servicing the vehicle, refer to the Precautions Section.

2. Place a clean shop cloth beneath the brake master cylinder to prevent brake fluid spills.

3. With the ignition OFF and the brakes cool, apply the brakes 3–5 times, or until the brake pedal effort increases significantly, in order to deplete the brake booster power reserve.

4. If you have performed a brake master cylinder bench bleeding on this vehicle, or if you disconnected the brake pipes from the master cylinder, you must perform the following steps:

a. Ensure that the brake master cylinder reservoir is full to the maximum-fill level. If necessary add GM approved brake fluid from a clean, sealed brake fluid container. If removal of the reservoir cap and diaphragm is necessary, clean the outside of the reservoir on and around the cap prior to removal.

b. With the rear brake pipe installed securely to the master cylinder, loosen and separate the front brake pipe from the front port of the brake master cylinder.

c. Allow a small amount of brake fluid to gravity bleed from the open port of the master cylinder.

d. Reconnect the brake pipe to the master cylinder port and tighten securely.

e. Have an assistant slowly depress the brake pedal fully and maintain steady pressure on the pedal.

f. Loosen the same brake pipe to purge air from the open port of the master cylinder.

g. Tighten the brake pipe, then have the assistant slowly release the brake pedal.

h. Wait 15 seconds, then repeat the above 5 steps until all air is purged from the same port of the master cylinder.

i. With the front brake pipe installed securely to the master cylinder, after all air has been purged from the front port of the master cylinder, loosen and separate the rear brake pipe from the master cylinder, then repeat the above 6 steps.

j. After completing the final master cylinder port bleeding procedure, ensure that both of the brake pipe-to-master cylinder fittings are properly tightened.

5. Fill the brake master cylinder reservoir to the maximum-fill level with GM approved brake fluid from a clean, sealed brake fluid container. Clean the outside of the reservoir on and around the reservoir cap prior to removing the cap and diaphragm.

6. Install the J-35589-A, Brake Pressure Bleeder Adapter, to the brake master cylinder reservoir.

7. Check the brake fluid level in the J-29532, Diaphragm Pressure Bleeder, or equivalent. Add GM approved brake fluid from a clean, sealed brake fluid container as

necessary to bring the level to approximately the half-full point.

8. Connect the J-29532, Diaphragm Pressure Bleeder, or equivalent, to the J-35589-A Brake Pressure Bleeder Adapter.

9. Charge the J-29532 Diaphragm Pressure Bleeder, or equivalent, air tank to 25–30 psi (175–205 kPa).

10. Open the J-29532, Diaphragm Pressure Bleeder, or equivalent, fluid tank valve to allow pressurized brake fluid to enter the brake system.

11. Wait approximately 30 seconds, then inspect the entire hydraulic brake system in order to ensure that there are no existing external brake fluid leaks. Any brake fluid leaks identified require repair prior to completing this procedure.

12. Install a proper box-end wrench onto the RIGHT REAR wheel hydraulic circuit bleeder valve.

13. Install a transparent hose over the end of the bleeder valve.

14. Submerge the open end of the transparent hose into a transparent container partially filled with GM approved brake fluid from a clean, sealed brake fluid container.

15. Loosen the bleeder valve to purge air from the wheel hydraulic circuit. Allow fluid to flow until air bubbles stop flowing from the bleeder, then tighten the bleeder valve.

16. With the right rear wheel hydraulic circuit bleeder valve tightened securely, after all air has been purged from the right rear hydraulic circuit, install a proper box-end wrench onto the LEFT REAR wheel hydraulic circuit bleeder valve.

17. Install a transparent hose over the end of the bleeder valve, then repeat steps 15–16.

18. With the left rear wheel hydraulic circuit bleeder valve tightened securely, after all air has been purged from the left rear hydraulic circuit, install a proper box-end wrench onto the RIGHT FRONT wheel hydraulic circuit bleeder valve.

19. Install a transparent hose over the end of the bleeder valve, then repeat steps 15–16.

20. With the right front wheel hydraulic circuit bleeder valve tightened securely, after all air has been purged from the right front hydraulic circuit, install a proper box-end wrench onto the LEFT FRONT wheel hydraulic circuit bleeder valve.

21. Install a transparent hose over the end of the bleeder valve, then repeat steps 15–16.

22. After completing the final wheel hydraulic circuit bleeding procedure, ensure that each of the 4 wheel hydraulic circuit bleeder valves are properly tightened.

23. Close the J-29532, Diaphragm Pressure Bleeder, or equivalent, fluid tank valve, then disconnect the J-29532, Diaphragm Pressure Bleeder, or equivalent, from the J-35589-A, Brake Pressure Bleeder Adapter.

24. Remove the J-35589-A, Brake Pressure Bleeder Adapter, from the brake master cylinder reservoir.

25. Fill the brake master cylinder reservoir to the maximum-fill level with GM approved brake fluid from a clean, sealed brake fluid container.

26. Slowly depress and release the brake pedal. Observe the feel of the brake pedal.

27. If the brake pedal feels spongy perform the following steps:

a. Inspect the brake system for external leaks.

b. Using a scan tool, perform the antilock brake system automated bleeding procedure to remove any air that may have been trapped in the Brake Pressure Modulator Valve (BPMV). Refer to Bleeding the ABS System.

28. Turn the ignition key ON, with the engine OFF. Check to see if the brake system warning lamp remains illuminated.

✳✳ CAUTION

If the brake system warning lamp remains illuminated, DO NOT allow the vehicle to be driven until it is diagnosed and repaired.

➡ If the brake system warning lamp remains illuminated, refer to Diagnostic Trouble Codes.

BRAKES   **FRONT DISC BRAKES**

✳✳ CAUTION

Dust and dirt accumulating on brake parts during normal use may contain asbestos fibers from production or aftermarket brake linings. Breathing excessive concentrations of asbestos fibers can cause serious bodily harm. Exercise care when servicing brake parts. Do not sand or grind brake lining unless equipment used is designed to contain the dust residue. Do not clean brake parts with compressed air or by dry brushing. Cleaning should be done by dampening the brake components with a fine mist of water, then wiping the brake components clean with a dampened cloth. Dispose of cloth and all residue containing asbestos fibers in an impermeable container with the appropriate label. Follow practices prescribed by the Occupational Safety and Health Administration (OSHA) and the Environmental Protection Agency (EPA) for the handling, processing, and disposing of dust or debris that may contain asbestos fibers.

BRAKE CALIPER

REMOVAL & INSTALLATION

See Figures 5 through 8.

1. Before servicing the vehicle, refer to the Precautions Section.
2. Inspect the fluid level in the brake master cylinder reservoir.
   a. If the brake fluid level is midway between the maximum-full point and the minimum allowable level, no brake fluid needs to be removed from the reservoir before proceeding.
   b. If the brake fluid level is higher than midway between the maximum-full point and the minimum allowable level, remove brake fluid to the midway point before proceeding.
3. Raise and safely support the vehicle.
4. Remove the tire and wheel assembly.
5. Compress the brake caliper pistons.
   a. Install 2 large C-clamps over the top of the caliper housing and against the back of the outboard brake pad.
   b. Slowly tighten the C-clamps until the caliper pistons are pushed completely into the caliper bores.
   c. Remove the C-clamps from the caliper.

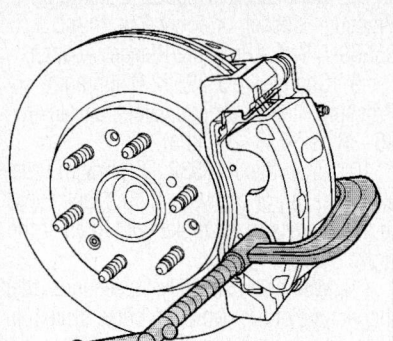

Fig. 5 Using a C-clamp to compress the brake caliper pistons

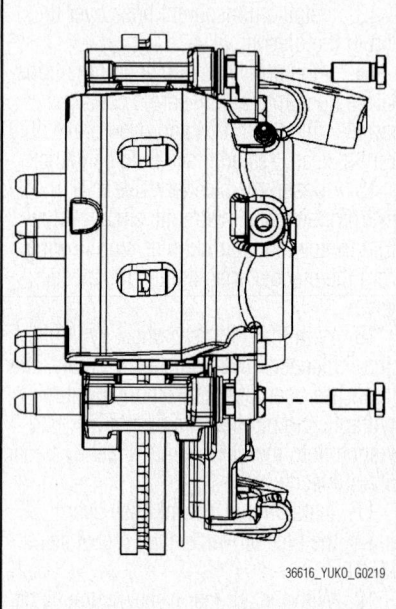

Fig. 6 Remove the brake caliper guide pin bolts from the brake caliper—1500 series

6. Clean all dirt and debris from the brake caliper and fittings.
7. Remove the brake hose to caliper bolt.
8. Remove the brake hose from the brake caliper.
9. Remove and discard the 2 copper brake hose gaskets.

➡Cap or plug the brake hose to prevent brake fluid leakage and contamination of the brake system.

➡Ensure that the washers are not still attached to the brake hose or the brake caliper. DO NOT re-use the washers, discard and replace with new.

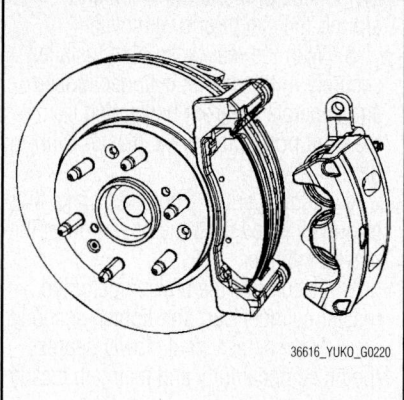

Fig. 7 Remove the brake caliper from the caliper mounting bracket—1500 series

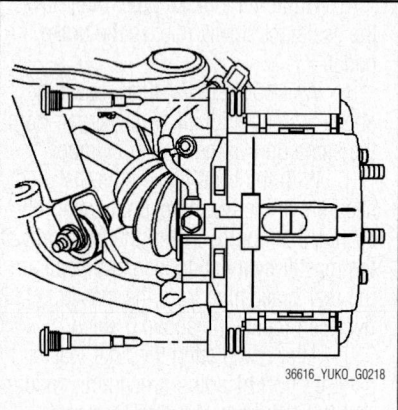

Fig. 8 Remove the brake caliper from the caliper mounting bracket—2500 series

✳✳ WARNING

Do not depress the brake pedal with the brake rotors/calipers and/or the brake drums removed. Damage to the brake system may result. If brake system damage occurs and is not repaired, vehicle damage and/or personal injury or death may result.

10. On the 1500 series: Use an open end wrench to hold the guide pin while loosening the caliper bolts.
11. Remove the brake caliper guide pin bolts from the brake caliper.
12. Remove the brake caliper from the caliper mounting bracket.

To install:

✳✳ WARNING

DO NOT use any air tools to remove or install the brake caliper bolts. Use hand tools ONLY.

13. Install the brake caliper to the caliper mounting bracket.

14. Install the brake caliper guide pin bolts and tighten to:

    a. 1500 series: 74 ft. lbs. (100 Nm).

    b. 2500 series: 80 ft. lbs. (108 Nm).

15. Remove the cap or plug from the brake hose-to-caliper fitting.

16. Assemble the 2 NEW copper brake hose gaskets to the brake-to-caliper bolt and the brake hose.

17. Install the brake hose-to-caliper bolt and tighten to:

    a. 1500 series: 30 ft. lbs. (40 Nm).

    b. 2500 series: 33 ft. lbs. (45 Nm).

18. Bleed the brake system. Refer to Bleeding The Brake System.

19. Install the tire and wheel assembly.

20. Fill the master cylinder reservoir to the proper level with clean brake fluid, if necessary.

DISC BRAKE PADS

REMOVAL & INSTALLATION

See Figures 5, 9, 8.

1. Before servicing the vehicle, refer to the Precautions Section.

2. Inspect the fluid level in the brake master cylinder reservoir.

    a. If the brake fluid level is midway between the maximum-full point and the minimum allowable level, no brake fluid needs to be removed from the reservoir before proceeding.

    b. If the brake fluid level is higher than midway between the maximum-full point and the minimum allowable level, remove brake fluid to the midway point before proceeding.

3. Raise and safely support the vehicle.

4. Remove the tire and wheel assembly.

5. Compress the brake caliper pistons.

    a. Install 2 large C-clamps over the top of the caliper housing and against the back of the outboard brake pad.

    b. Slowly tighten the C-clamps until the caliper pistons are pushed completely into the caliper bores.

    c. Remove the C-clamps from the caliper.

➡**DO NOT use any air tools to remove the guide pin bolts. Use hand tools ONLY.**

6. On 1500 series vehicles, use an open end wrench to hold the guide pin while loosening the brake caliper guide pin bolt.

7. Remove the lower brake caliper guide pin bolt.

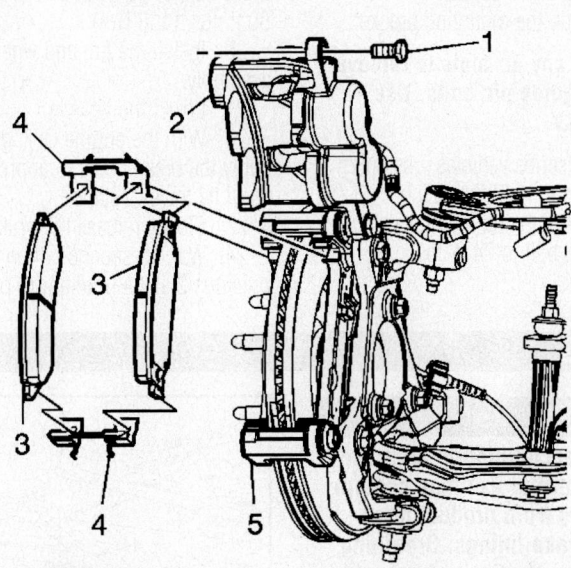

1. Guide pin bolt
2. Brake caliper
3. Brake pads
4. Spring clips
5. Mounting bracket

36616_YUKO_G0222

Fig. 9 Expanded view of disc brake pad components—1500 series

✳✳ WARNING

Support the brake caliper with heavy mechanic wire, or equivalent, whenever it is separated from its mount and the hydraulic flexible brake hose is still connected. Failure to support the caliper in this manner will cause the flexible brake hose to bear the weight of the caliper, which may cause damage to the brake hose and in turn may cause a brake fluid leak.

➡**DO NOT disconnect the flexible brake hose from the brake caliper.**

8. Rotate the brake caliper upward until it rests on the brake caliper mounting bracket and support it with heavy mechanics wire, or equivalent.

9. Remove the brake pads.

➡**If installing the original brake pads and spring clips, mark the position of the pads and spring clips for proper installation.**

➡**If installing new brake pads, install new pad spring clips. Do not reuse the old brake pad spring clips with new brake pads.**

10. Remove the brake pad spring clips from the mounting bracket.

To install:

➡**Use care when cleaning the brake caliper pistons to avoid damaging the piston dust seals.**

11. If installing new brake pads, thoroughly clean the brake caliper piston faces and caliper housing-to-brake pad contact surfaces of all disc brake pad insulator adhesive residue using denatured alcohol. Allow to dry.

12. Thoroughly clean the pad hardware mating surfaces of the caliper bracket of any corrosion or debris with denatured alcohol and allow to dry.

13. Apply a very thin coating of high temperature silicone brake lubricant to the pad mating surfaces of the caliper bracket.

14. Install the spring clips to the mounting bracket.

    a. Install the NEW spring clips if replacing the brake pads.

    b. Install the original spring clips in their original position if installing the original brake pads.

15. If installing new brake pads, remove the adhesive backing paper from the brake pad insulators.

➡**If installing the original brake pads, position the brake pads as marked during the removal procedure.**

16. Install the brake pads.

17. Rotate the brake caliper into the proper position on the mounting bracket.

➡ **DO NOT use any air tools to remove or tighten the guide pin bolts. Use hand tools ONLY.**

18. On 1500 series vehicles, use an open end wrench to hold the caliper guide pin while tightening the brake caliper guide pin bolt to 74 ft. lbs. (100 Nm).

19. On 2500 series vehicles, install the brake caliper guide pin bolts and tighten to 80 ft. lbs. (108 Nm).

20. Install the tire and wheel assembly.

21. Lower the vehicle.

22. With the engine OFF, gradually apply the brake pedal to approximately ⅔ of its travel distance.

23. Slowly release the brake pedal.

24. Wait 15 seconds, then repeat the previous 2 steps until a firm pedal is

obtained to properly seat the brake caliper pistons and pads.

25. Fill the brake master cylinder reservoir to the proper level with clean brake fluid, if necessary.

26. Firmly apply and maintain pressure on the brake pedal for 30 seconds to seat the brake pad insulators to the brake caliper pistons and caliper housing. Repeat this step 1 additional time.

27. Burnish the brake pads and rotors, as needed.

BRAKES   REAR DISC BRAKES

❋❋ CAUTION

Dust and dirt accumulating on brake parts during normal use may contain asbestos fibers from production or aftermarket brake linings. Breathing excessive concentrations of asbestos fibers can cause serious bodily harm. Exercise care when servicing brake parts. Do not sand or grind brake lining unless equipment used is designed to contain the dust residue. Do not clean brake parts with compressed air or by dry brushing. Cleaning should be done by dampening the brake components with a fine mist of water, then wiping the brake components clean with a dampened cloth. Dispose of cloth and all residue containing asbestos fibers in an impermeable container with the appropriate label. Follow practices prescribed by the Occupational Safety and Health Administration (OSHA) and the Environmental Protection Agency (EPA) for the handling, processing, and disposing of dust or debris that may contain asbestos fibers.

BRAKE CALIPER

REMOVAL & INSTALLATION

See Figures 10 through 12.

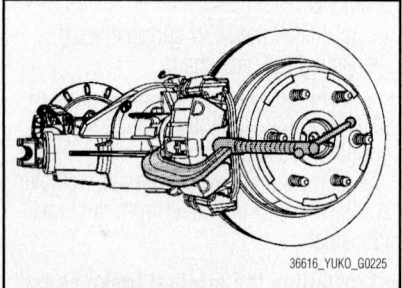

Fig. 10 Compress the caliper piston using a large C-clamp—1500 series shown

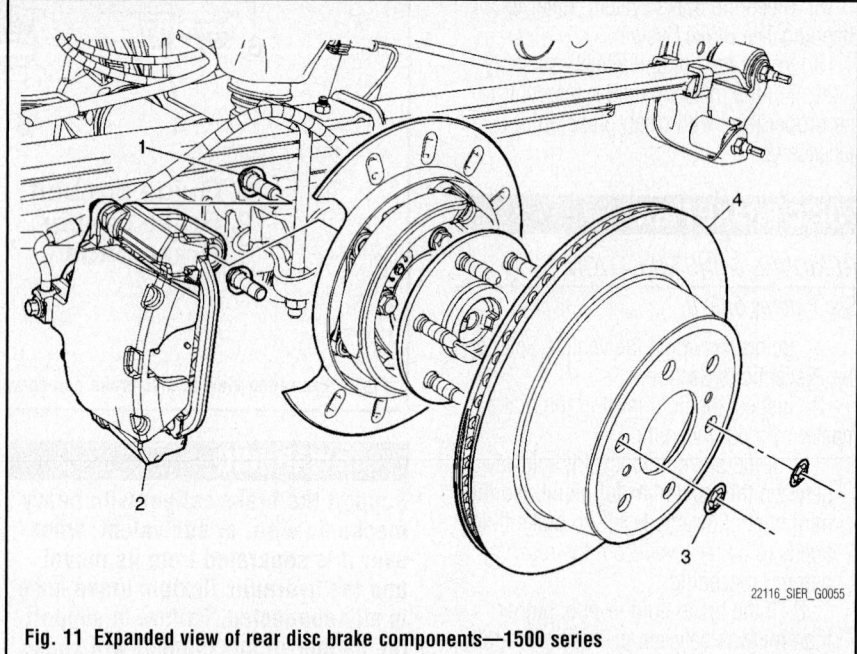

Fig. 11 Expanded view of rear disc brake components—1500 series

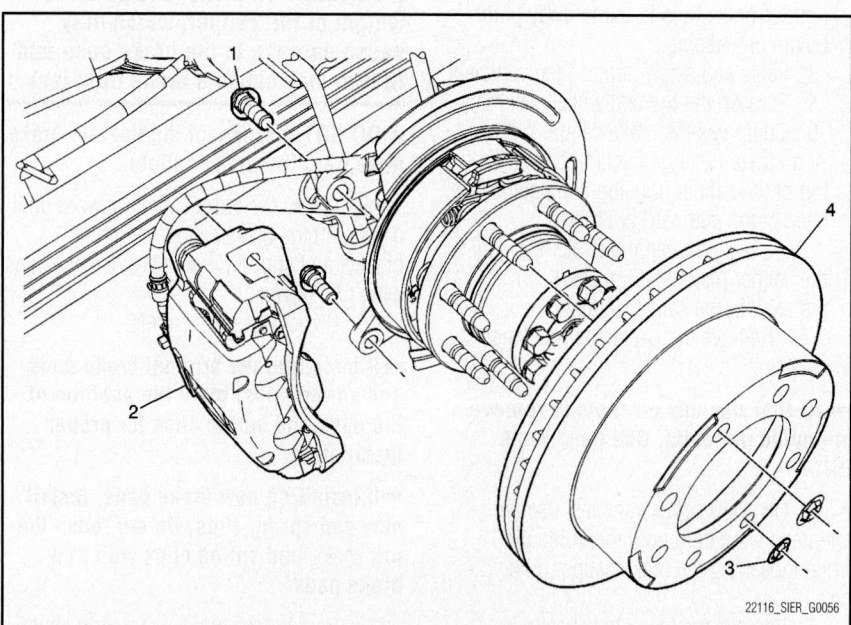

Fig. 12 Expanded view of rear disc brake components—2500 series

1. Before servicing the vehicle, refer to the Precautions Section.

2. Inspect the fluid level in the brake master cylinder reservoir.

   a. If the fluid level is midway between the maximum-full point and the minimum allowable level, no fluid needs to be removed from the reservoir before proceeding.

   b. If the fluid level is higher than midway between the maximum-full point and the minimum allowable level, remove fluid to the midway point before proceeding.

3. Release the park brake, if necessary.

4. Raise and safely support the vehicle.

5. Remove the tire and wheel assembly.

6. Clean all dirt and foreign material from the brake hose fitting.

7. Compress the caliper piston.

   a. Install a large C-clamp over the top of the caliper housing and against the back of the outboard pad.

   b. Slowly tighten the C-clamp until the piston is pushed completely into the caliper bore.

   c. Remove the C-clamp from the caliper.

➡**Cap or plug the brake pipe to prevent brake fluid leakage and contamination of the brake system.**

8. Remove the brake hose-to-caliper bolt. Position the brake hose to the side.

➡**Ensure that the copper gaskets are not attached to the brake caliper or the brake hose. DO NOT re-use the copper gaskets, replace with NEW.**

9. Remove and discard the 2 copper brake hose gaskets.

➡**DO NOT use any air tools to remove or tighten the guide pin bolts. Use hand tools only.**

10. On 1500 series vehicles, use an open end wrench to back up the caliper guide pin while removing the guide pin bolt.

11. On 2500 series vehicles, remove the brake caliper guide pin bolts from the brake caliper.

12. Remove the brake caliper from the mounting bracket.

   To install:

13. Install the brake caliper on to the mounting bracket.

14. Perform the following procedure before installing the brake caliper guide pin bolts:

   a. Remove all traces of the original adhesive patch.

   b. Clean the threads of the bolt with brake parts cleaner, or the equivalent, and allow to dry.

   c. Apply Threadlocker GM P/N 36616493 to the threads of the bolt.

15. On 1500 series vehicles, use an open end wrench to hold the guide pins while tightening the guide pin bolts. Tighten the bolts to 28 ft. lbs. (38 Nm).

16. On 2500 series vehicles, install the brake caliper guide pin bolts and tighten to 80 ft. lbs. (108 Nm).

17. Remove the rubber cap or plug from the exposed brake hose fitting end.

18. Install the 2 NEW copper gaskets to the brake hose bolt and the brake hose fitting.

19. Install the brake hose to caliper bolt and tighten to:

   a. On 1500 series vehicles, 30 ft. lbs. (40 Nm).

   b. On 2500 series vehicles, 33 ft. lbs. (45 Nm).

20. Bleed the hydraulic brake system. Refer to Bleeding The Brake System.

21. Install the tire and wheel assembly.

22. Fill the master cylinder reservoir to the proper level with clean brake fluid, if necessary.

DISC BRAKE PADS

REMOVAL & INSTALLATION

See Figures 10, 13 and 14.

1. Before servicing the vehicle, refer to the Precautions Section.

2. Inspect the fluid level in the brake master cylinder reservoir.

   a. If the fluid level is midway between the maximum-full point and the minimum allowable level, no fluid needs to be removed from the reservoir before proceeding.

   b. If the fluid level is higher than midway between the maximum-full point and the minimum allowable level, remove fluid to the midway point before proceeding.

3. Release the park brake, if necessary.

4. Raise and safely support the vehicle.

5. Remove the tire and wheel assembly.

6. Clean all dirt and foreign material from the brake hose fitting.

7. Compress the caliper piston.

   a. Install a large C-clamp over the top of the caliper housing and against the back of the outboard pad.

   b. Slowly tighten the C-clamp until the piston is pushed completely into the caliper bore.

   c. Remove the C-clamp from the caliper.

➡**DO NOT use any air tools to remove the guide pin bolts. Use hand tools only.**

8. On 1500 series vehicles, use an open end wrench to hold the guide pin while loosening the guide pin bolt.

9. Remove the lower guide pin bolt from the brake caliper.

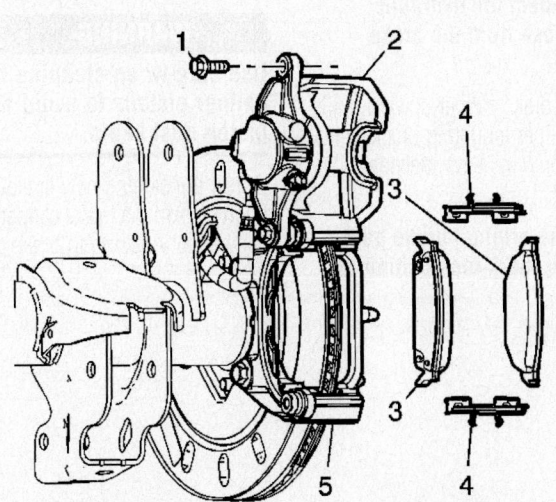

1. Lower guide pin bolt
2. Brake caliper
3. Brake pads
4. Spring clips
5. Mounting bracket

36616_YUKO_G0226

Fig. 13 Rear disc brake pad removal—1500 series

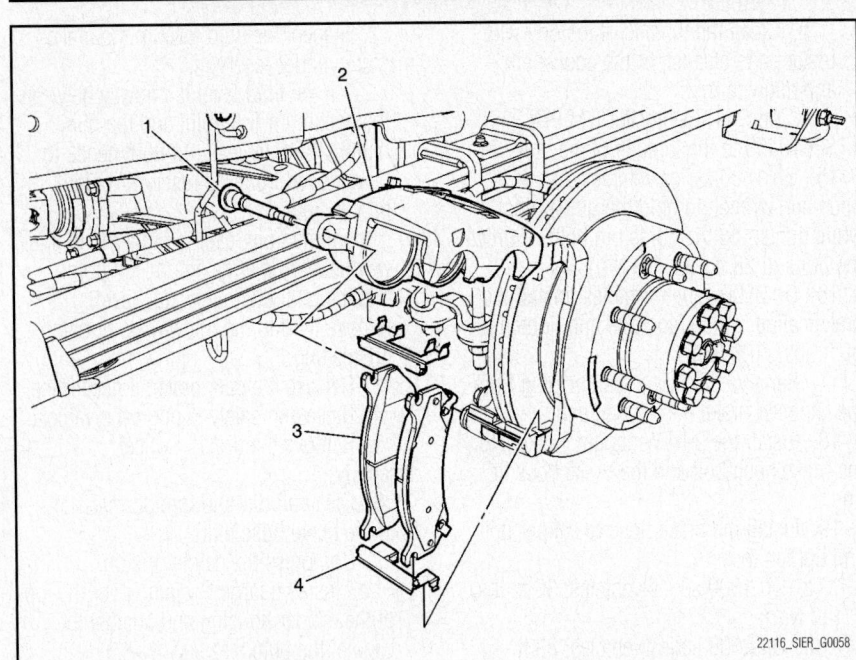

Fig. 14 Rear disc brake pad removal—2500 series

22116_SIER_G0058

✳✳ WARNING

Support the brake caliper with heavy mechanic wire, or equivalent, whenever it is separated from its mount and the hydraulic flexible brake hose is still connected. Failure to support the caliper in this manner will cause the flexible brake hose to bear the weight of the caliper, which may cause damage to the brake hose and in turn may cause a brake fluid leak.

➡ **Do not disconnect the hydraulic brake flexible hose from the brake caliper.**

10. Rotate the brake caliper upward until it stops on the caliper mounting bracket and support the caliper with heavy mechanics wire or equivalent.

➡ **If installing the original brake pads and spring clips, mark the position of** the brake pads and spring clips for proper installation. If installing new brake pads, install new pad spring clips. Do not reuse the old pad spring clips with new brake pads.

11. Remove the brake pads and spring clips from the mounting bracket.

To install:

12. Thoroughly clean the pad hardware mating surfaces of the caliper bracket of any corrosion or debris with denatured alcohol and allow to dry.

✳✳ WARNING

Use care when cleaning the brake caliper pistons to avoid damaging the piston dust seals.

13. If installing new brake pads, thoroughly clean the brake caliper piston faces and caliper housing to brake pad contact surfaces of all disc brake pad insulator adhesive residue with denatured alcohol and allow to dry.

14. Apply a very thin coating of high temperature silicone brake lubricant to the pad hardware mating surfaces of the caliper bracket only.

15. Install the spring clips on the caliper mounting bracket.

16. If installing new brake pads, remove the adhesive backing paper from the disc brake pad insulators.

➡ **If installing the original brake pads, note the locations marked prior to removal.**

17. Install the brake pads.

18. Remove the mechanics wire and rotate the brake caliper into position on the mounting bracket.

19. Install NEW caliper guide pin bolts.

20. On 1500 series vehicles, use an open end wrench to hold the caliper guide pin while tightening the guide pin bolt to 28 ft. lbs. (38 Nm).

21. On 2500 series vehicles, tighten the brake caliper bolts to 80 ft. lbs. (108 Nm).

22. Install the tire and wheel assembly.

23. Lower the vehicle.

24. With the engine OFF, gradually apply the brake pedal to approximately ⅔ of its travel distance.

25. Slowly release the brake pedal.

26. Wait 15 seconds, then repeat previous 2 steps until a firm pedal is obtained, to properly seat the brake caliper pistons and brake pads.

27. Fill the brake master cylinder reservoir to the proper level with clean brake fluid.

28. Firmly apply and maintain pressure on the brake pedal for 30 seconds to seat the brake pad insulators to the brake caliper pistons and caliper housing. Repeat this step 1 additional time.

29. Burnish the brake pads and rotors.

BRAKES

PARKING BRAKE

PARKING BRAKE CABLES

ADJUSTMENT

The parking brake pedals are equipped with automatic adjusters. The Park Brake Cable Equalizer evenly distributes input force to both the left and right park brake units and the threaded park brake cable equalizers are also used to remove slack in park brake cables.

PARKING BRAKE SHOES

REMOVAL & INSTALLATION

1500 Series

See Figure 15.

1. Before servicing the vehicle, refer to the Precautions Section.
2. Raise and safely support the vehicle.
3. Remove the tire and the wheel assembly.
4. Remove the caliper and mounting bracket as an assembly.
5. Relieve the tension on the park brake cables by loosening the nut at the equalizer.
6. Remove the parking brake cable from the lever.
7. Remove the rotor.
8. Turn the adjustment screw to the fully home position in the notched adjustment nut.
9. Remove the park brake shoe retaining bolts.
10. Remove the park brake shoe assembly from the backing plate by removing the tips from the slots and sliding the shoe towards the retaining spring until the shoe is disengaged from the spring.
11. Remove the park brake shoe assembly from the vehicle by placing one of the open ends of the shoe over the axle flange and rotating the shoe until it has cleared the flange.

To install:

12. Clean the debris and the dust from the park brake components using a clean towel.
13. Align the slots in both the adjusting screw and tappet to be parallel with the backing plate face.
14. Install the park brake shoe assembly to the vehicle by placing one of the open ends of the shoe over the axle flange and rotating the shoe until it is behind the flange.
15. Position the park brake shoe on the inboard side of the actuation.

16. Slide the parking brake shoe into position and seat into the retaining spring.
17. Install the brake shoe retaining bolts and tighten to 11 ft. lbs. (15 Nm).
18. Inspect the shoe assembly position. The shoe must be central on the backing plate with both tips located in the slots.
19. Adjust the park brake shoe.
20. Install the rotor.
21. Install the park brake cable to the park brake lever.
22. Tighten the nut to the intermediate cable at the equalizer.

23. Install the caliper and mounting bracket as an assembly.
24. Install the tire and wheel assembly.
25. Remove the safety stands.
26. Lower the vehicle.

2500 Series

See Figure 16.

1. Before servicing the vehicle, refer to the Precautions Section.
2. Disable the park brake cable automatic adjuster.
3. Raise and safely support the vehicle.

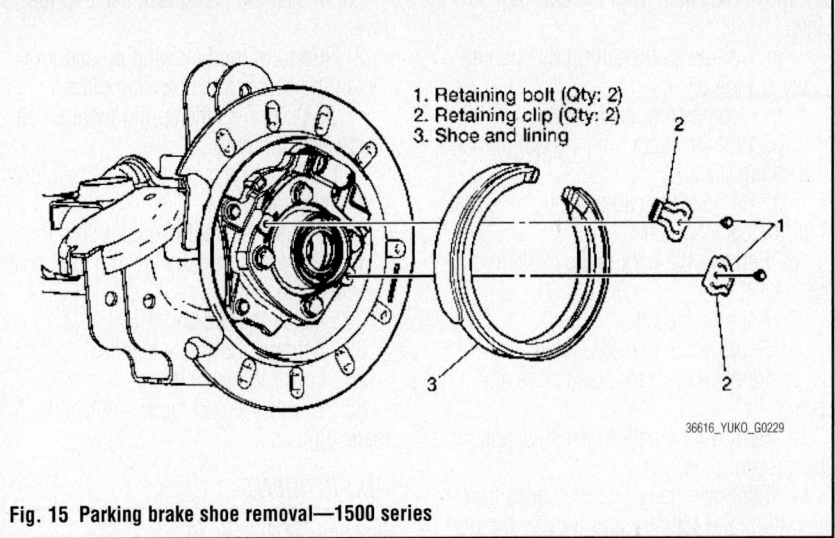

1. Retaining bolt (Qty: 2)
2. Retaining clip (Qty: 2)
3. Shoe and lining

36616_YUKO_G0229

Fig. 15 Parking brake shoe removal—1500 series

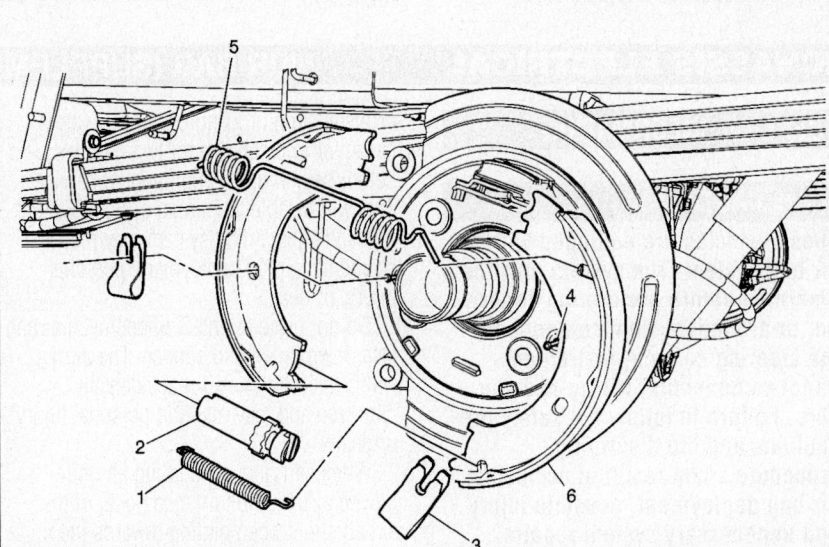

1. Parking brake shoe adjuster spring
2. Parking brake shoe adjuster
3. Parking brake shoe hold-down spring (qty. 2)
4. Parking brake shoe hold-down spring pin (qty. 2)
5. Parking brake shoe return spring
6. Parking brake shoe (qty. 2)

22116_SIER_G0062

Fig. 16 Parking brake shoe removal—2500 series

4. Remove the tire and the wheel.

5. Perform the following procedure to remove the cable from the backing plate:

    a. Compress the spring by pushing toward the lever.

    b. Depress the locking tabs.

    c. Pull the cable housing out of the backing plate.

    d. Remove the cable through the slot in the backing plate.

6. Remove the park brake cable from the lever.

7. Remove the rotor.

8. Remove the rear axle shaft.

9. Remove the park brake shoe return spring.

10. Remove the park brake shoe anchor springs and pins.

11. Separate the tips of the shoes from the park brake actuator and remove the park brake shoes and adjuster assembly from the vehicle.

To install:

12. Clean the debris and the dust from the park brake components using a clean shop cloth.

13. Install the adjuster assembly to the park brake shoes.

14. Separate the tips of the shoes and install the park brake shoes to the park brake actuator.

15. Install the park brake shoe anchor springs and pins.

16. Install the park brake shoe return spring.

17. Adjust the park brake shoe.

18. Install the rear axle shaft.

19. Install the rotor.

20. Install the park brake cable to the lever.

21. Perform the following procedure to install the cable to the backing plate:

    a. Compress the spring by pushing towards the lever.

    b. Route the cable through the slot in the backing plate.

    c. Push the cable housing into the backing plate until the locking tabs snap into place.

22. Install the tire and wheel.

23. Remove the safety stands.

24. Lower the vehicle.

25. Enable the park brake cable automatic adjuster.

ADJUSTMENT

See Figures 17 and 18.

Special Tool:

• J-21177-A: Drum-to-Brake Shoe Clearance Gage

1. Before servicing the vehicle, refer to the Precautions Section.

2. Set the J 21177-A so that it contacts the inside diameter of the rotor.

3. Position the J 21177-A over the shoe and the lining at the widest point.

4. Turn the adjuster nut until the lining just contacts the J 21177-A.

5. Repeat steps 2 through 4 for the opposite side.

6. The clearance between the park brake shoe and the rotor should be 0.026 inch (0.66 mm).

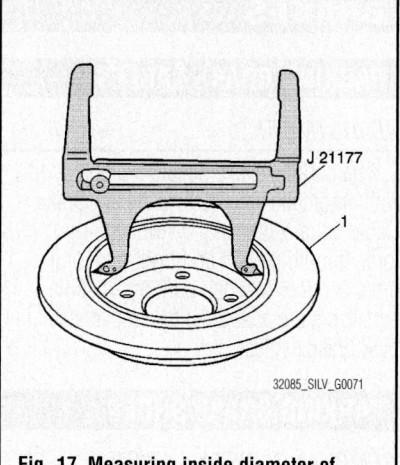

Fig. 17 Measuring inside diameter of brake rotor

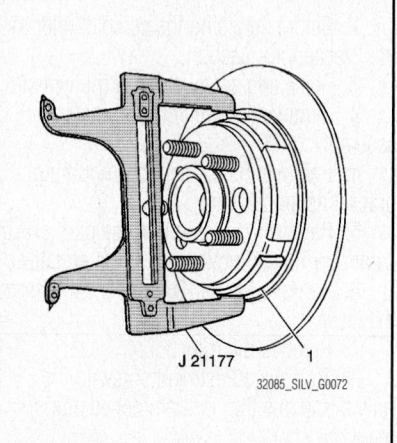

Fig. 18 Measuring outside diameter of brake rotor

CHASSIS ELECTRICAL   AIR BAG (SUPPLEMENTAL RESTRAINT SYSTEM)

GENERAL INFORMATION

✳✳ CAUTION

These vehicles are equipped with an air bag system. The system must be disarmed before performing service on, or around, system components, the steering column, instrument panel components, wiring and sensors. Failure to follow the safety precautions and the disarming procedure could result in accidental air bag deployment, possible injury and unnecessary system repairs.

SERVICE PRECAUTIONS

Disconnect and isolate the battery negative cable before beginning any airbag system component diagnosis, testing, removal, or installation procedures. Allow system capacitor to discharge for two minutes before beginning any component service. This will disable the airbag system. Failure to disable the airbag system may result in accidental airbag deployment, personal injury, or death.

Do not place an intact undeployed airbag face down on a solid surface. The airbag will propel into the air if accidentally deployed and may result in personal injury or death.

When carrying or handling an undeployed airbag, the trim side (face) of the airbag should be pointing towards the body to minimize possibility of injury if accidental deployment occurs. Failure to do this may result in personal injury or death.

Replace airbag system components with OEM replacement parts. Substitute parts may appear interchangeable, but internal differences may result in inferior occupant protection. Failure to do so may result in occupant personal injury or death.

Wear safety glasses, rubber gloves, and long sleeved clothing when cleaning powder residue from vehicle after an airbag deployment. Powder residue emitted from a deployed airbag can cause skin irritation. Flush affected area with cool water if irritation is experienced. If nasal or throat irritation is experienced, exit the vehicle for fresh air until the irritation ceases. If irritation continues, see a physician.

Do not use a replacement airbag that is not in the original packaging. This may result in improper deployment, personal injury, or death.

The factory installed fasteners, screws and bolts used to fasten airbag components have a special coating and are specifically designed for the airbag system. Do not use substitute fasteners. Use only original equipment fasteners listed in the parts catalog when fastener replacement is required.

During, and following, any child restraint anchor service, due to impact event or vehicle repair, carefully inspect all mounting hardware, tether straps, and anchors for proper installation, operation, or damage. If a child restraint anchor is found damaged in any way, the anchor must be replaced. Failure to do this may result in personal injury or death.

Deployed and non-deployed airbags may or may not have live pyrotechnic material within the airbag inflator.

Do not dispose of driver/passenger/curtain airbags or seat belt tensioners unless you are sure of complete deployment. Refer to the Hazardous Substance Control System for proper disposal.

Dispose of deployed airbags and tensioners consistent with state, provincial, local, and federal regulations.

After any airbag component testing or service, do not connect the battery negative cable. Personal injury or death may result if the system test is not performed first.

If the vehicle is equipped with the Occupant Classification System (OCS), do not connect the battery negative cable before performing the OCS Verification Test using the scan tool and the appropriate diagnostic information. Personal injury or death may result if the system test is not performed properly.

Never replace both the Occupant Restraint Controller (ORC) and the Occupant Classification Module (OCM) at the same time. If both require replacement, replace one, then perform the Airbag System test before replacing the other.

Both the ORC and the OCM store Occupant Classification System (OCS) calibration data, which they transfer to one another when one of them is replaced. If both are replaced at the same time, an irreversible fault will be set in both modules and the OCS may malfunction and cause personal injury or death.

If equipped with OCS, the Seat Weight Sensor is a sensitive, calibrated unit and must be handled carefully. Do not drop or handle roughly. If dropped or damaged, replace with another sensor. Failure to do so may result in occupant injury or death.

If equipped with OCS, the front passenger seat must be handled carefully as well. When removing the seat, be careful when setting on floor not to drop. If dropped, the sensor may be inoperative, could result in occupant injury, or possibly death.

If equipped with OCS, when the passenger front seat is on the floor, no one should sit in the front passenger seat. This uneven force may damage the sensing ability of the seat weight sensors. If sat on and damaged, the sensor may be inoperative, could result in occupant injury, or possibly death.

DISARMING THE SYSTEM

1. Before servicing the vehicle, refer to the Precautions Section.
2. Turn the ignition switch to **OFF**.
3. Disconnect the negative battery cable and isolate it from accidental reconnection. Insulate the cable end with high-quality electrical tape or a similar non-conductive wrapping.
4. Wait at least 1 minute for the system capacitor to discharge before performing any service. The airbag system is designed to retain enough voltage to deploy the airbag for a short period of time after the battery has been disconnected.

➡**DTC's will be lost when the negative battery cable is disconnected.**

There are several reasons for disabling the SIR system, such as repairs to the SIR system or servicing a component near or attached to an SIR component. There are several ways to disable the SIR system depending on what type of service is being performed.

• If the vehicle was involved in an accident with an air bag deployment: Disconnect the negative battery cable
• When performing SIR diagnostics: Follow the appropriate SIR service manual diagnostic procedure(s)
• When removing or replacing an SIR component or a component attached to an SIR component: Disconnect the negative battery cable
• If the vehicle is suspected of having shorted electrical wires: Disconnect the negative battery cable
• When performing electrical diagnosis on components other than the SIR system: Remove the SIR/Airbag fuse(s) when indicated by the diagnostic procedure to disable the SIR system

ARMING THE SYSTEM

1. Before servicing the vehicle, refer to the Precautions Section.
2. Be sure the ignition switch is in the **OFF** position.
3. Install the fuses, if removed.
4. Connect the negative battery cable.

✳✳ CAUTION

As an added precaution, make sure no one is in the vehicle when reconnecting the negative battery cable.

5. To confirm proper system operation, turn the ignition switch to the **ON** position. The SRS indicator light should light for at least 7 seconds and then go off.
6. If the AIR BAG warning indicator does not operate as described, perform a Diagnostic System Check.

CLOCKSPRING CENTERING

Centering Coil

See Figures 19 and 20.

✳✳ WARNING

The new SIR coil assembly will be centered. Improper alignment of the SIR coil assembly may damage the unit, causing an inflatable restraint malfunction.

➡**If a double wire harness strap is installed onto the wire harness assembly and column, you must reuse the holder for the wire straps during installation. Remove the wire harness strap(s) where necessary.**

1. Before servicing the vehicle, refer to the Precautions Section.
2. Verify that the following conditions are met before centering the SIR coil:
  a. The wheels on the vehicle are straight ahead.
  b. The block tooth of the steering shaft assembly is in the 12 o'clock position.
  c. The ignition switch is in the LOCK position.

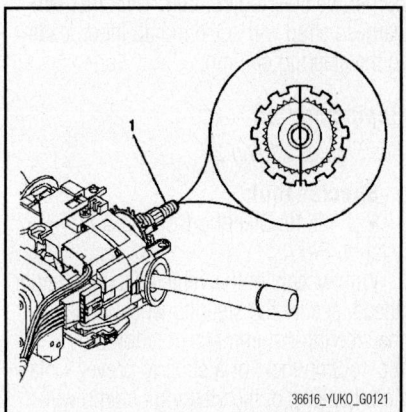

36616_YUKO_G0121

Fig. 19 The block tooth (1) of the steering shaft assembly should be in the 12 o'clock position—SIR coil alignment

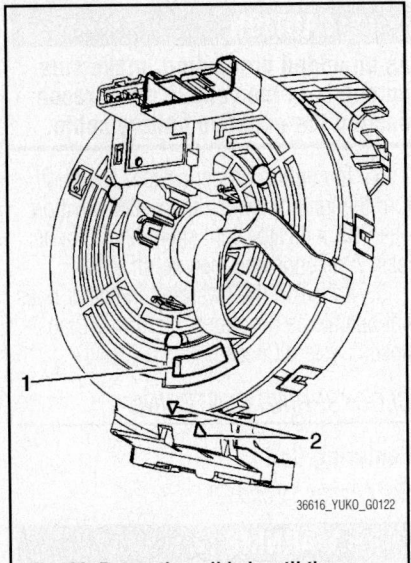

Fig. 20 Rotate the coil hub until the centering window appears yellow (1) and both arrows (2) line up

3. The front of the SIR coil has a centering window. To center the SIR coil, perform the following steps:

   a. Hold the SIR coil with the face up.

   b. Rotate the coil hub clockwise until the coil ribbon stops.

   c. Rotate the coil hub slowly, counterclockwise until the centering window appears yellow and both arrows line up. This is the CENTER position.

   d. While holding the coil hub in the CENTER position, align the SIR coil with the horn tower and slide onto the steering shaft assembly.

4. If a double wire harness strap is installed onto the wire harness assembly and column, you must route the wires up against the steering column. One wire harness strap will surround one lead from the coil to the steering column. The other wire harness strap will surround all other leads to the steering column.

Replacing Coil

See Figures 21 and 22.

Special Tool:

• J 42640: Steering Column Anti-rotation Pin

With wheels of the vehicle facing straight ahead, secure the steering wheel utilizing the steering column anti-rotation pin, steering column lock, or a strap to prevent rotation. Locking of the steering column will prevent damage and a possible malfunction of the SIR system. The steering wheel must be secured in position before disconnecting the following components:

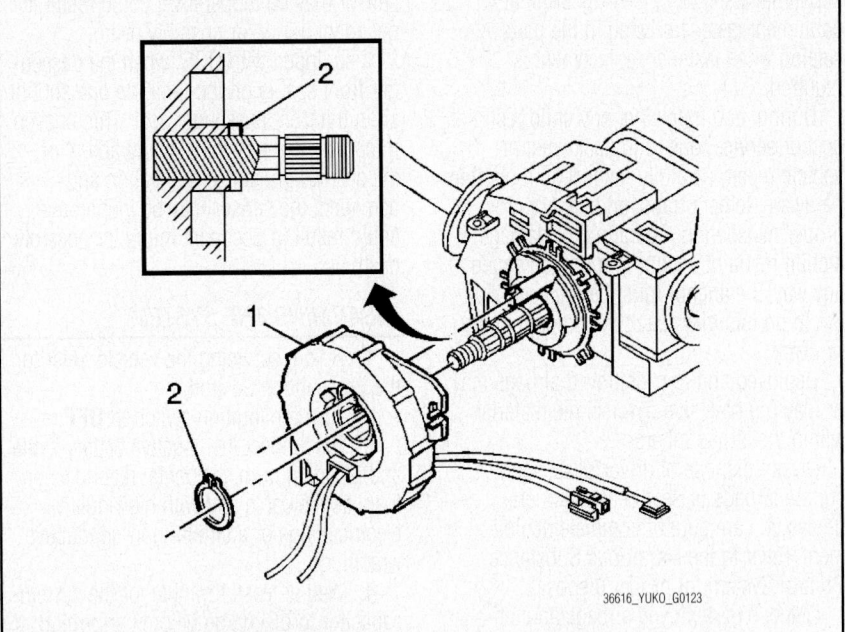

Fig. 21 Remove and discard the retaining ring (2). Remove the inflatable restraint steering wheel module coil (1) from the steering shaft

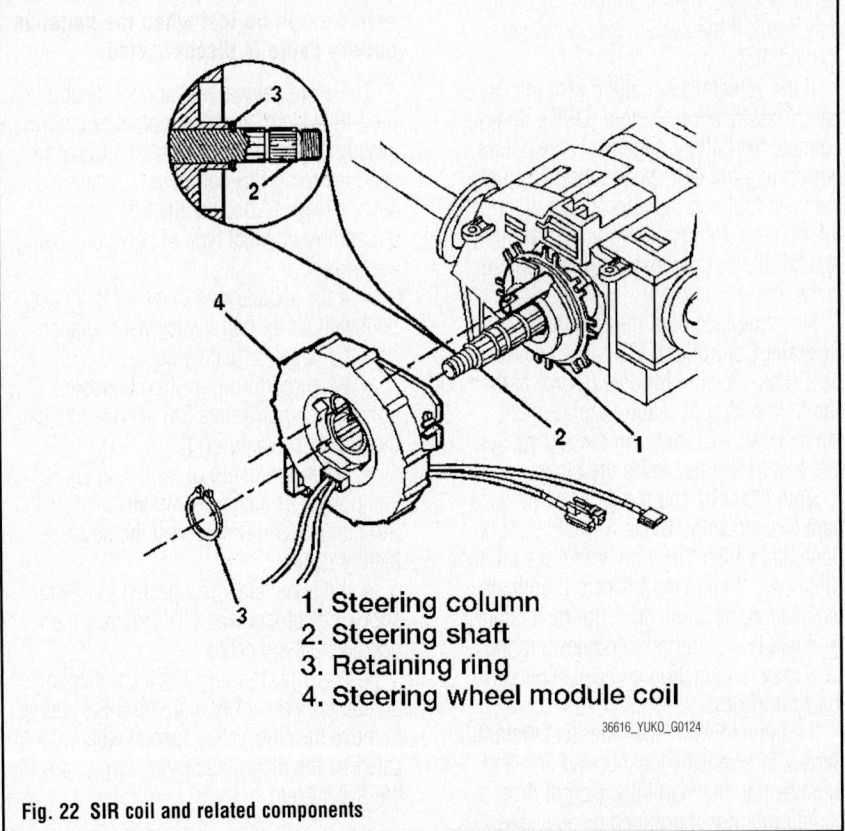

1. Steering column
2. Steering shaft
3. Retaining ring
4. Steering wheel module coil

Fig. 22 SIR coil and related components

• The steering column
• The intermediate shaft(s)
• The steering gear

After disconnecting these components, do not rotate the steering wheel or move the front tires and wheels. Failure to follow this

procedure may cause the SIR coil assembly to become un-centered and cause possible damage to the SIR coil. If you think the SIR coil has became un-centered, refer to the centering procedure to re-center the SIR Coil.

1. Before servicing the vehicle, refer to the Precautions Section.

2. Verify the following before removing the inflatable restraint steering wheel module coil:

a. The wheels on the vehicle are straight ahead.

b. The anti-rotation pin, J 42640, is installed or the ignition and start switch is in the LOCK position.

c. Remove the steering wheel. Refer to Steering Wheel, removal & installation.

d. Remove the steering column shroud.

e. Disconnect any electrical connectors as needed.

3. Remove the inflatable restraint steering wheel module coil retaining ring and discard it. DO NOT reuse the ring.

4. Remove the inflatable restraint steering wheel module coil from the steering shaft.

To install:

✳✳ WARNING

The new SIR coil assembly will be centered. Improper alignment of the SIR coil assembly may damage the unit, causing an inflatable restraint malfunction.

➡ **Do not remove the centering tab from the new inflatable restraint steering wheel module coil until the installation is complete. If the centering tab is missing, then re-center the assembly.**

5. If reusing the existing inflatable restraint steering wheel module coil it MUST be centered. Refer to Clockspring Centering, Centering Coil.

6. Align the inflatable restraint steering wheel module coil with the horn tower on the turn signal switch cancel cam.

7. Slide the inflatable restraint steering wheel module coil onto the steering shaft. Firmly seat the new inflatable restraint steering wheel module coil retaining ring into the appropriate groove on the steering shaft.

8. Remove and discard the centering tab from the new inflatable restraint steering wheel module coil.

9. Connect any electrical connectors, as needed.

10. Install the steering column shroud.

11. Install the steering wheel. Refer to Steering Wheel, removal & installation.

12. Remove the anti-rotation pin J 42640, as required.

DRIVE TRAIN   AUTOMATIC TRANSMISSION

AUTOMATIC TRANSMISSION ASSEMBLY

REMOVAL & INSTALLATION

4L60-E, 4L65-E, and 4L70-E Transmissions

See Figures 23 and 24.

Special Tool:
• J 21366: Converter Holding Strap

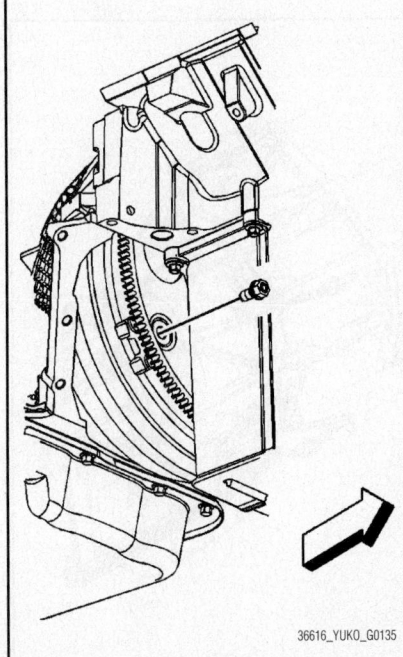

Fig. 23 Remove the flywheel-to-torque converter bolts

1. Before servicing the vehicle, refer to the Precautions Section.

2. Disconnect the negative battery cable.

3. Raise and safely support the vehicle.

4. Remove the driveshaft.

5. Properly support the transmission with a transmission jack.

6. Remove the transmission crossmember and transmission mount.

7. Remove the catalytic converter pipe.

8. If equipped with 4WD, remove the front driveshaft.

9. Remove the torque converter access plug.

10. Remove the left flywheel inspection cover.

11. Remove the starter motor. Refer to Starter, removal & installation.

12. Remove the right flywheel inspection cover.

13. Remove the flywheel-to-torque converter bolts.

14. Lower the transmission to gain access to the top and sides of the transmission.

15. Disconnect the vent tube hose and the electrical connections from the transfer case, if equipped with 4WD.

16. Remove the transfer case, if equipped with 4WD.

17. Remove the 2 bolts securing the heat shield and remove the transmission heat shield.

18. Remove the range selector cable from the transmission.

19. Disconnect the transmission vent hose.

20. Disconnect the park/neutral position switch connector.

21. Remove the wire harness from the bracket.

22. Remove the bolt that secures the fuel line bracket to the left side of the transmission.

23. Disconnect the main electrical connector and vehicle speed sensor from the transmission.

24. Remove the nut that secures the fuel line bracket to the transmission torque converter housing.

25. Disconnect the transmission oil cooler lines from the transmission.

26. Plug the transmission oil cooler line connectors in the transmission case.

27. Remove the 5 studs and one bolt securing the transmission to the engine.

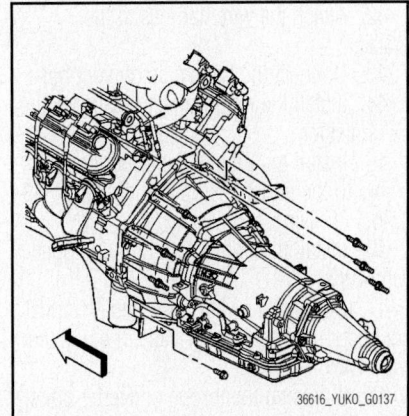

Fig. 24 Remove the studs and bolt securing the transmission to the engine— 4L60-E, 4L65-E, and 4L70-E transmissions

28. Pull the transmission straight back.

29. Install the J 21366 onto the transmission bell housing to retain the torque converter.

30. Remove the transmission from the vehicle while removing the fluid level indicator tube.

To install:

31. Flush the transmission oil cooler and cooling lines, if necessary.

32. Install the J 21366 onto the transmission bell housing to retain the torque converter.

33. Support the transmission with a transmission jack.

34. Raise the transmission into place while installing the fluid indicator tube.

35. Remove the J 21366 from the transmission.

36. Slide the transmission straight onto the locating pins while lining up the marks on the flywheel and the torque converter. The torque converter must rotate freely by hand.

➡**Be sure to use new fasteners, as required.**

37. Install the studs and bolt securing the transmission to the engine and tighten to 37 ft. lbs. (50 Nm).

38. Install the nut that secures the fuel line bracket to the transmission torque converter housing. Tighten the nut to 18 ft. lbs. (25 Nm).

39. Install the bolt that secures the fuel line bracket to the left side of the transmission and tighten the bolt to 89 inch lbs. (10 Nm).

40. Connect the main electrical connector and vehicle speed sensor to the transmission.

41. Connect the park/neutral position switch connector.

42. Attach the wire harness to the bracket.

43. Connect the transmission vent hose.

44. Install the range selector cable to the transmission.

45. Install the 2 bolts securing the heat shield to the transmission and tighten to 13 ft. lbs. (17 Nm).

46. Install the transfer case, if equipped with 4WD.

47. Connect the vent hose and electrical connectors to the transfer case, if equipped with 4WD.

48. If reusing the torque converter bolts, clean the bolt threads and apply LOCTITE 242, GM P/N 36616382, or equivalent, to the threads prior to installation.

49. Install the flywheel-to-torque con-

verter bolts and tighten to 46 ft. lbs. (63 Nm).

50. Install the starter motor. Refer to Starter, removal & installation.

51. Install the left flywheel inspection cover and bolt and tighten to 89 inch lbs. (10 Nm).

52. Install the torque converter access plug.

53. If the vehicle is equipped with a transfer case, install the front driveshaft.

54. Install the catalytic converter pipe.

55. Install the transmission mount and transmission crossmember.

56. Remove the transmission jack.

57. Install the rear driveshaft.

58. Connect the oil cooler lines to the transmission.

59. Lower the vehicle.

60. Connect the negative battery cable.

61. Fill the transmission with the proper amount and type of transmission fluid.

➡**It is recommended that the Transmission Adaptive Pressure (TAP) information be reset. Resetting the TAP values using a scan tool will erase all learned values in all cells. As a result, the Engine Control Module (ECM), Powertrain Control Module (PCM), or Transmission Control Module (TCM) will need to relearn TAP values. Transmission performance may be affected as new TAP values are learned.**

62. Reset the TAP values.

6L50, 6L80, and 6L90 Transmissions

See Figures 23 and 25.

Special Tool

• J 21366: Converter Holding Strap

1. Before servicing the vehicle, refer to the Precautions Section.

2. Disconnect the negative battery cable.

3. Raise and safely support the vehicle.

4. Remove the rear driveshaft.

5. Properly support the transmission with a transmission jack.

6. Remove the transmission crossmember and the transmission mount.

7. Remove the catalytic converter pipe.

8. If the vehicle is equipped with 4WD, remove the front driveshaft.

9. Remove the torque converter access plug.

10. Remove the left flywheel inspection cover.

11. Remove the starter motor. Refer to Starter, removal & installation.

12. Remove the right flywheel inspection cover.

13. Remove the flywheel-to-torque converter bolts.

14. Lower the transmission to gain access to the top and sides of the transmission.

15. Disconnect the vent tube hose and the electrical connections from the transfer case, if equipped with 4WD.

16. Remove the transfer case, if equipped with 4WD.

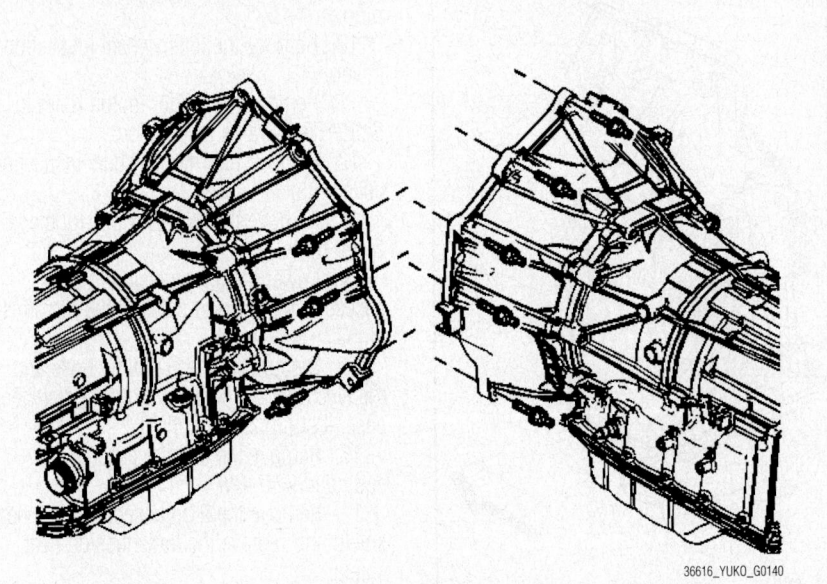

36616_YUKO_G0140

Fig. 25 Remove the 8 bolts securing the transmission to the engine—6L50, 6L80, and 6L90 transmissions

17. Remove the 2 bolts securing the heat shield to the transmission and remove the transmission heat shield.

18. Remove the range selector cable retaining clip from the transmission range selector cable.

19. Remove the range selector cable from the range selector lever ball stud and the range selector cable bracket.

20. Disconnect the transmission vent hose.

21. Disconnect the transmission electrical connector from the transmission.

22. Remove the wire harness from the transmission.

23. Remove the bolt that secures the fuel line bracket to the left side of the transmission.

24. Disconnect the transmission oil cooler lines from the transmission.

25. Plug the transmission oil cooler line connectors in the transmission case.

26. Remove the 8 bolts securing the transmission to the engine.

27. Pull the transmission straight back.

28. Install the J 21366 onto the transmission bell housing to retain the torque converter.

29. Remove the transmission from the vehicle while removing the fluid level indicator tube.

To install:

30. Flush the transmission oil cooler and cooling lines, if necessary.

31. Install the J 21366 onto the transmission bell housing to retain the torque converter.

32. Support the transmission with a transmission jack.

33. Raise the transmission into place while installing the fluid indicator tube.

34. Remove the J 21366 from the transmission.

35. Slide the transmission straight onto the locating pins while lining up the marks on the flywheel and the torque converter. The torque converter must rotate freely by hand.

➡ **Be sure to use new fasteners, as required.**

36. Install the 8 bolts securing the transmission to the engine and tighten to 37 ft. lbs. (50 Nm).

37. Connect the transmission vent hose.

38. Install the wire harness to the transmission.

39. Connect the transmission electrical connector to the transmission.

40. Install the range selector cable to the range selector cable bracket and the range selector lever ball stud.

41. Install the range selector cable retaining clip to the transmission range selector cable.

42. Install the transmission heat shield. Tighten the bolts to 13 ft. lbs. (17 Nm).

43. Install the transfer case, if equipped with 4WD.

44. Connect the vent hose and electrical connectors to the transfer case, if equipped with 4WD.

45. If reusing the torque converter bolts, clean the bolt threads and apply LOCTITE 242, GM P/N 36616382, or equivalent, to the threads prior to installation.

46. Install the flywheel-to-torque converter bolts and tighten to 46 ft. lbs. (63 Nm).

47. Install the right flywheel inspection cover and bolt. Tighten the bolt to 89 inch lbs. (10 Nm).

48. Install the starter motor. Refer to Starter, removal & installation.

49. Install the left flywheel inspection cover and bolt. Tighten the bolt to 89 inch lbs. (10 Nm).

50. Install the torque converter access plug.

51. If the vehicle is equipped with a transfer case, install the front driveshaft.

52. Install the catalytic converter pipe.

53. Install the transmission mount and the transmission crossmember.

54. Remove the transmission jack.

55. Install the rear driveshaft.

56. Connect the oil cooler lines to the transmission.

57. Lower the vehicle.

58. Connect the negative battery cable.

59. Fill the transmission with the proper amount and type of transmission fluid.

➡ **It is recommended that the Transmission Adaptive Pressure (TAP) information be reset. Resetting the TAP values using a scan tool will erase all learned values in all cells. As a result, the Engine Control Module (ECM), Powertrain Control Module (PCM), or Transmission Control Module (TCM) will need to relearn TAP values. Transmission performance may be affected as new TAP values are learned.**

60. Reset the TAP values.

61. If a replacement transmission is installed, program the TCM.

TRANSFER CASE ASSEMBLY

REMOVAL & INSTALLATION

See Figures 26 and 27.

1. Before servicing the vehicle, refer to the Precautions Section.

2. Raise and safely support the vehicle.

3. Remove the transfer case shield, if equipped.

4. Remove the rear driveshaft.

5. Remove the front driveshaft.

6. Drain the fluid from the transfer case.

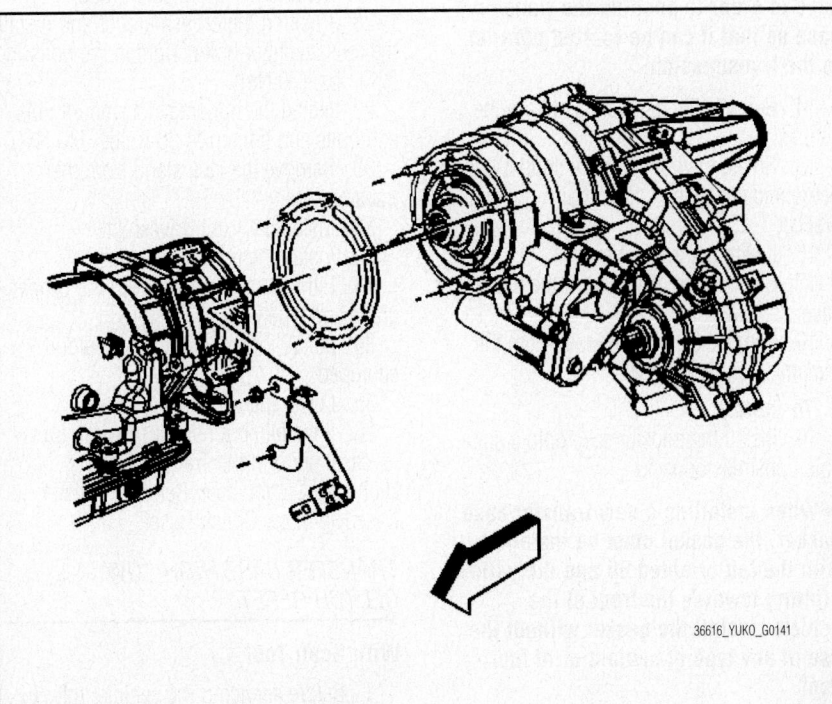

Fig. 26 Transfer case removal—BW 4485-NR3

36616_YUKO_G0141

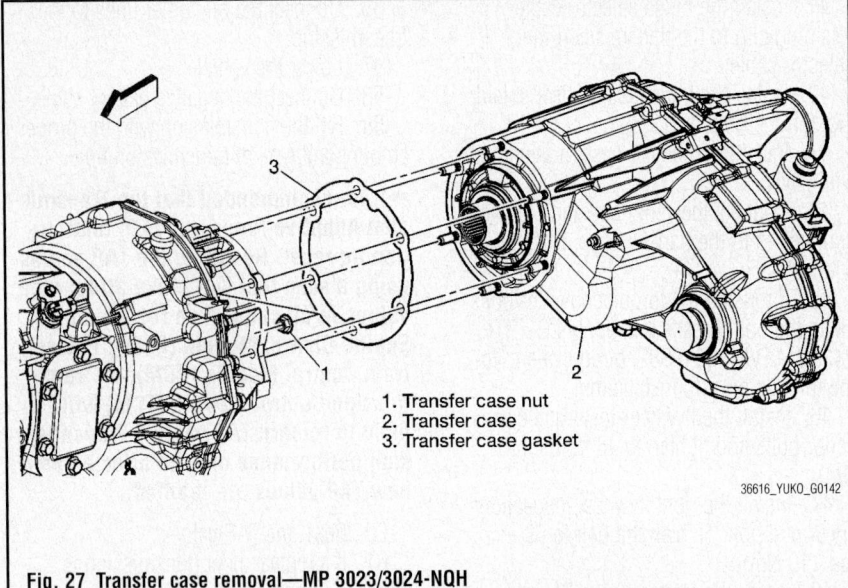

36616_YUKO_G0142

1. Transfer case nut
2. Transfer case
3. Transfer case gasket

Fig. 27 Transfer case removal—MP 3023/3024-NQH

7. Support the transmission with a suitable jack stand.

8. Remove the transmission mount nuts and bolts.

9. Remove the crossmember bolts and the crossmember.

10. Remove the transmission mount.

11. Install a suitable transmission jack to the transfer case.

12. Remove the transfer case adapter nuts.

13. Remove the fuel pipe bracket from the studs.

➥**Pull straight back on the transfer case in order to position the transfer case so that it can be rotated parallel to the transmission.**

14. Remove the transfer case from the adapter.

15. Rotate the transfer case so that it is perpendicular to the torsion bar mounting bracket.

16. Lower the transfer case.

17. Remove the gasket from the transfer case.

18. Remove the transfer case from the transmission jack.

To install:

19. Install the transfer case onto a suitable transmission jack.

➥**When installing a new transfer case gasket, the gasket must be installed with the tab oriented up and the yellow printing towards the front of the vehicle. Install the gasket without the use of any type of sealant or of lubricant.**

20. Install a NEW transfer case gasket.

21. Rotate the transfer case so that it is parallel to the torsion bar mounting bracket.

22. Raise the transfer case into position.

23. Rotate the transfer case so that it is aligned with the adapter.

24. Install the transfer case to the adapter.

25. Install the fuel pipe bracket onto the studs.

➥**Ensure that the gasket is flush to the transmission prior to installing the nuts.**

26. Install the transfer case adapter nuts and tighten to 37 ft. lbs. (50 Nm).

27. Install the transmission mount.

28. Position the crossmember and install the crossmember bolts. Tighten the bolts to 52 ft. lbs. (70 Nm).

29. Install the transmission mount nuts and bolts and tighten to 30 ft. lbs. (40 Nm).

30. Remove the jack stand from the transmission.

31. Install the front driveshaft.

32. Install the rear driveshaft.

33. Fill the transfer case with the proper grade and type fluid.

34. Install the transfer case shield, if equipped.

35. Lower the vehicle.

36. If installing a new or repaired transfer case, perform the Transfer Case High/Low Clutch reset. Refer to Transfer Case High/Low Clutch Reset.

TRANSFER CASE HIGH/LOW CLUTCH RESET

With Scan Tool

1. Before servicing the vehicle, refer to the Precautions Section.

2. Turn the ignition ON, go to the special functions heading in the scan tool.

3. Select Clutch Reset Procedure (Motor Learn Procedure).

4. When the Clutch Reset Procedure is initiated, you should hear the motor engage, indicating a successful learn procedure.

Without Scan Tool

This procedure uses the transfer case shift control switch.

1. Before servicing the vehicle, refer to the Precautions Section.

2. Turn the ignition to ACCESSORY, place the transfer case shift control switch into the 2 high mode.

3. Turn the switch clockwise past 4 low into the neutral request mode and hold for 30 seconds.

4. An audible noise from the motor should occur indicating a successful learn procedure.

FRONT AXLE SHAFT, BEARING & SEAL

REMOVAL & INSTALLATION

8.25 S4WD (Part-Time) and 9.25 Axles

See Figure 28.

1. Before servicing the vehicle, refer to the Precautions Section.

2. Raise and safely support the vehicle.

3. Drain the differential carrier assembly.

4. If only replacing the right side inner shaft and/or housing, follow the steps below. If only replacing the left side inner shaft, proceed to step 19.

5. Remove the stabilizer shaft link assembly.

6. Disconnect the electrical connector from the electric motor actuator.

7. Disconnect the wire harness from the inner axle shaft housing.

8. Remove the drive shaft inboard flange bolts from the inner axle shaft.

9. Disconnect the wheel drive shaft from the inner axle shaft.

10. Remove the inner axle shaft housing nuts from the bracket.

11. For 2500 series vehicles, remove the front axle mounting bracket to frame nuts.

12. Slide the front axle mounting bracket towards the engine. It may be necessary to pull down on the inner axle housing and/or push up on the mounting bracket in order to gain clearance.

13. Remove the inner axle shaft housing bolts from the differential carrier case.

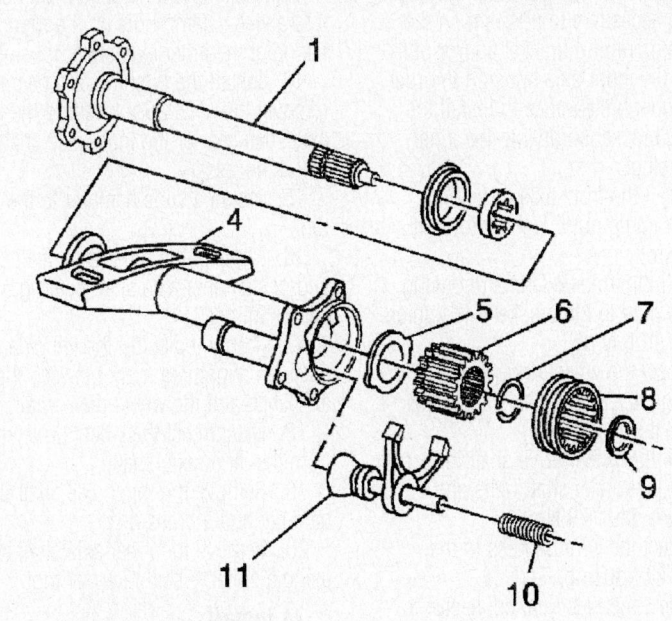

1. Inner axle shaft
4. Inner shaft housing
5. Thrust washer
6. Clutch gear
7. Washer
8. Clutch sleeve
9. Inner sleeve
10. Clutch fork inner spring
11. Clutch for assembly

06025-AVAL-G15

Fig. 28 Exploded view of the front axle assembly—8.25 S4WD and 9.25 axles

14. Carefully remove the inner axle shaft housing assembly from the differential carrier assembly.

15. For the 8.25 inch axle, remove the following components from the inner axle shaft housing:

  a. The clutch fork inner spring.
  b. The clutch fork assembly.
  c. The clutch shaft shim.
  d. The clutch sleeve.
  e. The clutch gear by doing the following:
    • Clamp the inner axle shaft housing in a vise. Clamp only on the mounting flange
    • Strike the inside surface of the shaft flange with a hammer and a brass drift in order to dislodge the front drive axle clutch gear from the inner axle shaft
    • The thrust washer

16. For the 9.25 inch axle, remove the following components from the inner axle shaft housing:

  a. The clutch fork inner spring.

  b. The clutch fork assembly.
  c. The clutch shaft shim.
  d. The clutch sleeve.
  e. The retainer ring.
  f. The thrust washers.

17. Remove the inner axle shaft. Tap out the inner axle shaft with a soft-faced mallet, if necessary.

18. Remove the inner axle seal and the bearing from the axle housing.

19. If only replacing the left side inner axle shaft, remove the wheel drive shaft inboard flange bolts from the inner axle shaft. Disconnect the wheel drive shaft from the inner axle shaft.

20. Remove the inner axle shaft using a hammer and a brass drift.

21. Install the inner axle shaft housing into a vise. Clamp only on the mounting flange of the inner axle shaft housing.

22. Install the bushing and bearing removal tool J-29369-1, 8.25 inch axle, or J-29369-2, 9.25 inch axle, behind the inner axle shaft seal or the inner axle shaft bearing as necessary.

23. Install a slide hammer to the removal tool.

24. Remove the inner axle shaft seal and/or the inner axle shaft bearing using the slide hammer.

25. If only replacing the left side seal, place an alignment mark between the inner axle shaft and the wheel drive shaft.

26. Disconnect the wheel drive shaft from the inner axle shaft.

27. Remove the inner axle shaft using a hammer and a brass drift.

28. Remove the inner axle shaft seal using a suitable seal remover tool.

To install:

29. Install the right side bearing with the square shoulder in using and axle bearing tube installer and a universal driver handle.

30. Install the new axle shaft seal using the sane tools.

31. Install the inner axle shaft into the inner axle shaft housing. Carefully tap the inner axle shaft into place with a soft-faced mallet.

32. Install the inner axle shaft and clutch fork assembly components into the inner shaft housing.

33. If only the left side inner axle shaft was removed, install the shaft by performing the following steps:

  a. Install the inner axle shaft into the differential case side gear using a soft-faced mallet until the retaining ring on the inner axle shaft is fully seated within the groove in the differential case side gear.

  b. Pull back on the inner axle shaft to ensure that the inner axle shaft is properly retained in the differential case side gear.

  c. Connect the halfshaft to the inner axle shaft.

  d. Install the halfshaft inboard flange to inner axle shaft bolts and tighten to 58 ft. lbs. (79 Nm).

34. If the right side inner axle shaft and/or housing was removed, install the shaft and/or housing using the following steps:

  a. Install the new inner axle shaft bearing and the seal to the axle housing.

  b. Install the inner axle shaft into the inner axle shaft housing. Carefully tap the inner axle shaft into place with a soft-faced mallet.

  c. Place the inner axle shaft housing on end so that the splines of the inner axle shaft is facing up.

35. For the 8.25 inch axle, install the following components into the inner axle shaft housing:

➡**Use chassis grease in order to hold the thrust washer in place.**

a. The thrust washer. Ensure the tabs on the thrust washer are aligned with the slots in the inner axle shaft housing.

b. The retainer ring into the clutch gear.

c. The clutch gear onto the inner axle shaft. Drive the clutch gear into place with a plastic hammer.

d. Install the original shim to the shaft. Use the chassis grease in order to hold the shim in place.

e. Install the inner axle housing assembly to the differential carrier case. Do not use sealer at this time.

f. Install the bolts.

g. Install a dial indicator on the axle tube end. The plunger of the indicator must be at a right angle to the axle flange.

h. Move the shaft back and forth and read the end play. The correct end play is 0.001–0.020 inch (0.03–0.51mm).

i. If the end play is incorrect, install a thicker or thinner shim as needed in order to bring the end play into the specified range.

j. Install the clutch gear shim, clutch sleeve, clutch fork assembly, and clutch fork inner spring.

36. For the 9.25 inch axle, install the following components into the inner axle shaft housing:

a. The thrust washer. Ensure the tabs on the thrust washer are aligned with the slots in the inner axle shaft housing.

b. The second thrust washer.

c. The retainer ring onto the inner axle shaft.

d. Determine the clutch gear shim thickness.

e. Install the clutch gear shim, clutch sleeve, clutch fork assembly and clutch fork inner spring.

f. Apply sealant to the inner axle housing to differential carrier sealing surface.

g. Install the inner axle shaft housing assembly to the differential carrier assembly.

h. Install the inner axle shaft housing bolts and tighten to 30 ft. lbs. (40 Nm) or 41 ft. lbs. (55 Nm) on 9.25 inch axles.

37. For 2500 series vehicles, perform the following steps in order to install the front axle mounting bracket to the inner axle shaft housing:

a. Slide the front axle mounting bracket towards the frame. Install the front axle mounting bracket studs into

the inner shaft housing mounting flange. It may be necessary to push up on the front axle mounting bracket and/or pull down on the inner axle housing in order to gain enough clearance to install the mounting bracket studs into the inner shaft housing.

b. Install the front axle mounting bracket to frame nuts. Tighten to 67 ft. lbs. (90 Nm).

38. Install the inner axle shaft housing washers and nuts to the bracket and tighten to 75 ft. lbs. (100 Nm).

39. Connect the wheel drive shaft inboard flange to the inner axle shaft and tighten to 30 ft. lbs. (40 Nm).

40. Install the wheel drive shaft inboard flange to the inner axle shaft bolts and tighten to 58 ft. lbs. (79 Nm).

41. Connect the wire harness to the inner axle shaft housing.

42. Connect the electrical connector to the front axle actuator.

43. Install the stabilizer shaft link assembly.

44. With either replacement procedure, fill the differential carrier assembly with axle lubricant.

45. Lower the vehicle.

8.25 F4WD (Full-Time) Axle

1. Before servicing the vehicle, refer to the Precautions Section.

2. Raise and safely support the vehicle.

3. Drain the differential carrier assembly.

4. If only replacing the right side inner shaft and/or housing, follow the steps below. If only replacing the left side inner shaft, proceed to step 16.

5. Remove the stabilizer shaft link assembly.

6. Remove the wheel drive shaft inboard flange bolts from the inner axle shaft.

7. Disconnect the wheel drive shaft from the inner axle shaft.

8. Disconnect the inner axle shaft from the differential case side gear using a hammer and brass drift.

Remove the inner axle shaft housing nuts from the bracket.

9. Remove the inner axle shaft housing bolts from the differential carrier assembly.

10. Remove the inner axle shaft and inner axle shaft housing from the vehicle.

11. Remove the inner axle shaft from the inner axle shaft housing.

12. Remove the inner axle shaft seal and the bearing from the inner axle shaft housing.

13. Install the inner axle shaft housing into a vise. Clamp only on the mounting flange of the inner axle shaft housing.

14. Install the bushing and bearing removal tool J–29369-1 behind the inner axle shaft seal or the inner axle shaft bearing as necessary.

15. Install a slide hammer to the removal tool.

16. Remove the inner axle shaft seal and/or the inner axle shaft bearing using the slide hammer.

17. If only replacing the left side seal, place an alignment mark between the inner axle shaft and the wheel drive shaft.

18. Disconnect the wheel drive shaft from the inner axle shaft.

19. Remove the inner axle shaft using a hammer and a brass drift.

20. Remove the inner axle shaft seal using a suitable seal remover tool.

To install:

21. Install the right side bearing with the square shoulder in using and axle bearing tube installer and a universal driver handle.

22. Install the new axle shaft seal using the sane tools.

23. Install the inner axle shaft into the inner axle shaft housing. Carefully tap the inner axle shaft into place with a soft-faced mallet.

24. Install the inner axle shaft and clutch fork assembly components into the inner shaft housing.

25. If only the left side inner axle shaft was removed, install the shaft by performing the following steps:

a. Install the inner axle shaft into the differential case side gear using a soft-faced mallet until the retaining ring on the inner axle shaft is fully seated within the groove in the differential case side gear.

b. Pull back on the inner axle shaft to ensure that the inner axle shaft is properly retained in the differential case side gear.

c. Connect the halfshaft to the inner axle shaft.

d. Install the halfshaft inboard flange to inner axle shaft bolts and tighten to 58 ft. lbs. (79 Nm).

26. If the right side inner axle shaft and/or housing was removed, install the shaft and/or housing using the following steps.

27. Install the new inner axle shaft bearing and the new seal to the inner axle shaft housing.

28. Install the inner axle shaft into the inner axle shaft housing. Do not install the

inner axle shaft completely into the inner axle shaft housing at this time.

29. Apply sealant to the inner axle housing to differential carrier sealing surface.

30. Install the inner axle shaft and the inner axle shaft housing to the differential carrier assembly.

31. Install the inner axle shaft housing bolts and tighten to 30 ft. lbs. (40 Nm).

32. Install the inner axle shaft housing nuts to the bracket and tighten to 75 ft. lbs. (100 Nm).

33. Install the inner axle shaft into the differential case side gear by doing the following:

34. Turn the inner axle shaft and align the splines of the inner axle shaft with the splines on the differential side gear.

35. Install the inner axle shaft into the differential case side gear using a soft–faced mallet until the retaining ring on the inner axle shaft is fully seated within the groove in the differential case side gear.

36. Pull back on the inner axle shaft to ensure that the inner axle shaft is properly retained in the differential case side gear.

37. Install the wheel drive shaft inboard flange to the inner axle shaft.

38. Install the wheel drive shaft inboard flange to inner axle shaft bolts and tighten to 58 ft. lbs. (79 Nm).

39. Install the stabilizer shaft link assembly.

40. Fill the differential carrier assembly with axle lubricant

41. Lower the vehicle.

FRONT HALFSHAFTS

REMOVAL & INSTALLATION

See Figures 29 and 30.

1. Before servicing the vehicle, refer to the Precautions Section.

2. Raise and safely support the vehicle.

3. Remove the wheel and tire assembly.

4. Insert a drift or a large screwdriver through the brake caliper into one of the brake rotor vanes in order to prevent the drive axle wheel drive shaft from turning.

5. Remove the nut and the washer from the hub.

➡**Do not reuse the hub nut. A NEW nut must be used when installing the wheel drive shaft.**

6. Remove the bolts securing the wheel drive shaft inboard flange to the output shaft flange.

7. Remove the drift from the rotor.

8. Remove the stabilizer shaft link from the lower control arm.

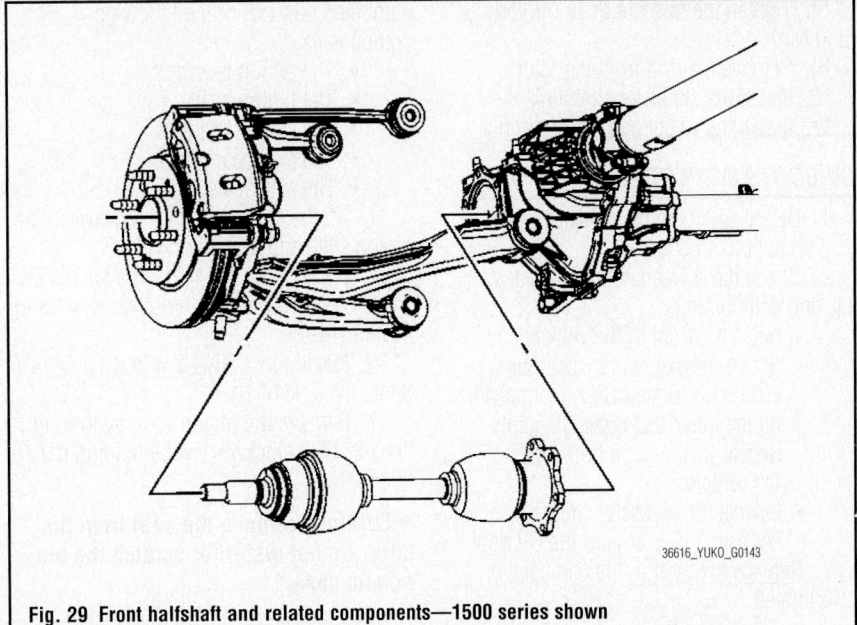

Fig. 29 Front halfshaft and related components—1500 series shown

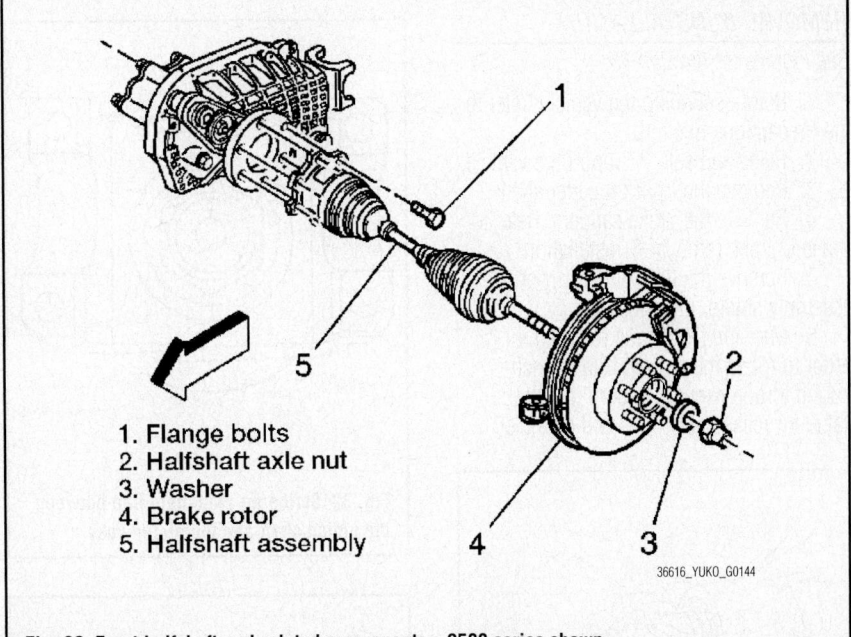

1. Flange bolts
2. Halfshaft axle nut
3. Washer
4. Brake rotor
5. Halfshaft assembly

Fig. 30 Front halfshaft and related components—2500 series shown

➡**Wrap shop towels around both the inner and the outer wheel drive shaft boots in order to avoid damage to the boots during removal and installation.**

9. Pull the wheel drive shaft through the lower control arm opening.

To install:

➡**Clean the steering knuckle and the wheel drive shaft splines and threads. These areas must be dry and free of grease, dirt, and contamination.**

10. Insert the wheel drive shaft splined shank into the knuckle hub.

➡**Use only a genuine GM front wheel drive shaft nut. Installation of anything but an OEM front wheel drive shaft nut could cause damage to the vehicle.**

11. Install the washer and the NEW hub nut to the wheel driveshaft. Do not tighten.

12. Install the wheel drive shaft inboard flange to the output shaft flange using the inboard flange bolts.

13. Insert a drift or a large screwdriver through the brake caliper into one of the brake rotor vanes in order to prevent the wheel drive shaft from turning. Tighten the inboard flange bolts to 58 ft. lbs. (78 Nm).

14. Tighten the hub nut to 177 ft. lbs. (240 Nm).

15. Remove the drift from the rotor.

16. Install the stabilizer shaft link.

17. Install the wheel and tire assembly.

CV-BOOTS INSPECTION

1. Before servicing the vehicle, refer to the Precautions Section.

2. Check the driveshaft boots for damage and deterioration:
- Raise the front of the vehicle
- Rotate the axle and inspect for cracked or ripped CV boot material on the inner and outer CV-joints. Repeat this step on both sides of the vehicle.
- Inspect for excessive grease deposits on or around the CV boot

3. Replace the boot if it is damaged or deteriorated.

FRONT PINION SEAL

REMOVAL & INSTALLATION

See Figures 31 through 35.

1. Before servicing the vehicle, refer to the Precautions Section.

2. Raise and safely support the vehicle.

3. Remove the front propeller shaft.

4. Remove the brake calipers. Refer to Brake Caliper, removal & installation.

5. Remove the differential carrier assembly shield, if equipped.

6. Measure the torque required in order to rotate the pinion. Use an inch-pound torque wrench. Record the torque value for reassembly. This will give the

combined preload for the following components:
- The pinion bearings
- The pinion seal
- The carrier bearings
- The axle bearings
- The axle seals

7. Scribe an alignment line between the pinion shaft and the pinion yoke.

8. Install the J 8614-01 onto the pinion.

9. Remove the pinion nut while holding the J 8614-01.

10. Install the J 8614-2 and the J 8614-3 into the J 8614-01.

11. Remove the pinion yoke by turning the J 8614-3 clockwise while holding the J 8614-01.

➡**Carefully remove the seal from the bore. Do not distort or scratch the aluminum case.**

12. Remove the oil seal using a suitable seal removal tool.

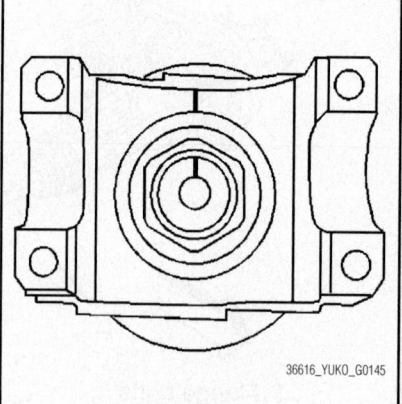

Fig. 32 Scribe an alignment line between the pinion shaft and the pinion yoke

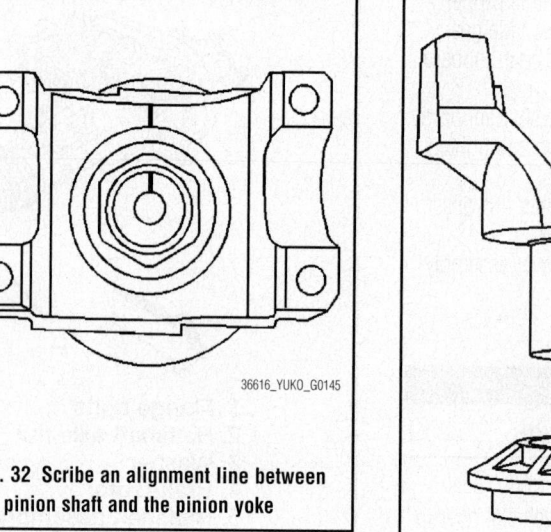

Fig. 33 Install the J 8614-01 (1), J 8614-2 (2), and J 8614-3 (3) for pinion yoke removal

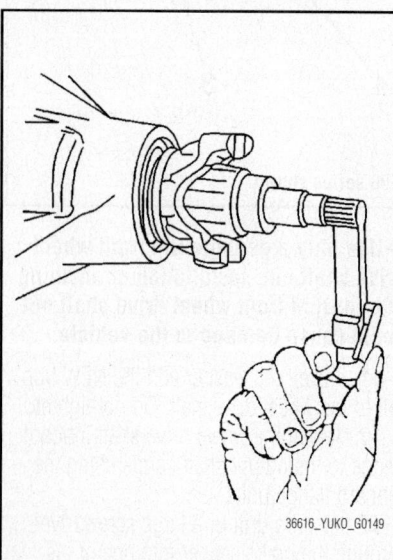

Fig. 31 Measuring the turning torque of the pinion

13. Remove the dust deflector from the pinion yoke using a soft-faced hammer.

To install:

14. Install the new deflector onto the pinion yoke using a soft-faced hammer.

✻✻ WARNING

Drive the seal in straight, not at an angle, as this will damage the aluminum housing.

15. Install the new oil seal:
- a. Position the oil seal in the bore.
- b. Install the J 21128 over the oil seal.
- c. Strike the J 21128 with a hammer until the seal flange seats on the axle housing surface.

16. Apply sealant GM P/N 12346004, or equivalent, to the splines of the drive pinion yoke.

17. Install the pinion yoke.

18. Align the reference marks made during removal.

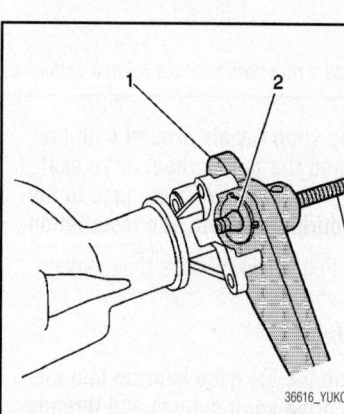

Fig. 34 Remove the dust deflector from the pinion yoke

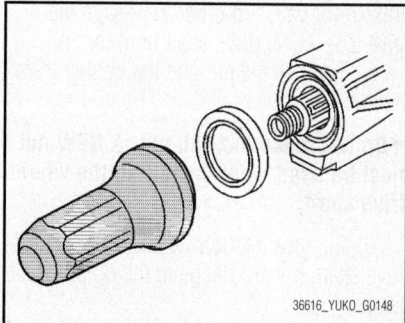

Fig. 35 Position the oil seal in the bore for installation

⁎⁑ WARNING

Do not hammer the pinion flange/yoke onto the pinion shaft. Pinion components may be damaged if the pinion flange/yoke is hammered onto the pinion shaft.

19. Seat the pinion yoke onto the pinion shaft by tapping it with a soft-faced hammer until a few pinion shaft threads show through the yoke.

20. Install the washer and a new pinion nut.

21. Install the J 8614-01 onto the pinion yoke.

➥ **If the rotating torque is exceeded, the pinion will have to be removed and a new collapsible spacer installed.**

22. Tighten the pinion nut while holding the J 8614-01. Tighten the pinion nut until the pinion end play is just taken up. Rotate the pinion while tightening the nut to seat the bearings.

23. Measure the rotating torque of the pinion using an inch-pound torque wrench.

24. Compare the measurement of the rotating torque to the measurement recorded earlier.

25. The rotating torque of the pinion nut should be 3–5 inch lbs. (0.40–0.57 Nm) greater than the torque recorded during removal.

26. If the rotating torque is not within specifications, continue to tighten the pinion nut. Tighten the pinion nut, in small increments, as needed, until the torque required in order to rotate the pinion is 3–5 inch lbs. (0.40–0.57 Nm) greater than the torque recorded during removal.

27. Once the specified torque is obtained, rotate the pinion several times to ensure the bearings have seated. Recheck the rotating torque and adjust if necessary.

28. Install the front propeller shaft.

29. Install the differential carrier assembly shield, if equipped.

30. Install the brake calipers. Refer to Brake Caliper, removal & installation.

31. Inspect the axle lubricant level and add if necessary.

32. Lower the vehicle.

REAR AXLE HOUSING

REMOVAL & INSTALLATION

See Figure 36.

1. Before servicing the vehicle, refer to the Precautions Section.

2. Raise and safely support the vehicle.

3. Remove the rear tires and wheels.

4. Remove the vent hose from the rear drive axle.

5. Remove the electronic suspension control sensor, if equipped.

6. Remove the rear wheel speed sensors from the rear drive axle.

7. Remove the rear brake calipers, and relocate to the side. Refer to Brake Caliper, removal & installation.

8. Drain the axle lubricant.

9. Remove the driveshaft.

10. Remove the rear axle tie rod.

➥ **The stabilizer shaft links do not have removed in the following procedure. Rotate the links upward toward the frame and of the way.**

11. Remove the rear stabilizer shaft, if equipped.

12. Remove the rear brake pipe retaining bracket bolt.

13. Remove the rear brake junction block retaining bolt at the rear axle cover.

14. Secure the rear brake pipes to the frame with mechanics wire, or equivalent.

15. Remove the rear brake pipe from the retaining strap.

16. Remove the brake pipe retaining bracket bolt.

➥ **Ensure that the rear drive axle is properly secured to the jack stand.**

17. Support the rear drive axle with an hydraulic jack stand.

➥ **It is not necessary to remove the control arms. Secure the control arms to the frame with the use of mechanics wire, or equivalent.**

18. Remove the lower control arm bolts from the rear the drive axle.

19. Remove the upper control arm bolts from the rear drive axle.

20. With the aid of an assistant, lower the drive axle.

21. Remove the rear coil springs.

22. Lower the rear drive axle assembly.

23. Remove the rear axle housing cover and gasket.

24. Remove the axle shafts. Refer to Axle Shaft, Bearing, and Seal, removal & installation.

25. Remove the differential assembly.

26. Remove the brake backing plates.

27. Remove the drive pinion shaft yoke and the seal. Refer to Pinion Seal, removal & installation.

28. Remove the drive pinion.

To install:

29. Install the drive pinion.

30. Install the differential assembly.

31. Adjust the differential side bearing preload.

32. Adjust the backlash.

33. Perform a gear tooth contact pattern check.

34. Install the brake backing plates.

35. Install the axle shafts.

36. Install the rear axle housing cover and gasket.

37. Position the rear drive axle assembly under the vehicle.

38. With the aid of an assistant, raise the rear drive axle into place.

39. Install the rear coil springs on the rear drive axle.

40. Install the upper control arms to the rear drive axle.

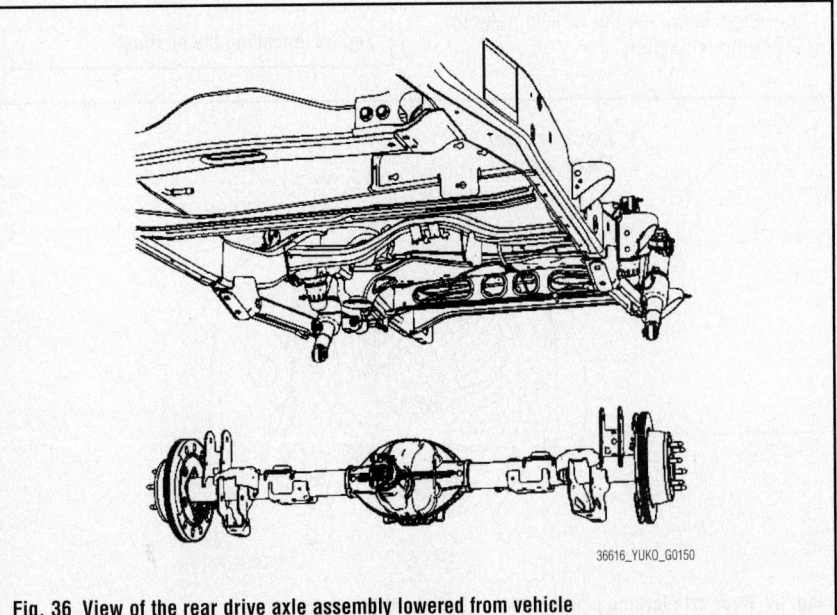

36616_YUKO_G0150

Fig. 36 View of the rear drive axle assembly lowered from vehicle

41. Install the lower control arms to the rear drive axle.

42. Install the lower shock absorber bolts to the rear drive axle.

43. Remove the hydraulic jack stand from the rear drive axle assembly.

➡️ **Be sure to use new fasteners, as required.**

44. Install the rear brake pipe retaining bracket bolt and tighten to 15 ft. lbs. (20 Nm).

45. Install the rear brake junction block retaining bolt at the rear axle cover and tighten to 15 ft. lbs. (20 Nm).

46. Install rear drive axle the vent hose.

➡️ **Rotate the stabilizer shaft links down into position to install them.**

47. Install the rear stabilizer shaft, if equipped.

48. Install the rear wheel speed sensors.

49. Install the rear axle tie rod.

50. Install the rear brake calipers.

51. Install the rear driveshaft.

52. Install the electronic suspension control sensor, if equipped.

53. Fill the rear drive axle with the proper type and amount of fluid.

54. Install the rear tires and wheels.

55. Remove the supports and lower the vehicle.

56. Calibrate the air level control, if needed.

REAR AXLE SHAFT, BEARING & SEAL

REMOVAL & INSTALLATION

See Figures 37 through 41.

1. Before servicing the vehicle, refer to the Precautions Section.

2. Raise and safely support the vehicle.

3. Remove the tire and wheel assemblies.

4. Drain the differential fluid. Be sure to properly dispose of used fluid.

5. Remove the wheel speed sensor.

6. Remove the caliper mounting bracket.

7. Remove the rear axle cover. Discard the gasket.

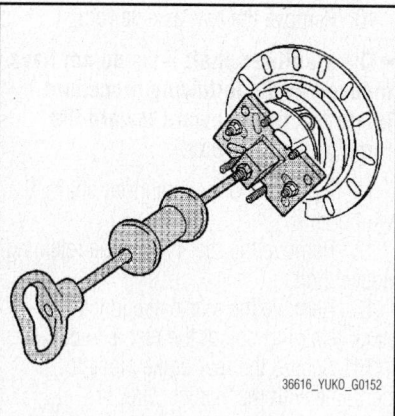
Fig. 38 Removing the axle shaft

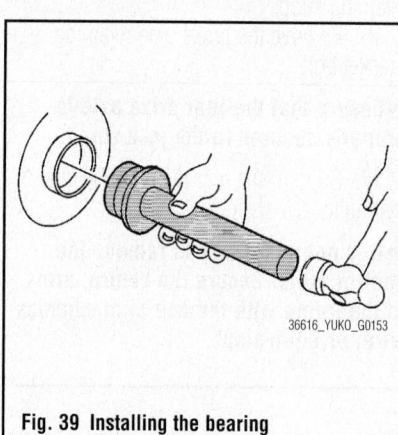
Fig. 39 Installing the bearing

8. Remove and discard the pinion gear shaft bolt.

9. Remove the pinion gear shaft, on non-locking differential equipped vehicles.

10. If equipped with locking differential, remove the pinion gear shaft part way from the differential case. Use a flat-bladed tool and rotate the lock until the lock aligns with the thrust block.

11. Push on the axle shaft and remove the lock.

12. Remove the axle shaft assembly.

➡️ **If the shaft is difficult to remove, install a slide hammer removal tool and remove the shaft.**

13. Carefully remove the seal and bearing from its mounting. Do not reuse the original seal.

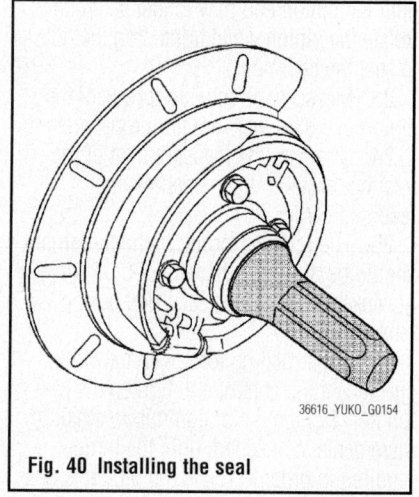
Fig. 40 Installing the seal

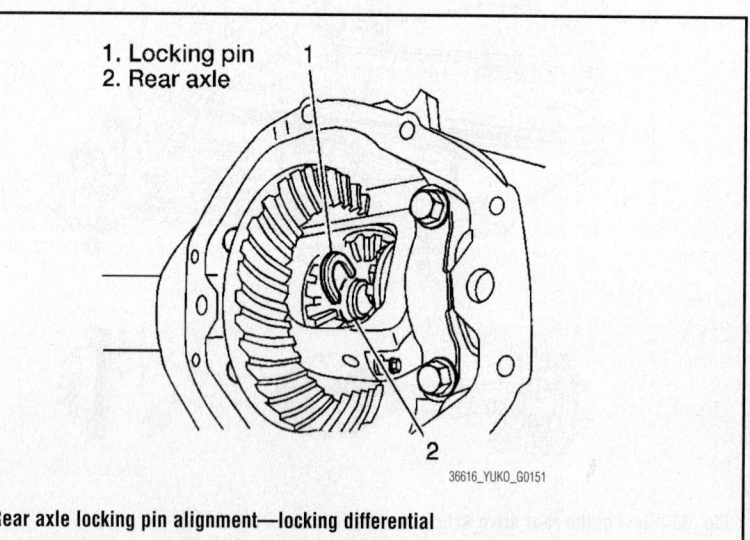
1. Locking pin
2. Rear axle

Fig. 37 Rear axle locking pin alignment—locking differential

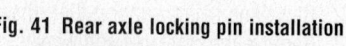
Fig. 41 Rear axle locking pin installation

To install:

➡️**Be sure to use new fasteners, as required.**

14. Position the bearing and seal to its mounting.

➡️**Be sure that the bearing is fully seated in the rear axle shaft housing.**

15. Using an installer tool and driver, install the bearing, then the seal. Drive the tool into the bore until the axle shaft seal bottoms flush with the tube.

16. Install the axle shaft to its mounting. Use care not to damage the seal.

➡️**Pull out on the axle shaft after the lock has been installed to ensure that the lock is seated properly.**

17. Install the lock in the axle, if equipped with a non-locking differential.

18. Install the lock on the axle shaft, if equipped with locking differential.

➡️**On a locking differential, keep the differential pinion shaft slightly withdrawn.**

19. Install the differential gear shaft. Install a new gear shaft bolt. Tighten to 25 ft. lbs (34 Nm), for 8.6 axle and 37 ft. lbs. (50 Nm), for 9.5 axle.

20. Continue the installation in the reverse order of the removal procedure.

21. Be sure to fill the differential with the proper grade and type fluid.

REAR PINION SEAL

REMOVAL & INSTALLATION

See Figures 42 through 46.

Special Tools:
• J 8614-01: Holder/Remover
• J 44414: Oil Seal Installer

➡️**Observe and mark the positions of all the driveline components, relative to the propeller shaft and the axles, prior to disassembly. These components include the propeller shafts, drive axles, pinion flanges, output shafts, etc. Reassemble all the components in the exact places in which you removed the parts. Follow any specifications, torque values, and any measurements made prior to disassembly.**

1. Before servicing the vehicle, refer to the Precautions Section.

2. Raise and safely support the vehicle.

3. Remove the tire and wheel assemblies.

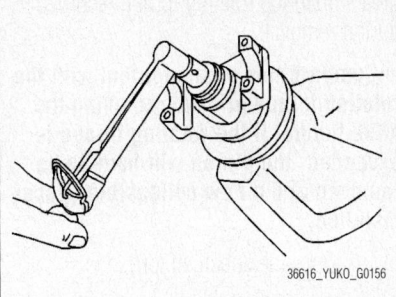

Fig. 42 Using an inch-pound torque wrench, measure the amount of torque required to rotate the pinion

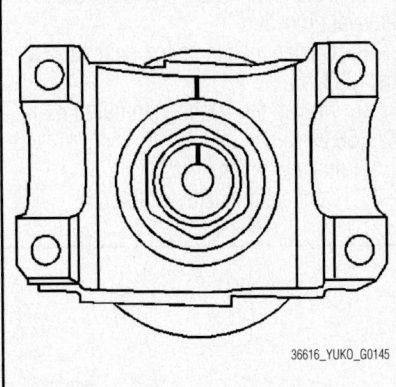

Fig. 43 Scribe an alignment line between the pinion shaft and the pinion yoke

4. Remove the rear wheel axle shafts, if equipped with the 10.5 inch axle.

5. Remove the rear brake rotors, if equipped with the 8.6 or 9.5 inch axle.

6. Remove the driveshaft from the vehicle.

7. Using an inch-pound torque wrench, measure the amount of torque required to rotate the pinion. Record this measurement for reassembly.

8. Place an alignment mark between the pinion and the pinion yoke.

9. Using the J 8614-01 holder/remover, remove the pinion nut.

10. Remove the washer.

➡️**Rotate the J 8614-3 clockwise to remove the yoke.**

11. Using the J 8614-2 and the J 8614-3, remove the pinion yoke.

12. Using a suitable tool, remove the drive pinion seal.

To install:

13. Using the J 44414 installer, install a new pinion oil seal.

14. Apply sealant to the splines of the pinion yoke.

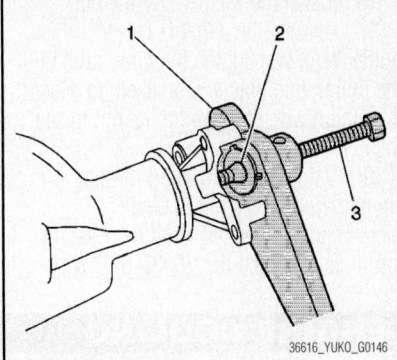

Fig. 44 Install the J 8614-01 (1), J 8614-2 (2), and J 8614-3 (3) for pinion yoke removal

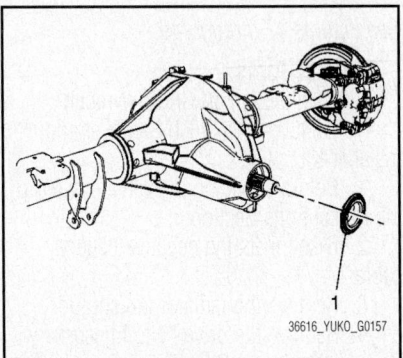

Fig. 45 Using a suitable tool, remove the drive pinion seal (1)

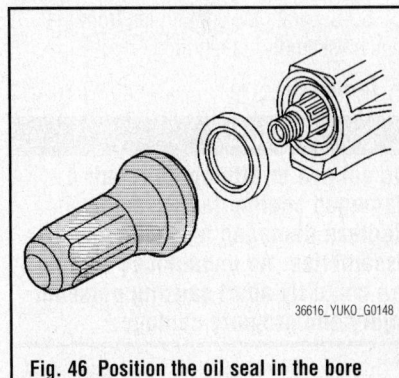

Fig. 46 Position the oil seal in the bore for installation

❊❊ WARNING

Do not hammer the pinion flange/yoke onto the pinion shaft. Pinion components may be damaged if the pinion flange/yoke is hammered onto the pinion shaft.

➡️**Align the reference marks and install the drive pinion yoke.**

15. Using a soft-faced hammer, install the drive flange onto the pinion shaft until a few treads show through the drive flange.

16. Install the washer and the nut.

17. Using a the J 8614-01 holder/remover, tighten the pinion nut until the pinion end play is just taken up. Rotate the pinion while tightening the nut to seat the bearing.

18. Using an inch-pound torque wrench, tighten the nut in small increments, as needed, until the rotating torque is 3–5 inch lbs. (0.40–0.57 Nm)

greater than the rotating torque recorded during removal.

➡ **Compare this measurement with the rotating torque prior to removing the drive flange. If the rotating torque is exceeded, the pinion will have to be removed and a new collapsible spacer installed.**

19. Once the specified torque is

obtained, rotate the pinion several times to ensure the bearings have seated.

20. Install the driveshaft assembly.

21. Install the axle shafts, if equipped with the 10.5 inch axle.

22. Install the rear brake rotors, if equipped with the 8.6 or 9.5 inch axle.

23. Install the tire and wheel assemblies.

24. Inspect and add axle lubricant to the axle housing, if necessary.

ENGINE COOLING

ENGINE FAN

REMOVAL & INSTALLATION

Belt Driven Fan

See Figures 47 through 49.

Special Tools:
- J 41240-5A: Fan Clutch Wrench
- J-48460: Fan Clutch Remover and Installer Kit

1. Before servicing the vehicle, refer to the Precautions Section.

2. Disconnect the negative battery cable.

3. Remove the radiator fan shroud.

4. Remove the drive belt, if necessary. Refer to Accessory Drive Belts, removal & installation.

5. Install the cooling fan removal tool. Remove the cooling fan from its mounting.

6. Separate the cooling fan from the clutch assembly, as required.

To install:

❋ CAUTION

Do not use or attempt to repair a damaged cooling fan assembly. Replace damaged fans with new assemblies. An unbalanced cooling fan could fly apart causing personal injury and property damage.

➡ **Be sure to use new fasteners, as required.**

7. Installation is the reverse of the removal procedure.

8. Tighten the fan clutch bolts to 17 ft. lbs. (23 Nm).

9. Tighten the cooling fan nut to 41 ft. lbs. (56 Nm).

10. Install the fan shroud.

11. Connect the battery cable.

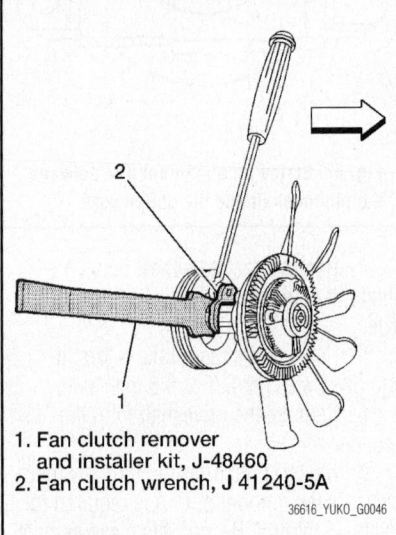

1. Fan clutch remover and installer kit, J-48460
2. Fan clutch wrench, J 41240-5A

36616_YUKO_G0046

Fig. 48 Cooling fan removal tool installation

Dual Electric Fans

See Figures 50 and 51.

1. Before servicing the vehicle, refer to the Precautions Section.

2. Disconnect the negative battery cable.

3. Remove the cooling fan and shroud.

4. Remove the cooling fan blade retainers.

5. Remove the cooling fan blades.

To install:

➡ **The electric cooling fan assembly uses a 5-blade fan and a 7-blade fan. It does not matter on which side the fan blades are installed. DO NOT install two 5-blade assemblies or two 7-blade assemblies, as this would cause a noise issue.**

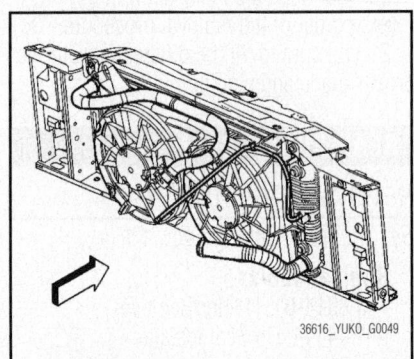

36616_YUKO_G0049

Fig. 50 View of electric fan shroud and related components

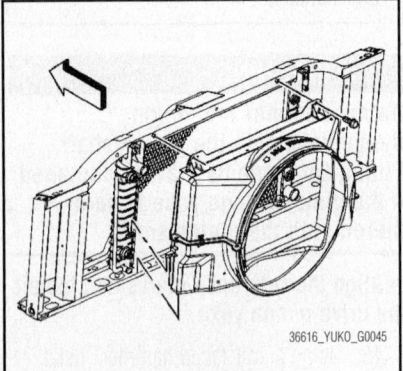

36616_YUKO_G0045

Fig. 47 Remove the radiator fan shroud

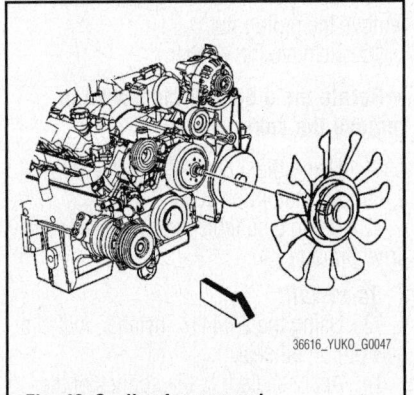

36616_YUKO_G0047

Fig. 49 Cooling fan removal

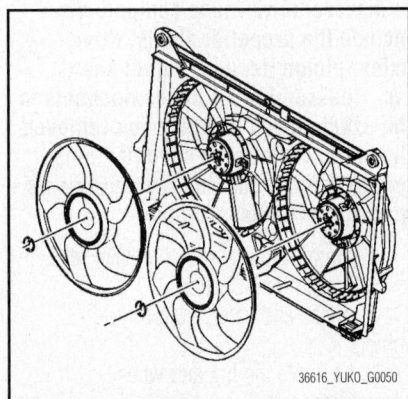

36616_YUKO_G0050

Fig. 51 Remove the cooling fan blades

➡ Be sure to use new fasteners, as required.

6. Install the cooling fan blades.
7. Install the cooling fan blade retainers.
8. Install the cooling fan and shroud.
9. Connect the negative battery cable.

RADIATOR

REMOVAL & INSTALLATION

See Figures 52 through 55.

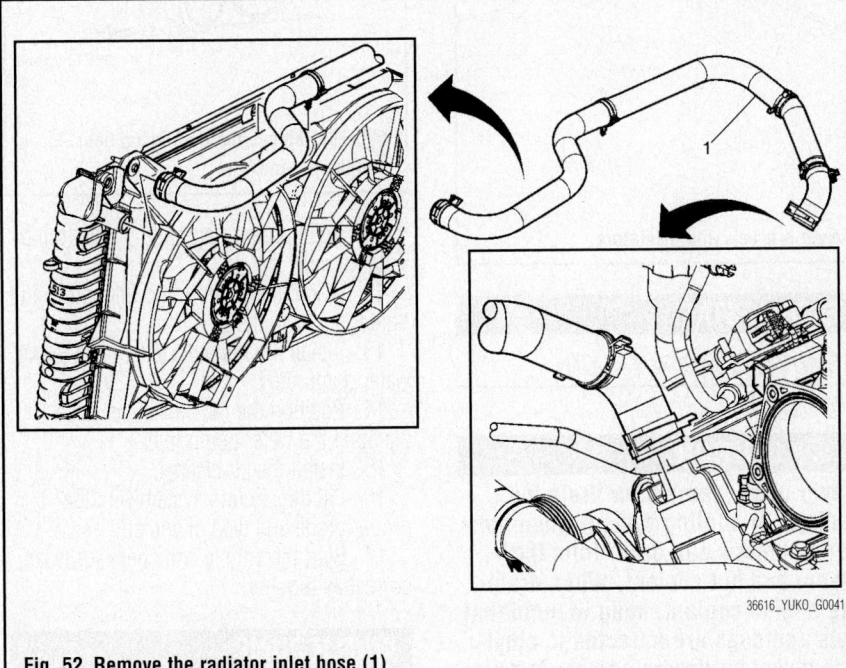

Fig. 52 Remove the radiator inlet hose (1)

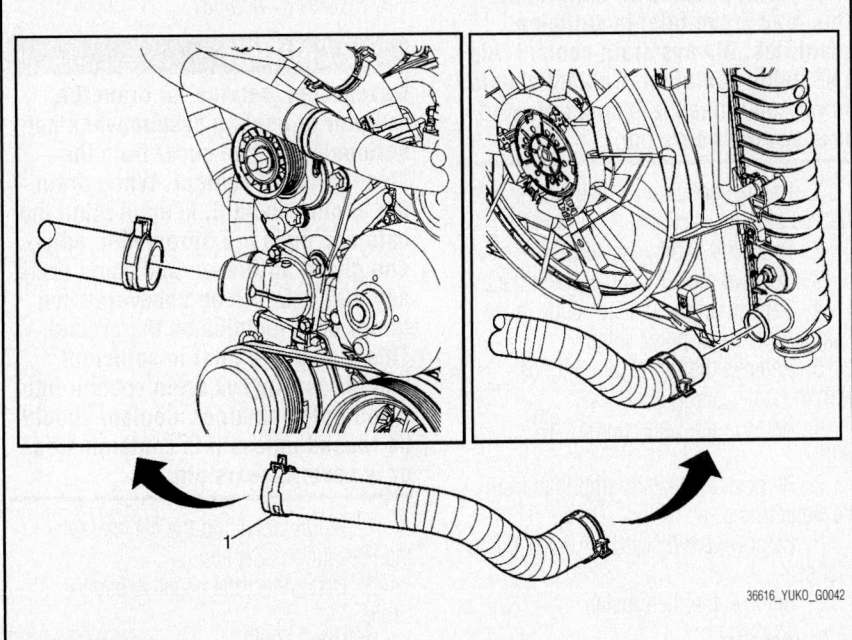

Fig. 53 Remove the radiator outlet hose

✳✳ CAUTION

Never open, service, or drain the radiator or cooling system when hot; serious burns can occur from the steam and hot coolant. When draining engine coolant, keep in mind that cats and dogs are attracted to ethylene glycol antifreeze and could drink any that is left in an uncovered container or in puddles on the ground. This may prove fatal in sufficient

quantities. Always drain coolant into a sealable container. Coolant should be reused unless it is contaminated or is several years old.

1. Before servicing the vehicle, refer to the Precautions Section.
2. Disconnect the negative battery cable.
3. Remove the surge tank inlet hose from the radiator.
4. Remove the air cleaner outlet duct.
5. Using Special Tool J 38185, reposition the radiator hose clamps.
6. Remove the radiator inlet and outlet hoses.
7. Disconnect the electrical connectors from the cooling fans.
8. Remove the clip attaching the wiring harness to the shroud.
9. Remove the transmission cooler line bolts from the fan shroud.
10. If necessary, open the engine oil cooler line clip and remove the cooler lines from the clip.
11. Remove the cooling fan shroud bolts.
12. Remove the cooling fans and shroud.
13. Remove the oil coolant lines, if equipped.
14. Remove the transmission fluid cooler hose from the radiator.
15. Remove the radiator from the lower brackets and insulators.

To install:

16. Install the radiator on the lower brackets and insulators.
17. Install the radiator retaining bolts and tighten to 18 ft. lbs. (25 Nm).

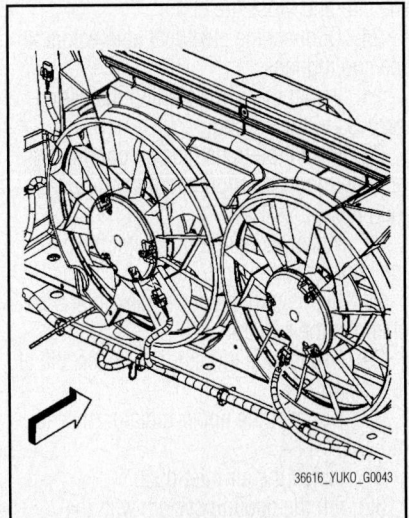

Fig. 54 Disconnect the electrical connectors from the cooling fans and remove the wiring harness from the shroud

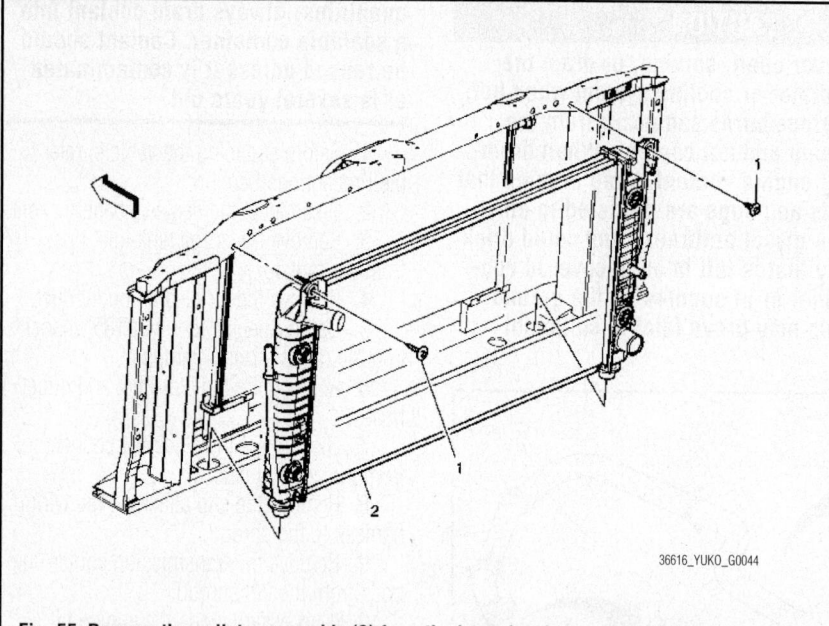

36616_YUKO_G0044

Fig. 55 Remove the radiator assembly (2) from the lower brackets and insulators

18. Install the quick-connect transmission fluid cooler hose to the radiator.

19. Install the transmission fluid cooler hose to the auxiliary oil cooler, if equipped.

20. Install the oil coolant lines, if equipped.

21. Install the cooling fan and shroud.

➡️**Insert the 3 lower tabs into the radiator support flange. Keeping the shroud parallel to the radiator will ensure the correct installation of the lower tabs.**

22. Install the cooling fan shroud bolts and tighten the bolts to 80 inch lbs. (9 Nm).

23. If equipped, install the cooler lines to the clip and close the clip.

24. Connect the electrical connectors to the cooling fans.

25. Install the clip attaching the wiring harness to the shroud.

26. Install the transmission cooling line bolts to the fan shroud and tighten to 35 inch lbs. (4 Nm).

27. Install the surge tank inlet hose to the radiator.

28. Reposition the surge tank inlet hose clamp at the radiator.

29. Engage the radiator inlet hose clip at the fan shroud.

30. Connect the upper radiator hose to radiator.

31. Install the air inlet duct.

32. Fill the cooling system with the proper grade and type of coolant.

33. Start the engine and check for leaks, correct as required.

THERMOSTAT

REMOVAL & INSTALLATION

See Figure 56.

✳✳ CAUTION

Never open, service, or drain the radiator or cooling system when hot; serious burns can occur from the steam and hot coolant. When draining engine coolant, keep in mind that cats and dogs are attracted to ethylene glycol antifreeze and could drink any that is left in an uncovered container or in puddles on the ground. This may prove fatal in sufficient quantities. Always drain coolant into a sealable container. Coolant should be reused unless it is contaminated or is several years old.

1. Before servicing the vehicle, refer to the Precautions Section.

2. Drain the cooling system.

3. Remove the air cleaner outlet duct.

4. Reposition the radiator outlet hose clamp at the water pump inlet.

5. Remove the radiator outlet hose from the water pump inlet.

6. Remove the water pump inlet bolts.

7. Remove the water pump inlet from the water pump.

8. Remove and discard the water pump inlet seal.

9. Remove the thermostat.

To install:

10. Install the thermostat.

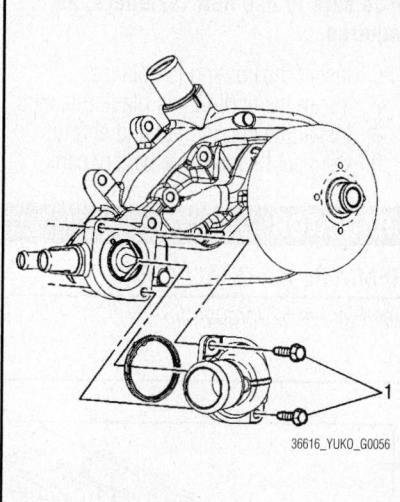

36616_YUKO_G0056

Fig. 56 Remove the thermostat housing and the thermostat

11. Position the water pump inlet to the water pump.

12. Install the water pump inlet bolts and tighten to 11 ft. lbs. (15 Nm).

13. Install the radiator outlet hose to the water pump inlet.

14. Position the radiator outlet hose clamp at the water pump inlet.

15. Install the air cleaner.

16. Fill the cooling system with the proper grade and type of coolant.

17. Start the engine and check for leaks, correct as required.

WATER PUMP

REMOVAL & INSTALLATION

See Figures 57 and 58.

✳✳ CAUTION

Never open, service, or drain the radiator or cooling system when hot; serious burns can occur from the steam and hot coolant. When draining engine coolant, keep in mind that cats and dogs are attracted to ethylene glycol antifreeze and could drink any that is left in an uncovered container or in puddles on the ground. This may prove fatal in sufficient quantities. Always drain coolant into a sealable container. Coolant should be reused unless it is contaminated or is several years old.

1. Before servicing the vehicle, refer to the Precautions Section.

2. Disconnect the negative battery cable.

3. Remove the air cleaner outlet duct.

4. Drain the cooling system.

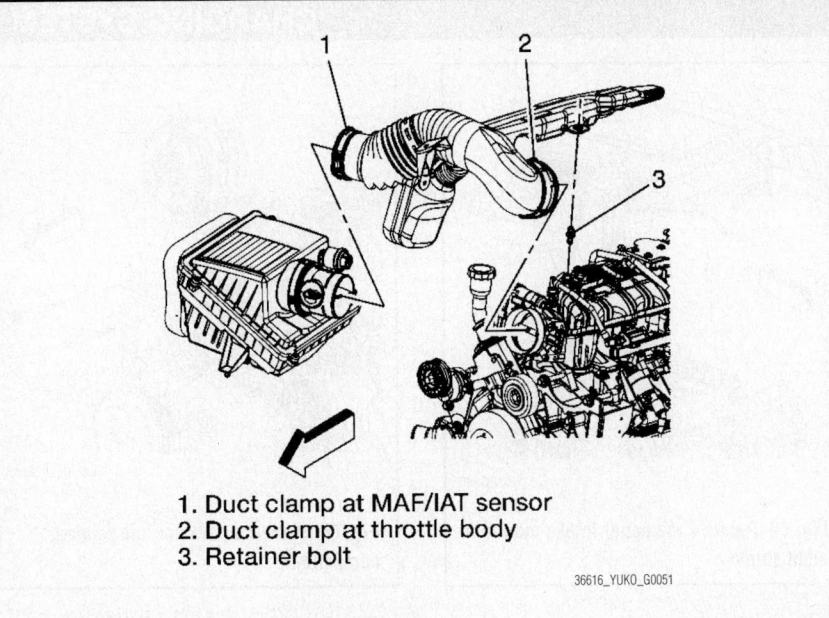

1. Duct clamp at MAF/IAT sensor
2. Duct clamp at throttle body
3. Retainer bolt

36616_YUKO_G0051

Fig. 57 View of air cleaner resonator outlet duct

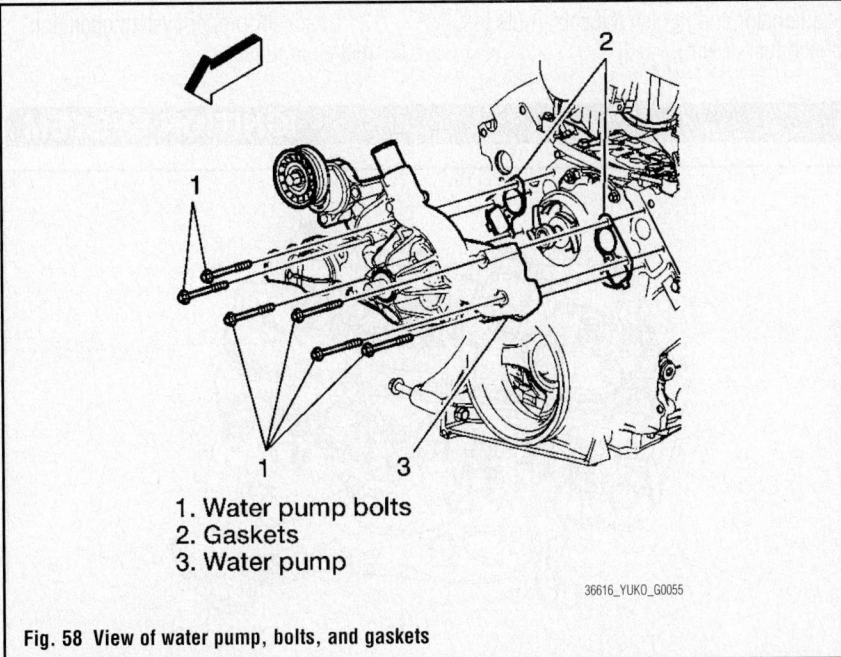

1. Water pump bolts
2. Gaskets
3. Water pump

36616_YUKO_G0055

Fig. 58 View of water pump, bolts, and gaskets

5. Reposition the radiator vent inlet hose clamp at the coolant air bleed pipe fitting.

6. Remove the radiator vent inlet hose from the coolant air bleed pipe fitting.

7. Reposition the radiator inlet hose clamp at the water pump.

8. Remove the radiator inlet hose from the water pump.

9. Reposition the radiator inlet hose and vent inlet hose out of the way.

10. Remove the accessory drive belt. Refer to Accessory Drive Belts, removal & installation.

11. Reposition the radiator outlet hose clamp at the water pump.

12. Remove the radiator outlet hose from the water pump.

13. Reposition the outlet hose out of the way.

14. Reposition the radiator surge tank outlet hose clamp at the water pump.

15. Remove the radiator surge tank outlet hose from the water pump.

16. Reposition the outlet hose out of the way.

17. Reposition the heater inlet hose clamp at the water pump.

18. Remove the heater inlet hose from the water pump.

19. Reposition the inlet hose out of the way.

20. Remove the water pump bolts.

21. Remove the water pump and gaskets. Discard the gaskets.

To install:

✳✳ WARNING

DO NOT use cooling system seal tabs, or similar compounds, unless otherwise instructed. The use of cooling system seal tabs, or similar compounds, may restrict coolant flow through the passages of the cooling system or the engine components. Restricted coolant flow may cause engine overheating and/or damage to the cooling system or the engine components/assembly.

➡All gasket surfaces are to be free of oil or other foreign material during assembly.

22. Position the water pump and NEW gaskets to the engine block.

23. Install the water pump bolts:
   a. Step 1: Tighten the bolts to 11 ft. lbs. (15 Nm).
   b. Step 2: Tighten the bolts to 22 ft. lbs. (30 Nm).

24. Install the heater inlet hose to the water pump and secure it with the hose clamp.

25. Install the radiator surge tank outlet hose to the water pump and secure it with the hose clamp.

26. Install the radiator outlet hose to the water pump and secure it with the hose clamp.

27. Install the accessory drive belt. Refer to Accessory Drive Belts, removal & installation.

28. Position the radiator inlet hose and vent inlet hose to the correct position.

29. Install the radiator inlet hose to the water pump.

30. Position the radiator inlet hose clamp at the water pump.

31. Install the radiator vent inlet hose to the coolant air bleed pipe fitting.

32. Position the radiator vent inlet hose clamp at the coolant air bleed pipe fitting.

33. Fill the cooling system with the proper grade and type of coolant.

34. Install the air cleaner outlet duct.

35. Start the engine and check for leaks, correct as required.

ENGINE ELECTRICAL

CHARGING SYSTEM

ALTERNATOR

REMOVAL & INSTALLATION

See Figures 59 and 60.

1. Before servicing the vehicle, refer to the Precautions Section.
2. Disconnect the negative battery cable.
3. Remove the upper intake manifold sight shield.
4. Remove the accessory drive belt. Refer to Accessory Drive Belts, removal & installation.
5. Disconnect the electrical connectors from the alternator.
6. Remove the alternator retaining bolts.
7. Remove the component from its mounting.

To install:

➡**Be sure to use new fasteners, as required.**

8. Position the alternator to its mounting.

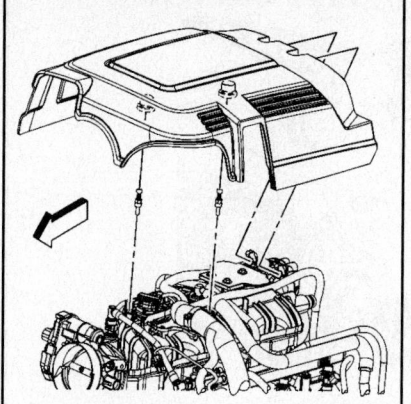

36616_YUKO_G0005

Fig. 59 Remove the upper intake manifold sight shield

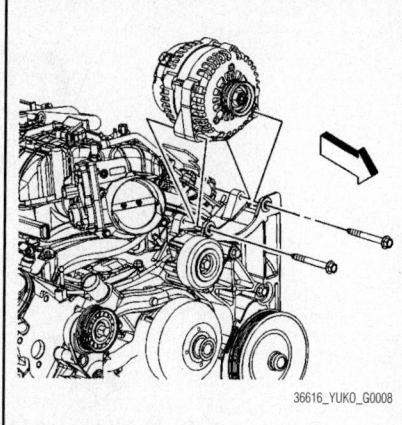

36616_YUKO_G0008

Fig. 60 View of alternator and related components

9. Tighten the retaining bolts to 41 ft. lbs. (55 Nm).
10. Connect the electrical connectors to the alternator and tighten the cable nuts to 80 inch lbs. (9 Nm).

11. Continue the installation in the reverse order of the removal procedure.
12. Connect the battery cable.
13. Check for proper system operation. Correct as required.

ENGINE ELECTRICAL

IGNITION SYSTEM

FIRING ORDER

See Figure 61.

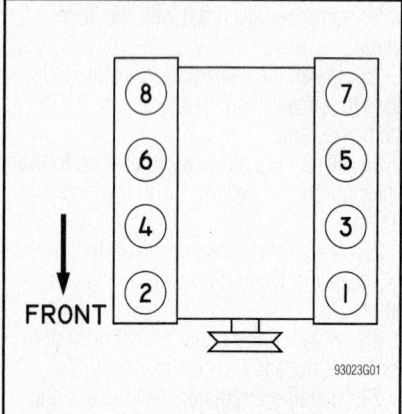

93023G01

Fig. 61 4.8L, 5.3L, 6.0L, and 6.2L Engines
Firing order: 1–8–7–2–6–5–4–3
Distributorless ignition system (one coil for each cylinder)

IGNITION COIL

REMOVAL & INSTALLATION

See Figures 59 through 64.

1. Before servicing the vehicle, refer to the Precautions Section.

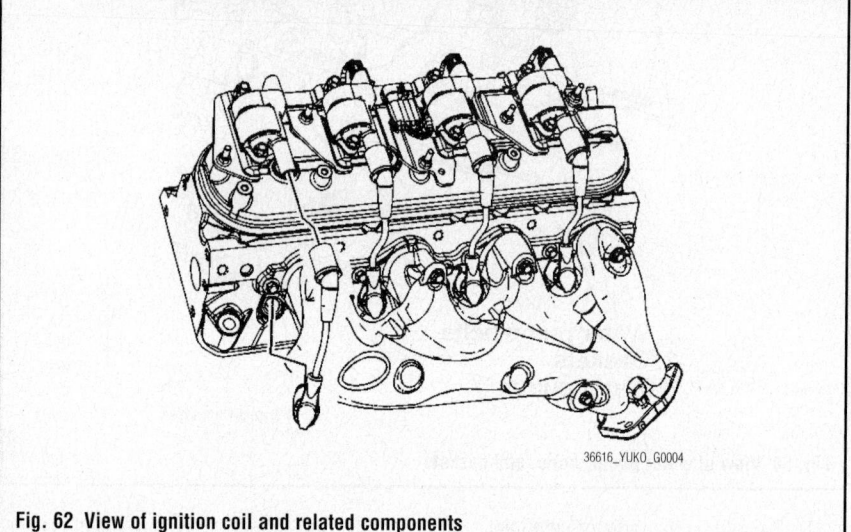

36616_YUKO_G0004

Fig. 62 View of ignition coil and related components

2. Disconnect the negative battery cable.
3. Remove the upper intake manifold sight shield.
4. Disconnect the spark plug wires at the ignition coils.
5. Disconnect the coil harness connector.
6. Remove the coil mounting bolts. Remove the coil from its mounting.

➡**Two different manufacturers of ignition coils are used on this vehicle. Refer to the illustrations for identification.**

To install:

➡**Be sure to use new fasteners, as required.**

7. Position the component on its mounting.
8. Tighten the retaining bolts to 89 inch lbs. (10 Nm).
9. Continue the installation in the reverse order of the removal procedure.
10. Connect the negative battery cable.

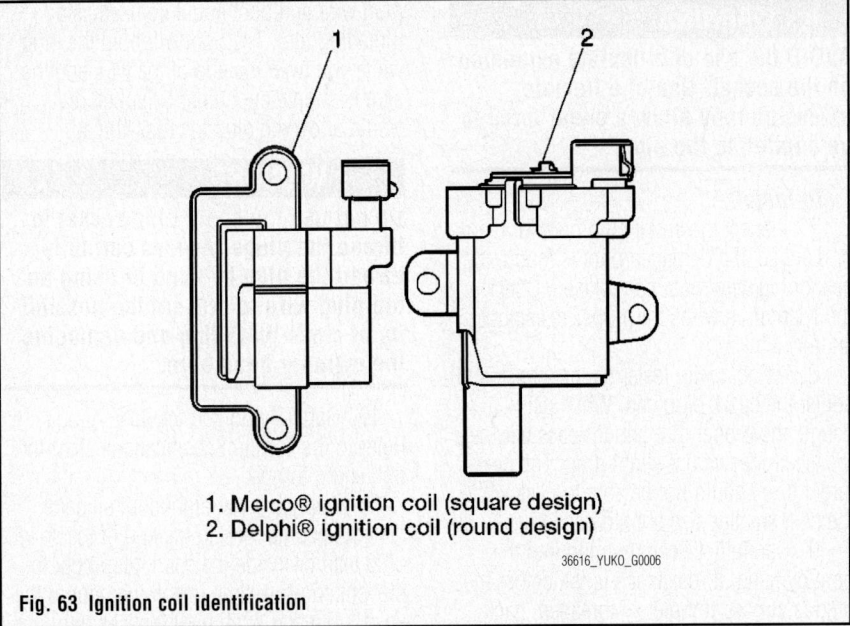

1. Melco® ignition coil (square design)
2. Delphi® ignition coil (round design)

36616_YUKO_G0006

Fig. 63 Ignition coil identification

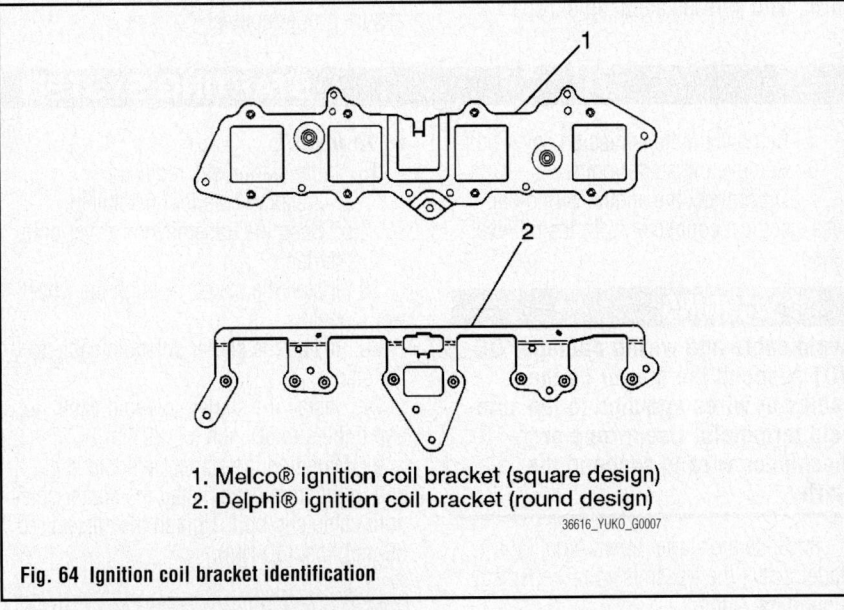

1. Melco® ignition coil bracket (square design)
2. Delphi® ignition coil bracket (round design)

36616_YUKO_G0007

Fig. 64 Ignition coil bracket identification

SPARK PLUGS

REMOVAL & INSTALLATION

See Figure 65.

All models were originally equipped with platinum-tipped spark plugs that can be in service for 100,000 miles (161,000 km). This holds true unless internal engine wear or damage and/or improperly operating emissions controls cause plug fouling. Remove and inspect the platinum plugs before the recommended mileage, as needed. Most platinum plugs should not be cleaned or re-gapped. If their condition is unsuitable, the plugs should be replaced.

When removing the spark plugs, work on 1 at a time. Don't start by removing the plug

wires all at once because, unless you number them, they may get mixed. Take time to number the wires with tape before removing them.

1. Before servicing the vehicle, refer to the Precautions Section.

2. Disconnect the negative battery cable.

✳✳ WARNING

If the vehicle has been run recently, allow the engine to thoroughly cool. Attempting to remove the plugs from a hot cylinder head could cause the plugs to seize and damage the threads in the cylinder head.

3. Check for access to the plugs on your vehicle. The wheel wells of some vehicles covered by this manual are designed to allow access to the sides of the engine. A rubber cover may be draped over the opening, and it may require removal of 1 or more plastic body snap fasteners before you can move it aside for clearance. If this is your best access point, raise and support the vehicle safely then remove the front tire and wheel assemblies.

➡**On some models, the engine cover may be removed to provide additional access to the spark plugs.**

4. Carefully twist the spark plug wire boot to loosen it, then pull upward and remove the boot from the plug. Be sure to pull on the boot and not on the wire, otherwise the connector located inside the boot may become separated.

➡**A spark plug wire removal tool is recommended as it will make removal**

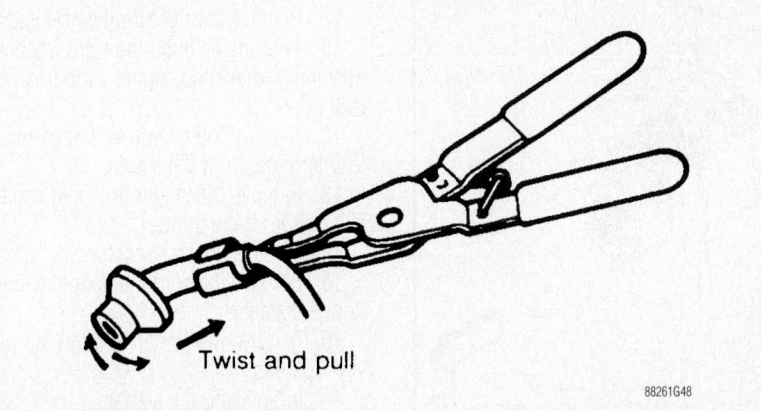

Twist and pull

88261G48

Fig. 65 A spark plug wire removal tool is recommended to prevent wire damage (and to make it easier)

easier and help prevent damage to the boot and wire assembly.

5. Using compressed air (and SAFETY GLASSES), blow any water or debris from the spark plug well to assure that no harmful contaminants are allowed to enter the combustion chamber when the spark plug is removed. If compressed air is not available, use a rag or a brush to clean the area.

→Remove the spark plugs when the engine is cold, if possible, to prevent damage to the threads. If plug removal is difficult, apply a few drops of penetrating oil or silicone spray to the area around the base of the plug, and allow it a few minutes to work.

6. Using a spark plug socket (usually a ⅝ inch socket on these engines) equipped with a rubber insert to properly hold the plug, turn the spark plug counterclockwise to loosen and remove the spark plug from the bore.

✳✳ WARNING

AVOID the use of a flexible extension on the socket. Use of a flexible extension may allow a shear force to be applied to the plug.

To install:

7. Inspect the spark plug boot for tears or damage. If a damaged boot is found, the spark plug wire must be replaced. Check the spark plug wires for proper resistance and/or damage.

8. Using a wire feeler gauge, check and adjust the spark plug gap. When using a gauge, the proper size should pass between the electrodes with a slight drag. The next larger size should not be able to pass while the next smaller size should pass freely.

9. Carefully thread the plug into the bore by hand. If resistance is felt before the plug is almost completely threaded, back the plug out and begin threading again. In small, hard to reach areas, an old spark plug wire and boot could be used as a threading tool. The boot will hold the plug while you twist the end of the wire and the wire is supple enough to twist before it would allow the plug to cross-thread.

✳✳ WARNING

Do not use the spark plug socket to thread the plugs. Always carefully thread the plug by hand or using an old plug wire to prevent the possibility of cross-threading and damaging the cylinder head bore.

10. Carefully tighten the spark plug. Refer to the Torque Specifications chart for tightening torque.

11. Apply a small amount of silicone dielectric compound to the end of the spark plug lead or inside the spark plug boot to prevent sticking, then install the boot to the spark plug and push until it clicks into place. Gently pull back on the boot to assure proper contact.

ENGINE ELECTRICAL

STARTER

REMOVAL & INSTALLATION

See Figures 66 and 67.

1. Before servicing the vehicle, refer to the Precautions Section.
2. Disconnect the negative battery cable.
3. Raise and safely support the vehicle.
4. Remove the oil pan skid plate, if equipped.

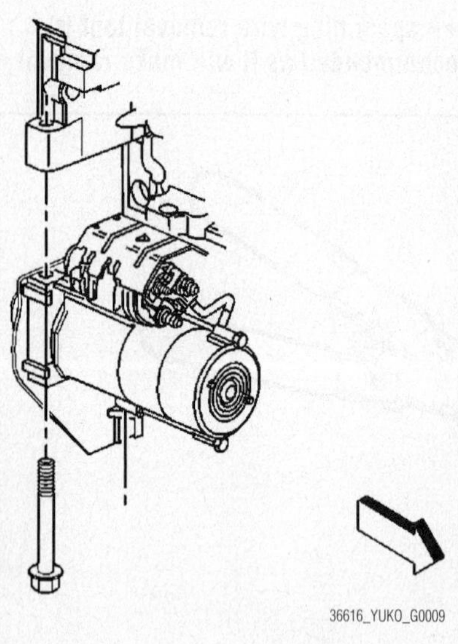

5. Remove the transmission cover bolt.
6. Remove the starter bolts.
7. Disconnect the engine wiring harness electrical connector from the oil level sensor.

✳✳ WARNING

Avoid cable and wiring damage. DO NOT suspend the starter by the cables or wires attached to the solenoid terminals. Use a rope or mechanics wire to suspend the starter.

8. Slide the starter forward until the starter clears the transmission. Properly support the starter.
9. Lower the vehicle half way.
10. Remove the right front wheel and tire.
11. Working through the right wheel well opening, remove the engine wiring harness lead nut.
12. Remove the engine wiring harness lead terminal from the starter.
13. Remove the starter solenoid cable clip bolt from the frame.
14. Remove the starter solenoid cable nut.
15. Remove the starter solenoid cable from the starter.
16. Remove the starter through the wheel well opening.
17. If replacing the starter:
   a. Unsnap the transmission cover from the starter.
   b. Remove the starter heat shield.

STARTING SYSTEM

To install:

18. If the starter was replaced:
   a. Install the starter heat shield.
   b. Snap the transmission cover onto the starter.
19. Install the starter through the wheel well opening.
20. Install the starter solenoid cable to the starter.
21. Install the starter solenoid cable nut and tighten to 80 inch lbs. (9 Nm).
22. Position the starter solenoid cable clip to the frame and install the starter solenoid cable clip bolt. Tighten the clip bolt to 89 inch lbs. (10 Nm).

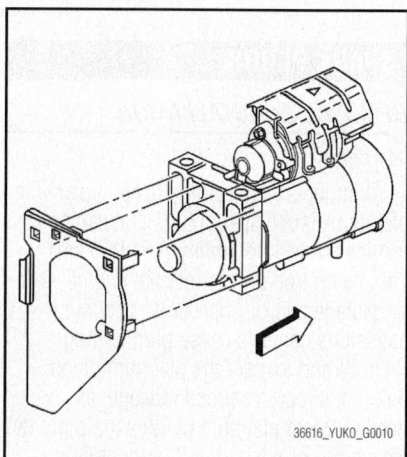

36616_YUKO_G0010

Fig. 67 Remove the starter through the wheel well opening

36616_YUKO_G0009

Fig. 66 Remove the starter bolts

23. Install the engine wiring harness lead terminal to the starter.

24. Install the engine wiring harness lead nut and tighten to 30 inch lbs. (3 Nm).

25. Position the starter into place.

26. Install the starter bolts and tighten the bolts to 37 ft. lbs. (50 Nm).

27. Install the right front wheel and tire.

28. Raise and safely support the vehicle.

29. Connect the engine wiring harness electrical connector to the oil level sensor.

30. Install the transmission cover bolt and tighten to 80 inch lbs. (9 Nm).

31. Install the oil pan skid plate, if equipped.

32. Lower the vehicle.

33. Connect the negative battery cable.

SOLENOID OR RELAY REPLACEMENT

See Figures 68 and 69.

1. Before servicing the vehicle, refer to the Precautions Section.

2. Remove the starter motor. Refer to Starter, removal & installation.

3. Reposition the M-terminal stud weather cover.

4. Clean the epoxy coating from the M-terminal stud.

5. Loosen the M-terminal stud nut.

6. Remove the cable from the M-terminal stud.

7. Remove the solenoid bolts.

8. Separate the solenoid from the housing and unhook the solenoid plunger from the drive gear lever.

9. Note that the spring is positioned against the drive gear lever and the drive gear lever is placed inside the solenoid plunger loop.

10. Remove the solenoid housing.

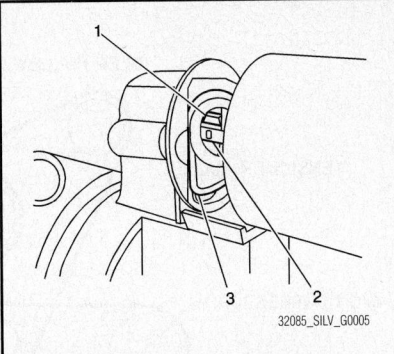

Fig. 68 The spring (3) is positioned against the drive gear lever (1) and the drive gear lever is placed inside the solenoid plunger loop (2)

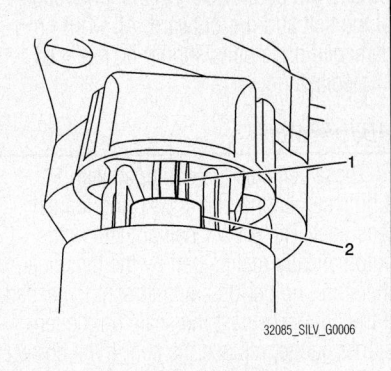

Fig. 69 Make sure that the drive gear lever (1) is properly installed into the solenoid plunger (2) loop

11. If necessary, remove the solenoid plunger and spring.

To install:

12. If necessary, install the solenoid plunger and spring.

13. Using Three Bond silicone 1207B, GM P/N 97720043, seal the starter solenoid attachment area.

✳✳ WARNING

Make sure that the drive gear lever is properly installed into the solenoid plunger loop. Improper installation of the drive gear lever will cause an abnormal or no operation condition of the starter.

14. Install the solenoid, making sure to insert the drive gear lever into the solenoid plunger loop, and perform the following:

    a. Pull the gear lever out away from the starter housing and pull the plunger out away from the solenoid.

    b. Tip the solenoid and insert the lever into the loop. Push the solenoid against the housing.

15. Install the solenoid bolts and tighten the bolts to 89 inch lbs. (10 Nm).

16. Wipe the excess silicone pressed out during the solenoid installation from around the base of the solenoid to make a weather proof seal.

17. Install the cable to the M-terminal stud between the washers and terminal nut.

18. Tighten the M-terminal stud nut to 71 inch lbs. (8 Nm).

19. Using Three Bond silicone 1207B, GM P/N 97720043, seal the M-terminal stud connection.

20. Reposition the M-terminal stud weather cover.

21. Bench test the starter in a free-run condition prior to installation.

22. Install the starter motor.

ENGINE MECHANICAL

➡ **Disconnecting the negative battery cable may interfere with the functions of the on board computer systems and may require the computer to undergo a relearning process, once the negative battery cable is reconnected.**

ACCESSORY DRIVE BELTS

ACCESSORY BELT ROUTING

See Figure 70.

INSPECTION

Inspect the drive belt for signs of glazing or cracking. A glazed belt will be perfectly smooth from slippage, while a good belt will have a slight texture of fabric visible.

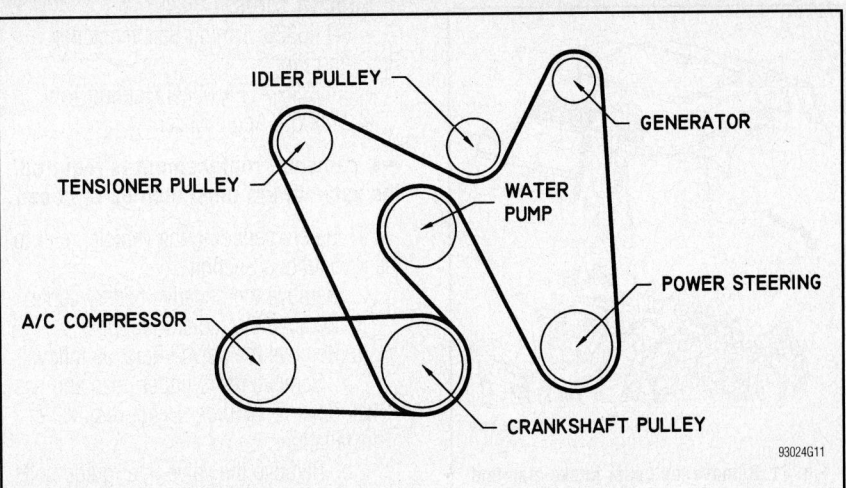

Fig. 70 Accessory drive belt routing—4.8L, 5.3L, 6.0L and 6.2L engines

Cracks will usually start at the inner edge of the belt and run outward. All worn or damaged drive belts should be replaced immediately.

ADJUSTMENT

These vehicles are equipped with a single serpentine belt and spring loaded tensioner. The proper belt adjustment is automatically maintained by the tensioner, therefore, no periodic adjustment is needed. If the pointer is past the scale on the tensioner gauge, replace the belt. If the correct belt tension cannot be achieved, make sure the correct belt is installed. If the correct tension is still not achieved, check for proper mounting on all accessory drive pulleys.

REMOVAL & INSTALLATION

See Figures 71 and 72.

1. Before servicing the vehicle, refer to the Precautions Section.
2. Remove the air cleaner outlet duct.
3. Remove the upper intake manifold sight shield.
4. Install a breaker bar with hex-head socket to the drive belt tensioner bolt.
5. Rotate the drive belt tensioner clockwise in order to relieve tension on the belt.
6. Remove the drive belt from the pulleys and the drive belt tensioner.
7. Slowly release the tension on the drive belt tensioner.
8. Remove the breaker bar and socket from the drive belt tensioner bolt.
9. Clean and inspect the belt surfaces of all the pulleys.

To install:

10. Route the drive belt around all the pulleys except the idler pulley.

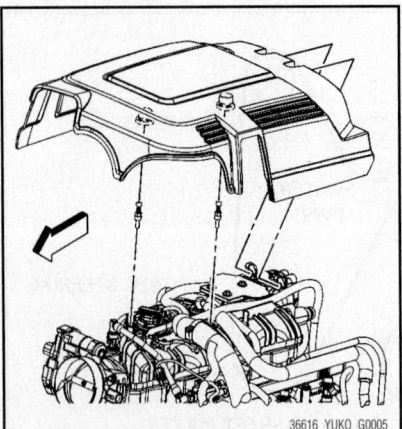

Fig. 71 Remove the upper intake manifold sight shield

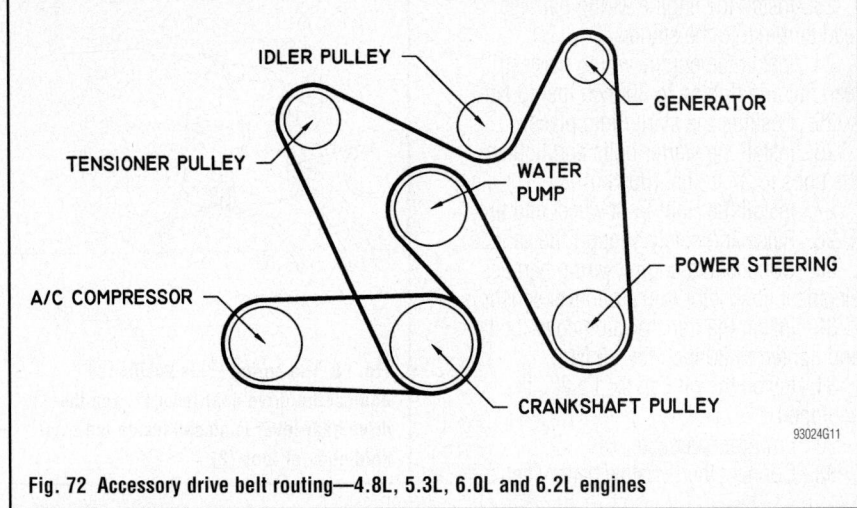

Fig. 72 Accessory drive belt routing—4.8L, 5.3L, 6.0L and 6.2L engines

11. Install the breaker bar with hex-head socket to the belt tensioner bolt.
12. Rotate the belt tensioner clockwise in order to relieve the tension on the tensioner.
13. Install the drive belt under the idler pulley.
14. Slowly release the tension on the belt tensioner.
15. Remove the breaker bar and socket from the belt tensioner bolt.
16. Inspect the drive belt for proper installation and alignment.
17. Install the upper intake manifold sight shield.
18. Install the air cleaner outlet duct.
19. Start the vehicle and inspect the drive belt for proper operation.

CAMSHAFT AND VALVE LIFTERS

REMOVAL & INSTALLATION

See Figures 73 through 83.

Special Tools:
• EN 46330: Timing Belt Tensioner Retaining Pin
• J 42386-A: Flywheel Holding Tool
• J 45059: Angle Meter

➡**If camshaft replacement is required, the valve lifters must also be replaced.**

1. Before servicing the vehicle, refer to the Precautions Section.
2. Remove the negative battery cable.
3. Remove the radiator support.
4. Remove the valve lifters, as follows:
   a. Remove the cylinder head and gasket. Refer to Cylinder Head, removal & installation.
   b. Remove the valve lifter guide bolts (211).

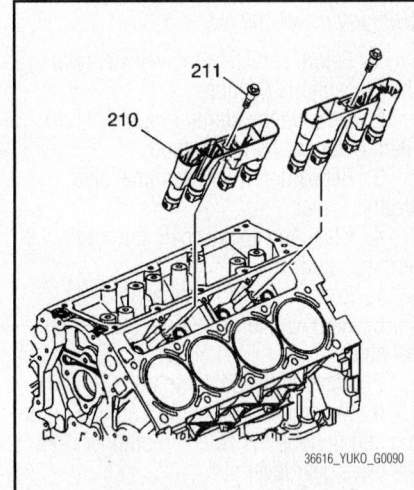

Fig. 73 Remove the valve lifter guide bolts (211) and valve lifter guides (210) with the lifters

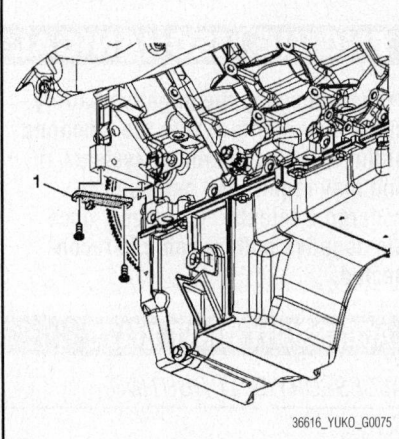

Fig. 74 Install Special Tool J 42386-A (1) and bolts. Use one M10 bolt (1.5 x 120mm) and another M10 bolt (1.5 x 45mm) for proper tool operation

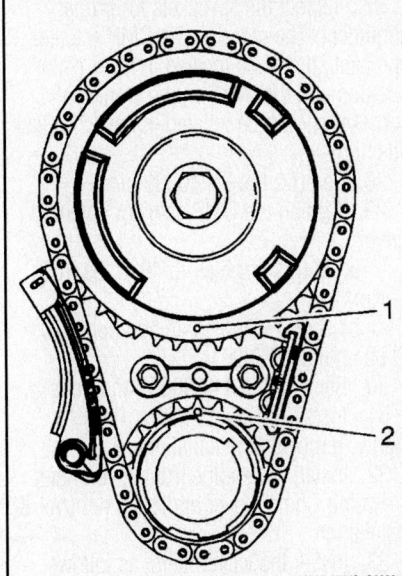

Fig. 75 Ensure the timing marks are properly aligned. The mark on the camshaft sprocket (1) should be located in the 6 o'clock position and the mark on the crankshaft sprocket (2) should be located in the 12 o'clock position

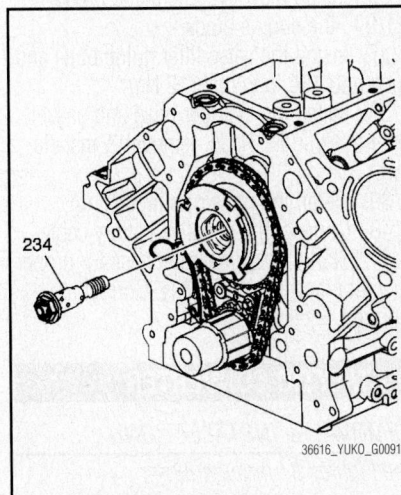

Fig. 76 Remove and discard the CMP actuator solenoid valve (234)

c. Remove the valve lifter guides (210) with the lifters. Note the installed position of the guides. The notched area of the guides is to align with the locating tab on the engine block.

d. Remove the valve lifters from the guide.

e. Organize or mark the components so that they can be installed in the same location from which they were removed, if required.

f. Clean and inspect the valve lifters, if required.

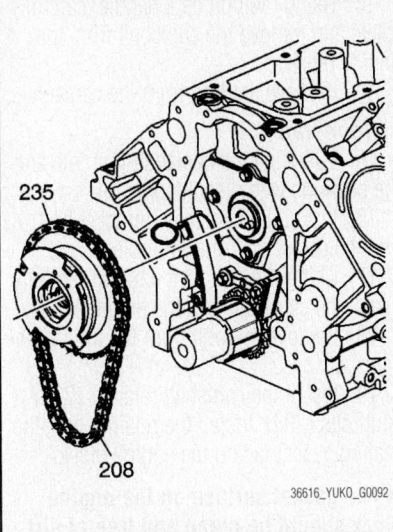

Fig. 77 Remove the CMP actuator (235) and timing chain (208)

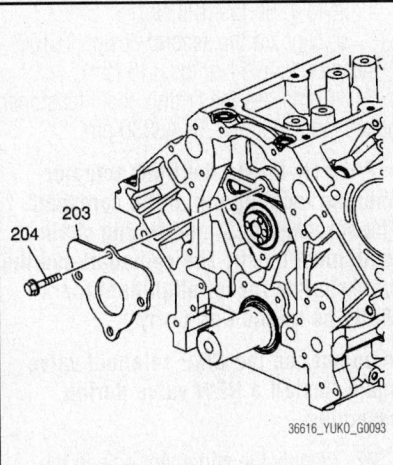

Fig. 78 Remove the camshaft retainer bolts (204) and retainer (203)

5. Remove the engine front cover. Refer to Timing Chain Cover and Seal, removal & installation.

6. Remove the starter motor. Refer to Starter, removal & installation.

7. Install Special Tool J 42386-A and bolts. Use one M10 bolt (1.5 x 120mm) and another M10 bolt (1.5 x 45mm) for proper tool operation. Tighten the J 42386-A bolts to 37 ft. lbs. (50 Nm).

➡️Ensure that the teeth of the J 42386-A mesh with the teeth of the engine flywheel.

8. Rotate the crankshaft sprocket until the Camshaft Position (CMP) actuator alignment mark and the crankshaft sprocket alignment mark are aligned.

9. Remove and discard the CMP actuator solenoid valve (234).

Fig. 79 Using the bolt as a handle, carefully rotate and remove the camshaft from the engine block

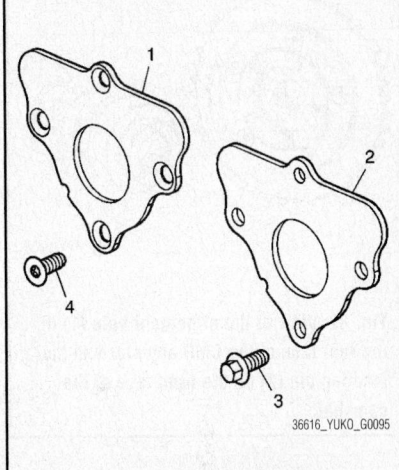

Fig. 80 Tighten the camshaft retainer bolts to specification, according to design illustrated

✳✳ WARNING

Do not turn the crankshaft assembly after the timing chain has been removed in order to prevent damage to the piston assemblies or the valves.

10. Remove the CMP actuator (235) and timing chain (208).

11. Remove the camshaft retainer bolts (204) and retainer (203).

✳✳ WARNING

All camshaft journals are the same diameter, so care must be used in removing or installing the camshaft to avoid damage to the camshaft bearings.

12. Install the camshaft sprocket bolt into the camshaft front bolt hole.

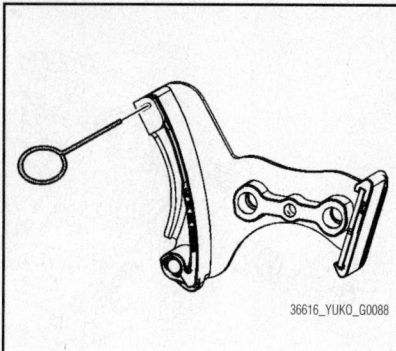

36616_YUKO_G0088

Fig. 81 Compress the timing chain tensioner guide and install the EN 46330 pin

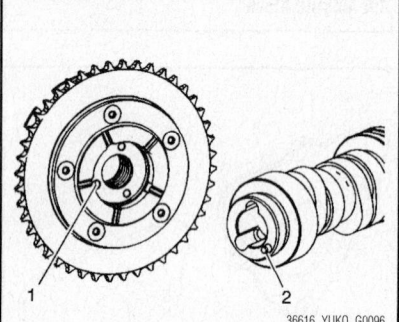

36616_YUKO_G0096

Fig. 82 View of the alignment hole (1) in the rear face of the CMP actuator and the locating pin (2) on the front face of the camshaft

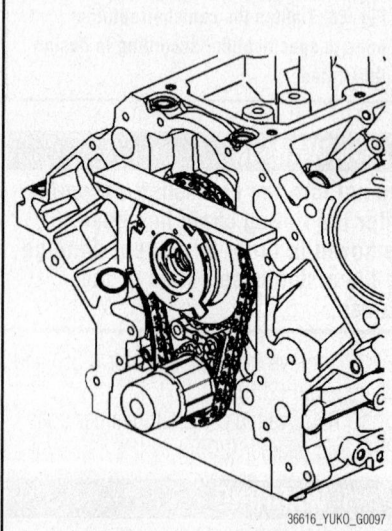

36616_YUKO_G0097

Fig. 83 Place a straight edge across the front face of the engine block. With the CMP actuator properly installed onto the front of the camshaft, the timing chain will not protrude beyond the front face of the engine block

13. Using the bolt as a handle, carefully rotate and remove the camshaft from the engine block.

14. Remove the bolt from the camshaft.

To install:

15. Lubricate the camshaft journals and the bearings with clean engine oil.

16. Install the camshaft sprocket bolt into the camshaft front bolt hole.

17. Using the bolt as a handle, carefully install the camshaft into the engine block.

18. Remove the bolt from the front of the camshaft.

19. Install the camshaft retainer (203) and bolts (204). Install the retainer with the sealing gasket facing the engine block.

➡**The gasket surface on the engine block should be clean and free of dirt and/or debris.**

20. Tighten the camshaft retainer bolts:
   a. Tighten the first design hex head bolts to 18 ft. lbs. (25 Nm).
   b. Tighten the second design TORX® head bolts to 11 ft. lbs. (15 Nm).

21. Compress the timing chain tensioner guide and install the EN 46330 pin.

➡**Properly locate the CMP actuator onto the locating pin of the camshaft. The sprocket teeth and timing chain teeth must mesh. The camshaft and the crankshaft sprocket alignment mark MUST be aligned properly.**

➡**Do not use the CMP solenoid valve again. Install a NEW valve during assembly.**

22. Identify the alignment hole in the rear face of the CMP actuator and the locating pin on the front face of the camshaft.

23. Align the CMP actuator so the timing mark is in the 6 o'clock position.

24. Install the CMP actuator (235) and timing chain (208). Align the hole in the face of the CMP actuator with the locating pin on the front face of the camshaft.

25. Place a straight edge across the front face of the engine block and inspect for proper installation of the CMP actuator and timing chain. With the CMP actuator properly and completely installed onto the front of the camshaft, the timing chain will not protrude beyond the front face of the engine block.

26. Install a NEW CMP actuator solenoid valve (234). With the CMP actuator properly positioned onto the camshaft, the CMP actuator solenoid valve can be threaded completely into the camshaft using light hand pressure. Tighten by hand until snug.

27. Inspect the sprockets for proper alignment. The mark on the CMP actuator sprocket should be located in the 6 o'clock position and the mark on the crankshaft sprocket should be located in the 12 o'clock position.

28. Remove the EN 46330 pin.

29. Tighten the CMP actuator solenoid valve:
   a. Step 1: Tighten to 48 ft. lbs. (65 Nm).
   b. Step 2: Tighten an additional 90° using the J 45059.

30. Remove the J 42386-A and bolts.

31. Install the starter motor. Refer to Starter, removal & installation.

32. Install the engine front cover. Refer to Timing Chain Cover and Seal, removal & installation.

33. Install the valve lifters, as follows:

34. Lubricate the valve lifters and engine block valve lifter bores with clean engine oil.

35. Insert the valve lifters into the lifter guides (210). Align the flat area on the top of the lifter with the flat area in the lifter guide bore. Push the lifter completely into the guide bore.

36. Install the valve lifters and guide (210) to the engine block.

37. Install the valve lifter guide bolts and tighten to 106 inch lbs. (12 Nm).

38. Install the cylinder head and gasket. Refer to Cylinder Head, removal & installation.

39. Install the radiator support.

40. Connect the negative battery cable.

41. Start the engine and check for proper operation and for fluid leaks. Correct as required.

CATALYTIC CONVERTER

REMOVAL & INSTALLATION
See Figures 84 through 88.

❊❊ CAUTION

In order to avoid being burned, do not service the exhaust system while it is still hot. Service the system when it is cool.

❊❊ CAUTION

Always wear protective goggles and gloves when removing exhaust parts as falling rust and sharp edges from worn exhaust components could result in serious personal injury.

1. Before servicing the vehicle, refer to the Precautions Section.

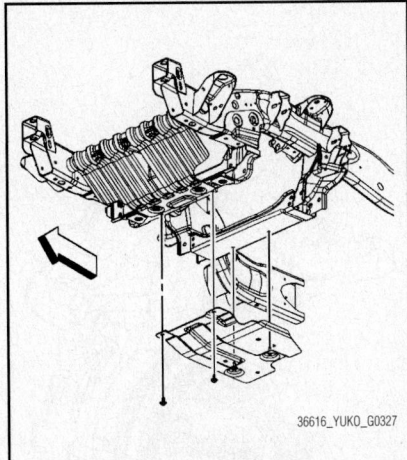

Fig. 84 Engine skid plate removal—1500 series

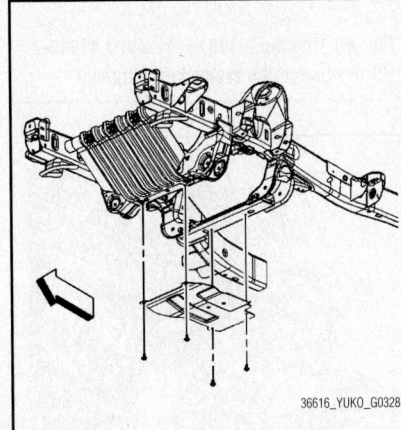

Fig. 85 Engine skid plate removal—2500 series

2. Remove the engine skid plate, if equipped.

3. Properly support the transmission assembly. Remove the transmission mount retaining bolts.

4. Remove the transmission crossmember.

5. Disconnect the electrical connectors from the CPA retainers and the oxygen sensors.

6. Remove the CPA retainers.

7. Remove the oxygen sensors. Refer to Heated Oxygen Sensor (HO2S), removal & installation.

8. Remove the converter-to-exhaust manifold nuts.

9. Remove the catalytic converter assembly from the vehicle.

To install:

➡ Use new fasteners, as required. Be sure to use new exhaust manifold seals.

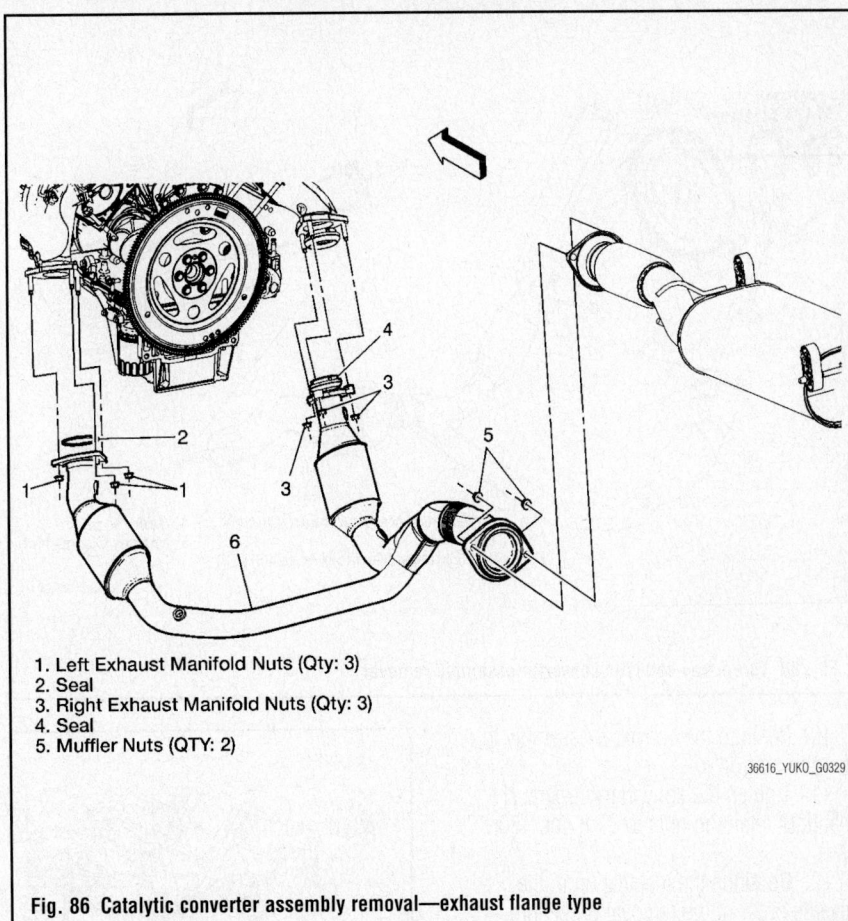

1. Left Exhaust Manifold Nuts (Qty: 3)
2. Seal
3. Right Exhaust Manifold Nuts (Qty: 3)
4. Seal
5. Muffler Nuts (QTY: 2)

Fig. 86 Catalytic converter assembly removal—exhaust flange type

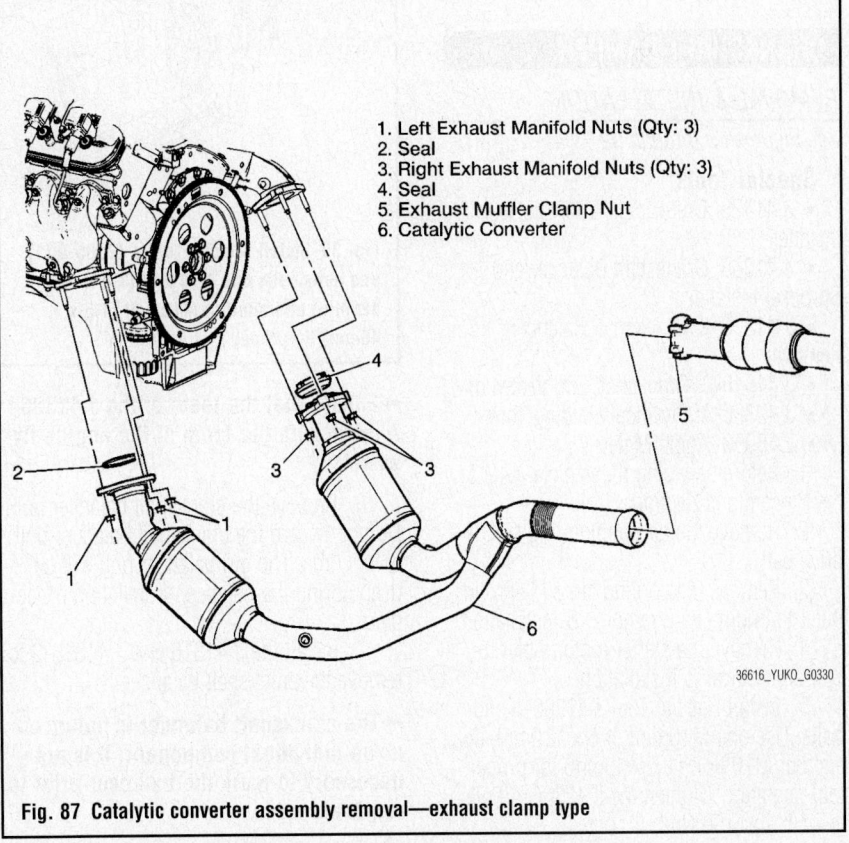

1. Left Exhaust Manifold Nuts (Qty: 3)
2. Seal
3. Right Exhaust Manifold Nuts (Qty: 3)
4. Seal
5. Exhaust Muffler Clamp Nut
6. Catalytic Converter

Fig. 87 Catalytic converter assembly removal—exhaust clamp type

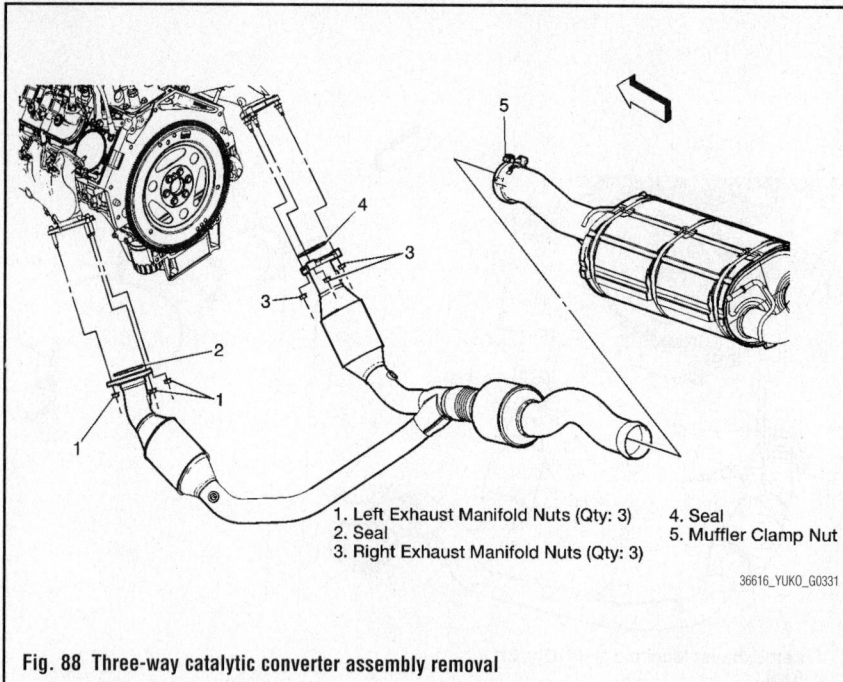

1. Left Exhaust Manifold Nuts (Qty: 3)
2. Seal
3. Right Exhaust Manifold Nuts (Qty: 3)
4. Seal
5. Muffler Clamp Nut

36616_YUKO_G0331

Fig. 88 Three-way catalytic converter assembly removal

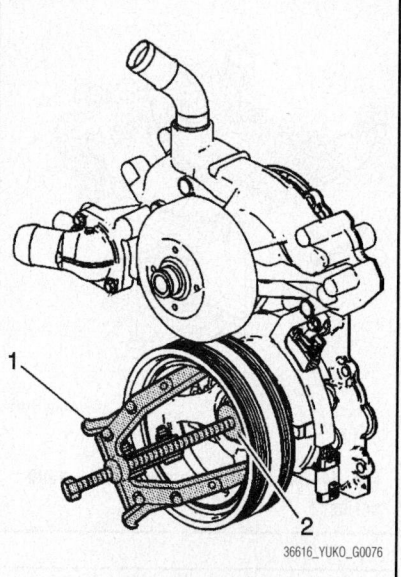

36616_YUKO_G0076

Fig. 90 Use the J 41816 (1) and J 41816-2 (2) to remove the crankshaft balancer

10. Position the converter assembly to its mounting.

11. Tighten the converter-to-exhaust manifold retaining nuts to 37 ft. lbs. (50 Nm).

12. Continue the installation in the reverse order of the removal procedure.

13. Start the engine and check for leaks. Correct as required.

CRANKSHAFT DAMPER

REMOVAL & INSTALLATION

See Figures 89 through 92.

Special Tools:
• J 41478: Crankshaft Front Oil Seal Installer
• J 41665: Crankshaft Balancer and Sprocket Installer
• J 41816-A: Crankshaft Balancer Remover
• J 41816-2: Crankshaft End Protector
• J 42386-A: Flywheel Holding Tool
• J 45059: Angle Meter

1. Before servicing the vehicle, refer to the Precautions Section.

2. Remove the air conditioning (A/C) drive belt.

3. Remove the cooling fan and shroud. Refer to Engine Fan, removal & installation.

4. Remove the starter motor. Refer to Starter, removal & installation.

5. Install Special Tool J 42386-A and bolts. Use one M10 bolt (1.5 x 120mm) and another M10 bolt (1.5 x 45mm) for proper tool operation. Tighten the J 42386-A bolts to 37 ft. lbs. (50 Nm).

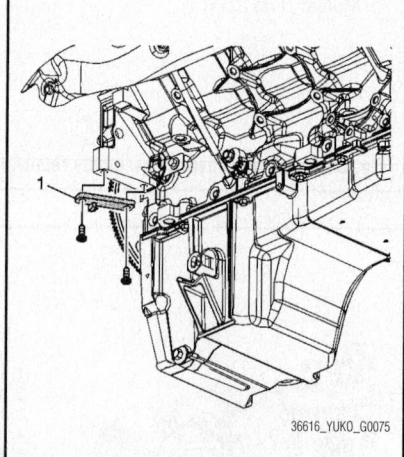

36616_YUKO_G0075

Fig. 89 Install Special Tool J 42386-A (1) and bolts. Use one M10 bolt (1.5 x 120mm) and another M10 bolt (1.5 x 45mm) for proper tool operation

➡**Ensure that the teeth of the J 42386-A mesh with the teeth of the engine flywheel.**

6. Remove the crankshaft balancer bolt. Do not discard the crankshaft balancer bolt at this time. The old balancer bolt will be used during the balancer installation procedure.

7. Install the J 41816 and J 41816-2 to remove the crankshaft balancer.

➡**The crankshaft balancer is balanced as an individual component. It is not necessary to mark the balancer prior to removal.**

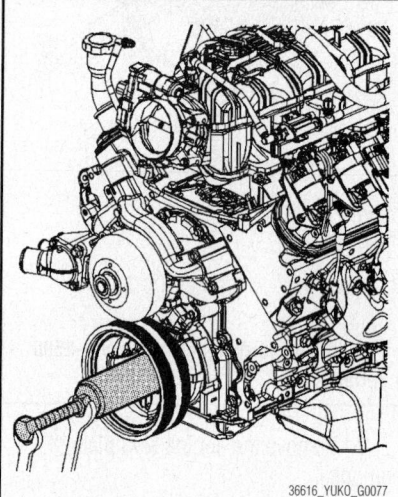

36616_YUKO_G0077

Fig. 91 Use the J 41665 and the threaded rod from the J 41478 to install the crankshaft balancer

To install:

➡**The crankshaft balancer installation and bolt tightening involves a 4-stage tightening process. The first pass ensures that the balancer is installed completely onto the crankshaft. The second, third, and fourth passes tighten the NEW bolt to the proper torque.**

➡**The used crankshaft balancer bolt will be used ONLY during the first pass of the balancer installation procedure. Install a NEW bolt and tighten as described in the second, third and**

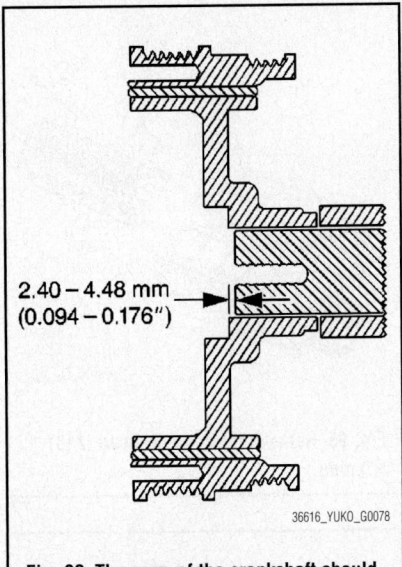

2.40 – 4.48 mm
(0.094 – 0.176")

36616_YUKO_G0078

Fig. 92 The nose of the crankshaft should be recessed 0.094–0.176 inch (2.4–4.48mm) into the balancer bore

fourth passes of the balancer bolt tightening procedure.

➡**The balancer should be positioned onto the end of the crankshaft as straight as possible prior to tool installation.**

8. Position the crankshaft balancer onto the end of the crankshaft.

9. Install the J 41665 and the threaded rod from the J 41478 to crankshaft balancer and install the balancer.

   a. Assemble the threaded rod, nut, washer, and installer. Insert the smaller end of the installer into the front of the balancer.

   b. Use a wrench and hold the hex end of the threaded rod.

   c. Use a second wrench and rotate the installation tool nut clockwise until the balancer is started onto the crankshaft.

   d. Remove the tool and reverse the installation tool.

➡**Position the larger end of the installer against the front of the balancer.**

   e. Use a wrench and hold the hex end of the threaded rod.

   f. Use a second wrench and rotate the installation tool nut clockwise until the balancer is installed onto the crankshaft.

   g. Remove the J 41665 and the threaded rod.

10. Install the USED crankshaft balancer bolt. Tighten the USED bolt to 240 ft. lbs. (330 Nm).

11. Remove the USED crankshaft balancer bolt.

➡**The nose of the crankshaft should be recessed 0.094–0.176 inch (2.4–4.48mm) into the balancer bore.**

12. Measure for a correctly installed balancer. If the balancer is not installed to the proper dimension, install the J 41665 and repeat the installation procedure.

13. Install the NEW crankshaft balancer bolt and tighten the bolt:

   a. Step 1: 37 ft. lbs. (50 Nm).

   b. Step 2: 140° using J 45059.

14. Remove the J 42386-A and bolts.

15. Install the starter motor. Refer to Starter, removal & installation.

16. Install the cooling fan and shroud. Refer to Engine Fan, removal & installation.

17. Install the A/C drive belt.

18. Perform the Crankshaft Position (CKP) system variation learn procedure. Refer to Crankshaft Position System Variation Learn.

CRANKSHAFT POSITION SYSTEM VARIATION LEARN

1. Before servicing the vehicle, refer to the Precautions Section.

2. Install a scan tool.

3. Monitor the Engine Control Module (ECM) for DTC's with a scan tool. If other DTC's are set, except DTC P0315, refer to Diagnostic Trouble Code (DTC) List for the applicable DTC that set.

4. Select the Crankshaft Position (CKP) variation learn procedure with a scan tool.

5. The scan tool should instruct you to perform the following:

   a. Accelerate to Wide Open Throttle (WOT).

   b. Release throttle when fuel cut-off occurs.

   c. Observe the fuel cut-off for applicable engine.

   d. The engine should not accelerate beyond calibrated RPM value.

   e. Release the throttle immediately if the value is exceeded.

   f. Block the drive wheels.

   g. Set the parking brake.

   h. DO NOT apply the brake pedal.

   i. Cycle the ignition from OFF to ON.

   j. Apply and hold the brake pedal.

   k. Start and idle the engine.

   l. Turn the A/C OFF.

   m. The vehicle must remain in Park or Neutral.

6. The scan tool monitors certain component signals to determine if all the conditions are met to continue with the procedure. The scan tool only displays the condition that inhibits the procedure. The scan tool monitors the following components:

   a. The CKP sensors activity—If there is a CKP sensor condition, refer to the applicable DTC that is set.

   b. The Camshaft Position (CMP) sensor activity—If there is a CMP sensor condition, refer to the applicable DTC that is set.

   c. The Engine Coolant Temperature (ECT)—If the ECT is not warm enough, idle the engine until the engine coolant temperature reaches the correct temperature.

7. Enable the CKP System Variation Learn Procedure with a scan tool.

➡**While the learn procedure is in progress, release the throttle immediately when the engine starts to decelerate. The engine control is returned to the operator and the engine responds to throttle position after the learn procedure is complete.**

8. Accelerate to WOT.

9. Release when the fuel cut-off occurs.

10. Test in progress.

11. The scan tool displays Learn Status: Learned this ignition.

   a. If the scan tool indicates that DTC P0315 ran and passed, the CKP Variation Learn Procedure is complete.

   b. If the scan tool indicates DTC P0315 failed or did not run, refer to DTC P0315. If any other DTC's are set, refer to the DTC List for the applicable DTC that is set.

12. Turn OFF the ignition for 30 seconds after the learn procedure is completed successfully.

13. The CKP Variation Learn Procedure is also required when the following service procedures have been performed, regardless of whether DTC P0315 is set:

- A CKP sensor replacement
- An engine replacement
- An ECM replacement
- An harmonic balancer replacement
- A crankshaft replacement
- Any engine repairs which disturb the CKP sensor relationship

CRANKSHAFT FRONT SEAL

REMOVAL & INSTALLATION

See Figures 93 and 94.

Special Tool:
- J 41478: Crankshaft Front Oil Seal Installer

1. Before servicing the vehicle, refer to the Precautions Section.

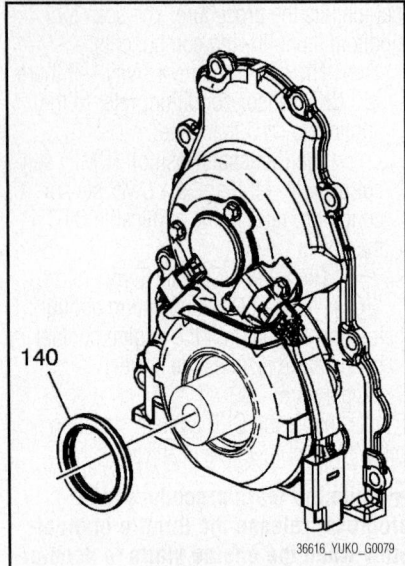

Fig. 93 Remove the crankshaft front oil seal (140) from the front cover

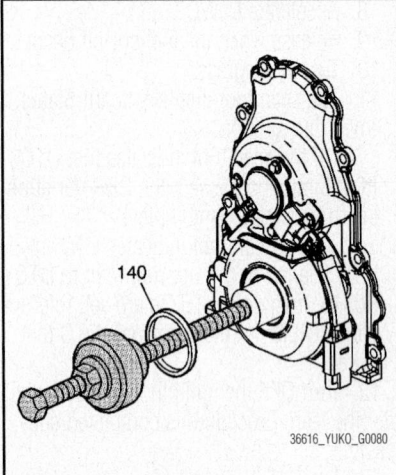

Fig. 94 Use the J 41478 in order to install the oil seal (140) into the cover bore

2. Remove the crankshaft balancer. Refer to Crankshaft Damper, removal & installation.

3. Remove the crankshaft front oil seal (140) from the front cover.

To install:

→Do not lubricate the oil seal sealing surface.

→Do not reuse the crankshaft front oil seal.

4. Lubricate the outer edge of the oil seal (140) with clean engine oil.

5. Lubricate the front cover oil seal bore with clean engine oil.

6. Install the crankshaft front oil seal (140) onto the J 41478 guide.

7. Install the J 41478 threaded rod (with nut, washer, guide, and oil seal) into the end of the crankshaft.

8. Use the J 41478 in order to install the oil seal into the cover bore.

   a. Use a wrench and hold the hex on the installer bolt.

   b. Use a second wrench and rotate the installer nut clockwise until the seal bottoms in the cover bore.

   c. Remove the J 41478.

   d. Inspect the oil seal for proper installation. The oil seal should be installed evenly and completely into the front cover bore.

9. Install the crankshaft balancer. Refer to Crankshaft Damper, removal & installation.

CYLINDER HEAD

REMOVAL & INSTALLATION

Left Side

See Figures 95 through 97.

Special Tools:

- J 45059: Angle Meter
- J 42385-200: Common Thread Repair Kit

1. Before servicing the vehicle, refer to the Precautions Section.

2. Release the fuel system pressure.

3. Disconnect the negative battery cable.

4. Remove the alternator bracket. Refer to Alternator, removal & installation.

5. Remove the intake manifold. Refer to Intake Manifold, removal & installation.

6. Remove the coolant air bleed pipe.

7. Remove the left exhaust manifold. Refer to Exhaust Manifold, removal & installation.

8. Remove the pushrods. Refer to Rocker Arms/Shafts, removal & installation.

9. Remove the engine ground strap bolt from the rear of the cylinder head.

10. Remove the ground strap from the cylinder head.

→The cylinder head bolts are of a torque-to-yield design and are NOT to be reused.

11. Remove and discard the cylinder head bolts (220, 221).

※※ WARNING

After removal, place the cylinder head on 2 wood blocks in order to prevent damage to the sealing surfaces.

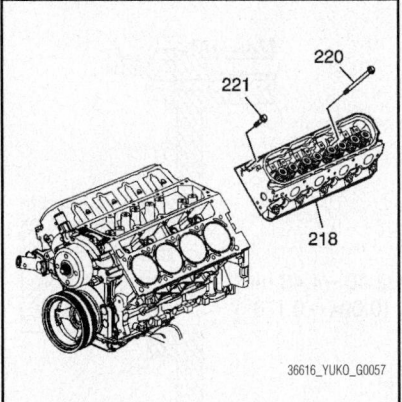

Fig. 95 Remove the cylinder head (218)— left side

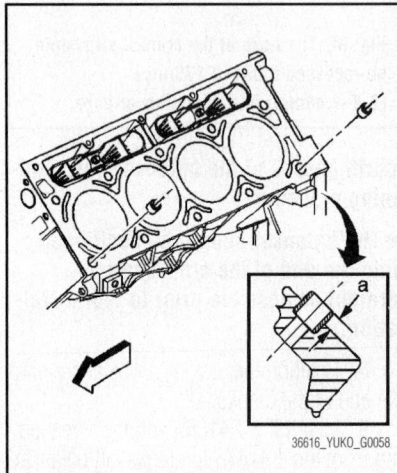

Fig. 96 Check the cylinder head locating pins for proper installation

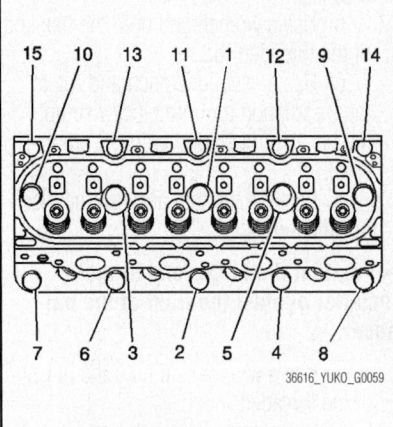

Fig. 97 Cylinder head bolt tightening sequence—left side

12. Remove the cylinder head (218).

13. Remove and discard the cylinder head gasket.

14. If required, clean and inspect the cylinder head.

To install:

⁕⁕ CAUTION

Wear safety glasses in order to avoid eye damage.

⁕⁕ WARNING

Clean all dirt, debris, and coolant from the engine block cylinder head bolt holes. Failure to remove all foreign material may result in damaged threads, improperly tightened fasteners or damage to components.

➡ If installing a new cylinder head, it is necessary to install a new engine coolant air bleed plug into the rear coolant passage of the cylinder head.

➡ Do not reuse the cylinder head bolts. Install NEW cylinder head bolts during assembly.

➡ Do not use any type of sealant on the cylinder head gasket (unless specified).

15. Clean the engine block cylinder head bolt holes, if required. Thread repair tool J 42385-107, found in J 42385-200, may be used to clean the threads of old thread-locking material.

16. Spray cleaner GM P/N 12346139, or equivalent into the hole.

17. Clean the cylinder head bolt holes with compressed air.

18. Check the cylinder head locating pins for proper installation using the following illustration. The specified measurement (a) from flush is 0.327 inch (8.3mm).

➡ When properly installed, with FRONT on the left side, the tab on the cylinder head gasket should be located left of center.

19. Install the NEW cylinder head gasket onto the locating pins.

20. Install the cylinder head (218) onto the locating pins.

21. Install the NEW cylinder head bolts (220, 221).

22. Tighten the cylinder head bolts in the sequence illustrated.

   a. Tighten the M11 cylinder head bolts (1–10) a first pass to 22 ft. lbs. (30 Nm).

   b. Tighten the M11 cylinder head bolts (1–10) a second pass to 90° using J 45059.

   c. Tighten the M11 cylinder head bolts (1–10) a final pass to 70° using J 45059.

   d. Tighten the M8 cylinder head bolts (11–15) to 22 ft. lbs. (30 Nm). Begin with the center bolt (11) and alternating side-to-side, work outward tightening all of the bolts.

23. Position the ground strap to the rear of the left cylinder head. Tighten the bolt to 12 ft. lbs. (16 Nm).

24. Install the pushrods. Refer to Rocker Arms/Shafts, removal & installation.

25. Install the left exhaust manifold. Refer to Exhaust Manifold, removal & installation.

26. Install the coolant air bleed pipe.

27. Install the intake manifold. Refer to Intake Manifold, removal & installation.

28. Install the alternator bracket. Refer to Alternator, removal & installation.

Right Side

See Figures 96, 98 and 99.

Special Tools:

- J 45059: Angle Meter
- J 42385-200: Common Thread Repair Kit

1. Before servicing the vehicle, refer to the Precautions Section.

2. Release the fuel system pressure.

3. Disconnect the negative battery cable.

4. Remove the oil level indicator.

5. Remove the intake manifold. Refer to Intake Manifold, removal & installation.

6. Remove the coolant air bleed pipe.

7. Remove the right exhaust manifold. Refer to Exhaust Manifold, removal & installation.

8. Remove the pushrods. Refer to Rocker Arms/Shafts, removal & installation.

9. Remove the negative battery cable stud from the front of the right cylinder head.

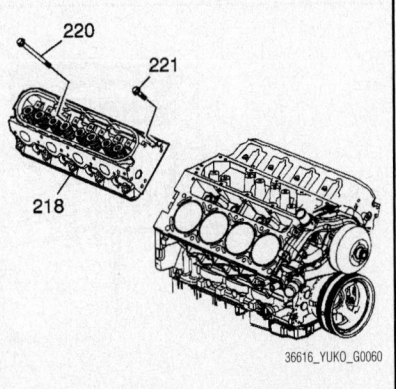

Fig. 98 Remove and discard the cylinder head bolts (220, 221) from the cylinder head (218)—right side

10. Remove the negative battery cable terminal and the engine harness terminal from the cylinder head.

➡ The cylinder head bolts are of a torque-to-yield design and are NOT to be reused.

11. Remove and discard the cylinder head bolts (220, 221).

⁕⁕ WARNING

After removal, place the cylinder head on 2 wood blocks in order to prevent damage to the sealing surfaces.

12. Remove the cylinder head (218).

13. Remove and discard the cylinder head gasket.

14. If required, clean and inspect the cylinder head.

To install:

⁕⁕ CAUTION

Wear safety glasses in order to avoid eye damage.

⁕⁕ WARNING

Clean all dirt, debris, and coolant from the engine block cylinder head bolt holes. Failure to remove all foreign material may result in damaged threads, improperly tightened fasteners, or damage to components.

➡ If installing a new cylinder head, it is necessary to install a new engine coolant air bleed plug into the rear coolant passage of the cylinder head.

➡ Do not reuse the cylinder head bolts. Install NEW cylinder head bolts during assembly.

➡ Do not use any type of sealant on the cylinder head gasket (unless specified).

15. Clean the engine block cylinder head bolt holes, if required. Thread repair tool J 42385-107, found in J 42385-200, may be

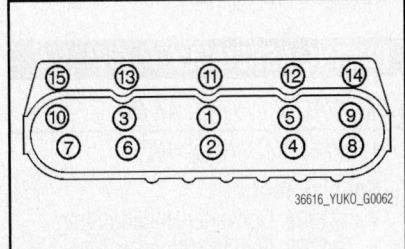

Fig. 99 Cylinder head bolt tightening sequence—right side

used to clean the threads of old thread-lock-ing material.

16. Spray cleaner GM P/N 12346139, or equivalent, into the bolt holes.

17. Clean the cylinder head bolt holes with compressed air.

18. Check the cylinder head locating pins for proper installation using the follow-ing illustration. The specified measurement (a) from flush is 0.327 inch (8.3mm).

➡**When properly installed, with FRONT on the right side, the tab on the cylin-der head gasket should be located right of center.**

19. Install the NEW cylinder head gasket onto the locating pins.

20. Install the cylinder head (218) onto the locating pins.

21. Install the NEW cylinder head bolts (220, 221).

22. Tighten the cylinder head bolts in the sequence illustrated.

    a. Tighten the M11 cylinder head bolts (1–10) a first pass to 22 ft. lbs. (30 Nm).

    b. Tighten the M11 cylinder head bolts (1–10) a second pass to 90° using J 45059.

    c. Tighten the M11 cylinder head bolts (1–10) a final pass to 70° using J 45059.

    d. Tighten the M8 cylinder head bolts (11–15) to 22 ft. lbs. (30 Nm). Begin with the center bolt (11) and alternating side-to-side, work outward tightening all of the bolts.

23. Position the negative battery cable terminal to the cylinder head.

24. Install the negative battery cable stud to the front of the right cylinder head and tighten the stud to 18 ft. lbs. (25 Nm).

25. Install the pushrods. Refer to Rocker Arms/Shafts, removal & installation.

26. Install the right exhaust manifold. Refer to Exhaust Manifold, removal & installation.

27. Install the coolant air bleed pipe.

28. Install the intake manifold. Refer to Intake Manifold, removal & installation.

29. Install the oil level indicator.

ENGINE ASSEMBLY

REMOVAL & INSTALLATION

See Figures 100 through 109.

Special Tools:
- J 21366: Converter Holding Strap
- J 41798: Engine Lifting Brackets

1. Before servicing the vehicle, refer to the Precautions Section.

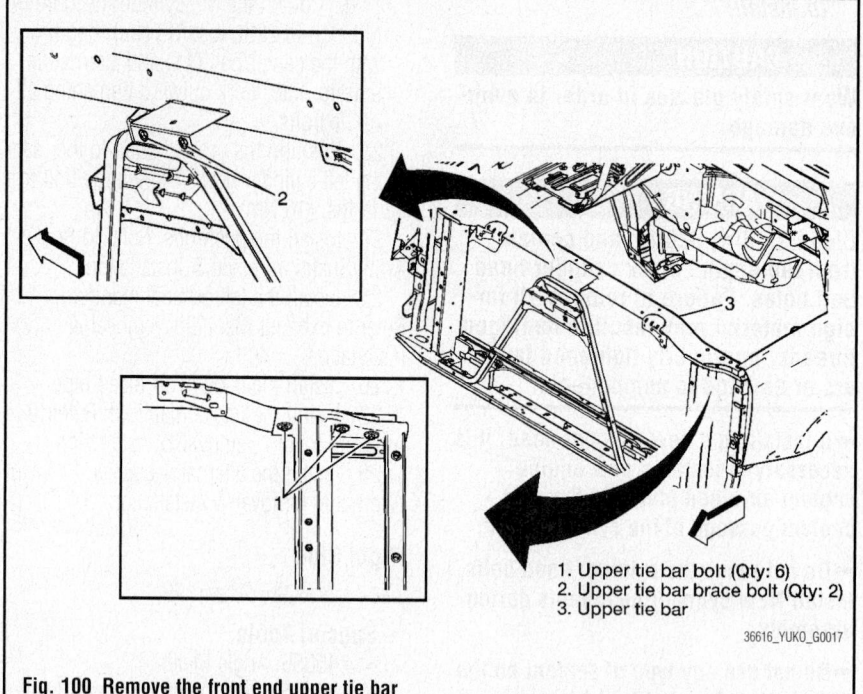

1. Upper tie bar bolt (Qty: 6)
2. Upper tie bar brace bolt (Qty: 2)
3. Upper tie bar

36616_YUKO_G0017

Fig. 100 Remove the front end upper tie bar

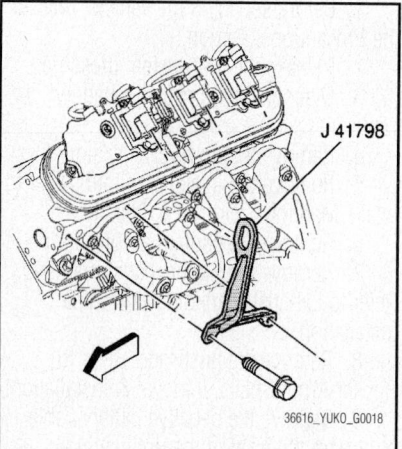

J 41798

36616_YUKO_G0018

Fig. 101 Install the J 41798 Engine Lift Bracket to the cylinder heads

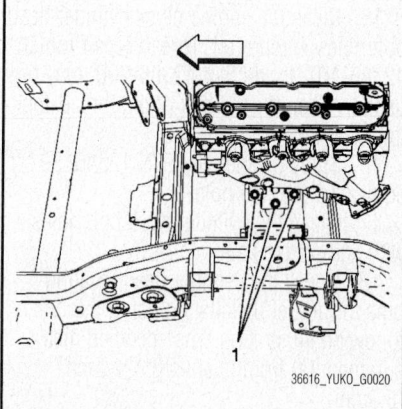

36616_YUKO_G0020

Fig. 103 Remove the left and right engine mount-to-frame bolts (1)—2500 series shown

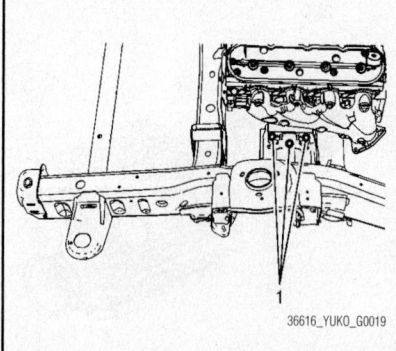

36616_YUKO_G0019

Fig. 102 Remove the left and right engine mount-to-frame bolts (1)—1500 series shown

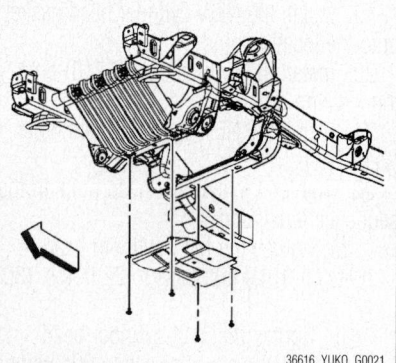

36616_YUKO_G0021

Fig. 104 Remove the oil pan skid plate bolts and plate—1500 series shown (2500 similar)

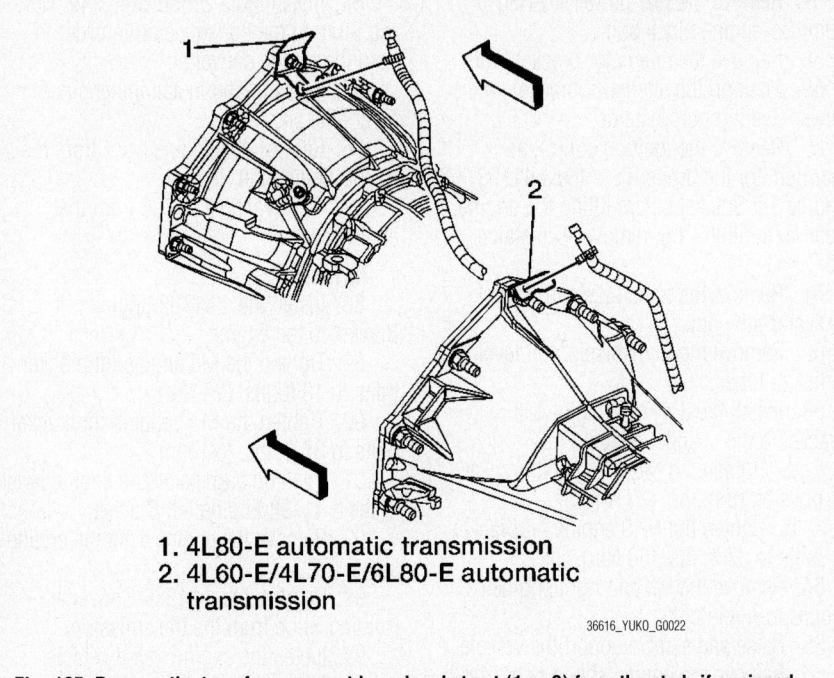

1. 4L80-E automatic transmission
2. 4L60-E/4L70-E/6L80-E automatic transmission

36616_YUKO_G0022

Fig. 105 Remove the transfer case vent hose bracket nut (1 or 2) from the stud, if equipped

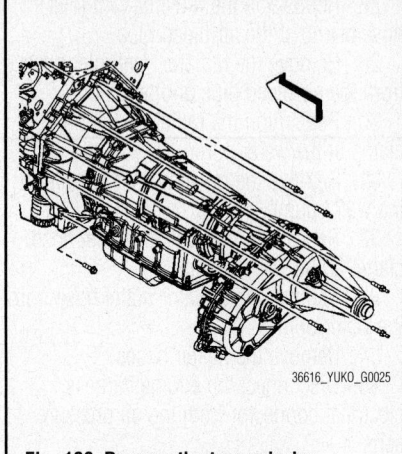

36616_YUKO_G0025

Fig. 108 Remove the transmission bolts/studs—6L80-E

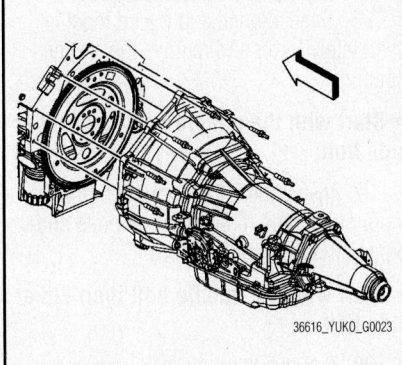

36616_YUKO_G0023

Fig. 106 Remove the transmission bolts/studs—4L60-E/4L70-E

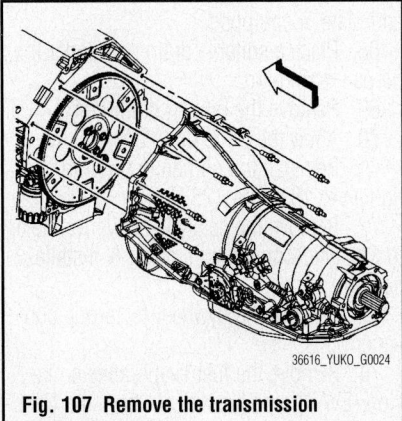

36616_YUKO_G0024

Fig. 107 Remove the transmission bolts/studs—4L80-E

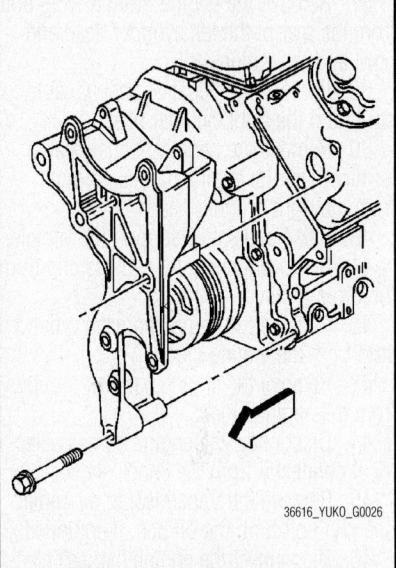

36616_YUKO_G0026

Fig. 109 Position the alternator bracket (with power steering pump) to the engine

2. Disconnect the negative battery cable.

3. Drain the cooling system.

4. Properly discharge the air conditioning system.

5. Properly relieve the fuel system pressure.

6. Open the hood and remove the ground strap nut at the hood stud.

7. Remove the ground strap from the stud.

8. Assemble 2 sets of the following:
   • An M6 bolt
   • Two 0.75 inch (19.05mm) flat washers
   • An M6 nut

9. Release the retainer securing the hood strut rod to the hood strut bracket stud.

10. Remove the hood strut rod from the stud.

11. Remove the air inlet grille end caps, lift the end cap up in order to disengage the retainers.

12. Have an assistant support the hood.

13. Remove the hood hinge bolts and set aside.

➡**There is a positive stop which limits the hood from being opened too far.**

14. Raise the hood until the service position notch in the upper hinge is reached.

15. Install the 2 sets of the M6 bolts to both the left and right side service notches and tighten finger tight.

16. Lower the hood until the bolts rest against the lower hinge, tighten the bolts to secure the hood to 15 ft. lbs. (20 Nm).

17. The hood is now set in the service position.

18. Remove the headlamps. Refer to Headlights, removal & installation.

19. Remove the grille support.

20. Disconnect the hood latch cable.

21. Remove the hood latch.

22. Remove the radiator support diagonal brace.

23. Remove the upper fan shroud bolts.

24. Remove the upper radiator bolts.

25. Remove the upper condenser bolts.

26. Remove the intake manifold. Refer to Intake Manifold, removal & installation.

27. Remove the radiator vent inlet hose from the radiator inlet hose clip.

28. Reposition the radiator vent inlet hose clamp at the air bleed pipe.

29. Remove the radiator vent inlet hose from the air bleed pipe and reposition.

30. Reposition the radiator inlet hose clamp at the water pump.

31. Remove the radiator inlet hose from the water pump.

32. Reposition the radiator outlet hose clamp at the water pump.

33. Remove the radiator outlet hose from the water pump.

34. Remove the heater hoses.

35. Disconnect the engine harness electrical connector from the oil pressure sensor.

36. Disconnect the engine harness electrical connector from the lifter oil manifold.

37. Remove the engine ground strap bolt from the rear of the left cylinder head and cowl and reposition.

38. Remove the negative battery cable stud from the right cylinder head.

39. Remove the negative battery cable terminal and the engine harness ground from the right cylinder head.

40. Raise and safely support the vehicle.

41. Remove the engine harness clip from the ground stud.

42. Remove the engine harness ground stud from the engine block.

43. Remove the engine harness grounds from the engine block.

44. Disconnect the engine harness electrical connector from the knock sensor.

45. Remove the transmission oil cooler line clip bolt from the oil pan, if equipped.

46. Disconnect the engine harness electrical connector from the Camshaft Position (CMP) sensor wire harness.

47. Remove the battery cable channel bolt.

48. Slide the channel pin out of the oil pan tab.

49. Disconnect the engine harness electrical connector from the A/C refrigerant pressure sensor.

50. Remove the starter motor. Refer to Starter, removal & installation.

51. Disconnect the engine harness electrical connector from the Crankshaft Position (CKP) sensor.

52. Disconnect the engine harness electrical connector from the knock sensor.

53. Disconnect the engine harness electrical connector from the oil level sensor.

54. Remove the engine harness clip from the transmission oil cooler line bracket.

55. Disconnect the coolant heater cord from the coolant heater, if equipped.

56. Lower the vehicle.

57. Remove the rear power steering pump-to-engine block bolt.

58. Remove the alternator bracket bolts.

59. Position the alternator bracket (with power steering pump) aside.

60. Remove the ignition coil(s), as required, for the proper fit of the J 41798 Engine Lift Bracket before lifting the engine. Refer to Ignition Coil, removal & installation.

61. Remove the transmission oil level indicator tube nut.

62. Remove the transmission oil level indicator tube.

63. Install the J 41798 Engine Lift Bracket to the cylinder heads.

   a. Tighten the M8 engine lift bracket bolts to 18 ft. lbs. (25 Nm).

   b. Tighten the M10 engine lift bracket bolts to 37 ft. lbs. (50 Nm).

64. Remove the left and right engine mount-to-frame bolts.

65. Raise and safely support the vehicle.

66. Remove the engine shield bolts and shield.

67. Remove the oil pan skid plate bolts and plate, if equipped.

68. Place a suitable drain pan under the oil pan drain plug.

69. Remove the oil pan drain plug.

70. Allow the oil to drain completely.

71. Reinstall the oil pan drain plug and tighten to 18 ft. lbs. (25 Nm).

72. Remove the catalytic converter. Refer to Catalytic Converter, removal & installation.

73. Remove the flywheel-to-torque converter bolts.

74. Remove the fuel/evaporative emission (EVAP) pipe bracket nut from the transmission stud.

75. Remove the fuel/EVAP pipe bracket from the stud. Reposition the bracket out of the way.

76. For the 4L80-E automatic transmission, remove the transfer case vent hose bracket nut from the stud, if equipped.

77. For the 4L60-E/4L70-E/6L80-E automatic transmission, remove the transfer case vent hose bracket nut from the stud, if equipped.

78. Reposition the transfer case vent hose bracket and hose out of the way, if equipped.

79. Remove the transmission bolts/studs.

80. Lower the vehicle.

81. Position and install an engine hoist to the J 41798 Engine Lift Bracket.

82. Install a floor jack under the transmission for support.

83. Remove the engine from the vehicle.

84. Install the J 21366 Converter Holding Strap to the transmission in order to hold the torque converter.

85. Position and install the engine onto an engine stand.

86. Remove the engine hoist from the J 41798 Engine Lift Bracket.

87. Remove the J 41798 from the engine.

To install:

88. Install the J 41798 Engine Lift Bracket to the engine.

89. Tighten the M8 engine lift bracket bolts to 18 ft. lbs. (25 Nm).

90. Tighten the M10 engine lift bracket bolts to 37 ft. lbs. (50 Nm).

91. Position and install the engine hoist to the J 41798 Engine Lift Bracket.

92. Remove the engine from the engine stand.

93. Remove the J 21366 Converter Holding Strap from the transmission.

94. Install the engine to the vehicle.

95. Align and install the engine to the transmission. Raise or lower the transmission as required using the floor jack.

96. Once aligned and mated together, completely lower and remove the engine hoist.

➡**Start with the middle bolt then either side bolt.**

97. Install the left and right engine mount to engine mount bracket bolts and tighten to 48 ft. lbs. (65 Nm).

➡**Start with the middle bolt then either side bolt.**

98. Remove the floor jack from under the transmission.

99. Raise and safely support the vehicle.

100. Install the transmission bolts/studs and tighten to 37 ft. lbs. (50 Nm).

101. Position the transfer case vent hose bracket and hose and install the bracket to the stud, if equipped.

102. If equipped, install the transfer case vent hose bracket nut to the stud and tighten to 15 ft. lbs. (20 Nm).

103. Position the fuel/EVAP pipe bracket and install the bracket to the stud.

104. Install the fuel/EVAP pipe bracket nut to the transmission stud and tighten to 15 ft. lbs. (20 Nm).

105. Align the torque converter bolt holes to the flywheel bolt holes.

106. Install the flywheel-to-torque converter bolts.

107. For the 4L60-E/4L70-E/6L80-E automatic transmission, tighten the bolts to 47 ft. lbs. (63 Nm).

108. For the 4L80-E automatic transmission, tighten the bolts to 44 ft. lbs. (60 Nm).

109. Install the catalytic converter. Refer to Catalytic Converter, removal & installation.

110. Lower the vehicle.

111. Remove the J 41798 Engine Lift Bracket from the cylinder heads.

112. Install the ignition coil(s) and spark plug wire(s), as required. Refer to Ignition Coil, removal & installation.

113. Install the transmission oil level indicator tube.

114. Install the transmission oil level indicator tube nut and tighten to 13 ft. lbs. (18 Nm).

115. Position the alternator bracket (with power steering pump) to the engine.

116. Install the alternator bracket bolts and tighten to 37 ft. lbs. (50 Nm).

117. Install the rear power steering pump-to-engine block bolt and tighten to 37 ft. lbs. (50 Nm).

118. Raise and safely support the vehicle.

119. Connect the coolant heater cord to the coolant heater, if equipped.

120. Connect the engine harness electrical connector to the CKP sensor.

121. Connect the engine harness electrical connector to the knock sensor.

122. Connect the engine harness electrical connector to the oil level sensor.

123. Install the engine harness clip to the transmission oil cooler line bracket.

124. Install the starter motor. Refer to Starter, removal & installation.

125. Connect the engine harness electrical connector to the A/C refrigerant pressure sensor.

126. Slide the channel pin into the oil pan tab.

127. Install the battery cable channel bolt and tighten to 106 inch lbs. (12 Nm).

128. Connect the engine harness electrical connector to the CMP sensor wire harness.

129. Position the transmission oil cooler line clip to the oil pan and install the bolt, if equipped, and tighten to 80 inch lbs. (9 Nm).

130. Connect the engine harness electrical connector to the knock sensor.

131. Position the engine harness grounds to the engine block.

132. Install the engine harness ground stud to the engine block and tighten to 12 ft. lbs. (16 Nm).

133. Install the engine harness clip to the ground stud.

134. Lower the vehicle.

135. Position the negative battery cable terminal and the engine harness ground to the right cylinder head.

136. Install the negative battery cable stud to the right cylinder head and tighten to 18 ft. lbs. (25 Nm).

137. Position the engine ground strap to the cylinder head and cowl.

138. Install the engine ground strap bolt to the rear of the left cylinder head and cowl and tighten to 12 ft. lbs. (16 Nm).

139. Connect the engine harness electrical connector to the oil pressure sensor.

140. Connect the engine harness electrical connector to the lifter oil manifold.

141. Install the heater hoses.

142. Install the radiator outlet hose to the water pump.

143. Position the radiator outlet hose clamp at the water pump.

144. Install the radiator inlet hose to the water pump.

145. Position the radiator inlet hose clamp at the water pump.

146. Position and install the radiator vent inlet hose to the air bleed pipe.

147. Position the radiator vent inlet hose clamp at the air bleed pipe.

148. Install the radiator vent inlet hose to the radiator inlet hose clip.

149. Position the alternator battery jumper to the engine.

150. Install the intake manifold. Refer to Intake Manifold, removal & installation.

151. Install the oil pan skid plate and bolts, if equipped, and tighten to 21 ft. lbs. (28 Nm).

152. Install the engine shield and bolts and tighten to 15 ft. lbs. (20 Nm).

153. Lower the vehicle.

154. Install the front end upper tie bar.

155. Install the hood latch.

156. With the aid of an assistant, raise the hood slightly until the hood hinge bolts can be removed from the service position notch.

157. With the aid of an assistant, lower the hood and install the hood hinge bolts to the hood hinges and tighten to 18 ft. lbs. (25 Nm).

158. Install the hood strut rod to the hood strut bracket stud.

159. Install the air inlet grille end caps, push down the end cap in order to engage the retainers.

160. Install the ground strap to the hood stud.

161. Install the ground strap nut at the hood stud and tighten to 80 inch lbs. (9 Nm).

162. Pre-lube the engine with clean engine oil.

163. Perform the CKP system variation learn procedure. Refer to Crankshaft Position System Variation Learn.

➡After an overhaul, the engine should be tested. Use the following procedure after the engine is installed in the vehicle.

164. Disable the ignition system.

165. Crank the engine several times. Listen for any unusual noises or evidence that parts are binding.

166. Enable the ignition system.

167. Start the engine and listen for unusual noises.

168. Check the vehicle oil pressure gauge or light and confirm that the engine has acceptable oil pressure.

169. Run the engine speed at about 1,000 RPM until the engine has reached normal operating temperature.

170. Listen for sticking lifters or other unusual noises.

171. Inspect for fuel, oil, and/or coolant leaks while the engine is running.

172. Perform a final inspection for the proper oil and coolant levels.

CRANKSHAFT POSITION SYSTEM VARIATION LEARN

1. Before servicing the vehicle, refer to the Precautions Section.

2. Install a scan tool.

3. Monitor the Engine Control Module (ECM) for DTC's with a scan tool. If other DTC's are set, except DTC P0315, refer to Diagnostic Trouble Code (DTC) List for the applicable DTC that set.

4. Select the Crankshaft Position (CKP) variation learn procedure with a scan tool.

5. The scan tool should instruct you to perform the following:

    a. Accelerate to Wide Open Throttle (WOT).

    b. Release throttle when fuel cut-off occurs.

    c. Observe the fuel cut-off for applicable engine.

    d. The engine should not accelerate beyond calibrated RPM value.

    e. Release the throttle immediately if the value is exceeded.

    f. Block the drive wheels.

    g. Set the parking brake.

    h. DO NOT apply the brake pedal.

    i. Cycle the ignition from OFF to ON.

    j. Apply and hold the brake pedal.

    k. Start and idle the engine.

    l. Turn the A/C OFF.

    m. The vehicle must remain in Park or Neutral.

6. The scan tool monitors certain component signals to determine if all the conditions are met to continue with the procedure. The scan tool only displays the condition

that inhibits the procedure. The scan tool monitors the following components:

    a. The CKP sensors activity—If there is a CKP sensor condition, refer to the applicable DTC that is set.

    b. The Camshaft Position (CMP) sensor activity—If there is a CMP sensor condition, refer to the applicable DTC that is set.

    c. The Engine Coolant Temperature (ECT)—If the ECT is not warm enough, idle the engine until the engine coolant temperature reaches the correct temperature.

    7. Enable the CKP System Variation Learn Procedure with a scan tool.

➡**While the learn procedure is in progress, release the throttle immediately when the engine starts to decelerate. The engine control is returned to the operator and the engine responds to throttle position after the learn procedure is complete.**

    8. Accelerate to WOT.

    9. Release when the fuel cut-off occurs.

    10. Test in progress.

    11. The scan tool displays Learn Status: Learned this ignition.

    a. If the scan tool indicates that DTC P0315 ran and passed, the CKP Variation Learn Procedure is complete.

    b. If the scan tool indicates DTC P0315 failed or did not run, refer to DTC P0315. If any other DTC's are set, refer to the DTC List for the applicable DTC that is set.

    12. Turn OFF the ignition for 30 seconds after the learn procedure is completed successfully.

    13. The CKP Variation Learn Procedure is also required when the following service procedures have been performed, regardless of whether DTC P0315 is set:

- A CKP sensor replacement
- An engine replacement
- An ECM replacement
- An harmonic balancer replacement
- A crankshaft replacement
- Any engine repairs which disturb the CKP sensor relationship

EXHAUST MANIFOLD

REMOVAL & INSTALLATION

Left Side

See Figures 110 through 113.

Special Tool:

- J 42640: Steering Column Anti-Rotation Pin

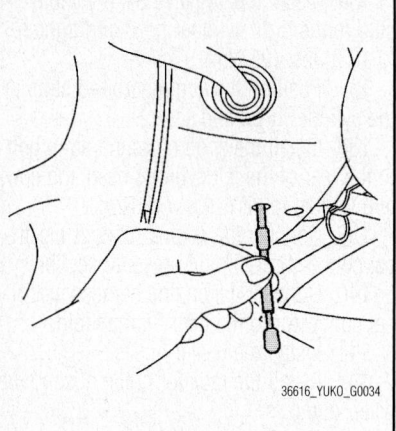

Fig. 110 Installing the steering column anti-rotation pin, tool J42640

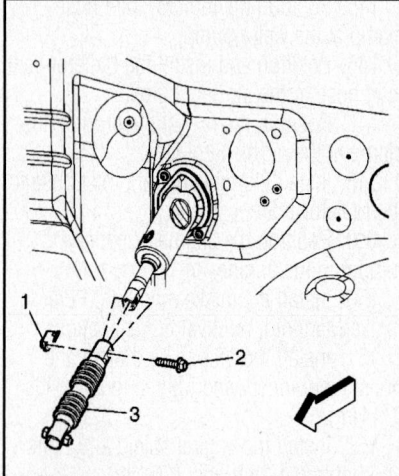

1. Nut
2. Coupling bolt
3. Upper intermediate steering shaft

36616_YUKO_G0035

Fig. 111 Disconnecting the upper intermediate shaft

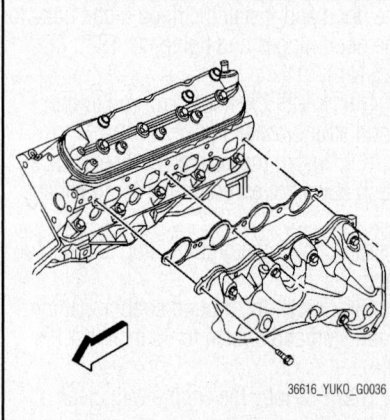

36616_YUKO_G0036

Fig. 112 Exhaust manifold and related components—left side

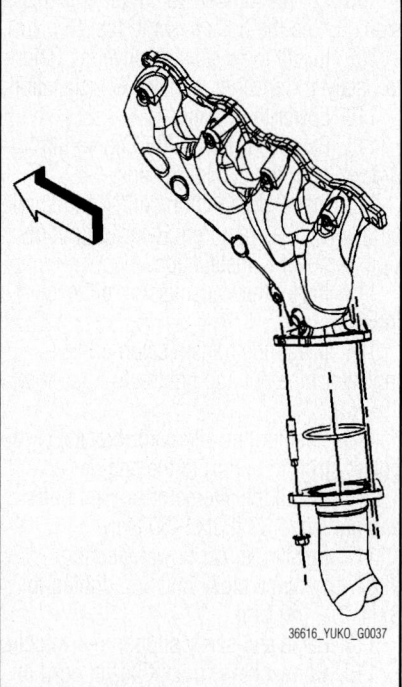

36616_YUKO_G0037

Fig. 113 Install the catalytic converter-to-exhaust manifold nuts—left side

    1. Before servicing the vehicle, refer to the Precautions Section.

    2. Disconnect the negative battery cable.

    3. Install tool J42640 into the steering column lower access hole. Lock the steering column.

    4. Remove the left wheelhouse assembly.

    5. Raise and safely support the vehicle.

    6. Disconnect the converter-to-exhaust manifold retaining nuts. Discard the gasket.

    7. Lower the vehicle part way in order to work through the wheel opening.

    8. Remove the spark plug wires from the spark plugs and from the ignition coils.

    9. Mark the relationship of the upper intermediate steering shaft to the steering column.

    10. Remove the steering shaft coupling bolt and nut from the upper intermediate shaft.

    11. Separate the upper intermediate steering shaft from the steering column, position both shafts out of the way.

    12. Remove the exhaust manifold bolts.

    13. Remove the exhaust manifold from the vehicle.

    14. Discard the exhaust manifold gasket and the catalytic converter seal.

    15. If replacing the exhaust manifold, remove the exhaust manifold heat shield bolts and the shield from the exhaust manifold.

To install:

➡️**Tighten the exhaust manifold bolts as specified. Improperly installed and/or leaking exhaust manifold gaskets may affect vehicle emissions and/or On-Board Diagnostic (OBD) II system performance.**

➡️**The cylinder head exhaust manifold bolt hole threads must be clean and free of debris or thread-locking material.**

➡️**Do not apply sealant to the first 3 threads of the bolt.**

16. If the exhaust manifold was replaced, position and install the exhaust manifold heat shield, and bolts to the exhaust manifold. Tighten the bolts to 80 inch lbs. (9 Nm).

17. Clean the threads of the exhaust manifold bolts.

18. Apply a 0.2 inch (5mm) wide band of threadlock GM P/N 36616493, or equivalent, to the threads of the exhaust manifold bolts.

19. Install a NEW catalytic converter seal to the catalytic converter.

20. Position the NEW exhaust manifold gasket and exhaust manifold to the cylinder head.

21. Ensure that the exhaust manifold is seated to the catalytic converter.

22. Install the exhaust manifold bolts in sequence by tightening the exhaust manifold bolts beginning with the center 2 bolts. Alternate from side-to-side, and work toward the outside bolts.

   a. Step 1: Tighten the bolts to 11 ft. lbs. (15 Nm).

   b. Step 2: Tighten the bolts to 15 ft. lbs. (20 Nm).

23. Using a flat punch, bend the gasket tab at the rear of the gasket around the cylinder head edge.

24. Position and align the marks on the upper intermediate steering shaft and the steering column.

25. Install the upper intermediate steering shaft to the steering column.

26. Install the steering shaft coupling bolt and nut to the upper intermediate steering shaft. Tighten the bolt/nut to 37 ft. lbs. (50 Nm).

27. Install the spark plug wires to the spark plugs and to the ignition coils.

28. Raise and safely support the vehicle.

29. Install the catalytic converter-to-exhaust manifold nuts. Tighten the nuts to 37 ft. lbs. (50 Nm).

30. Partially lower the vehicle.

31. Install the left wheelhouse liner.

32. Remove the J 42640 from the steering column lower access hole.

33. Start the engine and check for exhaust noise and leaks. Correct as required.

Right Side

See Figures 114 through 116.

1. Before servicing the vehicle, refer to the Precautions Section.

2. Disconnect the negative battery cable.

3. Remove the oxygen sensor. Refer to Heated Oxygen Sensor (HO2S), removal & installation.

4. Raise and safely support the vehicle.

5. Remove the catalytic converter-to-exhaust manifold nuts.

6. Remove the front wheel house liner (right side).

7. Partially lower the vehicle in order to work through the wheel opening.

8. Remove the spark plug wires from the spark plugs and from the ignition coils.

9. Remove the oil level indicator tube from the engine block.

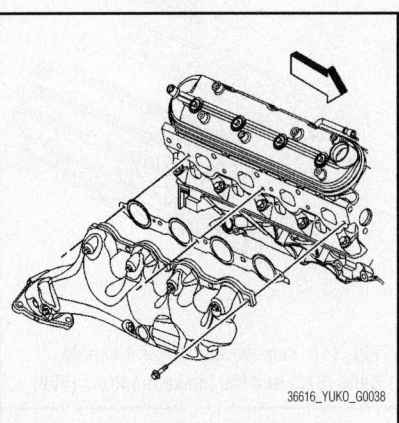

36616_YUKO_G0038

Fig. 114 Remove the exhaust manifold bolts and exhaust manifold—right side

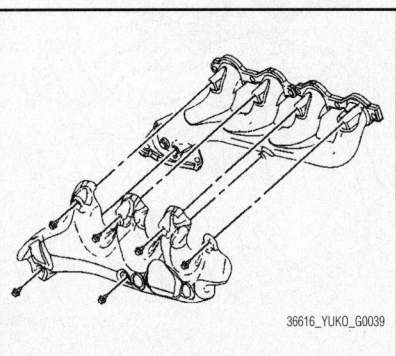

36616_YUKO_G0039

Fig. 115 Removed the exhaust manifold heat shield, as needed

10. Remove the exhaust manifold bolts and exhaust manifold.

11. Remove and discard the exhaust manifold gasket.

12. Remove and discard the exhaust manifold seal.

13. If replacing the exhaust manifold, remove the exhaust manifold heat shield bolts and shield from the exhaust manifold.

To install:

➡️**Tighten the exhaust manifold bolts as specified. Improperly installed and/or leaking exhaust manifold gaskets may affect vehicle emissions and/or On-Board Diagnostics (OBD) II system performance.**

➡️**The cylinder head exhaust manifold bolt hole threads must be clean and free of debris or thread-locking material.**

➡️**Do not apply sealant to the first 3 threads of the bolt.**

14. If the exhaust manifold was replaced, position and install the exhaust manifold heat shield and bolts to the exhaust manifold. Tighten the bolts to 80 inch lbs. (9 Nm).

15. Clean the threads of the exhaust manifold bolts.

16. Apply a 0.2 inch (5mm) wide band of threadlock GM P/N 36616493, or equivalent, to the threads of the exhaust manifold bolts.

17. Install a NEW catalytic converter seal to the exhaust manifold.

18. Position the NEW exhaust manifold gasket and exhaust manifold to the cylinder head.

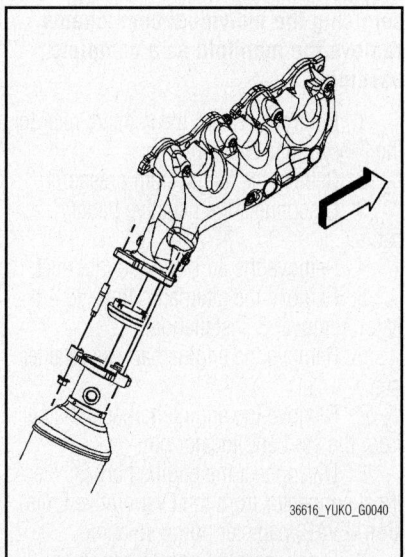

36616_YUKO_G0040

Fig. 116 Install the catalytic converter-to-exhaust manifold nuts—right side

19. Ensure that the catalytic converter seal is seated to the catalytic converter.

20. Install the exhaust manifold bolts in sequence by tightening the exhaust manifold bolts beginning with the center 2 bolts. Alternate from side-to-side, and work toward the outside bolts.

　a. Step 1: Tighten the bolts to 11 ft. lbs. (15 Nm).

　b. Step 2: Tighten the bolts to 15 ft. lbs. (20 Nm).

21. Using a flat punch, bend the gasket tab at the rear of the gasket around the cylinder head edge.

22. Install the oil level indicator tube to the engine block.

23. Install the spark plug wires to the spark plugs and to the ignition coils.

24. Raise and safely support the vehicle.

25. Install the catalytic converter-to-exhaust manifold nuts. Tighten the nuts to 37 ft. lbs. (50 Nm).

26. Partially lower the vehicle in order to work through the wheel opening.

27. Install the front wheel house liner (right front).

28. Install the oxygen sensor. Refer to Heated Oxygen Sensor (HO2S), removal & installation.

29. Start the engine and check for exhaust noise and leaks. Correct as required.

INTAKE MANIFOLD

REMOVAL & INSTALLATION

See Figures 117 through 119.

➡**The intake manifold, throttle body, fuel injection rail, and fuel injectors may be removed as an assembly. If not servicing the individual components, remove the manifold as a complete assembly.**

1. Before servicing the vehicle, refer to the Precautions Section.

2. Relieve the fuel system pressure.

3. Disconnect the negative battery cable.

4. Remove the air cleaner outlet duct.

5. Remove the alternator. Refer to Alternator, removal & installation.

6. Remove the engine harness retainer nut.

7. Remove the engine harness retainer from the stud and locator pin.

8. Disconnect the engine harness electrical connector from the Evaporative Emission (EVAP) canister purge solenoid.

9. Disconnect the engine wiring harness electrical connector from the Manifold Absolute Pressure (MAP) sensor.

10. Remove the Connector Position Assurance (CPA) retainer.

11. Disconnect the engine harness electrical connector from the ignition coil harness electrical connector.

12. Disconnect the engine harness electrical connectors from the left side fuel injectors.

13. Remove the engine harness clip from the ignition coil bracket stud.

14. Remove the CPA retainer.

15. Disconnect the engine harness electrical connector from the ignition coil harness electrical connector.

16. Disconnect the engine harness electrical connector from the throttle actuator.

17. Remove the engine harness clip from the ignition coil bracket stud.

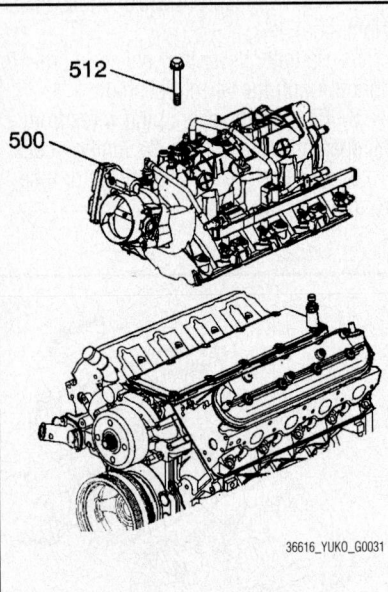

Fig. 117 Remove the intake manifold bolts (512) and the intake manifold (500)

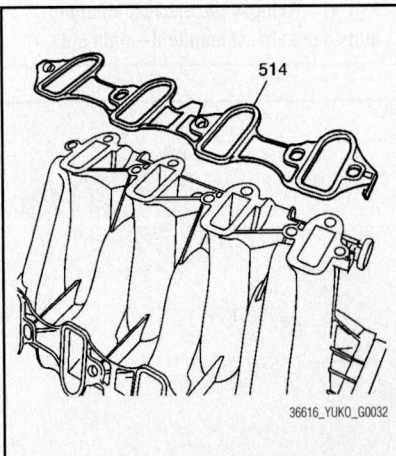

Fig. 118 Install NEW intake manifold gaskets to the intake manifold

18. Disconnect the engine harness electrical connectors from the right side fuel injectors.

19. Remove the engine harness clip and bolt.

20. Disconnect the engine harness electrical connector from the Engine Coolant Temperature (ECT) sensor.

21. Gather the engine harness branches and tie the harness up out of the way to the front of the engine compartment.

22. Reposition the brake booster vacuum hose clamp at the booster.

23. Remove the brake booster vacuum hose from the booster fitting.

24. Secure the brake booster vacuum hose to the intake manifold.

25. Disconnect the EVAP canister purge tube quick connect fitting from the EVAP canister purge solenoid.

26. Disconnect the fuel feed line quick connect fitting from the fuel rail.

27. Remove the Positive Crankcase Ventilation (PCV) hose from the intake manifold fitting.

28. Position the hose out of the way.

29. Loosen the intake manifold bolts (512).

➡**The aid of an assistant may be helpful in holding the engine harness up out of the way so the upper intake manifold cover does not get caught against the engine harness.**

30. Remove the intake manifold (500).

31. Cover the cylinder head passages in order to prevent dirt or debris from entering the passages.

32. Remove and discard the intake manifold gaskets.

33. If replacing the intake manifold, perform the following steps, otherwise proceed to step 21 of the installation procedure.

34. Place the intake manifold on a clean work surface.

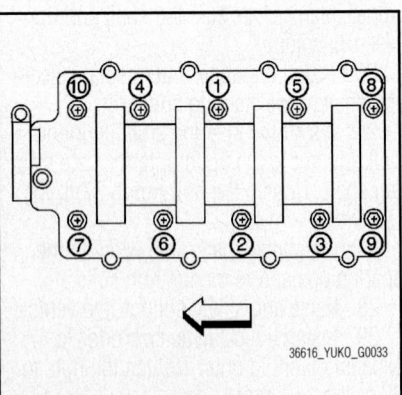

Fig. 119 Intake manifold bolt tightening sequence

35. Reposition the brake booster vacuum hose clamp at the intake manifold.

36. Remove the brake booster vacuum hose from the intake manifold nipple.

37. Remove the upper intake manifold cover nut.

38. Remove the upper intake manifold cover.

39. Remove the MAP sensor retainer.

40. Remove the MAP sensor.

41. Disconnect the EVAP tube quick connect fitting at the intake manifold.

42. Disengage the retainer securing the EVAP canister purge solenoid to the fuel rail.

43. Remove the EVAP tube and purge solenoid.

44. Remove the throttle body bolts/nuts.

45. Remove the throttle body.

46. Remove and discard the throttle body gasket.

47. Remove the fuel rail bolts.

➡**Lift evenly on both sides of the fuel rail until all injectors are removed from their bores.**

48. Remove the fuel rail.

49. Remove and discard the fuel injector lower O-ring seals.

➡**Evenly push in the RED collar in order to remove the nipple.**

50. Remove the brake booster vacuum hose nipple.

To install:

51. If the intake manifold was replaced, perform the following steps, otherwise proceed to step 21.

➡**Evenly push in the RED collar in order to install the nipple.**

52. Install the brake booster vacuum hose nipple to the NEW intake manifold.

53. Install NEW fuel injector lower O-ring seals onto the injectors.

54. Lubricate the NEW O-ring seals with clean engine oil.

➡**Push down firmly on both sides of the rail until all the injectors have been seated into their bores.**

55. Install the fuel rail.

56. Install the fuel rail bolts and tighten to 89 inch lbs. (10 Nm).

57. Install a NEW throttle body gasket to the intake manifold.

58. Install the throttle body.

59. Install the throttle body bolts/nuts and tighten to 89 inch lbs. (10 Nm).

60. Install the EVAP tube and purge solenoid.

61. Install the EVAP canister purge solenoid to the fuel rail bracket and engage the retainer.

62. Connect the EVAP tube quick connect fitting at the intake manifold.

63. Lubricate the MAP sensor seal with clean engine oil.

64. Install the MAP sensor.

65. Install the MAP sensor retainer.

66. Install the upper intake manifold cover.

67. Install the upper intake manifold cover nut until snug

68. Install the brake booster vacuum hose to the intake manifold nipple.

69. Position the brake booster vacuum hose clamp at the intake manifold.

70. Secure the brake booster vacuum hose to the intake manifold.

71. Install NEW intake manifold gaskets to the intake manifold.

72. Remove the covers from the cylinder head passages.

73. Install the intake manifold (500).

➡**The aid of an assistant may be helpful in holding the engine harness up out of the way so the upper intake manifold cover does not get caught against the engine harness.**

74. Tighten the intake manifold bolts (512) until snug.

75. Tighten the intake manifold bolts to specifications:

    a. Tighten the bolts a first pass, in the sequence shown, to 44 inch lbs. (5 Nm).

    b. Tighten the bolts a final pass, in the sequence shown, to 89 inch lbs. (10 Nm).

76. Position and install the PCV hose to the intake manifold fitting.

77. Connect the fuel feed line quick connect fitting to the fuel rail.

78. Connect the EVAP canister purge tube quick connect fitting to the EVAP canister purge solenoid.

79. Secure the brake booster vacuum hose to the intake manifold.

80. Install the brake booster vacuum hose to the booster fitting.

81. Position the brake booster vacuum hose clamp at the booster.

82. Untie the engine harness branches from the front of the engine compartment and position them over the engine.

83. Connect the engine harness electrical connector to the ECT sensor.

84. Position the engine harness clips to the bracket.

85. Connect the engine harness electrical connectors to the right side fuel injectors.

86. Install the engine harness clip to the ignition coil bracket stud.

87. Connect the engine harness electrical connector to the throttle actuator.

88. Connect the engine harness electrical connector to the ignition coil harness electrical connector.

89. Install the engine harness clip to the ignition coil bracket stud.

90. Connect the engine harness electrical connectors to the left side fuel injectors.

91. Connect the engine harness electrical connector to the ignition coil harness electrical connector.

92. Install the CPA retainer.

93. Connect the engine wiring harness electrical connector to the MAP sensor.

94. Connect the engine harness electrical connector to the EVAP canister purge solenoid.

95. Install the engine harness retainer to the stud and locator pin.

96. Install the engine harness retainer nut and tighten to 44 inch lbs. (5 Nm).

97. Install the alternator. Refer to Alternator, removal & installation.

98. Install the air cleaner outlet duct.

OIL PAN

REMOVAL & INSTALLATION

See Figures 120 through 126.

➡**The original oil pan gasket is retained and aligned to the oil pan by rivets. When installing a new gasket, it is not necessary to install new rivets. DO NOT reuse the oil pan gasket. When installing the oil pan, install a NEW oil pan gasket.**

1. Before servicing the vehicle, refer to the Precautions Section.

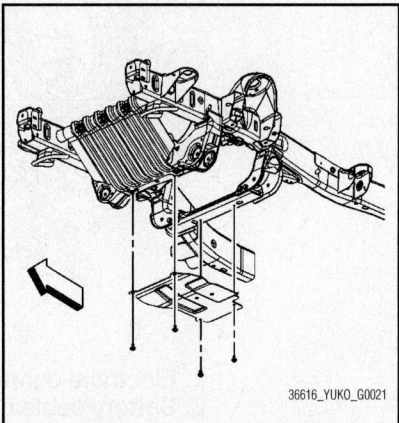

36616_YUKO_G0021

Fig. 120 Remove the oil pan skid plate bolts and plate—1500 series shown (2500 simiiar)

2. Disconnect the negative battery cable.

3. Raise and safely support the vehicle.

4. Remove the oil pan skid plate bolts and skid plate, if equipped.

5. Remove the front differential carrier, if equipped.

6. Unbolt the steering rack and hang downward.

7. Drain the engine oil.

8. Re-install the oil pan drain plug until snug.

9. Remove the oil filter and drain completely.

10. Re-install the oil filter until snug.

11. Remove the right side transmission cover bolt.

12. Remove the left side transmission cover bolt and cover.

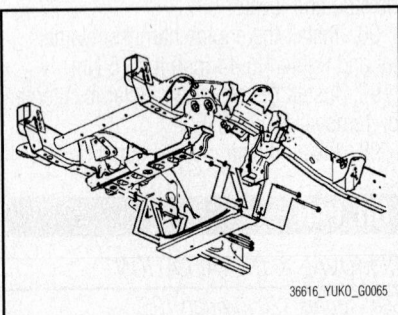

Fig. 121 Remove the crossbar bolts/nuts and crossbar—2500 series shown (1500 similar)

1. Electrical connector
2. Battery cable channel bolt
3. Channel pin

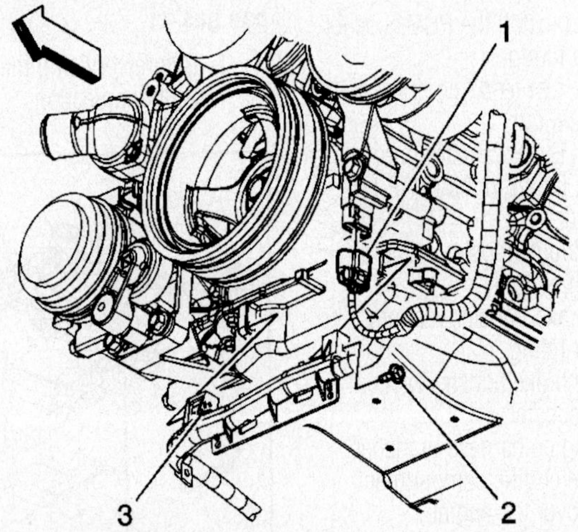

Fig. 122 Remove the battery cable channel bolt and slide the channel pin out of the oil pan tab

13. Remove the crossbar bolts/nuts and crossbar.

14. Remove the 2 lower transmission bolts.

15. Disconnect the engine harness electrical connector from the oil level sensor.

16. Remove the engine harness clip from the transmission oil cooler line bracket.

17. Remove the battery cable channel bolt.

18. Slide the channel pin out of the oil pan tab.

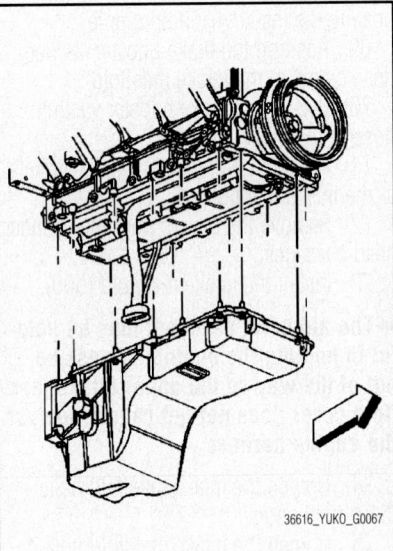

Fig. 123 Remove the oil pan bolts and the oil pan

19. Remove the oil cooler lines from the clip, if equipped.

20. Remove the transmission oil cooler line clip bolt and clip from the oil pan.

21. Remove the oil pan bolts.

22. Remove the oil pan.

❊❊ WARNING

DO NOT allow foreign material to enter the oil passages of the oil pan, cap, or cover the openings as required.

23. If reusing the oil pan, perform the following steps:

　a. Drill out the oil pan gasket rivets, if necessary.

　b. Remove the oil pan gasket from the pan.

　c. Discard the oil pan gasket.

　d. Discard the rivets, if necessary.

To install:

❊❊ WARNING

The alignment of the structural oil pan is critical. The rear bolt hole locations of the oil pan provide mounting points for the transmission bell housing. To ensure the rigidity of the powertrain and correct transmission alignment, it is important that the rear of the block and the rear of the oil pan must NEVER protrude beyond the engine block and transmission bell housing plane.

➡Do not reuse the oil pan gasket. It is not necessary to rivet the NEW gasket to the oil pan.

➡Be sure to align the oil gallery passages in the oil pan and engine block properly with the oil pan gasket.

24. If reusing the oil pan, place a NEW oil pan gasket onto the oil pan.

25. Apply a 0.2 inch (5mm) bead of sealant 0.8 inch (20mm) long to the engine block. Apply the sealant directly onto the tabs of the front cover gasket that protrudes into the oil pan surface.

26. Apply a 0.2 inch (5mm) bead of sealant 0.8 inch (20mm) long to the engine block. Apply the sealant directly onto the tabs of the rear cover gasket that protrudes into the oil pan surface.

27. Pre-assemble the oil pan gasket and bolts to the pan:

　a. Install the gasket onto the pan.

　b. Install the oil pan bolts to the pan and through the gasket.

28. Install the oil pan, oil pan gasket, and bolts to the engine block as an assembly.

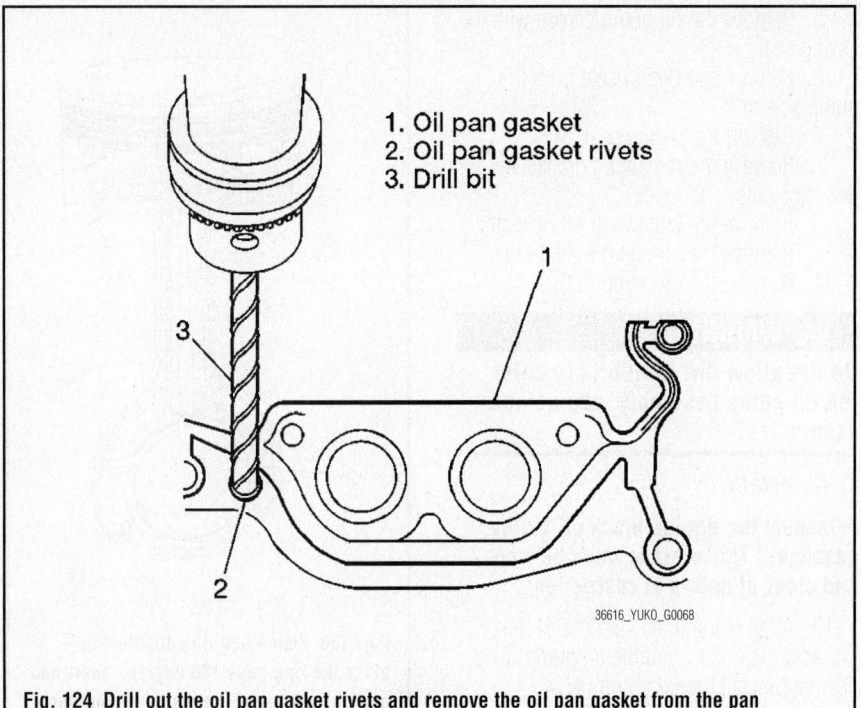

1. Oil pan gasket
2. Oil pan gasket rivets
3. Drill bit

36616_YUKO_G0068

Fig. 124 Drill out the oil pan gasket rivets and remove the oil pan gasket from the pan

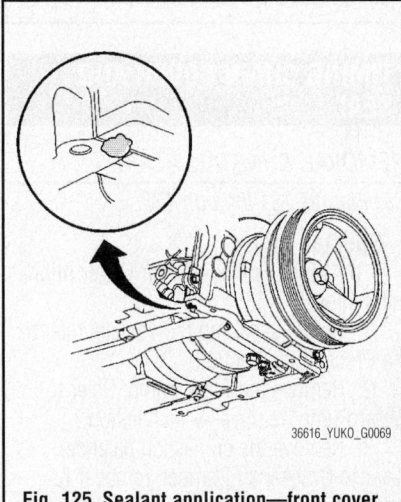

36616_YUKO_G0069

Fig. 125 Sealant application—front cover gasket tabs

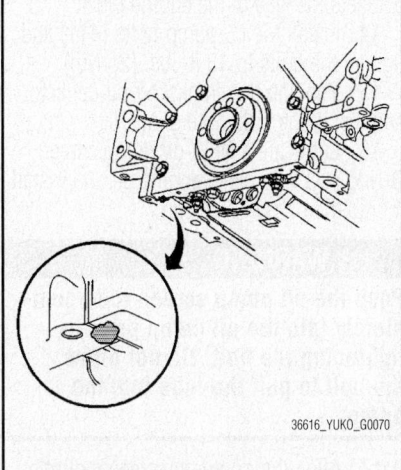

36616_YUKO_G0070

Fig. 126 Sealant application—rear cover gasket tabs

29. Hand thread the oil pan bolts into the engine block until snug. Do not tighten at this time.

30. For vehicles with a 6L80-E automatic transmission, position the oil cooler bracket and install the lower right transmission stud until snug and the lower left transmission bolt until snug.

31. For vehicles with a 4L60-E/4L70-E/4L80-E automatic transmission, install the 2 lower transmission bolts until snug.

32. Tighten the oil pan and oil pan-to-oil pan front cover bolts to 18 ft. lbs. (25 Nm).

33. Tighten the oil pan-to-rear cover bolts to 106 inch lbs. (12 Nm).

34. Tighten the transmission bolts/stud to 37 ft. lbs. (50 Nm).

35. Position the transmission oil cooler line clip and install the bolt to the oil pan. Tighten the bolt to 80 inch lbs. (9 Nm).

36. Install the oil cooler lines to the clip.

37. Position the channel and slide the channel pin into the oil pan tab.

38. Install the battery cable channel bolt and tighten the bolt to 106 inch lbs. (12 Nm).

39. Connect the engine harness electrical connector to the oil level sensor.

40. Install the engine harness clip to the transmission oil cooler line bracket.

41. For both the 1500 and 2500 series, perform the following steps prior to installing the crossbar bolts:

 a. Remove all traces of the original adhesive patch.

 b. Clean the threads of the bolts with denatured alcohol, or equivalent, and allow to dry.

 c. Apply threadlock GM P/N 36616493, or equivalent, to the bolt threads.

42. Install the crossbar and crossbar bolts/nuts and tighten the nuts to:

 a. For 1500 series vehicles, 74 ft. lbs. (100 Nm).

 b. For 2500 series vehicles, 89 ft. lbs. (120 Nm).

43. Position the left side transmission cover and install the cover bolt. Tighten the bolt to 106 inch lbs. (12 Nm).

44. Install the right side transmission cover bolt. Tighten the bolt to 106 inch lbs. (12 Nm).

45. Install a NEW oil filter. Tighten the oil filter to 22 ft. lbs. (30 Nm).

➡**Lubricate the NEW oil filter seal with clean engine oil.**

46. Ensure that the oil pan drain plug is tight. Tighten the drain plug to 18 ft. lbs. (25 Nm).

47. Install the front differential carrier, if equipped.

48. Raise the steering rack in place and install the steering rack bolts.

 a. Tighten the left side steering rack bolts to 148 ft. lbs. (200 Nm).

 b. Tighten the right side steering rack bolts to 74 ft. lbs. (100 Nm).

49. If equipped, position the oil pan skid plate and tighten the bolts to 21 ft. lbs. (28 Nm).

50. Lower the vehicle.

51. Fill the engine with the proper type and amount of NEW engine oil.

52. Start the engine and inspect for leaks.

OIL PUMP

REMOVAL & INSTALLATION

See Figures 127 through 129.

1. Before servicing the vehicle, refer to the Precautions Section.

2. Remove the oil pan. Refer to Oil Pan, removal & installation.

3. Remove the engine front cover. Refer to Timing Chain Cover and Seal, removal & installation.

4. Remove the oil pump screen bolt and nuts.

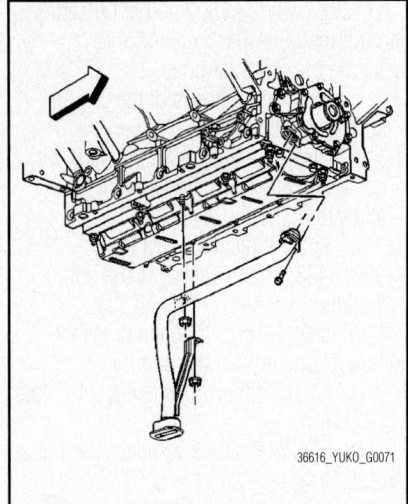

Fig. 127 View of oil pick-up tube and screen

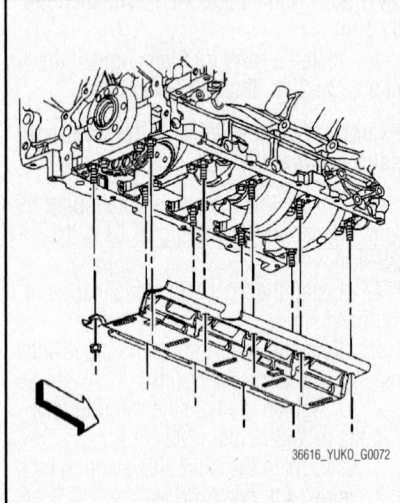

Fig. 128 Remove the crankshaft oil deflector

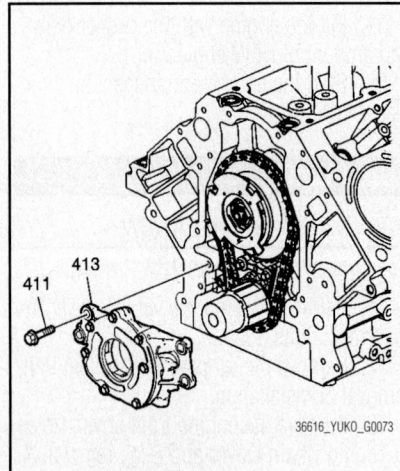

Fig. 129 Remove the oil pump bolts (411) and the oil pump (413)

5. Remove the oil pump screen with the O-ring seal.

6. Remove the O-ring seal from the pump screen.

7. Discard the O-ring seal.

8. Remove the remaining crankshaft oil deflector nuts.

9. Remove the crankshaft oil deflector.

10. Remove the oil pump bolts (411).

11. Remove the oil pump (413).

❋❋ WARNING

Do not allow dirt or debris to enter the oil pump assembly, cap as necessary.

To install:

➥Inspect the engine block oil galley passages. These areas must be free and clear of debris or restrictions.

12. Align the splined surfaces of the crankshaft sprocket and the oil pump drive gear and install the oil pump (413).

13. Install the oil pump (413) onto the crankshaft sprocket until the pump housing contacts the face of the engine block.

14. Install the oil pump bolts (411) and tighten the bolts to 18 ft. lbs. (25 Nm).

15. Position the crankshaft oil deflector and install the nuts until snug.

16. Lubricate a NEW oil pump screen O-ring seal with clean engine oil and install it onto the oil pump screen.

❋❋ WARNING

Push the oil pump screen tube completely into the oil pump prior to tightening the bolt. Do not allow the bolt to pull the tube into the pump.

17. Align the oil pump screen mounting brackets with the correct crankshaft bearing cap studs.

18. Install the oil pump screen.

19. Install the oil pump screen bolt and nuts.

   a. Tighten the bolt to 106 inch lbs. (12 Nm).

   b. Tighten the nuts to 18 ft. lbs. (25 Nm).

20. Install the engine front cover. Refer to Timing Chain Cover and Seal, removal & installation.

21. Install the oil pan. Refer to Oil Pan, removal & installation.

PISTON AND RING

POSITIONING

See Figure 130.

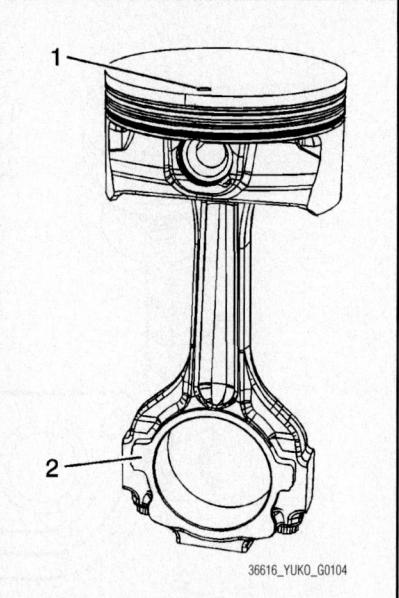

Fig. 130 Piston and ring positioning— place the ring gaps 180 degrees apart; the mark on the top of the piston (1) and the tab (2) on the side of the connecting rod should face the front of the engine

TIMING CHAIN COVER AND SEAL

REMOVAL & INSTALLATION

See Figures 131 through 133.

Special Tool:

• J 41476: Front and Rear Cover Alignment Tool

1. Before servicing the vehicle, refer to the Precautions Section.

2. Remove the water pump. Refer to Water Pump, removal & installation.

3. Remove the crankshaft balancer. Refer to Crankshaft Damper, removal & installation.

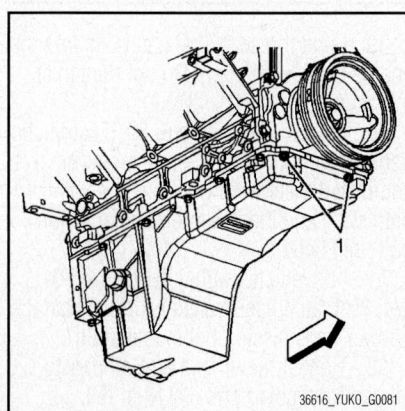

Fig. 131 Remove the oil pan-to-front cover bolts (1)

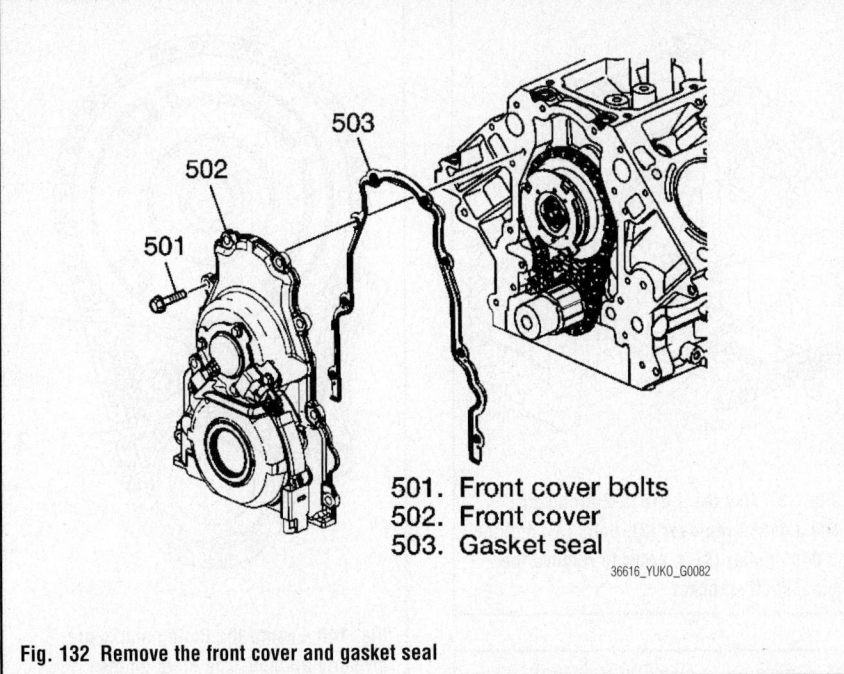

501. Front cover bolts
502. Front cover
503. Gasket seal

36616_YUKO_G0082

Fig. 132 Remove the front cover and gasket seal

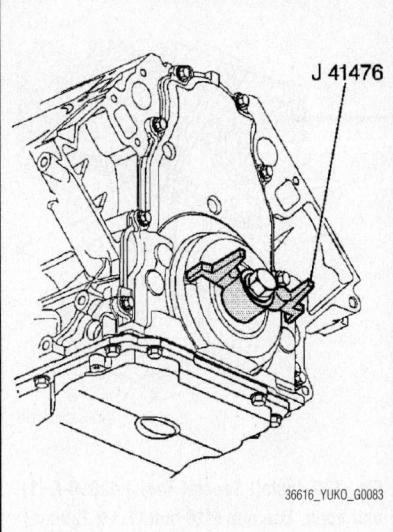

J 41476

36616_YUKO_G0083

Fig. 133 Align the tapered legs of the J 41476 with the machined alignment surfaces on the front cover

4. Disconnect the engine harness electrical connector from the Camshaft Position (CMP) sensor wire harness electrical connector.

5. Remove the oil pan-to-front cover bolts.

6. Remove the front cover bolts (501).

7. Remove the front cover (502) and gasket seal (503).

8. Discard the front cover gasket.

9. Remove the crankshaft front oil seal. Refer to Crankshaft Front Seal, removal & installation.

10. If replacing the engine front cover, perform the following steps:

a. Remove the CMP sensor wire harness bolts.

b. Disconnect the CMP sensor wire harness from the CMP sensor.

c. Remove the CMP sensor wire harness and the CMP sensor.

d. Remove the CMP actuator magnet bolts and magnet.

e. Remove and discard the CMP actuator magnet gasket.

To install:

➡**Do not reuse the crankshaft oil seal or front cover gasket. Do not apply any type of sealant to the front cover gasket, unless specified.**

❊❊ WARNING

The special tool in this procedure is used to properly center the front crankshaft front oil seal. All gasket surfaces should be free of oil or other foreign material during assembly.

The crankshaft front oil seal MUST be centered in relation to the crankshaft. An improperly aligned front cover may cause premature front oil seal wear and/or engine oil leaks.

11. If replacing the front cover, perform the following steps:

a. Install a NEW CMP actuator magnet gasket onto the magnet.

b. Install the CMP actuator magnet and bolts. Tighten the bolts to 106 inch lbs. (12 Nm).

c. Inspect the CMP sensor O-ring seal for cuts or damage. If the seal is not cut or damaged, it may be reused.

d. Lubricate the O-ring seal with clean engine oil.

e. Install the CMP sensor. Position the CMP sensor wire harness to the front cover.

f. Connect the CMP sensor wire harness to the CMP sensor.

g. Install the CMP sensor wire harness bolts and tighten to 106 inch lbs. (12 Nm).

12. Apply a 0.20 inch (5mm) bead of sealant, 0.80 inch (20mm) long, to the oil pan-to-engine block junction.

13. Position the NEW engine front cover gasket (503) and front cover (502) to the engine.

14. Install the front cover bolts (501) until snug. Do not over-tighten.

15. Install the oil pan-to-front cover bolts until snug. Do not over-tighten.

16. Install J 41476 to the front cover.

17. Align the tapered legs of the J 41476 with the machined alignment surfaces on the front cover.

18. Install the crankshaft balancer bolt until snug. Do not over-tighten.

19. Tighten the oil pan-to-front cover bolts to 18 ft. lbs. (25 Nm).

20. Tighten the engine front cover bolts to 18 ft. lbs. (25 Nm).

21. Remove the J 41476.

22. Connect the engine harness electrical connector to the CMP sensor wire harness electrical connector.

23. Install a NEW crankshaft front oil seal. Refer to Crankshaft Front Seal, removal & installation.

24. Install the water pump. Refer to Water Pump, removal & installation.

TIMING CHAIN AND SPROCKETS

REMOVAL & INSTALLATION

See Figures 134 through 140.

Special Tools:

• J 8433: Two Jaw Puller
• J 41558: Crankshaft Sprocket Remover
• J 41816-2: Crankshaft End Protector
• EN 46330: Timing Belt Tensioner Retaining Pin
• J 41478: Crankshaft Front Oil Seal Installer
• J 41665: Crankshaft Balancer and Sprocket Installer
• J 42386-A: Flywheel Holding Tool
• J 45059: Angle Meter

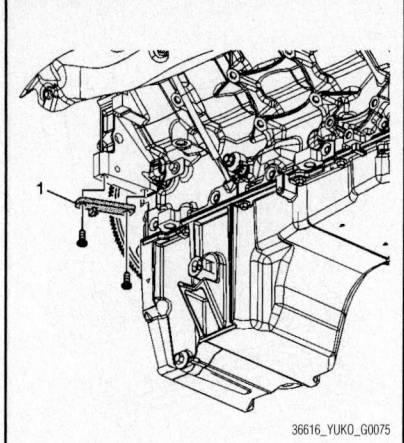

Fig. 134 Install Special Tool J 42386-A (1) and bolts. Use one M10 bolt (1.5 x 120mm) and another M10 bolt (1.5 x 45mm) for proper tool operation

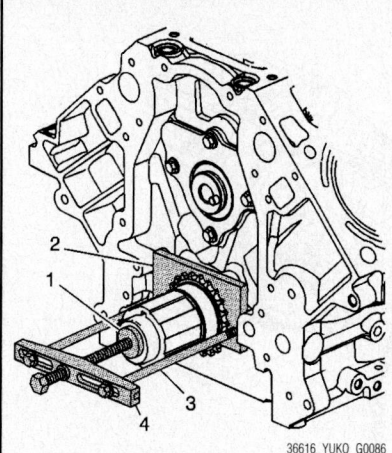

Fig. 137 Use the J 41816-2 protector (1), the J 41558 remover (2), bolts (3), and the J 8433 puller (4) in order to remove the crankshaft sprocket

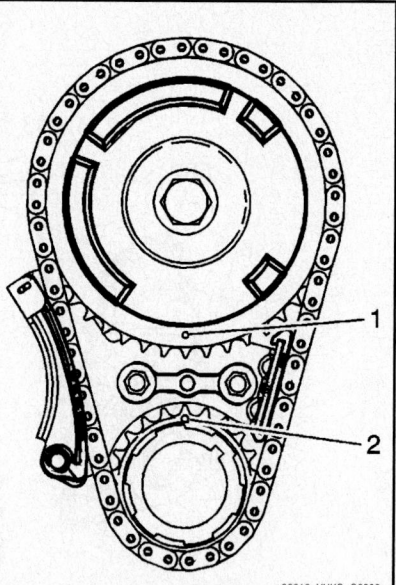

Fig. 140 Ensure the timing marks are properly aligned. The mark on the camshaft sprocket (1) should be located in the 6 o'clock position and the mark on the crankshaft sprocket (2) should be located in the 12 o'clock position

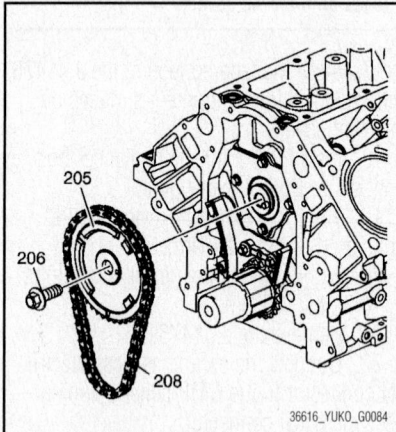

Fig. 135 Remove and discard the camshaft sprocket bolt (206). Remove the camshaft sprocket (205) and timing chain (208)

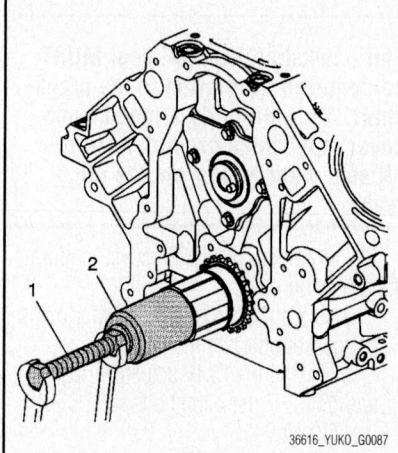

Fig. 138 Use the J 41478 installer (1) and the J 41665 installer (2) in order to install the crankshaft sprocket

❊❊ WARNING

Do not turn the crankshaft assembly after the timing chain has been removed in order to prevent damage to the piston assemblies or the valves.

1. Before servicing the vehicle, refer to the Precautions Section.
2. Disconnect the negative battery cable.
3. Drain the cooling system.
4. Remove the front cover and seal. Refer to Timing Chain Cover and Seal, removal & installation.
5. Remove the starter.
6. Install the J 42386-A tool and bolts. Use one M10 bolt (1.5 x 120mm) and another M10 bolt (1.5 x 45mm) for proper tool operation. Tighten the J 42386-A tool bolts to 37 ft. lbs. (50 Nm).
7. Remove and discard the camshaft sprocket bolt (206).
8. Remove the camshaft sprocket (205) and timing chain (208).
9. Remove the bolts (231) and timing chain tensioner (232).
10. Use the J 41816-2 protector, the J 41558 remover, bolts, and the J 8433 puller in order to remove the crankshaft sprocket.
11. Remove the crankshaft sprocket.
12. Remove the crankshaft sprocket key, as required.

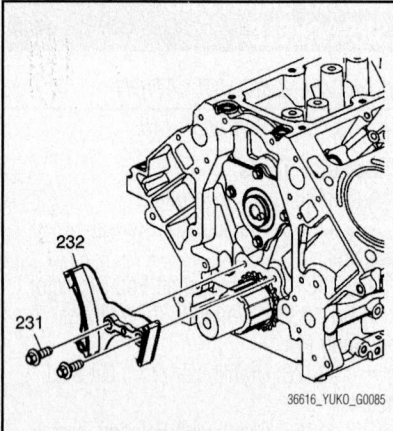

Fig. 136 Remove the bolts (231) and timing chain tensioner (232)

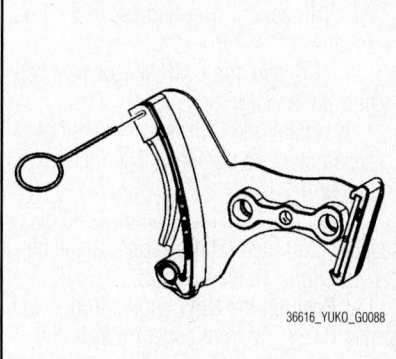

Fig. 139 Compress the timing chain tensioner guide and install the EN 46330 pin

13. Remove the J 42386-A tool and bolts.

To install:

14. Install the key into the crankshaft keyway, if previously removed.

15. Tap the key into the keyway until both ends of the key bottom onto the crankshaft.

16. Position the crankshaft sprocket onto the front of the crankshaft. Align the crankshaft key with the crankshaft sprocket keyway.

17. Use the J 41478 installer and the J 41665 installer in order to install the crankshaft sprocket.

18. Install the sprocket onto the crankshaft until fully seated against the crankshaft flange.

19. Rotate the crankshaft sprocket until the alignment mark is in the 12 o'clock position.

20. Compress the timing chain tensioner guide and install the EN 46330 pin.

21. Install the timing chain tensioner and bolts. Tighten the timing chain tensioner bolts to 18 ft. lbs. (25 Nm).

➡**Do not use the camshaft sprocket bolt again. Install a NEW bolt during assembly. The sprocket teeth and timing chain must mesh and the camshaft and the crankshaft sprocket alignment marks MUST be aligned properly.**

22. Install the camshaft sprocket (205), timing chain (208), and NEW bolt (206).

23. Inspect the sprockets for proper alignment. The mark on the camshaft sprocket should be located in the 6 o'clock position and the mark on the crankshaft sprocket should be located in the 12 o'clock position.

24. Remove the EN 46330 pin.

25. Install the J 42386-A tool and bolts. Use one M10 bolt (1.5 x 120mm) and another M10 bolt (1.5 x 45mm) for proper tool operation. Tighten the J 42386-A tool bolts to 37 ft. lbs. (50 Nm).

26. Tighten the camshaft sprocket bolt.

　a. Step 1: Tighten to 55 ft. lbs. (75 Nm).

　b. Step 2: Tighten an additional 50° using the J 45059 meter.

27. Remove the J 42386-A tool and bolts.

28. Install the starter.

29. Install the front cover. Refer to Timing Chain Cover and Seal, removal & installation.

30. Start the engine and check for proper operation. Correct as required.

31. Check for leaks, correct as required.

VALVE COVERS

REMOVAL & INSTALLATION

Left Side

See Figures 141 and 142.

1. Before servicing the vehicle, refer to the Precautions Section.

2. Remove the upper intake manifold sight shield.

3. Remove the Connector Position Assurance (CPA) retainer.

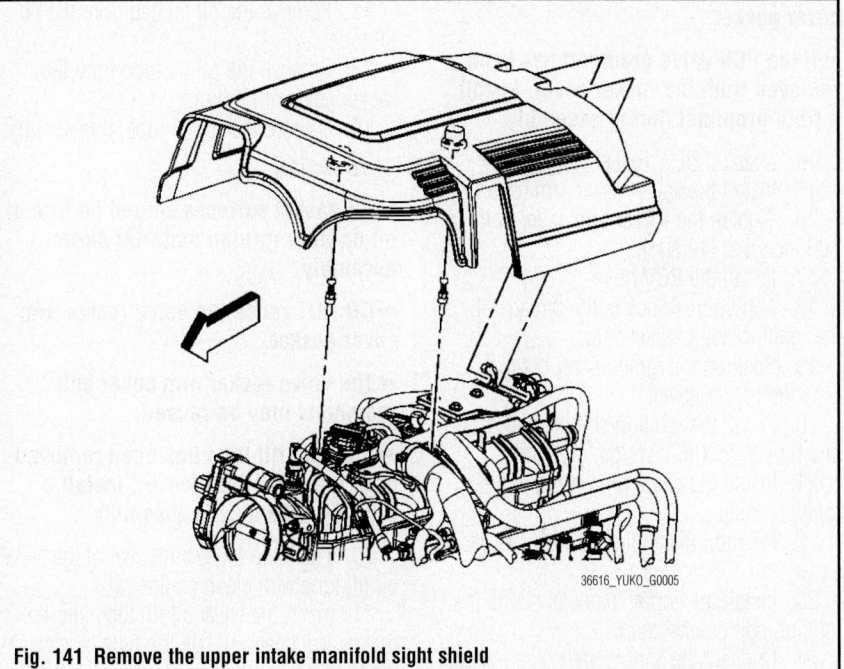

Fig. 141 Remove the upper intake manifold sight shield

4. Disconnect the engine harness electrical connector from the ignition coil wire harness.

5. Remove the engine harness clip from the ignition coil bracket stud.

6. Reposition the engine harness, as necessary.

7. Remove the spark plug wires from the ignition coils. Twist each plug wire ½ turn. Pull only on the boot in order to remove the wire from the ignition coil.

8. Remove the ignition coil bracket studs.

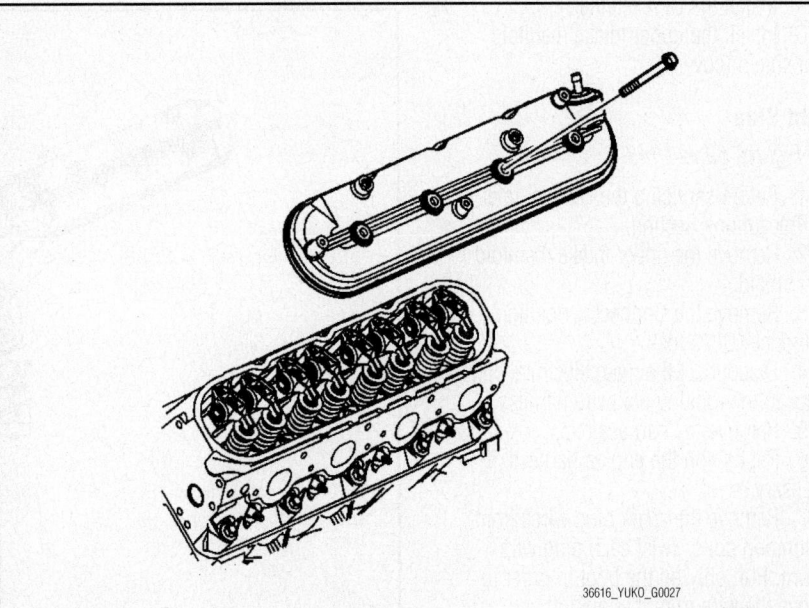

Fig. 142 Remove the valve rocker arm cover—left side

9. Remove the ignition coil bracket.

10. Remove the Positive Crankcase Ventilation (PCV) hose.

11. Loosen the valve rocker arm cover bolts.

12. Remove the valve rocker arm cover.

13. Remove and discard the old gasket.

To install:

➥All gasket surfaces should be free of oil and/or other foreign material during assembly.

➥DO NOT reuse the valve rocker arm cover gasket.

➥If the PCV valve grommet has been removed from the rocker cover, install a NEW grommet during assembly.

14. Install a NEW rocker cover gasket.

15. Install the valve rocker arm cover.

16. Tighten the rocker arm cover bolts to 106 inch lbs. (12 Nm).

17. Install the PCV hose.

18. Apply threadlock to the threads of the ignition coil bracket studs.

19. Position the ignition coil bracket onto the rocker cover.

20. Install the ignition coil bracket studs and tighten to 106 inch lbs. (12 Nm).

21. Install the spark plug wires to the ignition coils.

22. Position the engine harness, as necessary.

23. Install the engine harness clip to the ignition coil bracket stud.

24. Connect the engine harness electrical connector to the ignition coil wire harness.

25. Install the CPA retainer.

26. Install the upper intake manifold sight shield (cover).

Right Side

See Figures 59 and 143.

1. Before servicing the vehicle, refer to the Precautions Section.

2. Remove the upper intake manifold sight shield.

3. Remove the Connector Position Assurance (CPA) lock.

4. Disconnect the main electrical connector to the ignition coil wire harness.

5. Remove the harness clips.

6. Reposition the engine harness, if necessary.

7. Remove the spark plug wires from the ignition coils. Twist each plug wire ½ turn. Pull only on the boot in order to remove the wire from the ignition coil.

8. Remove the surge tank outlet hose from the heater hose bracket.

9. Remove the heater hose bracket bolt from the front of the right cylinder head.

10. If necessary, remove the ignition coil bracket studs from the rocker arm cover.

11. If necessary, remove the ignition coils and bracket from the rocker cover.

12. Remove the vent hose from the valve rocker arm cover.

13. Remove the valve rocker arm cover bolts.

14. Remove the valve rocker arm cover.

15. Remove the gasket from the rocker cover.

16. Discard the OLD gasket.

17. Remove the oil fill cap from the oil fill tube.

18. Remove the oil fill tube from the rocker cover, if required.

19. Discard the oil fill tube, if necessary.

To install:

➥All gasket surfaces should be free of oil or other foreign material during assembly.

➥DO NOT reuse the valve rocker arm cover gasket.

➥The valve rocker arm cover bolt grommets may be reused.

➥If the oil fill tube has been removed from the rocker arm cover, install a NEW fill tube during assembly.

20. Lubricate the O-ring seal of the NEW oil fill tube with clean engine oil.

21. Insert the NEW oil fill tube into the rocker arm cover. Rotate the tube clockwise until locked in the proper position.

22. Install the oil fill cap into the tube. Rotate the cap clockwise until locked in the proper position.

23. Install a NEW rocker cover gasket into the valve rocker arm cover.

24. Install the valve rocker arm cover onto the cylinder head.

25. Install new rocker arm cover grommets, if necessary.

26. Install the rocker arm cover bolts and grommets and tighten the bolts to 106 inch lbs. (12 Nm).

27. Install the vent hose to the valve rocker arm cover.

28. Apply threadlock, GM P/N 36616382, or equivalent, to the threads of the bracket bolts.

29. If necessary, install the ignition coils and bracket to the rocker arm cover.

30. If necessary, install the ignition coil bracket studs to the rocker cover and tighten the studs to 106 inch lbs. (12 Nm).

31. Install the heater hose bracket and nut to the front of the right cylinder head and tighten to 80 inch lbs. (9 Nm).

32. Install the surge tank outlet hose to the heater hose bracket.

33. Install the spark plug wires to the ignition coils.

34. Position the engine harness, if necessary.

35. Install the harness clips.

36. Connect the main electrical connector feeding the ignition coils.

37. Install the CPA lock.

38. Install the upper intake manifold sight shield.

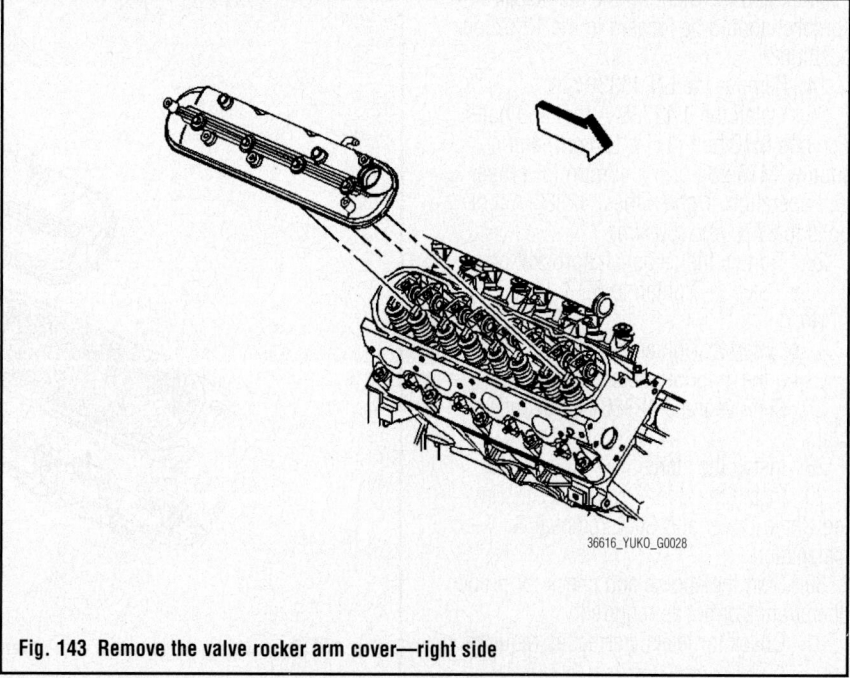

Fig. 143 Remove the valve rocker arm cover—right side

36616_YUKO_G0028

ENGINE PERFORMANCE & EMISSION CONTROLS

COMPONENT LOCATIONS

See Figures 144 through 149.

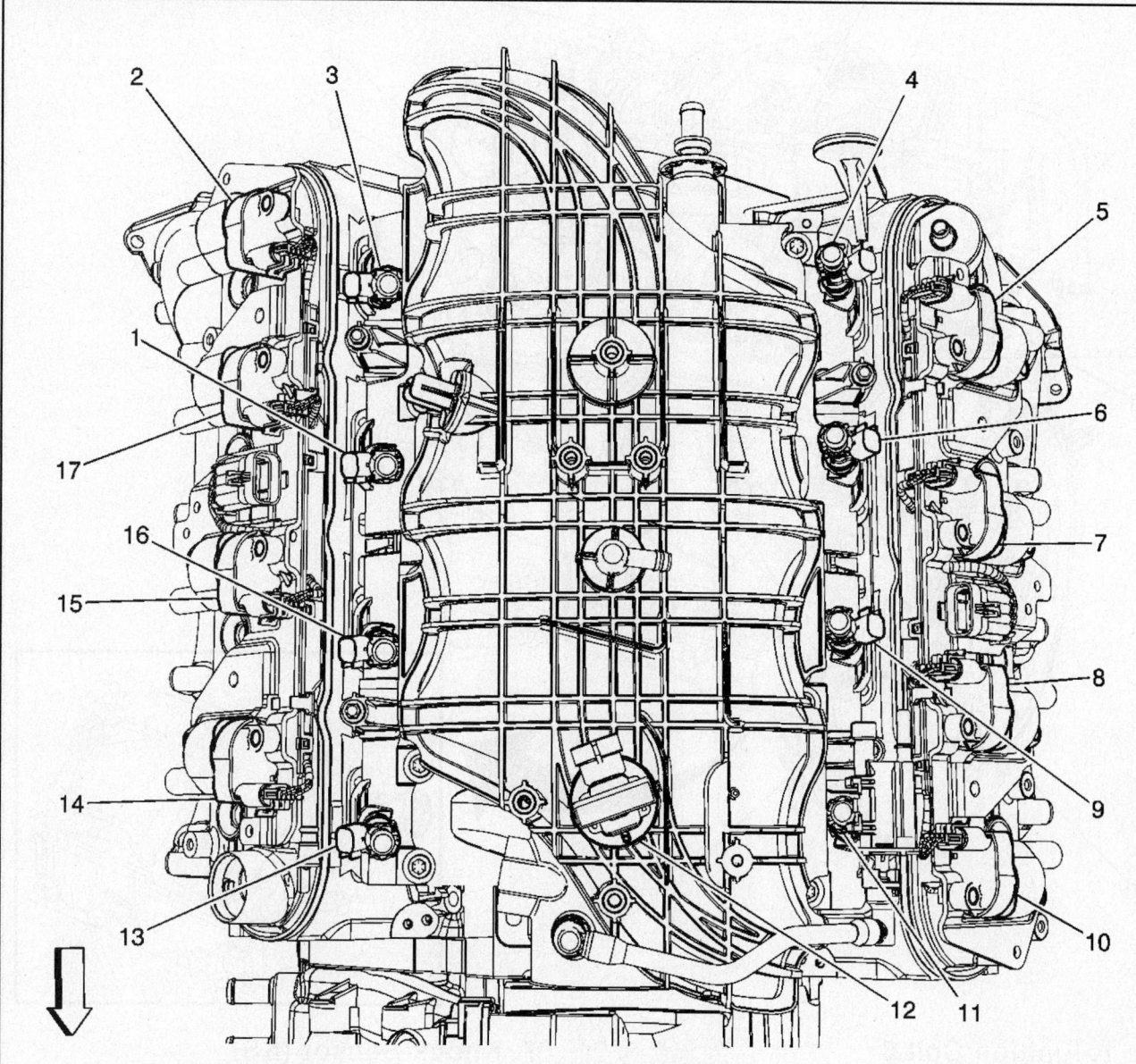

1. Fuel Injector 6
2. Ignition Coil 8
3. Fuel Injector 8
4. Fuel Injector 7
5. Ignition Coil 7
6. Fuel Injector 5
7. Ignition Coil 5
8. Ignition Coil 3
9. Fuel Injector 3
10. Ignition Coil 1
11. Fuel Injector 1
12. Manifold Absolute Pressure (MAP) Sensor
13. Fuel Injector 2
14. Ignition Coil 2
15. Ignition Coil 4
16. Fuel Injector 4
17. Ignition Coil 6

22116_SIER_G0116

Fig. 144 Top of engine component locations—4.8L, 5.3L, 6.0L and 6.2L engines

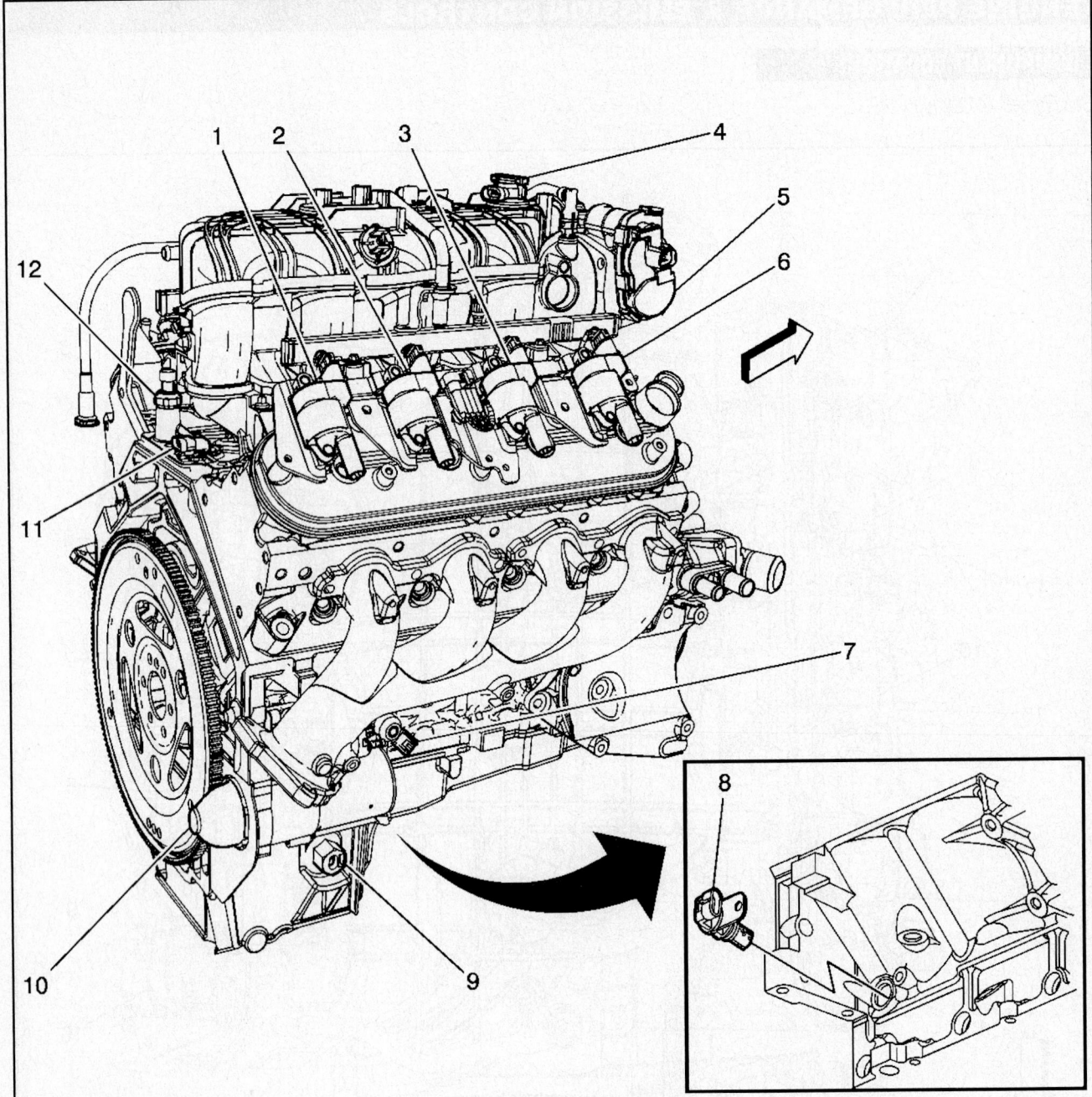

1. Ignition Coil 8
2. Ignition Coil 6
3. Ignition Coil 4
4. Manifold Absolute Pressure
   (MAP) Sensor
5. Throttle Body
6. Ignition Coil 2

7. Knock Sensor (KS)
8. Crankshaft Position (CKP) Sensor
9. Engine Oil Level Switch
10. Starter
11. Valve Lifter Oil Manifold
    (VLOM) Assembly
12. Engine Oil Pressure Sensor

22116_SIER_G0117

Fig. 145 Right side of the engine component locations—4.8L, 5.3L, 6.0L and 6.2L engines

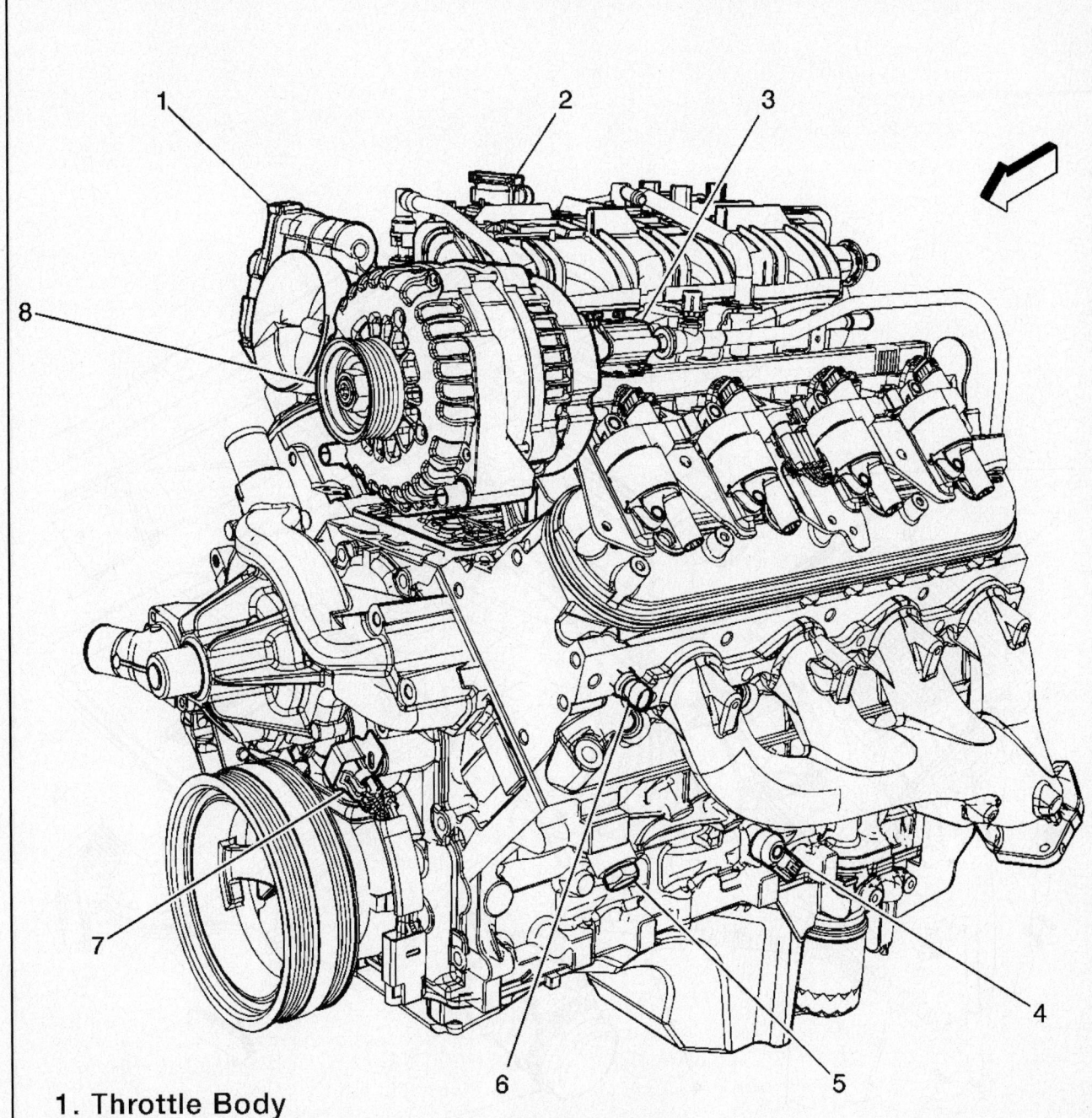

1. Throttle Body
2. Manifold Absolute Pressure (MAP) Sensor
3. Evaporative Emission (EVAP) Canister Purge Solenoid Valve
4. Knock Sensor (KS)
5. Engine Block Heater
6. Engine Coolant Temperature (ECT) Sensor
7. Camshaft Position (CMP) Sensor
8. Generator

22116_SIER_G0118

Fig. 146 Front of engine component locations—4.8L, 5.3L, 6.0L and 6.2L engines

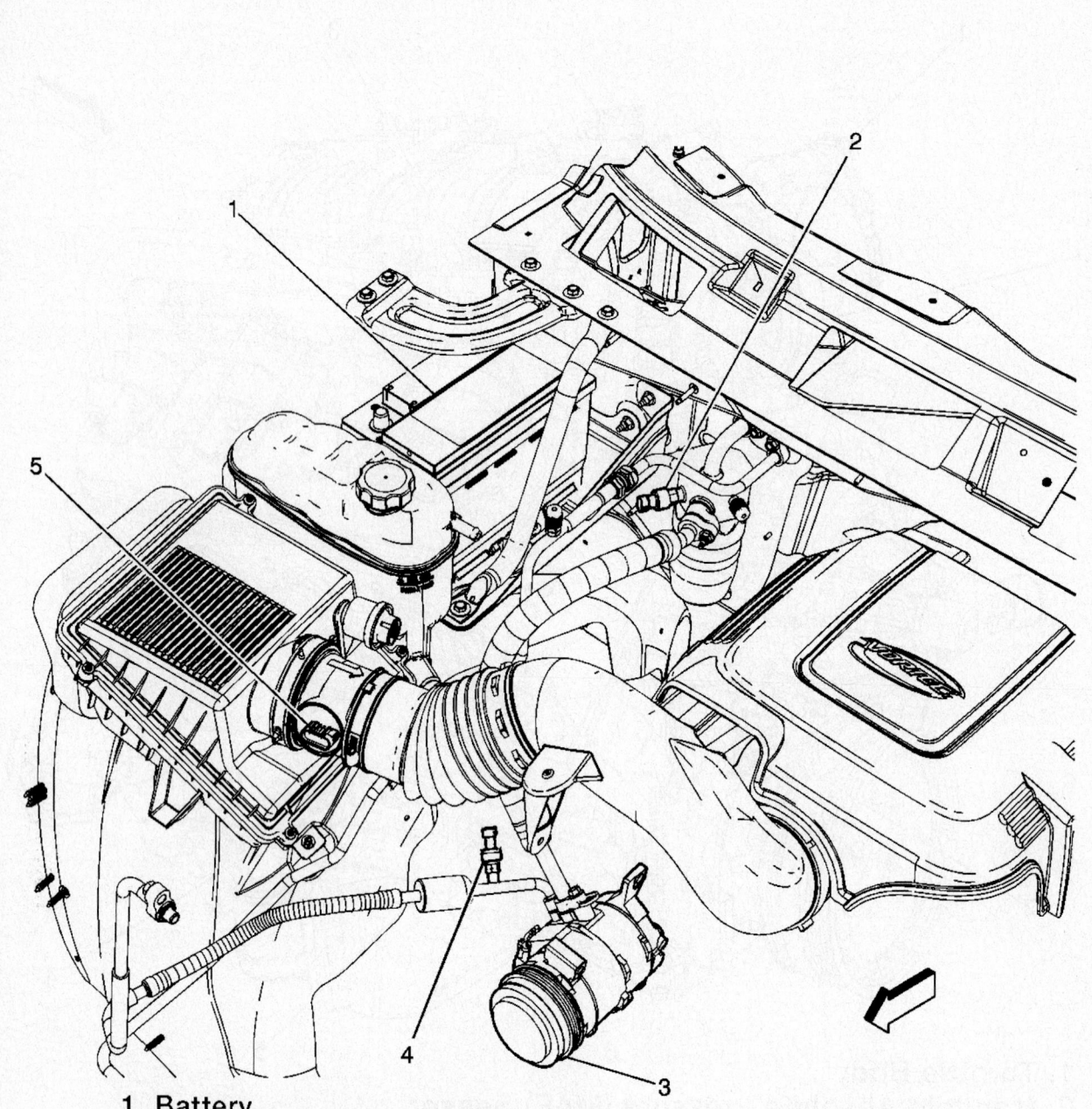

1. Battery
2. A/C Low Pressure Switch
3. A/C Compressor Clutch
4. A/C Refrigerant Pressure Switch
5. Mass Air Flow (MAF)/Intake Air Temperature (IAT) Sensor

22116_SIER_G0119

Fig. 147 Right rear of engine component locations—4.8L, 5.3L, 6.0L and 6.2L engines

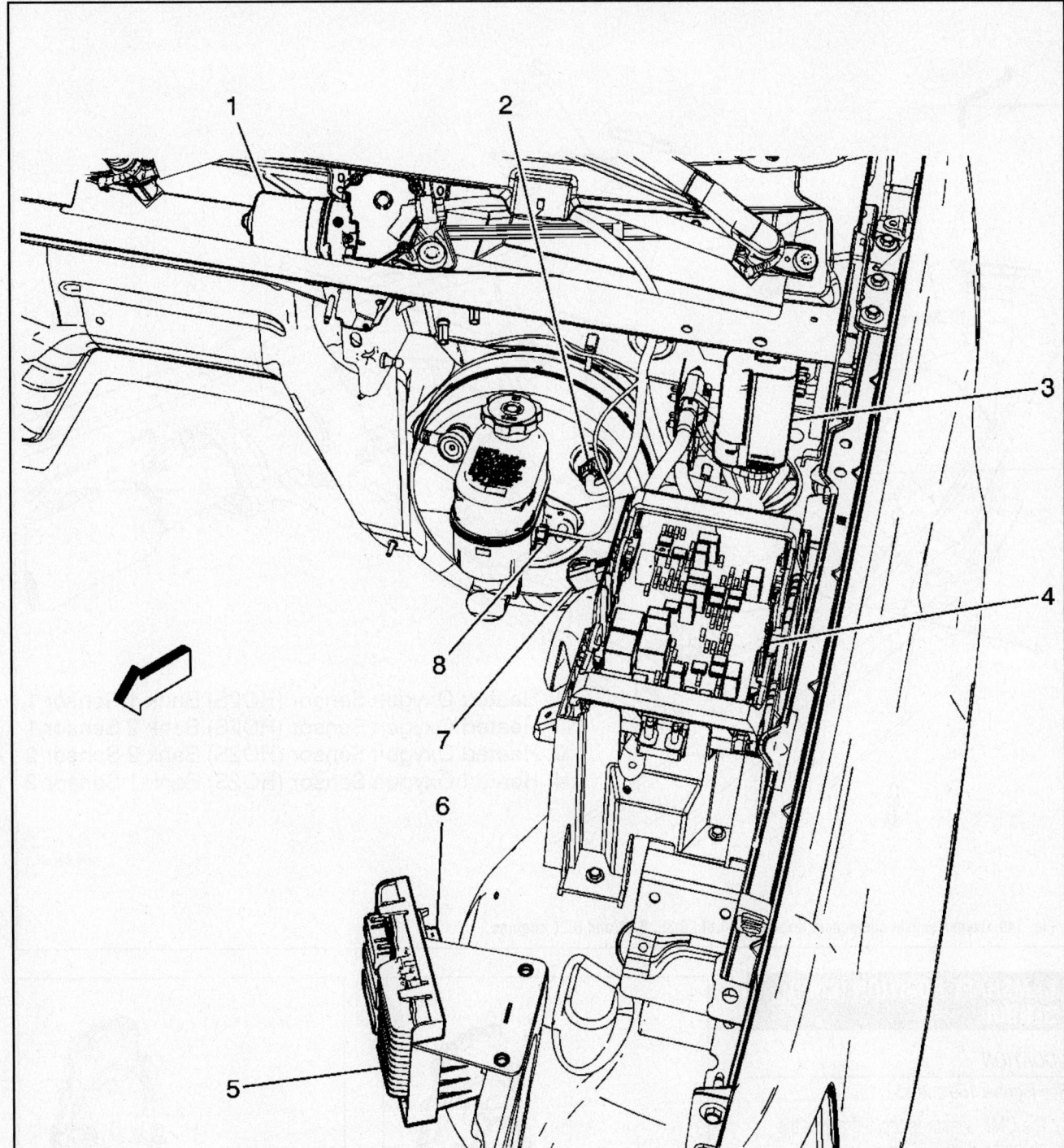

1. **Windshield Wiper Motor**
2. **Power Brake Booster**
3. **Windshield Washer Solvent Heater**
4. **Fuse Block**
5. **Powertrain Control Module (PCM)**
6. **Transmission Control Module (TCM)**
7. **Brake Booster Vacuum Sensor**
8. **Brake Fluid Level Switch**

22116_SIER_G0120

Fig. 148 Left of engine component locations—4.8L, 5.3L, 6.0L and 6.2L engines

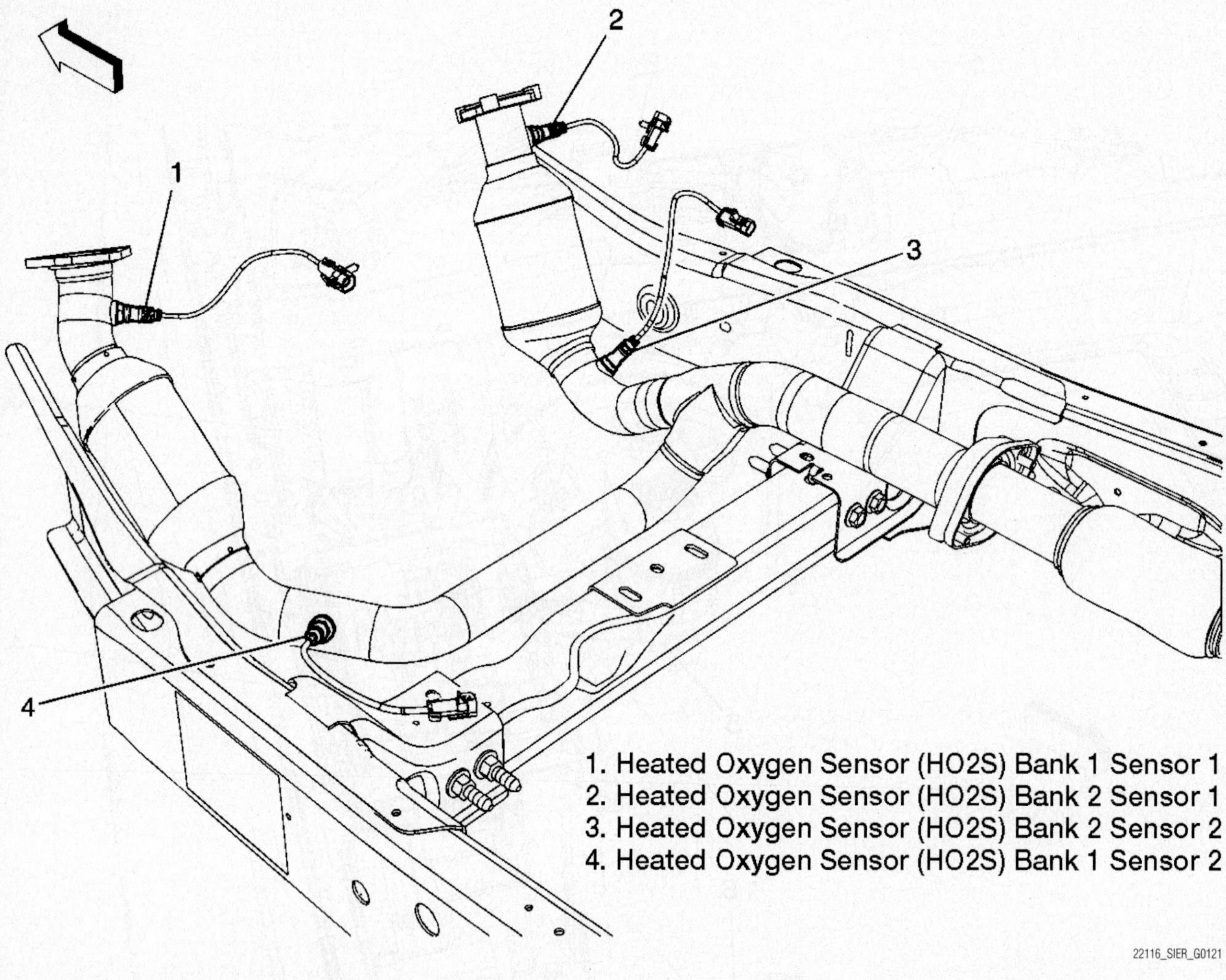

1. Heated Oxygen Sensor (HO2S) Bank 1 Sensor 1
2. Heated Oxygen Sensor (HO2S) Bank 2 Sensor 1
3. Heated Oxygen Sensor (HO2S) Bank 2 Sensor 2
4. Heated Oxygen Sensor (HO2S) Bank 1 Sensor 2

22116_SIER_G0121

Fig. 149 Oxygen sensor component locations—4.8L, 5.3L, 6.0L and 6.2L engines

CAMSHAFT POSITION (CMP) SENSOR

LOCATION

See Figures 150 and 151.

The CMP sensor is located above the crankshaft pulley.

REMOVAL & INSTALLATION

1. Before servicing the vehicle, refer to the Precautions Section.
2. Disconnect the negative battery cable.
3. Raise and support the vehicle safely.
4. Unplug the harness connector from the CMP sensor.
5. Remove the CMP sensor harness bolts, then remove the sensor from the engine.

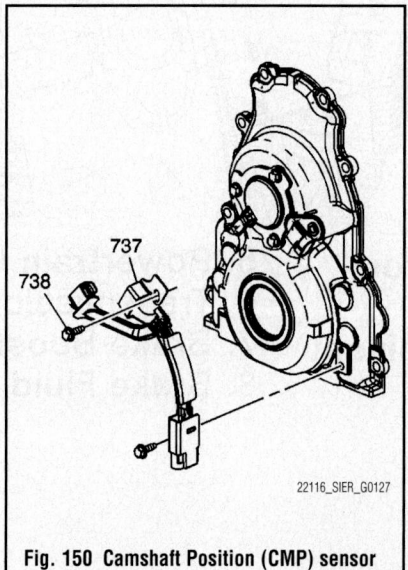

22116_SIER_G0127

Fig. 150 Camshaft Position (CMP) sensor location and harness mounting—type one

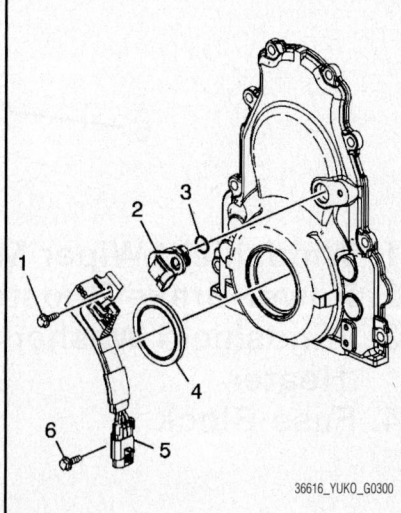

36616_YUKO_G0300

Fig. 151 Camshaft Position (CMP) sensor location and harness mounting—type two

To install:

➡ **Be sure to use new fasteners, as required.**

6. Installation is the reverse of removal.

7. Lubricate a new O-ring with clean engine oil. Tighten the bolt to 106 inch lbs. (12 Nm).

CRANKSHAFT POSITION (CKP) SENSOR

LOCATION

See Figure 152.

The CKP sensor is located on the side of the engine block.

REMOVAL & INSTALLATION

See Figure 152.

➡ **Use of a scan tool is required to complete this procedure. Anytime the CKP sensor is replaced, the variation learn procedure must be performed.**

1. Before servicing the vehicle, refer to the Precautions Section.

2. Disconnect the negative battery cable.

3. Raise and safely support the vehicle.

4. Remove the starter.

5. Working through the wheel well opening, unplug the harness connector from the sensor.

6. Clean the area around the sensor to prevent debris from entering the engine.

7. Remove the bolt securing the sensor, then remove it from the engine.

To install:

➡ **Be sure to use new fasteners, as required.**

8. Installation is the reverse of removal.

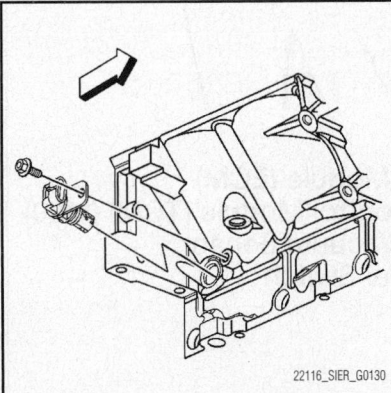

Fig. 152 Crankshaft Position (CKP) sensor location

22116_SIER_G0130

9. Lubricate a new O-ring with clean engine oil.

10. Tighten the bolt to 18 ft. lbs. (25 Nm).

11. Connect the scan tool to the vehicle and perform the CKP sensor variation learn procedure. Refer to Crankshaft Position System Variation Learn.

CRANKSHAFT POSITION SYSTEM VARIATION LEARN PROCEDURE

1. Before servicing the vehicle, refer to the Precautions Section.

2. Install a scan tool.

3. Monitor the Engine Control Module (ECM) for Diagnostic Trouble Codes (DTC's) with a scan tool. If other DTC's are set, except DTC P0315, refer to Diagnostic Trouble Codes for the applicable DTC that set.

4. Select the CKP variation learn procedure with a scan tool.

5. The scan tool instructs you to perform the following:

a. Accelerate to Wide Open Throttle (WOT).

b. Release throttle when fuel cut-off occurs.

c. Observe fuel cut-off for applicable engine.

d. Engine should not accelerate beyond calibrated RPM value.

e. Release throttle immediately if value is exceeded.

f. Block drive wheels.

g. Set parking brake.

h. DO NOT apply brake pedal.

i. Cycle ignition from OFF to ON.

j. Apply and hold brake pedal.

k. Start and idle engine.

l. Turn A/C OFF.

m. Vehicle must remain in Park or Neutral.

n. The scan tool monitors certain component signals to determine if all the conditions are met to continue with the procedure. The scan tool only displays the condition that inhibits the procedure. The scan tool monitors the following components:

- CKP sensors activity: If there is a CKP sensor condition, refer to the applicable DTC that set.
- Camshaft Position (CMP) sensor activity: If there is a CMP sensor condition, refer to the applicable DTC that set.
- Engine Coolant Temperature (ECT): If the ECT is not warm enough, idle the engine until the engine coolant temperature reaches the correct temperature.

6. Enable the CKP System Variation Learn Procedure with a scan tool.

➡ **Important: While the learn procedure is in progress, release the throttle immediately when the engine starts to decelerate. The engine control is returned to the operator and the engine responds to throttle position after the learn procedure is complete.**

7. Accelerate to WOT.

8. Release when the fuel cut-off occurs.

9. Test in progress.

10. The scan tool displays Learn Status: Learned this ignition. If the scan tool indicates that DTC P0315 ran and passed, the CKP Variation Learn Procedure is complete. If the scan tool indicates DTC P0315 failed or did not run, refer to DTC P0315. If any other DTC's set, refer to Diagnostic Trouble Codes for the applicable DTC that set.

11. Turn OFF the ignition for 30 seconds after the learn procedure is completed successfully.

12. The CKP Variation Learn Procedure is also required when the following service procedures have been performed, regardless of whether DTC P0315 is set:

- A CKP sensor replacement
- An engine replacement
- An ECM replacement
- An harmonic balancer replacement
- A crankshaft replacement
- Any engine repairs which disturb the CKP sensor relationship

ENGINE CONTROL MODULE (ECM)

LOCATION

See Figure 153.

The Engine Control Module (ECM) is located on a bracket on the left side of the engine compartment.

REMOVAL & INSTALLATION

See Figure 154.

Service of the Engine Control Module (ECM) should normally consist of either replacement of the ECM or Electrically Erasable Programmable Read Only Memory (EEPROM) programming. If the diagnostic procedures call for ECM replacement, inspect the ECM first to see if the replacement is the correct part. If the ECM is faulty, remove the ECM and install the new service ECM.

The new service ECM will not be programmed. You must program the new ECM. DTC P0602 indicates the EEPROM is not programmed or has malfunctioned.

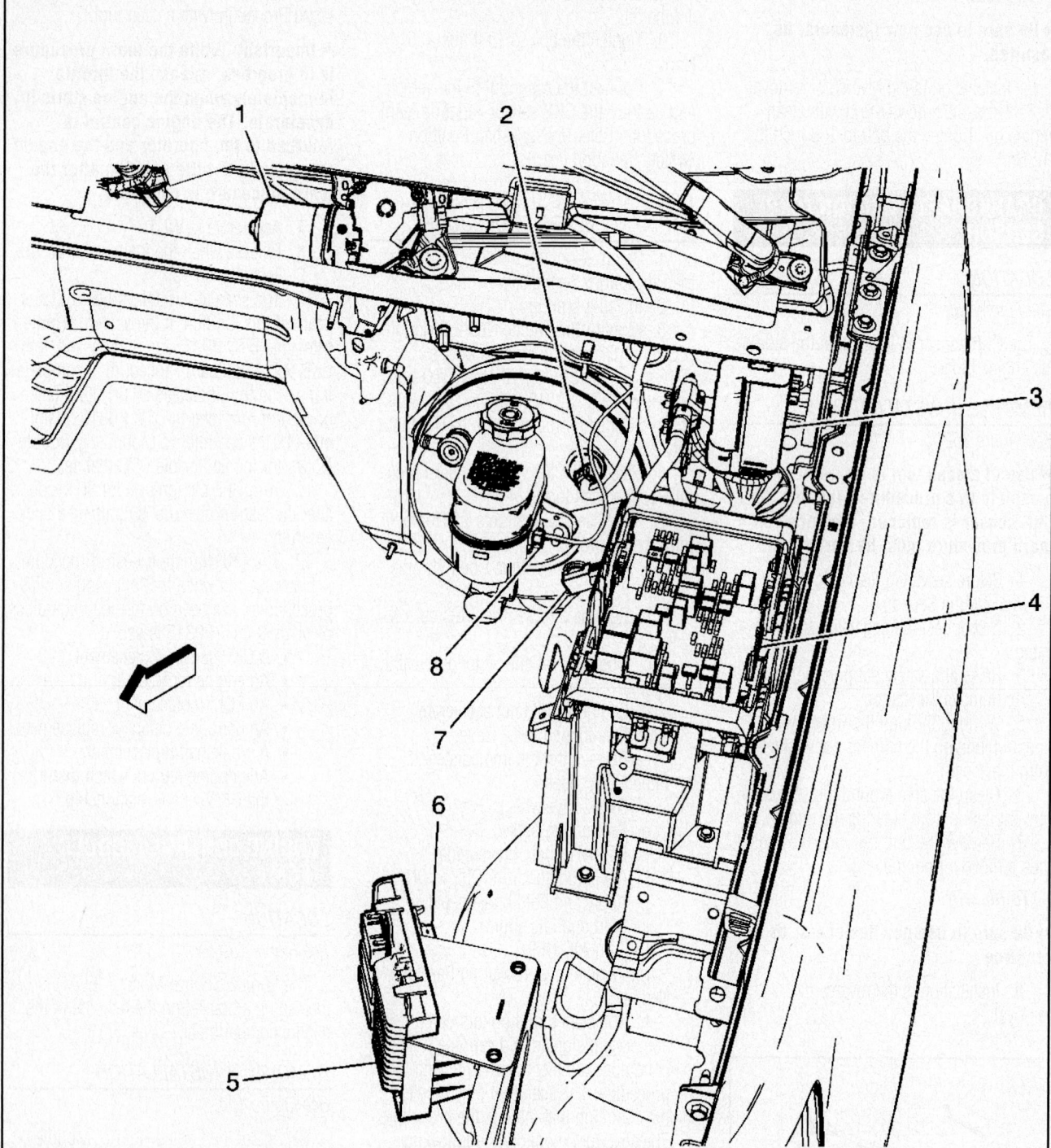

1. Windshield Wiper Motor
2. Power Brake Booster (JD9)
3. Windshield Washer Solvent Heater (XA7)
4. Fuse Block - Underhood
5. Engine Control Module (ECM)
6. Transmission Control Module (TCM) (M30)
7. Brake Booster Vacuum Sensor
8. Brake Fluid Level Switch

36616_YUKO_G0307

Fig. 153 Engine Control Module (ECM) location

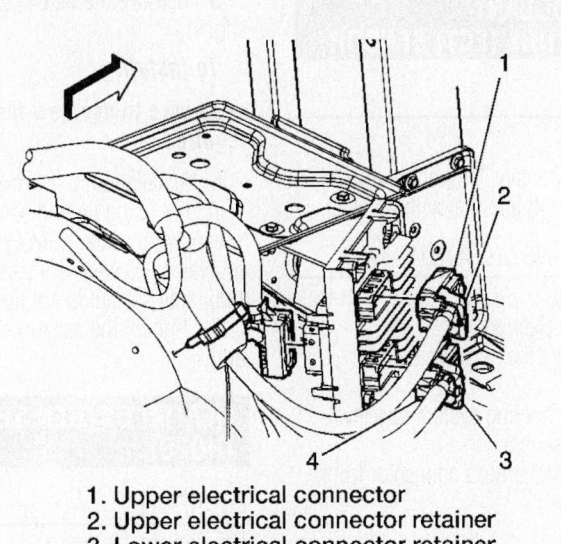

1. Upper electrical connector
2. Upper electrical connector retainer
3. Lower electrical connector retainer
4. Lower electrical connector

36616_YUKO_G0308

Fig. 154 Engine Control Module (ECM) removal

❋❋ WARNING

In order to prevent any possible electrostatic discharge damage to the ECM, do not touch the connector pins or the soldered components on the circuit board.

❋❋ WARNING

Control module damage may result when the metal case contacts battery voltage. DO NOT contact the control module metal case with battery voltage when servicing a control module, using battery booster cables, or when charging the vehicle battery.

❋❋ WARNING

Always turn the ignition OFF when installing or removing the ECM connectors in order to prevent damage to the components.

➡ It is necessary to record the remaining engine oil life. If the replacement module is not programmed with the remaining engine oil life, the engine oil life will default to 100 percent. If the replacement module is not programmed with the remaining engine oil life, the engine oil will need to be changed at 3,000 miles (5,000 km) from the last engine oil change.

1. Before servicing the vehicle, refer to the Precautions Section.

2. Using a scan tool, retrieve the percentage of remaining engine oil. Record the remaining engine oil life.

3. Disconnect the negative battery cable.

4. Disengage the engine wiring harness upper and lower electrical connector retainers and remove the connectors from the ECM.

5. Disengage the retainer tabs securing the ECM to the bracket.

6. Remove the ECM.

To install:

7. Install the bottom ECM tabs into the bracket.

8. Push the ECM in securing the ECM to the bracket.

9. Position the engine wiring harness lower and upper electrical connectors and engage the retainers securing the connectors to the ECM.

10. Connect the negative battery cable.

11. If a NEW ECM was installed, program the ECM. Refer to Reset Procedure.

RESET PROCEDURE

Special Tool:
• EL-49642: Service Programming System (SPS) Programming Support Tool

➡ **DO NOT reprogram a FlexFuel (E85) vehicle while the fuel composition learn function is active. If necessary, drive the vehicle until the scan tool indicates that the fuel composition learn parameter is inactive. Programming with the fuel composition learn active will result in fuel trim DTC's.**

If the ECM is replaced, the following procedures must be performed:
1. ECM Reprogramming.
2. The CKP System Variation Learn.
3. The Throttle/Idle Learn procedure.
4. Theft Deterrent reprogramming.
5. Fuel Composition Diagnostic.
6. Engine Oil Life Remaining. When available, use a scan tool to reset the engine oil life remaining back to the original percentage recorded before the module was replaced.
7. Transmission Fluid Life Remaining. When available, use the scan tool to reset the Transmission Fluid Life Remaining back to the original percentage recorded before the module was replaced.

Review the information below to ensure proper programming protocol.

• DO NOT program a control module unless you are directed by a service procedure or you are directed by a General Motors Corporation service bulletin. Programming a control module at any other time will not permanently correct for a fault or DTC being set.

• It is essential that the TIS terminal, MDI, and/or Scan Tool, is equipped with the latest software before performing service programming.

• Due to the time requirements of programming a controller, install EL-49642 SPS Programming Support Tool to maintain system voltage. Stable battery voltage is critical during programming. Any fluctuation, spiking, over voltage, or loss of voltage will interrupt programming. If the above tool is not available, connect a fully charged 12 volt jumper or booster pack disconnected from the AC voltage supply.

• Some modules will require additional programming/setup events to be performed before or after programming.

• Some vehicles may require the use of a CANDi or MDI module for programming.

• Review the appropriate service information for these procedures. DTC's may set during programming. Clear DTC's after programming is complete. Clearing powertrain DTC's will set the Inspection/Maintenance (I/M) system status indicators to NO.

Ensure the following conditions are met before programming a control module:

8. Vehicle system voltage:
   a. There is not a charging system concern. All charging system concerns must be repaired before programming a control module.
   b. Battery voltage is greater than 12 volts, but less than 16 volts. The battery must be fully charged before programming the control module.

c. Turn OFF or disable any system that may put a load on the vehicles battery, such as the following components:

- Interior lights
- Twilight sentinel
- Daytime running lights (DRL)– Applying the parking brake, on most vehicles, disables the DRL system
- Heating, Ventilation, and Air Conditioning (HVAC) systems
- Engine cooling fans, radio, etc.

9. The ignition switch must be in the proper position. SPS prompts you to turn ON the ignition, with the engine OFF. DO NOT change the position of the ignition switch during the programming procedure, unless instructed to do so.

10. Make certain all tool connections are secure, including the following components and circuits:

a. Scan Tool.

b. The RS-232 communication cable port.

c. The connection at the Data Link Connector (DLC).

d. The voltage supply circuits (MDI).

e. The USB, Ethernet, or Wireless communication port

f. The connection at the Data Link Connector (DLC)

11. DO NOT disturb the tool harnesses while programming. If an interruption occurs during the programming procedure, programming failure or control module damage may occur.

12. DO NOT turn OFF the ignition if the programming procedure is interrupted or unsuccessful. Ensure that all control module and DLC connections are secure and the TIS terminal operating software is up to date. Attempt to reprogram the control module.

a. If the control module cannot be programmed, turn the ignition OFF for at least 1 minute.

b. Turn the ignition ON and attempt to reprogram the control module. The control module should program.

c. If the control module cannot be programmed, replace the control module.

13. After programming, perform the following to avoid future misdiagnosis:

a. Turn the ignition OFF for 30 seconds.

b. Turn the ignition ON, with the engine OFF.

c. Use the scan tool in order to retrieve history DTC's from all modules.

d. Clear all history DTC's.

ENGINE COOLANT TEMPERATURE (ECT) SENSOR

LOCATION

See Figure 155.

The Engine Coolant Temperature (ECT) Sensor is threaded into the cylinder head.

REMOVAL & INSTALLATION

1. Before servicing the vehicle, refer to the Precautions Section.

2. Disconnect the negative battery cable.

3. Drain the cooling system to a level below the ECT sensor.

4. Unplug the harness connector from the ECT sensor.

22116_SIER_G0134

Fig. 155 Engine Coolant Temperature (ECT) sensor location

5. Remove the ECT sensor from the engine.

To install:

➡ **Be sure to use new fasteners, as required.**

6. Installation is the reverse of removal.

7. If reusing the old sensor, coat the threads with sealant GM P/N 12346004, or equivalent. New sensors are already coated; additional sealant is not needed.

8. Tighten the sensor to 15 ft. lbs. (20 Nm).

HEATED OXYGEN SENSOR (HO2S)

LOCATION

See Figures 156 and 157.

The Heated Oxygen Sensors (HO2S) are threaded into the exhaust pipes.

REMOVAL & INSTALLATION

➡ **Replace the sensor if the pigtail wiring, connector, or terminal is damaged. The external clean air reference is obtained by way of the sensor signal and heater wires. Any attempt to repair the wires or connectors could result in obstruction of the air reference. Make sure the lead wires are not sharply bent or kinked as the air reference could become blocked.**

1. Before servicing the vehicle, refer to the Precautions Section.

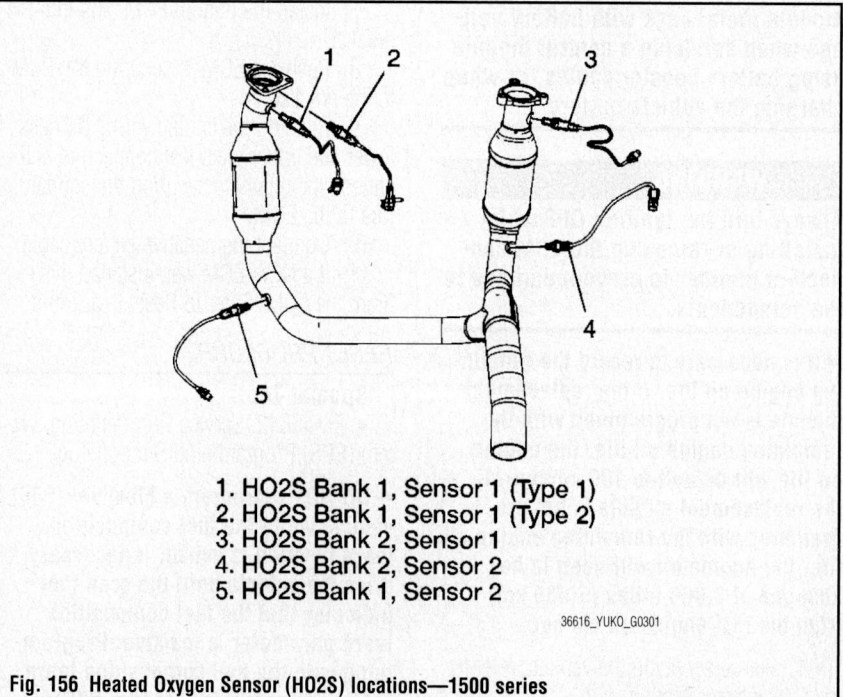

1. HO2S Bank 1, Sensor 1 (Type 1)
2. HO2S Bank 1, Sensor 1 (Type 2)
3. HO2S Bank 2, Sensor 1
4. HO2S Bank 2, Sensor 2
5. HO2S Bank 1, Sensor 2

36616_YUKO_G0301

Fig. 156 Heated Oxygen Sensor (HO2S) locations—1500 series

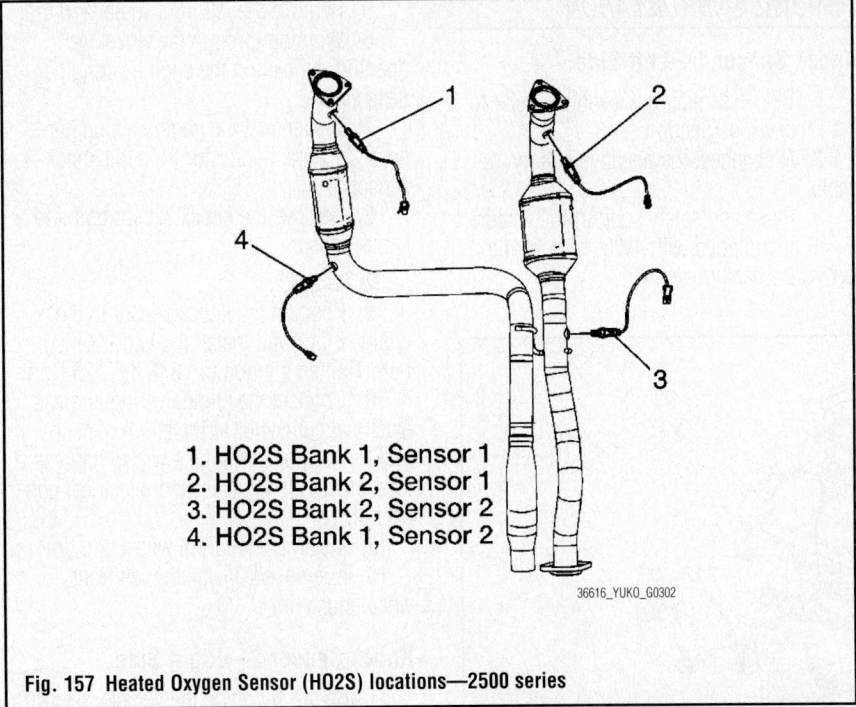

1. HO2S Bank 1, Sensor 1
2. HO2S Bank 2, Sensor 1
3. HO2S Bank 2, Sensor 2
4. HO2S Bank 1, Sensor 2

36616_YUKO_G0302

Fig. 157 Heated Oxygen Sensor (HO2S) locations—2500 series

2. Disconnect the negative battery cable.
3. Raise and safely support the vehicle.
4. On bank 1, sensor 1, if equipped with 4WD, unbolt the front driveshaft from the front differential.
5. On bank 2, sensor 1, remove the right side wheelhouse liner.
6. Disconnect the CPA retainer.
7. Unplug the sensor connector. Remove the clip from the engine harness.
8. Remove the sensor from the exhaust pipe.

To install:

➡A special anti-seize compound is used on the HO2S threads. The compound consists of liquid graphite and glass beads. The graphite tends to burn away, but the glass beads remain, making the sensor easier to remove. New, or service replacement sensors already have the compound applied to the threads. If the sensor is removed from an exhaust component and if for any reason the sensor is to be reinstalled, the threads must have anti-seize compound applied before the reinstallation.

9. Position the sensor on its mounting.
10. If reusing the old sensor, coat the threads with anti-seize compound GM P/N 12377953, or equivalent.
11. Tighten the sensor to 31 ft. lbs. (42 Nm).
12. Continue the installation in the reverse order of the removal procedure.

INTAKE AIR TEMPERATURE (IAT) SENSOR

LOCATION

See Figure 158.

The Intake Air Temperature (IAT) sensor is integrated with the Mass Airflow (MAF) sensor; it is located on the air cleaner assembly.

REMOVAL & INSTALLATION

➡Use care when handling the Mass Air Flow (MAF)/Intake Air Temperature (IAT) sensor. Do not dent, puncture, or otherwise damage the honey cell located at the air inlet end of the MAF/IAT. Do not touch the sensing elements or allow anything including cleaning solvents and lubricants to come in contact with them. Use a small amount of a non-silicone based lubricant, on the air duct only, to aid in installation.

1. Before servicing the vehicle, refer to the Precautions Section.
2. Remove the air cleaner outlet resonator from the MAF/IAT sensor.
3. Disconnect the engine wiring harness electrical connector from the MAF/IAT sensor.
4. Loosen the MAF/IAT sensor adapter clamp.
5. Remove the MAF/IAT sensor from the air cleaner assembly.

To install:

➡The embossed arrow on the MAF/IAT sensor indicates the proper air flow direction. The arrow must point toward the engine.

6. Install the MAF/IAT sensor to the air cleaner assembly.
7. Tighten the MAF/IAT sensor adapter clamp to 35 inch lbs. (4 Nm).

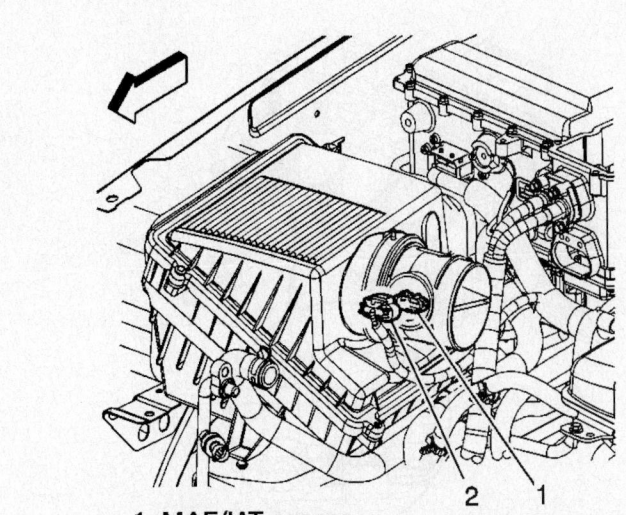

1. MAF/IAT sensor
2. Engine harness electrical connector

36616_YUKO_G0303

Fig. 158 Mass Airflow (MAF)/Intake Air Temperature (IAT) sensor location

8. Connect the engine wiring harness electrical connector to the MAF/IAT sensor.

9. Install the air cleaner outlet resonator.

KNOCK SENSOR (KS)

LOCATION

See Figures 159 and 160.

The Knock Sensor (KS) is located on the side of the engine block.

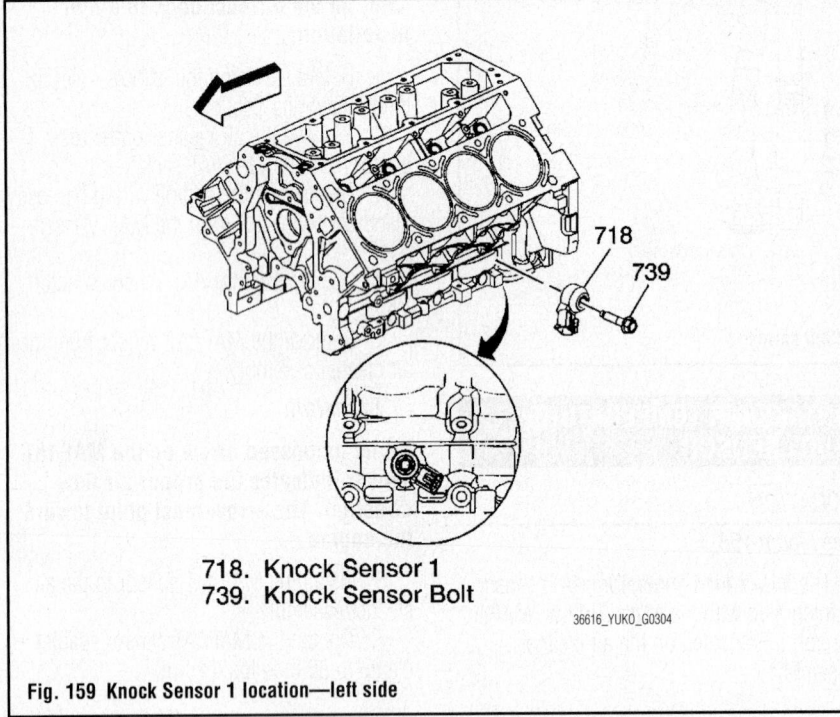

718. Knock Sensor 1
739. Knock Sensor Bolt

36616_YUKO_G0304

Fig. 159 Knock Sensor 1 location—left side

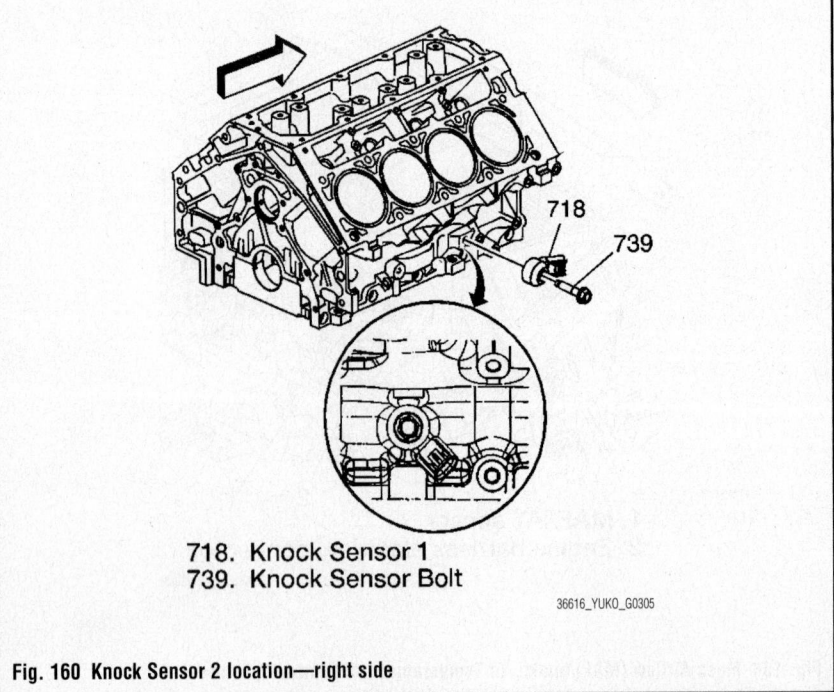

718. Knock Sensor 1
739. Knock Sensor Bolt

36616_YUKO_G0305

Fig. 160 Knock Sensor 2 location—right side

REMOVAL & INSTALLATION

Knock Sensor 1—Left Side

1. Before servicing the vehicle, refer to the Precautions Section.

2. Disconnect the negative battery cable.

3. Raise and safely support the vehicle.

4. If equipped with 4WD, remove the left front wheelhouse liner.

5. Remove the left front wheel and tire.

6. Working through the wheel well opening, reposition the engine wiring harness sleeve.

7. Disconnect the engine wiring harness electrical connector from the knock sensor.

8. Remove the knock sensor bolt and knock sensor.

To install:

9. Position the knock sensor to the engine block and install the knock sensor bolt. Tighten the bolt to 18 ft. lbs. (25 Nm).

10. Connect the engine wiring harness electrical connector to the knock sensor.

11. Position the engine wiring harness sleeve over the knock sensor electrical connection.

12. Install the left front wheel and tire.

13. If removed, install the left front wheelhouse liner.

Knock Sensor 2—Right Side

1. Before servicing the vehicle, refer to the Precautions Section.

2. Disconnect the negative battery cable.

3. Raise and safely support the vehicle.

4. If equipped with 4WD, remove the right front wheelhouse liner.

5. Remove the right front wheel and tire.

6. Working through the wheel well opening, disconnect the engine wiring harness electrical connector from knock sensor.

7. Remove the knock sensor bolt and knock sensor.

To install:

8. Position the knock sensor to the engine block and install the knock sensor bolt. Tighten the bolt to 18 ft. lbs. (25 Nm).

9. Connect the engine wiring harness electrical connector to knock sensor.

10. Install the right front wheel and tire.

11. If removed, install the right front wheelhouse liner.

MANIFOLD ABSOLUTE PRESSURE (MAP) SENSOR

LOCATION

See Figure 161.

The Manifold Absolute Pressure (MAP) sensor is located on the intake manifold.

REMOVAL & INSTALLATION

See Figure 162.

1. Before servicing the vehicle, refer to the Precautions Section.

2. Remove the intake manifold sight shield.

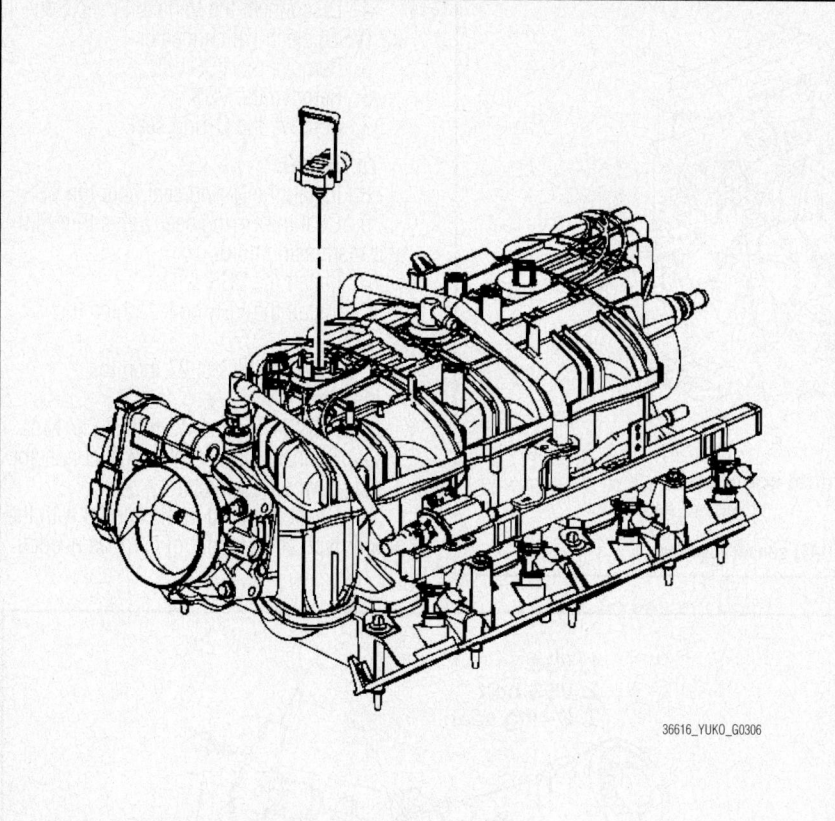

36616_YUKO_G0306

Fig. 161 Manifold Absolute Pressure (MAP) sensor location

3. Disconnect the engine wiring harness electrical connector from the Manifold Absolute Pressure (MAP) sensor.
4. Remove the MAP sensor retainer.
5. Remove the MAP sensor.

To install:

➡**Lightly coat the MAP sensor seal with clean engine oil before installing the sensor.**

6. Install the MAP sensor.
7. Install the MAP sensor retainer.
8. Connect the engine harness wiring electrical connector to the MAP sensor.
9. Install the intake manifold sight shield.

MASS AIR FLOW (MAF) SENSOR

LOCATION

See Figure 163.

The Mass Air Flow (MAF) sensor is integrated with the Intake Air Temperature (IAT) sensor; it is located on the air cleaner assembly.

REMOVAL & INSTALLATION

➡**Use care when handling the Mass Air Flow (MAF)/Intake Air Temperature (IAT) sensor. Do not dent, puncture, or otherwise damage the honey cell located at the air inlet end of the MAF/IAT. Do not touch the sensing elements or allow anything including cleaning solvents and lubricants to come in contact with them. Use a small amount of a non-silicone based lubricant, on the air duct only, to aid in installation.**

1. Before servicing the vehicle, refer to the Precautions Section.
2. Remove the air cleaner outlet resonator from the MAF/IAT sensor.
3. Disconnect the engine wiring harness electrical connector from the MAF/IAT sensor.
4. Loosen the MAF/IAT sensor adapter clamp.
5. Remove the MAF/IAT sensor from the air cleaner assembly.

To install:

➡**The embossed arrow on the MAF/IAT sensor indicates the proper air flow direction. The arrow must point toward the engine.**

6. Install the MAF/IAT sensor to the air cleaner assembly.
7. Tighten the MAF/IAT sensor adapter clamp to 35 inch lbs. (4 Nm).

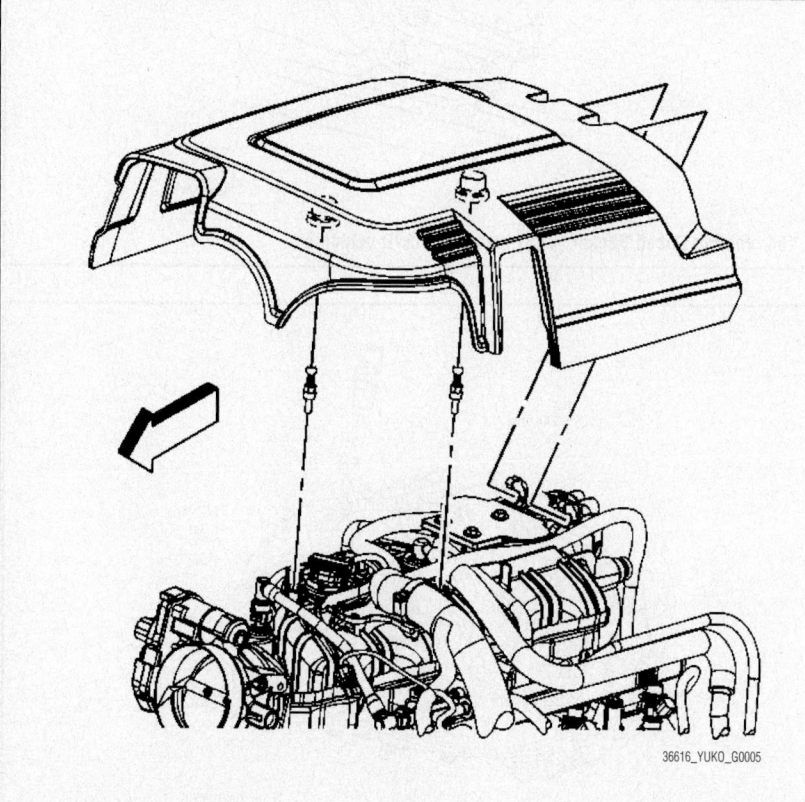

36616_YUKO_G0005

Fig. 162 Remove the upper intake manifold sight shield

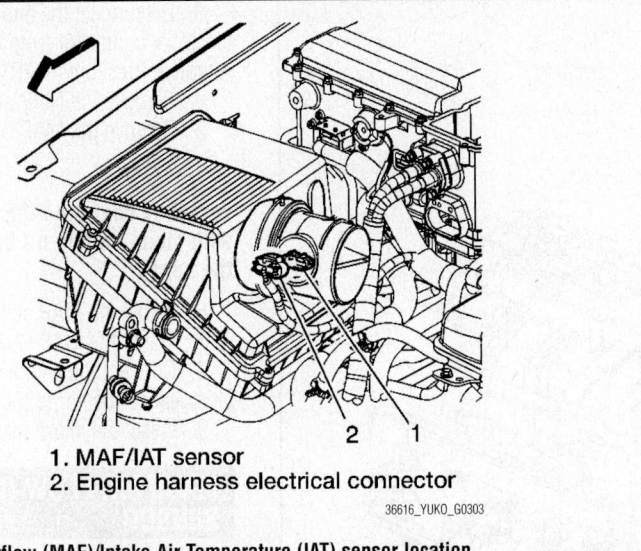

1. MAF/IAT sensor
2. Engine harness electrical connector

36616_YUKO_G0303

Fig. 163 Mass Airflow (MAF)/Intake Air Temperature (IAT) sensor location

8. Connect the engine wiring harness electrical connector to the MAF/IAT sensor.
9. Install the air cleaner outlet resonator.

THROTTLE POSITION SENSOR (TPS)

LOCATION

The Throttle Position Sensor (TPS) is integral to the throttle body. If it is determined, that the TPS signal is faulty, the throttle body assembly must be replaced. Refer to Throttle Body, removal & installation.

REMOVAL & INSTALLATION

The Throttle Position Sensor (TPS) is not serviceable as a standalone part. The throttle body position sensor is an integral part of the throttle body. If the throttle position sensor requires replacement, replace the throttle body assembly.

VEHICLE SPEED SENSOR (VSS)

LOCATION

See Figures 164 and 165.

The Vehicle Speed Sensor (VSS) is located on the tail section of the transmission on 2WD models. On 4WD models, the VSS is located on the transfer case.

REMOVAL & INSTALLATION

See Figures 164 and 165.

1. Before servicing the vehicle, refer to the Precautions Section.
2. Raise and safely support the vehicle.
3. Remove the transfer case shield, if equipped with 4WD.

4. Disconnect the Vehicle Speed Sensor (VSS) electrical connector.
5. Remove the VSS bolt.
6. Remove the VSS.
7. Remove the O-ring seal.

To install:

8. Install the O-ring seal onto the VSS.
9. Coat the O-ring seal with a thin film of transmission fluid.
10. Install the VSS.
11. Install the VSS bolt. Tighten the bolt to:
   a. 2WD vehicles, 97 inch lbs. (11 Nm).
   b. 4WD vehicles, 13 ft. lbs. (17 Nm).
12. Connect the VSS electrical connector.
13. Lower the vehicle.
14. Check the fluid levels and fill with the proper type and amount of fluid, as needed.

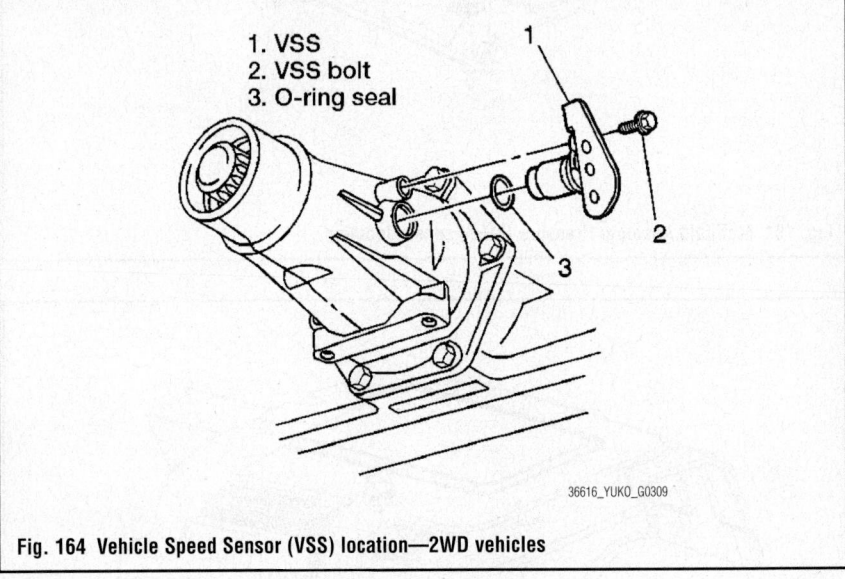

1. VSS
2. VSS bolt
3. O-ring seal

36616_YUKO_G0309

Fig. 164 Vehicle Speed Sensor (VSS) location—2WD vehicles

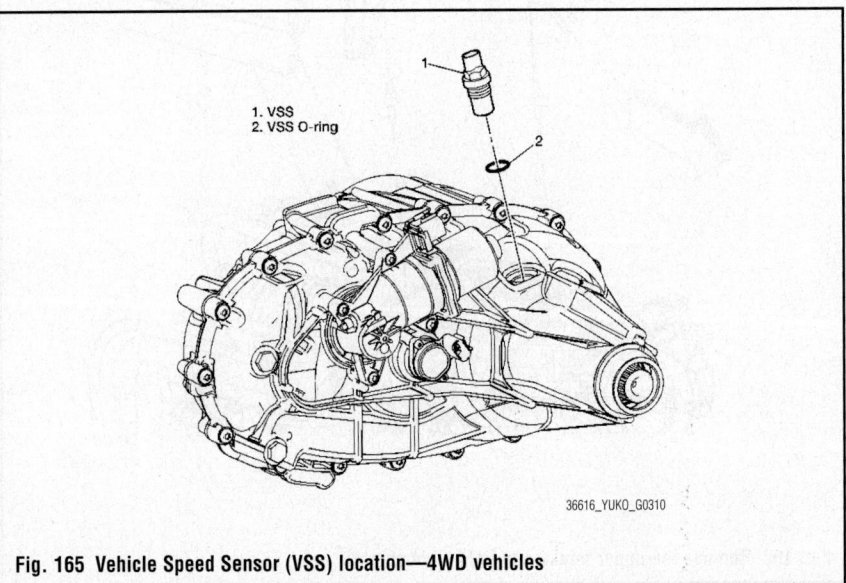

1. VSS
2. VSS O-ring

36616_YUKO_G0310

Fig. 165 Vehicle Speed Sensor (VSS) location—4WD vehicles

FUEL

GASOLINE FUEL INJECTION SYSTEM

FUEL SYSTEM SERVICE PRECAUTIONS

Safety is the most important factor when performing, not only fuel system maintenance, but any type of maintenance. Failure to conduct maintenance and repairs in a safe manner may result in serious personal injury or death. Maintenance and testing of the vehicle's fuel system components can be accomplished safely and effectively by adhering to the following rules and guidelines.

• To avoid the possibility of fire and personal injury, always disconnect the negative battery cable unless the repair or test procedure requires that battery voltage be applied.

• Always relieve the fuel system pressure prior to disconnecting any fuel system component (injector, fuel rail, pressure regulator, etc.), fitting, or fuel line connection. Exercise extreme caution whenever relieving fuel system pressure to avoid exposing skin, face, and eyes to fuel spray. Please be advised that fuel under pressure may penetrate the skin or any part of the body that it contacts.

• Always place a shop towel or cloth around the fitting or connection prior to loosening to absorb any excess fuel due to spillage. Ensure that all fuel spillage (should it occur) is quickly removed from the engine surfaces. Ensure that all fuel soaked cloths or towels are deposited into a suitable waste container.

• Always keep a dry chemical (Class B) fire extinguisher near the work area.

• Do not allow fuel spray or fuel vapors to come into contact with a spark or an open flame.

• Always use a back-up wrench when loosening and tightening fuel line connection fittings. This will prevent unnecessary stress and torsion to the fuel line piping.

• Always replace worn fuel fitting O-rings with new. Do not substitute fuel hose or equivalent where fuel pipe is installed.

Before servicing the vehicle, make sure to also refer to the precautions in the beginning of this section.

RELIEVING FUEL SYSTEM PRESSURE

❊❊ CAUTION

The fuel system is under constant high pressure even with engine OFF.

Until the fuel pressure has been properly relieved from the system, do not attempt to open the fuel system. Do not smoke or use open flames/sparks when servicing the fuel system. Wear protective clothing and eye protection. Make sure the area in which the vehicle is being serviced is in a well-ventilated area and free of flames/sparks.

❊❊ CAUTION

Remove the fuel tank cap and relieve the fuel system pressure before servicing the fuel system in order to reduce the risk of personal injury. After you relieve the fuel system pressure, a small amount of fuel may be released when servicing the fuel lines, the fuel injection pump, or the connections. In order to reduce the risk of personal injury, cover the fuel system components with a shop towel before disconnection. Place the shop towel in an approved container when the disconnection is complete.

1. Before servicing the vehicle, refer to the Precautions Section.
2. Disconnect the negative battery cable.
3. Loosen the fuel cap.
4. Remove the fuel rail service port cap.
5. Wrap a shop towel around the fuel rail service port and using a small flat tip tool, depress (open) the fuel rail test port valve.
6. Remove the shop towel. Properly dispose of the towel.
7. Install the service port cap.
8. Install the engine cover, as required.
9. Tighten the fuel cap.

FUEL FILTER

REMOVAL & INSTALLATION

The fuel filter is part of the fuel pump module located in the fuel tank. It is serviced as part of the fuel pump module. Refer to Fuel Pump Module, removal & installation.

FUEL PUMP MODULE

REMOVAL & INSTALLATION
See Figures 166 and 167.

Special Tool:
• J 45722: Fuel Sender Lock Ring Wrench

❊❊ CAUTION

Gasoline or gasoline vapors are highly flammable. A fire could occur if an ignition source is present. Never drain or store gasoline in an open container, due to the possibility of fire or explosion. Have a dry chemical (Class B) fire extinguisher nearby.

1. Before servicing the vehicle, refer to the Precautions Section.
2. Disconnect the negative battery cable.
3. Properly relieve the fuel system pressure.
4. Remove the fuel tank. Refer to Fuel Tank, removal & installation.
5. Disconnect the fuel and Evaporative Emission (EVAP) lines from the fuel tank module.

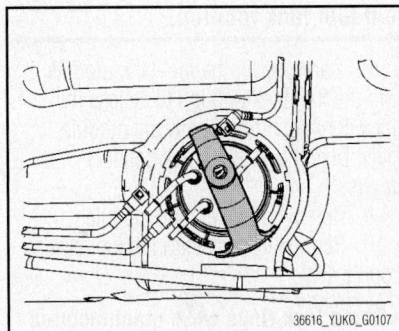

Fig. 166 Disconnect the fuel and EVAP lines from the fuel tank module and use the J 45722 and a long breaker bar to rotate the ring clockwise unlocking the fuel tank module lock ring

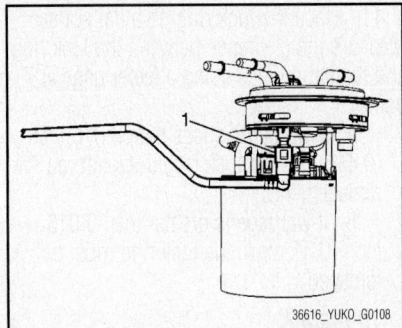

Fig. 167 Carefully lift the fuel tank module from the fuel tank enough to access the quick connect fitting (1) below the module cover and disconnect the quick connect fittings

6. Using the J 45722 and a long breaker bar, rotate the ring clockwise unlocking the fuel tank module lock ring.

7. Remove the lock ring.

❊❊ WARNING

Avoid damaging the lock ring. Use only J-45722 to prevent damage to the lock ring.

❊❊ WARNING

Do Not handle the fuel sender assembly by the fuel pipes. The amount of leverage generated by handling the fuel pipes could damage the joints.

❊❊ WARNING

Do NOT use impact tools. Significant force will be required to release the lock ring. The use of a hammer and screwdriver is not recommended. Secure the fuel tank in order to prevent fuel tank rotation.

8. Carefully lift the fuel tank module from the fuel tank enough to access the quick connect fitting below the module cover. Disconnect the quick connect fittings.

9. Remove the fuel tank module.

10. Remove and discard the fuel tank module seal.

➡Some lock rings were manufactured with **DO NOT REUSE** stamped into them. These lock rings may be reused if they are not damaged or warped.

➡Inspect the lock ring for damage due to improper removal or installation procedures. If damage is found, install a NEW lock ring.

11. Place the lock ring on a flat surface. Measure the clearance between the lock ring and the flat surface using a feeler gage at 7 points.

a. If warpage is less than 0.016 inch (0.41 mm), the lock ring does not require replacement.

b. If warpage is greater than 0.016 inch (0.41 mm), the lock ring must be replaced.

To install:

12. Install the NEW fuel tank module seal onto the fuel tank.

13. Pull the vent line in the fuel tank up, as far as possible, for ease of installation.

14. Position the fuel tank module part way into the fuel tank.

15. Connect the quick connect fitting to the module cover.

16. Install the fuel tank module into the fuel tank.

17. Place the lock ring into position.

➡Replace the fuel sender seal when installing the fuel sender assembly. Replace the lock ring if necessary. DO NOT apply any type of lubrication in the seal groove. Ensure the lock ring is installed with the correct side facing upward.

18. Rotate the lock ring counterclockwise using the J 45722 until fully seated.

19. Connect the fuel and EVAP lines to the fuel tank module.

20. Install the fuel tank. Refer to Fuel Tank, removal & installation.

21. Start the engine and check for leaks. Correct as required.

FUEL RAIL & INJECTORS

REMOVAL & INSTALLATION

See Figures 168 and 169.

➡An 8-digit identification number is located on the fuel rail. Refer to this identification number when servicing or when part replacement is required.

1. Before servicing the vehicle, refer to the Precautions Section.

2. Remove the air cleaner outlet duct.

3. Relieve the fuel system pressure. Refer to Relieving Fuel System Pressure.

4. Remove the engine wiring harness bracket nut.

5. Disconnect the engine wiring harness electrical connector from the following:

a. The Evaporative Emission (EVAP) purge solenoid.

b. The alternator.

c. The Manifold Absolute Pressure (MAP) sensor.

6. Remove the Connector Position Assurance (CPA) retainer.

7. Disconnect the engine wiring harness electrical connector from the ignition coil main electrical connector.

8. Disconnect the engine wiring harness electrical connectors from the fuel injectors and perform the following:

a. Mark the connectors to their corresponding injectors to ensure correct reassembly.

b. Pull the CPA retainer on the connector up 1 click.

c. Push in on the connector tab.

d. Disconnect the fuel injector electrical connector.

9. Remove the CPA retainer.

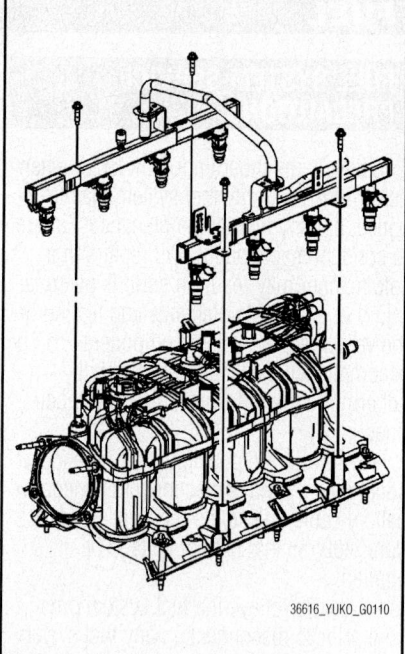

36616_YUKO_G0110

Fig. 168 Remove the bolts and the fuel rail assembly

10. Disconnect the engine wiring harness electrical connector from the electronic throttle control.

11. Remove the engine wiring harness clip from the alternator battery jumper cable and the ignition coil bracket stud.

12. Remove the negative battery cable stud from the right cylinder head and remove the negative battery cable terminal and engine wiring harness ground terminal.

13. Remove the wiring harness clip bolt from the alternator bracket.

14. Gather the branches of the engine wiring harness and reposition aside.

15. Remove the Positive Crankcase Ventilation (PCV) hose.

16. Disconnect the chassis fuel feed pipe quick connect fitting from the fuel rail.

17. Disconnect the EVAP tube quick connect fitting at the intake manifold.

18. Disconnect the chassis EVAP tube quick connect fitting at the EVAP canister purge solenoid.

19. Disengage the retainer securing the EVAP canister purge solenoid to the fuel rail.

20. Remove the EVAP tube and purge solenoid.

21. Remove the fuel rail bolts.

❊❊ WARNING

Remove the fuel rail assembly carefully in order to prevent damage to the injector electrical connector terminals and the injector spray tips.

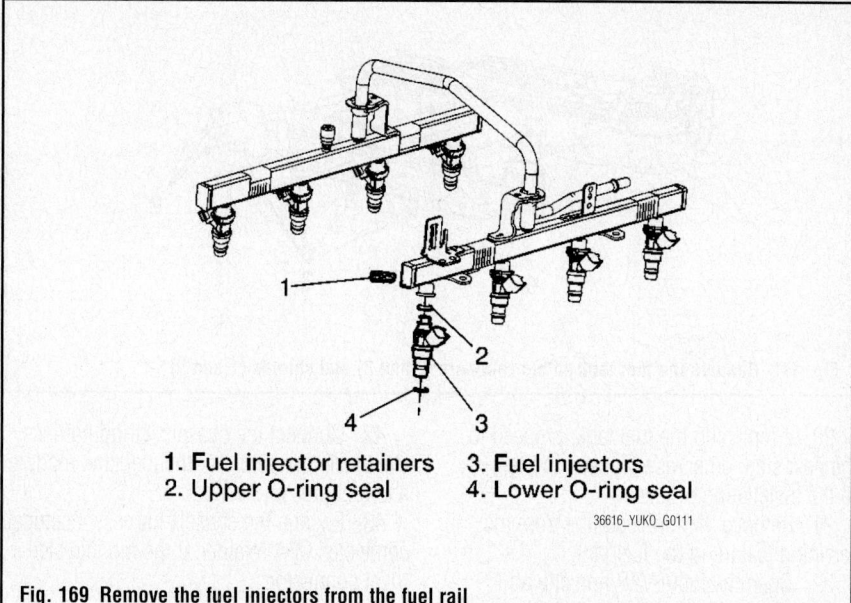

1. Fuel injector retainers
2. Upper O-ring seal
3. Fuel injectors
4. Lower O-ring seal

36616_YUKO_G0111

Fig. 169 Remove the fuel injectors from the fuel rail

Support the fuel rail after the fuel rail is removed in order to avoid damaging the fuel rail components.

➡Cap the fittings and plug the holes when servicing the fuel system in order to prevent dirt and other contaminants from entering open pipes and passages.

➡Before removal, clean the fuel rail with a spray type engine cleaner, such as GM X- 30A or equivalent, if necessary. Follow the package instructions. Do not soak the fuel rail in liquid cleaning solvent.

➡Lift evenly on both sides of the fuel rail until all injectors are removed from their bores.

22. Remove the fuel rail assembly.
23. Remove the fuel injector retainers.
24. Remove the fuel injectors from the fuel rail.
25. Remove and discard the fuel injector upper and lower O-ring seals.

To install:
26. Lubricate the NEW fuel injector O-ring seals with clean engine oil.
27. Install the NEW fuel injector upper and lower O-ring seals onto the injectors.
28. Install the fuel injectors into the fuel rails.
29. Install the fuel injector retainers.
30. Ensure the fuel injector lower O-ring seals are adequately lubricated, if not, lubricate the fuel injector lower O-ring seals with clean engine oil.
31. Position the fuel rail onto the intake manifold.

32. Firmly push down on both the centers of the left and right fuel rails, until the rails are fully seated against the intake manifold.

➡Push down firmly on both sides of the rail until all injectors have been seated into their bores.

33. Install the fuel rail bolts and tighten to 89 inch lbs. (10 Nm).
34. Install the EVAP tube and purge solenoid.
35. Install the EVAP canister purge solenoid to the fuel rail bracket and engage the retainer.
36. Connect the chassis EVAP tube quick connect fitting at the EVAP canister purge solenoid.
37. Connect the EVAP tube quick connect fitting at the intake manifold.
38. Connect the chassis fuel feed pipe quick connect fitting to the fuel rail.
39. Install the PCV hose.
40. Gather the branches of the engine wiring harness and position them over the top of the engine.
41. Position the engine wiring harness clip to the alternator bracket and install the clip bolt. Tighten the bolt to 80 inch lbs. (9 Nm).
42. Position the negative battery cable terminal and engine wiring harness ground terminal to the right cylinder head.
43. Install the negative battery cable stud to the cylinder head. Tighten the stud to 18 ft. lbs. (25 Nm).
44. Connect the engine wiring harness electrical connector to the ignition coil main electrical connector.
45. Install the CPA retainer.

46. Connect the engine wiring harness electrical connector to the electronic throttle control.
47. Connect the engine wiring harness electrical connectors to the fuel injectors and perform the following:
   a. Ensure that the CPA retainer is pulled out 1 click.
   b. Connect the electrical connectors to their corresponding injectors.
   c. Push the CPA retainer in 1 click.
   d. Ensure that the connector is secured.
48. Install the engine wiring harness clip to the alternator battery jumper cable, the ignition coil bracket stud, and the ignition coil main electrical connector.
49. Install the CPA retainer.
50. Connect the engine wiring harness electrical connector to the MAP sensor, the alternator, and the EVAP purge solenoid.
51. Install the engine wiring harness bracket nut and tighten to 44 inch lbs. (5 Nm).
52. Connect the negative battery cable.
53. Use the following procedure in order to inspect for leaks:
   a. Turn the ignition ON, with the engine OFF, for 2 seconds.
   b. Turn the ignition OFF for 10 seconds.
   c. Turn the ignition ON, with the engine OFF.
   d. Inspect for leaks.
54. Install the air cleaner outlet duct.

FUEL TANK

REMOVAL & INSTALLATION

Single and Dual Tank (Front)
See Figures 170 and 171.

➡Clean the fuel and Evaporative Emission (EVAP) connections and surrounding areas prior to disconnecting the lines in order to avoid possible system contamination.

1. Before servicing the vehicle, refer to the Precautions Section.
2. Relieve the fuel system pressure. Refer to Relieving Fuel System Pressure.
3. Drain the fuel tank. Refer to Fuel Tank Draining.
4. Disconnect the fuel tank vent line quick connect fitting from the fuel fill pipe vent line.
5. Disconnect the chassis EVAP line quick connect fitting from the fuel tank line.
6. Disconnect the fuel tank fuel feed line quick connect fitting from the chassis line.

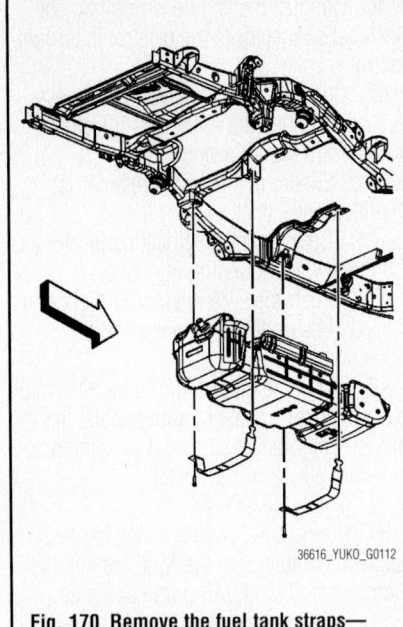

36616_YUKO_G0112

Fig. 170 Remove the fuel tank straps—single and dual tank (front)

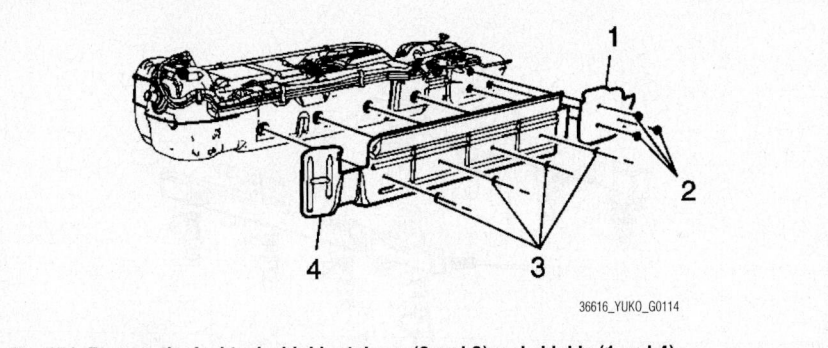

36616_YUKO_G0114

Fig. 171 Remove the fuel tank shield retainers (2 and 3) and shields (1 and 4)

7. Cap the fuel and EVAP lines in order to prevent possible fuel and/or EVAP system contamination.

8. Disconnect the fuel tank EVAP lines from the EVAP canister.

9. Cap the EVAP lines in order to prevent possible EVAP system contamination.

10. Disconnect the fuel tank EVAP line quick connect fitting at the fuel tank vent valve.

11. Using an adjustable jack, support the fuel tank.

12. Remove the fuel tank strap bolts.

13. Remove the fuel tank straps.

✳✳ WARNING

Do not bend the fuel tank straps. Bending the fuel tank straps may damage the straps.

➡**Carefully lower the fuel tank until the EVAP line can be repositioned.**

14. With the aid of an assistant, carefully lower the rear of the fuel tank.

15. Slide the front of the tank away from the frame.

16. Lower the fuel tank slightly until the chassis wiring harness electrical connectors can be accessed.

17. Disconnect the chassis wiring harness electrical connectors from the fuel pump module and the fuel pressure sensor.

18. Completely lower the fuel tank.

19. With the aid of an assistant, place the fuel tank in a suitable work area.

20. If replacing the fuel tank, proceed to the next step, otherwise proceed to Step 11 in the installation procedure.

21. Remove the fuel feed line from the retaining feature in the fuel tank.

22. Open the fuel/EVAP line clip and remove the fuel feed line from the clip.

23. Disconnect the fuel feed line quick connect fitting at the fuel tank module.

24. Remove the fuel feed line from the fuel tank.

25. Remove the fuel tank shield retainers and shields.

26. Open the fuel tank clips and remove the EVAP lines from the clips.

27. Disconnect the EVAP line quick connect fitting at the fuel tank module.

28. Remove the EVAP lines from the fuel tank.

29. Remove the fuel pump. Refer to Fuel Pump Module, removal & installation.

To install:

30. If the fuel tank was replaced perform the following steps, otherwise proceed to Step 11.

31. Install the fuel pump. Refer to Fuel Pump Module, removal & installation.

32. Install the EVAP lines to the fuel tank.

33. Connect the EVAP line quick connect fitting at the fuel tank module.

34. Install the EVAP lines to the fuel tank clips and close the clips.

35. Install the fuel tank shields and retainers.

36. Install the fuel feed line to the fuel tank.

37. Connect the fuel feed line quick connect fitting at the fuel tank module.

38. Install the fuel feed line to the clip and close the clip.

39. Install the fuel feed line to the retaining feature in the fuel tank.

40. Place the fuel tank onto a suitable jack.

41. With the aid of an assistant, partially raise the fuel tank until the electrical connections can be made.

42. Connect the chassis wiring harness electrical connectors to the fuel tank module and fuel pressure sensor.

43. Engage the chassis harness electrical connector CPA retainer at the module electrical connector.

➡**Carefully raise the fuel tank until the EVAP line can be positioned.**

44. Completely raise the fuel tank.

45. Install the fuel tank straps and bolts. Tighten the bolts to 30 ft. lbs. (40 Nm).

46. Remove the adjustable jack from the fuel tank.

47. Connect the fuel tank EVAP line quick connect fitting at the fuel tank vent valve.

48. Remove the caps from the fuel and EVAP lines and connect the fuel tank EVAP lines to the EVAP canister.

49. Connect the chassis EVAP line quick connect fitting to the fuel tank line.

50. Connect the fuel tank fuel feed line quick connect fitting to the chassis line.

51. Connect the fuel tank vent line quick connect fitting to the fuel fill pipe line.

52. Install the fuel fill hose to the fuel tank. Ensure that the notch in the hose is aligned with the notch on the fuel tank.

53. Tighten the fuel fill hose clamp to 22 inch lbs. (3 Nm).

54. Lower the vehicle.

55. Refill the fuel tank.

56. Install the fuel fill cap.

57. Connect the negative battery cable.

58. Use the following procedure in order to inspect for leaks:

   a. Turn the ignition ON, with the engine OFF, for 2 seconds.

   b. Turn the ignition OFF for 10 seconds.

   c. Turn the ignition ON, with the engine OFF.

   d. Inspect for fuel leaks. Repair as needed.

Dual Tank (Rear)

See Figures 172 through 174.

➡**Clean all fuel and Evaporative Emission (EVAP) line connections and surrounding areas prior to disconnecting the lines in order to avoid possible fuel and/or EVAP system contamination.**

1. Before servicing the vehicle, refer to the Precautions Section.
2. Relieve the fuel system pressure. Refer to Relieving Fuel System Pressure.
3. Remove the spare tire stowage lock cylinder.
4. Remove the spare tire.
5. Drain the fuel tank. Refer to Fuel Tank Draining.
6. Remove the rear exhaust insulator.

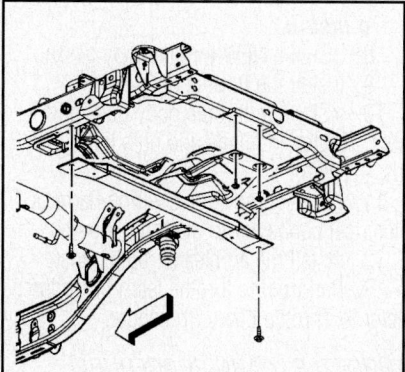

Fig. 172 Remove the spare tire hoist crossmember bolts and crossmember

7. Remove the spare tire hoist crossmember bolts and crossmember.
8. Disconnect the rear fuel tank EVAP line quick connect fittings from the EVAP canister.
9. Disconnect the fuel and EVAP intermediate line quick connect fittings from the front tank.
10. Disconnect the chassis harness electrical connector from the fuel pressure sensor.
11. Support the fuel tank with a suitable jack.
12. Remove the fuel tank strap bolts.

❊❊ WARNING

Do not bend the fuel tank straps. Bending the fuel tank straps may damage the straps.

13. Remove the fuel tank straps.
14. With the aid of an assistant, lower the rear tank until the intermediate line connections can be reached.
15. Disconnect the fuel and EVAP intermediate line quick connect fittings from the rear tank.
16. Remove the fuel and EVAP intermediate lines.
17. Cap the fuel and EVAP lines in order to prevent possible EVAP/fuel system contamination.
18. Disconnect the chassis harness electrical connector from the fuel tank module.
19. Completely lower the fuel tank.

20. With the aid of an assistant, remove the tank from the jack.
21. If replacing the fuel tank proceed to the next step, otherwise proceed to Step 6 in the installation procedure.
22. Disconnect the EVAP line quick connect fittings from the fuel tank module.
23. Remove the EVAP lines from the fuel tank.
24. Remove the fuel pump. Refer to Fuel Pump Module, removal & installation.

To install:

25. If the fuel tank was replaced perform the following steps, otherwise proceed to Step 6.
26. Install the fuel pump. Refer to Fuel Pump Module, removal & installation.
27. Install the EVAP lines to the fuel tank.
28. Connect the EVAP line quick connect fittings to the fuel tank module.
29. Install the EVAP lines to the fuel tank.
30. With the aid of an assistant, install the tank onto the jack.
31. Partially raise the fuel tank.
32. Connect the chassis harness electrical connector to the fuel tank module.
33. Remove the caps from the fuel and EVAP lines.
34. Install the fuel and EVAP intermediate lines.
35. Connect the fuel and EVAP intermediate lines to the rear tank.
36. With the aid of an assistant, completely raise the rear tank.
37. Install the fuel tank straps and bolts. Tighten the bolts to 30 ft. lbs. (40 Nm).
38. Remove the adjustable jack from under the fuel tank.
39. Connect the chassis harness electrical connector to the fuel pressure sensor.
40. Connect the fuel and EVAP intermediate line quick connect fittings to the front tank.
41. Connect the rear fuel tank EVAP line quick connect fittings to the EVAP canister.
42. Install the spare tire hoist crossmember and bolts. Tighten the bolts to 37 ft. lbs. (50 Nm).
43. Install the rear exhaust insulator.
44. Install the fuel fill hose to the fuel tank.
45. Tighten the fuel fill hose clamp at the fuel tank to 22 inch lbs. (3 Nm).
46. Lower the vehicle.
47. Install the spare tire.

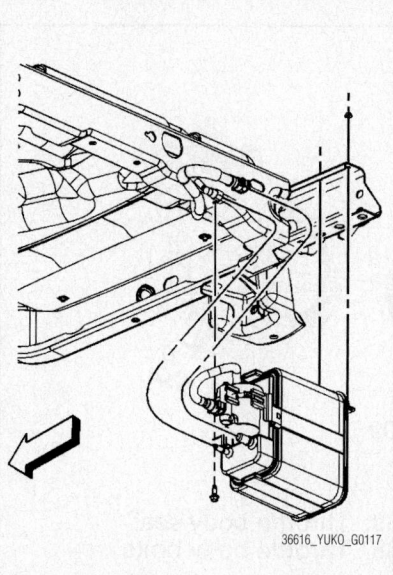

Fig. 173 Disconnect the rear fuel tank EVAP line quick connect fittings from the EVAP canister

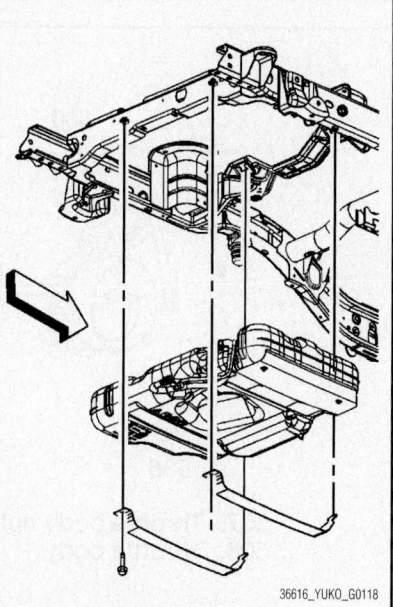

Fig. 174 Removal of the fuel tank—dual tank (rear)

48. Install the spare tire stowage lock cylinder.

49. Install the fuel tank filler housing.

50. Install the fuel tank filler housing-to-fuel tank fill pipe bolts. Tighten the bolts to 20 inch lbs. (2 Nm).

51. Install the fuel tank filler housing-to-body TORX® screws and retainer. Tighten the screws to 20 inch lbs. (2 Nm).

52. Refill the fuel tank.

53. Install the fuel fill cap.

54. Connect the negative battery cable.

55. Use the following procedure in order to inspect for leaks:

a. Turn the ignition ON, with the engine OFF, for 2 seconds.

b. Turn the ignition OFF for 10 seconds.

c. Turn the ignition ON, with the engine OFF.

d. Inspect for fuel leaks. Repair as necessary.

FUEL TANK DRAINING

Special Tool:
- J 45004: Fuel Tank Siphon Hose

❋❋ CAUTION

Gasoline or gasoline vapors are highly flammable. A fire could occur if an ignition source is present. Never drain or store gasoline in an open container due to the possibility of fire or explosion.

❋❋ CAUTION

Place a dry chemical (Class B) fire extinguisher nearby before performing any on-vehicle service procedures. Failure to follow these precautions may result in personal injury.

1. Before servicing the vehicle, refer to the Precautions Section.

2. Loosen the fuel fill cap in order to relieve the fuel tank vapor pressure.

3. Raise and safely support the vehicle.

4. Loosen the fuel fill hose clamp at the front tank.

5. Remove the fuel fill hose from the fuel tank.

6. Insert the siphon hose from the J 45004 into the fuel tank.

7. Attach the siphon hose from the J 45004 to the pump devise hose.

8. Using an air or hand operated pump device, drain as much fuel from the tank as possible.

IDLE SPEED

ADJUSTMENT

The idle speed is control by the Powertrain Control Module (PCM). No adjustment is necessary or possible.

THROTTLE BODY

REMOVAL & INSTALLATION

See Figure 175.

❋❋ CAUTION

DO NOT place fingers in or around the throttle body plate. If the throttle body is energized, the throttle plate could move causing personal injury. Always disconnect the negative battery cable prior to servicing the throttle body.

➡ **DO NOT move the throttle plate while power is connected to the throttle body. This may cause fault codes to set.**

❋❋ WARNING

Handle the electronic throttle control components carefully. Use cleanliness in order to prevent damage. Do not drop the electronic throttle control components. Do not roughly handle the electronic throttle control components. Do not immerse the electronic throttle control components in cleaning solvents of any type.

❋❋ WARNING

DO NOT, for any reason, insert a screwdriver or other small hand tools into the throttle body to hold open the throttle plate, as the wedge inside the throttle body could be damaged.

1. Before servicing the vehicle, refer to the Precautions Section.

2. Disconnect and isolate the negative battery cable at the battery.

3. Remove the air cleaner outlet duct.

4. Disconnect the engine wiring harness electrical connector from the throttle body.

5. Remove the throttle body bolts and nuts.

6. Remove the throttle body.

7. Remove and discard the throttle body seal.

To install:

8. Install a NEW throttle body gasket.

9. Install the throttle body.

10. Install the throttle body bolts and nuts. Tighten the bolts and nuts to 89 inch lbs. (10 Nm).

11. Connect the engine wiring harness electrical connector to the throttle body.

12. Install the air cleaner outlet duct.

13. Perform the throttle learn procedure. Refer to Throttle Learn Procedure.

THROTTLE LEARN PROCEDURE

After the throttle body is cleaned or replaced, perform the RESET procedure.

After the ECM/PCM is flashed or replaced, perform the LEARN procedure.

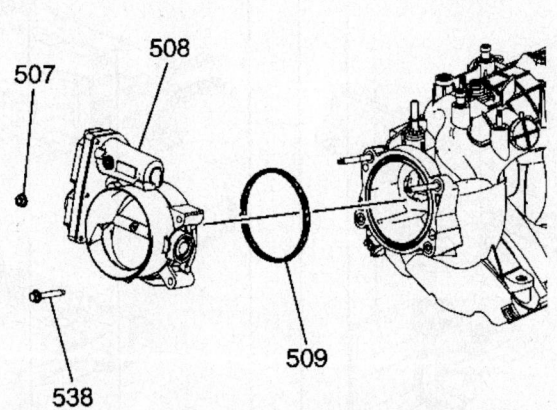

507. Throttle body nuts
508. Throttle body
509. Throttle body seal
538. Throttle body bolts

36616_YUKO_G0109

Fig. 175 Throttle body removal

1. Perform the following if the ECM/PCM is flashed or replaced.

➡ **Do NOT perform this procedure if DTC's are set. Refer to Diagnostic Trouble Codes.**

2. Start and idle the engine for 3 minutes.

3. With a scan tool, monitor the Desired Idle Speed and the actual Engine Speed.

4. The ECM will start to learn the new idle cells and the Desired Idle Speed should start to decrease.

5. Turn the ignition OFF for 60 seconds.

6. Start and idle the engine for 3 minutes.

➡ **During the drive cycle, the check engine light may come on with idle speed DTC's. If idle speed codes are set, clear the codes so the ECM can continue to learn.**

7. After the 3 minute run time, the engine should be idling normal. If the engine idle speed has not been learned, the vehicle will need to be driven at speeds above 44 mph (70 km/h) with several decelerations and extended idles.

8. After the drive cycle, the engine should be idling normally. If the engine idle speed has not been learned, turn OFF the ignition for 60 seconds and repeat Step 6.

9. Once the engine speed has returned to normal, clear any DTC's.

Throttle Reset Procedure

This procedure is to be performed after the throttle body is cleaned or replaced.

1. With the ignition ON and engine OFF, perform the Idle Learn Reset in Module Setup with a scan tool.

2. Start the engine and monitor the TB Idle Airflow Compensation parameter. The TB Idle Airflow Compensation value should equal 0 percent and the engine should be idling at a normal idle speed.

3. Clear any DTC's.

HEATING & AIR CONDITIONING SYSTEM

BLOWER MOTOR

REMOVAL & INSTALLATION

Except Cadillac

See Figures 176 and 177.

1. Before servicing the vehicle, refer to the Precautions Section.

2. Remove the sound insulator panel, if equipped.

3. Remove the blower motor insulating cover screws.

4. Disconnect the electrical connector from the blower motor.

5. Remove the blower motor insulating cover.

6. Pull the retaining tab down while turning the blower motor counterclockwise in order to disengage the blower motor from the heater/ventilation module.

7. Remove the blower motor.

To install:

8. Install the blower motor.

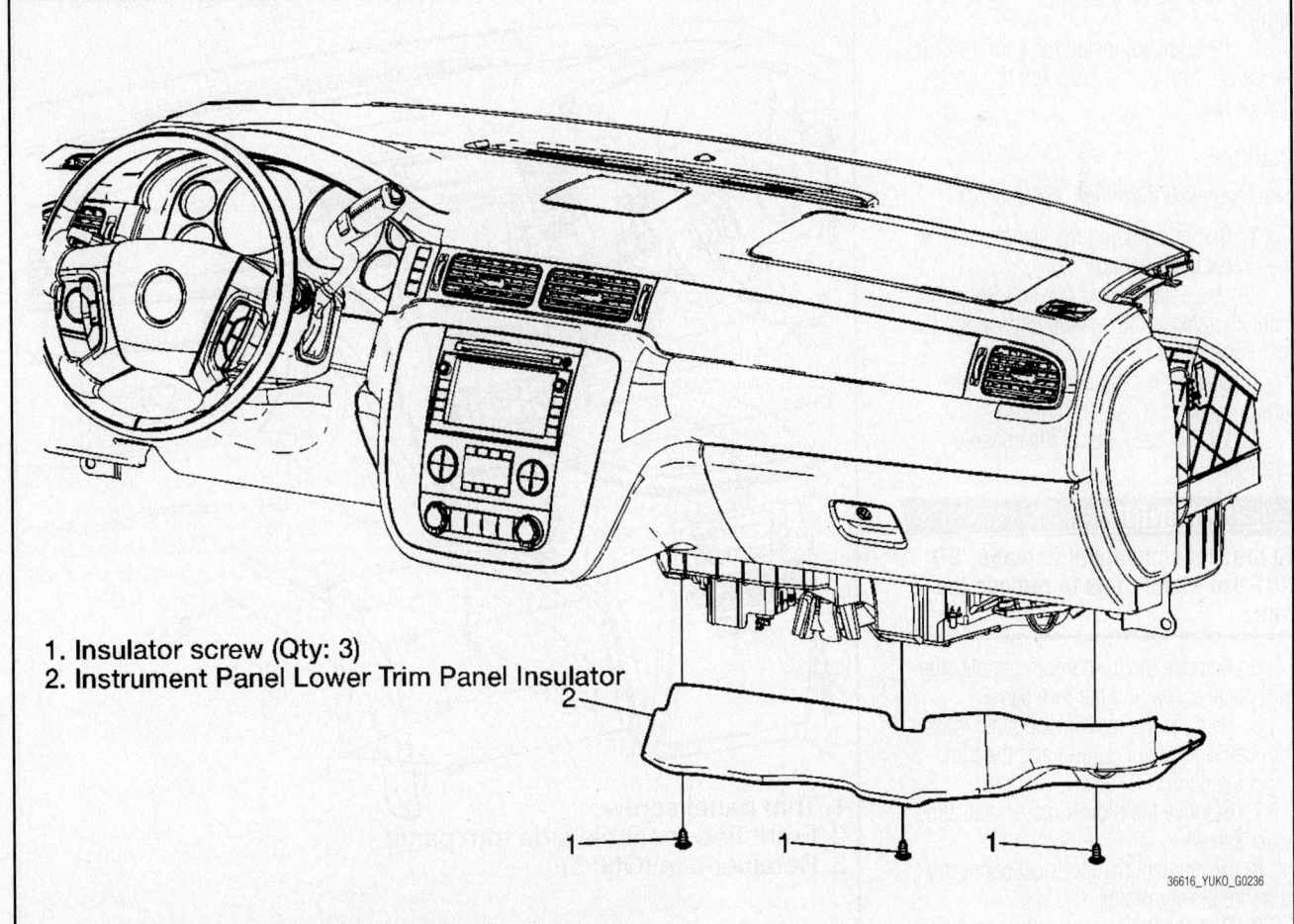

1. Insulator screw (Qty: 3)
2. Instrument Panel Lower Trim Panel Insulator

36616_YUKO_G0236

Fig. 176 Remove the sound insulator panel, if equipped—except Cadillac

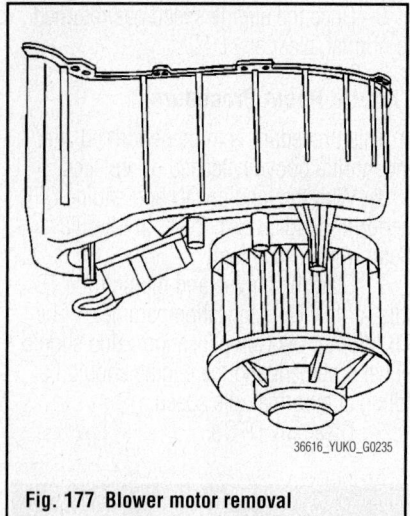

Fig. 177 Blower motor removal

9. Install the blower motor to the heater/ventilation module. Turn the blower assembly clockwise until the retaining tab locks into place.

10. Install the blower motor insulating cover.

11. Connect the electrical connector to the blower motor.

12. Install the blower motor insulating cover screws and tighten to 14 inch lbs. (2 Nm).

13. If equipped, install the sound insulator panel. Tighten the fasteners to 18 inch lbs. (2 Nm).

Cadillac

See Figures 178 through 180 and 177.

1. Before servicing the vehicle, refer to the Precautions Section.

2. Use a flat-bladed plastic trim tool to carefully release the retainer clips along the rear edge of the bezel.

3. Disconnect the electrical connections.

4. Lift the bezel out of the console assembly.

✳ WARNING

To prevent component damage, DO NOT use metal tools to remove the trim.

5. Remove the front floor console side trim panel screw and the trim panel.

6. Remove the instrument panel lower trim panel insulator screws and the trim panel insulator.

7. Remove the blower motor insulating cover screws.

8. Disconnect the electrical connector from the blower motor.

9. Remove the blower motor insulating cover.

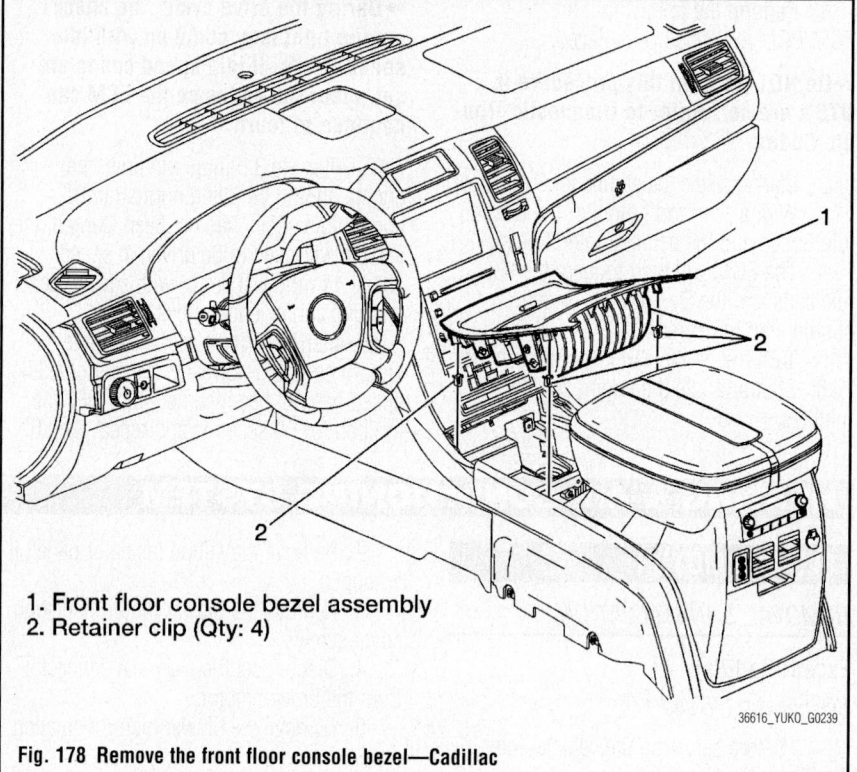

1. Front floor console bezel assembly
2. Retainer clip (Qty: 4)

Fig. 178 Remove the front floor console bezel—Cadillac

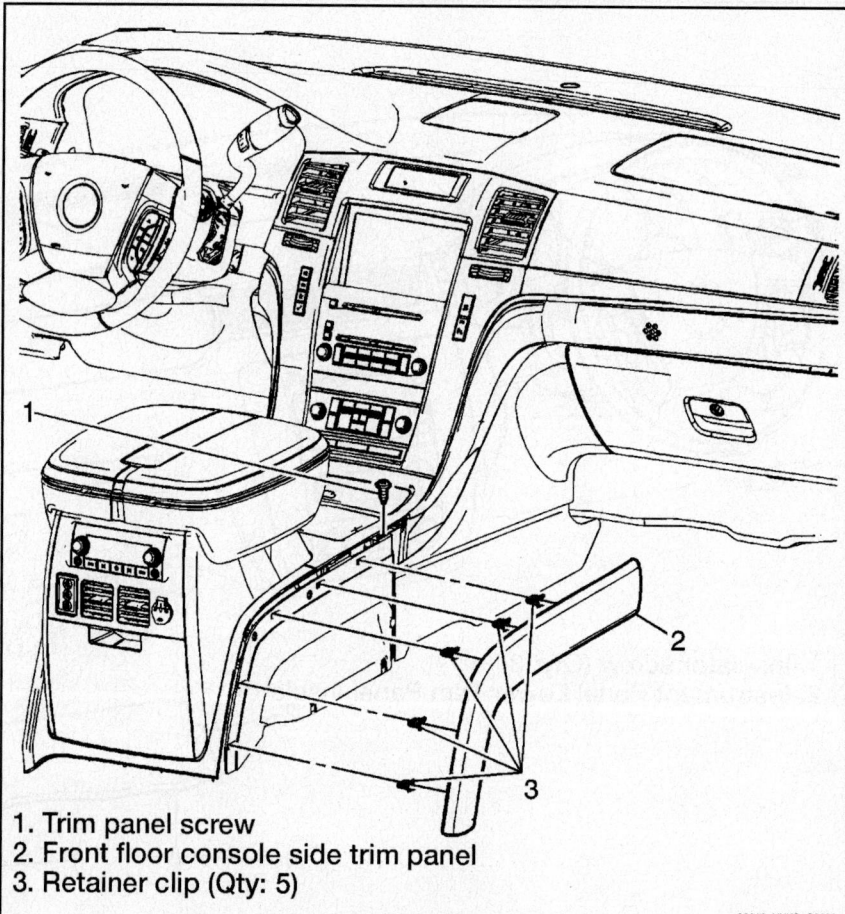

1. **Trim panel screw**
2. **Front floor console side trim panel**
3. **Retainer clip (Qty: 5)**

Fig. 179 Remove the right console trim panel—Cadillac

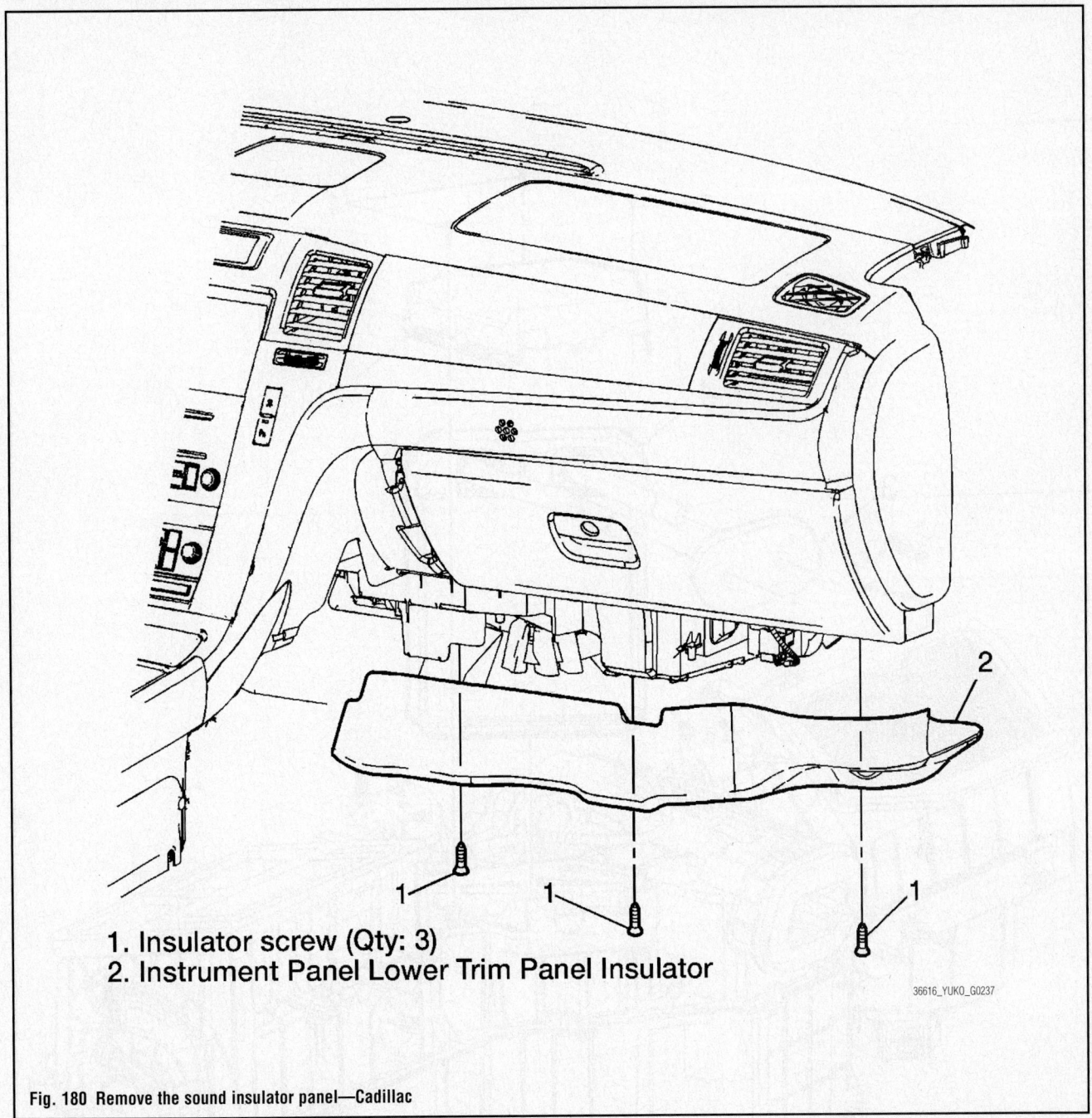

1. Insulator screw (Qty: 3)
2. Instrument Panel Lower Trim Panel Insulator

36616_YUKO_G0237

Fig. 180 Remove the sound insulator panel—Cadillac

10. Pull the retaining tab down while turning the blower motor counterclockwise in order to disengage the blower motor from the heater/ventilation module.

11. Remove the blower motor.

To install:

12. Install the blower motor.

13. Install the blower motor to the heater/ventilation module. Turn the blower assembly clockwise until the retaining tab locks into place.

14. Install the blower motor insulating cover.

15. Connect the electrical connector to the blower motor.

16. Install the blower motor insulating cover screws and tighten to 14 inch lbs. (2 Nm).

17. Installation continues in the reverse of the removal procedure.

18. Install the sound insulator panel. Tighten the fasteners to 18 inch lbs. (2 Nm).

HEATER CORE

REMOVAL & INSTALLATION

See Figure 181.

1. Before servicing the vehicle, refer to the Precautions Section.

2. Disconnect the negative battery cable.

3. Remove the HVAC Unit. Refer to HVAC Module Assembly, removal & installation.

4. Disconnect the wiring harness retainer from the heater core cover.

5. Remove the heater core cover screws and the cover.

6. Remove the heater core pass through seal.

7. Remove the heater core from the HVAC module assembly.

To install:

8. Installation is the reverse of the removal procedure.

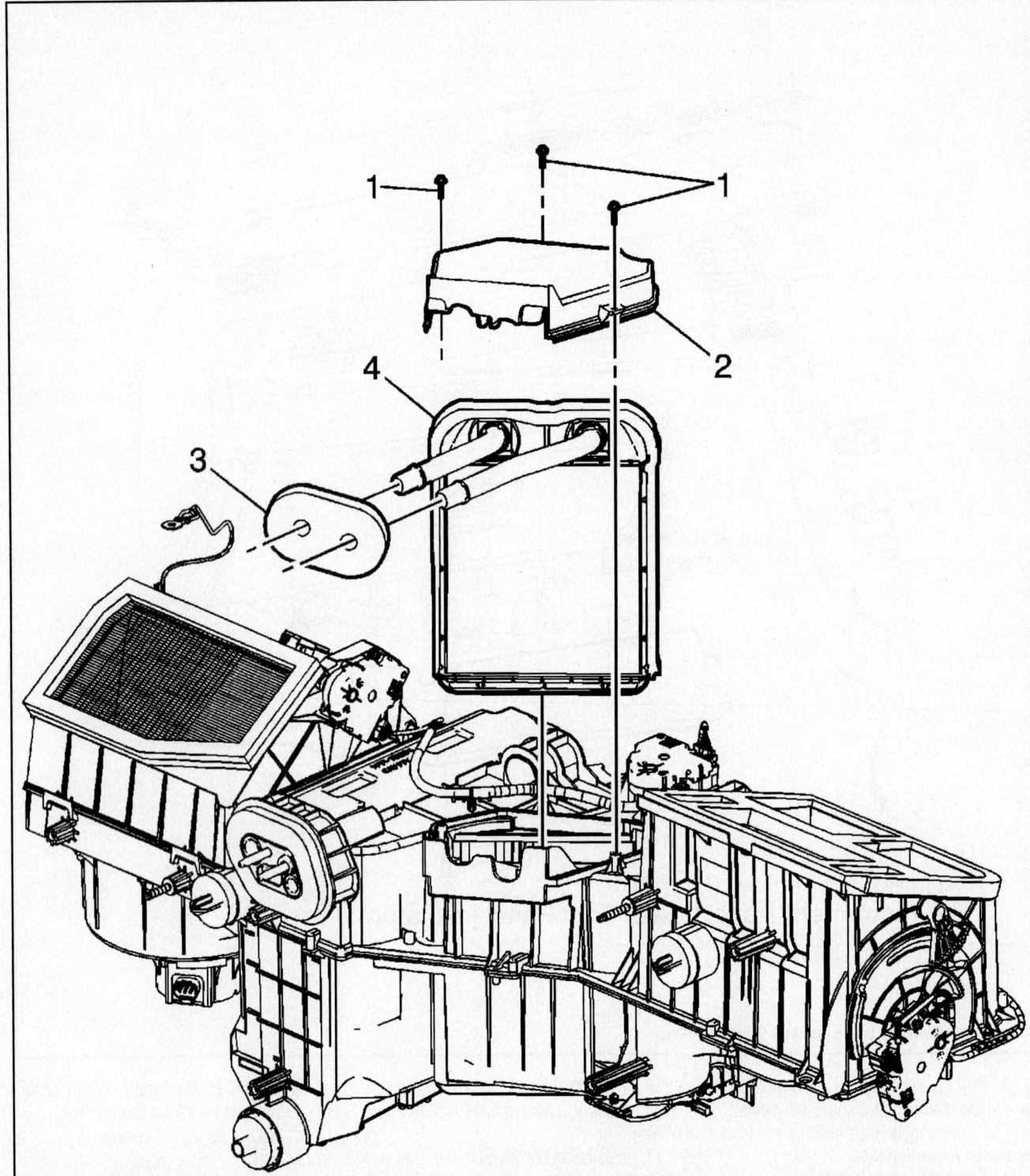

1. Heater core cover screw
2. Heater core cover
3. Heater core pass through seal
4. Heater core

36616_YUKO_G0240

Fig. 181 Remove the heater core from the HVAC module assembly

9. Install the heater core into the HVAC unit.

10. Tighten the heater core cover and screws to 14 inch lbs. (2 Nm).

11. Install the HVAC Unit into the vehicle. Refer to HVAC Module Assembly, removal & installation.

HVAC MODULE ASSEMBLY

REMOVAL & INSTALLATION

See Figures 182 through 198.

Special Tool:
- J 43181: Heater Line QC Release Tool

✳✳ CAUTION

When performing service on or near the SRS components, or SRS wiring, the SRS must be disabled. Failure to observe the correct procedure could cause deployment of the SRS components. Serious injury can occur.

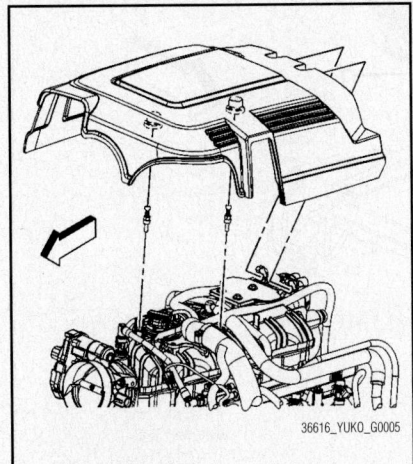

Fig. 182 Remove the upper intake manifold sight shield

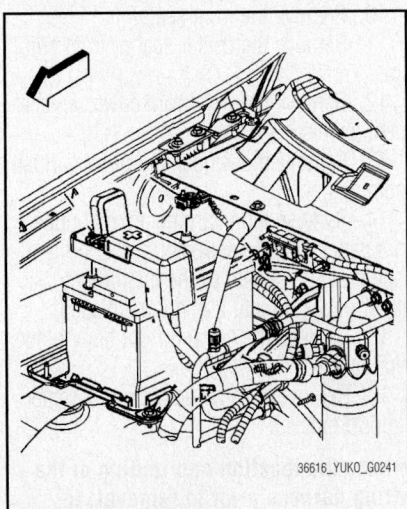

Fig. 183 Battery removal

1. Before servicing the vehicle, refer to the Precautions Section.

2. Disable the SRS system. Refer to Air Bag (Supplemental Restraint System), disarming the system.

3. Drain the cooling system. Properly dispose of used coolant.

4. Disconnect and plug the heater hoses at the HVAC unit using the J 43181, Heater Line QC Release Tool.

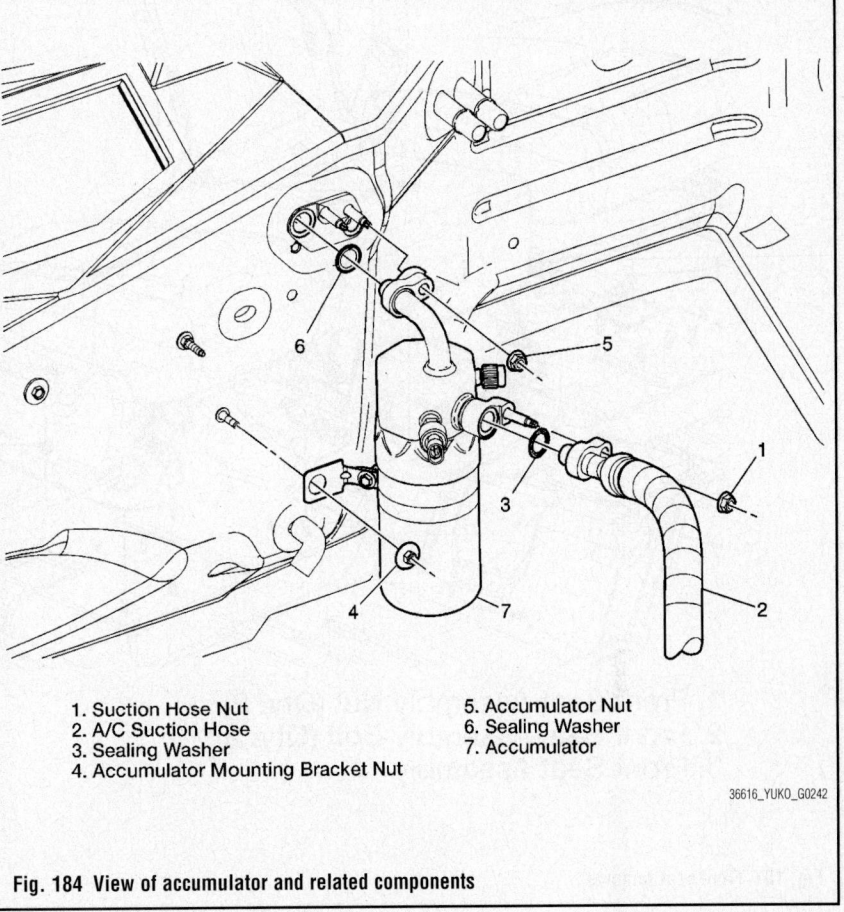

1. Suction Hose Nut
2. A/C Suction Hose
3. Sealing Washer
4. Accumulator Mounting Bracket Nut
5. Accumulator Nut
6. Sealing Washer
7. Accumulator

Fig. 184 View of accumulator and related components

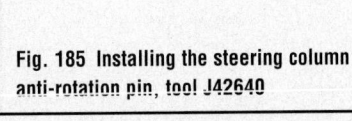

Fig. 185 Installing the steering column anti-rotation pin, tool J42640

5. Remove the upper intake manifold sight shield, if equipped.

6. Remove the battery.

7. Properly discharge the air conditioning system. Remove the accumulator.

8. Lock the steering column using tool J42640 through the access hole in the lower column trim cover.

9. Remove the steering shaft coupling nut and bolt at the steering column.

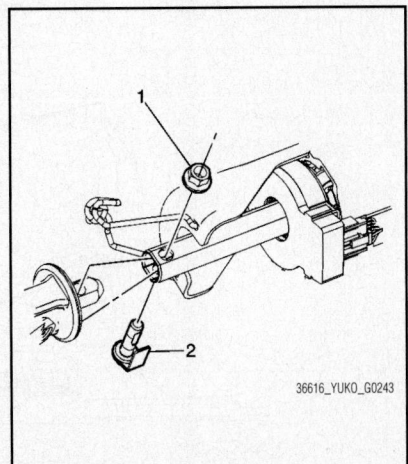

Fig. 186 Steering shaft coupling nut location

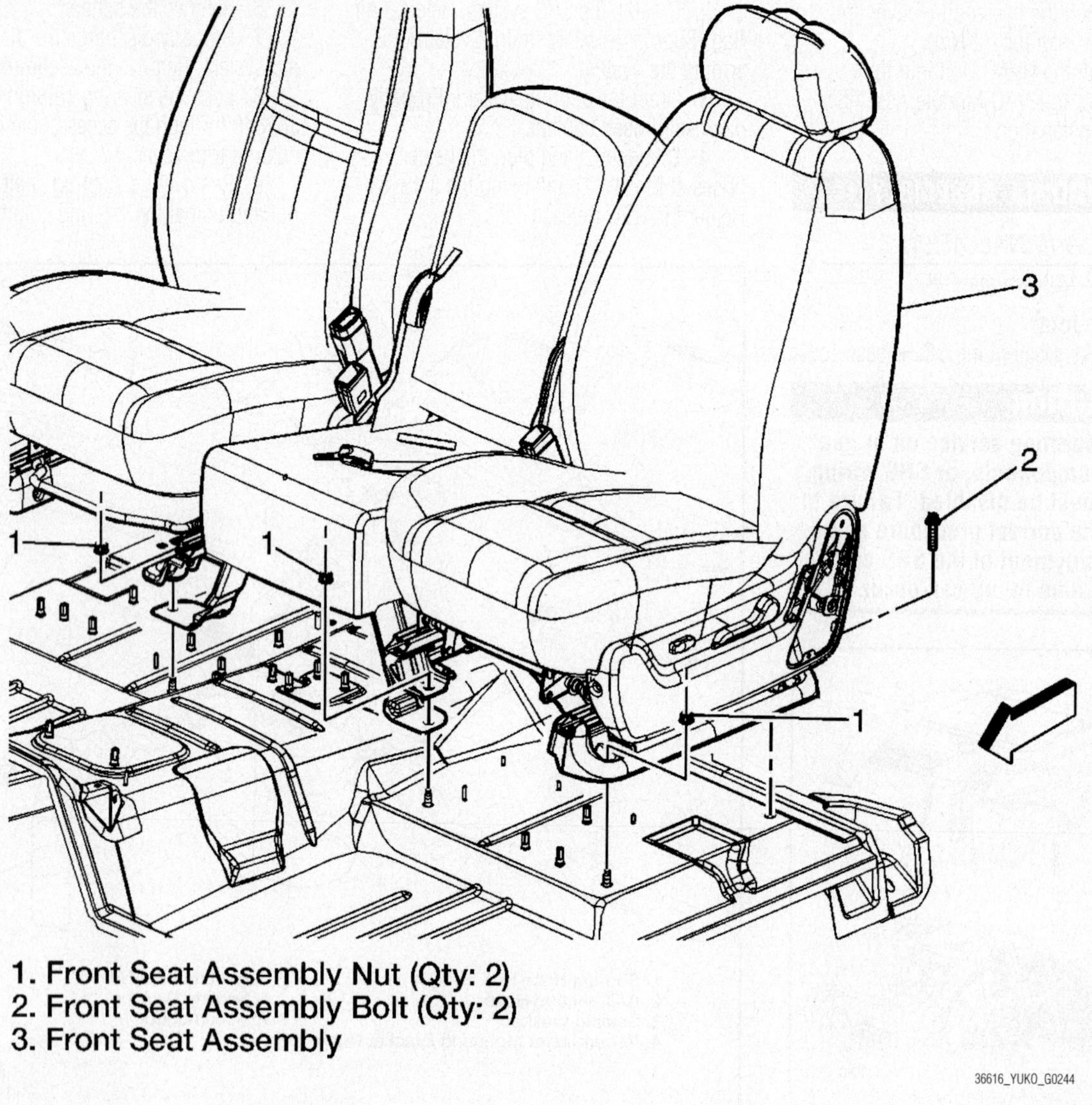

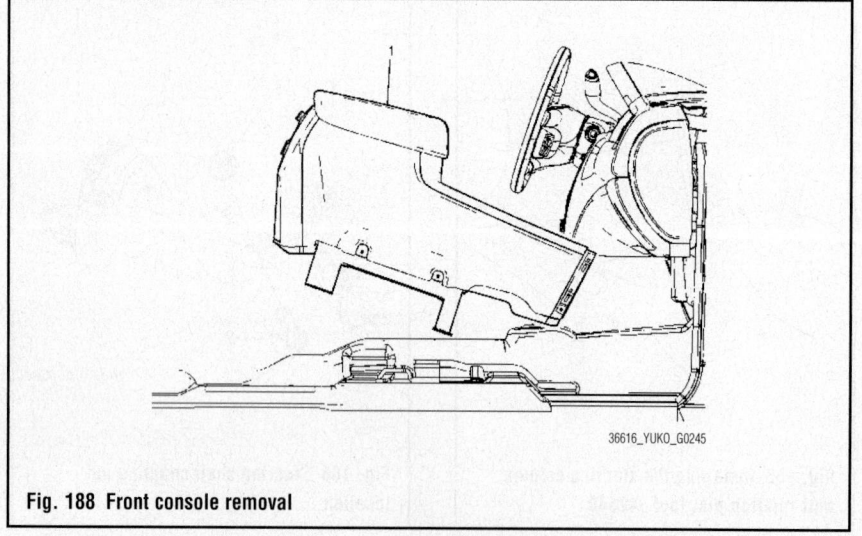

1. Front Seat Assembly Nut (Qty: 2)
2. Front Seat Assembly Bolt (Qty: 2)
3. Front Seat Assembly

36616_YUKO_G0244

Fig. 187 Front seat removal

Fig. 188 Front console removal

36616_YUKO_G0245

10. Remove the front seats.

11. Remove the center seat or front console.

12. Remove the outer trim cover replacement panels.

13. Remove the windshield pillar garnish moldings.

14. Remove the instrument panel upper trim panel with the defroster nozzle grille. Tape the light sensor to the instrument upper panel, so that it is not misplaced.

15. Remove the left and right body hinge trim panels.

16. Remove the instrument panel center support bracket.

→Note the location and routing of the wiring harness prior to removal, to ensure proper assembly.

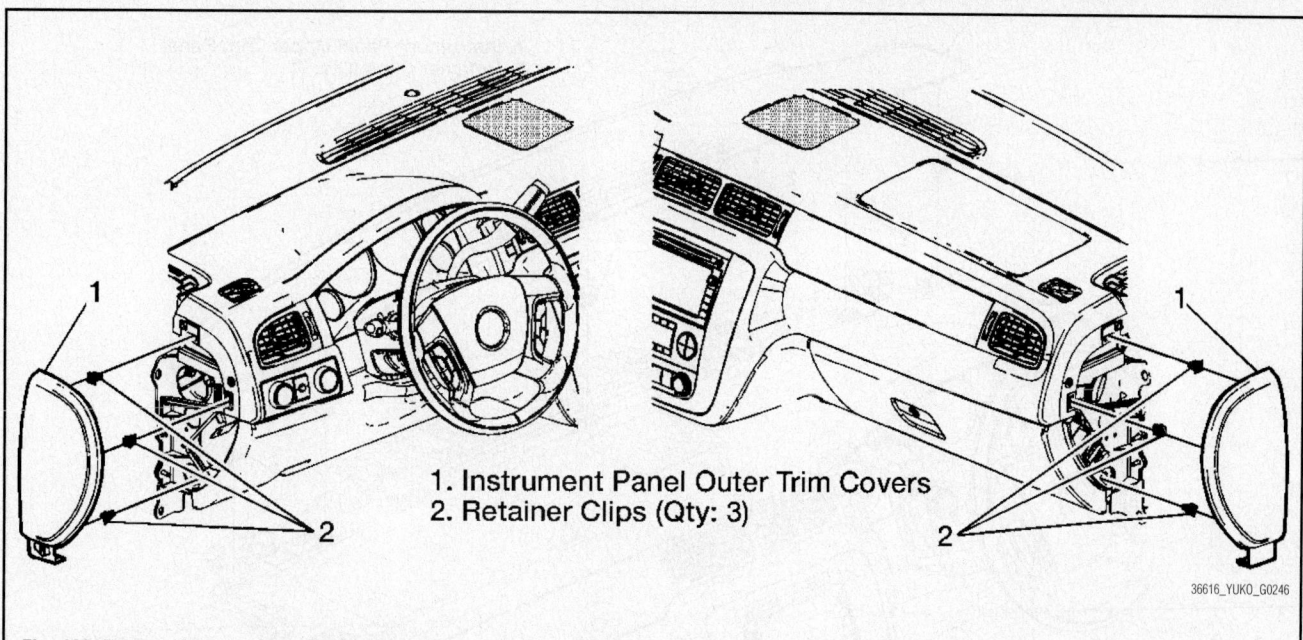

1. Instrument Panel Outer Trim Covers
2. Retainer Clips (Qty: 3)

36616_YUKO_G0246

Fig. 189 Remove the outer trim cover replacement panels

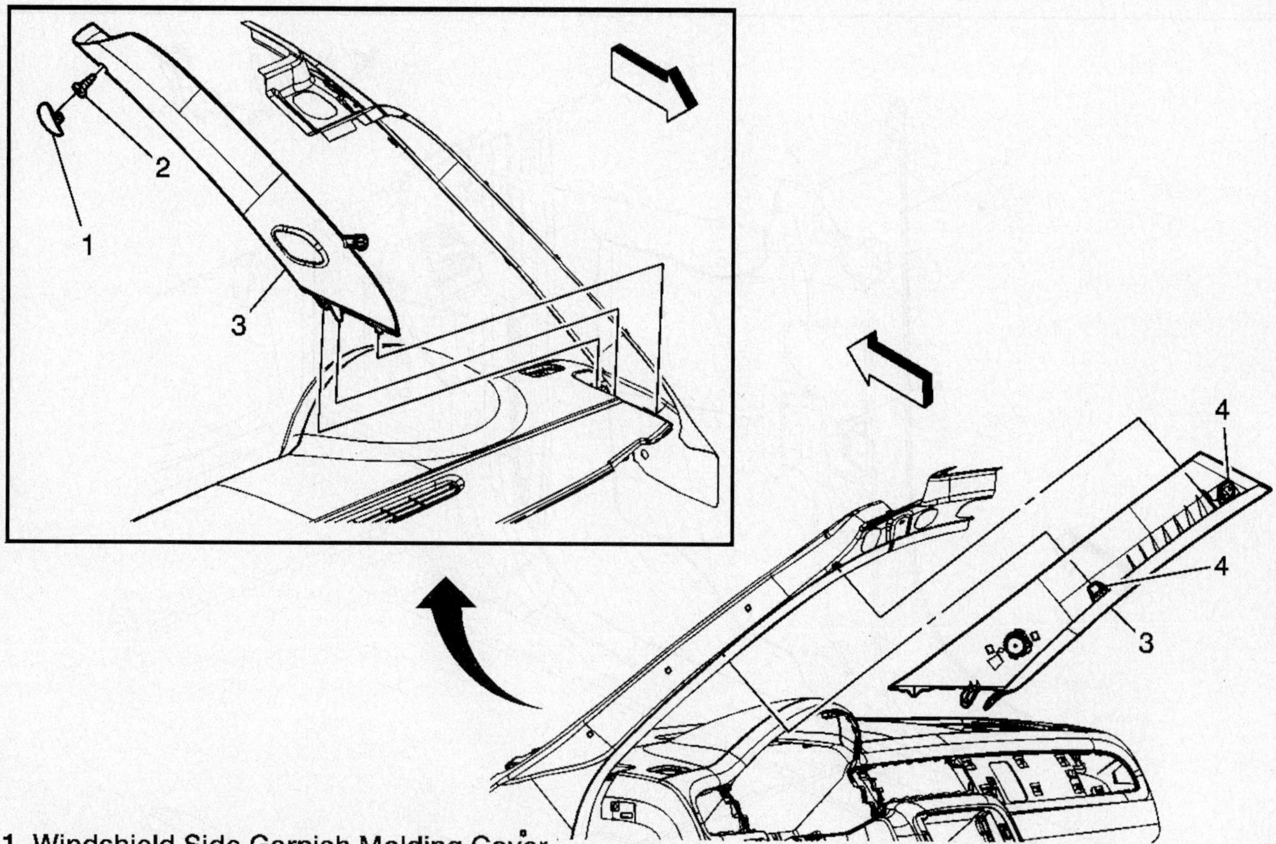

1. Windshield Side Garnish Molding Cover
2. Windshield Side Garnish Molding Screw
3. Windshield Side Garnish Molding Assembly
4. Windshield Side Garnish Molding Retainer (Qty: 2)

36616_YUKO_G0247

Fig. 190 Windshield pillar garnish molding removal

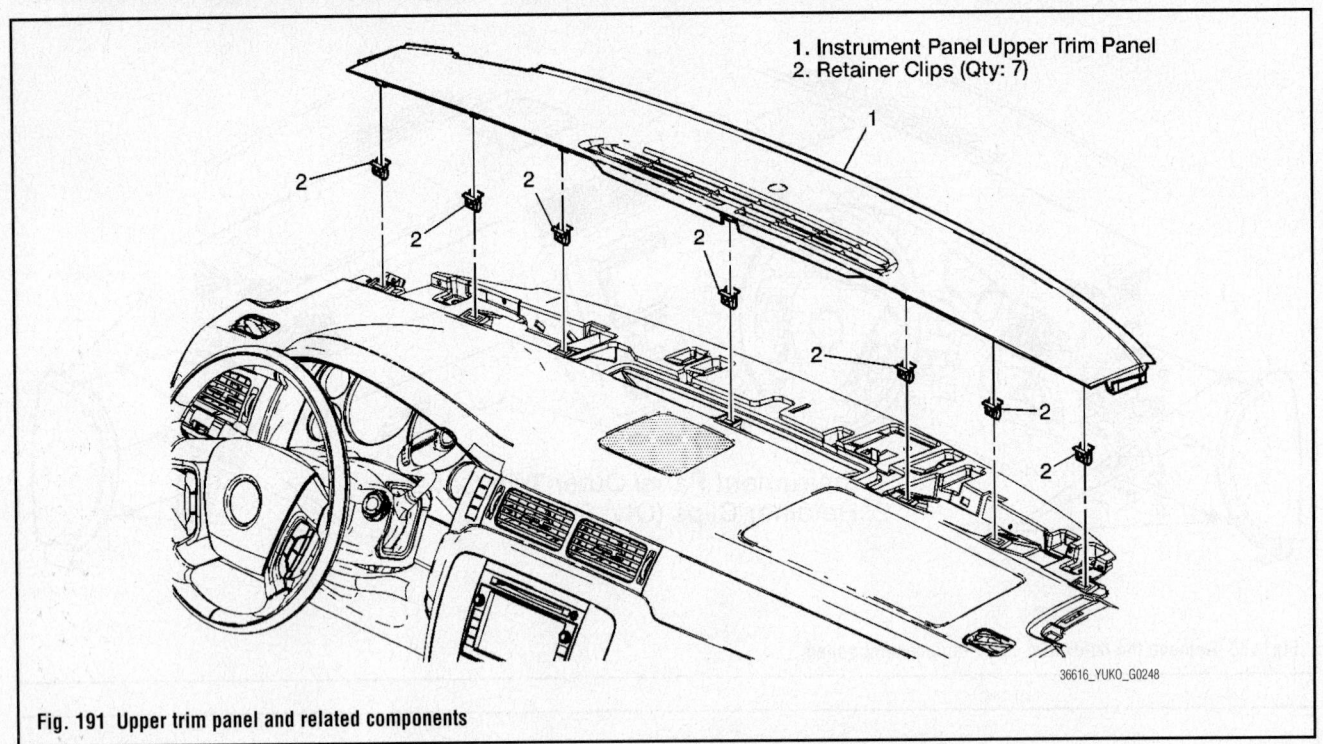

1. Instrument Panel Upper Trim Panel
2. Retainer Clips (Qty: 7)
1
2
2
2
2
2
2
2
36616_YUKO_G0248

Fig. 191 Upper trim panel and related components

1
2
2
1. Front Hinge Pillar Trim Panel Assembly
2. Front Hinge Pillar Trim Panel Assembly Retainer (Qty: 2)
36616_YUKO_G0249

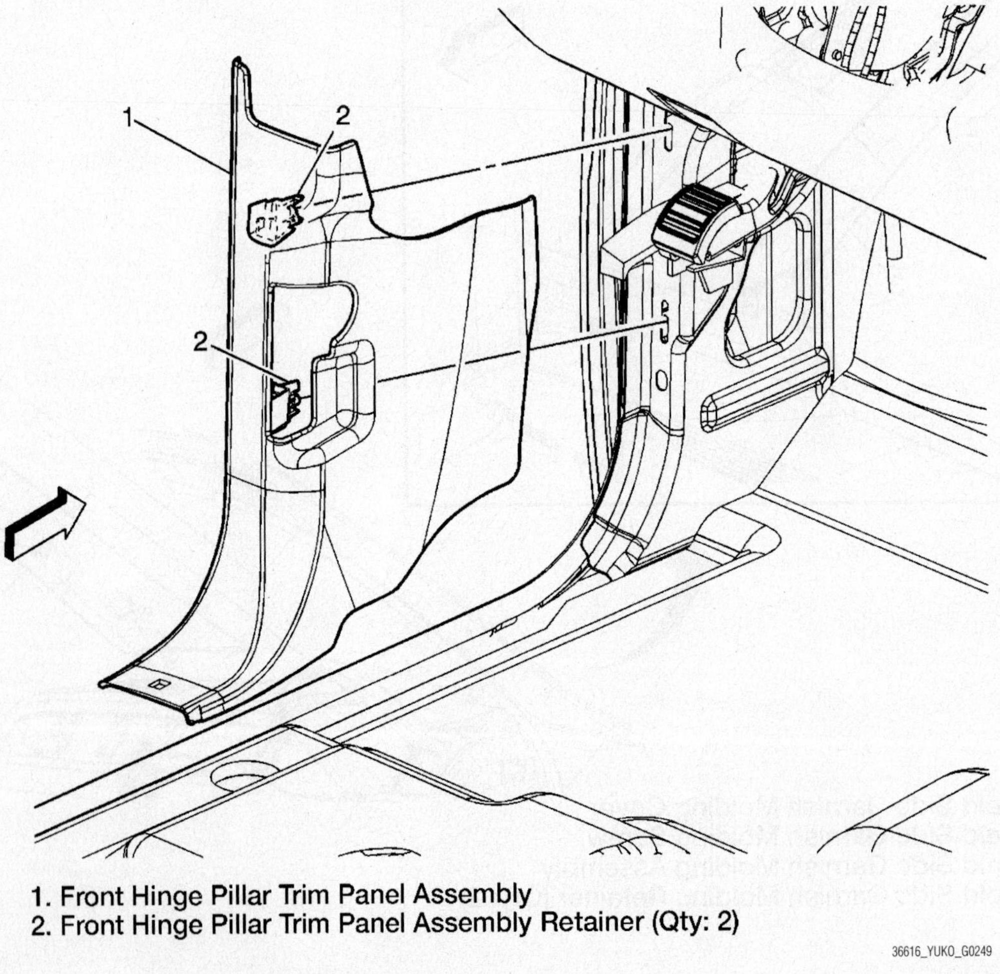

Fig. 192 Body hinge trim panel and related components

17. On the right side, disconnect the electrical connections to the instrument panel electrical center. Disconnect the electrical connector for the SRS module. Disconnect the antenna lead. Release the wire looms securing the harnesses to the instrument panel.

18. On the left side, disconnect the electrical connections to the instrument panel

electrical center. Disconnect the ground wires from the upper left cowl panel. Remove the body wiring harness junction block, from its bracket. Release the wire looms securing the harnesses to the instrument panel.

19. Remove the 4 bolts securing the instrument panel upper trim panel to the cowl.

20. Remove the 2 bolts securing the instrument carrier support to the cowl.

➡ **These bolts are located down inside the instrument panel and can be seen thru the windshield.**

21. Remove the 4 bolts releasing the instrument panel assembly from the vehicle.

22. With the aid of an assistant pull the assembly rearward, in the vehicle until the locator pin on each side clears the opening.

23. Remove the assembly from the vehicle, or position the assembly in the service position.

24. Remove the HVAC module drain hose.

25. Disconnect the electrical harnesses and the ground connections from the HVAC module.

26. Locate the rear engine cover on rear of intake manifold.

27. Reposition the acoustic foam (if applicable) down from the access location.

➡ **Ensure that any wiring harness does not interfere with the drilling process of the rear engine cover.**

28. Drill a 1 inch (25mm) diameter hole in the rear engine cover to access the HVAC module retaining nut located behind rear engine cover.

29. Remove the nuts and bolts from the HVAC module.

30. Carefully remove the HVAC module from the vehicle.

To install:

31. If replacing the HVAC module, transfer the components from the old HVAC module as necessary.

32. Install the HVAC module.

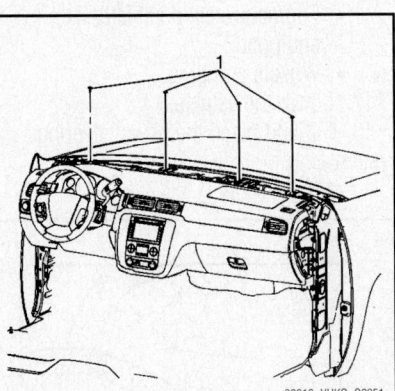

Fig. 193 Instrument panel center support and related components

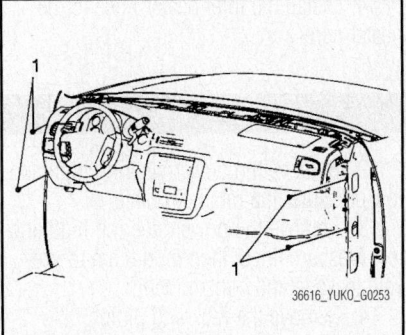

Fig. 196 Instrument panel side retaining bolt locations

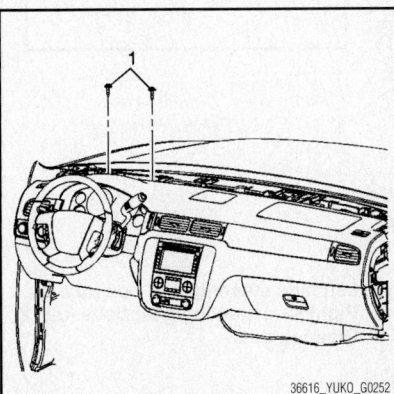

Fig. 194 Upper trim panel-to-cowl retaining bolt locations

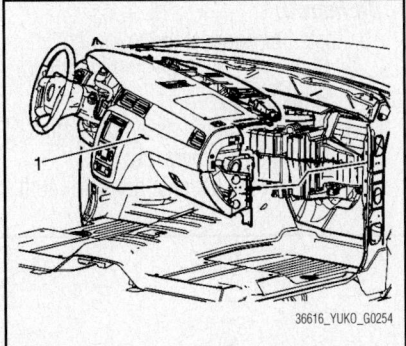

Fig. 197 Instrument panel in service position

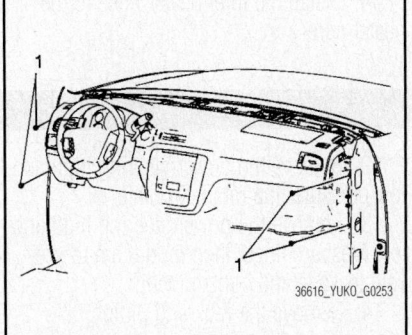

Fig. 195 Instrument panel-to-cowl retaining bolt locations

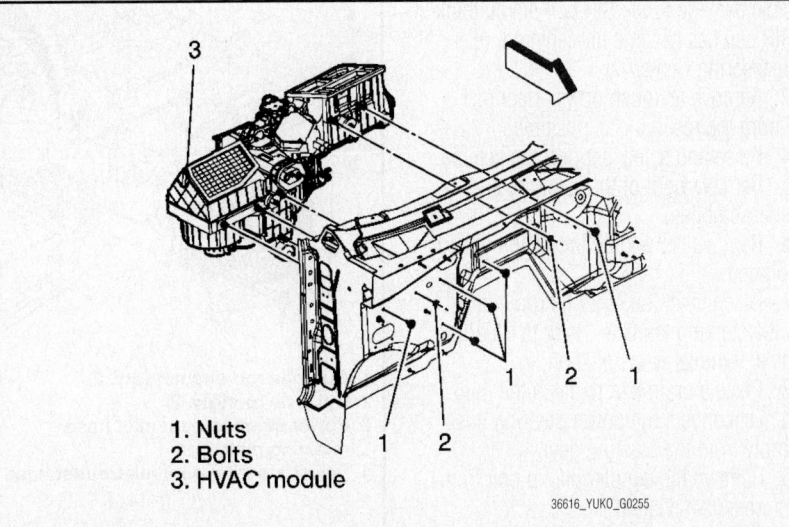

1. Nuts
2. Bolts
3. HVAC module

Fig. 198 Remove the retaining nuts and bolts from the HVAC module assembly

➡**Be sure to use new fasteners, as required.**

33. Install the nuts to the HVAC module and tighten to 80 inch lbs. (9 Nm).

34. Install the bolts to the HVAC module and tighten to 35 inch lbs. (4 Nm).

35. Reposition acoustic foam (if applicable) to original position or cover the access hole with equivalent foam tape.

36. Connect the electrical harness and the ground connections.

37. Install the HVAC module drain hose.

38. Install the instrument panel.

39. Install the upper intake manifold sight shield.

40. Install the battery.

41. Install the A/C accumulator.

42. Install the surge tank outlet hose to the heater core.

43. Firmly push the quick connect onto the heater core pipe until an audible click is heard.

44. Install the inlet heater hose to the heater core.

45. Firmly push the quick connect onto the heater core pipe until an audible click is heard.

46. Fill the cooling system with the proper type and amount of fluid.

47. Enable the SRS system. Refer to Air Bag (Supplemental Restraint System), arming the system.

48. Evacuate and charge the A/C system.

49. Check for proper function of installed components and for any fluid leakage. Repair as needed.

STEERING

POWER RACK & PINION STEERING GEAR

REMOVAL & INSTALLATION

See Figure 199.

Special Tool:
- J-42640: Steering Column Anti-Rotation Pin

1. Before servicing the vehicle, refer to the Precautions Section.

2. With the wheels of the vehicle facing straight ahead, secure the steering wheel utilizing the steering column anti-rotation pin, steering column lock, or a strap to prevent rotation. Locking of the steering column will prevent damage and a possible malfunction of the SIR system. The steering wheel must be secured in position before disconnecting the following components: the steering column, the intermediate shaft(s), or the steering gear. After disconnecting these components, do not rotate the steering wheel or move the front tires and wheels. Failure to follow this procedure may cause the SIR coil assembly to become un-centered and cause possible damage to the SIR coil. If you think the SIR coil has became un-centered, refer to Clockspring Centering.

3. Remove as much power steering fluid from the reservoir as possible.

4. Raise and safely support the vehicle.

5. Remove both of the front tire and wheel assemblies.

6. Remove the engine protection shield if equipped.

7. Disconnect the outer tie rod end from the steering knuckle. Refer to Steering Knuckle, removal & installation.

8. Place a drain pan to catch the fluid.

9. Disconnect the power steering hose assembly from the steering gear.

10. Remove the coupler clamp bolt from the intermediate shaft.

11. Separate the intermediate shaft from the steering gear.

12. Remove the power steering high and low pressure line retaining plate.

13. Remove the power steering high and low pressure lines, then plug them to prevent leakage and contamination.

14. Remove the rack and pinion assembly mounting nuts, washers, and bolts.

15. Remove the rack and pinion assembly from the vehicle.

To install:

16. Install or connect the following:
- Rack and pinion assembly into the vehicle
- Rack and pinion assembly mounting bolts, washers and nuts. Tighten the left side bolts to 148 ft. lbs. (200 Nm) and the right side bolts to 74 ft. lbs. (100 Nm).
- Intermediate shaft to the rack and pinion assembly
- Coupler clamp bolt to the intermediate shaft. Tighten the bolt to 33 ft. lbs. (45 Nm).
- Low pressure line and high pressure line. Tighten the retaining plate to 106 inch lbs. (12 Nm)
- Outer tie rod ends
- Engine protection shield, if equipped
- Wheels and tires

17. Lower the vehicle.

18. Fill and bleed the power steering system.

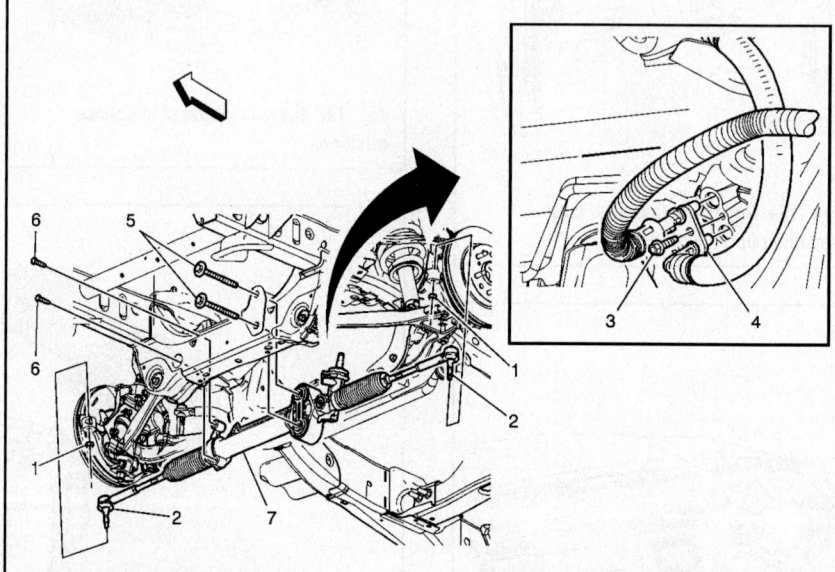

1. Outer tie rod end nut (qty. 2)
2. Outer tie rod (qty. 2)
3. Power steering gear inlet hose retaining plate bolt
4. Power steering gear inlet/outlet hose (qty. 2)
5. Left side steering gear bolt (qty. 2)
6. Right side steering gear bolts (qty. 2)
7. Steering gear

22116_SIER_G0046

Fig. 199 Exploded view of the rack and pinion steering gear assembly

POWER RECIRCULATING BALL STEERING GEAR

REMOVAL & INSTALLATION

See Figures 200 and 201.

Special Tools:
• J-24319-B: Steering Linkage and Tie Rod Puller
• J-42640: Steering Column Anti-Rotation Pin

With the wheels of the vehicle facing straight ahead, secure the steering wheel utilizing the steering column anti-rotation pin, steering column lock, or a strap to prevent rotation. Locking of the steering column will prevent damage and a possible malfunction of the SIR system. The steering wheel must be secured in position before disconnecting the following components: the steering column, the intermediate shaft(s), or the steering gear. After disconnecting these components, do not rotate the steering wheel or move the front tires and wheels. Failure to

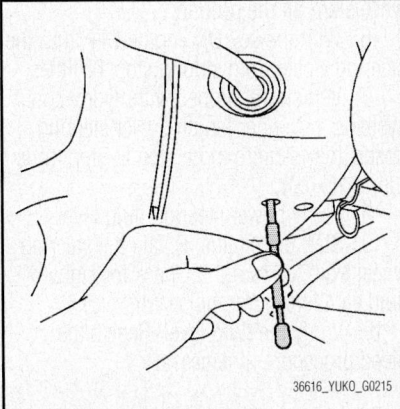

Fig. 200 With the front wheels of the vehicle in the straight ahead position, use the J-42640 Pin in order to lock the steering column

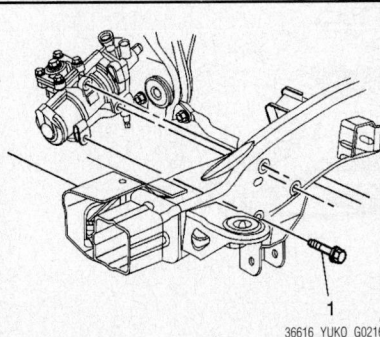

Fig. 201 Remove the steering gear bolts (1) and remove the steering gear from the vehicle

follow this procedure may cause the SIR coil assembly to become un-centered and cause possible damage to the SIR coil. If you think the SIR coil has became un-centered, refer to Clockspring Centering.

1. Before servicing the vehicle, refer to the Precautions Section.
2. With the front wheels of the vehicle in the straight ahead position, use the J-42640 Pin in order to lock the steering column.
3. Remove as much power steering fluid from the power steering fluid reservoir as possible.
4. Place drain pans under the vehicle.
5. Raise and safely support the vehicle.
6. Remove the engine shield, if equipped.
7. Disconnect the steering hoses from the steering gear.
8. Disconnect the steering shaft coupling from the steering gear.

✷✷ WARNING

Do not start the vehicle with any power steering gear inlet or outlet hoses disconnected. When disconnected, plug or cap all openings of components. Failure to do so could result in contamination or loss of power steering fluid and damage to the system.

9. Remove the pitman arm nut and discard.
10. Use the J-24319-B Puller in order to disconnect the pitman arm from the relay rod.
11. Remove the steering gear bolts.
12. Remove the steering gear from the vehicle.

To install:

13. Transfer the pitman arm if necessary. Refer to Steering Linkage, Pitman Arm, removal & installation.
14. Position the steering gear in the vehicle.

➡Start all of the steering gear bolts by hand and fully seat the bolts before finalizing the torque.

15. Install the steering gear bolts.

➡Use the correct fastener in the correct location. Replacement fasteners must be the correct part number for that application. Do not use paints, lubricants, or corrosion inhibitors on fasteners, or fastener joint surfaces, unless specified. These coatings affect fastener torque and joint clamping force and may damage the fastener. Use the correct tightening sequence and specifi-

cations when installing fasteners in order to avoid damage to parts and systems. When using fasteners that are threaded directly into plastic, use extreme care not to strip the mating plastic part(s). Use hand tools only, and do not use any kind of impact or power tools. Fastener should be hand tightened, fully seated, and not stripped.

16. Tighten the steering gear bolts to 110 ft. lbs. (150 Nm).
17. Connect the pitman arm to the relay rod.
18. Install the pitman arm nut and tighten to 46 ft. lbs. (62 Nm).
19. Connect the power steering hoses to the steering gear. Tighten the hose fittings to 24 ft. lbs. (32 Nm).
20. Connect the steering shaft coupling to the steering gear.
21. Install the engine shield, if equipped.
22. Lower the vehicle.
23. Remove the J-42640 Pin from the steering column.
24. Fill and bleed the power steering system.
25. Remove the drain pans.
26. Clean any excess fluid from the vehicle.

POWER STEERING PUMP

REMOVAL & INSTALLATION

See Figure 202.

1. Before servicing the vehicle, refer to the Precautions Section.
2. Remove the accessory drive belt. Refer to Accessory Drive Belts, removal & installation.
3. Remove as much power steering fluid from the power steering fluid reservoir as possible.
4. Remove the engine shield. Refer to Engine Shield Replacement.

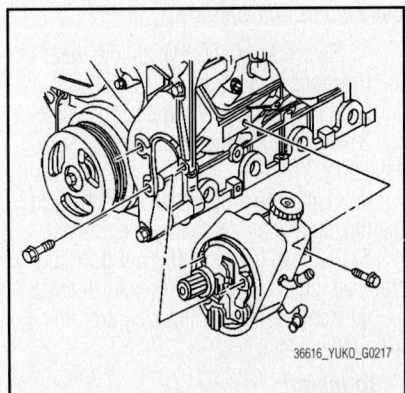

Fig. 202 Power steering pump assembly removal

5. Place drain pans under the vehicle as needed.

6. Disconnect the power steering gear inlet hose from the power steering pump assembly from underneath the vehicle.

7. Disconnect the power steering fluid cooler hose clamp and the power steering fluid cooler hose from the power steering pump assembly.

8. If equipped with hydroboost, disconnect the power brake booster outlet hose clamp and disconnect the power brake booster outlet hose from power steering pump assembly.

9. Remove the power steering pump bracket bolt from the side of the engine.

10. Remove the power steering pump bolts.

11. Remove the power steering pump assembly from the vehicle.

To install:

12. Install all transferable parts, as needed.

13. Install the power steering pump assembly to the vehicle.

➡**Start all the bolts by hand before finalizing each torque.**

14. Install the power steering pump bracket bolt to the side of the engine. Tighten the bolt to 37 ft. lbs. (50 Nm).

15. Install the power steering pump bolts. Tighten the bolts to 37 ft. lbs. (50 Nm).

16. Connect the power steering fluid cooler hose and the power steering fluid cooler hose clamp to the power steering pump assembly.

17. If equipped with hydroboost, connect the power brake booster outlet hose and the power brake booster outlet hose clamp to the power steering pump assembly.

18. Connect the power steering gear inlet hose to the power steering pump assembly from underneath the vehicle. Tighten the fitting to 24 ft. lbs. (32 Nm).

19. Clean any excess power steering fluid from the vehicle and remove the drain pans.

20. Install the engine shield, if equipped.

21. Fill and bleed the power steering system.

BLEEDING

⁕⁕ **CAUTION**

The fluid level should be checked with the engine OFF to prevent personal injury from moving parts and to assure an accurate fluid level reading.

⁕⁕ **WARNING**

If the air is not purged from the power steering system correctly, pump failure could result.

1. Before servicing the vehicle, refer to the Precautions Section.

2. Observe the following:
- Use clean, new power steering fluid only.
- Hoses touching the frame, body, or engine may cause system noise. Verify that the hoses do not touch any other part of the vehicle.
- Loose connections may not leak, but could allow air into the steering system. Verify that all hose connections are tight.
- Power steering fluid level must be maintained throughout bleed procedure.

3. Fill the pump reservoir with fluid to the minimum system level, FULL COLD level, or the middle of the hash mark on the cap stick fluid level indicator.

➡**With hydro-boost only, the oil level will appear falsely high if the hydro-boost accumulator is not fully charged. Do not apply the brake pedal with the engine OFF. This will discharge the hydro-boost accumulator.**

4. If equipped with hydro-boost, fully charge the hydro-boost accumulator using the following procedure:
   a. Start the engine.
   b. Firmly apply the brake pedal 10–15 times.
   c. Turn the engine OFF.

5. Raise the vehicle until the front wheels are off the ground.

6. With the key ON engine OFF, turn the steering wheel from stop to stop 12 times.

7. Vehicles equipped with hydro-boost systems, or longer length power steering hoses, may require more stop to stop turns (up to 15–20).

8. Verify power steering fluid level.

9. Start the engine. Rotate the steering wheel from left to right. Check for signs of fluid aeration (pump noise/whining).

10. Verify the fluid level. Repeat the bleed procedure, if necessary.

SUSPENSION

FRONT SUSPENSION

CONTROL LINKS

REMOVAL & INSTALLATION

See Figures 203 and 204.

1. Before servicing the vehicle, refer to the Precautions Section.

2. Raise and safely support the vehicle.

3. Remove the tire and wheel assembly.

4. Using the proper size wrench, hold the link stud while removing the link nut.

5. Remove the retaining nut from the stabilizer shaft and the lower control arm.

6. Remove the stabilizer/control link from the vehicle.

To install:

7. Remove all traces of the original adhesive patch, if required. Apply

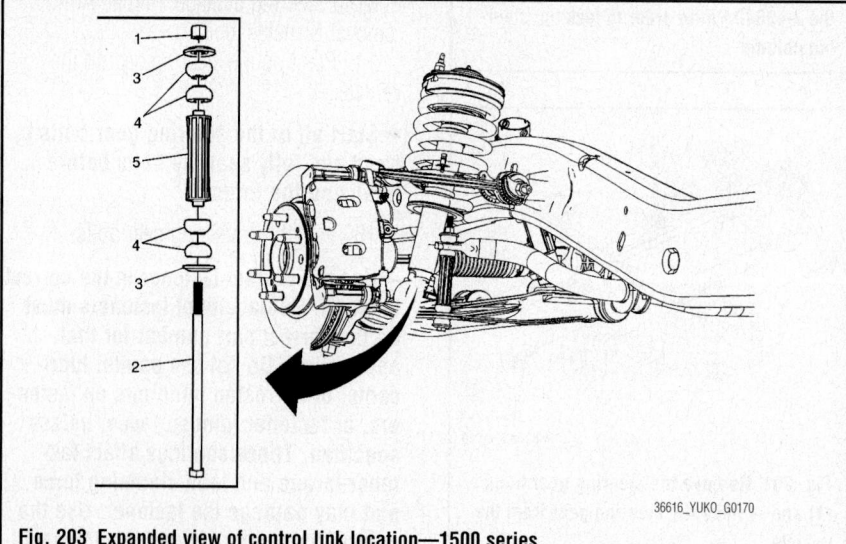

Fig. 203 Expanded view of control link location—1500 series

36616_YUKO_G0170

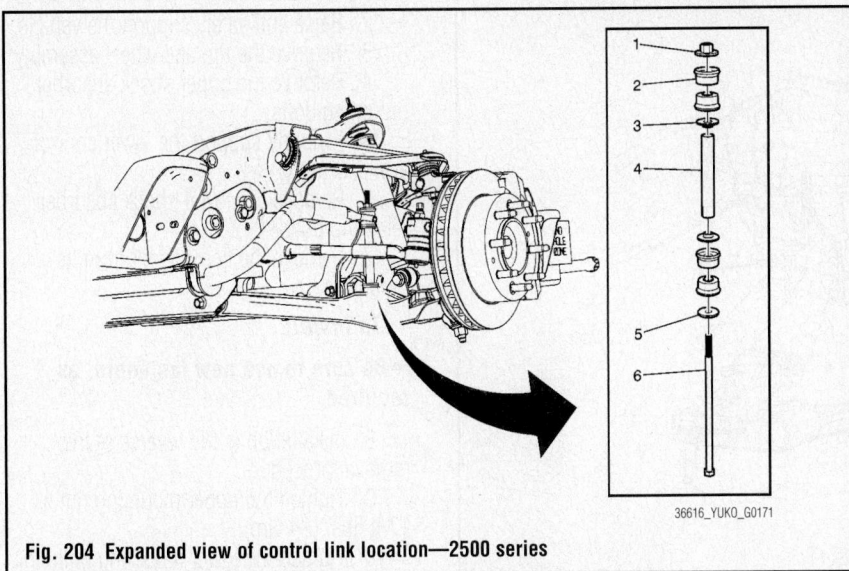

Fig. 204 Expanded view of control link location—2500 series

Threadlocker GM P/N 36616382 on the threads of the bolts.

8. Install the control link on the lower control arm and stabilizer shaft.

9. Hand tighten the stabilizer shaft link nuts.

10. Using the proper size wrench to hold the link stud, tighten the link nut to 17 ft. lbs. (23 Nm).

11. Install the tire and wheel assembly.

12. Remove the support and lower the vehicle.

LOWER BALL JOINT

REMOVAL & INSTALLATION

The following service procedure applies to vehicles equipped with cast iron lower control arms only. For those vehicles equipped with an aluminum lower control arm, the ball joint is NOT serviced separately. If the ball joint in the aluminum lower control arm is found to have excessive wear and is damaged, replace the lower control arm as an assembly.

1. Before servicing the vehicle, refer to the Precautions Section.

2. Raise and safely support the vehicle.

3. Remove the tire and wheel assembly.

4. Remove the lower control arm from the vehicle. Refer to Lower Control Arm, removal & installation.

5. Place the lower control arm in a vise.

6. Using a chisel, remove the securing crimps from the ball joint body, if equipped.

7. Using a press, remove the ball joint from the lower control arm.

To install:

➡ Use the outer flange of the ball joint in order to press the ball joint into place.

8. Install the ball joint using a press.

9. Place the lower control arm in a bench vise.

10. Using a punch, install the crimps to the ball joint.

11. Install the lower control arm in the vehicle. Refer to Lower Control Arm, removal & installation.

12. Install the tire and wheel.

13. Lower the vehicle.

14. Verify the wheel alignment, adjust as needed.

LOWER CONTROL ARM

REMOVAL AND & INSTALLATION

See Figures 205 and 206.

Special Tools:
- J 43631: Ball Joint Separator
- J 45851: Ball Joint Separator Protector Adapters

➡ **For vehicles equipped with the aluminum lower control arm, the ball joint is NOT service separately. If the ball joint in the aluminum lower control arm is found to have excessive wear and is damaged, replace the lower control arm as an assembly.**

1. Before servicing the vehicle, refer to the Precautions Section.

2. Raise and safely support the vehicle.

3. Remove the tire and wheel assembly.

4. Remove the stabilizer shaft link from the lower control arm.

5. Remove the front halfshaft, if equipped with 4WD. Refer to Halfshafts, removal & installation.

6. Using mechanics wire or equivalent, support the knuckle assembly and upper control arm.

7. Remove and discard the lower ball joint retaining nut.

8. Remove the lower shock bolts from the lower control arm.

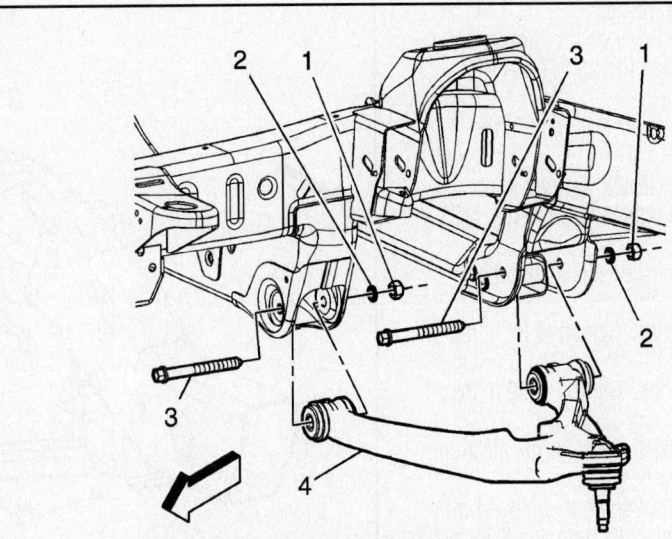

1. Lower control arm nuts
2. Lower control arm washers
3. Lower control arm bolts
4. Lower control arm

Fig. 205 Lower control arm removal—1500 series

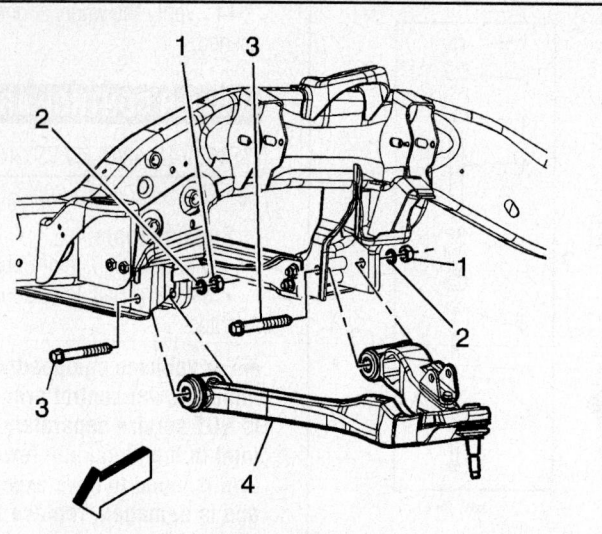

1. Lower control arm nuts
2. Lower control arm washers
3. Lower control arm bolts
4. Lower control arm

36616_YUKO_G0169

Fig. 206 Lower control arm removal—2500 series

9. Using the J 43631 and the J 45851, remove the lower ball joint from the steering knuckle.

10. Remove the lower control arm nuts and washers.

11. Remove the control arm bolts.

12. Remove the control arm.

To install:

13. Install the lower control arm.

14. Install the lower control arm bolts.

15. Install the washers.

16. Install the lower control arm retaining nuts and tighten to 129 ft. lbs. (175 Nm).

17. Install the lower ball joint in the steering knuckle.

18. Install the NEW lower ball joint retaining nut and tighten to 92 ft. lbs. (125 Nm).

19. Install the lower shock absorber mount bolts:

    a. 1500 series: Tighten to 37 ft. lbs. (50 Nm).

    b. 2500 series: Tighten to 59 ft. lbs. (80 Nm).

20. Remove the support for the steering knuckle and upper control arm.

21. Install the halfshaft, if equipped with 4WD. Refer to Halfshafts, removal & installation.

22. Install the stabilizer shaft link to the lower control arm.

23. Install the tire and wheel.

24. Lower the vehicle.

25. Align the front end.

SHOCK ABSORBERS

REMOVAL & INSTALLATION

See Figure 207.

1. Before servicing the vehicle, refer to the Precautions Section.

2. Raise and safely support the vehicle.

3. Remove the tire and wheel assembly.

4. Remove the upper shock absorber mounting bolts.

5. Properly support the lower control arm assembly.

6. Remove the lower shock absorber retaining bolts.

7. Remove the component from its mounting.

To install:

➡Be sure to use new fasteners, as required.

8. Installation is the reverse of the removal procedure.

9. Tighten the upper mounting nut to 17 ft. lbs. (24 Nm).

10. Tighten the lower mounting bolts to 59 ft. lbs. (80 Nm).

STABILIZER BAR

REMOVAL & INSTALLATION

See Figures 208 through 210.

1. Before servicing the vehicle, refer to the Precautions Section.

2. Raise and safely support the vehicle.

3. Remove the tire and wheel assembly.

4. Remove the engine shield, if equipped.

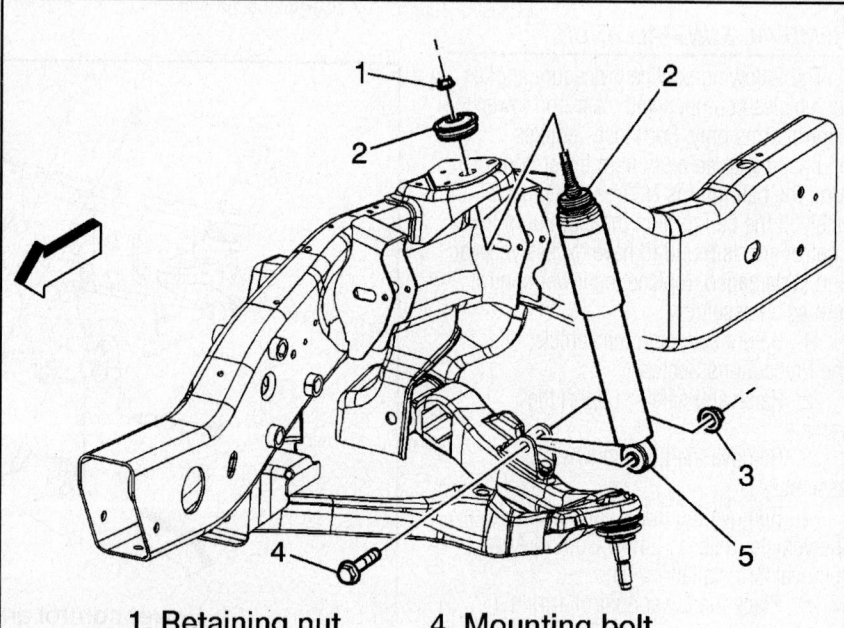

1. Retaining nut
2. Insulator (Qty: 2)
3. Retaining nut
4. Mounting bolt
5. Shock absorber

36616_YUKO_G0158

Fig. 207 Shock absorber mounting—2500 series

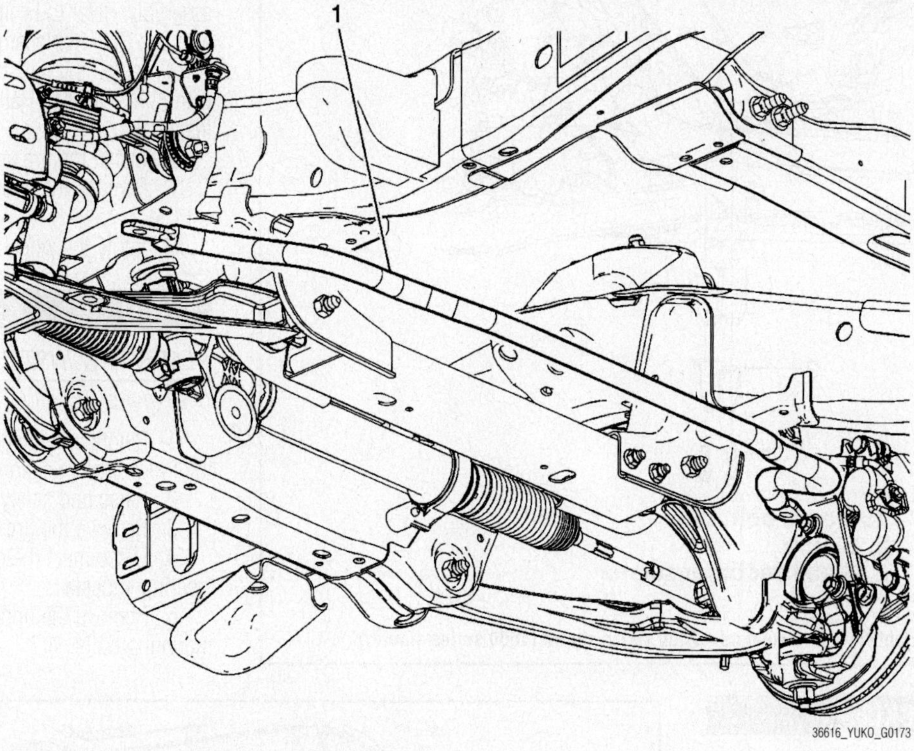

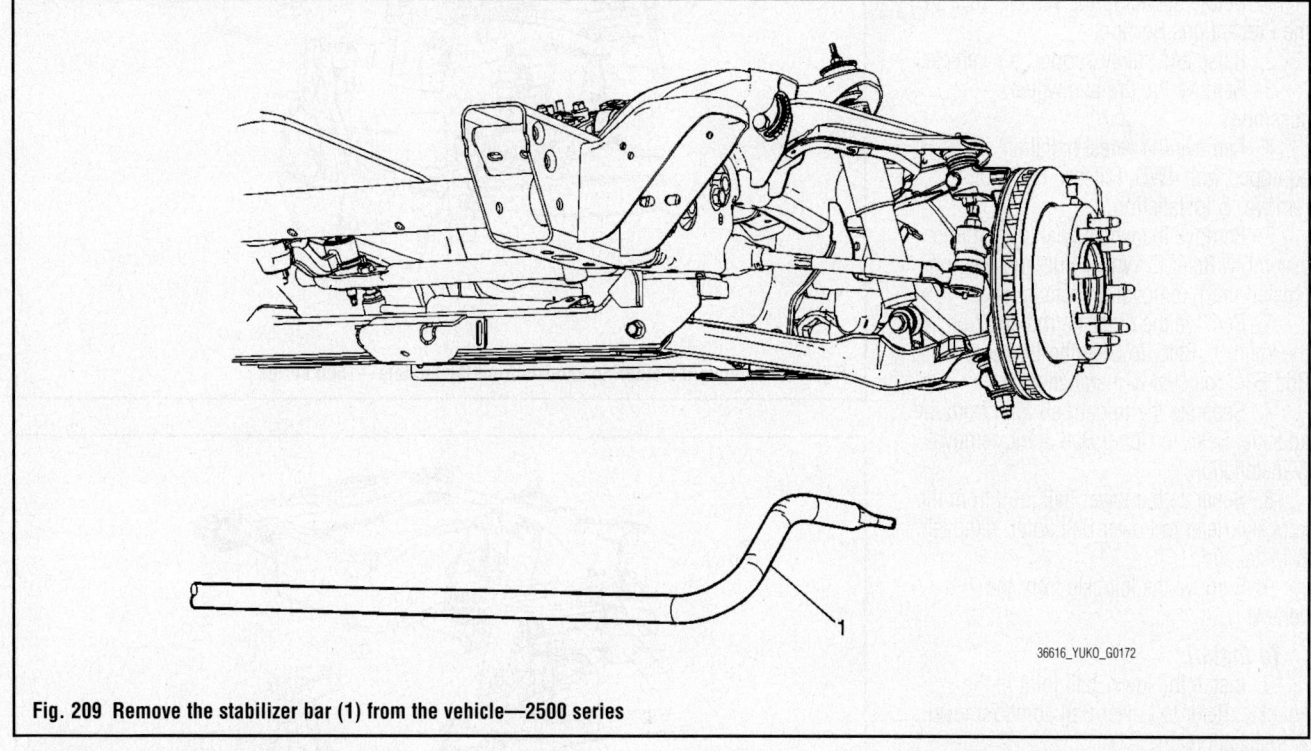

Fig. 208 Remove the stabilizer bar (1) from the vehicle—1500 series

36616_YUKO_G0173

Fig. 209 Remove the stabilizer bar (1) from the vehicle—2500 series

36616_YUKO_G0172

5. Remove the stabilizer bar link. Refer to Control Links, removal & installation.

6. Remove the stabilizer bar insulator.

7. Remove the stabilizer bar from the vehicle.

To install:

8. Install the stabilizer bar to the vehicle.

9. Install the stabilizer bar insulators. Tighten the clamp bolts to 37 ft. lbs. (50 nm).

➡**Ensure that the slit in the insulator is facing the front of the vehicle when installed.**

10. Installation continues in the reverse of the removal procedure.

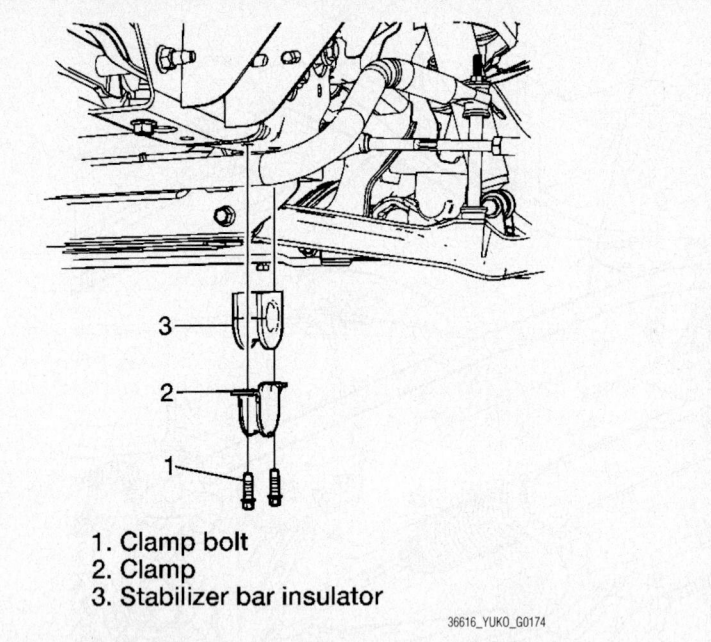

1. Clamp bolt
2. Clamp
3. Stabilizer bar insulator

36616_YUKO_G0174

Fig. 210 Install the stabilizer bar insulators—2500 series shown (1500 series similar)

STEERING KNUCKLE

REMOVAL & INSTALLATION

See Figures 211 and 212.

1. Before servicing the vehicle, refer to the Precautions Section.
2. Raise and safely support the vehicle.
3. Remove the tire and wheel assembly.
4. Remove the wheel halfshaft, if equipped with 4WD. Refer to Halfshafts, removal & installation.
5. Remove the wheel bearing and hub assembly. Refer to Wheel Hub and Bearing (sealed unit), removal & installation.
6. Remove the outer tie rod end from the knuckle. Refer to Steering Linkage, Tie Rod End, removal & installation.
7. Separate the upper ball joint from the knuckle. Refer to Upper Ball Joint, removal & installation.
8. Separate the lower ball joint from the knuckle. Refer to Lower Ball Joint, removal & installation.
9. Remove the knuckle from the vehicle.

To install:

10. Install the lower ball joint in the knuckle. Refer to Lower Ball Joint, removal & installation.
11. Install upper ball joint in the knuckle. Refer to Upper Ball Joint, removal & installation.
12. Install the outer tie rod end in the knuckle. Refer to Steering Linkage, Tie Rod End, removal & installation.

13. Install the wheel bearing and hub assembly. Refer to Front Wheel Hub, Bearing, and Seal Replacement.
14. Install the halfshaft, if equipped with 4WD. Refer to Halfshafts, removal & installation.
15. Install the tire and wheel.
16. Remove the support and lower the vehicle.
17. Verify the wheel alignment.

STRUT

REMOVAL & INSTALLATION

See Figures 213 and 214.

1. Before servicing the vehicle, refer to the Precautions Section.
2. Raise and safely support the vehicle.
3. Remove the tire and wheel assembly.
4. Disconnect the outer tie rod from the steering knuckle.
5. Remove the upper shock absorber mounting bolts.

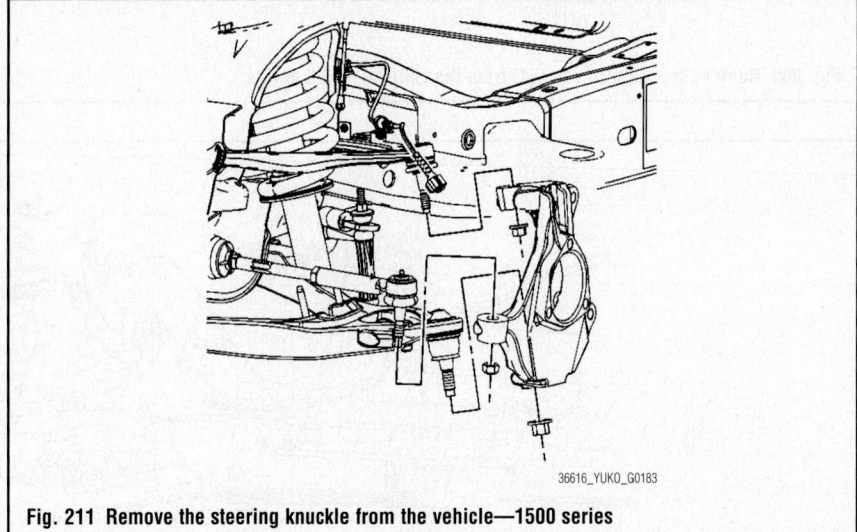
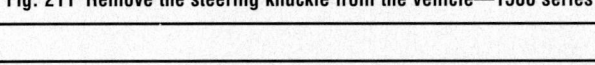

36616_YUKO_G0183

Fig. 211 Remove the steering knuckle from the vehicle—1500 series

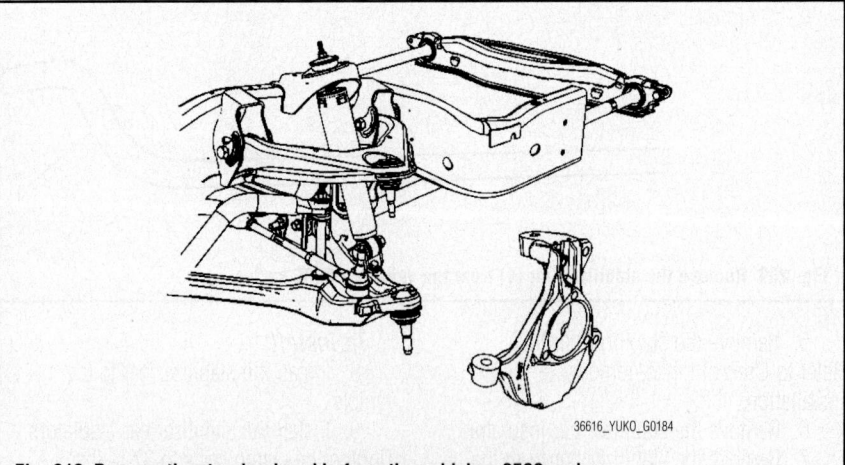

36616_YUKO_G0184

Fig. 212 Remove the steering knuckle from the vehicle—2500 series

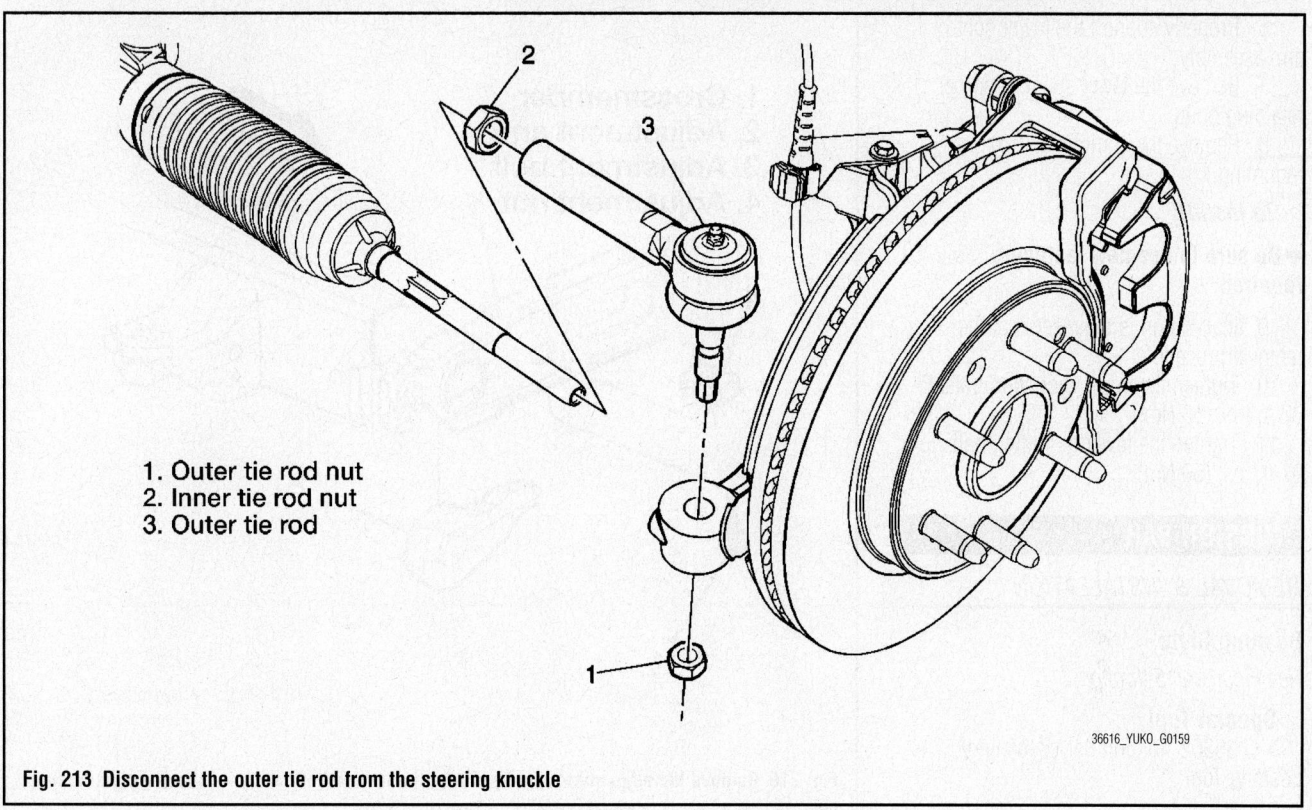

1. Outer tie rod nut
2. Inner tie rod nut
3. Outer tie rod

36616_YUKO_G0159

Fig. 213 Disconnect the outer tie rod from the steering knuckle

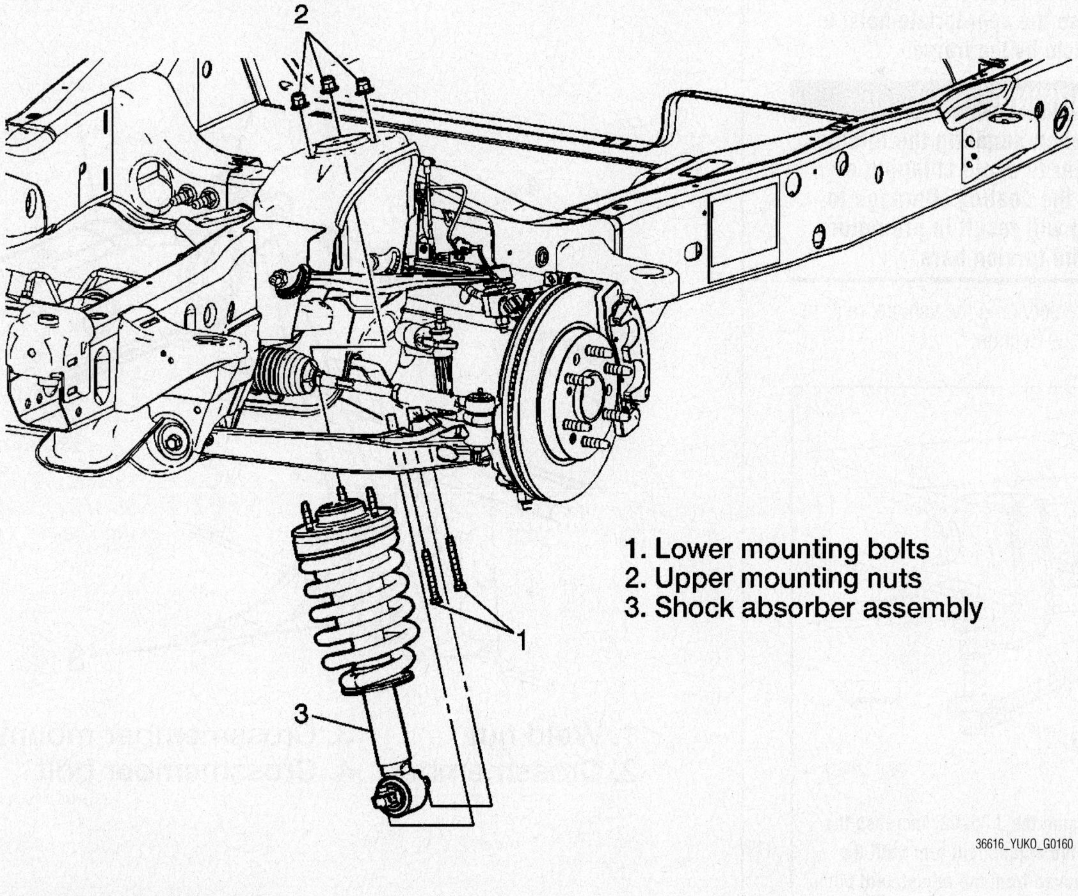

1. Lower mounting bolts
2. Upper mounting nuts
3. Shock absorber assembly

36616_YUKO_G0160

Fig. 214 Shock absorber assembly removal

6. Properly support the lower control arm assembly.

7. Remove the lower shock absorber retaining bolts.

8. Remove the component from its mounting.

To install:

➡ **Be sure to use new fasteners, as required.**

9. Installation is the reverse of the removal procedure.

10. Tighten the upper mounting bolts to 37 ft. lbs. (50 Nm).

11. Tighten the lower mounting bolts to 37 ft. lbs. (50 Nm).

TORSION BAR

REMOVAL & INSTALLATION

Bushing Style

See Figures 215 through 217.

Special Tool:
- J 36202: Torsion Bar Unloading/Loading Tool

➡ **When lifting the vehicle to service the torsion bars or related components, DO NOT lift the vehicle by the front suspension. Use the appropriate hoist to lift the vehicle by the frame.**

✳✳ WARNING

Use care when handling the torsion bars in order to avoid chipping or scratching the coating. Damage to the coating will result in premature failure of the torsion bars.

1. Before servicing the vehicle, refer to the Precautions Section.

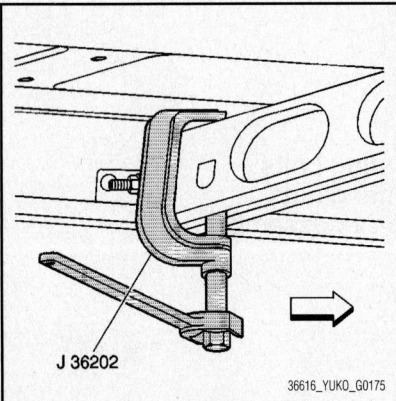

Fig. 215 Using the J 36202, increase the tension on the adjustment arm until the load is removed from the adjustment bolt and the adjuster nut

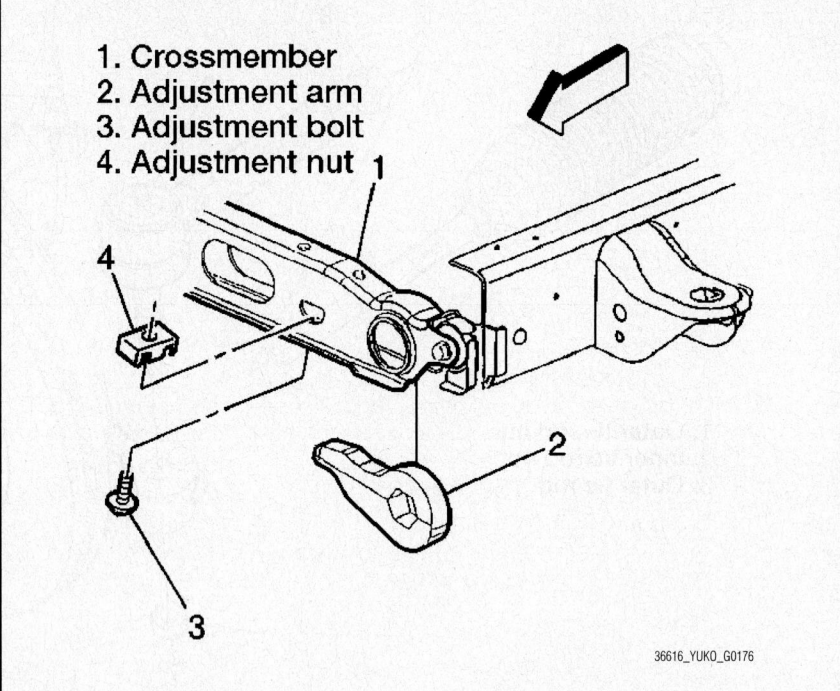

1. Crossmember
2. Adjustment arm
3. Adjustment bolt
4. Adjustment nut

36616_YUKO_G0176

Fig. 216 Remove the adjustment arm by sliding the torsion bar forward—bushing style torsion bar

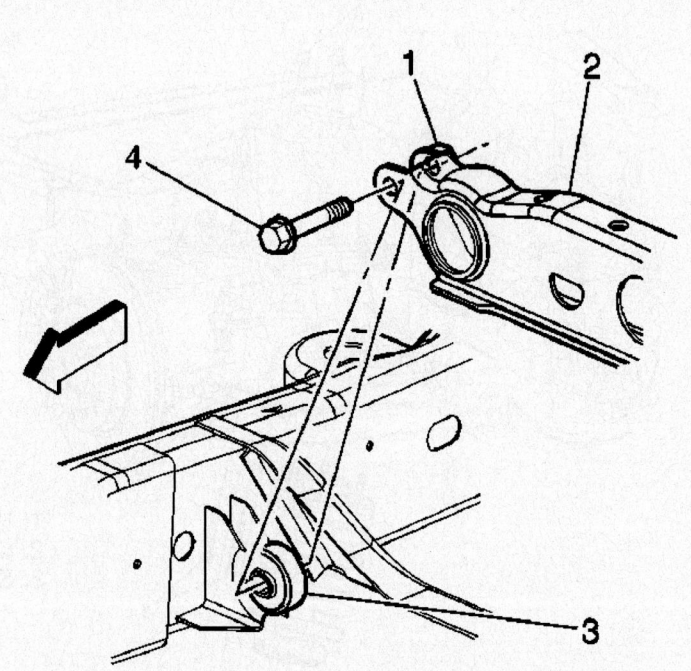

1. Weld nut
2. Crossmember
3. Crossmember mount
4. Crossmember bolt

36616_YUKO_G0177

Fig. 217 Remove the torsion bar from the crossmember—bushing style torsion bar

2. Raise and safely support the vehicle.

3. Install the J 36202 to the adjustment arm and the crossmember.

4. Using the J 36202, increase the tension on the adjustment arm until the load is removed from the adjustment bolt and the adjuster nut.

➡**Mark the adjustment bolt and count the number of times that is required to remove the adjustment bolt.**

5. Remove the adjustment bolt and the adjustment nut from the crossmember.

6. Remove the J 36202, allowing the torsion bar to unload.

7. Remove the adjustment arm by sliding the torsion bar forward.

8. Remove the torsion bar crossmember bolt from the weld nut.

9. Remove the crossmember from the crossmember mount.

10. Remove the torsion bar from the crossmember.

11. Remove the torsion bars from the vehicle.

To install:

➡**The left and right torsion bars are different and are not interchangeable.**

12. Position the torsion bar in the lower control arm.

13. Install the torsion bar in the crossmember on the crossmember mount.

14. Install the torsion bar crossmember bolt in the weld nut and tighten to 81 ft. lbs. (110 Nm).

15. Install the adjustment arm in the crossmember.

16. Install the adjuster bolt and the adjuster nut.

17. Install the torsion bar into the adjustment arm until the torsion bar is fully seated.

18. Install the J 36202 to the adjustment arm and the crossmember.

19. Using the J 36202, increase the tension on the adjustment arm to load the torsion bar.

20. Turn the adjuster bolt the same amount of turns as it took to remove it.

21. Remove the J 36202 from the crossmember.

22. Remove the safety stands and lower the vehicle.

23. Measure the Z height. Refer to Trim Height Inspection.

Link Style

See Figures 215, 218 and 219.

Special Tool:

• J 36202: Torsion Bar Unloading/
Loading Tool

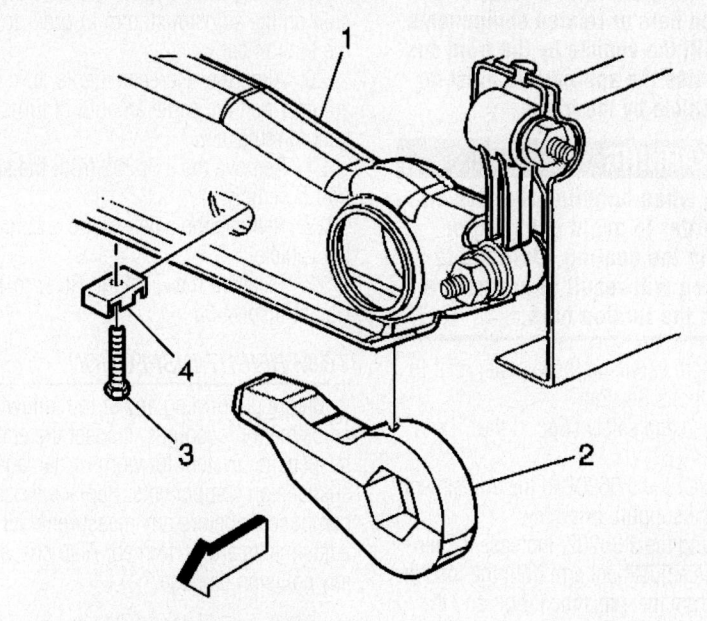

1. Support assembly
2. Adjustment arm
3. Adjustment bolt
4. Adjuster nut

36616_YUKO_G0181

Fig. 218 Remove the adjustment arm from the support assembly—link style torsion bar

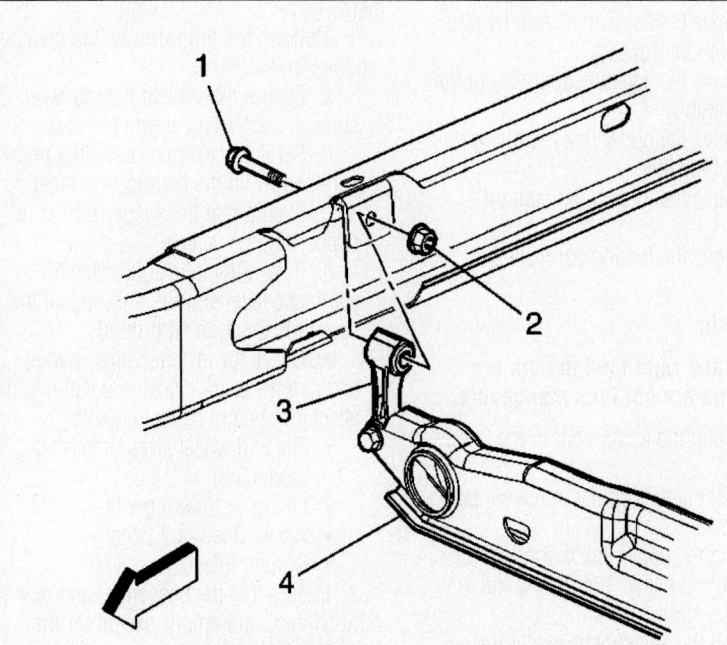

1. Upper link mounting bolt
2. Upper link mounting nut
3. Link
4. Torsion bar support assembly

36616_YUKO_G0182

Fig. 219 Removing the torsion bar—link style torsion bar

➡**When lifting the vehicle to service the torsion bars or related components, DO NOT lift the vehicle by the front suspension. Use the appropriate hoist to lift the vehicle by the frame.**

❈❈ WARNING

Use care when handling the torsion bars in order to avoid chipping or scratching the coating. Damage to the coating will result in premature failure of the torsion bars.

1. Before servicing the vehicle, refer to the Precautions Section.

2. Raise and safely support the vehicle.

3. Install the J 36202 to the adjustment arm and the support assembly.

4. Using the J 36202, increase the tension on the adjustment arm until the load is removed from the adjustment bolt and the adjuster nut.

➡**Create a reference point for the adjustment bolt to the support. Count the number of times that is required to remove the adjustment bolt.**

5. Remove the adjustment bolt and the adjuster nut from the support assembly.

6. Remove the J 36202, allowing the torsion bar to unload.

7. Remove the adjustment arm by sliding the torsion bar forward.

8. Remove the adjustment arm from the support assembly.

9. Remove the upper link mounting bolt and nut from the link.

10. Remove the torsion bar support assembly.

11. Remove the torsion bar from the vehicle.

To install:

➡**The left and right torsion bars are different and are not interchangeable.**

12. Position the torsion bar in the lower control arm.

13. Install the torsion bar in the support assembly.

14. Install the upper link mounting nut and the bolt in the link. Tighten the nut to 70 ft. lbs. (95 Nm).

15. Install the adjustment arm in the support assembly.

16. Install the adjuster bolt and the adjustment nut.

17. Slide the torsion bar rearward until the torsion bar is fully seated in the adjustment arm.

18. Install the J 36202 on the adjustment arm and the support assembly.

19. Using the J 36202, increase the tension on the adjustment arm in order to load the torsion bar.

20. Align the reference marks, turn the adjuster bolt the same amount of turns as it took to remove it.

21. Remove the J 36202 from the support assembly.

22. Remove the safety stand and lower the vehicle.

23. Measure the Z height. Refer to Trim Height Inspection.

TRIM HEIGHT INSPECTION

Before performing any of the following adjustment procedures, inspect the entire suspension system for worn or damaged suspension components. Replace those components before any measurements or adjustments are performed. Also check for any collision damage.

Trim Height Measurements

Trim height is a predetermined measurement relating to vehicle ride height. Incorrect trim heights can cause the vehicle to bottom over bumps, damage to the suspension components, and symptoms similar to wheel alignment problems. Check the trim heights when diagnosing suspension concerns and before checking the wheel alignment.

1. Perform the following before measuring the trim heights:

a. Ensure the vehicle is on a level surface, such as an alignment rack.

b. Set the tire pressures to the pressure shown on the certification label.

c. Ensure that the suspension is fully supporting the vehicle.

d. If the vehicle is equipped with automatic level control, ensure that the system is functioning properly.

e. Check for installed after market accessories or modifications that could affect trim height measurements:

- Tire and wheel sizes other than production
- Lifting or lowering kits
- Wheel Opening Flares
- Ground Effects

2. Ensure that the passenger and rear compartments are empty, except for the spare tire.

3. Check the fuel level. Add additional weight if necessary to simulate a full tank of fuel. One U.S. gallon of gasoline weighs approximate 6.5 lbs. One liter of gasoline weighs 0.70 kg.

4. Close all doors, lift gate/trunk, and the hood.

5. Remove the alignment rack floating pins, where applicable.

Z Height Measurement

See Figures 220 and 221.

➡**For vehicles equipped with torsion bars, check the Z height before performing the alignment.**

The Z height dimension measurement determines the proper ride height for the front end of the vehicle. Vehicles equipped with torsion bars use adjust arms in order to adjust the Z height dimension. Vehicles without torsion bars have no adjustment and could require replacement of suspension components.

1. Before servicing the vehicle, refer to the Precautions Section.

2. Jounce the front suspension of the vehicle by pushing the vehicle down and lifting up.

3. Allow the vehicle to settle and take a measurement.

➡**Perform the following steps for both sides of the vehicle.**

4. Set the top edge of the level on the reference surface of the steering knuckle and extend the level directly under the front end of the front attachment bolt of the lower control arm.

5. While keeping the level in contact with the knuckle reference surface, adjust the level up/down until the bubble indicates it is horizontally level.

6. Measure the distance between the center of the bolt and the top of the level for the first measurement.

7. Keep the top edge of the level on the reference surface of the steering knuckle and move the level directly under the rear end of the rear attachment bolt of the lower control arm.

8. Measure the distance between the center of the bolt and the top of the level for the second measurement.

9. Average the measurements between the step 6 and step 8.

10. Record the measurement.

Z Height Adjustment

See Figure 222.

1. Before servicing the vehicle, refer to the Precautions Section.

2. For vehicles equipped with torsion bar suspension, turn the bolt that contacts the torsion bar adjusting arm as needed.

3. For vehicles without torsion bars, replace worn or damaged components as necessary.

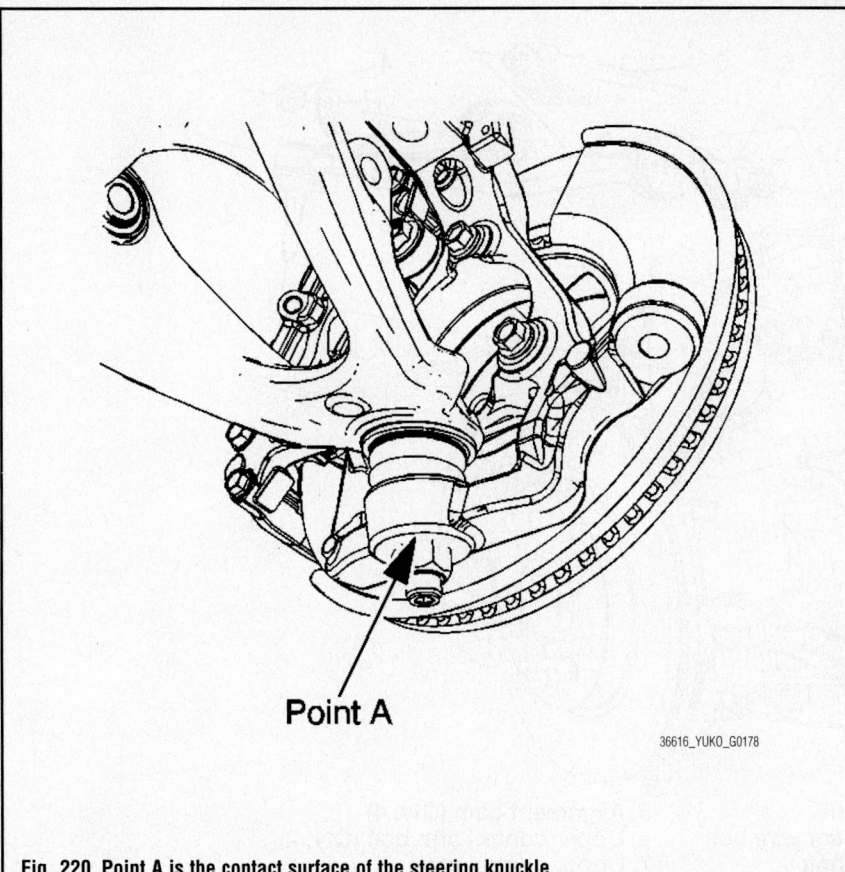

Fig. 220 Point A is the contact surface of the steering knuckle

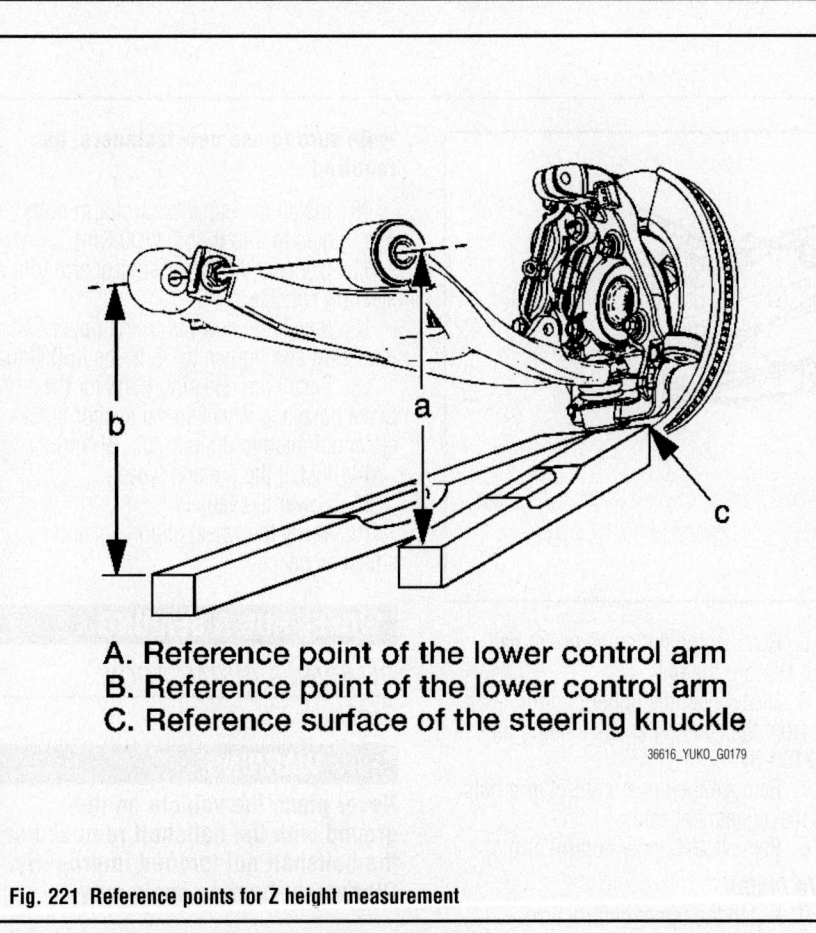

A. Reference point of the lower control arm
B. Reference point of the lower control arm
C. Reference surface of the steering knuckle

Fig. 221 Reference points for Z height measurement

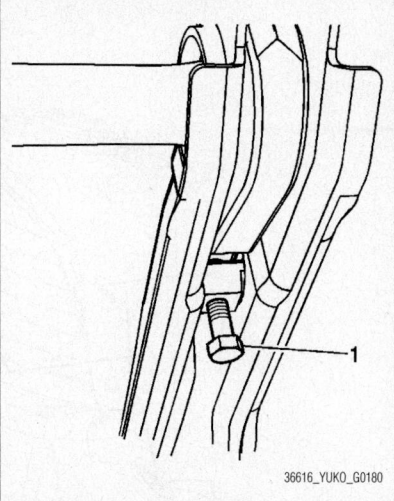

Fig. 222 For vehicles equipped with torsion bar suspension, turn the bolt (1) that contacts the torsion bar adjusting arm as needed

UPPER BALL JOINT

REMOVAL & INSTALLATION

The upper ball joint is integrated with the upper control arm. If worn or damaged, the entire control arm must be replaced.

UPPER CONTROL ARM

REMOVAL & INSTALLATION

See Figures 223 through 225.

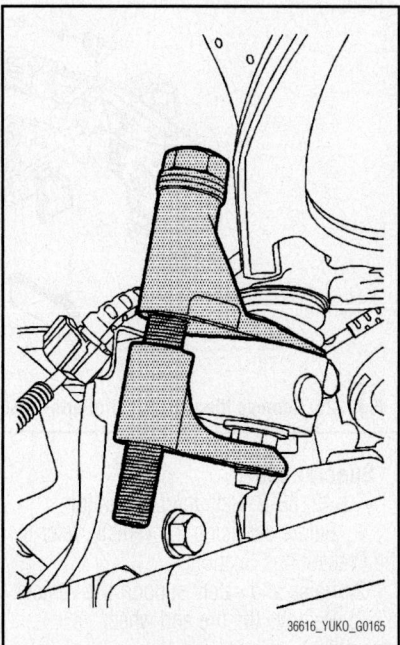

Fig. 223 Disconnect the upper control arm from the steering knuckle using the J-42188-B

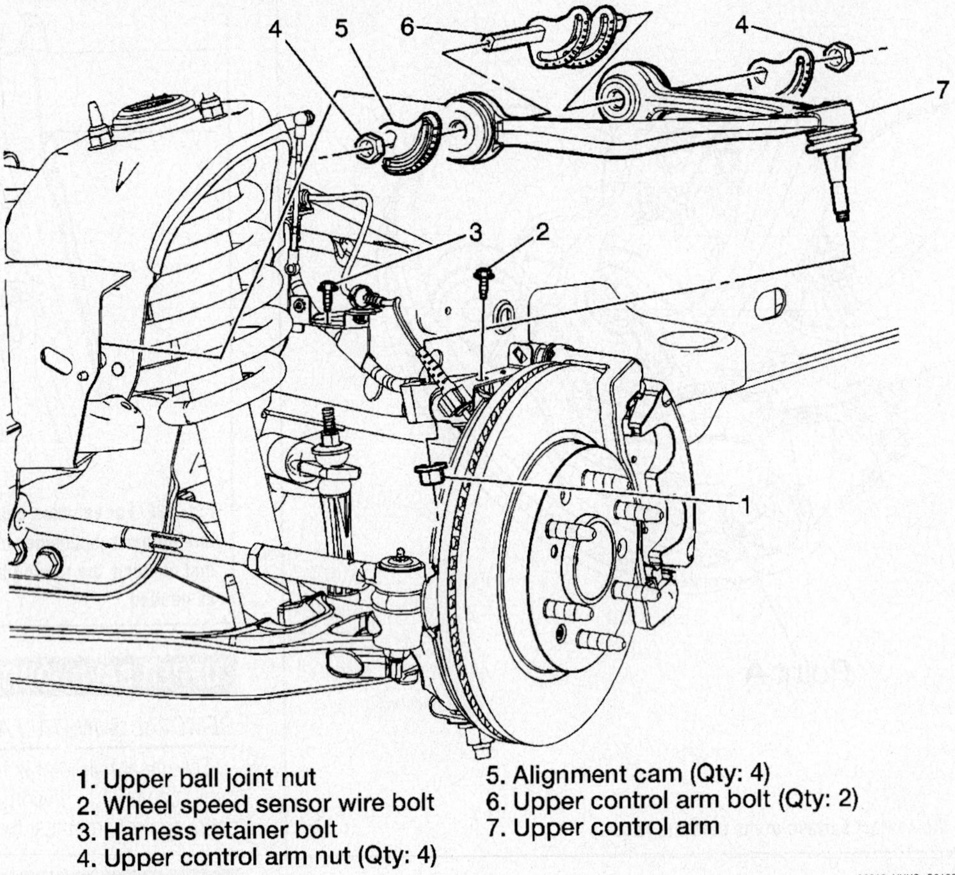

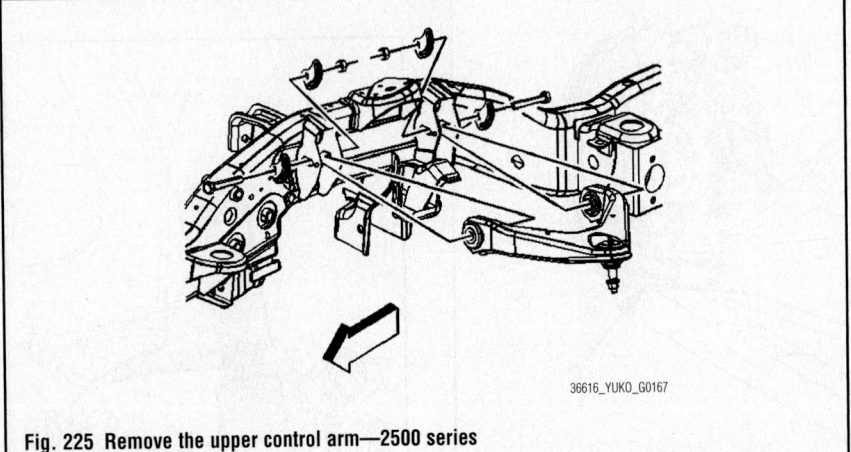

1. Upper ball joint nut
2. Wheel speed sensor wire bolt
3. Harness retainer bolt
4. Upper control arm nut (Qty: 4)
5. Alignment cam (Qty: 4)
6. Upper control arm bolt (Qty: 2)
7. Upper control arm

36616_YUKO_G0166

Fig. 224 Remove the upper control arm—1500 series

36616_YUKO_G0167

Fig. 225 Remove the upper control arm—2500 series

Special Tool:
• J-42188-B: Ball Joint Separator
1. Before servicing the vehicle, refer to the Precautions Section.
2. Raise and safely support the vehicle.
3. Remove the tire and wheel assembly.
4. Remove the retaining bolt for the brake hose and the wheel speed sensor brackets.

5. Remove the nut at the upper ball joint. Discard the nut.
6. Disconnect the upper control arm from the steering knuckle using the J-42188-B.
7. Remove the upper control arm nuts and the adjustment cams.
8. Remove the upper control arm.

To install:
9. Install the upper control arm.

➡Be sure to use new fasteners, as required.

10. Install the upper control arm bolts and tighten to 140 ft. lbs. (190 Nm).
11. Connect the upper control arm to the steering knuckle.
12. Install the new nut to the upper ball joint stud and tighten to 39 ft. lbs. (50 Nm).
13. Install the retaining bolts for the brake hose and wheel speed sensor brackets and tighten to 80 inch lbs. (9 Nm).
14. Install the tire and wheel.
15. Lower the vehicle.
16. Verify the wheel alignment and adjust as needed.

WHEEL HUB & BEARING

REMOVAL & INSTALLATION
See Figure 226.

❊❊ WARNING

Never place the vehicle on the ground with the halfshaft removed or the halfshaft nut torqued improperly. Otherwise, bearing seals may

become dislodged causing premature wear and/or damage to the hub and bearing assembly.

1. Before servicing the vehicle, refer to the Precautions Section.
2. Raise and safely support the vehicle.
3. Remove the tire and wheel.
4. Remove the brake rotor. Refer to Front Disc Brakes, Rotor, removal & installation.
5. Remove the wheel speed sensor and brake hose mounting bracket bolt from the steering knuckle.
6. Disconnect the electrical connection for the wheel speed sensor.
7. If equipped with 4WD:
   a. Remove the wheel halfshaft nut retaining cover.

✳✳ WARNING

Wheel halfshaft boots, seals, and clamps should be protected from sharp objects any time service is performed on or near the half-shaft(s). Damage to the boot(s), the seal(s), or the clamp(s) may cause lubricant to leak from the joint and lead to increased noise and possible failure of the wheel halfshaft.

   b. Wrap a shop towel around the inner and outer wheel halfshaft boot.
   c. Remove the halfshaft assembly retaining nut and washer. Refer to Halfshafts, removal & installation.
8. Remove the wheel hub and bearing mounting bolts.
9. Remove the wheel hub and bearing and splash shield from the vehicle.

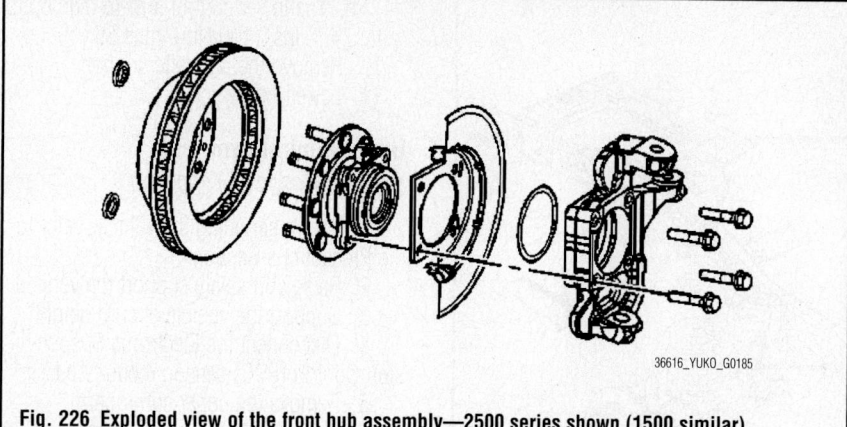

Fig. 226 Exploded view of the front hub assembly—2500 series shown (1500 similar)

36616_YUKO_G0185

10. Remove the O-ring seal from the steering knuckle bore.
11. Remove the wheel speed sensor from the wheel hub and bearing.
12. Clean and inspect the O-ring seal.
13. Replace the seal if the following conditions exist:
   • Nicks
   • Cuts
   • Dry or brittle
   • Compression set

To install:
14. Clean all corrosion or contaminates from the steering knuckle bore, and the hub and bearing assembly.
15. Lubricate the steering knuckle bore with wheel bearing grease, or the equivalent.
16. Install the O-ring to the steering knuckle.
17. Install the wheel speed sensor to the wheel hub and bearing. Tighten the sensor mounting bolt to 13 ft. lbs. (18 Nm).
18. Install the wheel hub and bearing and splash shield to the vehicle.

19. Install the wheel hub and bearing mounting bolts. Tighten the wheel hub-to-knuckle bolts to 133 ft. lbs. (180 Nm).
20. If equipped with 4WD, install the nut and washer retaining the wheel halfshaft assembly to the wheel hub and bearing. Refer to Halfshafts, removal & installation.
21. Connect the electrical connection for the wheel speed sensor.
22. Install the wheel speed sensor and brake hose mounting bracket bolt to the steering knuckle. Tighten the bolt to 106 inch lbs. (12 Nm).
23. Install the brake rotor. Refer to Front Disc Brakes, Rotor, removal & installation.
24. Install the tire and wheel.

ADJUSTMENT

Both 2WD and 4WD models have sealed front wheel bearings. These wheel bearings are designed to last for the life of the vehicle and are unable to be adjusted. If a wheel bearing exhibits any roughness or resistance to rotation, the bearing must be replaced.

SUSPENSION

COIL SPRING

REMOVAL & INSTALLATION

See Figure 227.

All 1500 series utility vehicles use a 5-link rear suspension system. The rear axle is attached to the frame with the upper control arms, lower control arms, and a track bar. Two coil springs and a link-mounted rear stabilizer shaft complete the system.
1. Before servicing the vehicle, refer to the Precautions Section.
2. Raise and safely support the vehicle.
3. Support the rear axle.
4. Disconnect the Electronic Suspension Control (ESC) sensor, if equipped.

5. Remove the stabilizer shaft link retaining nut from the frame. Refer to Control Arms/Links, removal & installation.
6. Remove the lower shock absorber nut and bolt from the rear axle.
7. Lower the rear axle until the springs are fully unloaded.

➡**Note the orientation of the spring as they are directional.**

8. Remove the coil spring and the upper insulator.

To install:
9. Install the coil spring and the upper insulator.
10. Raise the rear axle.
11. Install the lower shock absorber

REAR SUSPENSION

retaining nut and bolt to the rear axle and tighten to 85 ft. lbs. (115 Nm).
12. Install the stabilizer shaft link to the frame and tighten 48 ft. lbs. (65 Nm), plus 40°. Refer to Control Arms/Links, removal & installation.
13. Connect the ESC sensor, if equipped.
14. Remove the rear axle support.
15. Lower the vehicle.

CONTROL ARMS/LINKS

REMOVAL & INSTALLATION

Lower Control Arm

See Figure 228.

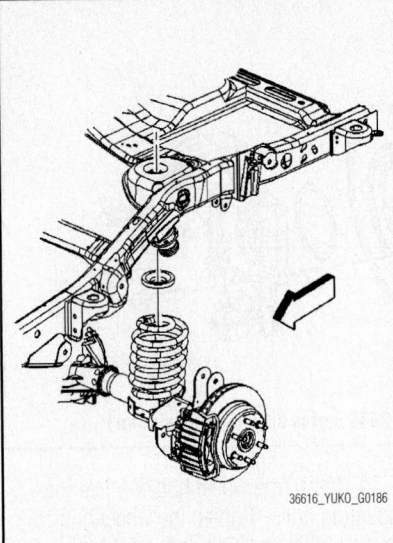

Fig. 227 Rear coil spring removal—1500 series

1. Before servicing the vehicle, refer to the Precautions Section.
2. Raise and safely support the vehicle.
3. Support the vehicle at curb height.
4. Remove the lower control arm retaining nuts.
5. Remove the lower control arm retaining bolt.
6. Remove the lower control arm.

To install:
7. Install the lower control arm.
8. Install the lower control arm retaining bolts.

➡**Do not tighten the bolts unless the suspension is at ride height.**

9. Install the lower control arm retaining nut and tighten:
   a. The lower control arm-to-frame bolts to: 74 ft. lbs. (100 Nm), plus 55°.

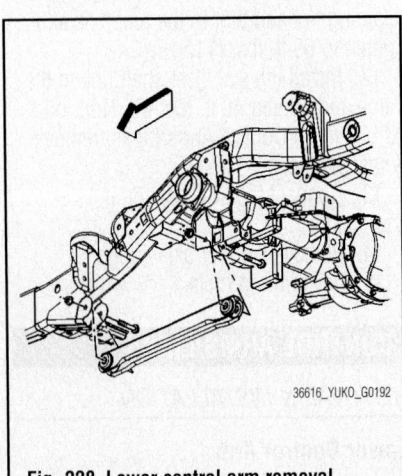

Fig. 228 Lower control arm removal

   b. The lower control arm-to-axle bolts to: 74 ft. lbs. (100 Nm), plus 55°.
10. Remove the rear axle support.
11. Lower the vehicle.

Upper Control Arm

See Figures 229 and 230.

1. Before servicing the vehicle, refer to the Precautions Section.
2. Raise and safely support the vehicle.
3. Support the vehicle at curb height.
4. Disconnect the Electronic Suspension Control (ESC) sensor, if equipped.
5. Remove the upper control arm retaining nut and bolt from the frame bracket.
6. Remove the upper control arm retaining nut and bolt from the axle bracket.
7. Remove the upper control arm.

To install:
8. Install the upper control arm.
9. Install the upper control arm retaining bolt and nut to the axle bracket.
10. Install the upper control arm retaining bolt to the frame bracket.

Fig. 229 Remove the upper control arm retaining nut and bolt from the frame bracket

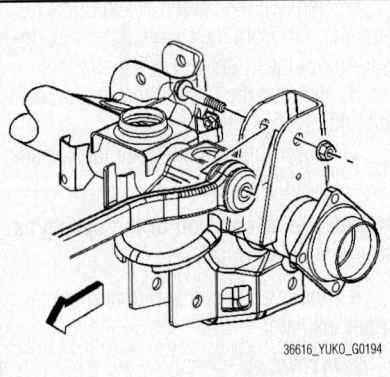

Fig. 230 Remove the upper control arm retaining nut and bolt from the axle bracket

➡**Do not tighten the nuts unless the suspension is at the curb height position.**

11. Install the upper control arm retaining nut and tighten to 118 ft. lbs. (160 Nm).
12. Connect the ESC sensor, if equipped.
13. Lower the vehicle.

Stabilizer Control Link

See Figure 231.

1. Before servicing the vehicle, refer to the Precautions Section.
2. Raise and safely support the vehicle.
3. Remove the stabilizer control link nuts and bolts.

➡**Use an Allen wrench to keep the lower stabilizer shaft ball stud from rotating while removing the outer nut.**

4. Remove the control link.

To install:
5. Install the stabilizer control link to the vehicle.

➡**When installing the inner stabilizer shaft link nut, ensure that it is tighten securely against the ball joint.**

6. Install the bolts and nuts and tighten to 48 ft. lbs. (65 Nm), plus 40°.
7. Lower the vehicle.

LEAF SPRING

REMOVAL & INSTALLATION

See Figures 232 through 234.

1. Before servicing the vehicle, refer to the Precautions Section.
2. Raise and safely support the vehicle.
3. Support the rear axle independently in order to relieve the tension on the leaf springs.
4. Remove the trailer hitch, if equipped.
5. Remove the fuel tank. Refer to Fuel Tank, removal & installation.
6. Remove the U-bolt nuts and the U-bolts.
7. Remove the spring spacer, if equipped.
8. Remove the anchor plate.
9. Remove the rear spring bracket nut and bolt.
10. Remove the front spring bracket nut and bolt.
11. Remove the leaf spring assembly from the vehicle.
12. Remove the rear leaf spring shackle, if needed.

To install:
13. Install the leaf spring assembly to the vehicle.

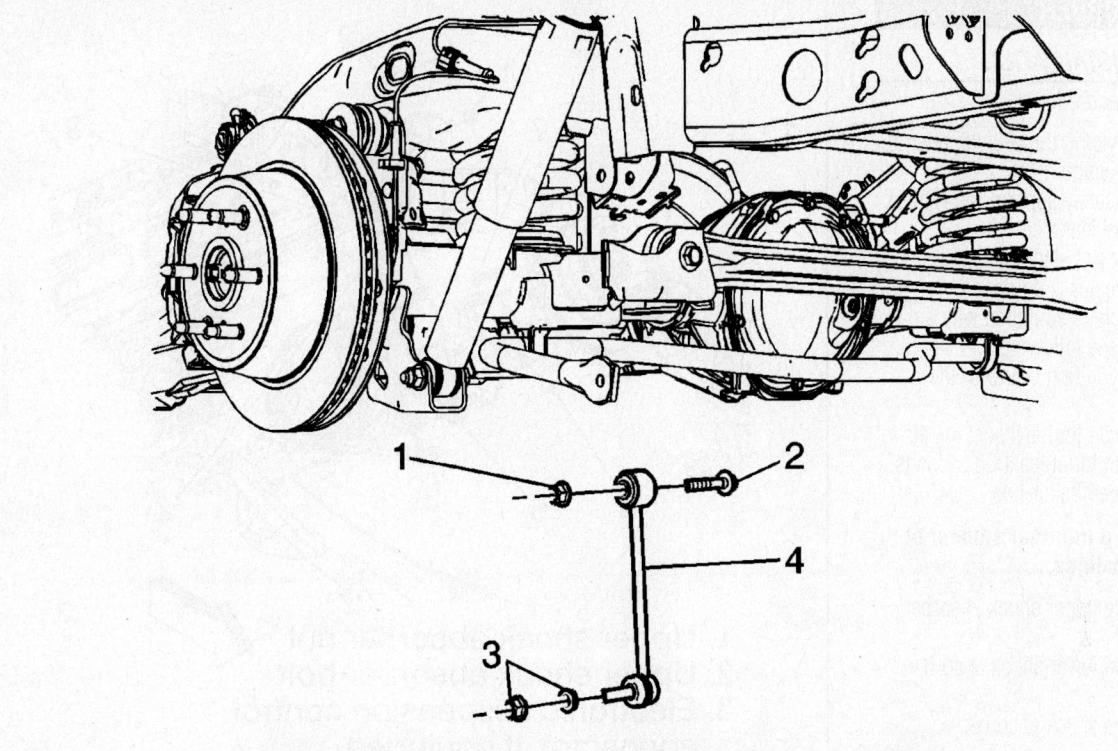

1. Upper link nut
2. Upper link bolt
3. Lower shaft nut (Qty: 2)
4. Rear stabilizer shaft

36616_YUKO_G0195

Fig. 231 Stabilizer control link removal

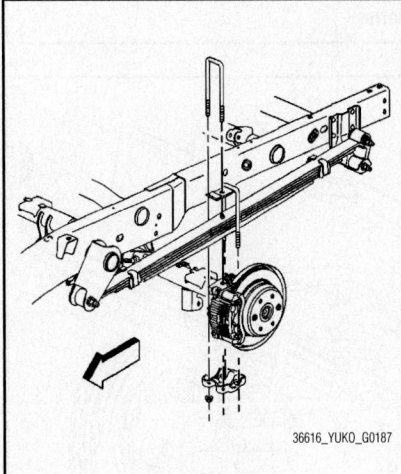

36616_YUKO_G0187

Fig. 232 Remove the U-bolts and anchor plate

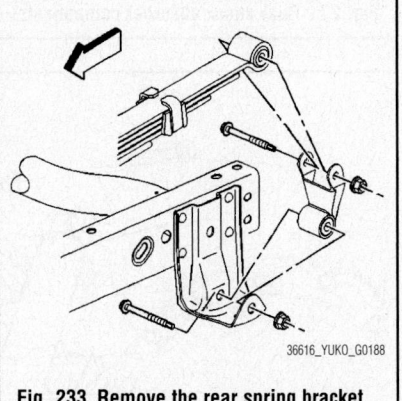

36616_YUKO_G0188

Fig. 233 Remove the rear spring bracket nut and bolt

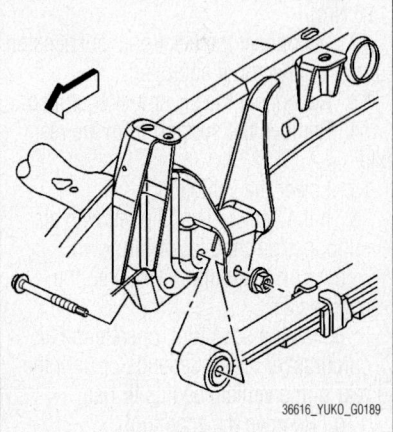

36616_YUKO_G0189

Fig. 234 Remove the front spring bracket nut and bolt

14. Install the front bolt and nuts but do not tighten.

15. Install the rear leaf spring hanger to shackle nut and bolt.

➡**Be sure to use new fasteners, as required.**

16. Install the rear leaf spring front nut and tighten to 125 ft. lbs. (170 Nm), plus 48°.

17. Tighten the rear leaf spring hanger nut and bolt to 70 ft. lbs. (95 Nm).

➡**Do not reuse the U-bolts.**

18. Install the spring spacer, if equipped.
19. Install the U-bolts.
20. Raise the rear axle until it touches the leaf spring and begins to apply light compression to the leaf spring.
21. Install the anchor plate.
22. Install and tighten the U-bolts in a criss-cross sequence:

a. 1500 series to 74 ft. lbs. (100 Nm).
b. 2500 series 118 ft. lbs. (160 Nm).

23. Install the fuel tank. Refer to Fuel Tank, removal & installation.
24. Install the trailer hitch, if equipped.
25. Remove the rear axle support.
26. Remove the safety stands.
27. Lower the vehicle.

SHOCK ABSORBER

REMOVAL & INSTALLATION

See Figures 235 and 236.

1. Before servicing the vehicle, refer to the Precautions Section.
2. Raise and safely support the vehicle.
3. Support the rear axle.
4. Disconnect the electronic suspension control connector, if equipped.
5. If the vehicle is equipped with air leveling, perform the following:
   a. Turn the ignition ON, with the engine OFF.
   b. With a scan tool, exhaust the air from the system for at least 60 seconds.
   c. Disconnect the air line.

➡**There will be a minimal amount of air left in the air lines.**

6. Remove the upper shock absorber nut and the bolt.
7. Remove the lower shock absorber nut and the bolt.
8. Remove the shock absorber.

To install:

9. Install the shock absorber.
10. Install the upper shock absorber nut and the bolt.
11. Install the lower shock absorber nut and bolt. Tighten the upper and lower shock absorber nuts and to 85 ft. lbs. (115 Nm).
12. Reconnect the electronic suspension control connector, if equipped.
13. Reconnect the air line, if equipped.
14. Remove the support from the rear axle.
15. Lower the vehicle.
16. If the vehicle is equipped with air leveling, perform the following:
    a. Turn the ignition ON, with the engine OFF.
    b. With a scan tool, operate the air compressor for 30 seconds or until the rear of the vehicle begins to rise.
    c. Remove the scan tool.
    d. Cycle the ignition OFF, then back ON (with the engine ON) to allow the air suspension system to regain the desired rear suspension position.
    e. Check for air leakage in the system.

WHEEL BEARINGS

REMOVAL & INSTALLATION

For wheel bearing removal, refer to Rear Drive Axle, Axle Shaft, Bearing & Seal, removal & installation.

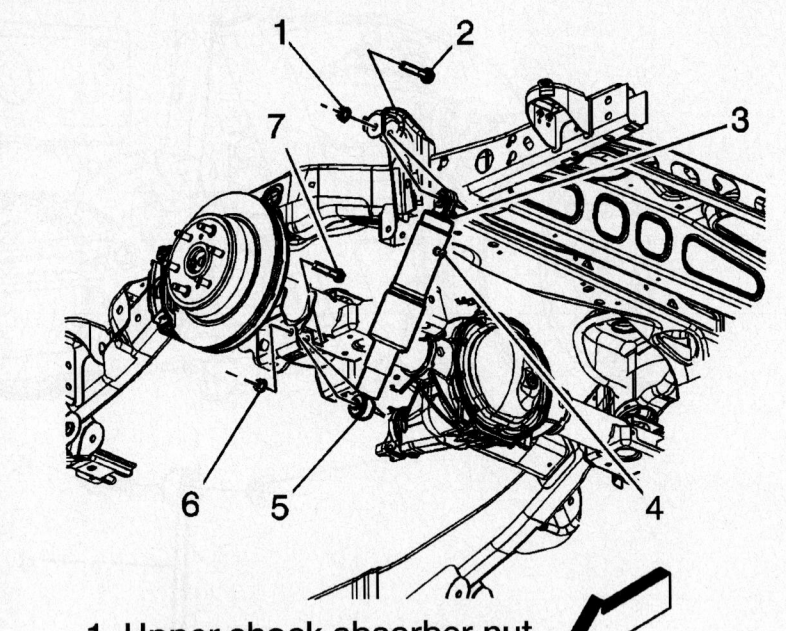

1. Upper shock absorber nut
2. Upper shock absorber bolt
3. Electronic suspension control connector, if equipped
4. Air line, if equipped
5. Shock absorber
6. Lower shock absorber nut
7. Lower shock absorber bolt

36616_YUKO_G0190

Fig. 235 Rear shock absorber components—1500 series

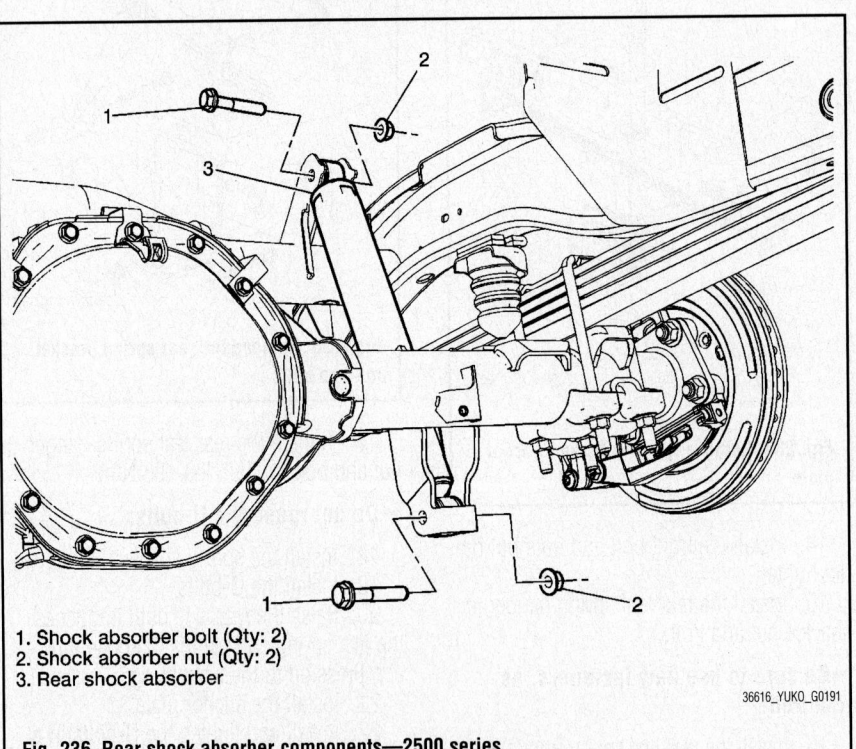

1. Shock absorber bolt (Qty: 2)
2. Shock absorber nut (Qty: 2)
3. Rear shock absorber

36616_YUKO_G0191

Fig. 236 Rear shock absorber components—2500 series

CHEVROLET AND PONTIAC

Aveo • Aveo 5 • G3

7

SPECIFICATIONS AND MAINTENANCE CHARTS

VEHICLE AND ENGINE IDENTIFICATION CHART

Engine								Model Year	
Code	Liters	Cu. In.	Cyl.	Fuel Sys.	Engine Type	Eng. Mfg.		Code	Year
6	1.6	97.5	4	MPI	DOHC	Daewoo		8	2008
E	1.6	97.5	4	MPI	DOHC	Daewoo		9	2009

MPI: Multi-port Fuel Injection

36616_AVEO_C0001

GENERAL ENGINE SPECIFICATIONS

Year	Model	Engine Displ. Liters	Engine VIN	Net Horsepower @ rpm	Net Torque @ rpm (ft. lbs.)	Bore x Stroke (in.)	Com-pression Ratio	Oil Pressure @ rpm
2008	Aveo	1.6	6	103@6200	107@3400	3.10x3.21	9.5:1	①
	Aveo 5	1.6	6	103@6200	107@3400	3.10x3.21	9.5:1	①
2009	Aveo	1.6	E	107@6400	105@3800	3.10x3.21	10.8:0	②
	Aveo 5	1.6	E	107@6400	105@3800	3.10x3.21	10.8:0	②
	G3	1.6	E	107@6400	105@3800	3.10x3.21	10.8:0	②

① The 1.6L LXT engine minimum oil pressure at idle should be 8.88 psi (30 kpa).

② The 1.6L LXV engine minimum oil pressure at idle should be 18.85 psi (130 kpa).

36616_AVEO_C0002

GASOLINE ENGINE TUNE-UP SPECIFICATIONS

Year	Engine Displacement Liters	Engine VIN	Spark Plugs Gap (in.)	Ignition Timing (deg.) MT	AT	Fuel Pump (psi)	Idle Speed (rpm) MT	AT	Valve Clearance In.	Ex.
2008	1.6	6	0.039-0.043	5	5	55-62	①	①	HYD	HYD
2009	1.6	E	0.039-0.043	5	5	53-60	①	①	HYD	HYD

NOTE: The Vehicle Emission Control Information label often reflects specification changes changes made during production.

The label figures must be used if they differ from those in this chart.

HYD: Hydraulic

① Controlled by the Powertrain Control Module (PCM) and cannot be manually adjusted.

36616_AVEO_C0003

CAPACITIES

Year	Model	Engine Displacement Liters	Engine ID/VIN	Engine Oil with Filter (qts.)	Transmission (pts.) 5-Spd	Transmission (pts.) Auto.	Drive Axle (front)	Fuel Tank (gal.)	Cooling System (qts.)
2008	Aveo	1.6	6	4.8	4.0	12.4 ①	②	11.9	6.7
	Aveo5	1.6	6	4.8	4.0	12.4 ①	②	11.9	6.7
2009	Aveo	1.6	E	4.8	4.0	12.4 ①	②	11.9	6.7
	Aveo5	1.6	E	4.8	4.0	12.4 ①	②	11.9	6.7
	G3	1.6	E	4.8	4.0	12.4 ①	②	11.9	6.7

NOTE: All capacities are approximate. Add fluid gradually and check to be sure a proper fluid level is obtained.

① Dry fill (Filter and fluid change 4.4 pts.)

② Included in transaxle capacity

36616_AVEO_C0004

FLUID SPECIFICATIONS

Year	Model	Engine Disp. Liters (VIN)	Engine Oil	Auto. Transaxle	Manual Transaxle	Power Steering Fluid	Brake Master Cylinder ①	Engine Coolant
2008	Aveo	1.6 (6)	5W-30	Type T-IV	75W-85 GL-4	DEXTRON® VI	DOT 3	Dexcool®
	Aveo 5	1.6 (6)	5W-30	Type T-IV	75W-85 GL-4	DEXTRON® VI	DOT 3	Dexcool®
2009	Aveo	1.6 (E)	5W-30	Type T-IV	75W-85 GL-4	DEXTRON® VI	DOT 3	Dexcool®
	Aveo 5	1.6 (E)	5W-30	Type T-IV	75W-85 GL-4	DEXTRON® VI	DOT 3	Dexcool®
	G3	1.6 (E)	5W-30	Type T-IV	75W-85 GL-4	DEXTRON® VI	DOT 3	Dexcool®

DOT: Department Of Transpotation

① Equivalent DOT 4 may be substituted

36616_AVEO_C0005

VALVE SPECIFICATIONS

Year	Engine Displacement Liters	Engine VIN	Seat Angle (deg.)	Face Angle (deg.)	Spring Test Pressure (lbs. @ in.)	Spring Installed Height (in.)	Stem-to-Guide Clearance (in.) Intake	Stem-to-Guide Clearance (in.) Exhaust	Stem Diameter (in.) Intake	Stem Diameter (in.) Exhaust
2008	1.6	6	44.5-45	45-45.25	NA	NA	NA	NA	0.2340-0.2350	0.2336-0.2342
2009	1.6	E	44.5-45	45-45.25	NA	NA	NA	NA	0.1955-0.1961	0.1945-0.1955

36616_AVEO_C0008

CAMSHAFT AND BEARING SPECIFICATIONS CHART

All measurements are given in inches.

Year	Engine Displacement Liters	Engine VIN	Journal Diameter	Brg. Oil Clearance	Shaft End-play	Runout	Journal Bore	Lobe Lift Intake	Lobe Lift Exhaust
2008	1.6	6	①	NA	0.0039-0.0079	NA	NA	0.2830	0.2830
2009	1.6	E	②	NA	0.0051-0.0085	NA	NA	1.8228	1.7835

NA: Not Available

① No. 1: 1.1785-1.1791 in.

  Nos. 2-5: 1.0604-1.0610 in.

② No. 1-5: 1.1000-1.1008 in.

36616_AVEO_C0007

CRANKSHAFT AND CONNECTING ROD SPECIFICATIONS

All measurements are given in inches.

Year	Engine Displ. Liters	Engine VIN	Crankshaft Main Brg. Journal Dia.	Crankshaft Main Brg. Oil Clearance	Crankshaft Shaft End-play	Crankshaft Thrust on No.	Connecting Rod Journal Diameter	Connecting Rod Oil Clearance	Connecting Rod Side Clearance
2008	1.6	6	2.1640-2.1650	0.0010-0.0017	0.0020-0.0110	NA	1.6900	0.0007-0.0027	0.0027-0.0090
2009	1.6	E	2.1646-2.1652	0.0006-0.0019	0.0039-0.0080	NA	1.8110	0.0007-0.0025	0.0028-0.0095

NA: Not available

36616_AVEO_C0006

PISTON AND RING SPECIFICATIONS

All measurements are given in inches.

Year	Engine Displ. Liters	Engine VIN	Piston Clearance	Ring Gap Top Comp.	Ring Gap Bottom Comp.	Ring Gap Oil Control	Ring Side Clearance Top Comp.	Ring Side Clearance Bottom Comp.	Ring Side Clearance Oil Control
2008	1.6	6	0.0008-0.0016	0.0060-0.0120	0.0120-0.0190	NA	0.0019-0.0031	0.0020-0.0030	NA
2009	1.6	E	0.0008-0.0016	0.0059-0.0118	0.0118-0.0197	0.0079-0.0276	0.0016-0.0031	0.0012-0.0028	0.0024-0.0059

NA: Not available

36616_AVEO_C0009

TORQUE SPECIFICATIONS
All readings in ft. lbs.

Year	Engine VIN	Engine Displacement Liters	Cylinder Head Bolts	Main Bearing Bolts	Rod Bearing Bolts	Crankshaft Damper Bolts	Flywheel Bolts	Manifold Intake	Manifold Exhaust	Spark Plugs	Oil Pan Drain Plug
2008	6	1.6	①	②	③	④	⑤	18	18	18	40
2009	6	1.6	①	②	③	④	⑤	18	18	18	40

① Step 1: 18 ft. lbs.
Step 2: plus 60 degrees
Step 3: plus 60 degrees
Step 4: plus 60 degrees
Step 4: plus 10 degrees

② Step 1: 37 ft. lbs.
Step 2: plus 45 degrees
Step 3: plus 15 degrees

③ Step 1: 18 ft. lbs.
Step 2: plus 30 degrees
Step 3: plus 15 degrees

④ Step 1: 70 ft. lbs.
Step 2: plus 30 degrees
Step 3: plus 15 degrees

⑤ Step 1: 25 ft. lbs.
Step 2: plus 30 degrees
Step 3: plus 15 degrees

36616_AVEO_C0010

WHEEL ALIGNMENT

Year	Model		Caster Range (+/-Deg.)	Caster Preferred Setting (Deg.)	Camber Range (+/-Deg.)	Camber Preferred Setting (Deg.)	Toe-in (Deg.)
2008	Aveo	Front	0.75	2.50	0.75	-0.40	0.07+/-0.17
		Rear	—	—	0.50	-1.50	0.25+/-0.33
	Aveo5	Front	0.75	2.50	0.75	-0.40	0.07+/-0.17
		Rear	—	—	0.50	-1.50	0.25+/-0.33
2009	Aveo	Front	0.75	2.50	0.75	-0.40	0.07+/-0.17
		Rear	—	—	0.50	-1.50	0.25+/-0.33
	Aveo5	Front	0.75	2.50	0.75	-0.40	0.07+/-0.17
		Rear	—	—	0.50	-1.50	0.25+/-0.33
	G3	Front	0.75	2.50	0.75	-0.40	0.07+/-0.17
		Rear	—	—	0.50	-1.50	0.25+/-0.33

36616_AVEO_C0011

TIRE AND WHEEL SPECIFICATIONS

Year	Model	OEM Tires		Tire Pressures (psi)		Wheel Size	Ball Joint Inspection	Lug Nut Torque (ft. lbs.)
		Standard	Optional	Front	Rear			
2008	Aveo	P185/60R14	P185/55R15	32	32	①	②	88
	Aveo5	P185/60R14	P185/55R15	32	32	①	②	88
2009	Aveo	P185/60R14	P185/55R15	32	32	①	②	88
	Aveo5	P185/60R14	P185/55R15	32	32	①	②	88
	G3	P185/60R14	P185/55R15	32	32	①	②	88

OEM: Original Equipment Manufacturer

PSI: Pounds Per Square Inch

① 14x5.5J and 15x6J

② Relpace if any noticable movement is present.

36616_AVEO_C0013

BRAKE SPECIFICATIONS

All measurements in inches unless noted

Year	Model		Brake Disc			Brake Drum Diameter			Minimum Lining Thickness	Brake Caliper	
			Original Thickness	Minimum Thickness	Maximum Runout	Original Inside Diameter	Max. Wear Limit	Maximum Machine Diameter		Bracket Bolts (ft. lbs.)	Mounting Bolts (ft. lbs.)
2008	Aveo	F	0.945	0.866	0.002	—	—	—	0.280	70	20
		R	—	—	—	7.870	7.910	NA	0.020	—	—
	Aveo5	F	0.945	0.866	0.002	—	—	—	0.280	70	20
		R	—	—	—	7.870	7.910	NA	0.020	—	—
2009	Aveo	F	0.945	0.866	0.002	—	—	—	0.280	70	20
		R	—	—	—	7.870	7.910	NA	0.020	—	—
	Aveo5	F	0.945	0.866	0.002	—	—	—	0.280	70	20
		R	—	—	—	7.870	7.910	NA	0.020	—	—
	G3	F	0.945	0.866	0.002	—	—	—	0.280	70	20
		R	—	—	—	7.870	7.910	NA	0.020	—	—

NA: Not available

36616_AVEO_C0012

SCHEDULED MAINTENANCE INTERVALS
2008-09 CHEVROLET AVEO, AVEO-5 & PONTIAC G3

TO BE SERVICED	TYPE OF SERVICE	VEHICLE MILEAGE INTERVAL (x1000)												
		7.5	15	22.5	30	37.5	45	52.5	60	67.5	75	82.5	90	97.5
Engine oil & filter	R	✓	✓	✓	✓	✓	✓	✓	✓	✓	✓	✓	✓	✓
Rotate tires	S/I	✓	✓	✓	✓	✓	✓	✓	✓	✓	✓	✓	✓	✓
Engine coolant strength hoses & clamps	S/I													
Air cleaner filter	R				✓				✓				✓	
Automatic transmission fluid & filter	R												✓	
Engine coolant	R				✓				✓				✓	
PCV valve	S/I				✓				✓				✓	
Spark plugs	R				✓				✓				✓	
Drive belts	S/I		✓		✓		✓		✓		✓		✓	
Front & rear brakes ①	S/I													
Fuel filter	R										✓			
Passenger compartment air filter	R		✓		✓		✓		✓		✓		✓	
Timing belt	S/I				✓		✓		✓				✓	
Evaporative canister	S/I				✓		✓		✓				✓	

R: Replace   S/I: Service or Inspect

① Change clutch/brake fluid every 24 months.

FREQUENT OPERATION MAINTENANCE (SEVERE SERVICE)

If a vehicle is operated under any of the following conditions it is considered severe service:

- Extremely dusty areas.

- 50% or more of the vehicle operation is in 32°C (90°F) or higher temperatures, or constant operation in temperatures below 0°C (32°F).

- Prolonged idling (vehicle operation in stop and go traffic.

- Frequent short running periods (engine does not warm to normal operating temperatures).

- Police, taxi, delivery usage or trailer towing usage.

Engine oil & filter: replace every 3000 miles.

Rotate tires initially at 6000 miles and every 9000 miles thereafter.

Air cleaner filter: change every 15,000 miles.

Engine coolant strength, hoses & clamps: check every 15,000 miles.

Exhaust system: check every 15,000 miles.

Automatic transmission fluid & filter: change every 21,000 miles.

36616_AVEO_C0014

PRECAUTIONS

Before servicing any vehicle, please be sure to read all of the following precautions, which deal with personal safety, prevention of component damage, and important points to take into consideration when servicing a motor vehicle:

• Never open, service or drain the radiator or cooling system when the engine is hot; serious burns can occur from the steam and hot coolant.

• Observe all applicable safety precautions when working around fuel. Whenever servicing the fuel system, always work in a well-ventilated area. Do not allow fuel spray or vapors to come in contact with a spark, open flame, or excessive heat (a hot drop light, for example). Keep a dry chemical fire extinguisher near the work area. Always keep fuel in a container specifically designed for fuel storage; also, always properly seal fuel containers to avoid the possibility of fire or explosion. Refer to the additional fuel system precautions later in this section.

• Fuel injection systems often remain pressurized, even after the engine has been turned **OFF**. The fuel system pressure must be relieved before disconnecting any fuel lines. Failure to do so may result in fire and/or personal injury.

• Brake fluid often contains polyglycol ethers and polyglycols. Avoid contact with the eyes and wash your hands thoroughly after handling brake fluid. If you do get brake fluid in your eyes, flush your eyes with clean, running water for 15 minutes. If eye irritation persists, or if you have taken

brake fluid internally, IMMEDIATELY seek medical assistance.

• The EPA warns that prolonged contact with used engine oil may cause a number of skin disorders, including cancer. You should make every effort to minimize your exposure to used engine oil. Protective gloves should be worn when changing oil. Wash your hands and any other exposed skin areas as soon as possible after exposure to used engine oil. Soap and water, or waterless hand cleaner should be used.

• All new vehicles are now equipped with an air bag system, often referred to as a Supplemental Restraint System (SRS) or Supplemental Inflatable Restraint (SIR) system. The system must be disabled before performing service on or around system components, steering column, instrument panel components, wiring and sensors. Failure to follow safety and disabling procedures could result in accidental air bag deployment, possible personal injury and unnecessary system repairs.

• Always wear safety goggles when working with, or around, the air bag system. When carrying a non-deployed air bag, be sure the bag and trim cover are pointed away from your body. When placing a non-deployed air bag on a work surface, always face the bag and trim cover upward, away from the surface. This will reduce the motion of the module if it is accidentally deployed. Refer to the additional air bag system precautions later in this section.

• Clean, high quality brake fluid from a sealed container is essential to the safe and

proper operation of the brake system. You should always buy the correct type of brake fluid for your vehicle. If the brake fluid becomes contaminated, completely flush the system with new fluid. Never reuse any brake fluid. Any brake fluid that is removed from the system should be discarded. Also, do not allow any brake fluid to come in contact with a painted surface; it will damage the paint.

• Never operate the engine without the proper amount and type of engine oil; doing so WILL result in severe engine damage.

• Timing belt maintenance is extremely important. Many models utilize an interference-type, non-freewheeling engine. If the timing belt breaks, the valves in the cylinder head may strike the pistons, causing potentially serious (also time-consuming and expensive) engine damage. Refer to the maintenance interval charts for the recommended replacement interval for the timing belt, and to the timing belt section for belt replacement and inspection.

• Disconnecting the negative battery cable on some vehicles may interfere with the functions of the on-board computer system(s) and may require the computer to undergo a relearning process once the negative battery cable is reconnected.

• When servicing drum brakes, only disassemble and assemble one side at a time, leaving the remaining side intact for reference.

• Only an MVAC-trained, EPA-certified automotive technician should service the air conditioning system or its components.

BRAKES

ANTI-LOCK BRAKE SYSTEM (ABS)

GENERAL INFORMATION

PRECAUTIONS

• Certain components within the ABS system are not intended to be serviced or repaired individually.

• Do not use rubber hoses or other parts not specifically specified for and ABS system. When using repair kits, replace all parts included in the kit. Partial or incorrect repair may lead to functional problems and require the replacement of components.

• Lubricate rubber parts with clean, fresh brake fluid to ease assembly. Do not use shop air to clean parts; damage to rubber components may result.

• Use only DOT 3 brake fluid from an unopened container.

• If any hydraulic component or line is removed or replaced, it may be necessary to bleed the entire system.

• A clean repair area is essential. Always clean the reservoir and cap thoroughly before removing the cap. The slightest amount of dirt in the fluid may plug an orifice and impair the system function. Perform repairs after components have been thoroughly cleaned; use only denatured alcohol to clean components. Do not allow ABS components to come into contact with any substance containing mineral oil; this includes used shop rags.

• The Anti-Lock control unit is a microprocessor similar to other computer units in the vehicle. Ensure that the ignition switch is **OFF** before removing or installing controller harnesses. Avoid static electricity discharge at or near the controller.

• If any arc welding is to be done on the vehicle, the control unit should be unplugged before welding operations begin.

WHEEL SPEED SENSORS

REMOVAL & INSTALLATION

Front

See Figures 1 and 2.

1. Before servicing the vehicle, refer to the precautions section.

2. Disconnect the negative battery cable.

3. Disconnect the electrical connector from the front wheel speed sensor.

4. Raise and suitably support the vehicle.

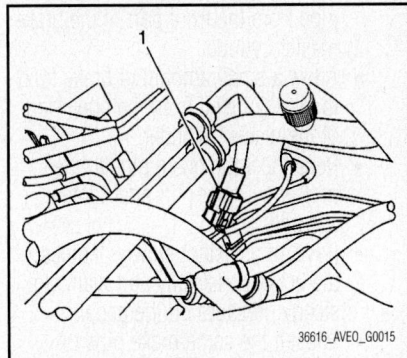

Fig. 1 Front speed sensor electrical connection (1) view

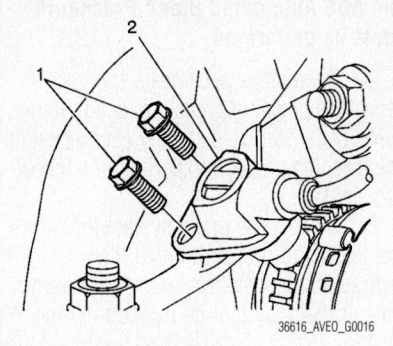

Fig. 2 Remove the bolts (2) and the front wheel speed sensor (1)

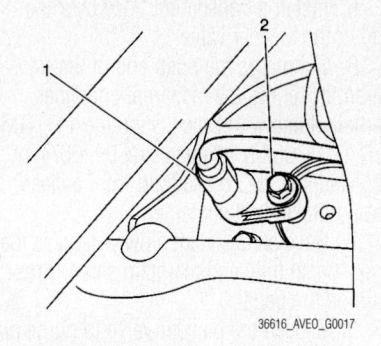

Fig. 3 Remove the bolt (2) and the rear wheel speed sensor (1)

5. Remove the wheel.

6. Remove the bolts and the front wheel speed sensor from the steering knuckle.

To install:

7. Install the bolts and front wheel speed sensor to the steering knuckle.

8. Tighten the bolts to 71 inch. lbs. (8 Nm).

9. Lower the vehicle.

10. Connect the electrical connector to the front wheel speed sensor.

11. Connect the negative battery cable.

Rear

See Figure 3.

1. Before servicing the vehicle, refer to the precautions section.

2. Raise and suitably support the vehicle.

3. Disconnect the electrical connector for the rear wheel speed sensor from the rear axle.

4. Remove the mounting bolt from the rear wheel speed sensor.

5. Remove the rear wheel speed sensor from the backing plate.

To install:

6. Install the rear wheel speed sensor (1) to the backing plate.

7. Install the rear wheel sensor mounting bolt.

8. Tighten the bolt to 71 inch. lbs. (8 Nm).

9. Connect the rear wheel speed sensor electrical connector.

10. Lower the vehicle.

11. Connect the negative battery cable.

BRAKES   BLEEDING THE BRAKE SYSTEM

BLEEDING PROCEDURE

Manual Procedure

➡**When adding fluid to the brake master cylinder reservoir, use only Delco Supreme 11®, GM P/N 12377967 (Canadian P/N 992667), or equivalent DOT-3 brake fluid from a clean, sealed brake fluid container. The use of any type of fluid other than the recommended type of brake fluid, may cause contamination which could result in damage to the internal rubber seals and/or rubber linings of hydraulic brake system components.**

1. Place a clean shop cloth beneath the brake master cylinder to prevent brake fluid spills.

With the ignition **OFF** and the brakes cool, apply the brakes 3–5 times, or until the brake pedal effort increases significantly, in order to deplete the brake booster power reserve.

2. If you have performed a brake master cylinder bench bleeding on this vehicle, or if you disconnected the brake pipes from the master cylinder, you must perform the following steps:

• Ensure that the brake master cylinder reservoir is full to the maximum-fill level. If necessary, add Delco Supreme 11®, GM P/N 12377967 (Canadian P/N 992667), or equivalent DOT-3 brake fluid from a clean, sealed brake fluid container. If removal of the reservoir cap and diaphragm is necessary, clean the outside of the reservoir on and around the cap prior to removal.

• With the rear brake pipe installed securely to the master cylinder, loosen and separate the front brake pipe from the front port of the brake master cylinder.

• Allow a small amount of brake fluid to gravity bleed from the open port of the master cylinder.

• Reconnect the brake pipe to the master cylinder port and tighten securely.

• Have an assistant slowly depress the brake pedal fully and maintain steady pressure on the pedal.

• Loosen the same brake pipe to purge air from the open port of the master cylinder.

• Tighten the brake pipe, then have the assistant slowly release the brake pedal.

• Wait 15 seconds, then repeat steps until all air is purged from the same port of the master cylinder.

• With the front brake pipe installed securely to the master cylinder, after all air has been purged from the front port of the master cylinder, loosen and separate the rear brake pipe from the master cylinder, then repeat steps.

• After completing the final master cylinder port bleeding procedure, ensure that both of the brake pipe-to-master cylinder fittings are properly tightened.

3. Fill the brake master cylinder reservoir with Delco Supreme 11®, GM P/N 12377967 (Canadian P/N 992667), or equivalent DOT-3 brake fluid from a clean, sealed brake fluid container. Ensure that the brake master cylinder reservoir remains at least half-full during this bleeding procedure. Add fluid as needed to maintain the proper level. Clean the outside of the reservoir on and around the reservoir cap prior to removing the cap and diaphragm.

4. Install a proper box-end wrench onto the RIGHT REAR wheel hydraulic circuit bleeder valve.

5. Install a transparent hose over the end of the bleeder valve.

6. Submerge the open end of the transparent hose into a transparent container partially filled with Delco Supreme 11®, GM P/N 12377967 (Canadian P/N 992667), or equivalent DOT-3 brake fluid from a clean, sealed brake fluid container.

7. Have an assistant slowly depress the brake pedal fully and maintain steady pressure on the pedal.

8. Loosen the bleeder valve to purge air from the wheel hydraulic circuit.

9. Tighten the bleeder valve, then have the assistant slowly release the brake pedal.

10. Wait 15 seconds, then repeat steps 8–10 until all air is purged from the same wheel hydraulic circuit.

11. With the right rear wheel hydraulic circuit bleeder valve tightened securely, after all air has been purged from the right rear hydraulic circuit, install a proper box-end wrench onto the LEFT FRONT wheel hydraulic circuit bleeder valve.

12. Install a transparent hose over the end of the bleeder valve, then repeat steps 7–11.

13. With the left front wheel hydraulic circuit bleeder valve tightened securely, after all air has been purged from the left front hydraulic circuit, install a proper box-end wrench onto the LEFT REAR wheel hydraulic circuit bleeder valve.

14. Install a transparent hose over the end of the bleeder valve, then repeat steps 7–11.

15. With the left rear wheel hydraulic circuit bleeder valve tightened securely, after all air has been purged from the left rear hydraulic circuit, install a proper box-end wrench onto the RIGHT FRONT wheel hydraulic circuit bleeder valve.

16. Install a transparent hose over the end of the bleeder valve, then repeat steps 7–11.

17. After completing the final wheel hydraulic circuit bleeding procedure, ensure that each of the 4 wheel hydraulic circuit bleeder valves are properly tightened.

18. Fill the brake master cylinder reservoir to the maximum-fill level with Delco Supreme 11®, GM P/N 12377967 (Canadian P/N 992667), or equivalent DOT-3 brake fluid from a clean, sealed brake fluid container.

19. Slowly depress and release the brake pedal. Observe the feel of the brake pedal.

➡️ **If it is determined that air was inducted into the system upstream of the ABS modulator prior to servicing,** the ABS Automated Bleed Procedure must be performed.

20. If the brake pedal feels spongy, repeat the bleeding procedure again. If the brake pedal still feels spongy after repeating the bleeding procedure, perform the following steps:

21. Inspect the brake system for external leaks and pressure bleed the hydraulic brake system in order to purge any air that may still be trapped in the system.

22. Turn the ignition key **ON**, with the engine **OFF**. Check to see if the brake system warning lamp remains illuminated.

➡️ **DO NOT allow the vehicle to be driven until it is diagnosed and repaired.**

Pressure Procedure

➡️ **When adding fluid to the brake master cylinder reservoir, use only Delco Supreme 11®, GM P/N 12377967 (Canadian P/N 992667), or equivalent DOT-3 brake fluid from a clean, sealed brake fluid container. The use of any type of fluid other than the recommended type of brake fluid, may cause contamination which could result in damage to the internal rubber seals and/or rubber linings of hydraulic brake system components.**

1. Place a clean shop cloth beneath the brake master cylinder to prevent brake fluid spills.

2. With the ignition **OFF** and the brakes cool, apply the brakes 3–5 times, or until the brake pedal effort increases significantly, in order to deplete the brake booster power reserve.

3. If you have performed a brake master cylinder bench bleeding on this vehicle, or if you disconnected the brake pipes from the master cylinder, you must perform the following steps:

- Ensure that the brake master cylinder reservoir is full to the maximum-fill level. If necessary, add Delco Supreme 11®, GM P/N 12377967 (Canadian P/N 992667), or equivalent DOT-3 brake fluid from a clean, sealed brake fluid container. If removal of the reservoir cap and diaphragm is necessary, clean the outside of the reservoir on and around the cap prior to removal.
- With the rear brake pipe installed securely to the master cylinder, loosen and separate the front brake pipe from the front port of the brake master cylinder.
- Allow a small amount of brake fluid to gravity bleed from the open port of the master cylinder.
- Reconnect the brake pipe to the master cylinder port and tighten securely.
- Have an assistant slowly depress the brake pedal fully and maintain steady pressure on the pedal.
- Loosen the same brake pipe to purge air from the open port of the master cylinder.
- Tighten the brake pipe, then have the assistant slowly release the brake pedal.
- Wait 15 seconds, then repeat steps until all air is purged from the same port of the master cylinder.
- With the front brake pipe installed securely to the master cylinder, after all air has been purged from the front port of the master cylinder, loosen and separate the rear brake pipe from the master cylinder, then repeat steps.
- After completing the final master cylinder port bleeding procedure, ensure that both of the brake pipe-to-master cylinder fittings are properly tightened.

4. Fill the brake master cylinder reservoir to the maximum-fill level with Delco Supreme 11®, GM P/N 12377967 (Canadian P/N 992667), or equivalent DOT-3 brake fluid from a clean, sealed brake fluid container. Clean the outside of the reservoir on and around the reservoir cap prior to removing the cap and diaphragm.

5. Install the J 35589-A to the brake master cylinder reservoir.

6. Check the brake fluid level in the J 29532 , or equivalent. Add Delco Supreme 11®, GM P/N 12377967 (Canadian P/N 992667), or equivalent DOT-3 brake fluid from a clean, sealed brake fluid container as necessary to bring the level to approximately the half-full point.

7. Connect the J 29532 , or equivalent, to the J 35589-A .

8. Charge the J 29532 , or equivalent, air tank to 25–30 psi (175–205 kPa).

9. Open the J 29532 , or equivalent, fluid tank valve to allow pressurized brake fluid to enter the brake system.

10. Wait approximately 30 seconds, then inspect the entire hydraulic brake system in order to ensure that there are no existing

external brake fluid leaks. Any brake fluid leaks identified require repair prior to completing this procedure.

11. Install a proper box-end wrench onto the RIGHT REAR wheel hydraulic circuit bleeder valve.

12. Install a transparent hose over the end of the bleeder valve.

13. Submerge the open end of the transparent hose into a transparent container partially filled with Delco Supreme 11®, GM P/N 12377967 (Canadian P/N 992667), or equivalent DOT-3 brake fluid from a clean, sealed brake fluid container.

14. Loosen the bleeder valve to purge air from the wheel hydraulic circuit. Allow fluid to flow until air bubbles stop flowing from the bleeder, then tighten the bleeder valve.

15. With the right rear wheel hydraulic circuit bleeder valve tightened securely, after all air has been purged from the right rear hydraulic circuit, install a proper box-end wrench onto the LEFT FRONT wheel hydraulic circuit bleeder valve.

16. Install a transparent hose over the end of the bleeder valve, then repeat steps 13–14.

17. With the left front wheel hydraulic circuit bleeder valve tightened securely, after all air has been purged from the left front hydraulic circuit, install a proper box-end wrench onto the LEFT REAR wheel hydraulic circuit bleeder valve.

18. Install a transparent hose over the end of the bleeder valve, then repeat steps 13–14.

With the left rear wheel hydraulic circuit bleeder valve tightened securely, after all air has been purged from the left rear hydraulic circuit, install a proper box-end wrench onto the RIGHT FRONT wheel hydraulic circuit bleeder valve

19. Install a transparent hose over the

end of the bleeder valve, then repeat steps 13–14.

20. After completing the final wheel hydraulic circuit bleeding procedure, ensure that each of the 4 wheel hydraulic circuit bleeder valves are properly tightened.

21. Close the J 29532 , or equivalent, fluid tank valve, then disconnect the J 29532 , or equivalent, from the J 35589-A .

22. Remove the J 35589-A from the brake master cylinder reservoir.

23. Fill the brake master cylinder reservoir to the maximum-fill level with Delco Supreme 11®, GM P/N 12377967 (Canadian P/N 992667), or equivalent DOT-3 brake fluid from a clean, sealed brake fluid container.

24. Slowly depress and release the brake pedal. Observe the feel of the brake pedal.

➡**If it is determined that air was inducted into the system upstream of the ABS modulator prior to servicing, the ABS Automated Bleed Procedure must be performed.**

25. If the brake pedal feels spongy, perform the following steps:

26. Inspect the brake system for external leaks.

27. Using a scan tool, perform the antilock brake system automated bleeding procedure to remove any air that may have been trapped in the BPMV.

28. Turn the ignition key **ON**, with the engine **OFF**. Check to see if the brake system warning lamp remains illuminated.

➡**DO NOT allow the vehicle to be driven until it is diagnosed and repaired.**

BLEEDING THE ABS SYSTEM

⁑ **WARNING**

The Auto Bleed Procedure may be terminated at any time during the

process by pressing the EXIT button. No further Scan Tool prompts pertaining to the Auto Bleed procedure will be given. After exiting the bleed procedure, relieve bleed pressure and disconnect bleed equipment per manufacturer's instructions. Failure to properly relieve pressure may result in spilled brake fluid causing damage to components and painted surfaces.**

1. Raise the vehicle on a suitable support.

2. Remove all four tire and wheel assemblies.

3. Inspect the battery state of charge.

4. Install a scan tool.

5. Turn ON the ignition, with the engine OFF.

6. With the scan tool, establish communications with the EBCM. Select Special Functions. Select Automated Bleed from the Special Functions menu.

7. Bleed the base brake system.

8. Follow the scan tool directions until the desired brake pedal height is achieved.

9. If the bleed procedure is aborted, a malfunction exists. Perform the following steps before resuming the bleed procedure:

10. If a DTC is detected, diagnose the appropriate DTC.

11. If the brake pedal feels spongy, perform the conventional brake bleed procedure again.

12. When the desired pedal height is achieved, press the brake pedal in order to inspect for firmness.

13. Remove the scan tool.

14. Install the tire and wheel assemblies.

15. Inspect the brake fluid level.

16. Road test the vehicle while inspecting that the pedal remains high and firm.

BRAKES

FRONT DISC BRAKES

BRAKE CALIPER

REMOVAL & INSTALLATION

See Figure 4.

1. Before servicing the vehicle, refer to the precautions section.
2. Raise and safely support the vehicle.
3. Mark the position of the front wheels relative to the wheel hubs and remove the wheels.
4. Remove the fitting and the washers that attach the brake hose to the caliper.
5. Disconnect the brake hose, and plug the openings in the caliper and the

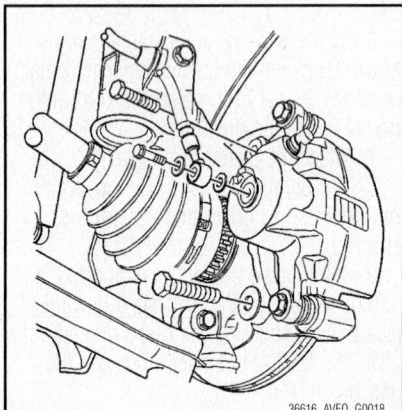

Fig. 4 Front brake caliper assembly removal

36616_AVEO_G0018

brake hose to prevent fluid loss and contamination.

6. Remove the caliper mounting bolts from the steering knuckle.
7. Remove the caliper assembly.

To install:

8. Ensure the slide pins are lubricated with silicone brake lubricant.
9. Install the caliper assembly with the mounting bolts.
10. Tighten the caliper-to-steering knuckle mounting bolts to 70 ft. lbs. (95 Nm).
11. Connect the brake hose and tighten the fitting to 30 ft. lbs. (40 Nm).
12. Install the front wheels
13. Lower the vehicle.
14. With the engine **OFF**, gradually apply and release the brake pedal several times in order to position the caliper piston and the pads.
15. Bleed the brake system.

DISC BRAKE PADS

REMOVAL & INSTALLATION

See Figure 5.

1. Before servicing the vehicle, refer to the precautions section.
2. Raise and suitably support the vehicle.
3. To maintain wheel balance, mark the relative positions of the wheel and the hub, and remove the front wheel.

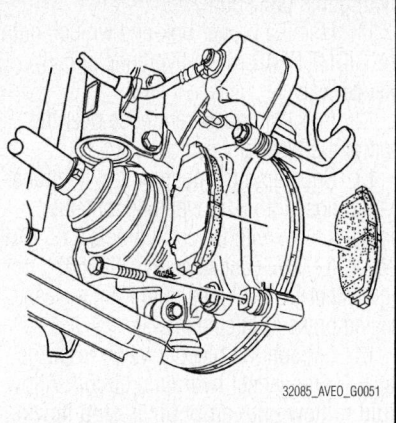

32085_AVEO_G0051

Fig. 5 Removal and installation of the front disc brake pads

4. Remove the lower guide pin bolt and rotate the caliper upward.
5. Remove the brake pads.

To install:

6. Compress the caliper piston into the bore.
7. Fit the pads into the caliper.
8. Ensure the slide pins are lubricated with silicone brake lubricant.
9. Install the caliper and tighten the mounting bolt to 20 ft. lbs. (27 Nm).
10. Align the marks that were made before the wheel removal and install the front wheels.
11. Lower the vehicle.

BRAKES

REAR DRUM BRAKES

BRAKE DRUM

REMOVAL & INSTALLATION

See Figure 6.

1. Before servicing the vehicle, refer to the precautions section.
2. Release the parking brake and apply the brake pedal ten times.
3. Raise and safely support the vehicle.
4. Remove the rear tire.
5. Remove the screws that retain the brake drum assembly.
6. Remove the brake drum from the hub.

To install:

7. Install the brake drum to the hub.
8. Install the screws that hold to the brake drum and tighten to 35 inch lbs. (4 Nm).
9. Install the rear tire.
10. Lower the vehicle.

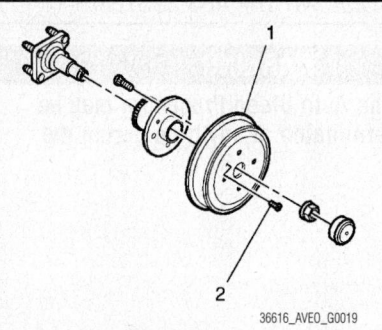

36616_AVEO_G0019

Fig. 6 Remove the screws (2) and brake drum (1)

✳✳ WARNING

If the clicking sound of the adjuster is not audible from either brake drum, the clearance between the brake shoes and the brake drum is adjusted.

11. Apply the brake pedal at least ten times in order to adjust the clearance between the brake shoes and the drum. Verify the clicking sound of the adjuster is not audible.
12. Adjust the parking brake. For additional information, refer to the following section, "Parking Brake Cables, Adjustment."

BRAKE SHOES

REMOVAL & INSTALLATION

See Figures 7 and 8.

1. Before servicing the vehicle, refer to the precautions section.
2. Raise and safely support the vehicle.
3. Remove the rear wheels.
4. Remove the brake drum.
5. Loosen the leading shoe hold-down return spring.
6. Disconnect the upper link of the connecting link spring of the leading shoe to relieve tension on the upper return spring.

7. Remove the upper return spring and the adjuster.

8. Disconnect the trailing shoe return spring.

9. Remove the trailing shoe and ining.

10. Disconnect the lower return spring.

To install:

11. Clean the adjuster assembly and apply Molykote® 111 grease to the brake shoe contact points.

12. Inspect the threads of the adjuster for smooth rotation.

13. Install the trailing shoe and lining assembly with the hold-down spring, the washer and the pin.

14. Properly route the parking brake cable and attach it to the shoe lever.

15. Install the lower return spring on the shoe.

16. Install the leading shoe and adjuster assembly against the backing plate.

17. Install the lower return spring to the leading shoe.

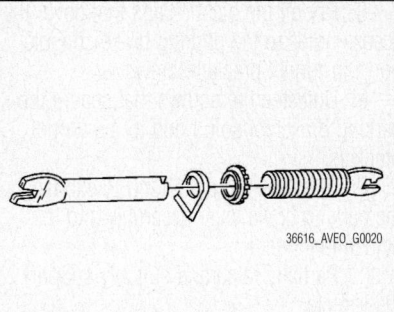

Fig. 8 Rear drum brake adjuster assembly

18. Install the adjuster assembly and turn it in as far as possible.

19. Position the spring clip toward the backing plate.

20. Install the leading shoe with the hold-down spring.

21. Attach the leading shoe upper link spring connection to apply tension to the return spring.

22. Install the upper return spring.

23. Ensure the adjuster assembly nut is drawn all the way to the stop.

24. Install the brake drum.

25. Lower the vehicle.

26. Adjust the parking brake.

ADJUSTMENT

See Figure 9.

1. Before servicing the vehicle, refer to the precautions section.

2. Remove the brake drum.

3. Using the rear brake adjuster nut, turn the adjuster assembly in until a sufficient amount of drag occurs on the brake drum.

4. Place the parking brake lever stops against the edge of the shoe web. If necessary, loosen the park brake cable at the equalizer.

5. Install the brake drum.

➡**If the clicking sound of the adjuster assembly is not audible from either brake drum, the clearance between the brake shoes and the drum is adjusted.**

6. Apply the brake pedal at least 10 times. Verify the clicking sound of the adjuster assembly is not audible from either brake drum.

7. Adjust the parking brake.

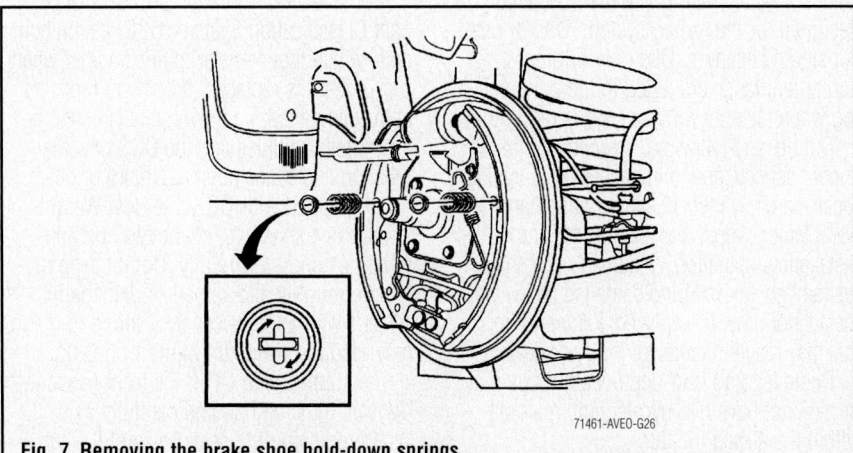

Fig. 7 Removing the brake shoe hold-down springs

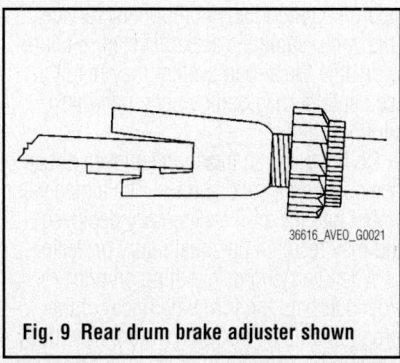

Fig. 9 Rear drum brake adjuster shown

BRAKES

PARKING BRAKE

PARKING BRAKE CABLES

ADJUSTMENT

See Figures 10 through 12.

1. Before servicing the vehicle, refer to the precautions section.

2. Adjust the rear brakes.

The rear drum brake shoes serve as the parking brakes.

3. Release the parking brake.

4. Raise and suitably support the vehicle.

5. Check the parking brake cables for free movement.

6. Lower the vehicle.

7. Move the front seats backward to ensure there is enough working space.

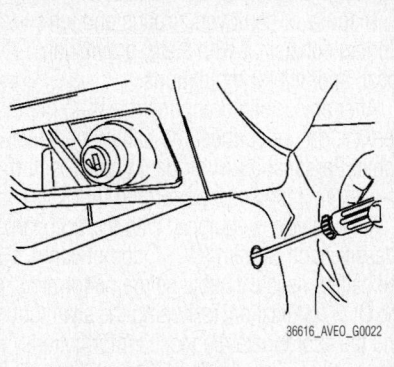

Fig. 10 Unfasten the screws that secure the parking brake console hood (1 of 2)

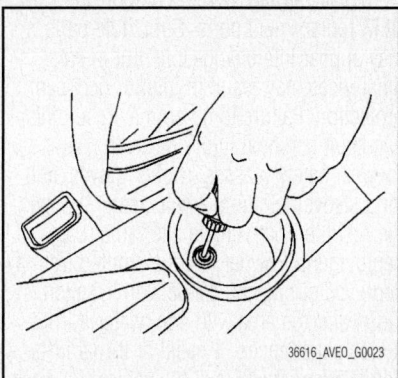

Fig. 11 Unfasten the screws that secure the parking brake console hood (2 of 2)

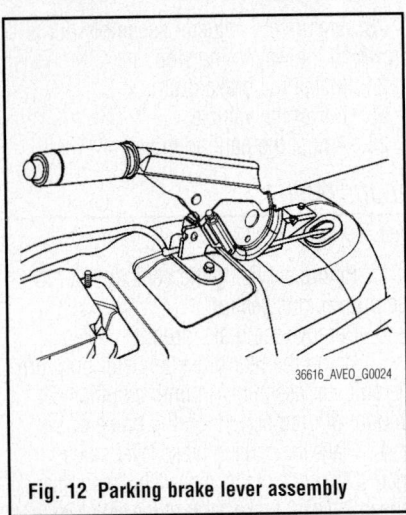

Fig. 12 Parking brake lever assembly

8. Pry off the plastic caps that cover the access holes to the parking brake console hood-to-tunnel bracket-screws.

9. Unfasten the screws that secure the parking brake console hood to the tunnel brackets.

10. Raise the console hood to expose the parking brake lever assembly and the adjustment nut.

11. Partially raise and suitably support the vehicle.

12. Turn the adjustment nut on the lever assembly until the wheels are difficult to turn.

13. Loosen the nut until the rear wheels are just free to turn.

14. Lower the vehicle.

15. Position the parking brake console hood and fasten it to the tunnel brackets with the screws.

16. Tighten the parking brake console hood-to-tunnel bracket screws 22 inch lbs. (2.5 Nm).

17. Snap in the plastic caps that cover the access holes to the parking brake console hood-to-tunnel bracket screws.

18. Adjust the front seats to their previous position.

PARKING BRAKE SHOES

REMOVAL & INSTALLATION

The rear drum brake shoes serve as the parking brakes. Refer to the procedures under Rear Drum Brakes.

CHASSIS ELECTRICAL

AIR BAG (SUPPLEMENTAL RESTRAINT SYSTEM)

GENERAL INFORMATION

SERVICE PRECAUTIONS

Disconnect and isolate the battery negative cable before beginning any airbag system component diagnosis, testing, removal, or installation procedures. Allow system capacitor to discharge for two minutes before beginning any component service. This will disable the airbag system. Failure to disable the airbag system may result in accidental airbag deployment, personal injury, or death.

Do not place an intact undeployed airbag face down on a solid surface. The airbag will propel into the air if accidentally deployed and may result in personal injury or death.

When carrying or handling an undeployed airbag, the trim side (face) of the airbag should be pointing towards the body to minimize possibility of injury if accidental deployment occurs. Failure to do this may result in personal injury or death.

Replace airbag system components with OEM replacement parts. Substitute parts may appear interchangeable, but internal differences may result in inferior occupant protection. Failure to do so may result in occupant personal injury or death.

Wear safety glasses, rubber gloves, and long sleeved clothing when cleaning powder residue from vehicle after an airbag deployment. Powder residue emitted from a deployed airbag can cause skin irritation. Flush affected area with cool water if irritation is experienced. If nasal or throat irritation is experienced, exit the vehicle for fresh air until the irritation ceases. If irritation continues, see a physician.

Do not use a replacement airbag that is not in the original packaging. This may result in improper deployment, personal injury, or death.

The factory installed fasteners, screws and bolts used to fasten airbag components have a special coating and are specifically designed for the airbag system. Do not use substitute fasteners. Use only original equipment fasteners listed in the parts catalog when fastener replacement is required.

During, and following, any child restraint anchor service, due to impact event or vehicle repair, carefully inspect all mounting hardware, tether straps, and anchors for proper installation, operation, or damage. If a child restraint anchor is found damaged in any way, the anchor must be replaced. Failure to do this may result in personal injury or death.

Deployed and non-deployed airbags may or may not have live pyrotechnic material within the airbag inflator.

Do not dispose of driver/passenger/curtain airbags or seat belt tensioners unless you are sure of complete deployment. Refer to the Hazardous Substance Control System for proper disposal.

Dispose of deployed airbags and tensioners consistent with state, provincial, local, and federal regulations.

After any airbag component testing or service, do not connect the battery negative cable. Personal injury or death may result if the system test is not performed first.

If the vehicle is equipped with the Occupant Classification System (OCS), do not connect the battery negative cable before performing the OCS Verification Test using the scan tool and the appropriate diagnostic information. Personal injury or death may result if the system test is not performed properly.

Never replace both the Occupant Restraint Controller (ORC) and the Occupant Classification Module (OCM) at the same time. If both require replacement, replace one, then perform the Airbag System test before replacing the other.

Both the ORC and the OCM store Occupant Classification System (OCS) calibration data, which they transfer to one another when one of them is replaced. If both are replaced at the same time, an irreversible fault will be set in both modules and the OCS may malfunction and cause personal injury or death.

If equipped with OCS, the Seat Weight Sensor is a sensitive, calibrated unit and must be handled carefully. Do not drop or handle roughly. If dropped or damaged, replace with another sensor. Failure to do so may result in occupant injury or death.

If equipped with OCS, the front passenger seat must be handled carefully as well. When removing the seat, be careful when setting on floor not to drop. If dropped, the sensor may be inoperative, could result in occupant injury, or possibly death.

If equipped with OCS, when the passenger front seat is on the floor, no one should sit in the front passenger seat. This uneven force may damage the sensing ability of the seat weight sensors. If sat on and damaged, the sensor may be inoperative, could result in occupant injury, or possibly death.

DISARMING THE SYSTEM

There are two ways to properly disarm the Supplemental Inflatable Restraint (SIR) System depending on the type of service that is being preformed:

• If the vehicle was involved in an accident with an air bag deployment, remove the negative battery cable.

• When performing SIR diagnostics follow the service manual diagnostic procedures and disable the SIR system when indicated to do so by removing the negative battery cable.

• When performing electrical diagnosis on components other than the SIR system, remove the SIR/Airbag fuse(s) when indicated by the diagnostic procedure.

• When removing or replacing a component attached to or near an SIR component, remove the negative battery cable as indicated in the procedure.

Negative Battery Cable

1. Turn the steering wheel so that the vehicles wheels are pointing straight ahead.
2. Place the ignition in the **OFF** position.
3. Remove the negative battery cable from the battery.
4. Wait 1 minute before servicing vehicle.
   Air Bag Fuse
1. Turn the steering wheel so that the vehicles wheels are pointing straight ahead.
2. Place the ignition in the **OFF** position.

➡ **With the AIR BAG fuse removed and the ignition switch in the ON position, the AIR BAG warning indicator illuminates. This is normal operation, and does not indicate an SIR system malfunction.**

3. Remove the cover for the instrument panel (I/P) fuse center.
4. Locate and remove the F1 Fuse from the I/P fuse center.

5. Wait 1 minute before servicing the vehicle.

ARMING THE SYSTEM

Negative Battery Cable

1. Place the ignition in the OFF position.
2. Connect the negative battery cable to the battery.
3. Use caution while reaching in and turn the ignition switch to the ON position. The AIR BAG indicator will flash then turn OFF.

Air Bag Fuse

1. Place the ignition in the OFF position.
2. Install the F1 Fuse in the interior fuse center.
3. Replace the fuse center cover.
4. Use caution while reaching in and turn the ignition switch to the ON position. The AIR BAG indicator will flash then turn OFF.

CLOCKSPRING CENTERING

See Figure 13.

✳✳ CAUTION

When servicing the steering column, the Supplemental Inflatable Restraint (SIR) System clock spring must be centered for proper steering wheel operation. Failure to properly center the SIR clock spring may result in reduced turn ability of the steering wheel causing the vehicle to improperly maneuver and may cause the SIR system to be inoperative.

✳✳ WARNING

Do not rotate the steering wheel or move the position of the steering gear once the intermediate shaft is disconnected. This will uncenter the Inflatable Restraint coil in the steering column. If the Inflatable Restraint coil becomes uncentered, it may be damaged during vehicle operation.

1. Turn the front wheels straight ahead.
2. Turn the lobe of the clock spring clockwise to lock. Do not force.
3. Turn the lobe of the clock spring counterclockwise approximately 3 turns to the Neutral position, with the front of the wheels straight ahead.
4. Properly align the pointed marks on the components of the clock spring.

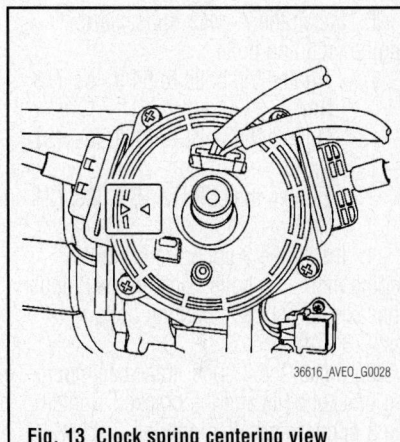

36616_AVEO_G0028

Fig. 13 Clock spring centering view

DRIVE TRAIN

AUTOMATIC TRANSAXLE ASSEMBLY

REMOVAL & INSTALLATION

See Figures 14 and 15.

1. Before servicing the vehicle, refer to the precautions section.
2. Disconnect the battery cables.
3. Remove the battery and battery tray.
4. Drain the transaxle fluid. Remove the left and right drive axle assemblies.
5. Disconnect the fluid cooler inlet and outlet hoses from the transaxle.
6. Disconnect the shift control cable from the transaxle. Install the J 28467-B to support the engine.
7. Disconnect the Input Shaft Speed

(ISS) sensor electrical connector. Disconnect the output shaft speed (OSS) sensor electrical connector.

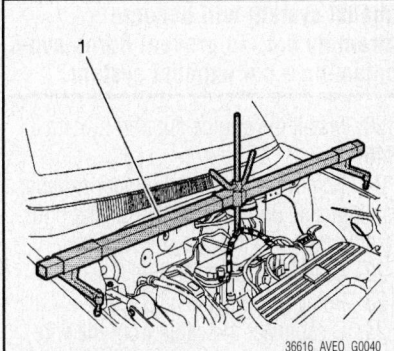

36616_AVEO_G0040

Fig. 14 J 28467-B—Installed to support the engine

8. Disconnect the Park/Neutral Position (PNP) sensor electrical connector.
9. Disconnect the transaxle electrical connector.
10. Remove the service hall cover.
11. Remove the torque converter bolts.
12. Remove the damping block connection nut and bolt.
13. Remove the rear mounting bracket bolts and rear mounting bracket.
14. Remove the 3 upper transaxle mounting bracket bolts.
15. Remove the 3 upper transaxle-to-engine mounting bolts.
16. Secure the transaxle to a transaxle jack and DW 260-120.
17. Remove the 7 lower transaxle-to-engine retaining bolts.
18. Carefully remove the transaxle from

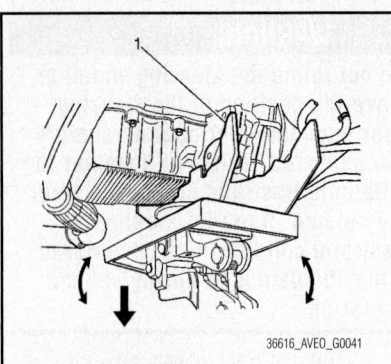

Fig. 15 Transaxle removal with a jack and DW 260-120 support (1)

the vehicle with the transaxle secured in the DW 260-120.

To install:

19. Secure the transaxle to the transaxle jack, then carefully position in the vehicle with the transaxle secured in the DW 260-120.

20. Install the 7 lower transaxle-to-engine retaining bolts.
- Tighten the bolts to 54 ft. lbs. (73 Nm).
- Tighten the bolts to 23 ft. lbs. (31 Nm).
- Tighten the bolts to 15 ft. lbs. (21 Nm).

21. Install the 3 upper transaxle-to-engine mounting bolts. Tighten the 3 upper transaxle-to-engine mounting bolts to 54 ft. lbs. (73 Nm).

22. Install the 3 upper transaxle mounting bracket bolts and the bracket. Tighten the 3 upper transaxle mounting bracket bolts to 44 ft. lbs. (60 Nm).

23. Install the rear mounting bracket bolts and the bracket. Tighten the rear mounting bracket bolts to 44 ft. lbs. (60 Nm).

24. Install the damping block connection nut and bolt. Tighten the damping block connection nut and bolt to 59 ft. lbs. (80 Nm).

25. Install the torque converter bolts. Tighten the torque converter bolts to 33 ft. lbs. (45 Nm).

26. Install the service hall cover.
- Connect the transaxle electrical connector.
- Connect the PNP sensor electrical connector.
- Connect the OSS sensor electrical connector.
- Connect the ISS sensor electrical connector.

27. Remove the J 28467-B .

28. Connect the shift control cable into the transaxle.

29. Connect the fluid cooler inlet and outlet hose into the transaxle.

30. Install the left and right drive axle assemblies.

31. Install the battery and battery tray

32. Fill the transaxle with fluid.

33. Measure the fluid level.

MANUAL TRANSAXLE ASSEMBLY

REMOVAL & INSTALLATION

Y4M Transaxle

See Figures 16 through 18.

1. Before servicing the vehicle, refer to the precautions section.

2. Remove the air cleaner assembly.

3. Remove the battery and battery tray.

4. Remove the shift cable pins.

5. Remove the washers.

6. Disconnect the select and the shift cable.

7. Remove the cable E-rings.

8. Disconnect the shift cables from the cable bracket.

9. Remove the engine wiring harness bending strap.

10. Remove the ground wire bolt.

11. Disconnect the ground wire.

12. Disconnect the backup lamp switch connector.

13. Remove the radiator lower hose bolts.

14. Disconnect the radiator lower hose.

15. Remove the Crankshaft Position (CKP) sensor bolt.

16. Disconnect the CKP sensor connector and remove the CKP sensor.

17. Disconnect the Vehicle Speed Sensor (VSS) connector.

18. Remove the VSS.

19. Remove the starter motor.

✳✳ CAUTION

While engine is operating, the exhaust system will become extremely hot. To prevent burns avoid contacting a hot exhaust system.

20. Install the engine support system J 28467-B.

21. Remove the transaxle upper exhaust manifold side bolt and the thermostat housing side bolt.

22. Drain the transaxle fluid.

23. Remove the cable adjust nut.

24. Disconnect the cable from the wire clip.

25. Disconnect the clutch cable from the transaxle mount hole.

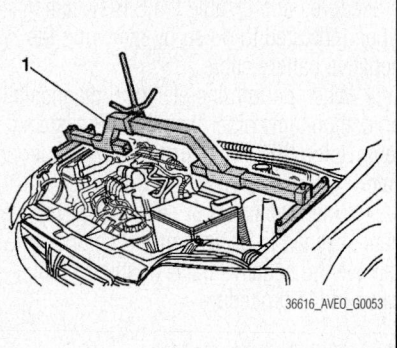

Fig. 16 Engine support system J 28467-B installed

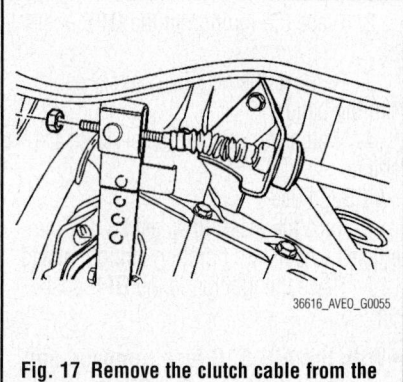

Fig. 17 Remove the clutch cable from the transaxle mount hole

26. Remove the front under longitudinal frames and stabilizer.

27. Remove the drive axle, only from the transaxle side.

28. Remove the clutch housing lower plate bolts and lower plate.

✳✳ CAUTION

While engine is operating, the exhaust system will become extremely hot. To prevent burns avoid contacting a hot exhaust system.

29. Remove the front exhaust pipe nuts from the exhaust manifold side.

30. Remove the gasket and separate the exhaust manifold pipe.

31. Remove the front exhaust pipe.

32. Remove the 3 transaxle mounting bracket bolts.

33. Support the transaxle with a transaxle support jack.

34. Remove the damping block connection nut and bolt.

35. Remove the 3 rear mounting bracket bolts.

36. Remove the rear mounting bracket from the transaxle.

37. Remove the 2 rear damping block retaining bolts.

38. Remove the rear damping block.
39. Remove the transaxle lower bolts.

➡ **Support the engine in the normal position when removing the transaxle. Damage to related parts can occur.**

40. Separate the transaxle, slide the transaxle sideways from the engine block.
41. Lower the transaxle to remove from the vehicle.

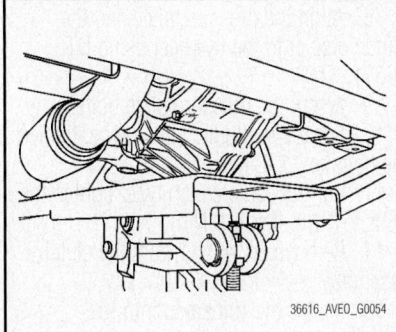

36616_AVEO_G0054

Fig. 18 Transaxle removal with support jack shown

To install:

42. Support the transaxle with a transaxle support jack.
43. Install the transaxle by inserting the transaxle input shaft into the clutch disc and sliding the transaxle sideways into the engine block.
44. Install the transaxle lower bolts.
45. Tighten the bolts to 55–65 Nm (41–48 lb ft).
46. Install the 2 rear damping block retaining bolts.
47. Tighten the bolts to 37–44 ft. lbs. (50–60 Nm).
48. Install the bracket, the 3 rear mounting bracket bolts, and the damping block connection nut.
   - Tighten the bracket bolts to 41–48 ft. lbs. (55–65 Nm).
   - Tighten the connection nut and bolt to 55–63 ft. lbs. (75–85 Nm)
49. Install the 3 rear transaxle mounting bracket bolts.
50. Tighten the bolts to 33–41 ft. lbs. (45–55 Nm).
51. Install the front exhaust pipe nuts.
52. Tighten the nuts to 18–25 ft. lbs. (25–35 Nm).
53. Install the clutch housing lower plate.
54. Install the clutch housing lower plate bolts.
55. Tighten the bolts to 71–106 inch lbs. (8–12 Nm).

56. Install the drive axle.
57. Install the front under longitudinal frames and stabilizer.
58. Install the clutch cable to the transaxle mount.
59. Install the cable to the wire clip.
60. Install the clutch cable adjusting nut.
61. Install the transaxle upper bolts.
62. Tighten the bolts to 41–48 ft. lbs. (55–65 Nm).
63. Install the starter motor.
64. Remove the engine support J 28467-B.
65. Install the VSS.
66. Install the VSS mounting bolt.
67. Tighten the bolt to 35–62 inch lbs. (4–7 Nm).
68. Connect the VSS connector.
69. Install the radiator lower hose and CKP sensor.
70. Tighten the connection nut and bolt to 55–63 ft. lbs. (75–85 Nm)
71. Tighten the sensor bolt to 44–70 inch lbs. (5–8 Nm).
72. Connect the ground wire and the backup lamp switch connector.
73. Install the engine wiring harness bending strap.
74. Tighten the bolt to 7–12 ft. lbs. (10–16 Nm).
75. Connect the shift cables to the cable bracket.
76. Install the cable E-rings.
77. Connect the select and shift cable.
78. Install the washers.
79. Install the shift cable pins.
80. Install the drain plug.
81. Tighten the drain plug to 18–22 ft. lbs. (25–30 Nm).
82. Remove the oil level plug.
83. Fill recommended fluid to the proper level and following specifications:
   - The classification is 75W-85
   - The capacity is 2.1 liters (2.21 quarts). (GL-4)
84. Install the oil level plug.
85. Tighten the oil level plug to 18–22 ft. lbs. (25–30 Nm).
86. Adjust the clutch cable.

D16 Transaxle

See Figures 19 through 22.

1. Before servicing the vehicle, refer to the precautions section.
2. Install the engine support system J 28467-B.
3. Remove the battery and battery tray.
4. Remove the shift linkage assembly.
5. Remove the drive axle shaft.
6. Disconnect the backup lamp switch electrical connector.

7. Disconnect the speedometer speed sensor electrical connector.
8. Remove the clutch release cylinder retaining bolts and the clutch release cylinder.
9. Remove the damping block connection nut and bolt.
10. Remove the rear mounting bracket bolts.
11. Remove the rear mounting bracket from the transaxle.

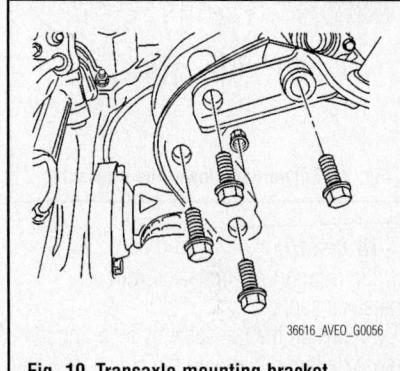

36616_AVEO_G0056

Fig. 19 Transaxle mounting bracket removal

12. Remove the rear damping block retaining bolts.
13. Remove the rear damping block from the front cross member.
14. Remove the cage retaining bolts.
15. Remove the transaxle upper mounting bracket bolts.
16. Remove the upper mounting bracket and cage.
17. Remove the transaxle upper retaining bolts.

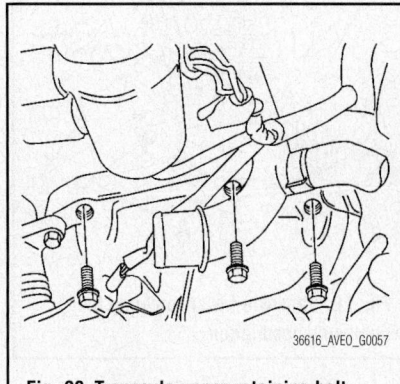

36616_AVEO_G0057

Fig. 20 Transaxle upper retaining bolt removal

18. Support the transaxle with a transaxle support jack.
19. Remove the transaxle lower retaining bolts.
20. Remove the transaxle.

21. Slide the transaxle sideways away from the engine block.

22. Lower the transaxle.

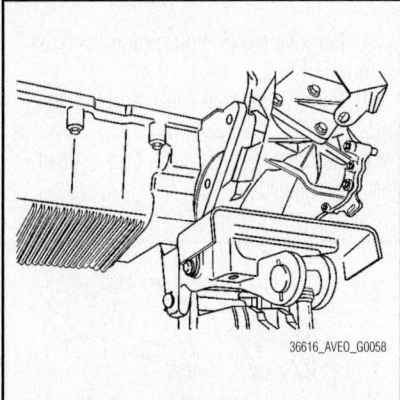

Fig. 21 Support and lower the transaxle

To install:

23. Support the transaxle with a transaxle support jack.

24. Install the transaxle by inserting the transaxle input shaft into the clutch disc and sliding the transaxle sideways into the engine block.

25. Install the transaxle lower retaining bolts and tighten as follows: (refer to graphic)

- Tighten the transaxle lower retaining bolts (1) to 54 ft. lbs. (73 Nm).
- Tighten the transaxle lower retaining bolts (2) to 23 ft. lbs. (31 Nm).
- Tighten the transaxle lower retaining bolt (3) to 15 ft. lbs. (21 Nm).

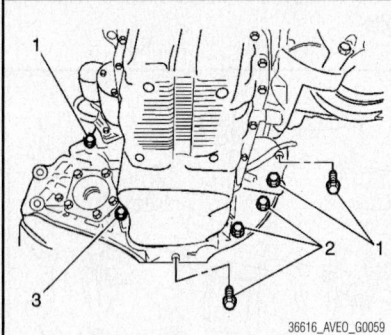

Fig. 22 Transaxle lower retaining bolt tightening description

26. Install the transaxle upper retaining bolts and tighten to 54 ft. lbs. (73 Nm).

27. Install the cage retaining bolt and cage.

28. Install the transaxle upper mounting bracket.

29. Install the transaxle upper mounting bracket bolts and tighten to 44 ft. lbs. (60 Nm).

30. Install the rear damping block retaining bolts and tighten to 41 ft. lbs. (55 Nm).

31. Install the rear damping block from the front cross member.

32. Install the rear mounting bracket and bracket bolts and tighten to 59 ft. lbs. (80 Nm).

33. Install the damping block connection nut and bolt and tighten to 59 ft. lbs. (80 Nm).

34. Install the clutch release cylinder.

35. Install the clutch release cylinder bolts and tighten to 15 ft. lbs. (20 Nm).

36. Connect the speedometer speed sensor electrical connector.

37. Connect the backup lamp switch electrical connector.

38. Remove the engine support J 28467-B.

39. Install the drive axle shaft.

40. Install the shift linkage assembly.

41. Install the battery and battery tray.

42. With the vehicle on a level surface and the fluid in the transaxle cold, remove the filler plug and check the fluid level. The fluid should come to the bottom edge of the plug hole.

43. If the level is low, add SAE 75W-85 GL-4 manual transaxle fluid through the filler plug hole until the fluid begins to run out.

44. Install the oil level plug.

45. Tighten the oil level plug to 21 ft. lbs. (28 Nm).

46. Bleed the hydraulic clutch system if needed.

CLUTCH DRIVEN DISC & PRESSURE PLATE

REMOVAL & INSTALLATION

See Figure 23.

1. Before servicing the vehicle, refer to the precautions section.

2. Disconnect the negative battery cable.

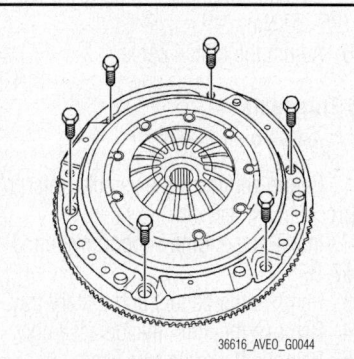

Fig. 23 Pressure plate bolts and the pressure plate

3. Remove the transaxle from the vehicle.

4. Remove the pressure plate bolts and the pressure plate.

5. Important: Support the pressure plate when you remove the last bolt.

6. Remove the clutch disc from the flywheel.

To install:

7. Coat the spline on the clutch disc with multi-purpose grease.

8. Align the pressure plate and the clutch disc onto the flywheel using DT 46551.

9. Install the pressure plate bolts.

10. For the hydraulic clutch type, tighten the bolts to 11 ft. lbs. (15 Nm).

11. For the cable clutch type, tighten the bolts to 13 ft. lbs. (18 Nm).

12. Remove DT 46551 from the clutch assembly.

13. Install the transaxle into the vehicle.

14. Connect the negative battery cable.

ADJUSTMENTS

See Figure 24.

If clutch engagement/disengagement is difficult or operating unsmooth, adjust the clutch cable (2) by adjusting clutch cable adjustment nut (1) until the desired free travel is obtained.

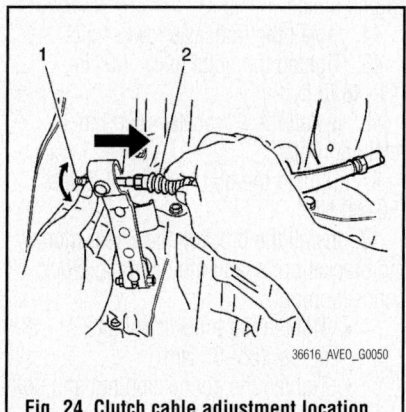

Fig. 24 Clutch cable adjustment location

Cable Type

See Figure 25.

This cable type of clutch engagement/disengagement system is designed to have no free travel in clutch pedal. Adjust the clutch cable adjusting nut until the below adjustment specifications are met:

- Clutch pedal travel for disengagement is (a) 4.7–5.1 inches (120–130 mm)
- Clearance between pedal and floor just

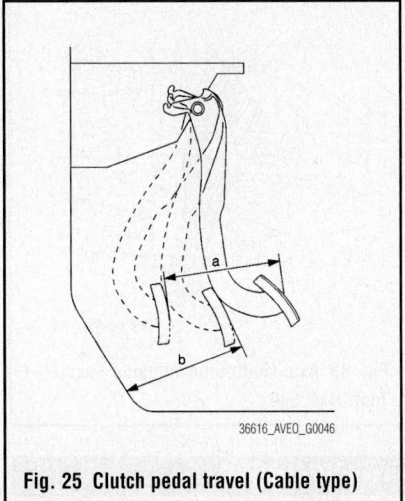
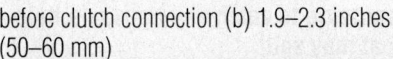

Fig. 25 Clutch pedal travel (Cable type)

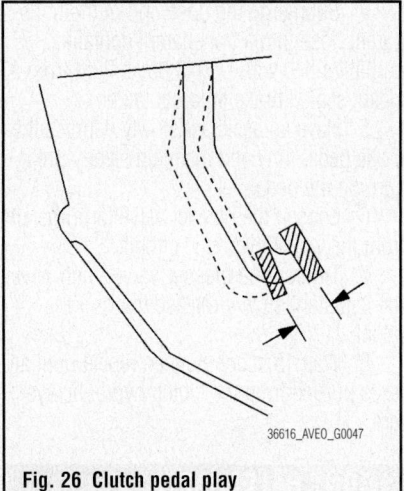

Fig. 26 Clutch pedal play

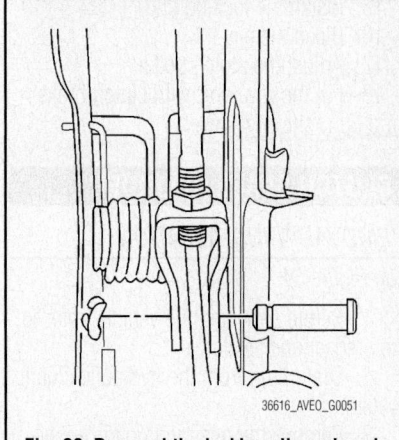

Fig. 29 Removal the locking clip and push rod fixing pin

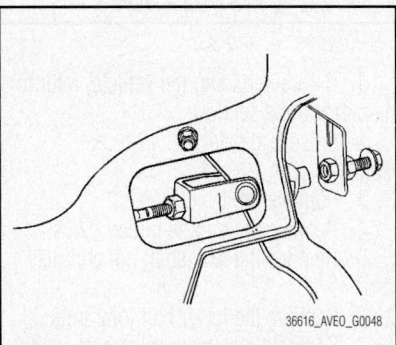

Fig. 27 Clutch pedal play adjustment location

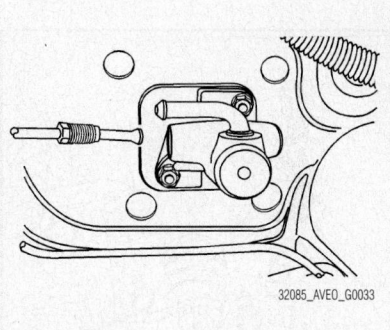

Fig. 30 Removal and installation of the master cylinder

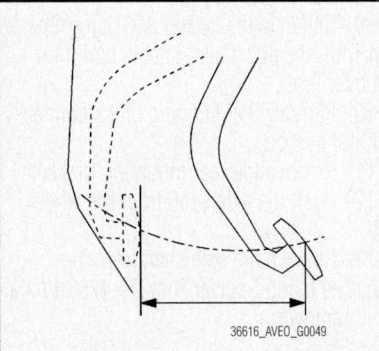

Fig. 28 Clutch pedal travel 4.7–4.9 inches (120–125 mm).

before clutch connection (b) 1.9–2.3 inches (50–60 mm)

❊❊ CAUTION

When performing this check, the vehicle could move suddenly. Personal injury or property damage may result. Make sure there is enough room around the vehicle, in case the vehicle does move. Do not use the accelerator pedal, and be ready to turn OFF the engine immediately if it starts.

After starting the engine, Inspect if the clearance between pedal and floor is within specified range. If the clutch adjustments cannot be obtained, Inspect for interference of the clutch pedal. If no interference or obstructions are found, the clutch cable may be worn and require replacement.

Clutch Cable Inspection

1. Inspect the clutch cable and replace it if any of the following conditions exists:
   - Excessively worn cable
   - Loose cable
   - Bent or distorted cable
   - Damaged boot
   - Worn end

Hydraulic Type

See Figures 26 through 28.

1. Determine the clutch pedal play. Depress the clutch pedal lightly with your hand and measure the distance when you feel resistance.
2. Adjust the clutch pedal play. Loosen the locknut and turn the pushrod.
3. Tighten the locknut after adjustment. The clutch pedal play is 0.4–0.5 inches (10–12 mm).
4. Measure the clutch pedal travel. Press the clutch pedal all the way to the floor.

Measure from the starting position to the ending position.

5. Adjust the clutch pedal travel. Loosen the locknut and turn the bolt.
6. Tighten the locknut after adjustment. The clutch pedal travel is 4.7–4.9 inches (120–125 mm).

CLUTCH MASTER CYLINDER

REMOVAL & INSTALLATION

See Figures 29 and 30.

Before disconnecting the reservoir tank hose, remove the clutch/brake fluid from the reservoir tank.

1. Before servicing the vehicle, refer to the precautions section.
2. Remove the locking clip.
3. Remove the push rod fixing pin and push rod.
4. Disconnect the hose clamp on the master cylinder.
5. Disconnect the master cylinder hose.
6. Remove the master cylinder pipe.
7. Remove the clutch master cylinder nuts.
8. Remove the clutch master cylinder.

To install:

9. Install the clutch master cylinder and clutch master cylinder nuts.
10. Tighten the clutch master cylinder nuts to 16 ft. lbs. (22 Nm).
11. Install the master cylinder pipe.
12. Connect the master cylinder hose.
13. Connect the hose clamp on the master cylinder.
14. Install the push rod fixing pin and push rod.

15. Install the locking clip.
16. Bleed the air.
17. Adjust the clutch pedal.
18. Fill the reservoir with clutch/brake fluid up to the MAX level.

CLUTCH SLAVE CYLINDER

REMOVAL & INSTALLATION

See Figure 31.

1. Before servicing the vehicle, refer to the precautions section.
2. Drain fluid from the hydraulic clutch system.
3. Remove the retaining bolt from the slave cylinder hose.
4. Remove the retaining bolts and remove the slave cylinder.

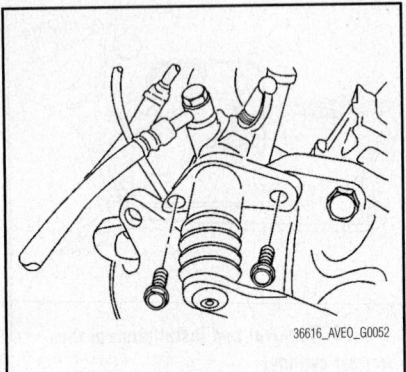

Fig. 31 Slave cylinder removal shown

To install:
5. Install the slave cylinder and tighten the retaining bolts to 15 ft. lbs. (20 Nm).
6. Install the retaining bolt to the slave cylinder hose.
7. Install fresh DOT-3 brake fluid and bleed the clutch hydraulic system.

CLUTCH HYDRAULIC SYSTEM BLEEDING

1. Fill the clutch master cylinder reservoir with DOT-3 brake fluid from a clean, sealed brake fluid container. Ensure that the clutch master cylinder reservoir remains at least half-full during this bleeding procedure. Add fluid as needed to maintain the proper level. Clean the outside of the reservoir on and around the reservoir cap prior to removing the cap and diaphragm.
2. Install a proper box-end wrench onto the slave cylinder hydraulic circuit bleeder valve.
3. Install a transparent hose over the end of the bleeder valve.

4. Submerge the open end of the transparent hose into a transparent container partially filled with DOT-3 brake fluid from a clean, sealed brake fluid container.
5. Have an assistant slowly depress the brake pedal fully and maintain steady pressure on the pedal.
6. Loosen the bleeder valve to purge air from the wheel hydraulic circuit.
7. Tighten the bleeder valve, then have the assistant slowly release the brake pedal.
8. Wait 15 seconds, then repeat until all air is purged from the clutch hydraulic system.

FRONT HALFSHAFTS

REMOVAL & INSTALLATION

See Figures 32 and 33.

1. Before servicing the vehicle, refer to the precautions section.
2. Raise and safely support the vehicle.
3. Remove the front wheels.
4. Remove the engine undercovers.
5. Remove the axle shaft nut and discard.
6. Remove the lower ball joint nuts.
7. Separate the steering knuckle from the lower ball joint using Special Tool KM-507-C or suitable ball joint remover tool.
8. Remove the tie rod nut.
9. Separate the tie rod end using Special Tool KM-507-C or suitable ball joint remover tool.
10. Remove the damping block connection nut and bolt.
11. Remove the rear mounting bracket.
12. Push the axle shaft from the wheel hub.
13. Remove the axle shaft from the transaxle using Special Tool DT-47539 Axle Shaft remover.

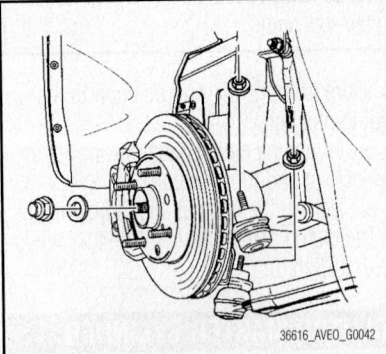

Fig. 32 Remove the axle nut, lower ball joint and tie rod end

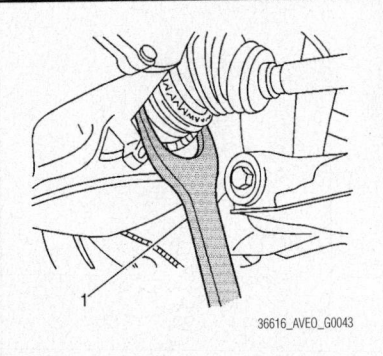

Fig. 33 Axle shaft removal using Special Tool DT-47539

✳✳ WARNING

Place a drain pan below the transaxle to catch any transaxle fluid that may spill.

➤**Cap the transaxle opening after the axle shaft has been removed to avoid contamination.**

To install:
14. Clean the hub seal and transaxle seal.
15. Install the axle shaft into the transaxle.
16. Install the wheel hub onto the axle-shaft.
17. Install the rear mounting bracket. Tighten the mounting bolts to 44 ft. lbs. (60 Nm).
18. Install the damping block connection nut and bolt and tighten to 59 ft. lbs. (80 Nm).
19. Mount the steering knuckle onto the lower ball joint.
20. Install the tie rod into the knuckle/strut and tighten the tie rod nut to 33 ft. lbs. (45 Nm)
21. Install the lower ball joint nut and tighten to 37 ft. lbs. (50 Nm).
22. Loosely install a new axle nut.

✳✳ CAUTION

Always use a new axle shaft nut when reinstalling.

23. Install the wheels, loosely install the lug nuts.
24. Lower the vehicle.
25. Tighten the lug nuts to 88 ft. lbs. (120 Nm).
26. Tighten the axle shaft nut to 221 ft. lbs. (300 Nm).
27. Peen the axle shaft nut with a punch and hammer until the nut is locked in place.
28. Install the engine undercovers.
29. Refill the transaxle with fluid to the correct level.

REAR AXLE HOUSING

REMOVAL & INSTALLATION

See Figure 34.

This is a non-drive axle.

1. Before servicing the vehicle, refer to the precautions section.
2. Raise and suitably support the vehicle.
3. Remove the rear wheels.
4. Disconnect the parking brake.
5. Disconnect the ABS sensor line.
6. Disconnect the brake pipes from the brake hoses at the rear axle brackets by removing the cap screws and the retaining clip. Cap or tape the brake hose openings to prevent entry of foreign matter. Unclip the brake hose from the rear axle brackets.
7. Place support jacks under the arms of the rear axle and raise the rear axle arms slightly. Remove the shock absorbers.
8. Remove the shock absorbers.
9. Lower the support jacks and remove the rear springs.
10. Remove the left rear axle mounting bolts and the right rear axle mounting

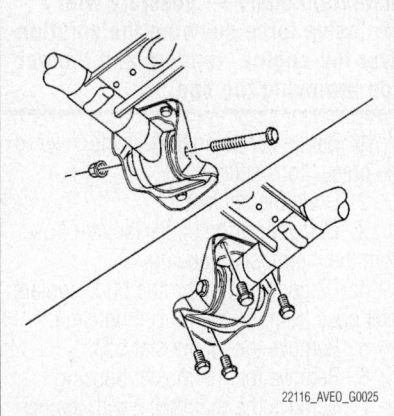

Fig. 34 Remove the rear axle mounting bolts and bracket bolts

bracket bolts from the underbody. Pry the rear axle slightly with a screw-driver, if required.

11. Remove the rear axle.

To install:

12. Raise the rear axle and loosely fasten it to the vehicle underbody mountings with the rear axle-to-body bracket bolt.

13. Install the rear springs and insulators.
14. Raise the rear axle arm with the support jacks. Attach the shock absorber to the axle with the lower attachment bolt.
15. Connect the brake pressure hoses into the bracket on the rear axle.
16. Mount the retaining clips.
17. Connect the brake pipes to the brake hoses.
18. Bleed the brakes.
19. Install the parking brake.
20. Lower the vehicle slightly and install the rear wheels.
21. At curb height, tighten the left rear axle-to-body bracket bolt and the right rear axle mounting bracket bolts.
22. Tighten the rear axle-to-body bracket bolt to 85 ft. lbs. (115 Nm).
23. Tighten the rear axle mounting bracket bolts to 52 ft. lbs. (70 Nm)
24. Adjust the rear wheel brakes. Bleed the brake system and check for leaks.
25. Connect the ABS sensor line.
26. Adjust the parking brake.
27. Lower the vehicle completely.

ENGINE COOLING

ENGINE FAN

REMOVAL & INSTALLATION

See Figure 35.

1. Before servicing the vehicle, refer to the precautions section.
2. Disconnect the negative battery cable.
3. Disconnect the cooling fan electrical connector(s) .
4. Remove the electric cooling fan mounting bolts.
5. Remove the electric cooling fan.

To install:

6. Install the electric cooling fan(s).
7. Install the electric cooling fan mounting bolts.
8. Tighten the electrical cooling fan mounting bolts to 35 inch lbs. (4 Nm).
9. Connect the cooling fan electrical connector.

RADIATOR

REMOVAL & INSTALLATION

See Figures 36 and 37.

1. Before servicing the vehicle, refer to the precautions section.
2. Disconnect the negative battery cable.
3. Drain the engine cooling system.
4. Remove the electric cooling fans.
5. Remove the upper radiator hose clamp.
6. Disconnect the upper radiator hose from the radiator.
7. Disconnect the lower radiator hose from the radiator.
8. Remove the lower radiator hose clamp.
9. Remove the hose clamp from the surge tank hose at the radiator.
10. Disconnect the surge tank hose from the radiator.

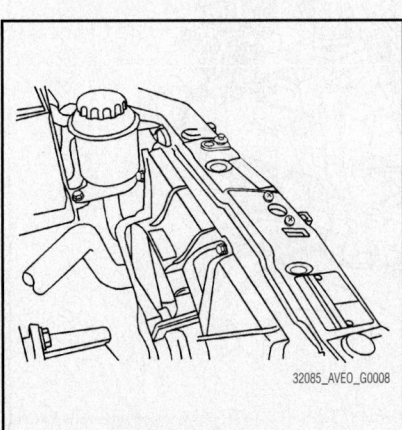

Fig. 35 Cooling fan mounting bolts

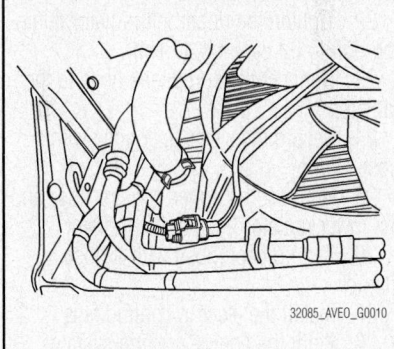

Fig. 36 Lower radiator hose

11. Remove the left upper radiator retaining bolt.
12. Remove the left upper radiator retaining bracket.
13. Remove the right upper radiator retaining bolt.
14. Remove the right upper radiator retaining bracket.

➡**The radiator still contains a substantial amount of coolant. Drain the remainder of the coolant from the radiator into a drain pan.**

15. Remove the radiator from the vehicle.

Fig. 37 Right upper radiator retaining bolt

To install:

Set the radiator into place in the vehicle with the radiator bottom posts in the rubber shock bumpers

16. Position the radiator retainers in place.

17. Install the upper right radiator retaining bracket.

18. Install the upper right radiator retaining bolt.

19. Tighten the upper right radiator retaining bolt to 62 inch lbs. (7 Nm).

20. Install the upper left radiator retaining bracket.

21. Install the upper left radiator retaining bolt.

22. Tighten the upper left radiator retaining bolt to 62 inch lbs. (7 Nm).

23. Connect the surge tank hose to the radiator.

24. Secure the surge tank hose with a hose clamp.

25. Connect the upper radiator hose and the lower radiator hose to the radiator.

26. Secure each hose with a hose clamp.

27. Install the electric cooling fans.

28. Refill the engine cooling system.

29. Connect the negative battery cable.

THERMOSTAT

REMOVAL & INSTALLATION

1,6L (LXT) Engine

See Figure 38.

✳✳ CAUTION

As long as there is pressure in the cooling system, the temperature can be considerably higher than the boiling temperature of the solution in the radiator without causing the solution to boil. Removal of the pressure cap while the engine is hot and pressure is high will cause the solution to boil

instantaneously — possibly with explosive force spewing the solution over the engine, fenders and the person removing the cap.

1. Before servicing the vehicle, refer to the precautions section.

2. Drain the coolant.

3. Disconnect the upper radiator hose from the thermostat housing.

4. Disconnect the throttle body coolant inlet hose from the thermostat housing.

5. Remove the thermostat bolts.

6. Remove the thermostat housing.

7. Remove the thermostat with the gasket.

8. Inspect the gasket for cracks or other damage.

9. Inspect the valve seat for foreign matter that could prevent the valve from seating properly.

10. Inspect the thermostat for proper operation.

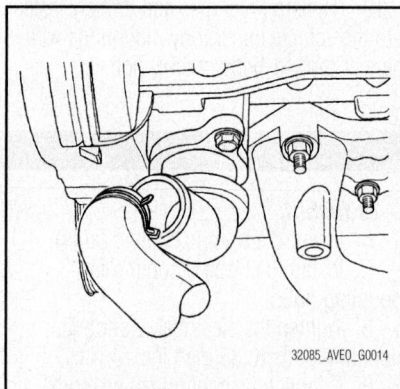

Fig. 38 Thermostat with bolts and housing

To install:

11. Install the thermostat with the bolts and the thermostat housing.

12. Tighten the mounting bolts to 15 ft. lbs. (20 Nm).

13. Secure the upper radiator hose to the thermostat housing with a hose clamp.

14. Connect the throttle body coolant inlet hose to the thermostat housing.

15. Refill the engine cooling system.

1.6L (LXV) Engine

See Figure 39.

✳✳ CAUTION

As long as there is pressure in the cooling system, the temperature can be considerably higher than the boiling temperature of the solution in the radiator without causing the solution to boil. Removal of the pressure cap while the engine is hot and pressure is high will cause the solution to boil instantaneously — possibly with explosive force spewing the solution over the engine, fenders and the person removing the cap.

1. Before servicing the vehicle, refer to the precautions section.

2. Disconnect the negative battery cable.

3. Drain the coolant.

4. Remove the upper radiator hose from the thermostat housing.

5. Disconnect the thermostat wiring harness plug.

6. Remove the thermostat bolts.

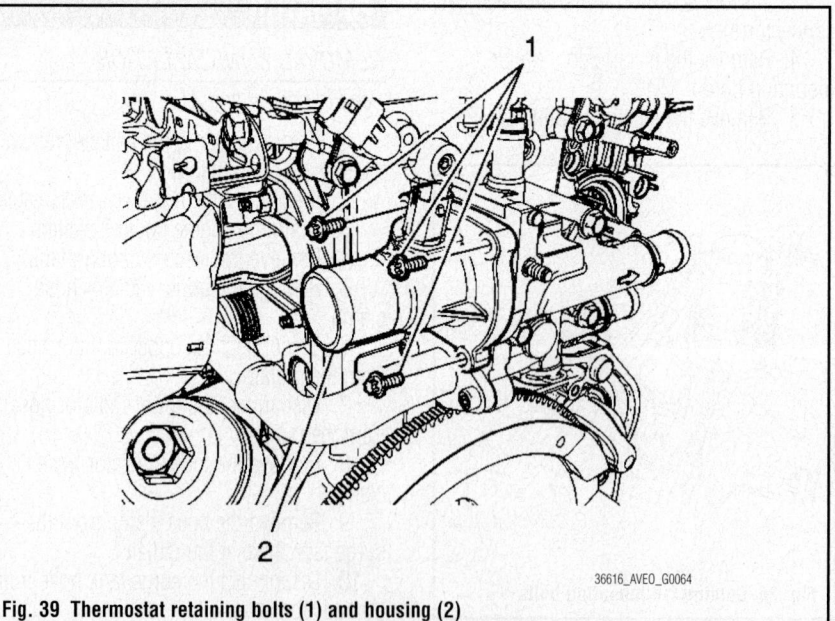

Fig. 39 Thermostat retaining bolts (1) and housing (2)

7. Remove the thermostat housing retaining bolts.

8. Remove the thermostat housing.

9. Remove the thermostat with the gasket.

10. Inspect the thermostat for proper operation.

11. Clean the thermostat housing and the cylinder head mating surfaces.

To install:

12. Fit the thermostat housing to the coolant distributor and use the NEW gasket.

13. Install the thermostat housing and tighten the retaining bolts to 6 ft. lbs. (8 Nm).

14. Connect the thermostat wiring harness plug.

15. Install the upper radiator hose to the thermostat housing.

16. Refill the engine with coolant and bleed the cooling system.

17. Connect the battery negative cable.

WATER PUMP

REMOVAL & INSTALLATION

1.6L (LXT) Engine

See Figure 40.

1. Before servicing the vehicle, refer to the precautions section.

2. Disconnect the negative battery cable.

3. Drain the cooling system.

4. Remove the rear timing belt cover.

5. Remove the water pump mounting bolts.

6. Remove the water pump.

7. Remove the seal ring from the water pump.

To install:

8. Install a new seal ring to the water pump and coat the sealing surface of the ring with Lubriplate®.

9. Install the water pump to the engine block, aligning the flange with the recess of the rear timing belt cover.

10. Install the water pump mounting bolts and tighten to 89 inch lbs. (10 Nm).

11. Install the rear timing belt cover.

12. Refill and bleed the cooling system.

13. Connect the negative battery cable.

14. Start the engine and check for leaks.

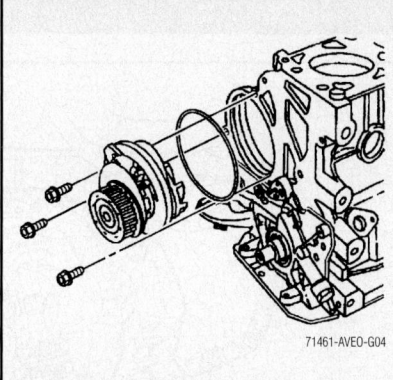

71461-AVEO-G04

Fig. 40 Water pump mounting—1.6L engine

1.6L (LXV) Engine

See Figure 41.

1. Before servicing the vehicle, refer to the precautions section.

2. Disconnect the negative battery cable.

3. Drain the engine coolant.

4. Remove the air cleaner assembly.

5. Remove the RH head lamp assembly. Refer to headlight Removal & Installation.

6. Relocate the A/C line if needed.

7. Remove the water pump pulley retaining bolts using EN-48356 fixture .

8. Remove the accessory belt.

9. Support the engine using an approved engine support system.

10. Remove the engine mount.

11. Remove the water pump pulley.

12. Remove the water pump retaining bolts.

13. Remove the water pump.

14. Remove the ring seal from the water pump.

15. Cleaning the mating surfaces of the water pump and the cylinder head

To install:

16. Install a new ring seal to the water pump.

17. Install the water pump and tighten the retaining bolts to 89 inch. lbs. (10 Nm).

18. Install the water pump pulley.

19. Install the engine mount.

20. Install the accessory belt.

21. Connect the A/C pipe retainer and fix the A/C hose.

22. Install the RH head lamp assembly.

23. Install the air cleaner assembly.

24. Refill and bleed the cooling system.

25. Connect the negative battery cable.

26. Start the engine and check for leaks.

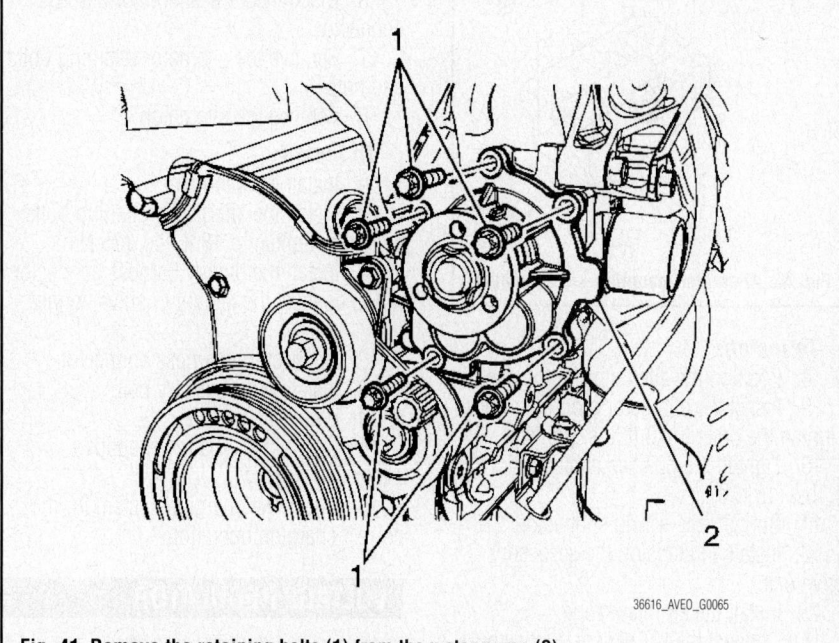

36616_AVEO_G0065

Fig. 41 Remove the retaining bolts (1) from the water pump (2)

ENGINE ELECTRICAL

CHARGING SYSTEM

ALTERNATOR

REMOVAL & INSTALLATION

1.6L (LXT) Engine

See Figure 42.

1. Before servicing the vehicle, refer to the precautions section.
2. Disconnect the negative battery cable.
3. Disconnect the Intake Air Temperature (IAT) sensor connector.
4. Disconnect the air intake tube
5. Remove the accessory drive belt.
6. Remove the alternator wiring connector.
7. Remove the alternator.

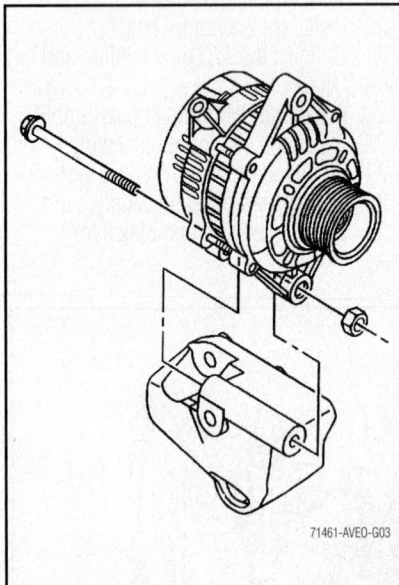

Fig. 42 Alternator mounting—1.6L engine

To install:

8. Position the alternator on the engine.
9. Install the alternator mounting bolts. Tighten the bolts to 18 ft. lbs. (25 Nm).
10. Tighten the positive cable nut to 11 ft. lbs. (15 Nm).
11. Connect the wiring connector.
12. Install and tension the accessory drive belt.
13. Install the air intake tube.
14. Connect the IAT sensor connector.
15. Connect the negative battery cable.
16. Check the charging system for the correct charging operation.

1.6L (LXV) Engine

See Figure 43.

1. Before servicing the vehicle, refer to the precautions section.

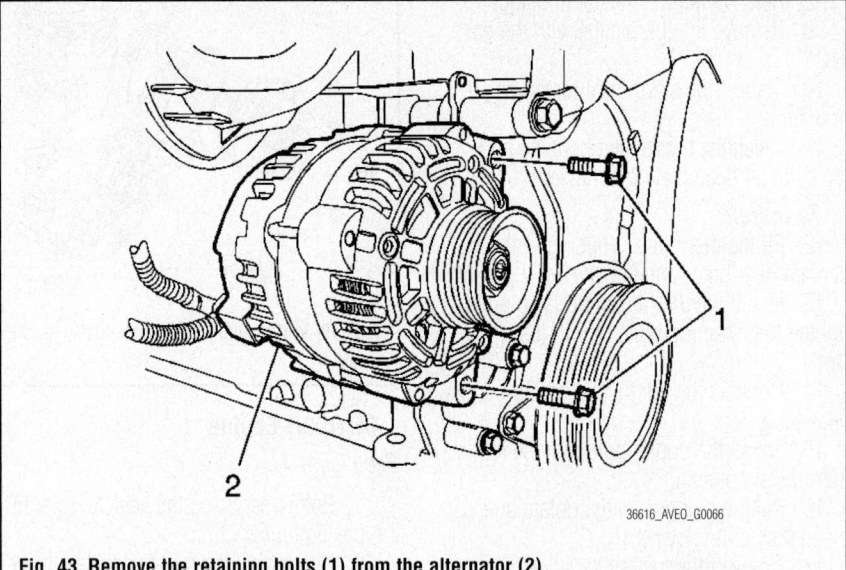

Fig. 43 Remove the retaining bolts (1) from the alternator (2)

2. Disconnect the negative battery cable.
3. Raise the vehicle.
4. Remove the accessory belt.
5. Remove the battery harness connector nut to disconnect the battery positive connector.
6. Disconnect the alternator harness connector.
7. Remove the alternator retaining bolts and nuts .
8. Remove the alternator.

To install:

9. Install the alternator.
10. Install the alternator retaining bolts and nuts, tighten to 18 ft. lbs. (25 Nm).
11. Install the battery harness connector nut to connect the battery positive connector.
12. Connect the harness connector.
13. Install the accessory belt.
14. Lower the vehicle.
15. Connect the battery negative cable.
16. Check the charging system for the correct charging operation.

VOLTAGE REGULATOR

REMOVAL & INSTALLATION

1.6L (LXT) Engine

See Figures 44 and 45.

1. Before servicing the vehicle, refer to the precautions section.
2. Disconnect the negative battery cable.
3. Remove the alternator.

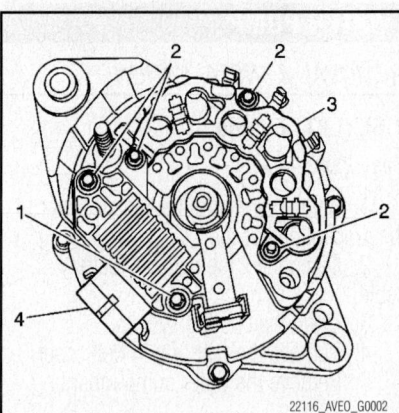

Fig. 44 Remove the screws (1 & 2) to access the regulator (3) and rectifier (4)—1.6L Engine

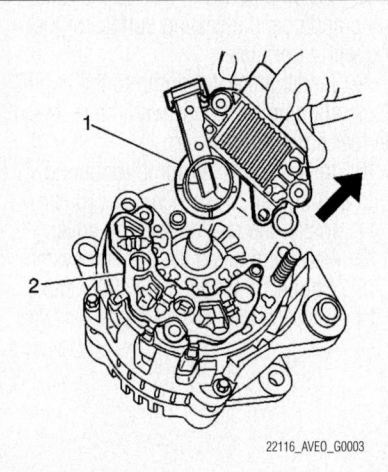

Fig. 45 Remove the rectifier (2) to access the voltage regulator (1)—1.6L Engine

4. Locate the four locking tabs on the alternator cover, and carefully pry the tabs using a suitable pry tool to remove the cover.

5. Remove the five screws that retain the voltage regulator and rectifier to the alternator.

6. Carefully lift up the rectifier and remove the voltage regulator.

To install:

7. Depress the voltage regulator brushes and insert a brush tube into the opening to keep brushes in the depressed position.

8. Install the voltage regulator on the alternator and ensure the battery ring terminal is positioned on the battery stud. Remove the brush tube.

9. Install the five mounting screws and tighten to 26 inch lbs. (3 Nm).

10. Snap the alternator cover into place.

11. Install the alternator.

12. Connect the negative battery cable.

ENGINE ELECTRICAL

FIRING ORDERS

See Figure 46.

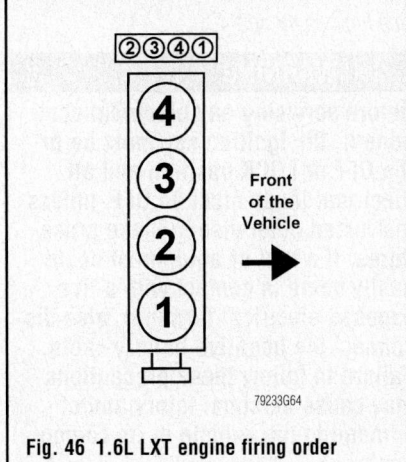

Fig. 46 1.6L LXT engine firing order 1-3-4-2

IGNITION COIL

REMOVAL & INSTALLATION

1.6L (LXT) Engine
See Figure 47.

✳ WARNING

Before servicing any electrical component, the ignition key must be in the OFF, or LOCK position and all electrical loads must be OFF, unless instructed otherwise in these procedures. If a tool or equipment could easily come in contact with a live exposed electrical terminal, also disconnect the negative battery cable. Failure to follow these precautions may cause personal injury and/or damage to the vehicle or its components.

1. Before servicing the vehicle, refer to the precautions section.

2. Disconnect the negative battery cable.

3. Disconnect the Electronic Ignition (EI) system ignition coil connector.

4. Note the ignition wire location and remove the ignition wire.

5. Remove the EI system ignition coil retaining nuts.

6. Remove the EI system ignition coil.

➡ Use the correct fastener in the correct location. Replacement fasteners must be the correct part number for that application. Fasteners requiring replacement or fasteners requiring the use of thread locking compound or sealant are identified in the service procedure. Do not use paints, lubricants, or corrosion inhibitors on fasteners or fastener joint surfaces unless specified. These coatings affect fastener torque and joint clamping force and may damage the fastener. Use the correct tightening sequence and specifications when installing fasteners in order to avoid damage to parts and systems.

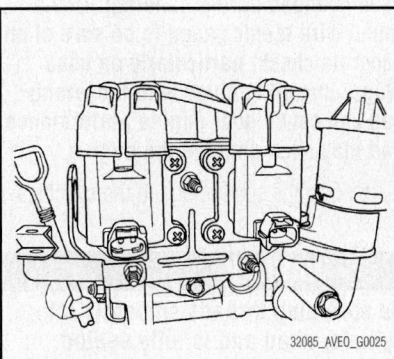

Fig. 47 The removal and installation of the ignition coil

To install:

7. Install the EI system ignition coil into the mounting location and install the retaining nuts. Tighten the EI system ignition coil retaining nuts to 89 inch lbs. (10 Nm).

8. Connect the EI system ignition coil connector.

9. Connect the negative battery cable.

IGNITION SYSTEM

1.6L (LXV) Engine

See Figures 48 and 49.

✳ WARNING

Before servicing any electrical component, the ignition key must be in the OFF, or LOCK position and all electrical loads must be OFF, unless instructed otherwise in these procedures. If a tool or equipment could easily come in contact with a live exposed electrical terminal, also disconnect the negative battery cable. Failure to follow these precautions may cause personal injury and/or damage to the vehicle or its components.

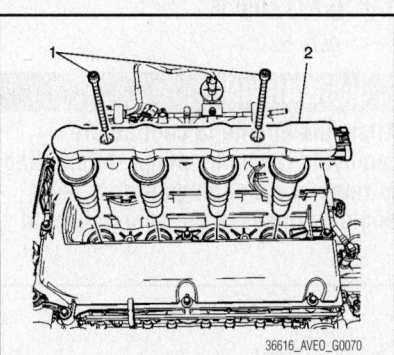

Fig. 48 Remove the ignition coil bolts (1) from the coil assembly (2)

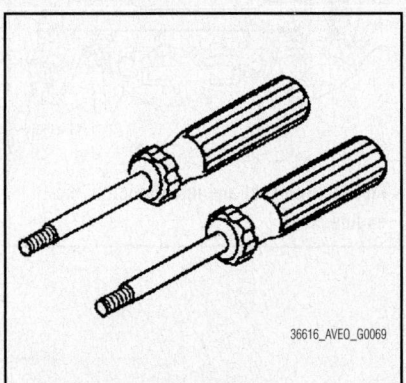

Fig. 49 Special tool KM-6009

1. Before servicing the vehicle, refer to the precautions section.
2. Detach the ignition coil cover.
3. Disconnect the ignition coil connector.
4. Remove the ignition coil bolts.
5. Install the KM-6009 to assist in the removal of the coil assembly.
6. Remove the ignition coil assembly.

To install:

7. Install the ignition coil assembly.
8. Install the ignition coil assembly retaining bolts. Tighten the bolts to 71 inch. lbs. (8 Nm).
9. Connect the ignition coil assembly connector.
10. Install the ignition coil cover.
11. Connect the battery negative cable.

IGNITION TIMING

INSPECTION

The ignition timing is controlled by the Engine Control Module (ECM). No adjustment is necessary or possible.

SPARK PLUGS

REMOVAL & INSTALLATION

1.6L (LXT) Engine

See Figure 50.

✳✳ WARNING

Allow the engine to cool before removing the spark plugs. Attempting to remove spark plugs from a hot engine can cause the spark plugs to

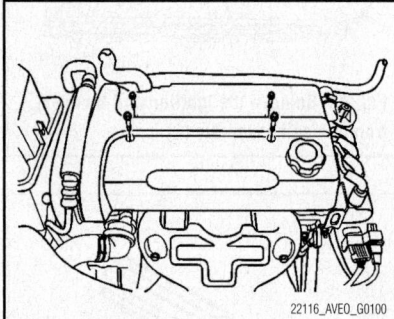

22116_AVEO_G0100

Fig. 50 Removal and installation of the engine cover

seize. This can damage the cylinder head threads.

✳✳ WARNING

Clean the spark plug recess area before removing the spark plug. Failure to do so can result in engine damage due to dirt or foreign material entering the cylinder head, or in contamination of the cylinder head threads. Contaminated threads may prevent proper seating of the new spark plug.

✳✳ WARNING

Use only the spark plugs specified for use in the vehicle. Do not install spark plugs that are either hotter or colder than those specified for the vehicle. Installing spark plugs of another type can severely damage the engine.

1. Turn OFF the ignition.
2. Loosen the 4 bolts and remove the engine cover.
3. Remove the spark plug wires from the spark plugs.
4. Remove the spark plugs from the engine.

To install:

➡ It is important to check the gap of all new and reconditioned spark plugs before installation. Pre-set gaps may have changed during handling. Use a round wire feeler gauge to be sure of an accurate check, particularly on used plugs. Installing plugs with the wrong gap can cause poor engine performance and may even damage the engine.

5. Gap the spark plugs to the specifications.

✳✳ WARNING

Be sure plug threads smoothly into cylinder head and is fully seated. Use a thread chaser if necessary to clean threads in cylinder head. Cross-threading or failing to fully seat spark plug can cause overheating of plug, exhaust blow-by, or thread damage. Follow the recom-

mended torque specifications carefully. Over or under-tightening can also cause severe damage to engine or spark plug.

6. Install the spark plugs to the engine.
7. Tighten the spark plugs to 18 ft. lbs. (25 Nm).
8. Install the spark plug wires to the spark plugs.
9. Install the engine cover and tighten the 4 bolts.
10. Tighten the engine cover bolts to 31 inch lbs. (3 Nm)

1.6L (LXV) Engine

See Figures 48 and 49.

✳✳ WARNING

Before servicing any electrical component, the ignition key must be in the OFF, or LOCK position and all electrical loads must be OFF, unless instructed otherwise in these procedures. If a tool or equipment could easily come in contact with a live exposed electrical terminal, also disconnect the negative battery cable. Failure to follow these precautions may cause personal injury and/or damage to the vehicle or its components.

1. Before servicing the vehicle, refer to the precautions section.
2. Detach the ignition coil cover.
3. Disconnect the ignition coil connector.
4. Remove the ignition coil bolts.
5. Install the KM-6009 to assist in the removal of the coil assembly.
6. Remove the ignition coil assembly.
7. Remove the spark plugs.

To install:

8. Install the spark plugs and tighten to 18 ft. lbs. (25 Nm).
9. Install the ignition coil assembly.
10. Install the ignition coil assembly retaining bolts. Tighten the bolts to 71 inch. lbs. (8 Nm).
11. Connect the ignition coil assembly connector.
12. Install the ignition coil cover.
13. Connect the battery negative cable.

ENGINE ELECTRICAL

STARTING SYSTEM

STARTER

REMOVAL & INSTALLATION

See Figure 51.

1. Before servicing the vehicle, refer to the precautions section.
2. Disconnect the negative battery cable.
3. Raise and support the vehicle safely.
4. Disconnect the starter electrical harness.
5. Remove the starter ground bolt.
6. Support the starter and remove the bolts.

7. Remove the starter from the vehicle.

To install:

8. Before servicing the vehicle, refer to the precautions in the beginning of this section.
9. Install the starter. Tighten the mounting bolts to 18 ft. lbs. (25 Nm). Tighten the solenoid nut to 8 ft. lbs. (10 Nm).
10. Install the ground bolt and tighten to 30 ft. lbs. (41 Nm).
11. Connect the starter electrical harness.
12. Connect the negative battery cable.

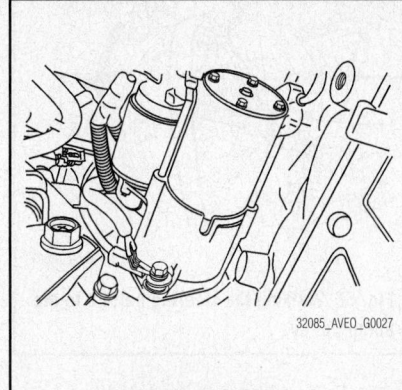

32085_AVEO_G0027

Fig. 51 Location of the starter

ENGINE MECHANICAL

ACCESSORY DRIVE BELTS

ACCESSORY BELT ROUTING

See Figure 52.

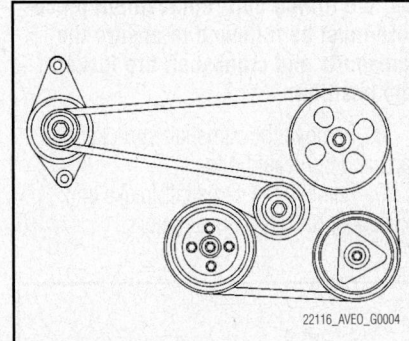

22116_AVEO_G0004

Fig. 52 Accessory drive belt routing— 1.6L engine

INSPECTION

Inspect the drive belt for signs of glazing or cracking. A glazed belt will be perfectly smooth from slippage, while a good belt will have a slight texture of fabric visible. Cracks will usually start at the inner edge of the belt and run outward. All worn or damaged drive belts should be replaced immediately.

ADJUSTMENT

It is not necessary to adjust belt tension on the accessory drive belt for the 1.6L engine. This engine is equipped with an automatic belt tensioner. The tensioner maintains correct belt tension at all times.

REMOVAL & INSTALLATION

See Figures 53 through 55.

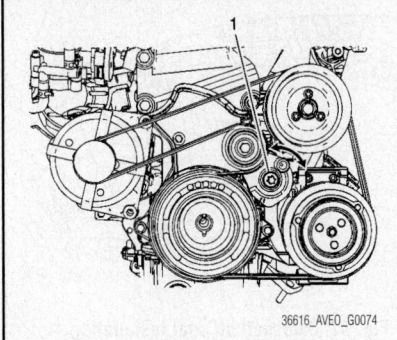

36616_AVEO_G0074

Fig. 53 Accessory drive belt and belt tensioner (1)

1. Before servicing the vehicle, refer to the precautions section.
2. Remove the engine front shield at the position of right front wheel.
3. Rotate the tensioner star-nut and remove the accessory belt.

To install:

4. Rotate the tensioner star-nut and install the accessory belt.
5. Install the engine front shield at the position of right front wheel.

Power Steering Belt 1.6L—LXV Engine

6. Before servicing the vehicle, refer to the precautions section.
7. Remove the engine accessory drive belt.
8. Remove the RH headlamp assembly.
9. Remove the air cleaner assembly.
10. Place a long bar in the opening between engine and pump drive belt. This will provide a guide function for the drive belt removal.
11. Using the bar push the drive belt into the opposite side of engine.

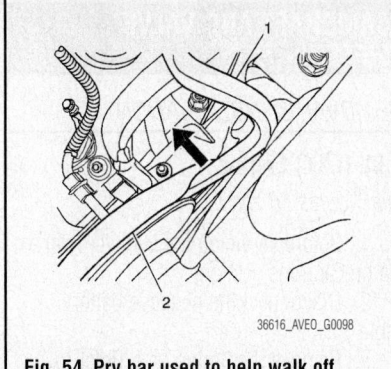

36616_AVEO_G0098

Fig. 54 Pry bar used to help walk off steering belt

12. Rotate the pulley using ⅜ inch hex bit socket in the power steering pump pulley shaft hole.
13. Rotate the power steering pump pulley clockwise while pushing the drive belt until the belt is fully removed from the pulley.

To install:

14. Route the power steering pump drive belt.
15. Align the drive belt on the water pump pulley first.
16. Position one of the three pulley holes on top point.
17. Through the pulley hole tie the driver belt to the pump pulley using a cable tie. This will provide a guide function for the drive belt installation.

Rotate the pulley using ⅜ inch hex bit socket in the power steering pump pulley shaft hole.

18. Rotate the power steering pump pulley clockwise until the belt is fully installed on the pulley.

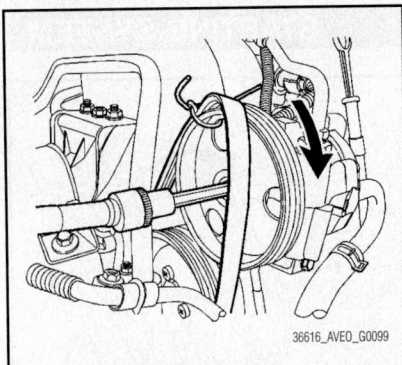

Fig. 55 Walking the steering belt on to the pump pulley

19. Remove the rope or cable tie.
20. Inspect for correct belt installation.
21. Install the air cleaner assembly.
22. Install the RH headlamp assembly.
23. Install the engine accessory belt.

CAMSHAFT AND VALVE LIFTERS

REMOVAL & INSTALLATION

1.6L (LXT) Engine

See Figures 56 and 57.

1. Before servicing the vehicle, refer to the precautions section.
2. Disconnect the negative battery cable.
3. Remove the timing belt. Refer to Timing Belt Removal & Installation.
4. Remove the engine appearance cover.
5. Disconnect the spark plug wires from the spark plugs.
6. Disconnect the crankcase ventilation tubes from the valve cover.
7. Disconnect the Camshaft Position (CMP) sensor.
8. Remove the valve cover and the valve cover gasket.
9. Remove the camshaft sprockets.
10. Remove the camshaft cap bolts in several steps in the sequence shown.

➡**Keep the camshaft caps in order for reinstallation.**

11. Remove the camshaft caps and camshafts.
12. Remove the camshaft oil seals.

To install:

13. Lubricate the camshaft journals and the camshaft caps with clean engine oil.
14. Install the intake/exhaust camshaft caps in their original positions, and tighten the cap bolts in the sequence shown to 12 ft. lbs. (16 Nm).

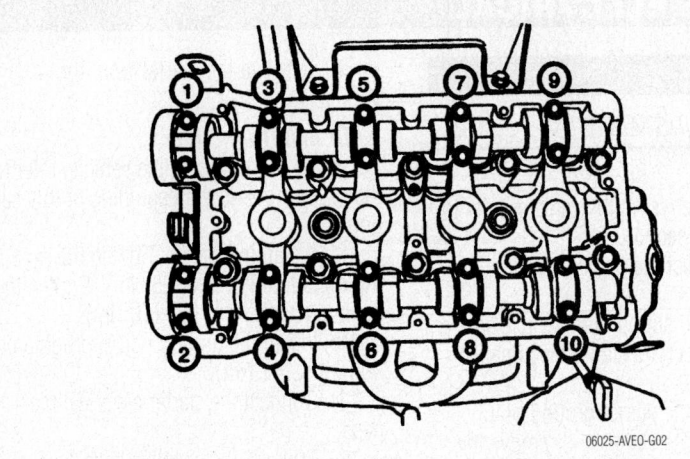

Fig. 56 Camshaft bearing cap bolt removal and installation sequence—1.6L engine

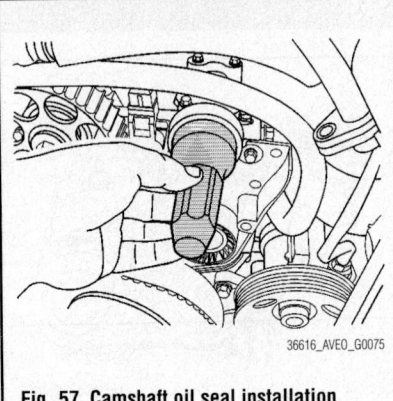

Fig. 57 Camshaft oil seal installation

15. Install new camshaft oil seals by using EN-48803 seal installer.
16. Install the camshaft sprockets. Tighten the bolt to 49 ft. lbs. (66 Nm).
17. Install the valve cover and gasket. Tighten the bolts nuts to 80 inch lbs. (9 Nm).
18. Connect the spark plugs wires to the spark plugs.
19. Connect the CMP sensor.
20. Install the engine appearance cover. Tighten the bolts to 27 inch lbs. (3 Nm).
21. Connect the ventilation tubes to the valve cover.
22. Install the timing belt. Refer to Timing Belt Removal & Installation.
23. Connect the negative battery cable.

1.6L (LXV) Engine

See Figures 58 through 62.

1. Before servicing the vehicle, refer to the precautions section.
2. Disconnect the negative battery cable.
3. Remove the air cleaner assembly.
4. Install the J 28647-B Engine Support Fixture.

5. Remove the accessory belt.
6. Remove the accessory belt tensioner.
7. Remove timing belt. Refer to timing belt and sprockets Removal & Installation.

➡**When removing the camshaft sprockets, the timing belt replacement procedure must be followed to ensure the camshafts and crankshaft are locked into position.**

8. Remove the camshaft sprocket bolt caps and sprocket bolts.
9. Remove the camshaft intake and exhaust sprockets with actuators.

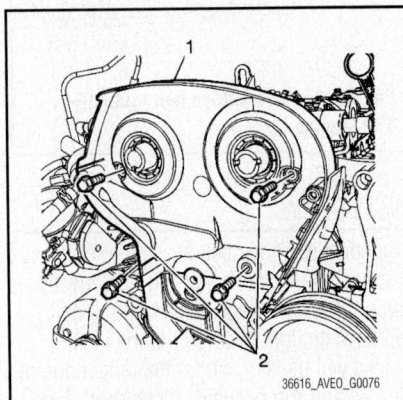

Fig. 58 Timing belt rear cover (1) and retaining bolts (2)

10. Remove the timing belt rear cover.
11. Remove the camshaft position solenoid valve housing.
12. Remove the camshaft cap bolts in sequence (1, 4, 2, 3).
13. Remove the camshaft caps.
14. Remove the intake and exhaust camshafts with the oil seals.

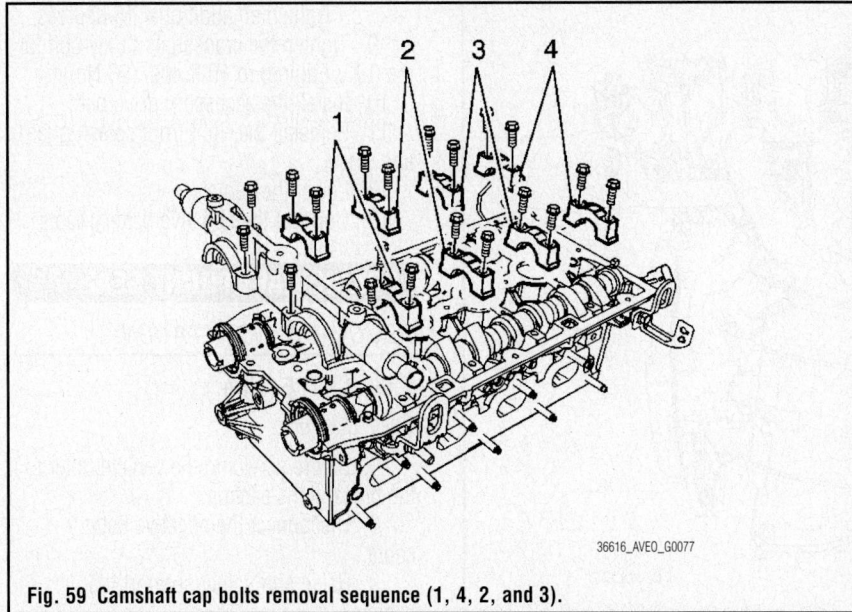

Fig. 59 Camshaft cap bolts removal sequence (1, 4, 2, and 3).

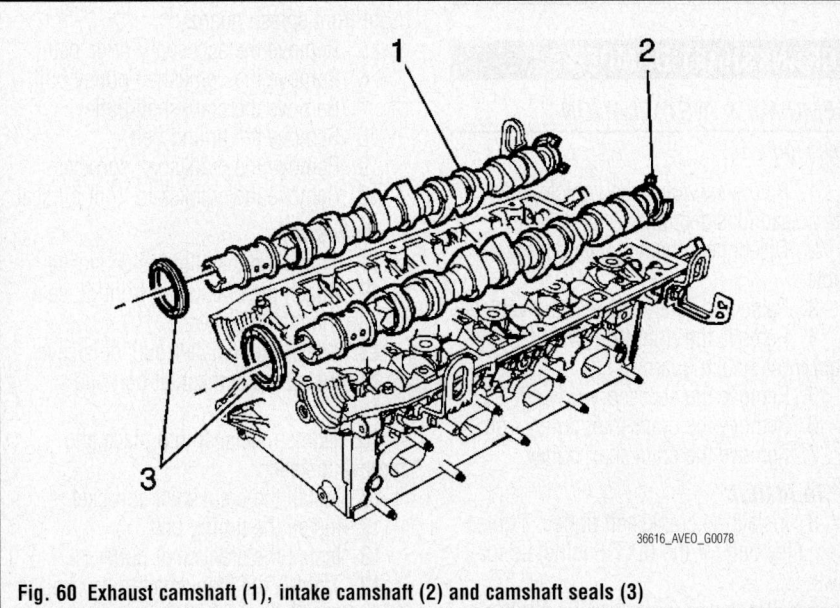

Fig. 60 Exhaust camshaft (1), intake camshaft (2) and camshaft seals (3)

To install:

15. Lubricate the camshaft bearing and cam surfaces with clean engine oil.

16. Install the camshafts on the cylinder head.

➡**The grooves adjacent to the sealing surfaces must remain free from sealant.**

17. Apply surface sealant LOCTITE® 574 to sealing surfaces (1) of the 1st camshaft bearing cap thinly and evenly.

18. Install the camshaft bearing caps in sequence (2, 3, 1, 4). Refer to the removal sequence graphic.

19. Install the camshaft position solenoid valve housing.

20. Tighten the camshaft bearing cap

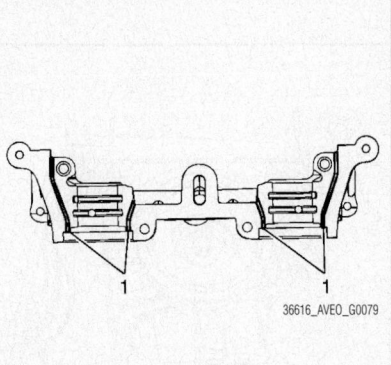

Fig. 61 Grooves (1) must remain free from sealant

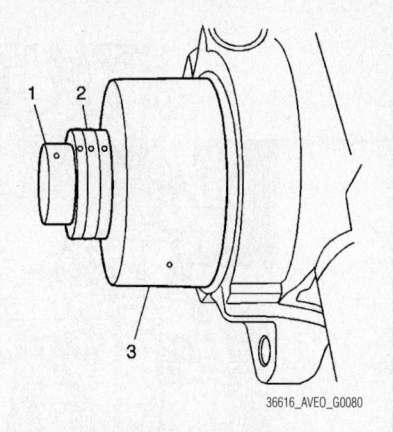

Fig. 62 Camshaft seal installation using special tool KM-422

and solenoid valve housing bolts to 71 inch. lbs. (8 Nm).

21. Install the new camshaft oil seals.

22. Install the KM-422 installer (3) with shims (2), with a total thickness of approximately 10 mm and tighten the camshaft bolt (1) manually.

23. Install the timing belt rear cover, tighten the bolts to 53 inch. lbs. (6 Nm).

24. Install the timing belt tensioner.

25. Install the camshaft intake and exhaust sprockets with actuators.

26. Tighten the camshaft sprocket bolts to 48 ft. lbs. (65 Nm).

27. Tighten the camshaft sprocket bolt cap to 37 ft. lbs. (50 Nm).

28. Install the timing belt. Refer to timing belt and sprockets Removal & Installation.

29. Install the accessory belt tensioner.

30. Install the accessory belt.

31. Remove the J 28647-B Engine Support Fixture.

32. Install the air cleaner assembly.

33. Connect the negative battery cable.

CATALYTIC CONVERTER

REMOVAL & INSTALLATION

See Figures 63 and 64.

1. Before servicing the vehicle, refer to the precautions section.

2. Disconnect the battery negative cable

3. Disconnect the front heated oxygen sensor connector.

4. Remove the oil level gage tube.

5. Remove the exhaust manifold heat shield.

6. Remove the catalytic converter upper flange nuts.

7. Remove the exhaust front pipe mounting bracket bolt.

8. Remove the catalytic converter lower flange nuts.

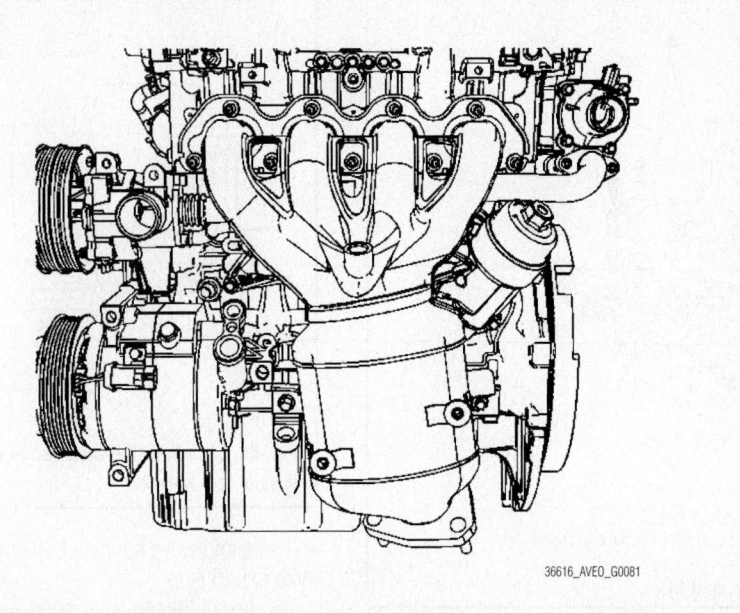

Fig. 63 Remove the catalytic converter upper flange nuts

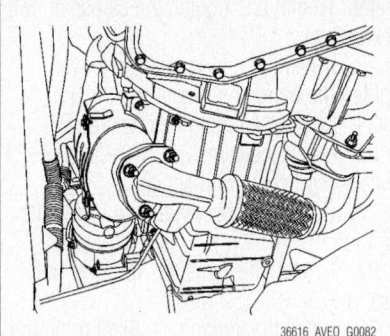

Fig. 64 Remove the catalytic converter lower flange nuts

9. Remove the catalytic converter and the gasket.

To install:

10. Install the catalytic converter and the gasket.

11. Install the catalytic converter lower flange nuts and the exhaust front pipe mounting bracket and tighten.
- The exhaust front pipe to catalytic converter nuts to 30 ft. lbs. (40 Nm).
- The exhaust front pipe mounting bracket bolt to 30 ft. lbs. (40 Nm).

12. Install the catalytic converter upper flange nuts to exhaust manifold nuts to 30 ft. lbs. (40 Nm).

13. Install the exhaust manifold heat shield and tighten to 6 ft. lbs. (8 Nm).

14. Install the oil level gage tube. Check engine oil level.

15. Connect the front heated oxygen sensor connector.

16. Connect the battery negative cable.

CRANKSHAFT DAMPER

REMOVAL & INSTALLATION

See Figure 65.

1. Before servicing the vehicle, refer to the precautions section.

2. Disconnect the negative battery cable.

3. Raise and safely support the vehicle.

4. Remove the right front wheel and right front splash guard.

5. Remove the accessory drive belt.

6. Remove the crankshaft pulley bolt.

7. Remove the crankshaft pulley.

To install:

8. Install the crankshaft pulley. Tighten the pulley bolt for the (LXT Engine) as follows:
   a. Tighten to 70 ft. lbs. (95 Nm).
   b. Tighten an additional 30 degrees.

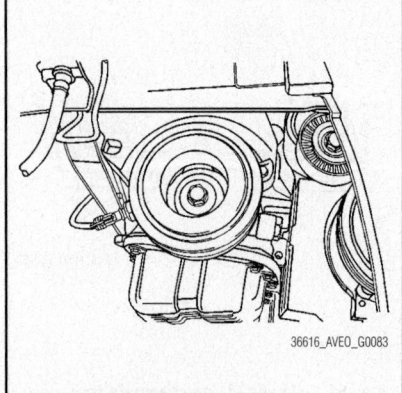

Fig. 65 Crankshaft pulley view

c. Tighten an additional 15 degrees.

9. Tighten the crankshaft pulley bolt for the (LXV Engine) to 19 ft. lbs. (25 Nm).

10. Install the accessory drive belt.

11. Reinstall the right front splash guard and wheel.

12. Lower the vehicle.

13. Connect the negative battery cable.

CRANKSHAFT FRONT SEAL

REMOVAL & INSTALLATION

1.6L (LXV) Engine

See Figure 66.

1. Before servicing the vehicle, refer to the precautions section.

2. Disconnect the negative battery cable.

3. Raise and safely support the vehicle.

4. Remove the right front wheel and right front splash guard.

5. Remove the accessory drive belt.

6. Remove the crankshaft pulley bolt.

7. Remove the crankshaft pulley.

8. Remove the timing belt.

9. Remove the crankshaft sprocket.

10. Remove the crankshaft front oil seal.

To install:

11. Attach the installer inside sleeve.

12. Attach the crankshaft front oil seal ring to the inside sleeve.

13. Attach the installer outside sleeve.

14. Install the crankshaft bolt and washer.

15. Tighten the seal into place and remove installer.

16. Install the crankshaft sprocket.

17. Install the timing belt.

18. Install the crankshaft pulley.

19. Tighten the crankshaft pulley bolt to 19 ft. lbs. (25 Nm).

20. Install the accessory drive belt.

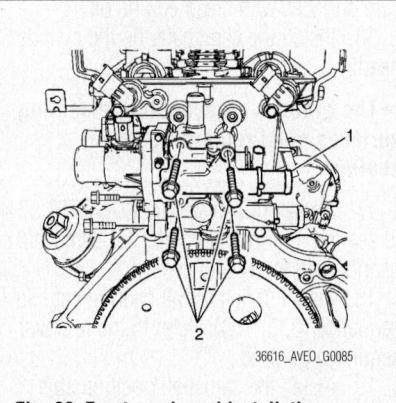

Fig. 66 Front crank seal installation

21. Reinstall the right front splash guard and wheel.

22. Lower the vehicle.

23. Connect the negative battery cable.

CYLINDER HEAD

REMOVAL & INSTALLATION

1.6L (LXT Engine)

See Figures 67 and 68.

1. Before servicing the vehicle, refer to the precautions section.

2. Properly relieve the fuel system pressure.

3. Disconnect the negative battery cable.

4. Drain the cooling system.

5. Disconnect the breather tube from the valve cover.

6. Disconnect the Intake Air Temperature (IAT) sensor connector.

7. Disconnect the air intake assembly from the throttle body.

8. Remove the air filter housing.

9. Disconnect the A/C Pressure (ACP) transducer connector.

10. Disconnect the Idle Air Control (IAC) valve connector and throttle position (TP) sensor connector.

11. Disconnect the throttle cable from the throttle body and the intake manifold.

12. Disconnect the engine coolant hose at the throttle body.

13. Disconnect the Manifold Absolute Pressure (MAP) sensor connector.

14. Disconnect the brake booster vacuum hose.

15. Disconnect the variable geometry induction solenoid (VGIS) connector.

16. Disconnect the VGIS vacuum tank hose.

17. Remove the engine appearance cover bolts and the cover.

18. Disconnect the breather tube from the valve cover.

19. Disconnect the crankcase ventilation tube from the valve cover.

20. Disconnect the Camshaft Position (CMP) sensor connector.

21. Disconnect the ignition wires from the spark plugs.

22. Disconnect the fuel injector harness connectors.

23. Disconnect the fuel line.

24. Remove the bracket nut from the power steering pressure pipe and remove the power steering pressure pipe.

25. Remove the accessory drive bolt.

26. Disconnect the Exhaust Gas Recirculation (EGR) valve connector.

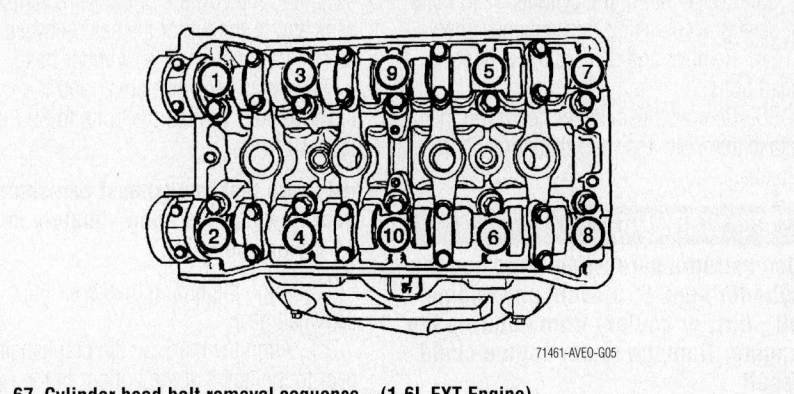

Fig. 67 Cylinder head bolt removal sequence—(1.6L EXT Engine)

71461-AVEO-G05

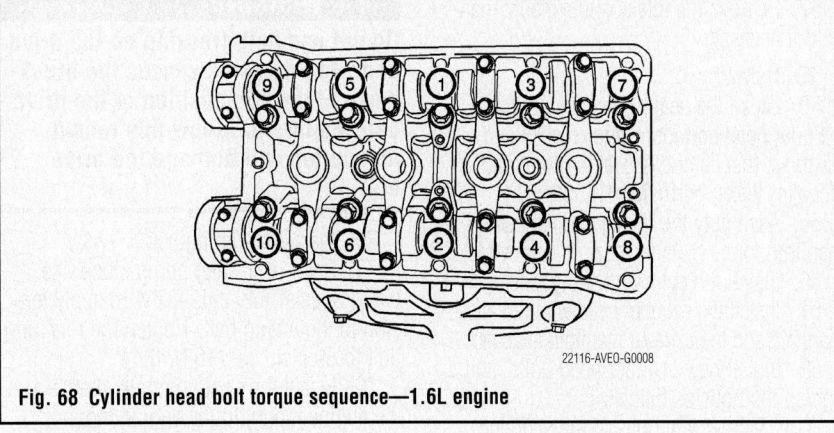

Fig. 68 Cylinder head bolt torque sequence—1.6L engine

22116-AVEO-G0008

27. Disconnect the ignition coil connector from the Electronic Ignition (EI) system.

28. Disconnect the front HO2S connector.

29. Raise and safely support the vehicle.

30. Remove the right front wheel.

31. Remove the engine under-cover.

32. Remove the canister purge solenoid valve at the intake manifold support bracket.

33. Remove the bracket bolts from the upper and lower intake manifold support.

34. Disconnect the connector from the Engine Coolant Temperature (ECT) sensor.

35. Remove the exhaust manifold heat shield.

36. Remove the catalytic converter.

37. Loosen the hose clamp on the upper radiator hose at the thermostat housing and disconnect the upper radiator hose.

38. Remove the cover from the upper front timing belt.

39. Remove the crankshaft damper.

40. Remove the cover from the lower front timing belt.

41. Align the camshaft gear timing marks.

42. Slightly loosen the water pump retaining bolts.

43. Rotate the coolant pump counter-

clockwise using Special Tool J 42492-A to relieve the timing belt tension.

44. Remove the timing belt. For additional information, refer to the following section, "Timing Belt & Sprockets, Removal & Installation."

45. Remove the valve cover.

✳✳ WARNING

Use extreme care when installing the camshaft not to nick, scratch, or damage the camshaft lobes or bearing surfaces.

46. While holding the intake camshaft firmly in place, remove the intake camshaft gear bolt and remove the intake camshaft gear.

47. While holding the exhaust camshaft firmly in place, remove the exhaust camshaft gear bolt and remove the exhaust camshaft gear.

48. Remove the bolts from the timing belt automatic tensioner and remove the timing belt automatic tensioner.

49. Remove the Camshaft Position (CMP) sensor.

50. Remove the timing belt idler pulley.

51. Remove the rear timing belt cover.

52. Disconnect the heater outlet hose from the coolant pipe.

53. Loosen all of the cylinder head bolts in several steps using the sequence shown.

54. Remove and discard the cylinder head bolts.

55. Remove the cylinder head with the intake manifold and the exhaust manifold attached.

❋❋ WARNING

Use extreme care when removing the cylinder head to prevent any engine oil , dirt, or coolant from entering the engine. Damage to the engine could result.

56. Remove the cylinder head gasket.

57. Remove the intake and exhaust manifold if necessary.

To install:

58. Clean the sealing surfaces of the cylinder head and inspect for cracks and warpage. Inspect the gasket and mating surfaces for leaks, corrosion and blow-by.

59. Assembly the intake and exhaust manifold to the cylinder head, if removed.

60. Install the cylinder head gasket.

61. Install the cylinder head with the intake manifold and the exhaust manifold attached.

62. Install new cylinder head bolts, and tighten the bolts as follows:

   a. Tighten the bolts in the sequence shown to 18 ft. lbs. (25 Nm).

   b. Tighten the bolts in the sequence shown an additional 60 degrees.

   c. Tighten the bolts in the sequence shown an additional 60 degrees for a second time.

   d. Tighten the bolts in the sequence shown an additional 60 degrees a third time.

   e. Tighten the bolts in the sequence shown an additional 10 degrees.

63. Connect the heater outlet hose to the coolant pipe.

64. Install the rear timing belt cover and tighten the bolts to 89 inch lbs. (10 Nm).

65. Install the CMP sensor. Tighten the bolts to 106 inch lbs. (12 Nm).

66. Install the timing belt idler pulley and tighten the bolt to 30 ft. lbs. (40 Nm).

67. Install the timing belt automatic tensioner. Tighten the bolts to 18 ft. lbs. (25 Nm).

68. Install the intake camshaft gear. While holding the intake camshaft firmly in place, tighten the intake camshaft gear bolt to 49 ft. lbs. (66 Nm).

69. Install the exhaust camshaft gear. While holding the exhaust camshaft firmly in place, tighten the exhaust camshaft gear bolt to 49 ft. lbs. (66 Nm).

70. Apply a small amount of gasket sealant to the corners of the front camshaft caps and to the top of the seal between the rear valve cover and the cylinder head.

71. Install the valve cover and the valve cover gasket. Tighten the bolts to 89 inch lbs. (10 Nm).

➡**Ensure that the exhaust camshaft gear dowel pin is approximately in the 11 o'clock position.**

72. Align the timing marks on the camshaft gear.

73. Align the mark on the crankshaft gear to the notch at the bottom of the rear timing belt cover.

❋❋ WARNING

Do not use belt dressing on the drive belt. Belt dressing causes the breakdown of the composition of the drive belt. Failure to follow this recommendation will damage the drive belt.

74. Install the timing belt.

75. Rotate the water pump clockwise using Special Tool J 42492-A to apply tension to the timing belt. Tighten the retaining bolt to 89 inch lbs. (10 Nm).

76. Install the retaining bolts that secure the engine mount to the engine mount bracket. Tighten to 44 ft. lbs. (60 Nm).

77. Install the lower front timing belt cover and tighten the bolts to 89 inch lbs. (10 Nm).

78. Install the crankshaft pulley. For additional information, refer to the following section, "Crankshaft Damper, Removal & Installation."

79. Install the upper front timing belt cover and tighten the bolts to 89 inch lbs. (10 Nm).

80. Connect the coolant hoses to the thermostat housing.

81. Install the catalytic converter.

82. Install the exhaust manifold heat shield.

83. Connect the ECT sensor connector.

84. Install the upper bolts to the intake manifold support bracket and tighten to 18 ft. lbs. (25 Nm).

85. Install the canister purge solenoid valve at the intake manifold support bracket.

86. Install the engine under-cover.

87. Connect the front HO2S connector.

88. Connect the EI system ignition coil connector.

89. Connect the EGR valve connector.

90. Install the accessory drive belt.

91. Reconnect the following:
- The fuel line at the fuel rail
- Fuel injector harness connectors
- Ignition wires to the spark plugs
- CMP sensor connector
- Crankcase ventilation tube to the valve cover
- Breather tube to the valve cover

92. Install the engine cover.

93. Reconnect the following:
- VGIS vacuum tank hose
- VGIS connector
- Brake booster vacuum hose
- MAP sensor connector
- Coolant hoses to the throttle body
- Throttle cable to the throttle body and the intake manifold
- TP sensor connector
- IAC valve connector
- A/C pressure transducer connector

94. Install the air intake assembly.

95. Connect the IAT sensor connector.

96. Connect the breather tube to the valve cover.

97. Connect the negative battery cable.

98. Refill the engine cooling system to the correct level.

99. Start the engine and check for leaks.

1.6L (LXV Engine)

See Figures 69 and 70.

1. Before servicing the vehicle, refer to the precautions section.

2. Drain the engine coolant.

3. Remove the fuel pump fuse.

4. Start the engine. Crank the engine after the engine stalls for 10 seconds to rid the fuel system of fuel pressure.

5. Disconnect the negative battery cable.

6. Remove the timing belt, refer to the following section, "Timing Belt & Sprockets, Removal & Installation."

7. Remove the timing belt tensioner.

8. Remove the camshaft.

9. Remove the timing belt rear cover.

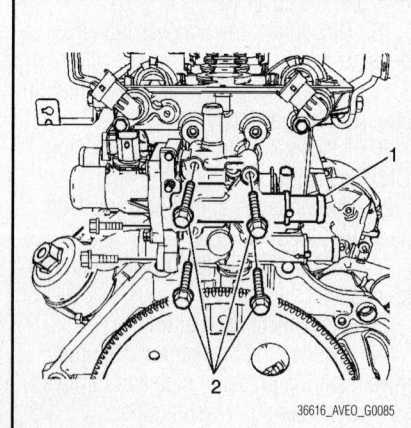

36616_AVEO_G0085

Fig. 69 Coolant distributor (1) mounting bolts (2)

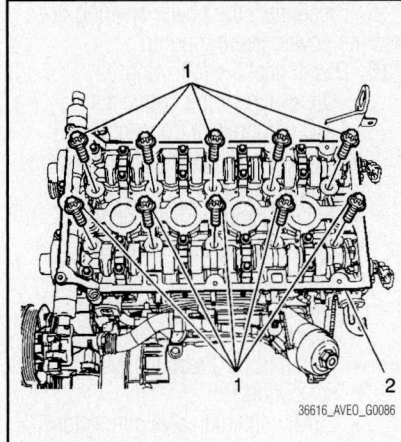

Fig. 70 Remove the bolts (1) from cylinder head (2)

10. Remove the intake manifold, refer to the following section, "Intake Manifold, Removal & Installation."

11. Remove the exhaust manifold, refer to the following section, "Exhaust Manifold, Removal & Installation."

12. Remove the coolant distributor.

13. Remove the cylinder head bolts.

14. Remove the cylinder head with the gasket.

15. Clean the sealing surfaces of the cylinder head and inspect for cracks and warpage. Inspect the gasket and mating surfaces for leaks, corrosion and blow-by.

To install:

16. Install new cylinder head bolts, and tighten the bolts as follows:
- Tighten the bolts in the sequence shown to 18 ft. lbs. (25 Nm).
- Tighten the bolts in the sequence an additional 90 degrees.
- Tighten the bolts in the sequence an additional 90 degrees for a second time.
- Tighten the bolts in the sequence an additional 90 degrees a third time.
- Tighten the bolts in the sequence an additional 45 degrees.

17. Install the coolant distributor.

18. Install the exhaust manifold.

19. Install the intake manifold. Install the timing belt rear cover and tighten to 53 inch. lbs. (6 Nm).

20. Install the camshaft.

21. Install and adjust the belt timing.

22. Connect the negative battery cable.

23. Refill and bleed the engine cooling system.

24. Start the engine and check for leaks.

ENGINE ASSEMBLY

REMOVAL & INSTALLATION

1.6L (LXT Engine)

See Figures 71 through 73.

1. Before servicing the vehicle, refer to the precautions section.

2. Properly relieve the fuel system pressure.

3. Drain the engine oil.

4. Disconnect the battery cables.

5. Remove the battery and the battery tray.

6. Properly discharge the Air Conditioning (A/C) system, if equipped, using a suitable refrigerant recovery station.

7. Drain the engine cooling system.

8. Remove the radiator and engine cooling fan.

9. Disconnect the upper radiator hose from the thermostat housing.

10. Disconnect the power steering hoses from the power steering pump, if equipped.

11. Disconnect the Intake Air Temperature (IAT) sensor connector.

12. Disconnect the breather tube from the valve cover.

13. Disconnect the air intake tube from the throttle body.

14. Remove the air intake assembly.

15. Remove the spark plug cover.

16. Disconnect the connector from the Idle Air Control (IAC) valve, Throttle Position Sensor (TPS), A/C Pressure (ACP) transducer, if equipped, and Camshaft Position (CMP) sensor.

17. Disconnect the throttle cable from the throttle body and from the intake manifold bracket.

18. Disconnect the connector from the Manifold Absolute Pressure (MAP) sensor.

19. Disconnect the ignition wires from the spark plugs.

20. Disconnect the surge tank coolant hose at the throttle body.

21. Disconnect the fuel injector electrical connectors.

22. Disconnect the electrical connector from the Exhaust Gas Recirculation (EGR) valve.

23. Disconnect the electrical connector at the Electronic Ignition (EI) system ignition coil.

24. Disconnect the oxygen sensor connector.

25. Disconnect the electrical connector from the Crankshaft Position Sensor (CPS).

26. Disconnect all of the necessary vacuum lines.

27. Disconnect the brake booster vacuum hose at the intake manifold.

28. Disconnect the fuel supply hose at the fuel rail.

29. Remove the mounting bolts from the battery tray support and remove the battery tray support.

30. Disconnect the lower radiator hose from the coolant pipe.

31. Remove the bolt from the A/C compressor pipe and hose assembly, if equipped.

32. Remove the A/C compressor pipe and hose assembly from the compressor.

33. Raise and safely support the vehicle.

34. Remove the front tires.

35. Remove the front splash shield and the engine undercover.

36. If equipped with Automatic Transmission (A/T):
- Disconnect the A/T oil cooler inlet/outlet pipe.
- Disconnect the A/T shift control cable.
- Disconnect all of the A/T electrical connectors.

37. Disconnect the electrical connector at the A/C compressor coil, if equipped.

38. Disconnect the connector from the rear Heat Oxygen Sensor (HO2S).

39. Remove the front exhaust pipe as follows:
- Remove the lower flange nuts from the exhaust manifold studs, retain the gasket, and then remove the bracket mounting bolts.
- Remove the nuts that secure the front muffler pipe. Retain the gasket.
- Remove the front exhaust pipe as a unit.

40. Remove the nut and bolt from the damping block connection.

41. Remove bolts from the rear mounting bracket. Remove the bracket.

42. Remove the A/T drive axle, if equipped.

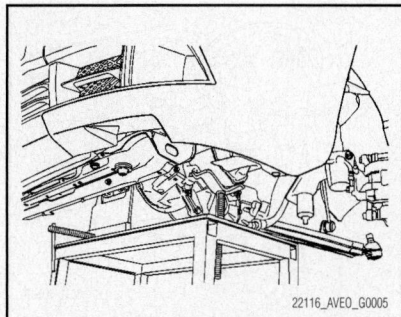

Fig. 71 Install a suitable engine lifting device to remove the engine/transaxle assembly from the vehicle.

43. Disconnect the electrical connector at the oil pressure switch.

44. Remove the battery harness connector nut from the alternator.

45. Disconnect the electrical connector from the alternator voltage regulator.

46. Disconnect the electrical connector from the EVAP emission canister purge solenoid.

47. Remove the bolts from the intake manifold support bracket and remove the intake manifold support bracket.

48. Disconnect the electrical connector from the Engine Coolant Temperature (ECT) sensor.

49. Remove the lower starter mounting bolt.

50. Remove the starter solenoid nuts in order to disconnect the electrical cable.

51. Remove the lower engine wiring harness.

52. Remove the rubber from the oil pan.

53. Remove the torque converter service cover and the bolts.

54. Install the engine lifting device.

55. Remove the retaining bolts from the engine mounting bracket, then remove the bracket from the engine block.

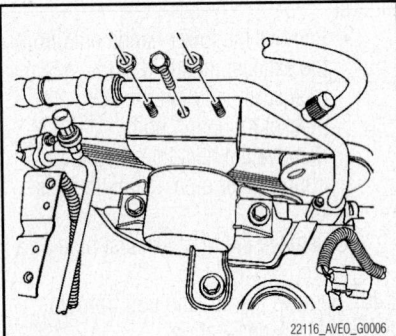

22116_AVEO_G0006

Fig. 72 Remove the mounting bracket retaining bolts . . .

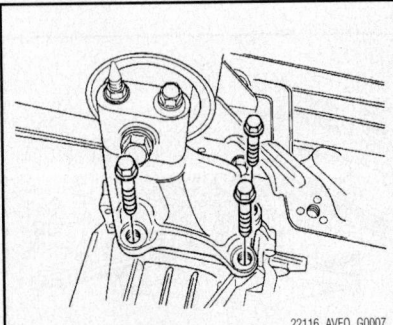

22116_AVEO_G0007

Fig. 73 . . . and remove the upper transaxle mounting bracket bolts to remove the engine assembly.

56. Remove the 3 bolts from the upper transaxle mounting bracket.

57. Verify at this point that the engine and transaxle assembly is not attached to the vehicle.

58. Lift up the vehicle slowly to separate the engine and transaxle assembly from the vehicle.

59. Separate the engine block from the transaxle to remove the engine.

To install:

60. Connect the engine to the transaxle, then lift the engine/transaxle assembly into the engine compartment using a suitable engine lifting device.

61. Install the right engine mount bracket to the engine block. Install and tighten the engine mounting bolts to 44 ft. lbs. (60 Nm).

62. Install the 3 upper transaxle mounting bolts and tighten to 44 ft. lbs. (60 Nm).

63. Install the service cover to the torque converter and tighten the bolts to 48 ft. lbs. (65 Nm).

64. The remainder of the installation is the reverse order of the removal procedure.

65. Refill the cooling system to the correct level.

66. Refill the engine with oil to the correct level.

67. Fill the A/C system, if equipped.

68. Bleed the power steering system, if equipped.

69. Start the engine and check for leaks.

1.6L (LXV Engine)

See Figures 74 and 75.

1. Before servicing the vehicle, refer to the precautions section.

2. Properly relieve the fuel system pressure.

3. Release the fuel pressure.

4. Disconnect the fuel pipe from the fuel rail.

5. Disconnect the EVAP hose from the EVAP canister solenoid valve.

6. Drain the engine coolant.

7. Remove the air cleaner assembly.

8. Remove the battery and tray.

9. Remove the fuse box bolts.

10. Discharge the A/C system, if equipped.

11. Remove the A/C inlet/outlet pipe bolt from the A/C compressor. Cover the compressor and pipe inlet/outlet ports.

12. Drain the power steering oil if equipped.

13. Remove the power steering pump pressure line union nut.

14. Remove the power steering pressure pipe retaining clamp bolt from the intake manifold.

15. Disconnect the power steering hose from the power steering pump.

16. Disconnect the following:

- Oil switch wiring connector
- A/C compressor connector
- Intake air temperature sensor connector
- A/C pressure sensor connector
- Cam position solenoid valve connector
- Electric Throttle Controller (ETC) connector
- Manifold Air Pressure (MAP) sensor connector
- EVAP solenoid valve connector
- Injector connectors
- Ignition coil connector
- Camshaft Position Sensor (CPS) connectors (right/left)
- Coolant temperature sensor connector
- Oxygen sensor connector
- Ground bolt
- Thermostat heater connector

17. Disconnect the following and pull the engine harness aside.

- Crankshaft Position (CKP) sensor connector
- Knock sensor connector
- Alternator connector
- Alternator B+ nut
- Oil level switch connector, if equipped
- Starter solenoid B+ nut
- Ground tightening nut
- Starter solenoid ground nut

18. Disconnect the coolant hose from water pump.

19. Disconnect the coolant hose from the thermostat housing.

20. Disconnect the heater core coolant inlet/outlet hoses from the coolant distributor.

21. Disconnect the ETC-to-coolant tank hose.

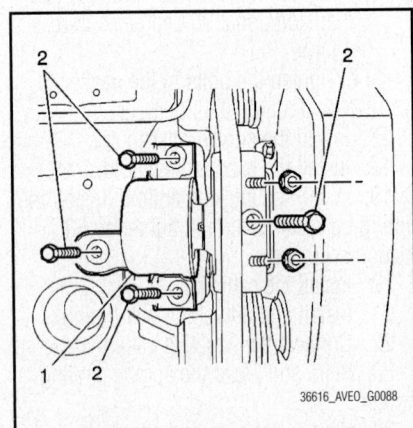

36616_AVEO_G0088

Fig. 74 Engine mount (1) retaining bolts (2)

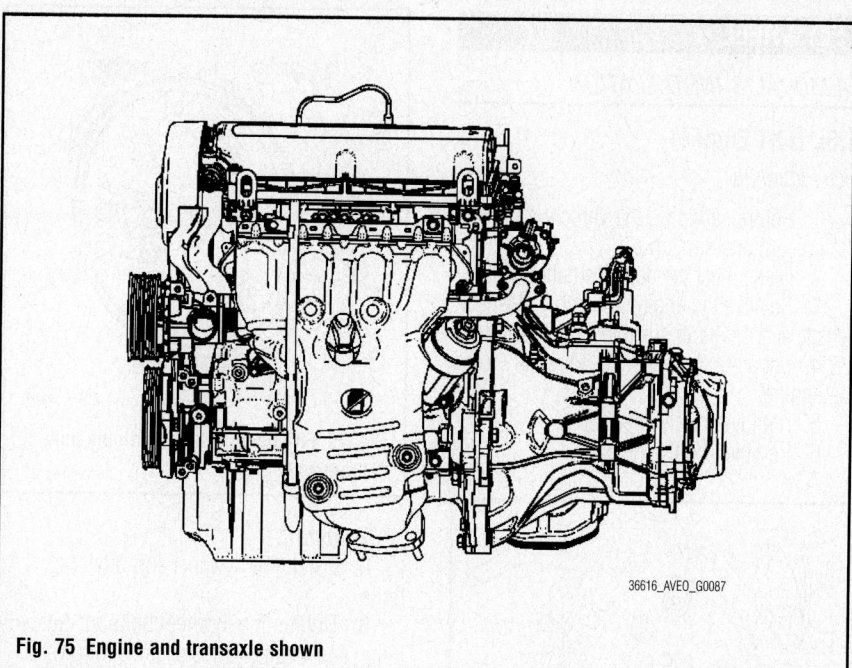

Fig. 75 Engine and transaxle shown

36616_AVEO_G0087

22. Disconnect the brake boost hose from the intake manifold.

23. Remove and disconnect the cables and wiring harness related to the automatic transaxle.

24. Disconnect the auto transaxle fluid cooler inlet/outlet hoses.

25. Remove and disconnect the cables and wiring harness related to the manual transaxle.

26. Remove the reaction rod.

27. Remove the exhaust front pipe.

28. Remove the drive axle shafts.

29. Raise the vehicle.

30. Install a suitable supporter under the vehicle engine and transaxle.

31. Lower the vehicle until engine assembly is on the supporter.

32. Remove the engine mount.

33. Remove the transaxle mount.

34. Separate the engine and the transaxle.

To install:

35. Assemble the engine to the transaxle.

36. Place the engine assembly on the supporter.

37. Raise the vehicle.

38. Locate the engine assembly with the supporter.

39. Lower the vehicle.

40. Install the engine mount and tighten the retaining bolts to 41 ft. lbs. (55 Nm).

41. Install the transaxle mount.

42. Install the drive axle shafts.

43. Install the exhaust front pipe.

44. Install the reaction rod.

45. Install and connect the cables and wiring harness related to the automatic transaxle.

46. Connect the auto transaxle fluid cooler inlet/outlet hoses.

47. Install and connect the cables and wiring harness related to the manual transaxle.

48. Connect the coolant hose to the water pump.

49. Connect the coolant hose to the thermostat housing.

50. Connect the heater core coolant inlet/outlet hoses to the coolant distributor.

51. Connect the ETC-to-coolant tank hose.

52. Connect the brake boost hose to the intake manifold

53. Position the engine harness and connect the following connectors:
- Crankshaft Position (CKP) sensor connector
- Knock sensor connector
- Alternator connector
- Alternator B+ nut, tighten to 11 ft. lbs. (15 Nm).
- Oil level switch connector, if equipped
- Starter solenoid B+ nut, tighten to 8 ft. lbs. (11 Nm).
- Ground nut, tighten to 9 ft. lbs. (12 Nm).
- Starter solenoid ground nut, tighten to 28 ft. lbs. (38 Nm).

54. Connect the following:
- Ignition coil connector
- Camshaft Position Sensor (CPS) connectors (right/left)
- Coolant temperature sensor connector

- Oxygen sensor connector
- Ground bolt, tighten to 9 ft. lbs. (12 Nm).
- Thermostat heater connector.
- Oil switch wiring connector
- A/C compressor connector

55. Install the power steering pump pressure line union nut.

56. Install the power steering pressure pipe retaining clamp bolt to the intake manifold.

57. Connect the power steering hose to the power steering pump

58. Install the A/C inlet/outlet pipe bolt from the A/C compressor if equipped. Remove coverings from the inlet/outlet connections.

59. Charge the A/C system.

60. Install the fuse box bolts.

61. Install the battery and tray.

62. Install the air cleaner assembly.

63. Connect the fuel pipe to the fuel rail.

64. Connect the EVAP hose to the EVAP canister solenoid valve.

65. Refill and bleed the cooling system.

66. Refill the engine with oil to the correct level.

67. Vacuum and recharge the A/C system, if equipped.

68. Refill and bleed the power steering system, if equipped.

69. Start the engine and check for leaks.

EXHAUST MANIFOLD

REMOVAL & INSTALLATION

1.6L (LXT Engine)

See Figures 76 and 77.

1. Before servicing the vehicle, refer to the precautions section.

➡Spray the exhaust system fasteners with penetrating lubricant before removing them to help prevent broken studs and bolts. The use of a 6-point

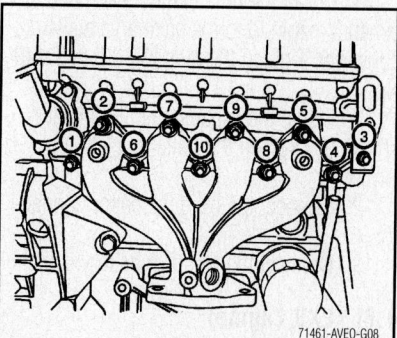

71461-AVEO-G08

Fig. 76 Exhaust manifold bolt removal sequence—1.6L engine

socket is highly recommended when removing exhaust system fasteners.

> **✳✳ CAUTION**
>
> **To prevent serious burns, allow the exhaust manifold to cool down before attempting to remove it.**

2. Disconnect the negative battery cable.

3. Disconnect the oxygen sensor connector

4. Remove the exhaust manifold heat shield

5. Remove the nuts that connect the exhaust manifold to the auxiliary catalytic converter.

6. Remove the exhaust manifold nuts in the sequence shown.

7. Remove the exhaust manifold and gasket.

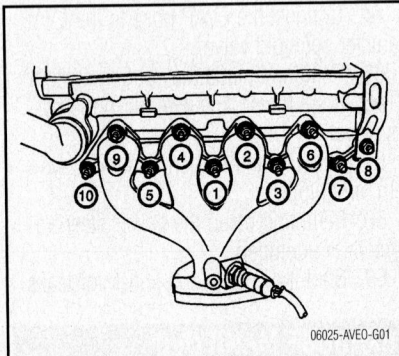

Fig. 77 Exhaust manifold bolt installation sequence—1.6L engine

To install:

8. Clean all gasket mating surfaces thoroughly.

9. Install a new exhaust manifold gasket and the exhaust manifold on the cylinder head. Start 2 nuts to hold the manifold in position. Tighten the nuts in sequence to 18 ft. lbs. (25 Nm).

10. Install the nuts that connect the exhaust manifold to the auxiliary catalytic converter. Tighten the nuts to 30 ft. lbs. (40 Nm).

11. Install the exhaust manifold heat shield and tighten the bolts to 11 ft. lbs. (15 Nm).

12. Connect the oxygen sensor connector.

13. Connect the negative battery cable.

1.6L (LXV Engine)

The exhaust manifold and catalytic converter are one unit. (refer to Catalytic Converter Removal & Installation).

FLYWHEEL

REMOVAL & INSTALLATION

1.6L (LXT Engine)

See Figure 78.

1. Before servicing the vehicle, refer to the precautions section.

2. Disconnect the negative battery cable.

3. Remove the engine assembly from the vehicle and mount in suitable engine stand.

4. Separate the transaxle assembly from the engine.

5. Remove the flywheel bolts.

6. Remove the flywheel.

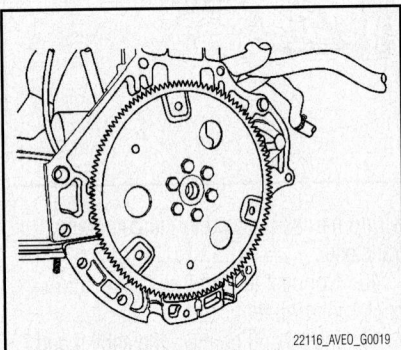

Fig. 78 Flywheel mounting location—1.6L Engine

To install:

7. Install the flywheel. Tighten the flywheel bolts as follows:

　a. Automatic transaxles: Tighten the bolts to 44 ft. lbs. (60 Nm).

　b. Manual Transaxles:
- Step 1: Tighten the bolts to 25 ft. lbs. (35 Nm).
- Step 2: Tighten the bolts an additional 30 degrees
- Step 3: Tighten the bolts an additional 15 degrees

8. Install the engine/transaxle assembly into the vehicle.

1.6L (LXV Engine)

See Figure 79.

1. Before servicing the vehicle, refer to the precautions section.

2. Install J 28647-B Engine Support Fixture.

3. Remove the transaxle.

4. Install KM-6625 locking device to block the crankshaft from turning.

5. Install the transaxle bolt with KM-6625 locking device .

6. Remove the flywheel bolts.

7. Remove the flywheel.

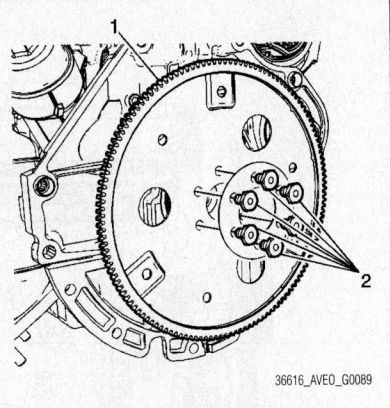

Fig. 79 Flywheel (1) and Retaining bolt (2) removal

To install:

8. Install the flywheel and retaining bolts.

9. Tighten the flywheel bolts for Automatic and Manual transaxles as follows:
- Step 1: Tighten the bolts to 25 ft. lbs. (35 Nm).
- Step 2: Tighten the bolts an additional 30 degrees
- Step 3: Tighten the bolts an additional 15 degrees

10. Remove KM-6625 locking device to block the crankshaft.

11. Install the transaxle.

12. Remove J 28647-B Engine Support Fixture.

INTAKE MANIFOLD

REMOVAL & INSTALLATION

1.6L (LXT Engine)

See Figures 80 and 81.

1. Before servicing the vehicle, refer to the precautions section.

2. Properly relieve the fuel system pressure.

3. Disconnect the negative battery cable.

4. Drain the cooling system.

5. Disconnect the Intake Air Temperature (IAT) sensor connector.

6. Disconnect the air intake assembly from the throttle body.

7. Disconnect the Idle Air Control (IAC) valve connector and Throttle Position Sensor (TPS) connector.

8. Remove the alternator adjusting bolt and the accessory drive belt.

9. Disconnect the Engine Coolant Temperature (ECT) sensor connector.

10. Disconnect the heater inlet hose from the cylinder head.

11. Disconnect the surge tank coolant hose at the throttle body.

12. Disconnect all of the necessary vacuum hoses, including the vacuum hose at the fuel pressure regulator and the brake booster vacuum hose at the intake manifold.

13. Disconnect the throttle body cable from the throttle body and the intake manifold.

14. Remove the fuel injector rail and fuel injectors as an assembly.

15. Remove the alternator adjusting bracket bolt from the intake manifold and remove the alternator adjusting bracket.

16. Remove the intake manifold support bracket bolts and the intake manifold support bracket.

17. Remove the intake manifold retaining nuts/bolts in the sequence shown.

18. Remove the intake manifold and gasket.

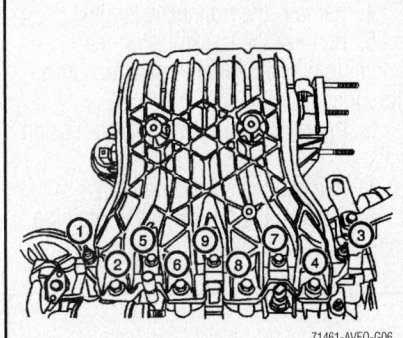

Fig. 80 Intake manifold bolt removal sequence—1.6L engine

To install:

19. Clean the sealing surfaces of the intake manifold and the cylinder head.

20. Install the intake manifold with a new gasket. Tighten the retaining nuts/bolts in the sequence shown to 18 ft. lbs. (25 Nm).

21. Install the intake manifold support bracket and tighten the bracket bolts to 18 ft. lbs. (25 Nm).

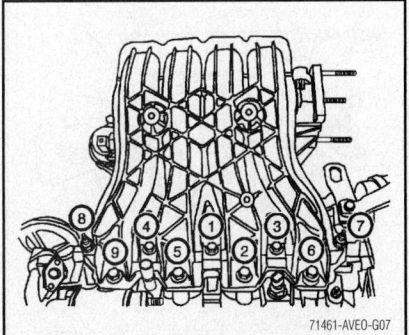

Fig. 81 Intake manifold bolt tightening sequence—1.6L engine

22. Install the intake manifold support bracket lower bolt-to-engine block.

23. Install the fuel rail and fuel injectors as an assembly.

24. Connect the throttle cable to the intake manifold and the throttle body.

25. Connect all of the necessary vacuum lines that were previously disconnected.

26. Connect the heater inlet hose to the cylinder head.

27. Connect the surge tank coolant hose to the throttle body.

28. Install the alternator adjusting bracket at the intake manifold and tighten the bracket bolts to 11 ft. lbs. (15 Nm).

29. Install the alternator adjusting bolt and the accessory drive belt.

30. Connect the ECT sensor connector, IAC valve connector and TPS connector.

31. Connect the air intake assembly to the throttle body.

32. Connect the IAT sensor connector.

33. Connect the Powertrain Control Module (PCM)/Engine Control Module (ECM) ground terminal to the intake manifold.

34. Reinstall the fuel pump fuse.

35. Connect the negative battery cable.

36. Refill the cooling system to the correct level.

37. Start the engine and check for leaks.

1.6L (LXV Engine)

See Figure 82.

1. Before servicing the vehicle, refer to the precautions section.

2. Disconnect the negative battery cable.

3. Properly relieve the fuel system pressure.

4. Remove the air cleaner assembly.

5. Remove the power steering pressure pipe clamp from the intake manifold.

6. Disconnect the following sensors and actuator connectors and the pull engine wiring harness aside:
- A/C pressure sensor (ACP) connector
- CAM position solenoid valve connector
- Electric throttle controller (ETC) connector
- Manifold air pressure (MAP) sensor connector
- EVAP solenoid valve connector
- Injector connectors

7. Disconnect the fuel line from the fuel rail.

8. Disconnect the ETC coolant inlet/outlet hoses and then pull it aside.

9. Remove the PCV hose from the ETC.

10. Remove the cylinder head cover.

11. Remove the Electric Throttle Controller (ETC).

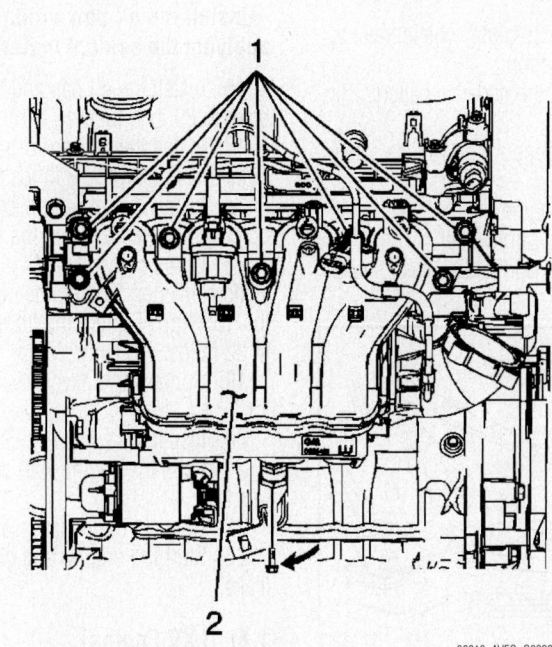

Fig. 82 Intake manifold (2) retaining bolts (1)

12. Remove the intake manifold with the gasket.

To install:

13. Install the intake manifold with a new gasket.

14. Tighten the intake manifold retaining bolts to 15 ft. lbs. (20 Nm).

15. Tighten the intake manifold lower bracket bolts to 71 inch. lbs. (8 Nm).

16. Install the Electric Throttle Controller (ETC).

17. Install the cylinder head cover.

18. Install the PCV hose to the ETC.

19. Connect the ETC coolant inlet/outlet hoses.

20. Connect the fuel line to the fuel rail.

21. Connect the following sensors and actuator connectors:

- ACP connector
- CAM position solenoid valve connector
- ETC connector
- MAP sensor connector
- EVAP solenoid valve connector
- Injector connectors

22. Install the power steering pressure pipe clamp to the intake manifold.

23. Install the air cleaner assembly.

24. Connect the battery negative cable.

OIL PAN

REMOVAL & INSTALLATION

1.6L (LXT Engine)

See Figures 83 and 84.

1. Before servicing the vehicle, refer to the precautions section.

2. Disconnect the negative battery cable.

3. Raise and support the vehicle safely on jack stands.

4. Drain the engine oil.

5. Remove the right wheel.

6. Remove the right side splash shield.

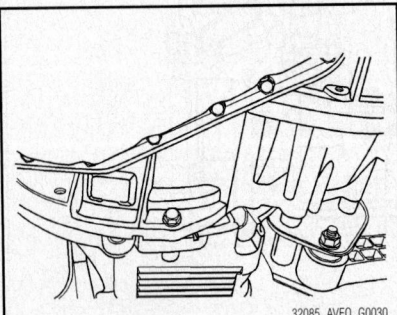

Fig. 83 Remove the bolts that secure the oil pan to the transaxle housing

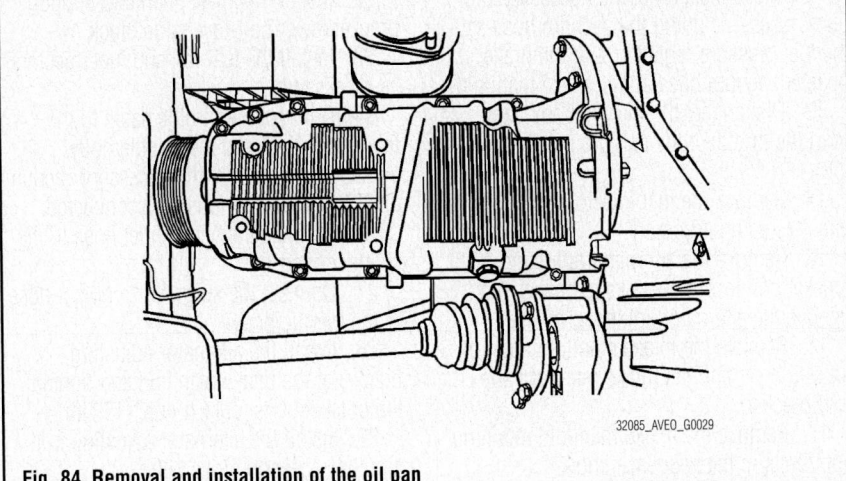

Fig. 84 Removal and installation of the oil pan

7. Disconnect the heated oxygen sensor connector.

8. Remove the catalytic converter lower flange nuts and nuts that secure the front exhaust pipe. Then remove the exhaust pipe and catalytic converter as a unit.

9. Remove the lower crossmember bracket, if necessary.

10. Remove the oil pan-to-transaxle case bolts.

11. Remove the oil pan-to-engine block bolts.

12. Remove the oil pan.

To install:

13. Clean the gasket mating surfaces thoroughly.

14. Coat the oil pan gasket with sealant.

➡ **Install the oil pan within 5 minutes of applying the sealant material.**

15. Install the oil pan and tighten the bolts to 89 inch lbs. (10 Nm).

16. Install the oil pan-to-transaxle case bolts and tighten to 18 ft. lbs. (25 Nm).

17. Install the oil pan-to-engine block bolts and tighten to 18 ft. lbs. (25 Nm).

18. Connect the exhaust pipe and catalytic converter. Tighten the nuts to 37 ft. lbs. (50 Nm). Tighten the front muffler nuts to 22 ft. lbs. (30 Nm).

19. Connect the oxygen sensor connector.

20. Install the splash shield and wheel.

21. Refill the engine with oil to the correct level.

22. Connect the negative battery cable.

23. Start the engine and check for leaks.

1.6L (LXV Engine)

See Figures 85 through 87.

1. Before servicing the vehicle, refer to the precautions section.

2. Disconnect the negative battery cable.

3. Drain the engine oil.

4. Remove the front exhaust pipe.

5. Remove the transmission rear mounting bracket, for automatic transmission only.

6. Remove the oil pan-to-transmission bolts.

7. Remove the oil pan bolts.

8. Remove the oil pan baffle retaining bolts.

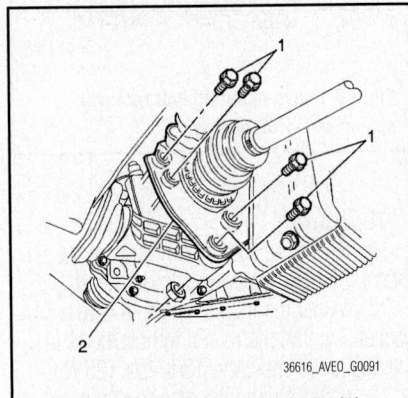

Fig. 85 Remove the retaining bolts (1) and the rear transmission bracket (2)

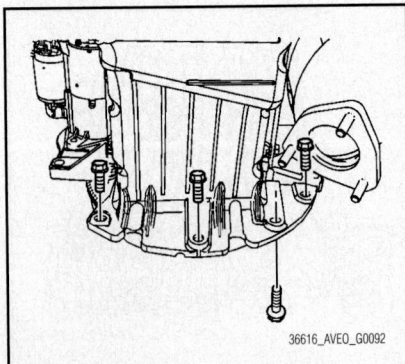

Fig. 86 Oil pan-to-transmission bolt removal

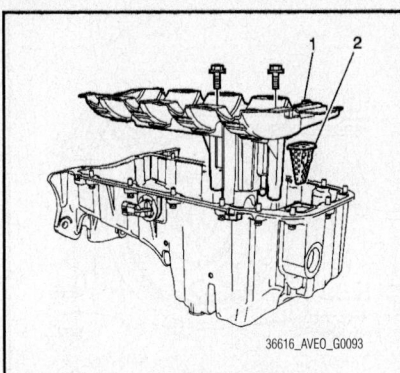

Fig. 87 Oil pan baffle (1) and suction filter (2)

9. Remove the oil pan baffle.
10. Remove the oil suction filter.

To install:

11. Install the oil suction filter to the oil pan.

12. Install the oil pan baffle and tighten the retaining bolts to 8 ft. lbs. (10Nm).

13. Clean the oil pan sealing surface.

14. Apply the oil pan sealant LOCTITE 5900® on the sealing surface.

15. Install the oil pan and bolts, Tighten the oil pan bolts to 10 ft. lbs. (14 Nm).

16. Install the oil pan-to-transmission bolts and tighten to 30 ft. lbs. (40 Nm).

17. Install the transmission rear mounting bracket, for automatic transmission only. Tighten the retaining bolts to 59 ft. lbs. (80 Nm).

OIL PUMP

REMOVAL & INSTALLATION

1.6L (LXT Engine)

See Figure 88.

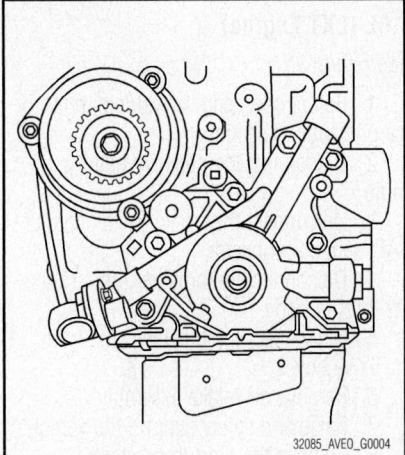

Fig. 88 Removal and installation of the oil pump

1. Before servicing the vehicle, refer to the precautions section.
2. Disconnect the negative battery cable.
3. Drain the engine oil.
4. Remove the power steering pump.
5. Remove the timing belt. (Refer to Timing belt and Sprockets Removal & Installation.)
6. Remove the rear timing belt cover.
7. Disconnect the oil pressure switch connector.
8. Remove the crankshaft position (CKP) sensor.
9. Remove the oil pan.
10. Remove the oil pump suction pipe and support bracket bolts.
11. Remove the oil pump mounting bolts.
12. Carefully separate the oil pump and gasket from the engine block and the oil pan and remove the oil pump.

To install:

13. Apply Loctite®242 to the oil pump bolts and RTV sealant to the new oil pump gasket.
14. Install the oil pump and gasket and tighten the bolts to 89 inch lbs. (10 Nm).
15. Install a new oil pump-to-crankshaft seal. Coat the lip of the seal with a thin coat of grease.
16. Coat the threads of the oil suction pipe and support bracket bolts with Loctite®242.
17. Install the oil suction pipe and bolts and tighten the bolts to 89 inch lbs. (10 Nm).
18. Install the oil pan.
19. Install the CKP sensor.
20. Connect the oil pressure switch connector.
21. Install the timing belt rear cover.
22. Install the timing belt. (Refer to Timing belt and Sprockets Removal & Installation.)
23. Refill the engine with oil to the correct level.
24. Connect the negative battery cable.
25. Start the engine and check for leaks.

1.6L (LXV Engine)

See Figures 89 and 90.

1. Before servicing the vehicle, refer to the precautions section.
2. Disconnect the negative battery cable.
3. Drain the engine coolant.
4. Drain the engine oil.
5. Remove the exhaust manifold.
6. Remove the timing belt. (Refer to Timing belt and Sprockets Removal & Installation.)

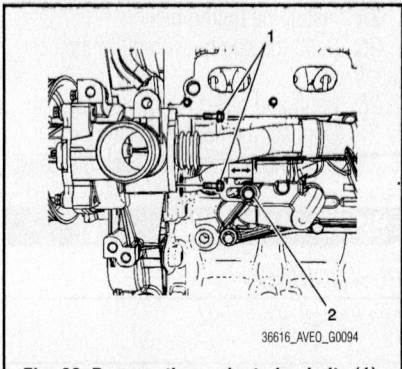

Fig. 89 Remove the coolant pipe bolts (1) and coolant pipe bracket bolt (2)

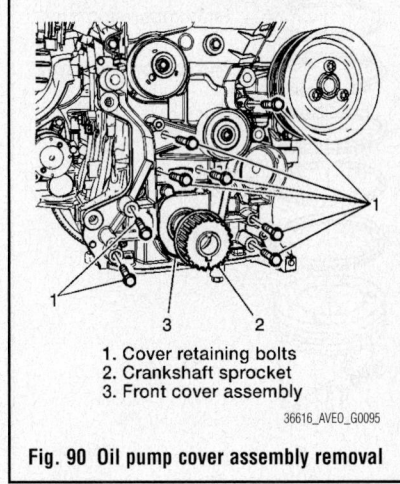

1. Cover retaining bolts
2. Crankshaft sprocket
3. Front cover assembly

Fig. 90 Oil pump cover assembly removal

7. Remove the oil pan. (Refer to Oil pan Removal & Installation.)
8. Remove the power steering pump and bracket
9. Remove the alternator.
10. Remove the A/C compressor.
11. Remove the engine coolant pipe bolts.
12. Remove the engine coolant pipe bracket bolt and then push the pipe into the oil cooler housing.
13. Remove the crankshaft sprocket.
14. Remove the engine front cover assembly with the gasket.

To install:

15. Install the engine front cover assembly with the new gasket.
16. Tighten the engine front cover assembly bolts to 15 ft. lbs. (20 Nm).
17. Install the crankshaft sprocket.
18. Install the engine coolant pipe bolts.
19. Install the engine coolant pipe bracket bolt and then push the pipe into the oil cooler housing.
20. Install the A/C compressor.
21. Install the alternator.
22. Install the power steering pump and bracket.
23. Install the oil pan.

24. Install the timing belt.
25. Refill the engine with oil to the correct level.
26. Refill and bleed the cooling system.
27. Connect the negative battery cable.
28. Start the engine and check for leaks.

PISTON AND RING

POSITIONING

See Figures 91 and 92.

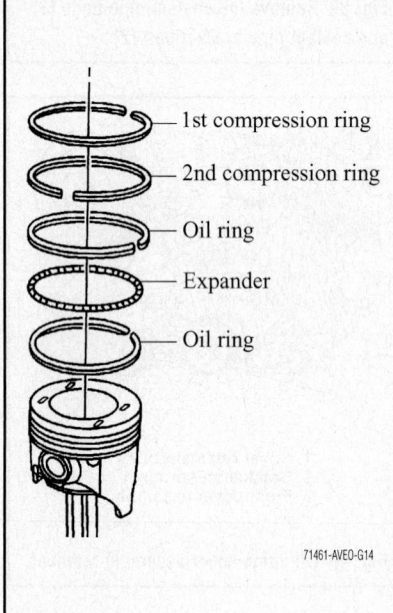

1st compression ring
2nd compression ring
Oil ring
Expander
Oil ring

71461-AVEO-G14

Fig. 91 Piston ring positioning—1.6L (LXT) engine

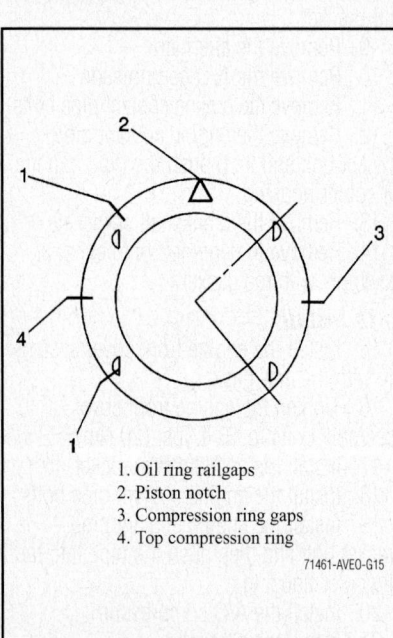

1. Oil ring railgaps
2. Piston notch
3. Compression ring gaps
4. Top compression ring

71461-AVEO-G15

Fig. 92 Piston ring gap positioning—1.6L (LXT) engine

REAR MAIN SEAL

REMOVAL & INSTALLATION

1.6L (LXT Engine)

See Figure 93.

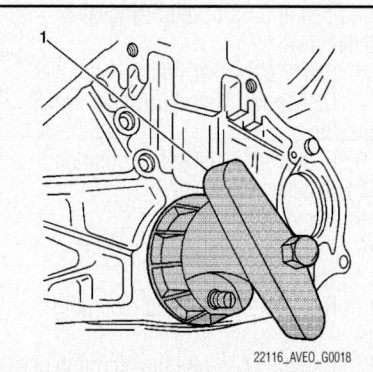

22116_AVEO_G0018

Fig. 93 Using Seal Installer Tool J-36972 (1) to install the rear main seal.

1. Before servicing the vehicle, refer to the precautions section.
2. Disconnect the negative battery cable.
3. Remove the engine.
4. Remove the flywheel or drive plate bolts.
5. Remove the flywheel or drive plate
6. Remove the crankshaft rear oil seal.

To install:
7. Inspect the crankshaft seal area for any damage that may cause the seal to leak. If damage is evident, service or replace the crankshaft as necessary.
8. Coat the crankshaft seal area and the seal lip with engine oil.
9. Using a crankshaft seal replacement tool (J-36972 or equivalent), install the seal. Tighten the bolts of the seal installer tool evenly so the seal is straight and seats without misalignment.
10. Install the flywheel or the drive plate. Tighten the flywheel bolts to 25 ft. lbs. (35 Nm). Plus an additional 30°, then another 15°. Tighten the drive plate bolts to 33 ft. lbs. (45 Nm).
11. Install the engine.
12. Connect the negative battery cable.

1.6L (LXV Engine)

See Figure 94.

1. Before servicing the vehicle, refer to the precautions section.
2. Disconnect the negative battery cable.
3. Remove the transaxle.
4. Remove the flywheel.

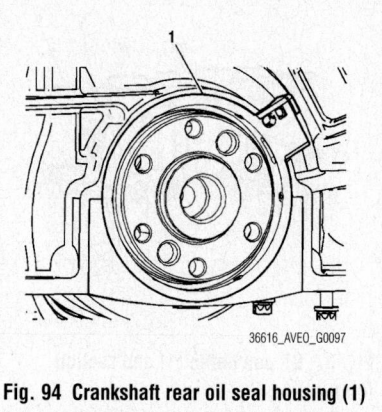

36616_AVEO_G0097

Fig. 94 Crankshaft rear oil seal housing (1)

5. Remove the Crankshaft Position (CKP) sensor.
6. Remove the crankshaft rear oil seal with housing.
7. Carefully install the new crankshaft rear oil seal using a suitable seal driver.
8. Install crankshaft position sensor and tighten the CKP sensor bolt to 40 inch. lbs. (4.5 Nm).
9. Install the flywheel.
10. Install the flywheel and retaining bolts.
11. Tighten the flywheel bolts for Automatic and Manual transmissions as follows:
  • Step 1: Tighten the bolts to 25 ft. lbs. (35 Nm).
  • Step 2: Tighten the bolts an additional 30 degrees
  • Step 3: Tighten the bolts an additional 15 degrees
12. Install the transaxle.
13. Connect the negative battery cable.

TIMING BELT FRONT COVER

REMOVAL & INSTALLATION

1.6L (LXT Engine)

See Figure 95.

1. Before servicing the vehicle, refer to the precautions section.
2. Disconnect the negative battery cable.
3. Disconnect the intake air temperature (IAT) sensor connector.
4. Disconnect the breather tube from the throttle body.
5. Disconnect the breather tube from the valve cover.
6. Remove air intake assembly.
7. Raise and safely support the vehicle.
8. Remove the right front wheel.
9. Remove the right front engine splash guard.
10. Remove the accessory drive belt. For additional information, refer to the following

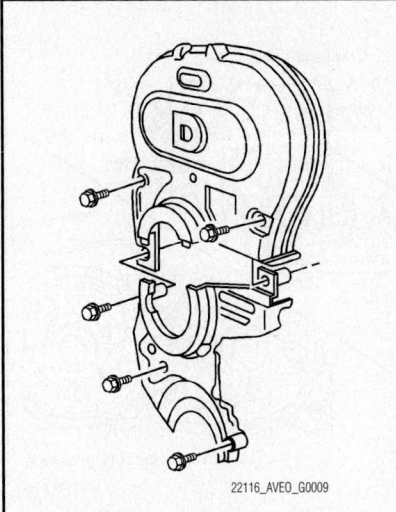

Fig. 95 Remove the upper and lower timing belt cover bolts to remove the timing belt front covers.

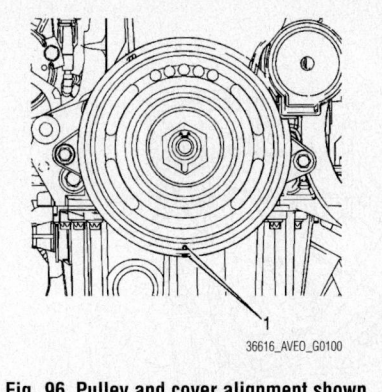

Fig. 96 Pulley and cover alignment shown

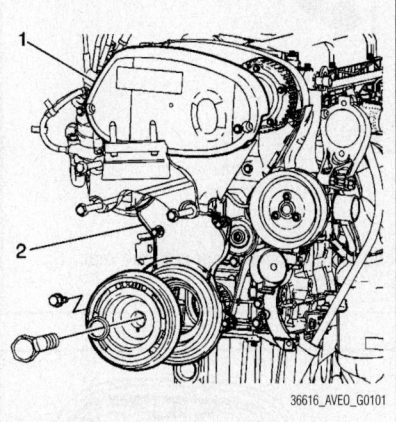

Fig. 97 Removing the crankshaft pulley and covers (1 and 2)

section, "Accessory Drive Belt, Removal & Installation."

11. Remove the crankshaft pulley.
12. Remove the upper front timing belt cover bolts.
13. Remove the upper front timing belt cover.
14. Remove the lower front timing belt cover bolts.
15. Remove the lower front timing belt cover.

To install:

16. Install the upper and lower timing belt covers.
17. Install the cover mounting bolts and tighten to 89 inch lbs. (10 Nm).
18. Install the crankshaft pulley.
19. Install the accessory drive belt.
20. Install the right front engine splash guard and wheel.
21. Lower the vehicle.
22. Install the air intake assembly.
23. Connect the breather tube to the valve cover.
24. Connect the breather tube to the throttle body.
25. Connect the IAT sensor connector.
26. Connect the negative battery cable.
27. Start the engine and check for leaks.

1.6L (LXV Engine)

See Figure 96.

1. Before servicing the vehicle, refer to the precautions section.
2. Disconnect the negative battery cable.
3. Remove the air cleaner assembly.
4. Install J 28647-B Engine Support Fixture .

5. Remove the accessory belt.
6. Remove the accessory belt tensioner.
7. Rotate the crankshaft pulley clockwise.
8. Align the notches between the pulley and the cover.
9. Remove the transmission bolt.
10. Install KM-6625 locking device to block the crankshaft.
11. Install the transmission bolt.
12. Remove the cylinder head cover.
13. Remove the engine mount.
14. Remove the crankshaft pulley.
15. Remove the timing belt upper cover.
16. Remove the engine mount bracket.
17. Remove the timing belt lower cover.
18. Remove the timing belt center cover.

To install:

19. Install the timing belt center cover.
20. Install the timing belt lower cover and tighten the bolts to 53 inch. lbs. (6 Nm).
21. Install the engine mount bracket and tighten the bolt to 48 ft. lbs. (65 Nm).
22. Install the timing belt upper cover and tighten the bolts to 35 ft. lbs. (47 Nm).
23. Install the crankshaft pulley with aligning crankshaft pulley notches and tighten it to 18 ft. lbs. (25 Nm).

24. Install the engine mount.
25. Install the cylinder head cover.
26. Install the accessory belt tensioner.
27. Install the accessory drive belt.
28. Connect the negative battery cable.

TIMING BELT AND SPROCKETS

REMOVAL & INSTALLATION

1.6L (LXT Engine)

See Figures 98 through 102.

1. Before servicing the vehicle, refer to the precautions section.
2. Disconnect the negative battery cable.
3. Disconnect the Intake Air Temperature (IAT) sensor connector.
4. Disconnect the air intake tube from the throttle body.
5. Disconnect the breather tube from the valve cover.
6. Remove the air filter housing bolts.
7. Remove the air filter housing.
8. Remove the right front wheel.
9. Remove the right front splash shield.
10. Remove the accessory drive belt.
11. Remove the crankshaft pulley bolt.
12. Remove the crankshaft pulley.
13. Remove the upper front timing belt cover bolts.
14. Remove the upper front timing belt cover by prying on the two tabs located on each side of the cover.
15. Remove the lower front timing belt cover bolts.
16. Remove the lower front timing belt cover.
17. Remove the power steering pump mounting bolts, if equipped with power steering.
18. Reinstall the crankshaft pulley bolt.
19. Using the crankshaft pulley bolt, rotate the crankshaft clockwise until the timing mark on the crankshaft gear aligns with the notch at the bottom of the rear timing cover.
20. Slightly loosen the water pump retaining bolts.
21. Using Special Tool J-42492-A, rotate the water pump counterclockwise to release the tension on the timing belt.
22. Removing the timing belt.
23. Remove the engine cover.
24. Disconnect the spark plug wires from the spark plugs.
25. Disconnect the crankcase ventilation tubes from the valve cover.
26. Disconnect the Camshaft Position (CMP) sensor.
27. Remove the valve cover and the valve cover gasket.

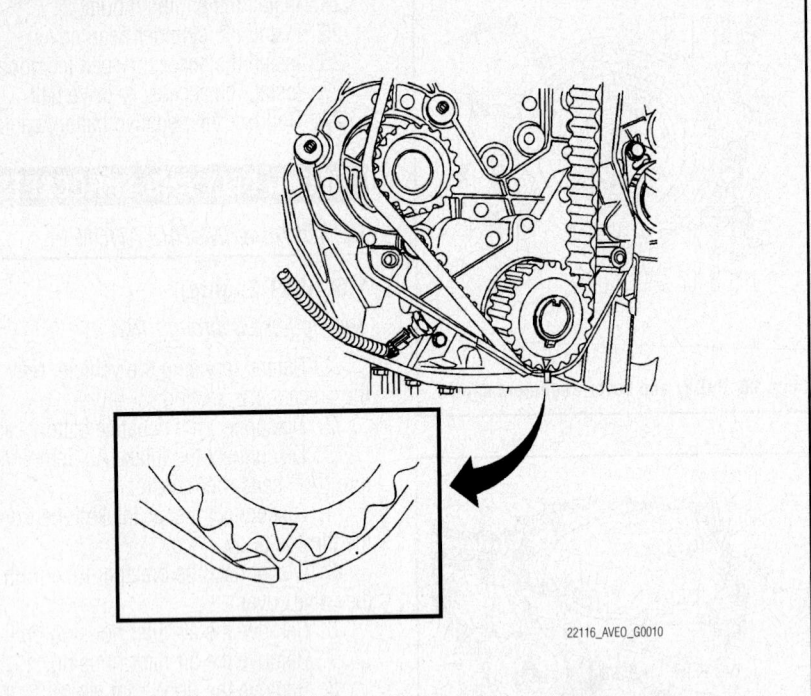

Fig. 98 Turn the crankshaft to align the timing mark on the crankshaft gear with the rear timing cover mark.

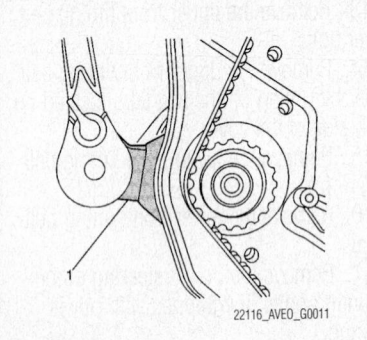

Fig. 99 Use Special Tool J-42492-A (1) to release the tension on the timing belt.

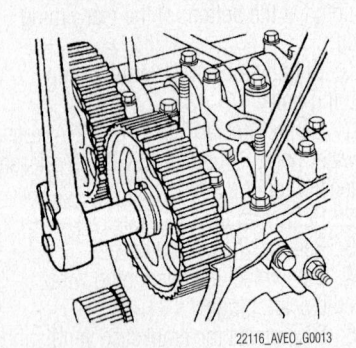

Fig. 100 Hold the camshaft firmly in place with a wrench to remove the camshaft gear bolt.

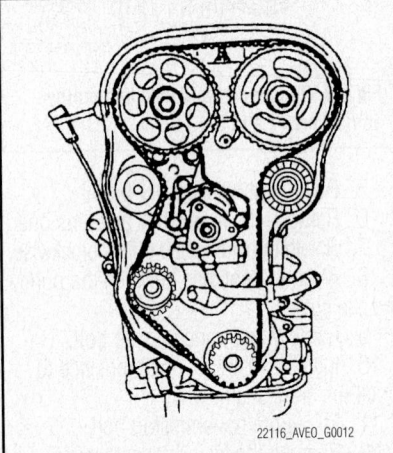

Fig. 101 Timing belt routing—1.6L engine

> ❈❈ **CAUTION**
>
> **Take extreme care to prevent any scratches, nicks or damage to the camshafts.**

28. While holding the intake camshaft firmly in place, remove the intake camshaft gear bolt.

29. Remove the intake camshaft gear.

30. While holding the exhaust camshaft firmly in place, remove the exhaust camshaft gear bolt.

31. Remove the exhaust camshaft gear.

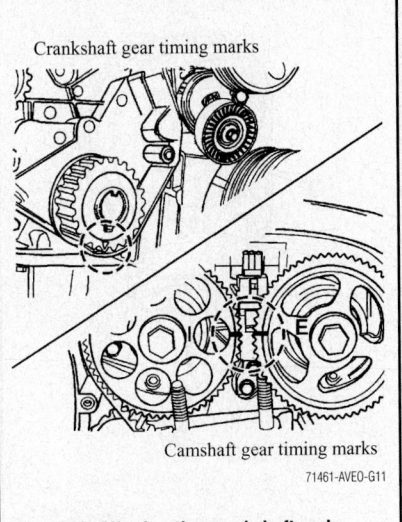

Fig. 102 Aligning the crankshaft and camshaft gear timing marks—1.6L engine

To install:

32. While holding the intake camshaft firmly in place, install the intake camshaft gear bolt. Tighten the bolt to 49 ft. lbs. (66 Nm)

33. While holding the exhaust camshaft firmly in place, install the intake camshaft gear bolt. Tighten the bolt to 49 ft. lbs. (66 Nm)

34. Install the valve cover and gasket.

35. Connect the CMP sensor.

36. Connect the crankshaft ventilation tubs to the valve cover.

37. Connect the spark plug wires.

38. Install the engine cover.

39. Ensure the timing mark on the crankshaft gear aligns with the notch at the bottom of the rear timing cover is aligned.

40. Align the timing marks on the camshaft gears.

41. Rotate the water pump clockwise using Special Tool J-42492-A until the adjusting arm pointer of the timing belt automatic tensioner is aligned with the notch in the timing belt automatic tensioner bracket.

42. Tighten the water pump retaining bolts.

43. Rotate the crankshaft 2 full turns clockwise using the crankshaft pulley bolt.

44. Loosen the water pump retaining bolts.

45. Rotate the water pump until the adjust arm pointer of the timing belt automatic tensioner is aligned with the pointer on the timing belt automatic tensioner bracket and second time.

46. Tighten the water pump retaining pump to 89 inch lbs. (10 Nm).

47. Remove the crankshaft pulley bolt.

48. Replace the power steering pump mounting bolts, if equipped with power steering.

49. Install the upper and lower front timing belt cover.

50. Install the upper and lower front timing belt cover bolts. Tighten to 89 inch. lbs. (10 Nm).

51. Install the crankshaft pulley.

52. Install the crankshaft pulley bolt.

53. Tighten the crankshaft pulley bolt as follows.

- Step 1: Tighten to 70 ft. lbs. (95 Nm)
- Step 2: Tighten an additional 30 degrees
- Step 3: Tighten an additional 15 degrees

54. Install the accessory drive belt.

55. Install the right front splash shield.

56. Install the right front wheel.

57. Install the air filter housing.

58. Install the air filter housing bolts.

59. Connect the air intake tube to the throttle body.

60. Connect the breather tube to the throttle body.

61. Connect the IAT sensor connector.

62. Connect the negative battery cable.

1.6L (LXV Engine)

See Figures 103 through 107.

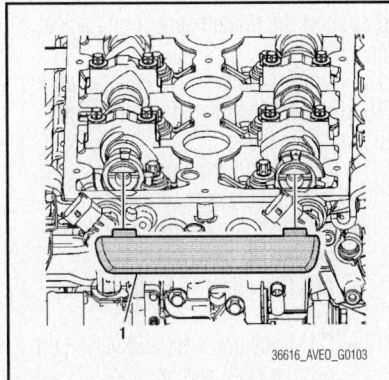

Fig. 103 Align the both camshaft horizontally

1. Before servicing the vehicle, refer to the precautions section.

2. Disconnect the negative battery cable.

3. Remove the air cleaner assembly.

4. Install J 28647-B Engine Support Fixture .

5. Remove the accessory belt.

6. Remove the accessory belt tensioner

7. Rotate the crankshaft pulley clockwise.

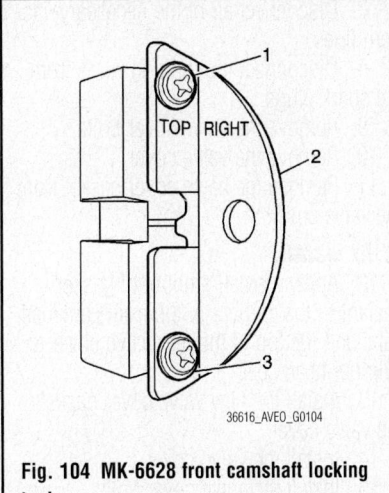

Fig. 104 MK-6628 front camshaft locking tool

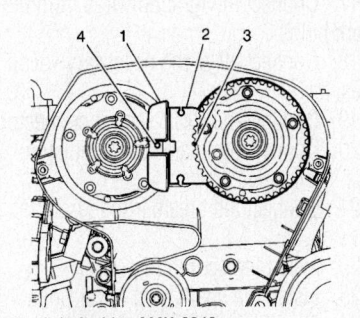

1. Left side of MK-6340
2. Right side of MK-6340
3. Intake sprocket alignment mark
4. Exhaust sprocket alignment mark

Fig. 105 Camshaft alignment with holding tool MK-6628

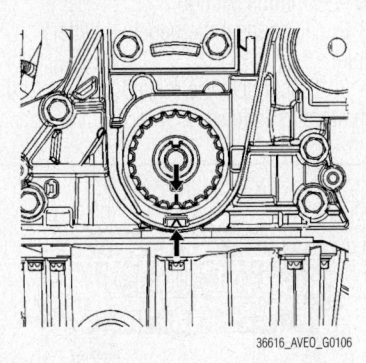

Fig. 106 Crankshaft sprocket alignment with front cover

8. Align the notches between the pulley and the cover.

9. Remove the cylinder head cover.

10. Remove the engine mount.

11. Remove the crankshaft pulley.

➡**Use proper holding tool to hold crankshaft while removing crankshaft bolt.**

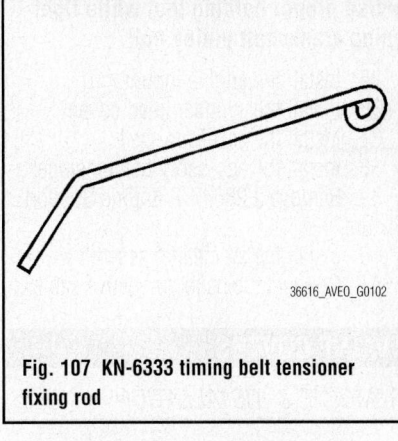

Fig. 107 KN-6333 timing belt tensioner fixing rod

12. Remove the timing belt upper cover.

13. Remove the engine mount bracket.

14. Remove the timing belt lower cover.

15. Remove the timing belt center cover.

16. Reinstall the crankshaft pulley bolt.

17. Align the both camshaft horizontally to install the MK-6628 locking tool .

18. Confirm that both camshaft sprocket spot marks and crankshaft sprocket are aligned.

19. Prepare the right half of MK-6340 locking tool.

20. Unscrew the bolts and detach the front panel from MK-6628 locking tool .

21. Confirm aligning between the intake side spot and the exhaust side spot on the camshaft sprockets.

22. If not aligned as shown, remove and install the camshaft sprocket to align.

23. Insert the left of into the intake camshaft sprocket side.

24. Insert the right of into the exhaust camshaft sprocket side.

25. Confirm alignment of the notches between the crankshaft sprocket and the cover.

26. Install KM-6333 rod during rotating the timing belt tensioner.

27. Remove the timing belt.

To install:

28. Install the timing belt and adjust. Remove the holding tools and verify marks and proper adjustment.

29. Pull out KM-6333 fixing rod.

30. Install the timing belt center cover.

31. Install the timing belt lower cover and tighten the bolts to 53 inch. lbs. (6 Nm).

32. Install the engine mount bracket and tighten the bolt to 48 ft. lbs. (65 Nm).

33. Install the timing belt upper cover and tighten the bolts to 35 inch. lbs. (4 Nm).

34. Install the crankshaft pulley with aligning crankshaft pulley notches and tighten to 18 ft. lbs.(25 Nm).

➥Use proper holding tool while tightening crankshaft pulley bolt.

35. Install the engine mount.
36. Install the cylinder head cover.
37. Install the accessory belt
38. Install the accessory belt tensioner
39. Remove J 28647-B Engine Support Fixture .
40. Install the air cleaner assembly.
41. Connect the battery negative cable.

VALVE COVERS

REMOVAL & INSTALLATION

1.6L (LXT Engine)

See Figures 108 and 109.

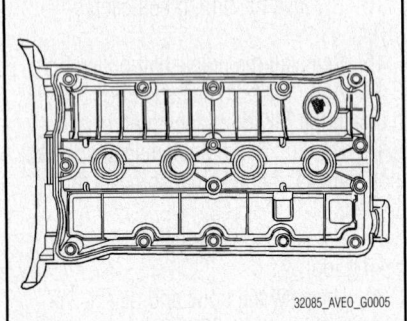

Fig. 108 Removal and installation of the valve cover

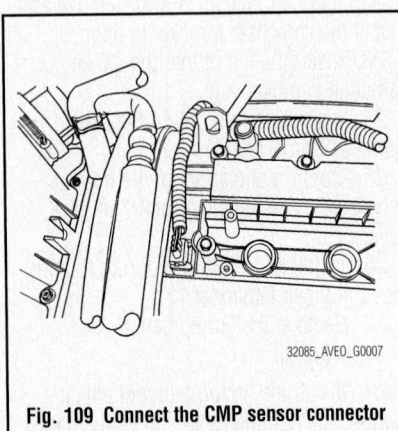

Fig. 109 Connect the CMP sensor connector

1. Before servicing the vehicle, refer to the precautions section.
2. Disconnect the negative battery cable.
3. Remove the engine cover bolts and cover.
4. Disconnect the breather tube from the valve cover.
5. Disconnect the crankcase ventilation tube from the valve cover.
6. Disconnect the Camshaft Position (CMP) sensor connect.

7. Disconnect all of the necessary vacuum lines.
8. Disconnect the ignition wires from the spark plugs.
9. Remove the valve cover bolts.
10. Remove the valve cover
11. Remove the valve cover gasket from the valve cover.

To install:

12. Apply a small amount of gasket sealant to the corners of the front camshaft caps and the top of the rear valve cover to cylinder head seal.
13. Install the new valve cover gasket to the valve cover.
14. Install the valve cover.
15. Install the valve cover bolts.
16. Tighten the valve cover bolts to 89 inch lbs. (10 Nm).
17. Connect the ignition wires from the spark plugs.
18. Connect all of the necessary vacuum lines.
19. Connect the CMP sensor connector
20. Connect the crankcase ventilation tube to the valve cover
21. Connect the breather tube from the valve cover
22. Install the spark plug cover.
23. Install the spark plug cover bolts.
24. Tighten the engine cover bolts to 27 inch lbs. (3 Nm).
25. Connect the negative battery cable

1.6L (LXV Engine)

See Figure 110.

1. Before servicing the vehicle, refer to the precautions section.
2. Disconnect the negative battery cable.
3. Disconnect the related sensors and actuators as follows:

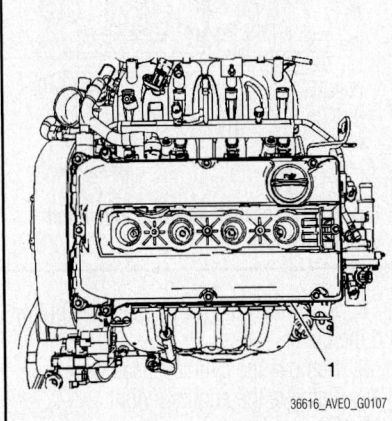

Fig. 110 1.6L LXV Engine valve cover shown (1)

- Oil switch wiring connector
- A/C compressor connector
- Manifold Air Temperature (MAT) sensor connector
- A/C Pressure (ACP) sensor connector.
- CAM position solenoid valve connectors right and left
- Manifold Air Pressure (MAP) sensor connector
- EVAP canister purge solenoid valve connector
- Fuel injector connectors
- Ignition coil assembly connector
- Camshaft Position Sensor (CPS) connectors right and left
4. Remove the ignition coil.
5. Detach the PCV clips from the PCV hose.
6. Remove the PCV hose from the cylinder head cover.
7. Remove the valve cover bolts.
8. Remove the valve cover.

To install:

9. Install the valve cover with a new gasket.
10. Install the valve cover bolts and tighten to 71 inch. lbs. (8 Nm).
11. Install the PCV hose to the cylinder head cover.
12. Attach the PCV clips to the PCV hose.
13. Install the ignition coil.
14. Position the engine wiring harness and connect the related sensor and actuator connector.
15. Connect the negative battery cable.
16. Connect the related sensors and actuators as follows:
- Oil switch wiring connector
- A/C compressor connector
- Manifold Air Temperature (MAT) sensor connector
- A/C Pressure (ACP) sensor connector.
- CAM position solenoid valve connectors right and left
- Manifold Air Pressure (MAP) sensor connector
- EVAP canister purge solenoid valve connector
- Fuel injector connectors
- Ignition coil assembly connector
- Camshaft Position Sensor (CPS) connectors right and left
17. Connect the negative battery cable.

VALVE LASH

ADJUSTMENT

See Figures 111 through 113.

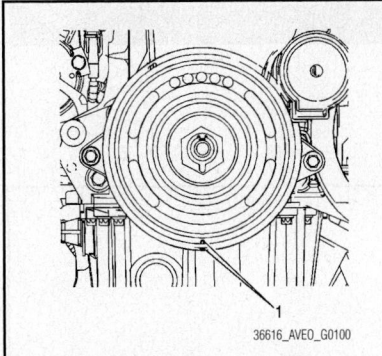

Fig. 111 Align the notches between the pulley and the cover

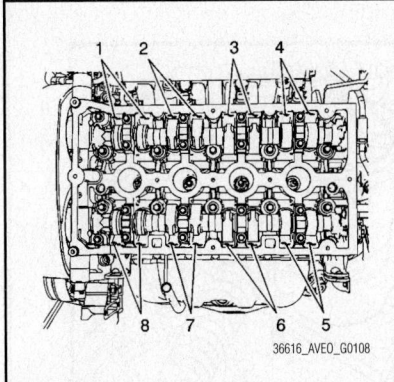

Fig. 112 Valve clearance reading positions

1. Before servicing the vehicle, refer to the precautions section.

2. Disconnect the negative battery cable.

3. Remove the valve cover.

4. Rotate the crankshaft pulley clockwise, aligning the notches between the pulley and the cover.

5. Measure the valve clearance at positions (2) and (6). Rotate the crankshaft pulley clockwise 180 degrees.

6. Measure the valve clearance at positions (3) and (7). Rotate the crankshaft pulley clockwise 180 degrees.

7. Measure the valve clearance at positions (4) and (8). Rotate the crankshaft pulley clockwise 180 degrees.

8. Measure the valve clearance at positions (1) and (5). Rotate the crankshaft pulley clockwise 180 degrees.

9. If the measured values are not within specifications, replace the valve tappets.

Part Number	ID Number	Value (mm)
24465260	04	3.060-3.050
24465261	06	3.050-3.070
24438041	08	3.070-3.090
24438145	10	3.090-3.110
24438146	12	3.110-3.130
24438147	14	3.130-3.150
24438148	16	3.150-3.170
24438149	18	3.170-3.190
24438150	20	3.190-3.210
24438151	22	3.210-3.230
55353764	24X	3.230-3.244
55353765	25X	3.244-3.258
55353766	27X	3.258-3.272
55353767	28X	3.272-3.286
55353768	30X	3.286-3.300
55353769	31X	3.300-3.314
55353770	32X	3.314-3.328
55353771	34X	3.328-3.342
55353772	35X	3.342-3.356
55353773	36X	3.356-3.370
55353774	38X	3.370-3.384
55353775	39X	3.384-3.398
55353776	41X	3.398-3.412
55353777	42X	3.412-3.426
55353778	43X	3.426-3.440
55353779	45	3.440-3.460
55353780	47	3.460-3.480
55353781	49	3.480-3.500
55353782	51	3.500-3.520
55353783	53	3.520-3.540
55353784	55	3.540-3.560
55353785	57	3.560-3.580
55353786	59	3.580-3.600

Fig. 113 Valve tappet selection chart

10. Specifications are as follows:
   - Intake Side: 0.21-0.29 mm (Nominal Value: 0.25 mm)
   - Exhaust Side: 0.27-0.35 mm (Nominal Value: 0.30 mm)

11. If the tappet is to be replaced continue as follows.

12. Remove the old tappet.

13. Locate the ID number inside old tappet.

14. Locate the ID number in the following table and record the value.

15. Perform the following calculation to determine the replacement tappet size.

16. Value of removed tappet + measured clearance - nominal value = new tappet size.

Example:
   - ID of old tappet = 20 = 3.20 mm, clearance was 0.31 mm, nominal value is 0.25 mm
   - 3.20 mm + 0.31 mm - 0.25 mm = 3.265 mm
   - 3.265 mm = 27X (ID number) = 55353766 (part number

ENGINE PERFORMANCE & EMISSION CONTROLS

COMPONENT LOCATIONS

See Figures 114 through 116.

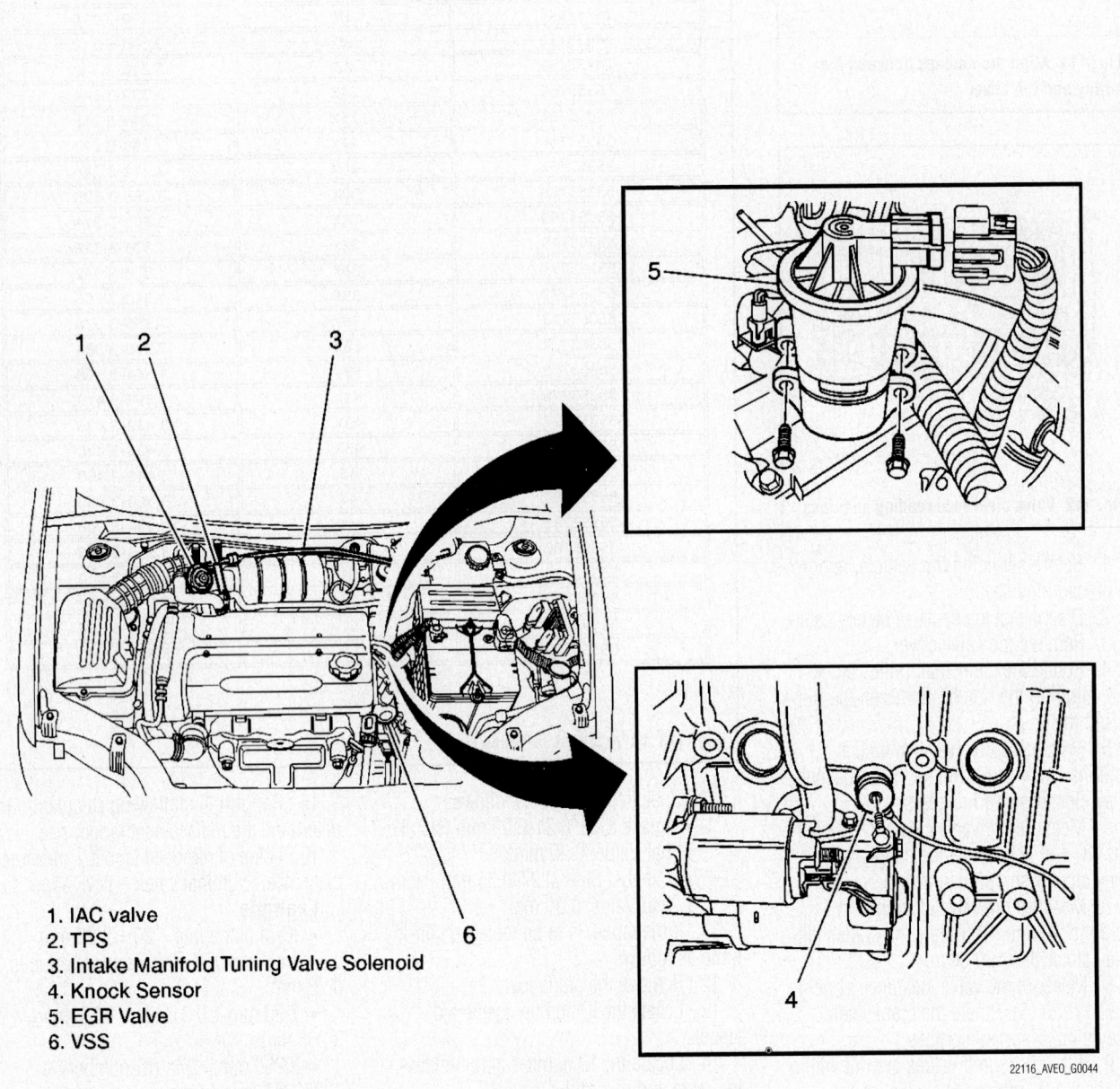

1. IAC valve
2. TPS
3. Intake Manifold Tuning Valve Solenoid
4. Knock Sensor
5. EGR Valve
6. VSS

22116_AVEO_G0044

Fig. 114 Component locations—1.6L LXT Engine (1 of 3)

CAMSHAFT POSITION (CMP) SENSOR

LOCATION

1.6L (LXT) Engine

See Figure 118.

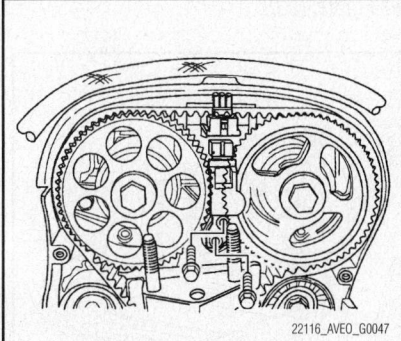

Fig. 118 The camshaft position sensor location view 1.6L (LXT Engine)

The Camshaft Position (CMP) Sensor for the 1.6L (LXT Engine) is located under the timing belt front cover.

1.6L (LXV) Engine

See Figure 119.

The Camshaft Position (CMP) Sensors for the 1.6L (LXV Engine) are located at the rear of the cylinder head. It consists of a left and a right sensor.

REMOVAL & INSTALLATION

1.6L (LXT) Engine

See Figure 118.

1. Before servicing the vehicle, refer to the precautions section.
2. Disconnect the negative battery cable.
3. Remove the engine appearance cover bolts and the nuts.
4. Remove the engine appearance cover.
5. Disconnect the Camshaft Position (CMP) sensor electrical connector.
6. Remove the timing belt front cover. For additional information, refer to the following section, "Timing Belt Front Cover, Removal & Installation."
7. Remove the CMP sensor bolts and CMP sensor.

To install:

8. Install the CMP sensor and tighten the bolts to 62 inch lbs. (7 Nm).
9. Install the timing belt front cover.
10. Connect the CMP sensor electrical connector.

11. Install the engine appearance cover.
12. Connect the negative battery cable.

1.6L (LXV) Engine

See Figure 119.

1. Before servicing the vehicle, refer to the precautions section.
2. Disconnect the negative battery cable.
3. Disconnect the Camshaft Position (CMP) sensor connectors.
4. Remove the CMP sensor bolt.
5. Remove the CMP sensor.

To install:

6. Install the CMP sensor.
7. Install the CMP sensor bolt and tighten to 53 inch lbs. (6 Nm).
8. Connect the CMP sensor connectors.
9. Connect the battery negative cable.

CRANKSHAFT POSITION (CKP) SENSOR

LOCATION

1.6L (LXT) Engine

See Figure 120.

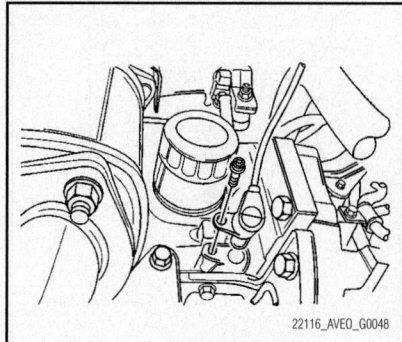

Fig. 120 Crankshaft Position (CKP) sensor location view 1.6L (LXT Engine)

1. Camshaft position sensor-intake side shown
2. Retaining bolt

Fig. 119 The camshaft position sensor location view 1.6L (LXV Engine)

The Crankshaft Position (CKP) sensor is located at the rear of the engine block underneath the oil filter.

1.6L (LXV) Engine

See Figure 121.

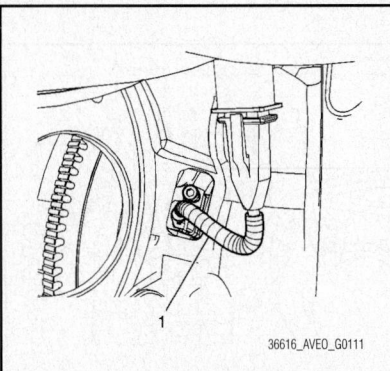

Fig. 121 Crankshaft Position (CKP) sensor (1) location view 1.6L (LXV Engine)

The Crankshaft Position (CKP) sensor is located in the transaxle housing underneath the starter motor.

REMOVAL & INSTALLATION

1.6L (LXT) Engine

See Figure 122.

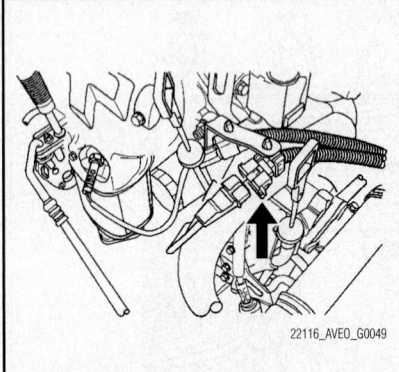

Fig. 122 Disconnect the crankshaft position sensor electrical connector.

1. Before servicing the vehicle, refer to the precautions section.
2. Disconnect the negative battery cable.
3. Disconnect the Crankshaft Position (CKP) sensor electrical connector.
4. Remove the CKP sensor bolt.
5. Remove the CKP sensor.

To install:

6. Install the CKP sensor and tighten the bolt to 58 inch lbs. (6.5 Nm).
7. Connect the CKP sensor electrical connector.
8. Connect the negative battery cable.

1.6L (LXV) Engine

See Figure 121.

1. Before servicing the vehicle, refer to the precautions section.
2. Disconnect the negative battery cable.
3. Remove the starter motor.
4. Remove the CKP sensor bolt.
5. Remove the CKP sensor.

To install:

6. Install the CKP sensor.
7. Install the CKP sensor bolt and tighten to 40 inch. lbs. (4.5 Nm).
8. Install the starter motor.
9. Connect the negative battery cable.

RELEARN PROCEDURE

1. Install a scan tool.
2. Monitor the ECM for DTCs with a scan tool. If other DTCs are set, except DTC P0315, refer to DTC list for the applicable DTC that set.
3. With a scan tool, select the CKP system variation learn procedure and perform the following:
   - Observe the fuel cut-off for the applicable engine.
   - Block the drive wheels.
   - Set the parking brake.
   - Place the vehicle's transmission in Park or Neutral.
   - Turn the air conditioning (A/C) OFF
   - Cycle the ignition from OFF to ON.
   - Apply and hold the brake pedal for the duration of the procedure.
   - Start and idle the engine.
   - Accelerate to wide open throttle (WOT). The engine should not accelerate beyond the calibrated fuel cut-off RPM value noted in step
   - Release the throttle immediately if the value is exceeded.
   - Release the throttle when fuel cut-off occurs.

➡**While the learn procedure is in progress, release the throttle immediately when the engine starts to decelerate. The engine control is returned to the operator and the engine responds to throttle position after the learn procedure is complete.**

4. The scan tool displays Learn Status: Learned this Ignition. If the scan tool indicates that DTC P0315 ran and passed, the CKP variation learn procedure is complete. If the scan tool indicates DTC P0315 failed or did not run, refer to DTC P0315. If any other DTCs set, refer to Diagnostic Trouble Code (DTC) List for the applicable DTC that set.

5. Turn OFF the ignition for 30 seconds after the learn procedure is completed successfully.

EVAPORATIVE EMISSION (EVAP) CANISTER

LOCATION

See Figure 123.

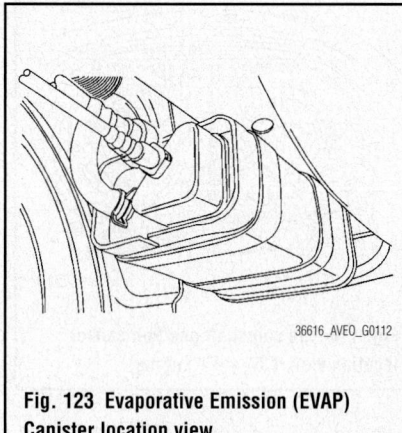

Fig. 123 Evaporative Emission (EVAP) Canister location view

The Evaporative Emission (EVAP) Canister is located next to the fuel tank.

REMOVAL & INSTALLATION

See Figure 123.

1. Before servicing the vehicle, refer to the precautions section.
2. Disconnect the negative battery cable.

✳✳ CAUTION

Do not allow smoking or the use of open flames in the area where work on the fuel or EVAP system is taking place. Anytime work is being done on the fuel system, disconnect the negative battery cable, except for those tests where battery voltage is required.

3. Raise and suitably support the vehicle.
4. Disconnect the canister fuel vapor hoses.
5. Remove the bolt that secures the canister flange to the vehicle.
6. Slide the canister out of the track holder.
7. Remove the canister.

To install:

8. Insert the canister into the track and slide it into position.
9. Install the canister flange bolt and tighten the bolt to 35 inch. lbs. (4 Nm).

10. Connect the canister fuel vapor hoses.

11. Lower the vehicle.

12. Connect the negative battery cable.

EVAPORATIVE EMISSION (EVAP) CANISTER PURGE SOLENOID VALVE

LOCATION

1.6L (LXT) Engine

See Figure 124.

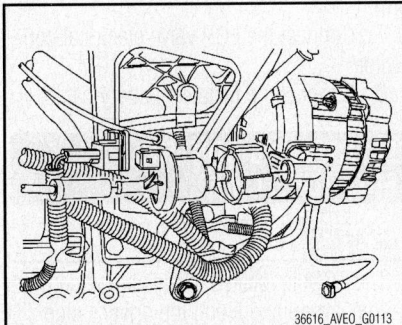

Fig. 124 Evaporative Emission (EVAP) Canister Purge Solenoid Valve 1.6L (LXT Engine)

The Evaporative Emission (EVAP) Canister Purge Solenoid Valve is located at the right side of the engine and sits behind the alternator.

1.6L (LXV) Engine

See Figure 125.

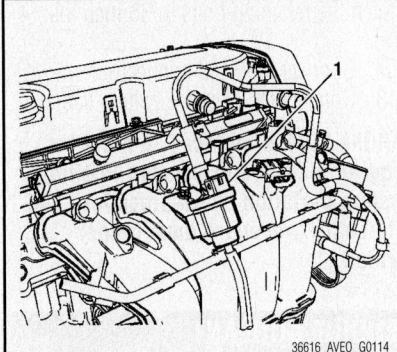

Fig. 125 Evaporative Emission (EVAP) Canister Purge Solenoid Valve (1) 1.6L (LXV Engine)

The Evaporative Emission (EVAP) Canister Purge Solenoid Valve is located at the right side of the engine and sits behind the alternator.

REMOVAL & INSTALLATION

1.6L (LXT) Engine

See Figure 124.

1. Before servicing the vehicle, refer to the precautions section.

2. Disconnect the negative battery cable.

> **✳✳ CAUTION**
>
> **Do not allow smoking or the use of open flames in the area where work on the fuel or EVAP system is taking place. Anytime work is being done on the fuel system, disconnect the negative battery cable, except for those tests where battery voltage is required.**

3. Disconnect the Evaporative Emission (EVAP) canister purge solenoid connector.

4. Disconnect the vacuum hoses from the EVAP canister purge solenoid.

5. Remove the EVAP canister purge solenoid from the intake manifold.

To install:

6. Attach the EVAP canister purge solenoid to the intake manifold.

7. Connect the vacuum hoses to the EVAP canister purge solenoid.

8. Connect the EVAP canister purge solenoid connector.

9. Connect the negative battery cable.

1.6L (LXV) Engine

See Figure 125.

1. Before servicing the vehicle, refer to the precautions section.

2. Disconnect the negative battery cable.

> **✳✳ CAUTION**
>
> **Do not allow smoking or the use of open flames in the area where work on the fuel or EVAP system is taking place. Anytime work is being done on the fuel system, disconnect the negative battery cable, except for those tests where battery voltage is required.**

3. Disconnect the EVAP canister purge valve upper and lower hoses.

4. Disconnect the EVAP canister purge valve connector.

5. Detach the EVAP canister purge valve.

To install:

6. Install the EVAP canister purge valve.

7. Connect the EVAP canister purge valve connector.

8. Connect the EVAP canister purge valve upper and lower hoses.

9. Connect the negative battery cable.

EVAPORATIVE EMISSION (EVAP) CANISTER VENT SOLENOID VALVE

LOCATION

1.6L (LXT) Engine

See Figure 126.

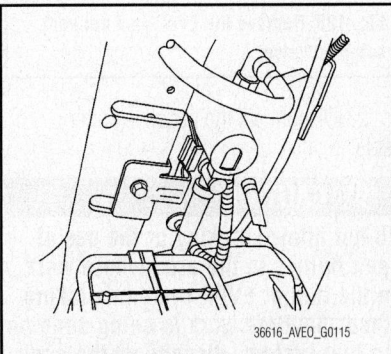

Fig. 126 Evaporative Emission (EVAP) Canister Vent Solenoid Valve 1.6L (LXT Engine)

The Evaporative Emission (EVAP) Canister Vent Solenoid Valve is located at the rear of the canister assembly.

1.6L (LXV) Engine

See Figure 127.

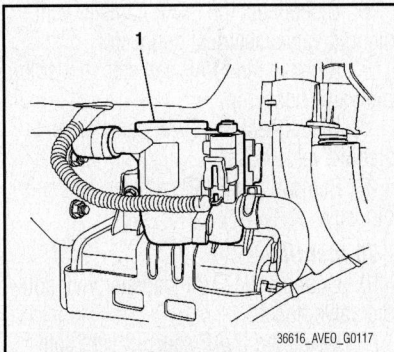

Fig. 127 Evaporative Emission (EVAP) Canister Vent Solenoid Valve 1.6L (LXV Engine)

The Evaporative Emission (EVAP) Canister Vent Solenoid Valve is located to the side of the canister assembly.

REMOVAL & INSTALLATION

1.6L (LXT) Engine

See Figure 128.

1. Before servicing the vehicle, refer to the precautions section.

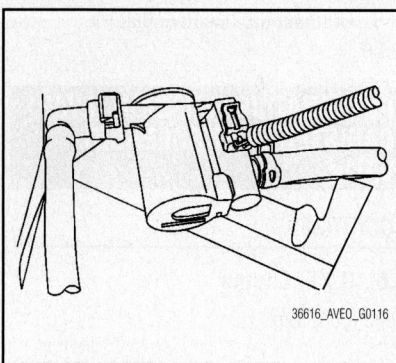

Fig. 128 Remove the EVAP canister vent solenoid valve

2. Disconnect the negative battery cable.

✳✳ CAUTION

Do not allow smoking or the use of open flames in the area where work on the fuel or EVAP system is taking place. Anytime work is being done on the fuel system, disconnect the negative battery cable, except for those tests where battery voltage is required.

3. Raise and suitably support the vehicle.
4. Remove the Evaporative Emission (EVAP) canister vent solenoid valve bracket bolt.
5. Remove the EVAP canister vent solenoid valve bracket.
6. Disconnect the EVAP canister vent solenoid valve electrical connector.
7. Remove the EVAP canister vent solenoid valve hose clip.
8. Disconnect the EVAP canister vent solenoid valve hoses.
9. Remove the EVAP canister vent solenoid valve.

To install:

10. Connect the EVAP canister vent solenoid valve hoses.
11. Install the EVAP canister vent solenoid valve hose clip.
12. Connect the EVAP canister vent solenoid valve electrical connector.
13. Install the EVAP canister vent solenoid valve bracket to the EVAP canister vent solenoid valve.
14. Install the bolt to the EVAP canister vent solenoid valve bracket.
15. Tighten the EVAP canister vent solenoid valve bracket bolt to 35 inch. lbs. (4 Nm).
16. Lower the vehicle.
17. Connect the negative battery cable, if disconnected.

1.6L (LXV) Engine

See Figure 127.

1. Before servicing the vehicle, refer to the precautions section.
2. Disconnect the negative battery cable.

✳✳ CAUTION

Do not allow smoking or the use of open flames in the area where work on the fuel or EVAP system is taking place. Anytime work is being done on the fuel system, disconnect the negative battery cable, except for those tests where battery voltage is required.

3. Raise and suitably support the vehicle.
4. Disconnect the EVAP canister vent solenoid valve connector.
5. Disconnect the EVAP canister vent hose.
6. Remove the EVAP canister vent assembly pushing it to the left side.

To install:

7. Install the EVAP canister vent assembly pushing it to the right side.
8. Connect the EVAP canister vent hose.
9. Connect the EVAP canister vent solenoid valve connector.
10. Lower the vehicle.
11. Connect the negative battery cable.

EXHAUST GAS RECIRCULATION (EGR) VALVE

LOCATION

1.6L (LXT) Engine

See Figure 129.

The Exhaust Gas Recirculation (EGR) Valve is located at the rear of the cylinder head.

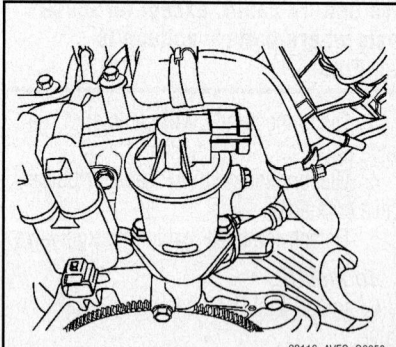

Fig. 129 Exhaust Gas Recirculation (EGR) Valve

REMOVAL & INSTALLATION

1.6L (LXT) Engine

See Figure 129.

1. Before servicing the vehicle, refer to the precautions section.
2. Disconnect the negative battery cable.
3. Disconnect the EGR valve electrical connector.
4. Remove the EGR valve retaining bolts.
5. Remove the EGR valve assembly.

To install:

6. Install the EGR valve assembly and tighten the retaining bolts to 22 ft. lbs. (30 Nm).
7. Connect the EGR valve electrical connector.
8. Connect the negative battery cable.

ELECTRONIC CONTROL MODULE (ECM)

LOCATION

The ECM is located in the engine compartment mounted along the driver's side fender area.

REMOVAL & INSTALLATION

1. Before servicing the vehicle, refer to the precautions section.
2. Disconnect the negative battery cable.
3. Disconnect the Engine Control Module (ECM) connectors.
4. Remove the ECM retaining nuts.
5. Remove the ECM from the ECM mount.

To install:

6. Position the ECM in place and tighten the retaining bolts to 35 inch lbs. (4 Nm).
7. Connect the ECM connectors.
8. Connect the negative battery cable.

➡ **If the ECM is replaced, it must be programmed, the Crankshaft Position System Variation Learn procedure and Idle Learn procedure must be performed.**

ENGINE COOLANT TEMPERATURE (ECT) SENSOR

LOCATION

1.6L (LXT) Engine

See Figure 130.

The Engine Coolant Temperature (ECT) Sensor is located on the cylinder head below the intake manifold.

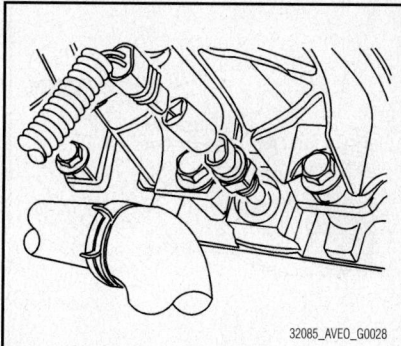

Fig. 130 Engine Coolant Temperature (ECT) location view

1.6L (LXV) Engine

ECT 1

See Figure 131.

The Engine Coolant Temperature (ECT) Sensor— ECT 1 is located at the rear of the cylinder head in the coolant jacket. It sits just below the intake camshaft sensor.

Fig. 131 Engine Coolant Temperature (ECT) location view—ECT 1

ECT 2

See Figure 132.

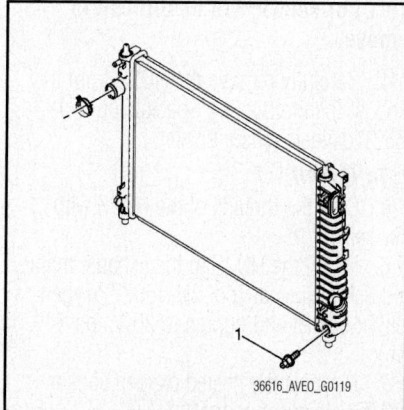

Fig. 132 Engine Coolant Temperature (ECT) location view (1)—ECT 2

The Engine Coolant Temperature (ECT) Sensor— ECT 2 is located at the bottom of the radiator.

REMOVAL & INSTALLATION

1.6L (LXT) Engine

See Figure 130.

1. Before servicing the vehicle, refer to the precautions section.
2. Disconnect the negative battery cable.
3. Relieve the coolant system pressure.
4. Disconnect the negative battery cable.
5. Drain the coolant below the Engine Coolant Temperature (ECT) sensor level.
6. Disconnect the ECT sensor connector.
7. Remove the ECT sensor.

➡**Use care when handling the coolant sensor. Damage to the coolant sensor will affect the operation of the fuel control system.**

To install:
8. Tighten the ECT sensor to 15 ft. lbs. (20 Nm).
9. Connect the ECT sensor connector.
10. Refill and bleed the cooling system.
11. Connect the negative battery cable.

1.6L (LXV) Engine

ECT 1

See Figure 131.

1. Before servicing the vehicle, refer to the precautions section.
2. Disconnect the negative battery cable.
3. Drain the engine coolant.
4. Disconnect the ECT sensor connector.
5. Remove the ECT retaining clip.
6. Remove the ECT from the coolant distributor.

To install:
7. Install the ECT to the coolant distributor.
8. Install the ECT retaining clip.
9. Connect the ECT sensor connector.
10. Refill and bleed the cooling system.
11. Connect the negative battery cable.

ECT 2

See Figure 132.

1. Before servicing the vehicle, refer to the precautions section.
2. Disconnect the negative battery cable.
3. Drain the engine coolant.

4. Drain the engine coolant.
5. Disconnect the ECT 2 sensor connector.
6. Remove the ECT 2 sensor from the radiator.

To install:
7. Install the ECT 2 sensor to the radiator. Tighten the ECT 2 sensor to 15 ft. lbs. (20 Nm).
8. Connect the ECT 2 sensor connector.
9. Refill and bleed the cooling system.
10. Connect the negative battery cable.

FUEL LEVEL SENDING UNIT

LOCATION

The fuel level sending unit is located in the fuel tank and is mounted to the fuel pump assembly.

REMOVAL & INSTALLATION

See Figures 133 through 135.

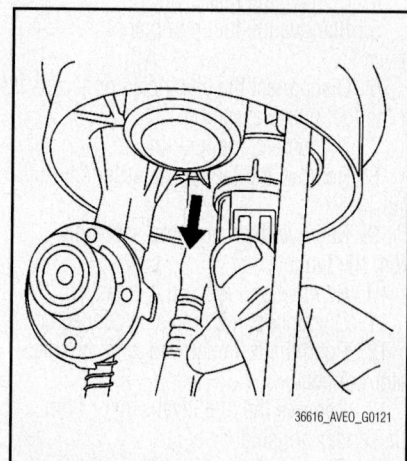

Fig. 133 Disconnect the insulator connector

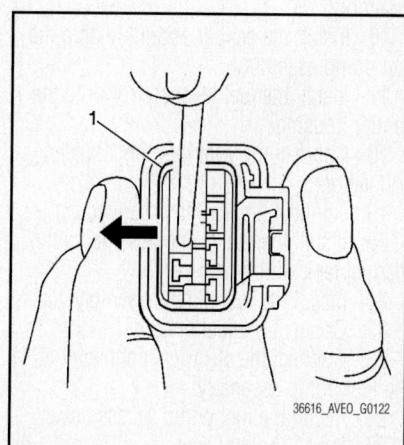

Fig. 134 Remove the fuel level sensor (1) from the sender housing

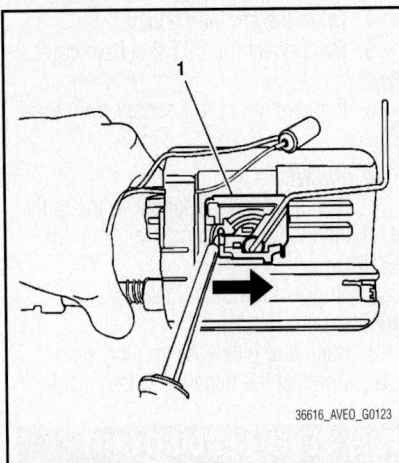

Fig. 135 Remove the fuel level sensor housing (1)

1. Before servicing the vehicle, refer to the precautions section.
2. Relieve the fuel system pressure.
3. Disconnect the negative battery cable.
4. Remove the rear seat.
5. Remove the fuel pump access cover.
6. Disconnect the electrical connector at the fuel pump assembly.
7. Disconnect the fuel lines.
8. Remove the fuel pump assembly clip.
9. Remove the fuel pump assembly from the tank.
10. Remove and discard the gasket.
11. Disconnect the insulator connector.
12. Push the terminal wedge in the insulator connector.
13. Remove the fuel level sensor from the sender housing.
14. Remove the sender housing.

To install:
15. Install the wires into the sender assembly.
16. Install the sender assembly onto the fuel pump assembly.
17. Install the fuel level sensor onto the sender housing.
18. Connect the wire into the insulator connector.
19. Connect the insulator connector
20. Install the fuel pump assembly into the fuel tank with a new gasket.
21. Install the fuel pump assembly clip.
22. Connect the fuel lines.
23. Connect the electrical connector at the fuel pump assembly.
24. Install the fuel pump access cover.
25. Install the rear seat.
26. Connect the negative battery cable.

FUEL TANK PRESSURE SENSOR (FTP)

LOCATION

The Fuel Tank Pressure Sensor (FTP) is located at the top of the fuel pump assembly. It can be accessed by removing the rear seat.

REMOVAL & INSTALLATION

1. Before servicing the vehicle, refer to the precautions section.
2. Relieve the fuel system pressure.
3. Remove the fuel fill cap.
4. Remove the rear seat.
5. Remove the fuel sender assembly access cover.
6. Disconnect the Fuel Tank Pressure (FTP) sensor electrical connector.
7. Remove the FTP from the fuel sender assembly.

To install:
8. Install the fuel tank pressure sensor.
9. Connect the fuel tank pressure sensor connector.
10. Install the fuel pump access cover.
11. Install the rear seat.
12. Connect the negative battery cable.

HEATED OXYGEN (HO2S) SENSOR

LOCATION

See Figures 136 and 137.

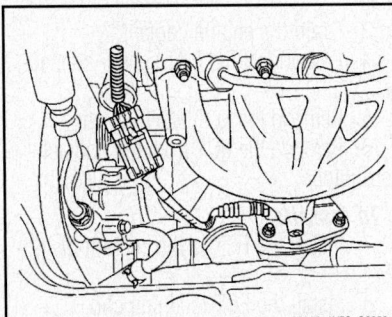

Fig. 136 Heated Oxygen (HO2S) Sensor (1) location view

The Heated Oxygen (HO2S) Sensor (1) is located at the exhaust manifold. The Heated Oxygen (HO2S) Sensor (2) is located after the catalytic converter in the front exhaust pipe.

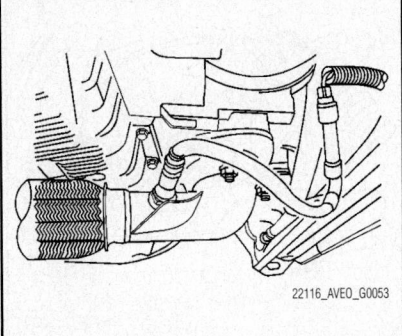

Fig. 137 Heated Oxygen (HO2S) Sensor (2) location view

REMOVAL & INSTALLATION

See Figures 136 and 137.

➡A special anti-seize compound is used on the oxygen sensor threads. This compound consists of a liquid graphite and glass beads. The graphite will burn away, but the glass beads will remain, making the sensor easier to remove. New or service sensors will already have the compound applied to the threads. If a sensor is removed from any engine and if for any reason it is to be reinstalled, the threads must have anti-seize compound applied before reinstallation.

➡Although there are two different Heated Oxygen sensors (front and rear), the procedure is the same for both.

1. Before servicing the vehicle, refer to the precautions section.
2. Disconnect the negative battery cable.
3. Disconnect the Heated Oxygen Sensor (HO2S) electrical connector.

➡Remove the oxygen sensors with the engine temperature above 120°F (48°C) or sensor will be difficult to remove.

4. Carefully remove the HO2S from the exhaust manifold using Special Tool EN-46577 oxygen sensor socket.

To install:
5. Coat the threads of the HO2S with anti-seize.
6. Install the HO2S to the exhaust manifold using Special Tool EN-46577 oxygen sensor socket and tighten to 30 ft. lbs. (40 Nm).
7. Connect the heated oxygen sensor (HO2S) electrical connector.
8. Connect the negative battery cable.

IDLE AIR CONTROL (IAC) VALVE

LOCATION

1.6L (LXT) Engine

See Figure 138.

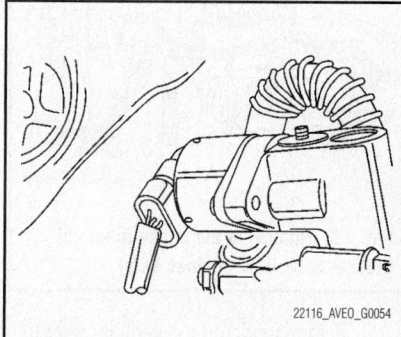

Fig. 138 Idle Air Control (IAC) Valve location view

The Idle Air Control (IAC) Valve is located at the throttle body.

REMOVAL & INSTALLATION

1.6L (LXT) Engine

See Figure 139.

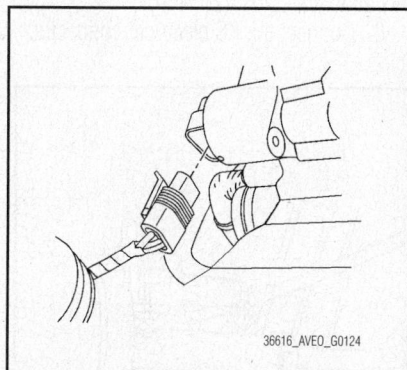

Fig. 139 Disconnect the Idle Air Control (IAC) valve connector

1. Before servicing the vehicle, refer to the precautions section.
2. Disconnect the negative battery cable.
3. Disconnect the Idle Air Control (IAC) valve connector.
4. Remove the IAC valve retaining bolts.

> **✴✴ WARNING**
>
> **Do not push or pull on the IAC valve pintle on IAC valves that have been in service. The force required to move the pintle may damage the threads on the worm drive.**

> **✴✴ WARNING**
>
> **Do not soak the IAC valve in any liquid cleaner or solvent, as damage may result.**

5. Remove the IAC valve.

To install:

> **✴✴ WARNING**
>
> **If installing a new IAC valve, be sure to replace it with an identical part. The IAC valve pintle shape and diameter are designed for the specific application. Measure the distance between the tip of the IAC valve pintle and the mounting flange. If the distance is greater than 1.1 inch. (28 mm), use finger pressure to slowly retract the pintle. The force required to retract the pintle will not damage the IAC valve. The purpose of the 1.1 inch. (28 mm), setting is to prevent the IAC pintle from bottoming out on the pintle seat. This 1.1 inch. (28 mm), setting is also an adequate setting for controlled idle on a restart.**

6. Clean the IAC valve O-ring seal area, the pintle valve seat, and the air passage with a suitable fuel system cleaner. Do not use methyl ethyl ketone.
7. Lubricate a new O-ring with engine oil. Install the new O-ring onto the valve.
8. Install the IAC valve into the throttle body. Tighten the retaining bolts to 27 inch lbs. (3 Nm).
9. Connect the IAC valve connector.
10. Connect the negative battery cable.
11. Perform the idle learn procedure.

IDLE LEARN PROCEDURE

1.6L (LXT) Engine

The Idle Learn Procedure listed below must be performed whenever the following occurs:
• The throttle body assembly is replaced
• The throttle body is cleaned
• The Engine Control Module (ECM) is replaced
• The Idle Air Control valve (IAC) is replaced
• Power disconnection (battery cable, ECM fuse, etc.) (Delphi ECM only)

1. Turn the ignition ON.
2. Turn the ignition OFF for 15 seconds.
3. Turn the ignition ON for 5 seconds.
4. Turn the ignition OFF for 15 seconds.
5. Start the engine in park/neutral.
6. Allow the engine to run until the engine coolant temperature is greater than 185°F (85°C).
7. Turn the A/C ON for 10 seconds, if equipped.
8. If the vehicle is equipped with an automatic transaxle, apply the parking brake. While pressing the brake pedal, place the transaxle in drive (D) for 10 seconds.
9. Turn the A/C OFF for 10 seconds, if equipped.
10. If the vehicle is equipped with an automatic transaxle, while pressing the brake pedal, place the transaxle in park/neutral.
11. Turn the ignition OFF. The idle learn procedure is complete.

INTAKE AIR TEMPERATURE (IAT) SENSOR

LOCATION

1.6L (LXT) Engine

See Figure 140.

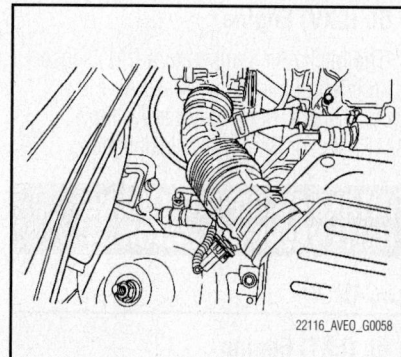

Fig. 140 Intake Air Temperature (IAT) Sensor location view

The Intake Air Temperature (IAT) Sensor is located in the air cleaner inlet duct. The IAT sensor is no longer replaced as a separate service item. If the intake air temperature sensor is faulty, replacement of the entire air cleaner inlet duct will be necessary.

1.6L (LXV) Engine

The Intake Air Temperature (IAT) sensor is an integral part of the Mass Air Flow (MAF) sensor. The MAF is located at the air intake system.

REMOVAL & INSTALLATION

1.6L (LXT) Engine

See Figure 140.

1. Before servicing the vehicle, refer to the precautions section.

2. Disconnect the negative battery cable.

3. Turn OFF the ignition.

4. Disconnect the electrical connector from the Intake Air Temperature (IAT) sensor.

5. Disconnect the breather tube from the air cleaner intake duct.

➡️The intake air temperature sensor is no longer replaced as a separate service item. If the intake air temperature sensor is faulty, replacement of the entire air cleaner inlet duct will be necessary.

6. Loosen the clamps securing the air cleaner intake duct.

7. Remove air cleaner intake duct.

To install:

8. Install the air cleaner intake duct.

9. Tighten the clamps securing the air cleaner intake duct to 27 inch. lbs. (3 Nm).

10. Connect the breather tube to the air cleaner intake duct.

11. Connect the electrical connector to the IAT sensor.

12. Connect the negative battery cable.

1.6L (LXV) Engine

The Intake Air Temperature (IAT) sensor is an integral part of the Mass Air Flow (MAF) sensor. Refer to Mass Air Flow (MAF) sensor Removal & Installation.

INTAKE MANIFOLD TUNING (IMT) VALVE ACTUATOR

LOCATION

1.6L (LXT) Engine

See Figure 141.

The Intake Manifold Tuning (IMT) Valve Actuator is located at the rear of the engine below the intake manifold.

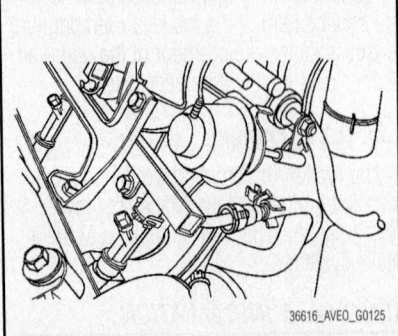

Fig. 141 Intake Manifold Tuning (IMT) Valve Actuator location view

REMOVAL & INSTALLATION

1.6L (LXT) Engine

See Figure 141.

1. Before servicing the vehicle, refer to the precautions section.

2. Disconnect the negative battery cable.

3. Disconnect the vacuum hose from the Intake Manifold Tuning (IMT) valve actuator.

➡️Ensure the IMT valve is closed before removing the IMT valve actuator retaining bolts and valve.

4. Remove the IMT valve actuator valve bolts.

5. Remove the IMT valve actuator valve from the IMT valve.

To install:

6. Install the IMT valve actuator valve to the IMT valve.

7. Install the IMT valve actuator valve bolts and tighten to 9 ft. lbs. (12 Nm).

8. Connect the vacuum hose to the IMT valve actuator valve.

9. Connect the negative battery cable.

KNOCK SENSOR (KS)

LOCATION

See Figure 142.

The Knock Sensor (KS) is located at the engine block and is mounted in front of the starter motor.

REMOVAL & INSTALLATION

See Figure 143.

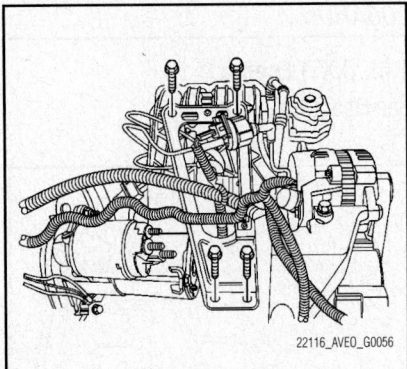

Fig. 143 Removing the intake manifold bracket bolts (LXT Engines only)

1. Before servicing the vehicle, refer to the precautions section.

2. Disconnect the negative battery cable.

3. Remove the intake manifold bracket bolts and bracket. (LXT Engines only).

4. Disconnect the Knock Sensor (KS) electrical connector.

5. Remove the knock sensor bolt.

6. Remove the knock sensor.

To install:

7. Install the knock sensor and tighten the bolt to 15 ft. lbs. (20 Nm).

8. Connect the KS electrical connector.

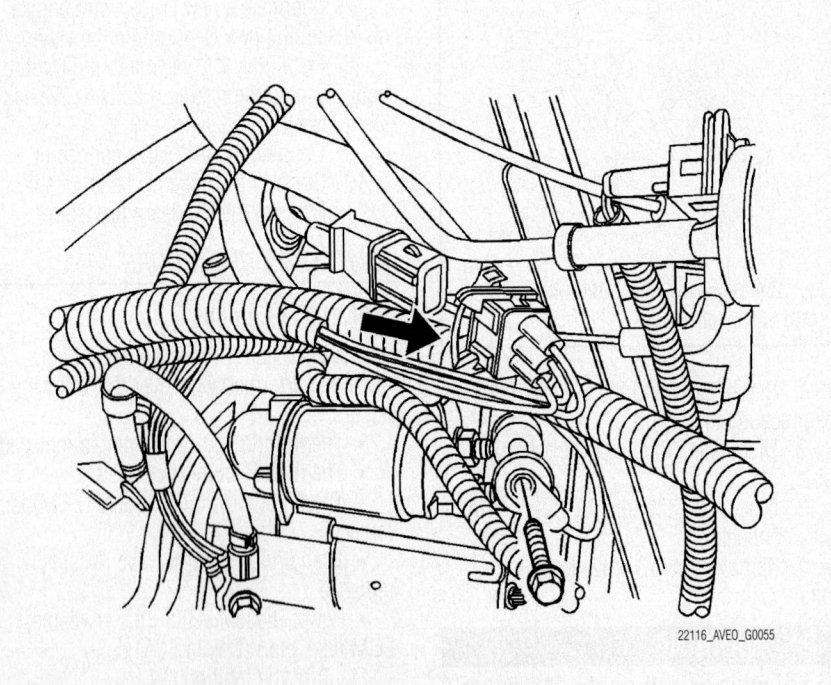

Fig. 142 Knock Sensor (KS) location view (LXT Engine) shown, (LXV) Engine similar

9. Install the intake manifold bracket. (LXT Engines only). Tighten the upper bolts to 18 ft. lbs. (25 Nm). Tighten the lower bolts to 33 ft. lbs. (45 Nm).

10. Connect the negative battery cable.

MALFUNCTION INDICATOR LIGHT (MIL)

RESET PROCEDURES

See Figure 144.

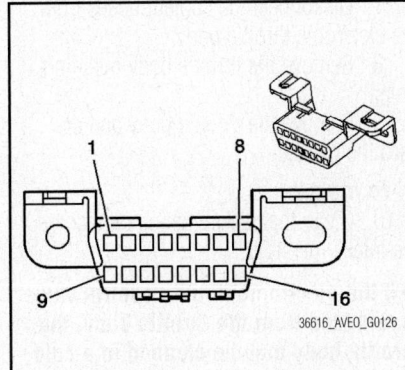

Fig. 144 Data Link Connector (DLC) and pin description

1. Install any components or connectors that may have been removed.

2. Perform any adjustment, programming or setup procedures that are required when a component or module is removed or replaced.

➡ **The DLC is located inside the drivers compartment, underneath the dash.**

3. Using a suitable scan tool connect to the Data Link Connector (DLC), clear any Diagnostic Trouble Codes (DTC).

4. Turn OFF the ignition for 60 seconds.

MASS AIR FLOW (MAF) SENSOR

LOCATION

1.6L (LXV) Engine

See Figure 145.

The Mass Air Flow (MAF) Sensor is located in the air induction system, after the air cleaner housing.

REMOVAL & INSTALLATION

1.6L (LXV) Engine

See Figure 146.

1. Before servicing the vehicle, refer to the precautions section.

2. Disconnect the negative battery cable.

Fig. 145 Mass Air Flow (MAF) Sensor location view

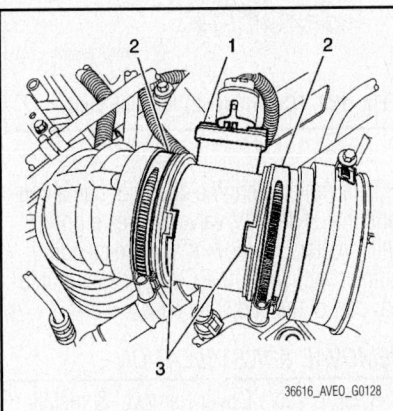

Fig. 146 Connector (1), clamps (2) and alignment notches (3)

3. Disconnect the Mass Air Flow (MAF) sensor connector.

4. Loosen the two clamps.

5. Remove the MAF sensor.

To install:

➡ **Ensure the MAF sensor is installed correctly. The arrow indicates direction of airflow and the tabs of the hoses and notches of the sensor must be aligned as illustrated. Failure to do so may cause drivability concerns and DTC's.**

6. Install the mass airflow sensor.

7. Tighten the clamps.

8. Connect the MAF sensor connector.

MANIFOLD ABSOLUTE PRESSURE (MAP) SENSOR

LOCATION

1.6L (LXT) Engine

See Figure 147.

The Manifold Absolute Pressure (MAP) Sensor is located at the intake manifold.

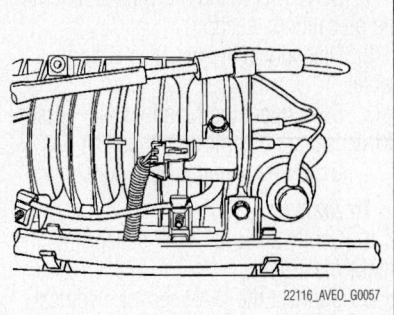

Fig. 147 Manifold Absolute Pressure (MAP) Sensor location view (LXT Engine)

1.6L (LXV) Engine

See Figure 148.

The Manifold Absolute Pressure (MAP) Sensor is located at the intake manifold.

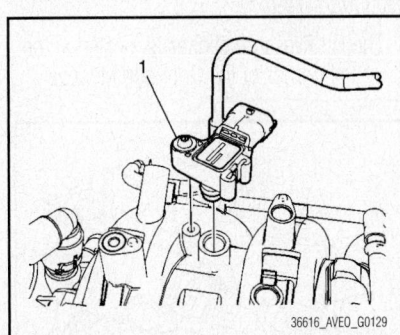

Fig. 148 Manifold Absolute Pressure (MAP) Sensor (1) location view (LXV Engine)

REMOVAL & INSTALLATION

1.6L (LXT) Engine

See Figure 147.

1. Before servicing the vehicle, refer to the precautions section.

2. Disconnect the negative battery cable.

3. Remove the Manifold Absolute Pressure (MAP) sensor electrical connector.

4. Disconnect the vacuum hose.

5. Remove the MAP sensor bolt.

6. Remove the MAP sensor.

To install:

7. Install the MAP sensor and tighten the bolt to 89 inch lbs. (10 Nm).

8. Connect the vacuum hose.

9. Connect the MAP sensor electrical connector.

10. Connect the negative battery cable.

1.6L (LXV) Engine

See Figure 148.

1. Before servicing the vehicle, refer to the precautions section.

2. Disconnect the negative battery cable.

3. Disconnect the Manifold Air Pressure (MAP) sensor electrical connector.

4. Gently remove the MAP sensor.

To install:

5. Gently snap the MAP sensor into the intake manifold.

6. Connect the MAP sensor electrical connector.

7. Connect the negative battery cable.

OIL PRESSURE SENSOR

LOCATION

1.6L (LXT) Engine

See Figure 149.

The Oil Pressure sensor is located at the lower left corner of the front engine cover.

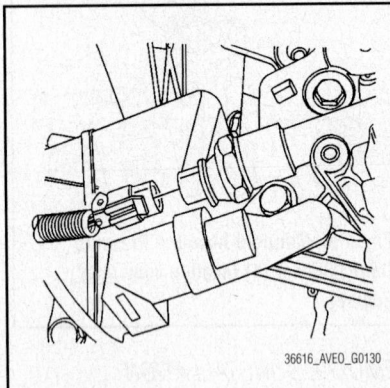

Fig. 149 Oil Pressure Sensor location view

REMOVAL & INSTALLATION

1.6L (LXT) Engine

See Figure 149.

1. Before servicing the vehicle, refer to the precautions section.

2. Disconnect the negative battery cable.

3. Disconnect the oil pressure sensor connector.

4. Remove the oil pressure sensor.

To install:

5. Add a small amount of gasket sealant to the oil pressure switch and install.

6. Tighten the oil pressure sensor to 30 ft. lbs. (40 Nm).

7. Connect the oil pressure sensor connector.

8. Connect the negative battery cable.

9. Check engine oil for the correct level.

POSITIVE CRANKCASE VENTILATION (PCV) VALVE

LOCATION

See Figure 150.

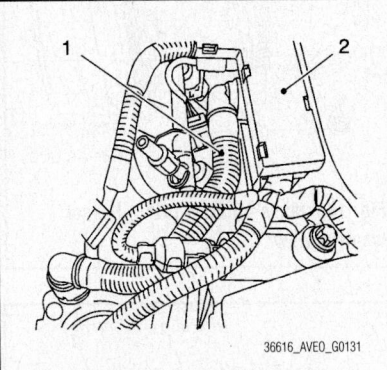

Fig. 150 PCV orifice (2) location view

This vehicles engine does not use a conventional style PCV valve, it uses a orifice which meters the flow at a rate depending on inlet vacuum. The PCV orifice is an integral part of the camshaft cover.

REMOVAL & INSTALLATION

Refer to Valve Cover Removal & Installation.

THROTTLE POSITION SENSOR (TPS)

LOCATION

The Throttle Position Sensor (TPS) is integral to the Electronic Throttle Control (ETC). It is located at the throttle body.

REMOVAL & INSTALLATION

1.6L (LXT) Engine

See Figure 151.

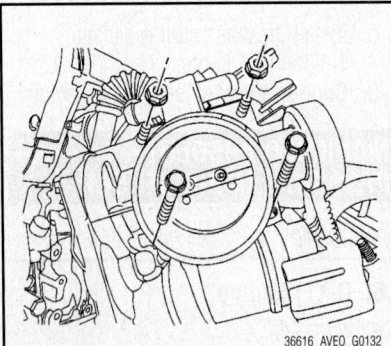

Fig. 151 Throttle body removal—1.6L (LXT Engine)

1. Before servicing the vehicle, refer to the precautions section.

2. Disconnect the negative battery cable.

3. Disconnect the intake air temperature sensor connector.

4. Remove the air cleaner inlet duct from the throttle body.

5. Disconnect the electronic throttle body connector.

6. Remove the IAC valve electrical connector if equipped.

7. Disconnect the coolant hoses from the electronic throttle body.

8. Remove the throttle body retaining bolts.

9. Remove the throttle body and discard the gasket.

To install:

10. Clean the gasket mating surface on the intake manifold.

➡**If the electronic throttle control valve is removed from the throttle body, the throttle body may be cleaned in a cold immersion type cleaner. Do not clean the electronic throttle control valve with any type of solvent or cleaner.**

11. Clean the throttle body.

12. Install the electronic throttle body assembly with a new gasket.

13. Install the electronic throttle body retaining nuts and bolts. Tighten the throttle body retaining bolts and nuts to 11 ft. lbs. (15 Nm).

14. Connect the electronic throttle body electrical connector.

15. Connect the IAC valve electrical connector if equipped.

16. Install the throttle body coolant hoses.

17. Install the air cleaner inlet duct to the throttle body.

18. Connect the negative battery cable.

19. Refill and bleed the cooling system.

1.6L (LXV) Engine

See Figure 152.

1. Before servicing the vehicle, refer to the precautions section.

2. Disconnect the negative battery cable.

3. Remove the air cleaner assembly.

4. Remove the air cleaner inlet duct from the throttle body.

5. Disconnect the ETC connector.

6. Disconnect the coolant inlet hose.

7. Disconnect the coolant outlet hose.

8. Disconnect the EVAP hose.

9. Detach the PCV breather hose.

10. Remove the throttle body bolts.

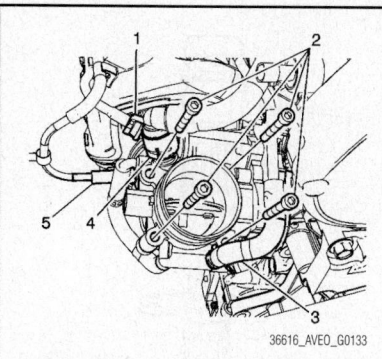

Fig. 152 Throttle body removal—1.6L (LXV Engine)

11. Remove the throttle body with the seal ring.

To install:

12. Install the throttle body with the seal ring. Install the retaining bolts and tighten to 71 inch. lbs. (8 Nm).
13. Connect the coolant inlet hose.
14. Connect the coolant outlet hose.
15. Connect the EVAP hose.
16. Connect the PCV breather hose.
17. Connect the ETC connector.
18. Install the air cleaner inlet duct to the throttle body.
19. Install the air-cleaner assembly.
20. Connect the negative battery cable.
21. Refill and bleed the cooling system.

THROTTLE & IDLE RELEARN PROCEDURE

1.6L (LXT) Engine

The Idle Learn Procedure listed below must be performed whenever the following occurs:
- The throttle body assembly is replaced
- The throttle body is cleaned
- The Engine Control Module (ECM) is replaced
- The Idle Air Control valve (IAC) is replaced
- Power disconnection (battery cable, ECM fuse, etc.) (Delphi ECM only)

1. Turn the ignition ON.
2. Turn the ignition OFF for 15 seconds.
3. Turn the ignition ON for 5 seconds.
4. Turn the ignition OFF for 15 seconds.
5. Start the engine in park/neutral.
6. Allow the engine to run until the engine coolant temperature is greater than 185°F (85°C).
7. Turn the A/C ON for 10 seconds, if equipped.
8. If the vehicle is equipped with an automatic transaxle, apply the parking brake. While pressing the brake pedal, place the transaxle in drive (D) for 10 seconds.

9. Turn the A/C OFF for 10 seconds, if equipped.
10. If the vehicle is equipped with an automatic transaxle, while pressing the brake pedal, place the transaxle in park/neutral.
11. Turn the ignition OFF. The idle learn procedure is complete.

1.6L (LXV) Engine

Without a scan tool

1. Start and idle the engine in park/neutral for 3 minutes.
2. With a scan tool, monitor the desired and the actual engine speed.
3. The ECM will start to learn the new idle cells and the desired engine speed should start to decrease.
4. Ignition OFF for 60 seconds.
5. Start and idle the engine in park/neutral for 3 minutes.
6. After the 3 minute run time the engine should be idling normal.

With a scan tool

7. Ignition ON, engine OFF, with a scan tool, perform the Idle Learn Reset in Module Setup.
8. Start the engine, monitor the TB Idle Airflow Compensation parameter. The TB Idle Airflow Compensation value should equal 0 percent and the engine should be idling at a normal idle speed.
9. Clear the DTCs with a scan tool.

VARIABLE CAMSHAFT TIMING OIL CONTROL SOLENOID

LOCATION

1.6L (LXV) Engine

See Figure 153.

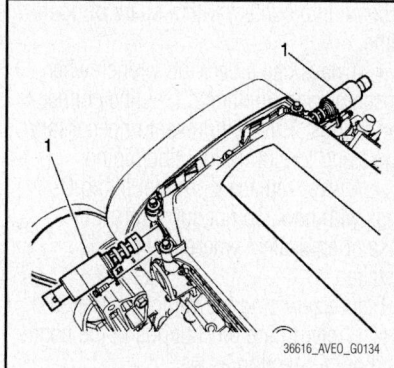

Fig. 153 Camshaft Position Actuator Valve location view

The Camshaft Position Actuator Valve is located at the front of the cylinder head, just behind the timing belt cover.

REMOVAL & INSTALLATION

1.6L (LXV) Engine

See Figure 153.

1. Before servicing the vehicle, refer to the precautions section.
2. Disconnect the negative battery cable.
3. Disconnect the camshaft position actuator valve connectors.
4. Remove the camshaft position actuator valve bolt.
5. Remove the camshaft position actuator valve and seal.

To install:

6. Install the camshaft position actuator valve and seal. Coat seal with clean engine oil prior to installation.
7. Install the camshaft position actuator valve bolt and tighten to 53 inch. lbs. (6 Nm).
8. Connect the camshaft position actuator valve connectors.
9. Connect the negative battery cable.

VEHICLE SPEED SENSOR (VSS)

LOCATION

Automatic Transaxle

See Figure 154.

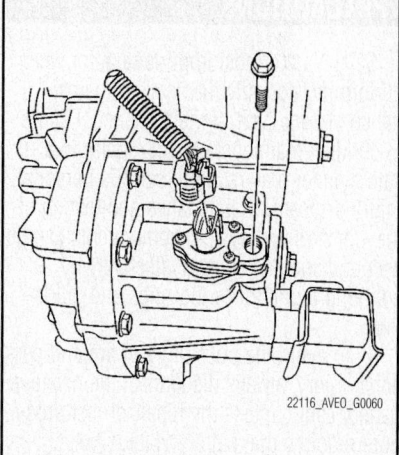

Fig. 154 Vehicle Speed Sensor (VSS) location view

The Vehicle Speed Sensor (VSS) or Output Shaft Speed (OSS) sensor is located on the upper position of the transaxle.

Manual Transaxle

See Figure 155.

The Vehicle Speed Sensor (VSS) or Output Shaft Speed (OSS) sensor is located on the upper position of the transaxle.

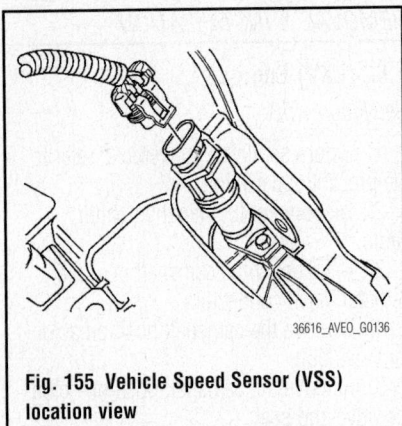

Fig. 155 Vehicle Speed Sensor (VSS) location view

REMOVAL & INSTALLATION

Automatic Transaxle

See Figure 154.

1. Before servicing the vehicle, refer to the precautions section.
2. Disconnect the negative battery cable.
3. Disconnect the Vehicle Speed Sensor (VSS) electrical connector.
4. Remove the VSS sensor retaining bolt.
5. Remove the VSS sensor from the transaxle.

To install:

6. Lubricate a new O-ring with clean automatic transmission fluid and install the O-Ring to the VSS.
7. Install the VSS and tighten the retaining bolts to 65 inch lbs. (74 Nm).
8. Connect the VSS electrical connector.
9. Connect the negative battery cable.

Manual Transaxle

See Figure 156.

1. Before servicing the vehicle, refer to the precautions section.
2. Disconnect the negative battery cable.
3. Disconnect the Vehicle Speed Sensor (VSS) electrical connector.
4. Remove the bolt and the speedometer driven gear assembly.
5. Remove the VSS from the speedometer driven gear.
6. Remove the O-ring from the speedometer driven gear housing.
7. Remove the driven gear pin and disconnect the driven gear.
8. Inspect for a damaged or torn O-ring.

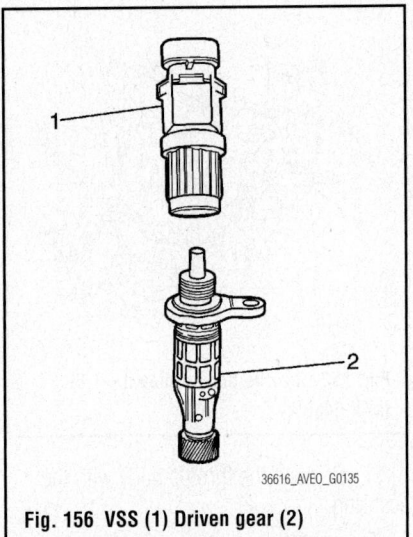

Fig. 156 VSS (1) Driven gear (2)

9. Inspect for a worn or damaged tooth on the driven gear.

To install:

10. Install the speedometer driven gear assembly to the transaxle housing mounting bolt and tighten to 62 inch. lbs. (7 Nm).
11. Connect the VSS connector.

FUEL

GASOLINE FUEL INJECTION SYSTEM

FUEL SYSTEM SERVICE PRECAUTIONS

Safety is the most important factor when performing not only fuel system maintenance but any type of maintenance. Failure to conduct maintenance and repairs in a safe manner may result in serious personal injury or death. Maintenance and testing of the vehicle's fuel system components can be accomplished safely and effectively by adhering to the following rules and guidelines.

• To avoid the possibility of fire and personal injury, always disconnect the negative battery cable unless the repair or test procedure requires that battery voltage be applied.

• Always relieve the fuel system pressure prior to disconnecting any fuel system component (injector, fuel rail, pressure regulator, etc.), fitting or fuel line connection. Exercise extreme caution whenever relieving fuel system pressure to avoid exposing skin, face and eyes to fuel spray. Please be advised that fuel under pressure may penetrate the skin or any part of the body that it contacts.

• Always place a shop towel or cloth around the fitting or connection prior to loosening to absorb any excess fuel due to spillage. Ensure that all fuel spillage (should it occur) is quickly removed from engine surfaces. Ensure that all fuel soaked cloths or towels are deposited into a suitable waste container.

• Always keep a dry chemical (Class B) fire extinguisher near the work area.

• Do not allow fuel spray or fuel vapors to come into contact with a spark or open flame.

• Always use a back-up wrench when loosening and tightening fuel line connection fittings. This will prevent unnecessary stress and torsion to fuel line piping.

• Always replace worn fuel fitting O-rings with new. Do not substitute fuel hose or equivalent where fuel pipe is installed.

Before servicing the vehicle, make sure to also refer to the precautions in the beginning of this section as well.

RELIEVING FUEL SYSTEM PRESSURE

See Figure 157.

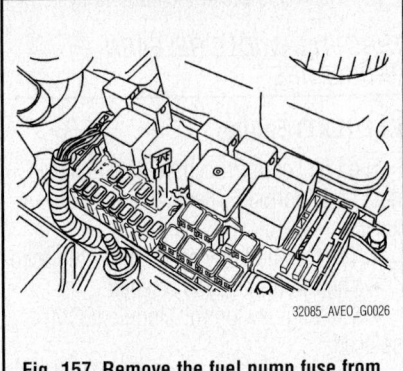

Fig. 157 Remove the fuel pump fuse from the engine fuse box

✳✳ WARNING

Remove the fuel tank cap and relieve the fuel system pressure before servicing the fuel system in order to reduce the risk of personal injury. After you relieve the fuel system pressure, a small amount of fuel may be released when servicing the fuel lines, the fuel injection pump, or the connections. In order to reduce the risk of personal injury, cover the fuel system components with a shop towel before disconnection. This will

catch any fuel that may leak out. Place the towel in an approved container when the disconnection is complete.

1. Remove the fuel cap.
2. Remove the fuel pump fuse from the engine fuse box.
3. Start the engine and allow the engine to stall.
4. Crank the engine for an additional 10 seconds.

FUEL FILTER

REMOVAL & INSTALLATION

1.6L (LXT) Engine

The fuel filter is contained within the fuel pump assembly inside the fuel tank. The fuel filter does not require regular replacement. For additional information, see Fuel Pump.

1.6L (LXV) Engine

See Figure 158.

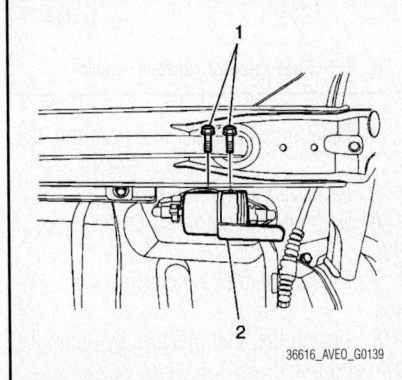

36616_AVEO_G0139

Fig. 158 Remove the fuel filter retaining bolts (1) and filter (2)

1. Before servicing the vehicle, refer to the precautions section.
2. Disconnect the negative battery cable.
3. Relieve the fuel pressure.
4. Disconnect the inlet and outlet fuel lines by moving the line connector lock forward and pulling the hose off of the fuel filter tube.
5. Remove the fuel filter bracket bolts.
6. Remove the fuel filter.

To install:
7. Install the fuel filter.
8. Install the fuel filter bracket bolts.
9. Connect the inlet and outlet quick connector lines.
10. Connect the negative battery cable.

FUEL PUMP

REMOVAL & INSTALLATION

See Figures 159 and 160.

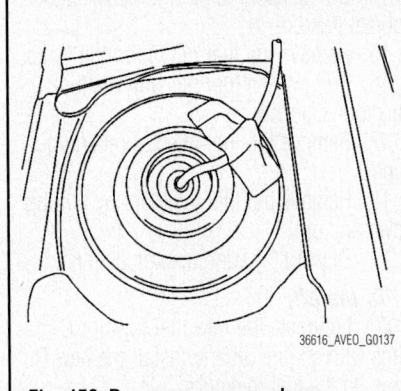

36616_AVEO_G0137

Fig. 159 Rear access cover shown

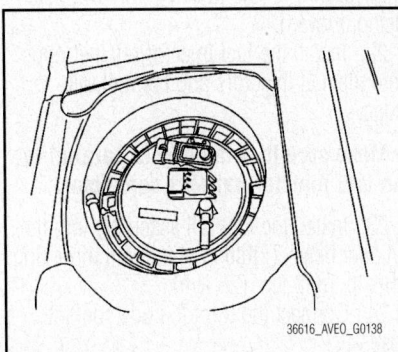

36616_AVEO_G0138

Fig. 160 Remove the fuel pump assembly from the tank

1. Before servicing the vehicle, refer to the precautions section.
2. Relieve the fuel system pressure.
3. Disconnect the negative battery cable.
4. Remove the rear seat.
5. Remove the fuel pump access cover.
6. Disconnect the electrical connector at the fuel pump assembly.
7. Disconnect the fuel line.
8. Remove the fuel pump assembly clip.
9. Remove the fuel pump assembly from the tank.
10. Remove and discard the gasket.

To install:
11. Clean the gasket mating surface on the fuel tank.
12. Position the new gasket in place.
13. Install the fuel pump into the fuel tank in the same location as removed for ease of line and connector installation.
14. Install the fuel pump assembly clip.
15. Connect the fuel pump assembly connector.

16. Install the fuel pump line.
17. Install the fuel pump access cover.
18. Install the EF10 fuse.
19. Connect the negative battery cable.
20. Perform an operational check of the fuel pump.
21. Install the rear seat.

FUEL TANK

REMOVAL & INSTALLATION

See Figure 161.

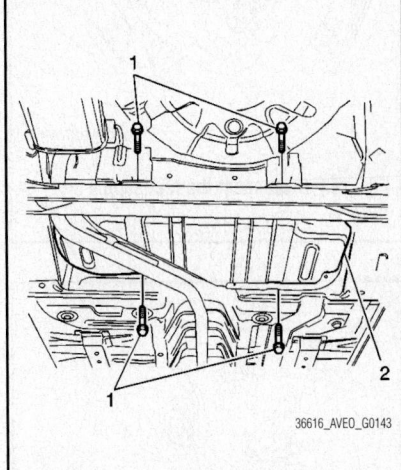

36616_AVEO_G0143

Fig. 161 Remove the retaining bolts (1) and the fuel tank (2)

1. Before servicing the vehicle, refer to the precautions section.
2. Properly relieve the fuel system pressure.
3. Disconnect the negative battery cable.
4. Using an air-operated pump, drain as much fuel as possible through the fuel fill pipe.
5. Disconnect the parking brake cable retainer clamps and the support along the fuel tank to provide clearance for the tank.
6. Remove the fuel tank filler tube clamp at the fuel tank.
7. Disconnect the fuel tank filler tube.
8. Disconnect the fuel tank filler tube at the fuel tank.
9. Disconnect the canister vapor tube at the control valve vapor tube.
10. Disconnect the fuel line near the right front of the fuel tank.
11. Disconnect the wiring harness clips and the fuel line clips as needed.
12. Remove the front exhaust pipe.
13. Support the fuel tank with a suitable jack.
14. Remove the fuel tank retaining bolts.
15. Carefully lower and remove the fuel tank.

FUEL RAIL & INJECTORS

REMOVAL & INSTALLATION

1.6L (LXT) Engine

See Figures 162 and 163.

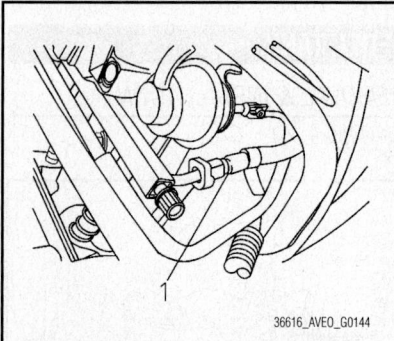

Fig. 162 Disconnect the fuel supply line (1)

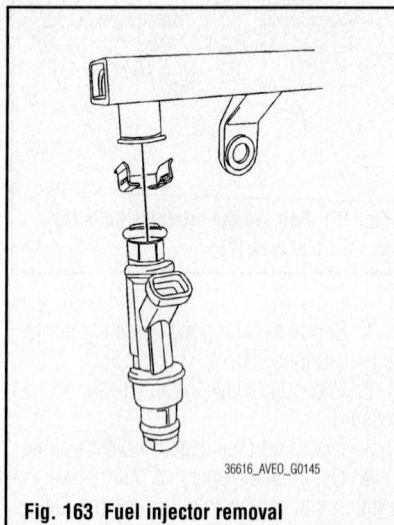

Fig. 163 Fuel injector removal

1. Before servicing the vehicle, refer to the precautions section.
2. Properly relieve the fuel system pressure.
3. Disconnect the negative battery cable.
4. Remove the engine appearance cover.
5. Disconnect the electronic throttle control connector.
6. Disconnect the Intake Air temperature (IAT) sensor.
7. Disconnect the Camshaft Position (CMP) sensor.
8. Disconnect the Manifold Absolute Pressure (MAP) sensor.
9. Disconnect the fuel injector harness connectors.
10. Remove the purge solenoid valve to intake manifold hose.

11. Remove the MAP sensor vacuum hose.
12. Remove the upper intake manifold bracket.
13. Disconnect the fuel supply line.
14. Disconnect the throttle body outlet coolant hose.
15. Remove the fuel rail mounting bolts.
16. Remove the fuel rail with the fuel injectors attached.
17. Remove the fuel injector retaining clips.
18. Remove the fuel injectors by pulling down and out.
19. Discard the fuel injector O-rings.

To install:

20. Lubricate the new fuel injector O-rings with engine oil and install the new O-rings on the fuel injectors.
21. Install the fuel injectors into the fuel rail sockets with the fuel injector terminals facing outward.
22. Install the fuel injector retainer clips onto the fuel injectors and the fuel rail ledge.

➡**Make sure that the clip is parallel to the fuel injector harness connector.**

23. Install the fuel rail assembly into the cylinder head. Tighten the fuel rail mounting bolts to 18 ft. lbs. (25 Nm).
24. Connect the throttle body coolant hose.
25. Connect the fuel supply line.
26. Install the intake manifold upper bracket with the bolts.
27. Install the MAP sensor vacuum hose.
28. Install the purge solenoid to intake manifold hose.
29. Connect the fuel injector harness connectors. Rotate each fuel injector as required to avoid stretching the wiring harness.
30. Connect the MAP sensor connector, CMP sensor and IAT sensor.
31. Connect the electronic throttle control connector.
32. Install the engine appearance cover.
33. Connector the negative battery cable.
34. Start the engine and check for leaks.

1.6L (LXV) Engine

See Figures 164 and 165.

1. Before servicing the vehicle, refer to the precautions section. Relieve the fuel pressure system.
2. Disconnect the negative battery cable.
3. Disconnect the injector connectors.

Fig. 164 Remove the fuel rail bolts (1) from the fuel rail (2)

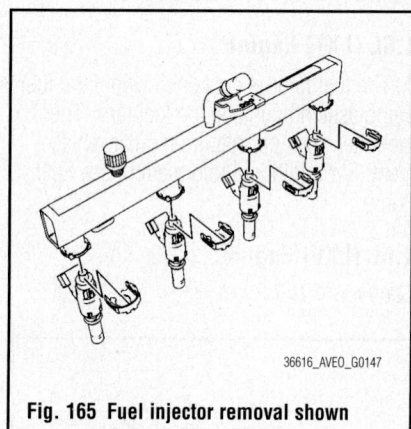

Fig. 165 Fuel injector removal shown

4. Disconnect the fuel line from the fuel rail.
5. Remove the fuel rail bolts.
6. Remove the fuel rail with the injectors.
7. Detach the fuel injector retainer clips.
8. Detach the fuel injectors by pulling down and out.
9. Discard the fuel injector O-rings.

To install:

10. Install the fuel injector O-rings.
11. Connect fuel injectors to the fuel rail.
12. Install the fuel injector retainer clips.
13. Install the fuel rail with the injectors to the intake manifold.
14. Install the fuel rail bolts and tighten to 71 inch. lbs. (8 Nm).
15. Connect the fuel line from the fuel rail and put a dust cap to avoid strange materials.
16. Connect the fuel injector connectors.
17. Connect the negative battery cable.
18. Start the engine and check for leaks.

To install:

19. Carefully raise the fuel tank into position using a suitable jack.

20. Install the fuel tank retaining nuts and tighten to 15 ft. lbs. (20 Nm).

21. Connect the fuel line.

22. Connect the wiring harness clips and the fuel line clips that were removed.

23. Connect the fuel pump electrical connector.

24. Connect the fuel vapor line.

25. Connect the fuel tank filler tube and the fuel tank vent tube.

26. Install the fuel tank filler tube clamp at the fuel tank.

27. Install the front exhaust pipe.

28. Install the parking brake cable support and retainer clamps.

29. Connect the negative battery cable.

30. Fill the fuel tank.

31. Start the engine and check for leaks.

IDLE SPEED

ADJUSTMENT

Idle speed is maintained by the Engine Control Module (ECM). No adjustment is necessary or possible.

THROTTLE BODY

REMOVAL & INSTALLATION

1.6L (LXT) Engine

See Figure 166.

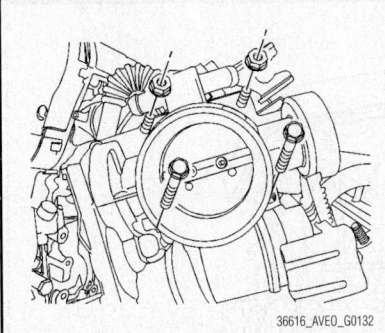

Fig. 166 Throttle body removal—1.6L (LXT Engine)

1. Before servicing the vehicle, refer to the precautions section.

2. Disconnect the negative battery cable.

3. Disconnect the intake air temperature sensor connector.

4. Remove the air cleaner inlet duct from the throttle body.

5. Disconnect the electronic throttle body connector.

6. Remove the IAC valve electrical connector if equipped.

7. Disconnect the coolant hoses from the electronic throttle body.

8. Remove the throttle body retaining bolts.

9. Remove the throttle body and discard the gasket.

To install:

10. Clean the gasket mating surface on the intake manifold.

➡**If the electronic throttle control valve is removed from the throttle body, the throttle body may be cleaned in a cold immersion type cleaner. Do not clean the electronic throttle control valve with any type of solvent or cleaner.**

11. Clean the throttle body.

12. Install the electronic throttle body assembly with a new gasket.

13. Install the electronic throttle body retaining nuts and bolts. Tighten the throttle body retaining bolts and nuts to 11 ft. lbs. (15 Nm).

14. Connect the electronic throttle body electrical connector.

15. Connect the IAC valve electrical connector if equipped.

16. Install the throttle body coolant hoses.

17. Install the air cleaner inlet duct to the throttle body.

18. Connect the negative battery cable.

19. Refill and bleed the cooling system.

1.6L (LXV) Engine

See Figure 167.

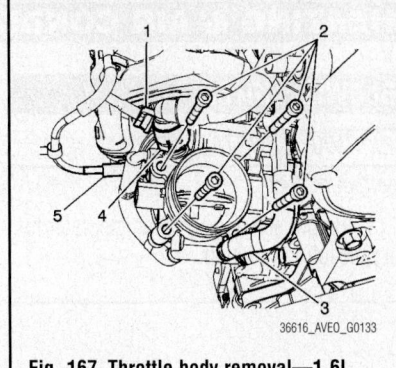

Fig. 167 Throttle body removal—1.6L (LXV Engine)

1. Before servicing the vehicle, refer to the precautions section.

2. Disconnect the negative battery cable.

3. Remove the air cleaner assembly.

4. Remove the air cleaner inlet duct from the throttle body.

5. Disconnect the ETC connector.

6. Disconnect the coolant inlet hose.

7. Disconnect the coolant outlet hose.

8. Disconnect the EVAP hose.

9. Detach the PCV breather hose.

10. Remove the throttle body bolts.

11. Remove the throttle body with the seal ring.

To install:

12. Install the throttle body with the seal ring. Install the retaining bolts and tighten to 71 inch. lbs. (8 Nm).

13. Connect the coolant inlet hose.

14. Connect the coolant outlet hose.

15. Connect the EVAP hose.

16. Connect the PCV breather hose.

17. Connect the ETC connector.

18. Install the air cleaner inlet duct to the throttle body.

19. Install the air-cleaner assembly.

20. Connect the negative battery cable.

21. Refill and bleed the cooling system.

HEATING & AIR CONDITIONING SYSTEM

BLOWER MOTOR

REMOVAL & INSTALLATION

See Figure 168.

1. Before servicing the vehicle, refer to the precautions section.

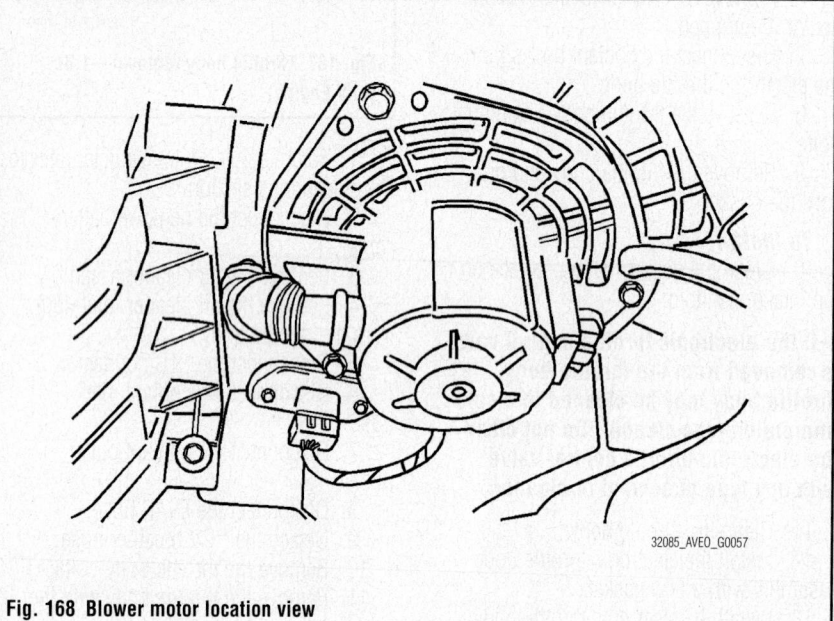

Fig. 168 Blower motor location view

2. Disconnect the negative battery cable.

3. Disconnect the blower motor electrical connector.

4. Remove the blower cooling hose.

5. Remove the screws that secure the motor to the heater/air distribution case.

6. Remove the motor and the seal from the heater/air distribution case by gently pulling the motor straight down and out.

To install:

7. Install the blower motor and seal, with the shock mount pads, in the heater/air distribution case. Hold the blower motor in position.

8. Install the screws to secure the blower motor to the heater/air distribution case.

9. Tighten the blower motor retaining screws to 53 inch lbs. (6 Nm).

10. Install the blower motor cooling hose.

11. Connect the electrical connector.

12. Connect the negative battery cable.

13. Confirm that the blower motor operates properly.

HEATER CORE

REMOVAL & INSTALLATION

Hatchback Models

See Figures 169 and 170.

❊❊ CAUTION

Refer to the applicable precautions for this system before performing the following operation. Failure to follow the warnings and cautions could result in possible personal injury or death.

1. Recover the air conditioning refrigerant, into a refrigerant recovery station.

2. Disconnect the negative battery cable.

3. Drain the cooling system into a clean container for reuse.

4. Disconnect the heater hoses at the firewall.

5. Remove the instrument panel.

6. Remove the A/C suction hose and liquid evaporator pipe connector block at the cowl.

7. From the firewall remove the screws that secure the heater/air distribution case. assembly to the cowl.

8. Remove the heater/air distribution case.

9. Disconnect the control cables from the case.

10. Remove the linkage lever. Note the position of all the levers to facilitate reassembly.

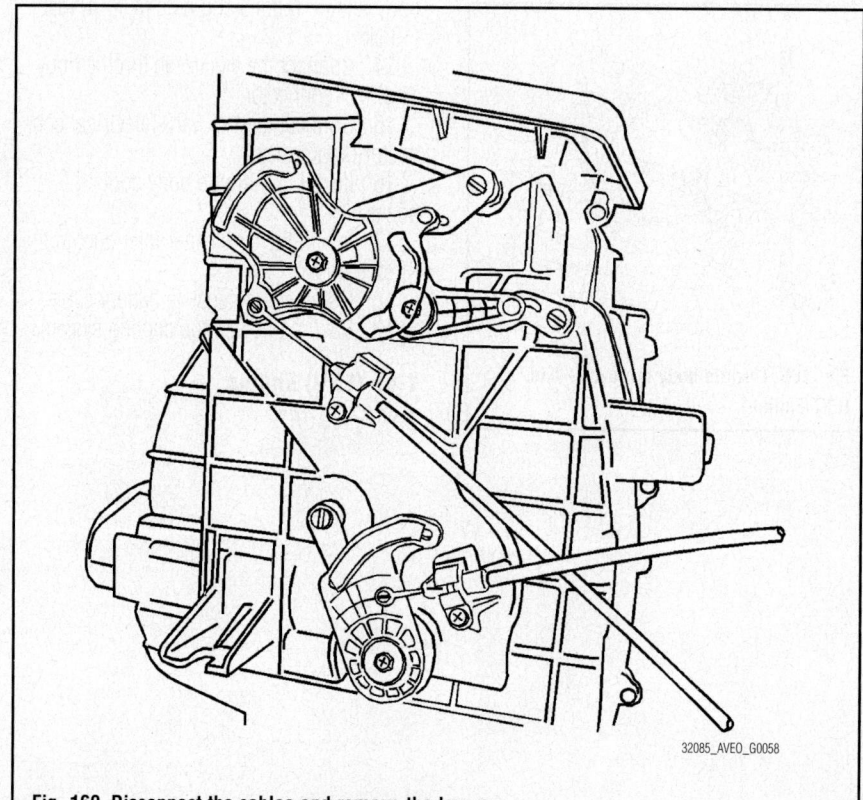

Fig. 169 Disconnect the cables and remove the levers

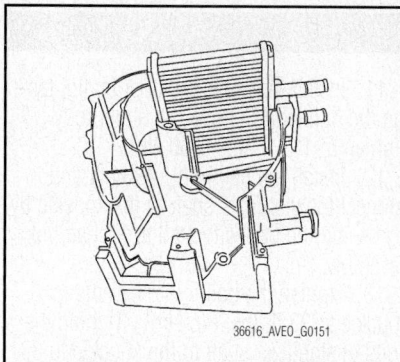

Fig. 170 Heater core removal—Hatchback models

11. Remove the screws that secure the heater core cover.

12. Slowly separate the lower heater core cover from the rest of the assembly. Retain the sealant.

13. Remove the screw and the bracket clamp that secure the heater core lines to the case.

14. Remove the spring clamp that secures the heater core body to the case.

15. Remove the heater core from the case.

To install:

16. Installation is the reverse of removal. Please note the following torque specifications:
- Tighten the instrument panel bolts to 15 ft. lbs. (20 Nm).
- Tighten the passenger air bag module mounting bolts to 97 inch lbs. (11 Nm).
- Tighten the driver air bag module mounting bolts to 71 inch lbs. (8 Nm).
- Tighten the steering wheel bolt to 28 ft. lbs. (38 Nm).

17. Connect the negative battery cable.

18. Vacuum and recharge the A/C system.

➡️**Any oil removed from the A/C system during the recovery process must be replenished at this time.**

19. Refill and bleed the cooling system.

20. Start the engine and check for leaks.

Sedan Models

See Figures 171 through 173.

✳✳ CAUTION

Refer to the applicable precautions for this system before performing the following operation. Failure to follow the warnings and cautions could result in possible personal injury or death.

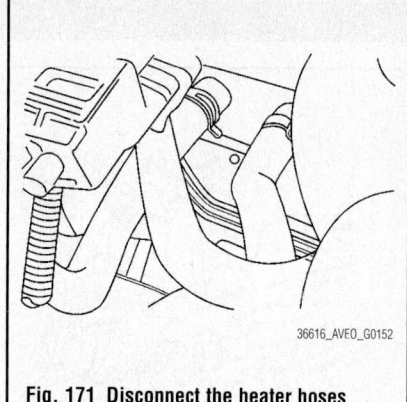

Fig. 171 Disconnect the heater hoses

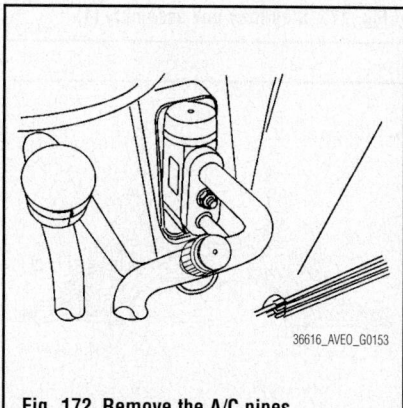

Fig. 172 Remove the A/C pipes

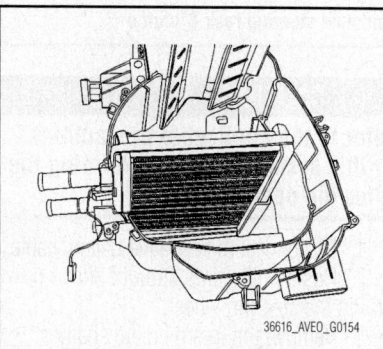

Fig. 173 Heater core removal—Sedan models

1. Recover the air conditioning refrigerant, into a refrigerant recovery station.

2. Disconnect the negative battery cable.

3. Drain the cooling system into a clean container for reuse.

4. Disconnect the heater hoses at the firewall.

5. Remove the nuts that secure the A/C suction hose and liquid evaporator pipe connector block at the cowl.

6. Remove the instrument panel assembly from the vehicle.

7. Remove the heater/air distribution case from the vehicle.

8. Remove the linkage screw from the lower heater core cover post.

9. Remove the linkage lever. Note the position of all the levers to facilitate reassembly.

10. Remove the screws that secure the heater core cover.

11. Slowly separate the lower heater core cover from the rest of the assembly. Retain the sealant.

12. Remove the screw and the bracket clamp that secure the heater core lines to the case.

13. Remove the spring clamp that secures the heater core body to the case.

14. Remove the heater core from the case.

To install:

15. Install the heater core into the case.

16. Secure the heater core lines to the case with the retaining bracket clamp and the screw.

17. Install the heater core body with the retaining spring clamp.

18. Reapply the sealant to the heater core cover mounting channel flange as removed.

19. Install the heater core cover.

20. Install the retaining screws.

21. Install the linkage lever onto the cover post with the screw.

22. Confirm proper operation of the actuating levers for the heater/air distribution case doors.

23. Install the heater/air distribution case.

24. Install and tighten the retaining screws to 71 inch. lbs. (8 Nm).

25. Install the instrument panel assembly. Tighten the instrument panel screws to 15 ft. lbs. (20 Nm).

26. Install the nuts that secure the A/C suction hose and liquid evaporator pipe connector block at the cowl. Install a new seal and tighten to 11 ft. lbs. (15 Nm).

27. Connect the heater hoses at the firewall.

28. Vacuum and recharge the A/C system.

➡️**Any oil removed from the A/C system during the recovery process must be replenished at this time.**

29. Connect the negative battery cable.

30. Refill and bleed the cooling system.

STEERING

MANUAL RACK & PINION STEERING GEAR

REMOVAL & INSTALLATION

See Figures 174 through 178.

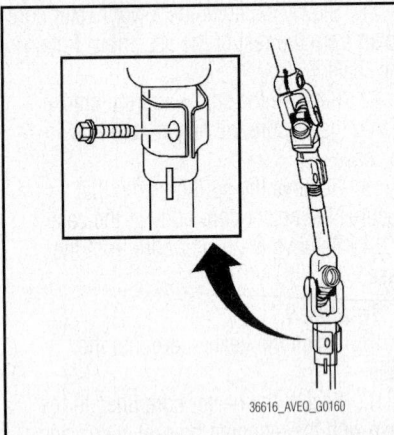

36616_AVEO_G0160

Fig. 174 Intermediate shaft disconnect location

36616_AVEO_G0161

Fig. 175 Disconnecting the outer tie rod end

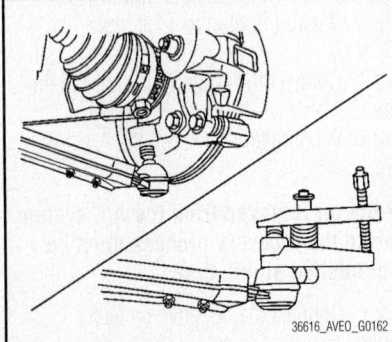

36616_AVEO_G0162

Fig. 176 Disconnecting the lower ball joint

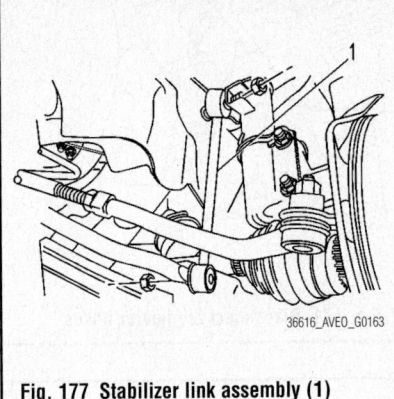

36616_AVEO_G0163

Fig. 177 Stabilizer link assembly (1)

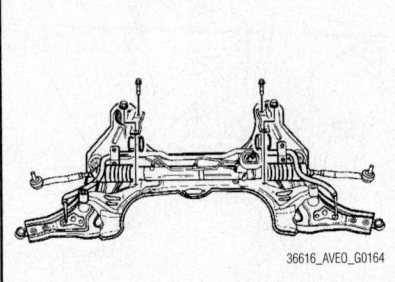

36616_AVEO_G0164

Fig. 178 Cross member removal with manual steering rack & pinion

❈❈ CAUTION

Refer to the applicable precautions for this system before performing the following operation.

1. Disconnect the negative battery cable.
2. Position the tires straight ahead by turning the steering wheel.
3. Remove the intermediate shaft.
4. Remove the front tires.
5. Disconnect the outer tie rod ends from the steering knuckle.
6. Disconnect the lower ball joints from the steering knuckle.
7. Remove the stabilizer link assemblies.
8. Remove the cross member by removing the nuts and bolts to the underbody.
9. Remove the rack and pinion assembly by disconnecting the steering gear retaining bracket nuts.

To install:

10. Install the rack and pinion assembly by connecting the steering gear retaining bracket nuts and tightening to 37 ft lbs. (50 Nm).

11. Install the cross member by tightening the nuts and bolts to the underbody. Tighten to 111 ft. lbs. (150 Nm).
12. Install the ball joint hex nuts and connect the stabilizer shaft to the knuckle by tightening the bolt with stabilizer shaft link assembly.
13. Tighten the ball joint hex nuts to knuckle to 33 ft. lbs. (45 Nm) . Tighten the bolts of stabilizer shaft to the knuckle to 33 ft. lbs. (45 Nm).
14. Install the intermediate shaft. Tighten to 33 ft. lbs. (45 Nm).
15. Install the outer tie rod hex nuts and tighten to 33 ft. lbs. (45 Nm).
16. Install the front tires and tighten to 88 ft. lbs. (120 Nm).
17. If the wheel cover is equipped with wheel nut caps, install the wheel nut caps and tighten to 53 inch. lbs. (6 Nm).
18. Check the wheel alignment and adjust as required.

POWER RACK & PINION STEERING GEAR

REMOVAL & INSTALLATION

See Figures 179 through 181.

❈❈ CAUTION

Refer to the applicable precautions for this system before performing the following operation.

1. Disconnect the negative battery cable.
2. Position the tires straight ahead by turning the steering wheel.
3. Remove the intermediate shaft.
4. Remove the front tires.
5. Drain the power steering fluid from the rack and pinion.
6. Disconnect the steering gear inlet and outlet pipe fittings.
7. Remove the outer tie rod hex nuts.
8. Remove the ball joint hex nuts and disconnect the stabilizer shaft from the knuckle by removing the stabilizer shaft link assembly.
9. Remove the cross member by removing the nuts and bolts to the underbody.
10. Remove the rack and pinion assembly by disconnecting the steering gear retaining bracket nuts.

To install:

11. Install the rack and pinion assembly by connecting the steering gear retaining bracket nuts.

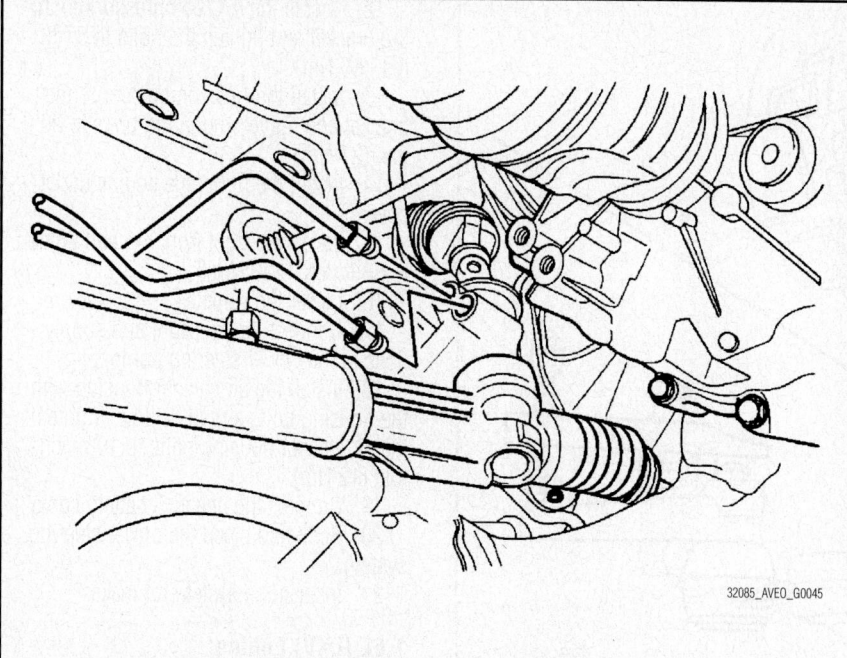

Fig. 179 Disconnect the steering gear inlet and outlet pipe fittings

12. Tighten the steering gear retaining bracket nuts to 37 ft. lbs. (50 Nm).

13. Install the cross member by tightening the nuts and bolts to the underbody. Tighten

14. Tighten the cross member by tightening the nuts and bolts to the underbody to 111 ft. lbs. (150 Nm).

15. Install the ball joint hex nuts and connect the stabilizer shaft to the knuckle by tightening the bolt with stabilizer shaft link assembly.

- Tighten the ball joint hex nuts to knuckle to 33 ft. lbs. (45 Nm).
- Tighten the bolts of the stabilizer shaft to the knuckle 33 ft. lbs. (45 Nm).

16. Install the outer tie rod hex nuts.

17. Tighten the outer tie rod hex nuts to 33 ft. lbs. (45 Nm).

18. Connect the steering gear inlet and outlet pipe fittings.

19. Tighten the nuts of the steering gear inlet and outlet pipe fittings to 16 ft. lbs. (22 Nm).

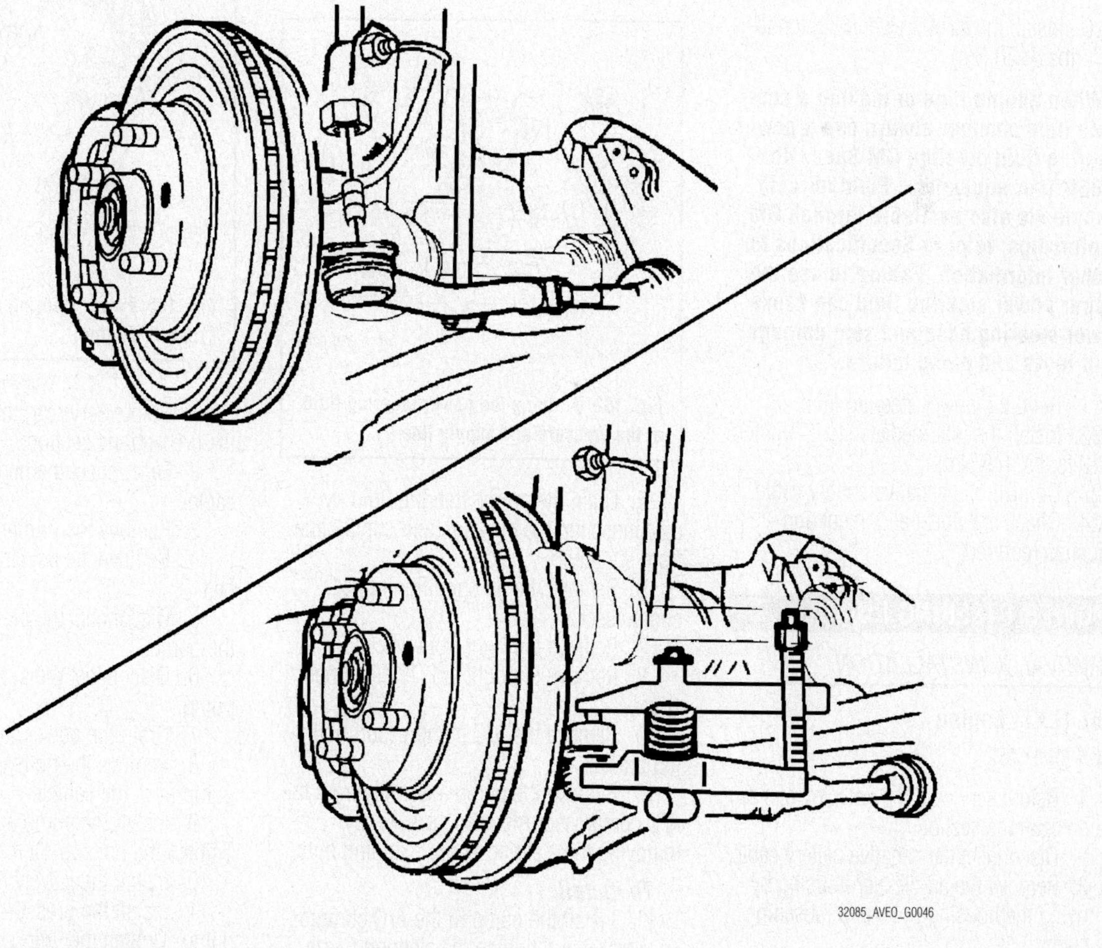

Fig. 180 Remove the outer tie rod hex nuts

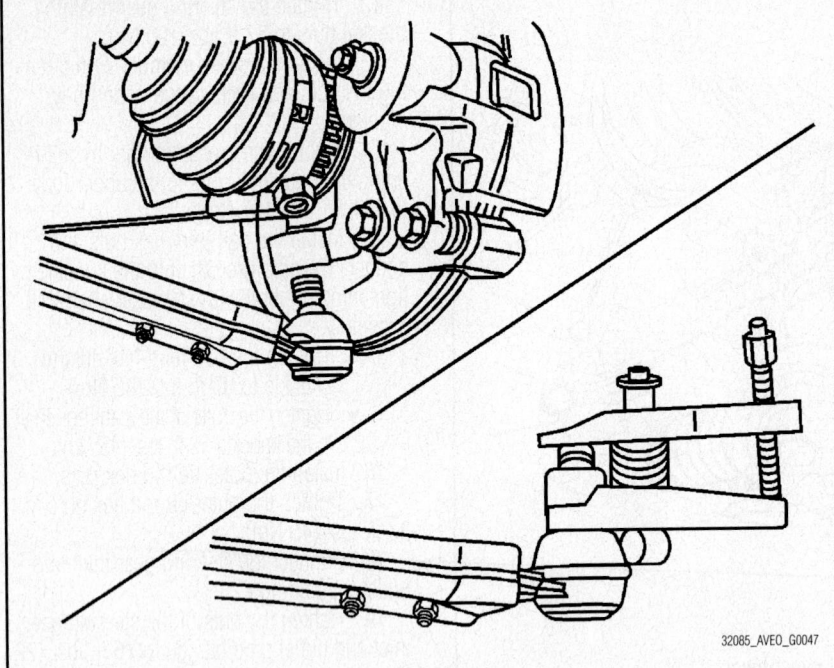

Fig. 181 Remove the ball joint hex nuts and disconnect the stabilizer shaft from the knuckle by removing the stabilizer shaft link assembly

20. Install the front tires and tighten to 88 ft. lbs. (120 Nm).

➡When adding fluid or making a complete fluid change, always use a power steering fluid meeting GM Spec. No. 9985010 or equivalent. Fluid for cold climates is also available through GM Dealerships; refer to Specifications for further information. Failure to use the proper power steering fluid can cause power steering hose and seal damage, fluid leaks and pump failure.

21. Refill the power steering fluid.
22. Install the intermediate shaft. Tighten to 33 ft. lbs. (45 Nm).
23. Connect the negative battery cable.
24. Check the wheel alignment and adjust as required.

POWER STEERING PUMP

REMOVAL & INSTALLATION

1.6L (LXT) Engine

See Figure 182.

1. Before servicing the vehicle, refer to the precautions section.
2. Disconnect the negative battery cable.
3. Remove the air cleaner housing by removing the housing bolts and loosening the clamp.
4. Raise the vehicle.

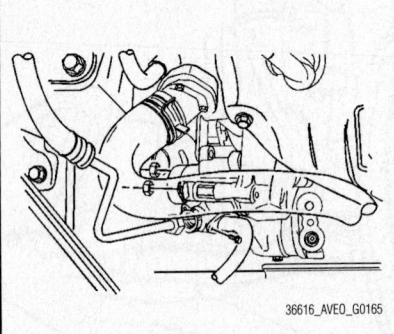

Fig. 182 Draining the power steering fluid at the pressure and supply line

5. Drain the power steering fluid by disconnecting the pressure and supply lines from the pump.
6. Remove the air conditioning A/C compressor.
7. Remove the right front wheel.
8. Remove the right side engine under cover.
9. Remove the A/C compressor mounting bracket.
10. Remove the pump assembly from the A/C compressor mounting bracket by removing the steering pump retaining nuts.

To install:

11. Install the pump to the A/C compressor bracket and tighten the steering pump retaining nuts to 18 ft. lbs. (25 Nm).

12. Install the A/C compressor mounting bracket and tighten the bolts to 37 ft. lbs. (50 Nm).
13. Install the A/C compressor to the bracket and tighten mounting bolts to 20 ft. lbs. (27 Nm).
14. Install the right side engine under cover
15. Install the right front tire and tighten to 88 ft. lbs. (120 Nm).
16. Lower the vehicle.
17. Connect the pressure and supply lines to the power steering pump.
18. Install the air cleaner housing with the housing bolts and the clamp. Tighten the air cleaner housing bolts to 106 inch. lbs. (12 Nm).
19. Connect the negative battery cable.
20. Refill and bleed the power steering system.
21. Inspect the system for leaks.

1.6L (LXV) Engine

See Figure 183.

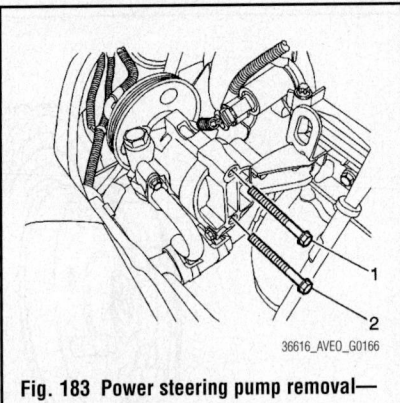

Fig. 183 Power steering pump removal— (1.6 LXV Engine)

1. Before servicing the vehicle, refer to the precautions section.
2. Disconnect the negative battery cable.
3. Remove the primary drive belt.
4. Remove the power steering pump belt.
5. Disconnect the pressure pipe from the pump.
6. Disconnect the supply hose from the pump.
7. Drain the power steering fluid.
8. Remove the bolts (1, 2) and the pump from the vehicle.
9. Install the pump and the bolts (1, 2). Tighten the bolts to 19 ft. lbs. (26 Nm).
10. Install the supply hose to the pump.
11. Install the pressure pipe to the pump. Tighten the union nut to 21 ft. lbs. (28 Nm).

12. Install the power steering pump drive belt.

13. Install the primary drive belt.

14. Fill the power steering fluid reservoir and bleed the power steering system.

15. Connect the negative battery cable.

16. Refill and bleed the power steering system.

17. Inspect the system for leaks.

BLEEDING

See Figure 184.

❋❋ WARNING

When adding fluid or making a complete fluid change, always use a power steering fluid meeting GM Spec. No. 9985010 or equivalent. Fluid for cold climates is also available through GM Dealerships; refer to Specifications for further information. Failure to use the proper power steering fluid can cause power steer-

ing hose and seal damage, fluid leaks and pump failure.

1. Turn the wheels all the way to the left and add the power steering fluid to

36616_AVEO_G0167

Fig. 184 Refill to max mark on the reservoir tank

the MIN mark on the fluid level indicator.

2. Start the engine. With the engine running at fast idle, recheck the fluid level. If necessary, add fluid to bring the level up to the MIN mark.

3. Bleed the system by turning the wheels from side to side without reaching the stop at either end. Keep the fluid level at the MIN mark. The air must be eliminated from the fluid before normal steering action can be obtained.

4. Return the wheels to the center position. Continue running the engine for 2-3 minutes.

5. Road test the car to be sure the steering functions normally and is free from noise.

6. Recheck the fluid level as described in steps 1 and 2. Make sure the fluid level is at the MAX mark after the system has stabilized at its normal operating temperature. Add fluid as needed.

SUSPENSION

FRONT SUSPENSION

COIL SPRING

REMOVAL & INSTALLATION

The coil spring is part of the strut assembly. For additional information, see MacPherson Strut.

FRONT SUSPENSION CROSSMEMBER

REMOVAL & INSTALLATION

See Figures 185 and 186.

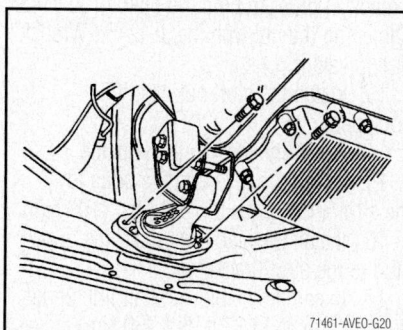

71461-AVEO-G20

Fig. 185 Removing engine reaction rod bolts

1. Before servicing the vehicle, refer to the precautions section.

2. Disconnect the negative battery cable.

3. Raise and support the vehicle.

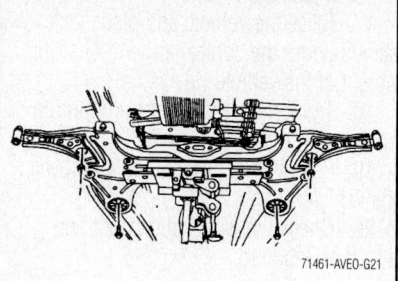

71461-AVEO-G21

Fig. 186 Removing front suspension crossmember

4. Drain the power steering fluid, if equipped.

5. Remove or disconnect the following:
   • Front wheels
   • Lower control arm ball joint and stabilizer bar link nut
   • Tie rod end ball joint
   • Engine mounting reaction rod bolts.
   • Steering gear feed and return lines
   • Steering column intermediate shaft lower joint
   • Crossmember mounting bolts and crossmember.

6. If the crossmember is being replaced, remove the stabilizer bar, steering gear and control arm from the crossmember.

To install:

7. If removed, install the stabilizer bar, steering gear and control arm to the crossmember.

8. Install the crossmember and tighten the bolts to 111 ft. lbs. (150 Nm)

9. Install or connect the following:
   • Intermediate shaft lower joint
   • Power steering lines
   • Engine reaction rod bolts and tighten the bolts to 44 ft. lbs. (60 Nm)
   • Tie rod end ball joint and tighten the bolts to 33 ft. lbs. (45 Nm)
   • Lower control arm ball joint and stabilizer bar link nut
   • Front wheels

10. Lower the vehicle

11. Refill and bleed the power steering fluid, if equipped.

LOWER BALL JOINT

REMOVAL & INSTALLATION

See Figure 187.

1. Before servicing the vehicle, refer to the precautions section.

2. Raise and safely support the vehicle so the weight of the vehicle rests on the stands, not the control arms.

3. Remove the wheels.

4. Separate the ball joint from the steering knuckle.

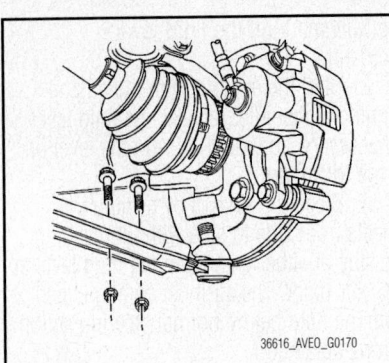

Fig. 187 Removal and installation of the ball joint

5. Remove the ball joint nuts and remove the ball joint.

To install:

6. Connect the ball joint to the control arm with the mounting bolts.

7. Install the nuts to secure the bolts from below the control arm and tighten to 111 ft. lbs. (150 Nm).

8. Install the ball joint to the steering knuckle and tighten the nut to 74 ft. lbs. (100 Nm).

9. Install the wheel and tighten to 88 ft. lbs. (120 Nm).

10. Lower the vehicle.

11. Check the wheel alignment and adjust as required.

LOWER CONTROL ARM

REMOVAL & INSTALLATION

See Figure 188.

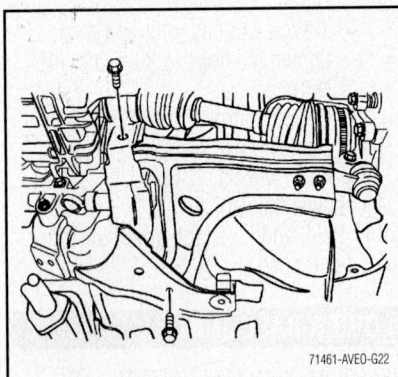

Fig. 188 Lower control arm mounting bolt locations

1. Before servicing the vehicle, refer to the precautions section.

2. Raise and support the vehicle so the weight rests on the stands, not on the control arms.

3. Remove the front wheels.

4. Remove the control arm link bolt and disconnect the stabilizer bar from the control arm.

5. Remove the ball joint-to-steering knuckle nut.

6. Separate the ball joint from the steering knuckle.

7. Remove the control arm mounting bolts and the bracket.

8. Remove the control arm.

To install:

9. Install the control arm.

10. Connect the front of the control arm to the body with the front mounting bolt and washer, but do not tighten.

11. Apply thread sealer to the control arm rear bolts.

12. Install the control arm rear bolts using new self-locking nuts, but do not tighten the nuts.

13. Install the stabilizer bar link bolt.

14. Install the ball joint to the steering knuckle and tighten the nut to 74 ft. lbs. (100 Nm).

15. Connect the retaining clip to the ball joint stud.

16. Install the wheels.

17. Raise the vehicle and place jack stands under the control arms to bear the weight of the vehicle.

18. Tighten the control arm mounting bolts to 81 ft. lbs. (110 Nm).

19. Remove the jack stands and lower the vehicle.

20. Check the wheel alignment and adjust as required.

MACPHERSON STRUT

REMOVAL & INSTALLATION

See Figures 189 and 190.

1. Before servicing the vehicle, refer to the precautions section.

2. Remove the strut nut cap, if equipped.

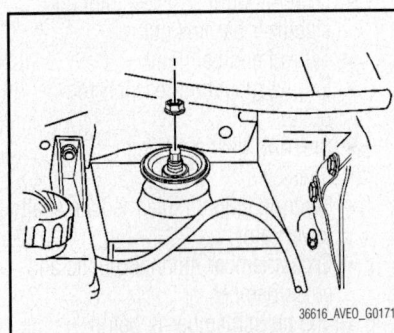

Fig. 189 Remove the strut assembly-to-body nut

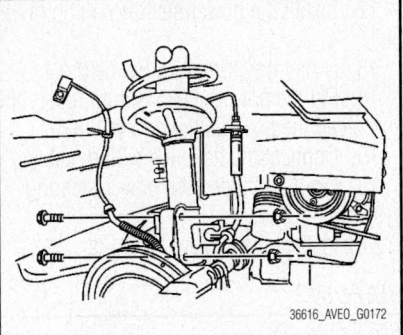

Fig. 190 Remove the strut assembly from the vehicle

3. Remove the strut assembly-to-body nut with the J-42468 Wrench or equivalent.

4. Raise and support the vehicle in order to access the bottom and the top of the strut.

5. Remove the front tire and wheel assembly.

6. Remove the ABS speed sensor wire, if equipped, from the strut bracket.

7. Remove the brake hose from the strut bracket.

8. Remove the stabilizer shaft link upper nut.

9. Remove the stabilizer shaft link upper stud from the strut bracket.

10. Remove the nuts and the bolts from the strut.

11. Remove the strut assembly from the vehicle.

To install:

12. Install the strut assembly into the vehicle with the strut assembly-to-body nut and tighten to 44 ft. lbs. (60 Nm). Use a wrench in order to hold the piston rod while tightening the nut with the J-42468 Wrench or equivalent.

13. Install the strut nut cap, if equipped.

14. Install the strut to the knuckle.

15. Install the nuts and the bolts to the strut and tighten to 74 ft. lbs. (100 Nm).

16. Install the stabilizer shaft link upper stud to the strut bracket.

17. Install the stabilizer shaft link upper nut and tighten to 37 ft. lbs. (50 Nm).

18. Install the brake hose to the strut bracket.

19. Install the ABS speed sensor wire, if equipped, to the strut bracket.

20. Install the front tire and tighten to 88 ft. lbs. (120 Nm).

21. Remove the jack stands and lower the vehicle.

22. Check the wheel alignment and adjust as required.

STEERING KNUCKLE

REMOVAL & INSTALLATION

See Figures 191 through 193.

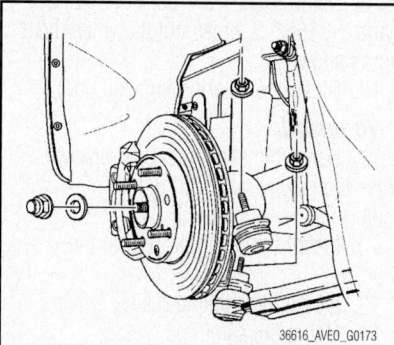

Fig. 191 Remove the axle shaft caulking nut, ball joint nut and tie rod nut

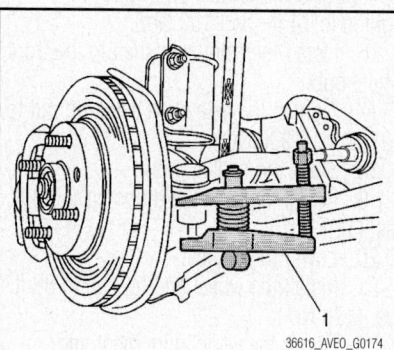

Fig. 192 Tie rod end removal with tool KM-507-C

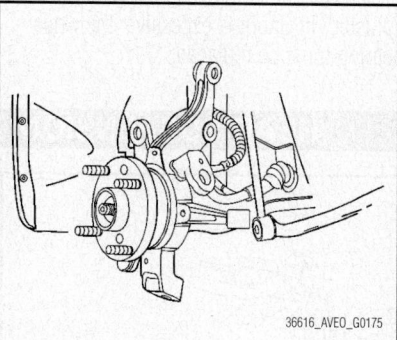

Fig. 193 Steering knuckle assembly removal

1. Before servicing the vehicle, refer to the precautions section.
2. Raise and support the vehicle.
3. Remove the front wheels.
4. Remove the axle shaft caulking nut. Discard the nut.
5. Remove the lower ball joint nut.
6. Remove the outer tie rod nut. Use the KM-507-C Ball Joint Remover in order to separate the lower ball joint and the outer tie rod end from the steering knuckle.

✳✳ WARNING

Support the brake caliper with heavy mechanic wire, or equivalent, whenever it is separated from its mount and the hydraulic flexible brake hose is still connected. Failure to support the caliper in this manner will cause the flexible brake hose to bear the weight of the caliper, which may cause damage to the brake hose and in turn may cause a brake fluid leak.

➡**DO NOT disconnect the hydraulic brake flexible hose from the caliper.**

7. Remove the brake caliper and the pads as an assembly and support the assembly with heavy mechanics wire, or equivalent. Verify there is no tension on the brake hose.
8. Remove the brake rotor.
9. Remove the ABS wheel speed sensor, if equipped.
10. Remove the front strut nuts and bolts.
11. Support the wheel drive shaft.
12. Remove the knuckle assembly.

To install:

13. Install the knuckle assembly to the front strut with the nuts and bolts and tighten to 74 ft. lbs. (100 Nm).
14. Install the ABS wheel speed sensor.
15. Install the brake rotor.
16. Install the brake caliper. Tighten the caliper-to-steering knuckle mounting bolts to 70 ft. lbs. (95 Nm).
17. Install the lower ball joint to the steering knuckle.
18. Install the lower ball joint nut and tighten to 41 ft. lbs. (55 Nm).
19. Install the outer tie rod end to the steering knuckle.
20. Install the outer tie rod nut and tighten to 33 ft. lbs. (45 Nm).
21. Loosely install a NEW axle shaft caulking nut.
22. Tighten the axle shaft caulking nut to 221 ft. lbs. (300 Nm).
23. Stake the caulking nut.
24. Install the wheel and tighten to 88 ft. lbs. (120 Nm).
25. Lower the vehicle.
26. Check the wheel alignment and adjust as required.

STABILIZER BAR

REMOVAL & INSTALLATION

See Figure 194.

1. Before servicing the vehicle, refer to the precautions section.
2. Raise and safely support the vehicle allowing the suspension to hang free.
3. Remove the wheels.
4. Remove the stabilizer bar-to-knuckle nut and the bar-to-link nut.
5. Remove the stabilizer bar links.
6. Remove the front crossmember assembly.
7. Remove the stabilizer bar from the crossmember by removing the U-clamp bolts.

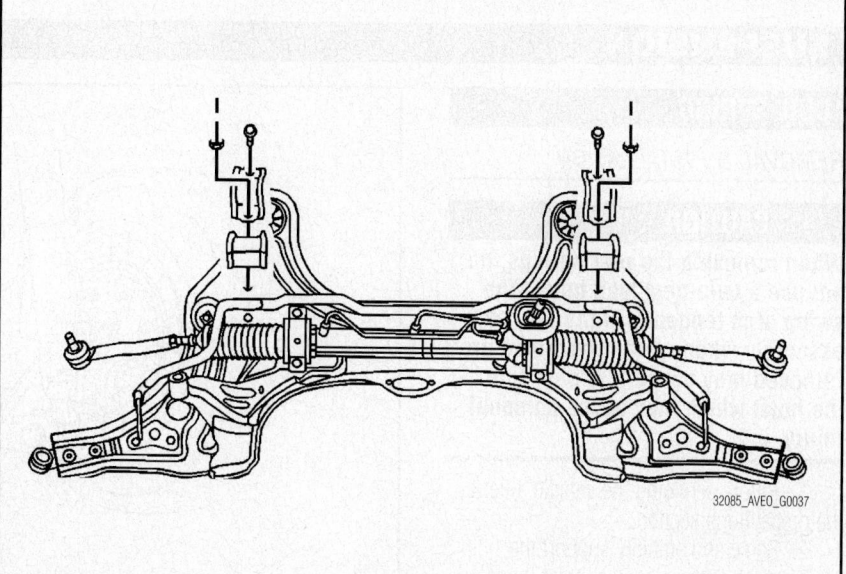

Fig. 194 Removal and installation of the stabilizer bar

To install:

8. Install or connect the following:
- Stabilizer bar and U-clamps. Tighten the clamp bolts to 18 ft. lbs. (25 Nm).
- Install the front crossmember assembly.

9. Install the stabilizer bar links.

10. Install the stabilizer bar-to-knuckle nut and the bar-to-link nut and tighten the nuts to 37 ft. lbs. (50 Nm).

11. Install the wheels.

12. Lower the vehicle.

13. Check the wheel alignment and adjust as required.

WHEEL BEARINGS

REMOVAL & INSTALLATION

See Figures 195 through 197.

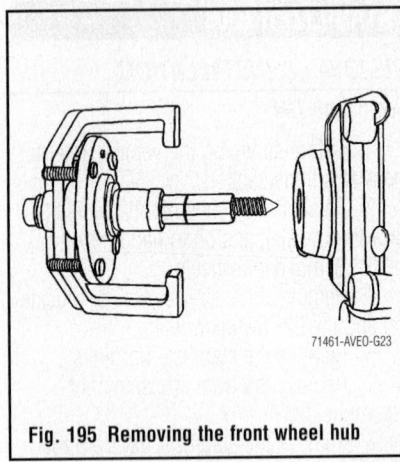

Fig. 195 Removing the front wheel hub

1. Before servicing the vehicle, refer to the precautions section.

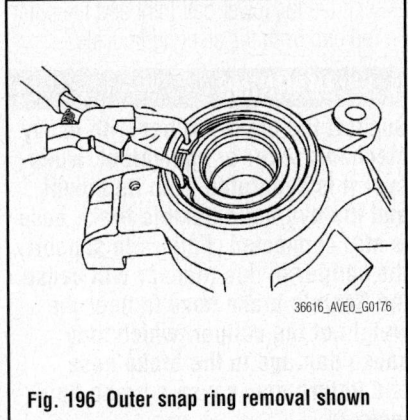

Fig. 196 Outer snap ring removal shown

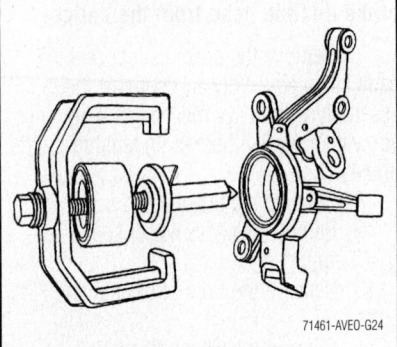

Fig. 197 Removing the front wheel bearing

2. Raise and support the vehicle.

3. Separate the front axle shaft from the front wheel hub.

4. Remove the front strut bolts and remove the steering knuckle.

5. Use a vise in order to hold the steering knuckle.

6. Remove the backing plate.

7. Using tools J-37105-1, -2, -3 and 500-2, press out the wheel hub as shown.

8. Remove the outer snap ring.

9. Using tools J-37105-1 and -2, 500-2 and J-36661-2, press out the wheel bearing as shown.

10. Clean the steering knuckle bore.

To install:

11. Using the same tools as removal, press the new wheel bearing into position.

12. Install the retaining ring to the knuckle.

13. Install the backing plate.

14. Using the same tools as removal, press the new wheel hub into position.

15. Install the knuckle assembly to the front strut with the nuts and bolts and tighten to 74 ft. lbs. (100 Nm).

16. Install the front axle shaft to the front wheel hub.

17. Tighten the axle shaft caulking nut to 221 ft. lbs. (300 Nm).

18. Stake the caulking nut.

19. Install the wheel and tighten to 88 ft. lbs. (120 Nm).

20. Lower the vehicle.

21. Install the wheel and tighten to 88 ft. lbs. (120 Nm).

22. Check the wheel alignment and adjust as required.

ADJUSTMENT

The wheel bearing assembly cannot be adjusted. If runout is excessive, the wheel bearing must be replaced.

SUSPENSION

REAR SUSPENSION

COIL SPRING

REMOVAL & INSTALLATION

✳✳ CAUTION

When removing the rear springs, do not use a twin-post type hoist. The swing arch tendency of the rear axle assembly when certain fasteners are removed may cause it to slip from the hoist which may cause personal injury.

1. Before servicing the vehicle, refer to the precautions section.

2. Raise and suitably support the vehicle. Use a frame contact hoist if possible and support the rear control arms with

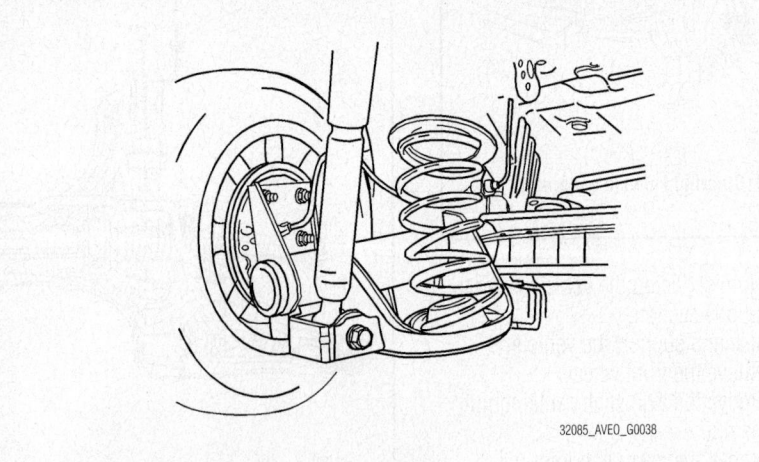

Fig. 198 Removal and installation of the coil spring

jack stands. If it becomes necessary to lift the vehicle with a twin-post hoist, lift the body and support the control arms with jack stands.

3. Remove the wheel.

4. Remove the right and the left shock absorber bolts.

5. Lower the rear axle and remove the springs and the top insulator.

To install:

❄❄ CAUTION

Prior to installing the springs, it will be necessary to install the upper insulators to the body and adhesive to keep them in position while raising the axle assembly and the springs.

6. Install the upper insulator and seat the lower bumper.

7. Install the springs and raise the axle.

8. Install the shock absorbers.

➡️**It will be necessary to bring the axle assembly to trim height prior to tightening the shock absorber attachment bolts.**

9. Install the wheel and tighten to 88 ft. lbs. (120 Nm).

10. Remove the jack stands and lower the vehicle.

SHOCK ABSORBER

REMOVAL & INSTALLATION

See Figures 199 and 200.

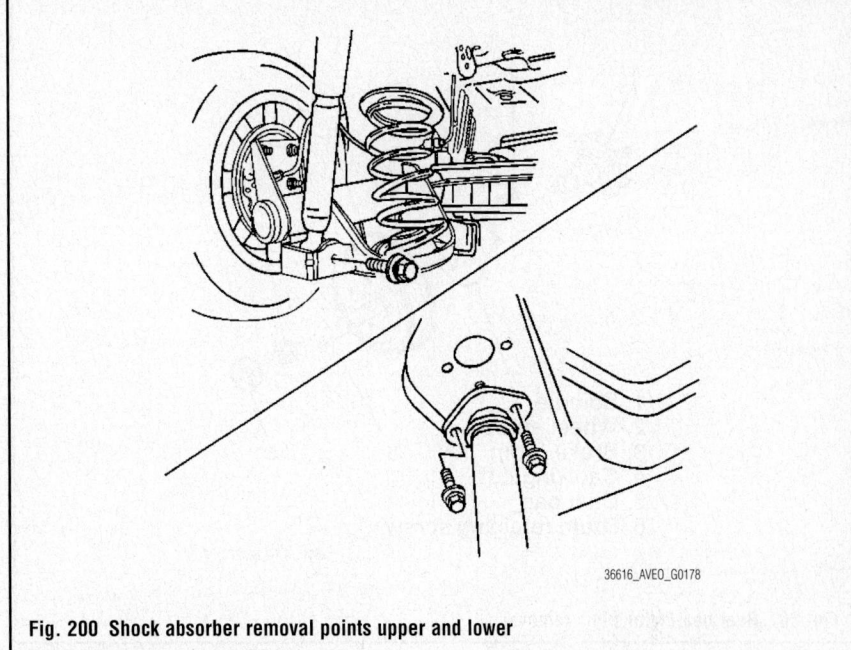

Fig. 200 Shock absorber removal points upper and lower

➡️**Remove only one shock at a time when both shocks are being replaced. Do not suspend the rear axle by the brake hoses. Damage to the brake hoses may result.**

1. Before servicing the vehicle, refer to the precautions section.

2. Remove the shock absorber-to-body bolts - upper.

➡️**When lifting the vehicle with a body hoist, it will be necessary to support the rear axle with adjustable jack stands.**

3. Raise the vehicle and support the rear axle assembly.

4. Remove the lower shock absorber-to-axle bolt.

5. Remove the shock absorber.

To install:

➡️**It will be necessary to bring the axle assembly to trim height prior to tightening the shock absorber attachment bolts.**

6. Insert the lower shock absorber-to-axle bolt through the shock absorber lower attachment bracket and into the axle.

7. Lower the vehicle enough to guide the upper shock stud on the body opening and loosely install the attaching bolts.

- Tighten the lower shock absorber-to-axle bolt to 53 ft. lbs. (72 Nm).
- Tighten the upper shock absorber-to-body bolt to 37 ft. lbs. (50 Nm).

WHEEL HUB & BEARING

REMOVAL & INSTALLATION

See Figure 201.

1. Before servicing the vehicle, refer to the precautions section.

2. Raise and suitably support the vehicle.

3. Remove the rear wheel speed sensor, if equipped.

4. Remove the wheel.

5. Remove the brake drum.

6. Unstake the caulking nut.

7. Remove the caulking nut.

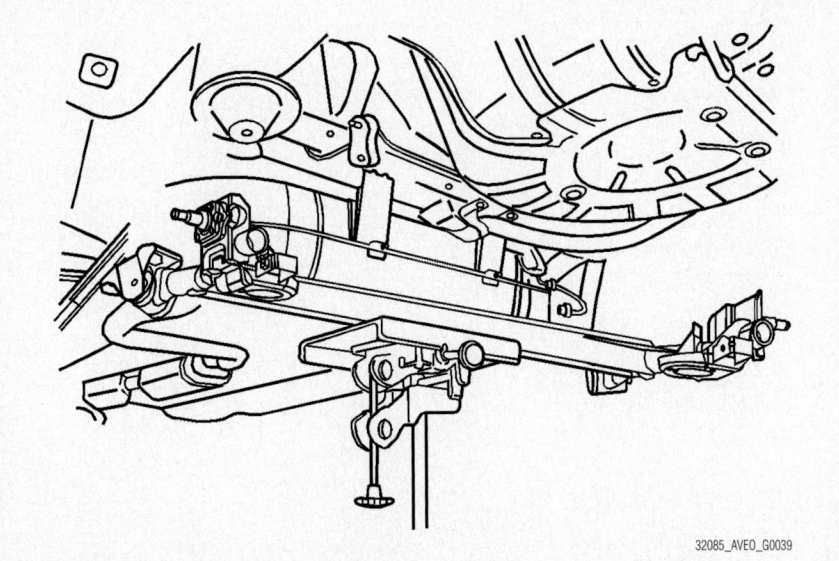

Fig. 199 Remove only one shock at a time when both shocks are being replaced. Never suspend the rear axle by the brake hoses.

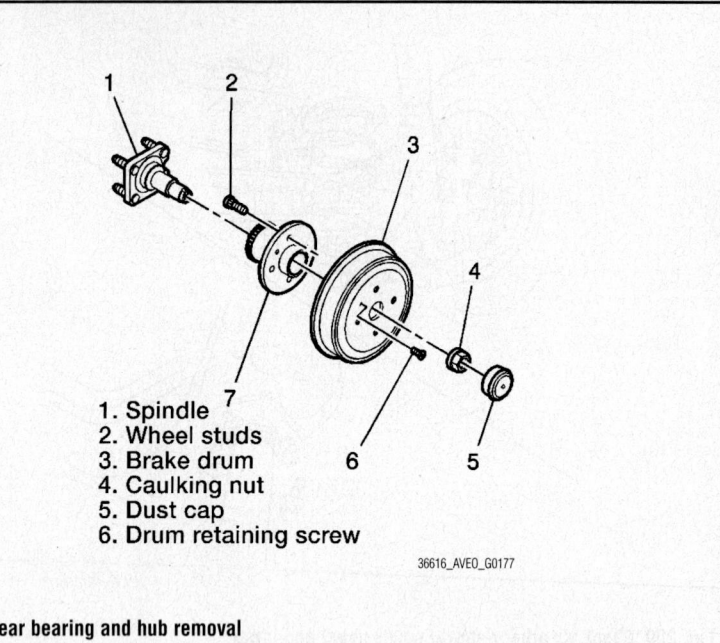

1. Spindle
2. Wheel studs
3. Brake drum
4. Caulking nut
5. Dust cap
6. Drum retaining screw

36616_AVEO_G0177

Fig. 201 Rear bearing and hub removal

8. Pull the wheel bearing and hub assembly straight off the spindle. The 2 inner wheel bearing races may not be secure.

To install:

9. Slide the wheel bearing and hub assembly straight onto the spindle. Use care in order to properly position the wheel bearing races on the spindle.

10. Install the caulking nut to the spindle and tighten to 140 ft. lbs. (190 Nm).

11. Stake the caulking nut.

12. Install the brake drum.

13. Install the rear wheel speed sensor, if equipped.

14. Install the wheel and tighten to 88 ft. lbs. (120 Nm).

15. Lower the vehicle.

ADJUSTMENT

The wheel bearing assembly cannot be adjusted. If runout is excessive, the wheel bearing must be replaced.

CHEVROLET

8

Camaro

SPECIFICATIONS AND MAINTENANCE CHARTS

ENGINE AND VEHICLE IDENTIFICATION

Engine							Model Year	
Code ①	Liters	Cu. In.	Cyl.	Fuel Sys.	Engine Type	Eng. Mfg.	Code ②	Year
V	3.6	217	6	SIDI	DOHC	GM	A	2010
W	6.2	376	8	SFI	OHV	GM		
J	6.2	376	8	SFI	OHV	GM		

SIDI: Sequential Direct Injection

SFI: Sequential Fuel Injection

DOHC: Dual overhead camshafts

OHV: Overhead Valves

① 8th position of VIN

② 10th position of VIN

36616_CAMA_C0001

GENERAL ENGINE SPECIFICATIONS

Year	Model	Engine Displacement Liters	Engine Series VIN	Net Horsepower @ rpm	Net Torque @ rpm (ft. lbs.)	Bore x Stroke (in.)	Com- pression Ratio	Oil Pressure @ rpm
2010	Camaro	3.6	V	304@6400	273@5200	3.70x3.37	11.4:1	20@2000
		6.2	W	400@5900	410@4300	4.00x3.62	10.7:1	18@2000
		6.2	J	426@5900	420@4600	4.00x3.62	10.4:1	18@2000

36616_CAMA_C0002

GASOLINE ENGINE TUNE-UP SPECIFICATIONS

Year	Engine Displacement Liters	Engine VIN	Spark Plug Gap (in.)	Ignition Timing (deg.)	Fuel Pump (psi)	Idle Speed (rpm)	Valve Clearance	
							Intake	Exhaust
2010	3.6	V	0.044	①	50-60	②	HYD	HYD
	6.2	W	0.040	①	50-60	②	HYD	HYD
	6.2	J	0.040	①	50-60	②	HYD	HYD

NOTE: The Vehicle Emission Control Information label often reflects specification changes made during production.

The label figures must be used if they differ from those in this chart.

NA: Not Available

HYD: Hydraulic

① Timing not adjustable

② Idle speed maintained by PCM. There is no recommended adjustment procedure.

36616_CAMA_C0003

CAPACITIES

Year	Model	Engine Displacement Liters	Engine VIN	Engine Oil with Filter (qts.)	Transmission (pts.)	Fuel Tank (gal.)	Cooling System (qts.)
2010	Camaro	3.6	V	6.0	①	18.8	②
		6.2	W	8.0	①	18.8	③
		6.2	J	8.0	①	18.8	③

NOTE: All capacities are approximate. Add fluid gradually and ensure a proper fluid level is obtained.

① Automatic: 13.4
   6 speed manual with V6 engine: 3.8
   6 speed manual with V8 engine: 8.4

② Automatic transmission: 10.8
   Manual transmission: 11.2

③ Automatic transmission: 11.4
   Manual transmission: 11.8

36616_CAMA_C0004

FLUID SPECIFICATIONS

Year	Model	Engine Displacement Liters	Engine ID/VIN	Engine Oil	Auto. Trans.	Manual Trans.	Power Steering Fluid	Brake Master Cylinder
2010	Camaro	3.6	V	5W-30	Dexron VI	①	Dexron VI	DOT 3
		6.2	W	5W-30	Dexron VI	①	Dexron VI	DOT 3
		6.2	J	5W-30	Dexron VI	①	Dexron VI	DOT 3

DOT: Department Of Transportation

① Aisin AY6 transmission: SAE 75W-90 (GL-5)
   Tremec transmission: GM part number 88861800 (88861801 Canada)

36616_CAMA_C0005

VALVE SPECIFICATIONS

Year	Engine Displacement Liters	Engine VIN	Seat Angle (deg.)	Face Angle (deg.)	Spring Test Pressure (lbs. @ in.)	Spring Installed Height (in.)	Stem-to-Guide Clearance (in.) Intake	Stem-to-Guide Clearance (in.) Exhaust	Stem Diameter (in.) Intake	Stem Diameter (in.) Exhaust
2010	3.6	VIN	45	44.25	NA	①	0.0010-0.0026	0.0014-0.0030	0.2344-0.2352	0.2341-0.2348
	6.2	W	46	45	②	2.08	0.0010-0.0026	0.0010-0.0026	0.3130-0.3140	0.3130-0.3140
	6.2	J	45.75	45	②	2.08	0.0010-0.0026	0.0010-0.0026	0.3130-0.3140	0.3130-0.3140

NA: Not Available

① Closed: 1.3779
   Open: 0.9449

② Closed: 90@1.80
   Open: 295@1.25

36616_CAMA_C0006

CAMSHAFT AND BEARING SPECIFICATIONS CHART

All measurements are given in inches.

Year	Engine Displ. Liters	Engine ID/VIN	Journal Dia.	Brg. Oil Clearance	Shaft End-play	Runout	Journal-to-Bore Clearance	Lobe Lift Intake	Lobe Lift Exhaust
2010	3.6	V	①	NA	0.0018-0.0085	NA	0.0016-0.0033	1.6687-1.6805	1.6703-1.6821
	6.2	W	2.1640-2.1660	NA	0.0010-0.0120	0.0020	NA	0.3240	0.3060
	6.2	J	2.1640-2.1660	NA	0.0010-0.0120	0.0020	NA	②	③

NA: Not Available

① Front No. 1: 1.3754-1.3764

Middle and rear No. 2-4: 1.0605- 1.0614

② Non active fuel management cylinders: 0.2940

Active fuel management cylinders: 0.2990

③ Non active fuel management cylinders: 0.2900

Active fuel management cylinders: 0.2950

36616_CAMA_C0007

CRANKSHAFT AND CONNECTING ROD SPECIFICATIONS

All measurements given in inches

Year	Engine Displacement Liters	Engine VIN	Crankshaft Main Brg. Journal Dia.	Crankshaft Main Brg. Oil Clearance	Crankshaft Shaft End-play	Crankshaft Thrust on No.	Connecting Rod Journal Diameter	Connecting Rod Oil Clearance	Connecting Rod Side Clearance
2010	3.6	V	2.2044-2.2050	0.0004-0.0024	0.0039-0.0130	NA	2.3472-2.3479	NA	0.0374-0.0140
	6.2	W	2.0991-2.0999	0.0008-0.0021	0.0015-0.0078	NA	2.2240-2.2250	NA	0.0043-0.0200
	6.2	J	2.0991-2.0999	0.0008-0.0021	0.0015-0.0078	NA	2.2240-2.2250	NA	0.0043-0.0200

NA: Not Available

36616_CAMA_C0008

PISTON AND RING SPECIFICATIONS

All measurements given in inches

Year	Engine Displacement Liters	Engine VIN	Piston Clearance	Ring Gap Top Compression	Ring Gap Bottom Compression	Ring Gap Oil Control	Ring Side Clearance Top Compression	Ring Side Clearance Bottom Compression	Ring Side Clearance Oil Control
2010	3.6	V	①	0.0059-0.0118	0.0110-0.0189	0.0059-0.0236	0.0012-0.0026	0.0006-0.0024	0.0012-0.0067
	6.2	W	②	0.0067-0.0150	0.0126-0.0248	0.0086-0.0310	0.0012-0.0033	0.0016-0.0033	0.0005-0.0079
	6.2	J	②	0.0067-0.0150	0.0126-0.0248	0.0086-0.0310	0.0012-0.0033	0.0016-0.0033	0.0005-0.0079

NA: Not Available

① Piston-to-bore clearance (Production): 0.0008 - 0.0013

Piston-to-bore clearance (Service limit): 0.0256

② Piston-to-bore clearance (Production): -0.0009 - +0.0000

Piston-to-bore clearance (Service limit): 0.0022

36616_CAMA_C0009

TORQUE SPECIFICATIONS
All measurements given in ft. lbs. unless otherwise noted

Year	Engine Displacement Liters	Engine VIN	Cylinder Head Bolts	Main Bearing Bolts	Rod Bearing Bolts	Crankshaft Damper Bolts	Flywheel Bolts	Manifold Intake	Manifold Exhaust	Spark Plugs	Oil Pan Drain Plug
2010	3.6	V	①	②	③	④	⑤	⑥	⑦	⑧	18
	6.2	W	⑨	⑩	⑪	⑪	⑫	⑬	⑭	⑮	18
	6.2	J	⑨	⑩	⑪	⑪	⑫	⑬	⑭	⑮	18

① M8 bolts- Step 1: 11ft. lbs. Step 2: 75 degrees

   M11 bolts- Step 1: 22 ft. lbs. Step 2: 150 degrees

② Inner- Step 1: 15 ft. lbs. Step 2: 80 degrees

   Outer- Step 1: 11 ft. lbs. Step 2: 110 degrees

   Side- Step 1: 22 ft. lbs. Step 2: 60 degrees

③ Step 1: 22 ft. lbs.

   Step 2: Counterclockwise, back off to zero

   Step 3: 18 ft. lbs.

   Step 4: 110 degrees

④ 74 ft. lbs. plus 150 degrees

⑤ Automatic- Step 1: 22 ft. lbs. Step 2: 45 degrees

   Manual: 49 ft. lbs.

⑥ Front cover M12: 48 ft. lbs.

   Intake manifold ball stud M6 89 inch lbs.

   Ball stud to cam cover M6: 44 inch lbs.

   Sight shield ball stud: 89 inch lbs.

   Tuning valve bolt 89 inch lbs.

   Long and short upper to cylinder head bolt: 18 ft lbs.

   Upper to lower intake manifold bolt 18 ft lbs.

⑦ Exhaust manifold bolt: 15 ft. lbs.

   Heat shield: 89 inch. lbs

⑧ New plug: 15 ft. lbs. Used plug 13 ft. lbs.

⑨ M11 bolts:

   Step 1: 22 ft. lbs.

   Step 2: +90 degrees

   Step 3: +70 degrees

   M8 bolts: 22 ft. lbs.

⑩ M10 cap bolts: 15 ft. lbs., then 80 degrees in sequence

   M10 cap studs: 15 ft. lbs., then 51 degrees in sequence

   M8 cap bolts (1-5): 15 ft. lbs., then 22 ft. lbs. in sequence

   M8 cap bolts (6-10): 15 ft. lbs., then 22 ft. lbs. in sequence

⑪ Step 1: 15 ft. lbs.

   Step 2: +85 degrees

⑫ Manual: Step 1: 15 ft. lbs. Step 2: 37 ft. lbs. Step 3: 74 ft. lbs.

   Automatic: Step 1: 15 ft. lbs. Step 2: 37 ft. lbs. Step 3: 74 ft. lbs.

⑬ Step 1: 44 inch lbs. Step 2: 89 inch lbs.

⑭ Bolts- Step 1: 11 ft. lbs., Step 2: 15 ft. lbs.

   Heat shield 80 inch lbs.

   Stud: 15 ft. lbs.

⑮ New plug: 15 ft. lbs. Used plug 11 ft. lbs.

36616_CAMA_C0010

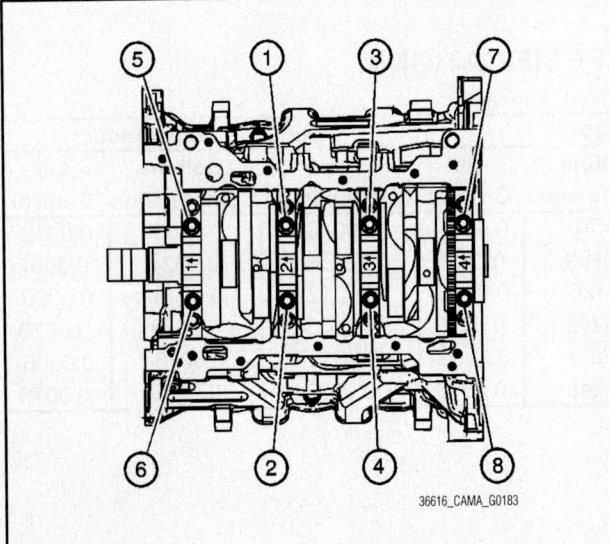

36616_CAMA_G0183

Fig. 1 Main bearing torque sequence (part one)—3.6L engines

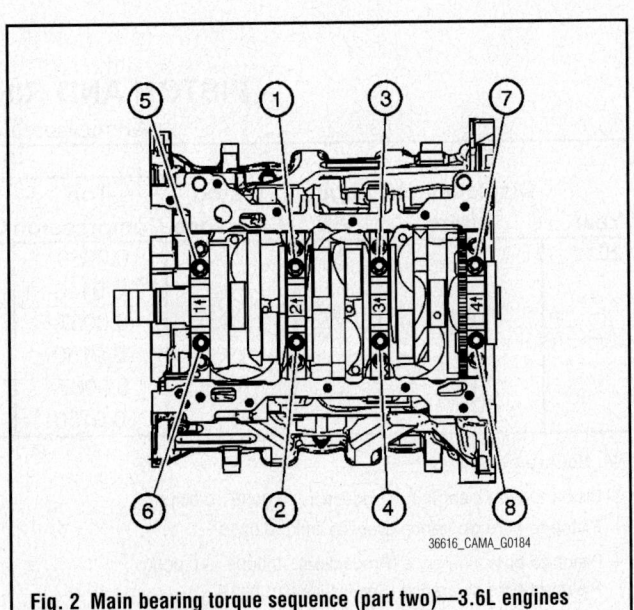

36616_CAMA_G0184

Fig. 2 Main bearing torque sequence (part two)—3.6L engines

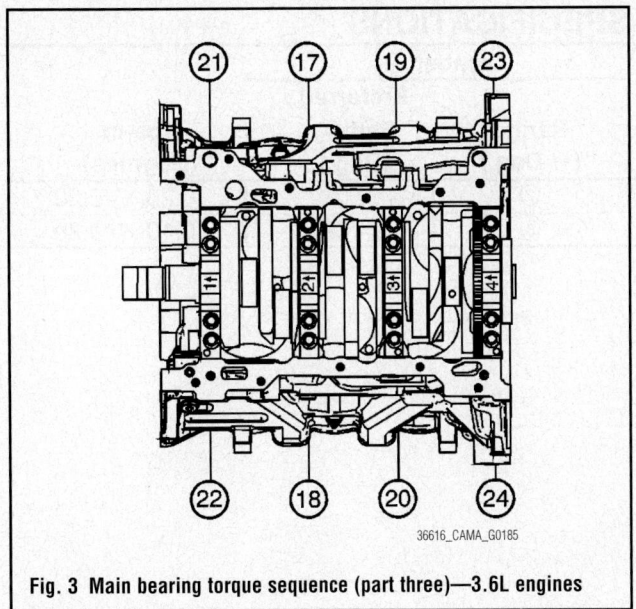

Fig. 3 Main bearing torque sequence (part three)—3.6L engines

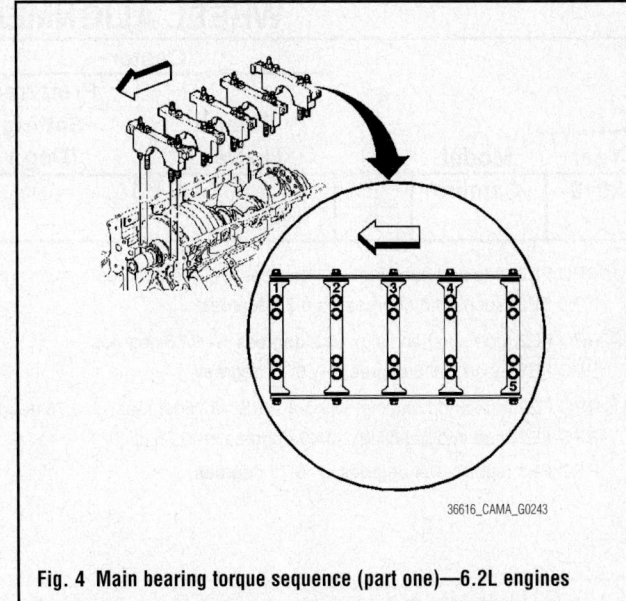

Fig. 4 Main bearing torque sequence (part one)—6.2L engines

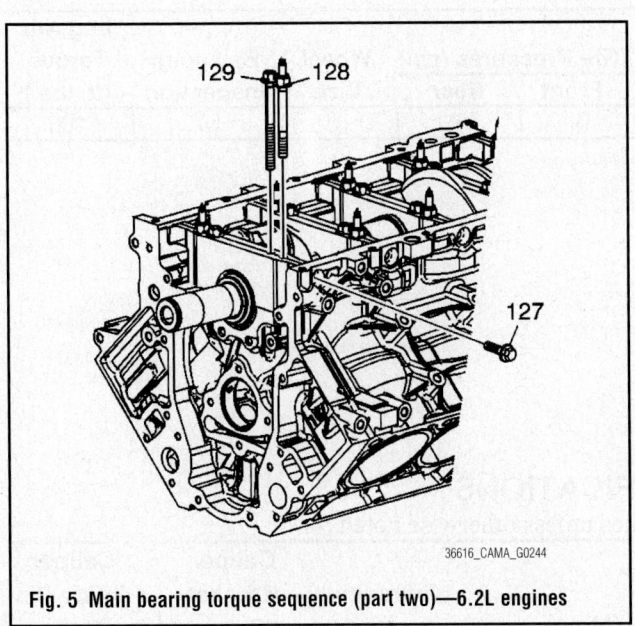

Fig. 5 Main bearing torque sequence (part two)—6.2L engines

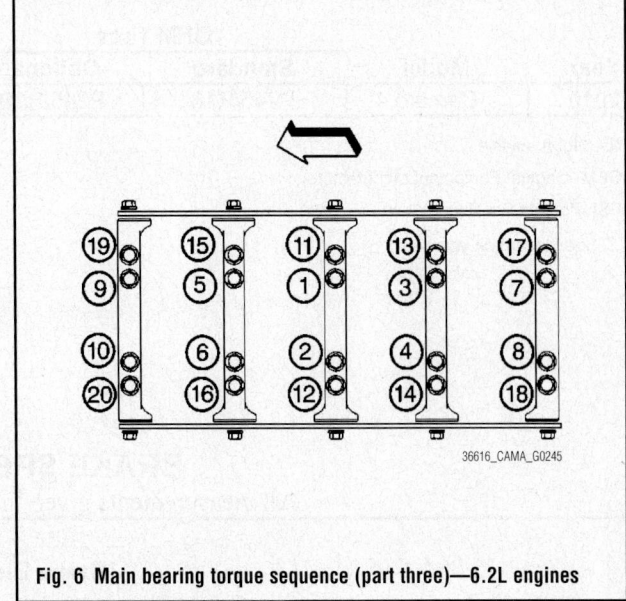

Fig. 6 Main bearing torque sequence (part three)—6.2L engines

WHEEL ALIGNMENT SPECIFICATIONS

Year	Model		Caster Range (+/-Deg.)	Caster Preferred Setting (Deg.)	Camber Range (+/-Deg.)	Camber Preferred Setting (Deg.)	Toe-in (Degrees)
2010	Camaro	F	①	①	②	②	0.20 +/- 0.20
		R	—	—	③	③	0.10 +/- 0.20

① RPO FE2 (ride and handling): 6.4 degrees +/- 0.75 degrees

RPO FE3 (sport): 6.6 degrees +/- 0.75 degrees

② RPO FE2 (ride and handling): -0.2 degrees +/- 0.75 degrees

RPO FE3 (sport): -0.8 degrees +/- 0.75 degrees

③ RPO FE2 (ride and handling) without WRS: -0.75degrees +/- 0.75 degrees

RPO FE2 (ride and handling): -0.40 degrees +/- 0.75 d

RPO FE3 (sport): -0.4 degrees +/- 0.75 degrees

36616_CAMA_C0011

TIRE, WHEEL AND BALL JOINT SPECIFICATIONS

Year	Model	OEM Tires Standard	OEM Tires Optional	Tire Pressures (psi) Front	Tire Pressures (psi) Rear	Wheel Size	Ball Joint Inspection	Lug Nut Torque (ft. lbs.)
2010	Camaro	P245/R18	P245/R19	①	①	②	NA	100

NA: Not Available

OEM: Original Equipment Manufacturer

PSI: Pounds Per Square Inch

① See placard on vehicle.

② 18" or 19"

36616_CAMA_C0012

BRAKE SPECIFICATIONS

All measurements given in inches unless otherwise noted

Year	Model		Original Thickness	Brake Disc Minimum Thickness	Maximum Runout	Minimum Lining Thickness	Caliper Bracket Bolts (ft. lbs.)	Caliper Guide Pin Bolts (ft. lbs.)
2010	Camaro	F	①	②	③	NA	④	⑤
		R	⑥	⑦	③	NA	⑧	⑤

NA: Not Available

① V6: 1.181 V8: 1.338

② V6: 1.122 V8: 1.220

③ V6: 0.002 V8: 0.001

④ 44 ft. lbs. plus 90 degrees

⑤ V6: 20 ft. lbs.

⑥ V6: 0.906 V8: 1.102

⑦ V6: 0.846 V8: 1.062

⑧ 30 ft. lbs. plus 90 degrees

36616_CAMA_C0013

MAINTENANCE I AND II SERVICE SCHEDULES
2010 Chevrolet Camaro

When the CHANGE ENGINE OIL light appears, certain services and inspections are required.

Required services are described as Maintenance I and Maintenance II.

The first service on a vehicle should be Maintenance I, and the second service should be Maintenance II.

Alternate between the 2 thereafter. However, in some cases, Maintenance II may be required more often.

Maintenance I: Use Maintenance I if the CHANGE ENGINE OIL light comes on within 10 months since vehicle was purchased or, if Maintenance II was performed.

Maintenance II: Use Maintenance II if the previous service performed was Maintenance I. Always use Maintenance II whenever the CHANGE ENGINE OIL light comes on 10 months or more since the last service, or, if the CHANGE ENGINE OIL light has not come on at all for one year.

Service	Maintenance I	II
Change the engine oil and filter. Reset the oil life system.	✓	✓
Visually inspect the vehicle for leaks or damage. A fluid loss in the vehicle system could indicate a problem. Inspect, repair, and add fluid to the system if necessary.	✓	✓
Inspect the engine air cleaner filter. If necessary, replace the filter.	--	✓
Rotate the tires. Inspect the tire inflation pressures and the tire wear.	✓	✓
Visually inspect the brake lines and hoses for proper hook-up, binding, leaks, cracks, chafing, etc. Inspect the disc brake pads for wear and the rotors for surface condition. Inspect the drum brake linings for wear or cracks. Inspect other brake parts, including drums, wheel cylinders, calipers, parking brake, etc. Inspect the parking brake adjustment.	✓	✓
Inspect the engine coolant and the windshield washer fluid levels. Add fluid as needed.	✓	✓
Inspect the suspension and steering components. Inspect the front and rear suspension and the steering system for damaged, loose or missing parts, or signs of wear. Inspect the power steering lines and the hoses for proper hook-up, binding, leaks, cracks, chafing, etc.	--	✓
Visually inspect the coolant hoses and replace the hoses if they are cracked, swollen, or deteriorated. Inspect all pipes, fittings and clamps; replace with GM parts as needed. To help ensure proper operation, a pressure test of the cooling system and pressure cap and cleaning the outside of the radiator and air conditioning condenser is recommended at least once a year.	--	✓
Inspect the front and rear suspension and the steering system for damaged, loose, or missing parts, or signs of wear. Inspect power steering lines and hoses for proper hook-up, binding, leaks, cracks, chafing, etc.	--	✓
Inspect the throttle system for interference or binding and for damaged or missing parts. Replace the parts as needed. Replace any components that have high effort or excessive wear. Do not lubricate the accelerator or the cruise control cables.	--	✓
Replace the passenger compartment air filter.	--	✓

To reset the CHANGE ENGINE OIL LIGHT:
1. Press the option button on the DIC until ENGINE OIL MONITOR appears on the DIC screen.
2. Press the set/reset button to reset the system. The next screen indicates that the CHANGE OIL SOON message has been reset. If the vehicle has the uplevel DIC, when the gages button is pressed and the OIL LIFE REMAINING mode appears, it should read 100 percent OIL LIFE REMAINING.
3. Turn the key to OFF.

Vehicles without Driver Information Center (DIC)
1. With the engine off, turn the ignition key to RUN.
2. Fully press and release the accelerator pedal slowly three times within five seconds.
3. Turn the key to OFF, then start the vehicle.

If the light or message comes back on when you start your vehicle, the oil life system has not reset. Repeat the procedure.

ADDITIONAL MAINTENANCE SERVICES
2010 Chevrolet Camaro

TO BE SERVICED	TYPE OF	VEHICLE MILEAGE INTERVAL (x1000)					
		25	50	75	100	125	150
Air cleaner filter	R	✓	✓	✓	✓	✓	✓
Accessory drive belt	I						✓
Auto. Trans. Fluid ①	R		✓		✓		✓
Cooling system hoses and clamps	S/I						✓
Engine coolant	R						✓
Fuel system	I	✓	✓	✓	✓	✓	✓
Exhaust system & heat shields	S/I	✓	✓	✓	✓	✓	✓
Spark plugs	R				✓		

R: Replace   S/I: Inspect and service, if necessary

① Replace if any of the following conditions are met:

Heavy city traffic where the outside temperature regularly reaches 32°C (90°F) or higher

Hilly or mountainous terrain

Frequent trailer towing

Taxi, police, or delivery service

Otherwise, change every 100,000 miles

36616_CAMA_C0015

PRECAUTIONS

Before servicing any vehicle, please be sure to read all of the following precautions, which deal with personal safety, prevention of component damage, and important points to take into consideration when servicing a motor vehicle:

• Never open, service or drain the radiator or cooling system when the engine is hot; serious burns can occur from the steam and hot coolant.

• Observe all applicable safety precautions when working around fuel. Whenever servicing the fuel system, always work in a well-ventilated area. Do not allow fuel spray or vapors to come in contact with a spark, open flame, or excessive heat (a hot drop light, for example). Keep a dry chemical fire extinguisher near the work area. Always keep fuel in a container specifically designed for fuel storage; also, always properly seal fuel containers to avoid the possibility of fire or explosion. Refer to the additional fuel system precautions later in this section.

• Fuel injection systems often remain pressurized, even after the engine has been turned **OFF**. The fuel system pressure must be relieved before disconnecting any fuel lines. Failure to do so may result in fire and/or personal injury.

• Brake fluid often contains polyglycol ethers and polyglycols. Avoid contact with the eyes and wash your hands thoroughly after handling brake fluid. If you do get brake fluid in your eyes, flush your eyes with clean, running water for 15 minutes. If eye irritation persists, or if you have taken

brake fluid internally, IMMEDIATELY seek medical assistance.

• The EPA warns that prolonged contact with used engine oil may cause a number of skin disorders, including cancer. You should make every effort to minimize your exposure to used engine oil. Protective gloves should be worn when changing oil. Wash your hands and any other exposed skin areas as soon as possible after exposure to used engine oil. Soap and water, or waterless hand cleaner should be used.

• All new vehicles are now equipped with an air bag system, often referred to as a Supplemental Restraint System (SRS) or Supplemental Inflatable Restraint (SIR) system. The system must be disabled before performing service on or around system components, steering column, instrument panel components, wiring and sensors. Failure to follow safety and disabling procedures could result in accidental air bag deployment, possible personal injury and unnecessary system repairs.

• Always wear safety goggles when working with, or around, the air bag system. When carrying a non-deployed air bag, be sure the bag and trim cover are pointed away from your body. When placing a non-deployed air bag on a work surface, always face the bag and trim cover upward, away from the surface. This will reduce the motion of the module if it is accidentally deployed. Refer to the additional air bag system precautions later in this section.

• Clean, high quality brake fluid from a

sealed container is essential to the safe and proper operation of the brake system. You should always buy the correct type of brake fluid for your vehicle. If the brake fluid becomes contaminated, completely flush the system with new fluid. Never reuse any brake fluid. Any brake fluid that is removed from the system should be discarded. Also, do not allow any brake fluid to come in contact with a painted surface; it will damage the paint.

• Never operate the engine without the proper amount and type of engine oil; doing so WILL result in severe engine damage.

• Timing belt maintenance is extremely important. Many models utilize an interference-type, non-freewheeling engine. If the timing belt breaks, the valves in the cylinder head may strike the pistons, causing potentially serious (also time-consuming and expensive) engine damage. Refer to the maintenance interval charts for the recommended replacement interval for the timing belt, and to the timing belt section for belt replacement and inspection.

• Disconnecting the negative battery cable on some vehicles may interfere with the functions of the on-board computer system(s) and may require the computer to undergo a relearning process once the negative battery cable is reconnected.

• When servicing drum brakes, only disassemble and assemble one side at a time, leaving the remaining side intact for reference.

• Only an MVAC-trained, EPA-certified automotive technician should service the air conditioning system or its components.

BRAKES   PRECAUTIONS

• Certain components within the Anti-Lock Brake System (ABS) system are not intended to be serviced or repaired individually.

• Do not use rubber hoses or other parts not specifically specified for and ABS system. When using repair kits, replace all parts included in the kit. Partial or incorrect repair may lead to functional problems and require the replacement of components.

• Lubricate rubber parts with clean, fresh brake fluid to ease assembly. Do not use shop air to clean parts; damage to rubber components may result.

• Use only the specified brake fluid from an unopened container.

• If any hydraulic component or line is removed or replaced, it may be necessary to bleed the entire system.

• A clean repair area is essential. Always clean the reservoir and cap thoroughly

before removing the cap. The slightest amount of dirt in the fluid may plug an orifice and impair the system function. Perform repairs after components have been thoroughly cleaned; use only denatured alcohol to clean components. Do not allow ABS components to come into contact with any substance containing mineral oil; this includes used shop rags.

• The Anti-Lock control unit is a microprocessor similar to other computer units in the vehicle. Ensure that the ignition switch is **OFF** before removing or installing controller harnesses. Avoid static electricity discharge at or near the controller.

• If any arc welding is to be done on the vehicle, the control unit should be unplugged before welding operations begin.

• For vehicles equipped with ON Star (RPO UE1), with battery backup, the backup battery is a redundant power supply to allow limited ON Star functionality in the event of a main battery power disruption to the ON Star module (VCIM). Do not disconnect the main vehicle battery or remove the ON Star fuse with the ignition key in any position other than OFF. Retained accessory power should be allowed to time out or be disabled by opening the driver's side door before disconnecting power. Disconnecting power to the module in any way while the ignition is ON or with the retained accessory power activated may cause activation of the ON Star backup battery system and will discharge and permanently damage the backup battery. Once the backup battery is activated it will stay on until it has completely discharged. The backup battery is not rechargeable.

GENERAL INFORMATION

PRECAUTIONS

• Certain components within the ABS system are not intended to be serviced or repaired individually.

• Do not use rubber hoses or other parts not specifically specified for and ABS system. When using repair kits, replace all parts included in the kit. Partial or incorrect repair may lead to functional problems and require the replacement of components.

• Lubricate rubber parts with clean, fresh brake fluid to ease assembly. Do not use shop air to clean parts; damage to rubber components may result.

• Use only DOT 3 brake fluid from an unopened container.

• If any hydraulic component or line is removed or replaced, it may be necessary to bleed the entire system.

• A clean repair area is essential. Always clean the reservoir and cap thoroughly before removing the cap. The slightest amount of dirt in the fluid may plug an orifice and impair the system function. Perform repairs after components have been thoroughly cleaned; use only denatured alcohol to clean components. Do not allow ABS components to come into contact with any substance containing mineral oil; this includes used shop rags.

• The Anti-Lock control unit is a microprocessor similar to other computer units in the vehicle. Ensure that the ignition switch is **OFF** before removing or installing controller harnesses. Avoid static electricity discharge at or near the controller.

• If any arc welding is to be done on the vehicle, the control unit should be unplugged before welding operations begin.

SPEED SENSORS

REMOVAL & INSTALLATION

➡**For vehicles equipped with ON Star (RPO UE1), with battery backup, the backup battery is a redundant power supply to allow limited ON Star functionality in the event of a main battery power disruption to the ON Star module (VCIM). Do not disconnect the main vehicle battery or remove the ON Star** fuse with the ignition key in any position other than OFF. Retained accessory power should be allowed to time out or be disabled by opening the driver's side door before disconnecting power. Disconnecting power to the module in any way while the ignition is ON or with the retained accessory power activated may cause activation of the ON Star backup battery system and will discharge and permanently damage the backup battery. Once the backup battery is activated it will stay on until it has completely discharged. The backup battery is not rechargeable and once it is activated, it must be replaced.

Front

See Figure 7.

1. Before servicing the vehicle, refer to the Precautions Section.
2. Disconnect the negative battery cable.
3. Disconnect the front wheel sensor electrical connector.
4. Release the sensor electrical connector retainer from the inner wheelhouse panel.
5. Feed the connector and harness thru the wheelhouse panel closeout.
6. Raise and support the vehicle safely.
7. Remove the tire and wheel assembly.

8. Release the sensor harness retainer from the outer wheelhouse panel.
9. Release the sensor wire harness from the front suspension strut.
10. Remove the sensor retaining bolt.
11. Remove the sensor from its mounting.

To install:

➡**Be sure to use new fasteners, as required.**

12. Position the sensor to its mounting.
13. Tighten the retaining bolt to 80 inch lbs. (9Nm).

Rear

See Figure 8.

1. Before servicing the vehicle, refer to the Precautions Section.
2. Disconnect the negative battery cable.
3. Raise and support the vehicle safely.
4. Remove the tire and wheel assembly.
5. Disconnect the rear wheel sensor electrical connector.
6. Remove the sensor retaining bolt.
7. Remove the sensor from its mounting.

To install:

➡**Be sure to use new fasteners, as required.**

8. Position the sensor to its mounting.
9. Tighten the retaining bolt to 80 inch lbs. (9 Nm).

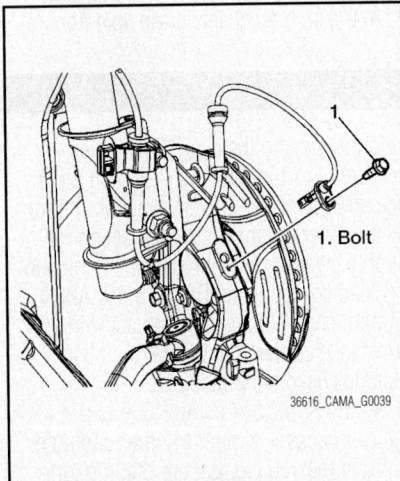

1. Bolt

36616_CAMA_G0039

Fig. 7 Front wheel speed sensor and related components

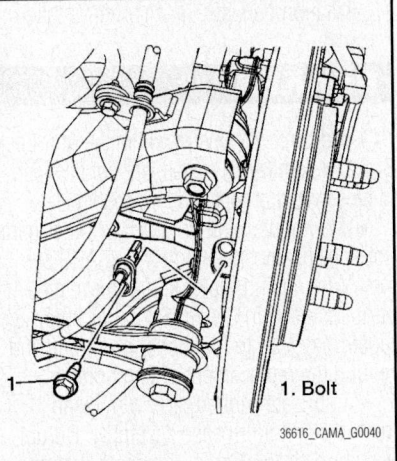

1. Bolt

36616_CAMA_G0040

Fig. 8 Rear wheel speed sensor and related components

BLEEDING PROCEDURE

✳✳ WARNING

When adding fluid to the brake master cylinder reservoir, use only Delco Supreme 11®, GM P/N 12377967 (Canadian P/N 992667), or equivalent DOT-3 brake fluid from a clean, sealed brake fluid container. The use of any type of fluid other than the recommended type of brake fluid may cause contamination which could result in damage to the internal rubber seals and/or rubber linings of hydraulic brake system components.

1. Before servicing the vehicle, refer to the Precautions Section.

2. Place a clean shop cloth beneath the brake master cylinder to prevent brake fluid spills.

3. With the ignition OFF and the brakes cool, apply the brakes 3–5 times, or until the brake pedal effort increases significantly, in order to deplete the brake booster power reserve.

4. If you have performed a brake master cylinder bench bleeding on this vehicle, or if you disconnected the brake pipes from the master cylinder, you must perform the following steps:

   a. Ensure that the brake master cylinder reservoir is full to the maximum-fill level. If necessary, add Delco Supreme 11®, GM P/N 12377967 (Canadian P/N 992667), or equivalent DOT-3 brake fluid from a clean, sealed brake fluid container. If removal of the reservoir cap and diaphragm is necessary, clean the outside of the reservoir on and around the cap prior to removal.

   b. With the rear brake pipe installed securely to the master cylinder, loosen and separate the front brake pipe from the front port of the brake master cylinder.

   c. Allow a small amount of brake fluid to gravity bleed from the open port of the master cylinder.

   d. Reconnect the brake pipe to the master cylinder port and tighten securely.

   e. Have an assistant slowly depress the brake pedal fully and maintain steady pressure on the pedal.

   f. Loosen the same brake pipe to purge air from the open port of the master cylinder.

   g. Tighten the brake pipe, then have the assistant slowly release the brake pedal.

   h. Wait 15 seconds, then repeat steps 3–7 until all air is purged from the same port of the master cylinder.

   i. With the front brake pipe installed securely to the master cylinder, after all air has been purged from the front port of the master cylinder, loosen and separate the rear brake pipe from the master cylinder, then repeat steps 3–8.

   j. After completing the final master cylinder port bleeding procedure, ensure that both of the brake pipe to master cylinder fittings are properly tightened.

5. Fill the brake master cylinder reservoir with Delco Supreme 11®, GM P/N 12377967 (Canadian P/N 992667), or equivalent DOT-3 brake fluid from a clean, sealed brake fluid container. Ensure that the brake master cylinder reservoir remains at least half-full during this bleeding procedure. Add fluid as needed to maintain the proper level. Clean the outside of the reservoir on and around the reservoir cap prior to removing the cap and diaphragm.

6. Install a proper box-end wrench onto the RIGHT REAR wheel hydraulic circuit bleeder valve.

7. Install a transparent hose over the end of the bleeder valve.

8. Submerge the open end of the transparent hose into a transparent container partially filled with Delco Supreme 11®, GM P/N 12377967 (Canadian P/N 992667), or equivalent DOT-3 brake fluid from a clean, sealed brake fluid container.

9. Have an assistant slowly depress the brake pedal fully and maintain steady pressure on the pedal.

10. Loosen the bleeder valve to purge air from the wheel hydraulic circuit.

11. Tighten the bleeder valve, then, have the assistant slowly release the brake pedal.

12. Wait 15 seconds, then repeat steps 8–10 until all air is purged from the same wheel hydraulic circuit.

13. With the right rear wheel hydraulic circuit bleeder valve tightened securely, after all air has been purged from the right rear hydraulic circuit, install a proper box-end wrench onto the LEFT FRONT wheel hydraulic circuit bleeder valve.

14. Install a transparent hose over the end of the bleeder valve, then, repeat steps 7–11.

15. With the left front wheel hydraulic circuit bleeder valve tightened securely, after all air has been purged from the left front hydraulic circuit, install a proper box-end wrench onto the LEFT REAR wheel hydraulic circuit bleeder valve.

16. Install a transparent hose over the end of the bleeder valve, then, repeat steps 7–11.

17. With the left rear wheel hydraulic circuit bleeder valve tightened securely, after all air has been purged from the left rear hydraulic circuit, install a proper box-end wrench onto the RIGHT FRONT wheel hydraulic circuit bleeder valve.

18. Install a transparent hose over the end of the bleeder valve, then, repeat steps 7–11.

19. After completing the final wheel hydraulic circuit bleeding procedure, ensure that each of the 4 wheel hydraulic circuit bleeder valves is properly tightened.

20. Fill the brake master cylinder reservoir to the maximum-fill level with Delco Supreme 11®, GM P/N 12377967 (Canadian P/N 992667), or equivalent DOT-3 brake fluid from a clean, sealed brake fluid container.

21. Slowly depress and release the brake pedal. Observe the feel of the brake pedal.

22. If the brake pedal feels spongy, repeat the bleeding procedure again. If the brake pedal still feels spongy after repeating the bleeding procedure, perform the following steps:

   a. Inspect the brake system for external leaks.

   b. Pressure bleed the hydraulic brake system in order to purge any air that may still be trapped in the system.

23. Turn the ignition key ON, with the engine OFF. Check to see if the brake system warning lamp remains illuminated.

⁑ CAUTION

Dust and dirt accumulating on brake parts during normal use may contain asbestos fibers from production or aftermarket brake linings. Breathing excessive concentrations of asbestos fibers can cause serious bodily harm. Exercise care when servicing brake parts. Do not sand or grind brake lining unless equipment used is designed to contain the dust residue. Do not clean brake parts with compressed air or by dry brushing. Cleaning should be done by dampening the brake components with a fine mist of water, then wiping the brake components clean with a dampened cloth. Dispose of cloth and all residue containing asbestos fibers in an impermeable container with the appropriate label. Follow practices prescribed by the Occupational Safety and Health Administration (OSHA) and the Environmental Protection Agency (EPA) for the handling, processing, and disposing of dust or debris that may contain asbestos fibers.

BRAKE CALIPER

REMOVAL & INSTALLATION

3.6L Engines

See Figure 9.

1. Before servicing the vehicle, refer to the Precautions Section.
2. If the brake fluid level is midway between the MAX point and the MIN point, no brake fluid needs to be removed from the master cylinder. Remove brake fluid from the master cylinder, as required.
3. Raise and safely support the vehicle.
4. Remove the wheel and tire assembly.
5. Install a C-clamp against the outer brake pad and the rear of the brake caliper body.
6. Slowly tighten the C-clamp until the caliper piston is compressed in its bore.
7. Disconnect and plug the brake line at the caliper.
8. Remove the gaskets. Discard them.
9. Remove and discard the caliper retaining bolts.
10. Remove the caliper from its mounting.

To install:

➡ **Be sure to use new fasteners, as required.**

11. Position the caliper to its mounting.
12. Tighten the retaining bolts to 20 ft. lbs. (27 Nm). Be sure to use new bolts.
13. Continue the installation in the reverse order of the removal procedure.
14. With the engine OFF, gradually apply the brake pedal to about two-thirds of its travel distance.
15. Slowly release the pedal.
16. Wait 15 seconds. Repeat the above until a firm pedal is achieved.
17. Be sure to fill the master cylinder with the proper grade and type brake fluid.
18. Bleed the brake system.

6.2L Engines

See Figure 10.

1. Before servicing the vehicle, refer to the Precautions Section.
2. If the brake fluid level is midway between the MAX point and the MIN point, no brake fluid needs to be removed from the master cylinder. Remove brake fluid from the master cylinder, as required.
3. Raise and safely support the vehicle.
4. Remove the wheel and tire assembly.
5. Remove the front disc pads.
6. Disconnect and plug the brake line at the caliper.
7. Remove the gaskets. Discard them.
8. Remove and discard the caliper retaining bolts.
9. Remove the caliper from its mounting.

To install:

➡ **Be sure to use new fasteners, as required.**

10. Position the caliper to its mounting.
11. Tighten the retaining bolts to 44 ft. lbs. (60 Nm), plus 90 degrees. Be sure to use new bolts.
12. Continue the installation in the reverse order of the removal procedure.
13. Be sure to fill the master cylinder with the proper grade and type brake fluid.
14. Bleed the brake system.

DISC BRAKE PADS

REMOVAL & INSTALLATION

3.6L Engines

See Figures 11 and 12.

1. Before servicing the vehicle, refer to the Precautions Section.
2. If the brake fluid level is midway between the MAX point and the MIN point, no brake fluid needs to be removed from the master cylinder. Remove brake fluid from the master cylinder, as required.
3. Raise and safely support the vehicle.

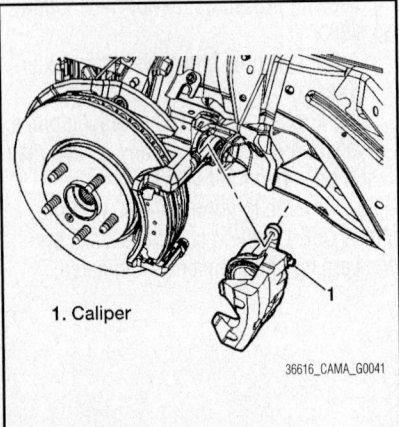

1. Caliper

36616_CAMA_G0041

Fig. 9 Front caliper and related components—3.6L engines

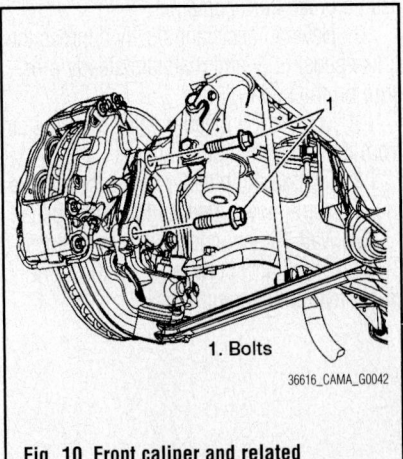

1. Bolts

36616_CAMA_G0042

Fig. 10 Front caliper and related components—6.2L engines

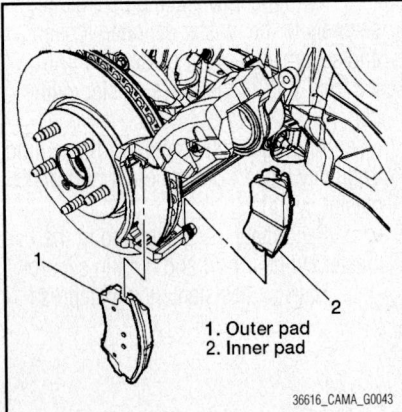

1. Outer pad
2. Inner pad

36616_CAMA_G0043

Fig. 11 Front brake pads and related components, part one—3.6L engines

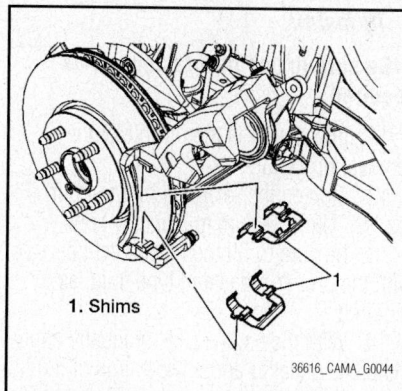

1. Shims

36616_CAMA_G0044

Fig. 12 Front brake pads and related components, part two—3.6L engines

4. Remove the wheel and tire assembly.

5. Install a C-clamp against the outer brake pad and the rear of the brake caliper body.

6. Slowly tighten the C-clamp until the caliper piston is compressed in its bore.

7. Remove the lower brake caliper guide pin bolt. Discard the bolt.

8. Support the caliper using mechanics wire. Do not disconnect the brake line hose or support the caliper using the hose.

9. Swing the caliper upward and remove the outer brake pad. Remove the inner brake pad.

10. Remove the brake pad springs.

To install:

➡**Be sure to use new fasteners, as required.**

11. Installation is the reverse of the removal procedure.

12. Tighten the retaining bolt to 20 ft. lbs. (27 Nm). Be sure to use new bolts.

13. Be sure to fill the master cylinder with the proper grade and type fluid, as required.

14. With the engine OFF, gradually apply the brake pedal to about two-thirds of its travel distance.

15. Slowly release the pedal.

16. Wait 15 seconds. Repeat the above until a firm pedal is achieved.

6.2L Engines

See Figure 13.

1. Before servicing the vehicle, refer to the Precautions Section.

2. If the brake fluid level is midway between the MAX point and the MIN point, no brake fluid needs to be removed from the master cylinder. Remove brake fluid from the master cylinder, as required.

3. Raise and safely support the vehicle.

4. Remove the wheel and tire assembly.

5. Hold the end of the brake spring down and carefully drive out the lower brake caliper pin from the caliper.

6. Remove the brake pad spring.

7. Carefully drive out the upper brake caliper pin from the caliper.

8. Using a spreader tool, carefully push the caliper pistons into the caliper bores until they are fully seated.

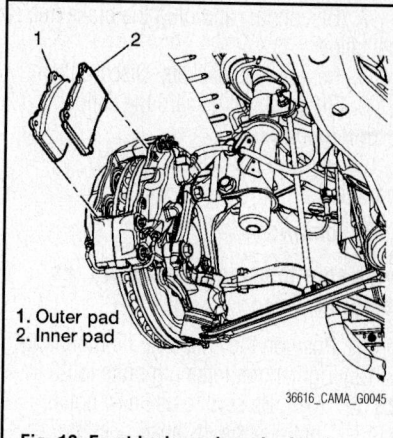

1. Outer pad
2. Inner pad

36616_CAMA_G0045

Fig. 13 Front brake pads and related components—6.2L engines

9. Remove the outer pad. Remove the inner pad.

To install:

➡**Be sure to use new fasteners, as required.**

10. Installation is the reverse of the removal procedure.

11. Be sure to fill the master cylinder with the proper grade and type fluid, as required.

12. With the engine OFF, gradually apply the brake pedal to about two-thirds of its travel distance.

13. Slowly release the pedal.

14. Wait 15 seconds. Repeat the above until a firm pedal is achieved.

BRAKES

REAR DISC BRAKES

✳✳ CAUTION

Dust and dirt accumulating on brake parts during normal use may contain asbestos fibers from production or aftermarket brake linings. Breathing excessive concentrations of asbestos fibers can cause serious bodily harm. Exercise care when servicing brake parts. Do not sand or grind brake lining unless equipment used is designed to contain the dust residue. Do not clean brake parts with compressed air or by dry brushing. Cleaning should be done by dampening the brake components with a fine mist of water, then wiping the brake components clean with a dampened cloth. Dispose of cloth and all residue containing asbestos fibers in an impermeable container with the appropriate label. Follow practices prescribed by the Occupational

Safety and Health Administration (OSHA) and the Environmental Protection Agency (EPA) for the handling, processing, and disposing of dust or debris that may contain asbestos fibers.

BRAKE CALIPER

REMOVAL & INSTALLATION

3.6L Engines

See Figure 14.

1. Before servicing the vehicle, refer to the Precautions Section.

2. If the brake fluid level is midway between the MAX point and the MIN point, no brake fluid needs to be removed from the master cylinder. Remove brake fluid from the master cylinder, as required.

3. Raise and safely support the vehicle.

4. Remove the wheel and tire assembly.

5. Install a C-clamp against the outer brake pad and the rear of the brake caliper body.

6. Slowly tighten the C-clamp until the caliper piston is compressed in its bore.

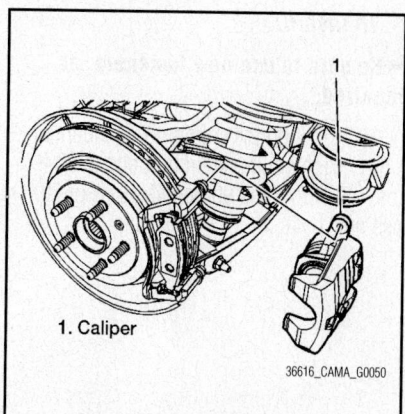

1. Caliper

36616_CAMA_G0050

Fig. 14 Rear caliper and related components—3.6L engines

7. Disconnect and plug the brake line at the caliper.

8. Remove the gaskets. Discard them.

9. Remove and discard the caliper retaining bolts.

10. Remove the caliper from its mounting.

To install:

➡**Be sure to use new fasteners, as required.**

11. Position the caliper to its mounting.

12. Tighten the retaining bolts to 20 ft. lbs. (27 Nm). Be sure to use new bolts.

13. Continue the installation in the reverse order of the removal procedure.

14. With the engine OFF, gradually apply the brake pedal to about two-thirds of its travel distance.

15. Slowly release the pedal.

16. Wait 15 seconds. Repeat the above until a firm pedal is achieved.

17. Be sure to fill the master cylinder with the proper grade and type brake fluid.

18. Bleed the brake system.

6.2L Engines

See Figure 15.

1. Before servicing the vehicle, refer to the Precautions Section.

2. If the brake fluid level is midway between the MAX point and the MIN point, no brake fluid needs to be removed from the master cylinder. Remove brake fluid from the master cylinder, as required.

3. Raise and safely support the vehicle.

4. Remove the wheel and tire assembly.

5. Remove the rear disc pads.

6. Disconnect and plug the brake line at the caliper.

7. Remove the gaskets. Discard them.

8. Remove and discard the caliper retaining bolts.

9. Remove the caliper from its mounting.

To install:

➡**Be sure to use new fasteners, as required.**

10. Position the caliper to its mounting.

11. Tighten the retaining bolts to 30 ft. lbs. (40 Nm), plus 90 degrees. Be sure to use new bolts.

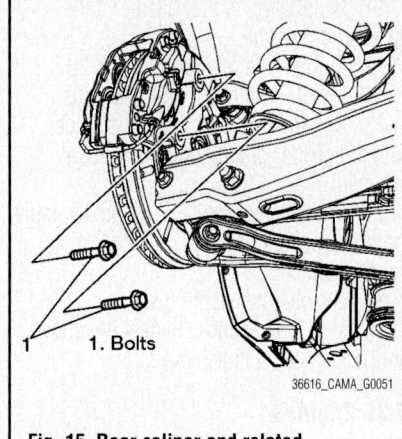

Fig. 15 Rear caliper and related components—6.2L engines

1. Bolts

36616_CAMA_G0051

12. Continue the installation in the reverse order of the removal procedure.

13. Be sure to fill the master cylinder with the proper grade and type brake fluid.

14. Bleed the brake system.

DISC BRAKE PADS

REMOVAL & INSTALLATION

3.6L Engines

1. Before servicing the vehicle, refer to the Precautions Section.

2. If the brake fluid level is midway between the MAX point and the MIN point, no brake fluid needs to be removed from the master cylinder. Remove brake fluid from the master cylinder, as required.

3. Raise and safely support the vehicle.

4. Remove the wheel and tire assembly.

5. Install a C-clamp against the outer brake pad and the rear of the brake caliper body.

6. Slowly tighten the C-clamp until the caliper piston is compressed in its bore.

7. Remove the lower brake caliper guide pin bolt. Discard the bolt.

8. Support the caliper using mechanics wire. Do not disconnect the brake line hose or support the caliper using the hose.

9. Swing the caliper upward and remove the outer brake pad. Remove the inner brake pad.

10. Remove the brake pad springs.

To install:

➡**Be sure to use new fasteners, as required.**

11. Installation is the reverse of the removal procedure.

12. Tighten the retaining bolt to 20 ft. lbs. (27 Nm). Be sure to use new bolts.

13. Be sure to fill the master cylinder with the proper grade and type fluid, as required.

14. With the engine OFF, gradually apply the brake pedal to about two-thirds of its travel distance.

15. Slowly release the pedal.

16. Wait 15 seconds. Repeat the above until a firm pedal is achieved.

6.2L Engines

1. Before servicing the vehicle, refer to the Precautions Section.

2. If the brake fluid level is midway between the MAX point and the MIN point, no brake fluid needs to be removed from the master cylinder. Remove brake fluid from the master cylinder, as required.

3. Raise and safely support the vehicle.

4. Remove the wheel and tire assembly.

5. Hold the end of the brake spring down and carefully drive out the lower brake caliper pin from the caliper.

6. Remove the brake pad spring.

7. Carefully drive out the upper brake caliper pin from the caliper.

8. Using a spreader tool, carefully push the caliper pistons into the caliper bores until they are fully seated.

9. Remove the outer pad. Remove the inner pad.

To install:

➡**Be sure to use new fasteners, as required.**

10. Installation is the reverse of the removal procedure.

11. Be sure to fill the master cylinder with the proper grade and type fluid, as required.

12. With the engine OFF, gradually apply the brake pedal to about two-thirds of its travel distance.

13. Slowly release the pedal.

14. Wait 15 seconds. Repeat the above until a firm pedal is achieved.

BRAKES

PARKING BRAKE CABLES

ADJUSTMENT

1. Before servicing the vehicle, refer to the Precautions Section.
2. Apply and release the park brake lever two or three times to set the cable tension.
3. Inspect for proper operation.
4. Correct as necessary.

PARKING BRAKE SHOES

REMOVAL & INSTALLATION

1. Before servicing the vehicle, refer to the Precautions Section.
2. Raise and support the vehicle safely.
3. Remove the rear tires and wheels.
4. Remove the rotors.
5. Retract the park brake shoe adjuster to ease removal.
6. Remove the upper park brake shoe retaining spring. Remove the park brake adjuster.
7. Remove the rear park brake shoe hold-down spring. Remove the lower park brake shoe retainer spring and the rear park brake shoe.
8. Remove the front park brake shoe hold-down spring. Remove the lower park brake shoe retainer spring and the front park brake shoe.

To install:

➡Be sure to use new fasteners, as required.

9. Lightly coat the park brake shoe contact areas of the backing plate with high temperature brake lubricant.
10. Install the shoes to their mountings.
11. Adjust the parking brake.

12. Continue the installation in the reverse order of the removal procedure.

ADJUSTMENT

See Figures 16 and 17.

➡**Adjustments are not necessary after replacing the park brake lever or park brake cables. The brake is adjusted automatically by cycling the park brake lever three times.**

➡**Do not operate the park brake lever with the rear rotors removed.**

1. Before servicing the vehicle, refer to the Precautions Section.
2. Apply and release the parking brake three times.
3. Verify that the parking brake pedal releases completely.
4. Raise and support the vehicle safely.
5. Remove the rear tires and wheels.
6. Remove the rotors.
7. Position tool J21177-A inside the

park brake drum at the widest point. Tighten the set screw on the tool.
8. Position the tool over the park brake shoe at the widest point.
9. Turn the adjuster on the tool until the park brake shoe just contacts the tool.
10. Repeat the above on the opposite side.
11. Install the rotors.
12. Install the tire and wheel assemblies.
13. Lower the vehicle to curb height.
14. Set and release the park lever three times.

➡**If the rear wheels rotate during the following test, readjust the parking brake shoes.**

15. Apply the parking brake. Inspect the wheel rotation.
16. The wheels should not rotate forward, drag or rotate backward.
17. Release the park brake lever. Verify that the wheels rotate freely.
18. Lower the vehicle.

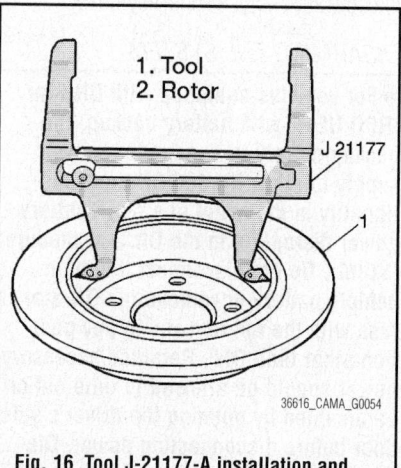

Fig. 16 Tool J-21177-A installation and park brake drum check

1. Tool
2. Rotor

J 21177

36616_CAMA_G0054

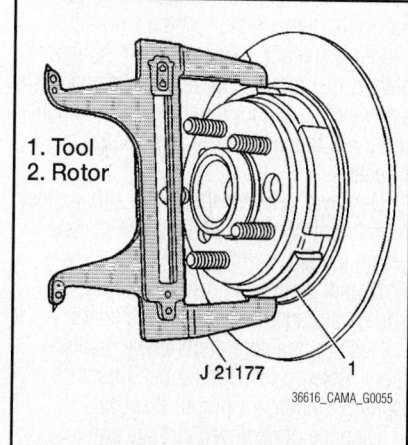

Fig. 17 Tool J-21177-A installation and park brake shoe clearance check

1. Tool
2. Rotor

J 21177

36616_CAMA_G0055

CHASSIS ELECTRICAL

GENERAL INFORMATION

✳✳ CAUTION

These vehicles are equipped with an air bag system. The system must be disarmed before performing service on, or around, system components, the steering column, instrument panel components, wiring and sensors. Failure to follow the safety precautions and the disarming procedure could result in accidental air bag deployment,

possible injury and unnecessary system repairs.

SERVICE PRECAUTIONS

Disconnect and isolate the battery negative cable before beginning any airbag system component diagnosis, testing, removal, or installation procedures. Allow system capacitor to discharge for two minutes before beginning any component service. This will disable the airbag system. Failure to disable the airbag system may result in accidental airbag deployment, personal injury, or death.

Do not place an intact undeployed airbag face down on a solid surface. The airbag will propel into the air if accidentally deployed and may result in personal injury or death.

When carrying or handling an undeployed airbag, the trim side (face) of the airbag should be pointing towards the body to minimize possibility of injury if accidental deployment occurs. Failure to do this may result in personal injury or death.

Replace airbag system components with OEM replacement parts. Substitute parts may appear interchangeable, but internal differences may result in inferior occupant protection. Failure to do so may result in occupant personal injury or death.

Wear safety glasses, rubber gloves, and long sleeved clothing when cleaning powder residue from vehicle after an airbag deployment. Powder residue emitted from a deployed airbag can cause skin irritation. Flush affected area with cool water if irritation is experienced. If nasal or throat irritation is experienced, exit the vehicle for fresh air until the irritation ceases. If irritation continues, see a physician.

Do not use a replacement airbag that is not in the original packaging. This may result in improper deployment, personal injury, or death.

The factory installed fasteners, screws and bolts used to fasten airbag components have a special coating and are specifically designed for the airbag system. Do not use substitute fasteners. Use only original equipment fasteners listed in the parts catalog when fastener replacement is required.

During, and following, any child restraint anchor service, due to impact event or vehicle repair, carefully inspect all mounting hardware, tether straps, and anchors for proper installation, operation, or damage. If a child restraint anchor is found damaged in any way, the anchor must be replaced. Failure to do this may result in personal injury or death.

Deployed and non-deployed airbags may or may not have live pyrotechnic material within the airbag inflator.

Do not dispose of driver/passenger/curtain airbags or seat belt tensioners unless you are sure of complete deployment. Refer to the Hazardous Substance Control System for proper disposal.

Dispose of deployed airbags and tensioners consistent with state, provincial, local, and federal regulations.

After any airbag component testing or service, do not Connect the negative battery cable. Personal injury or death may result if the system test is not performed first.

If the vehicle is equipped with the Occupant Classification System (OCS), do not Connect the negative battery cable before performing the OCS Verification Test using the scan tool and the appropriate diagnostic information. Personal injury or death may result if the system test is not performed properly.

Never replace both the Occupant Restraint Controller (ORC) and the Occupant Classification Module (OCM) at the same time. If both require replacement, replace one, then perform the Airbag System test before replacing the other.

Both the ORC and the OCM store Occupant Classification System (OCS) calibration data, which they transfer to one another when one of them is replaced. If both are replaced at the same time, an irreversible fault will be set in both modules and the OCS may malfunction and cause personal injury or death.

If equipped with OCS, the Seat Weight Sensor is a sensitive, calibrated unit and must be handled carefully. Do not drop or handle roughly. If dropped or damaged, replace with another sensor. Failure to do so may result in occupant injury or death.

If equipped with OCS, the front passenger seat must be handled carefully as well. When removing the seat, be careful when setting on floor not to drop. If dropped, the sensor may be inoperative, could result in occupant injury, or possibly death.

If equipped with OCS, when the passenger front seat is on the floor, no one should sit in the front passenger seat. This uneven force may damage the sensing ability of the seat weight sensors. If sat on and damaged, the sensor may be inoperative, could result in occupant injury, or possibly death.

DISARMING THE SYSTEM

➡For vehicles equipped with ON Star (RPO UE1), with battery backup, the backup battery is a redundant power supply to allow limited ON Star functionality in the event of a main battery power disruption to the ON Star module (VCIM). Do not disconnect the main vehicle battery or remove the ON Star fuse with the ignition key in any position other than OFF. Retained accessory power should be allowed to time out or be disabled by opening the driver's side door before disconnecting power. Disconnecting power to the module in any way while the ignition is ON or with the retained accessory power activated may cause activation of the ON Star backup battery system and will discharge and permanently damage the backup battery. Once the backup battery is activated it will stay on until it has completely discharged. The backup battery is not rechargeable and once it is activated, it must be replaced.

➡When performing service on or near the SRS components, or SRS wiring the SRS must be disabled. Failure to observe the correct procedure could cause deployment of the SRS components. Serious injury can occur.

1. Position the steering wheel so the front wheels are in the straight ahead position.

2. Be sure the ignition switch is in the **OFF** position.

3. Disconnect the negative battery cable.

➡The SDM may have more than one fused power input. To ensure that there is no unwanted SRS deployment, personal injury, or unnecessary SRS system repairs, remove all fuses supplying power to the SDM. With all SDM fuses removed and the ignition switch in the ON position, the AIR BAG warning indicator will illuminate. This is normal and does not indicate a SRS system malfunction.

4. Locate and remove the fuses supplying power to the SDM.

5. Wait one minute before working on the vehicle.

ARMING THE SYSTEM

1. Before servicing the vehicle, refer to the Precautions Section.

2. Be sure the ignition switch is in the **OFF** position.

3. Install the fuses.

4. Connect the negative battery cable.

5. Turn the ignition switch to the **ON** position.

6. If the system is operating properly the AIR BAG indicator will flash

7. Correct problems as required.

CLOCKSPRING CENTERING

See Figures 18 and 19.

➡For vehicles equipped with ON Star (RPO UE1), with battery backup, the backup battery is a redundant power supply to allow limited ON Star functionality in the event of a main battery power disruption to the ON Star module (VCIM). Do not disconnect the main vehicle battery or remove the ON Star fuse with the ignition key in any position other than OFF. Retained accessory power should be allowed to time out or be disabled by opening the driver's side door before disconnecting power. Disconnecting power to the module in any way while the ignition is ON or with the retained accessory power activated may cause activation of the ON Star backup battery system and will discharge and permanently damage the backup battery. Once the backup battery is activated it will stay on until it has completely discharged. The backup battery is not rechargeable and once it is activated, it must be replaced.

1. Before servicing the vehicle, refer to the Precautions Section.

2. Disconnect the negative battery cable.

➡The new SIR coil assembly will be centered. Improper alignment of the SIR coil assembly may damage the unit, causing an inflatable restraint malfunction.

3. Remove the steering wheel.

4. Verify that the front wheels are in the straight ahead position, the centering mark of the steering shaft is in the 6 o'clock position.

5. Turn the lobe of the clockspring clockwise until the coil ribbon stops. Do not force.

6. Turn the lobe of the clock spring counterclockwise approximately three turns to the neutral position.

7. Properly align until the centering window turns yellow. This indicates the center position. See illustration.

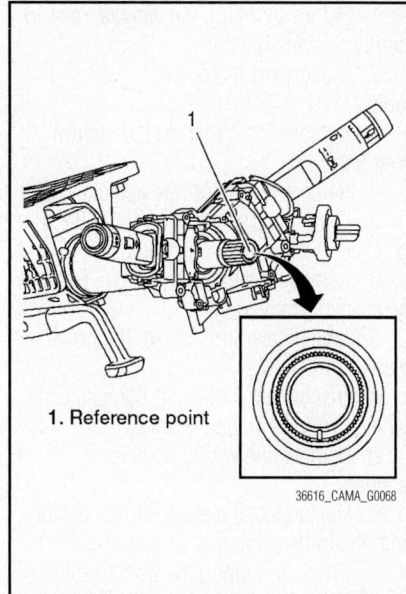

1. Reference point

36616_CAMA_G0068

Fig. 18 SRS coil alignment

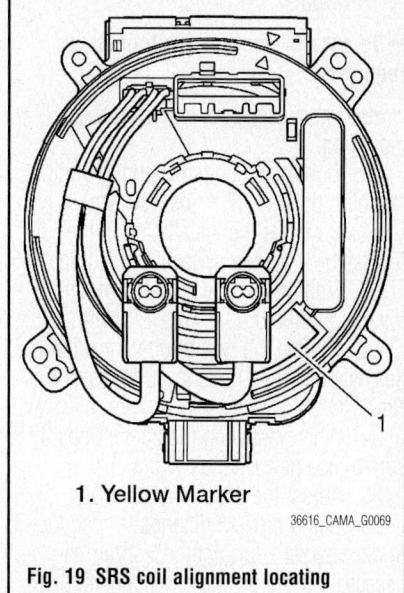

1. Yellow Marker

36616_CAMA_G0069

Fig. 19 SRS coil alignment locating point (yellow)

DRIVE TRAIN

AUTOMATIC TRANSMISSION ASSEMBLY

REMOVAL & INSTALLATION

See Figure 20.

➡For vehicles equipped with ON Star (RPO UE1), with battery backup, the backup battery is a redundant power supply to allow limited ON Star functionality in the event of a main battery power disruption to the ON Star module (VCIM). Do not disconnect the main vehicle battery or remove the ON Star fuse with the ignition key in any position other than OFF. Retained accessory power should be allowed to time out or be disabled by opening the driver's side door before disconnecting power. Disconnecting power to the module in any way while the ignition is ON or with the retained accessory power activated may cause activation of the ON Star backup battery system and will discharge and permanently damage the backup battery. Once the backup battery is activated it will stay on until it has completely discharged. The backup battery is not rechargeable and once it is activated, it must be replaced.

1. Before servicing the vehicle, refer to the Precautions Section.

2. Disconnect the negative battery cable.

3. Raise and support the vehicle safely.

4. Drain the transmission fluid. Be sure to properly dispose of used fluid.

5. Remove the exhaust system. Remove the catalytic converters.

6. Matchmark and remove the driveshaft.

7. Disconnect the transmission shift linkage.

8. Remove the vent hose.

9. Disconnect the wiring harness connectors from the transmission.

10. Remove the wiring harness retainers.

11. Remove the oxygen sensor wire harness retainers from the transmission.

12. Remove the transmission cooler lines. Be sure to catch used fluid in a drain pan. Discard the O-rings, new ones must be used.

13. Remove the transmission close out plug.

14. Matchmark the flexplate to the torque converter.

15. Remove the starter.

16. Remove the right side torque converter cover.

17. Remove and discard the torque converter to flexplate retaining bolts. Rotate the balancer clockwise to gain access to the bolts. Discard the bolts, new ones must be used.

18. Properly support the transmission using a transmission jack or suitable jack.

19. Remove the transmission mount support.

20. Slightly lower the transmission to gain access to the upper transmission to engine retaining bolts.

21. Disconnect the wire harness from the top of the transmission.

22. Position the vent tube to the side.

23. Remove the transmission to engine mounting bolts in the sequence shown in the illustration.

24. Remove the two remaining transmission bolts from the transmission.

25. Pull the transmission free from the engine dowels.

26. Be sure that there is sufficient clearance between the wiring harnesses, vent tube and cooler pipes to allow removal of the unit.

27. Check that nothing is still attached to the transmission to prevent removal.

28. Carefully lower the transmission from the vehicle.

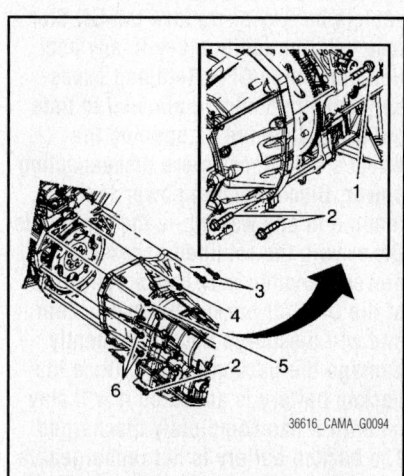

36616_CAMA_G0094

Fig. 20 Transmission to engine mounting bolt removal sequence

To install:

➡ **Be sure to use new fasteners, as required.**

29. Position the transmission to its mounting.

30. Tighten the transmission to engine retaining bolts to 37 ft. lbs. (50 Nm).

31. Continue the installation in the reverse order of the removal procedure.

32. Tighten the transmission mount retaining bolts to 43 ft. lbs. (58 Nm).

33. Tighten the new torque converter to flexplate retaining bolts to 48 ft. lbs. (65 Nm).

34. When installing the cooler lines be sure to use new O-rings.

35. Adjust the shift control linkage.

36. Using the GM diagnostic scan tool or aftermarket equivalent reprogram the necessary systems and components. Be sure to follow the scan tool manufacturer's directions.

37. Fill the transmission with the proper grade and type transmission fluid.

38. Start the engine and check for leaks. Correct as required.

39. Road test the vehicle.

MANUAL TRANSMISSION ASSEMBLY

REMOVAL & INSTALLATION

Aisin Transmission

See Figure 21.

➡ **For vehicles equipped with ON Star (RPO UE1), with battery backup, the backup battery is a redundant power supply to allow limited ON Star functionality in the event of a main battery power disruption to the ON Star module (VCIM). Do not disconnect the main vehicle battery or remove the ON Star fuse with the ignition key in any position other than OFF. Retained accessory power should be allowed to time out or be disabled by opening the driver's side door before disconnecting power. Disconnecting power to the module in any way while the ignition is ON or with the retained accessory power activated may cause activation of the ON Star backup battery system and will discharge and permanently damage the backup battery. Once the backup battery is activated it will stay on until it has completely discharged. The backup battery is not rechargeable and once it is activated, it must be replaced.**

1. Before servicing the vehicle, refer to the Precautions Section.

2. Disconnect the negative battery cable.

3. Remove the transmission control lever knob.

4. Raise and support the vehicle safely.

5. Drain the transmission fluid. Be sure to properly dispose of used fluid.

6. Remove the exhaust system. Remove the catalytic converters.

7. Matchmark and remove the driveshaft.

8. Disconnect the wiring harness connectors from the transmission.

9. Remove the wiring harness retainers.

10. Disconnect the electrical connector from the transmission.

11. Properly support the transmission using a transmission jack or suitable jack.

12. Remove the transmission mount support.

13. Remove the transmission shift control assembly.

14. Remove the clutch hose from the slave cylinder.

15. Disconnect the hydraulic hose from the slave cylinder.

16. Remove the transmission to engine mounting bolts in the sequence shown in the illustration.

17. Pull the transmission free from the engine dowels.

18. Be sure that there is sufficient clearance between the wiring harnesses, vent tube and cooler pipes to allow removal of the unit.

19. Check that nothing is still attached to the transmission to prevent removal.

20. Carefully lower the transmission from the vehicle.

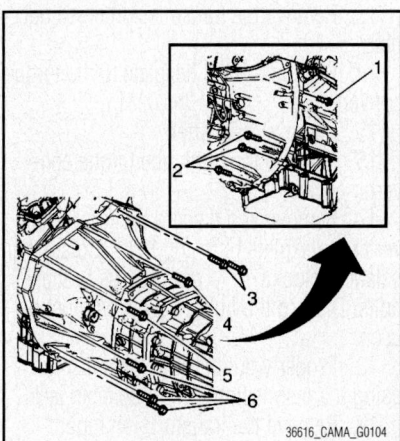

Fig. 21 Transmission to engine mounting bolt removal sequence—Aisin Transmission

To install:

➡ **Be sure to use new fasteners, as required.**

21. Position the transmission to its mounting.

22. Tighten the transmission to engine retaining bolts to 37 ft. lbs. (50 Nm).

23. Continue the installation in the reverse order of the removal procedure.

24. Tighten the transmission mount retaining bolts to 43 ft. lbs. (58 Nm).

25. With the ignition OFF, crank the engine several times. Listen for any unusual noises or evidence that parts are binding.

26. Place the transmission in neutral, start the engine and listen for any unusual noises or evidence that parts are binding.

27. With the engine running raise and safely support the vehicle.

28. Perform a final inspection for the proper fluid level.

29. Lower the vehicle.

30. Road test the vehicle.

Tremac Transmission

See Figure 22.

➡ **For vehicles equipped with ON Star (RPO UE1), with battery backup, the backup battery is a redundant power supply to allow limited ON Star functionality in the event of a main battery power disruption to the ON Star module (VCIM). Do not disconnect the main vehicle battery or remove the ON Star fuse with the ignition key in any position other than OFF. Retained accessory power should be allowed to time out or be disabled by opening the driver's side door before disconnecting power. Disconnecting power to the module in any**

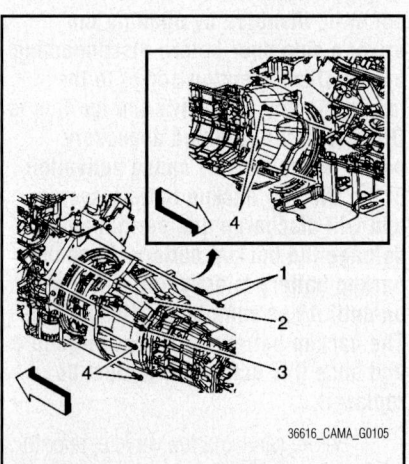

Fig. 22 Transmission to engine mounting bolt removal sequence—Tremec Transmission

way while the ignition is ON or with the retained accessory power activated may cause activation of the ON Star backup battery system and will discharge and permanently damage the backup battery. Once the backup battery is activated it will stay on until it has completely discharged. The backup battery is not rechargeable and once it is activated, it must be replaced.

1. Before servicing the vehicle, refer to the Precautions Section.
2. Disconnect the negative battery cable.
3. Remove the transmission control lever knob.
4. Raise and support the vehicle safely.
5. Drain the transmission fluid. Be sure to properly dispose of used fluid.
6. Remove the exhaust system. Remove the catalytic converters.
7. Matchmark and remove the driveshaft.
8. Properly support the transmission using a transmission jack or suitable jack.
9. Remove the transmission mount support.
10. Lower the transmission to gain access to the top of the unit.
11. Remove the transmission shift control assembly.
12. Disconnect the wiring harness connectors from the transmission.
13. Remove the wiring harness retainers.
14. Remove the clutch hose from the slave cylinder.
15. Remove the transmission to engine mounting bolts in the sequence shown in the illustration.
16. Pull the transmission free from the engine dowels.
17. Be sure that there is sufficient clearance between the wiring harnesses, vent tube and cooler pipes to allow removal of the unit.
18. Check that nothing is still attached to the transmission to prevent removal.
19. Carefully lower the transmission from the vehicle.

To install:

➥Be sure to use new fasteners, as required.

20. Position the transmission to its mounting.
21. Tighten the transmission to engine retaining bolts to 37 ft. lbs. (50 Nm).
22. Continue the installation in the reverse order of the removal procedure.
23. Tighten the transmission mount retaining bolts to 43 ft. lbs. (58 Nm).
24. Road test the vehicle.

CLUTCH

REMOVAL & INSTALLATION

See Figures 23 through 25.

➥When the clutch driven plate requires replacement the engine flywheel must also be replaced along with the clutch pressure plate.

➥For vehicles equipped with ON Star (RPO UE1), with battery backup, the backup battery is a redundant power supply to allow limited ON Star functionality in the event of a main battery power disruption to the ON Star module (VCIM). Do not disconnect the main vehicle battery or remove the ON Star fuse with the ignition key in any position other than OFF. Retained accessory power should be allowed to time out or be disabled by opening the driver's side door before disconnecting power. Disconnecting power to the module in any way while the ignition is ON or with the retained accessory power activated may cause activation of the ON Star backup battery system and will discharge and permanently damage the backup battery. Once the backup battery is activated it will stay on until it has completely discharged. The backup bat-

tery is not rechargeable and once it is activated, it must be replaced.

1. Before servicing the vehicle, refer to the Precautions Section.
2. Disconnect the negative battery cable.
3. Raise and support the vehicle safely.
4. Remove the transmission.
5. Remove the clutch pressure plate retaining bolts.
6. Remove the clutch pressure plate and clutch from the dowel pins on the flywheel.

To install:

➥Be sure to use new fasteners, as required.

➥When the clutch driven plate requires replacement the engine flywheel must also be replaced along with the clutch pressure plate.

➥The splined portion of the driven plate protrudes out of the plate more

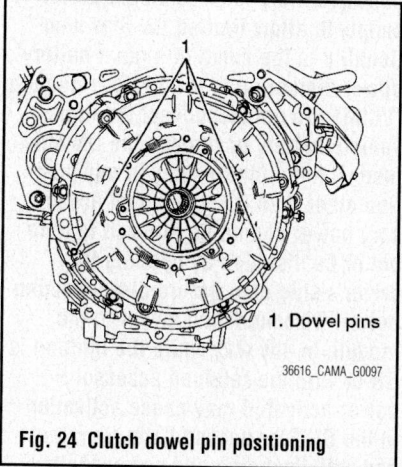

1. Dowel pins

36616_CAMA_G0097

Fig. 24 Clutch dowel pin positioning

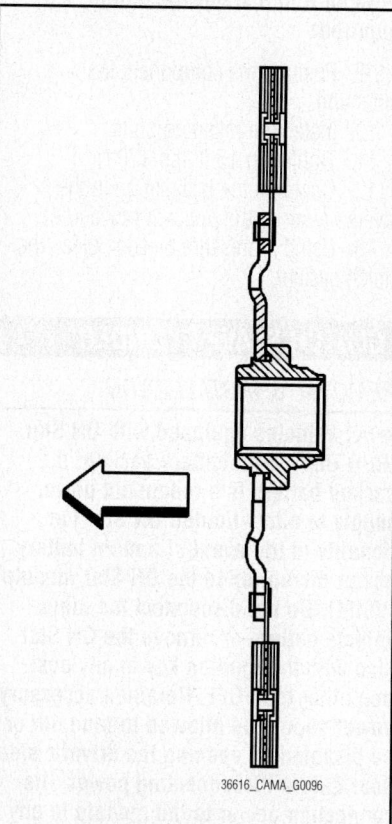

36616_CAMA_G0096

Fig. 23 Clutch positioning

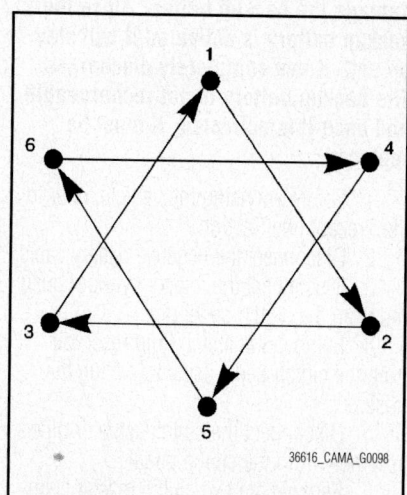

36616_CAMA_G0098

Fig. 25 Clutch retaining bolt tightening sequence

on one side than the other. The side that protrudes out more is the transmission side. The arrow in the illustration indicates front of vehicle, or flywheel side of the driven plate.

7. Install the clutch assembly to the flywheel.

8. Tighten the retaining bolts finger tight.

9. Ensure that all three dowel pins are visibly seated thru the clutch cover dowel pin holes, as shown in the illustration.

10. Using a clutch alignment tool, align the driven plate to the pilot bushing.

11. Tighten the retaining bolts to specification and in the proper sequence.

12. Continue the installation in the reverse order of the removal procedure.

CLUTCH MASTER CYLINDER

REMOVAL & INSTALLATION

See Figure 26.

➡ For vehicles equipped with ON Star (RPO UE1), with battery backup, the backup battery is a redundant power supply to allow limited ON Star functionality in the event of a main battery power disruption to the ON Star module (VCIM). Do not disconnect the main vehicle battery or remove the ON Star fuse with the ignition key in any position other than OFF. Retained accessory power should be allowed to time out or be disabled by opening the driver's side door before disconnecting power. Disconnecting power to the module in any way while the ignition is ON or with the retained accessory power activated may cause activation of the ON Star backup battery system and will discharge and permanently damage the backup battery. Once the backup battery is activated it will stay on until it has completely discharged. The backup battery is not rechargeable and once it is activated, it must be replaced.

1. Before servicing the vehicle, refer to the Precautions Section.

2. Disconnect the negative battery cable.

3. Disconnect the master cylinder push rod from the clutch pedal pin.

4. Remove the clutch fluid reservoir from the clutch pedal assembly. Plug the hose.

5. Disconnect the clutch actuator pipe assembly from the clutch pedal.

6. Remove the two clutch master cylinder fasteners from the right side of the clutch pedal assembly.

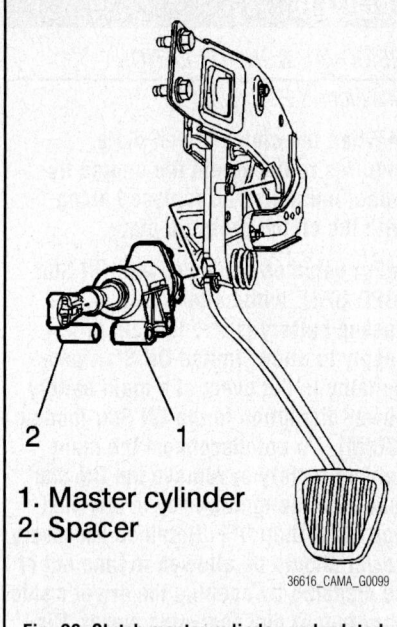

1. Master cylinder
2. Spacer

36616_CAMA_G0099

Fig. 26 Clutch master cylinder and related components

7. Remove the two clutch master cylinder fasteners from the left side of the clutch pedal assembly.

8. Remove the master cylinder and the spacer from the clutch pedal assembly.

To install:

➡ Be sure to use new fasteners, as required.

9. Position the component to its mounting.

10. Install the retaining bolts.

11. Tighten to 15 ft. lbs. (20 Nm).

12. Continue the installation in the reverse order of the removal procedure.

13. Using a pressure bleeder, bleed the clutch system.

CLUTCH SLAVE CYLINDER

REMOVAL & INSTALLATION

➡ For vehicles equipped with ON Star (RPO UE1), with battery backup, the backup battery is a redundant power supply to allow limited ON Star functionality in the event of a main battery power disruption to the ON Star module (VCIM). Do not disconnect the main vehicle battery or remove the ON Star fuse with the ignition key in any position other than OFF. Retained accessory power should be allowed to time out or be disabled by opening the driver's side door before disconnecting power. Disconnecting power to the module in any way while the ignition is ON or with the

retained accessory power activated may cause activation of the ON Star backup battery system and will discharge and permanently damage the backup battery. Once the backup battery is activated it will stay on until it has completely discharged. The backup battery is not rechargeable and once it is activated, it must be replaced.

Aisin Transmission

See Figure 27.

1. Before servicing the vehicle, refer to the Precautions Section.

2. Disconnect the negative battery cable.

3. Remove the transmission.

4. Remove the component retaining bolts. Remove the component.

5. Discard the O-ring.

To install:

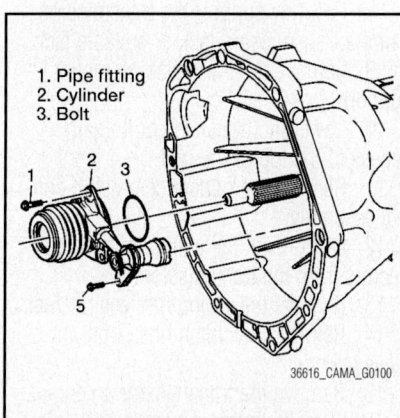

1. Pipe fitting
2. Cylinder
3. Bolt

36616_CAMA_G0100

Fig. 27 Clutch slave cylinder and related components—Aisin transmission

➡ Be sure to use new fasteners, as required.

6. Position the component to its mounting.

7. Tighten the retaining bolts to 15 ft. lbs. (20 Nm).

8. Continue the installation in the reverse order of the removal procedure.

Tremec Transmission

See Figure 28.

1. Before servicing the vehicle, refer to the Precautions Section.

2. Disconnect the negative battery cable.

3. Remove the transmission.

4. Disconnect the pipe fitting from the cylinder.

5. Remove the component retaining bolts. Remove the component.

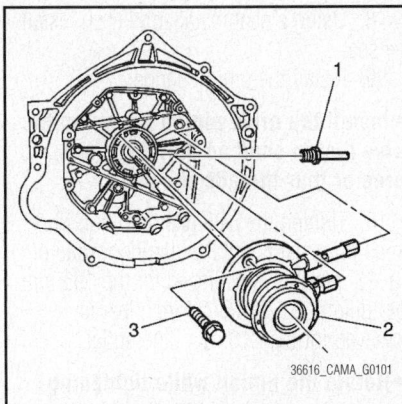

Fig. 28 Clutch slave cylinder and related components—Tremec transmission

To install:

→ Be sure to use new fasteners, as required.

6. Position the component to its mounting.

7. Tighten the retaining bolts to 115 inch. lbs. (10 Nm).

8. Continue the installation in the reverse order of the removal procedure.

REAR AXLE HOUSING

REMOVAL & INSTALLATION

1. Before servicing the vehicle, refer to the Precautions Section.

2. Raise and support the vehicle safely.

3. Remove the tire and wheel assemblies.

4. Matchmark and remove the rear driveshaft, if equipped.

5. Matchmark and remove the halfshaft assemblies, if equipped.

6. Properly support the rear differential assembly, using a suitable jack.

7. Remove the vent tube.

8. Remove the rear differential mount nut and bolt.

9. Remove the front differential nuts and bolts.

10. Remove the rear differential assembly from the vehicle.

To install:

→ Be sure to use new fasteners, as required.

11. Position the assembly to its mounting.

12. Install the retaining bolts.

13. Tighten them to 59 ft. lbs. (80 Nm).

14. Continue the installation in the reverse order of the removal procedure.

15. Be sure to fill the differential with the proper grade and type differential fluid.

REAR AXLE SHAFT, BEARING & SEAL

REMOVAL & INSTALLATION

→ At this time the manufacturer does not provide service information for this component.

REAR HALFSHAFTS

REMOVAL & INSTALLATION

See Figures 29 through 31.

1. Before servicing the vehicle, refer to the Precautions Section.

2. Raise and support the vehicle safely.

3. Remove the tire and wheel assemblies.

→ If equipped with Brembo brakes, do not place the drift or flat bladed tool against the bottom. Damage to the bottom cross over tube could result causing brake failure.

4. Insert the drift or suitable pry tool in the cooling fins of the brake rotor against the brake caliper.

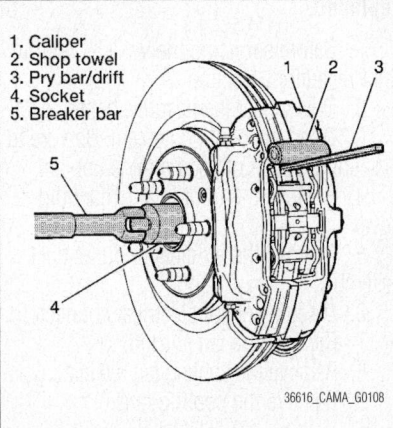

1. Caliper
2. Shop towel
3. Pry bar/drift
4. Socket
5. Breaker bar

Fig. 29 Nut removal—Brembo brakes

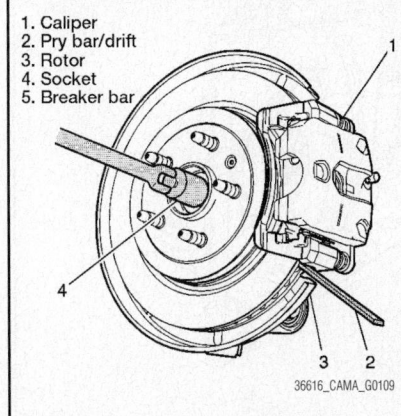

1. Caliper
2. Pry bar/drift
3. Rotor
4. Socket
5. Breaker bar

Fig. 30 Nut removal—except brakes

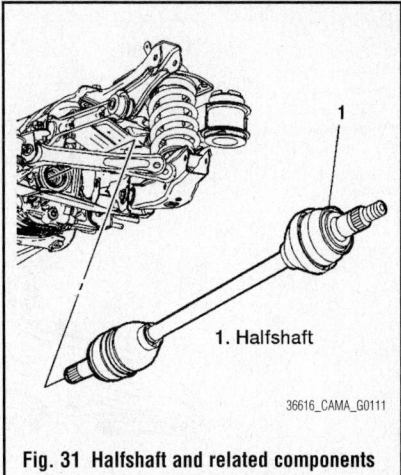

1. Halfshaft

Fig. 31 Halfshaft and related components

5. Place a clean shop towel between the drift or pry tool, if equipped with Brembo brakes.

6. Using a breaker bar and socket loosen the halfshaft nut.

7. Remove and discard the nut.

8. Use the proper tool and separate the halfshaft from the knuckle.

9. Install a protector over the halfshaft.

10. Remove the knuckle assembly.

11. Remove the halfshaft from the vehicle.

To install:

→ Be sure to use new fasteners, as required.

12. Position the halfshaft to its mounting.

13. Continue the installation in the reverse order of the removal procedure.

14. Tighten the wheel nut to 199 ft. lbs. (270 Nm).

REAR PINION SEAL

REMOVAL & INSTALLATION

See Figure 32.

1. Before servicing the vehicle, refer to the Precautions Section.

2. Raise and support the vehicle safely.

3. Matchmark and remove the rear driveshaft.

4. Remove the pinion flange retaining bolt. Discard the bolt.

5. Using a puller remove the flange from its mounting.

6. Using a seal removal tool, remove the seal from its mounting.

To install:

→ Be sure to use new fasteners, as required.

7. Position the seal on its mounting.

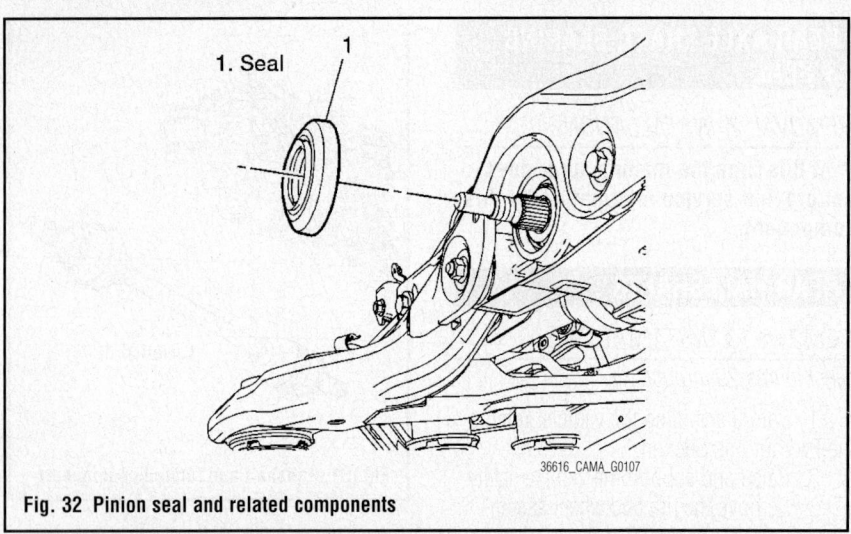

1. Seal

Fig. 32 Pinion seal and related components

36616_CAMA_G0107

8. Using a seal installation tool, install the seal.
9. Install the pinion flange.

➡**Install the drive pinion flange on the drive pinion shaft so that there are three or four threads showing.**

10. Tighten the new retaining nut, in small increments until a rotating torque of 18–23 inch lbs is achieved for the 195 mm rear differential or 18–27 inch lbs. is achieved for the 218 mm differential.

➡**Rotate the pinion while tightening the pinion nut to seat the bearings.**

11. Using a hammer, stake the two sides of the drive pinion nut to the grooves in the drive pinion gear.

ENGINE COOLING

ENGINE FAN

REMOVAL & INSTALLATION

See Figure 33.

➡For vehicles equipped with ON Star (RPO UE1), with battery backup, the backup battery is a redundant power supply to allow limited ON Star functionality in the event of a main battery power disruption to the ON Star module (VCIM). Do not disconnect the main vehicle battery or remove the ON Star fuse with the ignition key in any position other than OFF. Retained accessory power should be allowed to time out or be disabled by opening the driver's side door before disconnecting power. Disconnecting power to the module in any way while the ignition is ON or with the retained accessory power activated may cause activation of the ON Star backup battery system and will discharge and permanently damage the backup battery. Once the backup battery is activated it will stay on until it has completely discharged. The backup battery is not rechargeable and once it is activated, it must be replaced.

1. Before servicing the vehicle, refer to the Precautions Section.
2. Disconnect the negative battery cable.
3. Drain the cooling system. Be sure to properly dispose of used engine coolant.
4. Remove the front intake manifold cover.
5. Remove the air cleaner outlet duct assembly.
6. Disconnect the electrical connectors.
7. Remove the fan shroud.
8. Remove the cooling fan retaining nuts.
9. Remove the cooling fans.

To install:

➡Be sure to use new fasteners, as required.

10. Installation is the reverse of the removal procedure.
11. Tighten the retaining nuts to 53 inch lbs. (6 Nm).

RADIATOR

REMOVAL & INSTALLATION

See Figure 34.

➡For vehicles equipped with ON Star (RPO UE1), with battery backup, the backup battery is a redundant power supply to allow limited ON Star functionality in the event of a main battery power disruption to the ON Star module (VCIM). Do not disconnect the main vehicle battery or remove the ON Star fuse with the ignition key in any position other than OFF. Retained accessory power should be allowed to time out or be disabled by opening the driver's side door before disconnecting power. Disconnecting power to the module in any way while the ignition is ON or with the retained accessory power activated may cause activation of the ON Star backup battery system and will discharge and permanently damage the backup battery. Once the backup battery is activated it will stay on until it has completely discharged. The backup battery is not rechargeable and once it is activated, it must be replaced.

1. Before servicing the vehicle, refer to the Precautions Section.

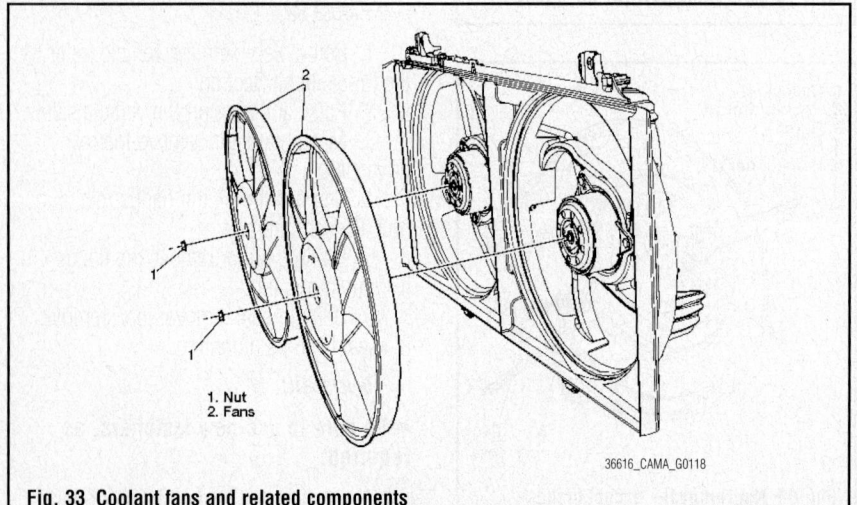

1. Nut
2. Fans

36616_CAMA_G0118

Fig. 33 Coolant fans and related components

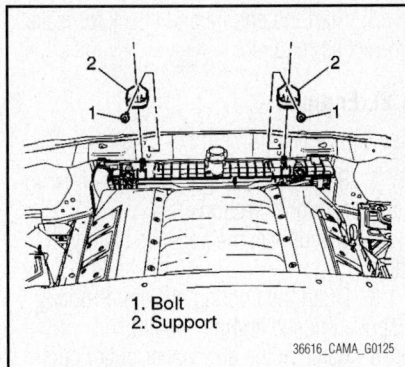

1. Bolt
2. Support

36616_CAMA_G0125

Fig. 34 Radiator support and related components

2. Disconnect the negative battery cable.

3. Drain the cooling system. Be sure to properly dispose of used engine coolant.

4. Remove the front intake manifold cover.

5. Remove the air cleaner outlet duct assembly.

6. Remove the radiator hoses.

7. Disconnect and plug the transmission cooler lines, as required.

8. Disconnect the electrical connectors.

9. Remove the fan shroud.

10. Remove the air conditioning condenser.

11. Remove the upper radiator support bolts. Remove the support.

12. Remove the radiator from the vehicle.

To install:

➡**Be sure to use new fasteners, as required.**

13. Position the radiator to its mounting.

14. Tighten the radiator support bolts to 80 inch lbs. (9 Nm).

15. Continue the installation in the reverse order of the removal procedure.

16. Be sure to properly recharge the air conditioning system.

17. Be sure to fill the cooling system with the proper grade and type engine coolant.

18. Start the engine and check for leaks, correct as required.

THERMOSTAT

REMOVAL & INSTALLATION

➡**For vehicles equipped with ON Star (RPO UE1), with battery backup, the backup battery is a redundant power supply to allow limited ON Star functionality in the event of a main battery power disruption to the ON Star module (VCIM). Do not disconnect the main vehicle battery or remove the ON Star fuse with the ignition key in any position other than OFF. Retained accessory power should be allowed to time out or be disabled by opening the driver's side door before disconnecting power. Disconnecting power to the module in any way while the ignition is ON or with the retained accessory power activated may cause activation of the ON Star backup battery system and will discharge and permanently damage the backup battery. Once the backup battery is activated it will stay on until it has completely discharged. The backup battery is not rechargeable and once it is activated, it must be replaced.**

3.6L Engines

See Figure 35.

1. Before servicing the vehicle, refer to the Precautions Section.

2. Disconnect the negative battery cable.

3. Drain the cooling system. Properly dispose of used engine coolant.

4. Remove the radiator outlet pipe.

5. Remove the front intake manifold cover.

6. Remove the rear intake manifold cover.

7. Remove the thermostat housing retaining bolts.

8. Remove the thermostat from its mounting.

9. Discard the gasket.

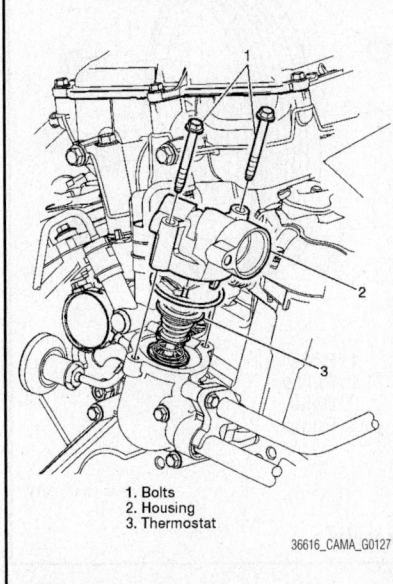

1. Bolts
2. Housing
3. Thermostat

36616_CAMA_G0127

Fig. 35 Thermostat and related components—3.6L engines

To install:

➡**Be sure to use new fasteners, as required.**

10. Using a new gasket, position the thermostat to its mounting.

11. Tighten the retaining bolts to 89 inch lbs. (10 Nm).

12. Continue the installation in the reverse order of the removal procedure.

13. Be sure to fill the cooling system with the proper grade and type engine coolant.

6.2L Engines

See Figure 36.

1. Before servicing the vehicle, refer to the Precautions Section.

2. Disconnect the negative battery cable.

3. Drain the cooling system. Properly dispose of used engine coolant.

4. Reposition the outlet hose clamp at the water pump inlet.

5. Remove the outlet hose from the water pump inlet.

6. Remove the water pump inlet bolts.

7. Remove the water pump inlet.

8. Remove and discard the O-ring.

9. Remove the thermostat from its mounting.

To install:

➡**Be sure to use new fasteners, as required.**

10. Using a new gasket, position the thermostat to its mounting.

11. Tighten the retaining bolts to 11 ft. lbs. (15 Nm).

12. Continue the installation in the reverse order of the removal procedure.

13. Be sure to fill the cooling system with the proper grade and type engine coolant.

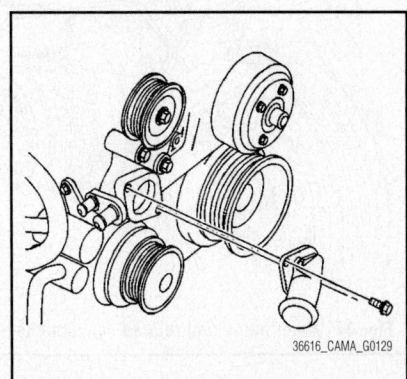

36616_CAMA_G0129

Fig. 36 Thermostat and related components—6.2L engines

WATER PUMP

REMOVAL & INSTALLATION

➡For vehicles equipped with ON Star (RPO UE1), with battery backup, the backup battery is a redundant power supply to allow limited ON Star functionality in the event of a main battery power disruption to the ON Star module (VCIM). Do not disconnect the main vehicle battery or remove the ON Star fuse with the ignition key in any position other than OFF. Retained accessory power should be allowed to time out or be disabled by opening the driver's side door before disconnecting power. Disconnecting power to the module in any way while the ignition is ON or with the retained accessory power activated may cause activation of the ON Star backup battery system and will discharge and permanently damage the backup battery. Once the backup battery is activated it will stay on until it has completely discharged. The backup battery is not rechargeable and once it is activated, it must be replaced.

3.6L Engines

See Figure 37.

1. Before servicing the vehicle, refer to the Precautions Section.
2. Disconnect the negative battery cable.
3. Drain the cooling system. Properly dispose of used engine coolant.
4. Remove the front intake manifold cover.
5. Remove the air cleaner outlet duct assembly.
6. Remove the drive belt.
7. Remove the water pump retaining bolts.
8. Remove the water pump from its mounting.
9. Discard the gasket.

To install:

➡Be sure to use new fasteners, as required.

10. Position the water pump to its mounting. Be sure to use a new gasket.
11. Tighten the retaining bolts to 89 inch lbs. (10 Nm).
12. Tighten the water pump pulley bolt to 89 inch lbs. (10 Nm).
13. Continue the installation in the reverse order of the removal procedure.
14. Be sure to fill the cooling system with the proper grade and type engine coolant.

15. Start the engine and check for leaks. Correct as required.

6.2L Engines

See Figure 38.

1. Before servicing the vehicle, refer to the Precautions Section.
2. Disconnect the negative battery cable.
3. Drain the cooling system. Properly dispose of used engine coolant.
4. Remove the air cleaner outlet duct assembly.
5. Remove the drive belt.
6. Remove the drive belt tensioner. Remove the drive belt idler pulley.
7. Remove the radiator hoses.
8. Remove the heater inlet hose.
9. Remove the water pump retaining bolts.
10. Remove the water pump from its mounting.
11. Discard the gasket.

To install:

➡Be sure to use new fasteners, as required.

12. Position the water pump to its mounting. Be sure to use a new gasket.
13. Tighten the retaining bolts to 22 ft. lbs. (30 Nm).
14. Continue the installation in the reverse order of the removal procedure.
15. Be sure to fill the cooling system with the proper grade and type engine coolant.
16. Start the engine and check for leaks. Correct as required.

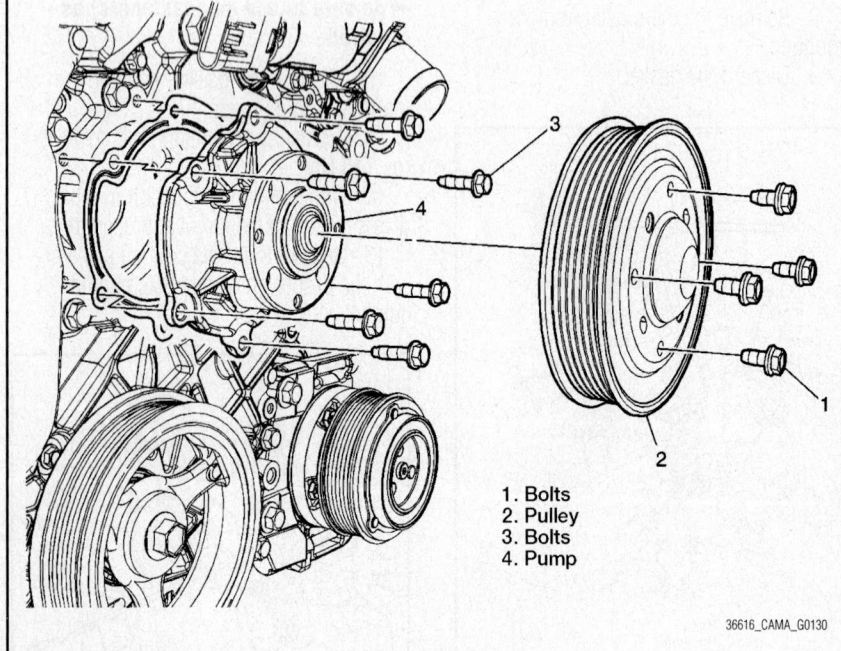

1. Bolts
2. Pulley
3. Bolts
4. Pump

36616_CAMA_G0130

Fig. 37 Water pump and related components—3.6L engines

1. Bolts
2. Pump

36616_CAMA_G0132

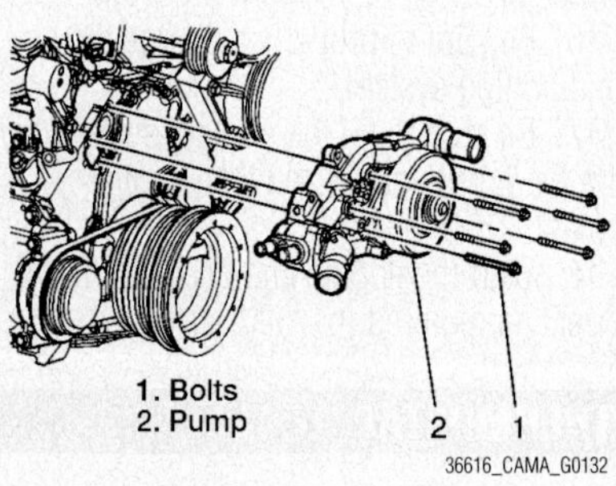

Fig. 38 Water pump and related components—6.2L engines

ALTERNATOR

REMOVAL & INSTALLATION

➡ **For vehicles equipped with ON Star (RPO UE1), with battery backup, the backup battery is a redundant power supply to allow limited ON Star functionality in the event of a main battery power disruption to the ON Star module (VCIM). Do not disconnect the main vehicle battery or remove the ON Star fuse with the ignition key in any position other than OFF. Retained accessory power should be allowed to time out or be disabled by opening the driver's side door before disconnecting power. Disconnecting power to the module in any way while the ignition is ON or with the retained accessory power activated may cause activation of the ON Star backup battery system and will discharge and permanently damage the backup battery. Once the backup battery is activated it will stay on until it has completely discharged. The backup battery is not rechargeable and once it is activated, it must be replaced.**

3.6L Engines

See Figure 39.

1. Before servicing the vehicle, refer to the Precautions Section.
2. Disconnect the negative battery cable.
3. Remove the front intake manifold cover.
4. Remove the radiator outlet pipe.
5. Remove the drive belt.
6. Disconnect the alternator electrical connectors.
7. Remove the alternator retaining bolts.
8. Remove the alternator from its mounting.

To install:

➡ **Be sure to use new fasteners, as required.**

9. Position the alternator to its mounting.
10. Tighten the retaining bolts to 43 ft. lbs. (58 Nm).
11. Tighten the nut to 11 ft. lbs. (15 Nm).
12. Continue the installation in the reverse order of the removal procedure.

6.2L Engines

See Figure 40.

1. Before servicing the vehicle, refer to the Precautions Section.
2. Disconnect the negative battery cable.
3. Remove the air cleaner assembly.
4. Remove the drive belt.
5. Remove the alternator positive cable.
6. Disconnect the alternator electrical connectors.
7. Remove the alternator retaining bolts.
8. Remove the alternator from its mounting.

To install:

➡ **Be sure to use new fasteners, as required.**

9. Position the alternator to its mounting.
10. Tighten the retaining bolts to 43 ft. lbs. (58 Nm).
11. Tighten the nut to 11 ft. lbs. (15 Nm).
12. Continue the installation in the reverse order of the removal procedure.

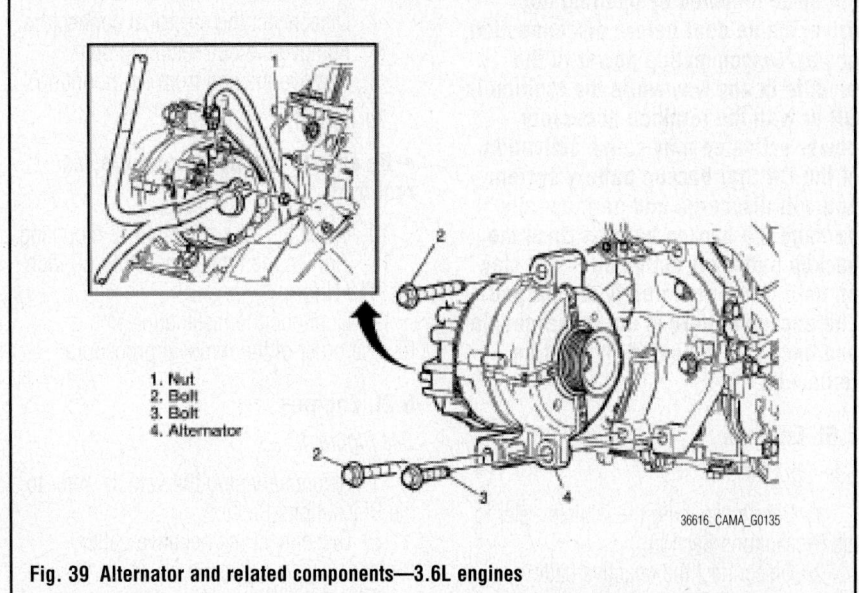

1. Nut
2. Bolt
3. Bolt
4. Alternator

36616_CAMA_G0135

Fig. 39 Alternator and related components—3.6L engines

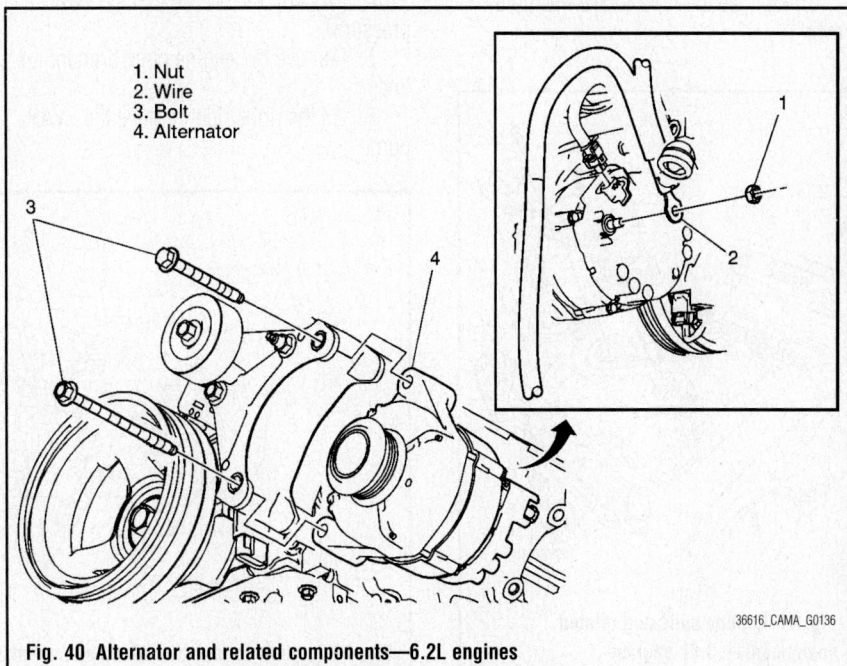

1. Nut
2. Wire
3. Bolt
4. Alternator

36616_CAMA_G0136

Fig. 40 Alternator and related components—6.2L engines

IGNITION COIL

REMOVAL & INSTALLATION

➡For vehicles equipped with ON Star (RPO UE1), with battery backup, the backup battery is a redundant power supply to allow limited ON Star functionality in the event of a main battery power disruption to the ON Star module (VCIM). Do not disconnect the main vehicle battery or remove the ON Star fuse with the ignition key in any position other than OFF. Retained accessory power should be allowed to time out or be disabled by opening the driver's side door before disconnecting power. Disconnecting power to the module in any way while the ignition is ON or with the retained accessory power activated may cause activation of the ON Star backup battery system and will discharge and permanently damage the backup battery. Once the backup battery is activated it will stay on until it has completely discharged. The backup battery is not rechargeable and once it is activated, it must be replaced.

3.6L Engines

See Figure 41.

1. Before servicing the vehicle, refer to the Precautions Section.
2. Disconnect the negative battery cable.
3. Remove the front intake manifold cover.

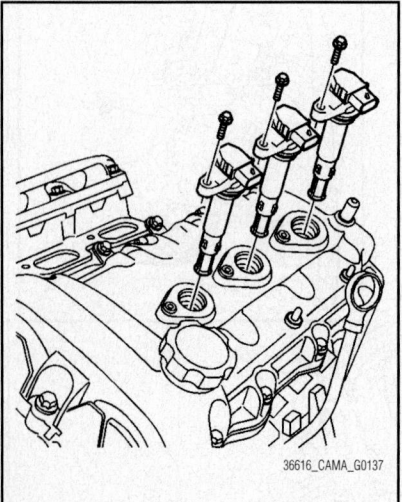

Fig. 41 Ignition coils and related components—3.6L engines

➡Do not disconnect the fuel pipes or hoses.

4. Remove the necessary components to gain access to the ignition coil.

➡Do not separate the upper intake manifold from the lower intake manifold.

5. Remove the intake manifold bolts.
6. Remove the intake manifold brace bolts.

➡Remove and reposition the upper intake manifold with the lower intake manifold in order to gain clearance for ignition coil removal.

7. Disconnect the electrical connectors.
8. Remove the coil retaining bolts.
9. Remove the coil from its mounting.

To install:

➡Be sure to use new fasteners, as required.

10. Install the ignition coil to its mounting.
11. Tighten the retaining bolt to 89 inch lbs. (10 Nm).
12. Continue the installation in the reverse order of the removal procedure.

6.2L Engines

See Figure 42.

1. Before servicing the vehicle, refer to the Precautions Section.
2. Disconnect the negative battery cable.
3. Remove the engine cover.
4. Properly relieve the fuel system pressure.
5. Remove the engine compartment fuel line.
6. On the right side, remove the EVAP purge pipe.

7. Reposition the engine wiring harness, as necessary.
8. Disconnect the spark plug wires.
9. Disconnect the main coil harness from the coil assembly.
10. Remove the coil assembly to rocker cover retaining bolts.
11. Remove the assembly from the engine.
12. Disconnect the coil to coil wiring harness connectors.
13. Remove the coil retaining bolts.
14. Remove the coils from their mounting.

To install:

➡Be sure to use new fasteners, as required.

15. Install the ignition coil to its mounting.
16. Tighten the retaining bolt to 106 inch lbs. (12 Nm).
17. Continue the installation in the reverse order of the removal procedure.

IGNITION TIMING

ADJUSTMENT

The ignition timing is not adjustable, and is set according to engine demand electronically. The Powertrain Control Module (PCM) controls the ignition timing for all driving conditions.

SPARK PLUGS

REMOVAL & INSTALLATION

➡For vehicles equipped with ON Star (RPO UE1), with battery backup, the backup battery is a redundant power

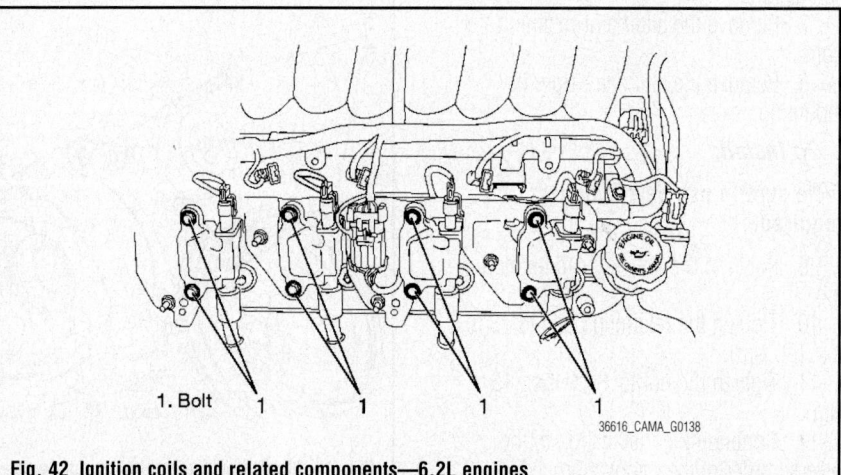

1. Bolt

Fig. 42 Ignition coils and related components—6.2L engines

supply to allow limited ON Star functionality in the event of a main battery power disruption to the ON Star module (VCIM). Do not disconnect the main vehicle battery or remove the ON Star fuse with the ignition key in any position other than OFF. Retained accessory power should be allowed to time out or be disabled by opening the driver's side door before disconnecting power. Disconnecting power to the module in any way while the ignition is ON or with the retained accessory power activated may cause activation of the ON Star backup battery system and will discharge and permanently damage the backup battery. Once the backup battery is activated it will stay on until it has

completely discharged. The backup battery is not rechargeable and once it is activated, it must be replaced.

3.6L Engines

1. Before servicing the vehicle, refer to the Precautions Section.
2. Disconnect the negative battery cable.
3. Remove the front intake manifold cover.
4. Remove the ignition coil.
5. Remove the spark plug from its mounting, using the proper removal tool.

To install:

➡Be sure to use new fasteners, as required.

6. Installation is the reverse of the removal procedure.

6.2L Engines

1. Before servicing the vehicle, refer to the Precautions Section.
2. Disconnect the negative battery cable.
3. Remove the intake manifold cover.
4. Remove the spark plug wires.
5. Remove the spark plug from its mounting, using the proper removal tool.

To install:

➡Be sure to use new fasteners, as required.

6. Installation is the reverse of the removal procedure.

ENGINE ELECTRICAL

STARTING SYSTEM

STARTER

REMOVAL & INSTALLATION

See Figures 43 and 44.

➡For vehicles equipped with ON Star (RPO UE1), with battery backup, the backup battery is a redundant power supply to allow limited ON Star functionality in the event of a main battery

power disruption to the ON Star module (VCIM). Do not disconnect the main vehicle battery or remove the ON Star fuse with the ignition key in any position other than OFF. Retained accessory power should be allowed to time out or be disabled by opening the driver's side door before disconnecting power. Disconnecting power to the module in any way while the ignition is

ON or with the retained accessory power activated may cause activation of the ON Star backup battery system and will discharge and permanently damage the backup battery. Once the backup battery is activated it will stay on until it has completely discharged. The backup battery is not rechargeable and once it is activated, it must be replaced.

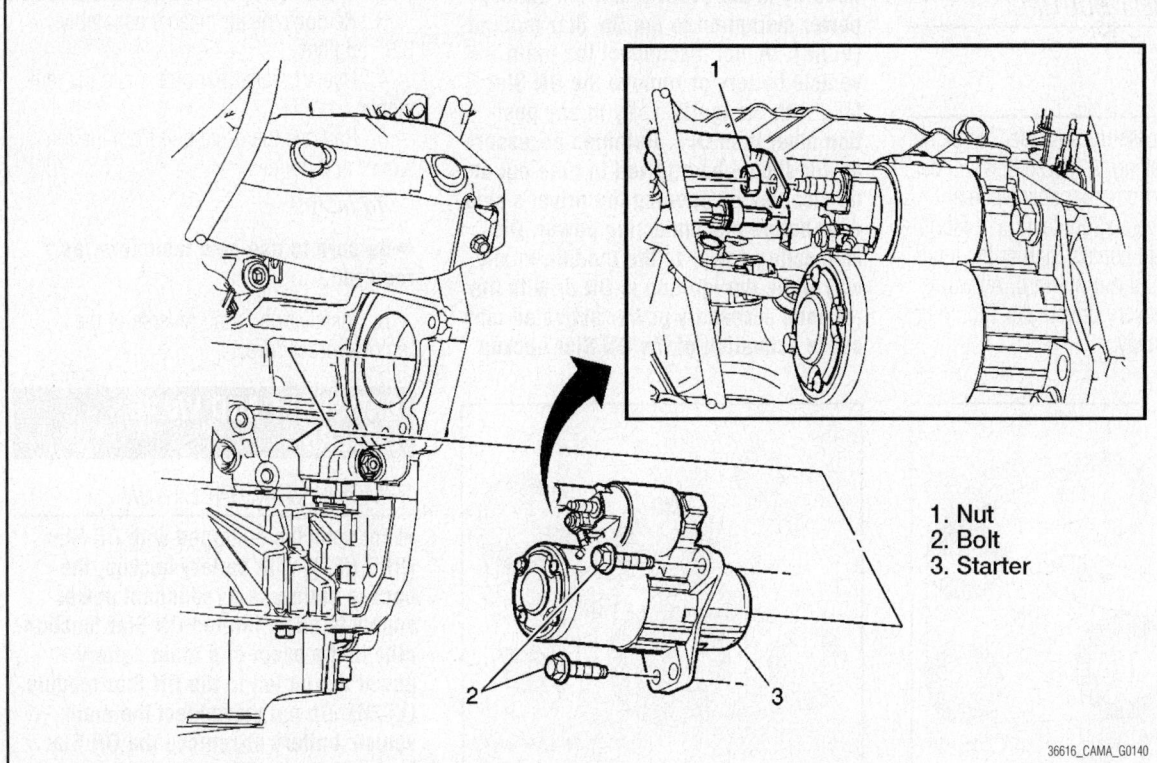

1. Nut
2. Bolt
3. Starter

36616_CAMA_G0140

Fig. 43 Starter and related components—3.6L engines

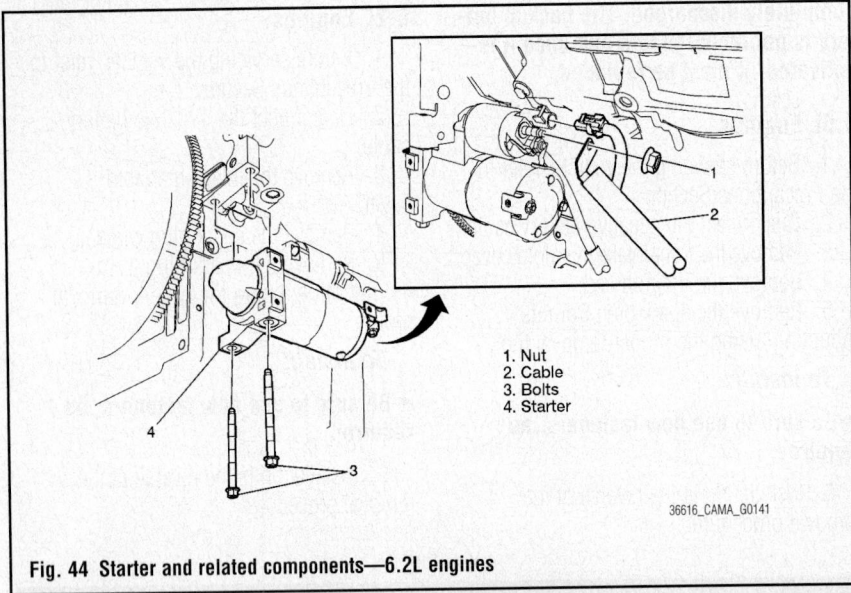

1. Nut
2. Cable
3. Bolts
4. Starter

36616_CAMA_G0141

Fig. 44 Starter and related components—6.2L engines

1. Before servicing the vehicle, refer to the Precautions Section.
2. Disconnect the negative battery cable.
3. Raise and safely support the vehicle.
4. Remove the starter heat shield.
5. Disconnect the electrical connectors.
6. Remove the starter retaining bolts.
7. Remove the starter from its mounting.

To install:

→ Be sure to use new fasteners, as required.

8. Position the starter to its mounting.
9. Tighten the retaining bolts to 43 ft. lbs. (58 Nm).
10. Continue the installation in the reverse order of the removal procedure.

ENGINE MECHANICAL

→ Disconnecting the negative battery cable may interfere with the functions of the on board computer systems and may require the computer to undergo a relearning process, once the negative battery cable is reconnected.

ACCESSORY DRIVE BELTS

ACCESSORY BELT ROUTING

See Figures 45 and 46.

INSPECTION

Inspect the accessory drive belt for signs of glazing or cracking. A glazed belt will be perfectly smooth from slippage, while a good belt will have a slight texture of fabric visible. Cracks will usually start at the inner edge of the belt and run outward. All worn or damaged accessory drive belts should be replaced immediately.

ADJUSTMENT

The accessory drive belt adjustment is maintained by an automatic tensioner.

REMOVAL & INSTALLATION

→ For vehicles equipped with ON Star (RPO UE1), with battery backup, the backup battery is a redundant power supply to allow limited ON Star functionality in the event of a main battery power disruption to the ON Star module (VCIM). Do not disconnect the main vehicle battery or remove the ON Star fuse with the ignition key in any position other than OFF. Retained accessory power should be allowed to time out or be disabled by opening the driver's side door before disconnecting power. Disconnecting power to the module in any way while the ignition is ON or with the retained accessory power activated may cause activation of the ON Star backup

battery system and will discharge and permanently damage the backup battery. Once the backup battery is activated it will stay on until it has completely discharged. The backup battery is not rechargeable and once it is activated, it must be replaced.

1. Before servicing the vehicle, refer to the Precautions Section.
2. Disconnect the negative battery cable.
3. Remove the air cleaner assembly, 3.6L engines.
4. Use a breaker bar and rotate the tensioner.
5. Remove the drive belt from the tensioner and pulleys.

To install:

→ Be sure to use new fasteners, as required.

6. Installation is the reverse of the removal procedure.

CAMSHAFT AND VALVE LIFTERS

REMOVAL & INSTALLATION

→ For vehicles equipped with ON Star (RPO UE1), with battery backup, the backup battery is a redundant power supply to allow limited ON Star functionality in the event of a main battery power disruption to the ON Star module (VCIM). Do not disconnect the main vehicle battery or remove the ON Star fuse with the ignition key in any position other than OFF. Retained accessory power should be allowed to time out or

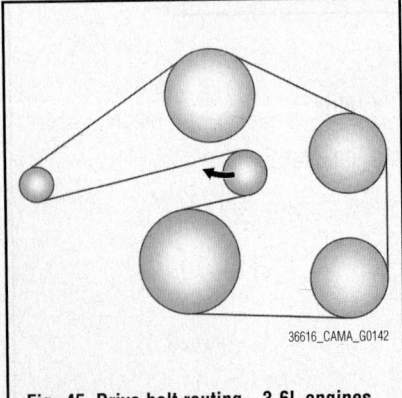

36616_CAMA_G0142

Fig. 45 Drive belt routing—3.6L engines

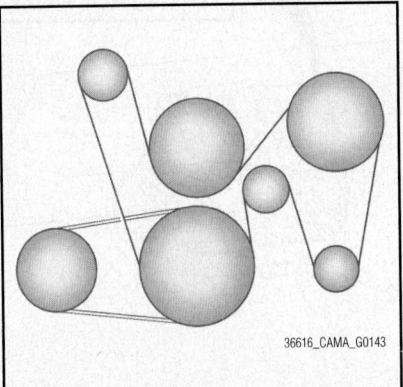

36616_CAMA_G0143

Fig. 46 Drive belt routing—6.2L engines

be disabled by opening the driver's side door before disconnecting power. Disconnecting power to the module in any way while the ignition is ON or with the retained accessory power activated may cause activation of the ON Star backup battery system and will discharge and permanently damage the backup battery. Once the backup battery is activated it will stay on until it has completely discharged. The backup battery is not rechargeable and once it is activated, it must be replaced.

3.6L Engines

Left Side

See Figures 47 through 52.

1. Before servicing the vehicle, refer to the Precautions Section.

2. Disconnect the negative battery cable.
3. Remove the intake manifold.
4. Remove the camshaft cover.
5. Remove the camshaft sensors.
6. Remove the camshaft position actuator solenoid.
7. Remove the crankshaft balancer.
8. Rotate the camshaft, using tool EN46111 until the camshafts are in a low tension position. The camshafts will be parallel with the camshaft cover rail.

➡A wrench must be used on the hex of the camshaft when loosening or tightening in order to prevent component damage.

➡Use an open wrench at the camshaft hex to prevent camshaft/engine rotation. Do not remove the camshaft position actuator bolt at this time.

9. Loosen the camshaft actuator bolt.

➡Be sure that the tips of the tool are fully engaged into the timing chain (see illustration 3 and 4). Install the tool (see illustration 1 and two) in order to retain the timing chain in place. Firmly tighten the tool.

10. Ensure that the components are marked for proper assembly (see illustration).
11. Mark the timing chain and the respective locations on the camshaft position actuators, numbers 1 thru 4.
12. Remove the camshaft position actuator bolt.
13. Remove the camshaft bearing cap bolts. Remove the bearing caps.

➡Observe the markings on the bearing caps. Each cap is marked to identify location.

Fig. 47 Camshaft positioning—3.6L engines

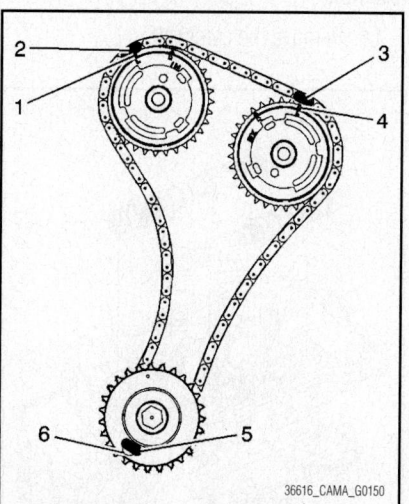

Fig. 49 Marking the timing chain (left side) numbers 1 thru 4—3.6L engines

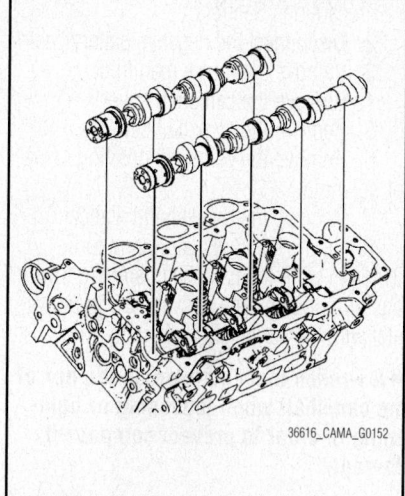

Fig. 51 Camshafts and related components (left side)—3.6L engines

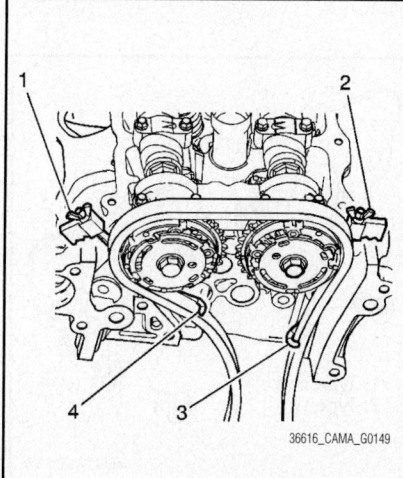

Fig. 48 Tool installation and number locating points—3.6L engines

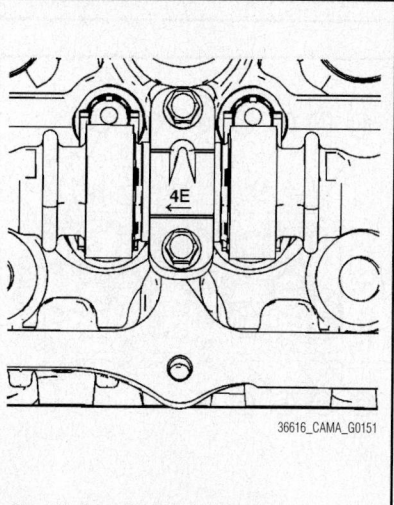

Fig. 50 Camshaft bearing cap identification—3.6L engines

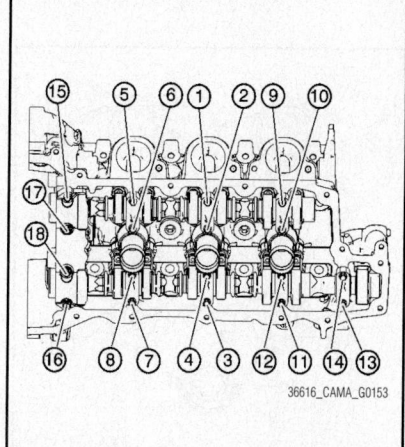

Fig. 52 Camshaft bearing cap tightening sequence (left side)—3.6L engines

14. Remove the camshafts.

To install:

➡**Be sure to use new fasteners, as required.**

15. Position the camshafts in their mountings.

16. Install the bearing caps.

17. Tighten to specification and in the sequence shown in the illustration. Specification is 89 inch lbs. (10 Nm). Loosen cap bolts 1 and 2 and 3 and 4. Retighten to 89 inch lbs. (10 Nm).

18. Install the chain, using the reference marks made during the removal procedure.

19. Continue the installation in the reverse order of the removal procedure.

Right Side

See Figures 53 through 55.

1. Before servicing the vehicle, refer to the Precautions Section.

2. Disconnect the negative battery cable.

3. Remove the intake manifold.

4. Remove the camshaft cover.

5. Remove the camshaft sensors.

6. Remove the camshaft position actuator solenoid.

7. Remove the crankshaft balancer.

8. Rotate the camshaft, using tool EN46111 until the camshafts are in a low tension position. The camshafts will be parallel with the camshaft cover rail.

➡**A wrench must be used on the hex of the camshaft when loosening or tightening in order to prevent component damage.**

➡**Use an open wrench at the camshaft hex to prevent camshaft/engine rotation. Do not remove the camshaft position actuator bolt at this time.**

9. Loosen the camshaft actuator bolt.

➡**Be sure that the tips of the tool are fully engaged into the timing chain (see illustration 3 and 4). Install the tool (see illustration 1 and two) in order to retain the timing chain in place. Firmly tighten the tool.**

10. Ensure that the components are marked for proper assembly (see illustration).

11. Mark the timing chain and the respective locations on the camshaft position actuators, numbers 15 thru 18.

12. Remove the camshaft position actuator bolt.

13. Remove the camshaft bearing cap bolts. Remove the bearing caps.

➡**Observe the markings on the bearing caps. Each cap is marked to identify location.**

14. Remove the camshafts.

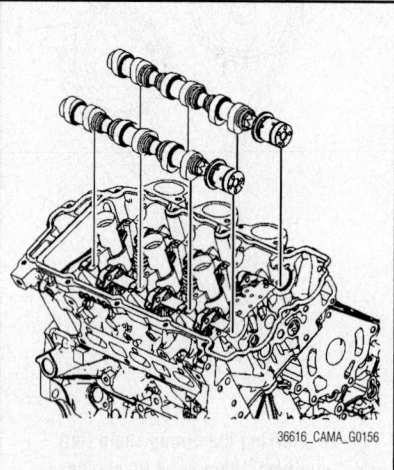

36616_CAMA_G0156

Fig. 54 Camshafts and related components (right side)—3.6L engines

To install:

➡**Be sure to use new fasteners, as required.**

15. Position the camshafts in their mountings.

16. Install the bearing caps.

17. Tighten to specification and in the sequence shown in the illustration. Specification is 89 inch lbs. (10 Nm). Loosen cap bolts 1 and 2 and 3 and 4. Retighten to 89 inch lbs. (10 Nm).

18. Install the chain, using the reference marks made during the removal procedure.

19. Continue the installation in the reverse order of the removal procedure.

6.2L Engines

See Figures 56 and 57.

➡**If camshaft replacement is necessary the valve lifters must also be replaced.**

1. Before servicing the vehicle, refer to the Precautions Section.

2. Disconnect the negative battery cable.

3. Position the engine at TDC on the compression stroke.

4. Drain the cooling system. Properly dispose of used coolant.

5. Properly discharge the air conditioning system, as required.

6. Remove the radiator, as required.

7. Remove the air conditioning condenser, as required.

8. Remove the radiator support.

9. Remove the intake manifold.

10. Remove the valve covers.

11. Remove the camshaft position actuator, as required.

12. Remove the exhaust manifold.

13. Remove the rocker arms, pushrods and lifters.

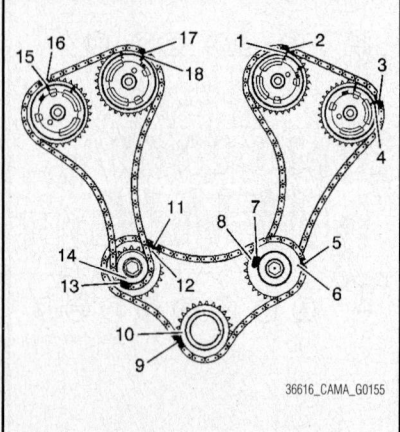

36616_CAMA_G0155

Fig. 53 Marking the timing chain (right side) numbers 15 thru 18—3.6L engines

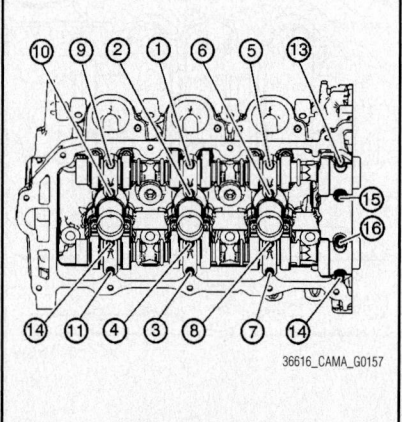

36616_CAMA_G0157

Fig. 55 Camshaft bearing cap tightening sequence (right side)—3.6L engines

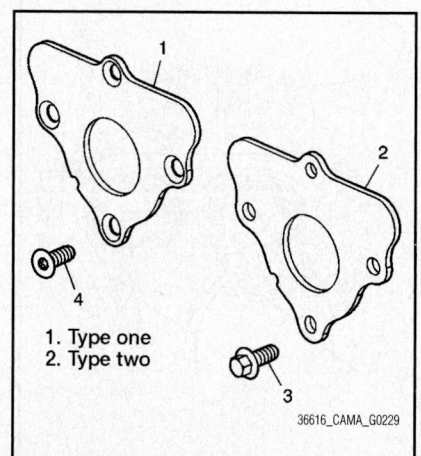

1. Type one
2. Type two

36616_CAMA_G0229

Fig. 56 Camshaft retainer plate identification—6.2L engines

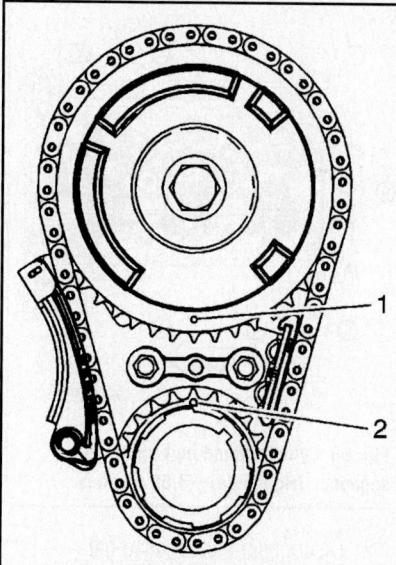

1. 6 o'clock position
2. 12 o'clock position

36616_CAMA_G0230

Fig. 57 Camshaft and crankshaft gear alignment—6.2L engines

14. Remove the engine front cover.
15. Remove the starter.
16. Remove the camshaft sprocket bolt.
17. Remove the camshaft sprocket and the timing chain.
18. Remove the camshaft retainer bolts and the retainer.
19. Install the camshaft sprocket bolt into the camshaft front hole bolt.
20. Using the bolt as a handle, carefully remove the camshaft.
21. Carefully remove the camshaft from the engine.

To install:

➥**Be sure to use new fasteners, as required.**

22. Lubricate the camshaft journals and bearings with clean engine oil.
23. Install the camshaft sprocket bolt into the camshaft front hole bolt.
24. Using the bolt as a handle, carefully install the camshaft.
25. Install the camshaft retainer and bolts. Be sure to use a new gasket.

➥**Install the retainer with the sealing gasket facing the engine block.**

26. Tighten the retainer bolts to specification. Type one (hex head bolt) 18 ft. lbs. (25 Nm). Type two (Torx® head bolt) 11 ft. lbs. (15 Nm).
27. Compress the timing chain tensioner guide. Install tool EN-46330.

28. Align the camshaft sprocket so the timing mark is in the six o'clock position.
29. Install the camshaft sprocket, timing chain and bolt.
30. Inspect for proper alignment.
31. Remove tool EN-46330.
32. Tighten the camshaft sprocket bolt to specification. Specification is pass one 66 ft. lbs. (90 Nm). Pass two plus 40 degrees.
33. Continue the installation in the reverse order of the removal procedure.

CATALYTIC CONVERTER

REMOVAL & INSTALLATION

➥**For vehicles equipped with ON Star (RPO UE1), with battery backup, the backup battery is a redundant power supply to allow limited ON Star functionality in the event of a main battery power disruption to the ON Star module (VCIM). Do not disconnect the main vehicle battery or remove the ON Star fuse with the ignition key in any position other than OFF. Retained accessory power should be allowed to time out or be disabled by opening the driver's side door before disconnecting power. Disconnecting power to the module in any way while the ignition is ON or with the retained accessory power activated may cause activation of the ON Star backup battery system and will discharge and permanently damage the backup battery. Once the backup battery is activated it will stay on until it has completely discharged. The backup battery is not rechargeable and once it is activated, it must be replaced.**

1. Before servicing the vehicle, refer to the Precautions Section.
2. Disconnect the negative battery cable.
3. Raise and support the vehicle safely.
4. Remove the converter heat shield.
5. Disconnect the required electrical connectors.
6. On the right side remove the oxygen sensors, as necessary.
7. Remove the retaining nuts.
8. Remove the clamp.
9. Remove the converter from its mounting.
10. Discard the gasket.

To install:

➥**Be sure to use new fasteners, as required.**

11. Position the converter to its mounting.
12. Be sure to use a new gasket.

13. Tighten the retaining nuts to 35 ft. lbs. (48 Nm).
14. Continue the installation in the reverse order of the removal procedure.

CRANKSHAFT FRONT SEAL

REMOVAL & INSTALLATION

3.6L Engines

1. Before servicing the vehicle, refer to the Precautions Section.
2. Disconnect the negative battery cable.
3. Remove the drive belts.
4. Remove the crankshaft balancer.
5. Use a flat bladed tool and remove the seal from its mounting. Discard the seal.

To install:

➥**Be sure to use new fasteners, as required.**

6. Position the new seal to its mounting.

➥**Do not lubricate the front oil seal or the balancer sealing surfaces.**

7. Using a seal installation tool, install the seal.
8. Continue the installation in the reverse order of the removal procedure.

6.2L Engines

See Figure 58.

1. Before servicing the vehicle, refer to the Precautions Section.
2. Disconnect the negative battery cable.
3. Remove the crankshaft balancer.
4. Carefully remove the oil seal from the front cover.

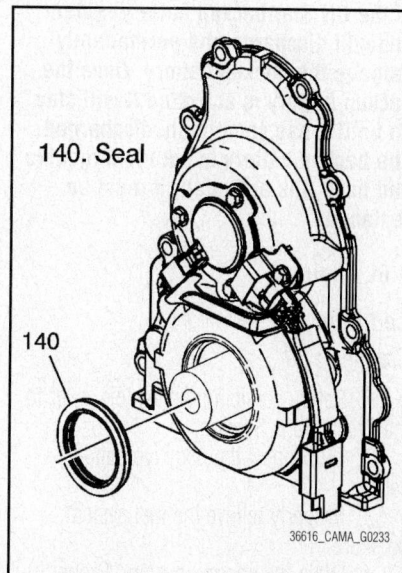

140. Seal

140

36616_CAMA_G0233

Fig. 58 Front cover oil seal and related components—6.2L engines

To install:

➡ **Be sure to use new fasteners, as required.**

➡ **Do not lubricate the oil seal sealing surface. Do not reuse the old seal.**

5. Lubricate the outer edge of the new seal with clean engine oil, prior to installation.

6. Lubricate the front cover oil seal bore with clean engine oil.

7. Using a seal installation tool, install the new seal.

8. Be sure that the seal is installed evenly and completely into the front cover bore.

9. Continue the installation in the reverse order of the removal procedure.

CYLINDER HEAD

REMOVAL & INSTALLATION

➡ **For vehicles equipped with ON Star (RPO UE1), with battery backup, the backup battery is a redundant power supply to allow limited ON Star functionality in the event of a main battery power disruption to the ON Star module (VCIM). Do not disconnect the main vehicle battery or remove the ON Star fuse with the ignition key in any position other than OFF. Retained accessory power should be allowed to time out or be disabled by opening the driver's side door before disconnecting power. Disconnecting power to the module in any way while the ignition is ON or with the retained accessory power activated may cause activation of the ON Star backup battery system and will discharge and permanently damage the backup battery. Once the backup battery is activated it will stay on until it has completely discharged. The backup battery is not rechargeable and once it is activated, it must be replaced.**

3.6L Engines

Left Side

See Figure 59.

1. Before servicing the vehicle, refer to the Precautions Section.

2. Disconnect the negative battery cable.

3. Properly relieve the fuel system pressure.

4. Drain the cooling system. Properly dispose of used engine coolant.

5. Remove the oil level indicator tube.

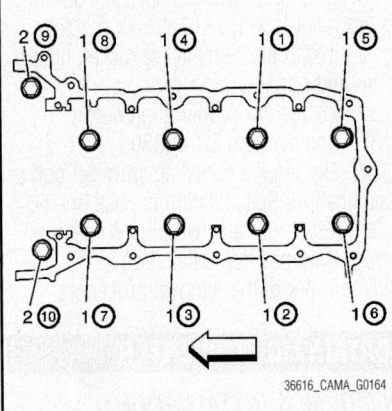

Fig. 59 Cylinder head bolt tightening sequence (left side)—3.6L engines

36616_CAMA_G0164

6. Remove the fuel pump.

7. Disconnect the coolant sensor electrical connector, after removing the heat shield.

8. Remove the wiring harness from the cylinder head. Disconnect the electrical connectors.

9. Remove the power steering pump bolts. Do not disconnect the pipes or hoses from the pump.

10. Remove the surge tank bracket from the rear of the cylinder head.

11. Remove the catalytic converter.

12. Remove the oil level indicator. Do not remove the oil filter adapter.

13. Remove the oil filter adapter upper bolt.

14. Remove the cylinder head retaining bolts. Discard the bolts.

15. Remove the cylinder head from the engine.

16. Discard the gasket.

➡ **The cylinder head is removed along with the exhaust manifold.**

17. Remove the exhaust manifold from the cylinder head, as required.

To install:

➡ **Be sure to use new fasteners, as required.**

18. Position the cylinder head to its mounting. Do not allow oil on the bolt head bosses.

19. Tighten the new retaining bolts to specification and in proper sequence.

20. Continue the installation in the reverse order of the removal procedure.

Right Side

See Figure 60.

1. Before servicing the vehicle, refer to the Precautions Section.

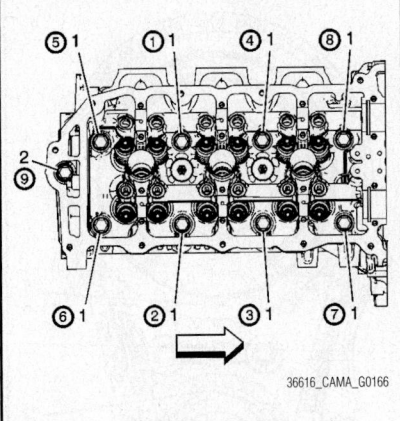

Fig. 60 Cylinder head bolt tightening sequence (right side)—3.6L engines

36616_CAMA_G0166

2. Disconnect the negative battery cable. Remove the negative battery cable.

3. Drain the cooling system. Properly dispose of used engine coolant.

4. Remove the coolant inlet pipe bolts.

5. Remove the catalytic converter.

6. Remove the wiring harness from the cylinder head. Disconnect the electrical connectors.

7. Remove the cylinder head retaining bolts. Discard the bolts.

8. Remove the cylinder head from the engine.

9. Discard the gasket.

➡ **The cylinder head is removed along with the exhaust manifold.**

10. Remove the exhaust manifold from the cylinder head, as required.

To install:

➡ **Be sure to use new fasteners, as required.**

11. Position the cylinder head to its mounting. Do not allow oil on the bolt head bosses.

12. Tighten the new retaining bolts to specification and in proper sequence.

13. Continue the installation in the reverse order of the removal procedure.

6.2L Engines

See Figures 61 through 64.

➡ **At this time the manufacturer does not provide service information for removal and installation of this component with the engine installed in the vehicle. To service the cylinder head gasket, remove the engine and position it in a suitable holding fixture.**

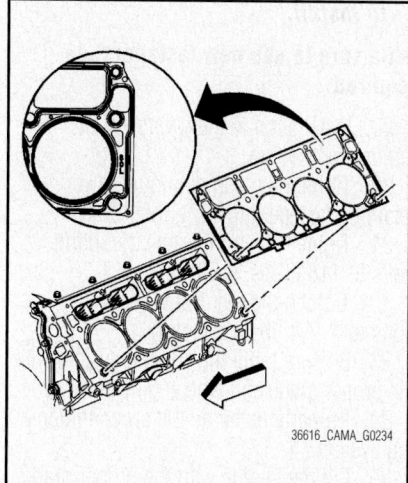

Fig. 61 Cylinder head gasket positioning (left)—6.2L engines

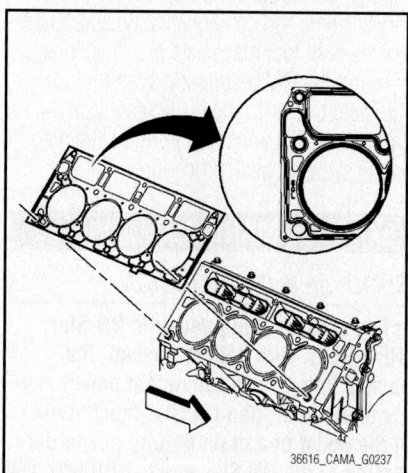

Fig. 62 Cylinder head gasket positioning (right)—6.2L engines

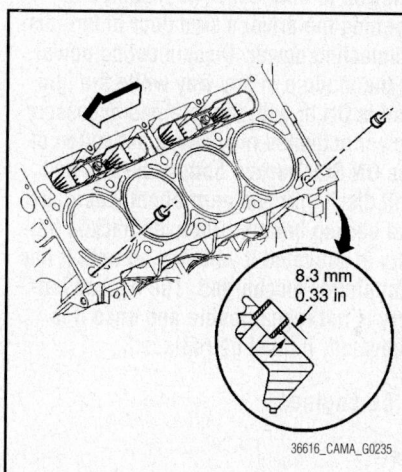

8.3 mm
0.33 in

Fig. 63 Cylinder head locating pin installation—6.2L engines

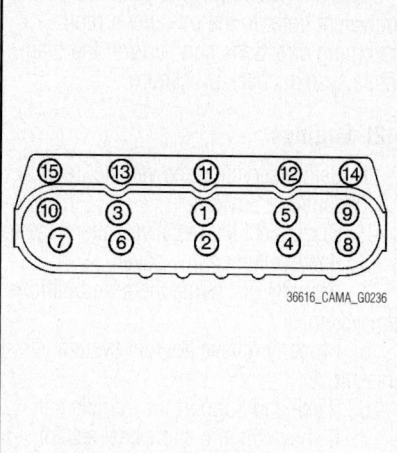

Fig. 64 Cylinder head bolt tightening sequence—6.2L engines

1. Before servicing the vehicle, refer to the Precautions Section.
2. Disconnect the negative battery cable.
3. Remove the engine and position it in a suitable holding fixture.

➡ The head bolts are of a torque to yield design and are not reusable. The bolts must be replaced.

4. Remove the valve covers.
5. Remove the intake manifold.
6. Remove the rocker arms and pushrods. Be sure to keep them in the proper order for reassembly.
7. Remove the cylinder head bolts. Discard the bolts.
8. Remove the cylinder head from its mounting.
9. Remove the cylinder head gasket. Discard the gasket.

To install:

➡ Be sure to use new fasteners, as required.

➡ Cylinder head gaskets must be installed in the proper direction and position.

10. Install the cylinder head locating pins.
11. Install the cylinder head gasket onto the locating pins.
12. Install the cylinder head onto its mounting.
13. Install the new cylinder head retaining bolts.
14. Tighten the bolts to specification and in the proper sequence.
15. Continue the installation in the reverse order of the removal procedure.

ENGINE ASSEMBLY

REMOVAL & INSTALLATION

➡ For vehicles equipped with ON Star (RPO UE1), with battery backup, the backup battery is a redundant power supply to allow limited ON Star functionality in the event of a main battery power disruption to the ON Star module (VCIM). Do not disconnect the main vehicle battery or remove the ON Star fuse with the ignition key in any position other than OFF. Retained accessory power should be allowed to time out or be disabled by opening the driver's side door before disconnecting power. Disconnecting power to the module in any way while the ignition is ON or with the retained accessory power activated may cause activation of the ON Star backup battery system and will discharge and permanently damage the backup battery. Once the backup battery is activated it will stay on until it has completely discharged. The backup battery is not rechargeable and once it is activated, it must be replaced.

3.6L Engines

See Figures 65 and 66.

1. Before servicing the vehicle, refer to the Precautions Section.
2. Disconnect the negative battery cable.
3. Remove the rear intake manifold cover.
4. Properly discharge the air conditioning system.
5. Properly relieve the fuel system pressure.

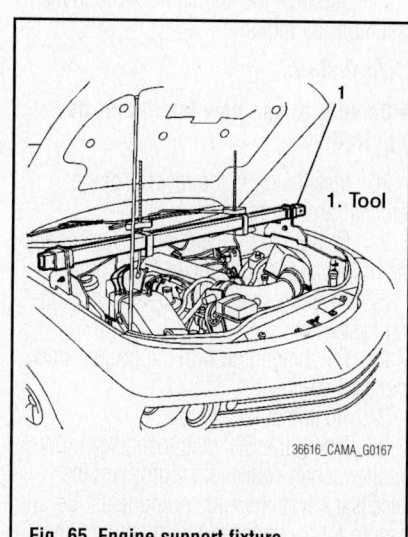

1. Tool

Fig. 65 Engine support fixture installation—3.6L engines

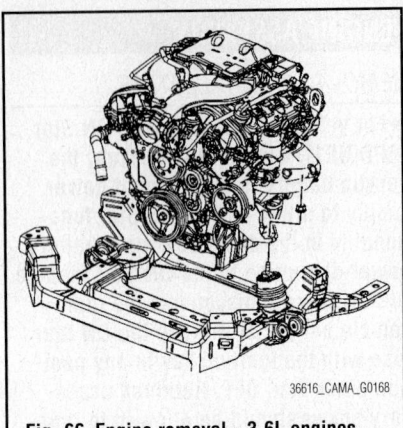

36616_CAMA_G0168

Fig. 66 Engine removal—3.6L engines

6. Drain the cooling system. Properly dispose of used coolant.

7. Drain the engine oil. Properly dispose of used engine oil.

8. Raise and support the vehicle safely.

9. Remove the front tire and wheel assemblies.

10. Remove the transmission.

11. Lower the vehicle.

12. Remove the air cleaner outlet duct.

13. Disconnect the heater core hose.

14. Remove the radiator hoses.

15. Disconnect all required electrical connectors and harness connectors.

16. Install the engine support fixture.

17. Raise and support the vehicle safely.

➡The engine is removed along with the sub-frame assembly. In order to accomplish this you will have to removal all components connected to the sub-frame unit

18. Lower the frame with the engine still attached.

19. Separate the engine from the frame assembly, as required.

To install:

➡Be sure to use new fasteners, as required.

20. Installation is the reverse of the removal procedure.

21. Be sure to fill the cooling system with the proper grade and type engine coolant.

22. Properly recharge the air conditioning system.

23. Fill the engine with the proper grade and type engine oil.

24. Road test the vehicle.

25. Using the GM diagnostic scan tool or aftermarket equivalent reprogram the necessary systems and components. Be sure to follow the scan tool manufacturer's directions.

Using the GM diagnostic scan tool, or equivalent, refer to the on-screen reprogramming directions and perform the diagnostic system check procedure.

6.2L Engines

1. Before servicing the vehicle, refer to the Precautions Section.

2. Disconnect the negative battery cable.

3. Remove the engine cover.

4. Properly discharge the air conditioning system.

5. Properly relieve the fuel system pressure.

6. Raise and support the vehicle safely.

7. Remove the tire and wheel assemblies.

8. Drain the engine oil. Properly dispose of used engine oil.

9. Drain the cooling system. Properly dispose of used engine coolant.

10. Remove the transmission.

11. Remove the air cleaner assembly.

12. Disconnect and plug the heater core hoses.

13. Disconnect and plug the refrigerant lines.

14. Disconnect the PCM electrical connectors.

15. Disconnect the fuel lines. Cap the lines to prevent dirt from entering the fuel system.

16. Disconnect the intermediate shaft from the steering gear.

17. Remove the front fascia.

18. Disconnect the outer tie rod ends from the steering knuckles

19. Disconnect the front lower control arm ball joints from the steering knuckles.

20. Disconnect the rear lower control arm ball joints from the steering knuckles.

21. Secure the front of the vehicle to a hoist.

22. Install tool J39580, under the frame.

23. Lower the vehicle to the frame support table.

24. Remove the six frame mounting bolts.

25. Carefully raise the body from the frame.

➡When raising the body be sure that the steering knuckles, electrical wiring and power steering lines are clear from the frame.

26. Remove the engine mount fasteners.

27. Disconnect all required hoses, lines, electrical connectors etc from the engine assembly.

28. Using a suitable engine lifting device, remove the engine from the frame.

To install:

➡Be sure to use new fasteners, as required.

29. Installation is the reverse of the removal procedure.

30. Tighten the engine mount lower retaining fasteners to 37 ft. lbs. (50 Nm).

31. Tighten the front frame mounting bolts to 118 ft. lbs. (160 Nm).

32. Tighten the rear frame mounting bolts to 177 ft. lbs. (240 Nm).

33. Be sure to fill the cooling system with the proper grade and type engine coolant.

34. Properly recharge the air conditioning system.

35. Fill the engine with the proper grade and type engine oil.

36. Road test the vehicle.

37. Using the GM diagnostic scan tool or aftermarket equivalent reprogram the necessary systems and components. Be sure to follow the scan tool manufacturer's directions.

Using the GM diagnostic scan tool, or equivalent, refer to the on-screen reprogramming directions and perform the diagnostic system check procedure.

EXHAUST MANIFOLD

REMOVAL & INSTALLATION

➡**For vehicles equipped with ON Star (RPO UE1), with battery backup, the backup battery is a redundant power supply to allow limited ON Star functionality in the event of a main battery power disruption to the ON Star module (VCIM). Do not disconnect the main vehicle battery or remove the ON Star fuse with the ignition key in any position other than OFF. Retained accessory power should be allowed to time out or be disabled by opening the driver's side door before disconnecting power. Disconnecting power to the module in any way while the ignition is ON or with the retained accessory power activated may cause activation of the ON Star backup battery system and will discharge and permanently damage the backup battery. Once the backup battery is activated it will stay on until it has completely discharged. The backup battery is not rechargeable and once it is activated, it must be replaced.**

3.6L Engines

Left

1. Before servicing the vehicle, refer to the Precautions Section.

2. Disconnect the negative battery cable.

3. Remove the heat shield.

4. Remove the manifold retaining nuts and bolts.

5. Remove the manifold from its mounting.

6. Discard the gasket.

To install:

➡️**Be sure to use new fasteners, as required.**

7. Position the manifold to its mounting. Be sure to use a new gasket.

8. Tighten the retaining nuts to 35 ft. lbs. (48 Nm). Tighten the retaining bolts to 15 ft. lbs. (20 Nm).

9. Continue the installation in the reverse order of the removal procedure.

10. Start the engine and check for exhaust leaks.

11. Correct, as required.

Right

1. Before servicing the vehicle, refer to the Precautions Section.

2. Disconnect the negative battery cable.

3. Remove the heat shield.

4. Remove the manifold retaining nuts and bolts.

5. Remove the manifold from its mounting.

6. Discard the gasket.

To install:

➡️**Be sure to use new fasteners, as required.**

7. Position the manifold to its mounting. Be sure to use a new gasket.

8. Tighten the retaining nuts to 35 ft. lbs. (48 Nm). Tighten the retaining bolts to 15 ft. lbs. (20 Nm).

9. Continue the installation in the reverse order of the removal procedure.

10. Start the engine and check for exhaust leaks.

11. Correct, as required.

6.2L Engines

Left

1. Before servicing the vehicle, refer to the Precautions Section.

2. Disconnect the negative battery cable.

3. Remove the intake manifold cover.

4. Remove the ignition coil assembly.

5. Remove the spark plugs.

6. Raise and safely support the vehicle.

7. Remove the catalytic converter. Discard the seal.

8. Disconnect the center steering shaft from the lower steering shaft. Separate the shafts and position aside.

9. Lower the vehicle.

10. Remove the exhaust manifold bolts.

11. Remove the manifold. Discard the gasket.

12. Remove the heat shield from the manifold.

To install:

➡️**Be sure to use new fasteners, as required.**

13. Position the manifold to its mounting. Be sure to use a new gasket.

➡️**Be sure to tighten the bolts to specification. Improperly installed or torqued bolts could cause a leaking exhaust manifold which could affect vehicle drivability.**

➡️**Be sure that the bolts are free of debris and/or thread locking material. Do not apply sealant to the first three threads of the bolt.**

14. Install the heat shield and bolts. Tighten to 80 inch lbs. (9 Nm).

15. Install the exhaust pipe studs. Tighten to 15 ft. lbs. (20 Nm).

16. Apply a 0.2 inch wide bead of threadlock to the threads of the bolts.

17. Install the exhaust manifold, using a new gasket.

18. Tighten the bolts to specification beginning with the center two bolts. Alternate from side to side and work toward the outside bolts.

19. First pass specification is 11 ft. lbs. (15 Nm). Final pass specification is 15 ft. lbs. (20 Nm).

20. Using a flat punch, bend over the exposed edge of the gasket at the rear of the cylinder head.

21. Continue the installation in the reverse order of the removal procedure.

Right

1. Before servicing the vehicle, refer to the Precautions Section.

2. Disconnect the negative battery cable.

3. Remove the intake manifold cover.

4. Remove the ignition coil assembly.

5. Remove the spark plugs.

6. Remove the oil level dipstick tube.

7. Raise and safely support the vehicle.

8. Remove the catalytic converter. Discard the seal.

9. Remove the starter.

10. Remove the exhaust manifold bolts.

11. Remove the manifold. Discard the gasket.

12. Remove the heat shield from the manifold.

To install:

➡️**Be sure to use new fasteners, as required.**

13. Position the manifold to its mounting. Be sure to use a new gasket.

➡️**Be sure to tighten the bolts to specification. Improperly installed or torqued bolts could cause a leaking exhaust manifold which could affect vehicle drivability.**

➡️**Be sure that the bolts are free of debris and/or thread locking material. Do not apply sealant to the first three threads of the bolt.**

14. Install the heat shield and bolts. Tighten to 80 inch lbs. (9 Nm).

15. Install the exhaust pipe studs. Tighten to 15 ft. lbs. (20 Nm).

16. Apply a 0.2 inch wide bead of threadlock to the threads of the bolts.

17. Install the exhaust manifold, using a new gasket.

18. Tighten the bolts to specification beginning with the center two bolts. Alternate from side to side and work toward the outside bolts.

19. First pass specification is 11 ft. lbs. (15 Nm). Final pass specification is 15 ft. lbs. (20 Nm).

20. Using a flat punch, bend over the exposed edge of the gasket at the rear of the cylinder head.

21. Continue the installation in the reverse order of the removal procedure.

INTAKE MANIFOLD

REMOVAL & INSTALLATION

➡️**For vehicles equipped with ON Star (RPO UE1), with battery backup, the backup battery is a redundant power supply to allow limited ON Star functionality in the event of a main battery power disruption to the ON Star module (VCIM). Do not disconnect the main vehicle battery or remove the ON Star fuse with the ignition key in any position other than OFF. Retained accessory power should be allowed to time out or be disabled by opening the driver's side door before disconnecting power. Disconnecting power to the module in any way while the ignition is ON or with the retained accessory power activated may cause activation of the ON Star backup battery system and will discharge and permanently damage the backup battery. Once the backup battery is activated it will stay on until it has completely discharged. The backup battery is not rechargeable and once it is activated, it must be replaced.**

3.6L Engines

See Figure 67.

1. Before servicing the vehicle, refer to the Precautions Section.

2. Disconnect the negative battery cable.

3. Remove the front intake manifold cover.

4. Remove the wiper transmission assembly.

5. Properly relieves the fuel system pressure.

6. Remove the fuel pipe shield.

7. Remove the air cleaner outlet duct.

8. Disconnect the brake booster vacuum hose from the manifold.

9. Disconnect the PCV valve from the manifold.

10. Disconnect the purge line from the manifold. Remove the bolt and position it to the side.

11. Disconnect the throttle body electrical connector. Remove the intake manifold bracket.

12. Unclip the engine wiring harness from the manifold.

13. Remove the intake manifold retaining bolts.

14. Remove the intake manifold from its mounting. Discard the gasket.

15. As required, disassemble the intake manifold.

To install:

➡**Be sure to use new fasteners, as required.**

16. If the intake manifold was disassembled, reassemble it. Be sure to use new gaskets.

17. Position the manifold to its mounting.

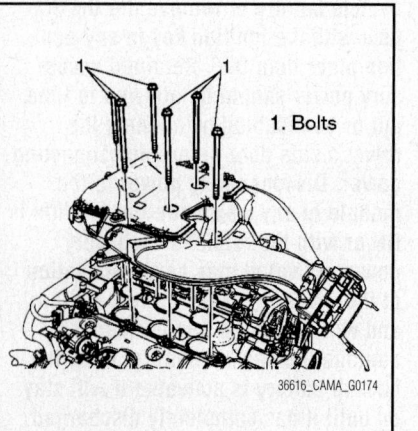

Fig. 67 Intake manifold and related components—3.6L engines

18. Tighten the retaining bolts to 17 ft. lbs. (23 Nm) in a criss-cross pattern.

19. Continue the installation in the reverse order of the removal procedure.

6.2L Engines

See Figures 68 and 69.

➡**The intake manifold, throttle body, fuel injection rail, and fuel injectors may be removed as an assembly. If not servicing the individual components, remove the manifold as a complete assembly.**

1. Before servicing the vehicle, refer to the Precautions Section.

2. Disconnect the negative battery cable.

3. Remove the intake manifold cover.

4. Remove the air cleaner assembly.

5. Disconnect the electrical connectors from the fuel injectors.

6. Properly relieves the fuel system pressure.

7. Disconnect the fuel feed pipe for the injectors.

8. Remove the PCV hose and pipe assembly.

9. Remove the vacuum hose for the brake booster.

10. Disconnect the MAP electrical connector. Remove the sensor.

11. Remove the EVAP clip, bolt, bracket, valve and tube.

12. Remove the intake manifold bolts and fuel rail stop bracket.

13. Remove the intake manifold from its mounting.

14. Remove the gaskets. Discard them.

To install:

➡**Be sure to use new fasteners, as required.**

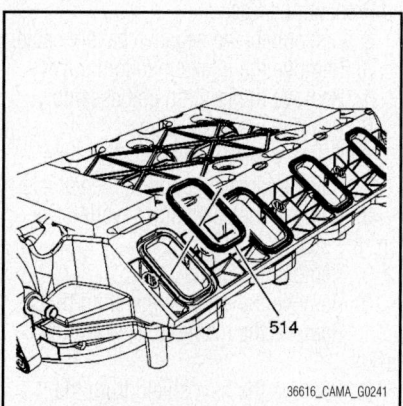

Fig. 68 Intake manifold and related components—6.2L engines

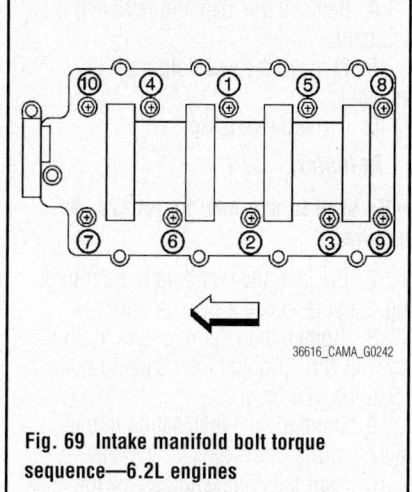

Fig. 69 Intake manifold bolt torque sequence—6.2L engines

15. Position the manifold to its mounting, using new gaskets.

16. Apply a 0.20 inch diameter bead of threadlocker to the threads of the intake manifold bolts. Install the bolts.

17. Tighten to specification and in the proper sequence:

a. First pass specification is 44 inch lbs. (5 Nm). Second pass specification is 89 inch lbs. (10 Nm).

18. Continue the installation in the reverse order of the removal procedure.

OIL PAN

REMOVAL & INSTALLATION

➡**For vehicles equipped with ON Star (RPO UE1), with battery backup, the backup battery is a redundant power supply to allow limited ON Star functionality in the event of a main battery power disruption to the ON Star module (VCIM). Do not disconnect the main vehicle battery or remove the ON Star fuse with the ignition key in any position other than OFF. Retained accessory power should be allowed to time out or be disabled by opening the driver's side door before disconnecting power. Disconnecting power to the module in any way while the ignition is ON or with the retained accessory power activated may cause activation of the ON Star backup battery system and will discharge and permanently damage the backup battery. Once the backup battery is activated it will stay on until it has completely discharged. The backup battery is not rechargeable and once it is activated, it must be replaced.**

3.6L Engines

See Figure 70.

1. Before servicing the vehicle, refer to the Precautions Section.
2. Disconnect the negative battery cable.
3. Remove the front bumper fascia.

→**Using mechanics wire properly support the radiator and condenser assembly to the body.**

4. Remove the intake manifold rear cover.
5. Install the engine support fixture.
6. Raise and support the vehicle safely.
7. Remove the tire and wheel assemblies.
8. Remove the electrical harness retainers, if equipped, retaining the engine harness to the frame.
9. Remove the stabilizer links from the struts.
10. Remove the steering gear.
11. Remove the power steering pipe fasteners (six bolts). Fasten the gear to the side using mechanics wire.
12. Separate the outer tie rods from the knuckles.
13. Disconnect the lower ball joints.
14. Remove the engine mounts lower retaining fasteners. Install tool J39580 to the frame.
15. Lower the vehicle to the frame support table.

16. Remove the six frame mounting bolts.
17. Carefully raise the body from the frame. Ensure that nothing will interfere with this step.
18. Remove the lower control arms.
19. Remove the stabilizer shaft.
20. Remove the frame from the support fixture.
21. Drain the engine oil. Be sure to properly dispose of used oil.
22. Remove the right side engine mount bracket.
23. Remove the oil pan retaining bolts.
24. Remove the component from its mounting.
25. Discard the gasket.

To install:

→**Be sure to use new fasteners, as required.**

26. Apply a 0.2 inch bead of sealant 0.8 inch long to the engine block.

→**Apply the sealant directly onto the tabs of the front cover gasket that protrude into the oil pan surface.**

→**The alignment of the oil pan is critical. The rear bolt hole locations of the pan provide mounting points for the transmission housing. To ensure the rigidity of the powertrain and correct**

transmission alignment it is important that the rear of the block and oil pan are flush or even. The rear of the oil pan must never protrude beyond the engine block and the transmission housing plane.

27. Using a new gasket. Position the pan to its mounting.
28. Tightening the retaining bolts to specification.
29. Continue the installation in the reverse order of the removal procedure.
30. Be sure to fill the engine with the proper grade and type engine oil.
31. Start the engine and check for leaks. Correct as required.

6.2L Engines

1. Before servicing the vehicle, refer to the Precautions Section.
2. Disconnect the negative battery cable.
3. Properly discharge the air conditioning system.
4. Remove the front bumper fascia.

→**Using mechanics wire properly support the radiator and condenser assembly to the body.**

5. Remove the intake manifold cover.
6. Install the engine support fixture.
7. Raise and support the vehicle safely.
8. Remove the tire and wheel assemblies.
9. Remove the electrical harness retainers, if equipped, retaining the engine harness to the frame.
10. Remove the stabilizer links from the struts.
11. Remove the steering gear.
12. Remove the power steering pipe fasteners (six bolts). Fasten the gear to the side using mechanics wire.
13. Separate the outer tie rods from the knuckles.
14. Disconnect the lower ball joints.
15. Remove the engine mounts lower retaining fasteners. Install tool J39580 to the frame.
16. Lower the vehicle to the frame support table.
17. Remove the six frame mounting bolts.
18. Carefully raise the body from the frame. Ensure that nothing will interfere with this step.
19. Remove the lower control arms.
20. Remove the stabilizer shaft.
21. Remove the frame from the support fixture.

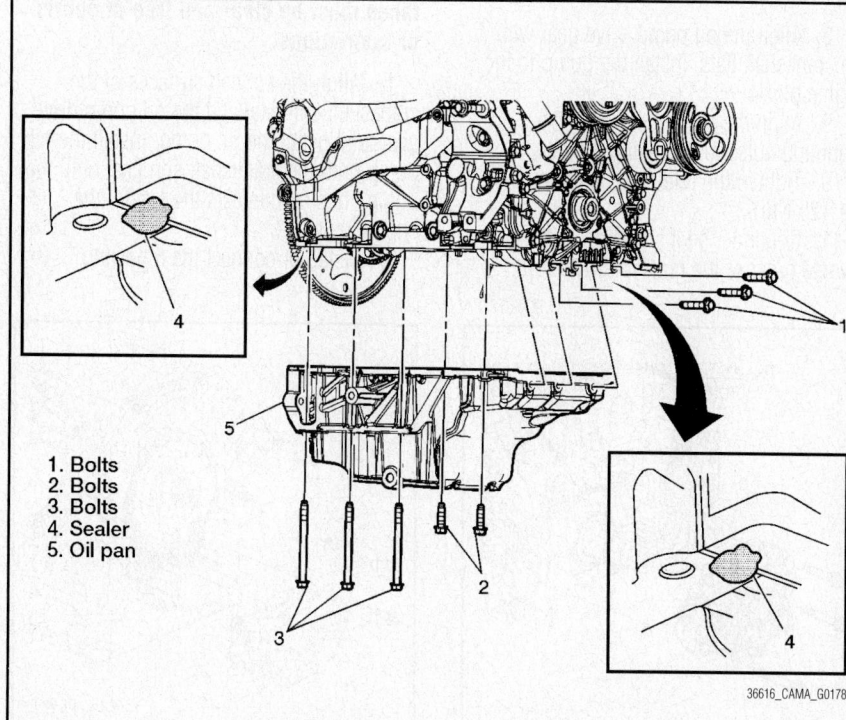

1. Bolts
2. Bolts
3. Bolts
4. Sealer
5. Oil pan

36616_CAMA_G0178

Fig. 70 Oil pan and related components—3.6L engines

22. Drain the engine oil. Be sure to properly dispose of used oil.

23. Remove the starter.

24. Remove the engine oil cooler.

25. Remove the A/C lines from the compressor and position them to the side. Cap the lines.

26. Reposition the engine wiring harness, as required.

27. Reposition the oil cooler lines, as required.

28. Remove the oil pan retaining bolts.

29. Remove the component from its mounting.

30. Discard the gasket.

To install:

➡Be sure to use new fasteners, as required.

31. Apply a 0.2 inch bead of sealant 0.8 inch long to the engine block.

➡Apply the sealant directly onto the tabs of the front cover gasket that protrude into the oil pan surface.

➡The alignment of the oil pan is critical. The rear bolt hole locations of the pan provide mounting points for the transmission housing. To ensure the rigidity of the powertrain and correct transmission alignment it is important that the rear of the block and oil pan are flush or even. The rear of the oil pan must never protrude beyond the engine block and the transmission housing plane.

32. Using a new gasket. Position the pan to its mounting.

33. Tightening the retaining bolts to specification.

34. Continue the installation in the reverse order of the removal procedure.

35. Be sure to fill the engine with the proper grade and type engine oil.

36. Start the engine and check for leaks. Correct as required.

OIL PUMP

REMOVAL & INSTALLATION

➡For vehicles equipped with ON Star (RPO UE1), with battery backup, the backup battery is a redundant power supply to allow limited ON Star functionality in the event of a main battery power disruption to the ON Star module (VCIM). Do not disconnect the main vehicle battery or remove the ON Star fuse with the ignition key in any position other than OFF. Retained accessory power should be allowed to time out or be disabled by opening the driver's side door before disconnecting power. Disconnecting power to the module in any way while the ignition is ON or with the retained accessory power activated may cause activation of the ON Star backup battery system and will discharge and permanently damage the backup battery. Once the backup battery is activated it will stay on until it has completely discharged. The backup battery is not rechargeable and once it is activated, it must be replaced.

3.6L Engines

See Figure 71.

1. Before servicing the vehicle, refer to the Precautions Section.

2. Disconnect the negative battery cable.

3. Remove the front cover.

➡Do not remove the left bank idler sprocket.

4. Remove the primary timing chain.

5. Remove the crankshaft sprocket.

6. Remove the oil pump retaining bolts.

7. Remove the oil pump from its mounting.

To install:

➡Be sure to use new fasteners, as required.

8. Align the oil pump drive gear with the crankshaft flats. Install the pump to the engine block.

9. Align the pump body with the mounting holes in the cylinder block.

10. Tighten the retaining bolts to 18 ft. lbs. (25 Nm).

11. Continue the installation in the reverse order of the removal procedure.

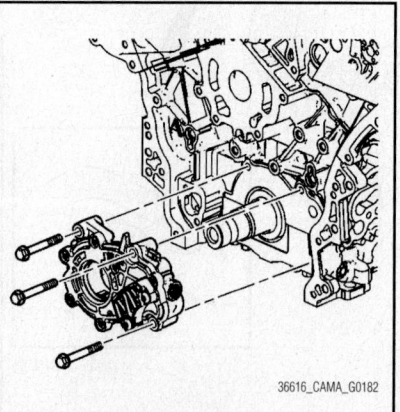

Fig. 71 Oil pump and related components—3.6L engines

36616_CAMA_G0182

6.2L Engines

See Figures 72 and 73.

1. Before servicing the vehicle, refer to the Precautions Section.

2. Disconnect the negative battery cable.

3. Raise and support the vehicle safely.

4. Remove or disconnect the following:
- Engine front cover
- Oil pan
- Oil pump screen bolt and nuts
- Oil pump screen with O–ring seal.
- O–ring seal from the pump screen. Discard the O–ring seal.
- Remaining crankshaft oil deflector nuts.
- Crankshaft oil deflector
- Oil pump bolts

➡Do not allow dirt or debris to enter the oil pump assembly, cap ends as necessary.

- Oil pump

➡The internal parts of the oil pump assembly are not serviced separately (excluding the spring). If the oil pump components are worn or damaged, replace the oil pump as an assembly. Do not attempt to repair the wire mesh portion of the pump and screen assembly.

To install:

➡Inspect the oil pump and engine block oil gallery passages. These surfaces must be clear and free of debris or restrictions.

5. Align the splined surfaces of the crankshaft sprocket and the oil pump drive gear and install the oil pump. Install the oil pump onto the crankshaft sprocket until the pump housing contacts the face of the engine block.

6. Install or connect the following:

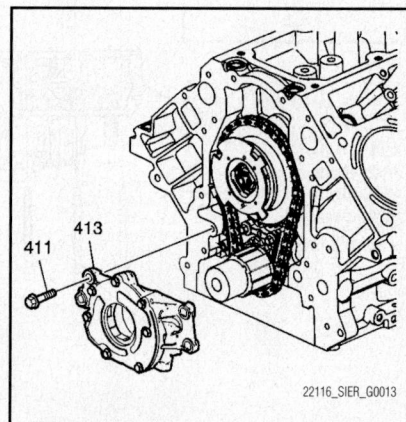

Fig. 72 Oil pump and related components—6.2L engines

411 413

22116_SIER_G0013

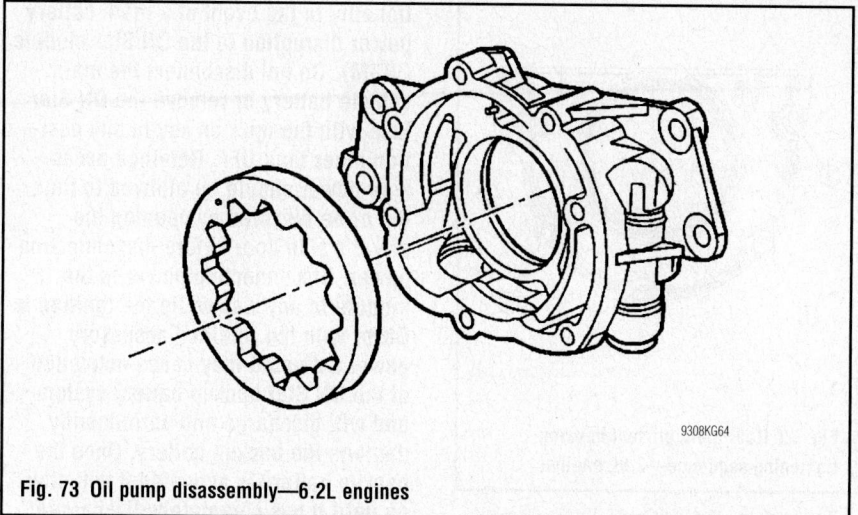

Fig. 73 Oil pump disassembly—6.2L engines

- Oil pump bolts. Tighten the oil pump bolts to 18 ft. lbs. (25 Nm).
- Crankshaft oil deflector

➡**Lubricate a NEW oil pump screen O–ring seal with clean engine oil.**

- NEW O–ring seal onto the oil pump screen

➡**Push the oil pump screen tube completely into the oil pump prior to tightening the bolt. Do not allow the bolt to pull the tube into the pump.**

7. Align the oil pump screen mounting brackets with the correct crankshaft bearing cap studs.

8. Install or connect the following:
- Oil pump screen
- Oil pump screen bolt and the deflector nuts. Tighten the bolt to 106 inch lbs. (12 Nm) and the nuts to 18 ft. lbs. (25 Nm).
- Oil pan
- Engine front cover

PISTON AND RING

POSITIONING

See Figures 74 and 75.

REAR MAIN SEAL

REMOVAL & INSTALLATION

➡**For vehicles equipped with ON Star (RPO UE1), with battery backup, the backup battery is a redundant power supply to allow limited ON Star functionality in the event of a main battery power disruption to the ON Star module (VCIM). Do not disconnect the main vehicle battery or remove the ON Star fuse with the ignition key in any position other than OFF. Retained**

accessory power should be allowed to time out or be disabled by opening the driver's side door before disconnecting power. Disconnecting power to the module in any way while the ignition is ON or with the retained accessory power activated may cause activation of the ON Star backup battery system and will discharge and permanently damage the backup battery. Once the backup battery is activated it will stay on until it has completely discharged. The backup battery is not rechargeable and once it is activated, it must be replaced.

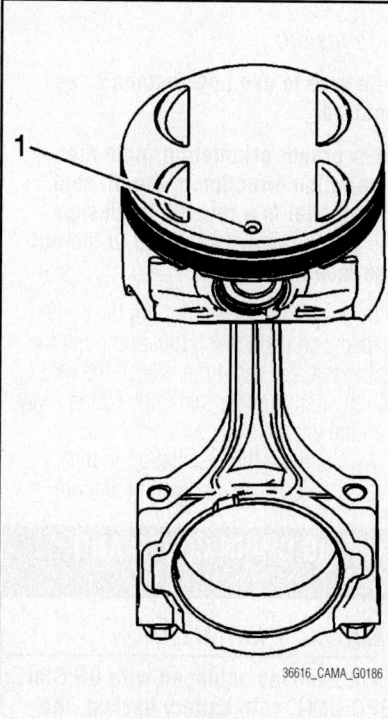

Fig. 74 Piston identification—3.6L engines

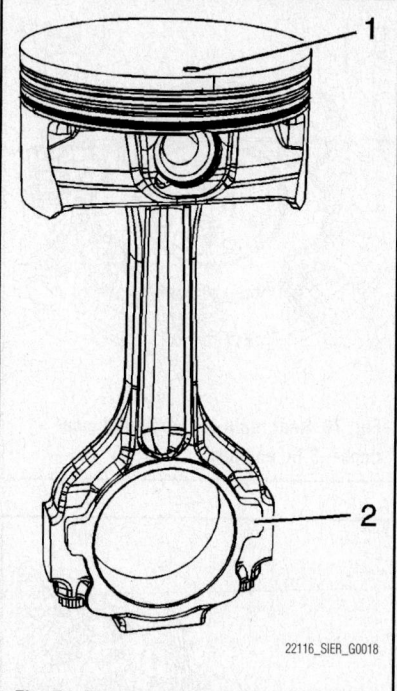

Fig. 75 Piston and connecting rod assembly—6.2L engines

3.6L Engines

See Figures 76 through 79.

1. Before servicing the vehicle, refer to the Precautions Section.

2. Disconnect the negative battery cable.

3. Remove the transmission.

4. Remove the flywheel or flexplate.

5. Remove the oil pan.

6. Remove the rear oil seal housing retaining bolts.

7. Use the pry points to separate the RTV sealant. See illustration.

8. Remove and discard the oil seal housing.

To install:

➡**Be sure to use new fasteners, as required.**

9. Using tools EN-46109 and EN-47839, install the rear oil seal housing.

➡**Place a 0.118 inch bead of RTV sealant to the new oil seal housing. See illustration. Do not allow engine oil on the area where the seal housing is to be installed.**

10. Position the component to its mounting.

11. Tighten the retaining bolts to 89 inch lbs. (10 Nm) and in the sequence shown in the illustration.

12. Continue the installation in the reverse order of the removal procedure.

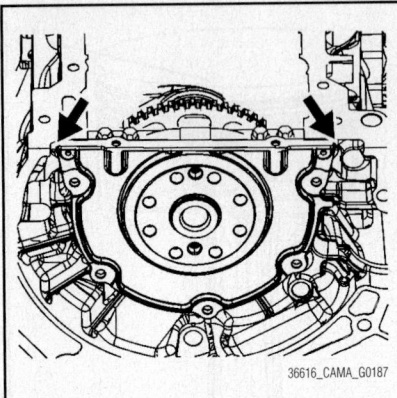

Fig. 76 Rear main seal pry point locations—3.6L engines

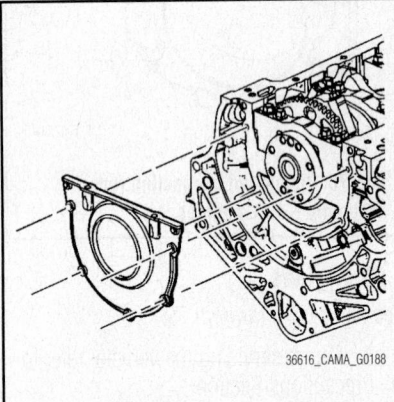

Fig. 77 Rear main oil seal housing and related components—3.6L engines

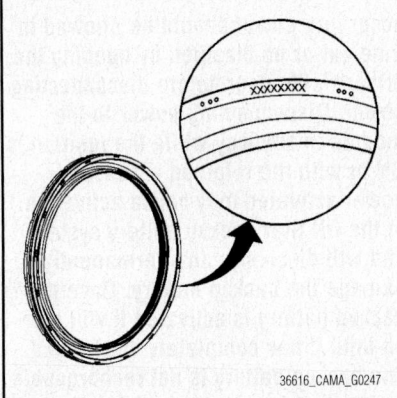

1. Sealant application point

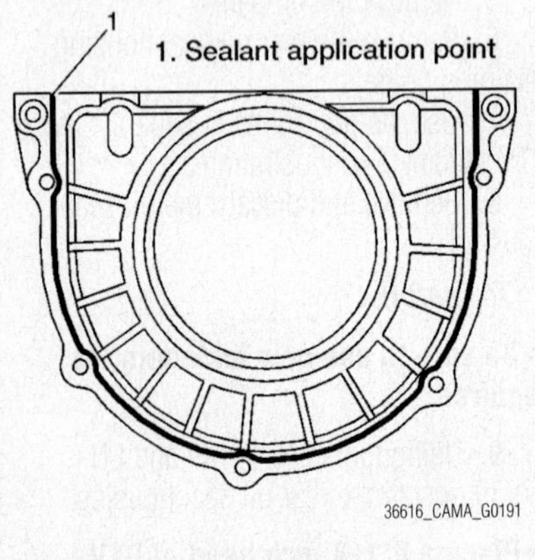

Fig. 78 Rear main oil seal RTV sealant application location—3.6L engines

6.2L Engines

See Figure 80.

1. Before servicing the vehicle, refer to the Precautions Section.
2. Disconnect the negative battery cable.
3. Remove the transmission.
4. Remove the flywheel or flexplate.
5. Remove and discard the oil seal.

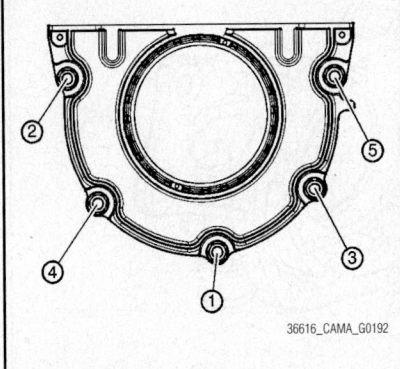

Fig. 79 Rear main oil seal housing tightening sequence—3.6L engines

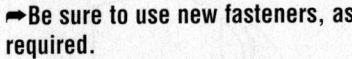

Fig. 80 Rear main seal orientation—6.2L engines

To install:

➡Be sure to use new fasteners, as required.

➡For proper orientation, note the installation direction of the oil seal. The oil seal is a reverse lip design. The part number is applied to the outside face of the seal.

6. Install the new seal onto the cone shaped seal installation tool and push the seal to the rear seal bore. Install the seal with the part number markings facing away from the engine.
7. Continue the installation in the reverse order of the removal procedure.

TIMING CHAIN COVER AND SEAL

REMOVAL & INSTALLATION

➡For vehicles equipped with ON Star (RPO UE1), with battery backup, the backup battery is a redundant power supply to allow limited ON Star func-

tionality in the event of a main battery power disruption to the ON Star module (VCIM). Do not disconnect the main vehicle battery or remove the ON Star fuse with the ignition key in any position other than OFF. Retained accessory power should be allowed to time out or be disabled by opening the driver's side door before disconnecting power. Disconnecting power to the module in any way while the ignition is ON or with the retained accessory power activated may cause activation of the ON Star backup battery system and will discharge and permanently damage the backup battery. Once the backup battery is activated it will stay on until it has completely discharged. The backup battery is not rechargeable and once it is activated, it must be replaced.

3.6L Engines

See Figures 81 through 83.

➡The front cover does not have to be removed to replace the oil seal.

1. Before servicing the vehicle, refer to the Precautions Section.
2. Disconnect the negative battery cable.
3. Remove the air inlet duct assembly.
4. Remove the front intake manifold cover.
5. Remove the rear intake manifold cover.
6. Remove the intake manifold.
7. Remove the valve covers.
8. Drain the cooling system. Properly dispose of used engine coolant.

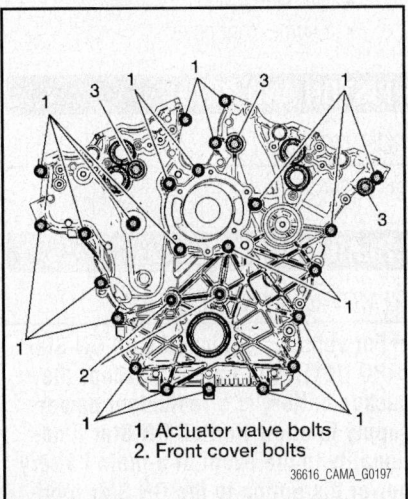

1. Actuator valve bolts
2. Front cover bolts

Fig. 81 Camshaft (right and left) position actuator valves and related components—3.6L engines

9. Disconnect the purge vent hose from the water inlet. Remove the water inlet at the radiator hose. Position it to the side.

10. Remove the drive belt.

11. Remove the A/C and power steering tensioner.

12. Remove the alternator bracket, with the tensioner.

➡**Do not drain the power steering fluid, or disconnect the lines.**

13. Remove the fluid reservoir and reposition the unit to gain access.

14. Remove the pump pulley.

15. Remove the upper front bolt and loosen the two remaining bolts.

16. Remove the crankshaft balancer.

17. Remove the camshaft position sensors.

➡**The camshaft position actuator valves must be removed from the front cover prior to removing the front cover or damage to the valves may occur.**

18. Remove the camshaft position actuator solenoid valve bolts (1) from the front cover. Remove the camshaft position actuator solenoid (2) from the front cover. See illustration.

19. Remove the engine front cover bolts (3). Depending upon the model these bolts may have already been removed. See illustration.

➡**There are a total of 23 bolts that must be removed plus the three optional bolts.**

20. Remove the engine front cover bolts. Carefully remove the cover from its mounting, with the water pump.

➡**Do not pry between the engine front cover and the camshaft position sensors or the camshaft position actuators to remove the cover. Use the pry points (2) and a bolt in the jackscrew hole (1) in order to remove the cover. See illustration.**

21. Replace the front cover seal, as required.

To install:

➡**Be sure to use new fasteners, as required.**

22. Position the front cover to its mounting.

23. Tighten the retaining bolts as follows. First sequence bolts 1 thru 23 14 ft. lbs. (20 Nm). Second sequence 14 ft. lbs. (20 Nm). Third sequence an additional 60 degrees. Bolt 24 48 ft. lbs. (65 Nm). Bolt 25 48 ft. lbs. (65 Nm), if equipped.

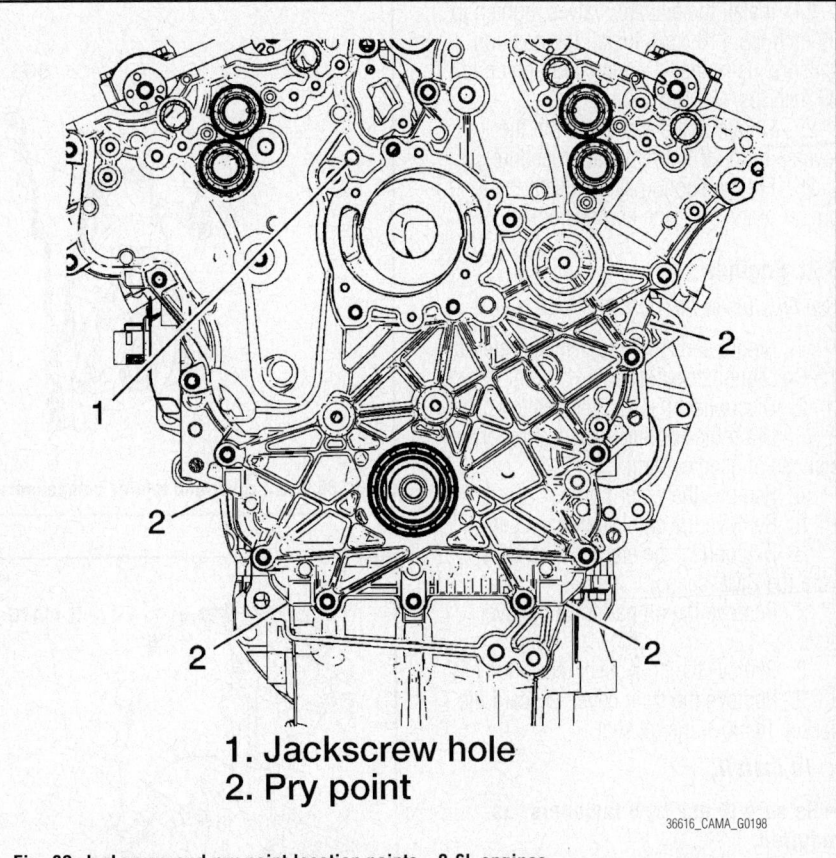

1. Jackscrew hole
2. Pry point

36616_CAMA_G0198

Fig. 82 Jackscrew and pry point location points—3.6L engines

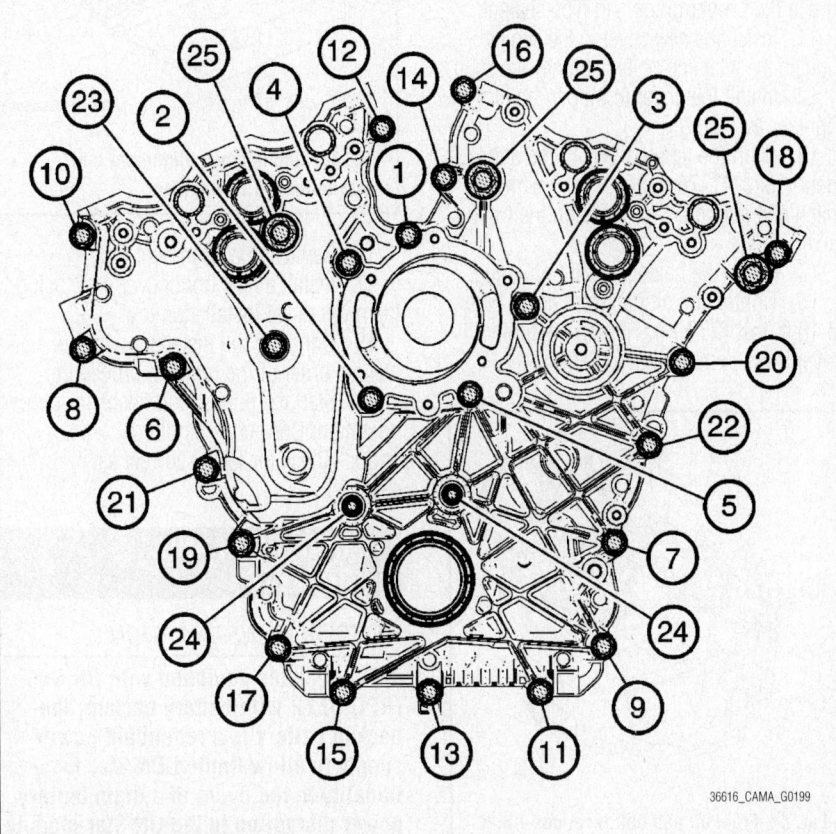

36616_CAMA_G0199

Fig. 83 Front cover bolt tightening sequence—3.6L engines

24. Install the actuator valves, tighten to 89 inch lbs. (10 Nm). Install the position sensors, using new O-rings and tighten to 89 inch lbs. (10 Nm).

25. Continue the installation in the reverse order of the removal procedure.

26. Fill the cooling system with the proper grade and type engine coolant.

6.2L Engines

See Figures 84 through 86.

1. Before servicing the vehicle, refer to the Precautions Section.

2. Disconnect the negative battery cable.

3. Drain the cooling system. Properly dispose of used coolant.

4. Remove the water pump.

5. Remove the crankshaft balancer.

6. Disconnect the electrical harness from the CMP sensor.

7. Remove the oil pan to front cover bolts.

8. Remove the front cover retaining bolts.

9. Remove the front cover. Discard the gasket. Remove the oil seal.

To install:

➡Be sure to use new fasteners, as required.

10. Apply a 0.20 inch of sealant to the engine block and oil pan junction. Be sure to use the proper grade and type sealant.

11. Install the new cover to the engine. Tighten the retaining bolts until they are snug.

12. Install the cover to oil pan bolts. Tighten until snug.

13. Align the tapered legs of the alignment tool J-41476 or equivalent, with the machined alignment surfaces on the front cover.

14. Install the balancer bolt until snug.

15. Tighten the oil pan front cover bolts to 18 ft. lbs. (25 Nm). Tighten the timing cover bolts to 18 ft. lbs (25 Nm).

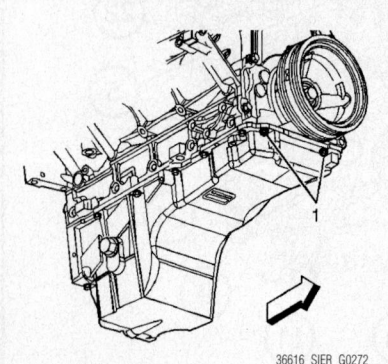

Fig. 84 Front oil pan bolt locations—6.2L engines

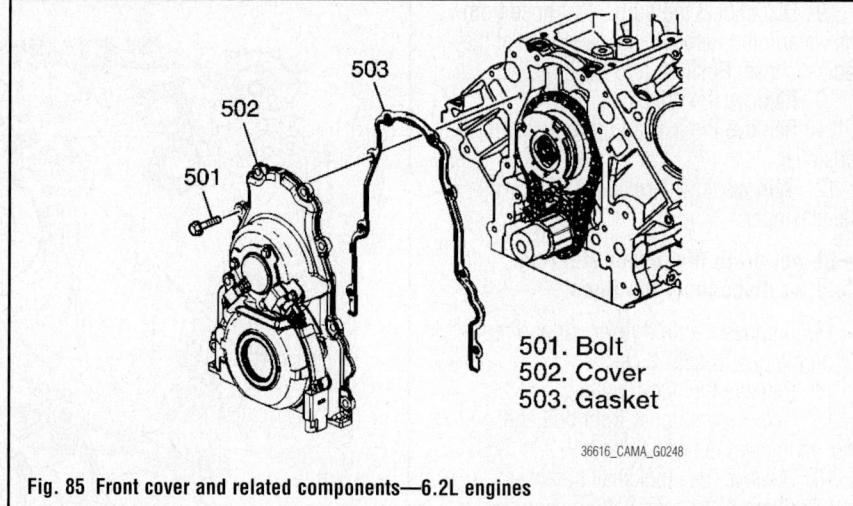

501. Bolt
502. Cover
503. Gasket

36616_CAMA_G0248

Fig. 85 Front cover and related components—6.2L engines

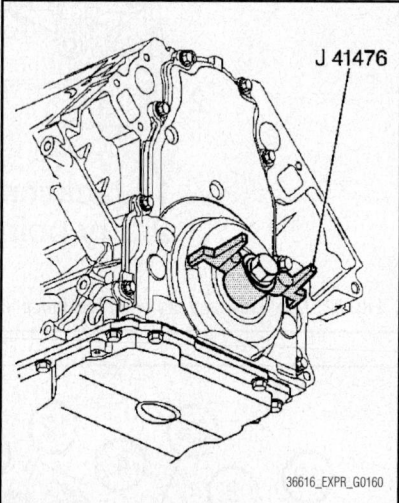

J 41476

36616_EXPR_G0160

Fig. 86 Timing cover alignment tool installation—6.2L engines

16. Remove the alignment tool.

17. Install a new front cover seal, using the proper seal installation tool.

18. Continue the installation in the reverse order of the removal procedure.

19. Start the engine and check for proper operation. Correct as required.

20. Check for leaks, correct as required.

TIMING CHAIN AND SPROCKETS

REMOVAL & INSTALLATION

➡For vehicles equipped with ON Star (RPO UE1), with battery backup, the backup battery is a redundant power supply to allow limited ON Star functionality in the event of a main battery power disruption to the ON Star module (VCIM). Do not disconnect the main

vehicle battery or remove the ON Star fuse with the ignition key in any position other than OFF. Retained accessory power should be allowed to time out or be disabled by opening the driver's side door before disconnecting power. Disconnecting power to the module in any way while the ignition is ON or with the retained accessory power activated may cause activation of the ON Star backup battery system and will discharge and permanently damage the backup battery. Once the backup battery is activated it will stay on until it has completely discharged. The backup battery is not rechargeable and once it is activated, it must be replaced.

3.6L Engines

Primary Chain

See Figures 87 through 92.

1. Before servicing the vehicle, refer to the Precautions Section.

2. Disconnect the negative battery cable.

3. Drain the cooling system. Properly dispose of used engine coolant.

4. Remove the front cover.

5. Remove the right bank secondary camshaft drive chain.

6. Remove the primary camshaft drive chain tensioner.

7. Remove the primary camshaft drive chain upper guide.

8. Remove the primary timing chain.

To install:

➡Be sure to use new fasteners, as required. Be sure that the crankshaft is in the stage one timing drive assembly position.

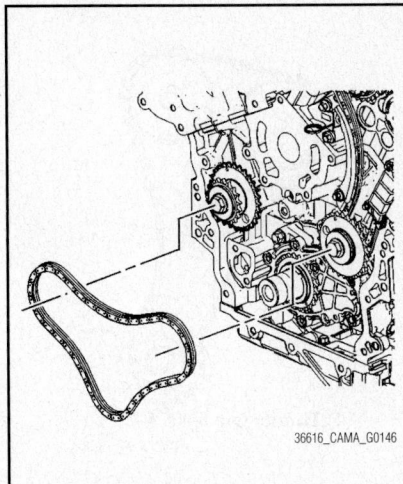

Fig. 87 Primary timing chain and related components—3.6L engines

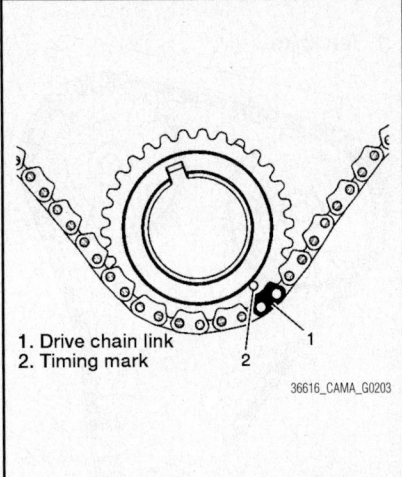

1. Drive chain link
2. Timing mark

Fig. 90 Primary timing chain installed configuration (view three)—3.6L engines

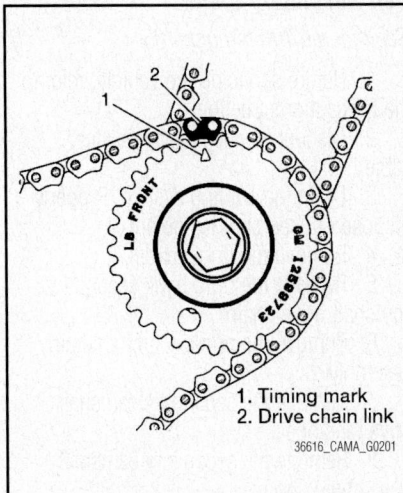

1. Timing mark
2. Drive chain link

Fig. 88 Primary timing chain installed configuration (view one)—3.6L engines

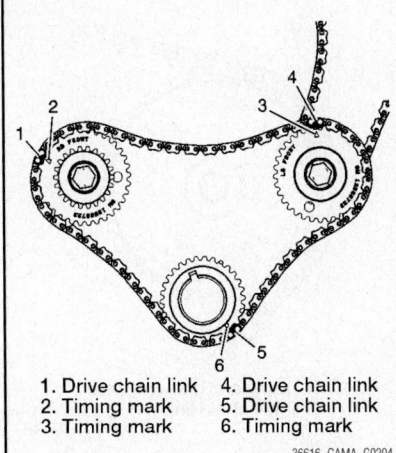

1. Drive chain link
2. Timing mark
3. Timing mark
4. Drive chain link
5. Drive chain link
6. Timing mark

Fig. 91 Primary timing chain installed configuration (view four)—3.6L engines

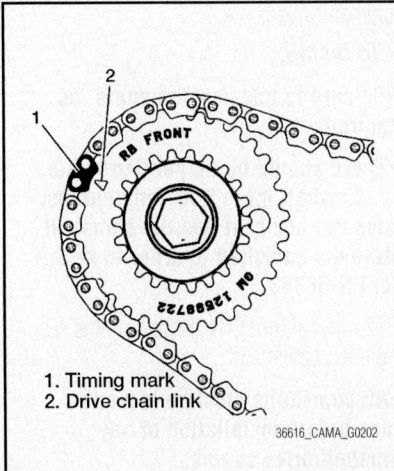

1. Timing mark
2. Drive chain link

Fig. 89 Primary timing chain installed configuration (view two)—3.6L engines

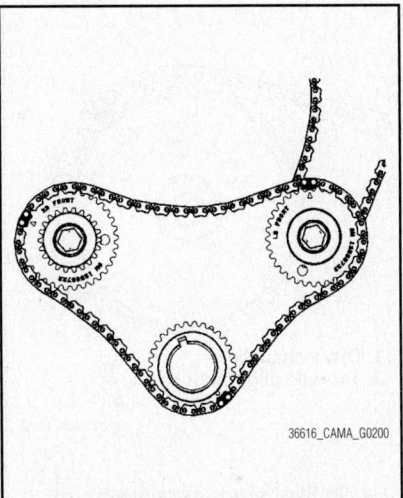

Fig. 92 Primary timing chain installed configuration (view five)—3.6L engines

9. Wrap the primary chain around the large sprockets of each camshaft drive chain idler and crankshaft sprocket.

10. The left camshaft drive chain idler timing mark will align with a timing chain link.

11. The right camshaft drive chain idler timing mark will align with a timing chain link.

12. The crankshaft sprocket timing mark will align with a camshaft drive chain link.

13. Be sure that all marks are properly aligned with the timing camshaft drive chain links.

14. Install the primary camshaft drive chain.

15. Continue the installation in the reverse order of the removal procedure.

Right Secondary Chain

See Figures 93 through 99.

1. Before servicing the vehicle, refer to the Precautions Section.

2. Disconnect the negative battery cable.

3. Drain the cooling system. Properly dispose of used engine coolant.

4. Remove the front cover.

5. Remove the secondary camshaft drive tensioner.

6. Remove the secondary camshaft drive chain shoe.

7. Remove the secondary camshaft drive chain guide.

8. Remove the right bank secondary camshaft drive chain.

To install:

➡**Be sure to use new fasteners, as required.**

9. Be sure that the crankshaft is in the stage two timing drive assembly position.

10. Install the camshaft drive chain.

11. Place the drive chain around the camshaft intermediate drive chain idler outer sprocket, aligning the drive chain link with the access hole made in the right camshaft intermediate chain inner sprocket.

12. Wrap the drive chain around both actuator drive sprockets.

13. Be sure that there are ten links between the drive chain links for the camshaft position actuator sprockets.

14. Align the exhaust camshaft position actuator sprocket alignment triangle mark with the timing drive chain link.

15. Align the intake camshaft position actuator sprocket alignment triangle mark with the timing drive chain link.

16. There will be twenty-two links between the camshaft intermediate chain idler camshaft chain link and each right camshaft position actuator sprocket drive chain link.

17. Continue the installation in the reverse order of the removal procedure.

Fig. 93 Right side secondary camshaft intermediate drive chain and related components—3.6L engines

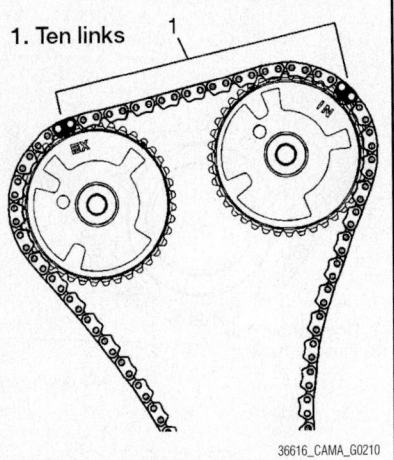

1. Ten links

Fig. 96 Right secondary camshaft installed configuration (view two)—3.6L engines

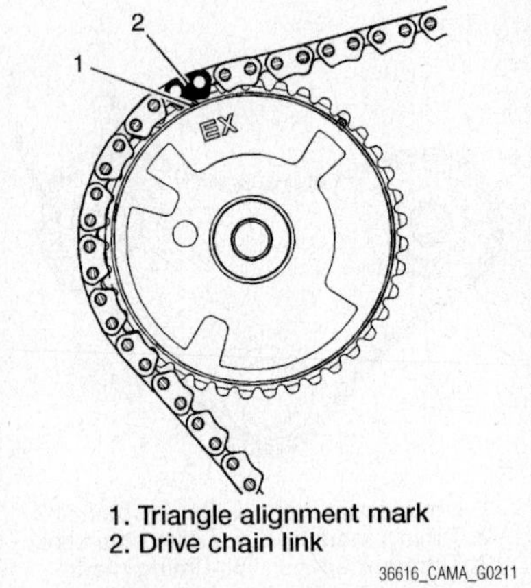

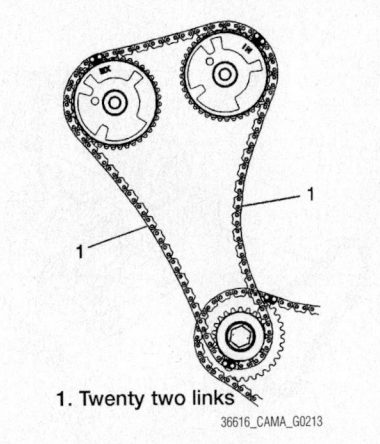

1. Twenty two links

Fig. 99 Right secondary camshaft installed configuration (view five)—3.6L engines

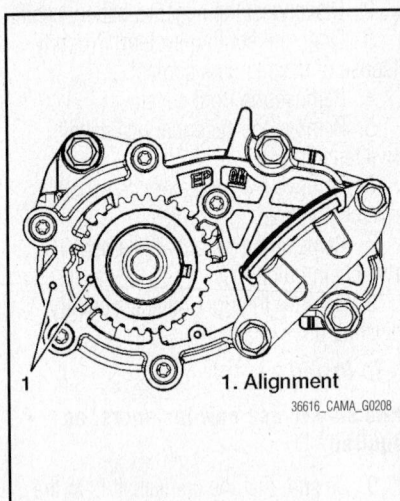

1. Alignment

Fig. 94 Right side stage two positioning—3.6L engines

1. Triangle alignment mark
2. Drive chain link

Fig. 97 Right secondary camshaft installed configuration (view three)—3.6L engines

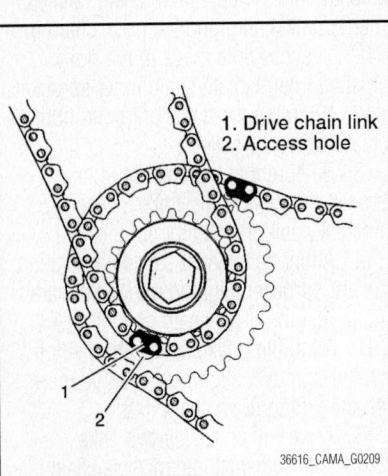

1. Drive chain link
2. Access hole

Fig. 95 Right secondary camshaft installed configuration (view one)—3.6L engines

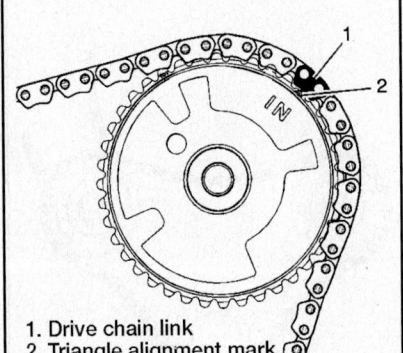

1. Drive chain link
2. Triangle alignment mark

Fig. 98 Right secondary camshaft installed configuration (view four)—3.6L engines

Left Secondary Chain

See Figures 100 through 105.

1. Before servicing the vehicle, refer to the Precautions Section.
2. Disconnect the negative battery cable.
3. Drain the cooling system. Properly dispose of used engine coolant.
4. Remove the front cover.
5. Remove the right bank secondary camshaft drive chain.
6. Remove the primary timing chain assembly.
7. Remove the secondary camshaft drive tensioner.
8. Remove the secondary camshaft drive chain shoe.
9. Remove the secondary camshaft drive chain guide.
10. Remove the drive chain idler.
11. Remove the left bank secondary camshaft drive chain.

To install:

➡Be sure to use new fasteners, as required.

➡There should be no need to rotate the camshaft more than ten degrees. Using the hex cast into the camshaft rotate the camshaft in order to install tool EN-48383.

12. Install tool EN-48383 onto the rear of the left camshafts.

➡All camshafts must be locked in place before installation of any camshaft drive chains.

13. Be sure that the crankshaft is in the stage one timing position with the crankshaft sprocket timing mark aligned to the

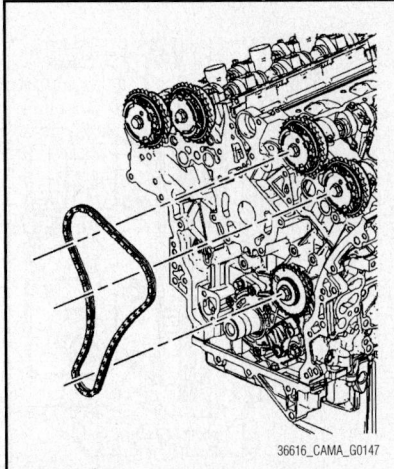

Fig. 100 Left side secondary camshaft intermediate drive chain and related components—3.6L engines

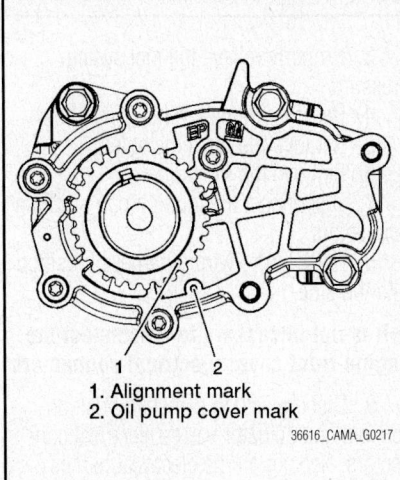

1. Alignment mark
2. Oil pump cover mark

36616_CAMA_G0217

Fig. 101 Left side stage one positioning—3.6L engines

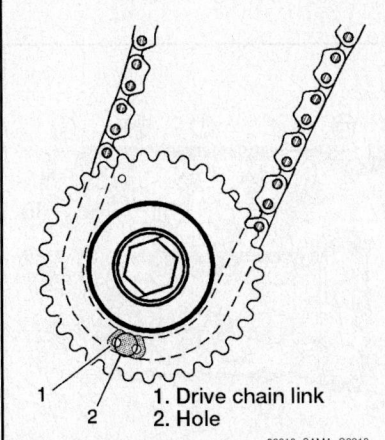

1. Drive chain link
2. Hole

36616_CAMA_G0218

Fig. 102 Left secondary camshaft installed configuration (view one)—3.6L engines

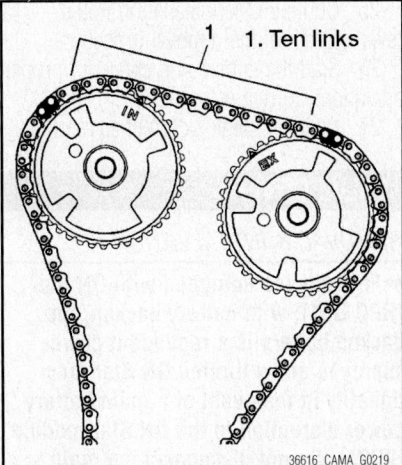

1. Ten links

36616_CAMA_G0219

Fig. 103 Left secondary camshaft installed configuration (view two)—3.6L engines

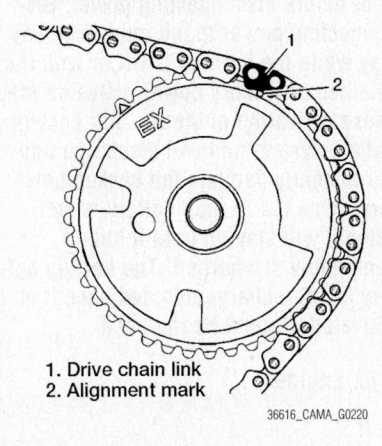

1. Drive chain link
2. Alignment mark

36616_CAMA_G0220

Fig. 104 Left secondary camshaft installed configuration (view three)—3.6L engines

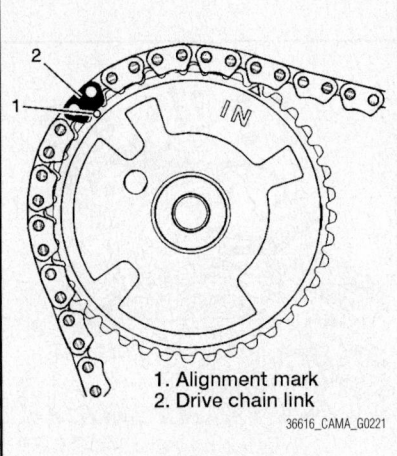

1. Alignment mark
2. Drive chain link

36616_CAMA_G0221

Fig. 105 Left secondary camshaft installed configuration (view four)—3.6L engines

stage one timing mark on the oil pump cover, using tool EN-48589.

14. Install the camshaft drive chain.

15. Place the drive chain around the camshaft intermediate drive chain idler outer sprocket, aligning the drive chain link with the access hole made in the right camshaft intermediate chain inner sprocket.

16. Wrap the drive chain around both actuator drive sprockets.

17. Be sure that there are ten links between the drive chain links for the camshaft position actuator sprockets.

18. Align the exhaust camshaft position actuator sprocket alignment triangle mark with the timing drive chain link.

19. Align the intake camshaft position actuator sprocket alignment triangle mark with the timing drive chain link.

20. Continue the installation in the reverse order of the removal procedure.

6.2L Engines

See Figure 106.

1. Before servicing the vehicle, refer to the Precautions Section.

2. Disconnect the negative battery cable.

3. Drain the cooling system. Properly dispose of used coolant.

4. Remove the water pump.

5. Remove the crankshaft balancer.

6. Remove the oil pan to front cover bolts.

7. Remove the front cover retaining bolts.

8. Remove the front cover. Discard the gasket. Remove the oil seal.

9. Remove the starter.

10. Remove the oil pump.

11. Remove the camshaft position actuator.

12. Remove the timing chain tensioner.

13. Rotate the crankshaft until the timing marks on the crankshaft and the camshaft sprockets are aligned.

➡**Do not turn the crankshaft assembly after the timing chain has been removed in order to prevent damage to the piston assemblies or the valves.**

14. Remove or disconnect the following:
- Camshaft sprocket bolts
- Camshaft sprocket and timing chain
- Crankshaft sprocket
- Crankshaft sprocket key

To install:

➡**Be sure to use new fasteners, as required.**

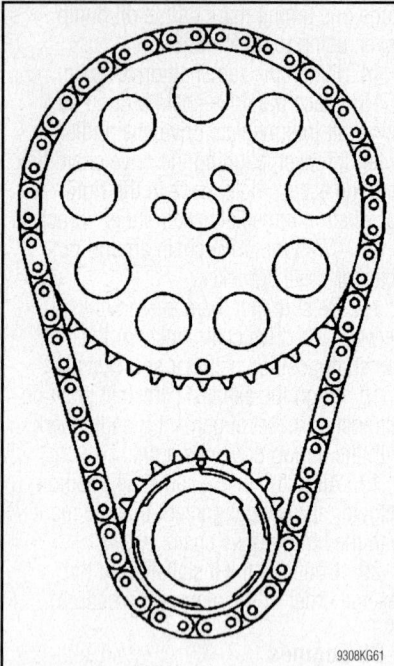

Fig. 106 Timing mark alignment—6.2L engines

15. Install or connect the following:
- Key into the crankshaft keyway
- Crankshaft sprocket onto the front of the crankshaft. Align the crankshaft key with the crankshaft sprocket keyway. Rotate the crankshaft sprocket until the alignment mark is in the 12 o'clock position.
- Camshaft sprocket and timing chain. Locate the camshaft sprocket alignment mark in the 6 o'clock position.
- Camshaft sprocket bolts and tighten to 26 ft. lbs. (35 Nm)

16. Install the oil pump.

17. Apply a 0.20 inch of sealant to the engine block and oil pan junction. Be sure to use the proper grade and type sealant.

18. Install the new cover to the engine. Tighten the retaining bolts until they are snug.

19. Install the cover to oil pan bolts. Tighten until snug.

20. Align the tapered legs of the alignment tool J-41476 or equivalent, with the machined alignment surfaces on the front cover.

21. Install the balancer bolt until snug.

22. Tighten the oil pan front cover bolts to 18 ft. lbs. (25 Nm). Tighten the timing cover bolts to 18 ft. lbs (25 Nm).

23. Remove the alignment tool.

24. Install a new front cover seal, using the proper seal installation tool.

25. Continue the installation in the reverse order of the removal procedure.

26. Start the engine and check for proper operation. Correct as required.

27. Check for leaks, correct as required.

VALVE COVERS

REMOVAL & INSTALLATION

➡For vehicles equipped with ON Star (RPO UE1), with battery backup, the backup battery is a redundant power supply to allow limited ON Star functionality in the event of a main battery power disruption to the ON Star module (VCIM). Do not disconnect the main vehicle battery or remove the ON Star fuse with the ignition key in any position other than OFF. Retained accessory power should be allowed to time out or be disabled by opening the driver's side door before disconnecting power. Disconnecting power to the module in any way while the ignition is ON or with the retained accessory power activated may cause activation of the ON Star backup battery system and will discharge and permanently damage the backup battery. Once the backup battery is activated it will stay on until it has completely discharged. The backup battery is not rechargeable and once it is activated, it must be replaced.

3.6L Engines

Left

See Figures 107 through 109.

1. Before servicing the vehicle, refer to the Precautions Section.

2. Disconnect the negative battery cable.

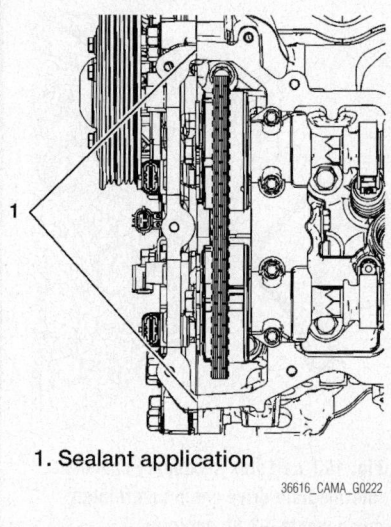

1. Sealant application

Fig. 108 Valve cover sealant application (left)—3.6L engines

3. Properly relieve the fuel system pressure.

4. Remove the upper intake manifold.

5. Remove the fuel pipe shield.

6. Remove the PCV pipe.

7. Disconnect the ignition coil electrical connectors.

8. Remove the wiring harness, position it to the side.

➡It is not necessary to disconnect the engine front cover electrical connectors

9. Disconnect the camshaft position sensors and actuator valves electrical connectors. Reposition the electrical harness.

10. Remove the ignition coils.

11. Remove the rocker cover retaining bolts.

12. Remove the rocker arm cover. Discard the gasket and grommets.

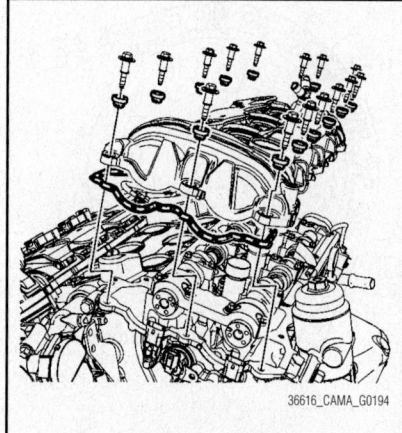

Fig. 107 Valve rocker arm cover and related components (left)—3.6L engines

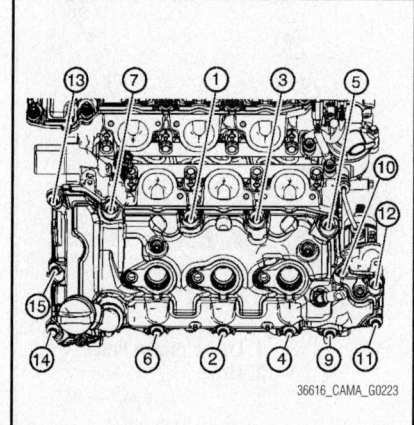

Fig. 109 Valve cover bolt tightening sequence (left)—3.6L engines

To install:

➡**Be sure to use new fasteners, as required.**

13. Install the guide tool EN-46101, or equivalent onto the spark plug tubes of the cylinder head.

14. Place a 0.3150 inch diameter bead by 0.1575 inch in height of RTV sealant on the engine front cover split lines.

15. Position the valve cover to its mounting.

16. Be sure to use a new gasket and retaining grommets.

17. loosely install the valve cover bolts.

18. Tighten the bolts to specification and in the proper sequence. Tighten first pass to 89 inch lbs. (10 Nm). Tighten second pass to 89 inch lbs. (10 Nm).

19. Remove the spark plug guide tool.

20. Continue the installation in the reverse order of the removal procedure.

Right

See Figures 110 through 112.

1. Before servicing the vehicle, refer to the Precautions Section.

2. Disconnect the negative battery cable.

3. Properly relieve the fuel system pressure.

4. Remove the upper intake manifold.

5. Disconnect the ignition coil electrical connectors.

6. Remove the wiring harness, position it to the side.

➡**It is not necessary to disconnect the engine front cover electrical connectors**

7. Disconnect the camshaft position sensors and actuator valves electrical connectors. Reposition the electrical harness.

8. Remove the ignition coils.

Fig. 110 Valve rocker arm cover and related components (right)—3.6L engines

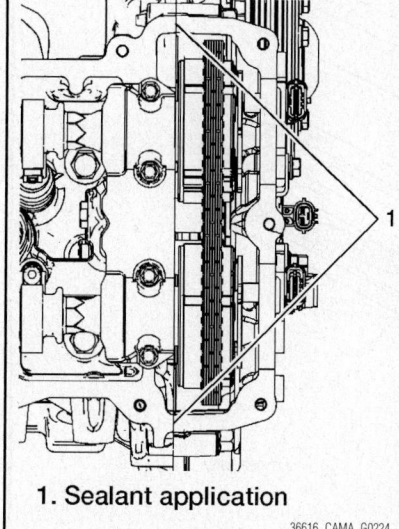

1. Sealant application

36616_CAMA_G0224

Fig. 111 Valve cover sealant application (right)—3.6L engines

9. Remove the rocker cover retaining bolts.

10. Remove the rocker arm cover. Discard the gasket and grommets.

To install:

➡**Be sure to use new fasteners, as required.**

11. Install the guide tool EN-46101, or equivalent onto the spark plug tubes of the cylinder head.

12. Place a 0.3150 inch diameter bead by 0.1575 inch in height of RTV sealant on the engine front cover split lines.

13. Position the valve cover to its mounting.

14. Be sure to use a new gasket and retaining grommets.

15. loosely install the valve cover bolts.

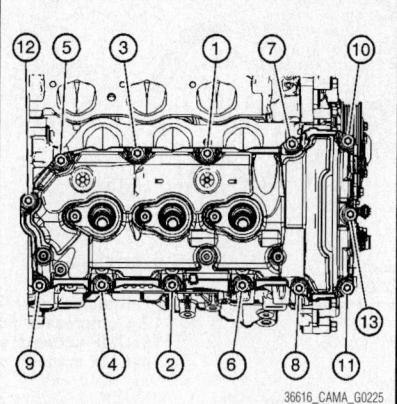

36616_CAMA_G0225

Fig. 112 Valve cover bolt tightening sequence (right)—3.6L engines

16. Tighten the bolts to specification and in the proper sequence. Tighten first pass to 89 inch lbs. (10 Nm). Tighten second pass to 89 inch lbs. (10 Nm).

17. Remove the spark plug guide tool.

18. Continue the installation in the reverse order of the removal procedure.

6.2L Engines

Left

1. Before servicing the vehicle, refer to the Precautions Section.

2. Disconnect the negative battery cable.

3. Remove the intake manifold cover.

4. Properly relieve the fuel system pressure.

5. Remove the PCV hoses and pipes.

6. Remove the ignition coils.

7. Loosen the valve rocker arm cover bolts.

8. Remove the valve rocker arm cover.

9. Remove and discard the old gasket.

10. If required, clean and inspect the rocker arm cover.

To install:

➡**Be sure to use new fasteners, as required.**

11. Using a new gasket, position the valve cover on the engine.

12. Install the retaining bolts. Tighten to 106 inch lbs. (12 Nm).

13. Continue the installation in the reverse order of the removal procedure.

14. Start the engine and check for leaks. Correct as required.

15. Remove the lower valve rocker arm cover bolts.

Right

See Figure 113.

1. Before servicing the vehicle, refer to the Precautions Section.

2. Disconnect the negative battery cable.

3. Remove the intake manifold cover.

4. Properly relieve the fuel system pressure.

5. Remove the PCV hoses and pipes.

6. Remove the ignition coils.

7. Loosen the valve rocker arm cover bolts.

8. Remove the valve rocker arm cover.

9. Remove and discard the old gasket.

10. If required, clean and inspect the rocker arm cover.

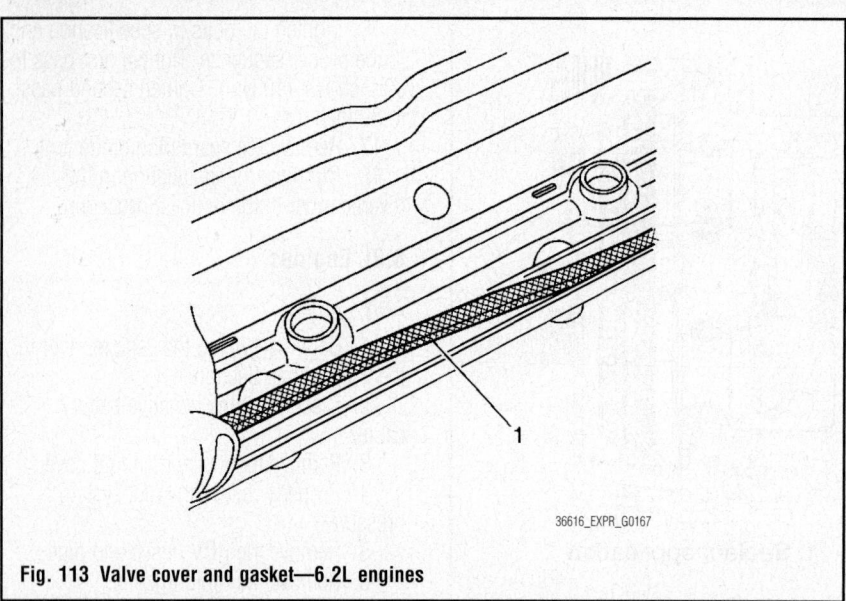

36616_EXPR_G0167

Fig. 113 Valve cover and gasket—6.2L engines

To install:

➡ **Be sure to use new fasteners, as required.**

11. Using a new gasket, position the valve cover on the engine.

12. Install the retaining bolts. Tighten to 106 inch lbs. (12 Nm).

13. Continue the installation in the reverse order of the removal procedure.

14. Start the engine and check for leaks. Correct as required.

VALVE LASH

ADJUSTMENT

The valve clearance cannot be adjusted on these engines. The engine is equipped with hydraulic lifters, and adjustment is not necessary.

ENGINE PERFORMANCE & EMISSION CONTROLS

COMPONENT LOCATIONS

See Figures 114 through 119.

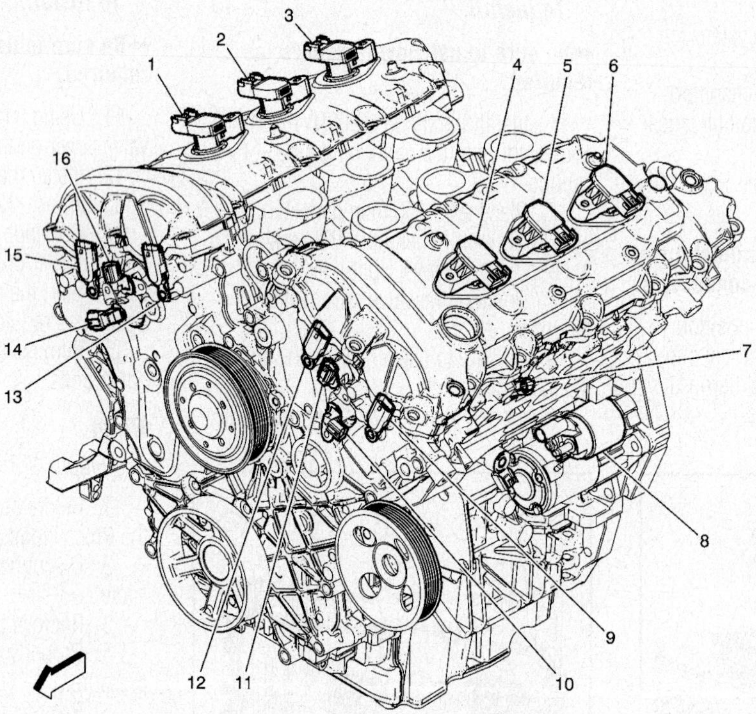

1. Throttle body
2. CMP actuator solenoid valve
3. CMP actuator solenoid valve
4. Coil 6
5. Coil 4
6. Coil 2
7. EOP sensor
8. High pressure fuel pump
9. ECT sensor
10. Starter
11. Knock sensor (2)
12. Compressor clutch
13. CMP actuator solenoid valve
14. CMP actuator solenoid valve

36616_CAMA_G0251

Fig. 114 Front left side engine components—3.6L engines

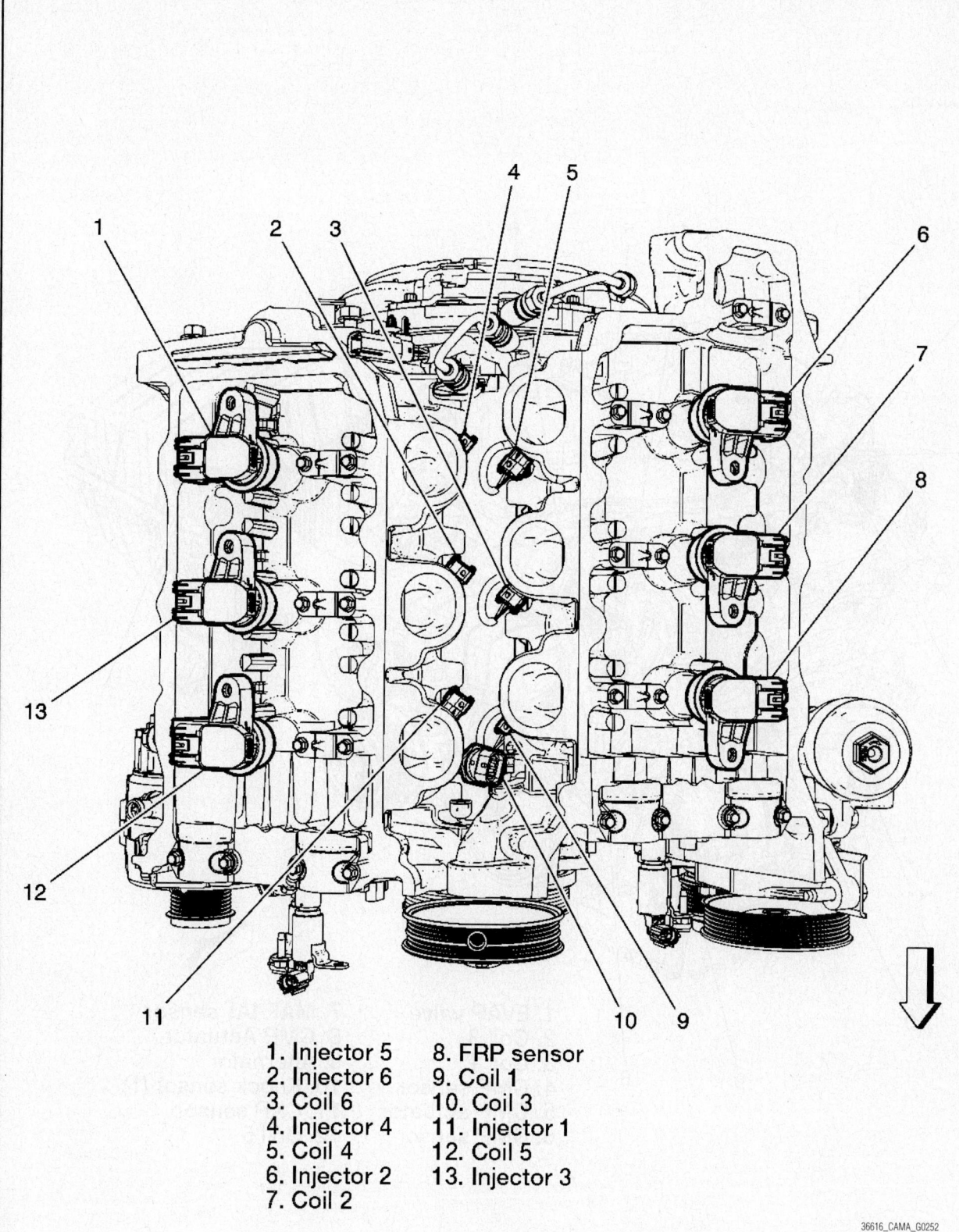

1. Injector 5
2. Injector 6
3. Coil 6
4. Injector 4
5. Coil 4
6. Injector 2
7. Coil 2
8. FRP sensor
9. Coil 1
10. Coil 3
11. Injector 1
12. Coil 5
13. Injector 3

36616_CAMA_G0252

Fig. 115 Top of engine components—3.6L engines

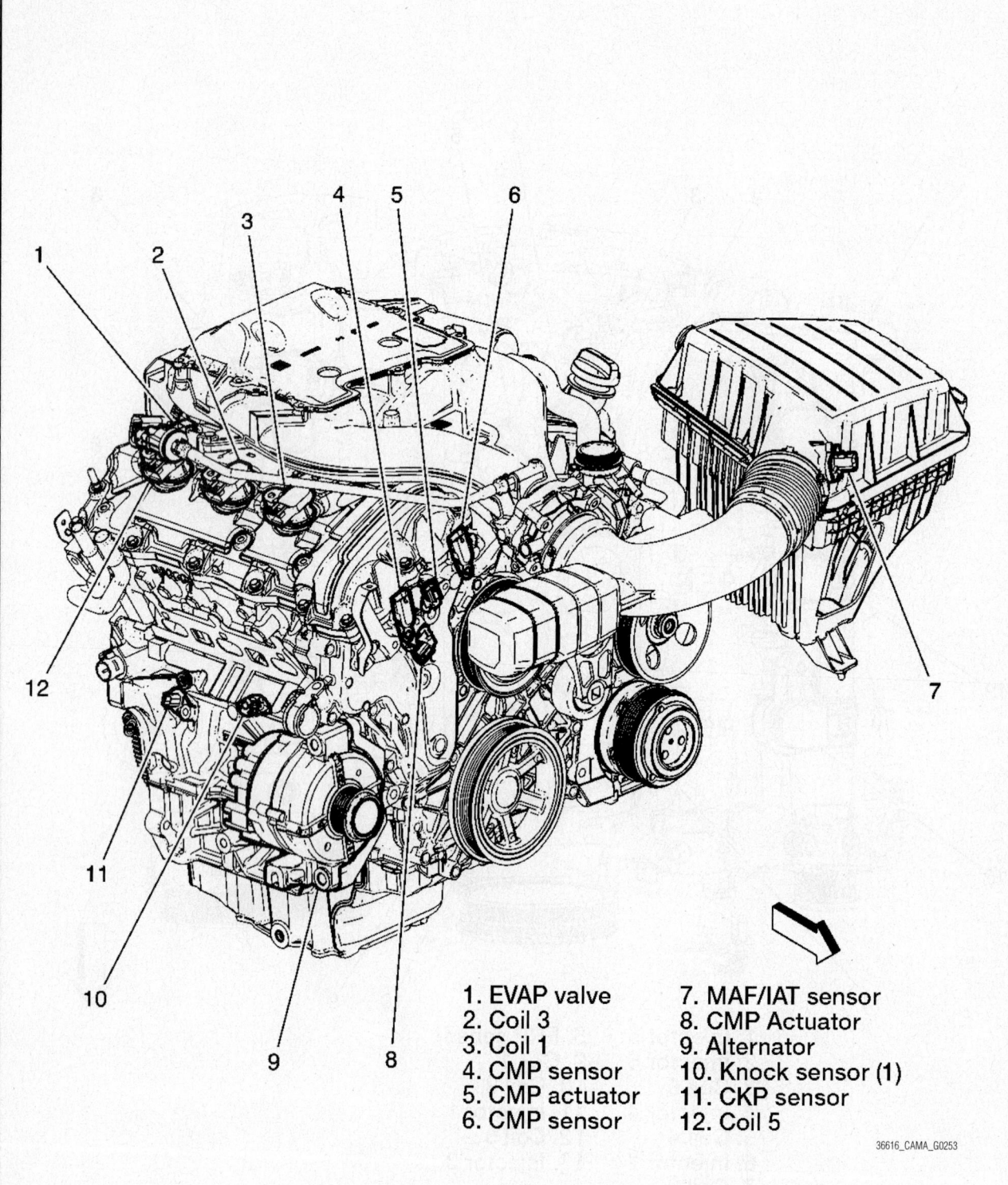

1. EVAP valve
2. Coil 3
3. Coil 1
4. CMP sensor
5. CMP actuator
6. CMP sensor
7. MAF/IAT sensor
8. CMP Actuator
9. Alternator
10. Knock sensor (1)
11. CKP sensor
12. Coil 5

36616_CAMA_G0253

Fig. 116 Front right side engine components—3.6L engines

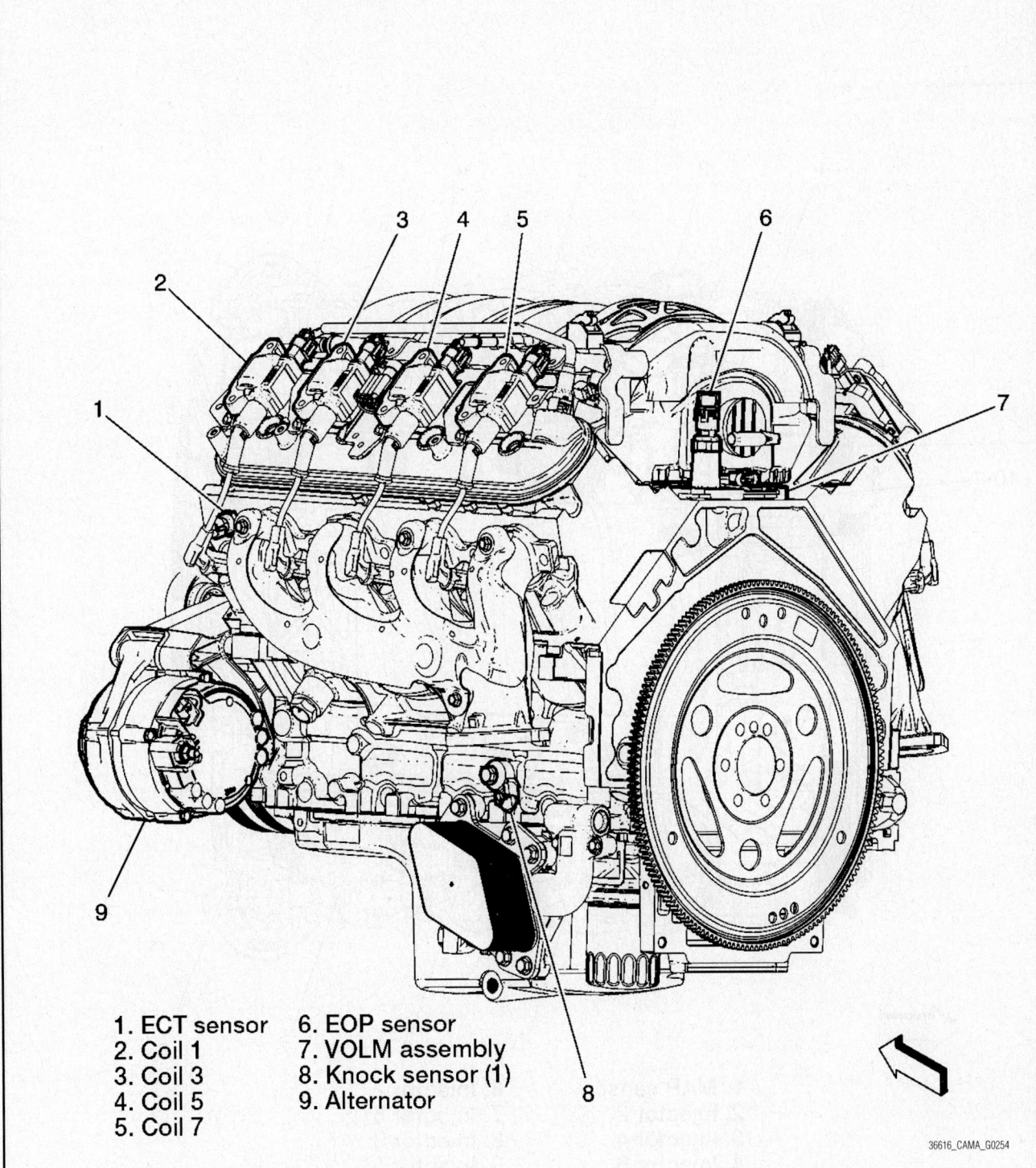

1. ECT sensor
2. Coil 1
3. Coil 3
4. Coil 5
5. Coil 7
6. EOP sensor
7. VOLM assembly
8. Knock sensor (1)
9. Alternator

36616_CAMA_G0254

Fig. 117 Left rear side engine components—6.2L engines

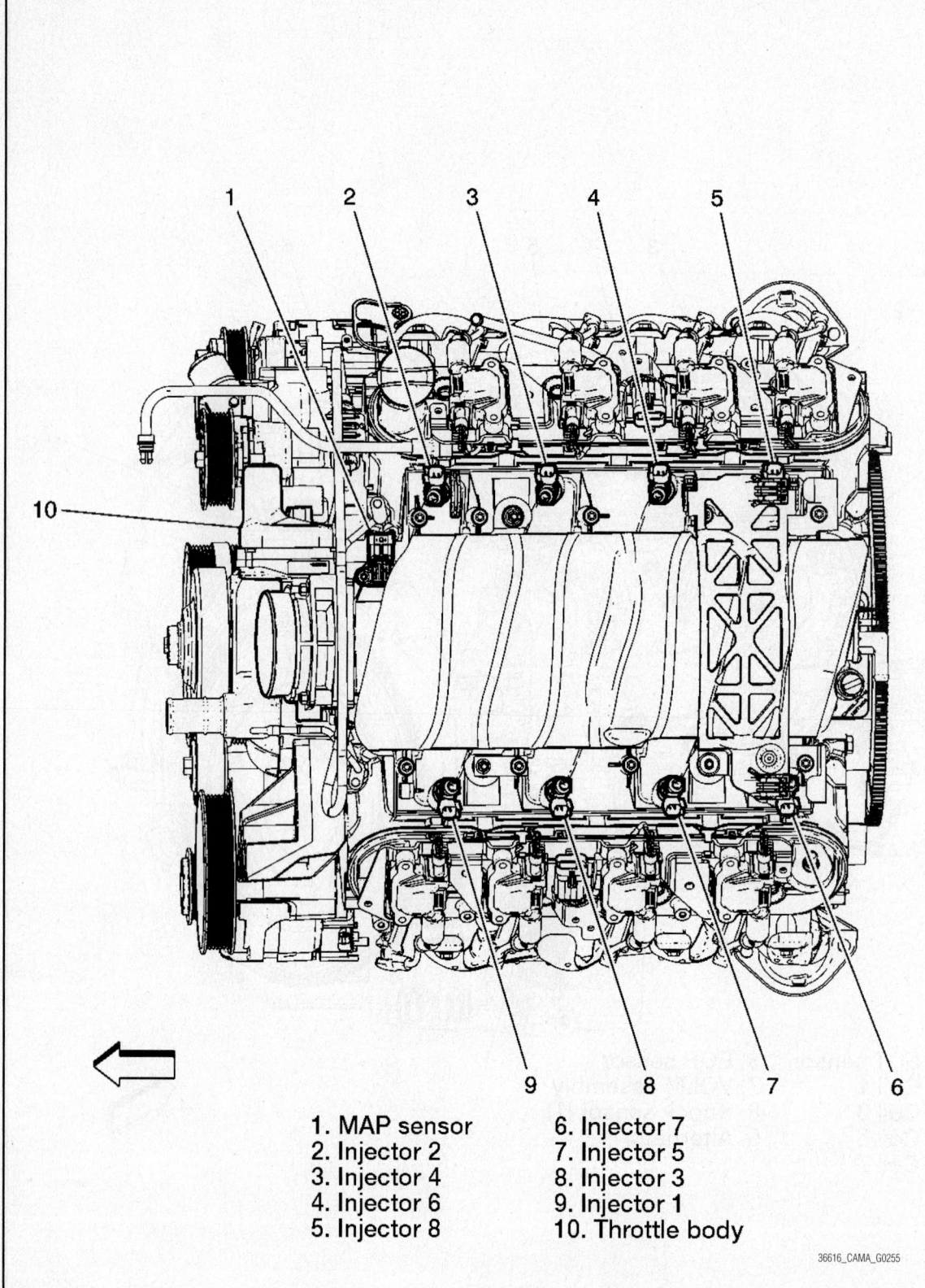

1. MAP sensor
2. Injector 2
3. Injector 4
4. Injector 6
5. Injector 8
6. Injector 7
7. Injector 5
8. Injector 3
9. Injector 1
10. Throttle body

36616_CAMA_G0255

Fig. 118 Top of engine components—6.2L engines

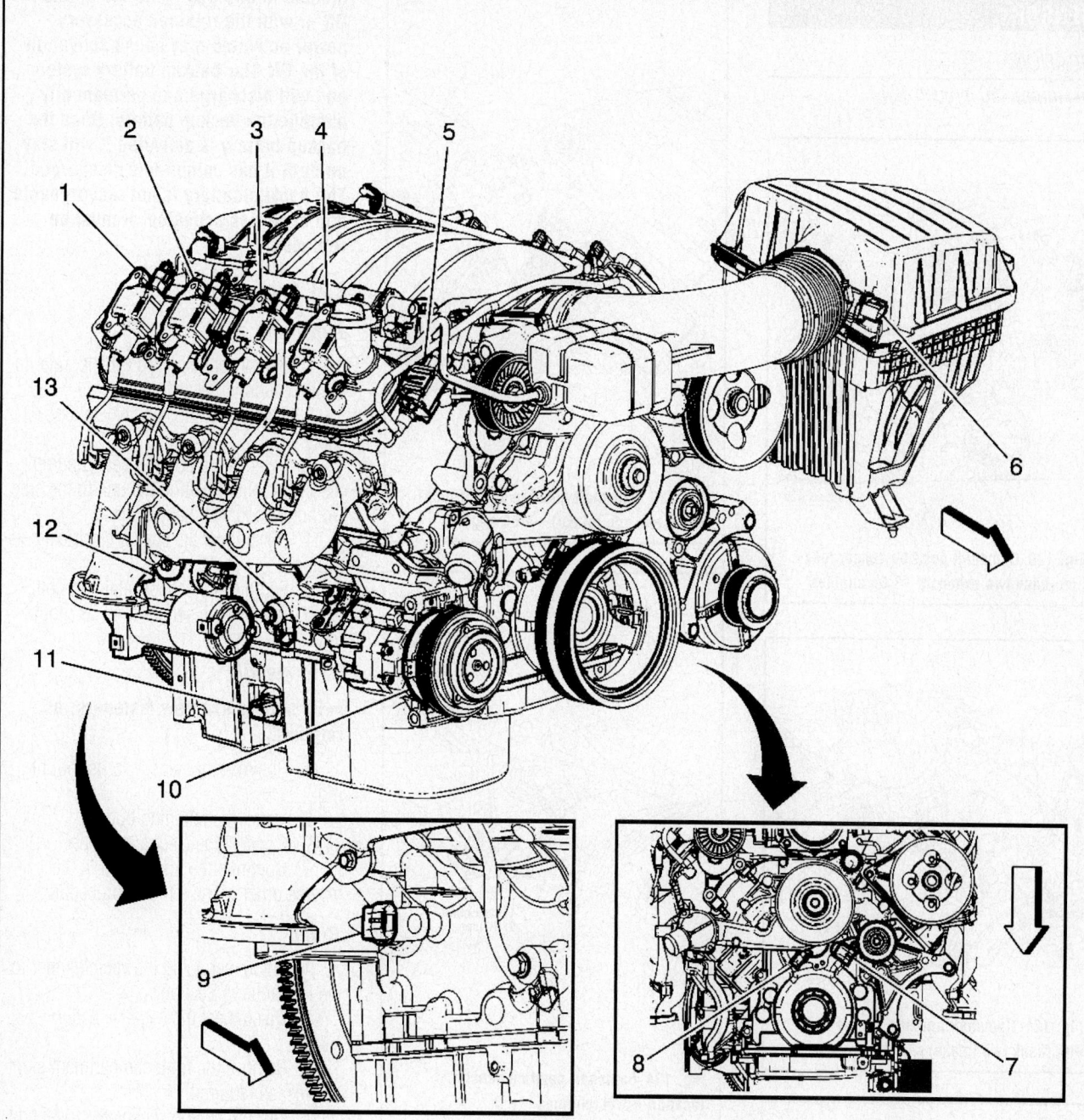

1. Coil 8
2. Coil 6
3. Coil 4
4. Coil 2
5. EVAP canister
6. MAF/IAT sensor
7. CMP sensor
8. CMP sensor
9. CKP sensor
10. Compressor clutch
11. Engine oil and level sensor
12. Starter
13 Knock sensor (2)

36616_CAMA_G0256

Fig. 119 Front right side engine components—6.2L engines

CAMSHAFT POSITION (CMP) SENSOR

LOCATION

See Figures 120 through 124.

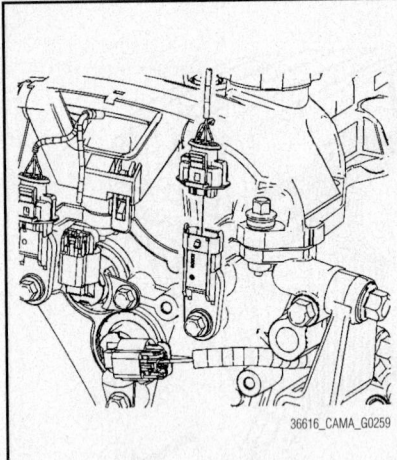

Fig. 120 Camshaft position sensor location (bank two exhaust)—3.6L engines

Fig. 121 Camshaft position sensor location (bank two intake)—3.6L engines

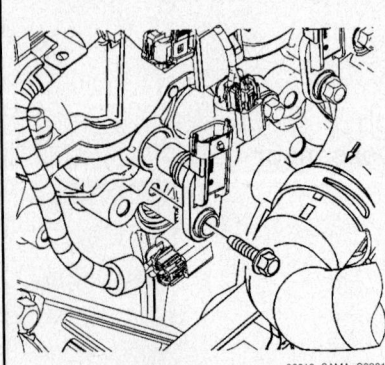

Fig. 122 Camshaft position sensor location (bank one exhaust)—3.6L engines

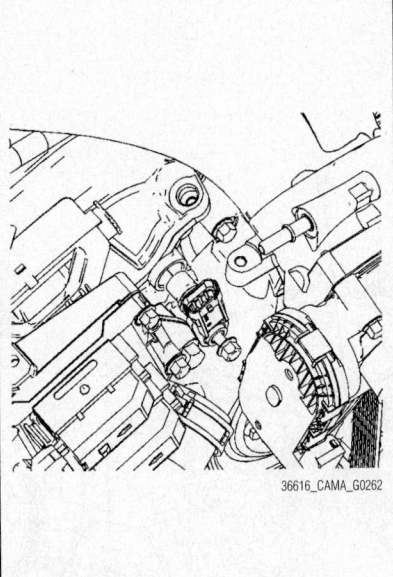

Fig. 123 Camshaft position sensor location (bank one intake)—3.6L engines

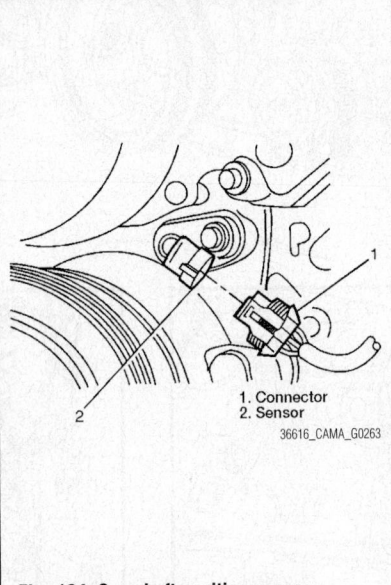

1. Connector
2. Sensor

Fig. 124 Camshaft position sensor location—6.2L engines

REMOVAL & INSTALLATION

➡**For vehicles equipped with ON Star (RPO UE1), with battery backup, the backup battery is a redundant power supply to allow limited ON Star functionality in the event of a main battery power disruption to the ON Star module (VCIM). Do not disconnect the main vehicle battery or remove the ON Star fuse with the ignition key in any position other than OFF. Retained accessory power should be allowed to time out or be disabled by opening the driver's side door before disconnecting**

power. **Disconnecting power to the module in any way while the ignition is ON or with the retained accessory power activated may cause activation of the ON Star backup battery system and will discharge and permanently damage the backup battery. Once the backup battery is activated it will stay on until it has completely discharged. The backup battery is not rechargeable and once it is activated, it must be replaced.**

3.6L Engines

Left

1. Before servicing the vehicle, refer to the Precautions Section.
2. Disconnect the negative battery cable.
3. Remove the power steering pump reservoir bolts. Position the unit to the side. Do not disconnect the fluid lines.
4. Disconnect the sensor electrical connector.
5. Remove the sensor retaining bolt.
6. Remove the sensor from its mounting.

To install:

➡**Be sure to use new fasteners, as required.**

7. Position the sensor to its mounting.
8. Install the retaining bolt.
9. Connect the electrical connector.
10. Continue the installation in the reverse order of the removal procedure.

Right

1. Before servicing the vehicle, refer to the Precautions Section.
2. Disconnect the negative battery cable.
3. Remove the front compartment sight shields, as required.
4. Disconnect the sensor electrical connector.
5. Remove the sensor retaining bolt.
6. Remove the sensor from its mounting.

To install:

➡**Be sure to use new fasteners, as required.**

7. Position the sensor to its mounting.
8. Install the retaining bolt.
9. Connect the electrical connector.
10. Continue the installation in the reverse order of the removal procedure.

6.2L Engines

1. Before servicing the vehicle, refer to the Precautions Section.
2. Disconnect the negative battery cable.
3. Remove the intake manifold cover.
4. Disconnect the electrical connector.
5. Remove the sensor retaining bolt.
6. Remove the sensor from its mounting.
7. Discard the O-ring.

To install:

➡**Be sure to use new fasteners, as required.**

8. Position the sensor to its mounting. Be sure to use a new O-ring.
9. Install the retaining bolt.
10. Connect the electrical connector.
11. Continue the installation in the reverse order of the removal procedure.

CRANKSHAFT POSITION (CKP) SENSOR

LOCATION

See Figures 125 and 126.

Refer to the accompanying illustrations for sensor location.

REMOVAL & INSTALLATION

➡**For vehicles equipped with ON Star (RPO UE1), with battery backup, the backup battery is a redundant power supply to allow limited ON Star functionality in the event of a main battery power disruption to the ON Star module (VCIM). Do not disconnect the main vehicle battery or remove the ON Star fuse with the ignition key in any position other than OFF. Retained accessory power should be allowed to time**

out or be disabled by opening the driver's side door before disconnecting power. Disconnecting power to the module in any way while the ignition is ON or with the retained accessory power activated may cause activation of the ON Star backup battery system and will discharge and permanently damage the backup battery. Once the backup battery is activated it will stay on until it has completely discharged. The backup battery is not rechargeable and once it is activated, it must be replaced.

3.6L Engines

1. Before servicing the vehicle, refer to the Precautions Section.
2. Disconnect the negative battery cable.
3. Raise and safely support the vehicle.
4. Remove the exhaust manifold heat shield.
5. Disconnect the electrical connector.
6. Remove the sensor retaining bolt.
7. Remove the sensor from its mounting.

To install:

➡**Be sure to use new fasteners, as required.**

8. Position the sensor to its mounting.
9. Install the retaining nuts/bolts.
10. Connect the electrical connector.
11. Continue the installation in the reverse order of the removal procedure.

6.2L Engines

1. Before servicing the vehicle, refer to the Precautions Section.
2. Disconnect the negative battery cable.

3. Raise and support the vehicle safely.
4. Remove the starter.
5. Disconnect the electrical connector.
6. Remove the sensor retaining bolt.
7. Remove the sensor from its mounting.

To install:

➡**Be sure to use new fasteners, as required.**

8. Position the sensor to its mounting.
9. Install the retaining bolt.
10. Connect the electrical connector.
11. Continue the installation in the reverse order of the removal procedure.

ENGINE COOLANT TEMPERATURE (ECT) SENSOR

LOCATION

See Figures 127 and 128.

Refer to the accompanying illustrations for sensor location.

REMOVAL & INSTALLATION

➡**For vehicles equipped with ON Star (RPO UE1), with battery backup, the backup battery is a redundant power supply to allow limited ON Star functionality in the event of a main battery power disruption to the ON Star module (VCIM). Do not disconnect the main vehicle battery or remove the ON Star fuse with the ignition key in any position other than OFF. Retained accessory power should be allowed to time out or be disabled by opening the driver's side door before disconnecting power. Disconnecting power to the module in any way while the ignition is ON or with the retained accessory power activated may**

36616_CAMA_G0265

Fig. 125 Crankshaft position sensor location—3.6L engines

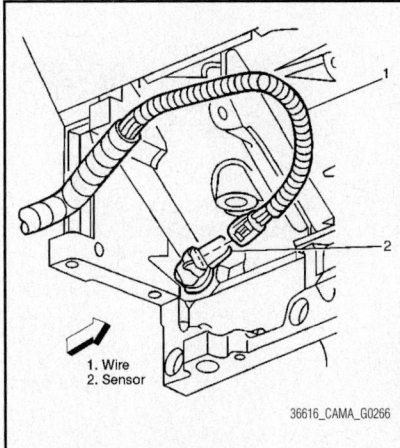

1. Wire
2. Sensor

36616_CAMA_G0266

Fig. 126 Crankshaft position sensor location—6.2L engines

36616_CAMA_G0268

Fig. 127 Engine coolant temperature sensor location—3.6L engines

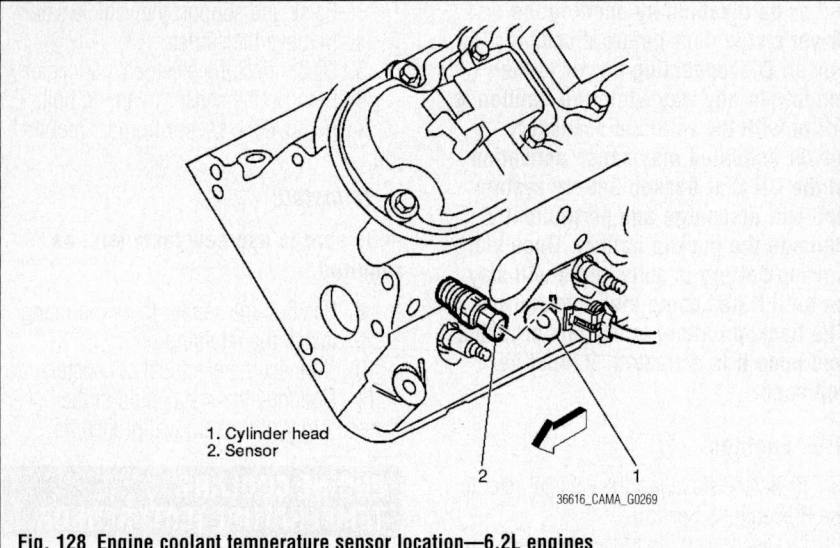

Fig. 128 Engine coolant temperature sensor location—6.2L engines

1. Cylinder head
2. Sensor

36616_CAMA_G0269

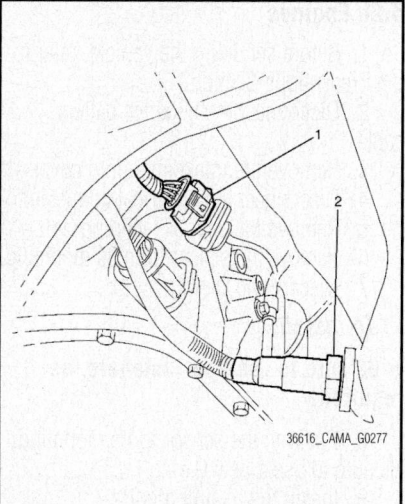

36616_CAMA_G0277

Fig. 130 Heated oxygen sensor location (bank one sensor two)—6.2L engines

cause activation of the ON Star backup battery system and will discharge and permanently damage the backup battery. Once the backup battery is activated it will stay on until it has completely discharged. The backup battery is not rechargeable and once it is activated, it must be replaced.

3.6L Engines

1. Before servicing the vehicle, refer to the Precautions Section.

2. Disconnect the negative battery cable.

3. Drain the cooling system. Properly dispose of used engine coolant.

4. Remove the dipstick indicator.

5. Slide the electrical connector shield off of the electrical connector.

6. Disconnect the electrical connector.

7. Remove the sensor from its mounting.

To install:

➡Be sure to use new fasteners, as required.

8. Position the sensor to its mounting. Tighten the sensor to 16 ft. lbs. (22 Nm).

9. Connect the electrical connector.

10. Continue the installation in the reverse order of the removal procedure.

6.2L Engines

1. Before servicing the vehicle, refer to the Precautions Section.

2. Disconnect the negative battery cable.

3. Raise and support the vehicle safely.

4. Drain the cooling system, below the level of the sensor. Properly dispose of used engine coolant.

5. Lower the vehicle.

6. Disconnect the electrical connector.

7. Remove the sensor from its mounting.

To install:

➡Be sure to use new fasteners, as required.

8. Coat the threads of the new sensor with sealer.

9. Position the sensor to its mounting. Tighten to 15 ft. lbs. (20 Nm).

10. Connect the electrical connector.

11. Continue the installation in the reverse order of the removal procedure.

HEATED OXYGEN (HO2S) SENSOR

LOCATION

See Figures 129 through 136.

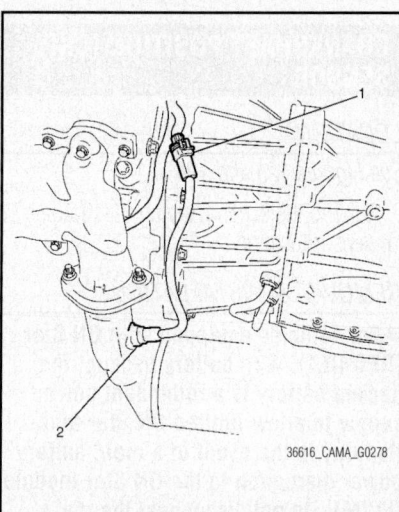

36616_CAMA_G0278

Fig. 131 Heated oxygen sensor location (bank two sensor one)—6.2L engines

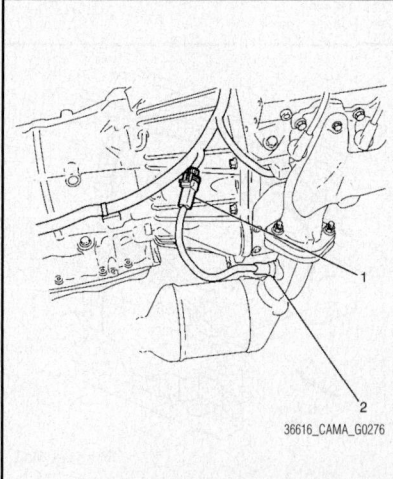

36616_CAMA_G0276

Fig. 129 Heated oxygen sensor location (bank one sensor one)—6.2L engines

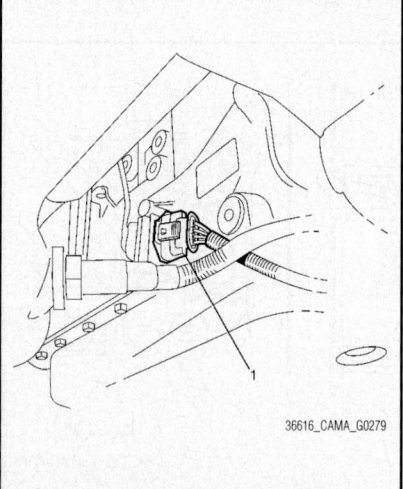

36616_CAMA_G0279

Fig. 132 Heated oxygen sensor location (bank two sensor two)—6.2L engines

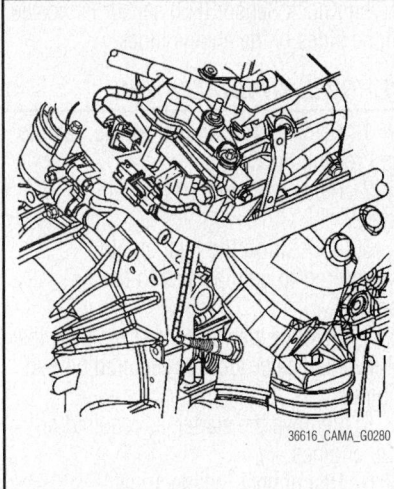

**Fig. 133 Heated oxygen sensor location
(bank one sensor one)—3.6L engines**

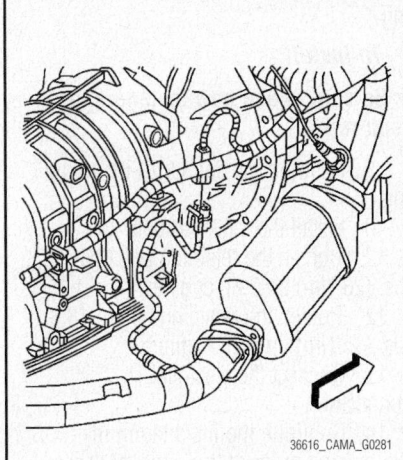

**Fig. 134 Heated oxygen sensor location
(bank one sensor two)—3.6L engines**

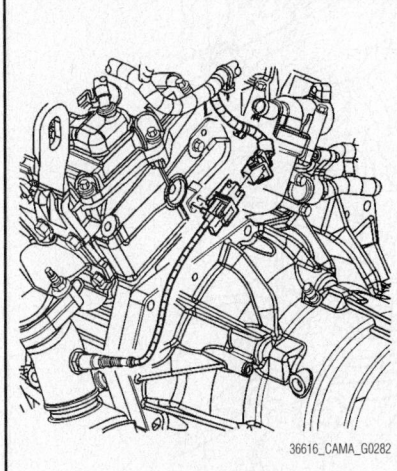

**Fig. 135 Heated oxygen sensor location
(bank two sensor one)—3.6L engines**

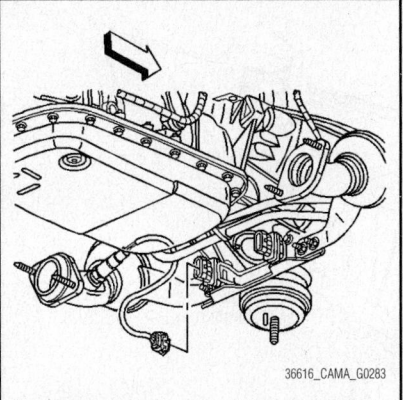

**Fig. 136 Heated oxygen sensor location
(bank two sensor two)—3.6L engines**

The Heated Oxygen Sensors (HO2S) are
threaded into the exhaust pipes.

REMOVAL & INSTALLATION

➡For vehicles equipped with ON Star
(RPO UE1), with battery backup, the
backup battery is a redundant power
supply to allow limited ON Star functionality in the event of a main battery
power disruption to the ON Star module
(VCIM). Do not disconnect the main
vehicle battery or remove the ON Star
fuse with the ignition key in any position other than OFF. Retained accessory power should be allowed to time
out or be disabled by opening the
driver's side door before disconnecting
power. Disconnecting power to the
module in any way while the ignition is
ON or with the retained accessory
power activated may cause activation
of the ON Star backup battery system
and will discharge and permanently
damage the backup battery. Once the
backup battery is activated it will stay
on until it has completely discharged.
The backup battery is not rechargeable
and once it is activated, it must be
replaced.

➡Replace the sensor if the pigtail
wiring, connector, or terminal is damaged. The external clean air reference
is obtained by way of the sensor signal
and heater wires. Any attempt to repair
the wires or connectors could result in
obstruction of the air reference. Make
sure the lead wires are not sharply
bent or kinked as the air reference
could become blocked.

3.6L Engines

1. Before servicing the vehicle, refer to
the Precautions Section.
2. Disconnect the negative battery cable.

3. Remove the front intake manifold
cover, as required.
4. Disconnect the electrical connector.

➡**Depending on which sensor is being
removed, it may be necessary to raise
and support the vehicle before disconnecting the electrical connector.**

5. Raise and support the vehicle safely.
6. Remove the sensor from its mounting.

To install:

➡**Be sure to use new fasteners, as
required.**

7. If reusing the old sensor, coat the
threads with GM antiseize compound
5613695 or equivalent.
8. New sensors are already coated;
additional compound is not needed.
9. Position the sensor to its mounting.
10. Tighten the sensor to 31 ft. lbs. (42
Nm).
11. Connect the electrical connector.
12. Continue the installation in the
reverse order of the removal procedure.

6.2L Engines

1. Before servicing the vehicle, refer to
the Precautions Section.
2. Disconnect the negative battery
cable.
3. Raise and support the vehicle
safely.
4. Disconnect the electrical connector.
5. Remove the sensor from its mounting.

To install:

➡**Be sure to use new fasteners, as
required.**

6. If reusing the old sensor, coat the
threads with GM antiseize compound
5613695 or equivalent.
7. New sensors are already coated;
additional compound is not needed.
8. Position the sensor to its mounting.
9. Tighten the sensor to 31 ft. lbs. (42
Nm).
10. Connect the electrical connector.
11. Continue the installation in the
reverse order of the removal procedure.

**INTAKE AIR TEMPERATURE
(IAT) SENSOR**

LOCATION

See Figures 137 and 138.

The Intake Air Temperature (IAT) Sensor
is integrated with the MAF sensor, it is
located on the air cleaner assembly.

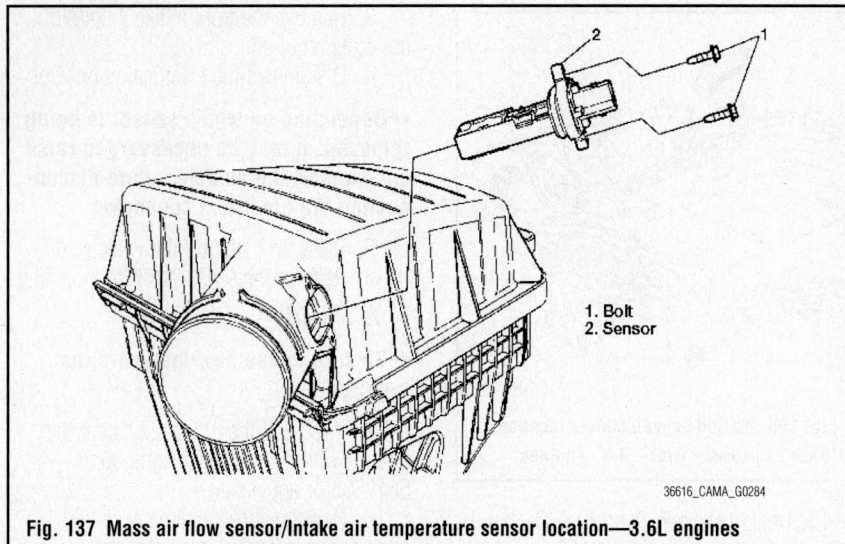

1. Bolt
2. Sensor

Fig. 137 Mass air flow sensor/Intake air temperature sensor location—3.6L engines

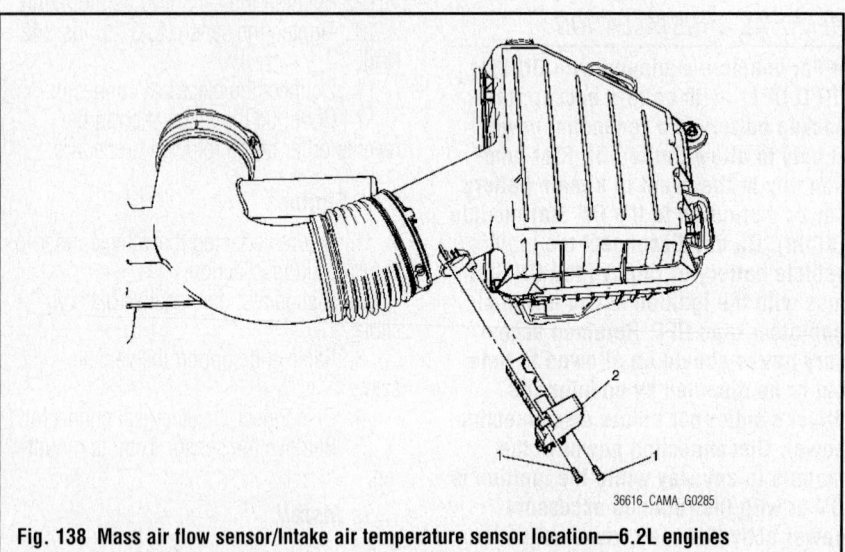

Fig. 138 Mass air flow sensor/Intake air temperature sensor location—6.2L engines

REMOVAL & INSTALLATION

1. Before servicing the vehicle, refer to the Precautions Section.
2. Disconnect the electrical connector.
3. Remove the sensor mounting screws.
4. Remove the sensor from its mounting.

To install:

➡Be sure to use new fasteners, as required.

5. Position the sensor to its mounting.
6. Install the retaining screws.
7. Connect the electrical connector.

KNOCK SENSOR (KS)

LOCATION

See Figures 139 through 141.

The Knock Sensor (KS) sensor is located on the sides of the engine block.

REMOVAL & INSTALLATION

1. Before servicing the vehicle, refer to the Precautions Section.
2. Raise and support the vehicle safely.
3. Reposition the heat shield as required to gain access to the sensor.
4. Remove the wiring harness from the oil level indicator tube, as required on 3.6L engines.
5. Remove the starter, as required on 6.2L engines.
6. Disconnect the electrical connector.
7. Remove the sensor retaining bolt.
8. Remove the sensor from its mounting.

To install:

➡Be sure to use new fasteners, as required.

9. Position the sensor to its mounting.
10. Install the retaining bolt.
11. Tighten the retaining bolt to 17 ft. lbs. (23 Nm) on 3.6L engines.
12. Tighten the retaining bolt to 18 ft. lbs. (25 Nm) on 6.2L engines.
13. Connect the electrical connector.
14. Continue the installation in the reverse order of the removal procedure.

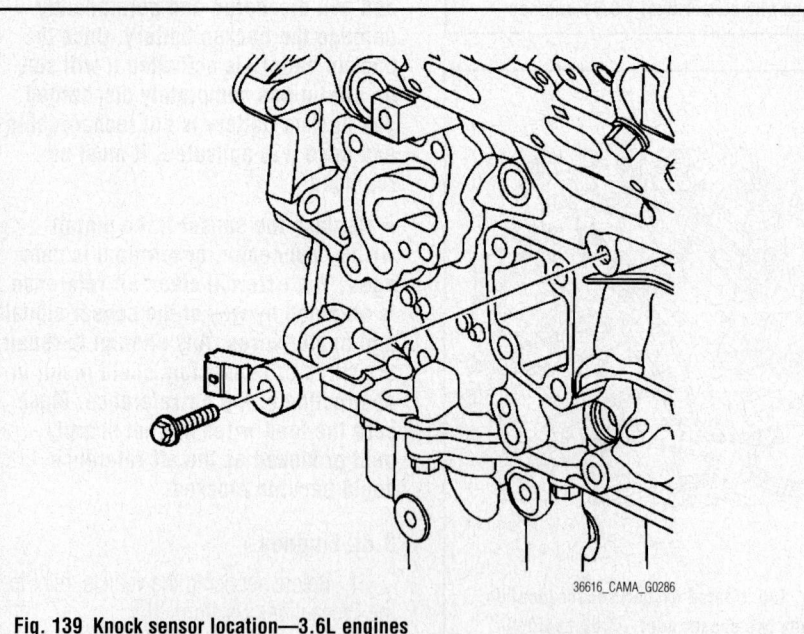

Fig. 139 Knock sensor location—3.6L engines

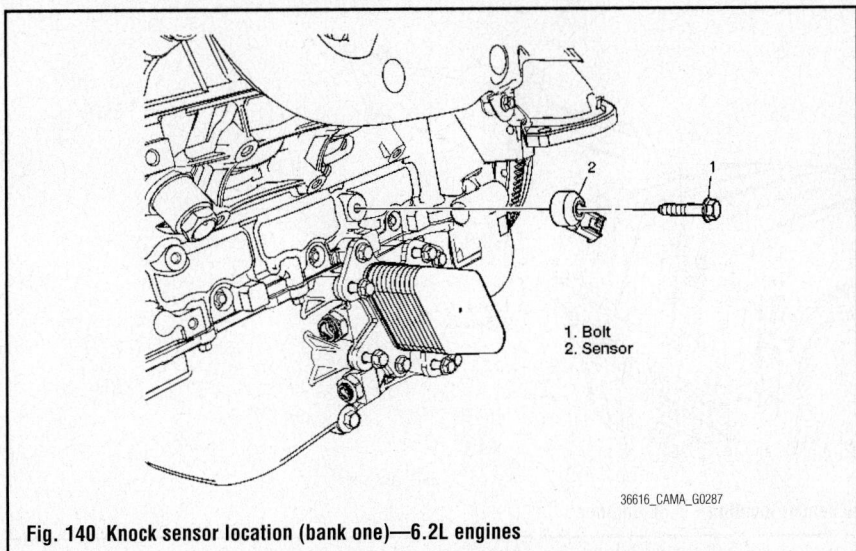

Fig. 140 Knock sensor location (bank one)—6.2L engines

1. Bolt
2. Sensor

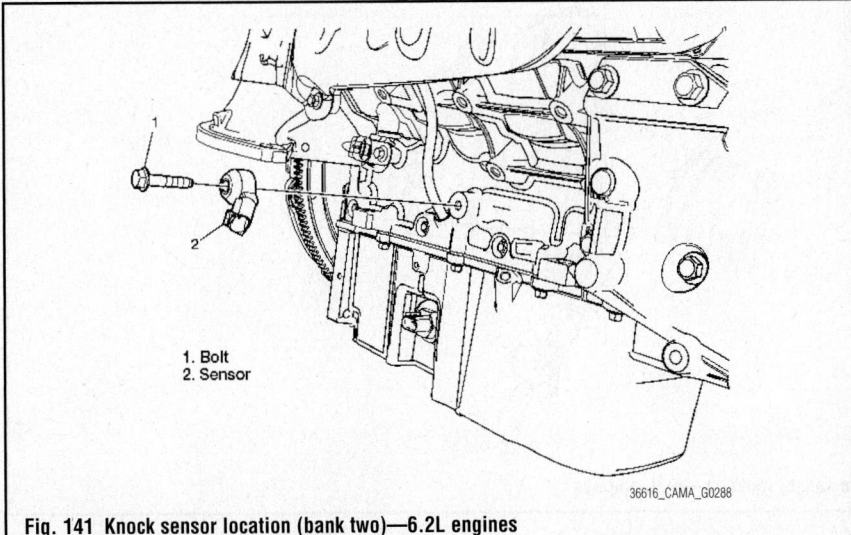

Fig. 141 Knock sensor location (bank two)—6.2L engines

1. Bolt
2. Sensor

MANIFOLD ABSOLUTE PRESSURE (MAP) SENSOR

LOCATION

See Figure 142.

The Manifold Absolute Pressure (MAP) Sensor It is located on the intake manifold.

REMOVAL & INSTALLATION

➡For vehicles equipped with ON Star (RPO UE1), with battery backup, the backup battery is a redundant power supply to allow limited ON Star functionality in the event of a main battery power disruption to the ON Star module (VCIM). Do not disconnect the main vehicle battery or remove the ON Star fuse with the ignition key in any position other than OFF. Retained accessory power should be allowed to time out or be disabled by opening the driver's side

door before disconnecting power. Disconnecting power to the module in any way while the ignition is ON or with the retained accessory power activated may cause activation of the ON Star backup battery system and will discharge and permanently damage the backup battery. Once the backup battery is activated it will stay on until it has completely discharged. The backup battery is not rechargeable and once it is activated, it must be replaced.

6.2L Engines

1. Before servicing the vehicle, refer to the Precautions Section.
2. Disconnect the negative battery cable.
3. Remove the intake manifold cover.
4. Disconnect the electrical connector.
5. Remove the sensor retaining screw.
6. Remove the sensor from its mounting.

To install:

➡Be sure to use new fasteners, as required.

7. Position the sensor to its mounting.
8. Install the retaining screw.
9. Connect the electrical connector.
10. Continue the installation in the reverse order of the removal procedure.

MASS AIR FLOW (MAF) SENSOR

LOCATION

See Figures 143 and 144.

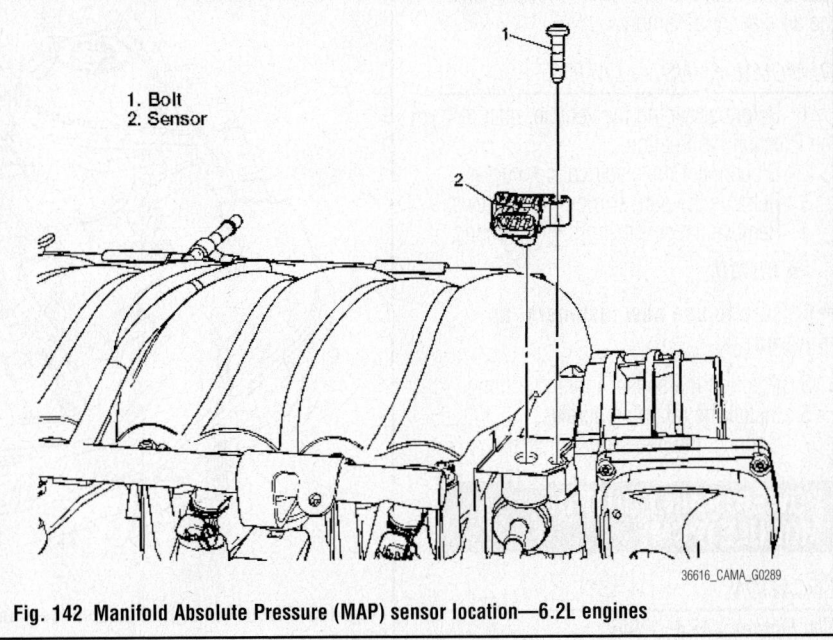

1. Bolt
2. Sensor

Fig. 142 Manifold Absolute Pressure (MAP) sensor location—6.2L engines

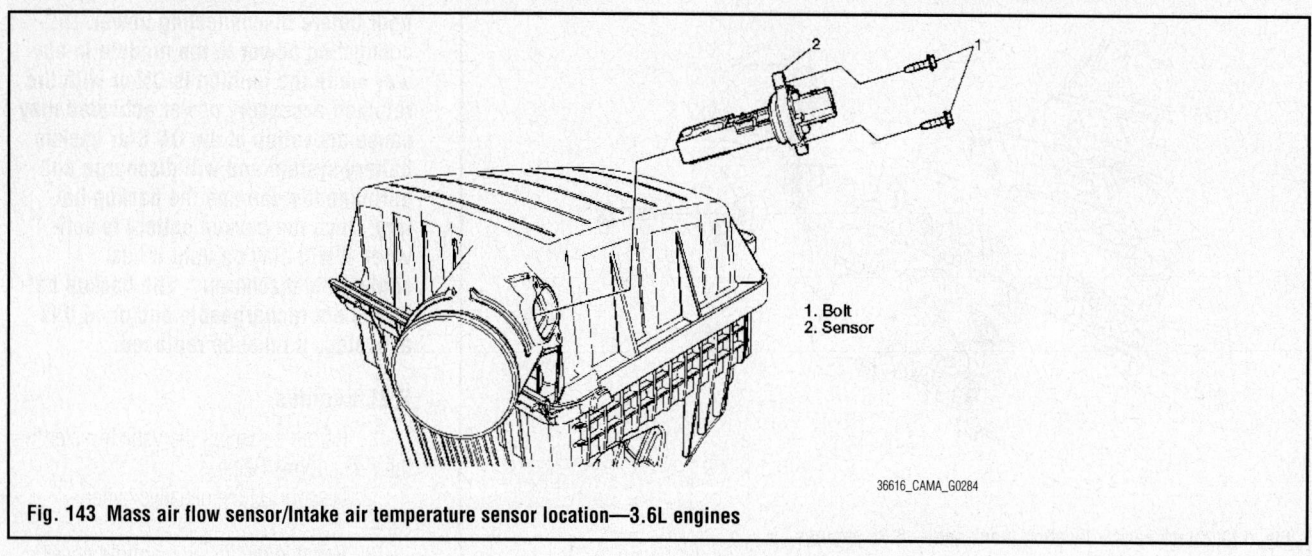

1. Bolt
2. Sensor

Fig. 143 Mass air flow sensor/Intake air temperature sensor location—3.6L engines

36616_CAMA_G0284

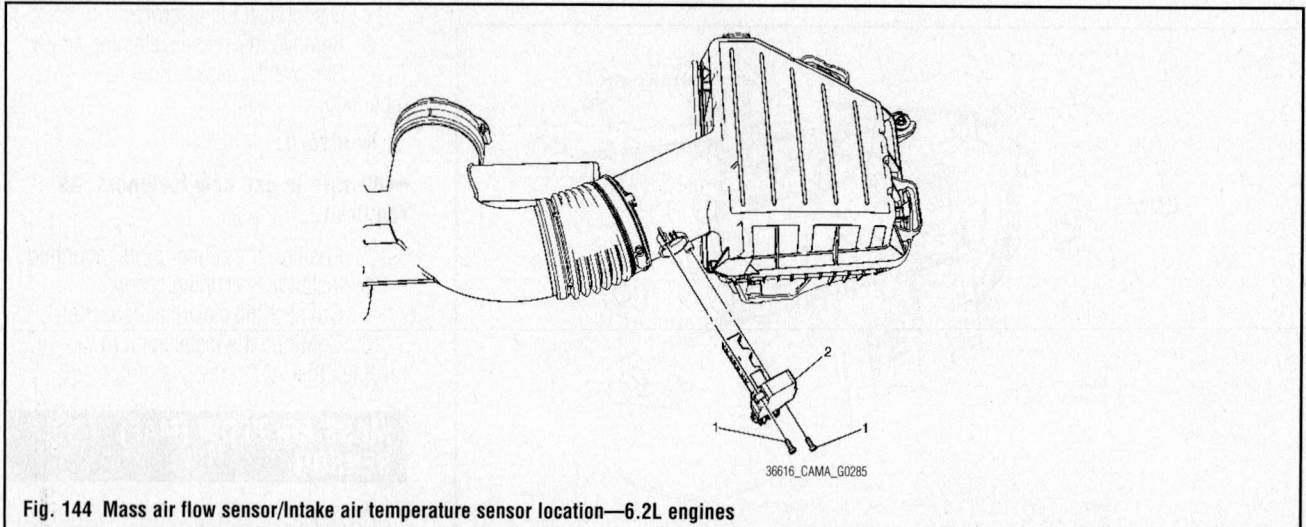

36616_CAMA_G0285

Fig. 144 Mass air flow sensor/Intake air temperature sensor location—6.2L engines

The Mass Air Flow (MAF) Sensor is integrated with the IAT sensor, it is located on the air cleaner assembly.

REMOVAL & INSTALLATION

1. Before servicing the vehicle, refer to the Precautions Section.
2. Disconnect the electrical connector.
3. Remove the sensor mounting screws.
4. Remove the sensor from its mounting.

To install:

➡ **Be sure to use new fasteners, as required.**

5. Position the sensor to its mounting.
6. Install the retaining screws.
7. Connect the electrical connector.

POWERTRAIN CONTROL MODULE (PCM)

LOCATION

See Figures 145 and 146.

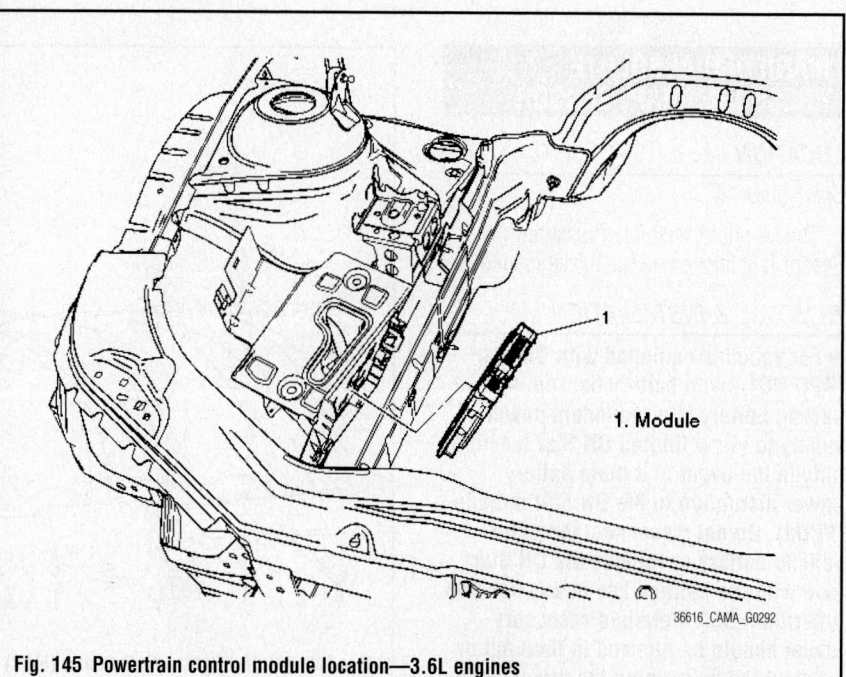

1. Module

Fig. 145 Powertrain control module location—3.6L engines

36616_CAMA_G0292

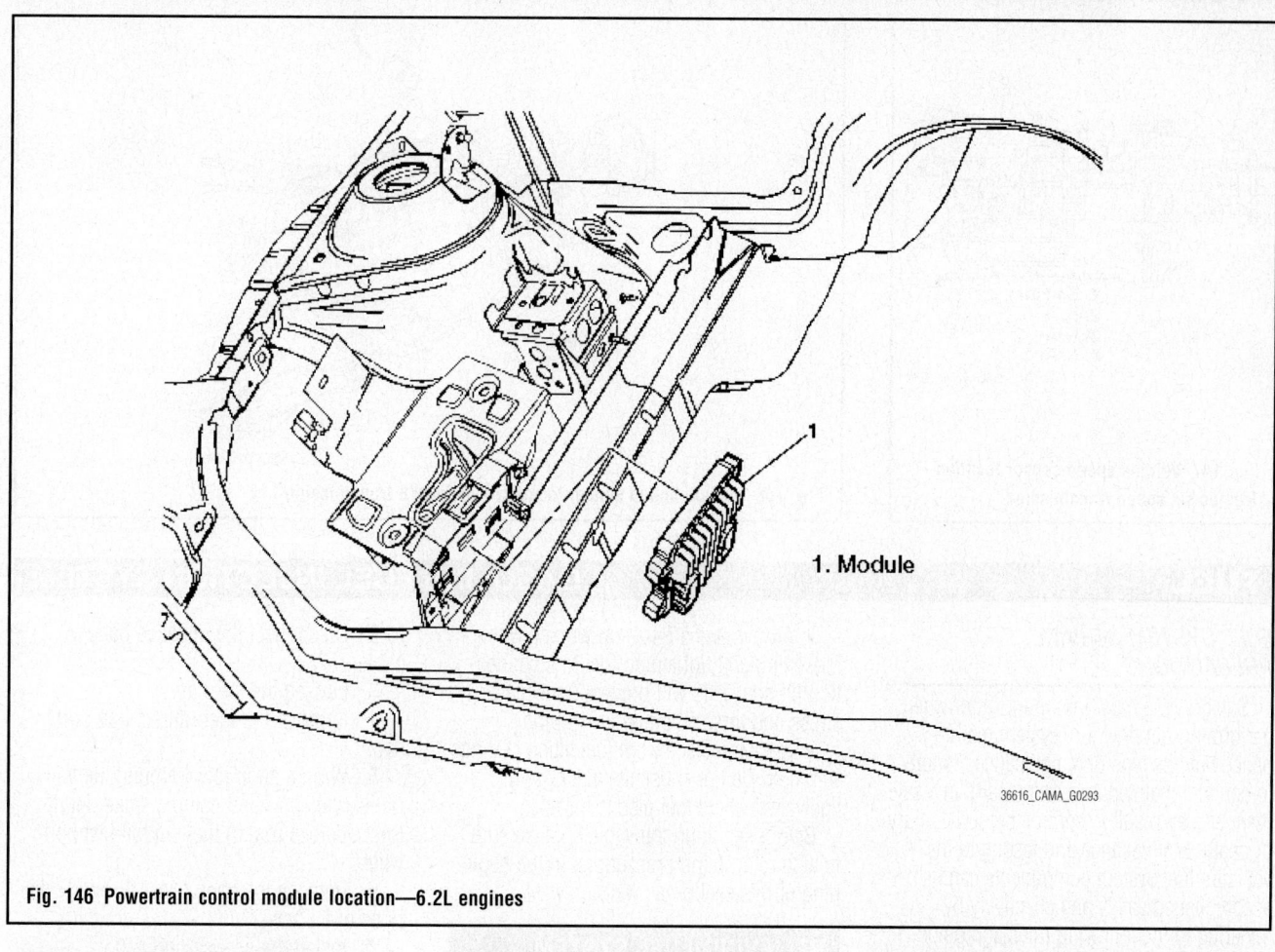

Fig. 146 Powertrain control module location—6.2L engines

REMOVAL & INSTALLATION

➡For vehicles equipped with ON Star (RPO UE1), with battery backup, the backup battery is a redundant power supply to allow limited ON Star functionality in the event of a main battery power disruption to the ON Star module (VCIM). Do not disconnect the main vehicle battery or remove the ON Star fuse with the ignition key in any position other than OFF. Retained accessory power should be allowed to time out or be disabled by opening the driver's side door before disconnecting power. Disconnecting power to the module in any way while the ignition is ON or with the retained accessory power activated may cause activation of the ON Star backup battery system and will discharge and permanently damage the backup battery. Once the backup battery is activated it will stay on until it has completely discharged. The backup battery is not rechargeable and once it is activated, it must be replaced.

➡It is necessary to record the remaining engine oil life. If the replacement module is not programmed with the remaining engine oil life, the engine oil life will default to 100 percent. If the replacement module is not programmed with the remaining engine oil life, the engine oil must be changed at 3,000 miles (5,000km) from the last oil change. A scan tool must be used to retrieve the PCM data. This information must be transferred to the new PCM.

1. Before servicing the vehicle, refer to the Precautions Section.
2. Disconnect the negative battery cable.
3. Disengage the harness connections from the PCM.
4. Disengage the retainer tabs securing the PCM to the bracket. Remove the PCM from the engine compartment.

To install:

➡Be sure to use new fasteners, as required.

5. Position the PCM on its mounting.
6. Continue the installation in the reverse order of the removal procedure.

➡If a new PCM was installed using the GM diagnostic scan tool, or equivalent, refer to the on-screen reprogramming directions and reprogram the PCM.

VEHICLE SPEED SENSOR (VSS)

LOCATION

See Figures 147 and 148.

REMOVAL & INSTALLATION

1. Before servicing the vehicle, refer to the Precautions Section.
2. Raise and safely support the vehicle.
3. Remove the transmission mount, Aisin AY6 transmission.
4. Disconnect the electrical connector.
5. Remove the sensor retaining bolt.
6. Remove the sensor from its mounting.

To install:

➡Be sure to use new fasteners, as required.

7. Position the sensor to its mounting.
8. Install the retaining bolt.
9. Connect the electrical connector.
10. Continue the installation in the reverse order of the removal procedure.

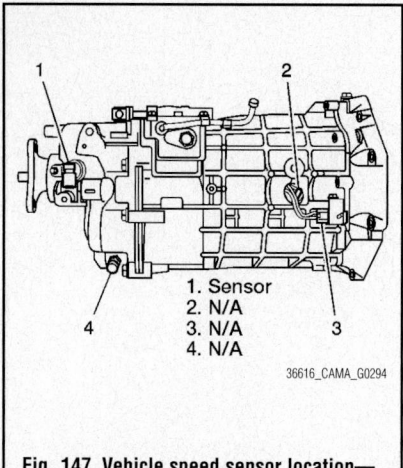

Fig. 147 Vehicle speed sensor location—Tremec six speed transmission

1. Sensor
2. N/A
3. N/A
4. N/A

36616_CAMA_G0294

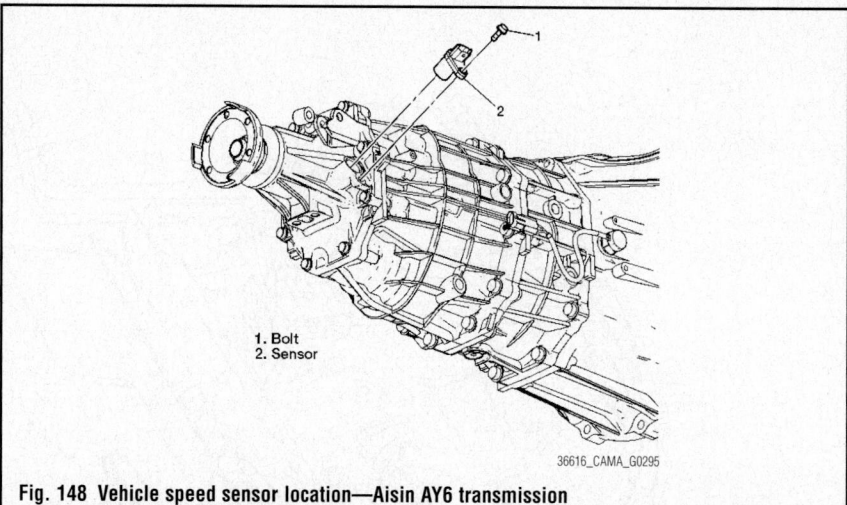

Fig. 148 Vehicle speed sensor location—Aisin AY6 transmission

1. Bolt
2. Sensor

36616_CAMA_G0295

FUEL

GASOLINE FUEL INJECTION SYSTEM

FUEL SYSTEM SERVICE PRECAUTIONS

Safety is the most important factor when performing not only fuel system maintenance but any type of maintenance. Failure to conduct maintenance and repairs in a safe manner may result in serious personal injury or death. Maintenance and testing of the vehicle's fuel system components can be accomplished safely and effectively by adhering to the following rules and guidelines.

• To avoid the possibility of fire and personal injury, always disconnect the negative battery cable unless the repair or test procedure requires that battery voltage be applied.

• Always relieve the fuel system pressure prior to disconnecting any fuel system component (injector, fuel rail, pressure regulator, etc.), fitting or fuel line connection. Exercise extreme caution whenever relieving fuel system pressure to avoid exposing skin, face and eyes to fuel spray. Please be advised that fuel under pressure may penetrate the skin or any part of the body that it contacts.

• Always place a shop towel or cloth around the fitting or connection prior to loosening to absorb any excess fuel due to spillage. Ensure that all fuel spillage (should it occur) is quickly removed from engine surfaces. Ensure that all fuel soaked cloths or towels are deposited into a suitable waste container.

• Always keep a dry chemical (Class B) fire extinguisher near the work area.

• Do not allow fuel spray or fuel vapors to come into contact with a spark or open flame.

• Always use a back–up wrench when loosening and tightening fuel line connection fittings. This will prevent unnecessary stress and torsion to fuel line piping.

• Always replace worn fuel fitting O–rings with new. Do not substitute fuel hose or equivalent where fuel pipe is installed.

Before servicing the vehicle, make sure to also refer to the precautions in the beginning of this section as well.

RELIEVING FUEL SYSTEM PRESSURE

PROCEDURE

3.6L Engines

➡A GM diagnostic scan tool, or equivalent, will be necessary to relieve the fuel system pressure. Follow the directions on the scan tool to accomplish this procedure.

6.2L Engines

➡Remove the fuel tank cap and relieve the fuel system pressure before servicing the fuel system in order to reduce the risk of personal injury. After you relieve the fuel system pressure, a small amount of fuel may be released when servicing the fuel lines, the fuel injection pump, or the connections. In order to reduce the risk of personal injury, cover the fuel system components with a shop towel before disconnection. Place the shop towel in an approved container when the disconnection is complete.

1. Before servicing the vehicle, refer to the Precautions Section.

2. Disconnect the negative battery cable.
3. Loosen the fuel cap.
4. Remove the fuel rail service port cap.
5. Wrap a shop towel around the fuel rail service port and using a small flat tip tool, depress (open) the fuel rail test port valve.
6. Remove the shop towel. Properly dispose of the towel.
7. Install the service port cap.
8. Install the engine cover, as required.
9. Tighten the fuel cap.

FUEL FILTER

REMOVAL & INSTALLATION

The fuel filter is integral with the fuel pump/sender assembly in the fuel tank.

FUEL PUMP

REMOVAL & INSTALLATION

3.6L Engines

See Figure 149.

➡For vehicles equipped with ON Star (RPO UE1), with battery backup, the backup battery is a redundant power supply to allow limited ON Star functionality in the event of a main battery power disruption to the ON Star module (VCIM). Do not disconnect the main vehicle battery or remove the ON Star fuse with the ignition key in any position other than OFF. Retained accessory power should be allowed to time out or be disabled by opening the driver's side door before disconnecting

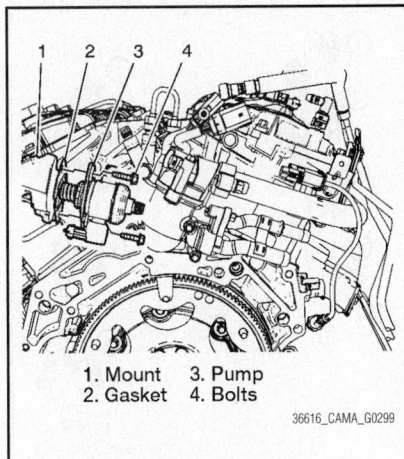

1. Mount   3. Pump
2. Gasket   4. Bolts

36616_CAMA_G0299

Fig. 149 Fuel pump and related components—3.6L engines

power. Disconnecting power to the module in any way while the ignition is ON or with the retained accessory power activated may cause activation of the ON Star backup battery system and will discharge and permanently damage the backup battery. Once the backup battery is activated it will stay on until it has completely discharged. The backup battery is not rechargeable and once it is activated, it must be replaced.

➡The following procedure is for servicing the right side fuel tank module. At this time the manufacturer does not provide service information for the left side.

1. Before servicing the vehicle, refer to the Precautions Section.
2. Disconnect the negative battery cable.
3. Properly relieve the fuel system pressure.
4. Remove the cross vehicle brace.
5. Remove the high pressure fuel pump shield.
6. Remove the intake manifold.
7. Remove the windshield wiper motor.
8. Disconnect the engine wiring harness electrical connector.
9. Remove the radiator surge tank outlet pipe.
10. Remove the low pressure feed pipe.
11. Remove the high pressure feed pipe.
12. Remove and discard the pump retaining bolts.
13. Remove the pump.
14. Discard the gasket. Discard the)-ring.
15. Remove the high pressure fuel pump roller lifter.

To install:

➡Be sure to use new fasteners, as required.

➡The camshaft must be in the base circle position before the high pressure fuel pump is installed.

16. Use tool EN-48896 to ensure that the camshaft lobe is in the base circle position. At the base circle the tool will be flush with the head.
17. Lubricate the pump cylinder and roller lifter with camshaft prelube, part number 36616501 (992704 Canada) or equivalent.
18. Install the fuel pump roller lifter.
19. Install the new pump O-ring.

➡The fuel pump gasket has a retaining feature to hold the pump retaining bolts in place.

20. Position the new pump gasket and bolts to the pump.
21. Install the pump to the cylinder head. Force will be felt while tightening the bolts. Tighten the bolts to 11 ft. lbs. (15 Nm).
22. Continue the installation in the reverse order of the removal procedure.
23. Turn ON the engine ignition, with the engine OFF for two seconds. Turn OFF the ignition, for ten seconds. Turn ON the ignition, with the engine OFF. Inspect for leaks. Correct as required.

FUEL PUMP MODULE

REMOVAL & INSTALLATION
See Figure 150.

➡For vehicles equipped with ON Star (RPO UE1), with battery backup, the backup battery is a redundant power supply to allow limited ON Star functionality in the event of a main battery power disruption to the ON Star module (VCIM). Do not disconnect the main vehicle battery or remove the ON Star fuse with the ignition key in any position other than OFF. Retained accessory power should be allowed to time out or be disabled by opening the driver's side door before disconnecting power. Disconnecting power to the module in any way while the ignition is ON or with the retained accessory power activated may cause activation of the ON Star backup battery system and will discharge and permanently damage the backup battery. Once the backup battery is activated it will stay on until it has completely discharged. The backup battery is not rechargeable

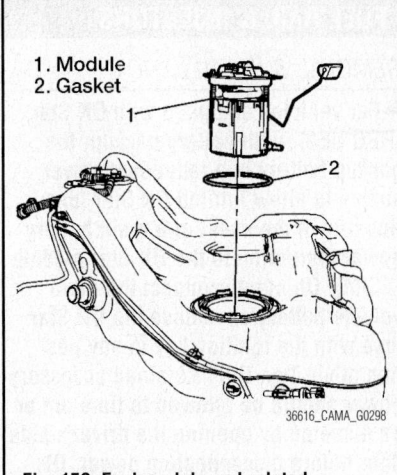

1. Module
2. Gasket

36616_CAMA_G0298

Fig. 150 Fuel module and related components—right side

and once it is activated, it must be replaced.

➡The following procedure is for servicing the right side fuel tank module. At this time the manufacturer does not provide service information for the left side.

1. Before servicing the vehicle, refer to the Precautions Section.
2. Disconnect the negative battery cable.
3. Properly relieve the fuel system pressure.
4. Raise and support the vehicle safely.
5. Drain the fuel tank.
6. Remove the fuel tank.
7. Disconnect the secondary fuel tank module electrical connector.
8. Rotate the lockring counterclockwise, using tool CH48482 or equivalent.
9. Remove the lockring.
10. Partially remove the primary fuel tank module in order to disconnect the fuel transfer hose quick connect fitting.
11. Remove the fuel tank module and seal.
12. Discard the seal.

To install:

➡Be sure to use new fasteners, as required.

13. Using a new seal, position the component to its mounting.
14. Partially install the fuel pump module in order to connect the fuel transfer hose quick connect fitting.
15. Rotate the lockring with the suitable tool and install it in position.
16. Continue the installation in the reverse order of the removal procedure.

FUEL RAIL & INJECTORS

REMOVAL & INSTALLATION

→For vehicles equipped with ON Star (RPO UE1), with battery backup, the backup battery is a redundant power supply to allow limited ON Star functionality in the event of a main battery power disruption to the ON Star module (VCIM). Do not disconnect the main vehicle battery or remove the ON Star fuse with the ignition key in any position other than OFF. Retained accessory power should be allowed to time out or be disabled by opening the driver's side door before disconnecting power. Disconnecting power to the module in any way while the ignition is ON or with the retained accessory power activated may cause activation of the ON Star backup battery system and will discharge and permanently damage the backup battery. Once the backup battery is activated it will stay on until it has completely discharged. The backup battery is not rechargeable and once it is activated, it must be replaced.

3.6L Engines

See Figures 151 through 153.

1. Before servicing the vehicle, refer to the Precautions Section.
2. Disconnect the negative battery cable.
3. Properly relieve the fuel system pressure.
4. Remove the cross vehicle brace.
5. Remove the fuel pump shield.
6. Remove the intake manifold.
7. Remove the high pressure fuel feed pipe.
8. Remove the fuel rail crossover pipe. Discard the pipe.
9. Remove the foam insulator from the fuel rails.
10. Disconnect the sensor electrical connector and cut the wire harness tie straps.
11. Remove the fuel rail bolts.

→Note the correct routing of the electrical wiring. Failure to reinstall the wiring properly could result in damage to the wiring.

12. Remove the fuel pressure sensor.
13. Remove and discard the direct fuel injector holddown clamps.

→The direct fuel injectors must be rebuilt whenever the injector has been released from the fuel rail or cylinder head.

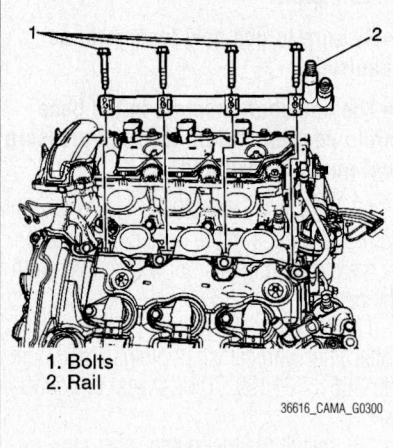

1. Bolts
2. Rail

36616_CAMA_G0300

Fig. 151 Fuel injector rail and related components—3.6L engines

14. Once the fuel rail is removed, remove the injectors. Be sure to rebuild them prior to installation.

To install:

→Be sure to use new fasteners, as required.

15. Install the rebuilt injectors to the cylinder head.
16. Install the new holddown clamps to the injector.
17. On the new fuel rail, lubricate the injector cups with silicon free engine oil.
18. Carefully place the fuel rail into position, placing the front into the rail over the front injector and rotating the rear downward.
19. Install the two outer bolts first, then the two inner bolts. Hand tighten.
20. Tighten the bolts in sequence and to 106 inch lbs. (12 Nm) for first pass and 17 ft lbs. (23 Nm) for second pass.
21. Install a new fuel rail crossover pipe. Install a new high pressure fuel pipe.
22. Continue the installation in the reverse order of the removal procedure.

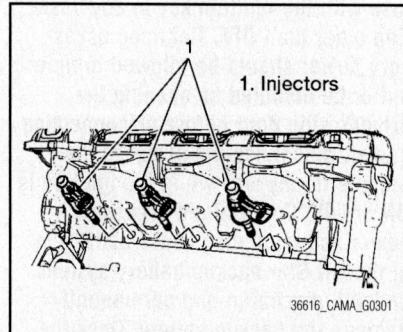

1. Injectors

36616_CAMA_G0301

Fig. 152 Fuel injectors and related components—3.6L engines

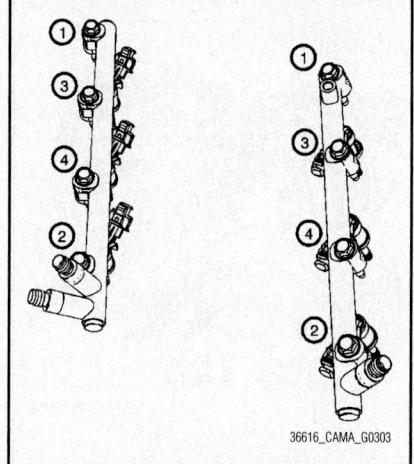

36616_CAMA_G0303

Fig. 153 Fuel injector rail tightening sequence—3.6L engines

23. Turn ON the engine ignition, with the engine OFF for two seconds. Turn OFF the ignition, for ten seconds. Turn ON the ignition, with the engine OFF. Inspect for leaks. Correct as required.

6.2L Engines

See Figure 154.

1. Before servicing the vehicle, refer to the Precautions Section.
2. Disconnect the negative battery cable.
3. Remove the intake manifold cover.
4. Properly relieve the fuel system pressure.

→Remove the fuel rail assembly carefully in order to prevent damage to the electrical connector terminals and the injector spray tips. Support the rail after rail removal. Cap all fittings and plug all holes.

5. Disconnect the fuel feed pipes from the fuel rail.
6. Disconnect the fuel injector electrical connectors from the injectors.
7. Disconnect the wiring harness from the rail, using the proper tool.
8. Remove the ground strap.
9. Remove the rail to intake manifold retaining bolts.
10. At the same time lift both sides of the rail and remove it from its mounting.

To install:

→Be sure to use new fasteners, as required.

11. Install the injectors to the fuel rail, as required. Be sure to use new gaskets.
12. Position the assembly to its mounting.
13. Apply a 0.02 inch bead of threadlock to the threads of the fuel rail retaining bolts.

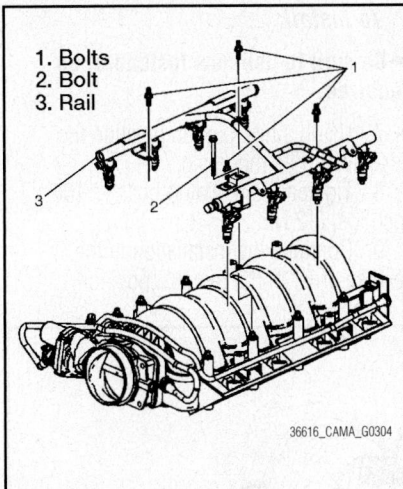

1. Bolts
2. Bolt
3. Rail

Fig. 154 Fuel injector rail and related components—6.2L engines

14. Tighten the retaining bolts to 89 inch lbs. (10 Nm).

15. Continue the installation in the reverse order of the removal procedure.

16. Turn ON the engine ignition, with the engine OFF for two seconds. Turn OFF the ignition, for ten seconds. Turn ON the ignition, with the engine OFF. Inspect for leaks. Correct as required.

FUEL TANK

REMOVAL & INSTALLATION

See Figure 155.

➡**For vehicles equipped with ON Star (RPO UE1), with battery backup, the backup battery is a redundant power supply to allow limited ON Star functionality in the event of a main battery power disruption to the ON Star module (VCIM). Do not disconnect the main vehicle battery or remove the ON Star fuse with the ignition key in any position other than OFF. Retained accessory power should be allowed to time**

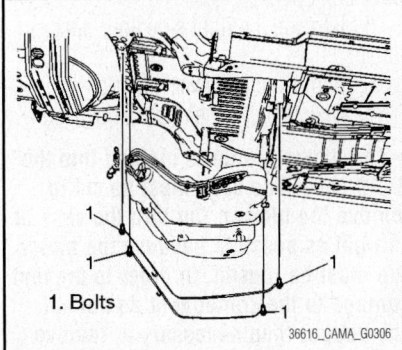

1. Bolts

Fig. 155 Fuel tank and related components

out or be disabled by opening the driver's side door before disconnecting power. Disconnecting power to the module in any way while the ignition is ON or with the retained accessory power activated may cause activation of the ON Star backup battery system and will discharge and permanently damage the backup battery. Once the backup battery is activated it will stay on until it has completely discharged. The backup battery is not rechargeable and once it is activated, it must be replaced.

➡**To avoid any vehicle damage or serious personal injury when major components are removed from the vehicle and the vehicle is supported by a hoist, support the vehicle with jack stands at the opposite end from which the components are being removed and strap the vehicle to a hoist.**

1. Before servicing the vehicle, refer to the Precautions Section.

2. Disconnect the negative battery cable.

3. Properly relieved the fuel system pressure.

4. Raise and safely support the vehicle.

5. Drain the fuel tank.

6. Remove the rear suspension support.

7. Disconnect the parking brake cables at the calipers and position them out of the way.

8. Disconnect the EVAP emission lines.

9. Disconnect the vent solenoid electrical connector.

10. Disconnect the EVAP emission line.

11. Disconnect the fuel tank electrical connector.

12. Disconnect the fuel feed line and the EVAP line.

13. Properly support the fuel tank.

14. Remove the fuel tank strap bolts.

15. Carefully remove the fuel tank from its mounting.

To install:

➡**Be sure to use new fasteners, as required.**

16. Position the tank to its mounting.

17. Install the retaining bolts.

18. Tighten to 37 ft. lbs. (50 Nm).

19. Continue the installation in the reverse order of the removal procedure.

20. Turn ON the engine ignition, with the engine OFF for two seconds. Turn OFF the ignition, for ten seconds. Turn ON the ignition, with the engine OFF. Inspect for leaks. Correct as required.

IDLE SPEED

ADJUSTMENT

Idle speed is maintained by the Engine Control Module (ECM). No adjustment is necessary or possible.

THROTTLE BODY

REMOVAL & INSTALLATION

➡**For vehicles equipped with ON Star (RPO UE1), with battery backup, the backup battery is a redundant power supply to allow limited ON Star functionality in the event of a main battery power disruption to the ON Star module (VCIM). Do not disconnect the main vehicle battery or remove the ON Star fuse with the ignition key in any position other than OFF. Retained accessory power should be allowed to time out or be disabled by opening the driver's side door before disconnecting power. Disconnecting power to the module in any way while the ignition is ON or with the retained accessory power activated may cause activation of the ON Star backup battery system and will discharge and permanently damage the backup battery. Once the backup battery is activated it will stay on until it has completely discharged. The backup battery is not rechargeable and once it is activated, it must be replaced.**

3.6L Engines

See Figure 156.

1. Before servicing the vehicle, refer to the Precautions Section.

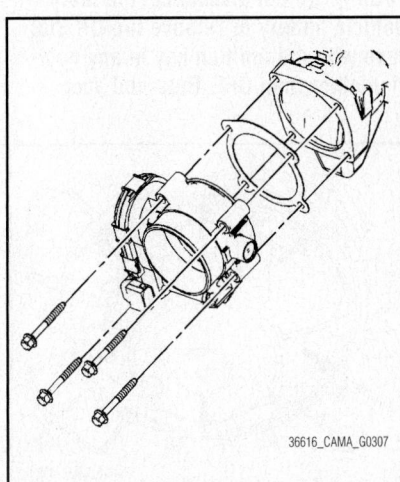

Fig. 156 Throttle body and related components—3.6L engines

2. Disconnect the negative battery cable.

3. Remove the air cleaner.

4. Disconnect the throttle body electrical connector.

5. Unlock and reposition the wiring harness conduit.

6. Remove the throttle body retaining bolts.

7. Remove the throttle body from its mounting. Discard the gasket.

To install:

➡**Be sure to use new fasteners, as required.**

8. Using a new gasket, position the assembly to its mounting.

9. Tighten the retaining bolts to 89 inch lbs. (10 Nm).

10. Continue the installation in the reverse order of the removal position.

6.2L Engines

See Figure 157.

1. Before servicing the vehicle, refer to the Precautions Section.

2. Disconnect the negative battery cable.

3. Remove the air cleaner.

4. Disconnect the throttle body electrical connector.

5. Remove the throttle body retaining bolts.

6. Remove the throttle body from its mounting. Discard the gasket.

To install:

➡**Be sure to use new fasteners, as required.**

7. Using a new gasket, position the assembly to its mounting.

8. Tighten the retaining bolts to 106 inch lbs. (12 Nm).

9. Continue the installation in the reverse order of the removal position.

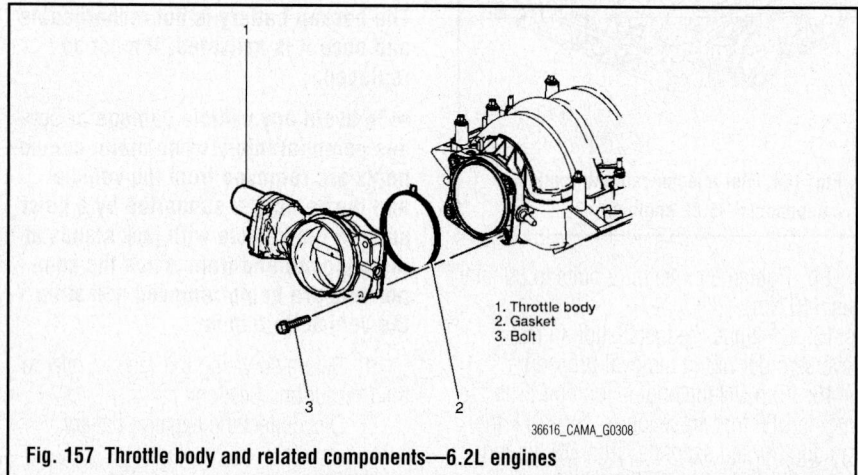

1. Throttle body
2. Gasket
3. Bolt

36616_CAMA_G0308

Fig. 157 Throttle body and related components—6.2L engines

HEATING & AIR CONDITIONING SYSTEM

BLOWER MOTOR

REMOVAL & INSTALLATION

See Figures 158 and 159.

➡**For vehicles equipped with ON Star (RPO UE1), with battery backup, the backup battery is a redundant power supply to allow limited ON Star functionality in the event of a main battery power disruption to the ON Star module (VCIM). Do not disconnect the main vehicle battery or remove the ON Star fuse with the ignition key in any position other than OFF. Retained acces-**

sory power should be allowed to time out or be disabled by opening the driver's side door before disconnecting power. Disconnecting power to the module in any way while the ignition is ON or with the retained accessory

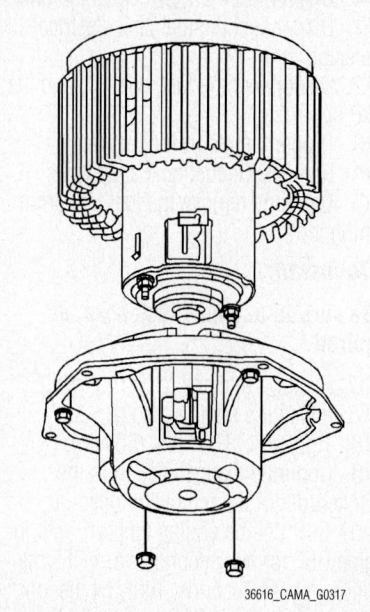

36616_CAMA_G0317

Fig. 159 Blower motor and blower motor cup assembly

power activated may cause activation of the ON Star backup battery system and will discharge and permanently damage the backup battery. Once the backup battery is activated it will stay on until it has completely discharged. The backup battery is not rechargeable and once it is activated, it must be replaced.

1. Before servicing the vehicle, refer to the Precautions Section.

2. Disconnect the negative battery cable.

3. Remove the glove box.

4. Remove the screws retaining the lower portion of the plastic instrument panel glove box opening.

5. Remove the right side floor duct outlet.

6. Remove the blower motor cover.

7. Disconnect the electrical connector.

➡**The blower motor is molded into the HVAC case. The case must be cut to remove the blower. Cut thru the case as straight as possible because the motor cup must be reused. In order to prevent damage to the component do not cut any deeper than necessary to remove the motor cup.**

8. Cut out the blower motor using a

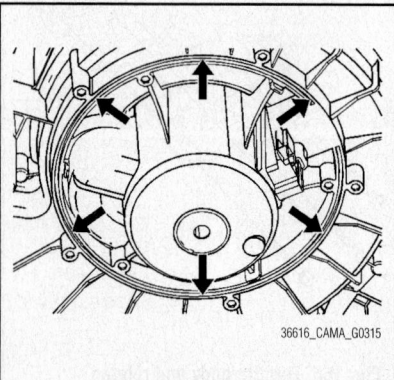

36616_CAMA_G0315

Fig. 158 Blower motor removal cut points

utility knife in the narrow of the lower case.

9. Remove the blower motor.
10. Remove the blower motor nuts.
11. Remove the motor from the motor cup.

To install:

➡**Be sure to use new fasteners, as required.**

12. Attach the assembly to the HVAC module. Use the service screws, provided.
13. Continue the installation in the reverse order of the removal procedure.

HEATER CORE

REMOVAL & INSTALLATION

See Figure 160.

➡**When performing service on or near the SRS components, or SRS wiring the SRS must be disabled. Failure to observe the correct procedure could cause deployment of the SRS components. Serious injury can occur.**

➡**For vehicles equipped with ON Star (RPO UE1), with battery backup, the backup battery is a redundant power supply to allow limited ON Star functionality in the event of a main battery power disruption to the ON Star module (VCIM). Do not disconnect the main vehicle battery or remove the ON Star fuse with the ignition key in any position other than OFF. Retained accessory power should be allowed to time out or be disabled by opening the driver's side door before disconnecting power. Disconnecting power to the module in any way while the ignition is ON or with the retained accessory power activated may cause activation of the ON Star backup battery system and will discharge and permanently damage the backup battery. Once the backup battery is activated it will stay on until it has completely discharged. The backup battery is not rechargeable and once it is activated, it must be replaced.**

1. Before servicing the vehicle, refer to the Precautions Section.
2. Position the steering wheel so the front wheels are in the straight ahead position.
3. Be sure the ignition switch is in the **OFF** position.
4. Disconnect the negative battery cable.

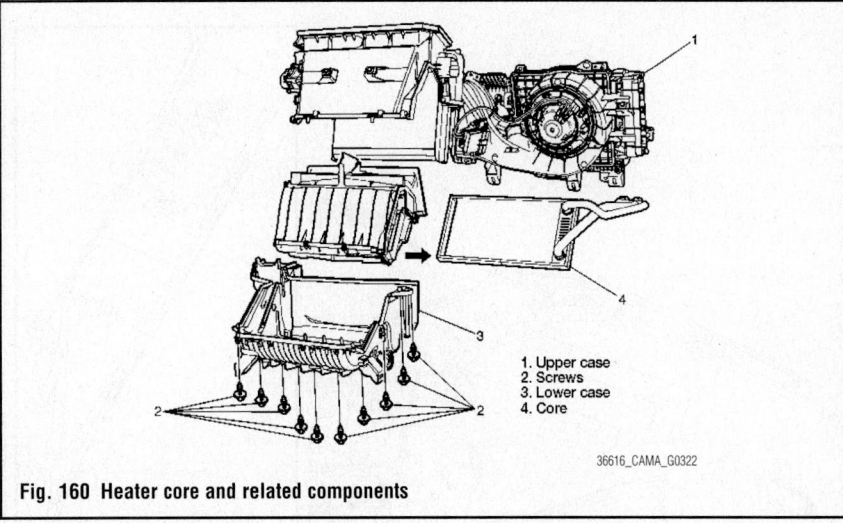

Fig. 160 Heater core and related components

1. Upper case
2. Screws
3. Lower case
4. Core

36616_CAMA_G0322

➡**The SDM may have more than one fused power input. To ensure that there is no unwanted SRS deployment, personal injury, or unnecessary SRS system repairs, remove all fuses supplying power to the SDM. With all SDM fuses removed and the ignition switch in the ON position, the AIR BAG warning indicator will illuminate. This is normal and does not indicate a SRS system malfunction.**

5. Locate and remove the fuses supplying power to the SDM.
6. Wait one minute before working on the vehicle.
7. Properly discharge the air conditioning system.
8. Drain the radiator. Properly dispose of used coolant.
9. Disconnect and plug the air conditioning hoses.
10. Disconnect and plug the heater hoses.
11. Remove the heater/AC unit from the vehicle.
12. Separate the upper and lower case halves.
13. Remove the evaporator temperature sensor.
14. Remove the evaporator from the case halves.

To install:

➡**Be sure to use new fasteners, as required.**

15. Position the evaporator in the case.
16. Tighten the case retaining screws to 13 inch lbs. (1.5 Nm).
17. Install the case assembly to its mounting.
18. Continue the installation in the reverse order of the removal procedure.
19. Enable the SRS system.

20. Properly recharge the air conditioning system.
21. Fill the cooling system with the proper grade and type engine coolant.
22. Using the GM diagnostic scan tool or aftermarket equivalent reprogram the necessary systems and components. Be sure to follow the scan tool manufacturer's directions.

HEATER/AC UNIT

REMOVAL & INSTALLATION

See Figures 161 through 172.

➡**For vehicles equipped with ON Star (RPO UE1), with battery backup, the backup battery is a redundant power supply to allow limited ON Star functionality in the event of a main battery power disruption to the ON Star module (VCIM). Do not disconnect the main vehicle battery or remove the ON Star fuse with the ignition key in any position other than OFF. Retained accessory power should be allowed to time out or be disabled by opening the driver's side door before disconnecting power. Disconnecting power to the module in any way while the ignition is ON or with the retained accessory power activated may cause activation of the ON Star backup battery system and will discharge and permanently damage the backup battery. Once the backup battery is activated it will stay on until it has completely discharged. The backup battery is not rechargeable and once it is activated, it must be replaced.**

1. Before servicing the vehicle, refer to the Precautions Section.

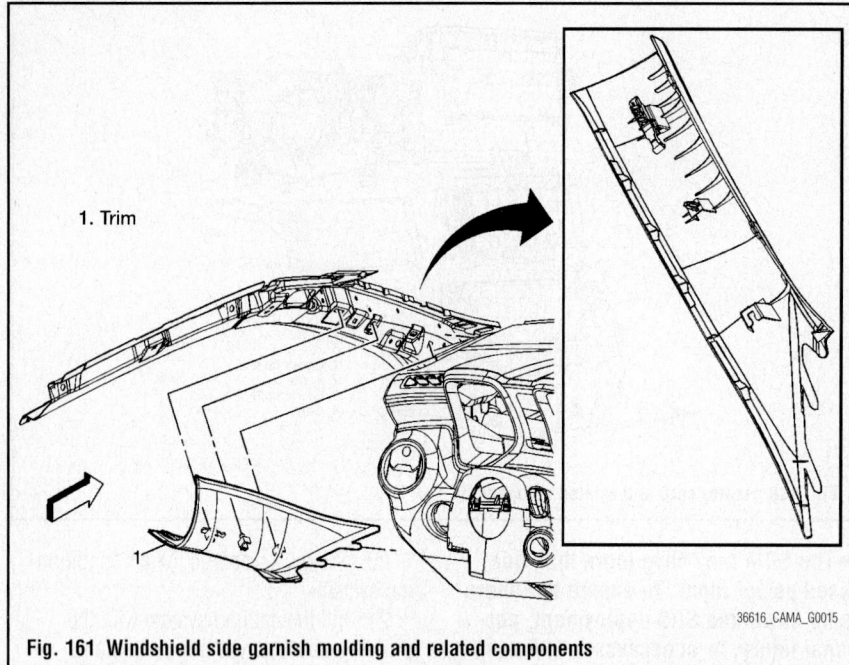

Fig. 161 Windshield side garnish molding and related components

1. Trim

36616_CAMA_G0015

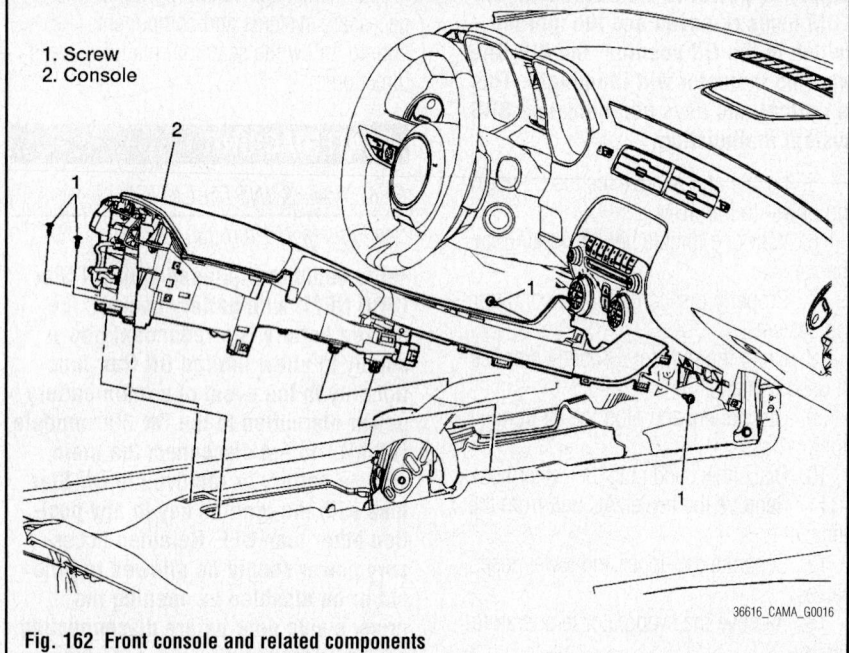

Fig. 162 Front console and related components

1. Screw
2. Console

36616_CAMA_G0016

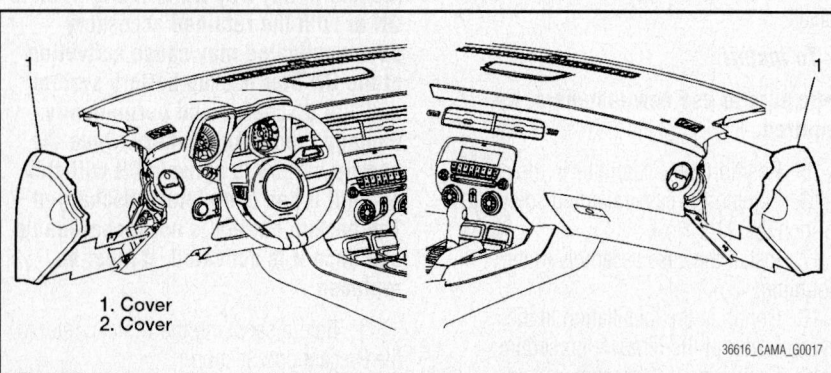

Fig. 163 Instrument panel right and left covers and related components

1. Cover
2. Cover

36616_CAMA_G0017

➡ When performing service on or near the SRS components, or SRS wiring the SRS must be disabled. Failure to observe the correct procedure could cause deployment of the SRS components. Serious injury can occur.

2. Position the steering wheel so the front wheels are in the straight ahead position.

3. Be sure the ignition switch is in the **OFF** position.

4. Disconnect the negative battery cable.

➡ The SDM may have more than one fused power input. To ensure that there is no unwanted SRS deployment, personal injury, or unnecessary SRS system repairs, remove all fuses supplying power to the SDM. With all SDM fuses removed and the ignition switch in the ON position, the AIR BAG warning indicator will illuminate. This is normal and does not indicate a SRS system malfunction.

5. Locate and remove the fuses supplying power to the SDM.

6. Wait one minute before working on the vehicle.

7. Properly discharge the air conditioning system.

8. Drain the radiator. Properly dispose of used coolant.

9. Disconnect and plug the air conditioning hoses.

10. Disconnect and plug the heater hoses.

11. Remove the windshield side garnish molding.

12. Remove the front floor console.

13. Remove the instrument panel right and left covers.

14. Remove the right and left air outlet ducts.

15. Remove the steering column shroud.

16. Remove the instrument panel cluster trim plate.

17. Remove the instrument cluster assembly.

18. Remove the steering wheel.

19. Remove the turn signal multifunction switch. Remove the wiper washer/switch.

20. Remove the radio control assembly. Remove the radio.

21. Remove the glove box.

22. Remove the instrument panel center air outlet grille.

23. Remove the communication interface module and battery.

24. Disconnect the DLC connector and the hood release handle.

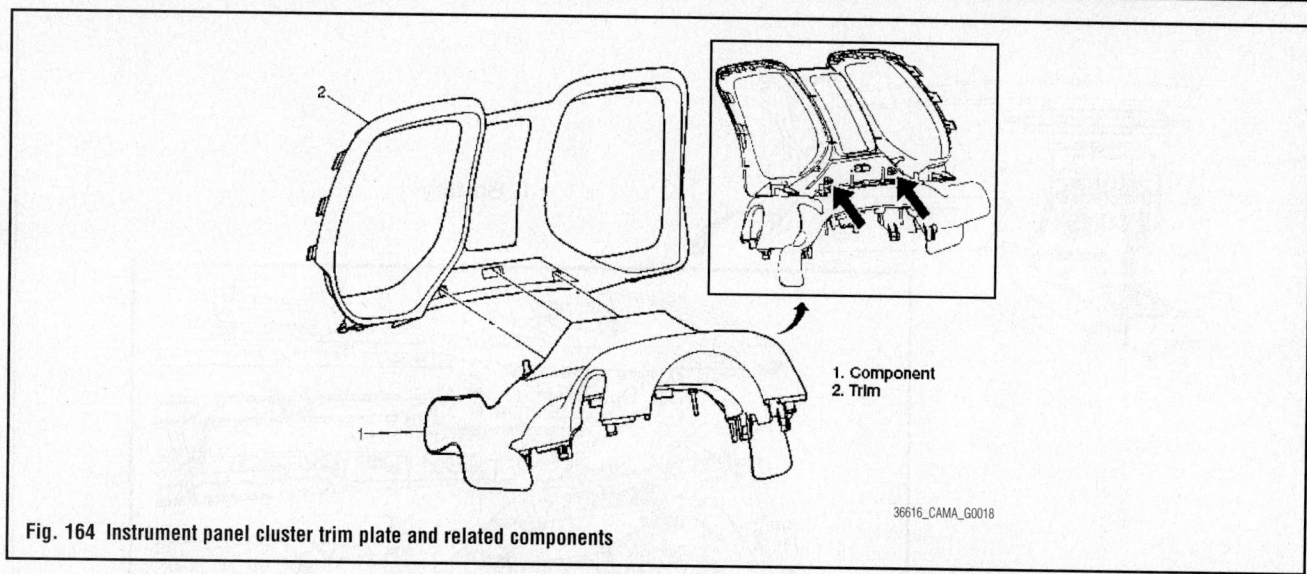

1. Component
2. Trim

36616_CAMA_G0018

Fig. 164 Instrument panel cluster trim plate and related components

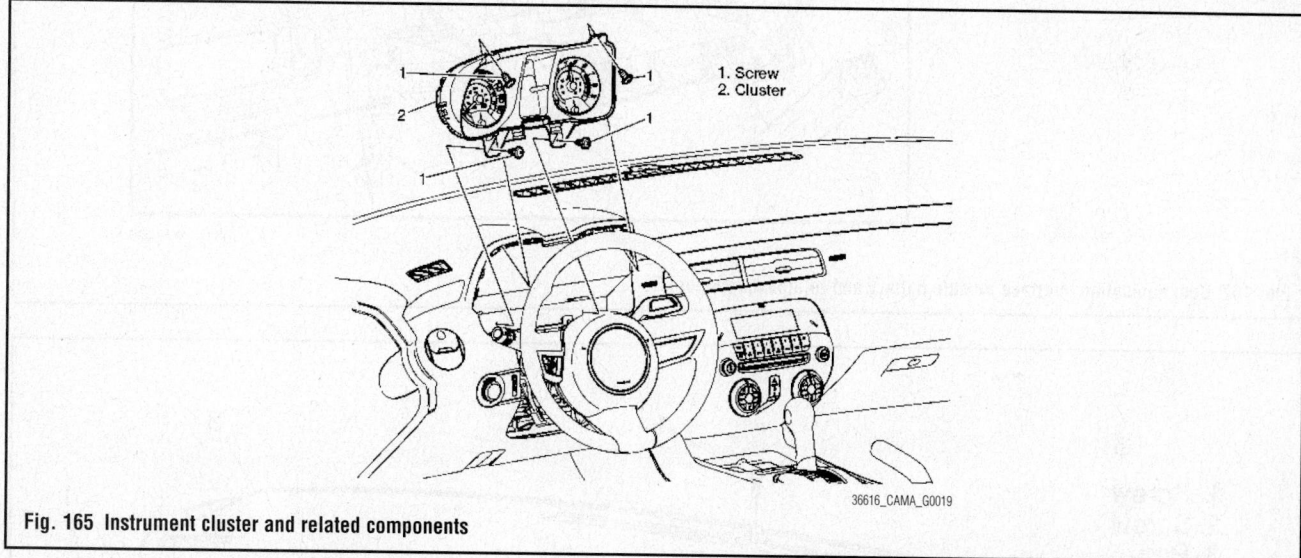

1. Screw
2. Cluster

36616_CAMA_G0019

Fig. 165 Instrument cluster and related components

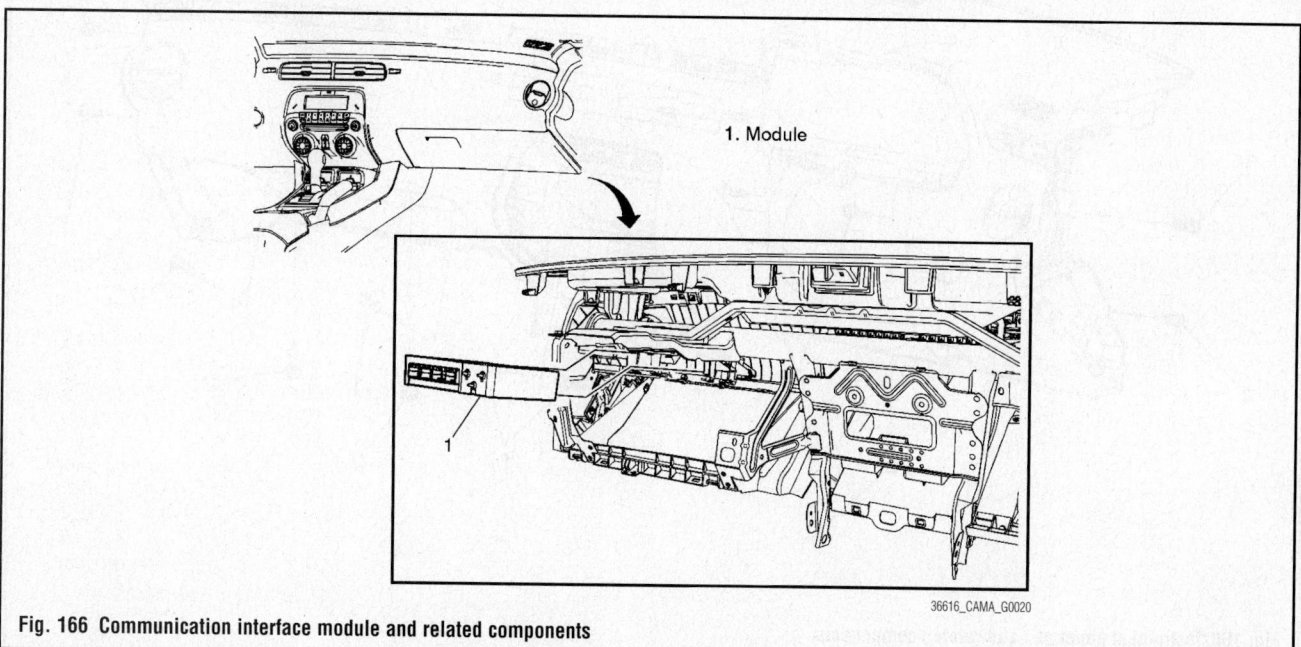

1. Module

36616_CAMA_G0020

Fig. 166 Communication interface module and related components

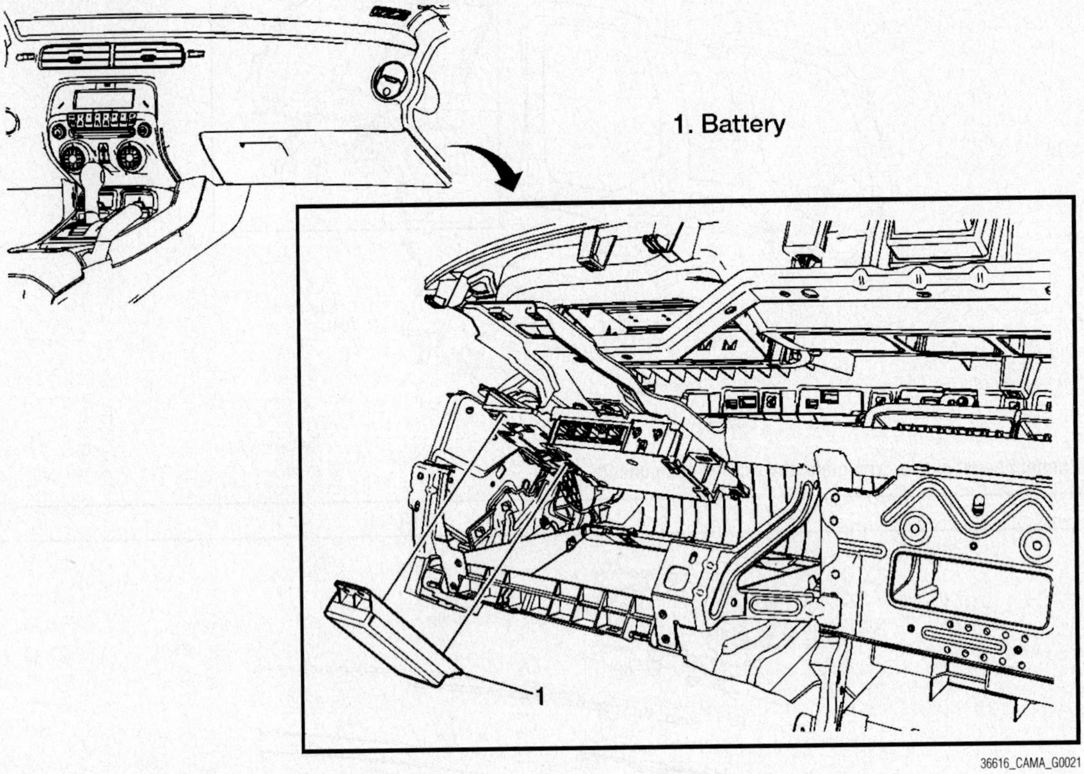

1. Battery

36616_CAMA_G0021

Fig. 167 Communication interface module battery and related components

1. Screw
2. Screw
3. Pad

36616_CAMA_G0014

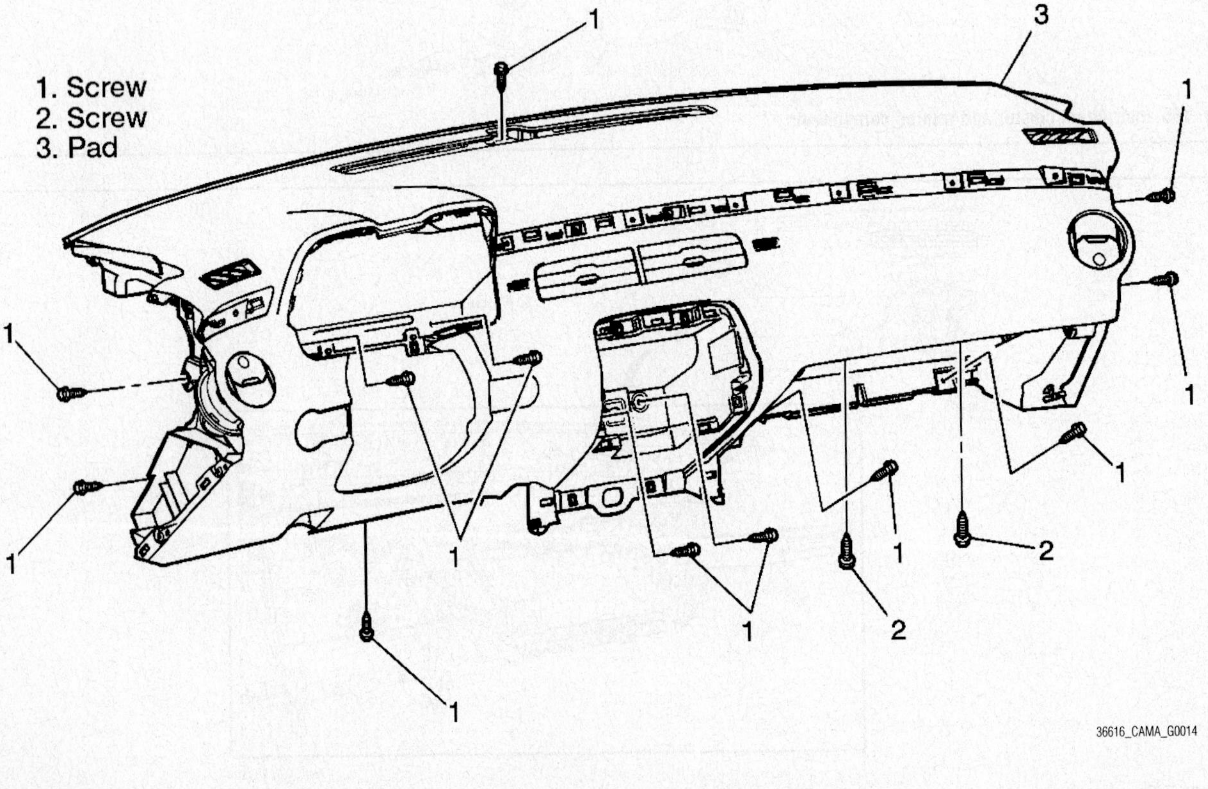

Fig. 168 Instrument panel pad and related components

1. Bolt

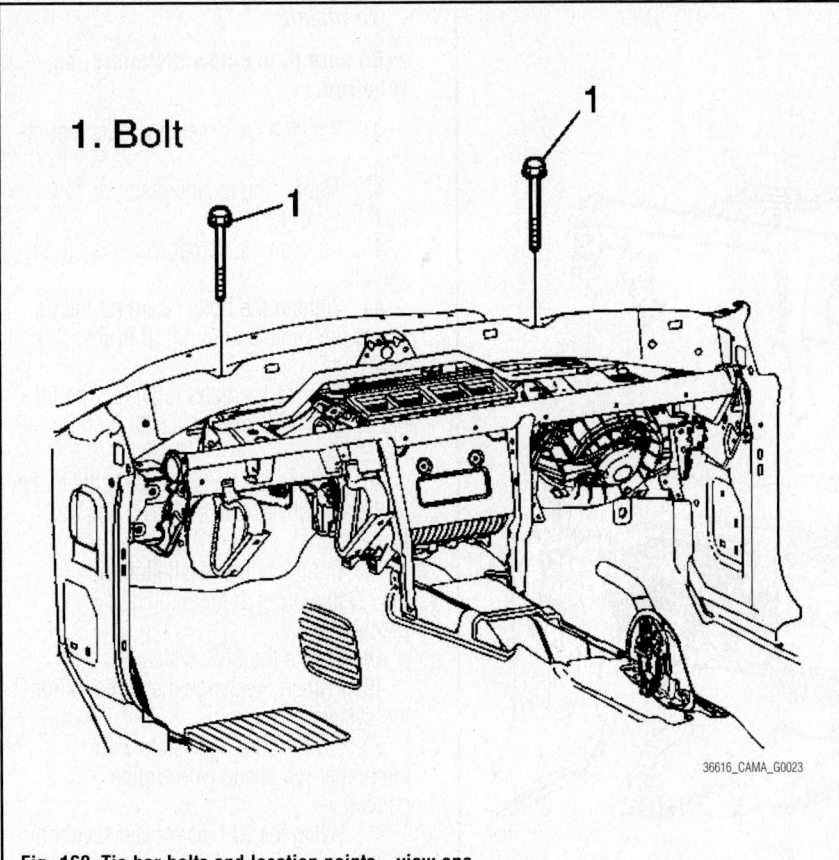

36616_CAMA_G0023

Fig. 169 Tie bar bolts and location points—view one

1. Screws

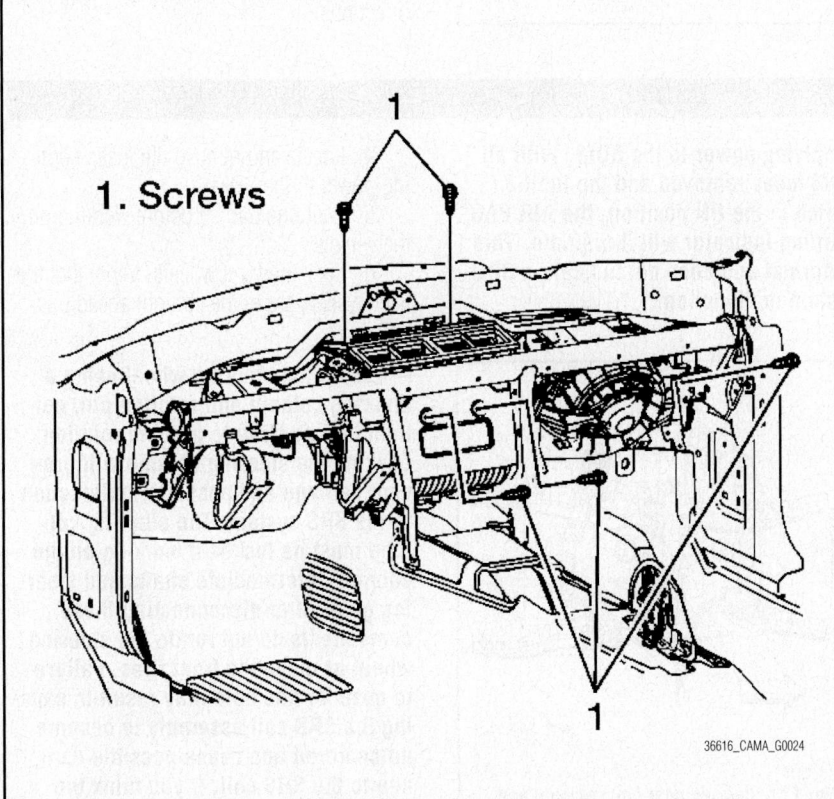

36616_CAMA_G0024

Fig. 170 Tie bar bolts and location points—view two

25. Remove the headlamp switch.

26. Remove the instrument panel retaining screws.

27. Remove the instrument panel inflatable restraint fasteners.

28. Remove the instrument panel trim pad.

29. Remove the steering column.

30. Remove the windshield.

31. Remove the fasteners securing the brake pedal assembly to the instrument panel tie bar.

32. Remove the fasteners securing the clutch pedal assembly to the instrument panel tie bar, if equipped.

➡**Note the location of the electrical connectors and the instrument panel electrical harness. This will aid in installation.**

33. Disconnect the fasteners securing the instrument panel electrical harness assembly to the instrument panel tie bar. Position it out of the way.

34. Remove the bolts retaining the instrument panel tie bar assembly to the windshield frame and plenum panel.

35. Remove the bolts retaining the instrument panel tie bar assembly to the HVAC module assembly.

36. Remove the bolts retaining the instrument panel tie bar assembly to the vehicle body.

37. Support the HVAC module assembly, as required.

38. Remove the tie bar assembly from its mounting.

39. Remove the heater/AC unit retaining screws.

40. Remove the component from its mounting.

1. Screws

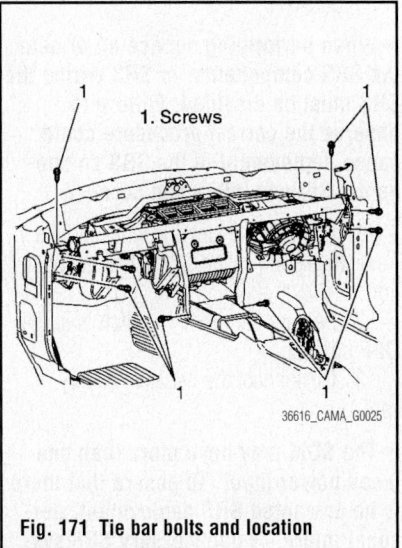

36616_CAMA_G0025

Fig. 171 Tie bar bolts and location points—view three

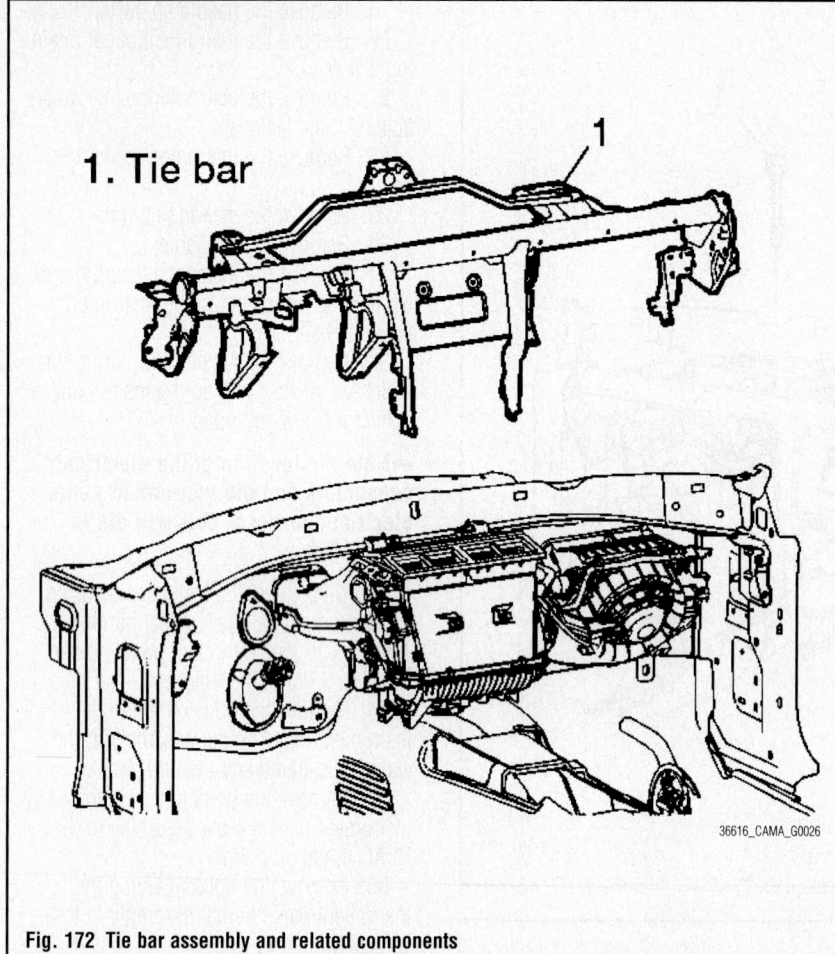

1. Tie bar

36616_CAMA_G0026

Fig. 172 Tie bar assembly and related components

To install:

➡ **Be sure to use new fasteners, as required.**

41. Position the assembly to its mounting.

42. Tighten the retaining screws to 89 inch lbs. (10 Nm).

43. Position the tie bar assembly in the vehicle.

44. Tighten the bolts retaining the tie bar to the vehicle body to 18 ft. lbs. (25 Nm).

45. Tighten the bolts retaining the tie bar to the HVAC module to 80 inch lbs. (9 Nm).

46. Tighten the bolts retaining the tie bar to the windshield frame to 16 ft. lbs. (22 Nm).

47. Continue the installation in the reverse order of the removal procedure.

48. Enable the SRS system.

49. Properly recharge the air conditioning system.

50. Fill the cooling system with the proper grade and type engine coolant.

51. Using the GM diagnostic scan tool or aftermarket equivalent reprogram the necessary systems and components. Be sure to follow the scan tool manufacturer's directions.

STEERING

POWER RACK & PINION STEERING GEAR

REMOVAL & INSTALLATION

See Figure 173.

➡ **When performing service on or near the SRS components, or SRS wiring the SRS must be disabled. Failure to observe the correct procedure could cause deployment of the SRS components. Serious injury can occur.**

1. Position the steering wheel so the front wheels are in the straight ahead position.

2. Be sure the ignition switch is in the **OFF** position.

3. Disconnect the negative battery cable.

➡ **The SDM may have more than one fused power input. To ensure that there is no unwanted SRS deployment, personal injury, or unnecessary SRS system repairs, remove all fuses supplying power to the SDM. With all SDM fuses removed and the ignition switch in the ON position, the AIR BAG warning indicator will illuminate. This is normal and does not indicate a SRS system malfunction.**

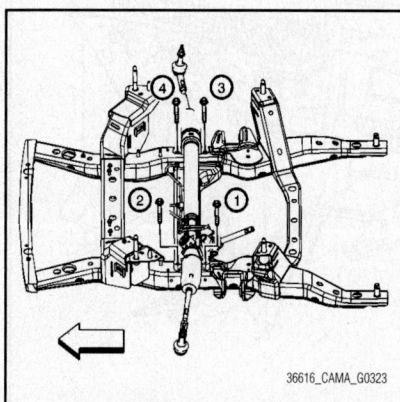

36616_CAMA_G0323

Fig. 173 Steering gear bolt removal and tightening sequence

4. Locate and remove the fuses supplying power to the SDM.

5. Wait one minute before working on the vehicle.

6. Lock the front wheels. Verify that the front wheels are in the straight ahead position.

➡ **Secure the steering wheel using a steering column anti rotation pin, column lock or strap to prevent rotation. Locking the steering column will prevent damage and possible malfunction to the SRS system. The steering column must be locked if working on the column, intermediate shafts and steering gear. After disconnecting these components do not rotate the steering wheel or move the front tires. Failure to observe this note may result in causing the SRS coil assembly to become un-centered and cause possible damage to the SRS coil. If you think the SRS coil has become un-centered, re-center it.**

7. Raise and support the vehicle safely.

8. Remove the tire and wheel assemblies.

9. Place a drain pan under the vehicle. Disconnect the power steering hoses from the gear. Plug the lines. Be sure to dispose of used power steering gear fluid properly.

10. Disconnect the two outer tie rods from the knuckles.

11. Disconnect the intermediate steering shaft from the steering gear pinion shaft.

12. On the driver's side disconnect the front wheel speed sensor. Disconnect the lower control arm from the knuckle. Push the front suspension toward the rear of the vehicle.

13. Remove the four bolts (1, 2, 3, 4), see illustration, from the steering gear.

14. Remove the steering gear thru the driver's side front wheelhouse.

To install:

➡**Be sure to use new fasteners, as required.**

15. Position the gear to its mounting.

16. Install the bolts in sequence, but do not tighten at this time.

17. Tighten the retaining bolts to 37 ft. lbs. (50 Nm) plus an additional 120 degrees, in sequence.

18. Continue the installation in the reverse order of the removal procedure.

19. Fill the power steering system with the proper grade and type fluid.

20. Bleed the system.

21. Check and adjust the wheel alignment, as required.

POWER STEERING PUMP

REMOVAL & INSTALLATION

➡**For vehicles equipped with ON Star (RPO UE1), with battery backup, the backup battery is a redundant power supply to allow limited ON Star functionality in the event of a main battery power disruption to the ON Star module (VCIM). Do not disconnect the main vehicle battery or remove the ON Star fuse with the ignition key in any position other than OFF. Retained accessory power should be allowed to time out or be disabled by opening the driver's side door before disconnecting power. Disconnecting power to the module in any way while the ignition is ON or with the retained accessory power activated may cause activation of the ON Star backup battery system and will discharge and permanently damage the backup battery. Once the**

backup battery is activated it will stay on until it has completely discharged. The backup battery is not rechargeable and once it is activated, it must be replaced.**

3.6L Engines

See Figure 174.

1. Before servicing the vehicle, refer to the Precautions Section.

2. Disconnect the negative battery cable.

3. Remove the front intake manifold cover.

4. Position a drain pan under the pump.

5. Disconnect and plug the power steering lines.

➡**Do not allow fluid to drain on the air conditioning compressor.**

6. Remove the air cleaner assembly.

7. Remove the drive belt.

8. Using a pulley removal tool, remove the power steering pulley from the pump.

9. Remove the retaining bolts.

10. Remove the pump and bracket from its mounting.

11. If equipped, remove the bolt and pump auxiliary bracket from the pump.

To install:

➡**Be sure to use new fasteners, as required.**

12. Position the pump to its mounting.

13. Install the retaining bolts in the proper sequence. Tighten the bolts to 43 ft. lbs (58 Nm), in the proper sequence, see illustration.

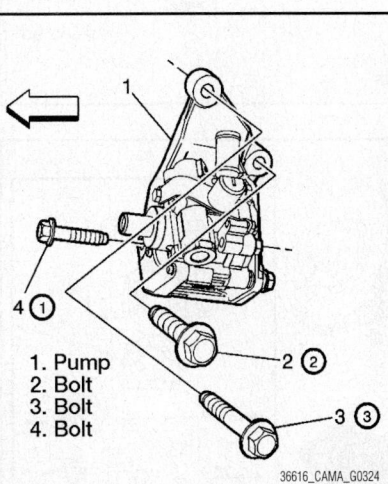

1. Pump
2. Bolt
3. Bolt
4. Bolt

36616_CAMA_G0324

Fig. 174 Power steering pump bolt removal and tightening sequence—3.6L engines

Continue the installation in the reverse order of the removal procedure.

14. Be sure to fill the system with the proper grade and type fluid.

15. Bleed the power steering system.

6.2L Engines

See Figure 175.

1. Before servicing the vehicle, refer to the Precautions Section.

2. Disconnect the negative battery cable.

3. Remove the front intake manifold cover.

4. Position a drain pan under the pump.

5. Disconnect and plug the power steering lines.

➡**Do not allow fluid to drain on the air conditioning compressor.**

6. Remove the air cleaner assembly.

7. Remove the drive belt.

8. Using a pulley removal tool, remove the power steering pulley from the pump.

9. Remove the retaining bolts.

10. Remove the pump and reservoir from its mounting.

To install:

➡**Be sure to use new fasteners, as required.**

11. Position the pump to its mounting.

12. Install the retaining bolts in the proper sequence. Tighten the bolts to 18 ft. lbs (25 Nm), in the proper sequence, see illustration.

Continue the installation in the reverse order of the removal procedure.

13. Be sure to fill the system with the proper grade and type fluid.

14. Bleed the power steering system.

BLEEDING

➡**At this time the manufacturer does not provide service information for this component.**

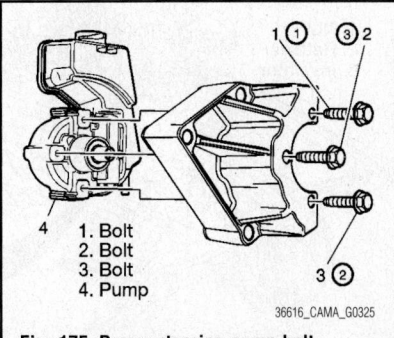

1. Bolt
2. Bolt
3. Bolt
4. Pump

36616_CAMA_G0325

Fig. 175 Power steering pump bolt removal and tightening sequence—6.2L engines

CONTROL LINKS

REMOVAL & INSTALLATION

Stabilizer Shaft Link

See Figure 176.

1. Before servicing the vehicle, refer to the Precautions Section.
2. Raise and support the vehicle safely.
3. Remove the tire and wheel assemblies.
4. Remove the link retaining nuts. Discard the nuts.
5. Remove the link from its mounting.

To install:

➡**Be sure to use new fasteners, as required.**

6. Position the link to its mounting.
7. Tighten the retaining nuts to 36 ft. lbs. (49 Nm).
8. Continue the installation in the reverse order of the removal procedure.

Stabilizer Shaft Insulator

See Figure 177.

1. Before servicing the vehicle, refer to the Precautions Section.
2. Raise and support the vehicle safely.
3. Remove the tire and wheel assemblies.
4. Remove the insulator retaining nuts. Discard the nuts.
5. Remove the insulator from its mounting.

To install:

➡**Be sure to use new fasteners, as required.**

6. Position the insulator to its mounting.
7. Tighten the retaining nuts to 13 ft. lbs. (17 Nm).
8. Continue the installation in the reverse order of the removal procedure.

LOWER CONTROL ARM

REMOVAL & INSTALLATION

Front Arm

See Figure 178.

➡**If servicing the steering knuckle, it is not necessary to completely remove the lower control arm from the vehicle. Separate the lower control arm from the steering knuckle.**

1. Before servicing the vehicle, refer to the Precautions Section.
2. Raise and support the vehicle safely.
3. Remove the tire and wheel assemblies.

➡**If removing the lower arm to service other suspension components, use paint to mark the adjuster to the frame.**

4. Loosen but do not remove the lower control arm nut.
5. Using a ball joint separator tool, or equivalent, separate the control arm from the steering knuckle.
6. Remove the control arm adjuster bolt, washer and nut.
7. Remove the control arm retaining nut. Discard the nut.
8. Remove the component from the vehicle.

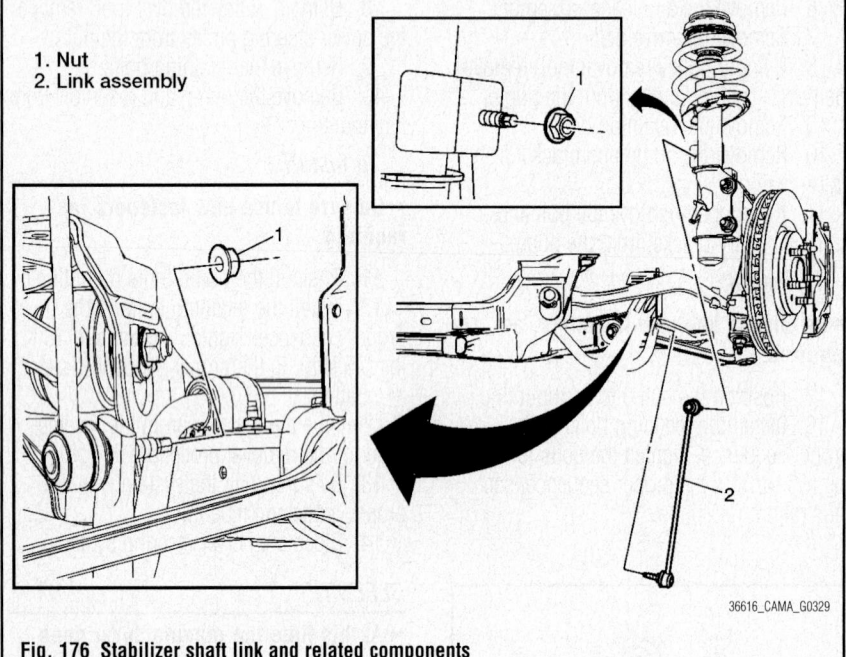

1. Nut
2. Link assembly

36616_CAMA_G0329

Fig. 176 Stabilizer shaft link and related components

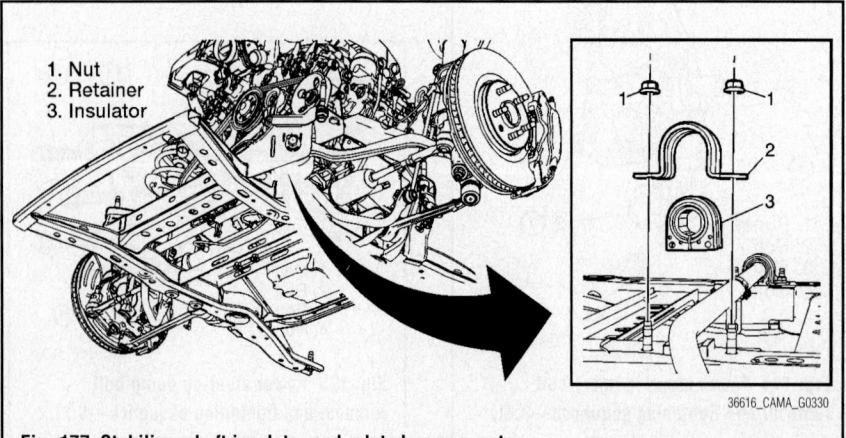

1. Nut
2. Retainer
3. Insulator

36616_CAMA_G0330

Fig. 177 Stabilizer shaft insulator and related components

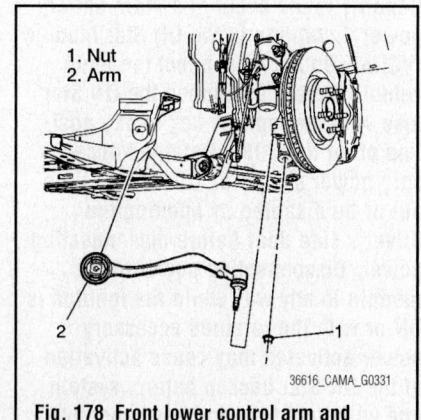

1. Nut
2. Arm

36616_CAMA_G0331

Fig. 178 Front lower control arm and related components

To install:

➡️**Be sure to use new fasteners, as required.**

9. Position the component to its mounting.

10. Install the adjuster bolt, washer and nut. Be sure to use the matchmarks made during removal for alignment.

11. Install the lower ball joint retaining nut. Tighten to 18 ft. lbs. (25 Nm), plus an additional 120 degrees.

12. Tighten the adjuster bolt to 37 ft. lbs. (50 Nm), plus an additional 150 degrees.

13. Continue the installation in the reverse order of the removal procedure.

14. Check and adjust the alignment, as required.

Rear (Front)Arm

See Figure 179.

➡️**If servicing the steering knuckle, it is not necessary to completely remove the lower control arm from the vehicle. Separate the lower control arm from the steering knuckle.**

1. Before servicing the vehicle, refer to the Precautions Section.

2. Raise and support the vehicle safely.

3. Remove the tire and wheel assemblies.

4. Loosen but do not remove the lower control arm nut.

5. Using a ball joint separator tool, or equivalent, separate the control arm from the steering knuckle.

6. Remove the control arm bolt, washer and nut.

7. Remove the control arm retaining nut. Discard the nut.

8. Remove the component from the vehicle.

To install:

➡️**Be sure to use new fasteners, as required.**

9. Position the component to its mounting.

10. Tighten the lower arm to steering knuckle nut to 18 ft. lbs. (25 Nm), plus an additional 120 degrees.

11. Tighten the lower control arm bolt to 37 ft. lbs. (50 Nm), plus an additional 120 degrees.

12. Continue the installation in the reverse order of the removal procedure.

13. Check and adjust the alignment, as required.

STABILIZER BAR

REMOVAL & INSTALLATION

See Figure 180.

1. Before servicing the vehicle, refer to the Precautions Section.

2. Raise and support the vehicle safely.

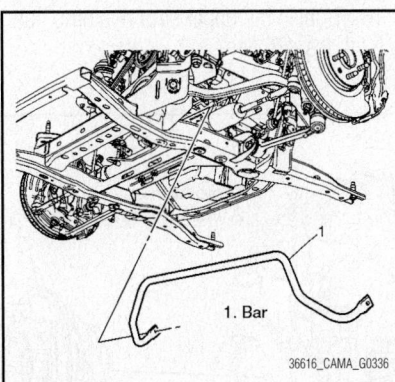

Fig. 180 Front stabilizer bar and related components

3. Remove the tire and wheel assemblies.

4. Remove the outer tie rod from the knuckle.

5. Remove the stabilizer links from the bar.

6. Remove the stabilizer insulators from the bar.

7. Remove the stabilizer bar from its mounting.

To install:

➡️**Be sure to use new fasteners, as required.**

8. Installation is the reverse of the removal procedure.

STEERING KNUCKLE

REMOVAL & INSTALLATION

See Figure 181.

1. Before servicing the vehicle, refer to the Precautions Section.

2. Raise and support the vehicle safely.

3. Remove the tire and wheel assemblies.

4. Remove the speed sensor from the steering knuckle.

5. Matchmark the strut and the steering knuckle.

6. Remove the strut bolts and nuts from the strut.

7. Remove the wheel/hub assembly from the steering knuckle.

8. Remove the outer tie rod from the knuckle.

9. Remove the front lower and rear lower control arms from the knuckle.

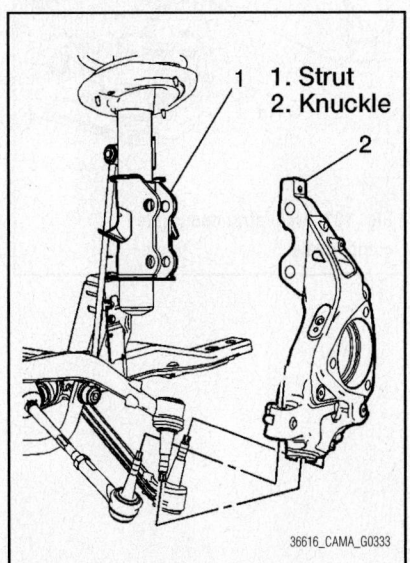

Fig. 181 Front steering knuckle and related components

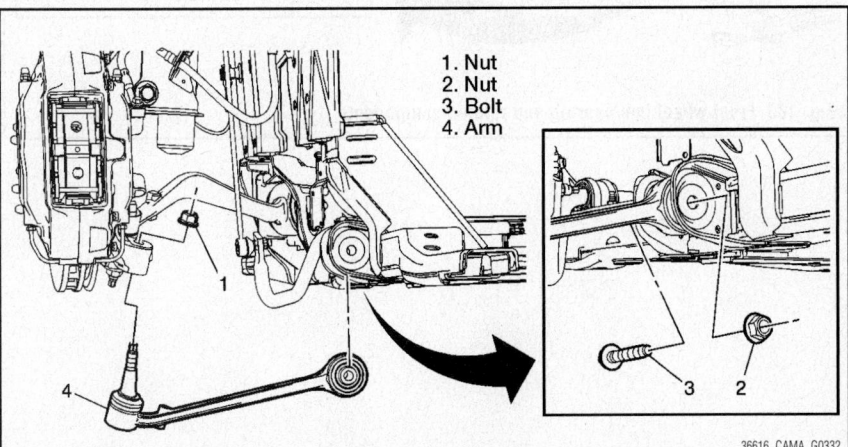

Fig. 179 Rear (front) lower control arm and related components

10. Remove the steering knuckle from its mounting.

To install:

→Be sure to use new fasteners, as required.

11. Position the component to its mounting.

12. When installing the mounting bolts be sure to use the reference marks made during the removal procedure, for alignment.

13. Continue the installation in the reverse order of the removal procedure.

14. Tighten the front suspension to strut bolts to 59 ft. lbs. (80 Nm), plus an additional 180 degrees.

15. Check and adjust the alignment, as required.

STRUT & SPRING ASSEMBLY

REMOVAL & INSTALLATION

See Figure 182.

1. Before servicing the vehicle, refer to the Precautions Section.

2. Raise and support the vehicle safely.

3. Remove the tire and wheel assemblies.

4. Remove the stabilizer shaft link from the strut.

5. Remove the speed sensor from the strut. It is not necessary to completely remove the sensor from the vehicle.

6. Remove the disc brake hose from the strut.

7. Matchmark the strut to the steering knuckle.

8. Using a floor jack, properly support the steering knuckle.

9. Remove the dust cover, if equipped.

10. Remove the lower strut nuts and bolts.

11. Remove the upper strut retaining nut and bolt.

12. Remove the strut from its mounting.

To install:

→Be sure to use new fasteners, as required.

13. Position the strut to its mounting.

14. Align the strut using the marks made during the removal procedure.

15. Tighten the lower strut nuts to 59 Ft. lbs. (80 Nm), plus an additional 180 degrees.

16. Tighten the upper strut retaining nut to 52 ft. lbs. (70 Nm).

17. Continue the installation in the reverse order of the removal procedure.

18. Check and adjust the alignment, as required.

WHEEL HUB & BEARING

REMOVAL & INSTALLATION

See Figure 183.

1. Before servicing the vehicle, refer to the Precautions Section.

2. Raise and support the vehicle safely.

3. Remove the tire and wheel assemblies.

4. Remove the wheel speed sensor.

5. Remove the rotor.

6. Remove the brake shield, if equipped.

7. Remove the hub/bearing retaining bolts.

8. Remove the component from its mounting.

To install:

→Be sure to use new fasteners, as required.

9. Installation is the reverse of the removal procedure.

10. Tighten the retaining bolts to 79 ft. lbs. (108 Nm).

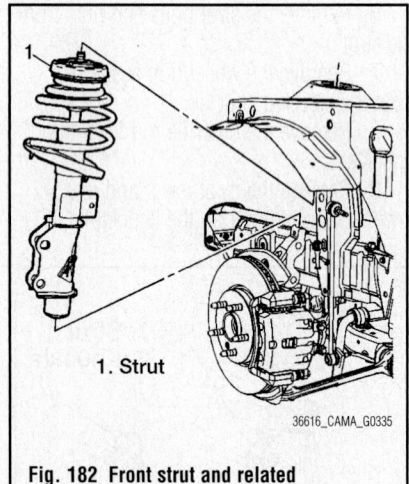

Fig. 182 Front strut and related components

1. Strut

36616_CAMA_G0335

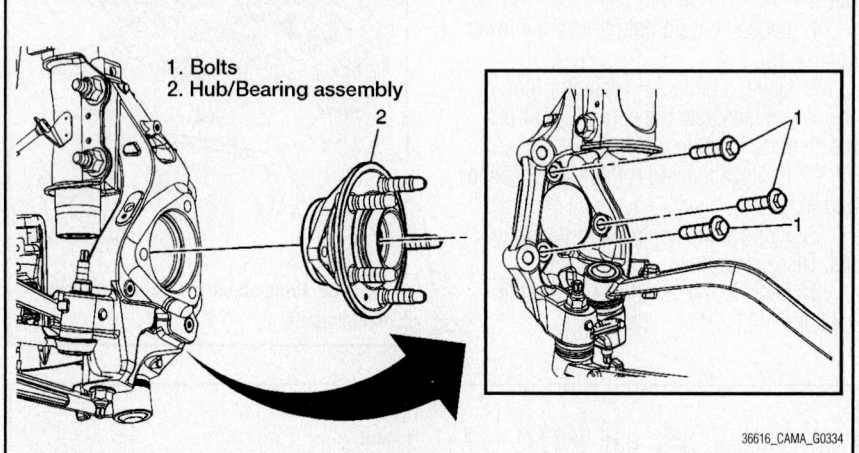

1. Bolts
2. Hub/Bearing assembly

36616_CAMA_G0334

Fig. 183 Front wheel hub/bearing and related components

CONTROL ARMS/LINKS

REMOVAL & INSTALLATION

Stabilizer Shaft Link

See Figure 184.

1. Before servicing the vehicle, refer to the Precautions Section.
2. Raise and support the vehicle safely.
3. Remove the link retaining nuts. Discard the nuts.
4. Remove the link from its mounting.

To install:

➡**Be sure to use new fasteners, as required.**

5. Position the link to its mounting.
6. Tighten the retaining nuts to 36 ft. lbs. (49 Nm).
7. Continue the installation in the reverse order of the removal procedure.

Stabilizer Shaft Insulator

See Figure 185.

1. Before servicing the vehicle, refer to the Precautions Section.
2. Raise and support the vehicle safely.
3. Remove the insulator retaining nuts. Discard the nuts.
4. Remove the insulator from its mounting.

To install:

➡**Be sure to use new fasteners, as required.**

5. Position the insulator to its mounting.
6. Tighten the retaining nuts to 16 ft. lbs. (22 Nm).
7. Continue the installation in the reverse order of the removal procedure.

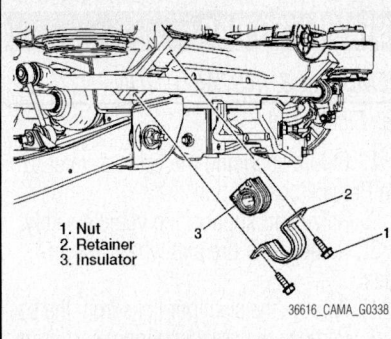

1. Nut
2. Retainer
3. Insulator

36616_CAMA_G0338

Fig. 185 Rear stabilizer shaft insulator and related components

LOWER CONTROL ARM

REMOVAL & INSTALLATION

See Figure 186.

1. Before servicing the vehicle, refer to the Precautions Section.
2. Raise and support the vehicle safely.
3. Remove the tire and wheel assemblies.
4. Mark the adjuster to the frame, before removing the bolt.
5. Support the rear knuckle using a suitable jack.
6. Remove the stabilizer link from the lower control arm.
7. Remove the lower shock absorber bolt.
8. Remove the lower control arm bolt and washer.
9. Remove the lower control arm adjuster bolt, washer and nut.
10. Remove the control arm from the vehicle.

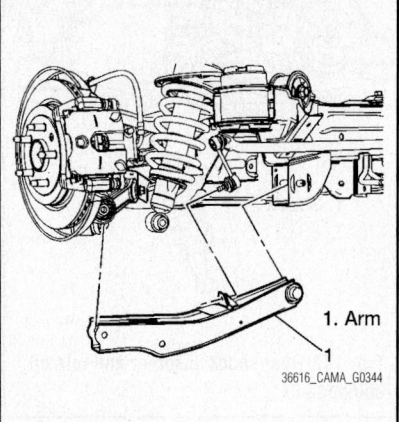

1. Arm

36616_CAMA_G0344

Fig. 186 Rear lower control arm and related components

To install:

➡**Be sure to use new fasteners, as required.**

11. Position the arm to its mounting.
12. Install the lower arm adjuster bolt. Be sure to use the reference marks made during removal.
13. Install the control arm nut, tighten to 30 ft. lbs. (40 Nm), plus 120 degrees.
14. Install the adjuster arm washer and nut. Tighten to 85 ft. lbs. (115 Nm).
15. Continue the installation in the reverse order of the removal procedure.
16. Check the alignment. Adjust as required.

SHOCK ABSORBER

REMOVAL & INSTALLATION

See Figure 187.

1. Before servicing the vehicle, refer to the Precautions Section.
2. Raise and support the vehicle safely.
3. Support the rear knuckle, using a suitable jack.
4. Remove the stabilizer link from the lower arm.
5. Remove the lower arm bolt from the knuckle.
6. Remove the shock lower retaining bolt and nut.
7. Remove the upper retaining bolts.
8. Remove the component from the vehicle.

To install:

➡**Be sure to use new fasteners, as required.**

9. Position the shock to its mounting.

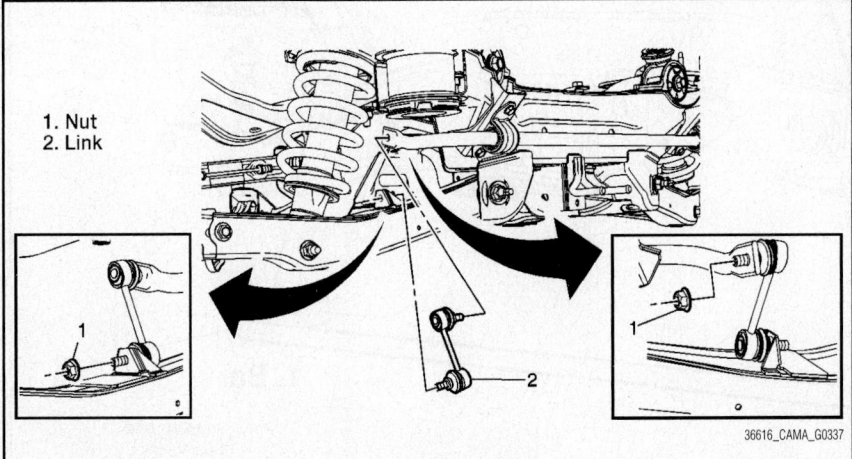

1. Nut
2. Link

36616_CAMA_G0337

Fig. 184 Rear stabilizer shaft link and related components

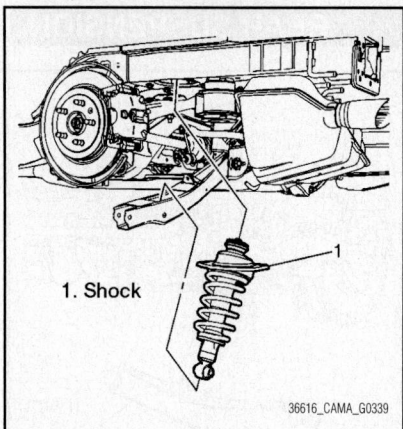

Fig. 187 Rear shock absorber and related components

1. Shock

36616_CAMA_G0339

10. Install the upper retaining bolts. Tighten to 43 ft. lbs. (58 Nm).

11. Install the lower bolt and nut. Tighten to 59 ft. lbs. (80 Nm).

12. Continue the installation in the reverse order of the removal procedure.

TESTING

1. Check the rubber parts for damage or deterioration.

2. Check for correct height and proper return of shock absorber to original height.

3. Check the shock absorber for abnormal resistance or unusual sounds.

4. Check for oil leakage around seals.

5. Replace if necessary.

STABILIZER BAR

REMOVAL & INSTALLATION

See Figure 188.

1. Before servicing the vehicle, refer to the Precautions Section.

2. Raise and support the vehicle safely.

3. Remove the tire and wheel assemblies.

4. Remove the stabilizer links from the bar.

5. Remove the stabilizer insulators from the bar.

6. Remove the stabilizer bar from its mounting.

To install:

➡**Be sure to use new fasteners, as required.**

7. Installation is the reverse of the removal procedure.

TRAILING ARM

REMOVAL & INSTALLATION

See Figure 189.

1. Before servicing the vehicle, refer to the Precautions Section.

2. Raise and support the vehicle safely.

3. Remove the tire and wheel assemblies.

4. Remove the retaining bolt.

5. Remove the retaining bolt and nut.

6. Remove the component from its mounting.

To install:

➡**Be sure to use new fasteners, as required.**

7. Position the component to its mounting.

8. Tighten the bolt and nut to 74 ft. lbs. (100 Nm).

9. Tighten the bolt to 30 ft. lbs. (40 Nm), plus 120 degrees

10. Continue the installation in the reverse order of the removal procedure.

11. Check the alignment. Adjust as required.

UPPER CONTROL ARM

REMOVAL & INSTALLATION

See Figure 190.

1. Before servicing the vehicle, refer to the Precautions Section.

2. Raise and support the vehicle safely.

3. Remove the tire and wheel assemblies.

4. Support the knuckle with a suitable jack.

5. Remove the brake hose from the control arm.

➡**The hose does not have to be completely removed from the arm. Just remove enough for clearance.**

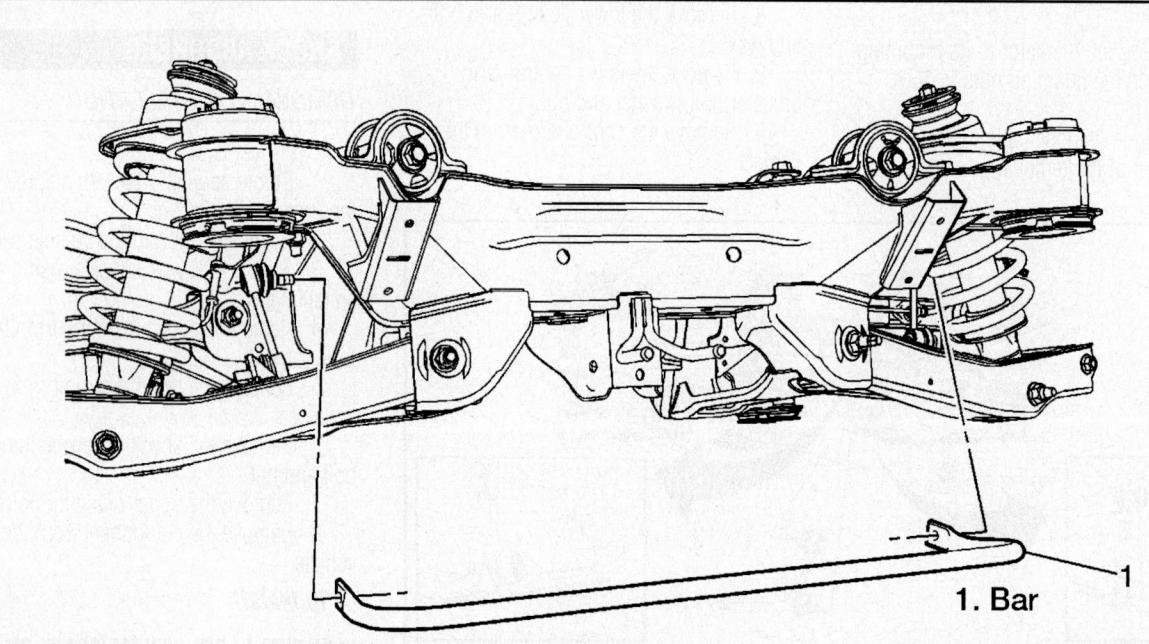

1. Bar

36616_CAMA_G0340

Fig. 188 Rear stabilizer bar and related components

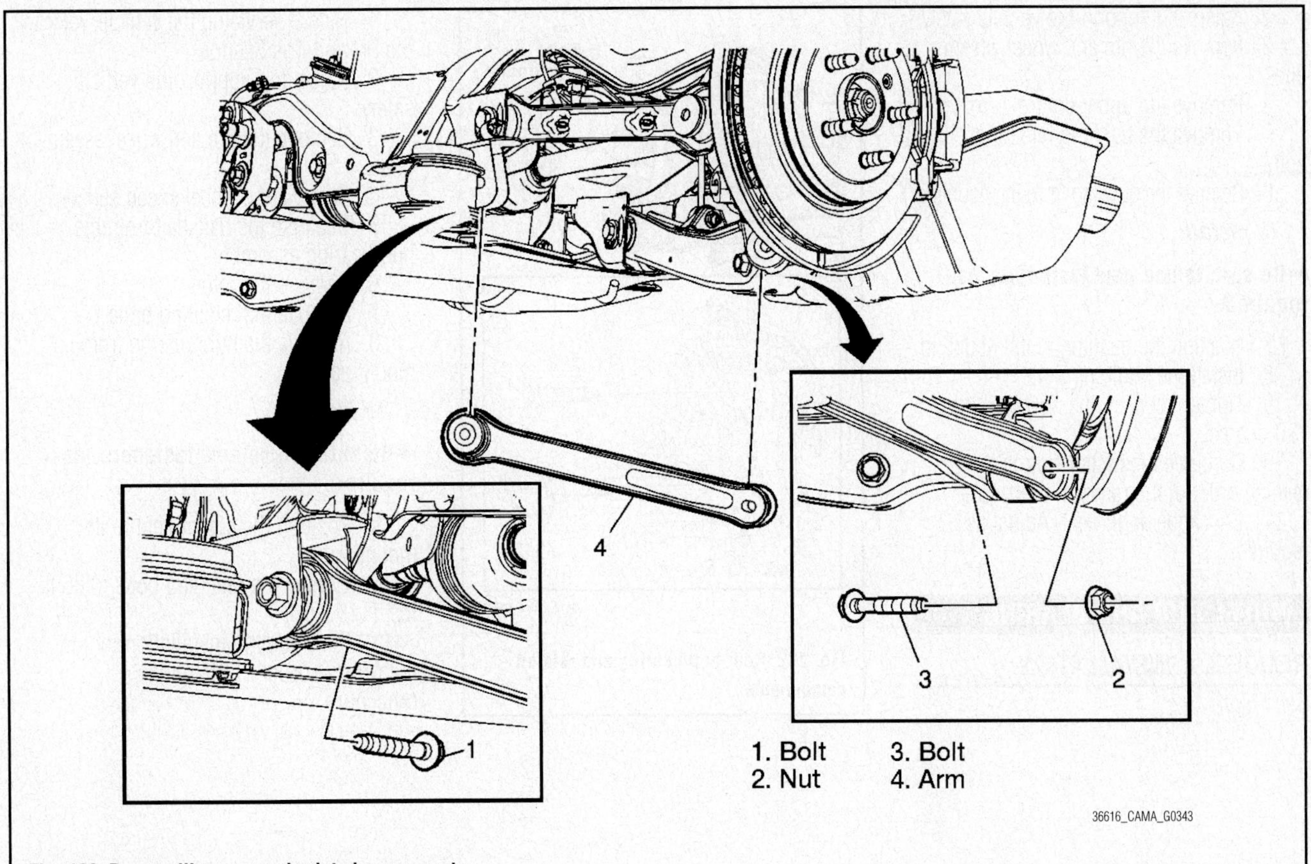

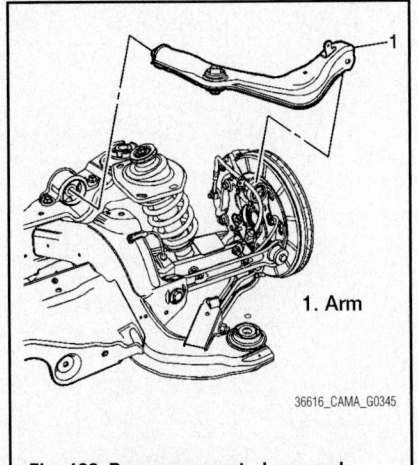

Fig. 189 Rear trailing arm and related components

1. Bolt   3. Bolt
2. Nut   4. Arm

36616_CAMA_G0343

6. Remove the control arm bushing bolt.

7. Remove the control arm bolt and nut from the knuckle.

8. Remove the bolt and nut from the frame.

9. Remove the arm from the vehicle.

To install:

➡**Be sure to use new fasteners, as required.**

10. Position the arm to its mounting.

11. Install the bolt and nut to the frame. Tighten to 59 ft. lbs. (80 Nm), plus 120 degrees.

12. Install the bolt and nut. Tighten to 44 ft. lbs. (60 Nm), plus 120 degrees.

13. Install the bolt and nut to the bushing. Tighten to 37 ft. lbs. (50 Nm), plus 120 degrees.

14. Continue the installation in the reverse order of the removal procedure.

15. Check the alignment. Adjust as required.

UPPER CONTROL ARM BUSHING

REMOVAL & INSTALLATION

See Figure 191.

1. Before servicing the vehicle, refer to the Precautions Section.

1. Arm

36616_CAMA_G0345

Fig. 190 Rear upper control arm and related components

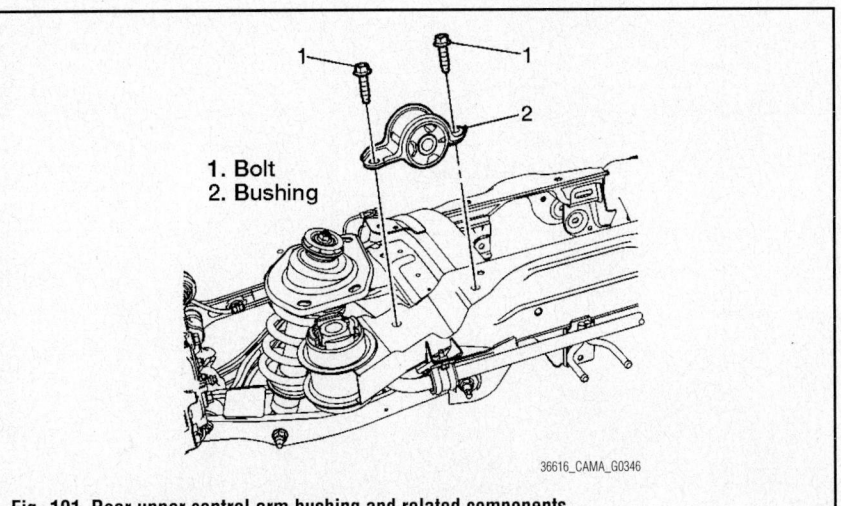

1. Bolt
2. Bushing

36616_CAMA_G0346

Fig. 191 Rear upper control arm bushing and related components

2. Raise and support the vehicle safely.

3. Remove the tire and wheel assemblies.

4. Remove the upper control arm.

5. Remove the bushing retaining bolts.

6. Remove the bushing from its mounting.

To install:

➡**Be sure to use new fasteners, as required.**

7. Position the bushing in its mounting.

8. Install the retaining bolts.

9. Tighten to 37 ft. lbs. (50 Nm), plus 120 degrees.

10. Continue the installation in the reverse order of the removal procedure.

11. Check the alignment. Adjust as required.

WHEEL HUB AND BEARING

REMOVAL & INSTALLATION

See Figure 192.

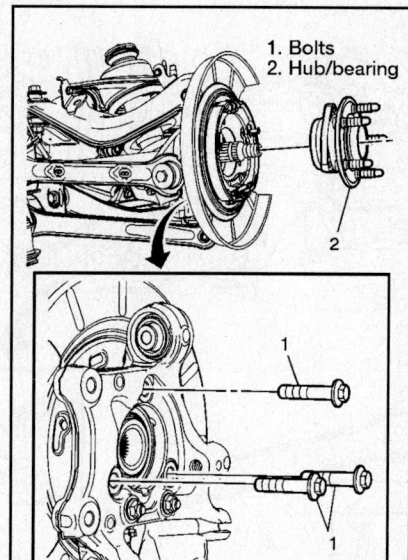

1. Bolts
2. Hub/bearing

36616_CAMA_G0341

Fig. 192 Rear hub/bearing and related components

1. Before servicing the vehicle, refer to the Precautions Section.

2. Raise and support the vehicle safely.

3. Remove the tire and wheel assemblies.

4. Remove the wheel speed sensor.

5. Separate the halfshaft from the hub/bearing assembly.

6. Remove the rotor.

7. Remove the retaining bolts.

8. Remove the hub/bearing from its mounting.

To install:

➡**Be sure to use new fasteners, as required.**

9. Position the component to its mounting.

10. Tighten the retaining bolts to 85 ft. lbs. (115 Nm).

11. Continue the installation in the reverse order of the removal procedure.

CHEVROLET AND GMC

Canyon • Colorado

9

SPECIFICATIONS AND MAINTENANCE CHARTS

ENGINE AND VEHICLE IDENTIFICATION

	Engine							Model Year	
Code ①	Liters (cc)	Cu. In.	Cyl.	Fuel Sys.	Engine Type	Eng. Mfg.	Code ②		Year
9	2.9 (2917)	178	4	SFI	DOHC	GM	8		2008
E	3.7 (3654)	223	5	SFI	DOHC	GM	9		2009
L	5.3 (5326)	325	8	SFI	OHV	GM			

SFI: Sequential Fuel Injection

MFI: Multi-point Fuel Injection

① 8th position of VIN

② 10th position of VIN

36616_CANY_C0001

GENERAL ENGINE SPECIFICATIONS

All measurements are given in inches.

Year	Model	Engine Displacement Liters	Engine Series VIN	Net Horsepower @ rpm	Net Torque @ rpm (ft. lbs.)	Bore x Stroke (in.)	Com- pression Ratio	Oil Pressure @ rpm
2008	Canyon/	2.9	9	185@5600	190@2800	3.76x4.02	10.3:1	12@1200
	Colorado	3.7	E	242@5600	242@4600	3.76x4.02	10.3:1	12@1200
2009	Canyon/	2.9	9	185@5600	190@2800	3.76x4.02	10.3:1	12@1200
	Colorado	3.7	E	242@5600	242@4600	3.76x4.02	10.3:1	12@1200
		5.3	L	300@5200	320@4000	3.78x3.62	9.95:1	24@4000

36616_CANY_C0002

GASOLINE ENGINE TUNE-UP SPECIFICATIONS

Year	Engine Displacement Liters	Engine VIN	Spark Plug Gap (in.)	Ignition Timing (deg.) MT	Ignition Timing (deg.) AT	Fuel Pump (psi)	Idle Speed (rpm) MT	Idle Speed (rpm) AT	Valve Clearance In.	Valve Clearance Ex.
2008	2.9	9	0.042	①	①	50-62	②	②	HYD	HYD
	3.7	E	0.042	①	①	50-62	②	②	HYD	HYD
2009	2.9	9	0.042	①	①	50-62	②	②	HYD	HYD
	3.7	E	0.042	①	①	50-62	②	②	HYD	HYD
	5.3	L	0.040	①	①	50-60	②	②	HYD	HYD

NOTE: The Vehicle Emission Control Information label often reflects specification changes made during production.

The label figures must be used if they differ from those in this chart.

HYD: Hydraulic

① Ignition timing is preset and cannot be adjusted

② Idle speed is maintained by the PCM

36616_CANY_C0003

CAPACITIES

Year	Model	Engine Displacement Liters	Engine VIN	Engine Oil with Filter (qts.)	Transmission (pts.) 5-Spd	Transmission (pts.) Auto.	Transfer Case (pts.)	Drive Axle Front (pts.)	Drive Axle Rear (pts.)	Fuel Tank (gal.)	Cooling System (qts.)
2008	Canyon/	2.9	9	5	①	②	2.8	3.2	③	19.5	10.4
	Colorado	3.7	E	6	①	②	2.8	3.2	③	19.5	10.6
2009	Canyon/	2.9	9	5	①	②	2.8	3.2	③	19.5	10.4
	Colorado	3.7	E	6	①	②	2.8	3.2	③	19.5	10.6
		5.3	L	6	①	②	2.8	3.2	③	19.5	13.7

NOTE: All capacities are approximate. Add fluid gradually and check to be sure a proper fluid level is obtained.

① 2WD models: 4.6
4WD models: 4.8

② Pan removal and refill: 10 pints.

③ 8.0 inch differential: 3.6 pints, 8.6 inch: 4.3 pints

36616_CANY_C0004

FLUID SPECIFICATIONS

Year	Model	Engine Displacement Liters	Engine ID/VIN	Engine Oil	Auto. Trans.	Drive Axle	Power Steering Fluid	Brake Master Cylinder
2008	Canyon/	2.9	9	5W-30	Dexron VI	75W-90	GM Part No. 89021184	DOT 3
	Colorado	3.7	E	5W-30	Dexron VI	75W-90	GM Part No. 89021184	DOT 3
2009	Canyon/	2.9	9	5W-30	Dexron VI	75W-90	GM Part No. 89021184	DOT 3
	Colorado	3.7	E	5W-30	Dexron VI	75W-90	GM Part No. 89021184	DOT 3
		5.3	L	5W-30	Dexron VI	75W-90	GM Part No. 89021184	DOT 3

DOT: Department Of Transpotation

36616_CANY_C0005

VALVE SPECIFICATIONS

Year	Engine Displacement Liters	Engine VIN	Seat Angle (deg.)	Face Angle (deg.)	Spring Test Pressure (lbs. @ in.)	Spring Installed Height (in.)	Stem-to-Guide Clearance (in.) Intake	Stem-to-Guide Clearance (in.) Exhaust	Stem Diameter (in.) Intake	Stem Diameter (in.) Exhaust
2008	2.9	9	NS	NS	130-142 @0.965	1.379	0.0011-0.0025	0.0015-0.0030	NS	NS
	3.7	E	NS	NS	130-142 @0.965	1.379	0.0011-0.0025	0.0015-0.0030	NS	NS
2009	2.9	9	NS	NS	130-142 @0.965	1.379	0.0011-0.0025	0.0015-0.0030	NS	NS
	3.7	E	NS	NS	130-142 @0.965	1.379	0.0011-0.0025	0.0015-0.0030	NS	NS
	5.3	L	46	45	220 @1.32	1.8	0.0037	0.0037	0.313	0.313

NS: Not Specified

36616_CANY_C0006

CAMSHAFT AND BEARING SPECIFICATIONS CHART

All measurements are given in inches.

Year	Engine Displ. Liters	Engine ID/VIN	Journal Dia.	Brg. Oil Clearance	Shaft End-play	Runout	Journal Bore	Lobe Height Intake	Lobe Height Exhaust
2008	2.9	9	①	0.0015-0.0033	②	NS	NS	1.635	1.615
	3.7	E	①	0.0015-0.0033	②	NS	NS	1.635	1.615
2009	2.9	9	①	0.0015-0.0033	②	NS	NS	1.635	1.615
	3.7	E	①	0.0015-0.0033	②	NS	NS	1.635	1.615
	5.3	L	0.2164-0.2166	0.0009-0.0038	0.001-0.012	0.002	③	0.283	0.283

NS: Not Specified

① All intake and exhaust No's. 2 through 7: 1.0612 - 1.0622 in.

　Exhaust No.1: 1.1794 - 1.1804 in.

② Exhaust: 0.0017 - 0.0084 in.

　Intake: 0.0020 - 0.0079 in.

③ Bearing Bore 1 and 5 Diameter: 2.345-2.347 in.

　Bearing Bore 2 and 4 Diameter: 2.325-2.327 in.

　Bearing Bore 3: 2.306-2.308 in.

36616_CANY_C0007

CRANKSHAFT AND CONNECTING ROD SPECIFICATIONS

All measurements are given in inches.

Year	Engine Displacement Liters	Engine VIN	Crankshaft Main Brg. Journal Dia.	Crankshaft Main Brg. Oil Clearance	Crankshaft Shaft End-play	Crankshaft Thrust on No.	Connecting Rod Journal Diameter	Connecting Rod Oil Clearance	Connecting Rod Side Clearance
2008	2.9	9	2.7567-2.7574	0.0004-0.0025	0.0044-0.0153	3	NS	0.0008-0.0025	0.0019-0.0137
	3.7	E	2.7567-2.7574	0.0004-0.0025	0.0044-0.0153	4	2.2340	0.0008-0.0025	0.0019-0.0137
2009	2.9	9	2.7567-2.7574	0.0004-0.0025	0.0044-0.0153	3	NS	0.0008-0.0025	0.0019-0.0137
	3.7	E	2.7567-2.7574	0.0004-0.0025	0.0044-0.0153	4	2.2340	0.0008-0.0025	0.0019-0.0137
	5.3	L	2.558	0.0008-0.0025	0.0015-0.0078	3	2.0987	0.0009-0.0030	0.00433-0.0200

36616_CANY_C0008

PISTON AND RING SPECIFICATIONS

All measurements are given in inches.

Year	Engine Displ. Liters	Engine VIN	Piston Clearance	Ring Gap			Ring Side Clearance		
				Top Compression	Bottom Compression	Oil Control	Top Compression	Bottom Compression	Oil Control
2008	2.9	9	0.0006-0.0014	0.00787-0.0157	0.0142-0.0201	0.0098-0.0299	0.0017-0.0037	0.0021-0.0037	0.0023-0.0085
	3.7	E	0.0004-0.0017	0.0079-0.0157	0.0142-0.0201	0.0098-0.0299	0.0017-0.0037	0.0021-0.0037	0.0023-0.0085
2009	2.9	9	0.0006-0.0014	0.00787-0.0157	0.0142-0.0201	0.0098-0.0299	0.0017-0.0037	0.0021-0.0037	0.0023-0.0085
	3.7	E	0.0004-0.0017	0.0079-0.0157	0.0142-0.0201	0.0098-0.0299	0.0017-0.0037	0.0021-0.0037	0.0023-0.0085
	5.3	L	①	0.009-0.0196	0.0173-0.030	0.007-0.032	0.00157-0.00335	0.00157-0.0031	0.0005-0.0078

① Service limit with skirt coating worn off: 0.0028 in.

36616_CANY_C0009

TORQUE SPECIFICATIONS

All readings in ft. lbs.

Year	Engine Displacement Liters	Engine VIN	Cylinder Head Bolts	Main Bearing Bolts	Rod Bearing Bolts	Crankshaft Damper Bolts	Flywheel Bolts	Manifold		Spark Plugs	Oil Pan Drain Plug
								Intake	Exhaust		
2008	2.9	9	①	②	③	④	⑤	⑥	⑦	13	19
	3.7	E	①	②	③	④	⑤	⑥	⑦	13	19
2009	2.9	9	①	②	③	④	⑤	⑥	⑦	13	19
	3.7	E	①	②	③	④	⑤	⑥	⑦	13	19
	5.3	L	⑧	⑨	⑩	⑪	⑫	⑬	⑭	11	18

① 1st pass: 22 ft. lbs.
2nd pass: Plus 155 degrees
Short end bolt
1st pass: 62 inch lbs.
2nd pass: plus 60 degrees
Long end bolt
1st pass: 62 inch lbs.
2nd pass: plus 120 degrees

② 1st pass: 18 ft. lbs.
2nd pass: plus 180 degrees

③ 1st pass: 18 ft. lbs.
2nd pass: plus 110 degrees

④ 1st pass: 110 ft. lbs.
2nd pass: plus 180 degrees

⑤ 1st pass: 30 ft. lbs.
2nd pass: plus 45 degrees

⑥ 89 inch lbs.

⑦ 1st pass: 15 ft. lbs.
Repeat twice more in sequence

⑧ M8 bolts
22 ft. lbs. in sequence
M11 bolts
1st pass: 22 ft. lbs.
2nd pass: plus 90 degrees
Final pass: plus 70 degrees

⑨ M8 bolts
18 ft. lbs.
M10 bolts
1st pass: 15 ft. lbs.
Final pass: plus 80 degrees
M10 studs
1st pass: 15 ft. lbs.
Final pass: plus 51 degrees

⑩ 1st pass: 15 ft. lbs.
Final pass: plus 85 degrees

⑪ 1st pass: 111 ft. lbs.
2nd pass: loosen 360 degrees
3rd pass: 37 ft. lbs.
Final pass: plus 230 degrees

⑫ 1st pass: 15 ft. lbs.
2nd pass: 37 ft. lbs.
Final pass: 74 ft. lbs.

⑬ 1st pass: 44 inch lbs.
Final pass: 89 inch lbs.

⑭ 1st pass: 11 ft. lbs.
Final pass: 15 ft. lbs.

36616_CANY_C0010

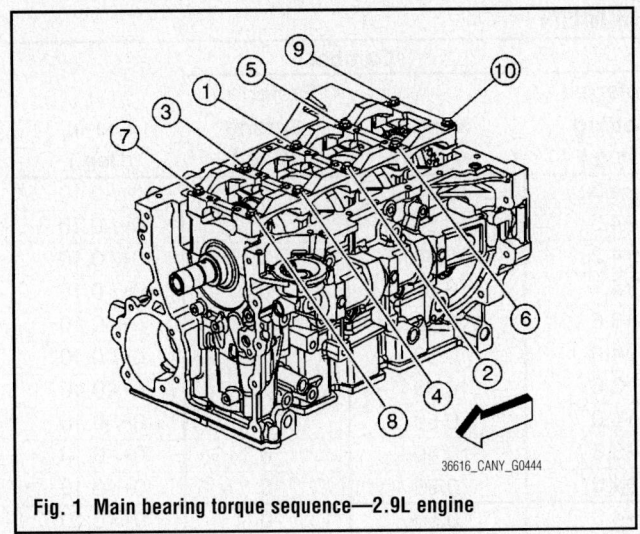

Fig. 1 Main bearing torque sequence—2.9L engine

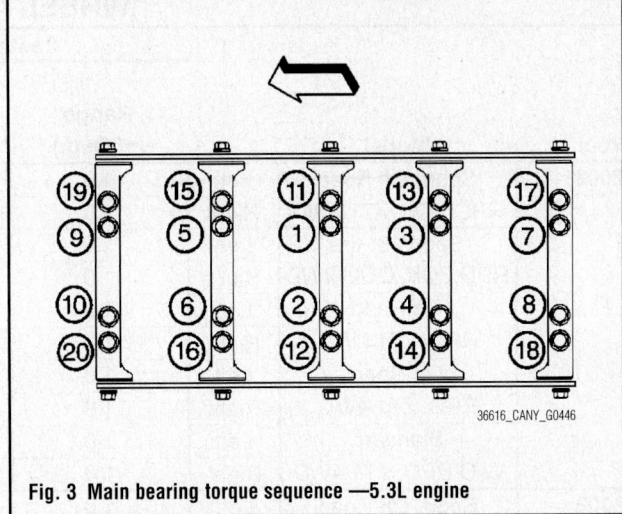

Fig. 3 Main bearing torque sequence —5.3L engine

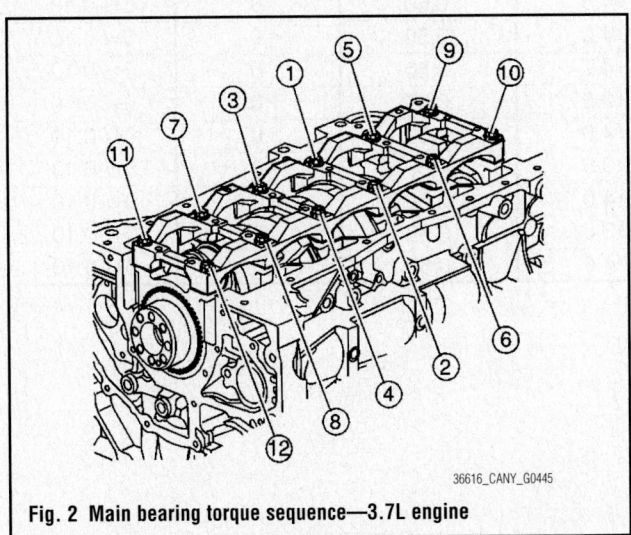

Fig. 2 Main bearing torque sequence—3.7L engine

WHEEL ALIGNMENT

Year	Model		Caster Range (+/-Deg.)	Caster Preferred Setting (Deg.)	Camber Range (+/-Deg.)	Camber Preferred Setting (Deg.)	Toe-in (Deg.)
2008	Sport, Off Road	Left	1.0	+4.3	0.50	0	0+/-0.10
	RPO:ZQ8, Z71 2WD	Right	1.0	+4.5	0.50	0	0+/-0.10
	Sport 18" tire	Left	1.0	+4.2	0.50	0	0+/-0.10
	RPO:ZQ8, QDG 2WD	Right	1.0	+4.7	0.50	0	0+/-0.10
	Off Road	Left	1.0	+3.6	0.50	0	0+/-0.10
	RPO: Z71 2WD	Right	1.0	+4.0	0.50	0	0+/-0.10
	Off Road	Left	1.0	+3.6	0.50	0	0+/-0.10
	RPO: Z71 4WD	Right	1.0	+4.0	0.50	0	0+/-0.10
	Standard	Left	1.0	+3.8	0.50	0	0+/-0.10
	W/O RPO: Z71 4WD	Right	1.0	+4.0	0.50	0	0+/-0.10
2009	Sport, Off Road	Left	1.0	+4.3	0.50	0	0+/-0.10
	RPO:ZQ8, Z71 2WD	Right	1.0	+4.5	0.50	0	0+/-0.10
	Sport 18" tire	Left	1.0	+4.2	0.50	0	0+/-0.10
	RPO:ZQ8, QDG 2WD	Right	1.0	+4.7	0.50	0	0+/-0.10
	Off Road	Left	1.0	+3.6	0.50	0	0+/-0.10
	RPO: Z71 2WD	Right	1.0	+4.0	0.50	0	0+/-0.10
	Off Road	Left	1.0	+3.6	0.50	0	0+/-0.10
	RPO: Z71 4WD	Right	1.0	+4.0	0.50	0	0+/-0.10
	Standard	Left	1.0	+3.8	0.50	0	0+/-0.10
	W/O RPO: Z71 4WD	Right	1.0	+4.0	0.50	0	0+/-0.10

36616_CANY_C0011

TIRE, WHEEL AND BALL JOINT SPECIFICATIONS

Year	Model	OEM Tires Standard	OEM Tires Optional	OEM Tires Optional	Tire Pres Front	Tire Pres Rear	Wheel Size	Ball Joint Inspection	Lug Nut Torque (ft. lbs.)
2008	Standard Cab 2WD	P215/70R16	None	None	①	①	16x7	NS	103
	Extended Cab 2WD	P215/70R16	P265/70R17	P235/50R18	①	①	17x7 18X8	NS	103
	Crew Cab 2WD	P215/70R16	P265/70R17	P235/50R18	①	①	17x7 18x8	NS	103
	Standard Cab 4WD	P235/75R16	None	None	①	①	16x7	NS	103
	Extended Cab 4WD	P235/75R16	P265/70R17	None	①	①	16x7 17X7	NS	103
	Crew Cab 4WD	P235/75R16	P265/70R17	None	①	①	16x7 17X7	NS	103
2009	Standard Cab 2WD	P215/70R16	None	None	①	①	16x7	NS	103
	Extended Cab 2WD	P215/70R16	P265/70R17	P235/50R18	①	①	17x7 18X8	NS	103
	Crew Cab 2WD	P215/70R16	P265/70R17	P235/50R18	①	①	17x7 18x8	NS	103
	Standard Cab 4WD	P235/75R16	None	None	①	①	16x7	NS	103
	Extended Cab 4WD	P235/75R16	P265/70R17	None	①	①	16x7 17X7	NS	103
	Crew Cab 4WD	P235/75R16	P265/70R17	None	①	①	16x7 17X7	NS	103

NS: Not Specified

OEM: Original Equipment Manufacturer

PSI: Pounds Per Square Inch

① Refer to placard on vehicle for proper inflation pressure

36616_CANY_C0012

BRAKE SPECIFICATIONS

All measurements in inches unless noted

Year	Model		Brake Disc Original Thickness	Brake Disc Minimum Thickness	Brake Disc Maximum Runout	Brake Drum Diameter Original Inside Diameter	Brake Drum Diameter Max. Wear Limit	Brake Drum Diameter Maximum Machine Diameter	Minimum Lining Thickness	Brake Caliper Bracket Bolts (ft. lbs.)	Brake Caliper Mounting Bolts (ft. lbs.)
2008	Canyon	F	1.140	1.080	0.002	NS	NS	NS	NS	133	47
	Colorado	R	NA	NA	NA	NS	NS	11.673	0.030	NA	NA
2009	Canyon	F	1.140	1.080	0.002	NS	NS	NS	0.070	133	47
	Colorado	R	NA	NA	NA	NS	NS	11.673	0.030	NA	NA

NS: Not Specified

NA: Not Applicable

36616_CANY_C0013

MAINTENANCE I AND II SERVICE SCHEDULES
2008-09 Canyon and Colorado

When the CHANGE ENGINE OIL light appears, certain services and inspections are required. Services are described below. Generally, it is recommended that the first service be Maintenance I, second service be Maintenance II, and that services are then alter

Required services are described as Maintenance I and Maintenance II.

The first service of a vehicle should be Maintance I, and the second service should be Maintenance II.

Alternate between the 2 services thereafter. However, in some cases, Maintenance II may be required more often.

Maintenance I: Use Maintenance I if the Service Engine Oil light comes on within 10 months since the vehicle was purcahses or, if Maintenance II was performed.

Maintenance II: Use Maintenance II if the previous service performed was Maintenance I. Always used Maintenance II whenever the CHANGE ENGINE OIL light comes on 10 months or more since the last service, or, if the CHANGE ENGINE OIL light has not come on a

Service	Maintenance I	Maintenance II
Change engine oil and filter. Reset oil life system.	✓	✓
Visually check for any leaks or damage. A fluid loss in the vehicle system could indicate a problem. Inspect, repair and add fluid to the system, if necessary.	✓	✓
Inspect engine air cleaner filter. If necessary, replace filter.	—	✓
Rotate tires and check inflation pressures and wear.	✓	✓
Visually inspect brake lines and hoses for proper hook-up, binding, leaks, cracks, chafing, etc. Inspect the disc brake pads for wear and the rotors for surface condition. Inspect the drum brake lings for wear or cracks. Inspect other brake parts, includi	✓	✓
Check engine coolant and windshield washer fluid levels and add fluid as needed.	✓	✓
Perform any needed additional services.	✓	✓
Inspect the suspension and steering components. Inspect the front and rear suspension systems and steering system for damaged, loose, or missing parts, or signs of wear. Inspect the power steering lines and the hoses for proper hook-up, binding, leaks, cr	—	✓
Inspect the coolant hoses and replace the hoses if they are crackes, swollen or deteriorated. Inspect all pipes, fittings and clamps; replace with OEM parts as needed. To help ensure proper operation, a pressure test of the cooling system and pressure cap	—	✓
Inspect wiper blades for wear or cracking		✓
Inspect restraint system components.		✓
Lubricate all key lock cylinders, latch assemblies and hinges		✓
Replace passenger compartment air filter.		✓

To reset the CHANGE ENGINE OIL LIGHT:

1. Turn the ignition key to ON/RUN with the engine off.

2. Press and release the stem in the lower center of the instrument cluster until the OIL LIFE message is displayed.

3. Once the alternating OIL LIFE and RESET messages appear, press and hold the stem until several beeps sound.

   This confirms that the oil life system has been reset.

4. Turn the ignition key to Off posiiton.

If the CHANGE OIL message comes back on when the vehicle is started, the engine oil life system has not reset. Repeat the procedure.

36616_CANY_C0014

ADDITIONAL MAINTENANCE SERVICES
Canyon and Colorado

TO BE SERVICED	TYPE OF SERVICE	VEHICLE MILEAGE INTERVAL (x1000)					
		25	50	75	100	125	150
Air cleaner filter	R		✓		✓		✓
Accessory drive belt	I						✓
Auto. Trans. Fluid ①	R		✓		✓		✓
Cooling system hoses and clamps	S/I						✓
Engine coolant: every 5 years, or	R						✓
Fuel system	I	✓	✓	✓	✓	✓	✓
Exhaust system & heat shields	S/I	✓	✓	✓	✓	✓	✓
Brake fluid ②	R						
Spark plugs	R				✓		

R: Replace

S/I: Inspect and service, if necessary

① Replace if any of the following condition are met:

Heavy city traffic where the outside temperature regularly reaches 90 degrees F (32 degrees C) or higher.

Hilly or mountainous terrain

Frequent trailer towing

Taxi, police or delivery service

Otherwise, change every 100,000 miles

② Drain, flush, and refill brake hydraulic system at a regular

service interval (I or II) every two years.

36616_CANY_C0015

PRECAUTIONS

Before servicing any vehicle, please be sure to read all of the following precautions, which deal with personal safety, prevention of component damage, and important points to take into consideration when servicing a motor vehicle:

• Never open, service or drain the radiator or cooling system when the engine is hot; serious burns can occur from the steam and hot coolant.

• Observe all applicable safety precautions when working around fuel. Whenever servicing the fuel system, always work in a well-ventilated area. Do not allow fuel spray or vapors to come in contact with a spark, open flame, or excessive heat (a hot drop light, for example). Keep a dry chemical fire extinguisher near the work area. Always keep fuel in a container specifically designed for fuel storage; also, always properly seal fuel containers to avoid the possibility of fire or explosion. Refer to the additional fuel system precautions later in this section.

• Fuel injection systems often remain pressurized, even after the engine has been turned **OFF**. The fuel system pressure must be relieved before disconnecting any fuel lines. Failure to do so may result in fire and/or personal injury.

• Brake fluid often contains polyglycol ethers and polyglycols. Avoid contact with the eyes and wash your hands thoroughly after handling brake fluid. If you do get brake fluid in your eyes, flush your eyes with clean, running water for 15 minutes. If eye irritation persists, or if you have taken brake fluid internally, IMMEDIATELY seek medical assistance.

• The EPA warns that prolonged contact with used engine oil may cause a number of skin disorders, including cancer. You should make every effort to minimize your exposure to used engine oil. Protective gloves should be worn when changing oil. Wash your hands and any other exposed skin areas as soon as possible after exposure to used engine oil. Soap and water, or waterless hand cleaner should be used.

• All new vehicles are now equipped with an air bag system, often referred to as a Supplemental Restraint System (SRS) or Supplemental Inflatable Restraint (SIR) system. The system must be disabled before performing service on or around system components, steering column, instrument panel components, wiring and sensors. Failure to follow safety and disabling procedures could result in accidental air bag deployment, possible personal injury and unnecessary system repairs.

• Always wear safety goggles when working with, or around, the air bag system. When carrying a non-deployed air bag, be sure the bag and trim cover are pointed away from your body. When placing a non-deployed air bag on a work surface, always face the bag and trim cover upward, away from the surface. This will reduce the motion of the module if it is accidentally deployed. Refer to the additional air bag system precautions later in this section.

• Clean, high quality brake fluid from a sealed container is essential to the safe and proper operation of the brake system. You should always buy the correct type of brake fluid for your vehicle. If the brake fluid becomes contaminated, completely flush the system with new fluid. Never reuse any brake fluid. Any brake fluid that is removed from the system should be discarded. Also, do not allow any brake fluid to come in contact with a painted surface; it will damage the paint.

• Never operate the engine without the proper amount and type of engine oil; doing so WILL result in severe engine damage.

• Timing belt maintenance is extremely important. Many models utilize an interference-type, non-freewheeling engine. If the timing belt breaks, the valves in the cylinder head may strike the pistons, causing potentially serious (also time-consuming and expensive) engine damage. Refer to the maintenance interval charts for the recommended replacement interval for the timing belt, and to the timing belt section for belt replacement and inspection.

• Disconnecting the negative battery cable on some vehicles may interfere with the functions of the on-board computer system(s) and may require the computer to undergo a relearning process once the negative battery cable is reconnected.

• When servicing drum brakes, only disassemble and assemble one side at a time, leaving the remaining side intact for reference.

• Only an MVAC-trained, EPA-certified automotive technician should service the air conditioning system or its components.

BRAKES

GENERAL INFORMATION

PRECAUTIONS

• Certain components within the ABS system are not intended to be serviced or repaired individually.

• Do not use rubber hoses or other parts not specifically specified for and ABS system. When using repair kits, replace all parts included in the kit. Partial or incorrect repair may lead to functional problems and require the replacement of components.

• Lubricate rubber parts with clean, fresh brake fluid to ease assembly. Do not use shop air to clean parts; damage to rubber components may result.

• Use only DOT 3 brake fluid from an unopened container.

• If any hydraulic component or line is removed or replaced, it may be necessary to bleed the entire system.

• A clean repair area is essential. Always clean the reservoir and cap thoroughly before removing the cap. The slightest amount of dirt in the fluid may plug an orifice and impair the system function. Perform repairs after components have been thoroughly cleaned; use only denatured alcohol to clean components. Do not allow ABS components to come into contact with any substance containing mineral oil; this includes used shop rags.

• The Anti-Lock control unit is a microprocessor similar to other computer units in the vehicle. Ensure that the ignition switch is **OFF** before removing or installing controller harnesses. Avoid static electricity discharge at or near the controller.

ANTI-LOCK BRAKE SYSTEM (ABS)

• If any arc welding is to be done on the vehicle, the control unit should be unplugged before welding operations begin.

WHEEL SPEED SENSORS

REMOVAL & INSTALLATION

Front

See Figure 4.

1. Before servicing the vehicle, refer to the Precautions Section, including brake dust precautions.

2. Within the engine compartment, disconnect the wheel speed sensor electrical connector.

3. Release the wheel speed sensor harness connector from the wheelhouse.

4. Raise and support the vehicle.

Fig. 4 Wheel speed sensor

5. Remove the wheel and tire.

6. Release the wheel speed sensor harness clips from the suspension upper control arm.

7. Release the wheel speed sensor harness grommet from the mounting bracket.

8. Remove the wheel speed sensor harness bracket bolt.

9. Thoroughly clean the wheel speed sensor mounting area of the steering knuckle of any dirt and debris.

10. Remove the wheel speed sensor bolt.

➥**Do not pry or lever against the wheel speed sensor to remove.**

11. Carefully remove the wheel speed sensor from the suspension knuckle by pulling straight upward.

To install:

12. Install the wheel speed sensor to the suspension knuckle.

13. Install the wheel speed sensor bolt and tighten to 71 inch lbs. (8 Nm).

14. Install the wheel speed sensor harness bracket bolt and tighten to 80 inch lbs. (9 Nm).

15. Install the wheel speed sensor har-

ness grommet to the mounting bracket.

16. Install the wheel speed sensor harness clips to the suspension upper control arm.

17. Install the wheel speed sensor harness connector to the wheelhouse.

18. Connect the wheel speed sensor electrical connector.

19. Install the tire and wheel assembly.

20. Perform the Diagnostic System Check. Refer to General Information.

Rear

See Figures 5 and 6.

1. Before servicing the vehicle, refer to the Precautions Section.

2. Raise and support the vehicle.

3. Remove the wheel speed sensor bolts.

4. Remove the wheel speed sensor from the drum brake backing plate by carefully pulling straight outward.

5. Release the wheel speed sensor harness retainers on the rear park brake cable. Release the harness from the retainers.

6. Disconnect the wheel speed sensor electrical connector.

7. Release the electrical connector and harness retainer from the frame.

8. Remove the wheel speed sensor assembly.

To install:

9. Position the wheel speed sensor assembly to the vehicle.

10. Connect the wheel speed sensor electrical connector.

11. Install the electrical connector and harness retainer to the frame.

12. Position the wheel speed sensor harness to the retainers on the rear park brake cable.

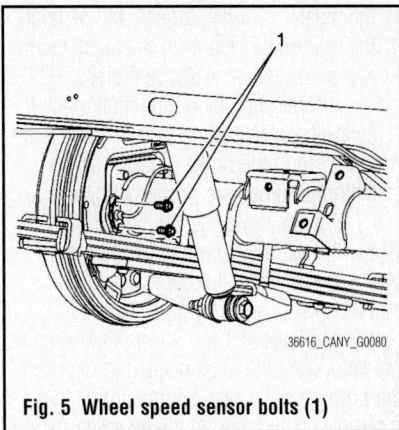

Fig. 5 Wheel speed sensor bolts (1)

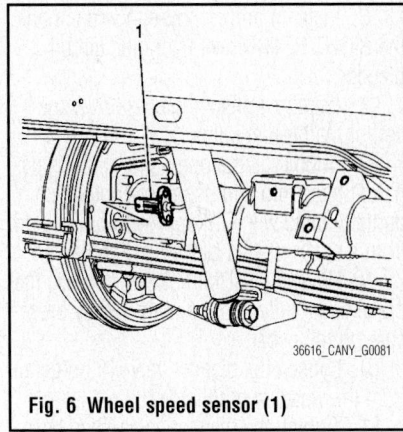

Fig. 6 Wheel speed sensor (1)

13. Fasten the wheel speed sensor harness retainers.

14. Install the wheel speed sensor to the drum brake backing plate.

15. Install the wheel speed sensor bolts and tighten to 13 ft. lbs. (17 Nm).

16. Lower the vehicle.

17. Perform the Diagnostic System Check. Refer to General Information.

BRAKES | **BLEEDING THE BRAKE SYSTEM**

BLEEDING PROCEDURE

Manual Bleeding

1. Before servicing the vehicle, refer to the Precautions Section.

2. Place a clean shop cloth beneath the brake master cylinder to prevent brake fluid spills.

3. With the ignition OFF and the brakes cool, apply the brakes 3–5 times, or until the brake pedal effort increases significantly, in order to deplete the brake booster power reserve.

4. If you have performed a brake master cylinder bench bleeding on this vehicle, or if you disconnected the brake pipes from the

master cylinder, you must perform the following steps:

a. Ensure that the brake master cylinder reservoir is full to the maximum-fill level. If necessary add GM approved brake fluid from a clean, sealed brake fluid container. If removal of the reservoir cap and diaphragm is necessary, clean the outside of the reservoir on and around the cap prior to removal.

b. With the rear brake pipe installed securely to the master cylinder, loosen and separate the front brake pipe from the front port of the brake master cylinder.

c. Allow a small amount of brake fluid to gravity bleed from the open port of the master cylinder.

d. Reconnect the brake pipe to the master cylinder port and tighten securely.

e. Have an assistant slowly depress the brake pedal fully and maintain steady pressure on the pedal.

f. Loosen the same brake pipe to purge air from the open port of the master cylinder.

g. Tighten the brake pipe, then have the assistant slowly release the brake pedal.

h. Wait 15 seconds, then repeat the above 5 steps until all air is purged from the same port of the master cylinder.

i. With the front brake pipe installed securely to the master cylinder, after all air has been purged from the front port of the master cylinder, loosen and separate the rear brake pipe from the master cylinder, then repeat the above 6 steps.

j. After completing the final master cylinder port bleeding procedure, ensure that both of the brake pipe-to-master cylinder fittings are properly tightened.

5. Fill the brake master cylinder reservoir with GM approved brake fluid from a clean, sealed brake fluid container. Ensure that the brake master cylinder reservoir remains at least half-full during this bleeding procedure. Add fluid as needed to maintain the proper level. Clean the outside of the reservoir on and around the reservoir cap prior to removing the cap and diaphragm.

6. Install a proper box-end wrench onto the RIGHT REAR wheel hydraulic circuit bleeder valve.

7. Install a transparent hose over the end of the bleeder valve.

8. Submerge the open end of the transparent hose into a transparent container partially filled with GM approved brake fluid from a clean, sealed brake fluid container.

9. Have an assistant slowly depress the brake pedal fully and maintain steady pressure on the pedal.

10. Loosen the bleeder valve to purge air from the wheel hydraulic circuit.

11. Tighten the bleeder valve, then have the assistant slowly release the brake pedal.

12. Wait 15 seconds, then repeat steps 8–10 until all air is purged from the same wheel hydraulic circuit.

13. With the right rear wheel hydraulic circuit bleeder valve tightened securely, after all air has been purged from the right rear hydraulic circuit install a proper box-end wrench onto the LEFT REAR wheel hydraulic circuit bleeder valve.

14. Install a transparent hose over the end of the bleeder valve, then repeat steps 8–12.

15. With the left rear wheel hydraulic circuit bleeder valve tightened securely, after all air purged from the left rear hydraulic circuit, install a proper box-end wrench onto the RIGHT FRONT wheel hydraulic circuit bleeder valve.

16. Install a transparent hose over the end of the bleeder valve, then repeat steps 8–12.

17. With the right front wheel hydraulic circuit bleeder valve tightened securely, after all air has been purged from the right front hydraulic circuit, install a proper box-end wrench onto the LEFT FRONT wheel hydraulic circuit bleeder valve.

18. Install a transparent hose over the end of the bleeder valve, then repeat steps 8–12.

19. After completing the final wheel hydraulic circuit bleeding procedure, ensure that each of the 4 wheel hydraulic circuit bleeder valves are properly tightened.

20. Fill the brake master cylinder reservoir to the maximum-fill level with GM approved brake fluid from a clean, sealed brake fluid container.

21. Slowly depress and release the brake pedal. Observe the feel of the brake pedal.

22. If the brake pedal feels spongy, repeat the bleeding procedure again. If the brake pedal still feels spongy after repeating the bleeding procedure, perform the following steps:

a. Inspect the brake system for external leaks.

b. Pressure bleed the hydraulic brake system in order to purge any air that may still be trapped in the system.

23. Turn the ignition key ON, with the engine OFF. Check to see if the brake system warning lamp remains illuminated.

➥If the brake system warning lamp remains illuminated, DO NOT allow the vehicle to be driven until it is diagnosed and repaired.

➥If the brake system warning lamp remains illuminated refer to Diagnostic Trouble Codes.

Pressure Bleeding

1. Before servicing the vehicle, refer to the Precautions Section.

2. Place a clean shop cloth beneath the brake master cylinder to prevent brake fluid spills.

3. With the ignition OFF and the brakes cool, apply the brakes 3–5 times, or until the brake pedal effort increases significantly, in order to deplete the brake booster power reserve.

4. If you have performed a brake master cylinder bench bleeding on this vehicle, or if you disconnected the brake pipes from the master cylinder, you must perform the following steps:

a. Ensure that the brake master cylinder reservoir is full to the maximum-fill level. If necessary add GM approved brake fluid from a clean, sealed brake fluid container. If removal of the reservoir cap and diaphragm is necessary, clean the outside of the reservoir on and around the cap prior to removal.

b. With the rear brake pipe installed securely to the master cylinder, loosen and separate the front brake pipe from the front port of the brake master cylinder.

c. Allow a small amount of brake fluid to gravity bleed from the open port of the master cylinder.

d. Reconnect the brake pipe to the master cylinder port and tighten securely.

e. Have an assistant slowly depress the brake pedal fully and maintain steady pressure on the pedal.

f. Loosen the same brake pipe to purge air from the open port of the master cylinder.

g. Tighten the brake pipe, then have the assistant slowly release the brake pedal.

h. Wait 15 seconds, then repeat the above 5 steps until all air is purged from the same port of the master cylinder.

i. With the front brake pipe installed securely to the master cylinder, after all air has been purged from the front port of the master cylinder, loosen and separate the rear brake pipe from the master cylinder, then repeat the above 6 steps.

j. After completing the final master cylinder port bleeding procedure, ensure that both of the brake pipe-to-master cylinder fittings are properly tightened.

5. Fill the brake master cylinder reservoir to the maximum-fill level with GM approved brake fluid from a clean, sealed brake fluid container. Clean the outside of the reservoir on and around the reservoir cap prior to removing the cap and diaphragm.

6. Install the J-35589-A Brake Pressure Bleeder Adapter to the brake master cylinder reservoir.

7. Check the brake fluid level in the J-29532 Diaphragm Pressure Bleeder, or equivalent , or equivalent. Add GM approved brake fluid from a clean, sealed brake fluid container as necessary to bring the level to approximately the half-full point.

8. Connect the J-29532 Diaphragm Pressure Bleeder, or equivalent , or equivalent, to the J-35589-A Brake Pressure Bleeder Adapter .

9. Charge the J-29532 Diaphragm Pressure Bleeder, or equivalent , or equivalent, air tank to 25–30 psi (175–205 kPa).

10. Open the J-29532 Diaphragm Pressure Bleeder, or equivalent , or equivalent, fluid tank valve to allow pressurized brake fluid to enter the brake system.

11. Wait approximately 30 seconds, then inspect the entire hydraulic brake system in order to ensure that there are no existing external brake fluid leaks. Any brake fluid leaks identified require repair prior to completing this procedure.

12. Install a proper box-end wrench onto the RIGHT REAR wheel hydraulic circuit bleeder valve.

13. Install a transparent hose over the end of the bleeder valve.

14. Submerge the open end of the transparent hose into a transparent container

partially filled with GM approved brake fluid from a clean, sealed brake fluid container.

15. Loosen the bleeder valve to purge air from the wheel hydraulic circuit. Allow fluid to flow until air bubbles stop flowing from the bleeder, then tighten the bleeder valve.

16. With the right rear wheel hydraulic circuit bleeder valve tightened securely, after all air has been purged from the right rear hydraulic circuit, install a proper box-end wrench onto the LEFT REAR wheel hydraulic circuit bleeder valve.

17. Install a transparent hose over the end of the bleeder valve, then repeat steps 14–15.

18. With the left rear wheel hydraulic circuit bleeder valve tightened securely, after all air has been purged from the left rear hydraulic circuit, install a proper box-end wrench onto the RIGHT FRONT wheel hydraulic circuit bleeder valve.

19. Install a transparent hose over the end of the bleeder valve, then repeat steps 14–15.

20. With the right front wheel hydraulic circuit bleeder valve tightened securely, after all air has been purged from the right front hydraulic circuit, install a proper box-end wrench onto the LEFT FRONT wheel hydraulic circuit bleeder valve.

21. Install a transparent hose over the end of the bleeder valve, then repeat steps 14–15.

22. After completing the final wheel hydraulic circuit bleeding procedure, ensure that each of the 4 wheel hydraulic circuit bleeder valves are properly tightened.

23. Close the J-29532 Diaphragm Pressure Bleeder, or equivalent, or equivalent, fluid tank valve, then disconnect the J-29532 Diaphragm Pressure Bleeder, or equivalent, or equivalent, from the J-35589-A Brake Pressure Bleeder Adapter.

24. Remove the J-35589-A Brake Pressure Bleeder Adapter from the brake master cylinder reservoir.

25. Fill the brake master cylinder reservoir to the maximum-fill level with GM approved brake fluid from a clean, sealed brake fluid container.

26. Slowly depress and release the brake pedal. Observe the feel of the brake pedal.

27. If the brake pedal feels spongy perform the following steps:

a. Inspect the brake system for external leaks.

b. Using a scan tool, perform the antilock brake system automated bleeding procedure to remove any air that may have been trapped in the Brake Pressure Modulator Valve (BPMV). Refer to Bleeding the ABS System.

28. Turn the ignition key ON, with the engine OFF. Check to see if the brake system warning lamp remains illuminated.

➡**If the brake system warning lamp remains illuminated, DO NOT allow the vehicle to be driven until it is diagnosed and repaired.**

➡**If the brake system warning lamp remains illuminated, refer to Diagnostic Trouble Codes.**

ABS AUTOMATED BLEED PROCEDURE

1. Install a scan tool to the vehicle.
2. Start the engine and allow the engine to idle.
3. Depress the brake pedal firmly and maintain steady pressure on the pedal.
4. Using the scan tool, begin the automated bleed procedure.

5. Follow the instructions on the scan tool to complete the automated bleed procedure. Release the brake pedal between each test sequence.

6. Turn the ignition OFF.

7. Remove the scan tool from the vehicle.

8. Fill the brake master cylinder reservoir to the maximum-fill level with Delco Supreme 11® GM P/N 12377967 or equivalent DOT-3 brake fluid from a clean, sealed brake fluid container.

9. Bleed the hydraulic brake system.

10. With the ignition OFF, apply the brakes 3–5 times, or until the brake pedal becomes firm, in order to deplete the brake booster power reserve.

11. Slowly depress and release the brake pedal. Observe the feel of the brake pedal.

12. If the brake pedal feels spongy, repeat the automated bleeding procedure. If the brake pedal still feels spongy after repeating the automated bleeding procedure inspect the brake system for external leaks.

13. Turn the ignition key ON, with the engine OFF; check to see if the brake system warning lamp remains illuminated.

14. If the brake system warning lamp remains illuminated, DO NOT allow the vehicle to be driven until it is diagnosed and repaired.

15. Drive the vehicle to exceed 8 mph to allow ABS initialization to occur. Observe brake pedal feel.

16. If the brake pedal feels spongy, repeat the automated bleeding procedure until a firm brake pedal is obtained.

BRAKES

FRONT DISC BRAKES

✳ CAUTION

Dust and dirt accumulating on brake parts during normal use may contain asbestos fibers from production or aftermarket brake linings. Breathing excessive concentrations of asbestos fibers can cause serious bodily harm. Exercise care when servicing brake parts. Do not sand or grind brake lining unless equipment used is designed to contain the dust residue. Do not clean brake parts with compressed air or by dry brushing. Cleaning should be done by dampening the brake components with a fine mist of water, then wiping the brake components clean with a dampened cloth. Dispose of cloth and all residue containing asbestos fibers in an impermeable container with the appropriate label. Follow practices prescribed by the Occupational Safety and Health Administration (OSHA) and the Environmental Protection Agency (EPA) for the handling, processing, and disposing of dust or debris that may contain asbestos fibers.

BRAKE CALIPER

REMOVAL & INSTALLATION
See Figures 7 and 8.

1. Before servicing the vehicle, refer to the Precautions Section, including brake fluid and brake dust precautions.
2. Raise and support the vehicle.
3. Remove the tire and wheel assembly.

➡**Do not reuse the brake hose fitting gaskets.**

4. Remove the brake hose fitting bolt (1), the brake hose fitting gaskets (2), and the brake hose fitting (3) from the brake

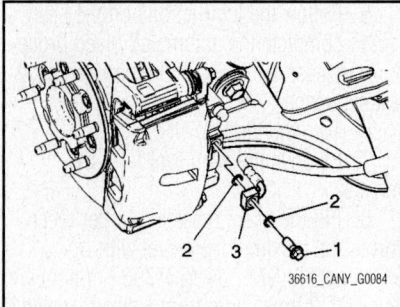

Fig. 7 Brake hose fitting bolt (1), brake hose fitting gaskets (2), and brake hose fitting (3)

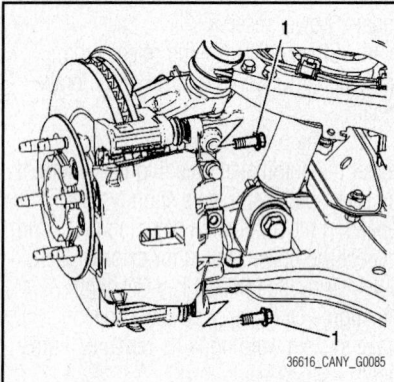

Fig. 8 Brake caliper guide pin bolts (1)

caliper. Cap the brake hose fitting to prevent brake fluid loss and contamination.

5. Discard the brake hose fitting gaskets.

6. Remove the brake caliper guide pin bolts (1).

7. Remove the brake caliper.

To install:

8. Install the brake caliper.

9. Install the brake caliper guide pin bolts and tighten to 47 ft. lbs. (64 Nm).

➡ **Install new brake hose fitting gaskets.**

10. Assemble the brake hose fitting bolt and new brake hose fitting gaskets to the brake hose fitting.

11. Install the brake hose assembly to the brake caliper and tighten the fitting bolt to 30 ft. lbs. (40 Nm).

12. Bleed the hydraulic brake system.

13. Install the tire and wheel assembly.

DISC BRAKE PADS

REMOVAL & INSTALLATION

See Figure 9.

1. Before servicing the vehicle, refer to the Precautions Section, including brake fluid and brake dust precautions.

2. Inspect the fluid level in the master cylinder reservoir.

3. If the brake fluid is midway between the maximum full point and the minimum allowable level, no brake fluid needs to be removed from the reservoir before proceeding.

4. If the brake fluid is higher than midway between the maximum full point and the minimum allowable level, remove brake fluid to the midway point before proceeding.

5. Raise and support the vehicle.

6. Remove the tire and wheel assembly.

7. Install a large C-clamp over the body of the brake caliper with the C-clamp ends against the rear of the caliper body and against the outboard brake pad.

8. Tighten the C-clamp evenly until the caliper pistons are compressed into the caliper bore.

9. Remove the lower brake caliper guide pin bolt.

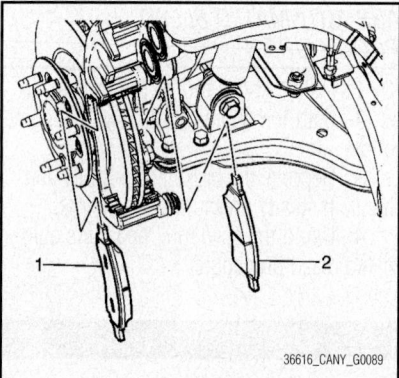

Fig. 9 Outer (1) and inner (2) brake pad

❄ WARNING

Support the brake caliper with heavy mechanic wire, or equivalent, whenever it is separated from its mount and the hydraulic flexible brake hose

is still connected. Failure to support the caliper in this manner will cause the flexible brake hose to bear the weight of the caliper, which may cause damage to the brake hose and in turn may cause a brake fluid leak.

10. Pivot the brake caliper upward and support with heavy mechanics wire or equivalent.

11. Remove the outer brake pad (1).

12. Remove the inner brake pad. (2).

13. If installing new disc brake pads, remove and discard the brake pad shims.

14. Thoroughly clean the brake caliper bracket mating surfaces and, if reusing the brake pads, clean the brake pad shims with denatured alcohol and allow to dry.

To install:

15. If installing new disc brake pads, install new brake pad shims.

16. Install the outer brake pad.

17. Install the inner brake pad.

❄ WARNING

Support the brake caliper with heavy mechanic wire, or equivalent, whenever it is separated from its mount and the hydraulic flexible brake hose is still connected. Failure to support the caliper in this manner will cause the flexible brake hose to bear the weight of the caliper, which may cause damage to the brake hose and in turn may cause a brake fluid leak.

18. Pivot the brake caliper downward and position to the brake caliper bracket.

19. Install the lower brake caliper guide pin bolt and tighten to 47 ft. lbs. (64 Nm).

20. Install the tire and wheel assembly.

21. Lower the vehicle.

22. With the engine OFF, gradually apply the brake pedal approximately ⅔ of its travel distance.

23. Slowly release the brake pedal.

24. Wait 15 seconds then repeat steps 8–9 until a firm brake pedal is obtained. This will properly seat the brake caliper pistons and the brake pads.

25. Fill the master cylinder reservoir to the proper level.

26. Burnish the brake pads and rotors.

BRAKE CALIPER

REMOVAL & INSTALLATION

See Figures 7 and 8.

1. Before servicing the vehicle, refer to the Precautions Section, including brake fluid and brake dust precautions.
2. Raise and support the vehicle.
3. Remove the tire and wheel assembly.

➡**Do not reuse the brake hose fitting gaskets.**

4. Remove the brake hose fitting bolt (1), the brake hose fitting gaskets (2), and the brake hose fitting (3) from the brake caliper. Cap the brake hose fitting to prevent brake fluid loss and contamination.
5. Discard the brake hose fitting gaskets.
6. Remove the brake caliper guide pin bolts (1).
7. Remove the brake caliper.

To install:

8. Install the brake caliper.
9. Install the brake caliper guide pin bolts and tighten to 47 ft. lbs. (64 Nm).

➡**Install new brake hose fitting gaskets.**

10. Assemble the brake hose fitting bolt and new brake hose fitting gaskets to the brake hose fitting.
11. Install the brake hose assembly to the brake caliper and tighten the fitting bolt to 30 ft. lbs. (40 Nm).
12. Bleed the hydraulic brake system.
13. Install the tire and wheel assembly.

DISC BRAKE PADS

REMOVAL & INSTALLATION

See Figure 9.

1. Before servicing the vehicle, refer to the Precautions Section, including brake fluid and brake dust precautions.
2. Inspect the fluid level in the master cylinder reservoir.
3. If the brake fluid is midway between the maximum full point and the minimum allowable level, no brake fluid needs to be removed from the reservoir before proceeding.
4. If the brake fluid is higher than midway between the maximum full point and the minimum allowable level, remove brake fluid to the midway point before proceeding.
5. Raise and support the vehicle.
6. Remove the tire and wheel assembly.
7. Install a large C-clamp over the body of the brake caliper with the C-clamp ends against the rear of the caliper body and against the outboard brake pad.
8. Tighten the C-clamp evenly until the caliper pistons are compressed into the caliper bore.
9. Remove the lower brake caliper guide pin bolt.

✳✳ WARNING

Support the brake caliper with heavy mechanic wire, or equivalent, whenever it is separated from its mount and the hydraulic flexible brake hose is still connected. Failure to support the caliper in this manner will cause the flexible brake hose to bear the weight of the caliper, which may cause damage to the brake hose and in turn may cause a brake fluid leak.

10. Pivot the brake caliper upward and support with heavy mechanics wire or equivalent.
11. Remove the outer brake pad (1).

12. Remove the inner brake pad (2).
13. If installing new disc brake pads, remove and discard the brake pad shims.
14. Thoroughly clean the brake caliper bracket mating surfaces and, if reusing the brake pads, clean the brake pad shims with denatured alcohol and allow to dry.

To install:

15. If installing new disc brake pads, install new brake pad shims.
16. Install the outer brake pad.
17. Install the inner brake pad.

✳✳ WARNING

Support the brake caliper with heavy mechanic wire, or equivalent, whenever it is separated from its mount and the hydraulic flexible brake hose is still connected. Failure to support the caliper in this manner will cause the flexible brake hose to bear the weight of the caliper, which may cause damage to the brake hose and in turn may cause a brake fluid leak.

18. Pivot the brake caliper downward and position to the brake caliper bracket.
19. Install the lower brake caliper guide pin bolt and tighten to 47 ft. lbs. (64 Nm).
20. Install the tire and wheel assembly.
21. Lower the vehicle.
22. With the engine OFF, gradually apply the brake pedal approximately ⅔ of its travel distance.
23. Slowly release the brake pedal.
24. Wait 15 seconds then repeat steps 8–9 until a firm brake pedal is obtained. This will properly seat the brake caliper pistons and the brake pads.
25. Fill the master cylinder reservoir to the proper level.
26. Burnish the brake pads and rotors.

✳✳ CAUTION

Dust and dirt accumulating on brake parts during normal use may contain asbestos fibers from production or aftermarket brake linings. Breathing excessive concentrations of asbestos fibers can cause serious bodily harm. Exercise care when servicing brake parts. Do not sand or grind brake lining unless equipment used is designed to contain the dust residue. Do not clean brake parts with compressed air or by dry brushing. Cleaning should be done by dampening the brake components with a fine mist of water, then wiping the brake components clean with a dampened cloth. Dispose of cloth and all residue containing asbestos fibers in an impermeable container with the appropriate label. Follow practices prescribed by the Occupational Safety and Health Administration (OSHA) and the Environmental Protection Agency (EPA) for the handling, processing, and disposing of dust or debris that may contain asbestos fibers.

BRAKE DRUM

REMOVAL & INSTALLATION

See Figure 10.

1. Before servicing the vehicle, refer to the Precautions Section, including the brake dust precautions.
2. Raise and support the vehicle.
3. Remove the tire and wheel assembly.
4. Remove and discard the brake drum retainers.
5. Remove the brake drum (1).
6. If the brake drum is difficult to

remove, retract the brake shoes using the following procedure:

   a. Remove the rubber adjuster access hole plug located below the wheel cylinder on the rear brake backing plate.

   b. Insert a small, flat bladed tool through the access hole at a slight downward angle to contact the adjuster lever.

   c. Insert a second small, flat bladed tool straight into the access hole just above the first tool to contact the adjuster teeth.

   d. While applying slight inward pressure on the first tool, rotate the adjuster counter clockwise using the second tool against the adjuster teeth.

   e. Continue to rotate the adjuster until the brake shoes are retracted and the brake drum can be removed.

7. Using the J-42450-A Wheel Hub Resurfacing Kit, clean the brake drum and rear axle flange mating surfaces of any accumulated dirt or corrosion.

To install:

8. Adjust the rear drum brakes.
9. Install the brake drum.
10. Install the tire and wheel assembly.

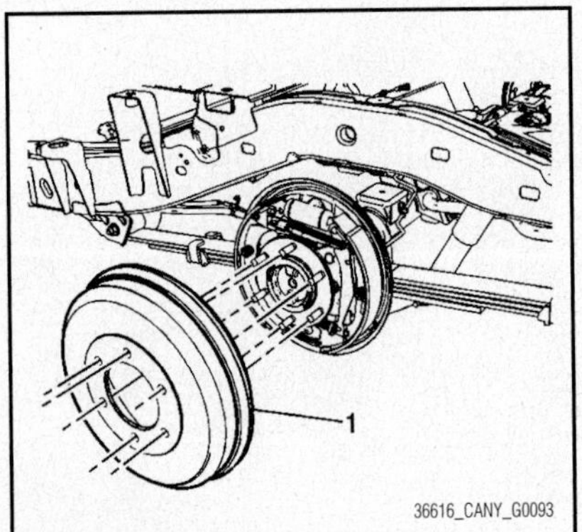

ADJUSTMENT

See Figures 11 and 12.

➡**The rear brakes must be adjusted manually after replacing the rear brake shoes.**

1. Before servicing the vehicle, refer to the Precautions Section.
2. Raise the vehicle.
3. Loosen the adjuster nut for the park brakes.
4. Remove the brake drum.
5. Using the J 21177-A (1), measure the inside diameter of the brake drum.

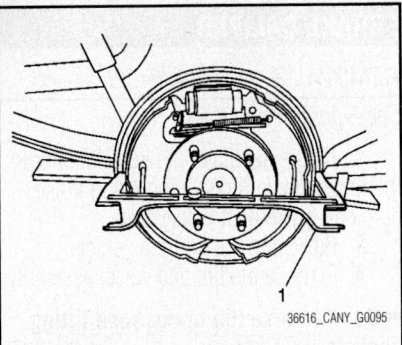

36616_CANY_G0095

Fig. 12 Adjust the brakes shoes until there is approximately .030 in. (0.76 mm) clearance between the rear brake shoes and the rear brake drum

➡**When performing the following service procedure, ensure that the J 21177-A (1) is level, before taking the measurement.**

6. Using the J 21177-A (1), adjust the brakes shoes until there is approximately .030 in. (0.76 mm) clearance between the rear brake shoes and the rear brake drum.
7. Install the brake drum.
8. With heavy force, apply the brake pedal 2 times in order to center and adjust the brake shoes.
9. Inspect the drums again for light drag. If necessary, repeat the previous step for adjusting the brakes.
10. Lower the vehicle.
11. Adjust the parking brake. Refer to Parking Brake Adjustment.

BRAKE SHOES

REMOVAL & INSTALLATION

See Figures 13 through 20.

1. Before servicing the vehicle, refer to the Precautions Section, including the brake dust precautions.
2. Remove the brake drum.
3. Remove the brake shoe adjuster spring.
4. Remove the brake shoe adjuster lever.
5. Carefully spread the top of the brake shoes away from the wheel cylinder and remove the brake shoe adjuster assembly.
6. Remove the brake shoe hold down springs and cups by compressing the springs inward and rotating the cups ¼ turn.
7. Rotate the forward brake shoe toward the rear axle flange.

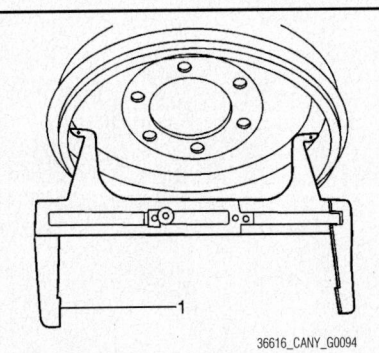

36616_CANY_G0093

Fig. 10 Brake drum

36616_CANY_G0094

Fig. 11 Measure the inside diameter of the brake drum

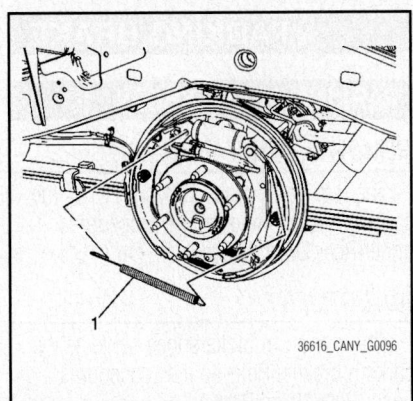

Fig. 13 Brake shoe adjuster spring (1)

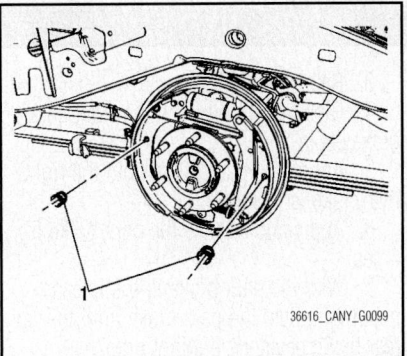

Fig. 16 Brake shoe hold down springs and cups (1)

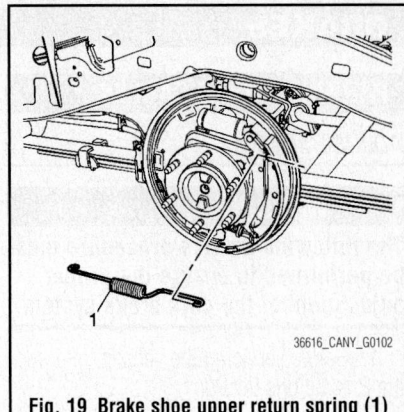

Fig. 19 Brake shoe upper return spring (1)

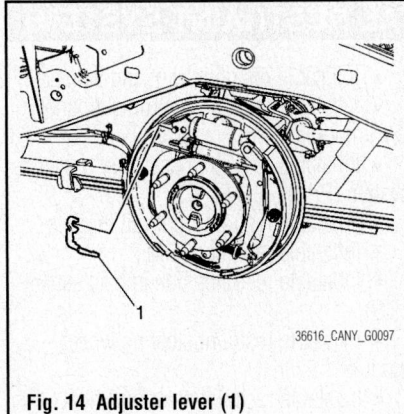

Fig. 14 Adjuster lever (1)

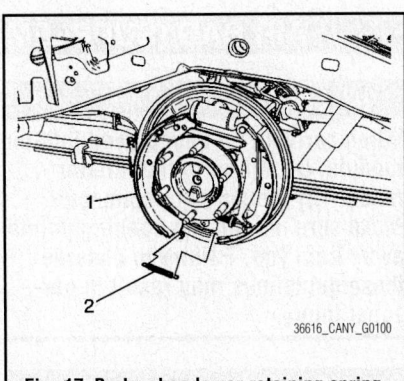

Fig. 17 Brake shoe lower retaining spring (2)

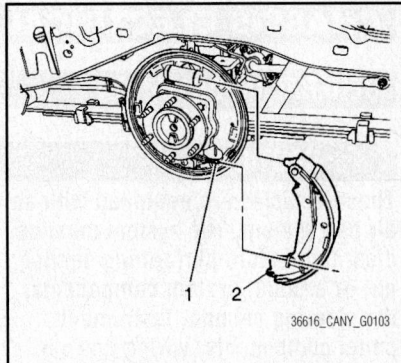

Fig. 20 Park brake cable fitting (1) and lever assembly (2)

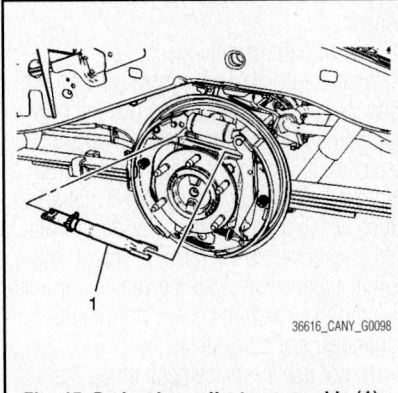

Fig. 15 Brake shoe adjuster assembly (1)

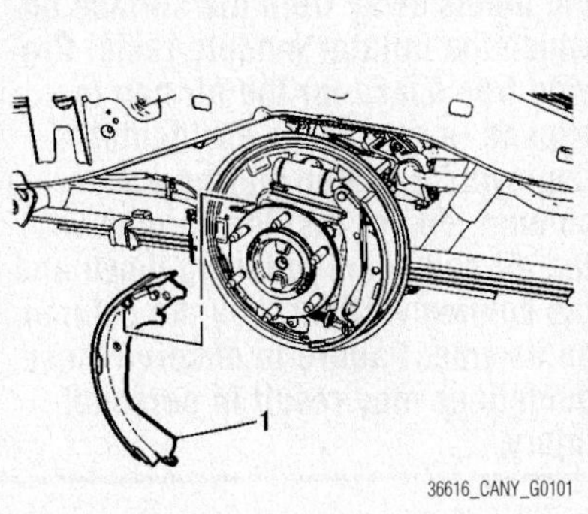

Fig. 18 Forward brake shoe (1)

8. Remove the brake shoe lower retaining spring.

9. Remove the forward brake shoe.

10. Remove the brake shoe upper return spring.

11. Release the park brake cable fitting (1) from the brake shoe park brake apply lever.

12. Remove the rear brake shoe and park brake lever assembly.

13. Remove the park brake lever from the brake shoe.

To install:

14. Clean the rear brake backing plate brake shoe contact points.

15. Apply a light coat of high temperature silicone brake lubricant to the rear brake backing plate brake shoe contact points.

16. Install the park brake lever to the brake shoe.

17. Install the park brake cable fitting to the brake shoe park brake apply lever and

position the brake shoe to the rear brake backing plate.

18. Install the brake shoe upper return spring.

19. Install the forward brake shoe.

20. Rotate the forward brake shoe toward the rear axle flange.

21. Install the brake shoe lower retaining spring.

22. Install the brake shoe hold down springs and cups by compressing the springs inward and rotating the cups ¼ turn.

23. Carefully spread the top of the brake shoes away from the wheel cylinder and install the brake shoe adjuster assembly.

24. Install the brake shoe adjuster lever.

25. Install the brake shoe adjuster spring.

26. Adjust the rear brake shoes. Refer to Brake Drum Adjustment.

27. Install the brake drum.

ADJUSTMENT

See Brake Drum Adjustment.

BRAKES

PARKING BRAKE CABLES

ADJUSTMENT

✳✳ WARNING

The following service procedure must be performed to ensure the proper adjustment of the park brake system.

1. Before servicing the vehicle, refer to the Precautions Section.
2. Release the park brake pedal.

3. Raise the vehicle.
4. Clean the threads on the front park brake cable.
5. Adjust the park brake until the right rear brake is locked.
6. Apply and release the park brake 5 times.
7. With the park brake in the release position, adjust the park brake until the right rear brake develops a slight drag.
8. Back off the adjusting nut 2 complete turns.

PARKING BRAKE

PARKING BRAKE SHOES

REMOVAL & INSTALLATION

The rear drum brake shoes serve as the parking brakes. Refer to the procedures under Rear Drum Brakes.

ADJUSTMENT

The rear drum brake shoes serve as the parking brakes. Refer to the procedures under Rear Drum Brakes.

CHASSIS ELECTRICAL

GENERAL INFORMATION

✳✳ CAUTION

These vehicles are equipped with an air bag system. The system must be disarmed before performing service on, or around, system components, the steering column, instrument panel components, wiring and sensors. Failure to follow the safety precautions and the disarming procedure could result in accidental air bag deployment, possible injury and unnecessary system repairs.

SERVICE PRECAUTIONS

✳✳ CAUTION

When performing service on or near the SIR components or the SIR wiring, the SIR system must be disabled. Refer to SIR Disabling and Enabling . Failure to observe the correct procedure could cause deployment of the SIR components, personal injury, or unnecessary SIR system repairs.

✳✳ CAUTION

The inflatable restraint Sensing and Diagnostic module (SDM) maintains a reserved energy supply. The reserved energy supply provides deployment power for the air bags. Deployment power is available for as much as 1 minute after disconnecting the vehicle power. Disabling the SIR system prevents deployment of the air bags from the reserved energy supply.

AIR BAG (SUPPLEMENTAL RESTRAINT SYSTEM)

✳✳ CAUTION

When carrying an undeployed inflator module: Do not carry the inflator module by the wires or connector. Make sure the air bag opening points away from you. Failure to observe these guidelines may result in personal injury.

✳✳ CAUTION

When storing an undeployed inflator module: Make sure the air bag opening points away from the surface on which the inflator module rests. Provide free space for the air bag to expand in case of an accidental deployment. When storing a steering column, do not rest the column with the air bag opening facing down and the column vertical. Lay the column on its side. Failure to observe these guidelines may result in personal injury.

The following are general service instructions which must be followed in order to properly repair the vehicle and return it to its original integrity:

• Do not handle the inflatable restraint vehicle rollover sensor when connected to vehicle power.

• Do not expose inflator modules to temperatures above 150°F (65°C).

• Verify the correct replacement part number. Do not substitute a component from a different vehicle.

• Use only original GM replacement parts available from your authorized GM dealer. Do not use salvaged parts for repairs to the SIR system.

Discard any of the following components if it has been dropped from a height of 3 ft. (91 cm) or greater:

• Inflatable restraint front end sensor
• Inflatable restraint instrument panel (I/P) module
• Inflatable restraint passenger presence system (PPS)
• Inflatable restraint roof rail module
• Inflatable restraint SDM
• Inflatable restraint side impact sensor (SIS)
• Inflatable restraint steering wheel module
• Inflatable restraint steering wheel module coil
• Inflatable restraint vehicle rollover sensor
• Seat belt pretensioner

Wear safety glasses, rubber gloves, and long sleeved clothing when cleaning powder residue from vehicle after an airbag deployment. Powder residue emitted from a deployed airbag can cause skin irritation. Flush affected area with cool water if irritation is experienced. If nasal or throat irritation is experienced, exit the vehicle for fresh air until the irritation ceases. If irritation continues, see a physician.

Do not use a replacement airbag that is not in the original packaging. This may result in improper deployment, personal injury, or death.

The factory installed fasteners, screws and bolts used to fasten airbag components have a special coating and are specifically designed for the airbag system. Do not use substitute fasteners. Use only original equipment fasteners listed in the parts catalog when fastener replacement is required.

During, and following, any child restraint anchor service, due to impact event or vehicle repair, carefully inspect all mounting hardware, tether straps, and anchors for proper installation, operation, or damage. If a child restraint anchor is found damaged in any way, the anchor must be replaced.

Failure to do this may result in personal injury or death.

Deployed and non-deployed airbags may or may not have live pyrotechnic material within the airbag inflator.

Do not dispose of driver/passenger/curtain airbags or seat belt tensioners unless you are sure of complete deployment. Refer to the Hazardous Substance Control System for proper disposal.

Dispose of deployed airbags and tensioners consistent with state, provincial, local, and federal regulations.

After any airbag component testing or service, do not connect the battery negative cable. Personal injury or death may result if the system test is not performed first.

If the vehicle is equipped with the Occupant Classification System (OCS), do not connect the battery negative cable before performing the OCS Verification Test using the scan tool and the appropriate diagnostic information. Personal injury or death may result if the system test is not performed properly.

Never replace both the Occupant Restraint Controller (ORC) and the Occupant Classification Module (OCM) at the same time. If both require replacement, replace one, then perform the Airbag System test before replacing the other.

Both the ORC and the OCM store Occupant Classification System (OCS) calibration data, which they transfer to one another when one of them is replaced. If both are replaced at the same time, an irreversible fault will be set in both modules and the OCS may malfunction and cause personal injury or death.

If equipped with OCS, the Seat Weight Sensor is a sensitive, calibrated unit and must be handled carefully. Do not drop or handle roughly. If dropped or damaged, replace with another sensor. Failure to do so may result in occupant injury or death.

If equipped with OCS, the front passenger seat must be handled carefully as well. When removing the seat, be careful when setting on floor not to drop. If dropped, the sensor may be inoperative, could result in occupant injury, or possibly death.

If equipped with OCS, when the passenger front seat is on the floor, no one should sit in the front passenger seat. This uneven force may damage the sensing ability of the seat weight sensors. If sat on and damaged, the sensor may be inoperative, could result in occupant injury, or possibly death.

DISARMING THE SYSTEM

✳✳ CAUTION

When performing service on or near the SIR components or the SIR wiring, the SIR system must be disabled. Refer to SIR Disabling and Enabling . Failure to observe the correct procedure could cause deployment of the SIR components, personal injury, or unnecessary SIR system repairs.

✳✳ CAUTION

The inflatable restraint Sensing and Diagnostic module (SDM) maintains a reserved energy supply. The reserved energy supply provides deployment power for the air bags. Deployment power is available for as much as 1 minute after disconnecting the vehicle power. Disabling the SIR system prevents deployment of the air bags from the reserved energy supply.

SIR component location affects how a vehicle should be serviced. There are parts of the SIR system installed in various locations around a vehicle. To find the location of the SIR components refer to SIR Identification Views in Chassis Electrical Component Locations.

There are several reasons for disabling the SIR system, such as repairs to the SIR system or servicing a component near or attached to an SIR component. There are several ways to disable the SIR system depending on what type of service is being performed. The following information covers the proper procedures for disabling/enabling the SIR system:

• If the vehicle was involved in an accident with an air bag deployment: Disconnect the negative battery cable(s).

• When performing SIR diagnostics: Follow the appropriate SIR service manual diagnostic procedure(s).

• When removing or replacing an SIR component or a component attached to an SIR component: Disconnect the negative battery cable(s).

• If the vehicle is suspected of having shorted electrical wires: Disconnect the negative battery cable(s)

• When performing electrical diagnosis on components other than the SIR system: Remove the SIR/Airbag fuse(s) when indicated by the diagnostic procedure to disable the SIR system.

➡DTCs will be lost when the negative battery cable is disconnected.

DISABLING AIR BAG FUSE PROCEDURE

✳✳ CAUTION

Refer to all precautions. Failure to observe the correct procedure could cause deployment of the SIR components, personal injury, or unnecessary SIR system repairs.

1. Turn the steering wheel so that the vehicles wheels are pointing straight ahead.
2. Place the ignition in the OFF position.

✳✳ CAUTION

The SDM may have more than one fused power input. To ensure there is no unwanted SIR deployment, personal injury, or unnecessary SIR system repairs, remove all fuses supplying power to the SDM. With all SDM fuses removed and the ignition switch in the ON position, the AIR BAG warning indicator illuminates. This is normal operation, and does not indicate a SIR system malfunction.

3. Locate and remove the fuse(s) supplying power to the SDM.
4. Wait 1 minute before working on the system.

DISABLING NEGATIVE BATTERY CABLE PROCEDURE

✳✳ CAUTION

Refer to all precautions. Failure to observe the correct procedure could cause deployment of the SIR components, personal injury, or unnecessary SIR system repairs.

1. Turn the steering wheel so that the vehicles wheels are pointing straight ahead.
2. Place the ignition in the OFF position.
3. Disconnect the negative battery cable from the battery.
4. Wait 1 minute before working on system.

ENABLING AIR BAG FUSE PROCEDURE

1. Place the ignition in the OFF position.
2. Install the fuse(s) supplying power to the SDM.

3. Turn the ignition switch to the ON position. The AIR BAG indicator will flash then turn OFF.

4. Perform the Diagnostic System Check if the AIR BAG warning indicator does not operate as described. Refer to General Information.

ENABLING NEGATIVE BATTERY CABLE PROCEDURE

1. Place the ignition in the OFF position.
2. Connect the negative battery cable to the battery.
3. Turn the ignition switch to the ON

position. The AIR BAG indicator will flash then turn OFF.

4. Perform the Diagnostic System Check if the AIR BAG warning indicator does not operate as described. Refer to General Information.

DRIVE TRAIN

AUTOMATIC TRANSMISSION ASSEMBLY

REMOVAL & INSTALLATION

2WD Models—2.9L & 3.7L Engines

See Figures 21 through 26.

1. Before servicing the vehicle, refer to the Precautions Section.
2. Ensure the vehicle is in the PARK position.
3. Remove the filler tube. Refer to Transmission Fluid Filler Tube & Seal Removal & Installation.
4. Drain the transmission fluid if necessary.
5. Remove the rear propeller shaft. Refer to Propeller Shaft Removal & Installation.

➡ **Do not pull on the boot portion of the cable.**

6. Complete the following in order to disconnect the range selector cable (3) from the transmission range selector lever ball stud:

    a. Insert a flat-bladed tool between the range selector cable end (5) and the range selector lever (1).

    b. Pry the range selector cable end (5) away from the range selector lever (1).

7. Remove the retainer (4) from the range selector cable (3).

8. Push the range selector cable locking tabs inward toward each other to release from the bracket (2).

9. Disconnect the following engine wiring harness electrical connectors:

- The heated oxygen sensor
- The transmission main connector
- The vehicle speed sensor (VSS)

10. Remove the screw securing the engine wiring harness to the right side of the transmission, and position the harness over the transmission.

11. Disconnect the park/neutral back up switch electrical connector.

12. Remove the screw securing the engine wiring harness to the left side of the transmission, and position the wiring harness aside.

13. Disconnect the transmission vent hose retainer (1) from the heater pipe bracket (2).

14. Remove the nuts securing the fuel hose/pipe bracket to the transmission.

15. Disconnect the fuel hose/pipe retainer from the range selector cable bracket, and position aside the fuel hose/pipe bundle.

16. Remove the inspection plug (3) from the transmission (1).

17. Mark the torque converter to flexplate/flywheel orientation to ensure proper realignment.

18. Remove the engine protection shield in order to access the harmonic balancer bolt.

19. Remove the service slot plug.

20. Repeat the following steps for all 3 torque converter bolts:

    a. Rotate the harmonic balancer center bolt clockwise ONLY, in order to access the torque converter bolt through the service slot.

    b. Remove the torque converter bolt using one of the following:

- 18 mm crowfoot wrench
- Short T50 TORX® bit

21. Place an oil pan under the transmission fluid cooler pipes.

22. Disconnect the transmission oil cooler pipes from the transmission ONLY. Refer to Transmission Fluid Cooler Hose/Pipe Removal & Installation.

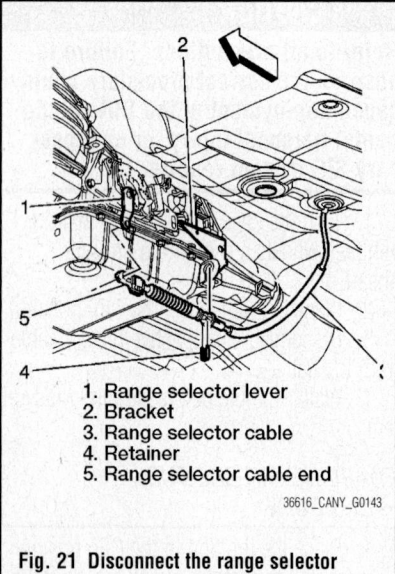

1. Range selector lever
2. Bracket
3. Range selector cable
4. Retainer
5. Range selector cable end

36616_CANY_G0143

Fig. 21 Disconnect the range selector cable

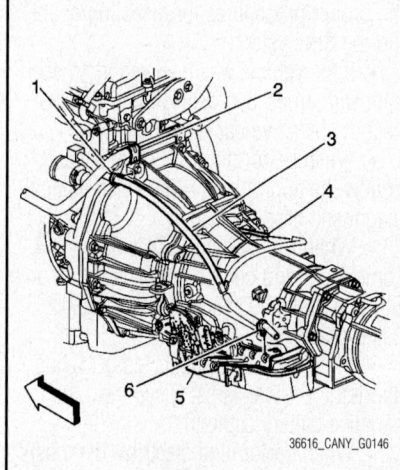

36616_CANY_G0146

Fig. 22 Disconnect the transmission vent hose retainer (1) from the heater pipe bracket (2)

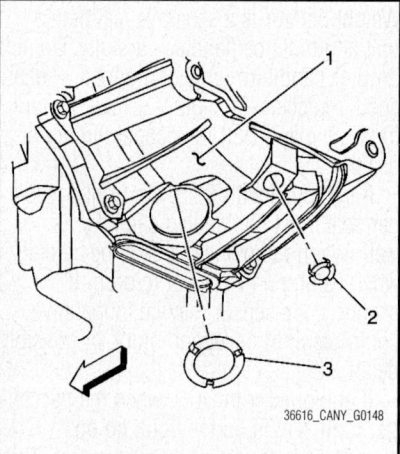

36616_CANY_G0148

Fig. 23 Remove the inspection plug (3), mark the torque converter to flexplate/flywheel orientation, and remove the engine protection shield

23. Plug the open outlet ports to prevent fluid loss and contamination.

24. Support and secure the transmission using a suitable transmission jack.

25. Remove the transmission crossmember. Refer to Transmission Support Crossmember Removal & Installation.

26. Remove the 9 transmission mounting bolts.

27. Remove the remaining transmission mounting bolts (2).

➡**Ensure clearance is maintained between the transmission and the following: The catalytic converter, the engine wiring harness, the fuel hose/pipe brackets, the heater pipe, and the transmission oil cooler pipes.**

28. Using the transmission jack, carefully lower the transmission from the vehicle.

29. Install the J 21366 onto the transmission bell housing to retain the torque converter.

30. Perform the flush and flow test on the automatic transmission oil cooler.

To install:

31. Remove the J 21366 from the transmission.

32. Ensure the torque converter is fully engaged with the transmission oil pump.

➡**Ensure clearance is maintained between the transmission and the following: The catalytic converter, the engine wiring harness, the fuel hose/pipe brackets, the heater pipe, and the transmission oil cooler pipes.**

33. Using the transmission jack, carefully raise the transmission to the engine.

34. Align the transmission with the engine dowels.

➡**Ensure the torque converter turns freely while tightening the transmission mounting bolts.**

35. Install the 2 transmission mounting bolts and tighten to 37 ft. lbs. (50 Nm).

➡**Ensure the studded mounting bolts are located in the correct position. The heater pipe must be secured with the 2 upper mounting bolts.**

36. Install the remaining transmission mounting bolts and tighten to 37 ft. lbs. (50 Nm).

37. Install the transmission crossmember.

38. Remove the transmission jack from under the vehicle.

39. Connect the transmission oil cooler pipes to the transmission.

40. Align the torque converter to flexplate/flywheel orientation marks made during the removal procedure.

41. Repeat the following steps for all 3 torque converter bolts:

   a. Rotate the harmonic balancer center bolt clockwise ONLY, in order to access the torque converter bolt holes in the flexplate/flywheel through the service slot.

   b. To aid in alignment of the torque converter to the flexplate/flywheel. Install all 3 torque converter bolts before fully tightening to 44 ft. lbs. (60 Nm), using one of the following:
- 18 mm crowfoot wrench
- Short T50 TORX® bit

42. Install the inspection plug to the transmission.

43. Install the service slot plug.

44. Install the nuts securing the fuel hose/pipe bracket to the transmission. Tighten the fuel hose/pipe bracket nuts to 15 ft. lbs. (20 Nm).

45. Connect the fuel hose/pipe retainer to the range selector cable bracket.

46. Connect the transmission vent hose retainer to the heater pipe bracket.

47. Install the screw securing the engine wiring harness to the left side of the transmission. Tighten the engine wiring harness retainer to transmission screw to 80 inch lbs. (9 Nm).

48. Connect the park/neutral back up switch electrical connector.

49. Lay the engine wiring harness over the transmission.

50. Connect the following engine wiring harness electrical connectors:
- The heated oxygen sensor
- The transmission main connector
- The Vehicle Speed (VSS) sensor

51. Install the screw securing the engine wiring harness to the right side of the transmission.

Tighten the engine wiring harness retainer to transmission screw to 80 inch lbs. (9 Nm).

52. Install the range selector cable to the bracket.

53. Install the retainer to the range selector cable.

54. Adjust the automatic transmission range selector cable. Refer to Range Selector Lever Cable Adjustment.

55. Install the rear propeller shaft.

56. Install the engine protection shield.

57. Install the filler tube.

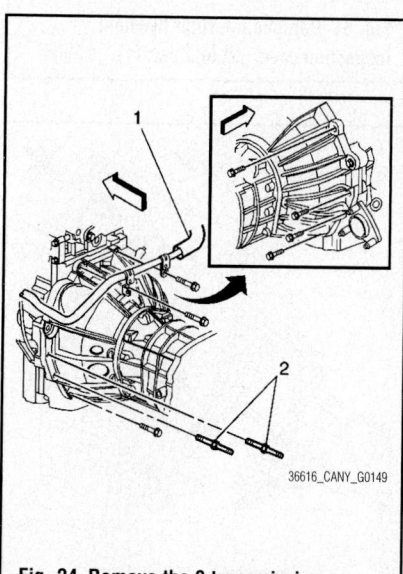

Fig. 24 Remove the 9 transmission mounting bolts

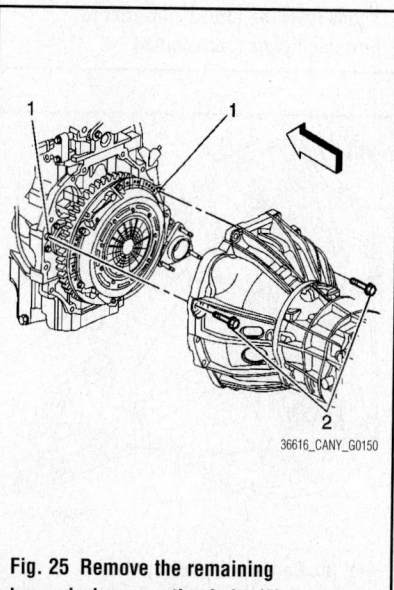

Fig. 25 Remove the remaining transmission mounting bolts (2)

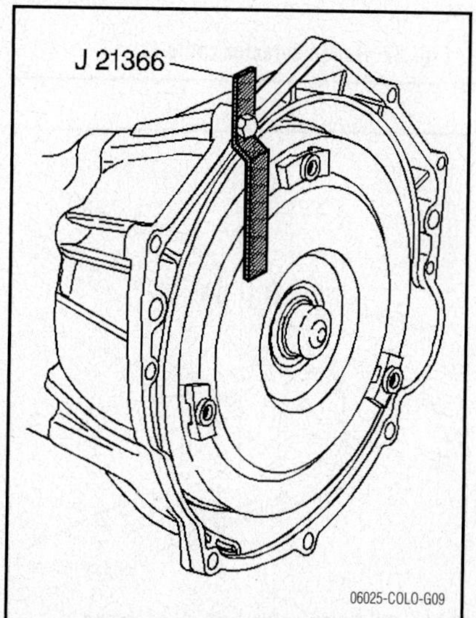

Fig. 26 Install the J 21366 onto the transmission bell housing

58. Fill the transmission fluid if necessary.
59. Lower the vehicle.

2WD Models—5.3L Engine

See Figures 27 through 34.

1. Before servicing the vehicle, refer to the Precautions Section.
2. Ensure the vehicle is in the park position.
3. Remove the filler tube. Refer to Transmission Fluid Filler Tube & Seal Removal & Installation.
4. Remove the right and left catalytic converters. Refer to Catalytic Converter Removal & Installation.
5. Remove the right heat shield bolts.
6. Remove the right heat shield.
7. Remove the left heat shield bolts.
8. Remove the left heat shield.

➡**Do not pull on the boot portion of the cable.**

9. Disconnect the range selector cable end (3) from the range selector lever.

10. Remove the retainer (1) from the range selector cable (2).
11. Push the range selector cable locking tabs (2) inward toward each other to release the cable from the bracket.
12. Disconnect the following engine wiring harness electrical connectors:
   a. The heated oxygen sensor
   b. The transmission main connector
   c. The Vehicle Speed (VSS) sensor
13. Remove the screw securing the engine wiring harness to the right side of the transmission, and position the harness over the transmission.
14. Disconnect the park/neutral back up switch electrical connector.
15. Remove the screw securing the engine wiring harness to the left side of the transmission, and position the wiring harness aside.
16. Remove the nut securing the fuel hose/pipe bracket to the transmission.

17. Remove the screw securing the fuel hose/pipe bracket to the transmission.
18. Remove the nut securing the fuel hose/pipe bracket to the transmission.
19. Remove the bolt (1) securing the fuel hose/pipe bracket (2) to the transmission crossmember.
20. Remove the inspection plug (3) from the transmission (1).
21. Mark the torque converter to flexplate/flywheel orientation to ensure proper realignment.
22. Remove the left flywheel inspection cover bolt (1).
23. Remove the left flywheel inspection cover (2).
24. Remove the starter motor. Refer to Starter Removal & Installation in Engine Electrical.
25. Remove the right flywheel inspection cover bolt (1).
26. Remove the right flywheel inspection cover (2).
27. Remove the engine protection shield.

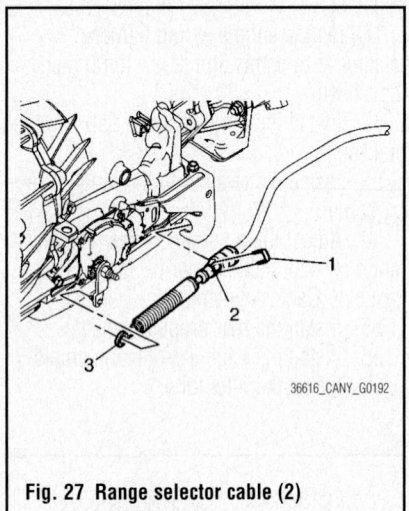

36616_CANY_G0192

Fig. 27 Range selector cable (2)

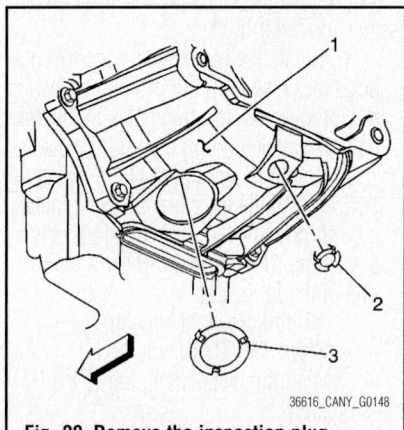
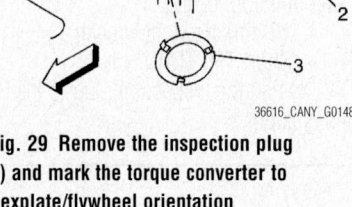

36616_CANY_G0148

Fig. 29 Remove the inspection plug 3) and mark the torque converter to flexplate/flywheel orientation

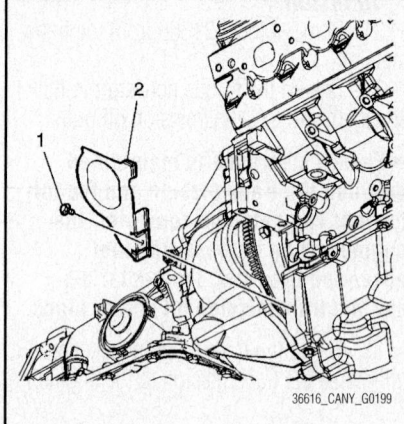

36616_CANY_G0199

Fig. 31 Remove the right flywheel inspection cover (2) and bolt (1)

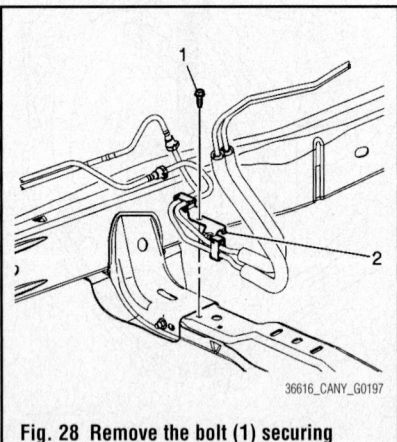

36616_CANY_G0197

Fig. 28 Remove the bolt (1) securing the fuel hose/pipe bracket (2) to the transmission crossmember

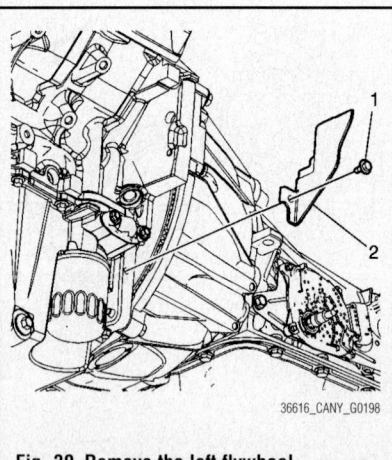

36616_CANY_G0198

Fig. 30 Remove the left flywheel inspection cover (2) and bolt (1)

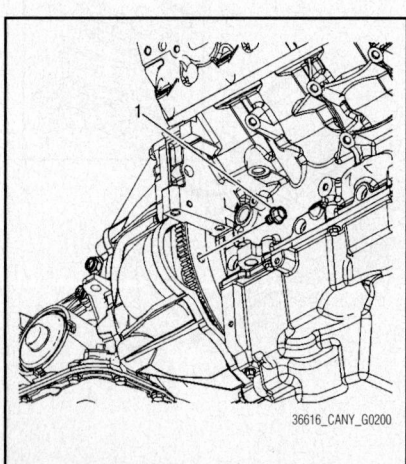

36616_CANY_G0200

Fig. 32 Remove the torque converter bolts

28. Repeat the following steps for all torque converter bolts (1):

    a. Rotate the harmonic balancer center bolt clockwise ONLY, in order to access the torque converter bolt.

    b. Remove the torque converter bolt:

- Place an oil pan under the transmission fluid cooler pipes.
- Disconnect the transmission oil cooler pipes from the transmission ONLY. Refer to Transmission Fluid Cooler Hose/Pipe Removal & Installation.
- Plug the open outlet ports to prevent fluid loss and contamination.
- Drain the transmission fluid if necessary. Refer to Automatic Transmission Fluid and Filter.
- Support and secure the transmission using a suitable transmission jack.
- Remove the transmission crossmember. Refer to Transmission Support Crossmember Removal & Installation.
- Remove the transfer case assembly. Refer to Transfer Case Assembly Removal & Installation.

29. Remove the 2 transmission mounting studs (1).

30. Remove the 6 transmission mounting bolts (2, 3).

31. Separate the transmission from the engine alignment dowels.

➡**Ensure clearance is maintained between the transmission and the following: The engine wiring harness, the fuel hose/pipe brackets, the transmission oil cooler pipes.**

32. Using the transmission jack, carefully lower the transmission from the vehicle.

33. Install the J 21366 onto the transmission bell housing to retain the torque converter.

34. Perform the flush and flow test on the automatic transmission oil cooler.

To install:

35. Remove the J 21366 from the transmission.

36. Ensure the torque converter is fully engaged with the transmission oil pump.

➡**Ensure clearance is maintained between the transmission and the following: The engine wiring harness, the fuel hose/pipe brackets, the transmission oil cooler pipes.**

37. Using the transmission jack, carefully raise the transmission to the engine.

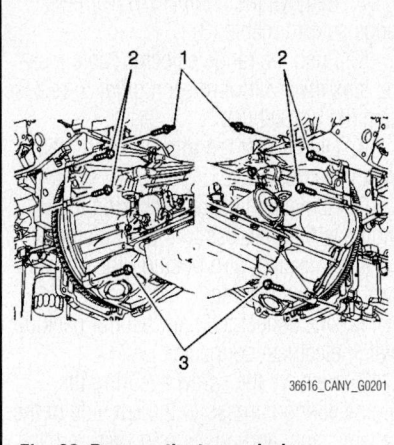

Fig. 33 Remove the transmission mounting studs (1) and bolts (2)

36616_CANY_G0201

38. Align the transmission with the engine alignment dowels.

➡**Ensure the torque converter turns freely while tightening the transmission mounting bolts.**

39. Install the 6 transmission mounting bolts and tighten to 37 ft. lbs. (50 Nm).

40. Install the 2 transmission mounting studs and tighten to 37 ft. lbs. (50 Nm).

41. Install the transfer case assembly.

42. Install the transmission crossmember.

43. Remove the transmission jack from under the vehicle.

44. Connect the transmission oil cooler pipes to the transmission.

45. Align the torque converter to flexplate/flywheel orientation marks made during the removal procedure.

46. Repeat the following steps for all 3 torque converter bolts:

    a. Rotate the harmonic balancer center bolt clockwise ONLY, in order to access the torque converter bolt holes.

    b. To aid in alignment of the torque converter to the flexplate/flywheel. Install all 3 torque converter bolts before fully tightening to 44 ft. lbs. (60 Nm).

47. Install the engine protection shield.

48. Install the right flywheel inspection cover.

49. Install the right flywheel inspection cover bolt and tighten to 89 inch lbs. (10 Nm).

50. Install the starter motor.

51. Install the left flywheel inspection cover.

52. Install the left flywheel inspection cover bolt and tighten to 89 inch lbs. (10 Nm).

53. Install the inspection plug to the transmission.

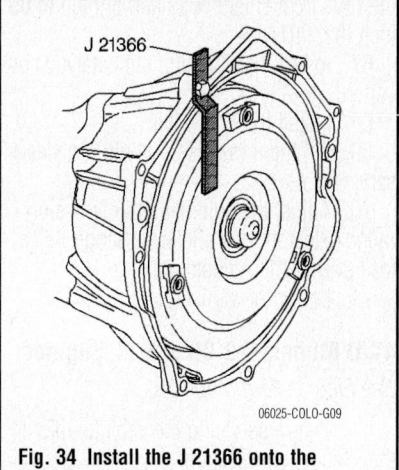

Fig. 34 Install the J 21366 onto the transmission bell housing

06025-COLO-G09

54. Install the bolt securing the fuel hose/pipe bracket to the transmission crossmember and tighten to 15 ft. lbs. (20 Nm).

55. Install the nut securing the fuel hose/pipe bracket to the transmission and tighten to 15 ft. lbs. (20 Nm).

56. Install the screw securing the fuel hose/pipe bracket to the transmission and tighten to 80 inch lbs. (9 Nm).

57. Install the nut securing the fuel hose/pipe bracket to the transmission and tighten to 15 ft. lbs. (20 Nm).

58. Connect the park/neutral back up switch electrical connector.

59. Install the screw securing the engine wiring harness to the left side of the transmission and tighten to 80 inch lbs. (9 Nm).

60. Connect the following engine wiring harness electrical connectors:

- The heated oxygen sensor
- The transmission main connector
- The VSS

61. Install the screw securing the engine wiring harness to the right side of the transmission and tighten to 80 inch lbs. (9 Nm).

➡**Ensure the range selector cable is routed exactly as originally positioned in the vehicle to avoid coming into contact with potential hazards such as hot, sharp, and moving objects.**

62. Install the range selector cable to the range selector cable bracket. Ensure the range selector cable retaining tabs fully engage the range selector cable bracket.

63. Install the retainer to the range selector cable.

64. Connect the range selector cable end to the transaxle range switch lever.

65. Install the left heat shield. Install the left heat shield bolts and tighten to 89 inch lbs. (10 Nm).

66. Install the right heat shield. Install

the right heat shield bolts and tighten to 89 inch lbs. (10 Nm).

67. Install the right and left catalytic converters.

68. Install the filler tube.

69. Fill the transmission fluid if necessary.

70. Adjust the automatic transmission range selector cable. Refer to Range Selector Lever Cable Adjustment.

71. Lower the vehicle.

4WD Models—2.9L & 3.7L Engines

See Figures 35 through 38.

1. Before servicing the vehicle, refer to the Precautions Section.

2. Ensure the vehicle is in the PARK position.

3. Remove the filler tube. Refer to Transmission Fluid Filler Tube and Seal Removal & Installation.

4. Drain the transmission fluid if necessary. Refer to Automatic Transmission Fluid & Filter.

5. Remove the transfer case assembly. Refer Transfer Case Assembly Removal & Installation.

➡ **Do not pull on the boot portion of the cable.**

6. Complete the following in order to disconnect the range selector cable (3) from the transmission range selector lever ball stud.

　a. Insert a flat-bladed tool between the range selector cable end (5) and the range selector lever (1).

　b. Pry the range selector cable end (5) away from the range selector lever (1).

7. Remove the retainer (4) from the range selector cable (3).

8. Push the range selector cable locking tabs inward toward each other to release from the bracket (2).

9. Disconnect the transmission main electrical connector.

10. Remove the screw securing the engine wiring harness to the right side of the transmission, and position the harness over the transmission.

11. Disconnect the park/neutral back up switch electrical connector.

12. Remove the screw securing the engine wiring harness to the left side of the transmission, and position the wiring harness aside.

13. Disconnect the transmission vent hose retainer from the heater pipe bracket.

14. Remove the nuts securing the fuel hose/pipe bracket to the transmission.

15. Disconnect the fuel hose/pipe retainer from the range selector cable bracket, and position aside the fuel hose/pipe bundle.

16. Remove the inspection plug (3) from the transmission (1).

17. Mark the torque converter to flexplate/flywheel orientation to ensure proper realignment.

18. Remove the engine protection shield in order to access the harmonic balancer bolt.

19. Remove the service slot plug.

20. Repeat the following steps for all 3 torque converter bolts:

　a. Rotate the harmonic balancer center bolt clockwise ONLY, in order to access the torque converter bolt through the service slot.

　b. Remove the torque converter bolt using one of the following:
- 18 mm crowfoot wrench
- Short T50 TORX® bit

21. Place an oil pan under the transmission fluid cooler pipes.

22. Disconnect the transmission oil cooler pipes from the transmission ONLY. Refer to Transmission Fluid Cooler Hose/Pipe Removal & Installation.

23. Plug the open outlet ports to prevent fluid loss and contamination.

24. Support and secure the transmission using a suitable transmission jack.

25. Remove the transmission crossmember. Refer to Transmission Support Crossmember Removal & Installation.

26. Remove the 7 transmission mounting bolts and 2 mounting studs.

27. Remove the remaining transmission mounting bolts.

➡ **Ensure clearance is maintained between the transmission and the following: The catalytic converter, the engine wiring harness, the fuel hose/pipe brackets, the heater pipe, and the transmission oil cooler pipes.**

28. Using the transmission jack, carefully lower the transmission from the vehicle.

29. Install the J 21366 onto the transmission bell housing to retain the torque converter.

30. Perform the flush and flow test on the automatic transmission oil cooler.

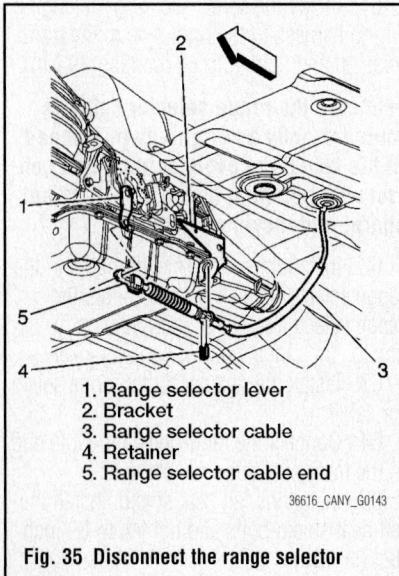

1. Range selector lever
2. Bracket
3. Range selector cable
4. Retainer
5. Range selector cable end

36616_CANY_G0143

Fig. 35 Disconnect the range selector cable

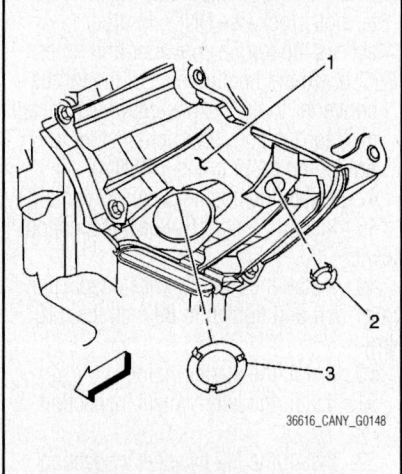

36616_CANY_G0148

Fig. 36 Remove the inspection plug (3), mark the torque converter to lexplate/flywheel orientation, and remove the engine protection shield

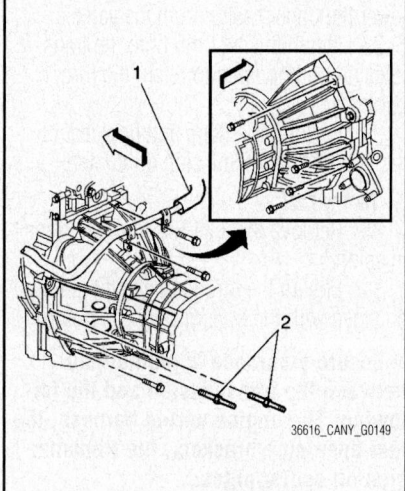

36616_CANY_G0149

Fig. 37 Remove the 7 transmission mounting bolts and 2 mounting studs

To install:

31. Remove the J 21366 from the transmission.

32. Ensure the torque converter is fully engaged with the transmission oil pump.

➡ **Ensure clearance is maintained between the transmission and the following: The catalytic converter, the engine wiring harness, the fuel hose/pipe brackets, the heater pipe, and the transmission oil cooler pipes.**

33. Using the transmission jack, carefully raise the transmission to the engine.

34. Align the transmission with the engine dowels.

➡ **Ensure the torque converter turns freely while tightening the transmission mounting bolts.**

35. Install the 2 transmission mounting bolts and tighten to 37 ft. lbs. (50 Nm).

➡ **Ensure the studded mounting bolts are located in the correct position. The heater pipe must be secured with the 2 upper mounting bolts.**

36. Install the remaining transmission mounting bolts and tighten to 37 ft. lbs. (50 Nm).

37. Install the transmission crossmember.

38. Remove the transmission jack from under the vehicle.

39. Connect the transmission oil cooler pipes to the transmission.

40. Align the torque converter to flexplate/flywheel orientation marks made during the removal procedure.

41. Repeat the following steps for all 3 torque converter bolts:

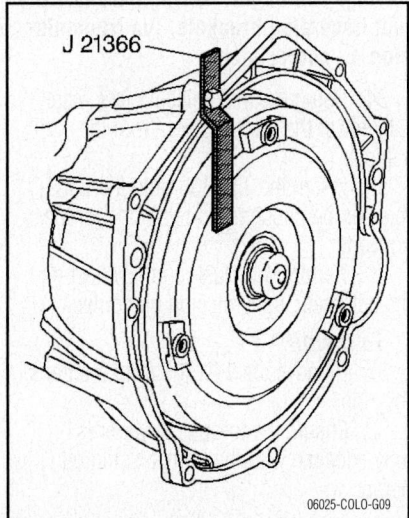

Fig. 38 Install the J 21366 onto the transmission bell housing

a. Rotate the harmonic balancer center bolt clockwise ONLY, in order to access the torque converter bolt holes in the flexplate/flywheel through the service slot.

b. To aid in alignment of the torque converter to the flexplate/flywheel. Install all 3 torque converter bolts before fully tightening to 44 ft. lbs. (60 Nm), using one of the following:
- 18 mm crowfoot wrench
- Short T50 TORX® bit

42. Install the inspection plug to the transmission.

43. Install the service slot plug.

44. Install the nuts securing the fuel hose/pipe bracket to the transmission. Tighten the fuel hose/pipe bracket nuts to 15 ft. lbs. (20 Nm).

45. Connect the fuel hose/pipe retainer to the range selector cable bracket.

46. Connect the transmission vent hose retainer to the heater pipe bracket.

47. Install the screw securing the engine wiring harness to the left side of the transmission. Tighten the engine wiring harness retainer to transmission screw to 80 inch lbs. (9 Nm).

48. Connect the park/neutral back up switch electrical connector.

49. Lay the engine wiring harness over the transmission.

50. Connect the transmission main electrical connector.

51. Install the screw securing the engine wiring harness to the right side of the transmission.
Tighten the engine wiring harness retainer to transmission screw to 80 inch lbs. (9 Nm).

52. Install the range selector cable to the bracket.

53. Install the retainer to the range selector cable.

54. Adjust the automatic transmission range selector cable. Refer to Range Selector Lever Cable Adjustment.

55. Install the transfer case assembly.

56. Install the engine protection shield.

57. Install the filler tube.

58. Fill the transmission fluid if necessary.

59. Lower the vehicle.

4WD Models—5.3L Engine

See Figures 39 through 48.

1. Before servicing the vehicle, refer to the Precautions Section.

2. Ensure the vehicle is in the park position.

3. Remove the filler tube. Refer to

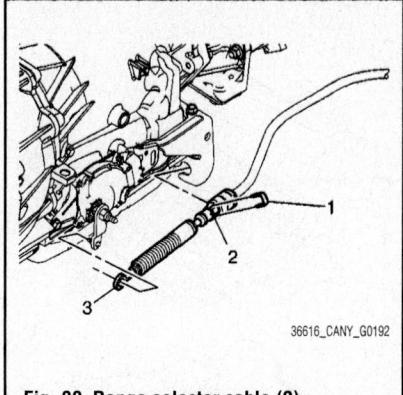

Fig. 39 Range selector cable (2)

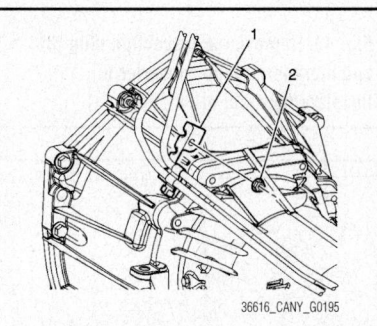

Fig. 40 Remove the nut (2) securing the fuel hose/pipe bracket (1) to the transmission

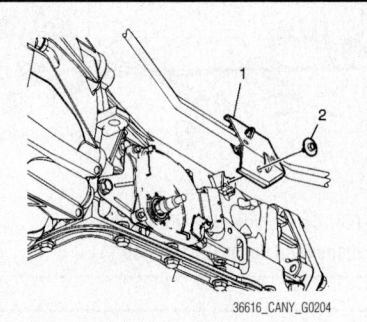

Fig. 41 Remove the screw (1) securing the fuel hose/pipe bracket to the transmission

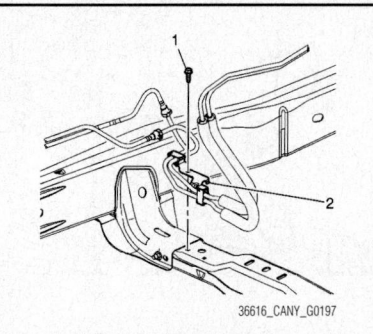

Fig. 42 Remove the bolt (1) securing the fuel hose/pipe bracket (2) to the transmission crossmember

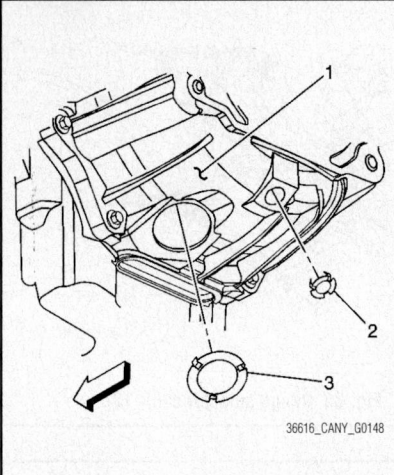

Fig. 43 Remove the inspection plug (3) and mark the torque converter to flexplate/flywheel orientation

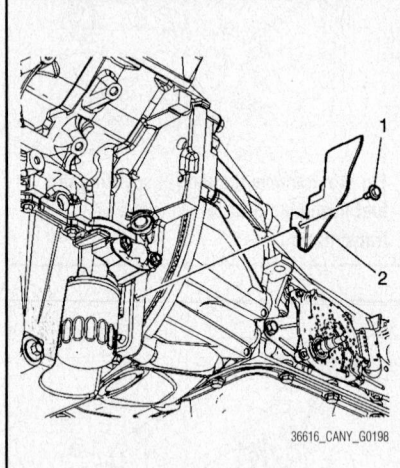

Fig. 44 Remove the left flywheel inspection cover (2) and bolt (1)

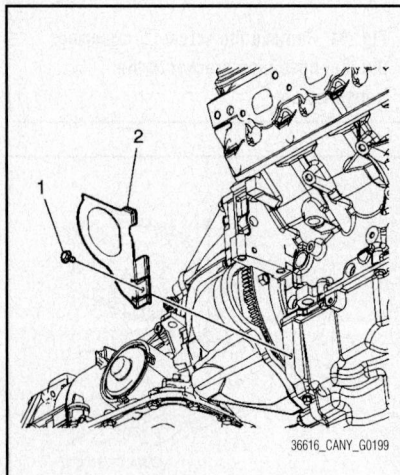

Fig. 45 Remove the right flywheel inspection cover (2) and bolt (1)

Transmission Fluid Filler Tube and Seal Removal & Installation.

4. Remove the right and left catalytic converters. Refer to Catalytic Converter Removal & Installation.

5. Remove the right heat shield bolts.

6. Remove the right heat shield.

7. Remove the left heat shield bolts.

8. Remove the left heat shield.

➡**Do not pull on the boot portion of the cable.**

9. Disconnect the range selector cable end (3) from the range selector lever.

10. Remove the retainer (1) from the range selector cable (2).

11. Push the range selector cable locking tabs (2) inward toward each other to release the cable from the bracket.

12. Disconnect the transmission main electrical connector.

13. Remove the screw securing the engine wiring harness to the right side of the transmission, and position the harness over the transmission.

14. Disconnect the park/neutral back up switch electrical connector.

15. Remove the screw securing the engine wiring harness to the left side of the transmission, and position the wiring harness aside.

16. Disconnect the transfer case vent hose retainer from the fuel hose/pipe bracket.

17. Disconnect the transmission vent hose retainer from the fuel hose/pipe bracket.

18. Remove the nut (2) securing the fuel hose/pipe bracket (1) to the transmission.

19. Remove the screw (2) securing the fuel hose/pipe bracket (1) to the transmission.

20. Disconnect the fuel hose/pipe retainer from the bracket on the transfer case adaptor, and position aside the fuel hose/pipe bundle.

21. Remove the bolt (1) securing the fuel hose/pipe bracket (2) to the transmission crossmember.

22. Remove the inspection plug (3) from the transmission (1).

23. Mark the torque converter to flexplate/flywheel orientation to ensure proper realignment.

24. Remove the left flywheel inspection cover bolt (1).

25. Remove the left flywheel inspection cover (2).

26. Remove the starter motor. Refer to Starter Removal & Installation in Engine Electrical.

27. Remove the right flywheel inspection cover bolt (1).

28. Remove the right flywheel inspection cover (2).

29. Remove the engine protection shield.

30. Repeat the following steps for all torque converter bolts (1):

a. Rotate the harmonic balancer center bolt clockwise ONLY, in order to access the torque converter bolt.

b. Remove the torque converter bolt:

- Place an oil pan under the transmission fluid cooler pipes.
- Disconnect the transmission oil cooler pipes from the transmission ONLY. Refer to Transmission Fluid Cooler Hose/Pipe Removal & Installation.
- Plug the open outlet ports to prevent fluid loss and contamination.
- Drain the transmission fluid if necessary.
- Support and secure the transmission using a suitable transmission jack.
- Remove the transmission crossmember. Refer to Transmission Support Crossmember Removal & Installation.
- Remove the transfer case assembly. Refer to Transfer Case Assembly Removal & Installation.

31. Remove the 2 transmission mounting studs (1).

32. Remove the 6 transmission mounting bolts (2, 3).

33. Separate the transmission from the engine alignment dowels.

➡**Ensure clearance is maintained between the transmission and the following: The engine wiring harness, the fuel hose/pipe brackets, the transmission oil cooler pipes.**

34. Using the transmission jack, carefully lower the transmission from the vehicle.

35. Install the J 21366 onto the transmission bell housing to retain the torque converter.

36. Perform the flush and flow test on the automatic transmission oil cooler.

To install:

37. Remove the J 21366 from the transmission.

38. Ensure the torque converter is fully engaged with the transmission oil pump.

➡**Ensure clearance is maintained between the transmission and the following: The engine wiring harness, the**

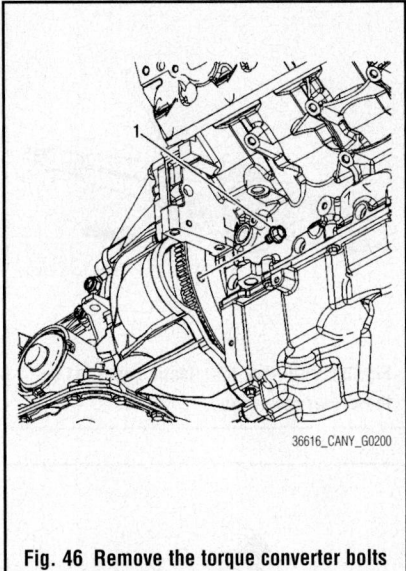

Fig. 46 Remove the torque converter bolts

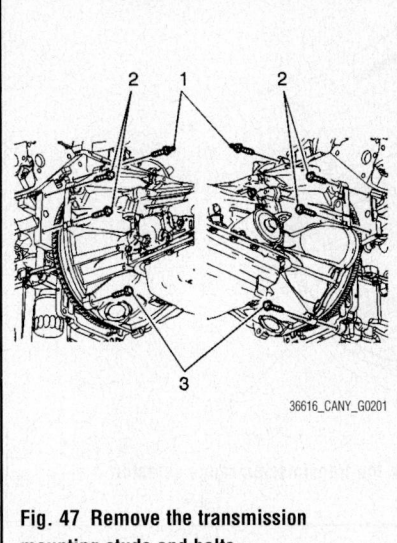

Fig. 47 Remove the transmission mounting studs and bolts

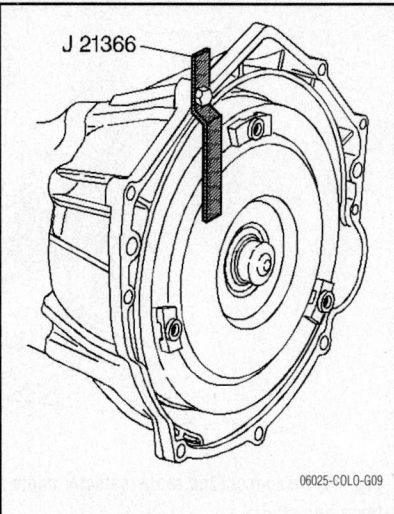

Fig. 48 Install the J 21366 onto the transmission bell housing

fuel hose/pipe brackets, the transmission oil cooler pipes.

39. Using the transmission jack, carefully raise the transmission to the engine.

40. Align the transmission with the engine alignment dowels.

➡**Ensure the torque converter turns freely while tightening the transmission mounting bolts.**

41. Install the 6 transmission mounting bolts and tighten to 37 ft. lbs. (50 Nm).

42. Install the 2 transmission mounting studs and tighten to 37 ft. lbs. (50 Nm).

43. Install the transfer case assembly.

44. Install the transmission crossmember.

45. Remove the transmission jack from under the vehicle.

46. Connect the transmission oil cooler pipes to the transmission.

47. Align the torque converter to flexplate/flywheel orientation marks made during the removal procedure.

48. Repeat the following steps for all 3 torque converter bolts:

   a. Rotate the harmonic balancer center bolt clockwise ONLY, in order to access the torque converter bolt holes.

   b. To aid in alignment of the torque converter to the flexplate/flywheel. Install all 3 torque converter bolts before fully tightening to 44 ft. lbs. (60 Nm).

49. Install the engine protection shield.

50. Install the right flywheel inspection cover.

51. Install the right flywheel inspection cover bolt and tighten to 89 inch lbs. (10 Nm).

52. Install the starter motor.

53. Install the left flywheel inspection cover.

54. Install the left flywheel inspection cover bolt and tighten to 89 inch lbs. (10 Nm).

55. Install the inspection plug to the transmission.

56. Install the bolt securing the fuel hose/pipe bracket to the transmission crossmember and tighten to 15 ft. lbs. (20 Nm).

57. Install the nut securing the fuel hose/pipe bracket to the transmission and tighten to 15 ft. lbs. (20 Nm).

58. Attach the fuel hose/pipe retainer to the bracket on the transfer case adaptor.

59. Install the screw securing the fuel hose/pipe bracket to the transmission and tighten to 80 inch lbs. (9 Nm).

60. Install the nut securing the fuel hose/pipe bracket to the transmission and tighten to 15 ft. lbs. (20 Nm).

61. Connect the transmission vent hose retainer to the fuel hose/pipe bracket.

62. Connect the transfer case vent hose retainer to the fuel hose/pipe bracket.

63. Connect the park/neutral back up switch electrical connector.

64. Install the screw securing the engine wiring harness to the left side of the transmission and tighten to 80 inch lbs. (9 Nm).

65. Connect the transmission main electrical connector.

66. Install the screw securing the engine wiring harness to the right side of the transmission and tighten to 80 inch lbs. (9 Nm).

➡**Ensure the range selector cable is routed exactly as originally positioned in the vehicle to avoid coming into contact with potential hazards such as hot, sharp, and moving objects.**

67. Install the range selector cable to the range selector cable bracket. Ensure the range selector cable retaining tabs fully engage the range selector cable bracket.

68. Install the retainer to the range selector cable.

69. Connect the range selector cable end to the transaxle range switch lever.

70. Install the left heat shield. Install the left heat shield bolts and tighten to 89 inch lbs. (10 Nm).

71. Install the right heat shield. Install the right heat shield bolts and tighten to 89 inch lbs. (10 Nm).

72. Install the right and left catalytic converters.

73. Install the filler tube.

74. Fill the transmission fluid if necessary.

75. Adjust the automatic transmission range selector cable. Refer to Range Selector Lever Cable Adjustment.

76. Lower the vehicle.

RANGE SELECTOR LEVER CABLE ADJUSTMENT—2.9L & 3.7L ENGINES

See Figures 49 through 51.

1. Ensure that the range selector cable is not restricted.

2. Ensure that the column shift control is in the PARK position.

3. Raise and support the vehicle.

❋❋ **WARNING**

Do not pull on the boot portion of the cable.

4. Complete the following in order to disconnect the range selector cable (3) from the transmission range selector lever ball stud.

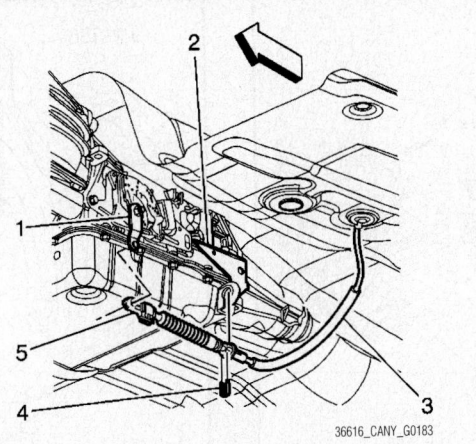

Fig. 49 Disconnect the range selector cable (3) from the transmission range selector lever ball stud

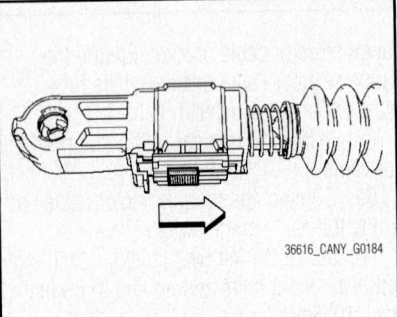

Fig. 50 Slide the secondary locking tab rearward to release the primary lock

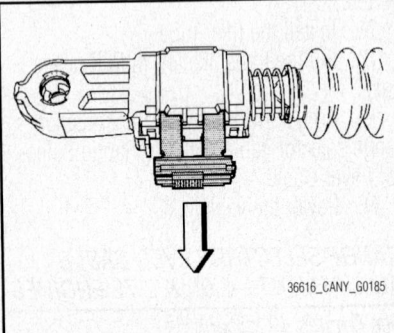

Fig. 51 Open the primary lock to disengage

a. Insert a flat-bladed tool between the range selector cable end (5) and the range selector lever (1).

b. Pry the range selector cable end (5) away from the range selector lever (1).

5. Ensure that the range selector lever is in the mechanical PARK position. Rotate the range selector lever fully clockwise.

6. Slide the secondary locking tab rearward to release the primary lock.

7. Open the primary lock to disengage.

8. Push the range selector cable end onto the transmission range selector lever ball stud to secure.

9. Close the primary lock to engage.

10. Slide the secondary locking tab forward to secure the primary lock.

11. Lower the vehicle.

12. Check the vehicle for proper operation.

RANGE SELECTOR LEVER CABLE ADJUSTMENT—5.3L ENGINES

See Figures 52 through 57.

1. Ensure that the shift control is in the park (P) position.

2. Raise and support the vehicle.

3. Ensure that the range selector cable is not restricted.

4. Pull back the plastic cover (1) on the center connector.

5. Pull up on the center tabs of the lock button (2).

❋❋ WARNING

This step must be performed correctly to avoid a misadjusted cable. Do not grasp the shift cable end (2) during this procedure.

6. Release the shift cable end (2) and allow the spring to tension/adjust the shift cable system.

7. Pull the cover (3) on the shift cable end (1) back.

8. Push the lock button (2) down to engage the locking teeth on the shift cable end (1).

9. Release the cover (1).

10. Verify the cover (1) conceals the lock (2).

11. If the cover (1) does not conceal the lock (2), the shift cable must be readjusted.

12. Lower the vehicle.

13. Check the vehicle for proper operation.

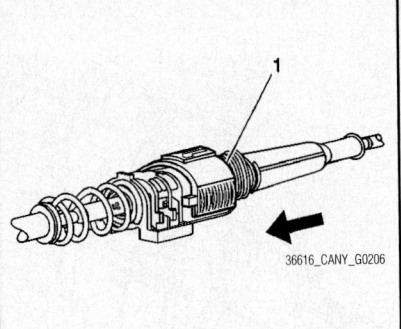

Fig. 52 Pull back the plastic cover (1) on the center connector

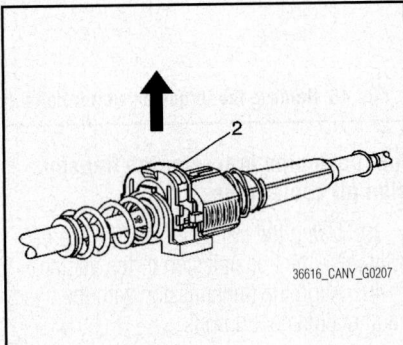

Fig. 53 Pull up on the center tabs of the lock button (2)

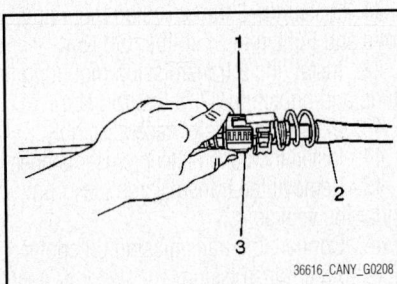

Fig. 54 Release the shift cable end (2) and allow the spring to tension/adjust the shift cable system and pull the cover (3) on the shift cable end (1) back

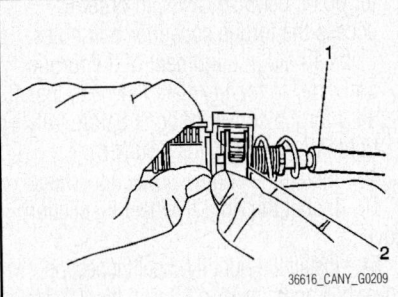

Fig. 55 Push the lock button (2) down to engage the locking teeth on the shift cable end (1)

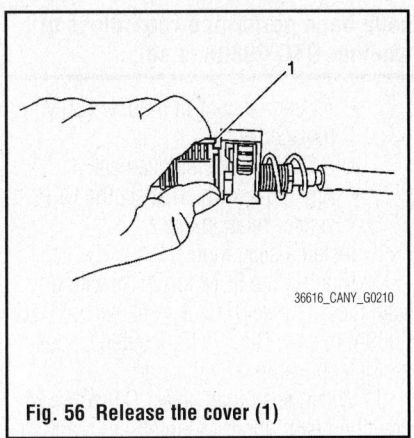

Fig. 56 Release the cover (1)

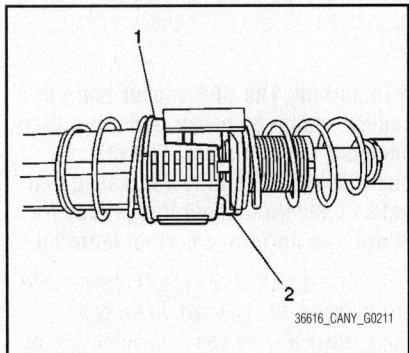

Fig. 57 Verify the cover (1) conceals the lock (2)

MANUAL TRANSMISSION ASSEMBLY

REMOVAL & INSTALLATION

See Figures 58 through 60.

1. Before servicing the vehicle, refer to the Precautions Section.
2. Remove the control lever and boot.
3. Drain the transmission fluid if necessary.
4. For RWD models, remove the rear propeller shaft. Refer to Propeller Shaft Removal & Installation.
5. For 4WD models, remove the transfer case assembly. Refer to Transfer Case Assembly Removal & Installation.
6. Using the J 42371, push back on the white plastic sleeve on the quick connect in order to separate the hydraulic clutch line from the clutch actuator quick connect. It is not necessary to plug the lower hose end or slave cylinder fitting as they are equipped with check valves, only minimal fluid loss may be experienced.
7. Disconnect the following engine wiring harness electrical connectors:
   - Backup lamp switch
   - Oxygen sensor
8. Disconnect the engine wiring harness clip from the clip bracket, and position the harness over the transmission.
9. Disconnect the Vehicle Speed (VSS) sensor electrical connector
10. Disconnect the engine wiring harness clips from the clip brackets, and position the harness aside.
11. Remove the nuts securing the fuel hose/pipe brackets to the transmission, and position aside.
12. Support and secure the transmission using a suitable transmission jack.
13. Remove the transmission crossmember. Refer to Transmission Support Crossmember Removal & Installation.
14. Remove the service slot plug.
15. Remove the 9 transmission mounting bolts.
16. Remove the remaining transmission mounting bolts (2).

➡**Do not allow the transmission to hang from the clutch assembly.**

17. Pull the transmission straight back off the clutch hub splines.

➡**Ensure clearance is maintained between the transmission and the following: The catalytic converter, the clutch assembly, the engine wiring harness, the fuel hose/pipe brackets, and the heater pipe.**

18. Using the transmission jack, carefully lower the transmission from the vehicle.

To install:

➡**Ensure clearance is maintained between the transmission and the following: The catalytic converter, the clutch assembly, the engine wiring harness, the fuel hose/pipe brackets, and the heater pipe.**

19. Using the transmission jack, carefully raise the transmission to the engine.

➡**Do not allow the transmission to hang from the clutch assembly.**

20. Align the transmission with the engine dowels.
21. Install the 2 transmission mounting bolts and tighten to 37 ft. lbs. (50 Nm).

➡**Ensure the studded mounting bolts are located in the correct position. The heater pipe must be secured with the 2 upper mounting bolts.**

22. Install the remaining transmission mounting bolts and tighten to 37 ft. lbs. (50 Nm).
23. Install the service slot plug.
24. Install the transmission crossmember.
25. Remove the transmission jack from under the vehicle.

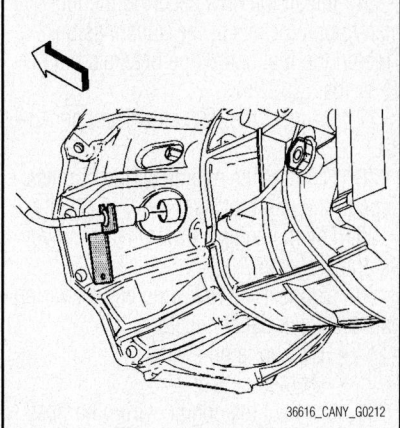

Fig. 58 Using the J 42371, push back on the white plastic sleeve on the quick connect in order to separate the hydraulic clutch line from the clutch actuator quick connect

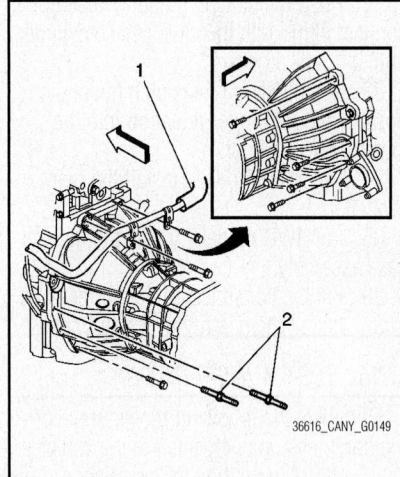

Fig. 59 Remove the 9 transmission mounting bolts

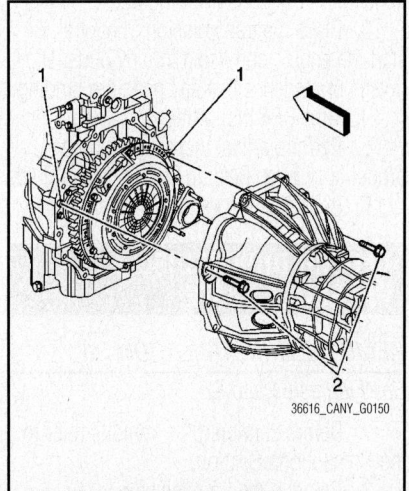

Fig. 60 Remove the remaining transmission mounting bolts (2)

26. Install the nuts securing the fuel hose/pipe brackets to the transmission. Tighten the fuel hose/pipe brackets nuts to 15 ft. lbs. (20 Nm).

27. Connect the VSS electrical connector.

28. Connect the engine wiring harness clips to the clip brackets.

29. Lay the engine wiring harness over the transmission.

30. Connect the following engine wiring harness electrical connectors:
- Backup lamp switch
- Oxygen sensor

31. Connect the engine wiring harness clip to the clip bracket.

✳✳ WARNING

Ensure the clutch hydraulic hose does not come in contact with any sharp or potential hot surfaces.

32. Push the clutch hydraulic hose quick connect fitting into the clutch slave cylinder, until a "click" is heard.

33. Tug gently on the clutch hydraulic hose to ensure proper retention into the clutch slave cylinder.

34. For RWD models, install the rear propeller shaft.

35. For 4WD models, install the transfer case assembly.

36. Fill the transmission fluid if removed.

37. Install the control lever and boot.

FINAL TEST & INSPECTION

Complete the following procedure after the transmission is installed in the vehicle:

1. With the ignition OFF or disconnected and clutch pedal depressed, crank the engine several times.

2. Listen for any unusual noises or evidence that any parts are binding.

3. Place the transmission in neutral, start the engine and listen for any unusual noises or evidence that any parts are binding.

4. Turn OFF the ignition.

5. Perform a final inspection for the proper fluid level. Refer to Transmission Fluid.

6. Road test the vehicle.

CLUTCH DRIVEN DISC & PRESSURE PLATE

REMOVAL & INSTALLATION

See Figures 61 and 62.

1. Before servicing the vehicle, refer to the Precautions Section.

2. Remove the transmission.

3. Remove the clutch pressure plate bolts (1). Discard the bolts.

4. Remove the clutch pressure plate (2) and driven disc (3) from the dowel pins (4) on the flywheel (5).

To install:

5. Install the clutch pressure plate (2) and driven plate (3) to the dowel pins (4) on the flywheel (5).

6. Install the clutch pressure plate bolts (1) finger tight.

7. Use the Snap-On® A145 Clutch Aligner Set, or equivalent, to align the clutch driven plate (3) to the clutch pilot bearing.

8. Tighten the NEW clutch pressure plate bolts in the sequence shown.

  a. Tighten the clutch pressure plate bolts in sequence to 15 ft. lbs. (20 Nm).

  b. Use the J 36660-A in order to tighten the clutch pressure plate bolts in sequence an additional 45 degrees.

9. Install the transmission.

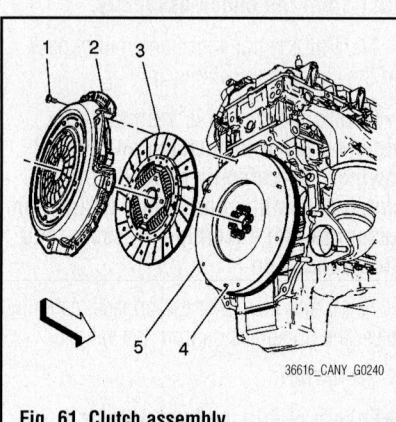

36616_CANY_G0240

Fig. 61 Clutch assembly

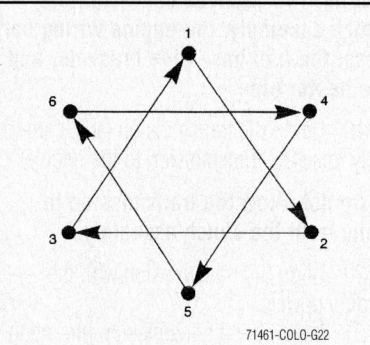

71461-COLO-G22

Fig. 62 Clutch pressure plate bolt tightening sequence

CLUTCH PEDAL POSITION SENSOR LEARN PROCEDURE

✳✳ WARNING

The Clutch Pedal Position (CPP) sensor learn procedure is required when the following service procedures

have been performed regardless of whether DTC P080A is set:

- An engine control module (ECM) replacement
- A CPP sensor replacement
- Any repairs which affect the CPP sensor relationship

1. Install a scan tool.

2. Monitor the ECM for DTCs with a scan tool. If other DTCs are set, except DTC P080A, refer to Diagnostic Trouble Codes for the applicable DTC that set.

3. With a scan tool, select Clutch Pedal Position Learn under Module Setup in Manual Transmission, and perform the following instructions displayed on the scan tool screen.

➡**Important: The CPP sensor learn procedure cannot be performed more than once per ignition cycle. The clutch pedal needs to be fully depressed and held steady throughout this procedure in order to perform a correct learning.**

4. The scan tool will display under CPP Learn Status: Not Learned, In Process, Complete, Fail-Low Volt, Fail-High Volt, or Fail Moving. The scan tool will display under CPP Learn Status Complete if the process was successful.

5. If the scan tool indicates that DTC P080A ran and passed this ignition the CPP sensor learn procedure is complete. If the scan tool indicates DTC P080A failed or did not run this ignition, refer to DTC P080A. If any other DTC is set, refer to Diagnostic Trouble Codes for the applicable DTC.

6. Turn OFF the ignition for 30 seconds after the learn procedure has successfully completed in order to store the CPP sensor variation values in ECM history.

CLUTCH MASTER CYLINDER

REMOVAL & INSTALLATION

See Figures 63 through 66.

1. Before servicing the vehicle, refer to the Precautions Section.

➡**A new retainer (3) is required after removal.**

2. Complete the following in order to disengage the retainer (3) from the clutch pedal pin.

  a. Insert a flat bladed tool (4) between the clutch master cylinder push rod (1) and the clutch pedal (2).

  b. Pry the clutch master cylinder push rod (1) away from the clutch pedal assembly (2).

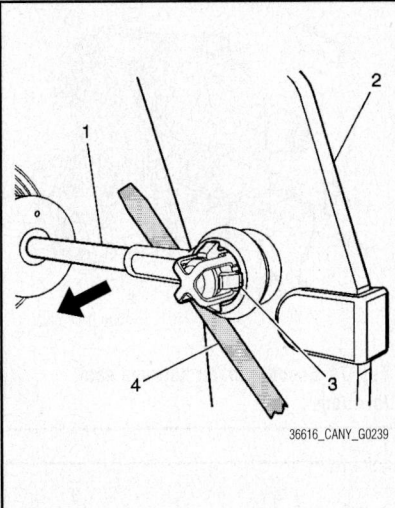

Fig. 63 Disengage the retainer (3) from the clutch pedal pin

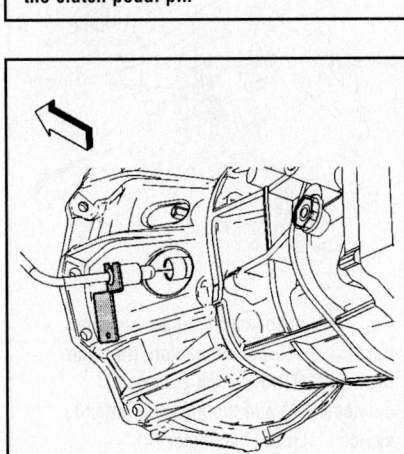

Fig. 64 Using clutch line separator J-42371, push back the white plastic sleeve on the quick connect in order to separate the hydraulic clutch hose from the clutch actuator quick connect

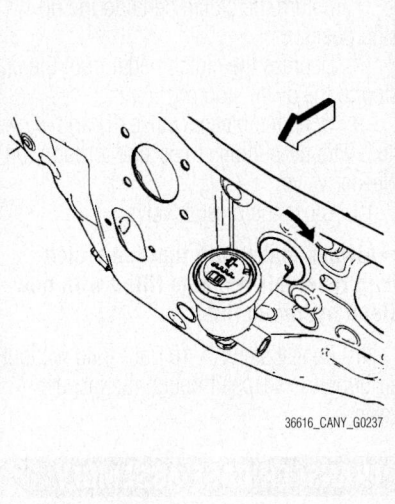

Fig. 65 Rotate the clutch master cylinder clockwise ⅛ turn

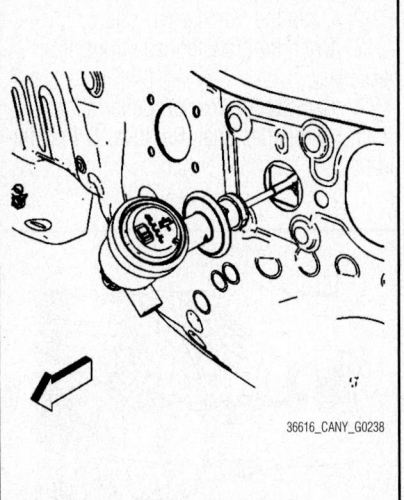

Fig. 66 Remove the clutch master cylinder with hydraulic hose from the cowl

c. Discard the retainer (3).

3. Raise and support the vehicle.

4. Using clutch line separator J-42371, push back the white plastic sleeve on the quick connect in order to separate the hydraulic clutch hose from the clutch actuator quick connect. It is not necessary to plug the lower hose end or slave cylinder fitting as they are equipped with check valves, only minimal fluid loss may be experienced.

5. Disconnect the clutch hydraulic hose retainer from the inner fender.

6. Lower the vehicle.

7. Rotate the clutch master cylinder clockwise ⅛ turn.

8. Remove the clutch master cylinder with hydraulic hose from the cowl.

To install:

9. Route the clutch hydraulic hose with master cylinder under the brake booster.

10. With the clutch fluid reservoir cap at the 1:30 position. Insert the clutch master cylinder into the cowl.

11. Rotate the clutch master cylinder counter clockwise ⅛ turn until fully seated. The clutch fluid reservoir cap will be vertical at the 12:00 position when the clutch master cylinder is properly installed.

12. Raise the vehicle.

❋❋ WARNING

Ensure the clutch hydraulic hose does not come in contact with any sharp or potentially hot surfaces.

13. Push the clutch hydraulic hose quick connect fitting into the clutch slave cylinder, until a "click" is heard.

14. Tug gently on the clutch hydraulic hose to ensure proper retention into the clutch slave cylinder.

15. Connect the clutch hydraulic hose retainer to the inner fender.

16. Lower the vehicle.

17. Insert a new retainer into the clutch master cylinder push rod.

18. Push the clutch master cylinder push rod onto the clutch pedal pin to secure.

19. Adjust the clutch release switch as follows:

20. Disconnect the clutch release switch electrical connector.

a. Rotate the clutch release switch counterclockwise, allowing the retainer to release.

b. Pull the clutch pedal to full stop.

c. While holding the clutch pedal at full stop, push the switch inward fully until the switch body contacts the clutch pedal arm. At this point the plunger in the switch should be pushed in.

d. Rotate the switch clockwise until a "click" is heard.

21. Adjust the clutch pedal position switch as follows:

a. Push the switch fully into the bracket, allowing the switch to ratchet in the retaining plate.

b. Depress the clutch pedal all the way to the floor.

22. Bleed the clutch hydraulic system, only if necessary.

CLUTCH SLAVE CYLINDER

REMOVAL & INSTALLATION

See Figure 67.

1. Before servicing the vehicle, refer to the Precautions Section.

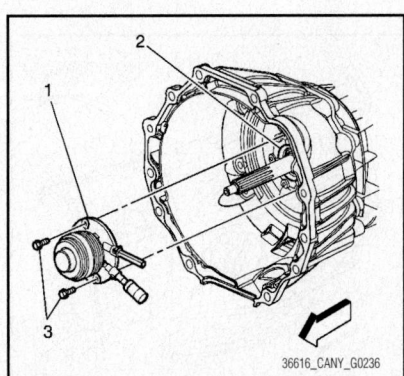

Fig. 67 Remove the control lever housing assembly bolts and gasket

2. Remove the transmission.

3. Remove the 2 clutch actuator cylinder bolts (3).

4. Remove the clutch actuator cylinder (1) from the input shaft bearing retainer (2).

To install:

5. Position the clutch actuator cylinder to the input shaft bearing retainer.

6. Install the 2 clutch actuator cylinder bolts and tighten the clutch actuator cylinder bolts to 71 inch lbs. (8 Nm).

7. Install the transmission.

CLUTCH HYDRAULIC SYSTEM BLEEDING

See Figure 68.

❄❄ CAUTION

DO NOT use fluid which has been bled from a hydraulic clutch system, in order to fill the clutch master cylinder reservoir, due to the possibility that the fluid may be aerated, have too much moisture content, or be contaminated and may cause system or vehicle damage.

1. Ensure the reservoir is filled to the fill line with new hydraulic fluid. Add fluid if required from a clean sealed container.

2. Pump the clutch pedal from the up stop to the down stop position at least 15 times.

3. With the pedal in the down stop position, open the bleeder valve (1) to release the trapped air.

4. Close the bleeder valve (1) and slowly return the clutch pedal to the up stop position.

5. Open the bleeder valve (1) and slowly depress the clutch pedal from the up stop to the down stop position until fluid escapes through the bleeder.

6. Close the bleeder valve.

7. Return the clutch pedal to the up stop position.

8. Depress the clutch pedal from the up stop to the down stop position.

9. Open the bleeder valve (1) and allow fluid with air bubbles to escape through the bleeder valve.

10. Close the bleeder valve.

➥**Always make sure that the clutch fluid reservoir remains filled with new clean hydraulic fluid.**

11. Repeat steps 7–10 until fluid without air bubbles escapes through the bleeder valve.

TRANSFER CASE ASSEMBLY

REMOVAL & INSTALLATION

See Figures 69 through 74.

1. Before servicing the vehicle, refer to the Precautions Section.

2. Drain the transfer case fluid.

3. Drain the transfer case fluid, if necessary.

4. Remove the rear propeller shaft. Refer to Propeller Shaft Removal & Installation.

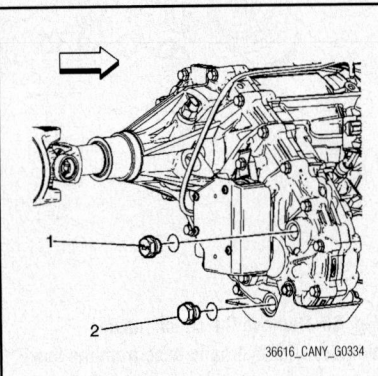

Fig. 69 Drain transfer case fluid, if necessary

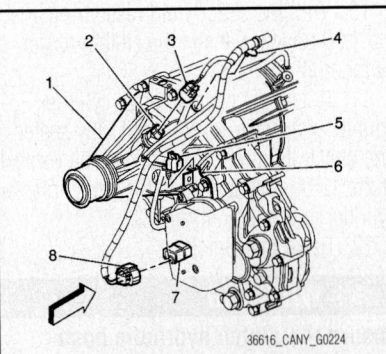

Fig. 70 Disconnect electrical connector (8) from encoder motor(7)

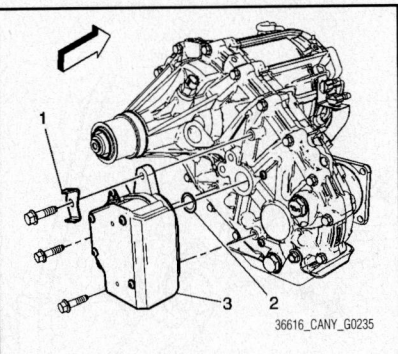

Fig. 71 Encoder motor bolt and seal locations

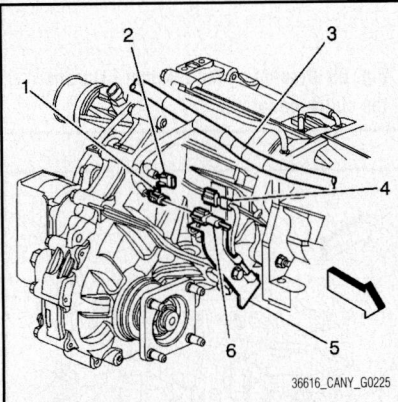

Fig. 72 Disconnect the engine wiring harness electrical connectors from the brown NEUTRAL switch electrical connector (6) and the gray 2/4 indicator switch electrical connector (4)

5. Remove the front propeller shaft. Refer to Front Propeller Shaft Replacement.

6. Remove the transfer case encoder motor, as follows:

a. Disconnect the following from the encoder motor (7):

- The electrical connector (8)
- The vent hose

b. Remove the encoder motor mounting bolts.

c. Remove the encoder motor (3) and O-ring seal (2) from the transfer case.

d. Discard the O-ring seal (2).

7. Disconnect the engine wiring harness electrical connectors from the following:

- The speed sensor
- The heated oxygen sensor pigtail

8. Disconnect the engine wiring harness electrical connectors (1, 2) from the following:

- The brown NEUTRAL switch electrical connector (6)
- The gray 2/4 indicator switch electrical connector (4)

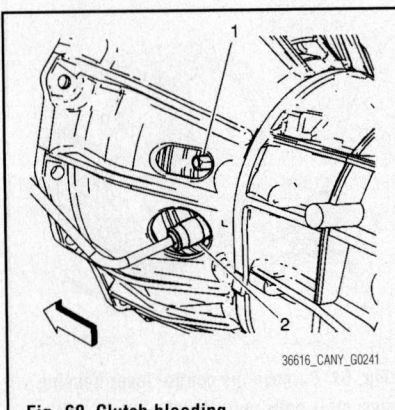

Fig. 68 Clutch bleeding

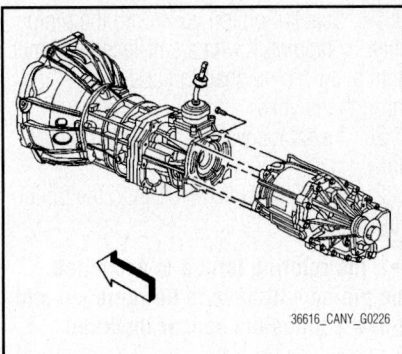

Fig. 73 Transfer case removal and installation—MA5 transmission

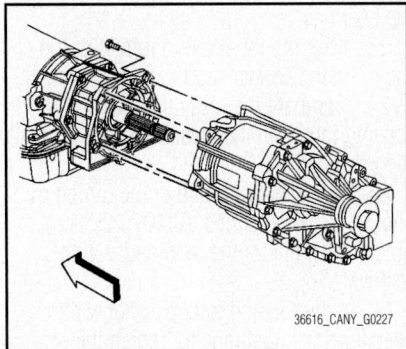

Fig. 74 Transfer case removal and installation—M30 transmission

9.Disconnect the engine wiring harness retainers from the transfer case.

10. Position the engine wiring harness aside.

11. If equipped with (MA5) complete the following:

    a. Remove the transfer case mounting bolts.

    b. With the aid of an assistant, carefully lower the transfer case from the vehicle.

12. If equipped with (M30) complete the following:

    a. Remove the transfer case mounting bolts.

    b. With the aid of an assistant, carefully lower the transfer case from the vehicle.

To install:

13. If equipped with (M30) complete the following:

    a. With the aid of an assistant, carefully raise the transfer case to the transfer case adapter, aligning the splines.

    b. Install the transfer case mounting bolts and tighten to 37 ft. lbs. (50 Nm).

14. If equipped with (MA5) complete the following:

    a. Lightly lubricate the transmission rear seal.

➡**Do not catch the input shaft on the transmission rear seal.**

    b. With the aid of an assistant, carefully raise the transfer case to the manual transmission, aligning the splines.

    c. Install the transfer case mounting bolts and tighten to 37 ft. lbs. (50 Nm).

15. Position the engine wiring harness to the transfer case assembly.

16. Connect the engine wiring harness retainers to the transfer case.

17. Connect the engine wiring harness electrical connectors to the following:

- The brown NEUTRAL switch electrical connector
- The gray 2/4 indicator switch electrical connector

18. Connect the engine wiring harness electrical connectors to the following:

- The speed sensor
- The heated oxygen sensor pigtail

19. Install the transfer case encoder motor, as follows:

➡**The actuator shaft in the transfer case may require rotating to the neutral position prior to installing the encoder motor. Do not rotate the actuator shaft using the encoder motor.**

20. Lightly lubricate the NEW O-ring seal with clean transfer case fluid.

21. Insert the O-ring seal into the transfer case.

➡**Ensure the encoder motor is seated flat against the transfer case.**

22. Position the encoder motor to the transfer case, aligning the actuator shaft.

23. Install the encoder motor mounting bolts, with the heated oxygen sensor bracket.

24. Tighten the encoder motor mounting bolts to 16 ft. lbs. (22 Nm).

25. Connect the following to the encoder motor:

- The electrical connector
- The vent hose

26. Install the front propeller shaft.

27. Install the rear propeller shaft.

28. Fill the transfer case with fluid, if previously drained.

29. Refill the transfer case.

FRONT HALFSHAFTS

REMOVAL & INSTALLATION

See Figures 75 and 76.

1. Before servicing the vehicle, refer to the Precautions Section.

2. Remove the tire and wheel assembly.

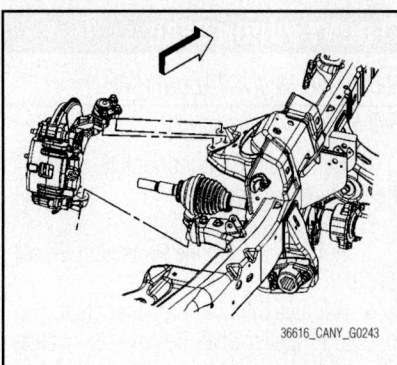

Fig. 75 Remove the steering knuckle assembly

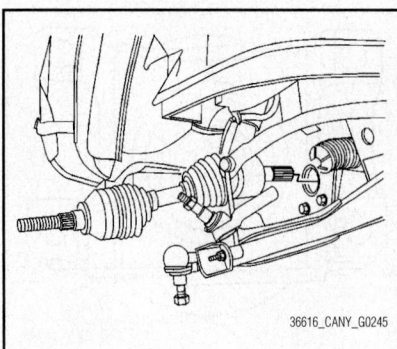

Fig. 76 Remove the front wheel drive shaft

3. DO NOT reuse the wheel drive shaft nut, replace with new.

4. Remove the wheel drive shaft nut and washer.

5. Remove the steering knuckle assembly.

6. Release the wheel drive shaft by placing a brass drift against the tripod housing. Firmly strike the brass drift with a hammer to release the drive shaft.

7. Remove the front wheel drive shaft from the vehicle.

To install:

➡**When installing the front wheel drive shaft, a snap or pop should be heard and felt when the front wheel drive shaft is properly seated in the differential case.**

8. Install the front wheel drive shaft in the front differential.

9. Install the steering knuckle assembly.

10. Install the new front wheel drive shaft nut and washer and tighten the nut to 191 ft. lbs. (260 Nm).

11. Check the fluid level of the front differential. Add fluid if necessary.

12. Install the tire and wheel assembly.

13. Lower the vehicle.

FRONT PINION SEAL

REMOVAL & INSTALLATION

See Figures 77 through 79.

1. Before servicing the vehicle, refer to the Precautions Section.
2. Raise the vehicle.
3. Remove the Engine Protection Shield (EPS).
4. Remove the front propeller shaft. Refer to Propeller Shaft Removal & Installation.
5. Remove the brake calipers. Refer to Brake Caliper Removal & Installation.

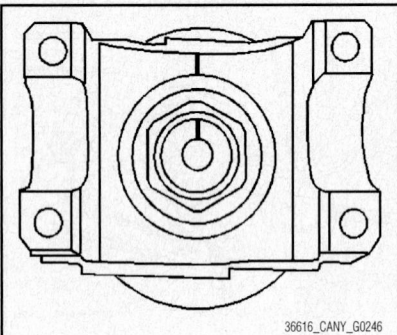

36616_CANY_G0246

Fig. 77 Scribe an alignment line between the pinion shaft and the pinion yoke

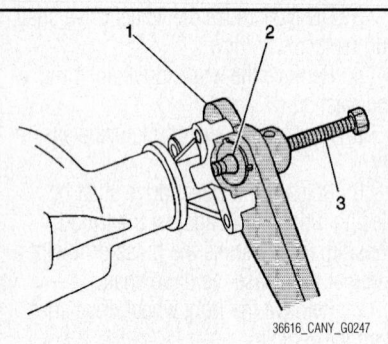

36616_CANY_G0247

Fig. 78 Install the J 8614-01 (1), J 8614-2 (2) and the J 8614-3 (3)

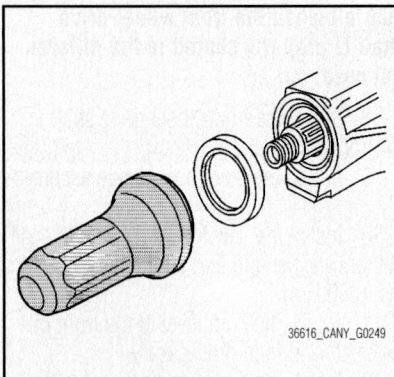

36616_CANY_G0249

Fig. 79 Position the oil seal in the bore

6. Measure the torque required in order to rotate the pinion. Use an inch-pound torque wrench. Record the torque value for reassembly. This will give the combined preload for the following components:

- The pinion bearings
- The pinion seal
- The carrier bearings
- The axle bearings
- The axle seals

7. Scribe an alignment line between the pinion shaft and the pinion yoke.
8. Install the J 8614-01 (1) onto the pinion as shown.
9. Remove the pinion nut while holding the J 8614-01 (1).
10. Install the J 8614-2 (2) and the J 8614-3 (3) into the J 8614-01 (1) as shown.
11. Remove the pinion yoke by turning the J 8614-3 (3) clockwise while holding the J 8614-01 (1).

➡**Carefully remove the seal from the bore. Do not distort or scratch the aluminum case.**

12. Remove the oil seal using a suitable seal removal tool.
13. Remove the dust deflector from the pinion yoke using a soft-faced hammer.

To install:

14. Install the new deflector onto the pinion yoke using a soft-faced hammer.

❊❊ WARNING

Drive the seal in straight, not at an angle, as this will damage the aluminum housing.

15. Install the new oil seal by doing the following:
    a. Position the oil seal in the bore.
    b. Install the J 21128 over the oil seal.
    c. Strike the J 21128 with a hammer until the seal flange seats on the axle housing surface.
16. Apply sealant GM P/N 12346004 (Canadian P/N 10953480) or equivalent to the splines of the drive pinion yoke.
17. Install the pinion yoke.
18. Align the reference marks made during removal.

❊❊ WARNING

Do not hammer the pinion flange/yoke onto the pinion shaft. Pinion components may be damaged if the pinion flange/yoke is hammered onto the pinion shaft.

19. Seat the pinion yoke onto the pinion shaft by tapping it with a soft-faced hammer until a few pinion shaft threads show through the yoke.
20. Install the washer and a new pinion nut.
21. Install the J 8614-01 onto the pinion yoke as shown.

➡**If the rotating torque is exceeded, the pinion will have to be removed and a new collapsible spacer installed.**

22. Tighten the pinion nut while holding the J 8614-01. Tighten the pinion nut until the pinion end play is just taken up. Rotate the pinion while tightening the nut to seat the bearings.
23. Measure the rotating torque of the pinion using an inch-pound torque wrench.
24. Compare the measurement of the rotating torque to the measurement recorded earlier.
25. The rotating torque of the pinion nut should be 3–5 inch lbs. (0.40–0.57 Nm) greater than the torque recorded during removal.
26. If the rotating torque is not within specifications, continue to tighten the pinion nut. Tighten the pinion nut, in small increments, as needed, until the torque required in order to rotate the pinion is 3–5 inch lbs. (0.40–0.57 Nm) greater than the torque recorded during removal.
27. Once the specified torque is obtained, rotate the pinion several times to ensure the bearings have seated. Recheck the rotating torque and adjust if necessary.
28. Install the front propeller shaft.
29. Install the EPS.
30. Install the brake calipers. Refer to Brake Caliper Removal & Installation.
31. Inspect the axle lubricant level, and add, if necessary.
32. Lower the vehicle.

REAR AXLE HOUSING

REMOVAL & INSTALLATION

1. Raise the vehicle.
2. Drain the axle lubricant.
3. Remove the rear axle assembly.
4. Remove the rear axle housing cover and gasket.
5. Remove the axle shafts. Refer to Axle Shaft, Bearing, and Seal Removal & Installation.
6. Remove the differential assembly.
7. Remove the brake backing plates.
8. Remove the drive pinion shaft yoke and the seal. Refer to Pinion Seal Removal & Installation.

9. Remove the drive pinion.

To install:

10. Install the drive pinion.
11. Install the differential assembly.
12. Adjust the differential side bearing preload.
13. Adjust the backlash.
14. Perform a gear tooth contact pattern check.
15. Install the brake backing plates.
16. Install the axle shafts.
17. Install the rear axle housing cover and gasket.
18. Install the rear axle.
19. Fill the axle with lubricant.
20. Lower the vehicle.

REAR AXLE SHAFT, BEARING & SEAL

REMOVAL & INSTALLATION

See Figures 80 through 82.

1. Before servicing the vehicle, refer to the Precautions Section.
2. Raise and support the vehicle.
3. Remove the rear tire and wheel assembly.
4. Remove the clip retaining the rear brake drum, if required.

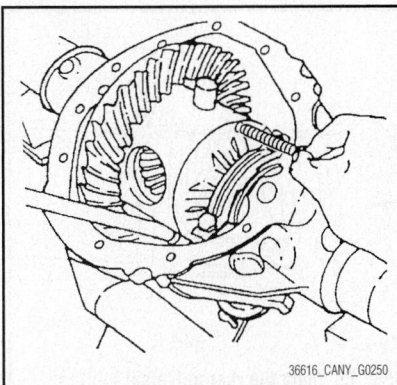

Fig. 80 Remove the lock pin bolt

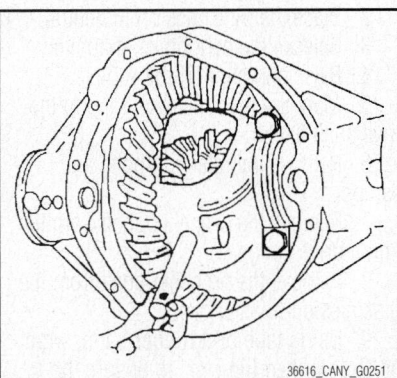

Fig. 81 Remove the pinion shaft

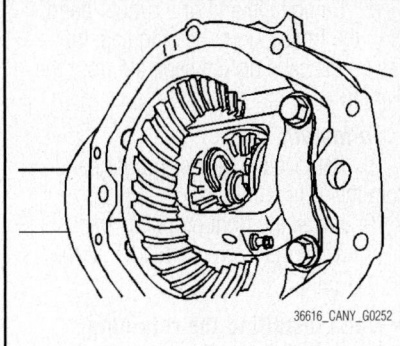

Fig. 82 Remove the C-lock from the rear axle

5. Remove the rear brake drums from the vehicle.
6. Remove the rear axle housing cover.
7. Remove the lock pin bolt.
8. Remove the pinion shaft.
9. Remove the C-lock from the rear axle.
10. Remove the rear axle shaft.
11. Using the J 44685 and the J 2619-01, remove the axle shaft bearing and seal.

To install:

12. Using the J 23690 and the J 8092, install the axle bearing.
13. Using the J 21128, install the axle shaft seal.
14. Install the rear axle shaft.
15. Install the C-lock to the rear axle.
16. Install the pinion shaft.
17. Install the lock bolt and tighten to 18 ft. lbs. (25 Nm).
18. Install the rear brake drums from the vehicle.
19. Install the rear axle housing cover and gasket.
20. Fill the rear axle with fluid.
21. Install the tire and wheel.

REAR PINION SEAL

REMOVAL & INSTALLATION

See Figures 77, 83 and 84.

➡**Observe and mark the positions of all the driveline components, relative to the propeller shaft and the axles, prior to disassembly. These components include the propeller shafts, drive axles, pinion flanges, output shafts, etc. Reassemble all the components in the exact places in which you removed the parts. Follow any specifications, torque values, and any measurements made prior to disassembly**

1. Raise the and support vehicle.
2. Remove the rear drum brakes.
3. Remove the propeller shaft.

Refer to Propeller Shaft Removal & Installation.

4. Use an inch-pound torque wrench, measure the amount of torque required to rotate the pinion. Record this measurement for reassembly. This will give the combined preload for the following components:
- The pinion bearings
- The pinion oil seal
- The differential case bearings
- The axle bearings
- The axle seals

5. Place an alignment mark between the pinion and the pinion yoke.
6. Using the J 8614-01 tool to hold the pinion nut, remove the pinion nut and the washer.

➡**Use a container in order to retrieve the lubricant.**

7. Using the J 8614-01 tool (1) to hold the pinion yoke, remove the pinion yoke by turning the J 8614-3 (3) clockwise.

➡**Do not damage the housing.**

8. Using a suitable tool, remove the pinion oil seal.

To install:

9. Using the J 33782 installer for the 8.0 inch, install the pinion seal.

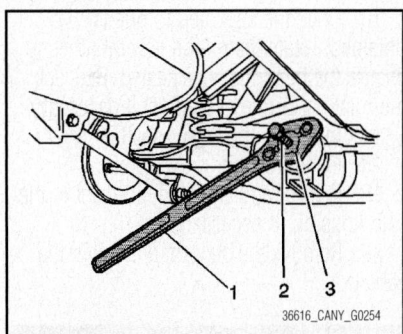

Fig. 83 Using the J 8614-01 tool (1) to hold the pinion yoke, remove the pinion yoke by turning the J 8614-3 (3) clockwise

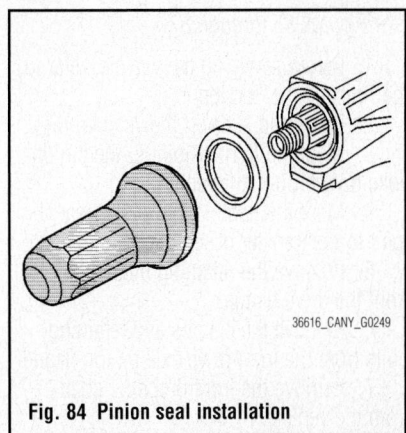

Fig. 84 Pinion seal installation

10. Apply sealant to the splines of the pinion yoke.

11. Align the reference marks and install the pinion yoke.

⚹⚹ WARNING

Do not hammer the pinion flange/yoke onto the pinion shaft. Pinion components may be damaged if the pinion flange/yoke is hammered onto the pinion shaft.

12. Using a soft-faced hammer, tap the pinion yoke until the threads on the pinion shaft can be seen.

13. Install the washer and a NEW pinion nut.

14. While holding the J 8614-01 tool, tighten the NEW pinion nut in small increments until the end play is just taken up.

➡**If the rotating torque is exceeded, the pinion will have to be removed and a new collapsible spacer installed.**

➡**Compare this measurement with the rotating torque recorded during removal.**

15. Using an inch pound torque wrench, measure the rotating torque of the pinion 3–5 lbs. (0–0.57 Nm) greater than the rotating torque recorded during removal.

16. Once the specified torque is obtained, rotate the pinion several times to ensure the bearings have seated. Recheck the rotating torque and adjust if necessary.

17. Install the propeller shaft.

18. Install the rear brake rotors.

19. Inspect and add axle lubricant to the axle housing, if necessary.

20. Remove the support and lower the vehicle.

PROPELLER SHAFT

REMOVAL & INSTALLATION

Front Propeller Shaft

See Figures 85 through 87.

1. Before servicing the vehicle, refer to the Precautions Section.

2. Raise and support the vehicle.

3. Mark the front U-joint to the pinion yoke on the front differential.

4. Mark the relationship of the rear U-joint to the transfer case drive flange.

5. Remove the retaining nuts and bolts from the drive flange.

6. Remove the clamps and retaining bolts from the front drive axle pinion flange.

7. Remove the front propeller shaft from the vehicle.

8. Using tape and or a rubber band, wrap the front U-joint bearing caps to ensure the caps do not separate from the U-joint.

To install:

9. Remove the tape or rubber band from the front U-joint

10. Install the front propeller shaft.

11. Align the reference marks on the front U-joint.

➡**When installing the retaining bolts, only tighten them finger tight to hold the front propeller shaft in position.**

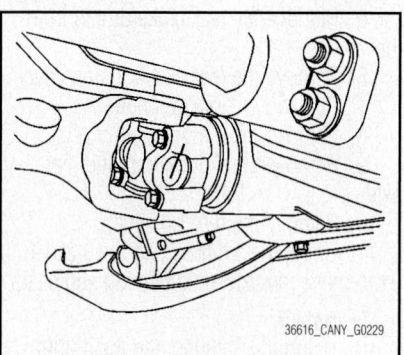

Fig. 85 Mark the front U-joint to the pinion yoke on the front differential

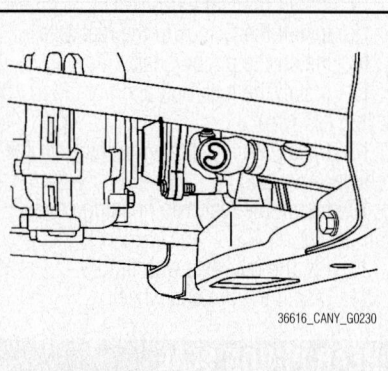

Fig. 86 Mark the relationship of the rear U-joint to the transfer case drive flange

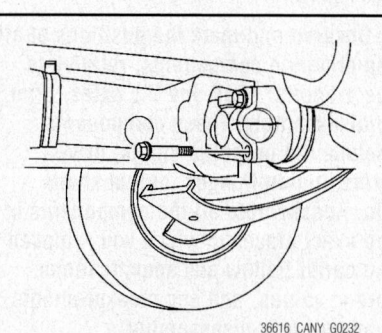

Fig. 87 Remove the clamps and retaining bolts from the front drive axle pinion flange

12. Install the front U-joint bolts and clamps.

13. Align the reference marks on the rear U-joint.

14. Install the propeller shaft to pinion flange bolts:
- Tighten the bolts from the propeller shaft to the pinion flange 15 ft. lbs. (20 Nm).
- Tighten the bolts for the front propeller U-joint clamps 15 ft. lbs. (20 Nm).

15. Lower the vehicle.

Rear Propeller Shaft

One-Piece Propeller Shaft

See Figures 88 and 89.

1. Before servicing the vehicle, refer to the Precautions Section.

⚹⚹ WARNING

When removing the propeller shaft, do not attempt to remove the shaft by pounding on the yoke ears or using a tool between the yoke and the universal joint. If the propeller shaft is removed by using such means, the injection joints may fracture and lead to premature failure of the joint.

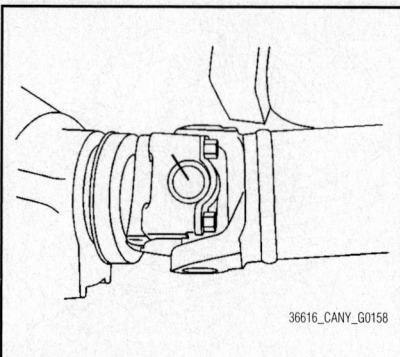

Fig. 88 Mark the rear universal joint to the drive shaft flange

2. Place the transmission in neutral.

3. Release the park brake, if applied.

4. Raise and support the vehicle.

5. Mark the rear universal joint to the drive shaft flange.

6. Remove the retaining bolts and clamps.

7. Remove the propeller shaft from the pinion drive flange.

8. Remove the propeller shaft from the transmission/transfer case.

9. Using tape or a rubber band, wrap the U-Joint bearing caps to ensure the bearing caps do not separate from the U-Joint.

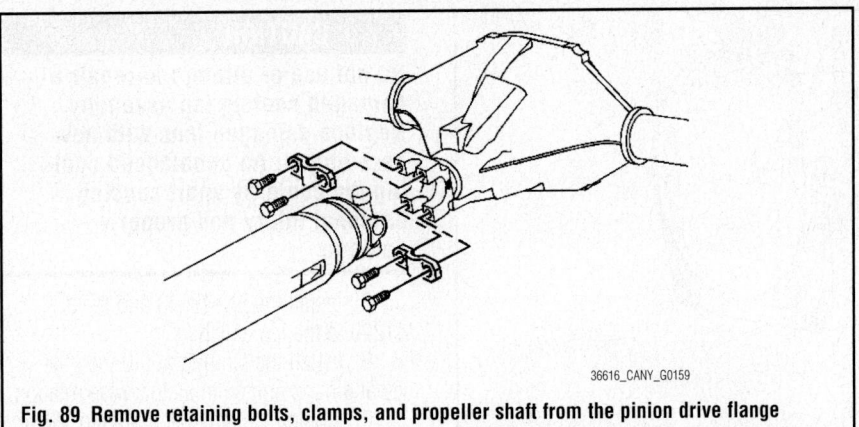

Fig. 89 Remove retaining bolts, clamps, and propeller shaft from the pinion drive flange

To install:

10. Remove the tape or rubber band from the U-Joint.

11. Install the propeller shaft in the transmission/transfer case.

12. Align the propeller shaft with the reference marks on the pinion flange.

13. Install the clamps and retaining bolts and tighten the bolts to 15 ft. lbs. (20 Nm).

14. Lower the vehicle.

Two-Piece Propeller Shaft

See Figure 89.

1. Before servicing the vehicle, refer to the Precautions Section.

✸✸ WARNING

When removing the propeller shaft, do not attempt to remove the shaft by pounding on the yoke ears or using a tool between the yoke and the universal joint. If the propeller shaft is removed by using such means, the injection joints may fracture and lead to premature failure of the joint.

2. Place transmission in neutral.

3. Release the park brake, if applied.

4. Raise and support the vehicle.

➡ **The following service procedure will ensure the proper alignment of all U-Joint to the transmission, center bearing support and the rear drive axle pinion flange.**

5. Rotate the propeller shafts so that all the external clips are aligned.

6. Mark the rear propeller shaft to the pinion drive flange, center bearing support, and transmission.

7. Remove the clamps and retaining bolts for the rear propeller shaft at the pinion drive flange and the center bearing.

8. Using tape or a rubber band, wrap the rear U-Joint bearing caps to ensure that they not separate from the U-Joint.

9. Remove the rear propeller shaft from the center bearing.

10. Remove the mounting bolts from the center bearing.

11. Remove the center bearing from the crossmember.

12. Remove the propeller shaft from the transmission.

To install:

13. Align the reference marks on the propeller shaft to the transmission.

14. Install the propeller shaft in the transmission.

15. Install the center bearing to the crossmember.

16. Install the center bearing mounting bolts and tighten to 59 ft. lbs. (80 Nm).

17. Rotate the propeller shaft so that the alignment marks and the pinion yoke are in alignment.

18. Remove the tape and or rubber band.

19. Position the U-Joint in the pinion yoke.

20. Install the clamps and retaining bolts and tighten the bolts to 22 ft. lbs. (30 Nm).

21. Double check the alignment marks to ensure that they are aligned properly

22. Lower the vehicle.

ENGINE COOLING

ENGINE COOLANT FAN SHROUD

REMOVAL & INSTALLATION

2.9L & 3.7L Engines

See Figure 90.

1. Before servicing the vehicle, refer to the Precautions Section.

2. Remove the radiator hose-outlet.

3. Release the differential vent hose retainer.

4. Release the A/C suction hose retainer.

5. Release the A/C discharge hose retainer.

6. Rotate the slip ring counterclockwise from under the fan shroud.

7. Remove the fan shroud (3).

To install:

8. Install the fan shroud to the vehicle.

9. Rotate the slip ring to the original position.

10. Install the differential vent hose retainer.

11. Install the A/C suction hose retainer.

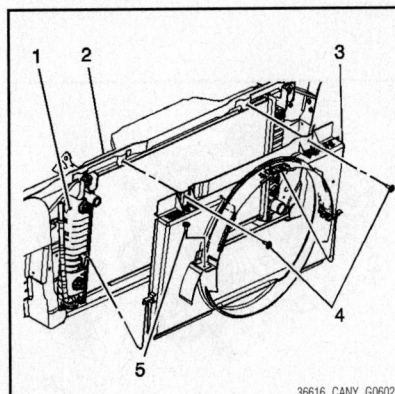

Fig. 90 Engine coolant fan shroud—2.9L and 3.7L engines

12. Install the A/C discharge hose retainer.

13. Install the radiator hose-outlet.

5.3L Engines

See Figure 91.

1. Before servicing the vehicle, refer to the Precautions Section.

2. Drain the cooling system. Refer to Engine Coolant Draining and Filling.

3. Remove the air cleaner assembly.

4. Unclip the lower section of the shroud assembly from the upper shroud for removal.

5. Remove the radiator inlet hose.

6. Remove the radiator outlet hose retainers.

7. Remove the A/C line retainers and reposition.

8. Remove the fan shroud.

To install:

9. Installation is the reverse of removal.

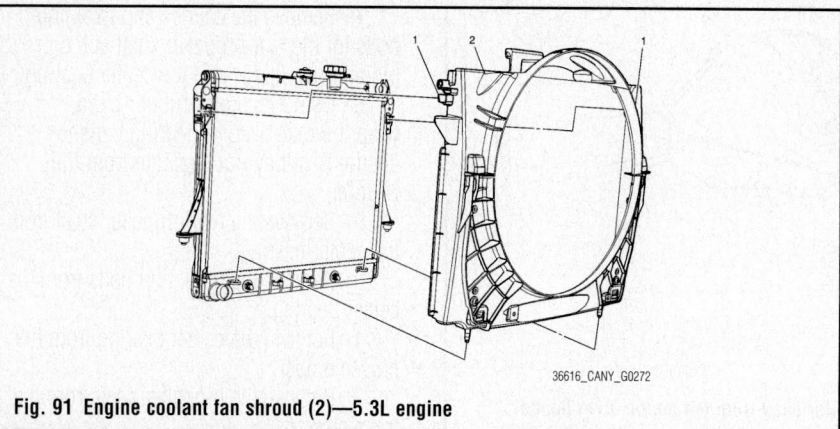

Fig. 91 Engine coolant fan shroud (2)—5.3L engine

ENGINE FAN

REMOVAL & INSTALLATION

2.9L & 3.7L Engines

See Figure 92.

1. Before servicing the vehicle, refer to the Precautions Section.
2. Remove the fan shroud. Refer to Engine Coolant Fan Shroud Removal & Installation.
3. Install the J 46406 and the J 41240-5A to the fan clutch.
4. Remove the fan hub nut in a counterclockwise rotation.

To install:

> ✳✳ **CAUTION**
>
> Do not use or attempt to repair a damaged cooling fan assembly. Replace damaged fans with new assemblies. An unbalanced cooling fan could fly apart causing personal injury and property damage.

5. Install the J 46406 and the J 41240-5A to the fan clutch.
6. Install the fan hub nut to the pulley and hand tighten in a clockwise rotation.

Tighten the fan clutch nut clockwise to 41 ft. lbs. (56 Nm).

7. Install the fan shroud.

5.3L Engines

See Figure 93.

1. Before servicing the vehicle, refer to the Precautions Section.
2. Remove the air cleaner outlet duct.
3. Remove the fan shroud. Refer to Engine Coolant Fan Shroud Removal & Installation.
4. Using J 41240 and EN-48543, loosen the fan clutch.
5. Remove the fan hub nut in a counterclockwise rotation (viewing fan from front of vehicle).

➡**If additional clearance is needed between tools substitute** 10/32 **thread ½ inch set screws on EN-48543 for the socket head cap screws as supplied use thread lock if needed.**

6. Remove the cooling fan (1) from the fan clutch.

To install:
7. Install the cooling fan to the fan clutch.

> ✳✳ **CAUTION**
>
> Do not use or attempt to repair a damaged cooling fan assembly. Replace damaged fans with new assemblies. An unbalanced cooling fan could fly apart causing personal injury and property damage.

8. Install the EN-48543 and the J 41240 to the fan clutch.
9. Install the fan hub nut to the pulley and hand tighten in a clockwise rotation.
10. Tighten the fan clutch nut clockwise to 41 ft. lbs. (56 Nm).
11. Install the fan shroud.
12. Install the air cleaner outlet duct.

RADIATOR

REMOVAL & INSTALLATION

See Figures 94 and 95.

1. Before servicing the vehicle, refer to the Precautions Section.

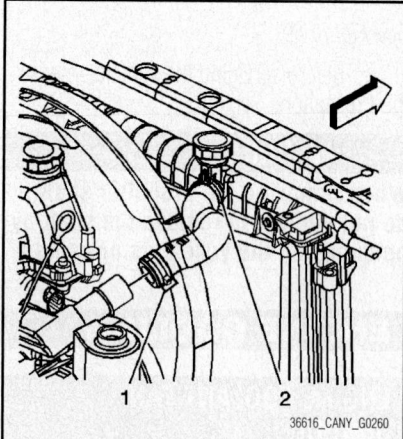

Fig. 94 Reposition the radiator outlet hose clamp (2) and remove the outlet radiator hose (1)

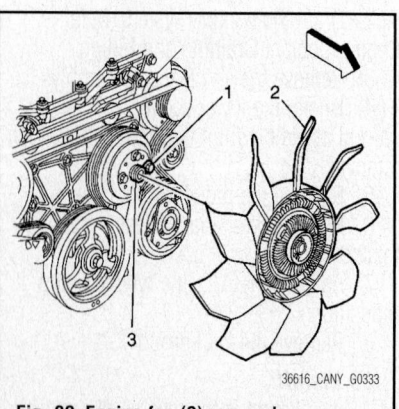

Fig. 92 Engine fan (2) removal

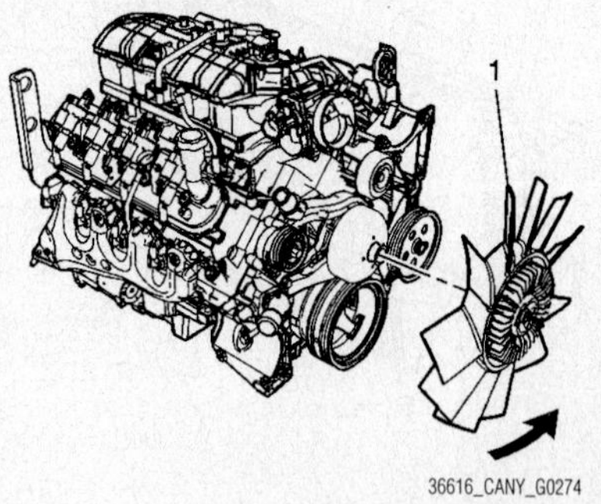

Fig. 93 Engine fan (1) removal

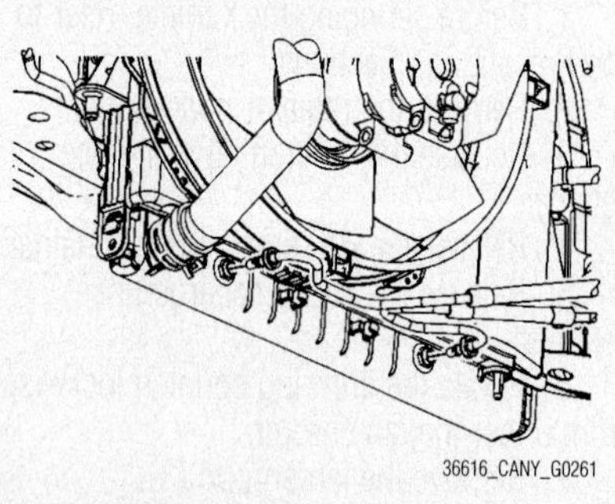

Fig. 95 Remove the transmission cooler lines from the radiator

2. Remove the fan shroud.

3. Raise the vehicle.

4. Using J 38185 reposition the radiator outlet hose clamp (2) from the radiator.

5. Remove the outlet radiator hose (1) from the radiator.

6. Remove the transmission cooler lines from the radiator. Refer to Transmission Fluid Cooler Hose/Pipe Quick-Connect Fitting Disconnection & Connection.

7. Lower the vehicle.

8. Remove the radiator vent inlet hose from the radiator.

9. Remove the radiator mounting bracket bolt.

10. Remove the radiator mount.

11. Remove the grill.

12. Remove the condenser mounting bolts.

13. Separate the condenser from the radiator.

14. Remove the radiator.

To install:

15. Install the radiator.

16. Install the condenser to the radiator.

17. Install the bolts retaining the condenser to the radiator and tighten to 21 ft. lbs. (28 Nm).

18. Install the grill.

19. Install the radiator mount bracket.

20. Install the radiator mounting bracket bolt and tighten to 21 ft. lbs. (28 Nm).

21. Raise the vehicle.

22. Install the radiator outlet hose to the radiator.

23. Using J 38185 reposition the radiator outlet hose clamp to the radiator.

24. Connect the transmission cooler lines to the radiator.

25. Lower the vehicle.

26. Install the radiator vent inlet hose to the radiator.

27. Install the fan shroud.

THERMOSTAT

REMOVAL & INSTALLATION

2.9L & 3.7L Engines

See Figures 96 and 97.

1. Before servicing the vehicle, refer to the Precautions Section.

2. Drain the cooling system. Refer to Engine Coolant Draining and Filling.

3. Raise and support the vehicle only high enough to access the thermostat housing (4) through the wheelhouse.

4. Remove the left wheelhouse liner.

5. Position the J 38185 to the clamp (3) in order to remove the radiator inlet hose (2) from the thermostat housing (4).

6. Remove the thermostat housing bolts.

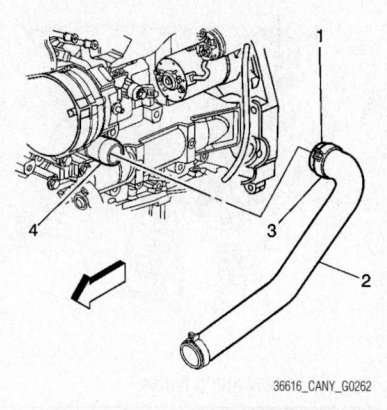

Fig. 96 Position the J 38185 to the clamp (3) in order to remove the radiator inlet hose (2) from the thermostat housing (4)

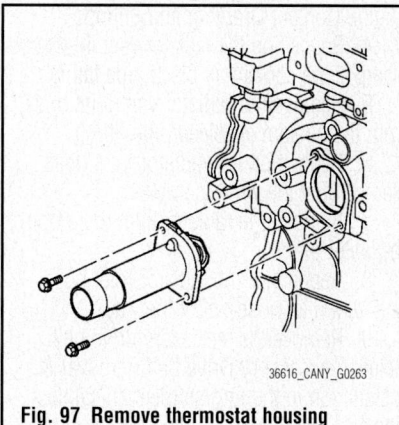

Fig. 97 Remove thermostat housing

7. Remove the thermostat housing from the engine block.

8. Clean and inspect the thermostat housing.

9. Clean and inspect the sealing surface of the engine block.

To install:

10. Position the thermostat housing to the engine block.

11. Install the thermostat housing bolts and tighten to 89 inch lbs. (10 Nm).

12. Position the J 38185 to the clamp in order to connect the radiator inlet hose to the thermostat housing.

13. Install the left wheelhouse liner.

14. Lower the vehicle.

15. Fill the cooling system.

16. Inspect all sealing surfaces for leaks after starting the engine.

5.3L Engine

See Figure 98.

1. Before servicing the vehicle, refer to the Precautions Section.

2. Remove the thermostat housing, as follows:

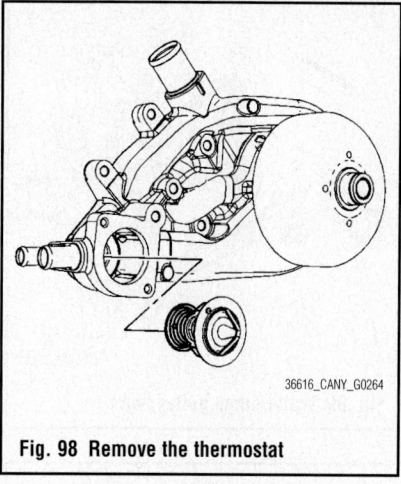

Fig. 98 Remove the thermostat

a. Drain the cooling system. Refer to Engine Coolant Draining and Filling.

b. Remove the air cleaner.

c. Reposition the radiator outlet hose clamp at the water pump inlet.

d. Remove the radiator outlet hose from the water pump inlet.

e. Remove the water pump inlet bolts.

f. Remove the water pump inlet from the water pump.

g. Remove and discard the water pump inlet seal.

3. Remove the thermostat.

To install:

4. Install the thermostat.

5. Install the thermostat housing, as follows:

a. Position the water pump inlet to the water pump.

b. Install the water pump inlet bolts and tighten to 11 ft. lbs. (15 Nm).

c. Install the radiator outlet hose to the water pump inlet.

d. Position the radiator outlet hose clamp at the water pump inlet.

e. Install the air cleaner.

f. Fill the cooling system.

WATER PUMP

REMOVAL & INSTALLATION

2.9L & 3.7L Engines

See Figures 99 and 100.

1. Before servicing the vehicle, refer to the Precautions Section.

2. Drain the cooling system. Refer to Engine Coolant Draining and Filling.

3. Remove the fan. Refer to Engine Fan Removal & Installation.

4. Remove the drive belt. Refer to Accessory Drive Belt Removal & Installation in the Engine Mechanical section.

5. Using the J 46406, secure the water

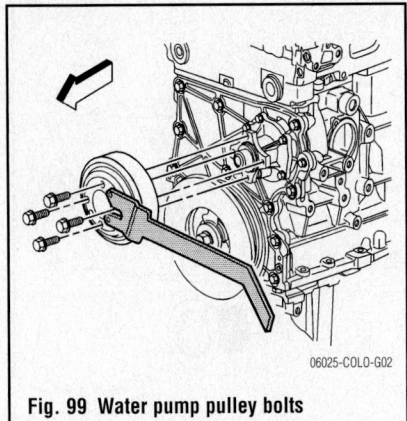

Fig. 99 Water pump pulley bolts

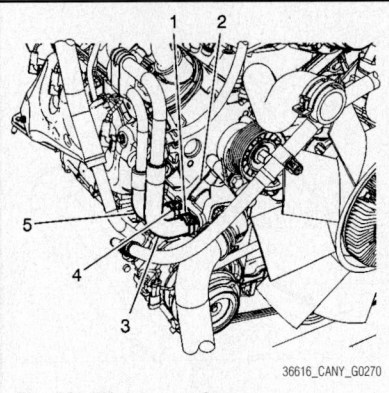

Fig. 101 Water pump hoses

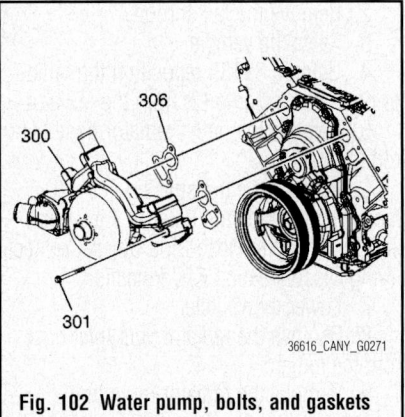

Fig. 102 Water pump, bolts, and gaskets

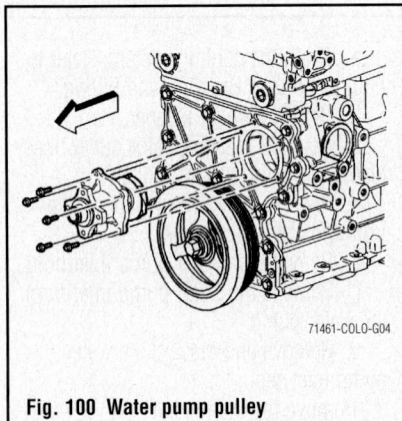

Fig. 100 Water pump pulley

pump pulley and remove the water pump pulley bolts.

6. Remove the J 46406.
7. Remove the water pump pulley.
8. Remove the water pump bolts.
9. Remove the water pump.
10. Discard the gasket.

To install:

11. Install a new water pump gasket.
12. Position the water pump to the engine.
13. Install the water pump bolts and tighten to 89 inch lbs. (10 Nm).
14. Install the water pump pulley.
15. Install the water pump pulley bolts.
16. Using the J 46406 , secure the water pump pulley while tightening the water pump pulley bolts. Tighten the bolts to 18 ft. lbs. (25 Nm).
17. Remove the J 41240.
18. Install the drive belt.
19. Install the fan.
20. Fill the cooling system with the specified coolant and concentration.
21. Inspect for leaks.

5.3L Engine

See Figures 101 and 102.

1. Before servicing the vehicle, refer to the Precautions Section.

2. Remove the air cleaner outlet duct. Refer to Air Cleaner Assembly Removal & Installation in the Engine Mechanical section.
3. Drain the cooling system. Refer to Engine Coolant Draining and Filling.
4. Reposition the radiator vent inlet hose clamp at the coolant air bleed pipe fitting.
5. Remove the radiator vent inlet hose from the coolant air bleed pipe fitting.
6. Reposition the radiator inlet hose clamp (3) at the water pump.
7. Remove the radiator inlet hose from the water pump.
8. Reposition the radiator inlet hose and vent inlet hose out of the way.
9. Remove the accessory drive belt. Refer to Accessory Drive Belt Removal & Installation in the Engine Mechanical section.
10. Reposition the radiator outlet hose clamp at the water pump.
11. Remove the radiator outlet hose from the water pump.
12. Reposition the outlet hose out of the way.
13. Reposition the radiator surge tank outlet hose clamp (1) at the water pump (2).
14. Remove the radiator surge tank outlet hose (3) from the water pump.
15. Reposition the outlet hose out of the way.
16. Reposition the heater inlet hose clamp (4) at the water pump.
17. Remove the heater inlet hose (5) from the water pump.
18. Reposition the inlet hose out of the way.
19. Remove the water pump bolts (301).
20. Remove the water pump (300) and gaskets (309). Discard the gaskets.

To install:

❊❊ WARNING

DO NOT use cooling system seal tabs, or similar compounds, unless otherwise instructed. The use of

cooling system seal tabs, or similar compounds, may restrict coolant flow through the passages of the cooling system or the engine components. Restricted coolant flow may cause engine overheating and/or damage to the cooling system or the engine components/assembly.

➡All gaskets surfaces are to be free of oil or other foreign material during assembly.

21. Position the water pump and NEW gaskets to the engine block.
22. Install the water pump bolts:
   a. Tighten the bolts a first pass to 11 ft. lbs. (15 Nm).
   b. Tighten the bolts a final pass to 22 ft. lbs. (30 Nm).
23. Position and install the heater inlet hose to the water pump.
24. Position the heater inlet hose clamp at the water pump.
25. Position and install the radiator surge tank outlet hose to the water pump.
26. Position the radiator surge tank outlet hose clamp at the water pump.
27. Position and install the radiator outlet hose to the water pump.
28. Position the radiator outlet hose clamp at the water pump.
29. Install the accessory drive belt.
30. Position the radiator inlet hose and vent inlet hose to the correct position.
31. Install the radiator inlet hose to the water pump.
32. Position the radiator inlet hose clamp at the water pump.
33. Install the radiator vent inlet hose to the coolant air bleed pipe fitting.
34. Position the radiator vent inlet hose clamp at the coolant air bleed pipe fitting.
35. Fill the cooling system.
36. Install the air cleaner outlet duct.

ENGINE ELECTRICAL

CHARGING SYSTEM

ALTERNATOR

REMOVAL & INSTALLATION

2.9L & 3.7L Engines

See Figures 103 through 106.

1. Before servicing the vehicle, refer to the Precautions Section.
2. Disconnect the battery negative cable.
3. Remove the drive belt.
4. Raise and support the vehicle only high enough to access the A/C compressor through the wheelhouse.
5. Remove the left front wheel.
6. Remove the left wheelhouse liner.
7. Disengage the A/C compressor electrical connector from the bracket.

➡**Evacuation of the A/C refrigerant will not be necessary.**

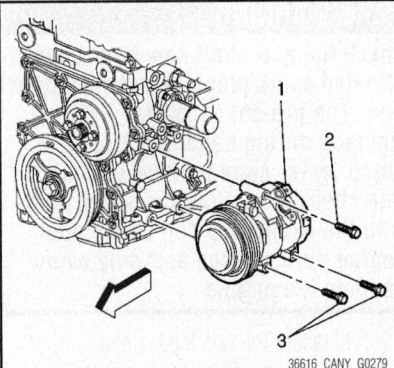

Fig. 103 Remove the A/C compressor mounting bolts (2, 3) ONLY. The upper mounting bolt (2) will remain with the A/C compressor (1)

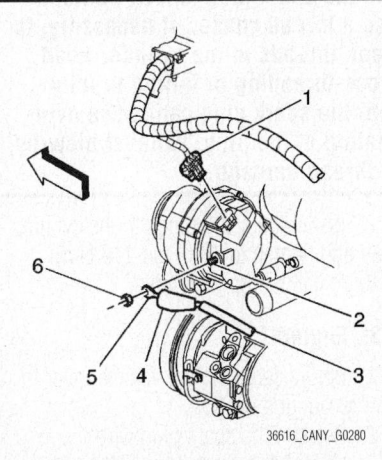

Fig. 104 Alternator removal—2.9L and 3.7L engines

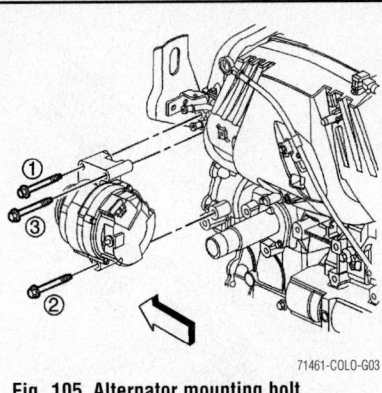

Fig. 105 Alternator mounting bolt tightening sequence—2.9L and 3.7L engines

8. Remove the A/C compressor mounting bolts (2, 3) ONLY. The upper mounting bolt (2) will remain with the A/C compressor (1).
9. Lower the vehicle.
10. Reposition the protective boot (4) from the alternator output BAT terminal (2) for access.
11. Remove the alternator output BAT terminal nut (6) and disconnect the alternator lead (5) from the alternator.
12. Disconnect the wiring harness connector (1) from the alternator.
13. Remove the 3 alternator mounting bolts.
14. Remove the engine lift bracket, in order to gain clearance to remove the alternator.
15. Position the A/C compressor forward, in order to gain clearance to remove the alternator.
16. Remove the alternator from the engine.

To install:

17. Position the alternator to the engine.
18. Install the engine lift bracket.
19. Install the alternator mounting bolts and tighten in sequence to 37 ft. lbs. (50 Nm).
20. Connect the alternator lead to the alternator and install the alternator output BAT terminal nut.
21. Tighten the nut to 15 ft. lbs. (20 Nm).
22. Press the protective boot on to the alternator output BAT terminal.
23. Connect the wiring harness connector to the alternator.
24. Raise and support the vehicle only high enough to access the A/C compressor through the wheelhouse. Position the A/C compressor to the engine.
25. Install the A/C compressor mounting bolts and tighten to 37 ft. lbs. (50 Nm).
26. Attach the A/C compressor electrical connector to the bracket.

27. Install the left wheelhouse liner.
28. Install the left front wheel.
29. Lower the vehicle.
30. Install the drive belt.
31. Connect the battery negative cable.

5.3L Engine

See Figure 106.

1. Before servicing the vehicle, refer to the Precautions Section.
2. Disconnect the negative battery cable.
3. Remove the intake manifold cover.
4. Remove the accessory drive belt.
5. Disconnect the engine wiring harness electrical connector (1) from the alternator.
6. Reposition the engine wiring harness/positive battery cable boot (5).
7. Remove the engine wiring harness/positive battery cable nut from the alternator.
8. Remove the engine wiring harness/positive battery cable (2) from the alternator.
9. Remove the alternator bolts.
10. Remove the alternator.

To install:

11. Install the alternator.
12. Install the alternator bolts and tighten the bolts to 37 ft. lbs. (50 Nm).
13. Install the engine wiring harness/positive battery cable to the alternator.
14. Install the engine wiring harness/positive battery cable nut to the alternator. Tighten the nut to 80 inch lbs. (9 Nm).
15. Position the engine wiring harness/positive battery cable boot.
16. Connect the engine wiring harness electrical connector to the alternator.
17. Install the accessory drive belt.
18. Install the intake manifold cover.
19. Connect the negative battery cable.

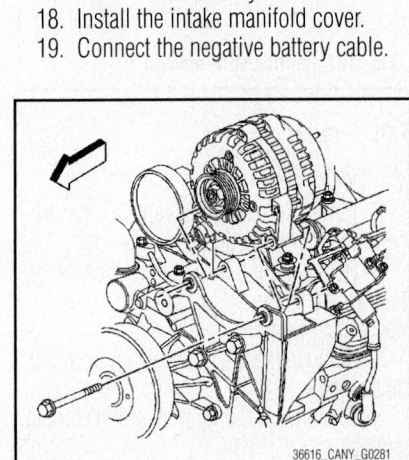

Fig. 106 Alternator removal—5.3L engine

ENGINE ELECTRICAL

IGNITION SYSTEM

IGNITION COIL

REMOVAL & INSTALLATION

2.9L & 3.7L Engines

See Figure 107.

1. Before servicing the vehicle, refer to the Precautions Section.
2. Remove the air cleaner resonator and outlet duct. Refer to Air Cleaner Assembly Removal & Installation in the Engine Mechanical section.
3. Disconnect the engine wiring harness electrical connectors from the ignition coils.
4. Remove the ignition coil bolts.
5. Remove the ignition coils from the camshaft cover.

To install:

6. Install the ignition coils to the camshaft cover.
7. Install the ignition coil bolts and tighten to 89 inch lbs. (10 Nm).
8. Connect the engine wiring harness electrical connectors to the ignition coils.
9. Install the air cleaner resonator and outlet duct.

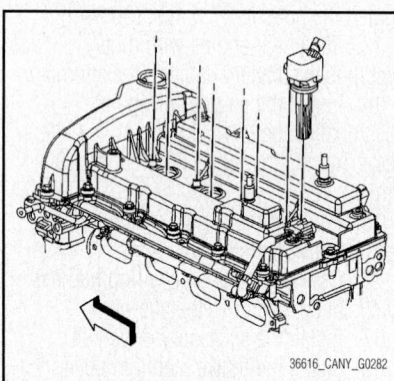

Fig. 107 Ignition coil removal

5.3L Engine

See Figure 108.

1. Before servicing the vehicle, refer to the Precautions Section.
2. Remove the intake manifold cover. Refer to Intake Manifold in the Engine Mechanical section.
3. Remove the spark plug wire from the ignition coil.
4. Disconnect the ignition coil electrical connector.
5. Remove the ignition coil bolts.
6. Remove the ignition coil.

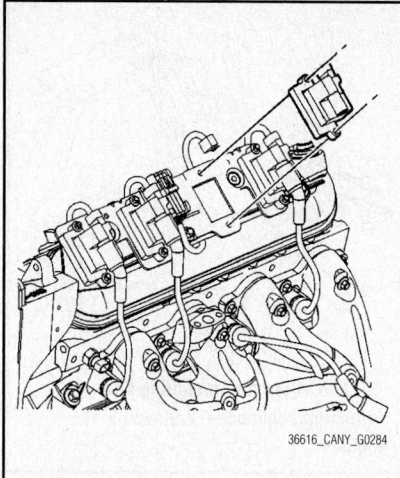

Fig. 108 Ignition coil removal

To install:

7. Install the ignition coil.
8. Install the ignition coil bolts. Tighten the bolts to 71 inch lbs. (8 Nm).
9. Connect the ignition coil electrical connector.
10. Connect the spark plug wire to the ignition coil.
11. Install the intake manifold cover.

SPARK PLUGS

REMOVAL & INSTALLATION

2.9L & 3.7L Engines

1. Before servicing the vehicle, refer to the Precautions Section.
2. Remove the ignition coils.

✴✴ CAUTION

Wear safety glasses when using compressed air, as flying dirt particles may cause eye injury.

✴✴ WARNING

Clean the spark plug recess area before removing the spark plug. Failure to do so could result in engine damage because of dirt or foreign material entering the cylinder head, or by the contamination of the cylinder head threads. The contaminated threads may prevent the proper seating of the new plug. Use a thread chaser to clean the threads of any contamination.

3. Clean the spark plug recesses with low pressure air.

✴✴ WARNING

Allow the engine to cool before removing the spark plugs. Attempting to remove the spark plugs from a hot engine may cause the plug threads to seize, causing damage to cylinder head threads.

4. Remove the spark plugs from the cylinder head.
5. Inspect the spark plugs.

To install:

✴✴ WARNING

Use only the spark plugs specified for use in the vehicle. Do not install spark plugs that are either hotter or colder than those specified for the vehicle. Installing spark plugs of another type can severely damage the engine.

✴✴ WARNING

Check the gap of all new and reconditioned spark plugs before installation. The pre-set gaps may have changed during handling. Use a round feeler gage to ensure an accurate check. Installing the spark plugs with the wrong gap can cause poor engine performance and may even damage the engine.

6. Measure the spark plug gap on the spark plugs to be installed. Compare the measurement to the gap specifications.

✴✴ WARNING

Be sure that the spark plug threads smoothly into the cylinder head and the spark plug is fully seated. Use a thread chaser, if necessary, to clean threads in the cylinder head. Cross-threading or failing to fully seat the spark plug can cause overheating of the plug, exhaust blow-by, or thread damage.

7. Install the spark plugs to the cylinder head and tighten to 13 ft. lbs. (18 Nm).
8. Install the ignition coils.

5.3L Engine

1. Before servicing the vehicle, refer to the Precautions Section.
2. Remove the spark plug wire.
3. Loosen the spark plug 1–2 turns.
4. Brush or using compressed air, blow away any dirt from around the spark plug.

5. Remove the spark plug. If removing more than one plug, place each plug in a tray marked with the corresponding cylinder number.

To install:

6. Correctly position the spark plug washer.

7. Inspect the spark plug gap. Adjust the gap as needed.

8. Hand start the spark plug in the corresponding cylinder.

9. Tighten the spark plug to 15 ft. lbs. (20 Nm).

10. Install the spark plug wire.

ENGINE MECHANICAL   STARTING SYSTEM

STARTER

REMOVAL & INSTALLATION

2.9L & 3.7L Engines

See Figures 109 and 110.

1. Before servicing the vehicle, refer to the Precautions Section.

2. Disconnect the negative battery cable.

3. Remove the intake manifold. Refer to Intake Manifold Removal & Installation in the Engine Mechanical section.

4. Remove the starter solenoid S terminal nut (3) and disconnect the lead (4) from the starter.

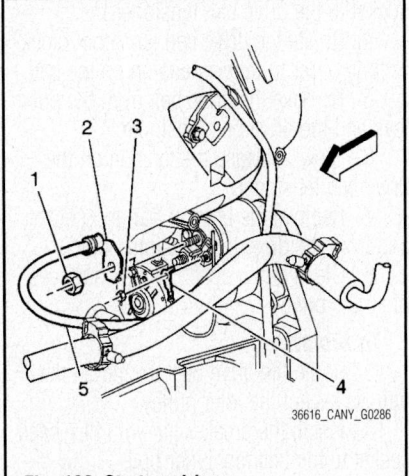

Fig. 109 Starter wiring

5. Remove the starter terminal nut (1) and disconnect the battery positive cable (2) from the starter.

6. Remove the starter motor mounting nut (1) and bolt (4).

7. Remove the starter motor (3) from the engine.

To install:

8. Position the starter motor over the stud.

9. Install the starter motor mounting nut and bolt and tighten to 37 ft. lbs. (50 Nm).

10. Connect the battery positive cable to the starter and install the starter terminal nut. Tighten the nut to 80 inch lbs. (9 Nm).

11. Connect the lead to the starter solenoid and install the starter solenoid S terminal nut. Tighten the nut to 31 inch lbs. (3.5 Nm).

12. Install the intake manifold.

13. Connect the negative battery cable.

5.3L Engine

See Figures 111 through 114.

1. Before servicing the vehicle, refer to the Precautions Section.

2. Disconnect the negative battery cable.

3. Remove the right front tire.

4. Remove the engine wiring harness/positive battery cable terminal nut (4) and cable terminal (5) from the starter.

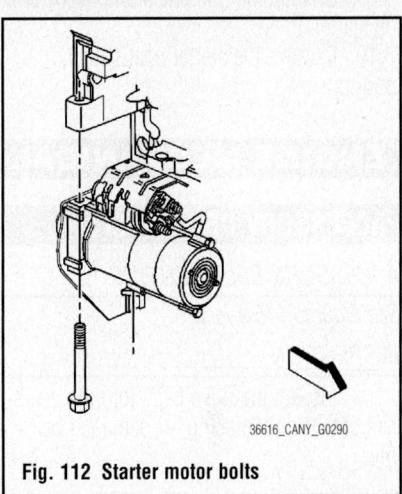

Fig. 112 Starter motor bolts

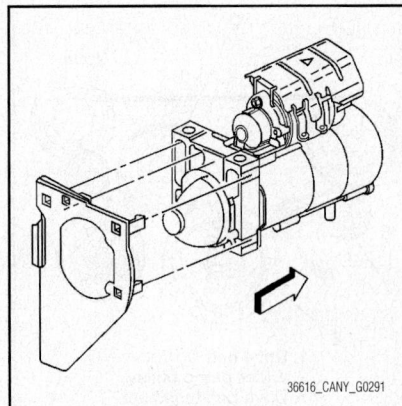

Fig. 113 Unsnap the transmission cover from the starter

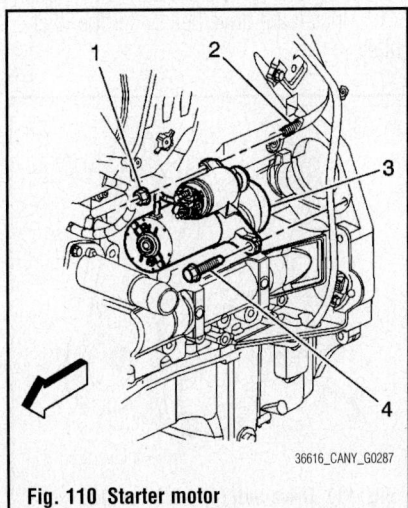

Fig. 110 Starter motor

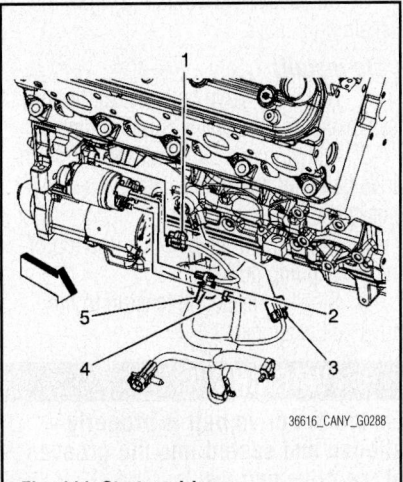

Fig. 111 Starter wiring

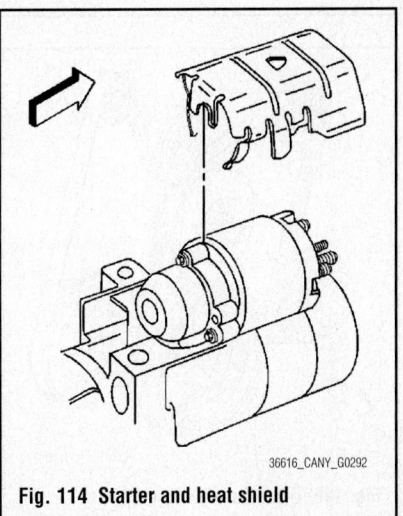

Fig. 114 Starter and heat shield

5. Disconnect the engine wiring harness electrical connector (2) from the starter motor.

6. Remove the front propeller shaft. Refer to Propeller Shaft Removal & Installation in the Drive Train section.

7. Remove the transmission cover bolt.

8. Remove the starter motor bolts.

9. Unsnap the transmission cover from the starter.

10. Remove the starter heat shield, if required.

11. Remove the starter.

To install:

12. Install the starter heat shield, if required.

13. Install the transmission cover to the starter.

14. Position the starter and install the starter motor bolts. Tighten the bolts to 37 ft. lbs. (50 Nm).

15. Install the transmission cover bolt and tighten to 106 inch lbs. (12 Nm).

16. Connect the engine wiring harness electrical connector to the starter motor.

17. Install the engine wiring harness/positive battery cable terminal to the starter and install the nut. Tighten the nut to 80 inch lbs. (9 Nm).

18. Install the front propeller shaft.

19. Install the right front tire.

20. Lower the vehicle.

21. Connect the negative battery cable.

ENGINE MECHANICAL

ACCESSORY DRIVE BELTS

ACCESSORY BELT ROUTING

See Figures 115 and 116.

INSPECTION

1. Inspect the drive belts for cuts, tears, sections of ribs missing, or damaged belt plies.

2. Inspection of the accessory drive pulleys should include inspecting for bends, dents or other damage that may prevent the drive belt from seating correctly in the pulley grooves or on the smooth surface of a pulley when the back side of the drive belts are used to drive the pulley.

ADJUSTMENT

No adjustment is necessary, as the belt tensioner applies constant pressure to keep the belt adjusted.

REMOVAL & INSTALLATION

2.9L & 3.7L Engines

See Figure 115.

1. Before servicing the vehicle, refer to the Precautions Section.

2. Install a ⅜ inch breaker bar into the drive belt tensioner (7) and rotate the tensioner (7) clockwise, enough to relieve the tension on the drive belt (1).

3. Slide the drive belt (1) from the water pump pulley (2).

4. Allow the drive belt tensioner (7) to return to the relaxed position.

5. Remove the drive belt (1) from the remaining pulleys.

To install:

6. Route the drive belt over all the pulleys, excluding the water pump pulley.

7. Install the ⅜ inch breaker bar on the drive belt tensioner and rotate the tensioner clockwise.

8. Route the drive belt over the top of the water pump pulley.

9. Slowly release the tension to the drive belt tensioner.

❄❄ WARNING

Ensure the drive belt is properly aligned and seated into the grooves of the drive pulleys.

10. Inspect for proper installation of the drive belt on the pulleys.

5.3L Engine

See Figure 117.

1. Before servicing the vehicle, refer to the Precautions Section.

2. Remove the air cleaner outlet duct. Refer to Air Cleaner Removal & Installation.

3. Install a breaker bar with hex-head socket to the drive belt tensioner bolt.

4. Rotate the drive belt tensioner clockwise in order to relieve tension on the belt.

5. Remove the drive belt from the pulleys and the drive belt tensioner.

6. Slowly release the tension on the drive belt tensioner.

7. Remove the breaker bar and socket and from the drive belt tensioner bolt.

8. Clean and inspect the belt surfaces of all the pulleys.

To install:

9. Route the drive belt around all the pulleys except the idler pulley.

10. Install the breaker bar with hex-head socket to the belt tensioner bolt.

11. Rotate the belt tensioner clockwise in order to relieve the tension on the tensioner.

12. Install the drive belt under the idler pulley.

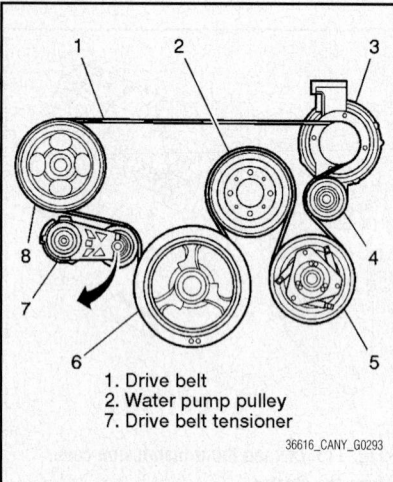

1. Drive belt
2. Water pump pulley
7. Drive belt tensioner

36616_CANY_G0293

Fig. 115 Drive belt—2.9L and 3.7L engines

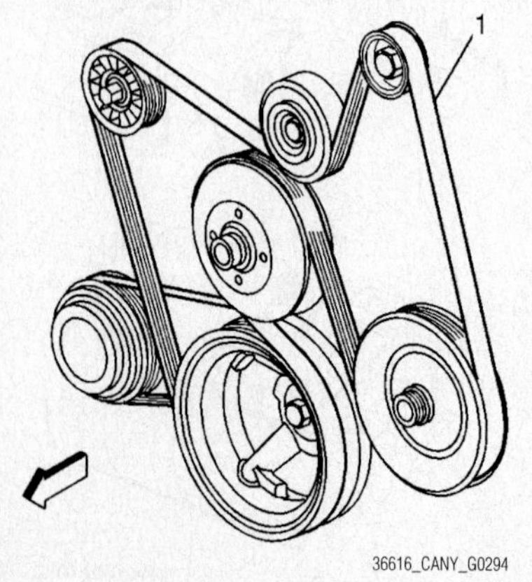

Fig. 116 Drive belt—5.3L engine

36616_CANY_G0294

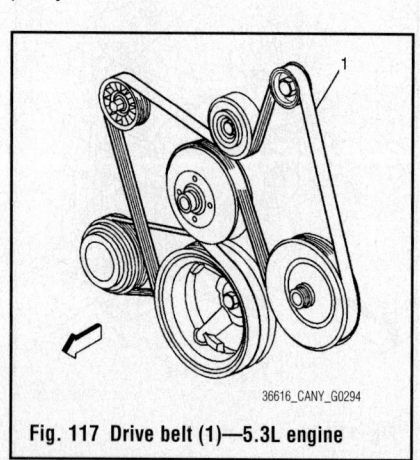

36616_CANY_G0294

Fig. 117 Drive belt (1)—5.3L engine

13. Slowly release the tension on the belt tensioner.

14. Remove the breaker bar and socket from the belt tensioner bolt.

15. Inspect the drive belt for proper installation and alignment.

16. Install the air cleaner outlet duct.

17. Start the vehicle and inspect the drive belt for proper operation.

BALANCE SHAFT

REMOVAL & INSTALLATION

See Figures 118 through 122.

1. Before servicing the vehicle, refer to the Precautions Section.

2. Remove the balance shaft drive chain, as follows:

  a. Remove the crankshaft rear oil seal housing. Refer to Rear Main Seal Removal & Installation.

➡**Important: Every 11 crankshaft rotations, 3 of the 5 dark links on the timing chain will line up with the timing marks.**

  b. Rotate the crankshaft until the correct timing chain and timing marks align:
  • The left hand balance shaft sprocket timing mark (1) is at the 12:00 position
  • The right hand balance shaft sprocket timing mark (2) is at the 2:30 position
  • The crankshaft sprocket timing mark (3) is at the 4:30 position
  • The 3 timing marks (1–3) on the sprockets line up with a dark link on the chain

  c. Remove the balance shaft chain tensioner bolts.

  d. Remove the balance shaft chain tensioner.

  e. Remove the balance shaft drive chain from the following:
  • The crankshaft sprocket
  • The left balance sprocket
  • The right balance sprocket

➡**Do not disassemble the balance shaft assembly. Remove and install the balance shaft as a complete assembly.**

➡**Rotate the balance shaft to check for free rotation. If the balance shaft does not turn free, inspect the balance shaft bearings and bearing surface for damage.**

3. Remove and discard the left balance shaft retaining bolt.

4. Remove the left balance shaft assembly.

5. Remove the right balance shaft assembly.

To install:

6. Lubricate the balance shaft bearing journals with clean engine oil.

7. Install the left balance shaft assembly with the counterweight down to prevent damage to the balance shaft bearings.

8. Install the right balance shaft assembly with the counterweight down to prevent damage to the balance shaft bearings.

9. Install a new balance shaft retaining bolt and tighten to 106 inch lbs. (12 Nm).

10. Install the balance shaft drive chain, as follows:

➡**Ensure the darkened links are facing outward.**

  a. Install the balance shaft drive chain to the following:
  • The left balance sprocket
  • The right balance sprocket
  • The crankshaft sprocket

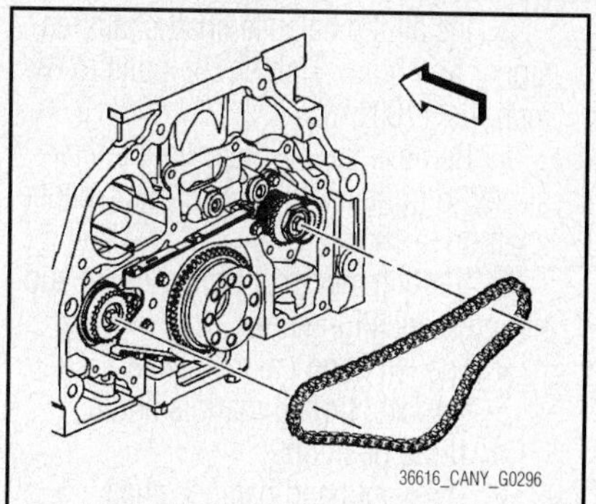

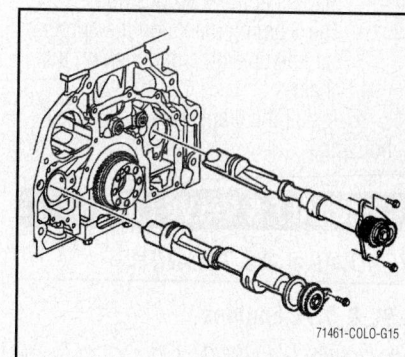

Fig. 120 Balance shaft drive chain—2.9L and 3.7L engines

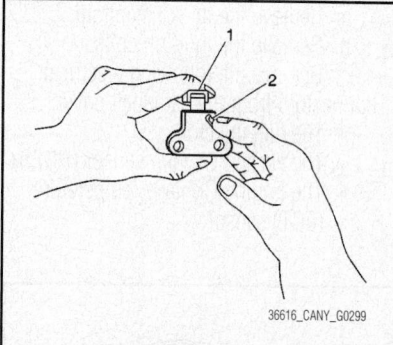

Fig. 121 Balance shaft—2.9L and 3.7L engines

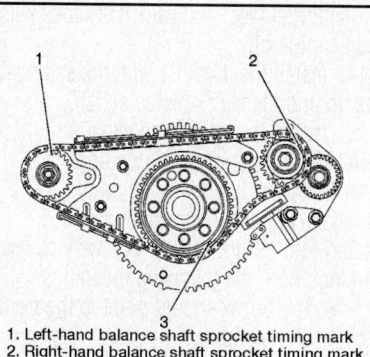

1. Left-hand balance shaft sprocket timing mark
2. Right-hand balance shaft sprocket timing mark
3. Crankshaft sprocket timing mark

36616_CANY_G0297

Fig. 118 Balance shaft timing chain and timing mark alignments—2.9L and 3.7L engines

36616_CANY_G0298

Fig. 119 Balance shaft timing chain tensioner—2.9L and 3.7L engines

Fig. 122 Collapse the balance shaft chain tensioner—2.9L and 3.7L engines

  b. Collapse the balance shaft chain tensioner using the following procedure:
  • Rotate the ratchet release lever clockwise and hold
  • Collapse the tensioner shoe and hold
  • Release the ratchet lever

  c. Slowly release the pressure on the shoe, until the ratchet lever moves to the first detent and a "click" is heard and felt.

  d. Insert a pin through the hole in the release lever in order to lock the tensioner shoe in the collapsed position.

➡**Important: Ensure the tensioner release lever is facing outward.**

e. Install the balance shaft chain tensioner and bolts. Tighten the bolts to 89 inch lbs. (10 Nm).

f. Remove the pin holding the tensioner to tighten any slack in the balance shaft drive chain.

g. Verify the correct timing chain and timing mark alignments:

- The left hand balance shaft sprocket timing mark is at the 12:00 position
- The right hand balance shaft sprocket timing mark is at the 2:30 position
- The crankshaft sprocket timing mark is at the 4:30 position
- The 3 timing marks on the sprockets line up with a dark link on the chain

h. Install the crankshaft rear oil seal housing.

CAMSHAFT & VALVE LIFTERS

REMOVAL & INSTALLATION

2.9L & 3.7L Engines

See Figures 123 through 128.

1. Before servicing the vehicle, refer to the Precautions Section.

2. Remove the camshaft cover, as follows:
   a. Remove the intake manifold.
   b. Remove the ignition coils.
   c. Remove the following electrical connectors from the camshaft cover:
   - The fuel injector
   - The Heated Oxygen sensor (HO2S)
   - The Engine Coolant Temperature (ECT) sensor

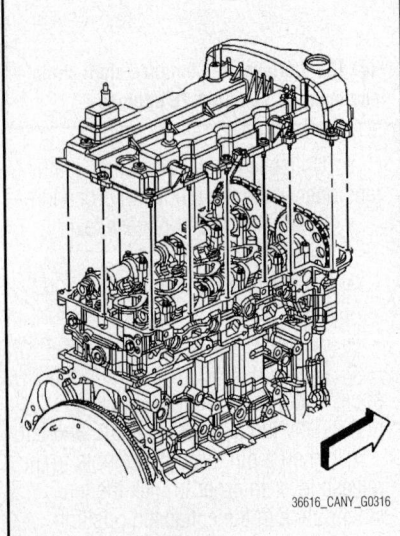

Fig. 123 Camshaft cover

d. Remove the camshaft cover ground wire bolt from the cover.

e. Remove the ground wire from cover.

f. Remove the camshaft cover bolts.

g. Remove the camshaft cover from the cylinder head.

h. Remove the seals from the camshaft cover.

i. Do not reuse the seals.

j. Clean and inspect the cylinder head sealing surface.

3. Remove the Camshaft Position (CMP) sensor. Refer to CMP Sensor Removal & Installation in Engine Performance & Emission Controls.

4. Rotate the crankshaft in the engine rotational direction clockwise, until the No. 1 piston is at top dead center (TDC) on the compression stroke.

✳✳ CAUTION

The camshaft holding tools must be installed on the camshafts to prevent camshaft rotation. When performing service to the valve train and/or timing components, valve spring pressure can cause the camshafts to

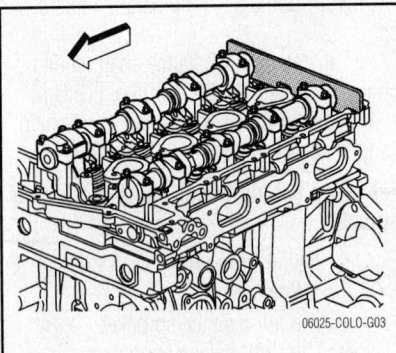

Fig. 124 Install the camshaft locking tool J-44221 to the rear of the camshafts.

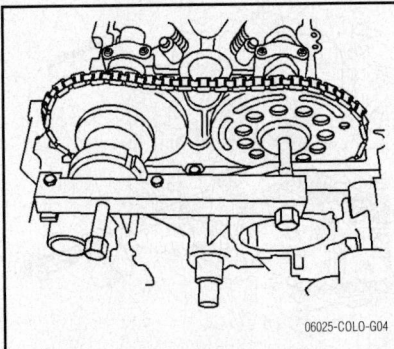

Fig. 125 Use Special Tool J-44222 camshaft sprocket holding tool to prevent the timing chain and sprockets from turning.

rotate unexpectedly and can cause personal injury.

5. Install the J 44221 to the rear of the camshafts.

6. Remove and discard the intake and the exhaust camshaft sprocket bolts.

✳✳ WARNING

In order to maintain timing chain tension, make sure the 2 bolts that hold J 44222 to the front of the cylinder head are completely tightened and the horizontal bolt into the exhaust camshaft phaser actuator sprocket is adjusted correctly before sliding the sprockets off the camshafts. Failure to do so may disturb the timing chain components.

7. Install the J 44222 onto the cylinder head and adjust the horizontal bolts into the camshaft sprockets in order to maintain chain tension and keep from disturbing the timing chain components.

8. Carefully slide the sprockets with the timing chain from the camshafts to the J 44222.

9. Alternately loosen the camshaft cap bolts a few turns at a time until all valve spring pressure has been released.

➡Place the camshaft caps in a rack to ensure the caps are installed in the same location from which they were removed.

10. Remove the camshaft caps.

11. Remove the J 44221 from the camshafts.

12. Remove the camshafts from the cylinder head.

To install:

13. Coat the camshaft journals, camshaft journal thrust face, and camshaft lobes with clean engine oil.

14. Install the J 44221 with the camshaft flats up and the No. 1 piston at TDC.

15. Install the intake and exhaust camshafts to their original positions.

16. Observe the markings on the camshaft caps. Each camshaft cap is marked in order to identify its location. The markings have the following meanings:

- The arrow should point to the front of the engine.
- The number indicates the position from the front of the engine.
- The "E" indicates the exhaust camshaft.
- The "I" indicates the intake camshaft.

17. Install the camshaft caps according to the identification marks.

18. Install the camshaft cap bolts. Tighten the bolts evenly in order to compress the valve springs before final torque. Tighten the bolts to 106 inch lbs. (12 Nm).

➡ **To aid in aligning the sprockets to the camshafts, use a 1 in. (25 mm) wrench on the hex of the camshafts to rotate.**

➡ **Ensure the alignment pins are properly engaged with the camshafts.**

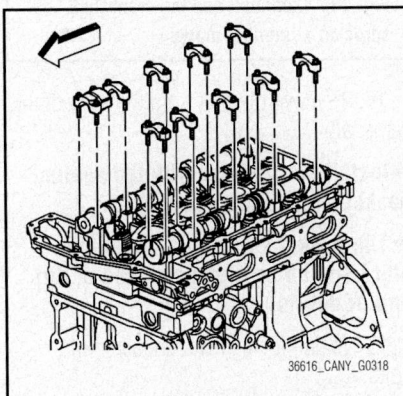

Fig. 126 Remove the camshaft caps

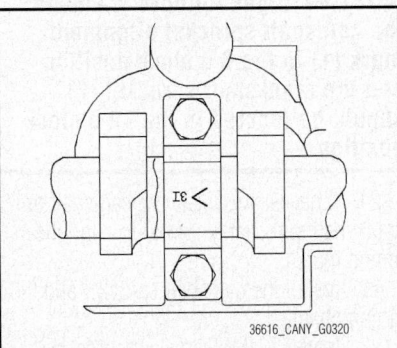

Fig. 127 Remove the camshaft

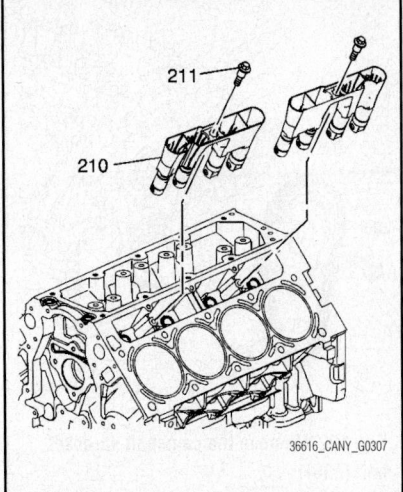

Fig. 128 Camshaft cap identification marks

19. Carefully slide the sprockets with the timing chain from the J 44222 to the camshafts.

20. Remove the J 44222 from the cylinder head.

21. Install the new intake camshaft sprocket bolt. Tighten the intake camshaft sprocket bolt to 15 ft. lbs. (20 Nm) plus an additional 100 degrees using the J 45059.

22. Install the new exhaust camshaft actuator bolt. Tighten the exhaust camshaft actuator bolt to 18 ft. lbs. (25 Nm) plus an additional 135 degrees using the J 45059.

23. Remove the J 44221 from the camshafts.

24. Install the CMP sensor.

25. Install the camshaft cover, as follows:

a. Install a NEW camshaft cover seal into the camshaft cover groove.

b. Install NEW ignition coil seals into the camshaft cover grooves.

c. Place the camshaft cover onto the cylinder head.

d. Install the camshaft cover bolts and tighten to 89 inch lbs. (10 Nm).

e. Position the ground wire to the camshaft cover. Ensure that the anti rotation tab is seated against the cover.

f. Install the camshaft cover ground wire bolt to the cover and tighten to 89 inch lbs. (10 Nm).

g. Install the following electrical connectors to the camshaft cover:

- The fuel injector
- The HO2S
- The ECT sensor

h. Install the ignition coils.

i. Install the intake manifold.

5.3L Engine

See Figures 129 through 136.

1. Before servicing the vehicle, refer to the Precautions Section.

2. Remove the condenser. Refer to Air Conditioning Condenser Removal & Installation.

3. Remove the engine front cover. Refer to Timing Chain Cover & Seal Removal & Installation.

4. Remove all of the valve lifters, as follows:

a. Remove the cylinder head and gasket. Refer to Cylinder Head Removal & Installation.

b. Remove the guide bolts (211).

c. Remove the guides (210) with lifters.

➡ **Note the installed position of the guides. The notched area of the guide is to align with the locating tab on the block.**

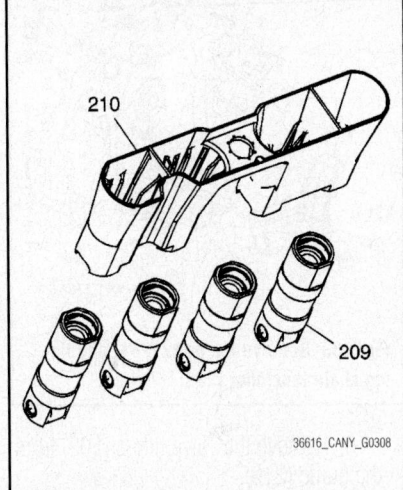

Fig. 129 Remove the guide bolts (211), and the guides (210) with lifters

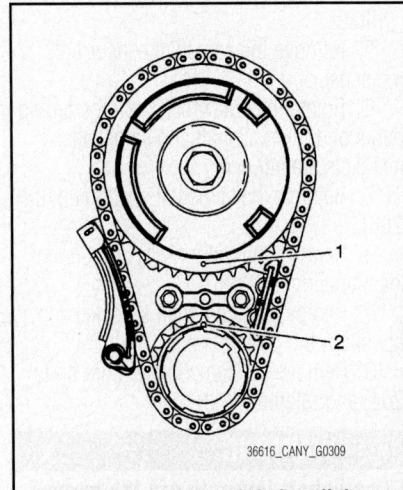

Fig. 130 Remove the valve lifters (209) from the guide (210)

Fig. 131 Rotate the crankshaft until the timing marks on the crankshaft and camshaft sprockets are aligned

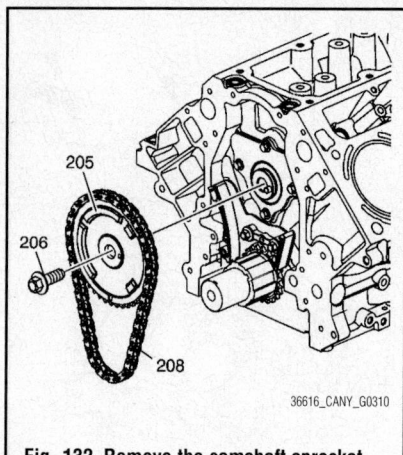

Fig. 132 Remove the camshaft sprocket bolt (206)

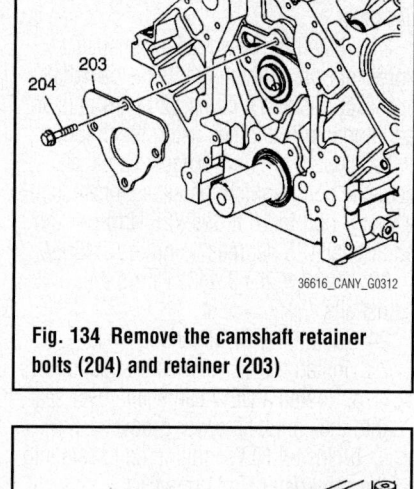

Fig. 134 Remove the camshaft retainer bolts (204) and retainer (203)

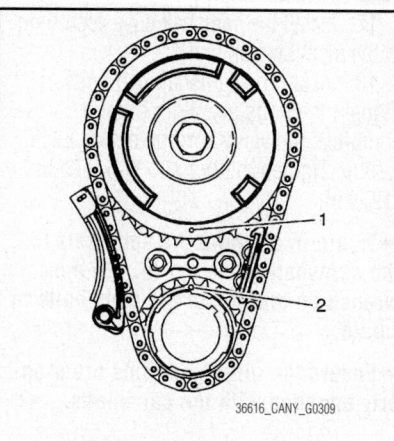

Fig. 136 Camshaft and the crankshaft sprocket alignment marks

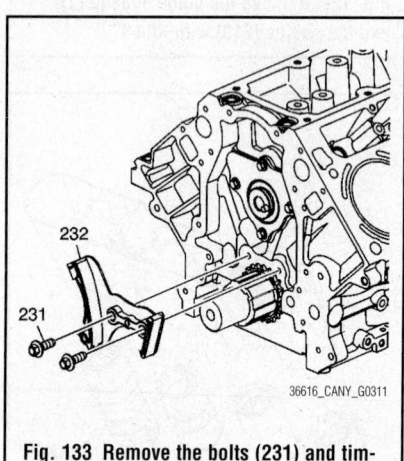

Fig. 133 Remove the bolts (231) and timing chain tensioner (232)

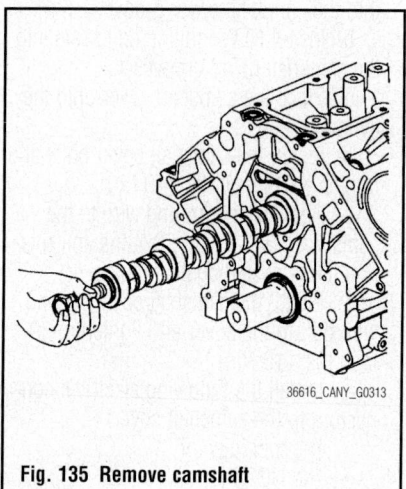

Fig. 135 Remove camshaft

d. Remove the valve lifters (209) from the guide (210).

e. Organize or mark the components so they can be installed in the same location from which they were removed.

f. Clean and inspect the valve lifters.

5. Remove the camshaft sensor bolt and sensor.

6. Rotate the crankshaft until the timing marks on the crankshaft and camshaft sprockets are aligned.

7. Remove the camshaft sprocket bolt (206).

8. Remove the bolts (231) and timing chain tensioner (232).

9. Remove the camshaft sprocket and reposition the timing chain.

10. Remove the camshaft retainer bolts (204) and retainer (203).

✳✳ WARNING

All camshaft journals are the same diameter, so care must be used in removing or installing the camshaft

to avoid damage to the camshaft bearings.

11. Install a bolt into the camshaft.

12. Using the bolt as a handle, carefully rotate and pull the camshaft out of the engine block.

13. Clean and inspect the camshaft and bearings.

To install:

➡ If camshaft replacement is required, the valve lifters must also be replaced.

14. Lubricate the camshaft journals and the bearings with clean engine oil.

✳✳ WARNING

All camshaft journals are the same diameter, so care must be used in removing or installing the camshaft to avoid damage to the camshaft bearings.

15. Using the bolt as a handle, carefully install the camshaft into the engine block.

16. Remove the bolt from the front of the camshaft.

➡ Install the retainer with the sealing gasket facing the engine block.

➡ The gasket surface on the engine block should be clean and free of dirt and/or debris.

17. Install the camshaft retainer and bolts.

18. Tighten the camshaft retainer bolts:
• Tighten the first design hex head bolts to 18 ft. lbs. (25 Nm).
• Tighten the second design TORX® head bolts to 11 ft. lbs. (15 Nm).

19. Compress the timing chain tensioner guide and install the EN 46330.

20. Install the timing chain tensioner and bolts. Tighten the timing chain tensioner bolts to 18 ft. lbs. (25 Nm).

✳✳ WARNING

Properly locate the camshaft sprocket locating pin with the camshaft sprocket alignment hole. The sprocket teeth and timing chain must mesh. The camshaft and the crankshaft sprocket alignment marks MUST be aligned properly. Locate the camshaft sprocket alignment mark (1) in the 6 o'clock position and the crankshaft sprocket (2) should be located in the 12 o'clock position.

21. If necessary, rotate the camshaft or crankshaft sprockets in order to align the timing marks.

22. Install the camshaft sprocket and the timing chain.

23. Install a NEW camshaft sprocket bolt.

24. Tighten the camshaft sprocket bolt:

- Tighten the camshaft sprocket bolt a first pass to 55 ft. lbs. (75 Nm).
- Tighten the camshaft sprocket bolt a final pass, an additional 50 degrees using the J 45059.

25. Remove the EN 46330.

26. Inspect the camshaft sensor O-ring seal. If the O-ring seal is not cut or damaged, it may be reused.

27. Lubricate the O-ring seal with clean engine oil.

28. Install the camshaft sensor and bolt. Tighten the bolt to 18 ft. lbs. (25 Nm).

29. Install the valve lifters, as follows:

➡ **When using the valve lifters again, install the lifters to their original locations.**

➡ **If camshaft replacement is required, the valve lifters must also be replaced.**

   a. Lubricate the valve lifters and engine block valve lifter bores with clean engine oil.

   b. Insert the valve lifters into the lifter guides. Align the flat area on the top of the lifter with the flat area in the lifter guide bore. Push the lifter completely into the guide bore.

   c. Install the valve lifters and guide assembly to the engine block.

   d. Install the valve lifter guide bolts and tighten to 106 inch lbs. (12 Nm).

30. Install the cylinder head and gasket.

31. Install the engine front cover.

32. Install the condenser.

CATALYTIC CONVERTER

REMOVAL & INSTALLATION

2.9L & 3.7L Engines

See Figure 137.

1. Before servicing the vehicle, refer to the Precautions Section.

> ✳✳ **CAUTION**
>
> **In order to avoid being burned, do not service the exhaust system while it is still hot. Service the system when it is cool.**

> ✳✳ **CAUTION**
>
> **Always wear protective goggles and gloves when removing exhaust parts as falling rust and sharp edges from worn exhaust components could result in serious personal injury.**

2. Raise and support the vehicle.

3. If equipped with 4WD, remove the right torsion bar. Refer to Torsion Bar Removal & Installation in the Suspension section.

4. Disconnect the Heated Oxygen Sensor (HO2S) at the sensor pigtail.

5. Remove the HO2S if replacement is necessary.

6. Remove the nuts securing the muffler to the catalytic converter.

7. Position the muffler rearward, enough to allow the studs located in the front to clear the catalytic converter pipe flange.

8. Remove the 3 nuts attaching the catalytic converter to the exhaust manifold.

9. Lower the catalytic converter from the vehicle.

10. Remove the exhaust manifold seal from the exhaust manifold flange. Discard the seal.

To install:

11. Install the NEW seal to the exhaust manifold flange.

> ✳✳ **WARNING**
>
> **When inspecting or replacing exhaust system components, make sure there is adequate clearance from all points on the underbody to prevent overheating of the floor pan and possible damage to the passenger compartment insulation and trim materials.**

12. Position the catalytic converter to the exhaust manifold.

13. Install the 3 nuts attaching the catalytic converter to the exhaust manifold. Do not tighten at this time.

14. Align the catalytic converter with the studs located in the front of the muffler.

15. Install the 2 nuts securing the muffler to the catalytic converter:

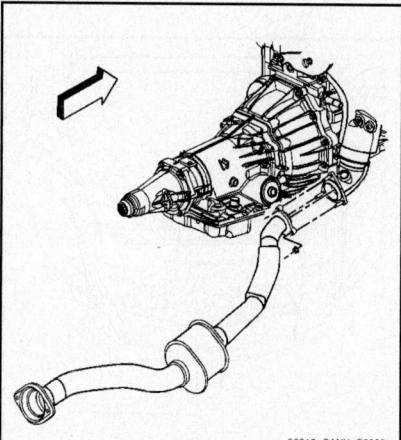

Fig. 137 Remove the 3 nuts attaching the catalytic converter to the exhaust manifold and lower the catalytic converter

36616_CANY_G0323

- Tighten the muffler nuts by hand until each contacts the metal flange.
- Tighten the muffler nuts to 33 ft. lbs. (45 Nm).
- Tighten the catalytic converter nuts previously installed in step 3 to 37 ft. lbs. (50 Nm).

16. Install the HO2S if previously removed.

17. Connect the HO2S at the sensor pigtail.

18. If equipped with 4WD, install the right torsion bar.

19. Lower the vehicle.

5.3L Engine

See Figures 138 and 139.

1. Before servicing the vehicle, refer to the Precautions Section.

> ✳✳ **CAUTION**
>
> **In order to avoid being burned, do not service the exhaust system while it is still hot. Service the system when it is cool.**

> ✳✳ **CAUTION**
>
> **Always wear protective goggles and gloves when removing exhaust parts as falling rust and sharp edges from worn exhaust components could result in serious personal injury.**

2. If equipped with 4WD, remove the right torsion bar. Refer to Torsion Bar Removal & Installation in the Suspension section.

3. Remove the Heated Oxygen Sensors (HO2S). Refer to HO2S Removal & Installation in the Engine Performance & Emission Controls section.

4. For the right side, remove the transmission support crossmember. Refer to Transmission Support Crossmember Removal & Installation in the Drive Train section.

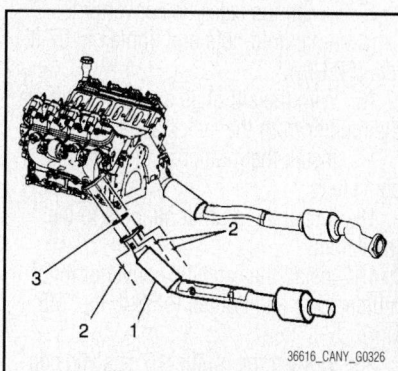

Fig. 138 Remove the catalytic converter (1) and seal (3)—5.3L engine, left side

36616_CANY_G0326

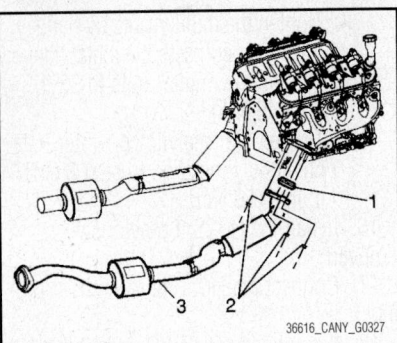

Fig. 139 Remove the catalytic converter (3) and seal (1)—5.3L engine, right side

5. Remove the catalytic converter to muffler nuts.

6. Loosen the muffler to catalytic converter clamp.

7. With the aid of an assistant, separate the muffler hangers from the insulators.

8. Separate the muffler from the catalytic converters.

9. Reposition the exhaust rearward as far as possible, and support using the rear axle and jack stands.

10. If equipped with 4WD, remove front propeller shaft. Refer to Front Propeller Shaft Removal & Installation in the Drive Train section.

11. Remove the catalytic converter to exhaust manifold nuts.

12. Remove the catalytic converter and seal.

To install:

13. Install the catalytic converter and seal.

14. If equipped with 4WD, install front propeller shaft.

➡**Ensure at least 7 mm of clearance between the bell housing and the catalytic converter. Use an assistant to hold and rotate the pipe counterclockwise while tightening the nuts.**

15. Install the catalytic converter to exhaust manifold nuts and tighten to 37 ft. lbs. (50 Nm).

16. With the aid of an assistant, remove the muffler from the jack stands.

17. Install the muffler to the catalytic converters.

18. Install the muffler hangers to the insulators.

19. Install catalytic converter to muffler nuts and tighten to 33 ft. lbs. (45 Nm).

20. Tighten the muffler to catalytic converter clamp to 32 ft. lbs. (43 Nm).

21. For the right side, install the transmission support crossmember.

22. Install the HO2S.

23. If equipped with 4WD, install the right torsion bar.

24. Inspect exhaust system for leaks.

CRANKSHAFT DAMPER

REMOVAL & INSTALLATION

2.9L & 3.7L Engines
See Figures 140 through 144.

1. Before servicing the vehicle, refer to the Precautions Section.

2. Remove the radiator. Refer to Radiator Removal & Installation in the Engine Cooling section.

3. Remove the drive belt. Refer to Accessory Drive Belt Removal & Installation.

4. Raise and support the vehicle.

5. Remove the service slot plug.

➡**The crankshaft balancer does not have a key-way; so the crankshaft could turn when tightening, causing an improper torque.**

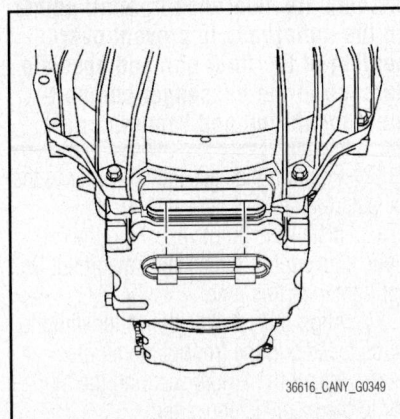

Fig. 140 Remove the service slot plug

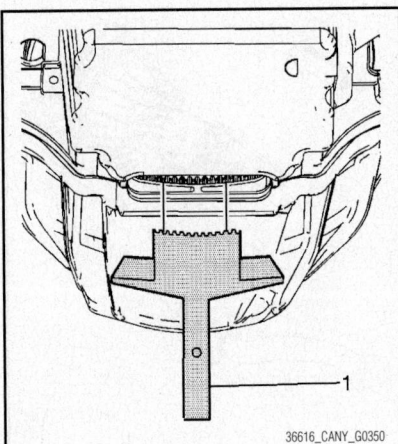

Fig. 141 Install the EN 46547 (1) into the flywheel teeth

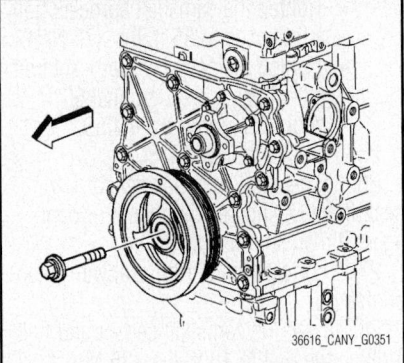

Fig. 142 Remove the crankshaft balancer bolt

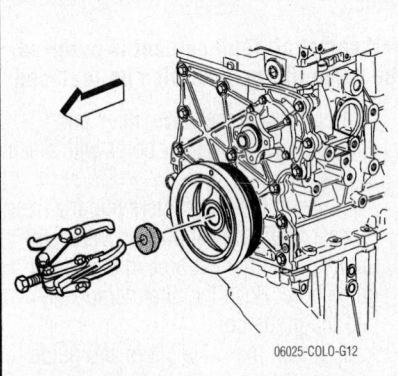

Fig. 143 Remove the crankshaft balancer using a suitable puller after installing End Protector J-41816-2.

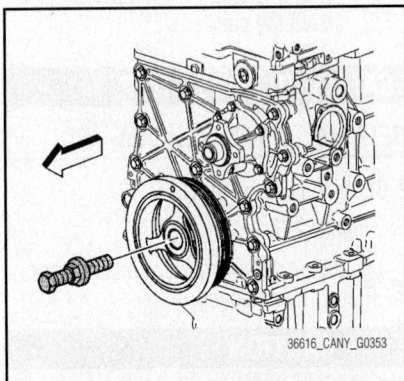

Fig. 144 Install the crankshaft balancer

6. Install the EN 46547 into the flywheel teeth.

7. Lower the vehicle.

8. Remove and discard the crankshaft balancer bolt.

9. Install the J 41816-2 and J 41816-A to the crankshaft balancer.

➡**Do not pull on outer edge of the crankshaft balancer.**

10. Remove the crankshaft balancer.

11. Remove the J 41816-2 and J 41816-A.

To install:

12. Install the crankshaft balancer using the EN-48034.

13. Remove the EN-48034.

14. Install the crankshaft balancer washer and NEW bolt and tighten to 111 ft. lbs. (150 Nm) plus an additional 180 degrees using the J 45059.

15. Raise and support the vehicle.

16. Remove the EN 46547 from the fly-wheel teeth.

17. Install the service slot plug.

18. Lower the vehicle.

19. Install the drive belt.

20. Install the radiator.

5.3L Engine

See Figures 145 through 150.

1. Before servicing the vehicle, refer to the Precautions Section.

2. Remove the air conditioning (A/C) drive belt.

3. Remove the cooling fan and shroud.

Refer to Engine Coolant Fan Shroud Removal & Installation.

4. Remove the starter motor. Refer to Starter Removal & Installation.

➡**Ensure that the teeth of the J 42386-A mesh with the teeth of the engine fly-wheel.**

5. Install the J 42386-A and bolts. Use one M10-1.5 x 120 mm and one M10-1.5 x 45 mm bolt for proper tool operation. Tighten the J 42386-A bolts to 37 ft. lbs. (50 Nm).

6. Remove the crankshaft balancer bolt. Do not discard the crankshaft balancer bolt at this time. The old balancer bolt will be used during the balancer installation procedure.

7. Install the J 41816 and J 41816-2 to the crankshaft balancer.

➡**The crankshaft balancer is balanced as an individual component. It is not necessary to mark the balancer prior to removal.**

8. Use the J 41816 and the J 41816-2 to remove the crankshaft balancer.

9. Remove the J 41816 and the J 41816-2 from the crankshaft balancer.

To install:

➡**The crankshaft balancer installation and bolt tightening involves a four stage tightening process. The first pass ensures that the balancer is installed completely onto the crankshaft. The second, third, and fourth passes tighten the NEW bolt to the proper torque.**

➡**The used crankshaft balancer bolt will be used ONLY during the first pass of the balancer installation procedure. Install a NEW bolt and tighten as described in the second, third and fourth passes of the balancer bolt tightening procedure.**

➡**The balancer should be positioned onto the end of the crankshaft as straight as possible prior to tool installation.**

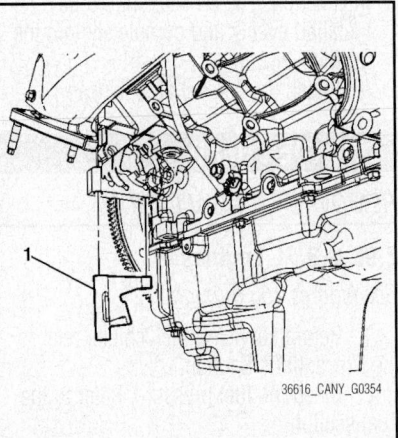

36616_CANY_G0354

Fig. 145 Install the J 42386-A (1) and bolts

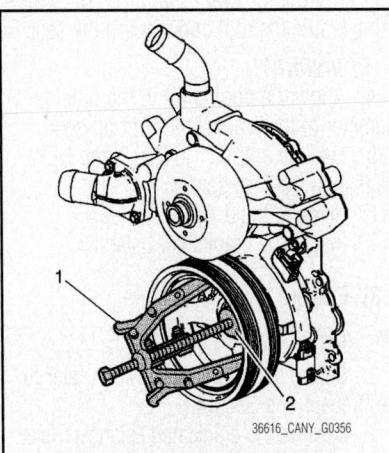

36616_CANY_G0356

Fig. 147 Install the J 41816 (1) and J 41816-2 (2) to the crankshaft balancer

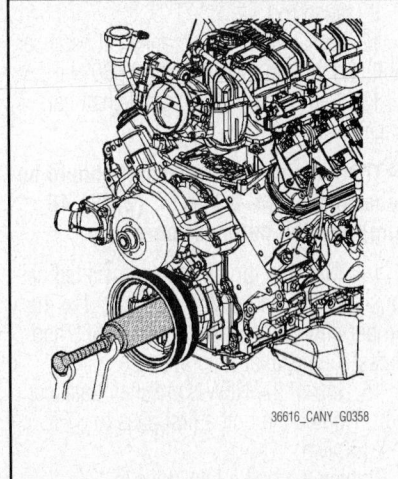

36616_CANY_G0358

Fig. 149 Install the crankshaft balancer

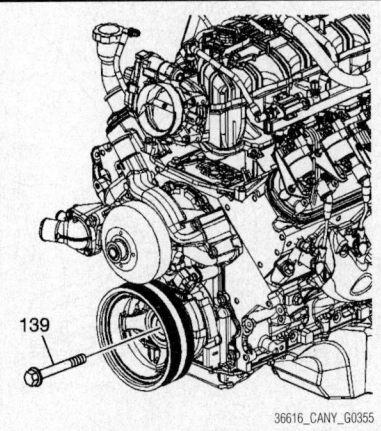

36616_CANY_G0355

Fig. 146 Remove the crankshaft balancer bolt (139)

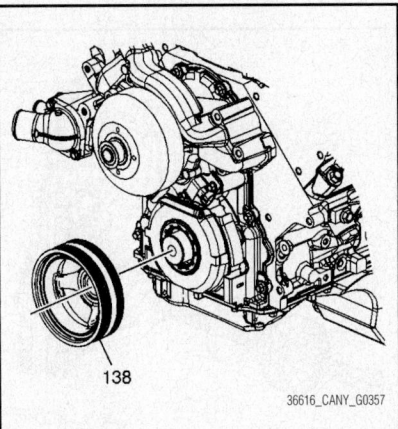

36616_CANY_G0357

Fig. 148 Remove the crankshaft balancer (138)

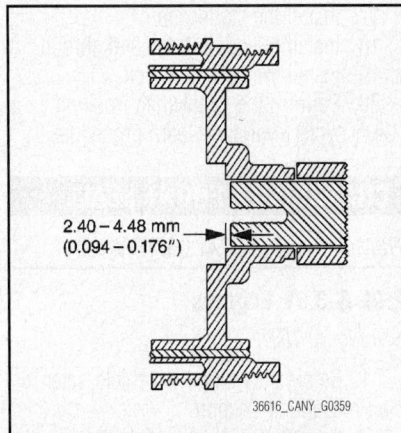

2.40 – 4.48 mm (0.094 – 0.176")

36616_CANY_G0359

Fig. 150 The nose of the crankshaft should be recessed 0.094–0.176 in. (2.4–4.48 mm)

10. Position the crankshaft balancer onto the end of the crankshaft.

11. Install the J 41665 and the threaded rod from the J 41478 to crankshaft balancer and install the balancer.

a. Assemble the threaded rod, nut, washer and installer. Insert the smaller end of the installer into the front of the balancer.

b. Use a wrench and hold the hex end of the threaded rod.

c. Use a second wrench and rotate the installation tool nut clockwise until the balancer is started onto the crankshaft.

d. Remove the tool and reverse the installation tool. Position the larger end of the installer against the front of the balancer.

e. Use a wrench and hold the hex end of the threaded rod.

f. Use a second wrench and rotate the installation tool nut clockwise until the balancer is installed onto the crankshaft.

g. Remove the J 41665 and the threaded rod.

12. Install the USED crankshaft balancer bolt and tighten to 240 ft. lbs. (330 Nm).

13. Remove the USED crankshaft balancer bolt.

➡ **The nose of the crankshaft should be recessed 0.094–0.176 in. (2.4–4.48 mm) into the balancer bore.**

14. Measure for a correctly installed balancer. If the balancer is not installed to the proper dimension, install the J 41665 and repeat the installation procedure.

15. Install the NEW crankshaft balancer bolt. Tighten the bolt a first pass to 37 ft. lbs. (50 Nm).

Tighten the bolt a final pass to 140 degrees using J 45059.

16. Remove the J 42386-A and bolts.

17. Install the starter motor.

18. Install the cooling fan and shroud.

19. Install the A/C drive belt.

20. Perform the Crankshaft Position (CKP) system variation learn procedure.

CRANKSHAFT FRONT SEAL

REMOVAL & INSTALLATION

2.9L & 3.7L Engines
See Figure 151.

1. Before servicing the vehicle, refer to the Precautions Section.

2. Remove the crankshaft balancer. Refer to Crankshaft Damper Removal & Installation.

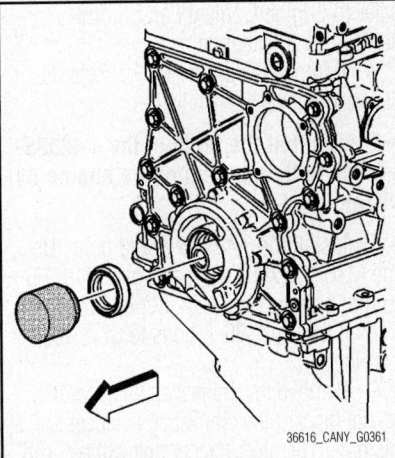

Fig. 151 Crankshaft front seal—2.9L and 3.7L engines

✳✳ WARNING

Do not damage the engine front cover or the crankshaft.

---

3. Pry out the crankshaft front oil seal using a suitable tool and discard the seal.

To install:

4. Apply the engine oil to the outside diameter of the crankshaft front oil seal.

5. Use the J 45951 to install the NEW crankshaft front oil seal.

6. Remove the J 45951.

7. Install the crankshaft balancer.

5.3L Engine
See Figure 152.

1. Before servicing the vehicle, refer to the Precautions Section.

2. Remove the crankshaft balancer. Refer to Crankshaft Damper Removal & Installation.

3. Remove the crankshaft front oil seal (1) from the front cover.

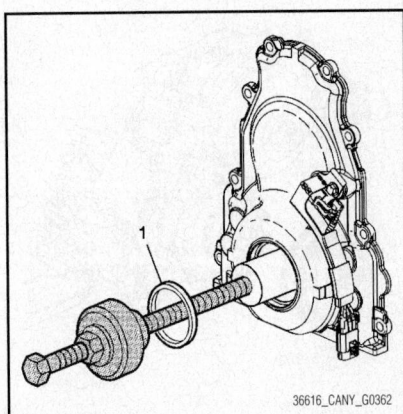

Fig. 152 Crankshaft front seal—5.3L engine

To install:

➡ **Do not lubricate the oil seal sealing surface.**

➡ **Do not reuse the crankshaft front oil seal.**

4. Lubricate the outer edge of the oil seal (1) with clean engine oil.

5. Lubricate the front cover oil seal bore with clean engine oil.

6. Install the crankshaft front oil seal (1) onto the J 41478 guide.

7. Install the J 41478 threaded rod (with nut, washer, guide, and oil seal) into the end of the crankshaft.

8. Use the J 41478 in order to install the oil seal into the cover bore.

a. Use a wrench and hold the hex on the installer bolt.

b. Use a second wrench and rotate the installer nut clockwise until the seal bottoms in the cover bore.

c. Remove the J 41478.

d. Inspect the oil seal for proper installation. The oil seal should be installed evenly and completely into the front cover bore.

9. Install the crankshaft balancer.

CYLINDER HEAD

REMOVAL & INSTALLATION

2.9L & 3.7L Engines
See Figures 153 through 172.

1. Before servicing the vehicle, refer to the Precautions Section.

2. Bleed the fuel pressure. Refer to the Fuel section.

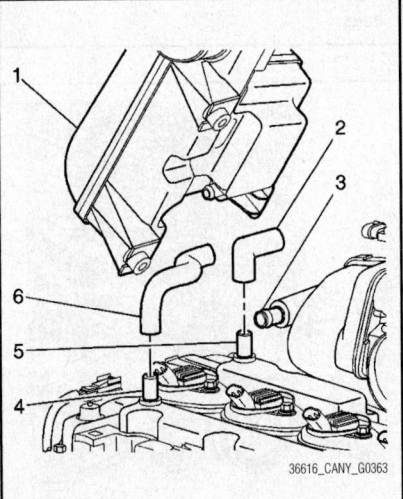

Fig. 153 Remove the Positive Crankcase Ventilation (PCV) pipes (2, 6) from the cam cover

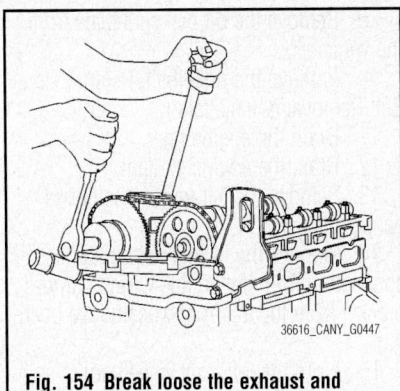

Fig. 154 Break loose the exhaust and intake camshaft sprocket bolts

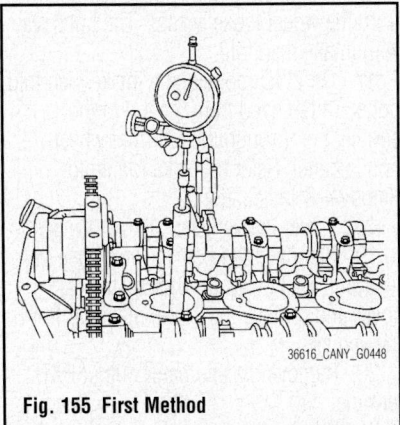

Fig. 155 First Method

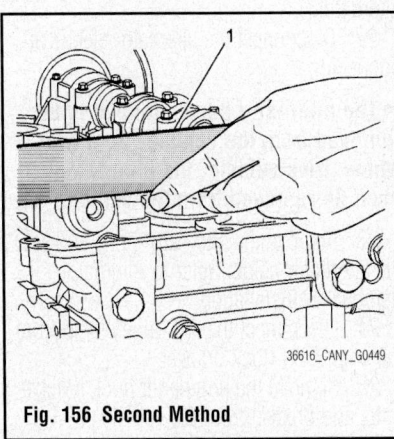

Fig. 156 Second Method

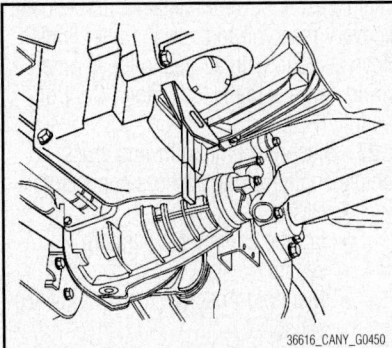

Fig. 157 Lock the flywheel with the EN 46547

Fig. 158 Place a reference mark on the harmonic balancer to the front cover for alignment purposes

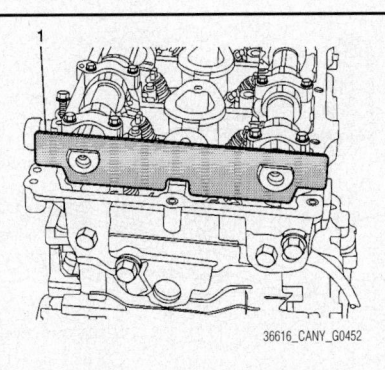

Fig. 159 Install J 44221 (1) to the back of the camshafts

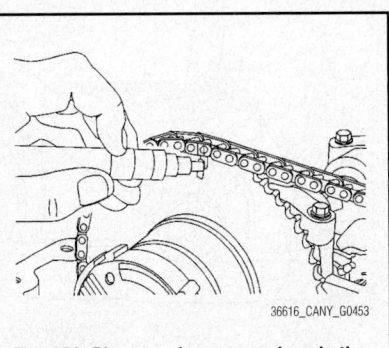

Fig. 160 Place a reference mark on both timing gear sprockets and the timing chain to mark location prior to disassembly

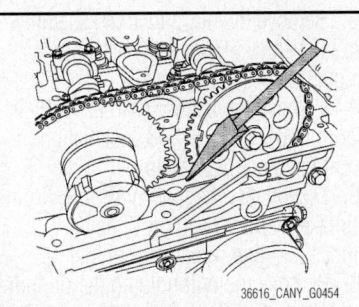

Fig. 161 Install EN-48464 with the proper orientation and seated square against the timing chain and the timing cover center bolt

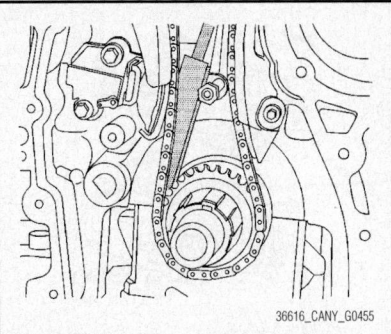

Fig. 162 Place the narrow ramp of the wedge tool so that it faces the timing chain

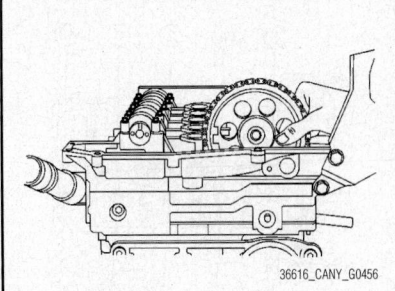

Fig. 163 Remove the exhaust and intake camshaft sprockets with the timing chain from the exhaust and intake camshafts

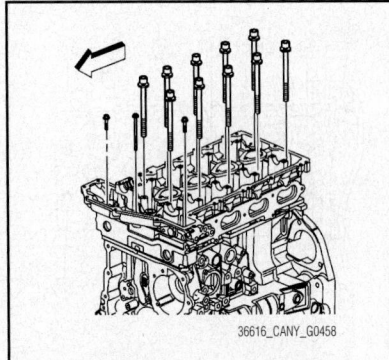

Fig. 164 Remove the cylinder head bolts—2.9L engine

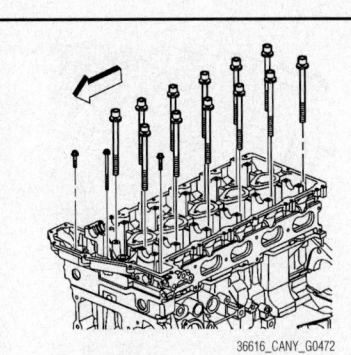

Fig. 165 Remove the cylinder head bolts—3.7L engine

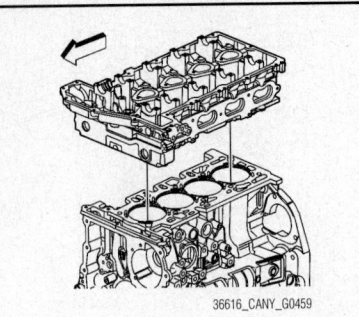

Fig. 166 Remove the cylinder head and gasket—2.9L engine shown, 3.7L engine similar

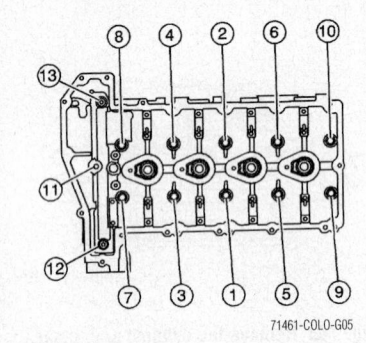

Fig. 167 Cylinder head bolt tightening sequence—2.9L engine

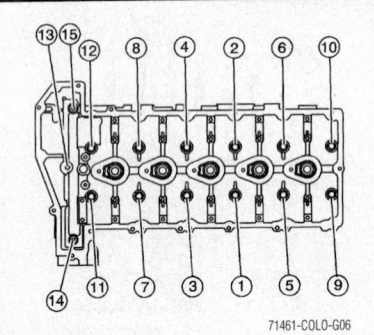

Fig. 168 Cylinder head bolt tightening sequence—3.7L engine

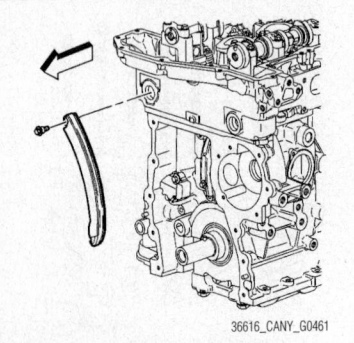

Fig. 169 Position the timing chain tensioner shoe to the engine

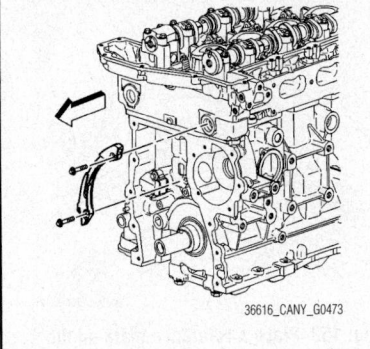

Fig. 170 Install the lower timing chain guide

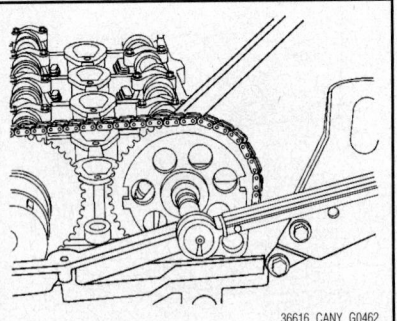

Fig. 171 Using J 45059, tighten the intake camshaft sprocket bolt

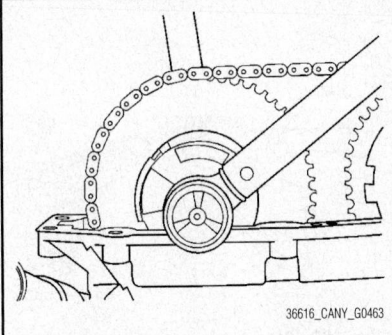

Fig. 172 Using J 45059, tighten the exhaust camshaft actuator sprocket bolt

3. Remove the air induction assembly from the vehicle. Refer to Air Cleaner Removal & Installation.

4. Remove the battery from the vehicle. Refer to Battery Removal & Installation, in the Engine Electrical section.

5. Disconnect the fuel/EVAP lines from the intake manifold and move aside. Includes fuel line removal from fuel rail.

6. Remove the bolt holding the oil indicator tube to the intake manifold and move the oil indicator tube aside. Do not remove.

7. Lift the vehicle.

8. Remove the engine shield from the vehicle.

9. Remove the oil pan skid plate from the vehicle.

10. Remove the drive belt. Refer to Drive Belt Removal & Installation.

11. Drain the engine oil.

12. Drain the engine coolant.

13. Remove the left front wheelhouse panel.

14. Remove the fir tree wiring harness connectors from the engine wiring harness bracket from the left front wheelhouse opening.

15. From the left front wheelhouse, remove the engine wiring harness bracket from the engine and set aside.

16. Remove the intake manifold bolts from the wheelhouse access. The bolts stay with intake manifold.

17. On 2WD models, the intake manifold bolts are removed from the top of the engine, not through the left front wheelhouse panel. Refer to Intake Manifold Removal & Installation.

18. Lower the vehicle.

19. Remove the Positive Crankcase Ventilation (PCV) pipes (2, 6) from the cam cover and remove the intake manifold from the vehicle.

20. Remove the alternator output BAT terminal nut.

21. Remove the alternator lead from the alternator.

22. Disconnect the alternator electrical connector.

➡**The alternator does not have to be removed from the vehicle. On a two-wheel drive vehicle, the alternator must be removed from the vehicle.**

23. Remove the alternator bolts and set the alternator aside. Refer to Alternator Removal & Installation.

24. Disconnect the A/C pipe clamp from the engine lift hook bracket.

25. Remove the engine lift hook bracket bolts and bracket from the vehicle.

26. Remove the bolts holding the windshield washer solvent container and coolant recovery reservoir to the right inner fender. Move aside to gain access to the engine wiring harness to the Powertrain Control Module (PCM).

27. Disconnect the following cross-vehicle engine wiring harness connectors:
- PCM
- Engine coolant temperature sensor
- Manifold Absolute Pressure (MAP) sensor
- Ignition coils
- Harness clamps at power steering pump

- Wiring harness fastener at right front inner fender
- Throttle body
- Camshaft sensors
- Exhaust camshaft actuator
- Fuel injectors
- HO2S 1

28. Set aside the cross-vehicle engine wiring harness on the left side of the vehicle.

29. If equipped, remove the secondary Air Injection (AIR) injection pipe block-off plate bolts from the cylinder head.

30. If equipped, remove the AIR injection pipe block-off plate.

31. Remove the bolts from the exhaust manifold heat shield. Refer to Exhaust Manifold Removal & Installation.

32. Remove the exhaust manifold heat shield.

33. Remove the exhaust manifold bolts.

34. Move the exhaust manifold back and away from the cylinder head.

35. Remove the bolts to all ignition coil assemblies and remove all ignition coil assemblies from the cam cover. Refer to Ignition Coil Module Removal & Installation, in the Engine Electrical system.

36. Remove all the spark plugs from the cylinder head. Refer to Spark Plug Removal & Installation, in the Engine Electrical system.

37. Remove the cam cover from the cylinder head. Refer to Camshaft Cover Replacement.

38. Remove the inlet radiator hose and clamp from the cylinder head.

39. Before performing one of the top dead center (TDC) procedures, break loose both the exhaust and intake camshaft sprocket bolts. Use a 1 in. (25 mm) open end wrench on the camshaft hexes to hold the camshaft from turning. **DO NOT** remove the bolts.

40. Perform one of the following methods for the service timing procedure:

   a. First Method: Rotate the engine clockwise by hand to TDC on the compression stroke by using a piston TDC indicator tool and/or dial indicator in the number 1 cylinder. The TDC indicator tool graduation marks on the shaft should note top of the piston stroke. When the piston is at TDC, the flats at the rear of the camshafts will be facing up and level when using a straight edge across the camshaft flats.

   b. Second Method: Rotate the crankshaft in the engine rotational direction clockwise until the number 1 piston is at TDC on the compression stroke. The word Delphi on the exhaust camshaft position actuator will be parallel with the cylinder head to cam cover mating surface. When the piston is at TDC, the flats at the rear of the camshafts will be facing up and level when using a straight edge across the camshaft flats. A 0.005 inch feeler gage should not slide under the straight edge (1).

41. Once TDC is located for the number 1 cylinder using above methods, raise the vehicle and lock the flywheel with the EN 46547.

42. Use a white paint pen or equivalent to place a reference mark on the harmonic balancer to the front cover for alignment purposes.

43. Lower the vehicle.

✳✳ CAUTION

The camshaft holding tools must be installed on the camshafts to prevent camshaft rotation. When performing service to the valve train and/or timing components, valve spring pressure can cause the camshafts to rotate unexpectedly and can cause personal injury.

➡**If the timing is correct, TDC compression stroke number 1 cylinder, the camshaft flats will be in the up position.**

44. Install J 44221 (1) to the back of the camshafts.

45. Remove the upper timing chain guide to the cylinder head.

46. Clean the timing chain and gears with brake cleaner or suitable solvent. Use a white paint pen or equivalent to place a reference mark on both timing gear sprockets and the timing chain to mark location prior to disassembly. It is recommended that the paint marks be in the 12 o'clock position.

✳✳ WARNING

DO NOT use excessive force to seat the wedge tool. If excessive force is used, you may damage the timing chain tensioner or break the front cover bolt requiring complete disassembly of the front engine.

47. Install EN-48464. It is important to install the tool with the proper orientation and to ensure that it is seated square against the timing chain and against the timing cover center bolt.

48. The narrow ramp of the wedge tool needs to be placed so that it faces the timing chain.

49. The wedge tool should be lightly seated using a couple of very light taps with a small plastic or brass hammer.

50. Once the tool is correctly installed, unscrew the handle and remove the handle.

✳✳ WARNING

Use a 25 mm open end wrench on the camshaft hexes to hold the camshaft from turning. It is critical that the crankshaft does not move and is held at TDC when the intake and exhaust camshaft sprocket bolts are removed.

✳✳ WARNING

If the crankshaft is not held in place, the wedge tool could be dislodged. If the crankshaft moves, or if the tool is not seated properly allowing the timing chain tensioner to extend, the repair will have to be completed by removing the front cover to release the timing chain tensioner.

51. Remove both upper cylinder head access hole plugs from the front of the cylinder head.

52. Remove the 1 long and 2 short cylinder head bolts next to the exhaust and intake timing chain tensioner shoes and discard the bolts.

53. Remove upper timing chain tensioner shoe bolt.

54. Remove upper timing chain tensioner guide bolt.

55. Remove the exhaust and the intake camshaft sprocket bolts. Discard the bolts.

56. Carefully remove the exhaust and intake camshaft sprockets with the timing chain from the exhaust and intake camshafts.

57. Remove the sprockets from the chain; tie a piece of mechanic's wire on the timing chain and let it drop.

58. Before removing the cylinder head bolts, use a drift punch and hammer to shock the bolts. This will ensure that the cylinder head bolts will not strip out the threads in the engine block or break. If a bolt breaks during engine disassembly, EN-47702 is available to assist in the removal of the remaining bolt segment.

59. Remove the cylinder head bolts. Discard the bolts.

60. Remove the cylinder head.

61. Place the cylinder head on a flat, clean surface with the combustion chambers face up, in order to prevent damage to the deck face.

62. Remove the cylinder head gasket.

63. Discard the gasket.

64. Remove all remaining gasket material from the engine block.

65. Inspect the cylinder head gasket mating surface on the engine block.

66. Clean and inspect the cylinder head. Refer to Cylinder Head Cleaning and Inspection.

67. Disassemble the cylinder head if necessary. Refer to Cylinder Head Disassemble.

To install:

68. Assemble the cylinder head if necessary.

69. Install the dowel pins, cylinder head locator, if necessary.

70. Position a NEW cylinder head gasket to the engine block.

➡**Ensure all wires, components, etc. are out of the way when installing the cylinder head.**

71. Install the cylinder head.

❊❊ WARNING

This component uses torque-to-yield bolts. When servicing this component do not reuse the bolts, New torque-to-yield bolts must be installed. Reusing used torque-to-yield bolts will not provide proper bolt torque and clamp load. Failure to install NEW torque-to-yield bolts may lead to engine damage.

72. Install **NEW** cylinder head bolts.

73. Tighten the NEW cylinder head bolts in the following sequence:

a. Tighten the cylinder head bolts (1–10) in sequence to 22 ft. lbs. (30 Nm). Use the J 45059 to rotate the cylinder head bolts (1–10) in sequence an additional 155 degrees.

b. Tighten the (2 short) end bolts (12–13) to 62 inch lbs. (7 Nm). Use the J 45059 to rotate the short cylinder head end bolts (12–13) an additional 60 degrees.

c. Tighten the (1 long) end bolt (11) to 62 inch lbs. (7 Nm). Use the J 45059 to rotate the long cylinder head end bolt (11) an additional 120 degrees.

❊❊ CAUTION

The camshaft holding tools must be installed on the camshafts to prevent camshaft rotation. When performing service to the valve train and/or timing components, valve spring pressure can cause the camshafts to rotate unexpectedly and can cause personal injury.

➡**Before installing the camshafts, refer to Camshafts Cleaning and Inspection.**

74. Install the camshafts with the flats up

using J 44221 (1). Refer to Camshaft Installation.

❊❊ WARNING

Tension must be always kept on the intake side of the timing chain to properly keep the engine in time. If the chain is loose the timing will be off, which may cause internal engine damage or set DTC P0017.

❊❊ WARNING

The exhaust camshaft actuator must be fully advanced during installation. Engine damage may occur if the camshaft actuator is not fully advanced.

75. Ensure that the camshaft position actuator is in the fully advanced position.

➡**To aid in aligning the actuator to the camshaft, use a 1 in. (25 mm) open end wrench on the hex of the camshaft to rotate. This will ensure the alignment pin is properly engaged with the camshaft and hand tighten the new exhaust camshaft sprocket bolt.**

76. Install the exhaust camshaft actuator/sprocket and chain onto the exhaust camshaft. Use the paint marks as an alignment guide.

➡**To aid in aligning the intake sprocket to the camshaft, use a 1 in. (25 mm) open end wrench on the hex of the camshaft to rotate. This will ensure the alignment pin is properly engaged with the camshaft and hand tighten the new intake camshaft sprocket bolt.**

77. Install the intake camshaft sprocket and chain onto the intake camshaft. Use paint marks as alignment guide.

78. Position the timing chain tensioner shoe to the engine.

79. Install the timing chain tensioner shoe bolt and tighten to 18 ft. lbs. (25 Nm).

80. Position the lower timing chain guide to the engine.

81. Install the lower timing chain guide bolts and tighten to 107 inch lbs. (12 Nm).

82. Install both upper timing chain tensioner shoe bolts and tighten to 18 ft. lbs. (25 Nm).

83. Install both upper cylinder head access hole plugs to the front of the cylinder head. Tighten the plugs to 44 inch lbs. (5 Nm).

84. Tighten the new intake camshaft sprocket bolt. Using J 45059, tighten the intake camshaft sprocket bolt to 15 ft. lbs. (20 Nm) plus 100 degrees.

85. Tighten the new exhaust camshaft actuator sprocket bolt. Using J 45059, tighten the exhaust camshaft actuator sprocket bolt to 18 ft. lbs. (25 Nm) plus 135 degrees.

86. Lift the vehicle and remove the EN 46547.

87. Lower the vehicle.

88. Remove the J 44221 from the back of the camshafts.

❊❊ WARNING

Ensure that the wedge tool is removed from engine prior to rotation. If the wedge tool is not removed, engine damage will result.

89. Install the handle of EN-48464 and remove the wedge portion of the tool from the engine.

❊❊ WARNING

It is critical that the engine is at TDC and not a couple of degrees off. If in doubt, repeat this step.

90. Rotate the engine clockwise by hand 2 complete revolutions to TDC number 1 on the compression stroke. Refer to First Method or Second Method for TDC. If you go past TDC, rotate the engine back approximately 45 degrees before TDC and then rotate clockwise up to TDC to ensure that the timing chain is tight (no slack) between the crank sprocket and the timing gears.

➡**DO NOT use the J 44221, installed to the back of the camshafts, as a method to verify timing.**

91. Both intake and exhaust camshaft flats should be facing up and flat and level with the cylinder head. If J 44221 (1) is used to verify cam timing, you could be off approximately one tooth and cause DTC P0017 to set. If a worn or new J 44221 is used to verify timing, the timing will be off.

92. To verify timing, set a straight edge across the flats of the camshafts.

93. A 0.005 inch feeler gage should not be able to slip under the straight edge. If the feeler gage slips under one or both camshaft flats, then the timing is off. Repeat step 20 and recheck. If the camshaft flats are still not flat, the camshaft timing will have to be reset. This may require removal and reinstallation of one or both camshaft sprockets.

94. Install the 1 long and 2 short cylinder head bolts next to the exhaust and intake timing chain tensioner shoes and tighten the bolts.

95. Position the upper timing chain guide to the cylinder head. Apply thread-

locker GM P/N 89021297 (Canadian P/N 10953488) to the upper timing chain guide bolt threads.

96. Install the upper timing chain guide bolts and tighten to 89 inch lbs. (10 Nm).

97. Install the radiator inlet hose and clamp to the cylinder head.

98. Clean and inspect the camshaft cover.

99. Install a NEW camshaft cover seal and NEW ignition control module seals to the cam cover. Position the camshaft cover to the cylinder head.

100. Install the camshaft cover bolts and tighten to 89 inch lbs. (10 Nm).

101. Check the gap on all of the spark plugs. The gap should be 0.042 in. (1.08 mm). Tighten all of the spark plugs to 13 ft. lbs. (18 Nm).

102. Install the ignition coils into the camshaft cover.

103. Install the ignition coil bolts and tighten to 89 inch lbs. (10 Nm).

104. Reposition the exhaust manifold to cylinder head and install the exhaust manifold bolts to the cylinder head.

105. If equipped, install a NEW AIR injection gasket, then the cover and pipe studs to the cylinder head.

Tighten the pipe studs to 18 ft. lbs. (25 Nm).

106. Install the exhaust manifold heat shield to the exhaust manifold.

107. Apply anti-seize GM P/N 12371386 (Canadian P/N 89021945) to the exhaust manifold heat shield nuts.

108. Install the exhaust manifold heat shield nuts and tighten to 89 inch lbs. (10 Nm).

109. Install the intake manifold to the cylinder head.

110. For 4WD models, raise the vehicle and install the blind intake manifold bolts from the left front wheelhouse access.

111. For 2WD models, the bolts are accessible from the top of the engine.

112. Reposition the engine wiring harness bracket to the engine and harnesses. Install the engine wiring harness bracket bolts and tighten to 89 inch lbs. (10 Nm).

113. Install the left front wheelhouse panel and the left wheel and tire.

114. Drain the engine oil again.

115. If removed, install the radiator outlet hose.

116. Install the oil pan skid plate and the engine shield.

117. Install the engine shield.

118. Lower the vehicle.

Install the cross-vehicle wiring harness connectors to the following components:

- PCM
- Map sensor
- Ignition coils
- Harness clamps at power steering pump
- Wiring harness fastener at right front inner fender
- Throttle body
- Camshaft sensors
- Exhaust camshaft actuator
- Fuel injectors
- HO2S 1

119. Install the windshield washer solvent container and coolant recovery reservoir bolts to the right inner fender. Tighten the bolts to 89 inch lbs. (10 Nm).

120. Install the PCV pipes to the intake manifold.

121. Reposition the oil indicator (dipstick) tube and tighten the bolt to the intake manifold.

122. Reposition the fuel/EVAP lines to the intake manifold retainer.

123. Install the following components:
- Alternator
- A/C compressor hose/pipe bracket clamp for the engine lift bracket

124. Drive belt

125. Install the battery.

126. Install the air induction assembly.

127. Install NEW engine oil.

128. Install NEW coolant.

129. Install a scan tool and start the engine.

130. Check for DTCs.

131. Road test the vehicle. DTC P0017 is a Type B diagnostic code. Three consecutive ignition key cycles must be performed during the road test with a minimum of a one minute run time between key cycles to verify that a DTC P0017 did not set. For further information on DTC P0017, refer to DTC P0017.

5.3L Engine

Left Side

See Figures 173 through 175.

1. Before servicing the vehicle, refer to the Precautions Section.

2. Remove the alternator bracket. Refer to Alternator Removal & Installation, in the Engine Electrical section.

3. Remove the intake manifold. Refer to Intake Manifold Removal & Installation.

4. Remove the coolant air bleed pipe.

5. Remove the left exhaust manifold. Refer to Exhaust Manifold Removal & Installation.

6. Remove the pushrods.

➡ The cylinder head bolts are of a torque-to-yield design and are NOT to be reused.

7. Remove and discard the cylinder head bolts (220, 221).

✱✱ WARNING

After removal, place the cylinder head on 2 wood blocks in order to prevent damage to the sealing surfaces.

8. Remove the cylinder head (218).

9. Remove and discard the cylinder head gasket.

10. If required, clean and inspect the cylinder head.

To install:

✱✱ CAUTION

Wear safety glasses in order to avoid eye damage.

✱✱ CAUTION

Clean all dirt, debris, and coolant from the engine block cylinder head bolt holes. Failure to remove all foreign material may result in damaged threads, improperly tightened fasteners or damage to components.

➡ If installing a new cylinder head it is necessary to install a new engine

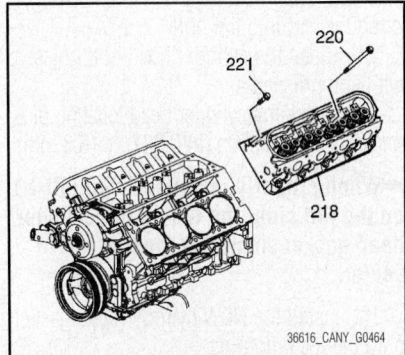

36616_CANY_G0464

Fig. 173 Remove the cylinder head bolts (220, 221) and cylinder head (218)

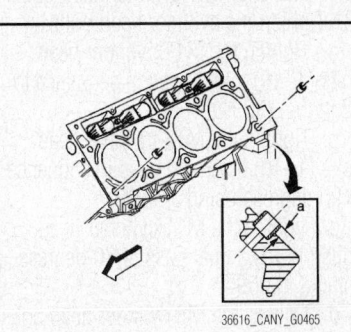

36616_CANY_G0465

Fig. 174 Check the cylinder head locating pins for proper installation (a) 0.327 in. (8.3 mm)

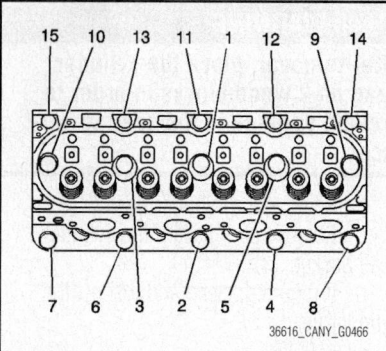

Fig. 175 Cylinder head bolt tightening sequence

coolant air bleed plug into the rear coolant passage of the cylinder head.

➡️**Do not reuse the cylinder head bolts. Install NEW cylinder head bolts during assembly.**

➡️**Do not use any type of sealant on the cylinder head gasket (unless specified).**

11. Clean the engine block cylinder head bolt holes, if required. Thread repair tool J 42385-107, found in J 42385-200 may be used to clean the threads of old threadlocking material.

12. Spray cleaner GM P/N 12346139, P/N 12377981 (Canadian P/N 10953463), or equivalent into the hole.

13. Clean the cylinder head bolt holes with compressed air.

14. Check the cylinder head locating pins for proper installation (a) 0.327 in. (8.3 mm).

➡️**When properly installed, with FRONT on the left side, the tab on the cylinder head gasket should be located left of center.**

15. Install the NEW cylinder head gasket onto the locating pins.

16. Install the cylinder head onto the locating pins.

17. Install the NEW cylinder head bolts.

18. Tighten the cylinder head bolts:

a. Tighten the M11 cylinder head bolts (1–10) a first pass in sequence to 22 ft. lbs. (30 Nm).

b. Tighten the M11 cylinder head bolts (1–10) a second pass in sequence to 90 degrees using J 45059.

c. Tighten the M11 cylinder head bolts (1–10) a final pass to 70 degrees using J 45059.

d. Tighten the M8 cylinder head bolts (11–15) to 22 ft. lbs. (30 Nm). Begin with the center bolt (11) and alternating side-to-side, work outward tightening all of the bolts.

19. Install the pushrods.
20. Install the left exhaust manifold.
21. Install the coolant air bleed pipe.
22. Install the intake manifold.
23. Install the alternator bracket.

Right Side

See Figures 176 through 178.

1. Before servicing the vehicle, refer to the Precautions Section.

2. Remove the oil level indicator.

3. Remove the intake manifold. Refer to Intake Manifold Removal & Installation.

4. Remove the coolant air bleed pipe.

5. Remove the right exhaust manifold. Refer to Exhaust Manifold Removal & Installation.

6. Remove the pushrods.

7. Remove the heater hose bracket bolt (1) from the front of the right cylinder head.

➡️**The cylinder head bolts are of a torque-to-yield design and are NOT to be reused.**

8. Remove and discard the cylinder head bolts (220, 221).

✴✴ WARNING

After removal, place the cylinder head on 2 wood blocks in order to prevent damage to the sealing surfaces.

9. Remove the cylinder head (218).

10. Remove and discard the cylinder head gasket.

11. If required, clean and inspect the cylinder head.

To install:

✴✴ CAUTION

Wear safety glasses in order to avoid eye damage.

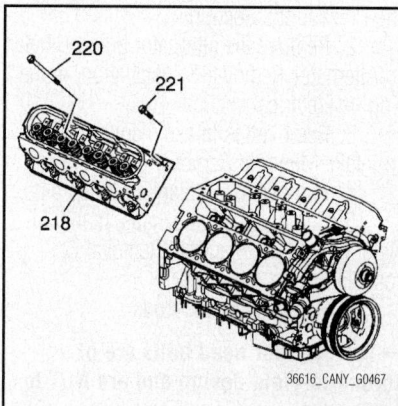

Fig. 176 Remove and discard the cylinder head (218) and bolts (220, 221)

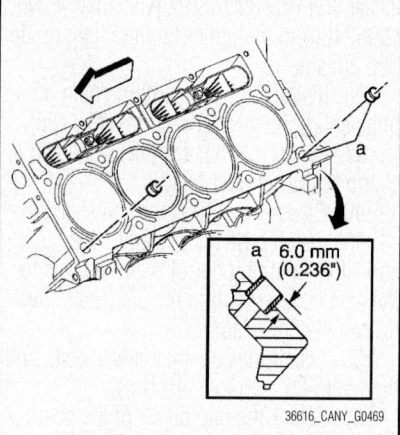

Fig. 177 Check the cylinder head locating pins for proper installation (a) 0.327 in. (8.3 mm)

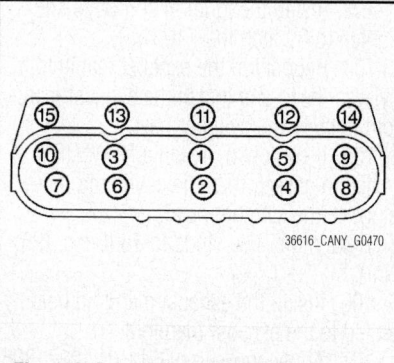

Fig. 178 Cylinder head bolt tightening sequence

✴✴ WARNING

Clean all dirt, debris, and coolant from the engine block cylinder head bolt holes. Failure to remove all foreign material may result in damaged threads, improperly tightened fasteners or damage to components.

➡️**If installing a new cylinder head it is necessary to install a new engine coolant air bleed plug into the rear coolant passage of the cylinder head.**

➡️**Do not reuse the cylinder head bolts. Install NEW cylinder head bolts during assembly.**

➡️**Do not use any type of sealant on the cylinder head gasket (unless specified).**

12. Clean the engine block cylinder head bolt holes, if required. Thread repair tool J 42385-107, found in J 42385-200 may be used to clean the threads of old threadlocking material.

13. Spray cleaner GM P/N 12346139, P/N 12377981 (Canadian P/N 10953463), or equivalent into the hole.

14. Clean the cylinder head bolt holes with compressed air.

15. Check the cylinder head locating pins for proper installation (a) 0.327 in. (8.3 mm).

➡ **When properly installed, with FRONT on the right side, the tab on the cylinder head gasket should be located right of center.**

16. Install the NEW cylinder head gasket (217) onto the locating pins.

17. Install the cylinder head (218) onto the locating pins.

18. Install the NEW cylinder head bolts (220, 221).

19. Tighten the cylinder head bolts:

   a. Tighten the M11 cylinder head bolts (1–10) a first pass in sequence to 22 ft. lbs. (30 Nm).

   b. Tighten the M11 cylinder head bolts (1–10) a second pass in sequence to 90 degrees using J 45059.

   c. Tighten the M11 cylinder head bolts (1–10) a final pass to 70 degrees in sequence using J 45059.

   d. Tighten the M8 cylinder head bolts (11–15) to 22 ft. lbs. (30 Nm). Begin with the center bolt (11) and alternating side-to-side, work outward tightening all of the bolts.

20. Install the heater hose bracket bolt to the front of the right cylinder head and tighten to 18 ft. lbs. (25 Nm).

21. Install the pushrods.

22. Install the right exhaust manifold.

23. Install the coolant air bleed pipe.

24. Install the intake manifold.

25. Install the oil level indicator.

ENGINE ASSEMBLY

REMOVAL & INSTALLATION

2.9L & 3.7L Engines

See Figures 179 through 185.

1. Before servicing the vehicle, refer to the Precautions Section.

2. Open the hood.

3. Remove the front hood seal by pulling downward on the seal, starting from one end.

4. Using a grease pencil or other suitable marking device, mark the position of the hood to the hinges.

5. With the aid of an assistant, remove the 4 bolts that retain the hood to the hood hinges.

6. With the aid of an assistant, remove the hood from the vehicle.

7. Remove the battery box. Refer to Battery Removal & Installation, in the Engine Electrical system.

8. Drain the engine coolant.

9. Remove the outlet radiator hose.

10. Remove the cooling fan. Refer to Fan Removal & Installation in the Engine Cooling section.

11. Remove the air cleaner assembly. Refer to Air Cleaner Removal & Installation.

12. Remove the air cleaner resonator and outlet duct. Refer to Air Cleaner Removal & Installation.

13. Remove the alternator. Refer to Alternator Removal & Installation.

14. Reinstall the engine lift bracket.

15. Position the J 38185 to the clamp in order to remove the radiator inlet hose from the water outlet housing.

36616_CANY_G0497

Fig. 179 Remove the studs securing the Secondary Air Injection (AIR) pipe cover

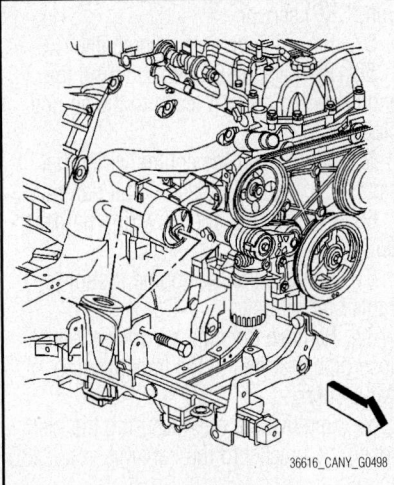

36616_CANY_G0498

Fig. 180 Remove the right engine mount-to-frame bracket bolt

16. Remove the washer solvent container/coolant recovery reservoir mounting bolts ONLY, in order to gain clearance to remove the engine wiring harness.

17. Disconnect the 2 engine wiring harness connectors from the powertrain control module (PCM).

18. Disconnect the engine wiring harness retainers from the wheelhouse.

19. Open the engine wiring harness retainer.

20. Disconnect the engine wiring harness retainers from the power steering pump.

21. Disconnect the engine wiring harness connectors from the following components:

   • The electric motor actuator connector (4WD only)
   • The oil pressure switch

22. Disconnect the engine wiring harness retainer from the camshaft cover.

23. Disconnect the engine wiring harness connectors from the following components:

   • The exhaust Camshaft Position (CMP) sensor
   • The exhaust camshaft actuator

24. Disconnect the following electrical connectors from the camshaft cover:

   • The fuel injector harness
   • The Heated Oxygen (HO2S) sensor
   • The Engine Coolant Temperature (ECT) sensor

25. Disconnect the engine wiring harness electrical connectors from the ignition coils.

26. Disconnect the engine wiring harness retainer from the camshaft cover.

27. Disconnect the engine wiring harness connector from the throttle body.

28. For 3.7L engines, disconnect the engine wiring harness connector from the intake CMP sensor.

29. Carefully disengage the engine wiring harness conduit from the camshaft cover.

30. Remove the transmission filler tube (M30 only).

31. Drain the engine oil, if necessary.

32. Remove the studs securing the Secondary Air Injection (AIR) pipe cover to the cylinder head.

   a. Install the AIR injection pipe cover studs, if applicable.

   b. Remove the AIR pipe cover and gasket.

   c. Discard the gasket.

33. Install the J 44220 in place of the AIR adapter.

34. Disconnect the inlet heater hose quick connect from the heater core, and secure to the engine.

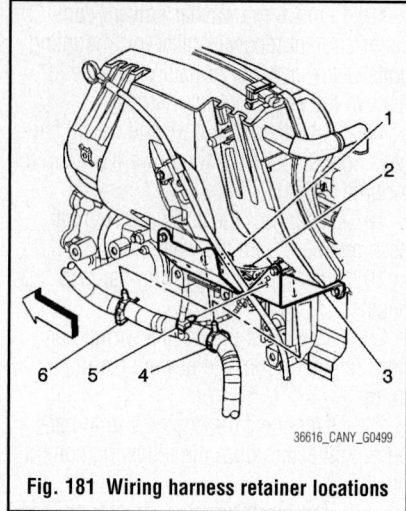

Fig. 181 Wiring harness retainer locations

35. Remove the power steering pump mounting bolts ONLY, and position aside.

36. Remove the right engine mount-to-frame bracket bolt.

37. Disconnect the engine wiring harness retainer from the intake manifold.

38. Position the engine wiring harness aside.

39. Disconnect the fuel feed pipe from the fuel rail.

40. Disconnect the evaporative emission EVAP pipe at the intake manifold.

41. Remove the oil level indicator and tube.

42. Disconnect the brake booster hose (6) from the brake booster.

43. Remove the Manifold Absolute Pressure (MAP) sensor. Refer to Manifold Absolute Pressure Sensor Removal & Installation in Engine Performance & Emission Controls.

44. Disconnect the MAP sensor wiring harness retainer (4) from the intake manifold (5).

45. Raise and support the vehicle only high enough to access the wiring harnesses through the wheelhouse. Disconnect the following wiring harness retainers from the engine wiring harness bracket:
   • The battery cable
   • The engine (4, 6)
   • The MAP sensor (5)

46. Remove the starter solenoid "S" terminal nut and disconnect the lead from the starter.

47. Remove the starter terminal nut and disconnect the battery positive cable from the starter.

48. Remove the bolt securing the battery negative cable to the engine block).

49. Disconnect the engine wiring harness connector from the Evaporative

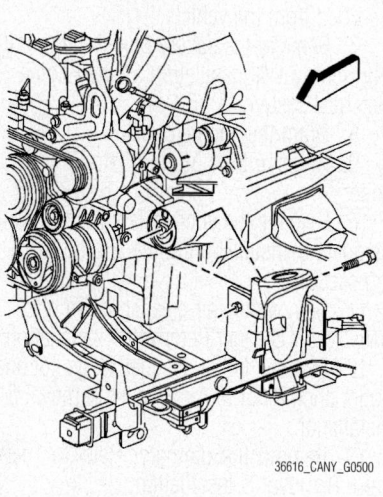

Fig. 182 Remove the left engine mount-to-frame bracket bolt location

Emission (EVAP) canister purge solenoid valve.

50. Disconnect the engine wiring harness connector from the Knock Sensor (KS).

51. Disconnect the coolant heater cord from the coolant heater, if equipped.

52. For 3.7L engines, disconnect the engine wiring harness connector from the No. 1 KS.

53. For 3.7L engines, disconnect the engine wiring harness retainer from the engine oil pan rail.

54. Remove the bolt securing the heater outlet hose/pipe to the left engine mount.

55. Position the J 38185 to the clamp in order to remove the heater outlet hose from the heater outlet hose fitting.

56. Disconnect the engine wiring harness connector from the Crankshaft Position (CKP) sensor.

57. Raise the vehicle completely.

58. Remove the 3 bolts securing the engine wiring ground leads to the engine block.

59. Disconnect the engine wiring harness retainer from the engine oil pan rail.

60. Position the engine wiring harness aside.

61. Remove the left engine mount-to-frame bracket bolt.

62. Remove the nuts securing the fuel hose/pipe brackets to the transmission (MA5 only).

63. Remove the nuts securing the fuel hose/pipe bracket to the transmission (M30 only).

64. Disconnect the fuel hose/pipe retainer from the range selector cable

bracket , and position aside the fuel hose/pipe bundle (M30 only).

65. Remove the applicable components in order to gain clearance to remove the engine:

   a. On 2WD models, remove the crossmember. Refer to Transmission Support Crossmember Removal & Installation in the Drive Train section.

   b. On 4WD models:
   • Remove the front propeller shaft. Refer to Front Propeller Shaft Removal & Installation in the Drive Train section.
   • Remove the differential carrier assembly bushing to frame bolts ONLY.
   • Position the differential carrier assembly forward.
   • Secure the pinion yoke, in order to prevent the differential carrier from rotating.

66. Remove the exhaust seal.

67. Remove the bolt securing the transmission oil cooler pipe bracket to the right side of the engine oil pan rail (M30 only).

68. Remove the inspection plug from the transmission (M30 only).

69. Mark the torque converter to flexplate/flywheel orientation to ensure proper realignment (M30 only).

70. Remove the service slot plug.

71. Repeat the following steps for all 3 torque converter bolts (M30 only):

   a. Rotate the harmonic balancer center bolt clockwise ONLY, in order to access the torque converter bolt through the service slot.

   b. Remove the torque converter bolt using one of the following:
   • 18 mm crowfoot wrench
   • Short T50 TORX® bit

72. Remove the 9 transmission mounting bolts.

73. Remove the remaining transmission mounting bolts.

74. Lower the vehicle.

75. Place a jack under the transmission for support.

76. Install an engine lift chain to the engine lift brackets and attach to an engine lift device.

77. Using the engine lift device, raise the engine only enough to remove the engine mounts.

78. Remove the bolts securing the following to the engine block:
   • The left engine mount
   • The right engine mount

79. Position the engine mounts away from the engine.

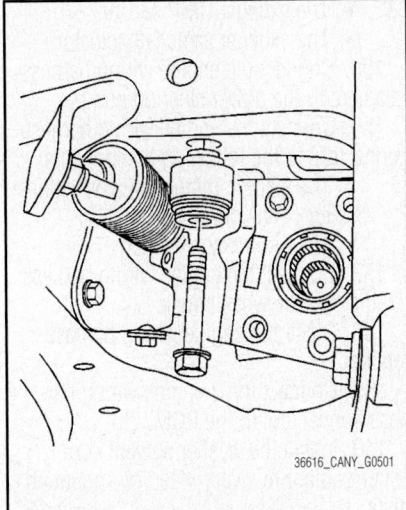

Fig. 183 Differential carrier assembly bushing to frame bolt location

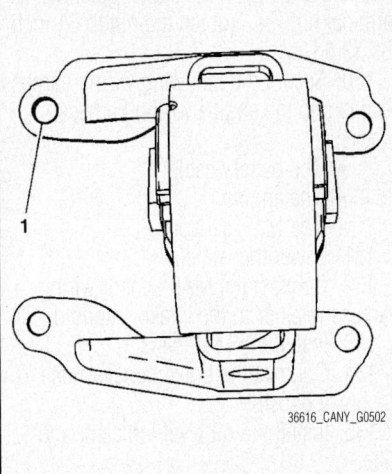

Fig. 184 Start bolt in this position first location—Right mount

➡**Ensure clearance is maintained between the engine and the following:**

- The A/C compressor
- The A/C hoses
- The engine mounts
- The engine wiring harness
- The fuel hose/pipes
- The heater outlet hose/pipe
- The power steering pump
- The radiator
- The transmission input shaft (MA5 only)
- The transmission oil cooler pipes (M30 only)

80. Carefully raise the engine from the engine compartment, ensuring the transmission stays supported.

81. If equipped with an automatic transmission, remove the automatic transmission flywheel locator.

82. Install the engine to an engine stand.

83. Remove the engine lift chain from the engine lift brackets.

To install:

84. Install an engine lift chain to the engine lift brackets and attach to an engine lift device.

85. Remove the engine from the engine stand.

86. If equipped with an automatic transmission, install the automatic transmission flywheel locator.

87. Ensure the torque converter is fully engaged with the transmission oil pump (M30 only).

➡**Ensure clearance is maintained between the engine and the following:**

- The A/C compressor
- The A/C hoses

- The engine mounts
- The engine wiring harness
- The fuel hose/pipes
- The heater outlet hose/pipe
- The power steering pump
- The radiator
- The transmission input shaft (MA5 only)
- The transmission oil cooler pipes (M30 only)

88. Carefully lower the engine into the engine compartment, aligning the engine dowels with the transmission.

➡**Ensure the torque converter turns freely while tightening the transmission mounting bolts (M30 only).**

89. Align the engine dowels with the transmission.

90. Loosely install the 2 transmission mounting bolts.

91. Ensure the dowels are fully engaged into the transmission.

92. Remove the jack from under the vehicle.

93. Position the engine mounts to the engine.

94. Install the bolts securing the right engine mount to the engine block.

95. The engine lift device may have to be raised or lowered slightly to install these bolts.

96. To aid in the installation of the bolts, start bolt in this position first. Tighten the bolts to 37 ft. lbs. (50 Nm).

97. Install the bolts securing the left engine mount to the engine block.

98. The engine lift device may have to be raised or lowered slightly to install these bolts.

99. To aid in the installation of the bolts,

start bolt in this position first. Tighten the bolts to 37 ft. lbs. (50 Nm).

100. Lower the engine fully on to the engine mounts.

101. Remove the engine lift chain from the engine lift brackets.

102. Raise and support the vehicle.

103. Tighten the 2 transmission mounting bolts previously installed to 37 ft. lbs. (50 Nm).

➡**Ensure the studded mounting bolts are located in the correct position.**

➡**The heater pipe must be secured with the 2 upper mounting bolts.**

104. Install the remaining transmission mounting bolts and tighten to 37 ft. lbs. (50 Nm).

105. Align the torque converter to flexplate/flywheel orientation marks made during the removal procedure (M30 only).

106. Repeat the following steps for all 3 torque converter bolts (M30 only):

a. Rotate the harmonic balancer center bolt clockwise ONLY, in order to access the torque converter bolt holes in the flexplate/flywheel through the service slot.

b. To aid in alignment of the torque converter to the flexplate/flywheel, install all 3 torque converter bolts before fully tightening using one of the following:

- 18 mm crowfoot wrench
- Short T50 TORX® bit
- Tighten the bolts to 44 ft. lbs. (60 Nm).

107. Install the inspection plug to the transmission (M30 only).

108. Install the bolt securing the transmission oil cooler pipe bracket to the right side of the engine oil pan rail (M30 only). Tighten the bolt to 15 ft. lbs. (20 Nm).

109. Install the exhaust seal.

110. Install the service slot plug.

111. Install the applicable components:

a. On 2WD models, install the crossmember.

b. On 4WD models:

- Position the differential carrier assembly to the frame.
- Install the differential carrier assembly bushing to frame bolts and tighten to 112 ft. lbs. (152 Nm).
- Install the front propeller shaft.

112. Install the nuts securing the fuel hose/pipe bracket to the transmission (M30 only). Tighten the nuts to 15 ft. lbs. (20 Nm).

113. Connect the fuel hose/pipe retainer to the range selector cable bracket (M30 only).

114. Install the nuts securing the fuel hose/pipe brackets to the transmission

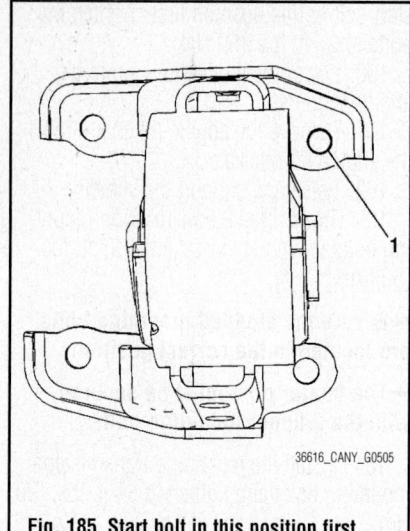

Fig. 185 Start bolt in this position first location—Left mount

36616_CANY_G0505

(MA5 only). Tighten the nuts to 15 ft. lbs. (20 Nm).

115. Install the left engine mount-to-frame bracket bolt and tighten to 63 ft. lbs. (85 Nm).

116. Connect the engine wiring harness retainer to the engine oil pan rail.

117. Install the 3 bolts securing the engine wiring ground leads to the engine block. Tighten the bolts to 15 ft. lbs. (20 Nm).

118. Lower the vehicle to chest level in order to access the components through the wheelhouse.

119. Connect the engine wiring harness connector to the CKP sensor.

120. Position the J 38185 to the clamp in order to connect the heater outlet hose to the heater outlet hose fitting.

121. Install the bolt securing the heater outlet hose/pipe to the left engine mount. Tighten the bolt to 80 inch lbs. (9 Nm).

122. For 3.7L engines, connect the engine wiring harness retainer to the engine oil pan rail.

123. Connect the engine wiring harness connector to the KS.

124. For 3.7L engines, connect the engine wiring harness connector to the KS 2.

125. Connect the coolant heater cord to the coolant heater, if equipped.

126. Connect the engine wiring harness connector to the EVAP canister purge solenoid valve.

127. Install the bolt securing the battery negative cable to the engine block. Tighten the bolt to 26 ft. lbs. (35 Nm).

128. Connect the battery positive cable to the starter and install the starter terminal nut. Tighten the nut to 80 inch lbs. (9 Nm).

129. Connect the lead (4) to the starter

solenoid and install the starter solenoid "S" terminal nut (3). Tighten the nut to 31 inch lbs. (3.5 Nm).

130. Secure the following wiring harness retainers to the engine wiring harness bracket:
- The battery cable
- The engine
- The MAP sensor

131. Lower the vehicle.

132. Connect the MAP sensor wiring harness retainer to the intake manifold.

133. Install the MAP sensor.

134. Connect the brake booster hose to the brake booster.

135. Install the oil level indicator and tube.

136. Connect the evaporative emission EVAP pipe at the intake manifold.

137. Connect the fuel feed pipe to the fuel rail.

138. Connect the engine wiring harness retainer to the intake manifold.

139. Install the right engine mount-to-frame bracket bolt and tighten to 63 ft. lbs. (85 Nm).

140. Position the power steering pump to the power steering pump bracket.

141. Install the power steering pump mounting bolts and tighten to 18 ft. lbs. (25 Nm).

142. Connect the inlet heater hose quick connect to the heater core.

143. Remove the J 44220 from the cylinder head.

144. Position the AIR pipe cover and NEW gasket to the cylinder head.

145. For 3.7L engines, install the AIR pipe cover studs and tighten to 18 ft. lbs. (25 Nm).

146. Install the transmission filler tube (M30 only).

147. Engage the engine wiring harness conduit to the camshaft cover.

148. For 3.7L engines, connect the engine wiring harness connector to the intake CMP sensor.

149. Connect the engine wiring harness retainer to the camshaft cover.

150. Connect the engine wiring harness connector to the throttle body.

151. Connect the engine wiring harness electrical connectors to the ignition coils.

152. Connect the engine wiring harness connectors to the following components:
- The fuel injector harness
- The HO2S
- The ECT sensor

153. Connect the engine wiring harness retainer to the camshaft cover.

154. Connect the engine wiring harness connectors to the following components:

- The exhaust CMP sensor
- The exhaust camshaft actuator

155. Connect the engine wiring harness retainers to the power steering pump.

156. Connect the engine wiring harness connectors to the following components:
- The electric motor actuator connector (4WD only)
- The oil pressure switch

157. Connect the engine wiring harness retainers to the wheelhouse.

158. Close the engine wiring harness retainer.

159. Connect the 2 engine wiring harness connectors to the PCM.

160. Install the washer solvent container/coolant recovery reservoir mounting bolts.

161. Position the J 38185 to the clamp in order to connect the radiator inlet hose to the water outlet housing.

162. Install the alternator.

163. Install the air cleaner resonator and outlet duct.

164. Install the air cleaner assembly.

165. Install the cooling fan.

166. Install the outlet radiator hose.

167. Fill the cooling system.

168. Install the battery box.

169. With the aid of an assistant, position the hood to the vehicle.

170. Partially install the 4 bolts that retain the hood to the hinges.

171. With the aid of an assistant, position the hood to the hinges at the previously marked locations. Tighten the bolts to 15 ft. lbs. (20 Nm).

172. Close the hood, inspect hood alignment, and adjust as necessary:

a. Open the hood and loosen the hinge to hood bolts.

b. Adjust the hood to fender position:
- The hood hinges are bolted to the inner fender and to the hood.
- Make fore and aft adjustments by elongating the hood-side hinge holes.
- Make vertical adjustments at the front by adjusting the hood bumpers up or down.
- Gap tolerances are 0.1–0.22 in. (2–6 mm).
- Flush tolerances are 0–0.06 in. (0–2 mm).

c. Adjust the hood bumpers.

d. Re-install the hinge to hood bolts and tighten to 15 ft. lbs. (20 Nm).

173. Install the front hood seal by pressing the retainers into the hood openings.

174. Fill the engine oil, if previously drained.

➠**After an overhaul, the engine should be tested. Use the Engine Testing procedure in this section after the engine is installed in the vehicle.**

5.3L Engine

See Figure 186.

1. Open the hood.
2. Remove the front hood seal by pulling downward on the seal, starting from one end.
3. Using a grease pencil or other suitable marking device, mark the position of the hood to the hinges.
4. With the aid of an assistant, remove the 4 bolts that retain the hood to the hood hinges.
5. With the aid of an assistant, remove the hood from the vehicle.
6. Place fender covers over both fenders.
7. Disconnect the negative battery cable.
8. Recover the refrigerant.
9. Remove the radiator. Refer to Radiator Removal & Installation.
10. Remove the intake manifold. Refer to Intake Manifold Removal & Installation.
11. Disconnect the oil pressure sensor and the oxygen sensors from the rear of the engine.
12. Disconnect the Engine Coolant Temperature (ECT) sensor.
13. Remove the ground terminal bolt.
14. Remove the retaining clips from the brackets.
15. Raise and suitably support the vehicle.
16. Remove the starter. Refer to Starter Removal & Installation.
17. Disconnect the following connectors:
   - Left and right side knock sensor electrical connector

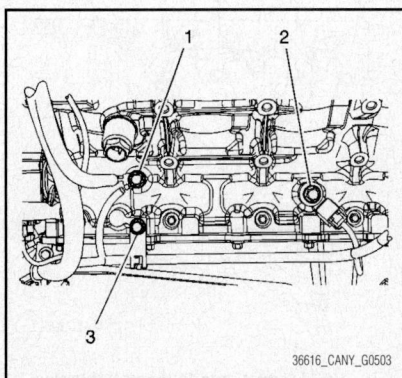

Fig. 186 Ground terminal bolt location

36616_CANY_G0503

   - A/C pressure switch electrical connector
   - Block heater electrical connector
18. Remove the ground terminal bolt.
19. Remove the engine harness bracket bolt.
20. Disconnect the engine wiring harness electrical connector from the Crankshaft Position (CKP) sensor.
21. Disconnect the engine wiring harness electrical connector from the Camshaft Position (CMP) sensor wire harness.
22. Remove the battery cable channel bolt.
23. Remove the battery cable channel from the oil pan.
24. Lower the vehicle.
25. Gather all branches of the engine wiring harness and reposition the harness off to the side.
26. Disconnect the engine wiring harness electrical connector from the alternator.
27. Reposition the engine wiring harness/positive battery cable boot.
28. Remove the engine wiring harness/positive battery cable nut from the alternator.
29. Remove the engine wiring harness/positive battery cable from the alternator.
30. Using J 38185, remove the inlet hose from the water outlet.
31. Using J 38185, remove the outlet hose from the water outlet.
32. Remove the heater inlet and outlet hoses.
33. Raise the vehicle.
34. Remove the catalytic converters. Refer to Catalytic Converter Removal & Installation.
35. Remove the 3 bracket bolts from both the right and the left side engine mounts.
36. Remove the torque converter bolts.
37. Remove the transmission oil level indicator tube.
38. Remove the transmission fluid cooler lines from the retainer located on the right side of the engine.
39. Remove the lower transmission bolts on the right and left side.
40. Remove the lower transmission bolt/studs.
41. Lower the vehicle.
42. Remove the 3 upper transmission bolts/studs.
43. Install an engine hoist to J 41798.
44. Install a floor jack under the transmission for support.
45. Separate the engine from the transmission.
46. Remove the engine.

47. Install the engine to an engine stand.
48. Install J 21366.

To install:

49. Remove J 21366.
50. Install an engine hoist to J 41798.
51. Remove the engine from the engine stand.
52. Install the engine.
53. Mate the engine to the transmission.
54. Remove the floor jack from under the transmission for support.
55. Install the 3 upper transmission bolts/studs and tighten to 37 ft. lbs. (50 Nm).
56. Raise the vehicle.
57. Install the lower transmission bolt/studs and tighten to 37 ft. lbs. (50 Nm).
58. Install the lower transmission bolts on the right and left side and tighten to 37 ft. lbs. (50 Nm).
59. Install the transmission fluid cooler lines to the right side of the engine.
60. Install the transmission oil level indicator tube.
61. Install the torque converter bolts and tighten to 44 ft. lbs. (60 Nm).
62. Install the 3 bracket bolts from both the right and the left side engine mounts.
63. Install the catalytic converters.
64. Lower the vehicle.
65. Install the heater inlet and outlet hoses.
66. Using J 38185, install the outlet hose to the water outlet.
67. Using J 38185, install the inlet hose to the water outlet.
68. Install the engine wiring harness/positive battery cable to the alternator.
69. Install the engine wiring harness/positive battery cable nut to the alternator and tighten the nut to 80 inch lbs. (9 Nm).
70. Position the engine wiring harness/positive battery cable boot.
71. Connect the engine wiring harness electrical connector to the alternator.
72. Gather all branches of the engine wiring harness and position the harness over the engine.
73. Raise the vehicle.
74. Install the starter.
75. Connect the following connectors:
   - Block heater electrical connector
   - A/C pressure switch electrical connector
   - Left and right side knock sensor electrical connector
76. Connect the engine wiring harness electrical connector to the CMP sensor wire harness.
77. Connect the engine wiring harness electrical connector to the CKP sensor.

78. Install the battery cable channel to the oil pan.

79. Install the battery cable channel bolt and tighten to 106 inch lbs. (12 Nm).

80. Install the engine harness bracket bolt.

81. Install the ground terminal bolt and tighten to 18 ft. lbs. (25 Nm).

82. Install the retaining clips to the brackets.

83. Install the ground terminal bolt and tighten to 18 ft. lbs. (25 Nm).

84. Connect the ECT sensor.

85. Connect the oil pressure sensor and the oxygen sensors at the rear of the engine.

86. Lower the vehicle.

87. Install the intake manifold.

88. Install the radiator.

89. Recharge the refrigerant.

90. Connect the negative battery cable.

91. Remove the fender covers from both fenders.

92. Prelube the engine.

93. Perform the CKP system variation learn procedure.

➡**After an overhaul, the engine should be tested. Use the Engine Testing procedure in this section after the engine is installed in the vehicle.**

ENGINE TESTING

2.9L & 3.7L Engines

1. With the ignition OFF or disconnected, crank the engine several times. Listen for any unusual noises or evidence that any parts are binding.

2. Start the engine and listen for abnormal conditions.

3. Check the vehicle oil pressure gage or light and confirm that the engine has acceptable oil pressure.

4. Run the engine at approximately 1000 RPM until the engine reaches normal operating temperature.

5. While the engine continues to idle raise and support the vehicle.

6. Inspect for oil, coolant, transmission fluid, and exhaust leaks while the engine is idling.

7. Lower the vehicle.

8. Perform the Crankshaft (CKP) variation learn procedure. Refer to Crankshaft Position System Variation Learn.

9. Perform a final inspection for the proper engine oil, transmission fluid and coolant levels.

10. Road test the vehicle.

5.3L Engines

1. Test the vehicle using the following procedure:

a. Disable the ignition system.

b. Crank the engine several times. Listen for any unusual noises or evidence that parts are binding.

c. Enable the ignition system.

d. Start the engine and listen for unusual noises.

e. Check the vehicle oil pressure gauge or light and confirm that the engine has acceptable oil pressure.

f. Run the engine speed at about 1,000 RPM until the engine has reached normal operating temperature.

g. Listen for sticking lifter and other unusual noises.

h. Inspect for fuel, oil and/or coolant leaks while the engine is running.

EXHAUST MANIFOLD

REMOVAL & INSTALLATION

2.9L & 3.7L Engines

See Figures 187 and 188.

1. Before servicing the vehicle, refer to the Precautions Section.

2. Remove the exhaust seal, as follows:

a. Raise and support the vehicle.

b. Remove the 3 nuts attaching the catalytic converter to the exhaust manifold.

c. Position the exhaust system rearward, enough to allow clearance to remove the seal.

d. Remove the exhaust manifold seal from the exhaust manifold flange. Discard the seal.

3. Remove the exhaust manifold heat shield, as follows:

a. Remove the air cleaner outlet duct. Refer to Air Cleaner Removal & Installation.

b. Remove the air cleaner assembly.

Refer to Air Cleaner Removal & Installation.

c. If equipped with M30, remove the transmission filler tube bracket nut from the A.I.R. adapter, and position aside.

d. Remove the Heated Oxygen Sensor (HO2S) from the exhaust manifold. Refer to Heated Oxygen Sensor Removal & Installation, in the Engine Performance & Emission Controls section.

e. Remove the 3 nuts securing the heat shield to the exhaust manifold.

f. Remove the heat shield.

4. Remove the exhaust manifold bolts.

5. Remove the exhaust manifold and the gasket from the engine. Discard the gasket.

To install:

6. Place a NEW exhaust manifold gasket on to the cylinder head.

7. Position the exhaust manifold to the cylinder head.

8. Apply threadlock GM P/N 12345493 (Canadian P/N 10953488) to the exhaust manifold bolt threads.

9. Install the exhaust manifold bolts.

10. Tighten the exhaust manifold bolts in sequence to 15 ft. lbs. (20 Nm).

11. Install the exhaust manifold heat shield, as follows:

a. Position the heat shield to the exhaust manifold.

b. Apply anti-seize GM P/N 12371386 (Canadian P/N 993128) to the exhaust manifold heat shield nuts.

c. Install the exhaust manifold heat shield nuts and tighten to 89 inch lbs. (10 Nm).

d. Install the HO2S to the exhaust manifold.

e. Position the transmission filler tube to the A.I.R. adapter if previously removed.

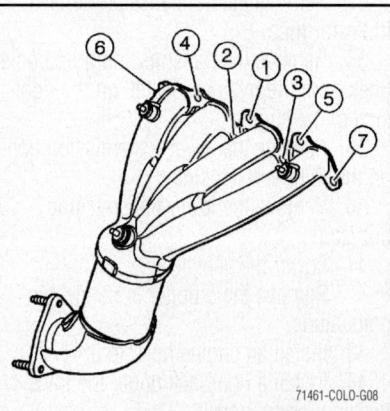

Fig. 187 Exhaust manifold bolt tightening sequence—2.9L engine

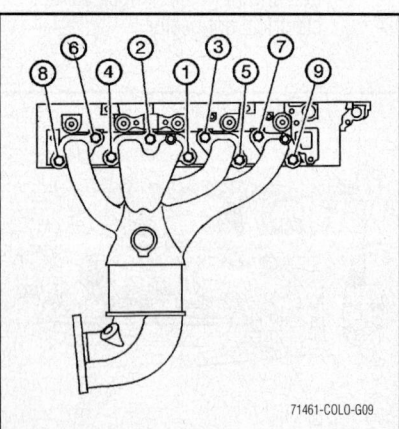

Fig. 188 Exhaust manifold bolt tightening sequence—3.7L engine

f. Install the transmission filler tube bracket nut and tighten to 9 ft. lbs. (12.5 Nm).

g. Install the air cleaner assembly and air cleaner outlet duct.

12. Install the exhaust seal, as follows:

a. Install the NEW seal to the exhaust manifold flange.

b. Position the catalytic converter to the exhaust manifold.

c. Install the 3 nuts attaching the catalytic converter to the exhaust manifold and tighten to 37 ft. lbs. (50 Nm).

d. Lower the vehicle.

5.3L Engine

Left Side

See Figures 189 through 191.

1. Before servicing the vehicle, refer to the Precautions Section.

2. Raise and suitably support the vehicle.

3. Remove the left front tire and wheel assembly.

4. Remove the left catalytic converter. Refer to Catalytic Converter Removal & Installation.

5. Remove the upper intake manifold sight shield, as follows:

a. Remove the oil fill cap.

b. Grasp the front of the intake manifold sight shield and lift up disengaging the grommets from the studs.

c. Remove the intake manifold sight shield from the retainer slots.

d. Remove the intake manifold sight shield retainer bolts and retainer, if required.

6. Remove the spark plugs. Refer to Spark Plug Removal & Installation.

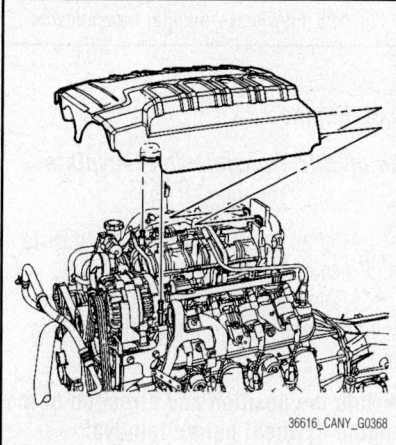

Fig. 189 Upper intake manifold sight shield—5.3L engine

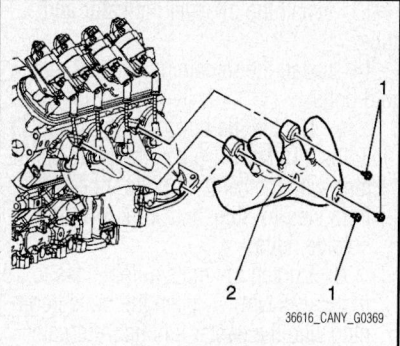

Fig. 190 Exhaust manifold heat shield — 5.3L engine, left side

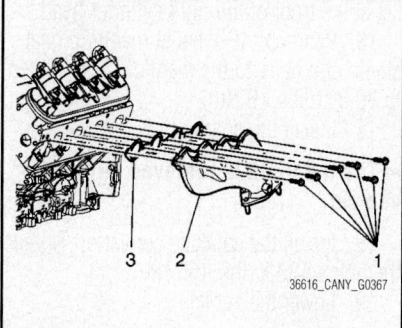

Fig. 191 Exhaust manifold (2), bolts (1), and gasket (3)—5.3L engine, left side

7. Remove the exhaust manifold heat shield bolts (1) and heat shield (2) from the exhaust manifold.

8. Working through the wheel well opening, remove the exhaust manifold bolts (1).

➡**The manifold is removed from below the vehicle.**

9. Remove the exhaust manifold (2) and gasket (3). Discard the gasket.

To install:

✷✷ WARNING

Tighten the exhaust manifold bolts as specified in the service procedure. Improperly installed and/or leaking exhaust manifold gaskets may affect vehicle emissions and/or On-Board Diagnostics (OBD) II system performance.

➡**The cylinder head exhaust manifold bolt hole threads must be clean and free of debris or threadlocking material.**

➡**Do not apply sealant to the first 3 threads of the bolt.**

10. Apply a 0.2 in. (5 mm) wide band of threadlock GM P/N 12345493, (Canadian

P/N 10953488), or equivalent to the threads of the exhaust manifold bolts.

11. Install one exhaust manifold bolt to the exhaust manifold and place the NEW gasket onto the bolt.

12. Working through the wheel well opening, install the remaining exhaust manifold bolts.

a. Tighten the bolts a first pass to 11 ft. lbs. (15 Nm). Tighten the bolts beginning with the center 2 bolts. Alternate from side-to-side, and work toward the outside bolts.

b. Tighten the bolts a final pass to 18 ft. lbs. (25 Nm). Tighten the bolts beginning with the center 2 bolts. Alternate from side-to-side, and work toward the outside bolts.

13. Using a flat punch, bend over the exposed edge of the exhaust manifold gasket at the rear of the left cylinder head.

14. Position the exhaust manifold heat shield and bolts to the manifold and tighten to 80 inch lbs. (9 Nm).

15. Install the spark plugs.

16. Install upper intake manifold sight shield, as follows:

a. Position the intake manifold sight shield on top of the intake manifold, aligning the holes, if required.

b. Install the intake manifold sight shield retainer bolts, if required. Tighten to 44 inch lbs. (5 Nm).

c. Install the intake manifold sight shield tabs into the slots in the retainer.

d. Align the intake manifold sight shield grommets with the studs.

e. Gently push down on the intake manifold sight shield over the grommets, seating the intake manifold sight shield.

f. Install the oil fill cap.

17. Install the catalytic converter. Tighten the nuts to 37 ft. lbs. (50 Nm).

18. Install the left front tire and wheel assembly.

19. Lower the vehicle.

Right Side

See Figures 192 and 193.

1. Before servicing the vehicle, refer to the Precautions Section.

2. Raise and suitably support the vehicle.

3. Remove the catalytic converter. Refer to Catalytic Converter Removal & Installation.

4. Remove the spark plugs. Refer to Spark Plug Removal & Installation.

5. Remove the exhaust manifold heat shield bolts (1) and shield (2).

6. Remove the oil level indicator and tube.

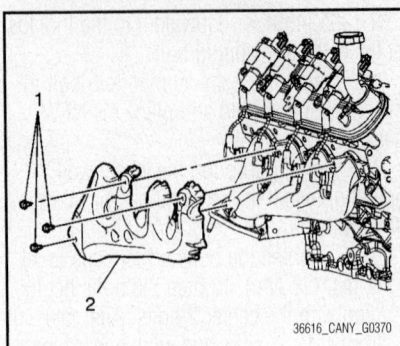

Fig. 192 Exhaust manifold heat shield — 5.3L engine, right side

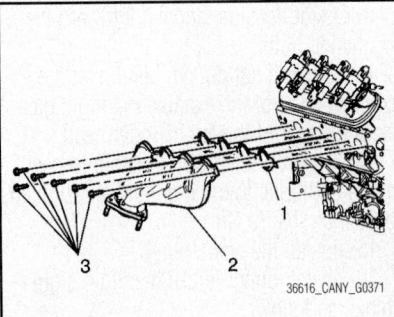

Fig. 193 Exhaust manifold (2), bolts (3), and gasket (1)—5.3L engine, right side

7. Remove the exhaust manifold bolts (3).
8. Remove the exhaust manifold (2) and gasket (1). Discard the gasket.

To install:

➡**Tighten the exhaust manifold bolts as specified in the service procedure. Improperly installed and/or leaking exhaust manifold gaskets may affect vehicle emissions and/or On-Board Diagnostics (OBD) II system performance.**

➡**The cylinder head exhaust manifold bolt hole threads must be clean and free of debris or threadlocking material.**

➡**Do not apply sealant to the first 3 threads of the bolt.**

9. Apply a 0.2 in, (5 mm) wide band of threadlock GM P/N 12345493, (Canadian P/N 10953488), or equivalent to the threads of the exhaust manifold bolts.
10. Ensure that the exhaust seal is still seated on the catalytic converter recess.
11. Install one exhaust manifold bolt to the exhaust manifold and place the NEW gasket onto the bolt.
12. Install the exhaust manifold to the catalytic converter flange and position the manifold to the cylinder head.

13. Install the oil level indicator and tube.
14. Install the remaining exhaust manifold bolts.
    a. Tighten the bolts a first pass to 11 ft. lbs. (15 Nm). Tighten the bolts beginning with the center 2 bolts. Alternate from side-to-side, and work toward the outside bolts.
    b. Tighten the bolts a final pass to 18 ft. lbs. (25 Nm). Tighten the bolts beginning with the center 2 bolts. Alternate from side-to-side, and work toward the outside bolts.
15. Using a flat punch, bend over the exposed edge of the exhaust manifold gasket at the front of the right cylinder head.
16. Position the exhaust manifold heat shield and bolts to the manifold and tighten to 80 inch lbs. (9 Nm).
17. Install the spark plugs.

➡**The manifold is removed below the vehicle.**

18. Install the catalytic converter. Tighten the nuts to 37 ft. lbs. (50 Nm).
19. Lower the vehicle.

FLYWHEEL/FLEXPLATE

REMOVAL & INSTALLATION

2.9L & 3.7L Engines

Automatic Transmission

See Figure 194.

1. Before servicing the vehicle, refer to the Precautions Section.
2. Remove the transmission. Refer to Transmission Removal & Installation.
3. Remove and discard the flywheel bolts.
4. Remove the flywheel.

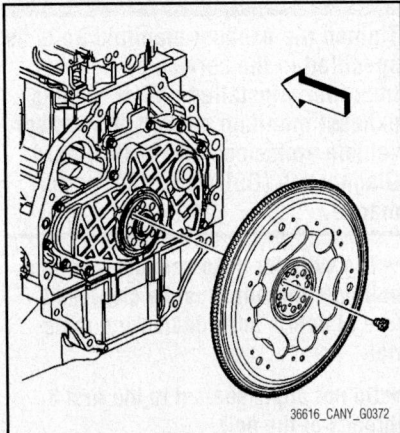

Fig. 194 Flywheel—automatic transmission

5. Clean and inspect the flywheel.

To install:
6. Position the flywheel to the crankshaft.
7. Install the new flywheel bolts and tighten to 30 ft. lbs. (40 Nm) plus an additional 45 degrees using the J 45059.
8. Install the transmission.

Manual Transmission

See Figure 195.

1. Before servicing the vehicle, refer to the Precautions Section.
2. Remove the clutch assembly. Refer to Clutch Removal & Installation.
3. Remove and discard the flywheel bolts.
4. Remove the flywheel.

To install:
5. Position the flywheel to the crankshaft.
6. Install the new flywheel bolts and tighten to 30 ft. lbs. (40 Nm) plus an additional 45 degrees using the J 45059.
7. Install the clutch assembly.

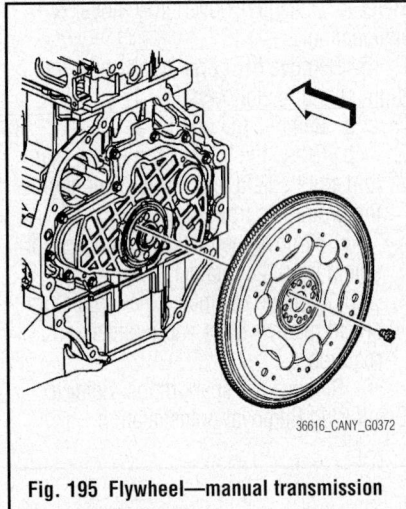

Fig. 195 Flywheel—manual transmission

5.3L Engine

Automatic Transmission Flexplate

See Figures 196 through 198.

1. Before servicing the vehicle, refer to the Precautions Section.
2. Remove the automatic transmission. Refer to Transmission Removal & Installation.

➡**Note the position and direction of the engine flywheel before removal.**

3. Remove the flywheel bolts.
4. Remove the flywheel.
5. Install two M11x1.5 mm bolts (1) to

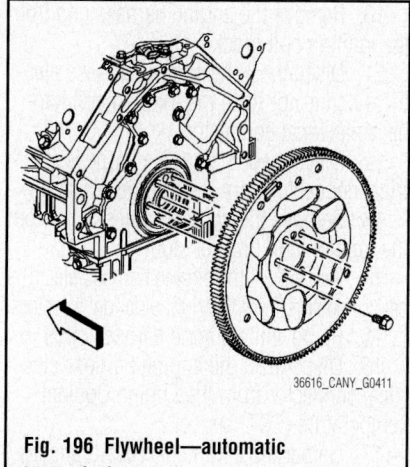

Fig. 196 Flywheel—automatic transmission

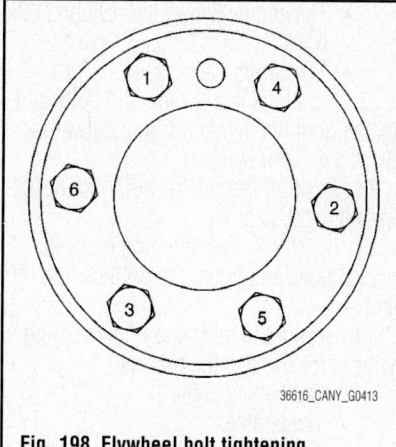

Fig. 198 Flywheel bolt tightening sequence—automatic transmission

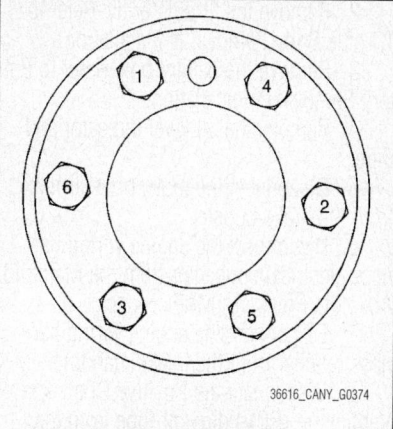

Fig. 200 Flywheel bolt tightening sequence—manual transmission

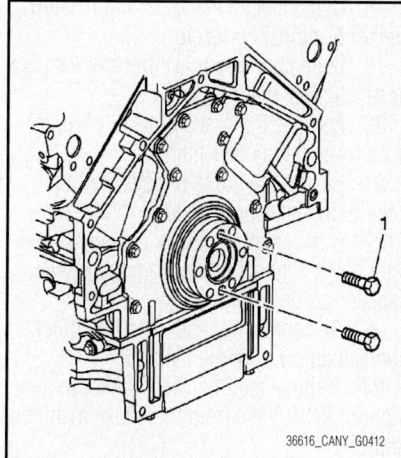

Fig. 197 Remove spacer—automatic transmission

the threaded holes of the spacer, if applicable.

6. Rotate the bolts clockwise to remove the spacer.

7. Remove the spacer from the rear of the crankshaft, if applicable.

To install:

➡**The flywheel does not use a locating pin for alignment and will not initially seat against the crankshaft flange or spacer, if applicable, but will be pulled onto the crankshaft by the engine flywheel bolts. This procedure requires a three stage tightening process.**

8. Install the spacer, if applicable, onto the rear of the crankshaft.

➡**Longer flywheel bolts must be used on applications using a flywheel spacer.**

9. Install the flywheel and bolts to the crankshaft.

10. Apply threadlock to the threads of the flywheel bolts.

11. Tighten the flywheel bolts:

a. Tighten the bolts (1–6) a first pass in sequence to 15 ft. lbs. (20 Nm).

b. Tighten the bolts (1–6) a second pass in sequence to 37 ft. lbs. (50 Nm).

c. Tighten the bolts (1–6) a final pass in sequence to 74 ft. lbs. (100 Nm).

12. Install the automatic transmission.

Flywheel

See Figures 199 and 200.

1. Before servicing the vehicle, refer to the Precautions Section.

2. Remove the transmission. Refer to Transmission Removal & Installation.

➡**Note the position and direction of the engine flywheel before removal.**

3. Remove and discard the flywheel bolts.

4. Remove the flywheel.

5. Clean and inspect the flywheel.

To install:

➡**The flywheel does not use a locating pin for alignment and will not initially**

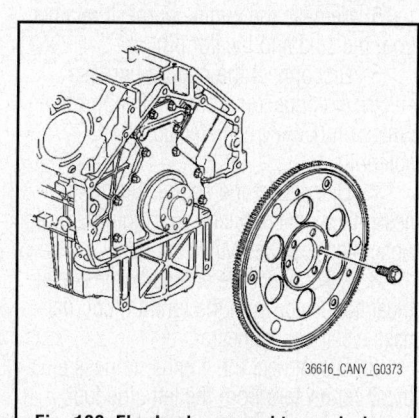

Fig. 199 Flywheel—manual transmission

seat against the crankshaft flange, but will be pulled onto the crankshaft by the engine flywheel bolts. This procedure requires a three stage tightening process.

6. Install the engine flywheel to the crankshaft.

7. Apply threadlock to the threads of the flywheel bolts.

8. Install the engine flywheel bolts:

- Tighten the bolts a first pass in sequence to 15 ft. lbs. (20 Nm).
- Tighten the bolts a second pass in sequence to 37 ft. lbs. (50 Nm).
- Tighten the bolts a final pass in sequence to 74 ft. lbs. (100 Nm).

9. Install the transmission.

INTAKE MANIFOLD

REMOVAL & INSTALLATION

2.9L & 3.7L Engines

See Figure 201.

1. Before servicing the vehicle, refer to the Precautions Section.

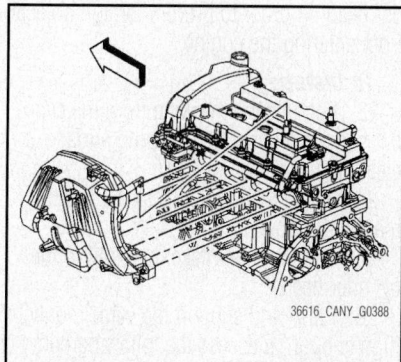

Fig. 201 Remove the intake manifold from the cylinder head

2. Remove the throttle body. Refer to Throttle Body Removal & Installation.

3. Remove the battery box. Refer to Battery Removal & Installation.

4. Remove the oil level indicator and tube.

5. Disconnect the brake booster hose from the brake booster.

6. Disconnect the engine wiring harness electrical connector from the Manifold Absolute Pressure (MAP) sensor.

7. Disconnect the engine wiring harness retainer from the intake manifold.

8. Disconnect the Positive Crankcase Ventilation (PCV) dirty air tube from the camshaft cover.

9. Remove the alternator. Refer to Alternator Removal & Installation.

10. Disconnect the engine wiring harness retainer from the intake manifold.

11. Remove the upper 2 bolts securing the engine wiring harness bracket to the intake manifold.

12. Raise and support the vehicle only high enough to access the remaining components through the wheelhouse.

13. Remove the left front wheel.

14. Remove the left front wheelhouse liner.

15. Disconnect the following wiring harness retainers from the engine wiring harness bracket:
- The battery cable
- The engine
- The MAP sensor

16. Remove the remaining engine wiring harness bracket lower bolt.

17. Remove the bracket from the engine compartment through the wheelhouse opening.

18. Remove the intake manifold bolts.

19. Lower the vehicle.

20. Remove the intake manifold from the cylinder head.

21. Remove the seal from the intake manifold. Discard the seal.

22. Mask off the open ports to the cylinder head, in order to prevent foreign objects from entering the engine.

To install:

23. Remove the masking from the cylinder head and ensure the sealing surface is clean and dry.

24. Install a NEW seal into the intake manifold groove.

25. Position the intake manifold to the cylinder head.

26. Raise and support the vehicle only high enough to access the following components through the wheelhouse:
- The intake manifold bolts

- The engine wiring harness bracket bolts
- The wiring harnesses

27. Install the intake manifold bolts and tighten from the inside working outward to 89 inch lbs. (10 Nm).

28. Position the engine wiring harness bracket to the engine.

29. Install the engine wiring harness bracket bolts and tighten to 89 inch lbs. (10 Nm).

30. Secure the following engine wiring harness retainers to the bracket:
- The battery cable
- The engine
- The MAP sensor

31. Install the left front wheelhouse liner.

32. Install the left front wheel.

33. Lower the vehicle.

34. Connect the engine wiring harness retainer to the intake manifold.

35. Install the alternator.

36. Connect the PCV dirty air tube to the camshaft cover.

37. Connect the engine wiring harness retainer to the intake manifold.

38. Connect the engine wiring harness electrical connector to the MAP sensor.

39. Connect the brake booster hose to the brake booster.

40. Install the oil level indicator and tube.

41. Install the battery box.

42. Install the throttle body.

5.3L Engine

See Figures 202 through 204.

1. Before servicing the vehicle, refer to the Precautions Section.

2. Remove the air cleaner outlet duct. Refer to Air Cleaner Removal & Installation.

3. Remove the alternator. Refer to Alternator Removal & Installation.

4. Remove the engine harness retainer nut.

5. Remove the engine harness retainer from the stud and locator pin.

6. Disconnect the engine harness electrical connector from the Evaporative Emission (EVAP) canister purge solenoid.

7. Disconnect the engine wiring harness electrical connector from the Manifold Absolute Pressure (MAP) sensor.

8. Disconnect the engine harness electrical connector from the ignition coil harness electrical connector.

9. Disconnect the engine harness electrical connectors from the left side fuel injectors.

10. Remove the engine harness clip from the ignition coil bracket stud.

11. Disconnect the engine harness electrical connector from the ignition coil harness electrical connector.

12. Disconnect the engine harness electrical connector from the throttle actuator.

13. Remove the engine harness clip from the ignition coil bracket stud.

14. Disconnect the engine harness electrical connectors from the right side fuel injectors.

15. Remove the engine harness clips.

16. Disconnect the engine harness electrical connector from the Engine Coolant Temperature (ECT) sensor.

17. Gather the engine harness branches and tie the harness up out of the way to the front of the engine compartment.

18. Disconnect the engine oil pressure sensor electrical connector.

19. Reposition the brake booster vacuum hose clamp at the booster.

20. Remove the brake booster vacuum hose from the booster fitting.

21. Secure the brake booster vacuum hose to the intake manifold.

22. Disconnect the EVAP canister purge tube quick connect fitting from the EVAP canister purge solenoid.

23. Disconnect the fuel feed line quick connect fitting from the fuel rail.

24. Remove the Positive Crankcase Ventilation (PCV) hose from the intake manifold fitting.

25. Position the hose out of the way.

26. Loosen the intake manifold bolts (512).

➡ **The aid of an assistant may be helpful in holding the engine harness up**

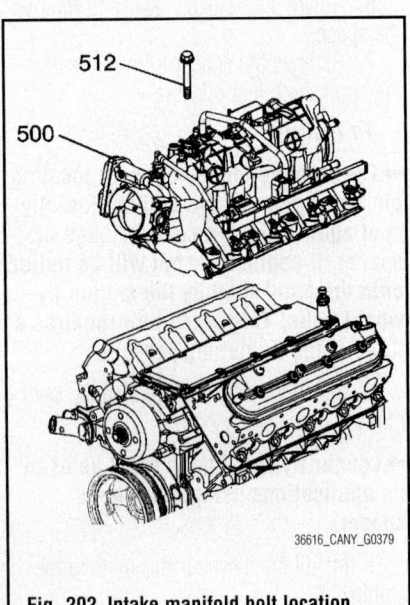

Fig. 202 Intake manifold bolt location

36616_CANY_G0379

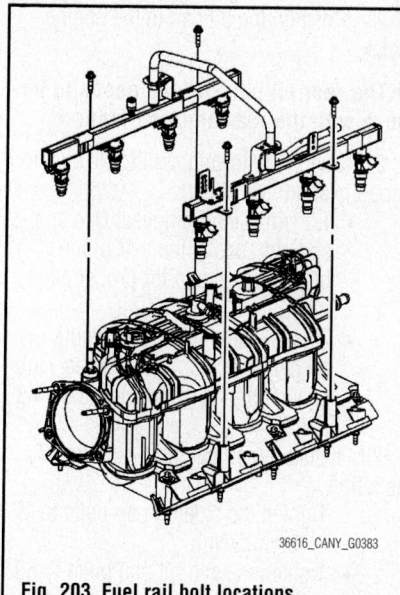

Fig. 203 Fuel rail bolt locations

out of the way so the upper intake manifold cover does not get caught against the engine harness.

27. Remove the intake manifold (500).
28. Cover the cylinder head passages in order to prevent dirt or debris from entering the passages.
29. Remove and discard the intake manifold gaskets.
30. If replacing the intake manifold, perform the following steps, otherwise proceed to step 21 of the installation procedure.
31. Place the intake manifold on a clean work surface.
32. Reposition the brake booster vacuum hose clamp at the intake manifold.
33. Remove the brake booster vacuum hose from the intake manifold nipple.
34. Remove the upper intake manifold cover nut.
35. Remove the upper intake manifold cover.
36. Remove the MAP sensor retainer.
37. Remove the MAP sensor.
38. Disconnect the EVAP tube quick connect fitting at the intake manifold.
39. Disengage the retainer securing the EVAP canister purge solenoid to the fuel rail.
40. Remove the EVAP tube and purge solenoid.
41. Remove the throttle body bolts/nuts.
42. Remove the throttle body.
43. Remove and discard the throttle body gasket.
44. Remove the fuel rail bolts.

➡**Lift evenly on both sides of the fuel rail until all injectors are removed from their bores.**

45. Remove the fuel rail.

46. Remove and discard the fuel injector lower O-ring seals.

➡**Evenly push in the RED collar in order to remove the nipple.**

47. Remove the brake booster vacuum hose nipple.

To install:

48. If the intake manifold was replaced perform the following steps, otherwise proceed to step 21.

➡**Evenly push in the RED collar in order to install the nipple.**

49. Install the brake booster vacuum hose nipple to the NEW intake manifold.
50. Install NEW fuel injector lower O-ring seals onto the injectors.
51. Lubricate the NEW O-ring seals with clean engine oil.

➡**Push down firmly on both sides of the rail until all the injectors have been seated into their bores.**

52. Install the fuel rail.
53. Install the fuel rail bolts and tighten to 89 inch lbs. (10 Nm).
54. Install a NEW throttle body gasket to the intake manifold.
55. Install the throttle body.
56. Install the throttle body bolts/nuts and tighten to 89 inch lbs. (10 Nm).
57. Install the EVAP tube and purge solenoid.
58. Install the EVAP canister purge solenoid to the fuel rail bracket and engage the retainer.
59. Connect the EVAP tube quick connect fitting at the intake manifold.
60. Lubricate the MAP sensor seal with clean engine oil.
61. Install the MAP sensor.
62. Install the MAP sensor retainer.
63. Install the upper intake manifold cover.
64. Install the upper intake manifold cover nut until snug
65. Install the brake booster vacuum hose to the intake manifold nipple.
66. Position the brake booster vacuum hose clamp at the intake manifold.
67. Secure the brake booster vacuum hose to the intake manifold.
68. Install NEW intake manifold gaskets to the intake manifold.
69. Remove the covers from the cylinder head passages.
70. Install the intake manifold.

➡**The aid of an assistant may be helpful in holding the engine harness up out of the way so the upper intake man-**

ifold cover does not get caught against the engine harness.

71. Tighten the intake manifold bolts until snug.
72. Tighten the intake manifold bolts to specifications:
   a. Tighten the bolts a first pass in the sequence shown to 44 inch lbs. (5 Nm).
   b. Tighten the bolts a final pass in the sequence shown to 89 inch lbs. (10 Nm).
73. Position and install the PCV hose to the intake manifold fitting.
74. Connect the fuel feed line quick connect fitting to the fuel rail.
75. Connect the EVAP canister purge tube quick connect fitting to the EVAP canister purge solenoid.
76. Unsecure the brake booster vacuum hose from the intake manifold.
77. Install the brake booster vacuum hose to the booster fitting.
78. Position the brake booster vacuum hose clamp at the booster.
79. Connect the engine oil pressure sensor electrical connector.
80. Untie the engine harness branches from the front of the engine compartment and position over the engine.
81. Connect the engine harness electrical connector to the ECT sensor.
82. Position the engine harness clips to the bracket.
83. Connect the engine harness electrical connectors to the right side fuel injectors.
84. Install the engine harness clip to the ignition coil bracket stud.
85. Connect the engine harness electrical connector to the throttle actuator.
86. Connect the engine harness electrical connector to the ignition coil harness electrical connector.
87. Install the engine harness clip to the ignition coil bracket stud.
88. Connect the engine harness electrical connectors to the left side fuel injectors.

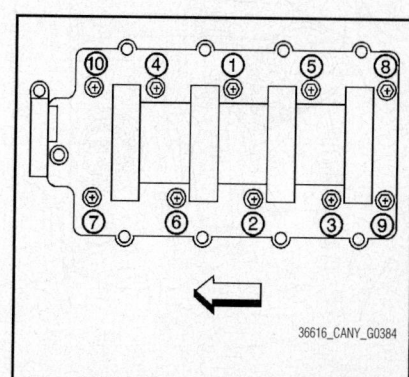

Fig. 204 Intake manifold bolt tightening sequence

89. Connect the engine harness electrical connector to the ignition coil harness electrical connector.

90. Install the CPA retainer.

91. Connect the engine wiring harness electrical connector to the MAP sensor.

92. Connect the engine harness electrical connector to the EVAP canister purge solenoid.

93. Install the engine harness retainer to the stud and locator pin.

94. Install the engine harness retainer nut and tighten to 44 inch lbs. (5 Nm).

95. Install the alternator.

96. Install the air cleaner outlet duct.

OIL PAN

REMOVAL & INSTALLATION

2.9L & 3.7L Engines

See Figures 205 through 207.

1. Before servicing the vehicle, refer to the Precautions Section.

2. Remove the oil level indicator and tube.

3. Remove the engine protection shield.

4. Drain the engine oil.

5. For 3.7L engines, remove the right front axle.

6. For 2WD models, remove the power steering gear. Refer to Power Rack & Pinion Steering Gear Removal & Installation.

7. For 4WD models:

   a. For 2.9L engines, remove the front propeller shaft. Refer to Propeller Shaft Removal & Installation.

   b. Remove the differential carrier assembly bushing to frame bolts ONLY.

   c. Pull the differential carrier assembly downward.

   d. Secure the pinion yoke, in order

to prevent the differential carrier from rotating.

8. Remove the service slot plug.

9. Remove the nuts securing the fuel hose/pipe bracket to the transmission, and position aside.

10. Remove 4 lower transmission mounting bolts that are attached to the oil pan.

11. For the 4WD only, remove the power steering gear mounting bolts ONLY. Refer to Power Rack & Pinion Steering Gear Removal & Installation.

12. Pull the power steering gear downward in order to gain access to the oil pan.

13. Disconnect the engine wiring harness retainers from the oil pan.

14. Remove the oil pan bolts.

15. Install 2 bolts in the threaded holes at the rear of the oil pan to act as jack screws and tighten evenly to release the oil pan from the engine block.

16. Remove the oil pan.

17. Remove the 2 bolts from the jack screw holes.

18. Clean and inspect the engine block sealing surface.

To install:

➡ **The oil pan must be installed within 10 minutes from when the sealer was applied.**

19. Apply a 0.22 in. (5.5 mm) bead of sealer to the oil pan in the areas marked (1).

20. Apply a 3 mm (0.12 in) bead of sealer to the oil pan in the area marked (2).

➡ **Use care not to allow the sealer to contact the oil pump pipe and screen assembly.**

21. Position the oil pan to the engine block.

➡ **The rear oil pan surface needs to be flush with the rear block surface.**

22. Use the following applicable step to properly align the oil pan:

   • Transmission Removed: Use a straight edge at the rear of the block and oil pan for proper alignment.

   • Transmission Installed: Ensure the oil pan is positioned fully rearward against the transmission mounting surface.

23. Install the oil pan bolts and tighten as follows:

   • Tighten the side oil pan bolts to 18 ft. lbs. (25 Nm).

   • Tighten the end oil pan bolts to 89 inch lbs. (10 Nm).

24. Connect the engine wiring harness retainers to the oil pan.

25. For the 4WD only, position the power steering gear upward to the frame assembly.

26. For the 4WD only, install the power steering gear mounting bolts.

27. Install the 4 lower transmission mounting bolts and tighten to 37 ft. lbs. (50 Nm).

28. Install the nuts securing the fuel hose/pipe bracket to the transmission. Tighten the nuts to 15 ft. lbs. (20 Nm).

29. Install the service slot plug.

30. For 3.7L engines, install the right front axle.

31. For 2WD models, install the power steering gear.

32. For 4WD models:

   a. Position the differential carrier assembly to the frame.

   b. Install the differential carrier

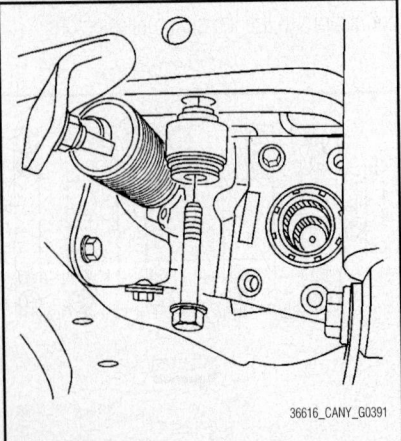

36616_CANY_G0391

Fig. 205 Remove the differential carrier assembly bushing to frame bolts ONLY

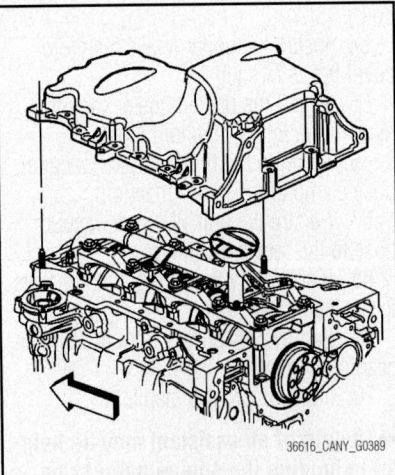

36616_CANY_G0389

Fig. 206 Oil pan removal

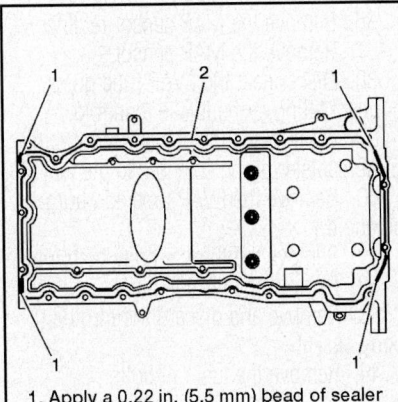

1. Apply a 0.22 in. (5.5 mm) bead of sealer
2. Apply a 0.12 in. (3 mm) bead of sealer

36616_CANY_G0390

Fig. 207 Oil pan sealant application

assembly bushing to frame bolts and tighten to 112 ft. lbs. (152 Nm).

c. For 2.9L engines, install the front propeller shaft.

33. Install the engine protection shield.

34. Install the oil level indicator and tube.

35. Fill the engine oil.

5.3L Engine

See Figures 208 through 211.

1. Before servicing the vehicle, refer to the Precautions Section.

2. Disconnect the negative battery cable.

3. Remove the oil level indicator tube.

4. Remove the front differential, if equipped.

5. Drain the engine oil.

6. Remove the transmission oil cooler lines from the retainer.

7. Remove the transmission oil cooler line retaining bracket bolt and bracket.

8. Remove the inner axle shaft.

9. Remove the starter. Refer to Starter Removal & Installation.

10. Remove the flywheel inspection cover from the left side of the transmission.

11. Remove the battery cable channel bolt from the front of the oil pan.

12. Remove the battery cable channel from the oil pan.

13. Loosen the 2 upper Air Conditioning (A/C) compressor bracket bolts.

14. Remove the 2 lower A/C compressor bracket bolts.

15. Position the A/C compressor aside and secure.

16. Remove the 2 lower bellhousing bolts (1).

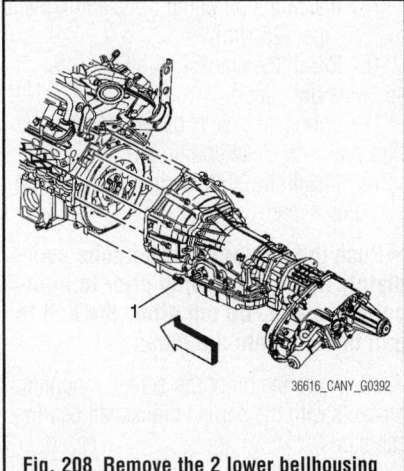

Fig. 208 Remove the 2 lower bellhousing bolts (1)

17. Remove the oil pan bolts.

18. Remove the oil pan by tilting the rear of the oil pan down to clear the transmission, pull the oil pan rearward past the front wire harness, then lower the oil pan clear of the vehicle.

➡The oil pan gasket is reusable. It is **NOT necessary to remove the oil pan gasket unless damaged.**

➡**DO NOT allow foreign material to enter the oil passages of the oil pan, cap or cover the openings as required.**

19. Drill out the oil pan gasket retaining rivets, if required.

20. Remove the gasket from the pan.

21. Discard the gasket and rivets.

22. Clean and inspect the oil pan.

To install:

✳✳ WARNING

The alignment of the structural oil pan is critical. The rear bolt hole locations of the oil pan provide mounting points for the transmission bellhousing. To ensure the rigidity of the powertrain and correct transmission alignment, it is important that the rear of the block and the rear of the oil pan must NEVER protrude beyond the engine block and transmission bellhousing plane.

➡**If replacing the oil pan gasket it is not necessary to rivet the NEW gasket to the oil pan.**

23. Apply a 0.2 in. (5 mm) bead of sealant 0.8 in. (20 mm) long to the engine block. Apply the sealant directly onto the tabs of the front cover gasket that protrudes into the oil pan surface.

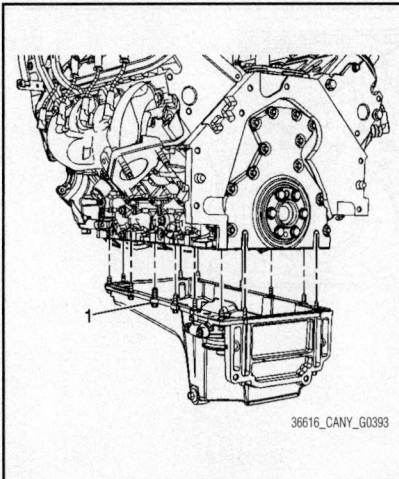

Fig. 209 Oil pan and bolts (1)

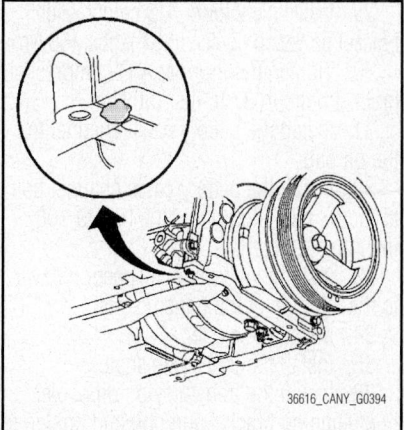

Fig. 210 Sealant application—front cover gasket tabs

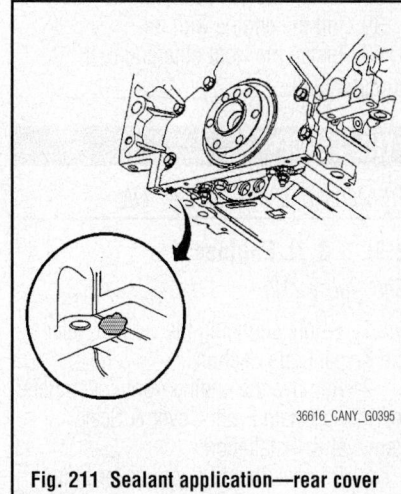

Fig. 211 Sealant application—rear cover gasket tabs

24. Apply a 0.2 in. (5 mm) bead of sealant 0.8 in. (20 mm) long to the engine block. Apply the sealant directly onto the tabs of the rear cover gasket that protrudes into the oil pan surface.

25. Pre-assemble the oil pan gasket and bolts to the pan:

a. Install the gasket onto the pan.

b. Install the oil pan bolts to the pan and through the gasket.

26. Install the oil pan, oil pan gasket, and bolts to the engine block as an assembly.

27. Hand thread the oil pan bolts into the engine block until snug. Do not tighten at this time.

28. Install the 2 lower bellhousing bolts:

a. Tighten the lower bellhousing bolts to 37 ft. lbs. (50 Nm).

b. Tighten the 2 rear oil pan to rear cover bolts to 106 inch lbs. (12 Nm).

c. Tighten the remaining oil pan bolts to 18 ft. lbs. (25 Nm).

29. Install the 2 lower A/C compressor bracket bolts and tighten to 37 ft. lbs. (50 Nm).

30. Tighten the 2 upper A/C compressor bracket bolts to 37 ft. lbs. (50 Nm).

31. Install the battery cable channel to the oil pan.

32. Install the battery cable channel bolt to the oil pan and tighten the bolt to 106 inch lbs. (12 Nm).

33. Install the flywheel inspection cover to the left side of the transmission.

34. Install the starter.

35. Install the inner axle shaft.

36. Install the transmission oil cooler line retaining bracket and bolt and tighten to 80 inch lbs. (9 Nm).

37. Install the transmission oil cooler lines to the retainer.

38. Install the oil level indicator tube.

39. Fill the engine with oil.

40. Install the front differential, if equipped.

OIL PUMP

REMOVAL & INSTALLATION

2.9L & 3.7L Engines

See Figure 212.

1. Before servicing the vehicle, refer to the Precautions Section.

2. Remove the engine front cover. Refer to Timing Chain Front Cover & Seal Removal & Installation.

3. Remove the oil pump cover bolts.

4. Remove the oil pump cover.

5. Mark the inner and the outer gears in relation to the oil pump housing.

6. Remove the inner and the outer oil pump gears.

7. Remove the oil pump pressure relief valve plug.

8. Remove the oil pump pressure relief valve and the spring.

To install:

9. Install the oil pump pressure relief valve and the spring.

10. Install the oil pump pressure relief valve plug and tighten to 10 ft. lbs. (14 Nm).

11. Install the oil pump outer and inner gears as removed.

12. Install the oil pump cover.

13. Install the oil pump cover bolts and tighten to 89 inch lbs. (10 Nm).

14. Install the engine front cover.

5.3L Engine

See Figures 213 and 214.

1. Before servicing the vehicle, refer to the Precautions Section.

2. Remove the oil pan. Refer to Oil Pan Removal & Installation.

3. Remove the engine front cover. Refer to Timing Chain Cover & Seal Removal & Installation.

4. Remove the oil pump screen bolt and nuts.

5. Remove the oil pump screen with O-ring seal.

6. Remove the O-ring seal from the pump screen.

7. Discard the O-ring seal.

8. Remove the remaining crankshaft oil deflector nuts.

9. Remove the crankshaft oil deflector.

10. Remove the oil pump bolts.

➡ **Do not allow dirt or debris to enter the oil pump assembly, cap end as necessary.**

11. Remove the oil pump.

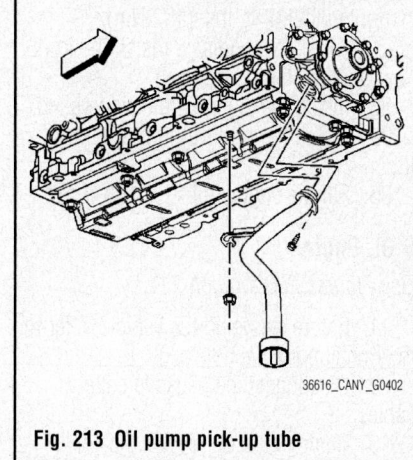

36616_CANY_G0402

Fig. 213 Oil pump pick-up tube

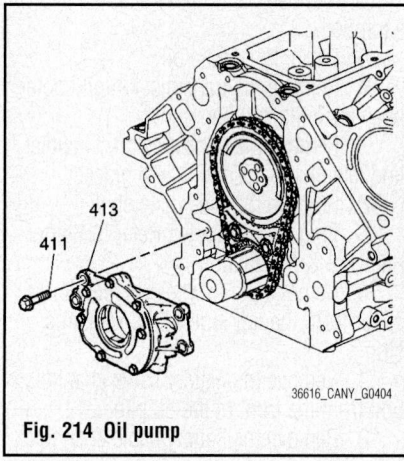

36616_CANY_G0404

Fig. 214 Oil pump

12. Clean and inspect the oil pump. Refer to Oil Pump Inspection.

To install:

13. Align the splined surfaces of the crankshaft sprocket and the oil pump drive gear and install the oil pump.

14. Install the oil pump onto the crankshaft sprocket until the pump housing contacts the face of the engine block.

15. Install the oil pump bolts and tighten to 18 ft. lbs. (25 Nm).

16. Install the crankshaft oil deflector and nuts until snug.

17. Lubricate a NEW oil pump screen O-ring seal with clean engine oil.

18. Install the NEW O-ring seal onto the oil pump screen.

➡ **Push the oil pump screen tube completely into the oil pump prior to tightening the bolt. Do not allow the bolt to pull the tube into the pump.**

19. Align the oil pump screen mounting brackets with the correct crankshaft bearing cap studs.

20. Install the oil pump screen.

21. Install the oil pump screen bolt and

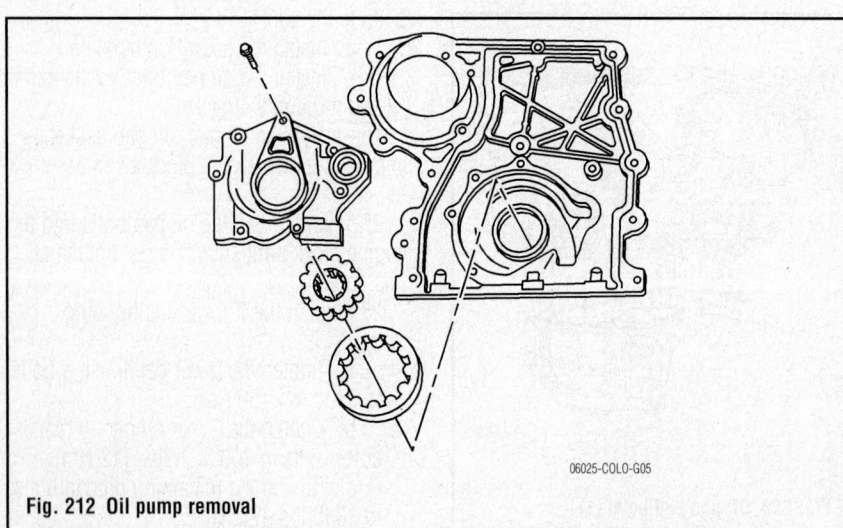

06025-COLO-G05

Fig. 212 Oil pump removal

nuts. Tighten the bolt to 106 inch lbs. (12 Nm) and tighten the nuts to 18 ft. lbs. (25 Nm).

22. Install the engine front cover.
23. Install the oil pan.

PISTON & RING

POSITIONING

See Figure 215.

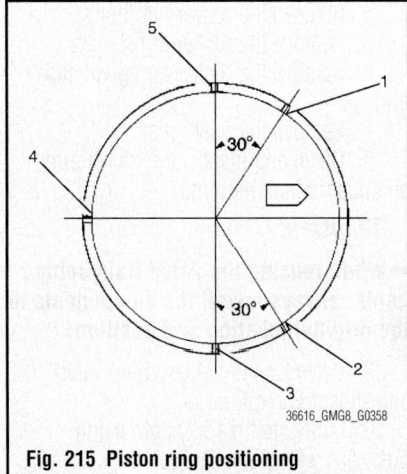

Fig. 215 Piston ring positioning

REAR MAIN SEAL

REMOVAL & INSTALLATION

2.9L & 3.7L Engines

See Figures 216 and 217.

1. Before servicing the vehicle, refer to the Precautions Section.
2. Remove the flywheel. Refer to Flywheel/Flexplate Removal & Installation.

✳✳ WARNING

Do not damage the crankshaft or seal bore.

3. Using a suitable tool, pry the crankshaft rear oil seal from the crankshaft rear oil seal housing.
4. Discard the seal.

To install:

5. Lightly lubricate the crankshaft rear oil seal lip with clean engine oil.
6. Position the plastic installation sleeve supplied with the new seal to the crankshaft.
7. Use the J 44215 with the J 8092 and a hammer to install the crankshaft rear oil seal into the crankshaft rear oil seal housing. Ensure the seal is installed square. The seal will bottom out in the housing when fully installed
8. Install the flywheel.

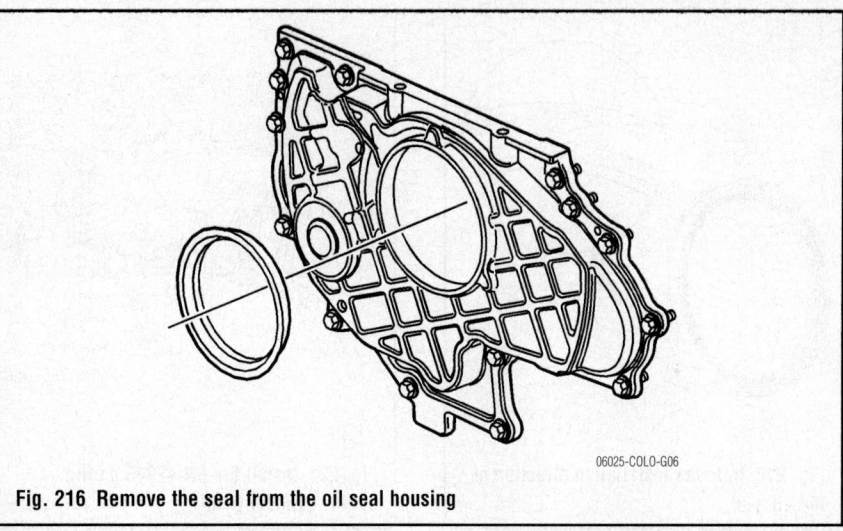

Fig. 216 Remove the seal from the oil seal housing

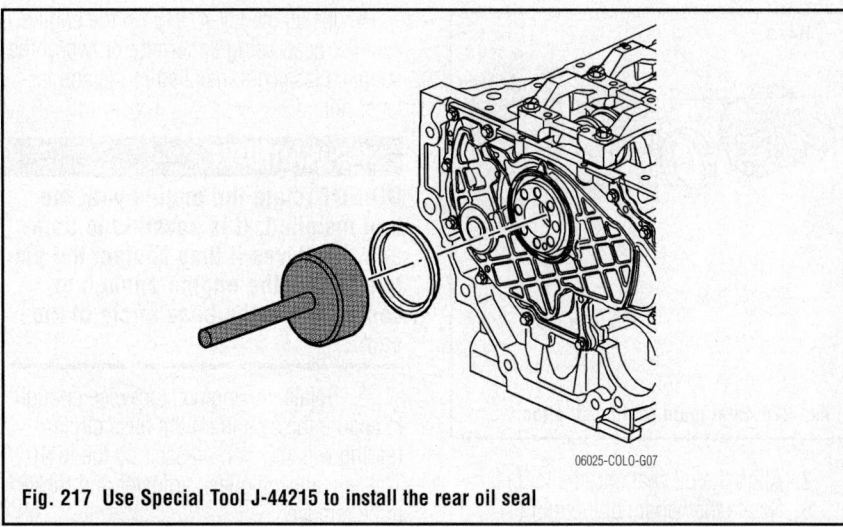

Fig. 217 Use Special Tool J-44215 to install the rear oil seal

5.3L Engine

See Figures 218 through 220.

1. Before servicing the vehicle, refer to the Precautions Section.
2. Remove the automatic transmission flexplate. Refer to Flywheel/Flexplate Removal & Installation.
3. Remove and discard the crankshaft rear oil seal (141).

To install:

✳✳ WARNING

For proper orientation, note the installation direction of the oil seal. The oil seal is a reverse-lip design. The part number is applied to the outside face of the seal, as shown.

4. Inspect the seal and identify the part number markings for proper orientation.
5. Install the J 41479 cone (2) and bolts onto the rear of the crankshaft. Tighten the bolts until snug. Do not overtighten.

6. Install the rear oil seal onto the tapered cone (2) and push the seal to the rear seal bore. Install the oil seal with the part number markings facing away from the engine.
7. Thread the J 41479 threaded rod into the tapered cone until the tool (1) contacts the oil seal.

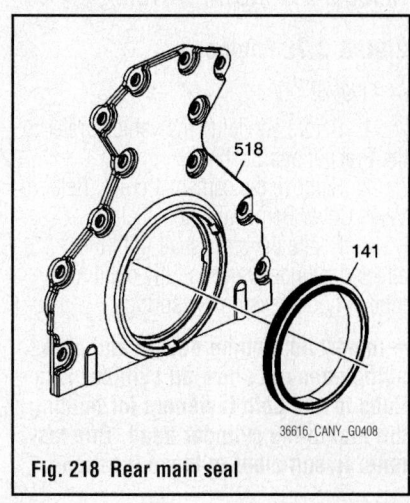

Fig. 218 Rear main seal

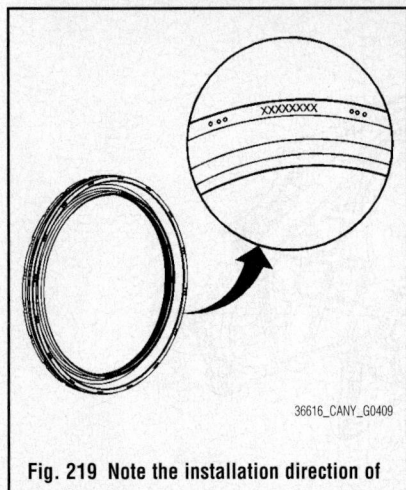

Fig. 219 Note the installation direction of the oil seal

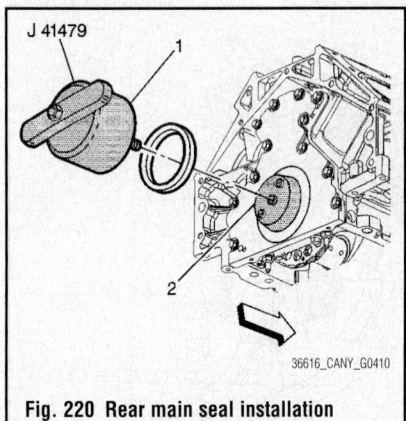

Fig. 220 Rear main seal installation

8. Align the oil seal into the tool (1).

9. Rotate the handle of the tool (1) clockwise until the seal enters the rear cover and bottoms into the cover bore.

10. Remove the J 41479.

11. Install the automatic transmission flexplate

ROCKER ARMS AND LIFTERS

REMOVAL & INSTALLATION

2.9L & 3.7L Engines

See Figure 221.

1. Before servicing the vehicle, refer to the Precautions Section.

2. Remove the camshaft cover. Refer to Valve Cover Removal & Installation.

3. Rotate the crankshaft until the affected cylinder valve is fully open (cam lobe fully depressing the spring).

➡**Important: Engine design and packaging does not allow all cylinder locations to use both fasteners for holding the tool to the cylinder head. One fastener is sufficient in these locations.**

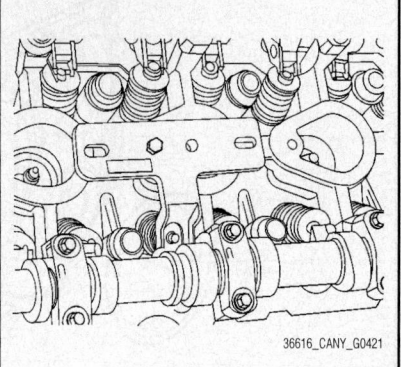

Fig. 221 Install the EN-47945 on the engine cylinder head

4. Install the EN-47945 on the engine cylinder head using either one or two of the supplied fasteners installed in the coil fastener hole.

✳✳ WARNING

DO NOT rotate the engine with the tool installed. It is possible to damage the valves if they contact the piston. Rotate the engine enough to come back to the base circle of the cam.

5. Rotate the engine clockwise enough to ensure the cam is on the base circle (spring will stay compressed by the tool). This will allow the lash adjuster and rocker to be removed.

6. Remove the valve rocker arm and valve lash adjuster.

7. Clean and inspect the valve rocker arm and valve lash adjuster.

To install:

8. Lubricate the valve rocker arm and fill the valve lash adjuster with oil.

9. Install the valve rocker arm and valve lash adjuster.

10. When the valve rocker arm and valve lash adjuster are in place, slowly rotate the engine counterclockwise enough that the cam lobe fully depresses the spring again.

11. Remove the EN-47945 from the cylinder head and repeat as required.

12. Install the camshaft cover.

5.3L Engine

See Figures 222 through 224.

1. Before servicing the vehicle, refer to the Precautions Section.

2. Remove the rocker arm cover. Refer to Valve Cover Removal & Installation.

➡The engine firing order is 1, 8, 7, 2, 6, 5, 4, 3. Cylinders 1, 3, 5 and 7 are the left bank.

3. Remove the number one cylinder spark plug. Refer to Spark Plug Removal & Installation.

➡Place the rocker arms, pushrods, and pivot support, in a rack so that they can be installed in the same location from which they were removed.

4. Remove the rocker arm bolts.

5. Remove the rocker arms.

6. Remove the rocker arm pivot support.

7. Remove the pushrods.

8. Clean and inspect the rocker arms and pushrods, if required.

To install:

➡When reusing the valve train components, always install the components to the original location and position.

9. Valve lash is net build, no valve adjustment is required.

10. Lubricate the rocker arms and pushrods with clean engine oil.

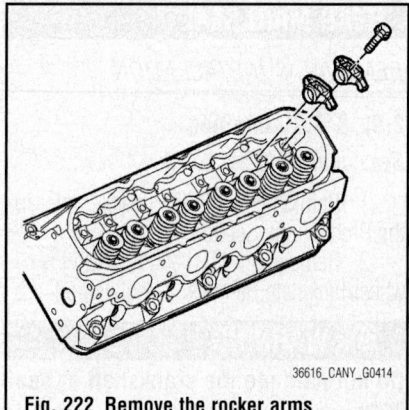

Fig. 222 Remove the rocker arms

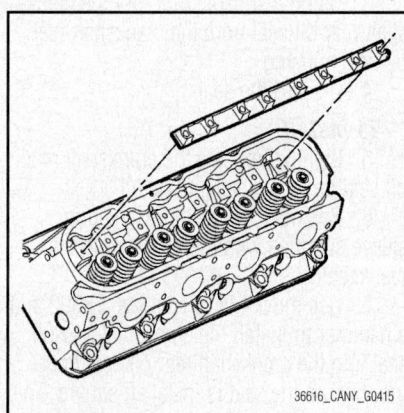

Fig. 223 Remove the rocker arm pivot support

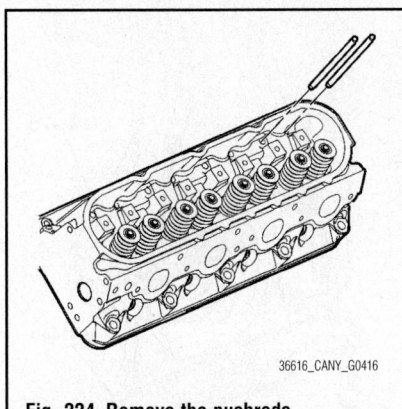

Fig. 224 Remove the pushrods

11. Lubricate the flange of the rocker arm bolts with clean engine oil. Lubricate the flange or washer surface of the bolt that will contact the rocker arm.

12. Install the rocker arm pivot support.

➡**Make sure that the pushrods seat properly to the valve lifter sockets.**

13. Install the pushrods.

➡**Make sure that the pushrods seat properly to the ends of the rocker arms. DO NOT tighten the rocker arm bolts at this time.**

14. Install the rocker arms and bolts.

➡**The engine firing order is 1, 8, 7, 2, 6, 5, 4, 3. Cylinders 1, 3, 5 and 7 are the left bank. Cylinders 2, 4, 6 and 8 are the right bank.**

15. Rotate the crankshaft until the number one piston is at top dead center (TDC) of the compression stroke. In this position, the number one cylinder rocker arms will be off lobe lift.

16. With the engine in the number one firing position, tighten the following rocker arm bolts:

- Tighten cylinders 1,2,7 and 8 exhaust valve rocker arm bolts to 22 ft. lbs. (30 Nm).
- Tighten cylinders 1,3,4 and 5 intake valve rocker arm bolts to 22 ft. lbs. (30 Nm).

17. Rotate the crankshaft 360 degrees.

18. Tighten the following rocker arm bolts:

- Tighten cylinders 3, 4, 5 and 6 exhaust valve rocker arm bolts to 22 ft. lbs. (30 Nm).
- Tighten cylinders 2, 6, 7 and 8 intake valve rocker arm bolts to 22 ft. lbs. (30 Nm).

19. Install the number one cylinder spark plug. Refer to Spark Plug Replacement.

20. Install the rocker arm cover.

TIMING CHAIN COVER AND SEAL

REMOVAL & INSTALLATION

2.9L & 3.7L Engines

See Figures 225 through 227.

1. Before servicing the vehicle, refer to the Precautions Section.

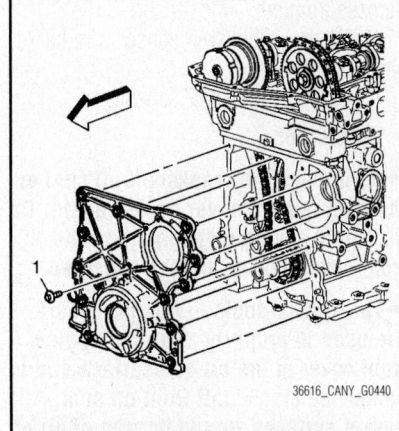

Fig. 225 Remove the engine front cover

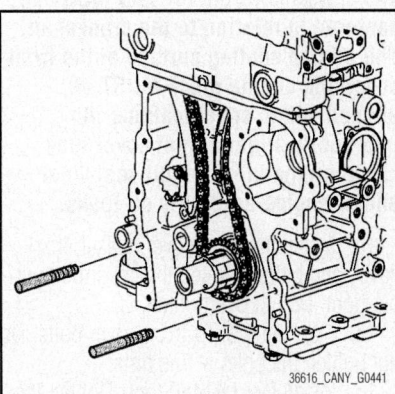

Fig. 226 Thread the J 44219 into the engine block

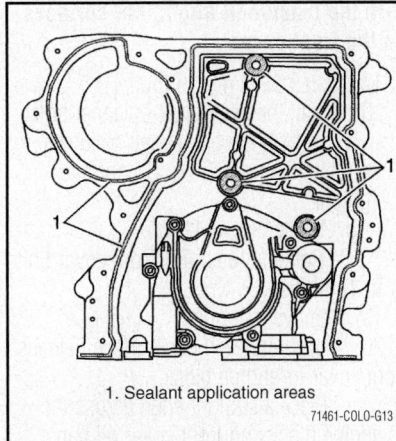

1. Sealant application areas

Fig. 227 Sealant application

2. Remove the water pump. Refer to Water Pump Removal & Installation.

3. Remove the crankshaft balancer. Refer to Crankshaft Damper Removal & Installation.

4. Remove the drive belt tensioner.

5. Remove the power steering pump.

6. Reposition A/C compressor on the side, if applicable.

7. Remove the oil pump pipe and screen assembly.

8. Lower the vehicle.

9. Remove the 7 mm center bolt (1).

10. Remove the remaining engine front cover bolts and discard the plastic bolt retainers if present.

11. Install 2 bolts into the threaded holes to act as jack screws and tighten evenly to release the engine front cover from the engine block.

12. Remove the engine front cover.

13. Remove the 2 bolts from the jack screw holes.

14. Remove the oil pump, if necessary. Refer to Oil Pump Removal & Installation.

15. Clean and inspect the engine block sealing surface.

To install:

16. Install the oil pump, if previously removed.

17. To aid in alignment of the cover, thread the J 44219 into the engine block.

➡**The engine front cover must be installed within 10 minutes from when the sealer was applied.**

18. Apply a 0.12 in. (3 mm) bead of sealer to the engine front cover.

19. Align the oil pump to the crankshaft sprocket splines.

20. Position the engine front cover over the J 44219, and to the engine block.

21. Install the engine front cover bolts.

22. Remove the J 44219 from the engine block.

23. Install the 2 remaining engine front cover bolts. Tighten the bolts to 89 inch lbs. (10 Nm). Tighten the small center bolt (1) last to 71 inch lbs. (8 Nm).

24. Install the oil pump pipe and screen assembly.

25. Install the power steering pump.

26. Install the drive belt tensioner.

27. Install the crankshaft balancer.

28. Install the water pump.

5.3L Engine

See Figures 228 through 232.

1. Remove the water pump. Refer to Water Pump Removal & Installation.

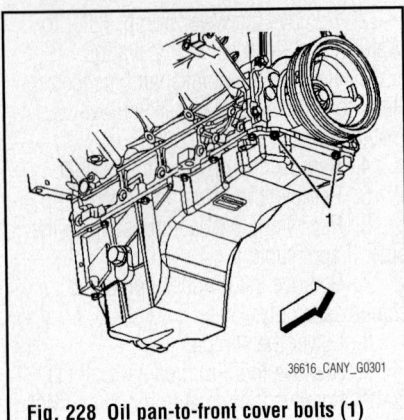

Fig. 228 Oil pan-to-front cover bolts (1)

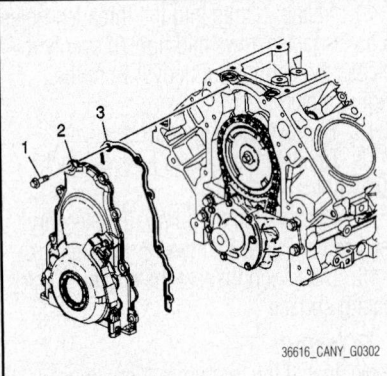

Fig. 229 Remove the front cover bolts (1), front cover (2) and gasket (3)

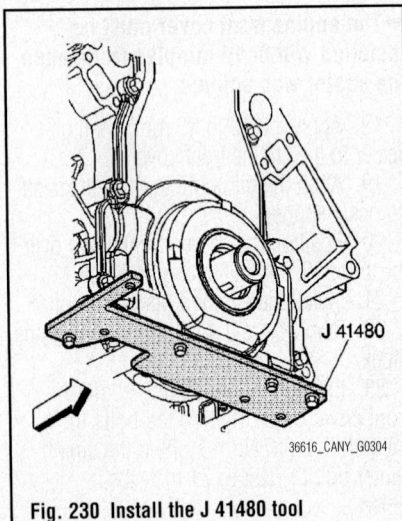

Fig. 230 Install the J 41480 tool

2. Remove the crankshaft balancer. Refer to Crankshaft Balancer Removal & Installation.

3. Disconnect the engine harness electrical connector (1) from the Camshaft Position (CMP) sensor wire harness electrical connector.

4. Remove the oil pan-to-front cover bolts (1).

5. Remove the front cover bolts (1).

6. Remove the front cover (2) and gasket (3).

7. Discard the front cover gasket.

8. Remove the crankshaft front oil seal.

9. If replacing the engine front cover perform the following steps, otherwise proceed to step 10 of the installation procedure.

10. Remove the CMP sensor wire harness bolts.

11. Disconnect the CMP sensor wire harness from the CMP sensor.

12. Remove the CMP sensor wire harness.

13. Remove the CMP sensor.

To install:

➡Do not use the crankshaft oil seal or the engine front cover gasket again. Do not apply any type of sealant to the front cover gasket, unless specified.

➡The special tools in this procedure are used to properly align the engine front cover at the oil pan surface and to center the crankshaft front oil seal. All gasket surfaces should be free of oil or other foreign material during assembly. The crankshaft front oil seal MUST be centered in relation to the crankshaft. The oil pan sealing surface at the front cover and engine block MUST be aligned within specifications. An improperly aligned front cover may cause premature front oil seal wear and/or engine assembly oil leaks.

14. Install the front cover gasket, front cover, and bolts. Tighten the cover bolts finger tight. Do not overtighten.

15. Start the tool-to-front cover bolts. Do not tighten the bolts at this time.

16. Install the J 41480 tool. Tighten the tool-to-engine block bolts to 18 ft. lbs. (25 Nm).

➡Align the tapered legs of the tool with the machined alignment surfaces on the front cover.

17. Install the J 41476 tool.

18. Install the crankshaft balancer bolt.
   a. Tighten the crankshaft balancer bolt by hand until snug. Do not overtighten.
   b. Tighten the J 41480.
   c. Tighten the engine front cover bolts to 18 ft. lbs. (25 Nm).

19. Remove the tools.

20. Measure the oil pan surface flatness, front cover-to-engine block:
   a. Place a straight edge across the engine block and front cover oil pan sealing surfaces.

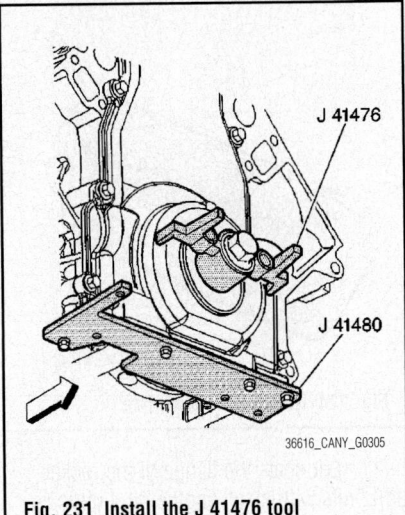

Fig. 231 Install the J 41476 tool

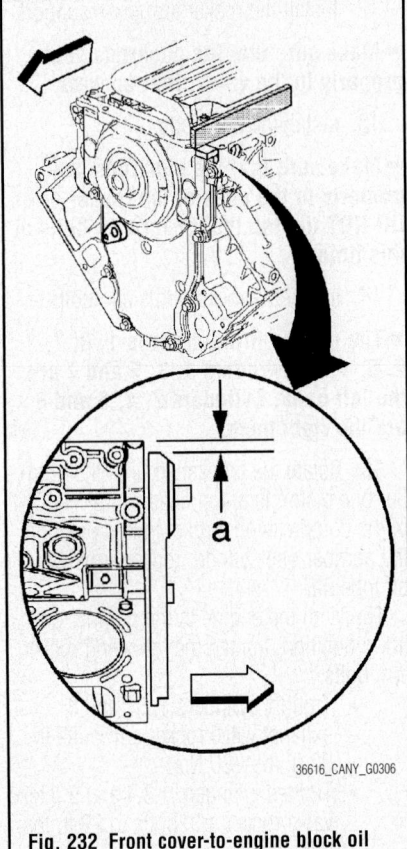

Fig. 232 Front cover-to-engine block oil pan surface alignment

➡Avoid contact with the portion of the gasket that protrudes into the oil pan surface.

   b. Insert a feeler gage between the front cover and the straight edge tool. The cover must be flush with the oil pan surface or no greater than 0.02 in. (0.5 mm) (a) below flush.

21. If the front cover-to-engine block oil pan surface alignment is not within

specifications, repeat the cover alignment procedure.

22. If the correct front cover-to-engine block alignment cannot be obtained, replace the front cover.

23. Inspect the CMP sensor O-ring seal for cuts or damage. If the seal is not cut or damaged, it may be used again.

24. Lubricate the O-ring seal with clean engine oil.

25. Install the O-ring seal onto the sensor.

26. Install the sensor to the cover.

27. Install the CMP sensor wire harness and bolts. Tighten the bolts to 106 inch lbs. (12 Nm).

28. Connect the engine harness electrical connector to the CMP sensor wire harness electrical connector.

29. Install a NEW crankshaft front oil seal.

30. Install the water pump.

TIMING CHAIN AND SPROCKETS

REMOVAL & INSTALLATION

2.9L & 3.7L Engines

See Figures 233 through 238.

1. Before servicing the vehicle, refer to the Precautions Section.

2. Remove No. 1 cylinder spark plug. Refer to Spark Plug Removal & Installation.

3. Remove the camshaft cover. Refer to Valve Cover Removal & Installation.

4. Remove the exhaust Camshaft Position (CMP) sensor. Refer to Camshaft Position Sensor Removal & Installation in the Engine Performance & Emission Control section.

5. Remove the intake CMP sensor. Refer to Camshaft Position Sensor Removal & Installation in the Engine Performance & Emission Control section.

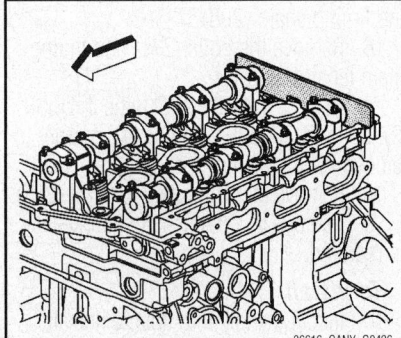

Fig. 233 Install the J 44221 to the rear of the camshafts

Fig. 234 Place the tee into the tensioner to hold the shoe in place

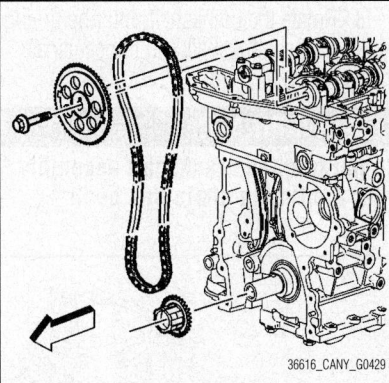

Fig. 235 Remove the intake camshaft timing chain and sprocket

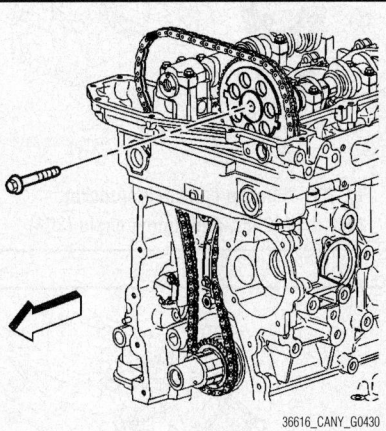

Fig. 236 Install the new intake camshaft sprocket bolt

6. Remove the engine front cover. Refer to Timing Chain Cover & Seal Removal & Installation.

7. Rotate the crankshaft in the engine rotational direction clockwise, until the No. 1 piston is at top dead center (TDC) on the compression stroke.

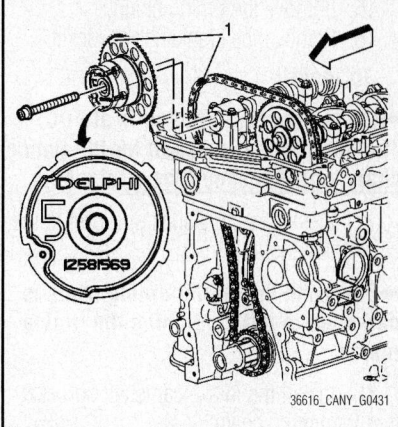

Fig. 237 Align the dark link (1) of the timing chain with the timing mark (1) on the exhaust camshaft position actuator sprocket

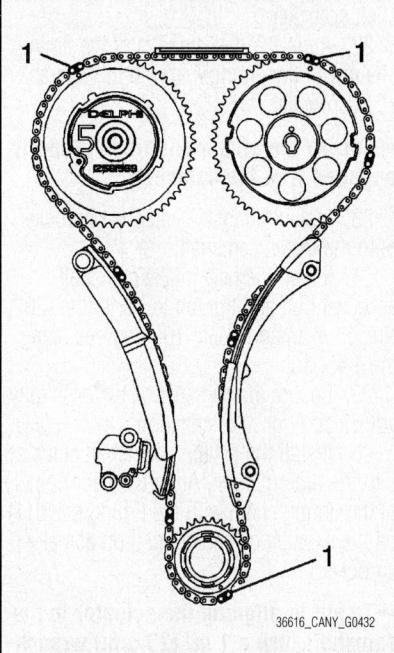

Fig. 238 The dark links (1) on the timing chain should be aligned with the marks on the sprockets

8. Install the J 44221 to the rear of the camshafts.

9. Release the tension on the timing chain by moving the tensioner shoe in.

10. Place the tee into the tensioner to hold the shoe in place.

11. Remove and discard the exhaust camshaft position actuator bolt.

12. Remove the exhaust camshaft position actuator.

13. Remove and discard the intake camshaft sprocket bolt.

14. Remove the intake camshaft sprocket.

15. Remove the timing chain.
16. Remove the crankshaft sprocket.

To install:

➡ **Ensure the No. 1 piston is at TDC. The pin on the crankshaft for the timing chain sprocket should be straight up.**

17. Install the crankshaft sprocket to the crankshaft snout.

➡ **Every 7th link of the timing chain is darkened to aid in aligning the timing marks.**

18. Install the intake camshaft sprocket into the timing chain.
19. Align the dark link (1) of the timing chain with the timing mark on the intake camshaft sprocket.
20. Feed the timing chain down through the opening in the cylinder head.
21. Install the timing chain on the crankshaft sprocket.
22. Align the dark link (2) of the timing chain with the timing mark on to the crankshaft sprocket.

➡ **Ensure the alignment pin is properly engaged with the camshaft**

23. Install the intake camshaft sprocket onto the intake camshaft.
24. Install the new intake camshaft sprocket bolt and tighten to 15 ft. lbs. (20 Nm) plus an additional 100 degrees using the J 45059.
25. Ensure the camshaft actuator is fully advanced prior to installation.
26. Install the exhaust camshaft actuator into the timing chain. Align the dark link (1) of the timing chain with the timing mark (1) on the exhaust camshaft position actuator sprocket.

➡ **To aid in aligning the actuator to the camshaft, use a 1 in. (25 mm) wrench on the hex of the camshaft to rotate. Ensure the alignment pin is properly engaged with the camshaft.**

27. Install the exhaust camshaft actuator onto the exhaust camshaft.
28. Install the new exhaust camshaft actuator bolt and tighten to 18 ft. lbs. (25 Nm) plus an additional 135 degrees using the J 45059.
29. Remove the tee in the timing chain tensioner to regain tension on the timing chain.
30. Remove the J 44221 from the camshafts.
31. The dark links (1) on the timing chain should be aligned with the marks on the sprockets as shown.
32. Install the engine front cover.
33. Install the intake CMP sensor.

34. Install the exhaust CMP sensor.
35. Install the camshaft cover.
36. Install No. 1 cylinder spark plug.

5.3L Engine

See Figures 239 through 247.

1. Before servicing the vehicle, refer to the Precautions Section.
2. Remove the oil pump. Refer to Oil Pump Removal & Installation.

> ❋❋ **WARNING**
>
> **Do not turn the crankshaft assembly after the timing chain has been removed in order to prevent damage to the piston assemblies or the valves.**

3. Rotate the crankshaft until the timing marks on the crankshaft and the camshaft sprockets are aligned.

> ❋❋ **WARNING**
>
> **Do not turn the crankshaft assembly after the timing chain has been**

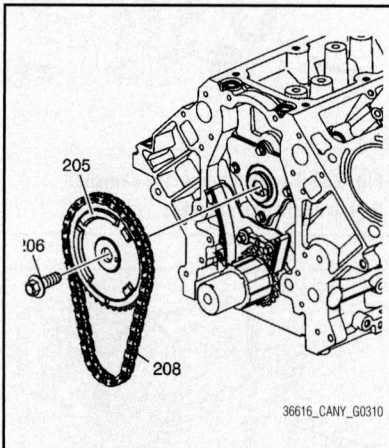

Fig. 239 Remove camshaft sprocket (205), bolt (206), and timing chain (208)

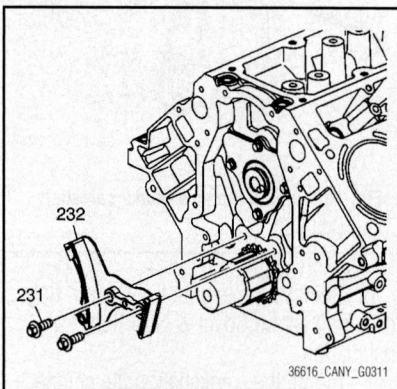

Fig. 240 Remove the bolts (231) and timing chain tensioner (232)

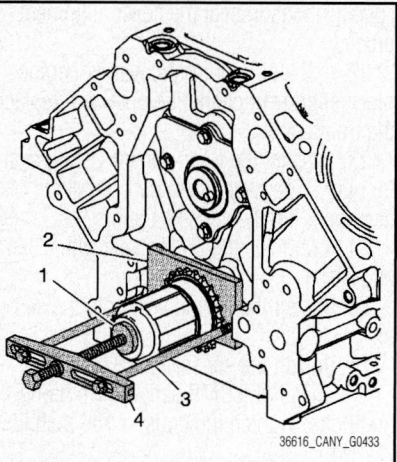

Fig. 241 Use the J 41816-2 (1), the J 41558 (2), bolts (3), and the J 8433 (4)

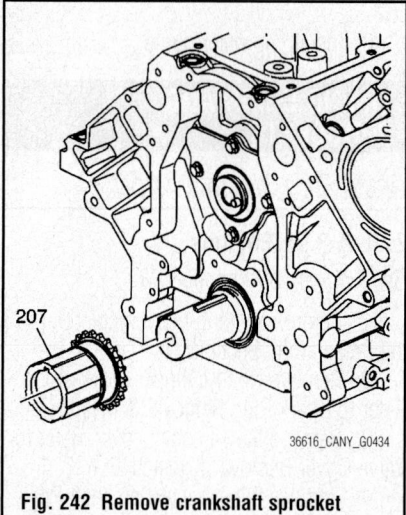

Fig. 242 Remove crankshaft sprocket (207)

removed in order to prevent damage to the piston assemblies or the valves.

4. Remove and discard the camshaft sprocket bolt (206).
5. Remove the camshaft sprocket (205) and timing chain (208).
6. Remove the bolts (231) and timing chain tensioner (232).
7. Use the J 41816-2 (1), the J 41558 (2), bolts (3), and the J 8433 (4) in order to remove the crankshaft sprocket.
8. Remove the crankshaft sprocket (207).
9. Remove the crankshaft sprocket key, as required.

To install:

10. Install the key into the crankshaft keyway, if previously removed.
11. Tap the key (122) into the keyway until both ends of the key bottom onto the crankshaft.

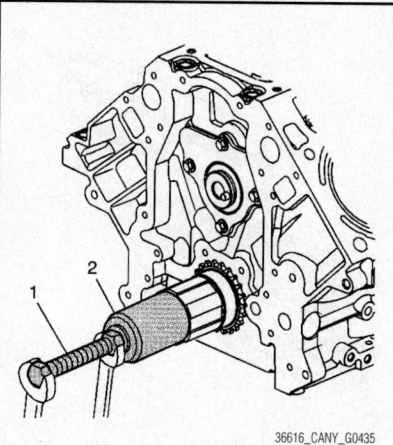

Fig. 243 Use the J 41478 (1) and the J 41665 (2) in order to install the crankshaft sprocket

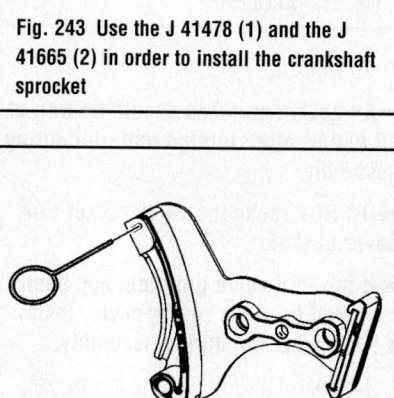

Fig. 244 Compress the timing chain tensioner guide and install the EN 46330

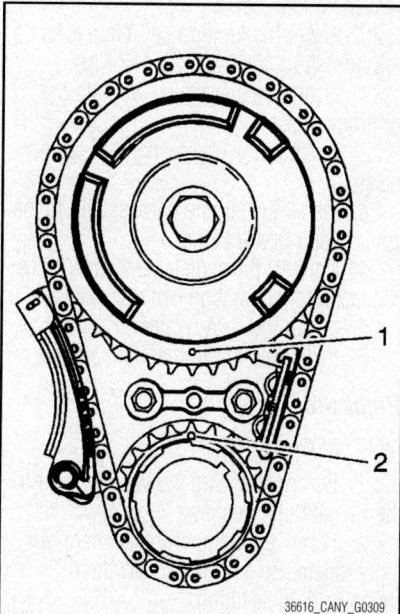

Fig. 245 Inspect the sprockets for proper alignment

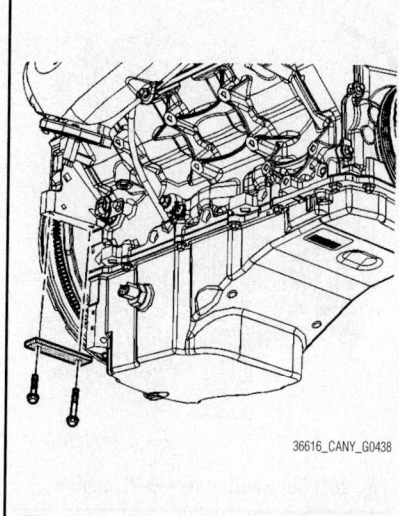

36616_CANY_G0438

Fig. 246 Install the J 42386-A and bolts

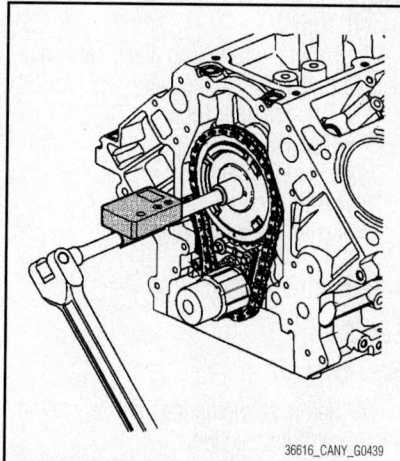

36616_CANY_G0439

Fig. 247 Tighten the camshaft sprocket bolt

12. Install the crankshaft sprocket (207) onto the front of the crankshaft. Align the crankshaft key with the crankshaft sprocket keyway.

13. Use the J 41478 (1) and the J 41665 (2) in order to install the crankshaft sprocket. Install the sprocket onto the crankshaft until fully seated against the crankshaft flange.

14. Rotate the crankshaft sprocket until the alignment mark is in the 12 o'clock position.

15. Compress the timing chain tensioner guide and install the EN 46330.

16. Install the timing chain tensioner (232) and bolts (231). Tighten the timing chain tensioner bolts to 18 ft. lbs. (25 Nm).

❋❋ WARNING

The sprocket teeth and timing chain must mesh. The camshaft and the

crankshaft sprocket alignment marks **MUST be aligned properly.**

17. Install the camshaft sprocket (205), timing chain (208), and bolt (206).

18. Inspect the sprockets for proper alignment. The mark on the camshaft sprocket (1) should be located in the 6 o'clock position and the mark on the crankshaft sprocket (2) should be located in the 12 o'clock position.

19. Remove the EN 46330.

➡**Do not apply threadlock to the flex plate bolts at this time.**

20. Temporarily install the automatic transmission flex plate and bolts.

21. Install the J 42386-A and bolts. Use 1 M10-1.5 x 120 mm bolt and 1 M10-1.5 x 45 mm bolt for proper tool operation. Tighten the J 42386-A bolts to 37 ft. lbs. (50 Nm).

22. Tighten the camshaft sprocket bolt a first pass to 55 ft. lbs. (75 Nm). Tighten the camshaft sprocket bolt a final pass an additional 50 degrees using the J 45059.

23. Remove the J 42386-A and bolts.

24. Remove the automatic transmission flex plate and bolts.

25. Install the oil pump.

VALVE COVERS/CAMSHAFT COVER

REMOVAL & INSTALLATION

2.9L & 3.7L Engines
See Figures 248 through 251.

1. Before servicing the vehicle, refer to the Precautions Section.

2. Remove the intake manifold. Refer to Intake Manifold Removal & Installation.

3. Remove the ignition coils. Refer to Ignition Coil Removal & Installation.

4. Remove the following electrical connectors from the camshaft cover:

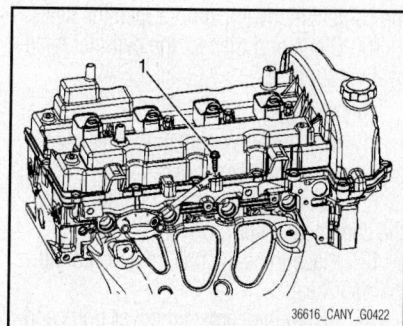

36616_CANY_G0422

Fig. 248 Camshaft cover ground wire bolt (1)—2.9L engine

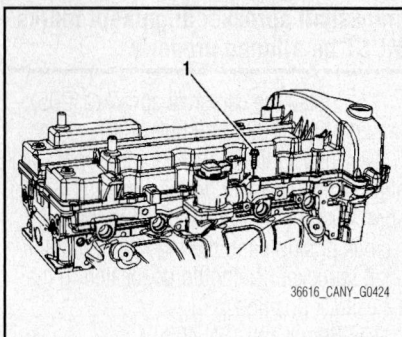

Fig. 249 Camshaft cover ground wire bolt (1)—3.7L engine

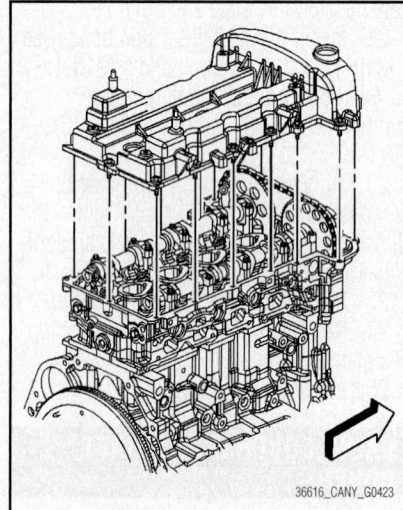

Fig. 250 Camshaft cover—2.9L engine

- The fuel injector
- The Heated Oxygen Sensor (HO2S)
- The Engine Coolant Temperature (ECT) sensor

5. Remove the camshaft cover ground wire bolt (1) from the cover.

6. Remove the ground wire from cover.

7. Remove the camshaft cover bolts.

8. Remove the camshaft cover from the cylinder head.

9. Remove and discard the seals from the camshaft cover. Do not reuse the seals.

10. Clean and inspect the cylinder head sealing surface.

To install:

11. Install a NEW camshaft cover seal into the camshaft cover groove.

12. Install NEW ignition coil seals into the camshaft cover grooves.

13. Place the camshaft cover onto the cylinder head.

14. Install the camshaft cover bolts and tighten to 89 inch lbs. (10 Nm).

15. Position the ground wire to the camshaft cover. Ensure that the anti rotation tab is seated against the cover.

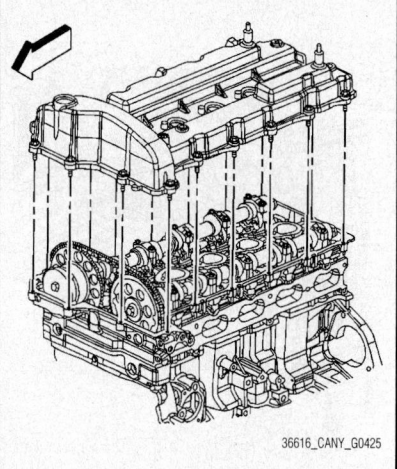

Fig. 251 Camshaft cover—3.7L engine

16. Install the camshaft cover ground wire bolt to the cover and tighten to 89 inch lbs. (10 Nm).

17. Install the following electrical connectors to the camshaft cover:
- The fuel injector
- The HO2S
- The ECT sensor

18. Install the ignition coils.

19. Install the intake manifold.

5.3L Engine

Left Side

See Figure 252.

1. Before servicing the vehicle, refer to the Precautions Section.

2. Remove the intake manifold cover. Refer to Intake Manifold Removal & Installation.

3. Remove the Connector Position Assurance (CPA) retainer.

4. Disconnect the engine harness electrical connector from the ignition coil wire harness.

5. Remove the engine harness clip from the ignition coil bracket stud.

6. Reposition the engine harness, as necessary.

7. Remove the spark plug wires from the ignition coils. Twist each plug wire ½ turn. Pull only on the boot in order to remove the wire from the ignition coil.

8. Remove the ignition coil bracket studs.

9. Remove the ignition coil bracket.

10. Remove the Positive Crankcase Ventilation (PCV) hose.

11. Loosen the valve rocker arm cover bolts.

12. Remove the valve rocker arm cover.

13. Remove and discard the old gasket.

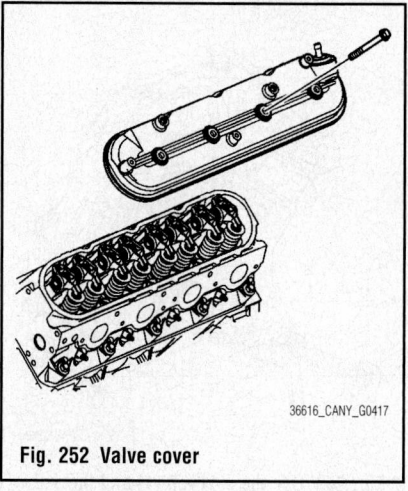

Fig. 252 Valve cover

To install:

➡ **All gasket surfaces should be free of oil and/or other foreign material during assembly.**

➡ **DO NOT reuse the valve rocker arm cover gasket.**

➡ **If the PCV valve grommet has been removed from the rocker cover, install a NEW grommet during assembly.**

14. Install a NEW rocker cover gasket.

15. Install the valve rocker arm cover.

16. Tighten the rocker arm cover bolts to 106 inch lbs. (12 Nm).

17. Install the PCV hose.

18. Apply threadlock to the threads of the ignition coil bracket studs.

19. Position the ignition coil bracket onto the rocker cover.

20. Install the ignition coil bracket studs and tighten to 106 inch lbs. (12 Nm).

21. Install the spark plug wires to the ignition coils.

22. Position the engine harness, as necessary.

23. Install the engine harness clip to the ignition coil bracket stud.

24. Connect the engine harness electrical connector to the ignition coil wire harness.

25. Install the CPA retainer.

26. Install the intake manifold cover.

Right Side

See Figures 253 and 254.

1. Before servicing the vehicle, refer to the Precautions Section.

2. Remove the upper intake manifold sight shield. Refer to Intake Manifold Removal & Installation.

3. Remove the Connector Position Assurance (CPA) lock.

4. Disconnect the main electrical connector to the ignition coil wire harness.

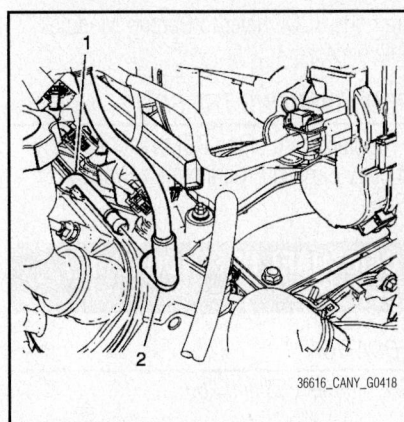

Fig. 253 Remove the vent hose (2) from the valve rocker arm cover (1)

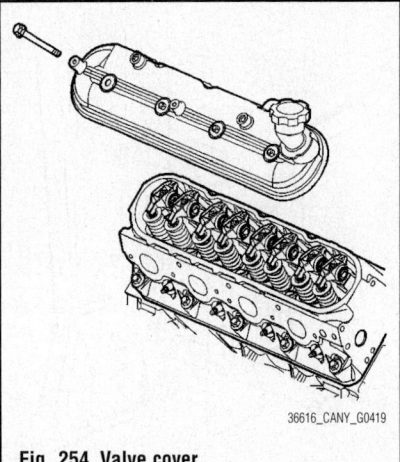

Fig. 254 Valve cover

5. Remove the harness clips.

6. Reposition the engine harness, if necessary.

7. Remove the spark plug wires from the ignition coils. Twist each plug wire ½ turn. Pull only on the boot in order to remove the wire from the ignition coil.

8. Remove the heater hose bracket bolt from the front of the right cylinder head.

9. If necessary, remove the ignition coil bracket studs from the rocker arm cover.

10. If necessary, remove the ignition coils and bracket from the rocker cover.

11. Remove the vent hose (2) from the valve rocker arm cover (1).

12. Remove the valve rocker arm cover bolts.

13. Remove the valve rocker arm cover.

14. Remove the gasket from the rocker cover.

15. Discard the OLD gasket.

16. Remove the oil fill cap from the oil fill tube.

17. Remove the oil fill tube from the rocker cover, if required.

18. Discard the oil fill tube.

To install:

➡ **All gasket surfaces should be free of oil or other foreign material during assembly.**

➡ **DO NOT reuse the valve rocker arm cover gasket.**

➡ **The valve rocker arm cover bolt grommets may be reused.**

➡ **If the oil fill tube has been removed from the rocker arm cover, install a NEW fill tube during assembly.**

19. Lubricate the O-ring seal of the NEW oil fill tube with clean engine oil.

20. Insert the NEW oil fill tube into the rocker arm cover. Rotate the tube clockwise until locked in the proper position.

21. Install the oil fill cap into the tube. Rotate the cap clockwise until locked in the proper position.

22. Install a NEW rocker cover gasket into the valve rocker arm cover.

23. Install the valve rocker arm cover onto the cylinder head.

24. Install new rocker arm cover grommets, if necessary.

25. Install the rocker arm cover bolts and grommets and tighten the bolts to 106 inch lbs. (12 Nm).

26. Install the vent hose to the valve rocker arm cover.

27. Apply threadlock to the threads of the bracket bolts.

28. If necessary, install the ignition coils and bracket to the rocker arm cover.

29. If necessary, install the ignition coil bracket studs to the rocker cover and tighten the studs to 106 inch lbs. (12 Nm).

30. Install the heater hose bracket bolt to the front of the right cylinder head.

31. Install the spark plug wires to the ignition coils.

32. Position the engine harness, if necessary.

33. Install the harness clips.

34. Connect the main electrical connector feeding the ignition coils.

35. Install the CPA lock.

36. Install the upper intake manifold sight shield.

ENGINE PERFORMANCE & EMISSION CONTROLS

ACCELERATOR PEDAL POSITION (APP) SENSOR

LOCATION

See Figure 255.

The APP sensor is located above the accelerator pedal arm.

REMOVAL & INSTALLATION

See Figure 255.

1. Before servicing the vehicle, refer to the Precautions Section.

2. Disconnect the Accelerator Pedal Position (APP) sensor electrical connector.

3. Remove the APP sensor nuts.

4. Remove the APP sensor from the vehicle.

To install:

5. Position the APP sensor over the studs.

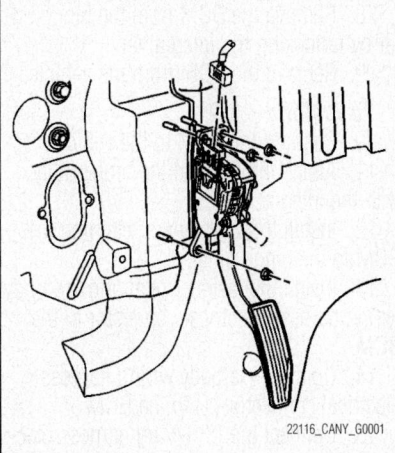

Fig. 255 Identifying accelerator pedal position sensor connector

6. Install the APP sensor nuts. Tighten the APP sensor mounting nuts to 80 inch lbs. (9 Nm).

7. Connect the APP sensor electrical connector.

8. Inspect below the pedal for binding, to ensure full range of motion.

BODY CONTROL MODULE (BCM)

REMOVAL & INSTALLATION

See Figures 256 through 258.

✷✷ WARNING

Replacement of the BCM requires a proprietary Service Programming System (SPS).

1. Before servicing the vehicle, refer to the Precautions Section.

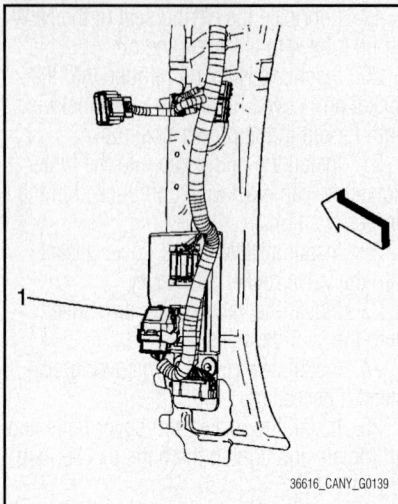

Fig. 256 Disconnect the body wiring harness electrical connector (1) from the BCM

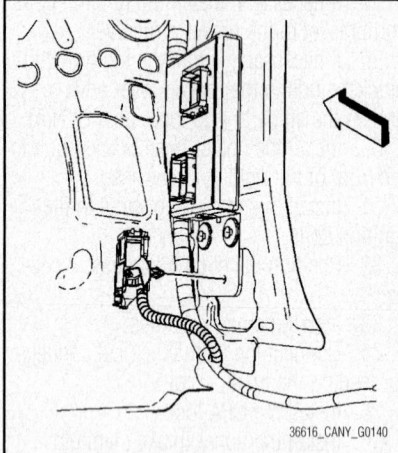

Fig. 257 Disconnect the I/P wiring harness electrical connector (1) from the BCM

❊❊ WARNING

The ignition switch should be in the OFF position when connecting or disconnecting the connectors to the Body Control Module (BCM).

❊❊ WARNING

Always disconnect the black body wiring harness connector FIRST and the gray instrument panel (I/P) wiring harness connector LAST.

❊❊ WARNING

Always connect the black body wiring harness connector FIRST and the gray I/P wiring harness connector LAST.

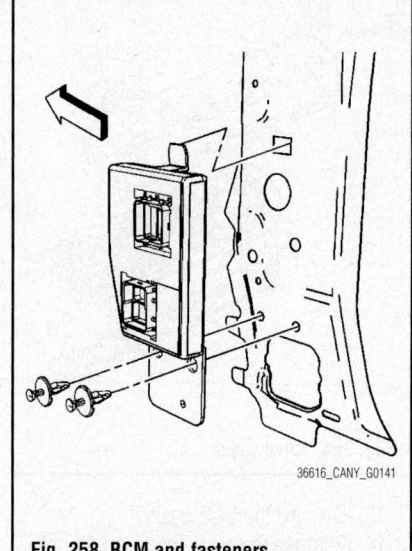

Fig. 258 BCM and fasteners

❊❊ WARNING

Do not open the BCM housing. The module does not have any serviceable components. The module may be replaced only as an assembly.

2. Ensure the ignition switch is in the OFF position.

3. Remove the right front hinge pillar trim panel. Refer to Body Hinge Pillar Trim Panel Removal & Installation, in Body Interior.

4. Disconnect the body wiring harness electrical connector (1) from the BCM.

5. Disconnect the I/P wiring harness electrical connector (1) from the BCM.

6. Release the fastener retaining the body wiring harness electrical connector to the BCM.

7. Remove the 2 fasteners retaining the BCM to the hinge pillar.

8. Remove the BCM from the hinge pillar by unlocking the integral tab.

9. Remove the BCM from the vehicle.

To install:

10. Position the BCM to the vehicle.

11. Attach the BCM to the hinge pillar with the integral tab.

12. Install the 2 fasteners retaining the BCM to the hinge pillar.

13. Install the fastener retaining the body wiring harness electrical connector to the BCM.

14. Connect the body wiring harness electrical connector (1) to the BCM.

15. Connect the I/P wiring harness electrical connector (1) to the BCM.

16. Install the right front hinge pillar trim panel.

17. If installing a replacement BCM, pro-

gram the BCM. Refer to Control Module References.

PROGRAMMING THE BCM

Replacement of the BCM requires a proprietary Service Programming System (SPS).

CAMSHAFT POSITION (CMP) SENSOR

LOCATION

See Figures 259 and 260.

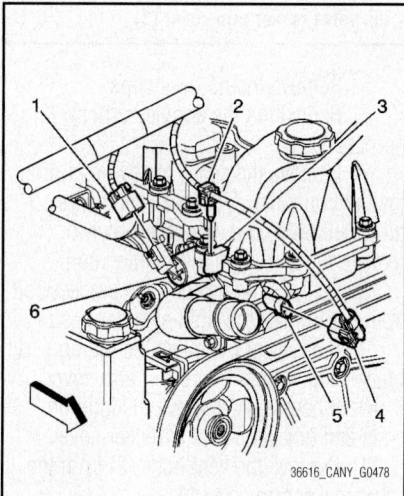

Fig. 259 Camshaft Position (CMP) sensor (5)—2.9L engine and exhaust CMP (5)—3.7L engine

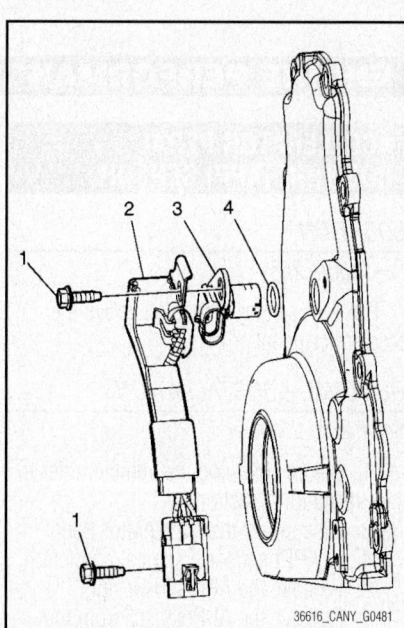

Fig. 260 Camshaft Position (CMP) sensor—5.3L engine

REMOVAL & INSTALLATION

2.9L Engine

See Figure 261.

1. Before servicing the vehicle, refer to the Precautions Section.

2. Disconnect the engine wiring harness electrical connector (4) from the Camshaft Position (CMP) sensor (5).

3. Remove the CMP sensor retaining bolt.

4. Remove the CMP sensor from the cylinder head.

5. Discard the O-ring seal.

To install:

6. Install a new O-ring seal to the CMP sensor.

7. Lightly lubricate the O-ring seal with clean engine oil.

8. Install the CMP sensor into the cylinder head.

9. Install the CMP sensor bolt.

10. Tighten the CMP sensor bolt to 89 inch lbs. (10 Nm).

11. Connect the engine wiring harness electrical connector (4) to the CMP sensor (5).

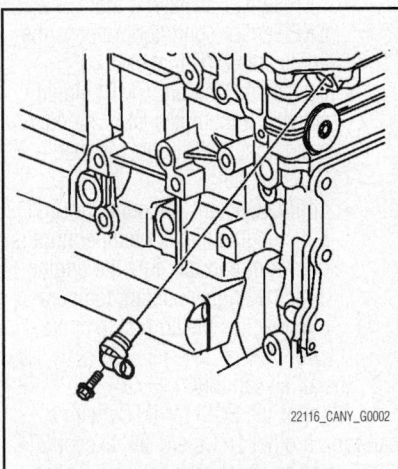

Fig. 261 Removing camshaft position sensor

3.7L Engine

Exhaust

See Figure 261.

1. Before servicing the vehicle, refer to the Precautions Section.

2. Disconnect the engine wiring harness electrical connector (4) from the exhaust Camshaft Position (CMP) sensor (5).

3. Remove the exhaust CMP sensor retaining bolt.

4. Remove the exhaust CMP sensor from the cylinder head.

5. Discard the O-ring seal.

To install:

6. Install a new O-ring seal to the exhaust CMP sensor.

7. Lightly lubricate the O-ring seal with clean engine oil.

8. Install the exhaust CMP sensor into the cylinder head.

9. Install the exhaust CMP sensor bolt.

10. Tighten the exhaust CMP sensor bolt to 89 inch lbs. (10 Nm).

11. Connect the engine wiring harness electrical connector (4) to the exhaust CMP sensor (5).

Intake

See Figures 262 and 263.

1. Before servicing the vehicle, refer to the Precautions Section.

2. Disconnect the engine wiring harness electrical connector from the intake Camshaft Position (CMP) sensor.

3. Remove the intake CMP sensor retaining bolt.

4. Remove the intake CMP sensor from the cylinder head.

To install:

5. Lightly lubricate the O-ring seal with clean engine oil.

6. Install the intake CMP sensor into the cylinder head.

7. Add sealer GM P/N 12346004 (Canadian P/N 10953480) to the CMP sensor bolt threads.

8. Install the intake CMP sensor bolt. Tighten the CMP sensor bolt to 89 inch lbs. (10 Nm).

9. Connect the engine wiring harness electrical connector to the intake CMP sensor.

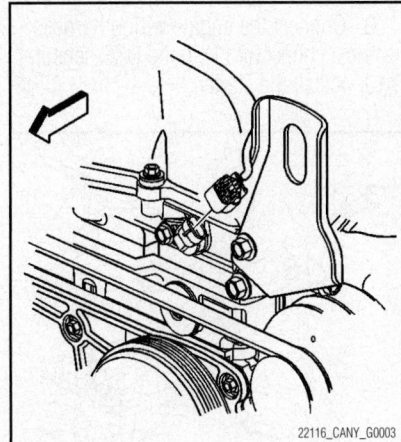

Fig. 262 Disconnecting CMP electrical connector–intake

Fig. 263 Removing camshaft position sensor–intake

5.3L Engine

See Figure 260.

1. Before servicing the vehicle, refer to the Precautions Section.

2. Disconnect the battery ground cable from the battery.

3. Clean the area around the Camshaft Position (CMP) sensor before removal in order to prevent debris from entering the engine.

4. Remove the CMP sensor bolts (1).

5. Remove the CMP sensor bracket assembly (2).

6. Remove the CMP sensor (3).

7. Remove the CMP sensor O-ring (4) from the CMP sensor and discard.

To install:

➡ Install a NEW O-ring to the camshaft sensor

➡ Before installing the camshaft sensor, apply a small amount of clean motor oil to the O-ring (3).

8. Install a NEW O-ring (4) to the CMP sensor.

9. Install the CMP sensor bracket assembly (2).

10. Install the CMP sensor bolts (1) and tighten to 106 inch lbs. (12 Nm).

CRANKSHAFT POSITION (CKP) SENSOR

LOCATION

See Figures 264 and 265.

On 2.9L and 3.7L engines, the Crankshaft Position (CKP) sensor is located at the left rear of the engine block below the starter motor.

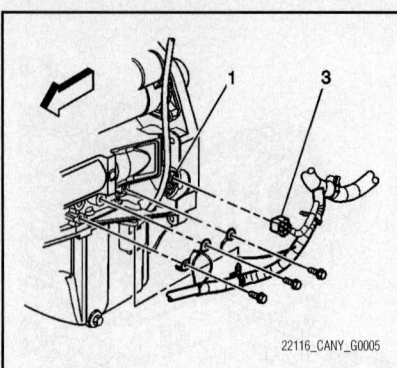

Fig. 264 Crankshaft Position (CKP) sensor (1)—2.9L and 3.7L engines

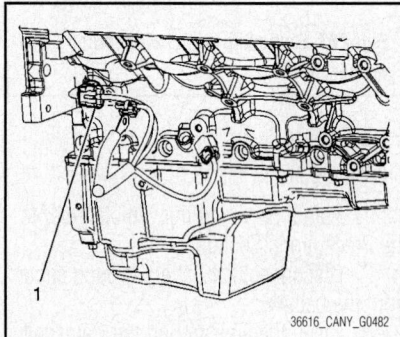

Fig. 265 Crankshaft Position (CKP) sensor—5.3L engine

On 5.3L engines, the CKP is located at the right rear of engine block, in back of starter motor.

REMOVAL & INSTALLATION

2.9L & 3.7L Engines

See Figures 264 and 266.

1. Before servicing the vehicle, refer to the Precautions Section.
2. Raise and support the vehicle.
3. Disconnect the engine wiring harness electrical connector (3) from the Crankshaft Position (CKP) sensor (1).

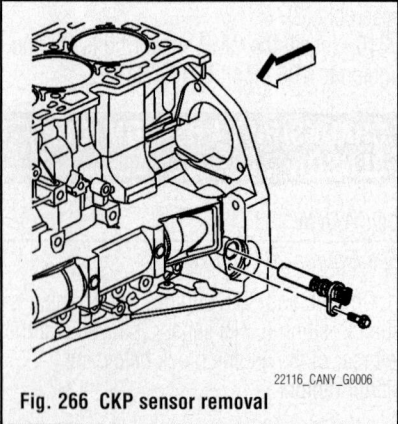

Fig. 266 CKP sensor removal

4. Remove the CKP sensor bolt.
5. Remove the CKP sensor from the engine block.
6. Discard the O-ring seals.

To install:

7. Install new O-ring seals to the CKP sensor.
8. Lightly lubricate the O-ring seals with clean engine oil.
9. Install the CKP sensor into the engine block.
10. Add sealer GM P/N 12346004 (Canadian P/N 10953480) to the CKP sensor bolt threads.
11. Install the CKP sensor bolt. Tighten the bolt to 89 inch lbs. (10 Nm).
12. Connect the engine wiring harness electrical connector (3) to the CKP sensor (1).
13. Lower the vehicle.
14. Perform the crankshaft (CKP) system variation learn procedure. Refer to Crankshaft Position System Variation Learn.

5.3L Engine

See Figures 265 and 267.

1. Before servicing the vehicle, refer to the Precautions Section.
2. Remove the starter. Refer to Starter Motor Removal & Installation.
3. Disconnect the engine wiring harness electrical connector (1) from the Crankshaft Position (CKP) sensor.
4. Clean the area around the CKP sensor before removal in order to avoid debris from entering the engine.
5. Remove the CKP sensor bolt.
6. Remove the CKP sensor.

To install:

7. Install the CKP sensor.
8. Install the CKP sensor bolt. Tighten the bolt to 18 ft. lbs. (25 Nm).
9. Connect the engine wiring harness electrical connector (1) to the CKP sensor.
10. Install the starter.

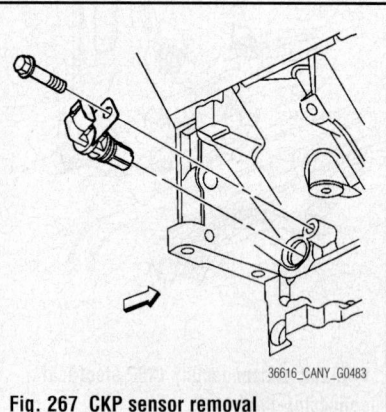

Fig. 267 CKP sensor removal

11. Perform the crankshaft position system variation learn procedure. Refer to Crankshaft Position System Variation Learn.

CRANKSHAFT POSTION SYSTEM VARIATION LEARN PROCEDURE

2.9L & 3.7L Engines

1. Important: The crankshaft position (CKP) system variation learn procedure is required when the following service procedures have been performed, regardless of whether DTC P0315 is set:

- Engine replacement
- Engine Control Module (ECM) replacement
- Crankshaft damper replacement
- Crankshaft replacement
- CKP sensor replacement
- Any engine repairs which disturb the crankshaft to CKP sensor relationship

2. Important: The scan tool monitors certain component signals to determine if all the conditions are met to continue with the CKP system variation learn procedure. The scan tool only displays the condition that inhibits the procedure. The scan tool monitors the following components:

- CKP sensor activity: If there is a CKP sensor condition, refer to the applicable DTC that set.
- Camshaft Position (CMP) signal activity: If there is a CMP signal condition, refer to the applicable DTC that set.
- Engine Coolant Temperature (ECT): If the engine coolant temperature is not warm enough, idle the engine until the engine coolant temperature reaches the correct temperature.

3. Install a scan tool.
4. Monitor the ECM for DTCs with a scan tool. If other DTCs are set, except DTC P0315, refer to Diagnostic Trouble Codes for the applicable DTC that set.
5. With a scan tool, select the CKP system variation learn procedure and perform the following:

a. Observe the fuel cut-off for the applicable engine.
b. Block the drive wheels.
c. Set the parking brake.
d. Place the vehicle's transmission in Park or Neutral.
e. Turn the air conditioning (A/C) OFF.
f. Cycle the ignition from OFF to ON.
g. Apply and hold the brake pedal for the duration of the procedure.
h. Start and idle the engine.

i. Accelerate to Wide Open Throttle (WOT). The engine should not accelerate beyond the calibrated fuel cut-off RPM value noted above. Release the throttle immediately if the value is exceeded.

➡Important: While the learn procedure is in progress, release the throttle immediately when the engine starts to decelerate. The engine control is returned to the operator and the engine responds to throttle position after the learn procedure is complete.

j. Release the throttle when fuel cut-off occurs.

6. The scan tool displays Learn Status: Learned this Ignition. If the scan tool indicates that DTC P0315 ran and passed, the CKP variation learn procedure is complete. If the scan tool indicates DTC P0315 failed or did not run, refer to DTC P0315. If any other DTCs set, refer to Diagnostic Trouble Codes for the applicable DTC that set.

7. Turn OFF the ignition for 30 seconds after the learn procedure is completed successfully.

5.3L Engine

1. Install a scan tool.

2. Monitor the Engine Control Module (ECM) for DTCs with a scan tool. If other DTCs are set, except DTC P0315, refer to Diagnostic Trouble Codes for the applicable DTC that set.

3. Select the CKP variation learn procedure with a scan tool.

4. The scan tool instructs you to perform the following:

a. Accelerate to Wide Open Throttle (WOT).

b. Release throttle when fuel cut-off occurs.

c. Observe fuel cut-off for applicable engine.

d. Engine should not accelerate beyond calibrated RPM value.

e. Release throttle immediately if value is exceeded.

f. Block drive wheels.

g. Set parking brake.

h. DO NOT apply brake pedal.

i. Cycle ignition from OFF to ON.

j. Apply and hold brake pedal.

k. Start and idle engine.

l. Turn A/C OFF.

m. Vehicle must remain in Park or Neutral.

n. The scan tool monitors certain component signals to determine if all the conditions are met to continue with the

procedure. The scan tool only displays the condition that inhibits the procedure. The scan tool monitors the following components:

- CKP sensors activity: If there is a CKP sensor condition, refer to the applicable DTC that set.
- Camshaft Position (CMP) sensor activity: If there is a CMP sensor condition, refer to the applicable DTC that set.
- Engine Coolant Temperature (ECT): If the ECT is not warm enough, idle the engine until the engine coolant temperature reaches the correct temperature.

5. Enable the CKP System Variation Learn Procedure with a scan tool.

➡Important: While the learn procedure is in progress, release the throttle immediately when the engine starts to decelerate. The engine control is returned to the operator and the engine responds to throttle position after the learn procedure is complete.

6. Accelerate to WOT.

7. Release when the fuel cut-off occurs.

8. Test in progress.

9. The scan tool displays Learn Status: Learned this ignition. If the scan tool indicates that DTC P0315 ran and passed, the CKP Variation Learn Procedure is complete. If the scan tool indicates DTC P0315 failed or did not run, refer to DTC P0315. If any other DTCs set, refer to Diagnostic Trouble Codes for the applicable DTC that set.

10. Turn OFF the ignition for 30 seconds after the learn procedure is completed successfully.

11. The CKP Variation Learn Procedure is also required when the following service procedures have been performed, regardless of whether DTC P0315 is set:

12. A CKP sensor replacement

13. An engine replacement

14. A ECM replacement

15. A harmonic balancer replacement

16. A crankshaft replacement

17. Any engine repairs which disturb the CKP sensor relationship

ENGINE COOLANT TEMPERATURE (ECT) SENSOR

LOCATION
See Figures 268 and 269.

REMOVAL & INSTALLATION
See Figures 268 and 269.

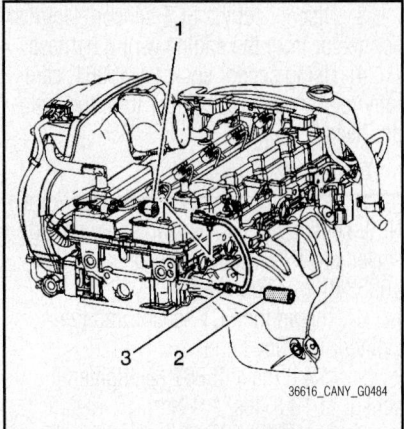

Fig. 268 Engine coolant temperature sensor (3)—2.9L and 3.7L engines

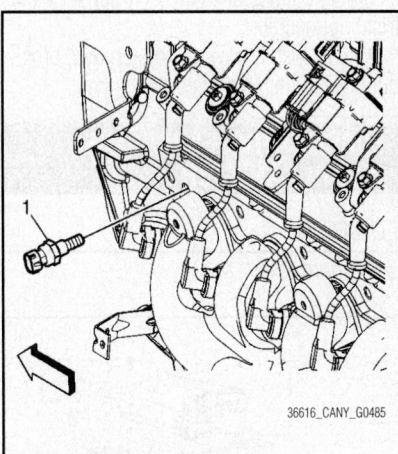

Fig. 269 Engine coolant temperature sensor (1)—5.3L engine

➡Use care when handling the coolant sensor. Damage to the coolant sensor will affect the operation of the fuel control system.

➡Replacement components must be the correct part number for the application. Components requiring the use of the thread locking compound, lubricants, corrosion inhibitors, or sealants are identified in the service procedure. Some replacement components may come with these coatings already applied. Do not use these coatings on components unless specified. These coatings can affect the final torque, which may affect the operation of the component. Use the correct torque specification when installing components in order to avoid damage.

1. Before servicing the vehicle, refer to the Precautions Section.

2. Partially drain the engine coolant below the level of the engine coolant temperature (ECT) sensor.

3. Disconnect the ECT sensor electrical connector from the engine wiring harness.

4. Using sensor socket J-45861, carefully remove the ECT sensor from the cylinder head.

To install:

5. If installing the original sensor or a NEW sensor without sealant, apply thread sealer GM P/N 12346004 (Canadian P/N 10953480) or equivalent.

6. Thread the ECT sensor into the cylinder head by hand.

7. Using the J 45861 (2), tighten the sensor to 10 ft. lbs. (14 Nm).

8. Install the ECT sensor electrical connector to the camshaft cover.

9. Connect the engine wiring harness electrical connector to the ECT sensor electrical connector.

10. To install, reverse the removal procedure. Refill the engine coolant.

EVAPORATIVE EMISSIONS (EVAP) CANISTER

LOCATION

See Figure 270.

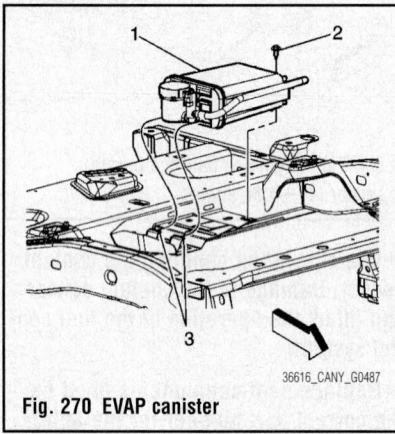

Fig. 270 EVAP canister

REMOVAL & INSTALLATION

See Figures 270 and 271.

❋❋ CAUTION

Before servicing the vehicle, refer to the Precautions Section, including Fuel and EVAP Precautions.

1. Raise and support the vehicle.

2. Disconnect the electrical connector from the Evaporative Emission (EVAP) canister vent solenoid valve (4).

3. Disengage the bracket retaining tab and remove the EVAP canister vent solenoid valve (4).

4. Disconnect the following from the EVAP canister (5):

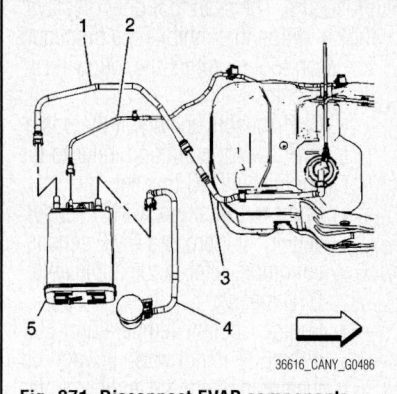

Fig. 271 Disconnect EVAP components

- The EVAP vent hose (1)
- The EVAP chassis hose/pipe (2)
- The EVAP canister vent solenoid valve (4)

5. Remove the bolt (2) securing the EVAP canister (1) to the crossmember.

6. Disengage the EVAP canister (1) from the crossmember bracket tabs (3).

7. Remove the EVAP canister (1) from the vehicle.

To install:

8. Position the EVAP canister (1) to the crossmember bracket tabs (3).

9. Install the bolt (2) securing the EVAP canister (1) to the crossmember. Tighten the evaporative emission (EVAP) canister bolt to 18 ft. lbs. (25 Nm).

10. Slide the EVAP canister vent solenoid valve (4) over the bracket. Ensure the valve (4) is properly retained to the bracket.

11. Connect the following to the EVAP canister (5):

- The EVAP vent hose (1)
- The EVAP chassis hose/pipe (2)
- The EVAP canister vent solenoid valve (4)

12. Connect the electrical connector to the EVAP canister vent solenoid valve (4).

13. Lower the vehicle.

HEATED OXYGEN (HO2S) SENSOR

LOCATION

See Figures 272 through 275.

REMOVAL & INSTALLATION

See Figures 272 through 275.

❋❋ WARNING

Be careful of the following:

- Do not remove the pigtail from either the heated oxygen sensor (HO2S) or the oxygen sensor (O2S).

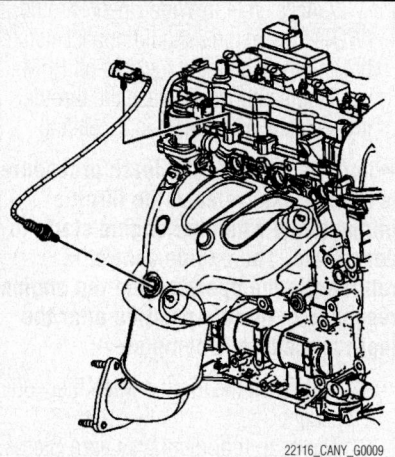

Fig. 272 Heated Oxygen (HO2S) Sensor location—2.9L and 3.7L engines Sensor 1

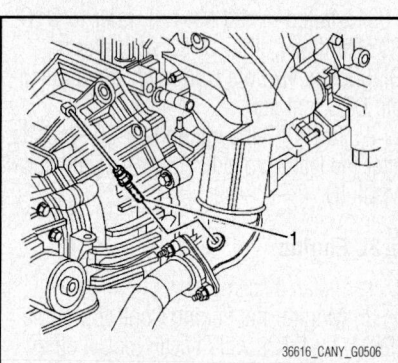

Fig. 273 Heated Oxygen (HO2S) Sensor location—2.9L and 3.7L engines Sensor 2

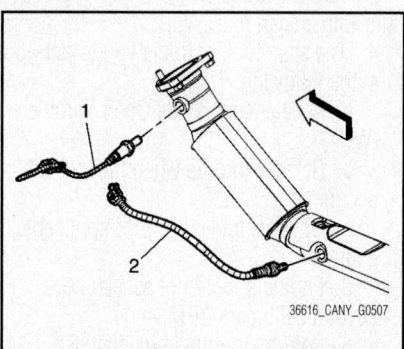

Fig. 274 Heated Oxygen (HO2S) Sensor location—5.3L Bank 1 Sensors 1 and 2

- Removing the pigtail or the connector will affect sensor operation.
- Handle the oxygen sensor carefully. Do not drop the HO2S. Keep the in-line electrical connector and the louvered end free of grease, dirt, or other contaminants. Do not use cleaning solvents of any type.
- Do not repair the wiring, connector or terminals. Replace the oxygen

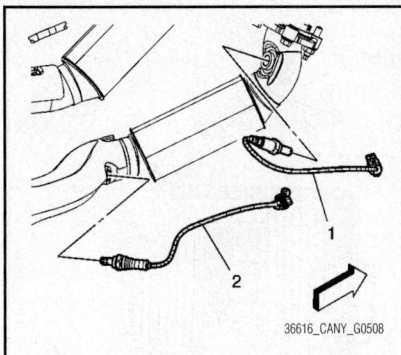

Fig. 275 Heated Oxygen (HO2S) Sensor location—5.3L Bank 2 Sensors 1 and 2

sensor if the pigtail wiring, connector, or terminal is damaged.

- This external clean air reference is obtained by way of the oxygen sensor signal and heater wires. Any attempt to repair the wires, connectors, or terminals could result in the obstruction of the air reference and degraded sensor performance.

✵✵ WARNING

The following guidelines should be used when servicing the heated oxygen sensor:

- Do not apply contact cleaner or other materials to the sensor or vehicle harness connectors. These materials may get into the sensor causing poor performance.
- Do not damage the sensor pigtail and harness wires in such a way that the wires inside are exposed. This could provide a path for foreign materials to enter the sensor and cause performance problems.
- Ensure the sensor or vehicle lead wires are not bent sharply or kinked. Sharp bends or kinks could block the reference air path through the lead wire.
- Do not remove or defeat the oxygen sensor ground wire, where applicable. Vehicles that utilize the ground wired sensor may rely on this ground as the only ground contact to the sensor. Removal of the ground wire will cause poor engine performance.
- Ensure that the peripheral seal remains intact on the vehicle harness connector in order to prevent damage due to water intrusion. The engine harness may be

repaired using Packard's Crimp and Splice Seals Terminal Repair Kit. Under no circumstances should repairs be soldered since this could result in the air reference being obstructed.

1. Raise and suitably support the vehicle.
2. Disconnect the HO2S electrical connector from the engine wiring harness electrical connector.
3. Remove the HO2S wiring from under the rear HO2S electrical connector.
4. Remove the HO2S

To install:

➡**A special anti-seize compound is used on the HO2S threads. The compound consists of liquid graphite and glass beads. The graphite tends to burn away, but the glass beads remain, making the sensor easier to remove. New, or service replacement sensors already have the compound applied to the threads. If the sensor is removed from an exhaust component and if for any reason the sensor is to be reinstalled, the threads must have anti-seize compound applied before the reinstallation. If reinstalling the old sensor, coat the threads with anti-seize compound GM P/N 12377953, or equivalent.**

✵✵ WARNING

Replacement components must be the correct part number for the application. Components requiring the use of the thread locking compound, lubricants, corrosion inhibitors, or sealants are identified in the service procedure. Some replacement components may come with these coatings already applied. Do not use these coatings on components unless specified. These coatings can affect the final torque, which may affect the operation of the component. Use the correct torque specification when installing components in order to avoid damage.

5. Install the HO2S.
6. Tighten the sensor to 31 ft. lbs. (42 Nm).
7. Route the HO2S wiring under the rear HO2S electrical connector.
8. Connect the HO2S electrical connector to the engine wiring harness electrical connector.
9. Lower the vehicle.

KNOCK SENSOR (KS)

LOCATION

See Figures 276 through 279.

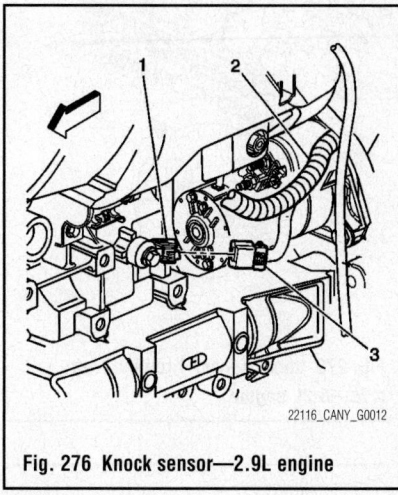

Fig. 276 Knock sensor—2.9L engine

REMOVAL & INSTALLATION

2.9L Engine

See Figure 276.

1. Before servicing the vehicle, refer to the Precautions Section.
2. Raise and support the vehicle only high enough to access the Knock Sensor (KS) through the wheelhouse.
3. Remove the left wheelhouse liner.
4. Disconnect the engine wiring harness electrical connector (3) from the KS (1).
5. Remove the KS retaining bolt.
6. Remove the KS (1) from the engine block.

To install:

7. Install the KS (1) and the retaining bolt to the engine block, positioning the electrical terminals rearward. Tighten the KS bolt to 18 ft. lbs. (25 Nm).

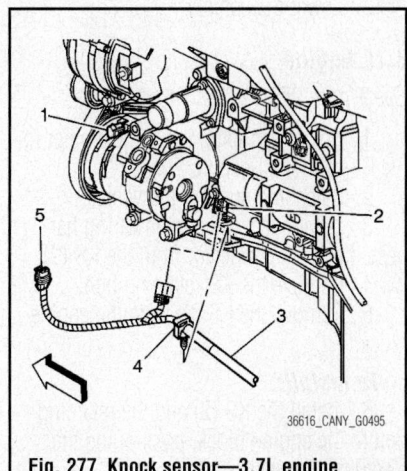

Fig. 277 Knock sensor—3.7L engine

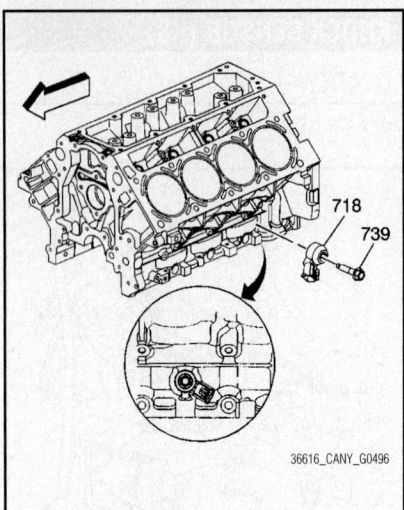

Fig. 278 Knock sensor 1 removal left side—5.3L engine

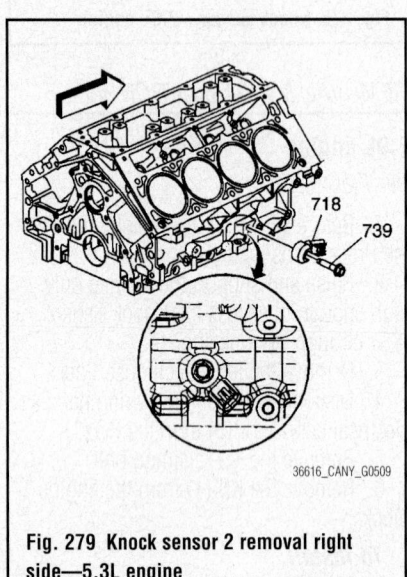

Fig. 279 Knock sensor 2 removal right side—5.3L engine

8. Connect the engine wiring harness electrical connector (3) to the KS (1).

9. Install the left wheelhouse liner.

10. Lower the vehicle.

3.7L Engine

See Figure 277.

1. Before servicing the vehicle, refer to the Precautions Section.

2. Raise and support the vehicle.

3. Disconnect the engine wiring harness electrical connector from the KS (2).

4. Remove the KS retaining bolt.

5. Remove the KS (2) from the engine block.

To install:

6. Install the KS (2) and the retaining bolt to the engine block, positioning the electrical terminals down.

7. Tighten the KS bolt to 18 ft. lbs. (25 Nm).

8. Connect the engine wiring harness electrical connector to the KS (2).

9. Lower the vehicle.

5.3L Engine

Knock Sensor 1

See Figure 278.

1. Before servicing the vehicle, refer to the Precautions Section.

2. Raise and suitably support the vehicle.

3. Disconnect the engine wiring harness electrical connector from the Knock Sensor (KS).

4. Remove the knock sensor bolt (739) and sensor (718).

To install:

5. Position the knock sensor (718) to the engine block and install the bolt (739).

6. Tighten the bolt to 15 ft. lbs. (20 Nm).

7. Connect the engine wiring harness electrical connector to the knock sensor.

8. Lower the vehicle.

Knock Sensor 2

See Figure 279.

1. Before servicing the vehicle, refer to the Precautions Section.

2. Raise and suitably support the vehicle.

3. Disconnect the engine wiring harness electrical connector from the Knock Sensor (KS).

4. Remove the knock sensor bolt (739) and sensor (718).

To install:

5. Position the knock sensor (718) to the engine block and install the bolt (739). Tighten the bolt to 15 ft. lbs. (20 Nm).

6. Connect the engine wiring harness electrical connector to the knock sensor.

7. Lower the vehicle.

MALFUNCTION INDICATOR LIGHT (MIL)

RESET PROCEDURE

Clearing Diagnostic Trouble Codes resets the MIL.

MASS AIR FLOW (MAF) SENSOR

LOCATION

See Figures 280 and 281.

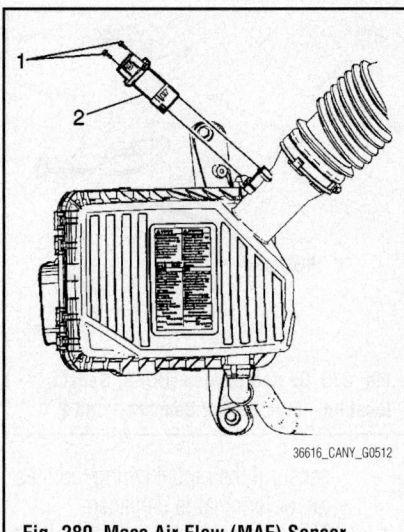

Fig. 280 Mass Air Flow (MAF) Sensor— 2.9L and 3.7L engine

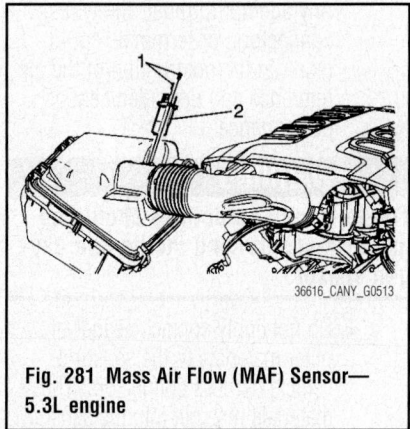

Fig. 281 Mass Air Flow (MAF) Sensor— 5.3L engine

REMOVAL & INSTALLATION

2.9L & 3.7L Engines

See Figure 280.

1. Before servicing the vehicle, refer to the Precautions Section.

※ WARNING

Handle the MAF sensor carefully. Do not drop the MAF sensor. Do not damage the screen located on the air inlet end of the MAF. Do not touch the sensing elements. Do not allow solvents and lubricants to come in contact with the sensing elements. Use a small amount of a soap based solution in order to aid in the installation.

2. Disconnect the engine wiring harness electrical connector (1) from the Mass Air Flow (MAF)/Intake Air Temperature (IAT) sensor (2).

3. Remove the MAF/IAT sensor screws.

4. Remove the MAF/IAT sensor from the air cleaner assembly.

To install:

5. Insert the MAF/IAT sensor into the air cleaner assembly.

6. Install the MAF/IAT sensor screws. Tighten the screws to 13 inch lbs. (1.5 Nm).

7. Connect the engine wiring harness electrical connector to the MAF/IAT sensor.

5.3L Engine

See Figure 281.

1. Before servicing the vehicle, refer to the Precautions Section.

✳✳ WARNING

Use care when handling the Mass Air Flow (MAF)/Intake Air Temperature (IAT) sensor. Do not dent, puncture, or otherwise damage the honeycell located at the air inlet end of the MAF/IAT. Do not touch the sensing elements or allow anything including cleaning solvents and lubricants to come in contact with them. Use a small amount of a non-silicone based lubricant, on the air duct only, to aid in installation.

2. Disconnect the engine wiring harness electrical connector from the MAF/IAT sensor.

3. Remove the MAF/IAT sensor screws (1).

4. Remove the MAF/IAT sensor (2) from the air cleaner upper housing.

To install:

✳✳ WARNING

The embossed arrow on the MAF/IAT sensor indicates the proper air flow direction. The arrow must point toward the engine.

5. Install the MAF/IAT sensor to the air cleaner upper housing.

6. Install the MAF/IAT sensor screws. Tighten the screws to 13 inch lbs. (1.5 Nm).

7. Connect the engine wiring harness electrical connector to the MAF/IAT sensor.

MANIFOLD ABSOLUTE PRESSURE (MAP) SENSOR

LOCATION

See Figures 282 and 283.

REMOVAL & INSTALLATION

2.9L & 3.7L Engines

See Figure 282.

1. Disconnect the Manifold Absolute Pressure (MAP) sensor electrical connector.

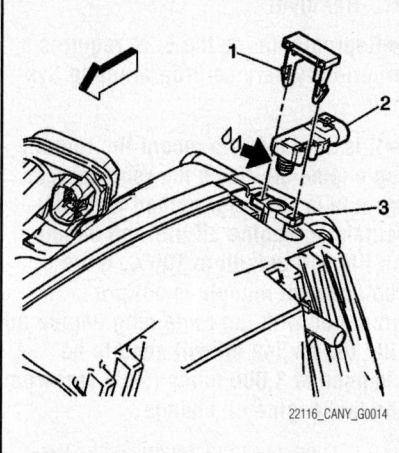

Fig. 282 MAP sensor location—2.9L engine

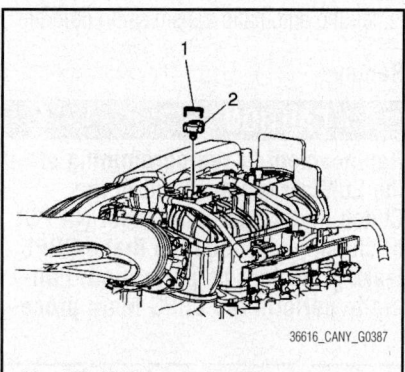

Fig. 283 MAP sensor location—5.3L engine

2. Press the retainer locking tabs inward, then pull the retainer up to remove.

3. Remove the MAP sensor (2) from the intake manifold (3).

4. Inspect the MAP sensor seal for damage, and replace as necessary.

To install:

5. Lightly lubricate the MAP sensor seal with clean engine oil, to aid in installation.

6. Install the MAP sensor into the intake manifold.

7. Install the MAP sensor retainer.

8. Connect the MAP sensor electrical connector.

5.3L Engine

See Figure 283.

1. Remove the upper intake manifold cover.

2. Disconnect the engine wiring harness electrical connector (1) from the Manifold Absolute Pressure (MAP) sensor.

3. Remove the MAP sensor retainer (1) from the intake manifold.

4. Remove the MAP sensor (2) from the intake manifold.

To install:

→Lightly coat the MAP sensor seal with clean engine oil before installing the sensor.

5. Install the MAP sensor into the intake manifold.

6. Install the MAP sensor retainer to the intake manifold.

7. Connect the engine wiring harness electrical connector to the MAP sensor.

8. Install the upper intake manifold cover.

POSITIVE CRANKCASE VENTILATION (PCV) VALVE

LOCATION

See Figures 284 and 285.

REMOVAL & INSTALLATION

2.9L Engine

See Figure 284.

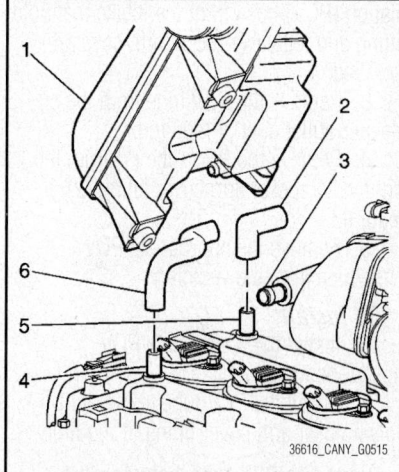

Fig. 284 Positive Crankcase Ventilation (PCV) Valve—2.9L and 3.7L engine

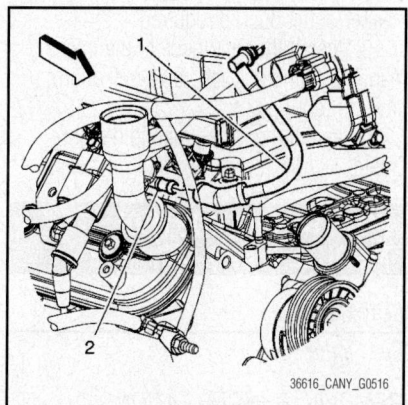

Fig. 285 Positive Crankcase Ventilation (PCV) Valve—5.3L engine

1. Remove the air cleaner resonator and outlet duct.

2. Disconnect the Positive Crankcase Ventilation (PCV) fresh air tube (6) from the air cleaner resonator (1).

3. Disconnect the PCV dirty air tube (2) from the following:
- The camshaft cover (5)
- The intake manifold (3)

To install:

4. Connect the PCV fresh air tube to the air cleaner resonator.

5. Connect the PCV dirty air tube to the following:
- The camshaft cover
- The intake manifold

6. Install the air cleaner resonator and outlet duct.

5.3L Engine

See Figure 285.

1. Remove the intake manifold sight shield.

2. Remove the Positive Crankcase Ventilation (PCV) hose from the intake manifold fitting and left valve rocker arm cover, if required.

3. Remove the PCV tube from the air cleaner outlet duct, if required.

4. Remove the PCV tube (1) from the right valve rocker arm cover fitting (2), if required.

5. Remove the appropriate PCV hose/tube from the vehicle.

To install:

6. Install the appropriate PCV hose/tube to the vehicle.

7. Install the PCV tube to the right valve rocker arm cover fitting, if required.

➡️**Route the PCV tube between the engine harness and alternator battery jumper cable.**

8. Install the PCV tube to the air cleaner outlet duct, if required.

9. Install the PCV hose to the intake manifold fitting and left valve rocker arm cover, if required.

10. Install the intake manifold sight shield.

POWERTRAIN CONTROL MODULE (PCM)

LOCATION

See Figure 286.

REMOVAL & INSTALLATION

See Figure 286.

Pre-Removal

➡️**Reprogramming the ECM requires a proprietary Service Programming System.**

➡️**It is necessary to record the remaining engine oil life. If the replacement module is not programmed with the remaining engine oil life, the engine oil life will default to 100%. If the replacement module is not programmed with the remaining engine oil life, the engine oil will need to be changed at 3,000 miles (5000 km) from the last engine oil change.**

1. Using a scan tool, retrieve the percentage of remaining engine oil and the remaining automatic transmission fluid life. Record the remaining engine oil and the remaining automatic transmission fluid life.

Removal

❋❋ CAUTION

Replacement or reprogramming of the ECM, or replacement of the Clutch Pedal Position Sensor (CPPS) or clutch pedal requires that a CPPS learn procedure be performed. Failure to perform the CPPS learn proce-

dure may result in personal injury or damage to the vehicle or its components if the vehicle is in gear and the starter motor is accidentally engaged. Refer to Clutch Pedal Position Sensor Learn Procedure in the Drive Train section.

❋❋ WARNING

Observe the following:

- Turn the ignition OFF when installing or removing the control module connectors and disconnecting or reconnecting the power to the control module (battery cable, PCM/ECM)/Transaxle Control Module (TCM) pigtail, control module fuse, jumper cables, etc.) in order to prevent internal control module damage.
- Control module damage may result when the metal case contacts battery voltage. DO NOT contact the control module metal case with battery voltage when servicing a control module, using battery booster cables, or when charging the vehicle battery.

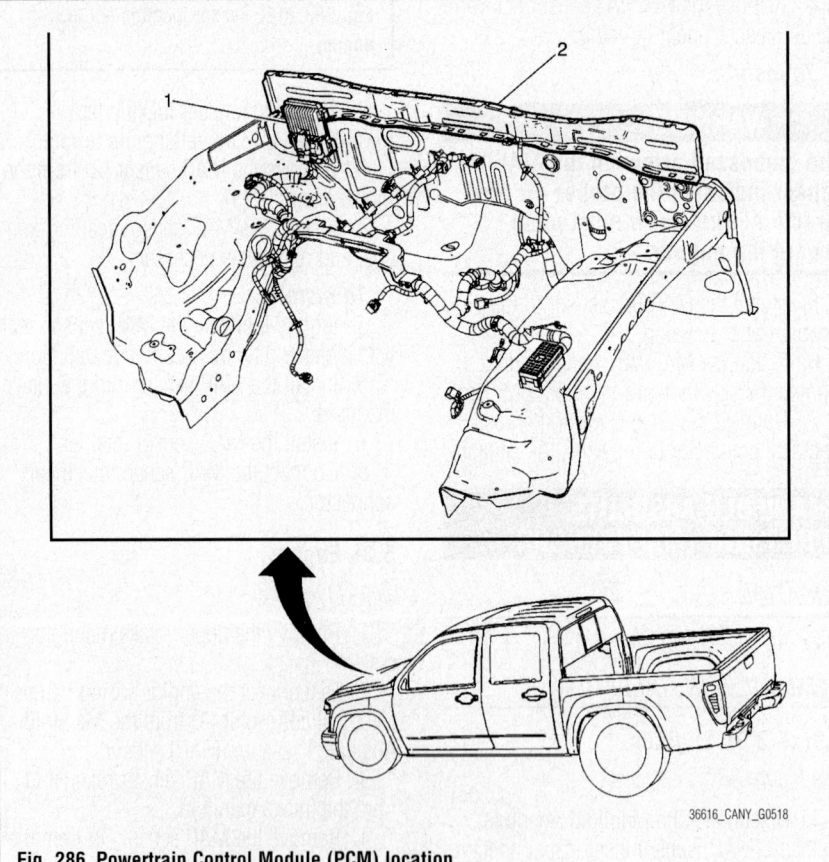

36616_CANY_G0518

Fig. 286 Powertrain Control Module (PCM) location

- In order to prevent any possible electrostatic discharge damage to the control module, do not touch the connector pins or the soldered components on the circuit board.
- Remove any debris from around the control module connector surfaces before servicing the control module. Inspect the control module connector gaskets when diagnosing or replacing the control module. Ensure that the gaskets are installed correctly. The gaskets prevent contaminant intrusion into the control module.
- The replacement control module must be programmed.

✸✸ CAUTION

Always turn the ignition off when installing or removing the ECM connectors in order to prevent damage to the components.

1. Turn the ignition OFF.
2. Disconnect the battery negative cable.

➡**Disconnect the rear electrical connector from the ECM first.**

3. Unlock the ECM electrical connector lock levers and disconnect the ECM electrical connectors.
4. Remove the ECM from the ECM housing by pushing both ECM retaining clips outwards.

To install:

5. Install the ECM to the ECM housing. Ensure the ECM retaining clips are located correctly.
6. Connect the ECM electrical connectors and lock the connector lock levers into place.
7. Connect the battery negative cable to the battery.
8. Program the ECM. Reprogramming the ECM requires a proprietary Service Programming System.
9. Turn OFF the ignition for at least 5 seconds after the programming event is complete.
10. Perform the Clutch Pedal Position Sensor Learn procedure. Refer to Clutch Pedal Position Sensor Learn Procedure in the Drive Train section.
11. Use the scan tool to clear all DTCs.

RESET

Reprogramming the ECM requires a proprietary Service Programming System.

VEHICLE SPEED SENSOR (VSS)

LOCATION
See Figure 287.

REMOVAL & INSTALLATION
See Figure 287.

1. Raise and support the vehicle.
2. Disconnect the wiring harness

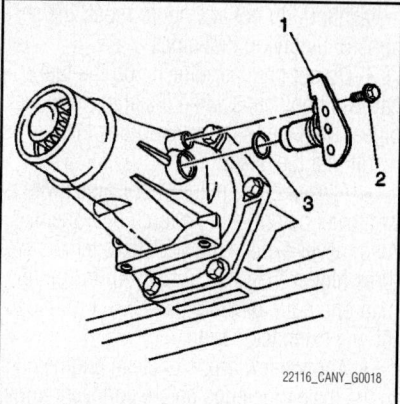

22116_CANY_G0018

Fig. 287 Vehicle Speed Sensor (VSS) (1) location

electrical connector from the Vehicle Speed Sensor (VSS).
3. Remove the harness connector.
4. Remove the bolt.
5. Remove the VSS.
6. Remove the O-ring seal.

To install:
7. Install the O-ring seal on the VSS.
8. Coat the O-ring seal with a thin film of transmission fluid.
9. Install the vehicle speed sensor into the transmission case.
10. Install the bolt and tighten to 97 inch lbs. (11 Nm).
11. Connect the wiring harness electrical connector to the VSS.
12. Lower the vehicle.
13. Refill the fluid as required.

FUEL
GASOLINE FUEL INJECTION SYSTEM

FUEL SYSTEM SERVICE PRECAUTIONS

Safety is the most important factor when performing not only fuel system maintenance but any type of maintenance. Failure to conduct maintenance and repairs in a safe manner may result in serious personal injury or death. Maintenance and testing of the vehicle's fuel system components can be accomplished safely and effectively by adhering to the following rules and guidelines:

- To avoid the possibility of fire and personal injury, always disconnect the negative battery cable unless the repair or test procedure requires that battery voltage be applied.
- Always relieve the fuel system pressure prior to disconnecting any fuel system component (injector, fuel rail, pressure regulator, etc.), fitting or fuel line connection.

After you relieve the fuel system pressure, a small amount of fuel may be released when servicing the fuel lines, the fuel injection pump, or the connections. In order to reduce the risk of personal injury, cover the fuel system components with a shop towel before disconnection. This will catch any fuel that may leak out. Place the towel in an approved container when the disconnection is complete. Please be advised that fuel under pressure may penetrate the skin or any part of the body that it contacts.

- Always place a shop towel or cloth around the fitting or connection prior to loosening to absorb any excess fuel due to spillage. Ensure that all fuel spillage (should it occur) is quickly removed from engine surfaces. Ensure that all fuel soaked cloths or towels are deposited into a suitable waste container.
- Always keep a dry chemical (Class B) fire extinguisher near the work area.

- Do not allow fuel spray or fuel vapors to come into contact with a spark or open flame.
- Always use a back-up wrench when loosening and tightening fuel line connection fittings. This will prevent unnecessary stress and torsion to fuel line piping.
- Always replace worn fuel fitting O-rings with new. Do not substitute fuel hose or equivalent where fuel pipe is installed.

Always wear safety goggles when working with fuel in order to protect the eyes from fuel splash.

Do not drain the fuel into an open container. Never store the fuel in an open container due to the possibility of a fire or an explosion.

When servicing fuel and Evaporative Emission (EVAP) pipes, reduce the risk of fire and personal injury by observing the following items:

- Replace all nylon fuel pipes that are nicked, scratched or damaged during installation, do not attempt to repair the sections of the nylon fuel pipes.

• Do not hammer directly on the fuel harness body clips when installing new fuel pipes. Damage to the nylon pipes may result in a fuel leak.

• Always cover nylon vapor pipes with a wet towel before using a torch near them. Also, never expose the vehicle to temperatures higher than 239°F (115°C) for more than one hour, or more than 194°F (90°C) for any extended period.

• Apply a few drops of clean engine oil to the male pipe ends before connecting fuel pipe fittings. This will ensure proper reconnection and prevent a possible fuel leak. (During normal operation, the O-rings located in the female connector will swell and may prevent proper reconnection if not lubricated.)

Always apply a few drops of clean engine oil to the male pipe ends before connecting the fuel pipe fittings in order to reduce the risk of fire and personal injury. This will ensure proper reconnection and prevent a possible fuel leak. During normal operation, the O-rings located in the female connector will swell and may prevent proper reconnection if not lubricated.

Clean all of the following areas before performing any disconnections in order to avoid possible contamination in the system:

• The fuel pipe connections
• The hose connections
• The areas surrounding the connections

Do not breathe the air through the EVAP component tubes or hoses. The fuel vapors inside the EVAP components may cause personal injury.

The fuel rail stop bracket must be installed onto the engine assembly. The stop bracket serves as a protective shield for the fuel rail in the event of a vehicle frontal crash. If the fuel rail stop bracket is not installed and the vehicle is involved in a frontal crash, fuel could be sprayed possibly causing a fire and personal injury from burns.

Verify that the lower (small) O-ring of each injector does not remain in the lower manifold in order to reduce the risk of fire and personal injury.

If the O-ring is not removed with the injector, the replacement injector with new O-rings will not seat properly in the injector socket. Improper seating could cause a fuel leak.

Before servicing the vehicle, make sure to also refer to the precautions in the beginning of this section as well.

RELIEVING FUEL SYSTEM PRESSURE

See Figure 288.

1. Before servicing the vehicle, refer to the Precautions Section.

❄❄ CAUTION

Gasoline or gasoline vapors are highly flammable. A fire could occur if an ignition source is present. Never drain or store gasoline or diesel fuel in an open container, due to the possibility of fire or explosion. Have a dry chemical (Class B) fire extinguisher nearby.

❄❄ CAUTION

Remove the fuel tank cap and relieve the fuel system pressure before servicing the fuel system in order to reduce the risk of personal injury. After you relieve the fuel system pressure, a small amount of fuel may be released when servicing the fuel lines, the fuel injection pump, or the connections. In order to reduce the risk of personal injury, cover the fuel system components with a shop towel before disconnection. This will catch any fuel that may leak out. Place the towel in an approved container when the disconnection is complete.

2. Disconnect the negative battery cable.
3. Remove the engine cover, if required.
4. Loosen the fuel fill cap in order to relieve the fuel tank vapor pressure.
5. Remove the fuel rail service port cap.

❄❄ CAUTION

Wrap a shop towel around the fuel pressure connection in order to

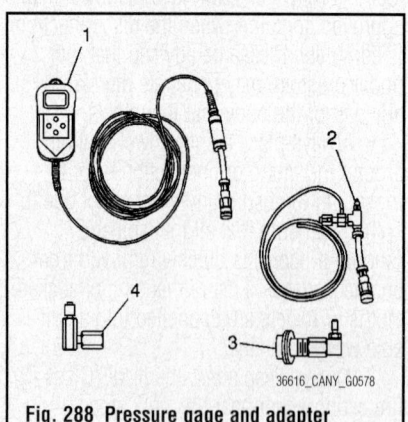

Fig. 288 Pressure gage and adapter

reduce the risk of fire and personal injury. The towel will absorb any fuel leakage that occurs during the connection of the fuel pressure gage. Place the towel in an approved container when the connection of the fuel pressure gage is complete.

6. Wrap a shop towel around the fuel rail service port.
7. Connect the J 42242 to the fuel rail service port.
8. Connect the CH-48027-3 (4) to the J 42242.
9. Connect the CH-48027-2 (2) to the CH-48027-3 (4).
10. Place the hose on the CH-48027-2 (2) into an approved gasoline container.
11. Open the valve on the CH-48027-2 (2) in order to bleed any fuel from the fuel rail.
12. Close the valve on the CH-48027-2 (2).
13. Remove the hose on the CH-48027-2 (2) from the approved gasoline container.

❄❄ WARNING

Clean all of the following areas before performing any disconnections in order to avoid possible contamination in the system: the fuel pipe connections, the hose connections, the areas surrounding the connections.

14. Connect the negative battery cable.

FUEL TANK MODULE/FUEL PUMP MODULE

REMOVAL & INSTALLATION

2.9L & 3.7L Engines
See Figure 289.

1. Before servicing the vehicle, refer to the Precautions Section.

❄❄ WARNING

Clean all of the following areas before performing any disconnections in order to avoid possible contamination in the system: the fuel pipe connections, the hose connections, the areas surrounding the connections.

2. Remove the fuel tank. Refer to Fuel Tank Removal & Installation.
3. Disconnect the Evaporative Emission (EVAP) line quick connect fittings from the module and the vent valve.
4. Remove the EVAP line from the clip on the side of the fuel tank.

5. Disengage the EVAP line from the retaining features molded into the fuel tank and remove the EVAP line.

6. Disconnect the fuel feed line quick connect fitting from the module.

7. Disengage the fuel feed line from the retaining feature molded into the fuel tank and remove the fuel line.

8. Install the J 45722 to the fuel pump module lock ring.

❋❋ WARNING

Avoid damaging the lock ring. Use only J-45722 to prevent damage to the lock ring.

❋❋ WARNING

Do Not handle the fuel sender assembly by the fuel pipes. The amount of leverage generated by handling the fuel pipes could damage the joints.

➡**Do NOT us impact tools. Significant force will be required to release the lock ring. The use of a hammer and screwdriver is not recommended. Secure the fuel tank in order to prevent fuel tank rotation.**

9. Using the J 45722 and a long breaker-bar, rotate the lock ring in a counterclockwise direction in order to unlock the lock ring.

10. Remove the J 45722 from the fuel pump module lock ring.

11. Raise the fuel pump module up from the fuel tank. Tilt the module in order to allow the fuel level sensor arm and float to clear the module opening.

12. Remove the fuel pump module.

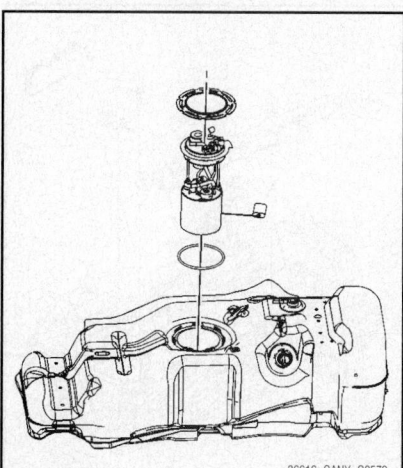

Fig. 289 Fuel tank module removal and installation

13. Remove and discard the fuel pump module seal.

❋❋ CAUTION

Drain the fuel from the fuel sender assembly into an approved container in order to reduce the risk of fire and personal injury. Never store the fuel in an open container.

14. Clean the fuel pump module sealing surface.

➡**Some lock rings were manufactured with DO NOT REUSE stamped into them. These lock rings may be reused if they are not damaged or warped. Inspect the lock ring for damage due to improper removal or installation procedures. If damage is found, install a NEW lock ring. Check the lock ring for flatness.**

15. Place the lock ring on a flat surface. Measure the clearance between the lock ring and the flat surface using a feeler gage at 7 points.

16. If warpage is less than 0.016 in. (0.41 mm), the lock ring does not require replacement.

17. If warpage is greater than 0.016 in. (0.41 mm), the lock ring must be replaced.

To install:

❋❋ CAUTION

In order to reduce the risk of fire and personal injury that may result from a fuel leak, always replace the fuel sender gasket when reinstalling the fuel sender assembly.

18. Clean any contamination from the male pipe ends of the fuel pump module.

19. Place a NEW fuel tank module seal onto the fuel tank.

20. Insert the fuel pump module into the fuel tank allowing the sensor arm and float to clear module opening.

21. Lower the module down into the fuel tank.

22. Press the fuel tank module downward, aligning the tang with the notch in the fuel tank.

23. Install the fuel pump module lock ring onto the fuel tank.

24. Install the J 45722 to the fuel pump module lock ring.

➡**Always replace the fuel module seal when installing the fuel pump module. Replace the lock ring if necessary. Do not apply any type of lubrication in the seal groove.**

➡**Ensure the lock ring is installed with the correct side facing upward. A correctly installed lock ring will only turn in a clockwise direction.**

25. Using the J 45722 and a long breaker-bar, rotate the lock ring in a clockwise direction on order to lock the lock ring.

26. Remove the J 45722 from the fuel pump module lock ring.

27. Connect the fuel feed line quick connect fitting to the module.

28. Engage the fuel feed line to the retaining feature molded into the fuel tank.

29. Connect the EVAP line quick connect fittings to the module and the vent valve.

30. Engage the EVAP line to the retaining feature molded into the fuel tank.

31. Install the EVAP line to the clip on the side of the fuel tank.

32. Install the fuel tank.

5.3L Engine

See Figure 290.

1. Before servicing the vehicle, refer to the Precautions Section.

❋❋ WARNING

Clean all of the following areas before performing any disconnections in order to avoid possible contamination in the system: the fuel pipe connections, the hose connections, the areas surrounding the connections.

2. Remove the fuel tank. Refer to Fuel Tank Removal & Installation.

3. Using a flare nut wrench and a back up wrench, disconnect the fuel feed line (2) fitting from the fuel tank module.

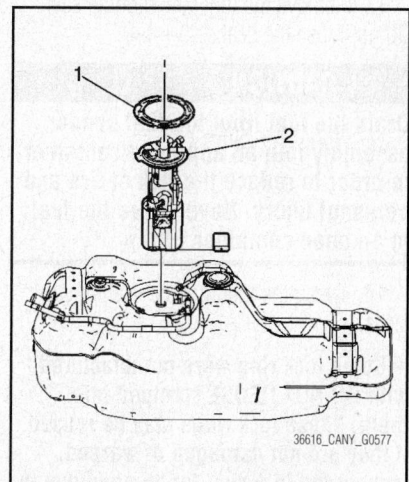

Fig. 290 Fuel tank module (2) removal and installation

4. Disconnect the EVAP vapor line (1) from the fuel tank vent valve.

5. Disconnect the EVAP vapor line (3) quick connect from the fuel tank module.

6. Reposition the fuel feed and EVAP lines in order to access the lock ring.

✳✳ WARNING

Avoid damaging the lock ring. Use only J-45722 to prevent damage to the lock ring.

✳✳ WARNING

DO NOT handle the fuel sender assembly by the fuel pipes. The amount of leverage generated by handling the fuel pipes could damage the joints.

➡**DO NOT use impact tools. Significant force will be required to release the lock ring. The use of a hammer and screwdriver is not recommended. Secure the fuel tank in order to prevent fuel tank rotation.**

7. Use the J 45722 and a long breaker-bar in order to unlock the fuel sender lock ring. Turn the J 45722 fuel sender lock ring in a counterclockwise direction.

8. Remove the cam lock ring from the fuel tank.

9. Raise the fuel tank module upward far enough to access the vapor line quick connect under the module cover.

10. Disconnect the vapor line quick connect from the fuel tank module.

11. Tilt the module, to allow the fuel level sensor arm and float to clear the fuel tank module opening.

12. Remove the fuel tank module from the fuel tank.

13. Remove the fuel tank module seal. Do not reuse the seal.

✳✳ CAUTION

Drain the fuel from the fuel sender assembly into an approved container in order to reduce the risk of fire and personal injury. Never store the fuel in an open container.

14. Clean the fuel module sealing surfaces.

➡**Some lock ring were manufactured with DO NOT REUSE stamped into them. These lock rings may be reused if they are not damaged or warped. Inspect the lock ring for damage due to improper removal or installation procedures. If damage is found, install a**

NEW lock ring. Check the lock ring for flatness.

15. Place the lock ring on a flat surface. Measure the clearance between to lock ring and the flat surface using a feeler gage at 7 points.

16. If the warpage is less than 0.016 in. (0.41 mm), the lock ring does not require replacement.

17. If the warpage is greater than 0.016 in. (0.41 mm), the lock ring must be replaced.

To install:

18. Clean any contamination from the male pipe ends of the fuel tank module.

✳✳ CAUTION

In order to reduce the risk of fire and personal injury that may result from a fuel leak, always replace the fuel sender gasket when reinstalling the fuel sender assembly.

19. Place the new fuel tank module seal on the fuel tank.

20. Insert the module into the fuel tank allowing the fuel level sensor arm and float to clear module opening.

21. Lower the module downward into the fuel tank.

22. Connect the vapor line quick connect to the fuel tank module.

23. Press the fuel tank module downward, aligning the locator tang with the locator notch in the fuel tank.

24. Position the cam lock ring to the fuel tank.

➡**Always replace the fuel sender seal when installing the fuel sender assembly. Replace the lock ring if necessary. Do not apply any type of lubrication in the seal groove.**

25. Ensure the lock ring is installed with the correct side facing upward. A correctly installed lock ring will only turn in a clockwise direction.

26. Use the J 45722 in order to install the fuel sender lock ring. Turn the fuel sender lock ring in a clockwise direction.

27. Position the fuel feed and EVAP lines to the module.

28. Connect the EVAP vapor line to the fuel tank vent valve.

29. Connect the EVAP vapor line quick connect to the fuel tank module.

30. Using a flare nut wrench and a back up wrench, connect the fuel feed line fitting to the fuel tank module. Tighten the fitting to 22 ft. lbs. (30 Nm).

31. Install the fuel tank.

FUEL RAIL & INJECTORS

REMOVAL & INSTALLATION

2.9L & 3.7L Engines

See Figures 291 and 292.

1. Before servicing the vehicle, refer to the Precautions Section.

2. Relieve the fuel system pressure. Refer to Relieving Fuel System Pressure.

3. Disconnect the fuel feed line quick connect fitting from the fuel rail.

4. Disconnect the Evaporative Emission (EVAP) purge tube from the throttle body control module and the EVAP canister purge solenoid valve.

5. Remove the intake manifold. Refer to Intake Manifold Removal & Installation.

6. Disconnect the engine wiring harness electrical connector from the fuel injector harness electrical connector.

7. Before removal, clean the fuel rail assembly and the cylinder head with a spray type engine cleaner, GM X-30A or equivalent, if necessary. Follow the package instructions. Do not soak the fuel rail in liquid cleaning solvent.

8. Remove the fuel rail bolts.

✳✳ WARNING

Remove the fuel rail assembly carefully in order to prevent damage to the injector electrical connector terminals and the injector spray tips. Support the fuel rail after the fuel rail is removed in order to avoid damaging the fuel rail components.

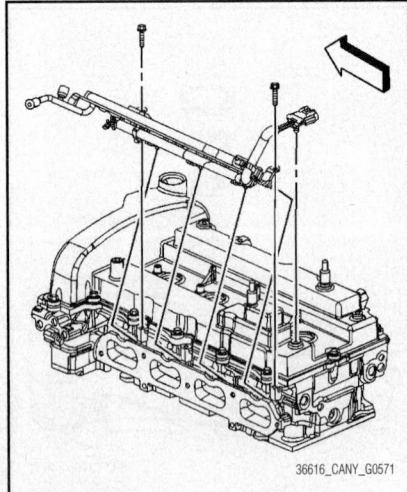

36616_CANY_G0571

Fig. 291 Remove the fuel rail bolts — 2.9L engine

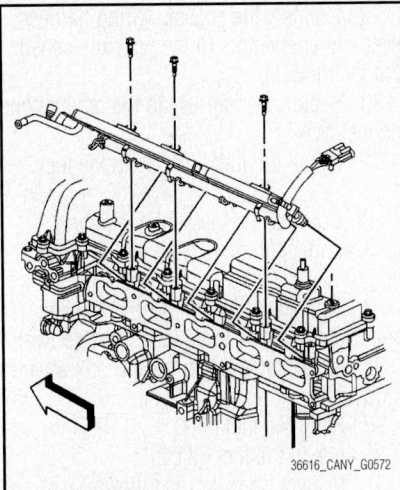

Fig. 292 Remove the fuel rail bolts —
3.7L engine

✳✳ WARNING

Cap the fittings and plug the holes when servicing the fuel system in order to prevent dirt and other contaminants from entering open pipes and passages.

9. Remove the fuel rail from the cylinder head.

10. Remove and discard the fuel injector lower O-ring seals from each fuel injector.

To install:

11. Lightly lubricate the NEW lower O-ring seals with mineral oil GM P/N 9981704.

12. Install the NEW O-ring seals onto the tip of each injector.

13. Position the fuel rail to the cylinder head, insert the spray tip ends of the fuel injectors into the cylinder head.

14. Push in the fuel rail until the rail is properly seated.

15. Install the fuel rail bolts and tighten to 89 inch lbs. (10 Nm).

16. Connect the engine wiring harness electrical connector to the fuel injector harness electrical connector.

17. Install the intake manifold.

18. Connect the EVAP purge tube to the throttle body control module and the EVAP canister purge solenoid valve.

19. Connect the fuel feed line quick connect fitting to the fuel rail.

20. Inspect for leaks:

   a. Turn ON the ignition, with the engine OFF for 2 seconds.

   b. Turn OFF the ignition for 10 seconds.

   c. Turn ON the ignition, with the engine OFF.

   d. Inspect for fuel leaks.

5.3L Engine

See Figures 293 and 294.

1. Before servicing the vehicle, refer to the Precautions Section.

➡**An 8-digit identification number is located on the fuel rail. Refer to this model identification number if servicing or part replacement is required.**

2. Relieve the fuel system pressure. Refer to Relieving Fuel System Pressure.

3. Remove the air cleaner outlet duct. Refer to Air Cleaner Removal & Installation.

4. Disconnect the engine wiring harness electrical connector from the Manifold Absolute Pressure (MAP) sensor.

5. Remove the Positive Crankcase Ventilation (PCV) foul air hose.

6. Remove the engine wiring harness clip from the ignition coil bracket stud.

7. Disconnect the engine wiring harness electrical connector from the throttle body.

8. Disconnect the engine wiring harness electrical connectors from the fuel injectors.

9. Disconnect the engine wiring harness electrical connector from the ignition coil harness.

10. Disconnect the engine wiring harness electrical connector from the alternator.

11. Disconnect the engine wiring harness electrical connector from the Evaporative Emission (EVAP) canister purge solenoid valve.

12. Remove the engine wiring harness bracket nut.

13. Remove the engine wiring harness bracket from the stud and reposition the harness as needed.

14. Remove the EVAP canister purge solenoid valve. Refer to EVAP Purge Sole-

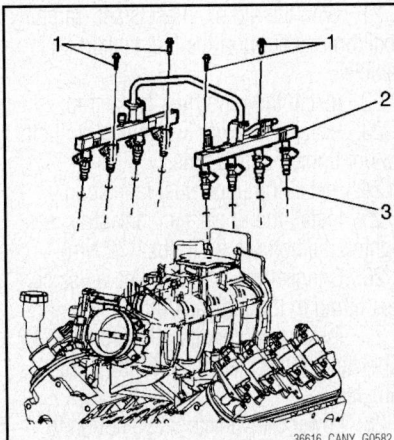

Fig. 293 Fuel rail and injector removal

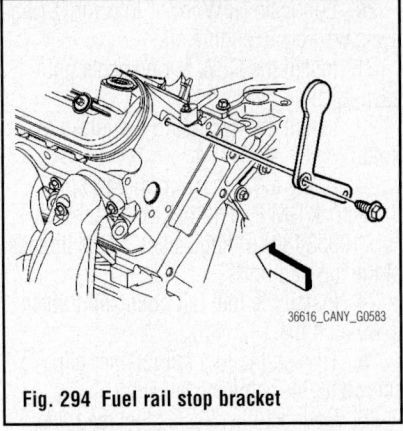

Fig. 294 Fuel rail stop bracket

noid Removal & Installation in the Engine Performance & Emission Control section.

15. Disconnect the chassis fuel feed line quick connect fitting from the fuel rail.

16. Remove the fuel rail bolts (1).

17. Loosen, but do not remove the fuel rail crossover pipe retainer clip screws.

✳✳ WARNING

Remove the fuel rail assembly carefully in order to prevent damage to the injector electrical connector terminals and the injector spray tips. Support the fuel rail after the fuel rail is removed in order to avoid damaging the fuel rail components.

✳✳ WARNING

Cap the fittings and plug the holes when servicing the fuel system in order to prevent dirt and other contaminants from entering open pipes and passages.

➡**Before removal, clean the fuel rail with a spray type engine cleaner, GM X-30A or equivalent, if necessary. Follow the package instructions. Do not soak the fuel rail in liquid cleaning solvent.**

18. Remove the fuel rail assembly (2).

19. Remove and discard the fuel injector lower O-ring seals (3).

To install:

✳✳ CAUTION

The fuel rail stop bracket must be installed onto the engine assembly. The stop bracket serves as a protective shield for the fuel rail in the event of a vehicle frontal crash. If the fuel rail stop bracket is not installed and the vehicle is involved in a frontal crash, fuel could be sprayed possibly causing a fire and personal injury from burns.

20. Lubricate NEW lower injector O-ring seals with clean engine oil.

21. Install the NEW O-ring seals onto each injector.

22. Install the fuel rail to the intake manifold.

23. Apply a 0.2 in. (5 mm) band of threadlock GM P/N 12345382 (Canadian P/N 10953489) or equivalent, to the threads of the fuel rail bolts.

24. Install the fuel rail bolts and tighten to 89 inch lbs. (10 Nm).

25. Tighten the fuel rail retainer clip screws to 34 inch lbs. (3.8 Nm).

26. Connect the chassis fuel feed line quick connect fitting to the fuel rail.

27. Install the EVAP canister purge solenoid valve.

28. Position the engine wiring harness as needed, and install the engine wiring harness bracket to the stud.

29. Install the engine wiring harness bracket nut and tighten to 80 inch lbs. (9 Nm).

30. Connect the engine wiring harness electrical connectors to the fuel injectors.

31. Connect the engine wiring harness electrical connector to the ignition coil harness.

32. Connect the engine wiring harness electrical connector to the EVAP canister purge solenoid valve.

33. Connect the engine wiring harness electrical connector to the alternator.

34. Connect the engine wiring harness electrical connector to the throttle body.

35. Install the engine wiring harness clip to the ignition coil bracket stud.

36. Install the PCV foul air hose.

37. Connect the engine wiring harness electrical connector to the MAP sensor.

38. Install the air cleaner outlet duct.

39. Install the fuel fill cap.

40. Connect the negative battery cable.

41. Use the following procedure in order to inspect for leaks:

    a. Turn the ignition ON, with the engine OFF, for 2 seconds.

    b. Turn the ignition OFF for 10 seconds.

    c. Turn the ignition ON, with the engine OFF.

    d. Inspect for fuel leaks.

FUEL TANK

REMOVAL & INSTALLATION

1. Before servicing the vehicle, refer to the Precautions Section.

2. Relieve the fuel system pressure. Refer to Relieving Fuel System Pressure.

3. Drain the fuel tank. Refer to Fuel Tank Draining.

4. Raise and support the vehicle, high enough to access the top of the fuel tank through the wheelhouse liner.

5. Remove the left rear pickup box wheelhouse liner.

6. Loosen the fuel fill hose clamp at the fuel tank.

7. Disconnect the Evaporative Emission (EVAP) line quick connect fitting from the fill tube vent tube.

8. Separate the fuel fill hose from the fuel tank.

9. Disconnect the chassis wiring harness electrical connectors from the pressure sensor and the module.

10. Disengage the harness from the retainer on the fuel tank.

11. Raise the vehicle completely.

12. Disconnect and remove the middle EVAP vapor line from the fuel tank and the EVAP canister.

13. Disconnect the fuel feed line quick connect fitting from the fuel tank line.

✳✳ CAUTION

Do not bend the fuel tank straps. Bending the fuel tank straps may damage the straps.

14. Remove the upper fuel tank strap bolt.

15. Remove the upper fuel tank strap.

16. Support the fuel tank with an adjustable jack.

17. Remove the lower fuel tank strap bolt.

18. Remove the lower fuel tank strap.

19. With the aid of an assistant, carefully lower the fuel tank from the vehicle.

20. Place the fuel tank in a suitable work area.

To install:

21. With the aid of an assistant, carefully position and support the fuel tank to the vehicle.

22. Install the lower fuel tank strap.

23. Install the lower fuel tank strap bolt. Do not tighten at this time.

24. Install the upper fuel tank strap.

25. Install the upper fuel tank strap bolt. Tighten the bolts to 24 ft. lbs. (32 Nm).

26. Connect the fuel feed line quick connect fitting to the fuel tank line.

27. Install and connect the middle EVAP vapor line to the fuel tank and the EVAP canister.

28. Lower the vehicle only enough to gain access to the fuel tank through the wheelhouse.

29. Connect the chassis wiring harness electrical connectors to the pressure sensor and the module.

30. Secure the harness to the retainer on the fuel tank.

31. Install the fuel fill hose to the fuel tank.

32. Connect the fuel tank EVAP line quick connect fitting to the fill tube vent tube.

33. Tighten the fuel fill hose at the fuel tank. Tighten clamp to 22 inch lbs. (2.5 Nm).

34. Install the left rear pickup box wheelhouse liner.

35. Refill the fuel tank.

36. Install the fuel fill cap.

37. Inspect for leaks, as follows:

    a. Turn ON the ignition, with the engine OFF for 10 seconds.

    b. Turn OFF the ignition for 10 seconds.

    c. Turn ON the ignition, with the engine OFF.

    d. Inspect for fuel leaks.

FUEL TANK DRAINING

✳✳ CAUTION

Gasoline or gasoline vapors are highly flammable. A fire could occur if an ignition source is present. Never drain or store gasoline or diesel fuel in an open container, due to the possibility of fire or explosion. Have a dry chemical (Class B) fire extinguisher nearby.

✳✳ CAUTION

Never drain or store fuel in an open container. Always use an approved fuel storage container in order to reduce the chance of fire or explosion.

✳✳ CAUTION

Place a dry chemical (Class B) fire extinguisher nearby before performing any on-vehicle service procedures. Failure to follow these precautions may result in personal injury.

1. Remove the fuel filler cap.

2. Install the J 42960-2 into the fuel fill pipe in order to hold the door open.

➡**Lubricate the fuel drain hose with J 36850 or equivalent to aid in hose insertion and removal. Do not use an unapproved lubricant.**

3. Insert the J 45004 into the fuel tank until the hose reaches the bottom of the fuel tank.

4. Use an air operated pump device in order to drain the fuel into an approved gasoline container.

5. Simultaneously twist and pull in order to remove the J 45004 from the fuel tank.

THROTTLE BODY

REMOVAL & INSTALLATION

2.9L & 3.7L Engines

See Figure 295.

1. Before servicing the vehicle, refer to the Precautions Section.

> ❊❊ **WARNING**
>
> **Handle the electronic throttle control components carefully. Use cleanliness in order to prevent damage. Do not drop the electronic throttle control components. Do not roughly handle the electronic throttle control components. Do not immerse the electronic throttle control components in cleaning solvents of any type.**

> ❊❊ **WARNING**
>
> **DO NOT for any reason, insert a screwdriver or other small hand tools into the throttle body to hold open the throttle plate, as the wedge inside the throttle body could be damaged.**

2. Remove the air cleaner resonator and outlet duct.

3. Disconnect the Evaporative Emission (EVAP) canister purge pipe from the throttle control module.

4. Disconnect the engine wiring harness

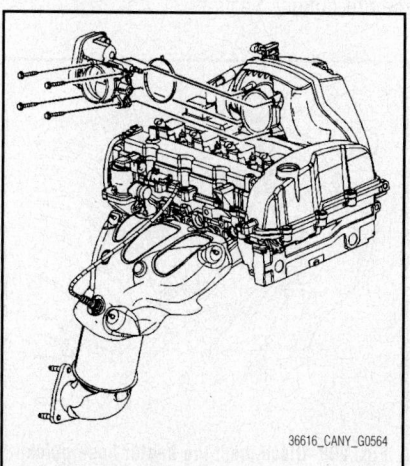

Fig. 295 Throttle body removal

electrical connector from the throttle body control module.

5. Remove the throttle control module bolts.

6. Remove the throttle body control module and the seal from the intake manifold.

7. Clean the gasket surface.

To install:

8. Install a NEW seal into the intake manifold groove.

9. Position the throttle body control module to the intake manifold.

10. Install the throttle body control module bolts and tighten to 89 inch lbs. (10 Nm).

11. Connect the engine wiring harness electrical connector to the throttle body control module.

12. Connect the EVAP canister purge pipe to the throttle body control module.

13. Install the air cleaner resonator and outlet duct.

14. Perform the throttle learn procedure.

5.3L Engine

See Figure 296.

1. Before servicing the vehicle, refer to the Precautions Section.

> ❊❊ **WARNING**
>
> **Handle the electronic throttle control components carefully. Use cleanliness in order to prevent damage. Do not drop the electronic throttle control components. Do not roughly handle the electronic throttle control components. Do not immerse the electronic throttle control components in cleaning solvents of any type.**

> ❊❊ **WARNING**
>
> **DO NOT for any reason, insert a screwdriver or other small hand**

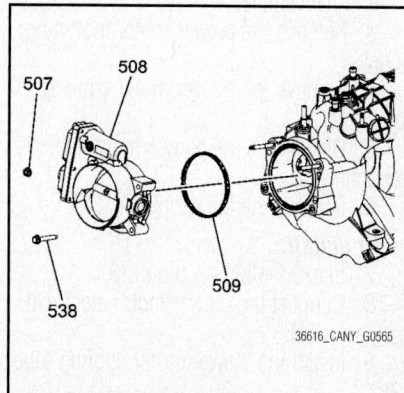

Fig. 296 Throttle body removal

tools into the throttle body to hold open the throttle plate, as the wedge inside the throttle body could be damaged.

2. Remove the air cleaner outlet duct. Refer to Air Cleaner Removal & Installation.

3. Disconnect the engine wiring harness electrical connector from the throttle body.

4. Remove the throttle body bolts (538) and nuts (507).

5. Remove the throttle body (508).

6. Remove and discard the throttle body seal (509).

To install:

7. Install a NEW throttle body gasket (509).

8. Install the throttle body (508).

9. Install the throttle body bolts (538) and nuts (507). Tighten the bolts and nuts to 89 inch lbs. (10 Nm).

10. Connect the engine wiring harness electrical connector to the throttle body.

11. Install the air cleaner outlet duct.

12. Perform the throttle learn/reset procedure.

THROTTLE LEARN PROCEDURE

2.9L & 3.7L Engines

With Scan Tool

1. Ignition ON, engine OFF. With a scan tool, perform the Idle Learn Reset in Module Setup.

2. Start the engine, monitor the TB Idle Airflow Compensation parameter. The TB Idle Airflow Compensation parameter value should equal 0 percent and the engine should be idling at a normal idle speed. If the engine is not idling normally, proceed with the Learn portion of the diagnostic.

3. Clear the DTCs and return to the diagnostic that referred you here.

Without Scan Tool

➡ **Do NOT perform the Without Scan Tool-Learn procedure if DTCs are set. Refer to Diagnostic Trouble Codes.**

1. The engine speed is between 450–4,000 RPM.

2. The Manifold Absolute Pressure (MAP) is greater than 5 kPa.

3. The Mass Air Flow (MAF) is greater than 2 g/s.

4. The ignition 1 voltage is greater than 10 volts.

5. Start and idle the engine in Park for 3 minutes.

6. With a scan tool, monitor desired and actual RPM.

7. The ECM will start to learn the new idle cells and Desired RPM should start to decrease.

8. Ignition OFF for 60 seconds.

9. Start and idle the engine in Park for 3 minutes.

➡During the drive cycle the check engine light may come on with idle speed DTCs. If idle speed codes are set, clear codes so the ECM can continue to learn.

10. After the 3 minute run time the engine should be idling normal.

a. If the engine idle speed has not been learned the vehicle will need to be driven at speeds above 44 mph (70 km/h) with several decelerations and extended idles.

11. After the drive cycle, the engine should be idling normally.

a. If the engine idle speed has not been learned, turn OFF the ignition for 60 seconds and repeat step 6.

12. Once the engine speed has returned to normal, clear DTCs.

5.3L Engine

After the throttle body is cleaned or replaced, perform the reset procedure. After the ECM/PCM is flashed or replaced, perform the learn procedure.

Learn Procedure

This procedure is to be performed after the ECM/PCM is flashed or replaced.

➡Do NOT perform this procedure if DTCs are set. Refer to Diagnostic Trouble Codes.

1. Start and idle the engine for 3 minutes.

2. With a scan tool, monitor the Desired Idle Speed and the actual Engine Speed.

3. The ECM will start to learn the new idle cells and Desired Idle Speed should start to decrease.

4. Ignition OFF for 60 seconds.

5. Start and idle the engine for 3 minutes.

➡During the drive cycle the check engine light may come on with idle speed DTCs. If idle speed codes are set, clear codes so the ECM can continue to learn.

6. After the 3 minute run time the engine should be idling normal.

a. If the engine idle speed has not been learned the vehicle will need to be driven at speeds above 44 mph (70 km/h) with several decelerations and extended idles.

7. After the drive cycle, the engine should be idling normally.

a. If the engine idle speed has not been learned, turn OFF the ignition for 60 seconds and repeat step 6.

8. Once the engine speed has returned to normal, clear DTCs and return to the diagnostic that referred you here.

Reset Procedure

This procedure is to be performed after the throttle body is cleaned or replaced.

1. Ignition ON, engine OFF, perform the Idle Learn Reset in Module Setup with a scan tool.

2. Start the engine and monitor the TB Idle Airflow Compensation parameter. The TB Idle Airflow Compensation value should equal 0 percent and the engine should be idling at a normal idle speed.

3. Clear the DTCs and return to the diagnostic that referred you here.

HEATING & AIR CONDITIONING SYSTEM

BLOWER MOTOR

REMOVAL & INSTALLATION

See Figure 297.

1. Before servicing the vehicle, refer to the Precautions Section.

2. Remove the right hinge pillar trim panel, as follows:

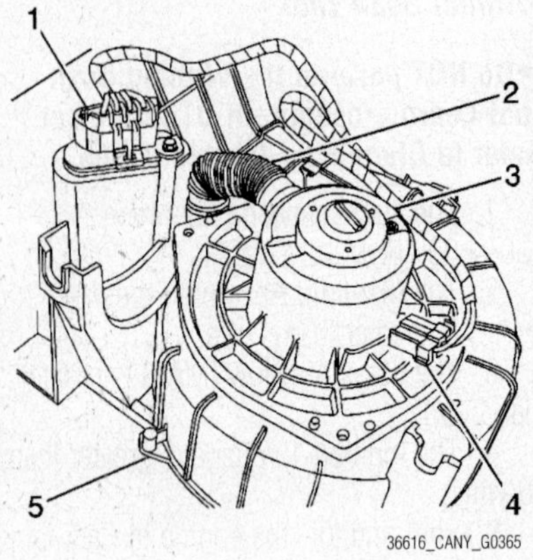

a. Remove the front door sill trim plate.

b. One at a time, grasp the hinge pillar trim panels and gently pull the panels away from the body to release the fasteners.

c. Remove any fasteners that may have pulled away from the panel and reinstall them to the back of the panel.

d. Slide the panels forward so the panels unhook from around the front door frame.

e. Remove the hinge pillar trim panel from the vehicle.

3. Remove the blower motor mounting screws.

4. Remove the blower motor cooling tube (2).

5. Disconnect the blower motor electrical connector (4).

6. Remove the blower motor (3).

To install:

7. Install the blower motor (3).

8. Connect the blower motor electrical connector (4).

9. Install the blower motor cooling tube (2).

10. Install the blower motor mounting screws. Tighten the screws to inch 18 lbs. (2 Nm).

11. Install the right hinge pillar trim panel.

HEATER CORE

REMOVAL & INSTALLATION

See Figures 298 and 299.

1. Before servicing the vehicle, refer to the Precautions Section.

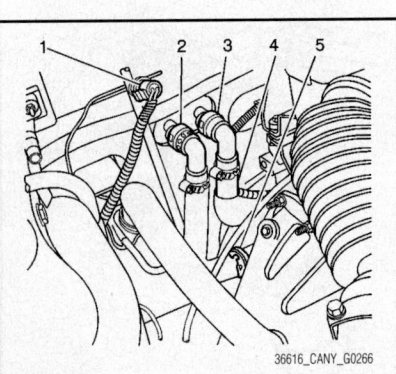

36616_CANY_G0266

Fig. 298 Disconnect the heater hose quick connects (2) and (3) from the heater core

36616_CANY_G0365

Fig. 297 Blower motor removal and installation

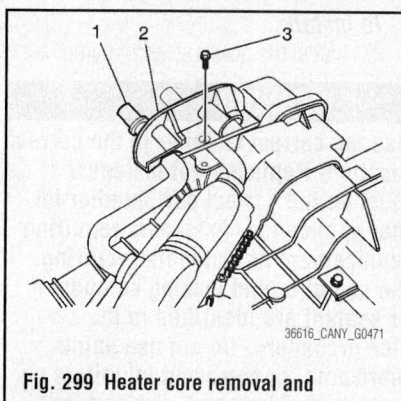

Fig. 299 Heater core removal and installation

2. Remove the HVAC module assembly, as follows:

    a. Drain the engine coolant.

    b. Recover the refrigerant.

    c. Remove the Instrument Panel (I/P) carrier.

    d. Release the heater hose clamps using J 43181.

    e. Disconnect the heater hose quick connects and from the heater core.

    f. Remove the retaining nut from the TXV stud.

    g. Remove the evaporator tube and suction hose from the TXV.

    h. Remove the radio antenna from the HVAC module.

    i. Reposition the carpet.

    j. Remove rear floor duct.

    k. Remove the HVAC module retaining nuts from the cowl.

    l. Remove the HVAC module assembly.

3. Remove the heater core pipes clamp screw (3).

4. Remove the heater core pipes clamp (2).

5. Remove the heater core clamp screws.

6. Remove the heater core clamp (2).

7. Remove the heater core from the HVAC module.

To install:

8. Install the heater core to the HVAC module.

9. Install the heater core clamp (2).

10. Install the heater core clamp screws and tighten to 18 inch lbs. (1.9 Nm).

11. Install the heater core pipes clamp (2).

12. Install the heater core pipes clamp screw (3) and tighten to 15 ft. lbs. (20 Nm).

13. Install the HVAC module assembly.

STEERING

POWER RACK & PINION STEERING GEAR

REMOVAL & INSTALLATION

See Figures 300 through 303.

1. Before servicing the vehicle, refer to the Precautions Section.

✳✳ CAUTION

With wheels of the vehicle facing straight ahead, secure the steering wheel utilizing steering column anti-rotation pin, steering column lock, or a strap to prevent rotation. Locking of the steering column will prevent damage and a possible malfunction of the SIR system. The steering wheel must be secured in position before disconnecting the following components: The steering column, The intermediate shaft(s),
the steering gear. After disconnecting these components, do not rotate the steering wheel or move the front tires and wheels. Failure to follow this procedure may cause the SIR coil assembly to become un-centered and cause possible damage to the SIR coil. If you think the SIR coil has became un-centered, refer to Clockspring Centering, in the Chassis Electrical section.

2. Raise and support the vehicle.

3. Remove both of the front tire and wheel assemblies.

4. Remove the engine protection shield if equipped.

5. Disconnect the outer tie rod end from the steering knuckle.

6. Place a drain pan to catch the fluid.

7. Disconnect the power steering hose assembly from the steering gear.

8. Remove the coupler clamp bolt from the intermediate shaft.

9. Separate the intermediate shaft from the steering gear.

10. Remove the steering gear vertical mounting nuts, the washers and the bolts.

11. Remove the steering gear horizontal mounting nuts, the washers and the bolts.

12. Remove the crossmember, **2WD ONLY**:

    a. Remove the crossmember mounting nuts and bolts.

    b. Remove the crossmember from the vehicle.

13. Remove the steering gear from the vehicle.

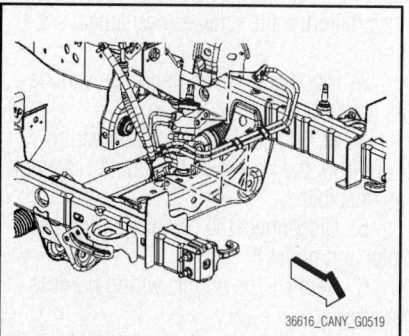

Fig. 300 Separate the intermediate shaft from the steering gear

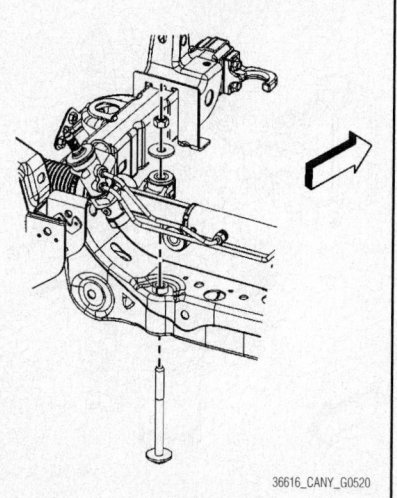

Fig. 301 Remove the steering gear vertical mounting nuts

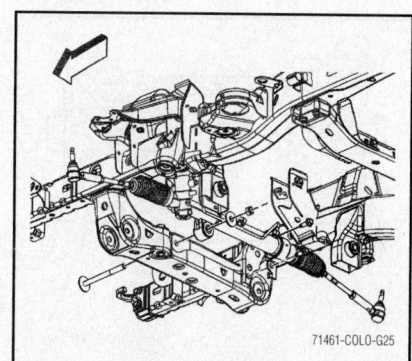

Fig. 302 Remove the steering gear horizontal mounting nuts

To install:

14. Install the steering gear into the vehicle.

15. Loose install the steering gear horizontal mounting nuts, the washers and the bolts.

16. Install the crossmember, **2WD ONLY**:

a. Position the crossmember to the vehicle.

b. Perform the following procedure before installing the bolts:

- Remove all traces of the original adhesive patch.
- Clean the threads of the bolt with denatured alcohol or equivalent and allow to dry.
- Apply Threadlocker GM P/N 12345493 (Canadian P/N 10953488).

✳✳ WARNING

Use the correct fastener in the correct location. Replacement fasteners must be the correct part number for that application. Fasteners requiring replacement or fasteners requiring the use of thread locking compound or sealant are identified in the service procedure. Do not use paints, lubricants, or corrosion inhibitors on fasteners or fastener joint surfaces unless specified. These coatings affect fastener torque and joint clamping force and may damage the fastener. Use the correct tightening sequence and specifications when installing fasteners in order to avoid damage to parts and systems.

c. Install the bolts and the nuts and tighten to 44 ft. lbs. (60 Nm).

17. Loose install the steering gear vertical mounting nuts, the washers and the bolts. Tighten the long bolts to 96 ft. lbs.

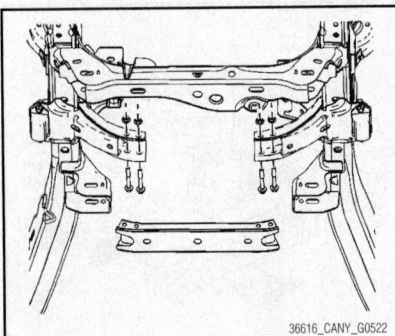

Fig. 303 Remove the crossmember—2WD only

(130 Nm). Tighten the isolator clamp bolts to 74 ft. lbs. (100 Nm).

18. Install the intermediate shaft to the steering gear.

19. Install the coupler clamp bolt to the intermediate shaft.

20. Connect the power steering hose assembly to the steering gear.

21. Install the engine protection shield, if equipped.

22. Install the outer tie rod end to the steering knuckle.

23. Install both of the front tire and wheel assemblies.

24. Lower the vehicle.

25. Bleed the power steering system.

POWER STEERING PUMP

REMOVAL & INSTALLATION

2.9L & 3.7L Engines

See Figure 304.

1. Before servicing the vehicle, refer to the Precautions Section.

2. Remove the air cleaner assembly. Refer to Air Cleaner Removal & Installation.

3. Remove the drive belt. Refer to Accessory Drive Belt Removal & Installation.

4. Remove the power steering pump pulley using J 25034-C.

5. Disconnect the oil pressure sensor harness clip from the pump body.

6. Install a drain pan under the vehicle.

7. Disconnect the power steering pressure hoses from the power steering pump.

8. Remove the power steering pump mounting bolts.

9. Remove the power steering pump.

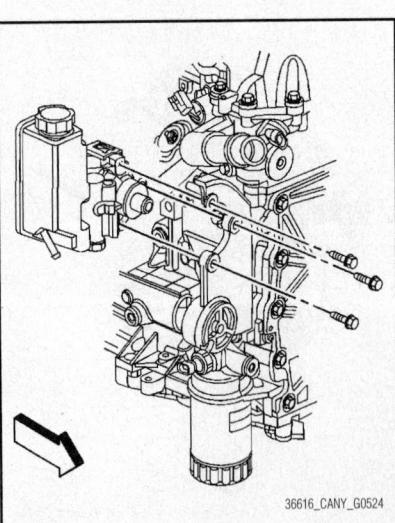

Fig. 304 Remove the power steering pump

To install:

10. Install the power steering pump.

✳✳ WARNING

Use the correct fastener in the correct location. Replacement fasteners must be the correct part number for that application. Fasteners requiring replacement or fasteners requiring the use of thread locking compound or sealant are identified in the service procedure. Do not use paints, lubricants, or corrosion inhibitors on fasteners or fastener joint surfaces unless specified. These coatings affect fastener torque and joint clamping force and may damage the fastener. Use the correct tightening sequence and specifications when installing fasteners in order to avoid damage to parts and systems.

11. Install the power steering pump mounting bolts and tighten to 18 ft. lbs. (25 Nm).

12. Connect the power steering pressure hoses to the power steering pump. Tighten the power steering pressure hose to 18 ft. lbs. (25 Nm).

13. Remove the drain pan from under the vehicle.

14. Connect the oil pressure sensor harness clip to the pump body.

15. Install the power steering pump pulley.

16. Install the drive belt.

17. Install the air cleaner assembly.

18. Bleed the power steering system.

19. Inspect the power steering system for leaks.

5.3L Engine

See Figures 305 and 306.

1. Before servicing the vehicle, refer to the Precautions Section.

2. Remove the accessory drive belt. Refer to Accessory Drive Belt Removal & Installation in the Engine Mechanical section.

3. Place drain pans under the vehicle as needed.

4. Remove as much power steering fluid from the power steering fluid reservoir as possible.

5. Disconnect the power steering gear inlet and outlet hose.

6. Remove the engine wiring harness bracket bolt.

7. Reposition the engine wiring harness bracket out of the way.

8. Remove the alternator bracket bolts

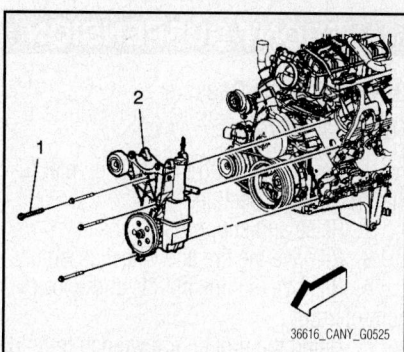

Fig. 305 Remove the alternator bracket bolts (1) and bracket (2) with the power steering pump and power steering fluid reservoir assembly attached

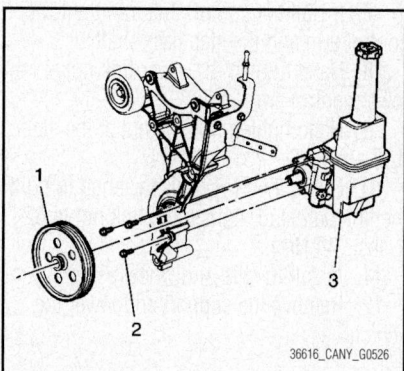

Fig. 306 Power steering pump removal

(1) and alternator bracket (2) with the power steering pump and power steering fluid reservoir assembly attached.

9. Remove the power steering pump pulley. Refer to Power Steering Pump Pulley Replacement.

10. Remove the power steering pump bolts (2).

11. Remove the power steering pump and power steering pump fluid reservoir assembly (3) from the alternator bracket.

12. Separate the power steering pump and the power steering fluid reservoir.

To install:

13. Connect the power steering pump and the power steering fluid reservoir.

14. Install the power steering pump and power steering pump fluid reservoir assembly to the alternator bracket.

✳✳ WARNING

Use the correct fastener in the correct location. Replacement fasteners must be the correct part number for that application. Fasteners requiring replacement or fasteners requiring the use of thread locking compound or sealant are identified in the service procedure. Do not use paints, lubricants, or corrosion inhibitors on fasteners or fastener joint surfaces unless specified. These coatings affect fastener torque and joint clamping force and may damage the fastener. Use the correct tightening sequence and specifications when installing fasteners in order to avoid damage to parts and systems.

15. Install the power steering pump bolts and tighten to 18 ft. lbs. (25 Nm).

16. Install the power steering pump pulley.

17. Install the alternator bracket and alternator bracket bolts to the vehicle with the power steering pump and power steering fluid reservoir assembly attached. Tighten the bolts to 37 ft. lbs. (50 Nm).

18. Position the engine wiring harness bracket.

19. Install the engine wiring harness bracket bolt and tighten to 30 ft. lbs. (40 Nm).

20. Connect the power steering gear inlet and outlet hose.

21. Clean any excess power steering fluid from the vehicle and remove the drain pans.

22. Install the accessory drive belt.

BLEEDING

✳✳ WARNING

Use clean, new power steering fluid type only.

➡ Hoses touching the frame, body or engine may cause system noise. Verify that the hoses do not touch any other part of the vehicle.

➡ Loose connections may not leak, but could allow air into the steering system. Verify that all hose connections are tight.

➡ Important: Power steering fluid level must be maintained throughout bleed procedure.

1. Fill pump reservoir with fluid to minimum system level, FULL COLD level, or middle of hash mark on cap stick fluid level indicator.

➡ Important: With hydro-boost only, the oil level will appear falsely high if the hydro-boost accumulator is not fully charged. Do not apply the brake pedal with the engine OFF. This will discharge the hydro-boost accumulator.

2. If equipped with hydro-boost, fully charge the hydro-boost accumulator using the following procedure:
   a. Start the engine.
   b. Firmly apply the brake pedal 10–15 times.
   c. Turn the engine OFF.

3. Raise the vehicle until the front wheels are off the ground.

4. Key on engine OFF, turn the steering wheel from stop to stop 12 times. Vehicles equipped with hydro-boost systems or longer length power steering hoses may require turns up to 15 to 20 stop to stops.

5. Verify power steering fluid level per operating specification.

6. Start the engine. Rotate steering wheel from left to right. Check for sign of cavitation or fluid aeration (pump noise/whining).

7. Verify the fluid level. Repeat the bleed procedure, if necessary.

SUSPENSION
FRONT SUSPENSION

COIL SPRING

REMOVAL & INSTALLATION

See Figure 307.

1. Before servicing the vehicle, refer to the Precautions Section.

2. Remove the shock absorber/spring assembly. Refer to Shock Absorber Removal & Installation.

➥**Important: Note the orientation between the mounting plate and the spring before removing the spring from the compressor**

3. Remove the spring and mounting plate from the spring compressor.

To install:

4. Assemble the mounting plate to the spring ensuring proper orientation.

5. Align the center line of any of the upper mounting studs with the center line of the lower shock mount.

6. Install the mounting plate and spring to the spring compressor.

7. Install the shock absorber/spring assembly

8. Lower the vehicle.

CONTROL LINKS

REMOVAL & INSTALLATION

Sport (ZQ8) & Increased Capacity (Z85) Chassis

See Figure 308.

1. Before servicing the vehicle, refer to the Precautions Section.

2. Raise and support the vehicle.

3. Remove the tire and wheel.

4. Using the proper size wrench, hold the link ball stud while removing the link nut.

5. Remove the retaining nut from the stabilizer shaft and the lower control arm.

6. Remove the stabilizer/control link from the vehicle.

To install:

7. Install the control link on the lower control arm and stabilizer shaft.

8. Hand tighten the stabilizer shaft link nuts

9. Using the proper size wrench to hold the link ball joint, tighten the link nut to 32 ft. lbs. (44 Nm).

10. Install the tire and wheel assembly.

11. Remove the support and lower the vehicle.

Off-Road (Z71) Chassis

See Figure 309.

1. Before servicing the vehicle, refer to the Precautions Section.

2. Raise and support the vehicle.

3. Remove the tire and wheel assembly.

4. Remove the link nut (1) at the lower control arm.

5. Using the proper size wrench to hold the link ball stud, remove the link nut (2) at the stabilizer shaft.

6. Remove the stabilizer/control link from the lower control arm and stabilizer shaft.

To install:

7. Install the control link into the lower control arm and the stabilizer shaft.

8. Hand tighten the lower link nut at the lower control arm.

9. Hand tighten the link nut at the stabilizer shaft.

10. Using the proper size wrench to hold the link ball stud, tighten the link nut to 32 ft. lbs. (44 Nm).

11. Install the tire and wheel assembly.

12. Remove the support and lower the vehicle.

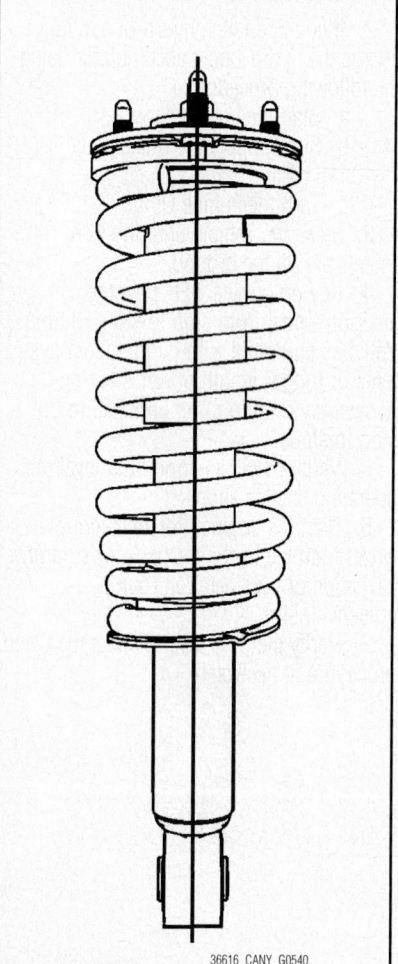

36616_CANY_G0540

Fig. 307 Align the center line of any of the upper mounting studs with the center line of the lower shock mount

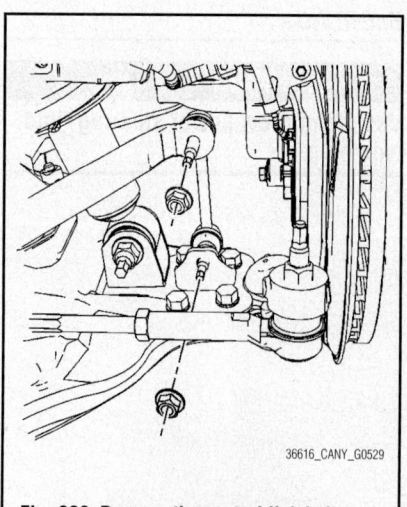

36616_CANY_G0529

Fig. 308 Remove the control link bolt

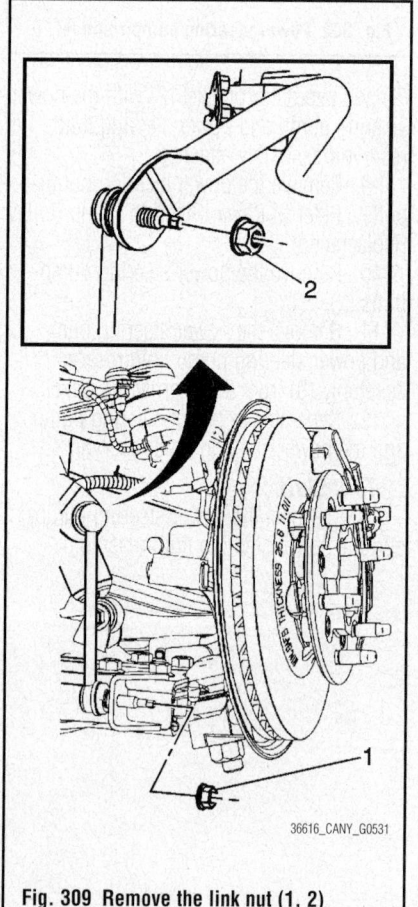

36616_CANY_G0531

Fig. 309 Remove the link nut (1, 2)

LOWER BALL JOINT

REMOVAL & INSTALLATION

2WD, Sport (ZQ8) & Increased Capacity (Z85) Chassis

See Figure 310.

1. Before servicing the vehicle, refer to the Precautions Section.
2. Remove the steering knuckle.
3. Remove the ball joint nuts and bolts from the lower control arm. Discard the nuts and bolts.
4. Remove the ball joint from the lower control arm.

To install:

5. Install the ball joint to the lower control arm.
6. Install the new ball joint nuts and bolts to the lower control arm and tighten the nuts to 32 ft. lbs. (44 Nm).
7. Install the steering knuckle.
8. Verify the wheel alignment.

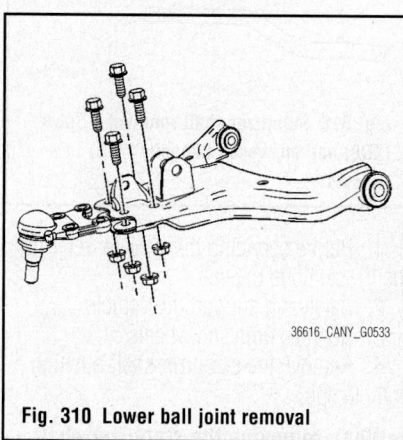

Fig. 310 Lower ball joint removal

4WD & 2WD, Off-Road (Z71) Chassis

See Figure 311.

1. Before servicing the vehicle, refer to the Precautions Section.
2. Remove the steering knuckle.
3. Remove the ball joint nuts and bolts from the lower control arm. Discard the nuts and bolts.
4. Remove the ball joint from the lower control arm.

To install:

5. Install the ball joint to the lower control arm.
6. Install the new ball joint nuts and bolts to the lower control arm and tighten to 47 ft. lbs. (64 Nm).
7. Install the steering knuckle.
8. Verify the wheel alignment.

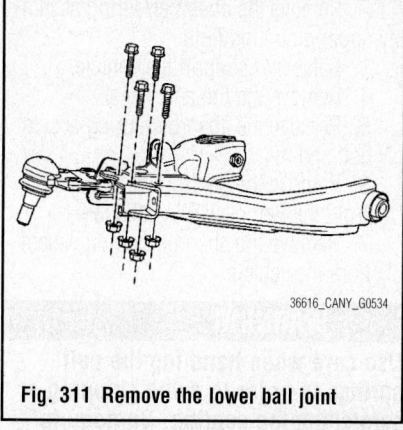

Fig. 311 Remove the lower ball joint

LOWER CONTROL ARM

REMOVAL & INSTALLATION

See Figures 312 and 313.

1. Before servicing the vehicle, refer to the Precautions Section.
2. Raise and support the vehicle.
3. Remove the tire and wheel assembly.
4. Remove the control links from the lower control arm. Refer to Control Link Removal & Installation.
5. Remove the shock absorber nut and through bolt. Refer to Shock Absorber Removal & Installation.
6. Remove the lower ball joint stud nut.
7. Disconnect the lower ball joint stud from the steering knuckle using J 43631.
8. Remove the lower control arm nuts and the alignment cams.
9. Remove the lower control arm bolts.
10. Remove the lower control arm.

To install:

11. Install the lower control arm.
12. Install the lower control arm bolts.

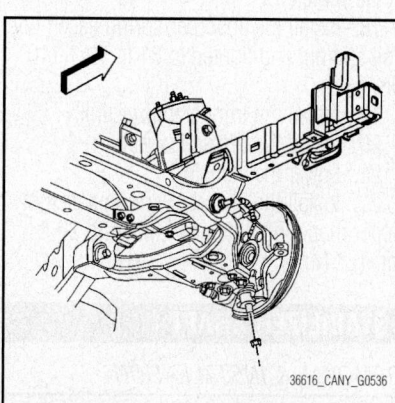

Fig. 312 Remove lower ball joint nut

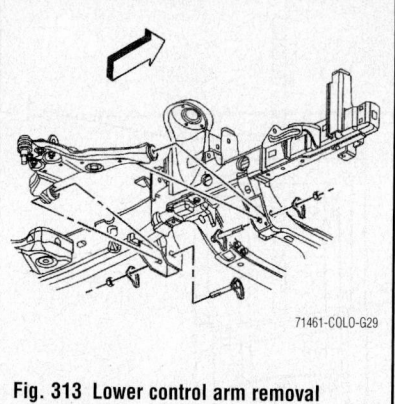

Fig. 313 Lower control arm removal

➡ **The fasteners must be tightened in sequence. Tighten the rear nut first then the front nut.**

13. Install the nuts and washers. Tighten the rear nut to 114 ft.lbs. (155 Nm). Tighten the front nut to 114 ft. lbs. (155 Nm).
14. Connect lower ball joint stud to the steering knuckle.
15. Install the nut to the ball joint stud and tighten to 102 ft. lbs. (138 Nm).
16. Install the shock absorber through bolt and nut.
17. Install the stabilizer shaft links to the lower control arm.
18. Install the tire and wheel assembly.
19. Lower the vehicle.
20. Verify the wheel alignment.

SHOCK ABSORBERS

REMOVAL & INSTALLATION

See Figures 00, 314 through 316.

1. Before servicing the vehicle, refer to the Precautions Section.

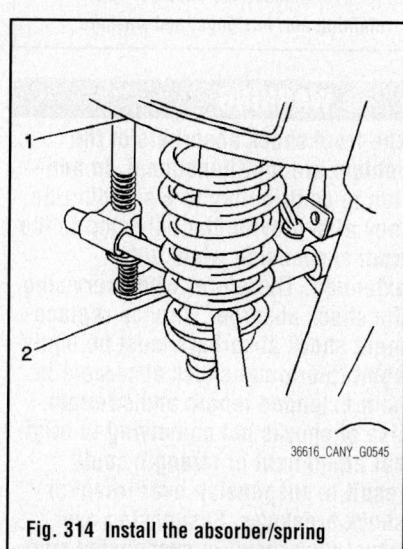

Fig. 314 Install the absorber/spring assembly (2) into the J 45400 (1)

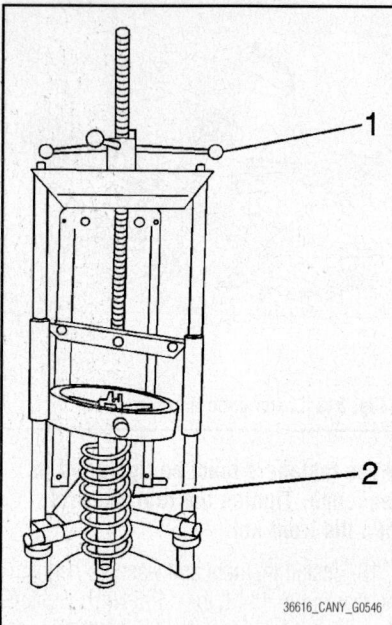

Fig. 315 Turn the spring compressor forcing screw (1) until the coil spring (2) is compressed

Fig. 316 Remove the absorber upper retaining nut, bushings, and washers

✳✳ WARNING

The front shock absorbers of the vehicle are multifunctional. In addition to contributing to a smooth ride they also provide the only stop to the front suspension when fully extended. Therefore, when servicing the shock absorber, service replacement shock absorbers must be equivalent to original shock absorbers in both extended length and strength. Use of shocks not complying to original equipment or strength could result in suspension over-travel or shock breakage. Suspension over-travel may result in suspension component breakage.

2. Remove the absorber/spring assembly upper mounting nuts.
3. Raise and support the vehicle.
4. Remove the tire and wheel.
5. Remove the absorber/spring assembly bolt and nut.
6. Remove the control link. Refer to Control Link Removal & Installation.
7. Remove the absorber/spring assembly from the vehicle.

✳✳ WARNING

Use care when handling the coil springs in order to avoid chipping or scratching the coating. Damage to the coating will result in premature failure of the coil springs.

8. Install the absorber/spring assembly (2) into the J 45400 (1).

➡ **The spring is compressed when the shock absorber moves freely.**

9. Turn the spring compressor forcing screw (1) until the coil spring (2) is compressed.
10. Remove the absorber upper retaining nut, bushings, and washers.
11. Remove the absorber from the assembly.
12. Do not remove the spring from the J 45400.

To install:
13. Install the absorber to the J 45400.
14. Install the absorber bushings and washers.

➡ **Ensure that the absorber bushings and tennon align correctly with the mounting bracket before securing the retaining nut.**

15. Install the absorber retaining nut and tighten to 15 ft. lbs. (20 Nm).
16. Remove the absorber/spring assembly from the J 45400.
17. Install the absorber/spring assembly to the vehicle.
18. Install the absorber/spring assembly bolt and nut and tighten to 81 ft. lbs. (110 Nm).
19. Install the front stabilizer link.
20. Install the tire and wheel
21. Lower the vehicle.
22. Install the absorber/spring assembly upper mounting nuts and tighten to 20 ft. lbs. (27 Nm).

STABILIZER SHAFT

REMOVAL & INSTALLATION
See Figures 317 and 318.

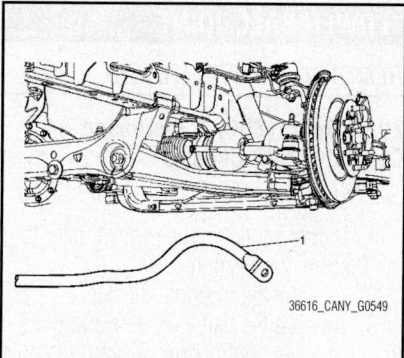

Fig. 317 Stabilizer shaft removal— Off-Road (Z71) chassis

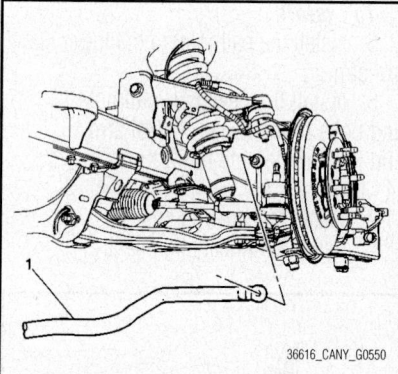

Fig. 318 Stabilizer shaft removal—Sport (ZQ8) and Increased Capacity (Z85) chassis

1. Before servicing the vehicle, refer to the Precautions Section.
2. Raise and support the vehicle.
3. Remove tires and wheels.
4. Remove the stabilizer shaft bushing and clamps.

➡ **When removing the stabilizer shaft, it may be necessary to rotate the stabilizer shaft down to clear the outer tie rod end and wheel drive shaft.**

5. Separate the stabilizer shaft from the control link.

To install:
6. Installation is the reverse of removal.

STEERING KNUCKLE

REMOVAL & INSTALLATION
See Figure 319.

1. Before servicing the vehicle, refer to the Precautions Section.
2. Raise and support the vehicle.
3. Remove the tire and wheel assembly.
4. Support the lower control arm with a suitable jack.

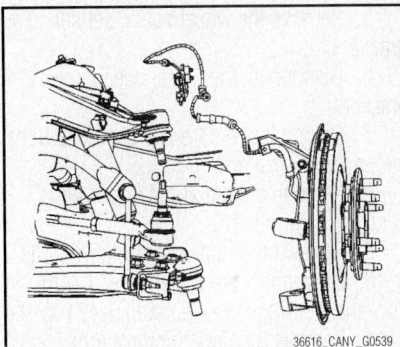

Fig. 319 Remove steering knuckle assembly

➡In the following service procedure, it is NOT necessary to separate the brake caliper and mounting bracket. Remove them as an assembly. Support the assembly with mechanics wire or equivalent.

Remove the brake caliper assembly and relocate to the side. Refer to Brake Caliper Removal & Installation.

➡Perform the following service procedure if the vehicle is equipped with 4WD. If the vehicle does not have 4WD, proceed to Step 7.

5. Separate the front wheel drive shaft from the steering knuckle.

6. Remove the speed senor wiring harness from the retaining clips on the upper control arm and frame.

7. Remove the outer tie rod end from the knuckle.

8. Separate the upper ball joint from the knuckle. Refer to Upper Ball Joint Removal & Installation.

9. Separate the lower ball joint from the knuckle. Refer to Lower Ball Joint Removal & Installation.

➡Remove the wheel hub and bearing assembly and knuckle as a unit.

10. Remove the knuckle from the upper and lower control arms.

11. Remove the wheel hub and bearing assembly from the knuckle. Refer to Front Wheel Bearing & Hub Removal & Installation.

To install:

12. Install the wheel hub and bearing assembly onto the knuckle.

13. Install the lower control arm/ball joint into the knuckle.

➡The following service procedure is for vehicles equipped with 4WD only. If the vehicle is not equipped with 4WD, proceed to Step 4.

14. Install the wheel drive shaft into the knuckle.

15. Install the upper control arm/ball joint into the knuckle.

16. Install the outer tie rod end into the knuckle.

17. Install the speed senor wiring harness in the retaining clips on the upper control arm and frame.

18. Install the brake caliper mounting bracket.

19. Install the wheel drive shaft retaining nut to specifications.

20. Remove the support from the lower control arm.

21. Install the tire and wheel.

22. Remove the support and lower the vehicle.

TORSION BAR

REMOVAL & INSTALLATION

See Figure 320.

1. Before servicing the vehicle, refer to the Precautions Section.

✳✳ WARNING

Use care when handling the torsion bars in order to avoid chipping or scratching the coating. Damage to the coating will result in premature failure of the torsion bars.

2. Raise and support the vehicle.

3. Allow the front suspension to hang in the rebound position.

4. Mark the adjuster bolt.

➡To aid in re-assembly record the number of turns that are required to remove the adjuster bolt.

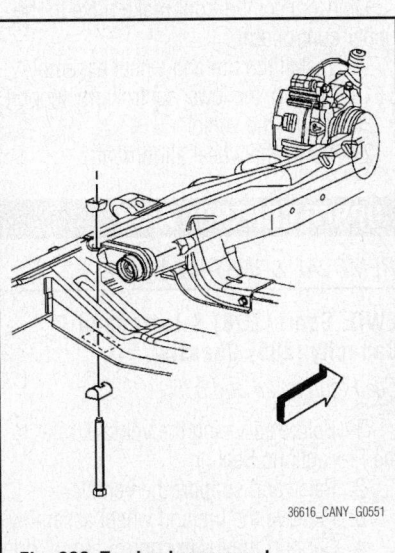

Fig. 320 Torsion bar removal

5. Remove the adjuster bolt, spacer and adjuster nut.

➡Take note that the torsion bars are specific to the left and right sides of the vehicle.

6. Remove the adjustment arms and torsion bars as a unit, moving it rearward to disengage the lower control arm.

To install:

7. Install the adjustment arms and torsion bars in relation to where the bars were removed.

8. Install the adjustment arm to the torsion bar and slide the torsion bar forward until the torsion bar fully engages the lower control arm.

9. Install the adjuster bolt, spacer and adjuster nut.

10. Lower the vehicle.

11. Check the Z-Height.

UPPER BALL JOINT

REMOVAL & INSTALLATION

2WD, Sport (ZQ8) & Increased Capacity (Z85) Chassis

See Figures 321 and 322.

1. Before servicing the vehicle, refer to the Precautions Section.

2. Raise and support the vehicle.

3. Remove the tire and wheel assembly.

4. Support the lower control arm with a suitable jack stand.

5. Disconnect the front brake hose from the upper control arm.

6. Remove the wheel speed sensor bracket bolt.

7. Disconnect the wheel speed sensor brackets.

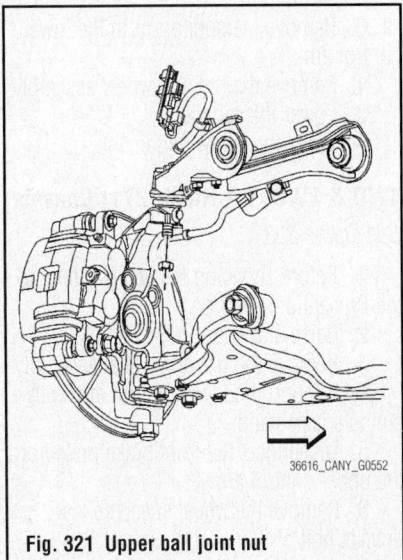

Fig. 321 Upper ball joint nut

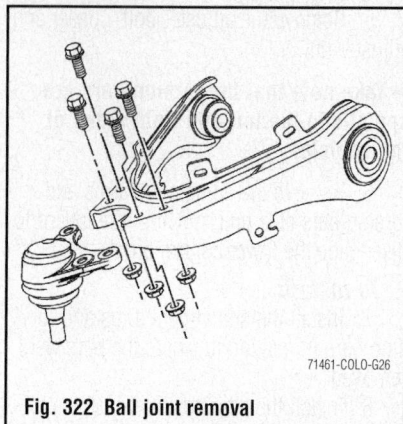

Fig. 322 Ball joint removal

8. Remove the nut from the upper ball joint. Discard the nut.

9. Disconnect the ball joint from the steering knuckle using the J-42188-B.

10. Remove the ball joint nuts and bolts from the upper control arm. Discard the nuts and bolts.

11. Remove the ball joint from the upper control arm.

To install:

12. Install the ball joint to the upper control arm.

13. Install the replacement bolts to the upper control arm.

14. Install the nuts to the bolts and tighten 12 ft. lbs. (16 Nm).

15. Connect the ball joint to the steering knuckle.

16. Install the new nut to the upper ball joint and tighten to 74 ft. lbs. (100 Nm).

17. Connect the wheel speed sensor brackets.

18. Install the wheel speed sensor bracket bolt and tighten to 15 ft. lbs. (20 Nm).

19. Connect the front brake hose to the upper control arm.

20. Remove the support from the lower control arm.

21. Remove the tire and wheel assembly.

22. Lower the vehicle.

23. Verify the wheel alignment.

4WD & 2WD, Off-Road (Z71) Chassis

See Figure 323.

1. Before servicing the vehicle, refer to the Precautions Section.

2. Raise and support the vehicle.

3. Remove the tire and wheel assembly.

4. Support the lower control arm with a suitable jack stand.

5. Disconnect the front brake hose from the upper control arm.

6. Remove the wheel speed sensor bracket bolt.

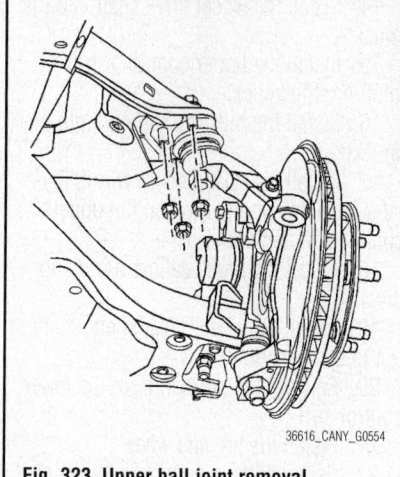

Fig. 323 Upper ball joint removal

7. Disconnect the wheel speed sensor brackets.

8. Disconnect the upper control arm from the ball stud by removing the retention nuts. Discard the nuts.

9. Remove the nut from the upper ball joint. Discard the nut.

10. Disconnect the ball joint from the steering knuckle using the J-42188-B.

11. Remove the ball joint from the steering knuckle.

To install:

12. Install the ball joint to the steering knuckle.

13. Install the new nut to the upper ball joint and tighten to 55 ft. lbs. (75 Nm).

14. Connect the upper control arm to the ball stud by installing the retention nuts. Tighten the nut to 35 ft. lbs. (47 Nm).

15. Connect the wheel speed sensor brackets.

16. Install the wheel speed sensor bracket bolt and tighten to 15 ft. lbs. (20 Nm).

17. Connect the front brake hose to the upper control arm.

18. Install the tire and wheel assembly.

19. Remove the lower control arm support.

20. Lower the vehicle.

21. Verify the wheel alignment.

UPPER CONTROL ARM

REMOVAL & INSTALLATION

2WD, Sport (ZQ8) & Increased Capacity (Z85) Chassis

See Figures 324 and 325.

1. Before servicing the vehicle, refer to the Precautions Section.

2. Raise and support the vehicle.

3. Remove the tire and wheel assembly.

4. Support the lower control arm at ride height.

5. Remove the wheel speed sensor bracket bolt.

6. Disconnect the wheel speed sensor brackets.

7. Disconnect the front brake hose from the upper control arm.

8. Remove the nut at the upper ball joint. Discard the nut.

9. Remove the upper control arm bolts.

10. Disconnect the upper control arm from the steering knuckle using J-42188-B.

11. Remove the upper control arm.

To install:

12. Install the upper control arm.

13. Install the upper control arm bolts and tighten to 118 ft. lbs. (160 Nm).

14. Connect the upper control arm to the steering knuckle.

15. Install the new nut to the upper ball joint stud and tighten the nut to 74 ft. lbs. (100 Nm).

16. Connect the wheel speed sensor brackets.

17. Install the wheel speed sensor bracket bolt and tighten to 15 ft. lbs. (20 Nm).

18. Connect the front brake hose to the upper control arm.

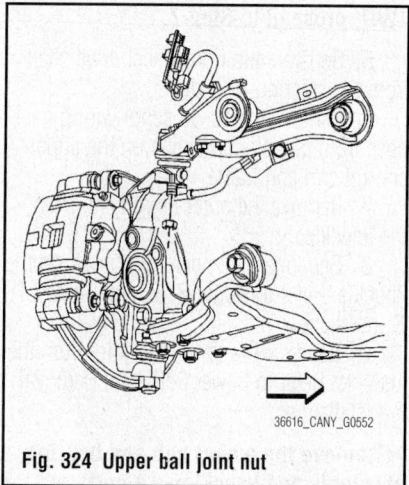

Fig. 324 Upper ball joint nut

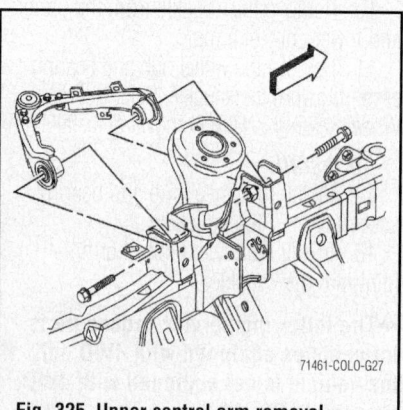

Fig. 325 Upper control arm removal

19. Remove the lower control arm support.

20. Install the tire and wheel assembly.

21. Lower the vehicle.

22. Verify the wheel alignment.

4WD & 2WD, Off-Road (Z71) Chassis

See Figure 326.

1. Before servicing the vehicle, refer to the Precautions Section.

2. Raise and support the vehicle.

3. Remove the tire and wheel assembly.

4. Support the lower control arm at ride height.

5. Remove the wheel speed sensor bracket bolt.

6. Disconnect the wheel speed sensor brackets.

7. Disconnect the front brake hose from the frame bracket.

8. Remove the front shock. Refer to Shock Absorber Removal & Installation.

9. Disconnect the upper control arm from the ball stud by removing the retention nuts.

10. Remove the upper control arm nuts and the adjustment cams.

11. Remove the upper control arm bolts.

12. Remove the upper control arm.

To install:

13. Install the upper control arm.

14. Install the upper control arm nuts and the adjustment cams.

15. Using the J 45938, tighten the nuts to 114 ft. lbs. (155 Nm).

16. Connect the upper control arm to the ball stud by installing the retention nuts and tighten to 47 ft. lbs. (64 Nm).

17. Connect the wheel speed sensor brackets.

18. Install the wheel speed sensor bracket bolt and tighten to 15 ft. lbs. (20 Nm).

19. Connect the front brake hose to the frame bracket.

20. Install the front shock.

21. Install the tire and wheel assembly.

22. Remove the lower control arm support.

23. Lower the vehicle.

24. Verify the wheel alignment.

WHEEL HUB & BEARING

REMOVAL & INSTALLATION

See Figure 327.

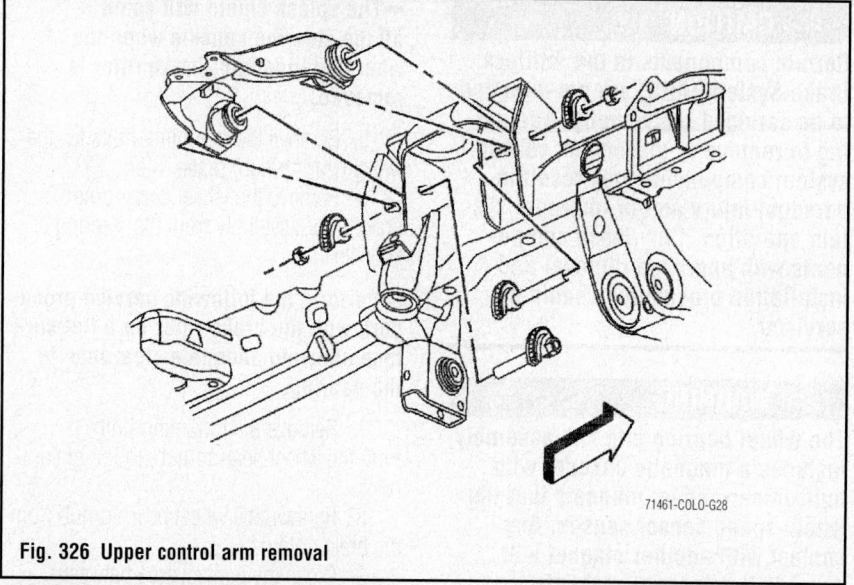

Fig. 326 Upper control arm removal

✳✳ CAUTION

Some models or aftermarket brake parts may contain asbestos fibers which can become airborne in dust. Breathing dust with asbestos fibers may cause serious bodily harm. Use a water-dampened cloth in order to remove any dust on brake parts. Equipment is available commercially in order to perform this washing function. These wet methods prevent fibers from becoming airborne. Avoid taking the following actions when you service wheel brake parts:

- Do not grind brake linings.
- Do not sand brake linings.
- Do not clean wheel brake parts with a dry brush or with compressed air.

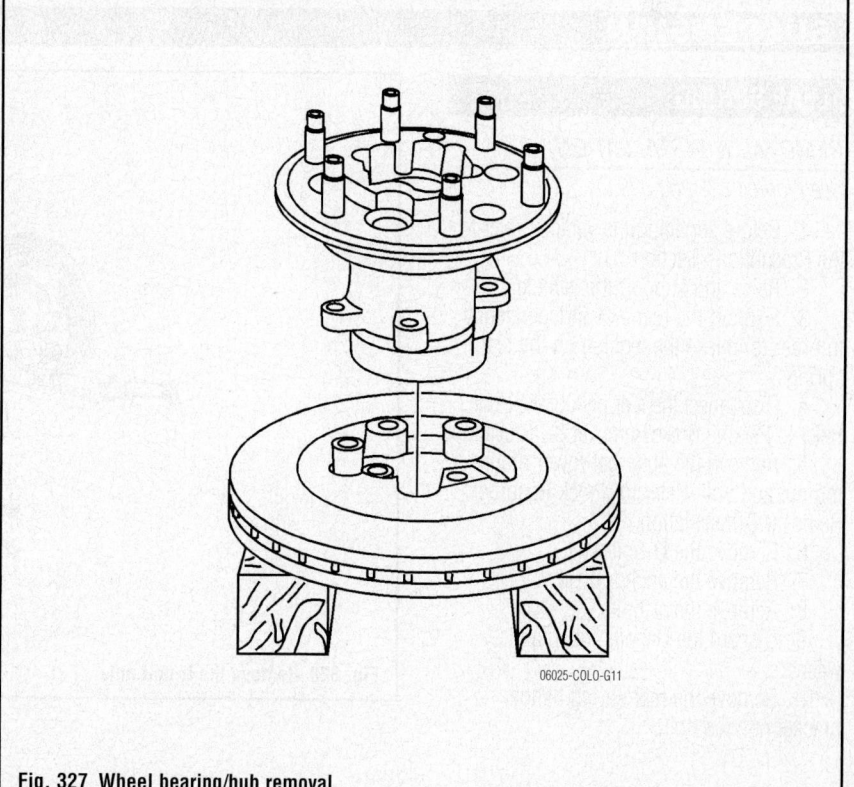

Fig. 327 Wheel bearing/hub removal

✴✴ CAUTION

Certain components in the Antilock Brake System (ABS) are not intended to be serviced individually. Attempting to remove or disconnect certain system components may result in personal injury and/or improper system operation. Only those components with approved removal and installation procedures should be serviced.

✴✴ WARNING

The wheel bearing and hub assembly includes a magnetic encoder with built-in permanent magnets that the wheel speed sensor senses. Any contact with another magnet will damage the encoder magnets. The damage will cause a diagnostic trouble code to be set and will require wheel bearing and hub replacement.

1. Before servicing the vehicle, refer to the Precautions Section.
2. Raise the vehicle.
3. Remove the wheel drive shaft nut, if needed.
4. Remove the front brake caliper mounting bracket. Refer to Brake Caliper Removal & Installation.

➡ The splash shield will come off the steering knuckle when the wheel bearing/hub, brake rotor is removed.

5. Remove the mounting bolts for the wheel bearing/hub, brake rotor.
6. Remove the wheel bearing/hub, brake rotor assembly from the steering knuckle.

➡ Perform the following service procedure with the brake rotor on a flat surface allowing adequate clearance to the bearing.

7. Remove the mounting bolt from the wheel bearing/hub, to the brake rotor.
8. Remove the wheel bearing/hub from the brake rotor.
9. Clean the contact area between the wheel bearing/hub and the brake rotor.

To install:

10. Position the wheel bearing/hub assembly on the brake rotor.
11. Install the mounting bolts from the wheel bearing/hub assembly to the brake rotor.

➡ The following service procedure is to be performed on a flat surface and to ensure that the brake rotor is securely attached to the hub assembly

prior to the final torquing procedure. DO NOT use air tools of any type for this procedure. The following procedure is to ensure that the wheel bearing hub/brake rotor assembly are securely attached to limit the movement of the wheel bearing hub/brake rotor assembly prior to the final torque.

12. Tighten the mounting bolts in crisscross pattern to 15 ft. lbs. (20 Nm).
13. Install the splash shield to the wheel bearing/hub, brake rotor assembly.
14. Install the wheel bearing/hub into the steering knuckle.

➡ When performing the following service procedure, DO NOT use air tools of any type to torque the brake rotor to hub bolts.

15. Install the wheel bearing/hub mounting bolts and tighten to 96 ft. lbs. (130 Nm).
16. Install the brake caliper mounting bracket to the steering knuckle.
17. Install the wheel drive shaft nut, if needed.
18. Tighten the brake rotor bolts to the final torque specification. Refer to Brake Rotor Replacement.
19. Lower the vehicle.

SUSPENSION   REAR SUSPENSION

LEAF SPRING

REMOVAL & INSTALLATION

See Figures 328 and 329.

1. Before servicing the vehicle, refer to the Precautions Section.
2. Raise and support the vehicle.
3. Support the rear axle independently in order to relieve the tension on the leaf springs.
4. Disconnect the rear park brake cable. Refer to Parking Brake Removal & Installation.
5. Remove the absorber lower mounting nut and bolt. Refer to Shock Absorber Removal & Installation.
6. Remove the U-bolt nuts.
7. Remove the anchor plate.
8. Remove the U-bolts.
9. Discard the U-bolts, nuts, and washers.
10. Remove the rear spring hanger bracket nut and bolt.

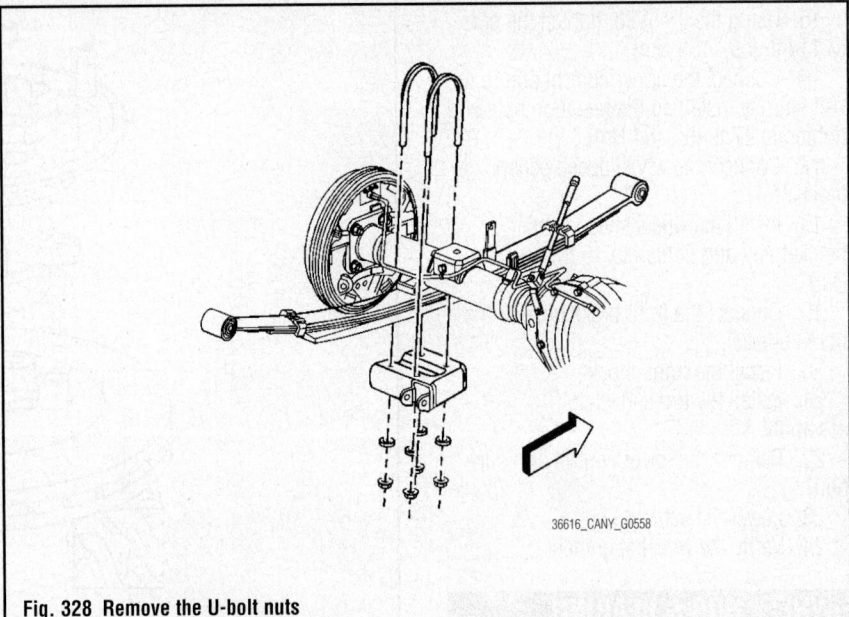

36616_CANY_G0558

Fig. 328 Remove the U-bolt nuts

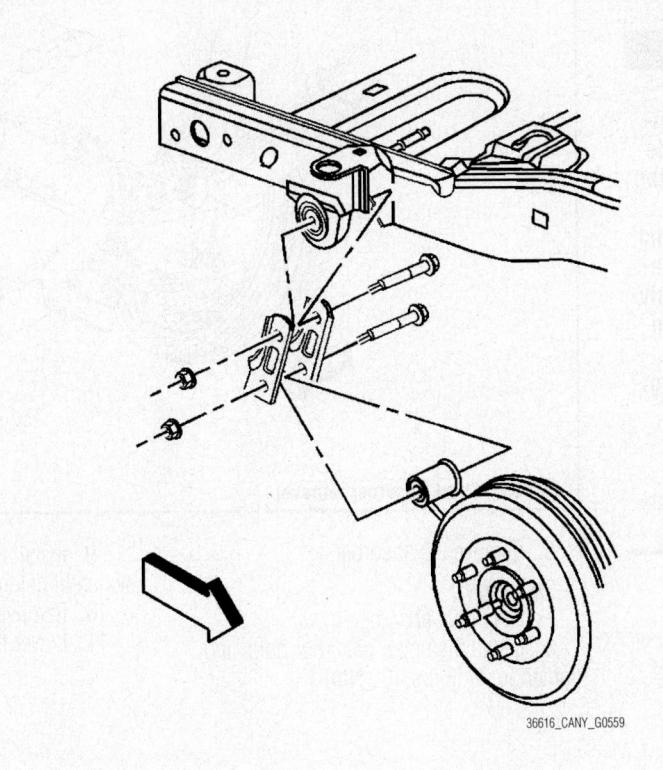

Fig. 329 Remove the rear spring hanger bracket nut and bolt

11. Remove the front spring bracket bolt.

12. Remove the leaf spring assembly from the vehicle.

To install:

13. Install the leaf spring assembly to the vehicle.

14. Install the front spring hanger bracket bolt.

15. Install the front spring hanger bracket nut.

16. Install the rear spring hanger bracket bolt.

17. Install the rear spring hanger bracket nut.

➡**Do not reuse the U-bolts.**

18. Install the new U-bolts.

19. Install the anchor plate.

20. Install new U-bolt washers and nuts and tighten the nuts to 56 ft. lbs. (76 Nm).

21. Install the absorber lower mounting nut and bolt.

22. Connect the rear park brake cable.

23. Remove the rear axle support.

24. Lower the vehicle.

25. With the vehicle weight on the tires and wheels, tighten the front hanger and rear shackle nut. Tighten the front hanger bracket nut to 92 ft. lbs. (125 Nm). Tighten the rear shackle nut to 63 ft. lbs. (85 Nm).

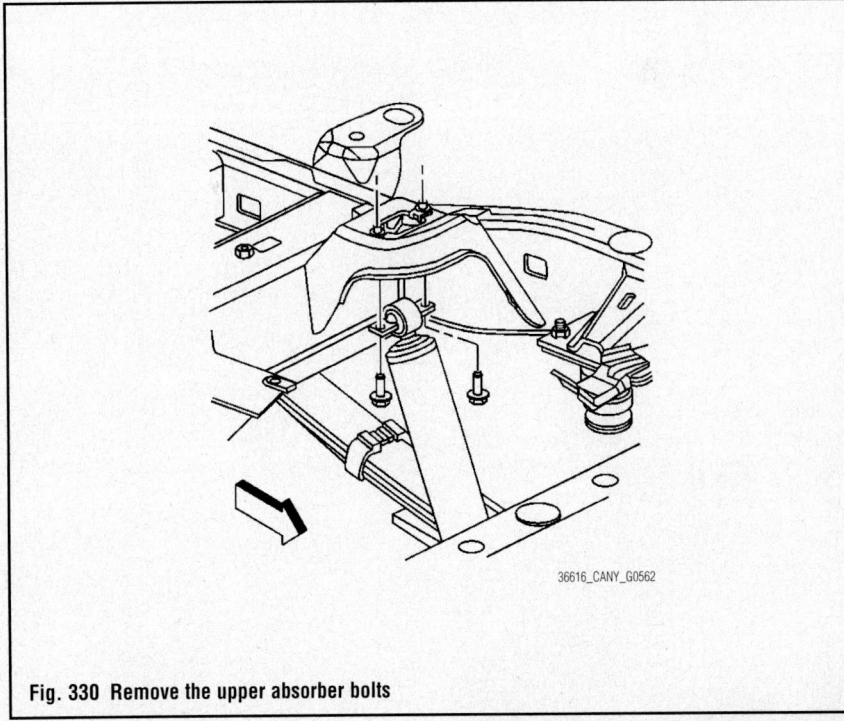

Fig. 330 Remove the upper absorber bolts

SHOCK ABSORBER

REMOVAL & INSTALLATION
See Figures 330 and 331.

1. Before servicing the vehicle, refer to the Precautions Section.

✳✳ WARNING

The front shock absorbers of the vehicle are multifunctional. In addition to contributing to a smooth ride they also provide the only stop to the front suspension when fully extended. Therefore, when servicing the shock absorber, service replacement shock absorbers must be equivalent to original shock absorbers in both extended length and strength. Use of shocks not complying to original equipment or strength could result in suspension over-travel or shock breakage. Suspension over-travel may result in suspension component breakage.

2. Raise and support the vehicle.
3. Support the rear axle at ride height.
4. Remove the upper absorber bolts.
5. Remove the lower absorber nut and the bolt.

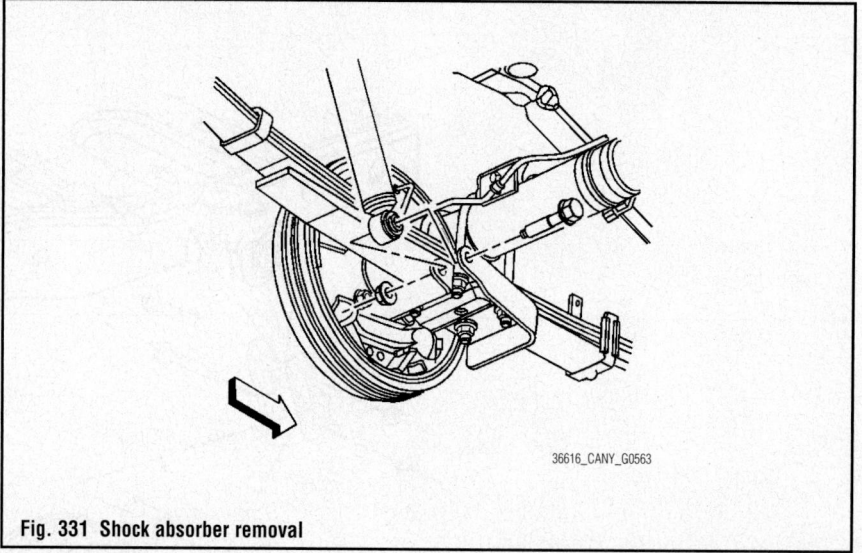

36616_CANY_G0563

Fig. 331 Shock absorber removal

6. Remove the absorber.

To install:

7. Install the absorber.
8. Install the upper absorber bolts and tighten to 26 ft. lbs. (35 Nm).

9. Install the lower absorber bolt and nut and tighten the nut to 70 ft. lbs. (95 Nm).
10. Remove the rear axle support.
11. Lower the vehicle.

SPECIFICATIONS AND MAINTENANCE CHARTS

ENGINE AND VEHICLE IDENTIFICATION

Engine							Model Year	
Code ①	Liters	Cu. In.	Cyl.	Fuel Sys.	Engine Type	Eng. Mfg.	Code ②	Year
A,M	2.0	122	4	DI	DOHC Turbo	GM	8	2008
F	2.2	134	4	MFI	DOHC	GM	9	2009
B	2.4	146	4	MFI	DOHC	GM		

MFI: Multi-port Fuel Injection

DI: Direct Injeciton

DOHC: Double Overhead Camshafts

① 8th digit of VIN

② 10th digit of VIN

36616_COBA_C0001

GENERAL ENGINE SPECIFICATIONS

All measurements are given in inches.

Year	Model	Engine Displacement Liters	Engine Series VIN	Net Horsepower @ rpm	Net Torque @ rpm (ft. lbs.)	Bore x Stroke (in.)	Compression Ratio	Oil Pressure @ rpm
2008	Cobalt SS	2.0	A,M	260@5300	260@2000	3.388x3.388	9.2:1	50-80@1000
	Cobalt LS, LT, G5	2.2	F	148@5600	152@4200	3.386x3.727	10.0:1	50-80@1000
	Cobalt LS, LT, G5	2.4	B	173@6200	163@4800	3.468x3.861	10.4:1	50-80@1000
2009	Cobalt SS	2.0	A,M	260@5300	260@2000	3.388x3.388	9.2:1	50-80@1000
	Cobalt LS, LT, G5	2.2	F	155@6100	150@4900	3.386x3.727	10.0:1	50-80@1000

36616_COBA_C0002

GASOLINE ENGINE TUNE-UP SPECIFICATIONS

Year	Engine Displacement Liters	Engine VIN	Spark Plug Gap (in.)	Ignition Timing (deg.) MT	Ignition Timing (deg.) AT	Fuel Pump (psi)	Idle Speed (rpm) MT	Idle Speed (rpm) AT	Valve Clearance In.	Valve Clearance Ex.
2008	2.0	A,M	0.035	①	NA	57-67	②	NA	HYD	HYD
	2.2	F	0.042	①	①	50-60	②	②	HYD	HYD
	2.4	B	0.042	①	①	50-60	②	②	HYD	HYD
2009	2.0	A,M	0.035	①	NA	57-67	②	NA	HYD	HYD
	2.2	F	0.042	①	①	50-60	②	②	HYD	HYD

NOTE: The Vehicle Emission Control Information label reflects specification changes made during production.

Follow the figures on the label if they differ from those in this chart.

HYD: Hydraulic

NA: Not Applicable

① Ignition timing is preset and cannot be adjusted

② Idle speed is maintained by the PCM

36616_COBA_C0003

CAPACITIES

Year	Model	Engine Displacement Liters	Engine VIN	Engine Oil with Filter (qts.)	Transmission (pts.) Manual	Transmission (pts.) Auto. ①	Fuel Tank (gal.)	Cooling System (qts.)
2008	Cobalt SS	2.0	A,M	5.0	②	NA	13.2	9.2
	Cobalt LS, LT, G5	2.2	F	5.0	②	14.0	13.5	7.4
	Cobalt LS, LT, G5	2.4	B	5.0	②	14.0	13.5	7.4
2009	Cobalt SS	2.0	A,M	5.0	②	NA	13.2	9.2
	Cobalt LS, LT, G5	2.2	F	5.0	②	14.0	13.5	7.4

NOTE: All capacities are approximate. Add fluid gradually and check to be sure a proper fluid level is obtained.

NA: Not Applicable

① Bottom pan removed

② Getrag M86: 3.8 pts. MU3: 4.0 pts.

36616_COBA_C0004

FLUID SPECIFICATIONS

Year	Model	Engine Displacement Liters	Engine ID/VIN	Engine Oil	Auto. Trans.	Manual Trans.	Power Steering Fluid	Brake Master Cylinder
2008	Cobalt SS	2.0	A,M	5W-30	NA	GM P/N 88862472	①	DOT 3
	Cobalt LS, LT, G5	2.2	F	5W-30	Dexron VI	Dexron VI	①	DOT 3
	Cobalt LS, LT, G5	2.4	B	5W-30	Dexron VI	Dexron VI	①	DOT 3
2009	Cobalt SS	2.0	A,M	5W-30	NA	GM P/N 88862472	①	DOT 3
	Cobalt LS, LT, G5	2.2	F	5W-30	Dexron VI	Dexron VI	①	DOT 3

DOT: Department Of Transportation

NA: Not Applicable

① These vehicles utilize an Electronic Power Steering (EPS) system

36616_COBA_C0005

VALVE SPECIFICATIONS

Year	Engine Displacement Liters	Engine VIN	Seat Angle (deg.)	Face Angle (deg.)	Spring Test Pressure (lbs. @ in.)	Spring Installed Height (in.)	Stem-to-Guide Clearance (in.) Intake	Stem-to-Guide Clearance (in.) Exhaust	Stem Diameter (in.) Intake	Stem Diameter (in.) Exhaust
2008	2.0	A,M	NS	NS	181-200 @1.279	1.279	0.0012-0.0022	0.0020-0.0026	0.2344-0.2355	0.2337-0.2343
	2.2	F	NS	NS	181-200 @1.279	1.279	0.0012-0.0022	0.0020-0.0026	0.2344-0.2355	0.2337-0.2343
	2.4	B	NS	NS	181-200 @1.279	1.279	0.0012-0.0022	0.0020-0.0026	0.2344-0.2355	0.2337-0.2343
2009	2.0	A,M	NS	NS	181-200 @1.279	1.279	0.0012-0.0022	0.0020-0.0026	0.2344-0.2355	0.2337-0.2343
	2.2	F	NS	NS	181-200 @1.279	1.279	0.0012-0.0022	0.0020-0.0026	0.2344-0.2355	0.2337-0.2343

NS: Not Specified

36616_COBA_C0006

CAMSHAFT AND BEARING SPECIFICATIONS CHART

All measurements are given in inches.

Year	Engine Displ. Liters	Engine ID/VIN	Journal Dia.	Brg. Oil Clearance	Shaft End-play	Thrust Surface	Journal Bore	Lobe Height Intake	Lobe Height Exhaust
2008	2.0	A,M	1.0604-1.0614 ①	NS	0.0016-0.0121	1.1828 1.1889 ②	NS	NS	NS
	2.2	F	1.0604-1.0614	NS	0.0016-0.0057	0.8268-0.8252	NS	NS	NS
	2.4	B	1.0604-1.0614	NS	0.0016-0.0057	0.8268-0.8252	NS	NS	NS
2009	2.0	A,M	1.0604-1.0614 ①	NS	0.0016-0.0121	1.1828 1.1889 ②	NS	NS	NS
	2.2	F	1.0604-1.0614	NS	0.0016-0.0057	0.8268-0.8252	NS	NS	NS

NS: Not Supplied

① Front journal diameter is 1.3774-1.3764

② Measured with actuator installed

36616_COBA_C0007

CRANKSHAFT AND CONNECTING ROD SPECIFICATIONS

All measurements are given in inches.

Year	Engine Displacement Liters	Engine VIN	Crankshaft Main Brg. Journal Dia.	Crankshaft Main Brg. Oil Clearance	Crankshaft Shaft End-play	Crankshaft Thrust on No.	Connecting Rod Journal Diameter	Connecting Rod Oil Clearance	Connecting Rod Side Clearance
2008	2.0	A,M	2.2045-2.2050	0.0012-0.0026	0.0012-0.0150	2	1.9291-1.9297	0.0011-0.0029	0.0028-0.0146
	2.2	F	2.2045-2.2050	0.0012-0.0026	0.0012-0.0150	2	1.9291-1.9297	0.0011-0.0029	0.0028-0.0146
	2.4	B	2.2045-2.2050	0.0012-0.0026	0.0012-0.0150	2	1.9291-1.9297	0.0011-0.0029	0.0028-0.0146
2009	2.0	A,M	2.2045-2.2050	0.0012-0.0026	0.0012-0.0150	2	1.9291-1.9297	0.0011-0.0029	0.0028-0.0146
	2.2	F	2.2045-2.2050	0.0012-0.0026	0.0012-0.0150	2	1.9291-1.9297	0.0011-0.0029	0.0028-0.0146

36616_COBA_C0008

PISTON AND RING SPECIFICATIONS

All measurements are given in inches.

Year	Engine Displ. Liters	Engine VIN	Piston Clearance	Ring Gap			Ring Side Clearance		
				Top Compression	Bottom Compression	Oil Control	Top Compression	Bottom Compression	Oil Control
2008	2.0	A,M	0.0004-0.0016	0.008-0.014	0.014-0.022	0.010-0.030	0.0016-0.0031	0.0010-0.0027	0.0009-0.0069
	2.2	F	0.0004-0.0016	0.008-0.014	0.014-0.022	0.010-0.030	0.0015-0.0031	0.0012-0.0027	0.0023-0.0081
	2.4	B	0.0004-0.0016	0.008-0.014	0.014-0.022	0.010-0.030	0.0015-0.0031	0.0012-0.0027	0.0023-0.0081
2009	2.0	A,M	0.0004-0.0016	0.008-0.014	0.014-0.022	0.010-0.030	0.0016-0.0031	0.0010-0.0027	0.0009-0.0069
	2.2	F	0.0004-0.0016	0.008-0.014	0.014-0.022	0.010-0.030	0.0015-0.0031	0.0012-0.0027	0.0023-0.0081

36616_COBA_C0009

TORQUE SPECIFICATIONS

All readings in ft. lbs.

Year	Engine Displacement Liters	Engine VIN	Cylinder Head Bolts	Main Bearing Bolts	Rod Bearing Bolts	Crankshaft Damper Bolts	Flywheel Bolts	Manifold		Spark Plugs	Oil Pan Drain Plug
								Intake	Exhaust		
2008	2.0	A,M	①	②	③	④	⑤	⑥	⑦	15	18
	2.2	F	①	②	③	④	⑤	⑧	⑨	15	18
	2.4	B	①	②	③	④	⑤	⑧	⑨	15	18
2009	2.0	A,M	①	②	③	④	⑤	⑥	⑦	15	18
	2.2	F	①	②	③	④	⑤	⑧	⑨	15	18

① Step 1: 22 ft. lbs.
　Step 2: plus 155 degrees

② Step 1: 15 ft. lbs.
　Step 2: plus 77 degrees for 2.0L engine
　Step 2: plus 70 degrees for 2.2 & 2.4L engine

③ Step 1: 18 ft. lbs.
　Step 2: plus 100 degrees

④ Step 1: 74 ft. lbs.
　Step 2: plus 125 degrees

⑤ Step 1: 39 ft. lbs.
　Step 2: plus 25 degrees

⑥ Manifold to Cylinder Head Bolt or Nut 18 ft. lbs.
　Manifold to Cylinder Head Stud 11 ft. lbs.

⑦ Manifold to Cylinder Head Bolt or Nut 120 inch lbs.
　Manifold to Cylinder Head Stud 15 ft. lbs.

⑧ Manifold to Cylinder Head Bolt or Nut 89 inch lbs.
　Manifold to Cylinder Head Stud 53 inch lbs.

⑨ Manifold to Cylinder Head Nut 124 inch lbs.
　Manifold to Cylinder Head Stud 89 inch lbs. - in 2 passes

36616_COBA_C0010

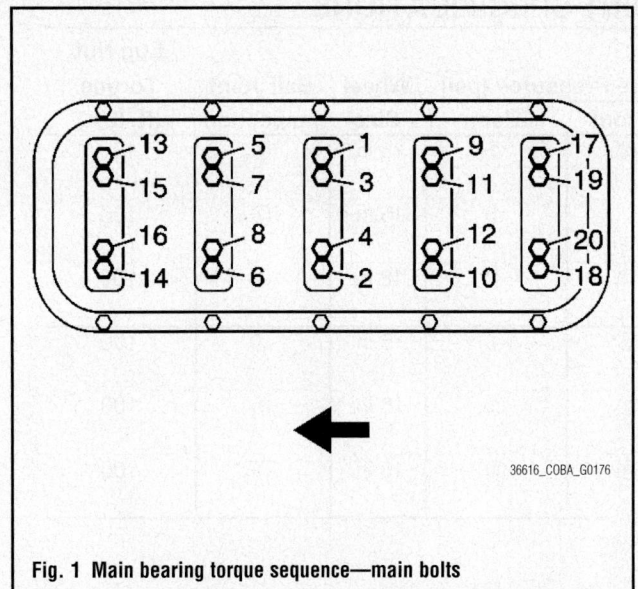

Fig. 1 Main bearing torque sequence—main bolts

36616_COBA_G0176

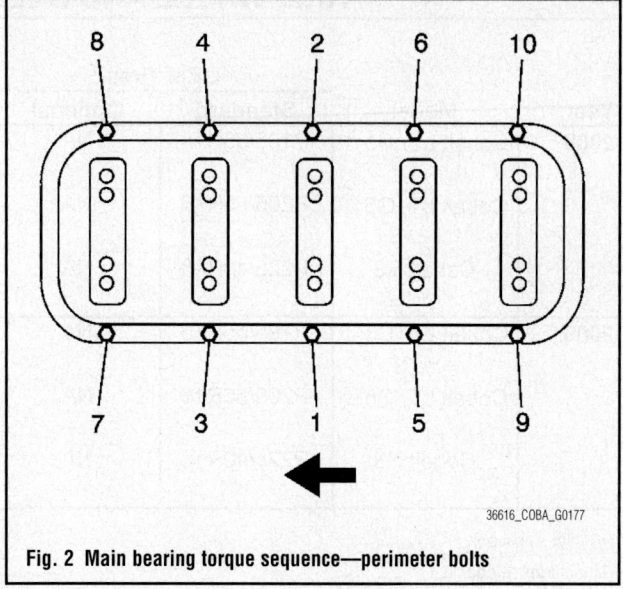

Fig. 2 Main bearing torque sequence—perimeter bolts

36616_COBA_G0177

WHEEL ALIGNMENT

Year	Model		Caster Range (+/-Deg.)	Caster Preferred Setting (Deg.)	Camber Range (+/-Deg.)	Camber Preferred Setting (Deg.)	Toe-in (Deg.)
2008	FE1(Soft Ride)	Front	0.75	+3.00	0.75	-1.00	0.20+/-0.20
	Suspension	Rear	NA	NA	0.75	-0.80	0.25+/-0.30
	FE3 & FE5 (Sport)	Front	0.75	+3.65	0.75	-1.05	0.20+/-0.20
	Suspension	Rear	NA	NA	0.75	-0.80	0.25+/-0.30
2009	FE1(Soft Ride)	Front	0.75	+3.00	0.75	-1.00	0.20+/-0.20
	Suspension	Rear	NA	NA	0.75	-0.80	0.25+/-0.30
	FE3 & FE5 (Sport)	Front	0.75	+3.65	0.75	-1.05	0.20+/-0.20
	Suspension	Rear	NA	NA	0.75	-0.80	0.25+/-0.30

NA Not Applicable

① FE5 with 225/40ZR18 tires: Front camber -125

36616_COBA_C0011

TIRE, WHEEL AND BALL JOINT SPECIFICATIONS

Year	Model	OEM Tires		Tire Pressures (psi)		Wheel Size	Ball Joint Inspection	Lug Nut Torque (ft. lbs.)
		Standard	Optional	Front	Rear			
2008	Cobalt LS, G5 ①	P195/65R15	NA	②	②	15 in.	③	100
	Cobalt LT, G5 ④	P205/55R16	NA	②	②	16 in.	③	100
	Cobalt SS	P225/40R18	NA	②	②	18 in.	③	100
2009	Cobalt LS, G5 ①	P195/65R15	NA	②	②	15 in.	③	100
	Cobalt LT, G5 ④	P205/55R16	NA	②	②	16 in.	③	100
	Cobalt SS	P225/40R18	NA	②	②	18 in.	③	100

NA: Not Applicable

① Includes model 1LT

② Refer to placard on vehicle for proper inflation pressure

③ Measure with appropriate tool and if the dial indicator reading is more than 0.020 inch (0.5 mm) of play, replace the lower control arm.

④ Includes models 2LT

36616_COBA_C0012

BRAKE SPECIFICATIONS

All measurements in inches unless noted

Year	Model		Brake Disc			Brake Drum Diameter			Minimum Lining Thickness	Brake Caliper	
			Original Thickness	Minimum Thickness	Maximum Runout	Original Inside Diameter	Max. Wear Limit	Maximum Machine Diameter		Bracket Bolts (ft. lbs.)	Mounting Bolts (ft. lbs.)
2008	Cobalt, G5	F	0.933	0.870	0.002	NA	NA	NA	0.039	96	25
		R	NA	NA	NA	9.060	9.094	9.075	0.020	NA	NA
	Cobalt, G5 ABS	F	0.933	0.870	0.002	NA	NA	NA	0.039	96	25
		R	0.551	0.465	0.002	NA	NA	NA	NS	85	25
	Cobalt, G5 ABS	F	1.023	①	0.002	NA	NA	NA	0.039	96	25
		R	②	③	0.002	NA	NA	NA	NS	85	25
2009	Cobalt, G5	F	0.933	0.870	0.002	NA	NA	NA	0.039	96	25
		R	NA	NA	NA	9.060	9.094	9.075	0.020	NA	NA
	Cobalt, G5 ABS	F	0.933	0.870	0.002	NA	NA	NA	0.039	96	25
		R	0.551	0.465	0.002	NA	NA	NA	NS	85	25
	Cobalt, G5 ABS	F	1.023	①	0.002	NA	NA	NA	0.039	96	25
		R	②	③	0.002	NA	NA	NA	NS	85	25

NS Not Supplied

NA Not Applicable

① Minimum thickness Cobalt SS: 0.945 Non-SS: 0.898

② Original thickness Cobalt SS: 0.783 Non-SS: 0.551

③ Minimum thickness Cobalt SS: 0.709 Non-SS: 0.465

36616_COBA_C0013

MAINTENANCE I AND II SERVICE SCHEDULES
Chevrolet Cobalt & Pontiac G5

When the CHANGE ENGINE OIL light appears, certain services and inspections are required.

Required services are described as Maintenance I and Maintenance II.

The first service on a vehicle should be Maintenance I, and the second service should be Maintenance II.

Alternate between the 2 thereafter. However, in some cases, Maintenance II may be required more often.

Maintenance I: Use Maintenance I if the CHANGE ENGINE OIL light comes on within 10 months since vehicle was purchased or, if Maintenance II was performed.

Maintenance II: Use Maintenance II if the previous service performed was Maintenance I. Always use Maintenance II whenever the CHANGE ENGINE OIL light comes on 10 months or more since the last service, or, if the CHANGE ENGINE OIL light has not come on at all for one year.

Service	Maintenance I	II
Change the engine oil and filter. Reset the oil life system.	✓	✓
Visually inspect the vehicle for leaks or damage. A fluid loss in the vehicle system could indicate a problem. Inspected, repair and add fluid to the system if necessary.	✓	✓
Inspect the engine air cleaner filter at each oil change, if regularily driven in dusty condition. If necessary, replace the filter.	--	✓
Rotate the tires. Inspect the tire inflation pressures and the tire wear.	✓	✓
Visually inspect the brake lines and hoses for proper hook-up, binding, leaks, cracks, chafing, etc. Inspect the disc brake pads for wear and the rotors for surface condition. Inspect the drum brake linings for wear or cracks. Inspect other brake parts, including drums, wheel cylinders, calipers, parking brake, etc. Inspect the parking brake	✓	✓
Inspect the engine coolant and the windshield washer fluid levels. Add fluid as needed.	✓	✓
Inspect the suspension and steering components. Inspect the front and rear suspension and the steering system for damaged, loose or missing parts, or signs of wear.	--	✓
Visually inspect the coolant hoses and replace the hoses if they are cracked, swollen or deteriorated. Inspect all pipes, fittings and clamps; replace with GM parts as needed. To help ensure proper operation, a pressure test of the cooling system and pressure cap and cleaning the outside of the radiator and air conditioning condenser is recommended at least once a year.	--	✓
Inspect wiper blades for wear, cracking, or contamination. Clean the windshield and wiper blades, if contaminated. Replace wiper blades that are worn or damaged.		✓
Look for any other loose or damaged safety belt system parts. If you see anything that might keep a safety belt system from doing its job, have it repaired. Have any torn or frayed safety belts replaced.	--	✓
Inspect the throttle system for interference or binding and for damaged or missing parts. Replace the parts as needed. Replace any components that have high effort or excessive wear. Do not lubricate the accelerator or the cruise control cables.	--	✓
Replace the passenger compartment air filter. Dusty conditions may require more frequent replacement.	--	✓

To reset the CHANGE ENGINE OIL LIGHT:

1. Turn the ignition switch to RUN with the engine OFF.

2. Press the Information and Reset buttons on the Driver Information Center (DIC) at the same time to enter the personalization menu.

3. Press the information button to scroll through the available personalization menu modes until the DIC display shows OIL-LIFE RESET.

4. Press and hold the reset button until the DIC display shows ACKNOWLEDGED. This will tell you the system has been reset.

5. Turn the key to OFF.

PRECAUTIONS

Before servicing any vehicle, please be sure to read all of the following precautions, which deal with personal safety, prevention of component damage, and important points to take into consideration when servicing a motor vehicle:

• Never open, service or drain the radiator or cooling system when the engine is hot; serious burns can occur from the steam and hot coolant.

• Observe all applicable safety precautions when working around fuel. Whenever servicing the fuel system, always work in a well-ventilated area. Do not allow fuel spray or vapors to come in contact with a spark, open flame, or excessive heat (a hot drop light, for example). Keep a dry chemical fire extinguisher near the work area. Always keep fuel in a container specifically designed for fuel storage; also, always properly seal fuel containers to avoid the possibility of fire or explosion. Refer to the additional fuel system precautions later in this section.

• Fuel injection systems often remain pressurized, even after the engine has been turned OFF. The fuel system pressure must be relieved before disconnecting any fuel lines. Failure to do so may result in fire and/or personal injury.

• Brake fluid often contains polyglycol ethers and polyglycols. Avoid contact with the eyes and wash your hands thoroughly after handling brake fluid. If you do get brake fluid in your eyes, flush your eyes with clean, running water for 15 minutes. If eye irritation persists, or if you have taken brake fluid internally, IMMEDIATELY seek medical assistance.

• The EPA warns that prolonged contact with used engine oil may cause a number of skin disorders, including cancer. You should make every effort to minimize your exposure to used engine oil. Protective gloves should be worn when changing oil. Wash your hands and any other exposed skin areas as soon as possible after exposure to used engine oil. Soap and water, or waterless hand cleaner should be used.

• All new vehicles are now equipped with an air bag system, often referred to as a Supplemental Restraint System (SRS) or Supplemental Inflatable Restraint (SIR) system. The system must be disabled before performing service on or around system components, steering column, instrument panel components, wiring and sensors. Failure to follow safety and disabling procedures could result in accidental air bag deployment, possible personal injury and unnecessary system repairs.

• Always wear safety goggles when working with, or around, the air bag system. When carrying a non-deployed air bag, be sure the bag and trim cover are pointed away from your body. When placing a non-deployed air bag on a work surface, always face the bag and trim cover upward, away from the surface. This will reduce the motion of the module if it is accidentally deployed. Refer to the additional air bag system precautions later in this section.

• Clean, high quality brake fluid from a sealed container is essential to the safe and proper operation of the brake system. You should always buy the correct type of brake fluid for your vehicle. If the brake fluid becomes contaminated, completely flush the system with new fluid. Never reuse any brake fluid. Any brake fluid that is removed from the system should be discarded. Also, do not allow any brake fluid to come in contact with a painted surface; it will damage the paint.

• Never operate the engine without the proper amount and type of engine oil; doing so WILL result in severe engine damage.

• Timing belt maintenance is extremely important. Many models utilize an interference-type, non-freewheeling engine. If the timing belt breaks, the valves in the cylinder head may strike the pistons, causing potentially serious (also time-consuming and expensive) engine damage. Refer to the maintenance interval charts for the recommended replacement interval for the timing belt, and to the timing belt section for belt replacement and inspection.

• Disconnecting the negative battery cable on some vehicles may interfere with the functions of the on-board computer system(s) and may require the computer to undergo a relearning process once the negative battery cable is reconnected.

• When servicing drum brakes, only disassemble and assemble one side at a time, leaving the remaining side intact for reference.

• Only an MVAC-trained, EPA-certified automotive technician should service the air conditioning system or its components.

BRAKES

GENERAL INFORMATION

PRECAUTIONS

• Certain components within the ABS system are not intended to be serviced or repaired individually.

• Do not use rubber hoses or other parts not specifically specified for and ABS system. When using repair kits, replace all parts included in the kit. Partial or incorrect repair may lead to functional problems and require the replacement of components.

• Lubricate rubber parts with clean, fresh brake fluid to ease assembly. Do not use shop air to clean parts; damage to rubber components may result.

• Use only DOT 3 brake fluid from an unopened container.

• If any hydraulic component or line is removed or replaced, it may be necessary to bleed the entire system.

• A clean repair area is essential. Always clean the reservoir and cap thoroughly before removing the cap. The slightest amount of dirt in the fluid may plug an orifice and impair the system function. Perform repairs after components have been thoroughly cleaned; use only denatured alcohol

ANTI-LOCK BRAKE SYSTEM (ABS)

to clean components. Do not allow ABS components to come into contact with any substance containing mineral oil; this includes used shop rags.

• The Anti-Lock control unit is a microprocessor similar to other computer units in the vehicle. Ensure that the ignition switch is OFF before removing or installing controller harnesses. Avoid static electricity discharge at or near the controller.

• If any arc welding is to be done on the vehicle, the control unit should be unplugged before welding operations begin.

BRAKES

BLEEDING PROCEDURE

Pressure Bleeding

1. Before servicing the vehicle, refer to the Precautions Section.

> ❋❋ **WARNING**
>
> **When adding fluid to the brake master cylinder reservoir, use only GM approved or equivalent DOT-3 brake fluid from a clean, sealed brake fluid container. The use of any type of fluid other than the recommended type of brake fluid may cause contamination which could result in damage to the internal rubber seals and/or rubber linings of hydraulic brake system components.**

> ❋❋ **WARNING**
>
> **Avoid spilling brake fluid onto painted surfaces, electrical connections, wiring, or cables. Brake fluid will damage painted surfaces and cause corrosion to electrical components. If any brake fluid comes in contact with painted surfaces, immediately flush the area with water. If any brake fluid comes in contact with electrical connections, wiring, or cables, use a clean shop cloth to wipe away the fluid.**

2. Place a clean shop cloth beneath the brake master cylinder to catch brake fluid spills.

3. With the ignition OFF and the brakes cool, apply the brakes 3–5 times, or until the brake pedal becomes firm, in order to deplete the brake booster power reserve.

4. If you have performed a brake master cylinder bench bleeding on this vehicle, or if you disconnected the brake pipes from the master cylinder, or if you have disconnected the brake pipes from the proportioning valve assembly or the brake modulator assembly, you must perform the following steps to bleed air at the ports of the hydraulic component:

   a. If removal of the reservoir cap and diaphragm is necessary, clean the outside of the reservoir on and around the cap prior to removal.

   b. With the brake pipes installed securely to the master cylinder, proportioning valve assembly, or brake modulator assembly, loosen and separate one of the brake pipes from the port of the component. For the proportioning valve assembly or the brake modulator assembly, perform these steps in the sequence of system flow; begin with the fluid feed pipes from the master cylinder.

   c. Allow a small amount of brake fluid to gravity bleed from the open port of the component.

   d. Reconnect the brake pipe to the component and tighten securely.

   e. Have an assistant slowly depress the brake pedal fully and maintain steady pressure on the pedal.

   f. Loosen the same brake pipe to purge air from the open port of the component.

   g. Tighten the brake pipe, then have the assistant slowly release the brake pedal.

   h. Wait 15 seconds, then repeat steps 3–7 until all air is purged from the same port of the component.

   i. With the brake pipe installed securely to the master cylinder, proportioning valve assembly, or brake modulator assembly, and after all air has been purged from the first port of the component that was bled, loosen and separate the next brake pipe from the component, then repeat steps 3.3–3.8 until each of the ports on the component has been bled.

   j. After completing the final component port bleeding procedure, ensure that each of the brake pipe-to-component fittings is properly tightened.

5. Clean the outside of the reservoir on and around the reservoir cap prior to removing the cap and diaphragm.

6. Install a pressure bleeder such as J 44894-A to the brake master cylinder reservoir.

7. Connect the J 29532, or equivalent, to the J 44894-A.

8. Charge the J 29532, or equivalent, air tank to 25–30 psi (175–205 kPa).

9. Open the J 29532, or equivalent, fluid tank valve to allow pressurized brake fluid to enter the brake system.

10. Wait approximately 30 seconds, then, inspect the entire hydraulic brake system in order to ensure that there are no existing external brake fluid leaks. Any brake fluid leaks identified require repair prior to completing this procedure.

11. Install a proper box-end wrench onto the RIGHT REAR wheel hydraulic circuit bleeder valve.

12. Install a transparent hose over the end of the bleeder valve.

13. Loosen the bleeder valve to purge air from the wheel hydraulic circuit. Allow fluid to flow until air bubbles stop flowing from the bleeder, then tighten the bleeder valve.

14. With the right rear wheel hydraulic circuit bleeder valve tightened securely, and after all air has been purged from the right rear hydraulic circuit, install a proper box-end wrench onto the LEFT FRONT wheel hydraulic circuit bleeder valve.

15. Install a transparent hose over the end of the bleeder valve, then repeat steps 13–14.

16. With the left front wheel hydraulic circuit bleeder valve tightened securely, and after all air has been purged from the left front hydraulic circuit, install a proper box-end wrench onto the LEFT REAR wheel hydraulic circuit bleeder valve.

17. Install a transparent hose over the end of the bleeder valve, then, repeat steps 13–14.

18. With the left rear wheel hydraulic circuit bleeder valve tightened securely, and after all air has been purged from the left rear hydraulic circuit, install a proper box-end wrench onto the RIGHT FRONT wheel hydraulic circuit bleeder valve.

19. Install a transparent hose over the end of the bleeder valve, then, repeat steps 13–14.

20. After completing the final wheel hydraulic circuit bleeding procedure, ensure that each of the 4 wheel hydraulic circuit bleeder valves is properly tightened.

21. Close the J 29532, or equivalent, fluid tank valve, then disconnect the J 29532, or equivalent, from the J 44894-A.

22. Remove the J 44894-A from the brake master cylinder reservoir.

23. Slowly depress and release the brake pedal. Observe the feel of the brake pedal.

24. If the brake pedal feels spongy perform the following steps:

   a. Inspect the brake system for external leaks.

   b. If equipped with anti-lock brakes, using a scan tool, perform the antilock brake system automated bleeding procedure to remove any air that may have been trapped in the Brake Pressure Modulator Valve (BPMV).

Manual Bleeding

1. Before servicing the vehicle, refer to the Precautions Section.

✳✳ WARNING

When adding fluid to the brake master cylinder reservoir, use only GM approved or equivalent DOT-3 brake fluid from a clean, sealed brake fluid container. The use of any type of fluid other than the recommended type of brake fluid may cause contamination which could result in damage to the internal rubber seals and/or rubber linings of hydraulic brake system components.

✳✳ WARNING

Avoid spilling brake fluid onto painted surfaces, electrical connections, wiring, or cables. Brake fluid will damage painted surfaces and cause corrosion to electrical components. If any brake fluid comes in contact with painted surfaces, immediately flush the area with water. If any brake fluid comes in contact with electrical connections, wiring, or cables, use a clean shop cloth to wipe away the fluid.

2. Place a clean shop cloth beneath the brake master cylinder to catch brake fluid spills.

3. With the ignition OFF and the brakes cool, apply the brakes 3–5 times, or until the brake pedal effort increases significantly, in order to deplete the brake booster power reserve.

4. If you have performed a brake master cylinder bench bleeding on this vehicle, or if you disconnected the brake pipes from the master cylinder, or if you have disconnected the brake pipes from the proportioning valve assembly or the brake modulator assembly, you must perform the following steps to bleed air at the ports of the hydraulic component:

   a. If removal of the reservoir cap and diaphragm is necessary, clean the outside of the reservoir on and around the cap prior to removal.

   b. With the brake pipes installed securely to the master cylinder, proportioning valve assembly, or brake modulator assembly, loosen and separate one of the brake pipes from the port of the component. For the proportioning valve assembly or the brake modulator assembly, perform these steps in the sequence of system flow; begin with the fluid feed pipes from the master cylinder.

   c. Allow a small amount of brake fluid to gravity bleed from the open port of the component.

   d. Reconnect the brake pipe to the component and tighten securely.

   e. Have an assistant slowly depress the brake pedal fully and maintain steady pressure on the pedal.

   f. Loosen the same brake pipe to purge air from the open port of the component.

   g. Tighten the brake pipe, then have the assistant slowly release the brake pedal.

   h. Wait 15 seconds, then repeat steps 3–7 until all air is purged from the same port of the component.

   i. With the brake pipe installed securely to the master cylinder, proportioning valve assembly, or brake modulator assembly, and after all air has been purged from the first port of the component that was bled, loosen and separate the next brake pipe from the component, then repeat steps 3–8 until each of the ports on the component has been bled.

   j. After completing the final component port bleeding procedure, ensure that each of the brake pipe-to-component fittings is properly tightened.

5. Ensure the brake master cylinder reservoir remains at least half-full during this bleeding procedure. Add fluid as needed to maintain the proper level. Clean the outside of the reservoir on and around the reservoir cap prior to removing the cap and diaphragm.

6. Install a proper box-end wrench onto the RIGHT REAR wheel hydraulic circuit bleeder valve.

7. Install a transparent hose over the end of the bleeder valve.

8. Have an assistant slowly depress the brake pedal fully and maintain steady pressure on the pedal.

9. Loosen the bleeder valve to purge air from the wheel hydraulic circuit.

10. Tighten the bleeder valve, then have the assistant slowly release the brake pedal.

11. Wait 15 seconds, then repeat steps 8–10 until all air is purged from the same wheel hydraulic circuit.

12. With the right rear wheel hydraulic circuit bleeder valve tightened securely, and after all air has been purged from the right rear hydraulic circuit, install a proper box-end wrench onto the LEFT FRONT wheel hydraulic circuit bleeder valve.

13. Install a transparent hose over the end of the bleeder valve, then repeat steps 7–11.

14. With the left front wheel hydraulic circuit bleeder valve tightened securely, and after all air has been purged from the left front hydraulic circuit, install a proper box-

end wrench onto the LEFT REAR wheel hydraulic circuit bleeder valve.

15. Install a transparent hose over the end of the bleeder valve, then repeat steps 7–11.

16. With the left rear wheel hydraulic circuit bleeder valve tightened securely, and after all air has been purged from the left rear hydraulic circuit, install a proper box-end wrench onto the RIGHT FRONT wheel hydraulic circuit bleeder valve.

17. Install a transparent hose over the end of the bleeder valve, then repeat steps 7–11.

18. After completing the final wheel hydraulic circuit bleeding procedure, ensure that each of the 4 wheel hydraulic circuit bleeder valves is properly tightened.

19. Slowly depress and release the brake pedal. Observe the feel of the brake pedal.

20. If the brake pedal feels spongy, repeat the bleeding procedure again. If the brake pedal still feels spongy after repeating the bleeding procedure, perform the following steps:

   a. Inspect the brake system for external leaks.

   b. Pressure bleed the hydraulic brake system in order to purge any air that may still be trapped in the system.

21. Turn the ignition key ON, with the engine OFF. Check to see if the brake system warning lamp remains illuminated.

✳✳ WARNING

DO NOT allow the vehicle to be driven until it is diagnosed and repaired.

BLEEDING THE ABS SYSTEM

1. Before servicing the vehicle, refer to the Precautions Section.

✳✳ WARNING

The Auto Bleed Procedure may be terminated at any time during the process by pressing the EXIT button. No further Scan Tool prompts pertaining to the Auto Bleed procedure will be given. After exiting the bleed procedure, relieve bleed pressure and disconnect bleed equipment per manufacturer's instructions. Failure to properly relieve pressure may result in spilled brake fluid causing damage to components and painted surfaces.

2. Raise and support the vehicle.

3. Remove all four tire and wheel assemblies.

4. Inspect the brake system for leaks and visual damage. Repair or replace components as needed.

5. Lower the vehicle.

6. Inspect the battery state of charge.

7. Install a scan tool.

8. Turn the ignition ON, with the engine OFF.

9. With the scan tool, establish communications with the ABS system. Select Special Functions. Select Automated Bleed from the Special Functions menu.

10. Raise and support the vehicle.

11. Following the directions given on the scan tool, pressure bleed the base brake system. Refer to Bleeding the Brake System.

12. Follow the scan tool directions until the desired brake pedal height is achieved.

13. If the bleed procedure is aborted, a malfunction exists. Perform the following steps before resuming the bleed procedure:

  a. If a Diagnostic Trouble Code (DTC) is detected, diagnose the appropriate DTC.

  b. If the brake pedal feels spongy, perform the conventional brake bleed procedure again.

14. When the desired pedal height is achieved, press the brake pedal to inspect for firmness.

15. Lower the vehicle.

16. Remove the scan tool.

17. Install the tire and wheel assemblies.

18. Inspect the brake fluid level.

19. Road test the vehicle while inspecting that the pedal remains high and firm.

20. Turn the ignition key ON, with the engine OFF. Check to see if the brake system warning lamp remains illuminated.

✲✲ WARNING

If there is a brake malfunction exists, DO NOT allow the vehicle to be driven until it is diagnosed and repaired.

BRAKES

FRONT DISC BRAKES

✲✲ CAUTION

Dust and dirt accumulating on brake parts during normal use may contain asbestos fibers from production or aftermarket brake linings. Breathing excessive concentrations of asbestos fibers can cause serious bodily harm. Exercise care when servicing brake parts. Do not sand or grind brake lining unless equipment used is designed to contain the dust residue. Do not clean brake parts with compressed air or by dry brushing. Cleaning should be done by dampening the brake components with a fine mist of water, then wiping the brake components clean with a dampened cloth. Dispose of cloth and all residue containing asbestos fibers in an impermeable container with the appropriate label. Follow practices prescribed by the Occupational Safety and Health Administration (OSHA) and the Environmental Protection Agency (EPA) for the handling, processing, and disposing of dust or debris that may contain asbestos fibers.

BRAKE CALIPER

REMOVAL & INSTALLATION

Non-Turbo Model

See Figures 3 and 4.

1. Before servicing the vehicle, refer to the Precautions Section.

2. Inspect the fluid level in the brake master cylinder reservoir.

3. If the brake fluid level is midway between the maximum-full point and the

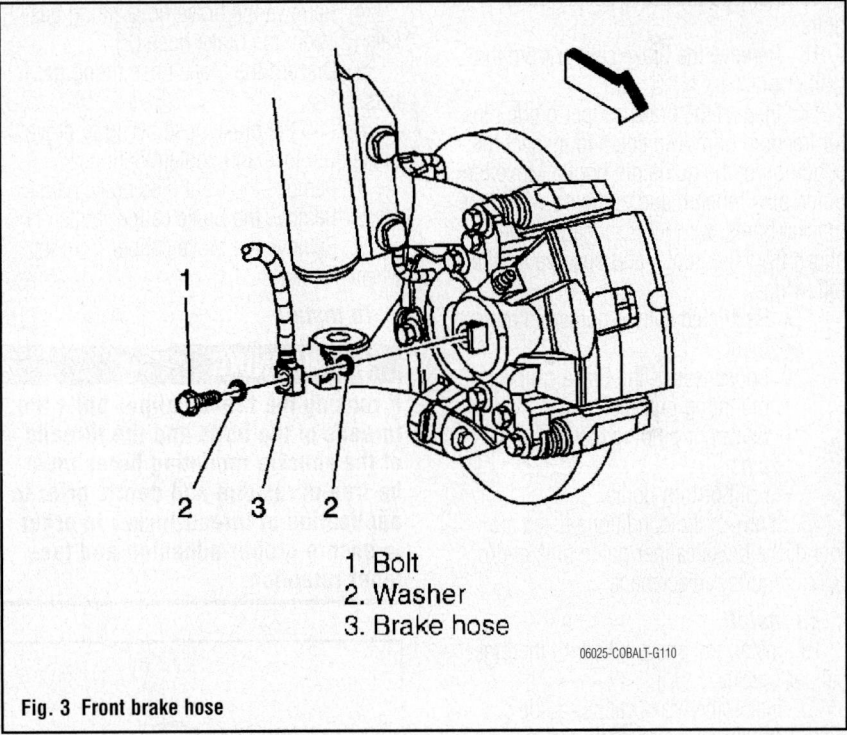

1. Bolt
2. Washer
3. Brake hose

06025-COBALT-G110

Fig. 3 Front brake hose

minimum allowable level, no brake fluid needs to be removed from the reservoir before proceeding.

4. If the brake fluid level is higher than midway between the maximum-full point and the minimum allowable level, remove brake fluid to the midway point before proceeding.

5. Raise and support the vehicle.

6. Remove the tire and wheel assembly.

7. Install and firmly hand tighten 2 wheel nuts to opposite wheel studs in order to retain the rotor to the hub.

8. Install a large C-clamp over the body of the brake caliper with the C-clamp ends

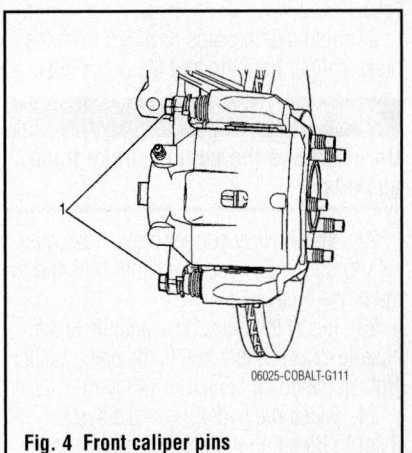

06025-COBALT-G111

Fig. 4 Front caliper pins

against the rear of the caliper body and against the outer brake pad.

9. Tighten the C-clamp until the caliper piston is compressed into the caliper bore enough to allow the caliper to slide past the brake rotor.

10. Remove the C-clamp from the caliper.

11. Remove the brake hose-to-caliper bolt from the brake caliper.

12. Remove the brake hose from the brake caliper.

13. Remove and discard the 2 copper brake hose gaskets. These gaskets may be stuck to the brake caliper and/or the brake hose end.

14. Cap or plug the opening in the brake caliper and the brake hose to prevent fluid loss and contamination.

15. Remove the brake caliper guide pin bolts.

16. Remove the brake caliper from the caliper bracket.

17. Inspect the brake caliper guide pins for freedom of movement, and inspect the condition of the guide pin boots. Move the guide pins inboard and outboard within the bracket bores, without disengaging the slides from the boots, and observe for the following:

- Restricted caliper guide pin movement
- Looseness in the brake caliper mounting bracket
- Seized or binding caliper guide pins
- Split or torn boots

18. If any of the conditions listed are found, the brake caliper guide pins and/or boots require replacement.

To install:

19. Install the brake caliper to the brake caliper bracket.

20. Install the brake caliper guide pin bolts. Tighten the bolts to 25 ft. lbs. (34 Nm).

21. Remove the caps or plugs from the brake caliper opening and the brake hose.

✲✲ WARNING

Do not reuse the copper brake hose gaskets.

22. Install NEW copper brake hose gaskets to the brake hose-to-caliper bolt and to the brake hose.

23. Install the brake hose and the brake hose-to-brake caliper bolt to the brake caliper. Tighten the bolt to 35 ft. lbs. (48 Nm).

24. Bleed the hydraulic brake system. Refer to Bleeding the Brake System.

25. Remove the wheel nuts retaining the brake rotor to the wheel hub.

26. Install the tire and wheel assembly.

27. Lower the vehicle.

28. With the engine OFF, gradually apply the brake pedal to approximately ⅔ of its travel distance.

29. Slowly release the brake pedal.

30. Wait 15 seconds, then gradually apply the brake pedal approximately ⅔ of its travel distance again until a firm brake pedal is obtained. This will properly seat the brake caliper pistons and brake pads.

Turbo Model

See Figures 5 and 6.

1. Raise and support the vehicle.
2. Remove the tire and wheel assembly.
3. Remove the brake hose fitting bolt (1).
4. Remove the brake hose fitting gaskets (2) from the brake hose (3).
5. Discard the brake hose fitting gaskets.
6. Cap the brake hose fitting to prevent brake fluid loss and contamination.
7. Remove the front disc brake pads.
8. Remove the brake caliper bolts (1).
9. Remove the brake caliper from the wheel knuckle.

To install:

✲✲ WARNING

If reusing the brake caliper bolts the threads of the bolts and the threads of the knuckle mounting holes must be free of residue and debris prior to application of thread-locker in order to ensure proper adhesion and fastener retention.

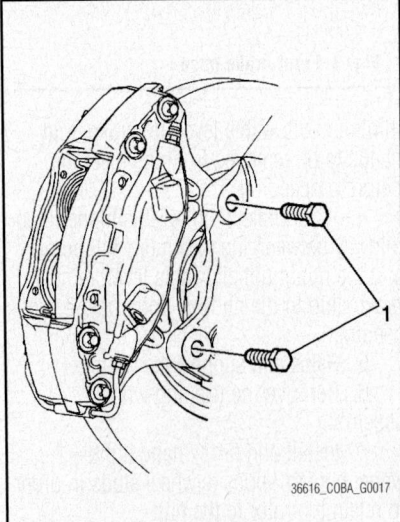

Fig. 5 Caliper bolt locations

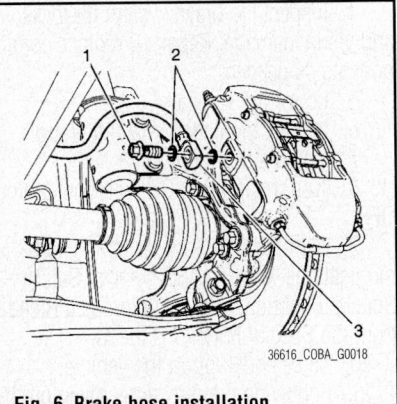

36616_COBA_G0018

Fig. 6 Brake hose installation

10. Prepare the bolts and the threaded holes for assembly:

a. Thoroughly clean the residue from the bolt threads by using denatured alcohol or equivalent and allow to dry.

b. Thoroughly clean the residue from the threaded holes by using denatured alcohol or equivalent and allow to dry.

11. Apply thread-locker GM P/N 12345493 (Canadian P/N 10953488), or equivalent to ⅔ of the threaded length of the caliper bolts. Ensure that there are no gaps in the thread-locker along the length of the filled area of the bolts.

12. Allow the thread-locker to cure approximately 10 minutes before installation.

13. Install the brake caliper to the wheel knuckle and tighten to 96 ft. lbs. (130 Nm).

➡ **Install NEW copper brake hose gaskets.**

14. Assemble the brake hose fitting bolt (1) and new fitting gaskets (2) to the brake hose (3).

15. Install the brake hose assembly to the brake caliper and tighten to 30 ft. lbs. (40 Nm).

16. Install the front disc brake pads.

17. Bleed the hydraulic brake system. Refer to Bleeding the Brake System.

18. With the engine OFF, gradually apply the brake pedal to approximately ⅔ of its travel distance.

19. Slowly release the brake pedal.

20. Wait 15 seconds, then repeat steps 10 and 11 until a firm brake pedal is obtained. This will properly seat the brake caliper pistons and brake pads.

21. Install the tire and wheel assembly.

22. Lower the vehicle.

DISC BRAKE PADS

REMOVAL & INSTALLATION

Non-Turbo Models

See Figure 7.

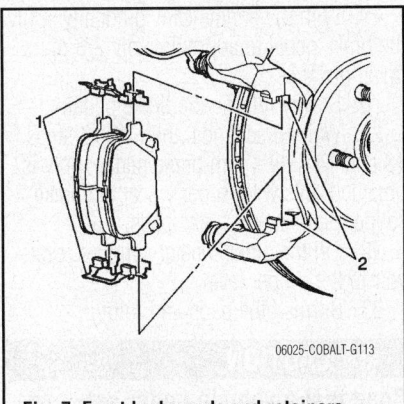

Fig. 7 Front brake pads and retainers

1. Before servicing the vehicle, refer to the Precautions Section.

2. Inspect the fluid level in the brake master cylinder auxiliary reservoir.

3. If the brake fluid level is midway between the maximum-full point and the minimum allowable level, no brake fluid needs to be removed from the reservoir before proceeding.

4. If the brake fluid level is higher than midway between the maximum-full point and the minimum allowable level, remove brake fluid to the midway point before proceeding.

5. Raise and support the vehicle.

6. Remove the tire and wheel assembly.

7. Install and firmly hand tighten 2 wheel nuts to opposite wheel studs in order to retain the rotor to the hub.

8. Using a piston compressing tool, the caliper piston is compressed into the caliper bore enough to allow the caliper to slide past the brake rotor. Or, install a large C-clamp over the body of the brake caliper with the C-clamp ends against the rear of the caliper body and against the outboard brake pad.

9. Tighten the C-clamp evenly until the caliper piston is compressed into the caliper bore enough to allow the caliper to slide past the brake rotor.

10. Remove the C-clamp from the caliper.

11. Remove the brake caliper lower guide pin bolt.

✳✳ WARNING

Support the brake caliper with heavy mechanic's wire, or equivalent, whenever it is separated from its mount and the hydraulic flexible brake hose is still connected. Failure to support the caliper in this manner will cause the flexible brake hose to bear the weight of the caliper, which may cause damage to the brake hose and in turn may cause a brake fluid leak.

12. Without disconnecting the hydraulic brake flexible hose, pivot the caliper upward and secure the caliper with heavy mechanics wire, or equivalent.

13. Remove the brake pads from the caliper mounting bracket.

14. Remove the brake pad retainers (1) from the caliper bracket.

15. Fully compress the piston in its bore.

16. Thoroughly clean the brake pad hardware mating surfaces of the caliper bracket (2), of any debris and corrosion.

17. Inspect the brake caliper guide pins for freedom of movement, and inspect the condition of the guide pin boots. Move the guide pins inboard and outboard within the bracket bores, without disengaging the slides from the boots, and observe for the following:

- Restricted caliper guide pin movement
- Looseness in the brake caliper mounting bracket
- Seized or binding caliper guide pins
- Split or torn boots

18. If any of the conditions listed are found, the brake caliper guide pins and/or boots require replacement.

To install:

19. Apply a very thin coating of high temperature silicone brake lubricant to the pad hardware mating surfaces of the caliper bracket (2) only.

20. Install the brake pad retainers to the brake caliper bracket.

➡**The wear sensor equipped disc brake pad must be mounted inboard of the rotor with the leading edge of the sensor facing the brake rotor during forward wheel rotation, or at the top of the pad when installed in vehicle position.**

21. Install the brake pads to the caliper bracket.

22. Remove the support, and rotate the brake caliper into position over the disc brake pads and to the caliper mounting bracket.

23. Install the lower brake caliper guide pin bolt. Tighten the bolt to 25 ft. lbs. (34 Nm).

24. Remove the wheel nuts retaining the brake rotor to the hub.

25. Install the tire and wheel assembly.

26. Lower the vehicle.

27. With the engine OFF, gradually apply the brake pedal approximately ⅔ of its travel distance.

28. Slowly release the brake pedal.

29. Wait 15 seconds, then gradually apply the brake pedal approximately ⅔ of its travel distance again until a firm brake pedal apply is obtained. This will properly seat the brake caliper pistons and brake pads.

30. Fill the master cylinder auxiliary reservoir to the proper level.

31. Burnish the pads and rotors.

✳✳ CAUTION

Road test a vehicle under safe conditions and while obeying all traffic laws. Do not attempt any maneuvers that could jeopardize vehicle control. Failure to adhere to these precautions could lead to serious personal injury and vehicle damage.

➡**Burnishing the brake pads and brake rotors is necessary in order to ensure that the braking surfaces are properly prepared after service has been performed on the disc brake system. This procedure should be performed whenever the disc brake rotors have been refinished or replaced, and/or whenever the disc brake pads have been replaced.**

a. Select a smooth road with little or no traffic.

b. Accelerate the vehicle to 48 km/h (30 mph).

➡**Use care to avoid overheating the brakes while performing this step.**

c. Using moderate to firm pressure, apply the brakes to bring the vehicle to a stop. Do not allow the brakes to lock.

d. Repeat steps 2 and 3 until approximately 20 stops have been completed. Allow sufficient cooling periods between stops in order to properly burnish the brake pads and rotors.

Turbo Model

See Figures 8 and 9.

1. Inspect the fluid level in the brake master cylinder reservoir.

2. If the brake fluid level is midway between the maximum-full point and the minimum allowable level, no brake fluid needs to be removed from the reservoir before proceeding.

3. If the brake fluid level is higher than midway between the maximum-full point and the minimum allowable level, remove brake fluid to the midway point before proceeding.

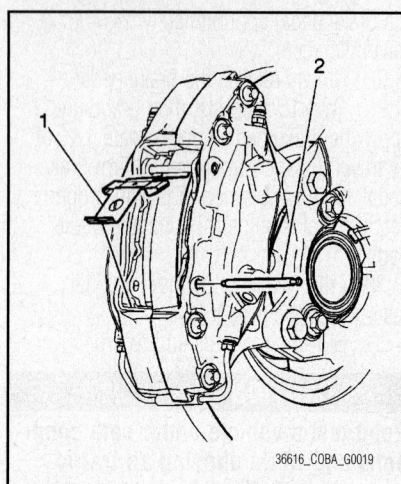

Fig. 8 Brake pad mounting pins and retainer

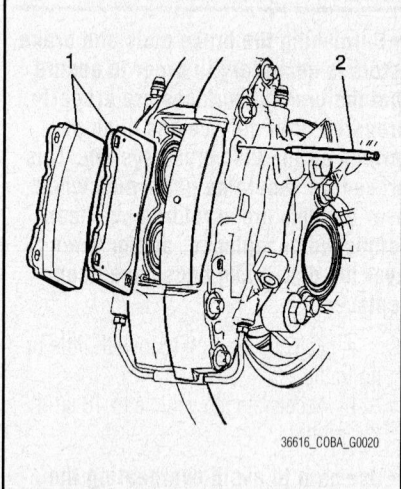

Fig. 9 Brake pad mounting pins and retainer installation

4. Raise and support the vehicle.
5. Remove the tire and wheel assembly.
6. Remove the front disc brake pads.

a. Holding the lower end of the retainer (1) down and using a hammer and punch carefully tap the lower caliper guide pin (2) inward out of the caliper.

b. Carefully rotate the brake pad retainer (1) upward.

c. Remove the brake pad retainer (1).

d. Using a hammer and punch carefully tap the upper caliper to brake pad mounting pin (2) inward out of the caliper.

e. Using a disc brake pad spreader, apply pressure to the brake pad backing plates until the caliper pistons are fully compressed into the caliper piston bores.

f. Remove the brake pads (1) from the caliper.

To install:

7. Inspect the brake caliper mounting pins. If damaged, or corroded replace the guide pin. Do not attempt to clean away any corrosion.

8. Inspect the brake caliper piston boot for damage and/or deterioration, replace if damaged or deteriorated.

9. Install the brake pads (1) to the caliper.

10. Install the upper caliper guide pin (2) through the caliper, inner and outer brake pads.

11. Using a hammer and punch, carefully seat the upper guide pin (2) to the outer caliper half. Ensure the caliper guide pin is seated into the outer caliper pin seat.

12. Install the brake pad retainer under the upper caliper pin assembly.

13. Rotate brake pad retainer down.

14. Carefully apply pressure downward on the lower end of the brake pad retainer.

15. Carefully install the lower caliper guide pin through the caliper, inner and outer brake pads.

16. Using a hammer and punch carefully seat the upper guide pin to the outer caliper half. Ensure the caliper guide pin is seated into the outer caliper pin seat. Ensure the brake pad retainer is centered and retaining both brake pads.

17. Install the tire and wheel assembly.

18. Lower the vehicle.

19. With the engine OFF, gradually apply the brake pedal to approximately 2/3 of its travel distance.

20. Slowly release the brake pedal.

21. Wait 15 seconds, then repeat steps 13 and 14 until a firm brake pedal apply is obtained; this will properly seat the brake caliper pistons and brake pads.

22. Fill the brake master cylinder reservoir to the proper level.

23. Burnish the pads and rotors:

❄❄ CAUTION

Road test a vehicle under safe conditions and while obeying all traffic laws. Do not attempt any maneuvers that could jeopardize vehicle control. Failure to adhere to these precautions could lead to serious personal injury and vehicle damage.

➡Burnishing the brake pads and brake rotors is necessary in order to ensure that the braking surfaces are properly prepared after service has been performed on the disc brake system. This procedure should be performed whenever the disc brake rotors have been refinished or replaced, and/or whenever the disc brake pads have been replaced.

a. Select a smooth road with little or no traffic.

b. Accelerate the vehicle to 48 km/h (30 mph).

➡Use care to avoid overheating the brakes while performing this step.

c. Using moderate to firm pressure, apply the brakes to bring the vehicle to a stop. Do not allow the brakes to lock.

d. Repeat steps 2 and 3 until approximately 20 stops have been completed. Allow sufficient cooling periods between stops in order to properly burnish the brake pads and rotors.

✳✳ CAUTION

Dust and dirt accumulating on brake parts during normal use may contain asbestos fibers from production or aftermarket brake linings. Breathing excessive concentrations of asbestos fibers can cause serious bodily harm. Exercise care when servicing brake parts. Do not sand or grind brake lining unless equipment used is designed to contain the dust residue. Do not clean brake parts with compressed air or by dry brushing. Cleaning should be done by dampening the brake components with a fine mist of water, then wiping the brake components clean with a dampened cloth. Dispose of cloth and all residue containing asbestos fibers in an impermeable container with the appropriate label. Follow practices prescribed by the Occupational Safety and Health Administration (OSHA) and the Environmental Protection Agency (EPA) for the handling, processing, and disposing of dust or debris that may contain asbestos fibers.

BRAKE CALIPER

REMOVAL & INSTALLATION

See Figures 10 through 12.

1. Before servicing the vehicle, refer to the Precautions Section.
2. Inspect the fluid level in the brake master cylinder auxiliary reservoir.
3. If the brake fluid level is midway between the maximum-full point and the

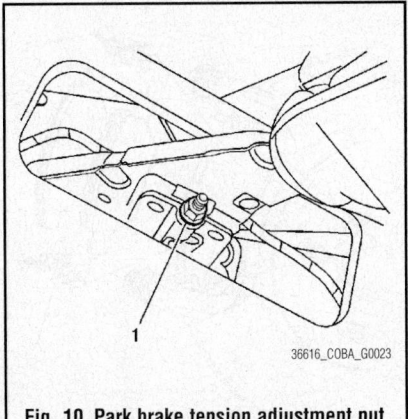

Fig. 10 Park brake tension adjustment nut

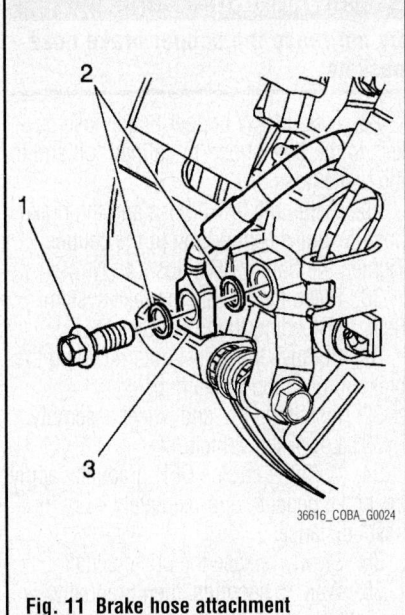

36616_COBA_G0024

Fig. 11 Brake hose attachment

minimum allowable level, no brake fluid needs to be removed from the reservoir before proceeding.

4. If the brake fluid level is higher than midway between the maximum-full point

and the minimum allowable level, remove brake fluid to the midway point before proceeding.

5. Release the park brake lever boot from the floor console by applying light pressure inward on the sides of the boot retainer, and pull the boot back.

6. Release the tension from the park brake cables. With the park brake lever in the released position, using ONLY HAND TOOLS, loosen the adjusting nut completely to the end of the front cable threaded rod.

7. Raise and support the vehicle.

8. Remove the tire and wheel assembly.

9. Install and firmly hand tighten 2 wheel nuts to opposite wheel studs in order to retain the rotor to the hub.

10. Release the park brake cable end from the lever on the caliper.

11. Release the retaining tabs securing the park brake cable to the bracket on the caliper.

12. Install a large C-clamp, over the body of the brake caliper with the C-clamp ends against the rear of the caliper body and against the outer brake pad.

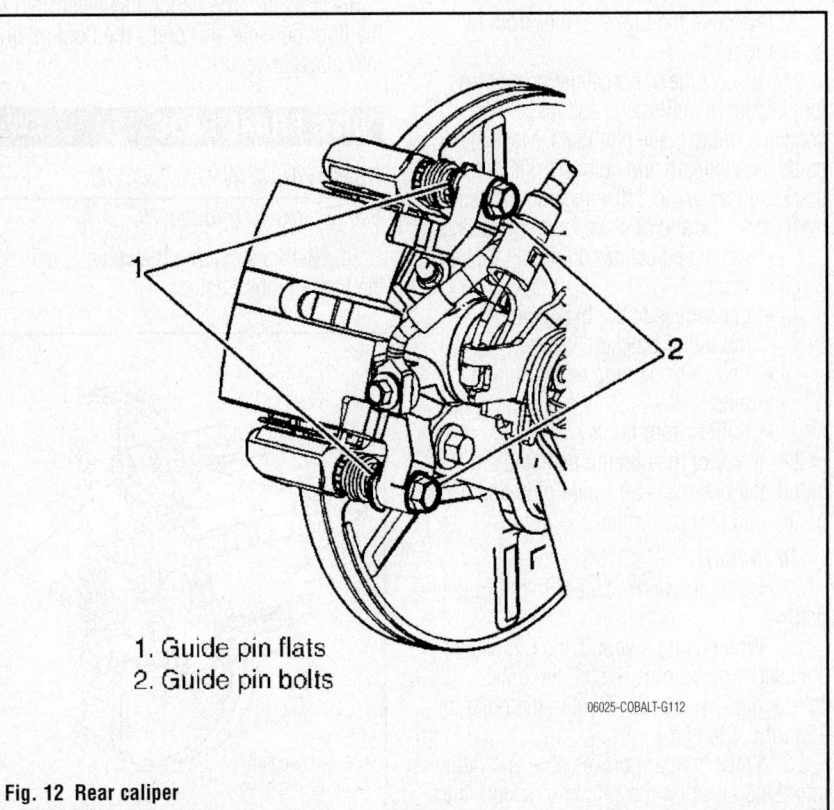

1. Guide pin flats
2. Guide pin bolts

06025-COBALT-G112

Fig. 12 Rear caliper

⁂ WARNING

When using a large C-clamp to compress a caliper piston into a caliper bore of a caliper equipped with an integral park brake mechanism, do not exceed more than 0.039 inch (1mm) of piston travel. Exceeding this amount of piston travel will cause damage to the internal adjusting mechanism and/or the integral park brake mechanism.

13. Tighten the C-clamp just enough to compress the caliper piston 0.039 inch (1mm) of travel only.

14. Remove the C-clamp from the caliper.

15. Remove the brake hose-to-caliper bolt from the brake caliper.

16. Remove the brake hose from the brake caliper.

17. Remove and discard the 2 copper brake hose gaskets. These gaskets may be stuck to the brake caliper and/or the brake hose end.

18. Cap or plug the opening in the brake caliper and the brake hose to prevent fluid loss and contamination.

19. While using a wrench on the flats of the caliper guide pins, remove the brake caliper guide pin bolts.

20. Remove the brake caliper from the caliper bracket.

21. Inspect the brake caliper guide pins for freedom of movement, and inspect the condition of the guide pin boots. Move the guide pins inboard and outboard within the bracket bores, without disengaging the slides from the boots, and observe for the following:

- Restricted caliper guide pin movement
- Looseness in the brake caliper mounting bracket
- Seized or binding caliper guide pins
- Split or torn boots

22. If any of the conditions listed are found, the brake caliper guide pins and/or boots require replacement.

To install:

23. Install the brake caliper to the caliper bracket.

24. While using a wrench on the flats of the caliper guide pins, install the brake caliper guide pin bolts. Tighten the bolts to 25 ft. lbs. (34 Nm).

25. Press the park brake cable end fitting into the bracket on the caliper to secure the retaining tabs.

26. Secure the park brake cable end to the lever on the caliper.

27. Remove the caps or plugs from the brake caliper opening and the brake hose.

⁂ WARNING

Do not reuse the copper brake hose gaskets.

28. Install NEW copper brake hose gaskets to the brake hose-to-caliper bolt and to the brake hose.

29. Install the brake hose and the brake hose-to-brake caliper bolt to the caliper. Tighten the bolt to 35 ft. lbs. (48 Nm).

30. Bleed the hydraulic brake system. Refer to Bleeding the Brake System.

31. Remove the wheel nuts retaining the brake rotor to the wheel hub.

32. Install the tire and wheel assembly.

33. Lower the vehicle.

34. With the engine OFF, gradually apply the brake pedal to approximately ⅔ of its travel distance.

35. Slowly release the brake pedal.

36. Wait 15 seconds, then gradually apply the brake pedal approximately ⅔ of its travel distance again until a firm brake pedal is obtained. This will properly seat the brake caliper pistons and brake pads.

37. Adjust the park brake cable tension. Refer to Parking Braked Cable Adjustment.

38. Position the park brake lever boot to the floor console and press the boot retainer into place to secure.

DISC BRAKE PADS

REMOVAL & INSTALLATION

See Figures 13 through 15.

1. Before servicing the vehicle, refer to the Precautions Section.

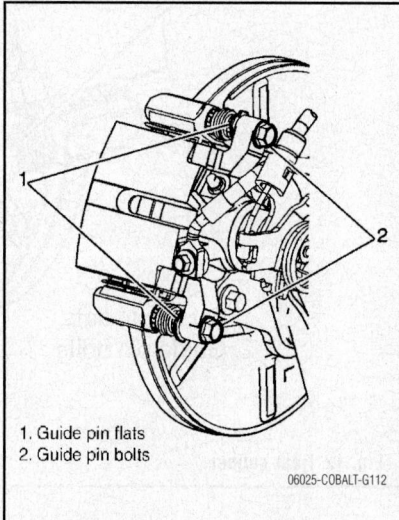

1. Guide pin flats
2. Guide pin bolts

06025-COBALT-G112

Fig. 13 Rear caliper guide pin bolts

2. Inspect the fluid level in the brake master cylinder auxiliary reservoir.

3. If the brake fluid level is midway between the maximum-full point and the minimum allowable level, no brake fluid needs to be removed from the reservoir before proceeding.

4. If the brake fluid level is higher than midway between the maximum-full point and the minimum allowable level, remove brake fluid to the midway point before proceeding.

5. Raise and support the vehicle.

6. Remove the tire and wheel assembly.

7. Install and firmly hand tighten 2 wheel nuts to opposite wheel studs in order to retain the rotor to the hub.

8. Install a large C-clamp, over the body of the brake caliper with the C-clamp ends against the rear of the caliper body and against the outer brake pad.

⁂ WARNING

When using a large C-clamp to compress a caliper piston into a caliper bore of a caliper equipped with an integral park brake mechanism, do not exceed more than 1mm (0.039 in.) of piston travel. Exceeding this amount of piston travel will cause damage to the internal adjusting mechanism and/or the integral park brake mechanism.

9. Tighten the C-clamp just enough to compress the caliper piston 0.039 inch (1mm) of travel only.

10. Remove the C-clamp from the caliper.

11. While using a wrench on the flats of the caliper guide pins, remove the brake caliper guide pin bolts.

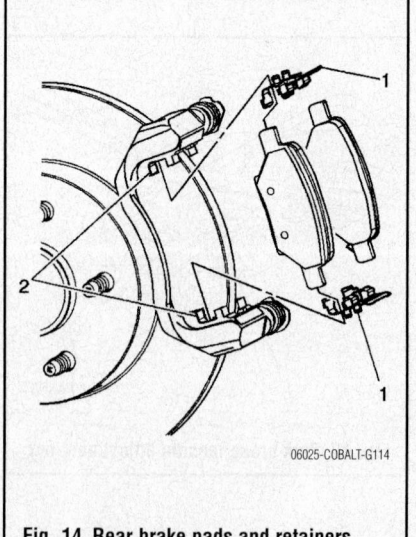

06025-COBALT-G114

Fig. 14 Rear brake pads and retainers

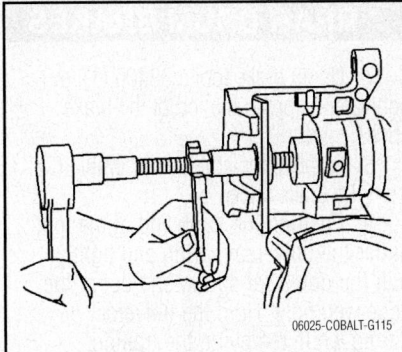

06025-COBALT-G115

Fig. 15 Using a spanner wrench type caliper piston installer, fully retract the piston into the rear caliper bore

✳✳ WARNING

Support the brake caliper with heavy mechanic's wire, or equivalent, whenever it is separated from its mount and the hydraulic flexible brake hose is still connected. Failure to support the caliper in this manner will cause the flexible brake hose to bear the weight of the caliper, which may cause damage to the brake hose and in turn may cause a brake fluid leak.

12. Without disconnecting the hydraulic brake flexible hose, remove the caliper from the mounting bracket and secure the caliper with heavy mechanics wire, or equivalent.

13. Remove the brake pads from the caliper mounting bracket.

14. Remove the brake pad retainers (1) from the caliper bracket.

15. Thoroughly clean the brake pad hardware mating surfaces of the caliper bracket (2), of any debris and corrosion.

16. Inspect the brake caliper guide pins for freedom of movement, and inspect the condition of the guide pin boots. Move the guide pins inboard and outboard within the bracket bores, without disengaging the slides from the boots, and observe for the following:

- Restricted caliper guide pin movement
- Looseness in the brake caliper mounting bracket
- Seized or binding caliper guide pins
- Split or torn boots

17. If any of the conditions listed are found, the brake caliper guide pins and/or boots require replacement.

18. Using a spanner wrench type caliper piston installer, fully retract the piston into the caliper bore.

To install:

19. Apply a very thin coating of high temperature silicone brake lubricant to the pad hardware mating surfaces of the caliper bracket only.

20. Install the brake pad retainers to the brake caliper bracket.

➡ **The wear sensor equipped disc brake pad must be mounted inboard of the rotor with the leading edge of the sensor facing the brake rotor during forward wheel rotation, or at the bottom of the pad when installed in vehicle position.**

21. Install the brake pads to the caliper bracket.

22. Remove the support, and install the caliper into position over the disc brake pads and to the caliper mounting bracket.

23. While using a wrench on the flats of the caliper guide pins, install the brake caliper guide pin bolts. Tighten the bolts to 25 ft. lbs. (34 Nm).

24. Remove the wheel nuts retaining the brake rotor to the hub.

25. Install the tire and wheel assembly.

26. Lower the vehicle.

27. With the engine OFF, gradually apply the brake pedal approximately ⅔ of its travel distance.

28. Slowly release the brake pedal.

29. Wait 15 seconds, then gradually apply the brake pedal approximately ⅔ of its travel distance again until a firm brake pedal apply is obtained. This will properly seat the brake caliper pistons and brake pads.

30. Fill the master cylinder auxiliary reservoir to the proper level.

31. Burnish the pads and rotors.

✳✳ CAUTION

Road test a vehicle under safe conditions and while obeying all traffic laws. Do not attempt any maneuvers that could jeopardize vehicle control. Failure to adhere to these precautions could lead to serious personal injury and vehicle damage.

➡ Burnishing the brake pads and brake rotors is necessary in order to ensure that the braking surfaces are properly prepared after service has been performed on the disc brake system. This procedure should be performed whenever the disc brake rotors have been refinished or replaced, and/or whenever the disc brake pads have been replaced.

    a. Select a smooth road with little or no traffic.

    b. Accelerate the vehicle to 48 km/h (30 mph).

➡ **Use care to avoid overheating the brakes while performing this step.**

    c. Using moderate to firm pressure, apply the brakes to bring the vehicle to a stop. Do not allow the brakes to lock.

    d. Repeat steps 2 and 3 until approximately 20 stops have been completed. Allow sufficient cooling periods between stops in order to properly burnish the brake pads and rotors.

BRAKE DRUM

REMOVAL & INSTALLATION

See Figure 16.

1. Before servicing the vehicle, refer to the Precautions Section.
2. Check to ensure that the park brake is fully released.
3. Raise and safely support the vehicle.
4. Remove the tire and wheel assembly.
5. Remove and discard the brake drum retainers (1), if equipped.
6. Remove the brake drum.
7. If the brake drum is to be reinstalled to the vehicle, use the J 41013 to clean any rust or corrosion from the hub/flange mating surface of the brake drum. If necessary, carefully remove any corrosion from the edge of the drum braking surface in order to ease installation.
8. Use the J 42450-A tool to clean the wheel hub flange.

To install:

9. If installing a new brake drum, use denatured alcohol or an equivalent approved brake cleaner and a clean shop towel to remove the protective coating from the friction surface of the drum.
10. Install the brake drum.
11. Install the tire and wheel assembly. Tighten lug nuts to 100 ft. lbs (140 Nm).
12. Apply the brakes approximately three times in order to seat and center the brake shoes within the drum.
13. Lower the vehicle.

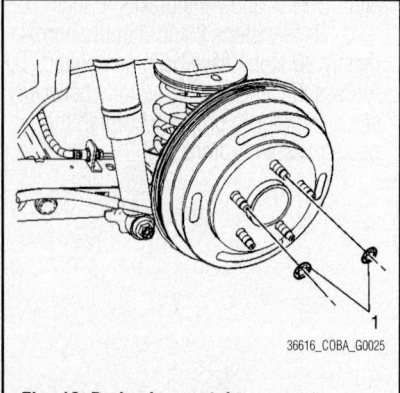

Fig. 16 Brake drum retainers

BRAKE SHOES

REMOVAL & INSTALLATION

2008 Models

See Figures 17 through 21.

1. Before servicing the vehicle, refer to the Precautions Section.
2. Raise and support the vehicle.
3. Remove the tire and wheel assembly.
4. Remove the brake drum.

❋❋ WARNING

Do not over stretch the adjuster spring. Damage can occur if the spring is over stretched.

5. Remove the adjuster spring. Disengage the adjuster spring hook end from the tab on the adjuster actuator lever, then release the spring from the brake shoe web hole.
6. Remove the adjuster actuator lever (1) from the pivot.

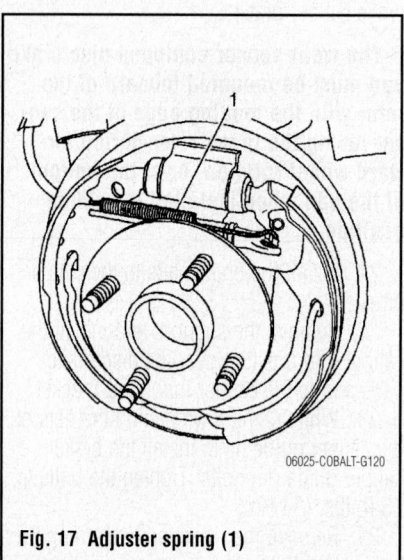

Fig. 17 Adjuster spring (1)

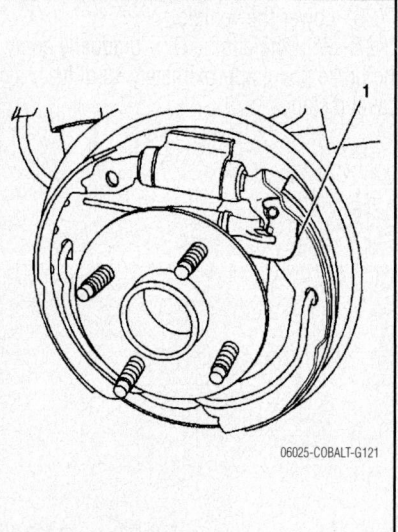

Fig. 18 Adjuster lever (1)

7. Using brake tool J 38400 (1), or equivalent, spread the top of the brake shoes apart.
8. Remove the adjuster assembly (2) from the brake shoes.
9. Position the hook end of the tool under the universal spring and lightly pull the universal spring end out of the shoe web hole. Hold the universal spring while removing the trailing brake shoe.
10. Release the park brake cable from the park brake lever on the trailing shoe.

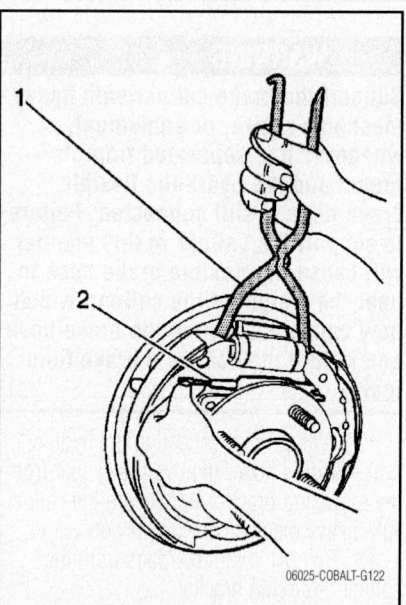

Fig. 19 Using brake tool J 38400 (1), or equivalent, spread the top of the brake shoes apart

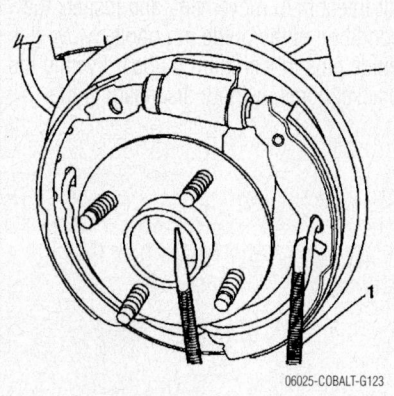

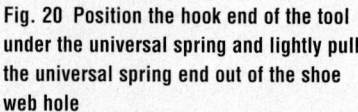

Fig. 20 Position the hook end of the tool under the universal spring and lightly pull the universal spring end out of the shoe web hole

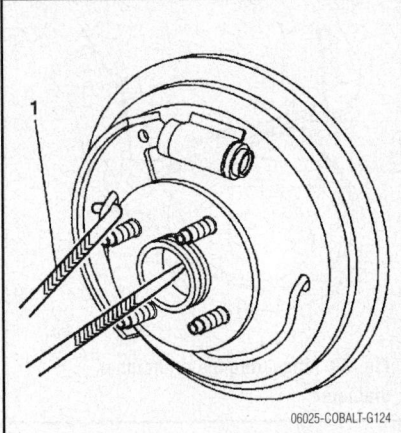

Fig. 21 Position the hook end of the tool under the universal spring and lightly pull the universal spring end out of the shoe web hole

11. Position the hook end of the tool under the universal spring and lightly pull the universal spring end out of the shoe web hole. Hold the universal spring while removing the leading brake shoe.

To install:
12. Measure the brake shoe lining thickness. Brake shoe lining minimum thickness is 0.020 inch (0.5mm).
13. If the brake shoe lining thickness is at or below the minimum specification, replace the brake shoes.
14. Apply a thin, light coat of high temperature silicone brake lubricant to the brake shoe contact surfaces of the brake backing plate.
15. Position the hook end of the tool under the universal spring and lightly pull the universal spring end out while installing the leading brake shoe. Ensure that the universal spring engages the brake shoe web hole.
16. Install the park brake cable to the park brake lever on the trailing brake shoe.
17. Position the hook end of the tool under the universal spring and lightly pull the universal spring end out while installing the trailing brake shoe. Ensure that the universal spring properly engages the brake shoe web hole.
18. Using the tool, spread the top of the brake shoes apart.
19. Install the adjuster assembly to the brake shoes.
20. Install the adjuster actuator lever to the brake shoe and the adjuster assembly. Ensure that the lever is properly engaged between the adjuster assembly and the brake shoe.

> ※※ **WARNING**
>
> **Do not over stretch the adjuster spring. Damage can occur if the spring is over stretched.**

21. Install the adjuster spring. Ensure that the loop end of the spring fully engages the tab on the actuator lever.
22. Adjust the drum brakes. Refer to Drum Brake Adjustment.
23. Install the brake drum.
24. Install the tire and wheel assembly.
25. Lower the vehicle.

2009 Models
See Figures 22 through 29.

1. Remove the brake drum. Refer to Brake Drum Replacement.
2. Remove the brake adjuster actuator lever spring (1).
3. Remove the brake adjuster actuator lever (1).
4. Remove the brake shoe hold down spring and cup (1) assemblies by compressing the spring and rotating the assembly 1/4 turn.
5. Remove the 2 hold down spring and cup assembly pins.
6. Spread the top of the brake shoes

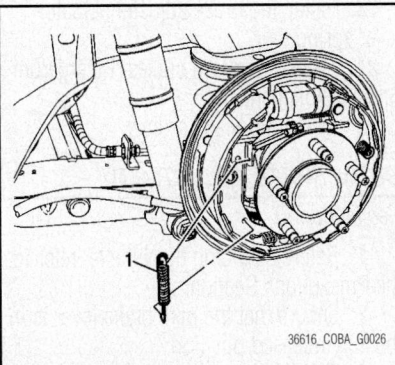

Fig. 22 Brake adjuster actuator lever spring

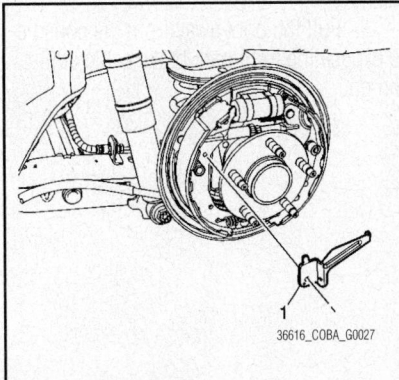

Fig. 23 Brake adjuster actuator lever

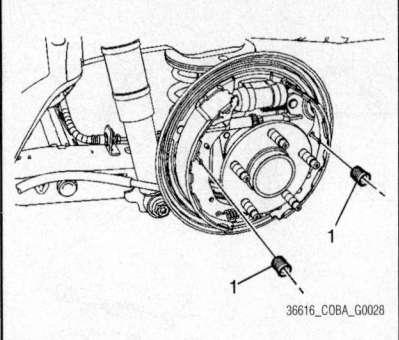

Fig. 24 Brake shoe hold down spring and cup

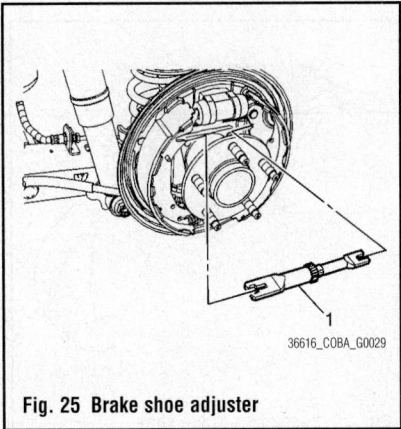

Fig. 25 Brake shoe adjuster

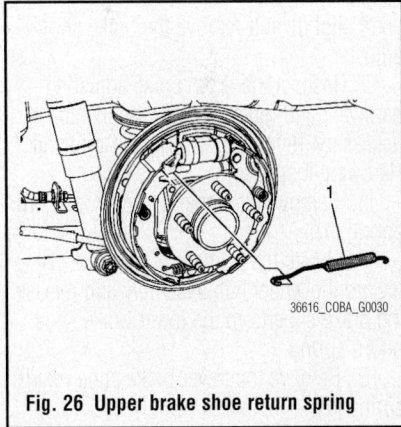

Fig. 26 Upper brake shoe return spring

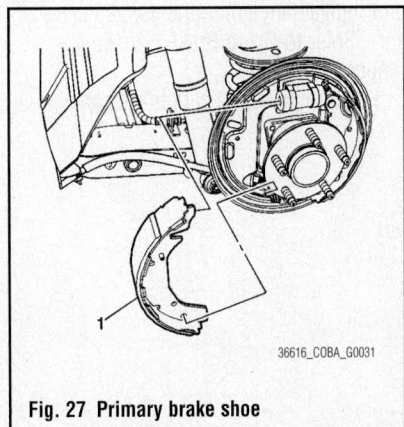

Fig. 27 Primary brake shoe

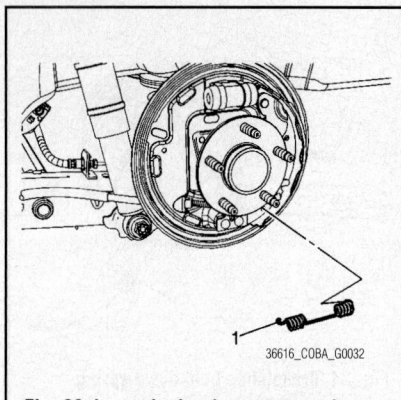

Fig. 28 Lower brake shoe return spring

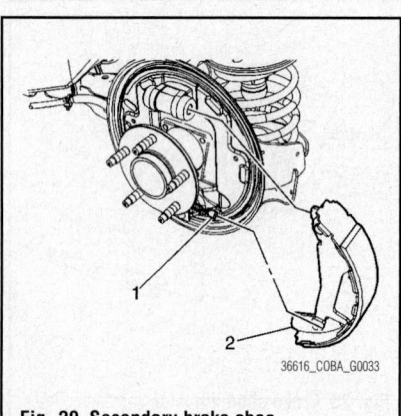

Fig. 29 Secondary brake shoe

apart slightly and remove the brake shoe adjuster (1).

7. Inspect the drum brake adjusting hardware and replace any components, as necessary. Refer to Drum Brake Adjusting Hardware Inspection.

8. Remove the upper brake shoe return spring (1).

9. Rotate the primary brake shoe (1) toward the wheel hub assembly and release the brake shoe from the lower brake shoe return spring.

10. Remove the lower brake shoe return spring (1).

11. Inspect the drum brake hardware and replace any components, as necessary. Refer to Drum Brake Hardware Inspection.

12. Compress the park brake cable

return spring and release the park brake cable fitting (1) from the park brake apply lever and remove the brake shoe (2).

To install:

13. Clean the drum brake backing plate of any dirt and debris.

14. Apply a light coat of high temperature brake lubricant to the drum brake backing plate brake shoe contact surfaces.

15. Compress the park brake cable return spring and install the park brake cable fitting to the park brake apply lever and position the brake shoe to the drum brake backing plate.

16. Install the lower brake shoe return spring.

17. Position the primary brake shoe to the drum brake backing plate and connect the brake shoe to the lower brake shoe return spring.

18. Install the upper brake shoe return spring.

19. Spread the top of the brake shoes apart slightly and install the brake shoe adjuster.

20. Install the 2 hold down spring and cup assembly pins.

21. Install the brake shoe hold down spring and cup assemblies by compressing the spring and rotating the assembly 1/4 turn.

22. Install the brake adjuster actuator lever.

23. Install the brake adjuster actuator lever spring.

24. Adjust the drum brakes. Refer Drum Brake Adjustment.

25. Install the brake drum.

DRUM BRAKE ADJUSTMENT

See Figure 30.

1. Before servicing the vehicle, refer to the Precautions Section.

2. Ensure that the park brake lever is in the fully released position.

3. Release the park brake lever boot from the floor console by applying light pressure inward on the sides of the boot retainer.

4. Pull the boot away from the console to expose the front park brake cable adjusting nut.

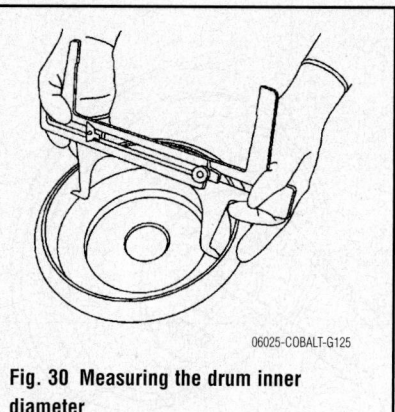

Fig. 30 Measuring the drum inner diameter

5. Release the tension from the park brake cable system at the front cable adjusting nut. Using ONLY HAND TOOLS, loosen the adjusting nut completely to the end of the front cable threaded rod.

6. Raise and support the vehicle.

7. Remove the rear tire and wheel assemblies.

8. Remove the brake drums.

9. Measure the inner diameter of the drum with a caliper such as tool J 21177-A at its widest point.

10. Firmly hand tighten the set screw on the tool.

11. Remove the tool from the brake drum and position it over the corresponding brake shoe assembly at its widest point.

12. While holding the tool in position, insert a 0.025 inch (0.635mm) (2008), insert a 0.015 inch (0.375mm) (2009) feeler gage between one side of the tool, and the corresponding brake shoe lining.

13. Rotate the brake shoe adjuster screw until the brake shoe linings contact the tool, and the feeler gage.

14. Repeat the above steps for the opposite brake drum and brake shoe assembly.

15. Install the brake drums.

16. Adjust the park brake.

17. Install the rear tire and wheel assemblies.

18. Lower the vehicle.

19. Position the park brake lever boot to the floor console and press the boot retainer into place to secure.

BRAKES PARKING BRAKE

PARKING BRAKE CABLES

ADJUSTMENT

Disc Brakes

See Figure 31.

1. Before servicing the vehicle, refer to the Precautions Section.

※※ WARNING

The park brake cable adjusting nut is a nylon lock type. Use ONLY HAND TOOLS whenever tightening or loosening the adjusting nut.

2. Apply and fully release the park brake several times. Verify that the park brake lever releases completely.

3. Turn ON the ignition. Verify the red BRAKE warning lamp is not illuminated.

4. If the red BRAKE warning lamp is illuminated, verify the following:
   - The park brake lever is in the fully released position and against the stop
   - There is no slack in the park brake cables

5. Turn OFF the ignition.

6. Release the park brake lever boot from the floor console by applying light pressure inward on the sides of the boot retainer, and pull the boot back.

7. With the park brake lever in the released position, loosen the adjusting nut (1) enough to completely relieve tension on the front cable.

8. Raise and support the vehicle. Raise the vehicle just enough to observe the rear calipers and rotate the rear tire and wheel assemblies.

9. With all tension relieved from the park brake cables, rotate the rear tire and

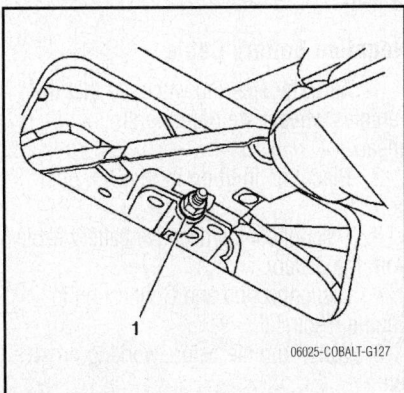

06025-COBALT-G127

Fig. 31 Parking brake adjusting nut

wheel assemblies, or the rear brake rotors if the wheels have been removed. Observe the amount of effort required for rotation, and the amount of drag if present.

10. Tighten the park brake cable adjusting nut until all slack is taken out of the front cable.

11. Further tighten the adjusting nut until one of the park brake levers on the rear calipers is just lifted off the stop on the caliper housing.

12. Slowly back off the adjusting nut until the park brake lever just rests on the stop.

13. Back off the adjusting nut one full turn.

14. Fully apply and release the park brake lever 3–5 times.

15. Raise the park brake lever 3 detent positions and attempt to rotate the rear tire and wheel assemblies, or the rear brake rotors.

➡**If rotating the tire and wheel assemblies, they should be difficult to rotate, but should not be locked. If rotating the brake rotors, they should be locked.**

16. Raise the park brake lever one additional detent position and attempt to rotate the rear tire and wheel assemblies, or the rear brake rotors. The tire and wheel assemblies, or the rear brake rotors should be locked.

17. Fully release the park brake lever.

18. Verify the park brake is released by rotating the rear tire and wheel assemblies, or the rear brake rotors. The rotors should rotate freely and exhibit no brake shoe drag from the park brake system.

19. With the lever released, if the rotors required more effort to rotate, or exhibited more drag than noted previously when all cable tension was relieved, check the park brake levers on the rear calipers. The levers should be on the stops.

20. If the levers are not against the stops, loosen the adjusting nut just until the levers rest against the stops, then repeat steps 14–18.

21. If the rotors still do not rotate freely, with the park lever fully released, park brake adjustment is not the cause of any drag in the brake system.

22. Lower the vehicle.

23. Position the park brake lever boot to the floor console and press the boot retainer into place to secure.

24. Release the park brake lever.

Drum Brakes

1. Before servicing the vehicle, refer to the Precautions Section.

2. Apply and fully release the park brake several times. Verify that the park brake lever releases completely.

3. Turn ON the ignition. Verify the red BRAKE warning lamp is not illuminated.

4. If the red BRAKE warning lamp is illuminated, verify the following:
   - The park brake lever is in the fully released position and against the stop
   - There is no slack in the park brake cables

5. Turn OFF the ignition.

6. Release the park brake lever boot from the floor console by applying light pressure inward on the sides of the boot retainer, and pull the boot back.

7. With the park brake lever in the released position, loosen the adjusting nut enough to completely relieve tension on the front cable.

8. Raise and support the vehicle. Raise the vehicle just enough to allow rear tire and wheel assembly removal and rear drum adjustment.

9. Remove the rear tire and wheel assemblies.

10. Adjust the rear drum brakes. Refer to Drum Brake Adjustment.

11. Ensure there is no brake shoe drag after adjustment by rotating the brake drums. If drag exists, re-center the brake shoes and perform the brake shoe adjustment again.

12. Install 2 wheel nuts to the wheel studs and firmly hand-tighten in order to retain the brake drums.

13. Raise the park brake lever 6 detent positions.

14. Tighten the park brake cable adjusting nut. Tighten the nut to 35 inch lbs. (4 Nm).

15. Attempt to rotate the rear brake drums. There should be no rotation forward or rearward.

16. Fully release the park brake lever.

17. Verify the park brake is released by rotating the rear brake drums. The drums should rotate freely and exhibit no brake shoe drag.

18. If the drums do not rotate freely, repeat the park brake cable adjustment procedure.

19. Raise the park brake lever 3 detent positions and attempt to rotate the rear

brake drums. One of the brake drums should not rotate forward or rearward. The other brake drum should not rotate forward or rearward, or should require substantial effort to rotate.

20. Raise the park brake lever one additional detent position and attempt to rotate the rear brake drums.

21. Verify that the left and right brake drums cannot be rotated.

22. Remove the wheel nuts retaining the brake drums.

23. Install the rear tire and wheel assemblies.

24. Lower the vehicle.

25. Position the park brake lever boot to the floor console and press the boot retainer into place to secure.

26. Release the park brake lever.

PARKING BRAKE SHOES

REMOVAL & INSTALLATION

The rear drum brake shoes and disc brake pads serve as the parking brakes. Refer to the procedures under Rear Drum Brakes and Rear Disc Brakes.

ADJUSTMENT

Refer to parking brake cables, adjustment.

CHASSIS ELECTRICAL

GENERAL INFORMATION

✳✳ CAUTION

These vehicles are equipped with an air bag system. The system must be disarmed before performing service on, or around, system components, the steering column, instrument panel components, wiring and sensors. Failure to follow the safety precautions and the disarming procedure could result in accidental air bag deployment, possible injury and unnecessary system repairs.

SERVICE PRECAUTIONS

✳✳ CAUTION

When performing service on or near the SIR components or the SIR wiring, the SIR system must be disabled. Refer to SIR Disabling and Enabling . Failure to observe the correct procedure could cause deployment of the SIR components, personal injury, or unnecessary SIR system repairs.

The inflatable restraint sensing and diagnostic module (SDM) maintains a reserved energy supply. The reserved energy supply provides deployment power for the air bags. Deployment power is available for as much as 1 minute after disconnecting the vehicle power. Disabling the SIR system prevents deployment of the air bags from the reserved energy supply.

General Service Instructions

1. The following are general service instructions which must be followed in order to properly repair the vehicle and return it to its original integrity:

a. Do not handle the inflatable restraint vehicle rollover sensor when connected to vehicle power.

AIR BAG (SUPPLEMENTAL RESTRAINT SYSTEM)

b. Do not expose inflator modules to temperatures above 65°C (150°F).

c. Verify the correct replacement part number. Do not substitute a component from a different vehicle.

d. Use only original GM replacement parts available from your authorized GM dealer. Do not use salvaged parts for repairs to the SIR system.

2. Discard any of the following components if it has been dropped from a height of 3 ft (91cm) or greater:

- Inflatable restraint front end sensor
- Inflatable restraint instrument panel (I/P) module
- Inflatable restraint passenger presence system (PPS)
- Inflatable restraint roof rail module
- Inflatable restraint SDM
- Inflatable restraint side impact sensor (SIS)
- Inflatable restraint steering wheel module
- Inflatable restraint steering wheel module coil
- Inflatable restraint vehicle rollover sensor
- Seat belt pretensioner

When carrying an undeployed inflator module:

- Do not carry the inflator module by the wires or connector.
- Make sure the air bag opening points away from you.

When storing an undeployed inflator module:

- Make sure the air bag opening points away from the surface on which the inflator module rests.
- Provide free space for the air bag to expand in case of an accidental deployment.
- When storing a steering column, do not rest the column with the air bag opening facing down and the column vertical. Lay the column on its side.
- Failure to observe these guidelines may result in personal injury.

DISABLING THE SYSTEM

Air Bag Fuse

✳✳ CAUTION

If you are performing service on or near the SIR components or the SIR wiring, observe all SIR System Precautions. Failure to follow the correct procedure could cause air bag deployment, unnecessary SIR system repairs, or personal injury or death.

1. Turn the steering wheel so that the vehicles wheels are pointing straight ahead.

2. Place the ignition in the OFF position.

➡ **The SDM may have more than one fused power input. To ensure there is no unwanted SIR deployment, personal injury, or unnecessary SIR system repairs, remove all fuses supplying power to the SDM. With all SDM fuses removed and the ignition switch in the ON position, the AIR BAG warning indicator illuminates. This is normal operation, and does not indicate a SIR system malfunction.**

3. Locate and remove the fuse(s) supplying power to the SDM. Refer to Fuses & Flashers.

4. Wait 1 minute before working on the system.

Negative Battery Cable

1. Turn the steering wheel so that the vehicles wheels are pointing straight ahead.

2. Place the ignition in the OFF position.

3. Disconnect the negative battery cable from the battery.

4. Disconnection and Connection in Engine Electrical.

5. Wait 1 minute before working on system.

ENABLING THE SYSTEM

Air Bag Fuse

1. Place the ignition in the OFF position.

2. Install the fuse(s) supplying power to the SDM. Refer to Fuses & Flashers.

3. Turn the ignition switch to the ON position. The AIR BAG indicator will flash then turn OFF.

4. Perform the Diagnostic System Check—Vehicle if the AIR BAG warning indicator does not operate as described. Refer to Diagnostic Trouble Codes.

Negative Battery Cable

1. Place the ignition in the OFF position.

2. Connect the negative battery cable to the battery.

3. Turn the ignition switch to the ON position. The AIR BAG indicator will flash then turn OFF.

4. Perform the Diagnostic System Check—Vehicle if the AIR BAG warning indicator does not operate as described.

CLOCKSPRING CENTERING

See Figures 32 and 33.

1. Before servicing the vehicle, refer to the Precautions Section.

※ CAUTION

If you are performing service on or near the SIR components or the SIR wiring, observe all SIR System Precautions. Failure to follow the correct

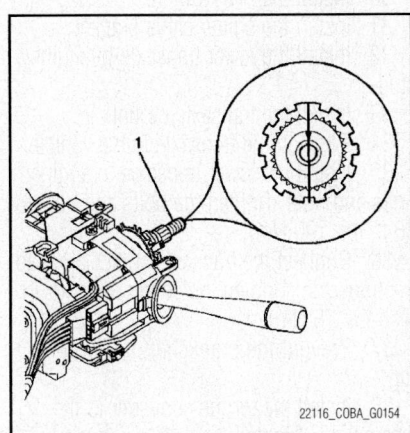

Fig. 32 The block tooth and the centering mark (1) of the steering shaft must be in the 12 o'clock position

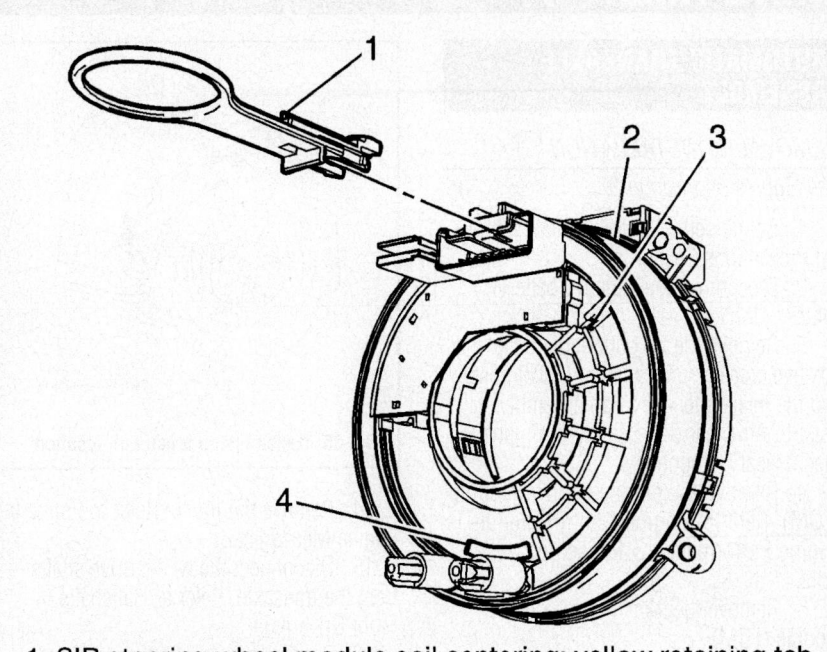

1. SIR steering wheel module coil centering: yellow retaining tab
2. Casing
3. Coil hub
4. Centering window

22116_COBA_G0155

Fig. 33 SIR steering wheel module coil centering: yellow retaining tab, casing, coil hub, and centering window

procedure could cause air bag deployment, unnecessary SIR system repairs, or personal injury or death.

2. Disable the SIR system. Refer to SIR Disabling and Enabling in Chassis Electrical.

※ CAUTION

The new Supplemental Inflatable Restraint (SIR) coil assembly will be centered. Improper alignment of the SIR coil assembly may damage the unit, causing an inflatable restraint malfunction.

3. Verify the following conditions before centering the SIR steering wheel module coil ("clockspring"):

- The wheels on the vehicle are straight ahead
- The block tooth and the centering mark (1) of the steering shaft must be in the 12 o'clock position

4. If available, remove the yellow retaining tab (1) from the SIR steering wheel module coil and save the tab for reassembly.

5. Hold the SIR steering wheel module coil face up by the casing (2).

6. Slowly turn the SIR steering wheel module coil hub (3) in a clockwise direction until the coil ribbon stops.

7. Slowly rotate the SIR steering wheel module coil hub (3) counterclockwise 2½ revolutions until the centering window (4) turns yellow. This indicates the **CENTER** position.

➡ If the retaining tab is not available, the use of tape to secure the SIR steering wheel module coil is recommended for installation to the steering column.

8. Install the yellow retaining tab (1) to the SIR steering wheel module coil.

9. Slide the centered SIR steering wheel module coil onto the steering shaft.

DRIVE TRAIN

AUTOMATIC TRANSAXLE ASSEMBLY

REMOVAL & INSTALLATION

See Figures 34 through 37.

1. Before servicing the vehicle, refer to the Precautions Section.

2. Disconnect the negative battery cable.

3. Remove the air outlet duct hose, the positive crankcase ventilation (PCV) hose, and the intake plenum as an assembly. Refer to Air Cleaner Assembly in Engine Mechanical Components.

4. Remove the engine control module (ECM). Refer to Engine Control Module in Engine Performance & Emission Controls.

5. Remove the transmission control module (TCM).

   a. Remove the transmission control module (TCM) cover.

   b. Disconnect the TCM electrical connector.

6. Remove the underhood electrical junction block.

7. Disconnect the transaxle wiring harness from the transaxle and the park/neutral position (PNP) switch.

8. Disconnect the shift cable from the shift linkage.

9. Disconnect the cable from the bracket.

10. Disconnect the engine ground wires at the engine block.

11. Remove the upper transmission to engine bolts and stud.

12. Support engine with engine support fixture, if available.

13. Remove the left transmission mount bolts.

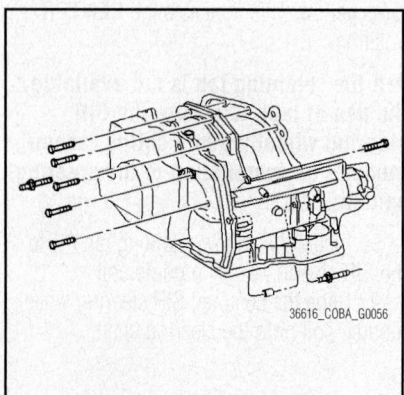

Fig. 34 Upper transmission to engine bolts and stud location

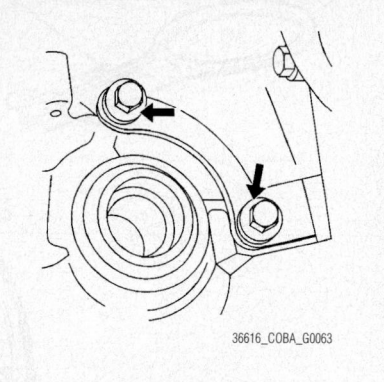

Fig. 35 Transmission brace bolt location

14. Remove the frame. Refer to Frame in Engine Mechanical.

15. Disconnect the wheel drive shafts from the transaxle. Refer to Halfshafts in Front Drive Axle.

16. Remove the 2 bolts from the transmission brace.

17. Remove the flywheel inspection cover.

18. Remove the starter. Refer to Starter in Engine Electrical.

19. Mark the relationship of the flywheel to the torque converter for reassembly.

20. Use the J 43653 to prevent the crankshaft from rotating.

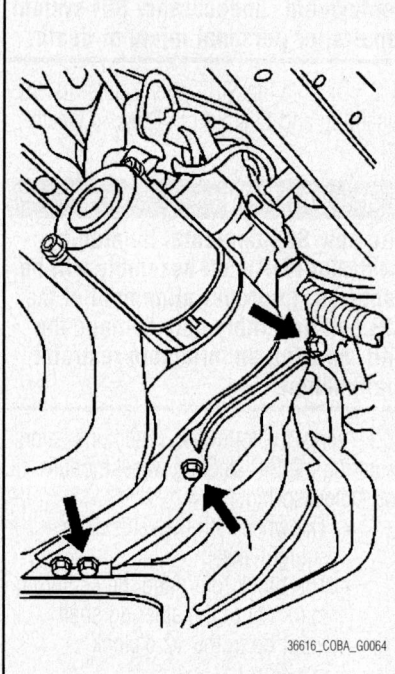

Fig. 36 Flywheel inspection cover bolt location

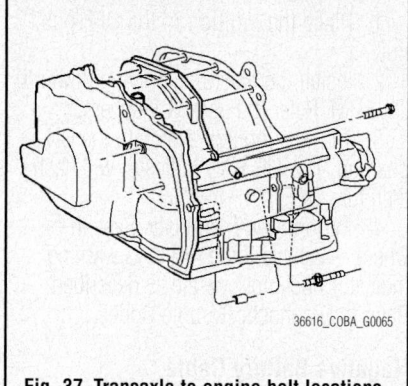

Fig. 37 Transaxle to engine bolt locations

21. Remove the torque converter to flywheel bolts.

22. Remove the transmission cooler lines by removing the nut holding the bracket to the transaxle case.

23. Disconnect the vehicle speed sensor (VSS) wiring harness from the sensor.

24. Support the transaxle with a suitable jack.

25. Remove the transaxle to engine bolts.

26. Separate the engine and the transaxle.

27. Remove the transaxle from the vehicle.

28. If installing a replacement transmission, transfer all necessary parts.

29. Flush the transmission cooler and lines.

To install:

30. Install the PNP switch.

31. Install the shifter cable bracket.

32. Install the lower transaxle to engine stud.

33. Install the transaxle mount.

34. Position the transaxle in the vehicle.

35. Install the lower transaxle to engine bolts and nuts. Tighten the bolts and nuts to 66 ft. lbs. (90 Nm).

36. Connect the transaxle cooler pipes to the transaxle. Tighten the cooler pipes to 71 inch lbs. (8 Nm).

37. Prevent the crankshaft from rotating.

38. Install the torque converter to flywheel bolts. Tighten the torque converter bolts to 46 ft. lbs. (62 Nm).

39. Install the halfshafts to the transaxle.

40. Connect the wiring harness to the VSS.

41. Install the starter.

42. Install the flywheel inspection cover

bolts. Tighten the bolts to 89 inch lbs. (10 Nm).

43. Install the upper transmission to engine bolts and stud and tighten all of the bolts to 66 ft. lbs. (90 Nm).

44. Install the transmission to engine brace bolts and tighten to 53 ft. lbs. (72 Nm).

45. Install the frame. Refer to Frame in Engine Mechanical.

46. Lower the vehicle.

47. Install the transaxle mount to body bolts. Tighten the bolts to 66 ft. lbs. (90 Nm).

48. Remove the engine support fixture.

49. Install the engine wiring harness grounds to the transaxle to engine mount stud and nut. Tighten the nut to 71 inch lbs. (8 Nm).

50. Install the shift linkage to the transaxle.

51. Connect the electrical connectors to the PNP switch and transaxle.

52. Connect the air duct hose to the intake plenum.

53. Connect the negative battery cable.

54. Inspect the transaxle fluid level.

➡️**It is recommended that transmission adaptive pressure (TAP) information be reset. Resetting the TAP values using a scan tool will erase all learned values in all cells. As a result, the ECM, powertrain control module (PCM), or TCM will need to relearn TAP values. Transmission performance may be affected as new TAP values are learned.**

MANUAL TRANSAXLE ASSEMBLY

REMOVAL & INSTALLATION

MU3 Transaxle

See Figures 38 through 42.

1. Before servicing the vehicle, refer to the Precautions Section.

2. Disconnect the negative battery cable.

3. Remove the cover from the underhood electrical center.

4. Release the forward lamp harness retainer from the ABS modulator bracket, or the proportioning valve bracket, to allow the underhood electrical center to be repositioned adequately.

5. Remove the underhood electrical center bracket from the vehicle and

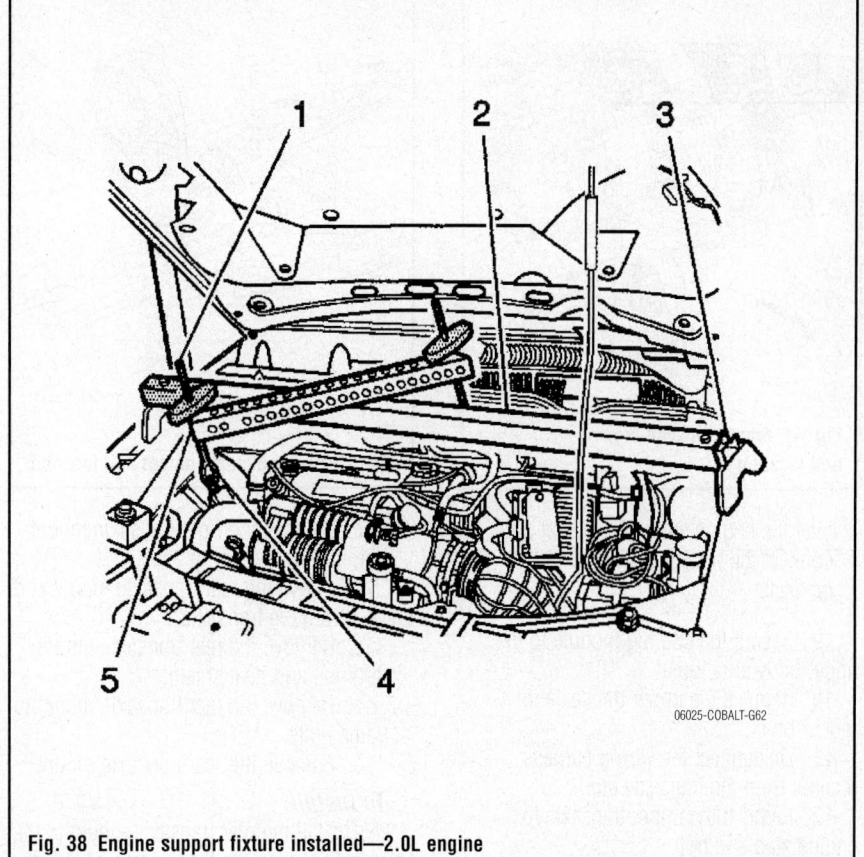

Fig. 38 Engine support fixture installed—2.0L engine

reposition the electrical center to access the bracket.

6. Release the wiring harness retainers above the brake booster, to allow the electrical center to be repositioned adequately.

7. Disconnect the hydraulic clutch hose from the clutch actuator cylinder and the clutch master cylinder. Refer to Clutch Actuator Assembly in Clutch.

8. Install the engine support fixture.

a. Place the engine support fixture long bar (2), from the J 28467-B across the engine compartment .

b. Install the engine support fixture legs (3) from the J 43405 on the engine support fixture long bar and center above the engine.

c. Install the engine support fixture hooks (4) and engine support fixture handle to the engine support cross bar.

d. Place the engine support cross bar

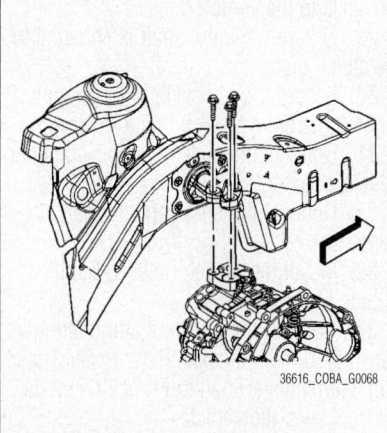

Fig. 39 Upper transaxle to mount bolt locations

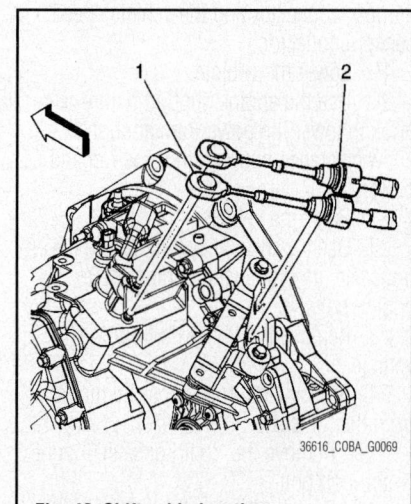

Fig. 40 Shift cable location

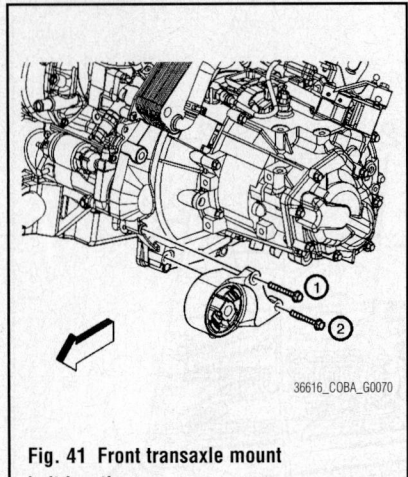

Fig. 41 Front transaxle mount bolt location

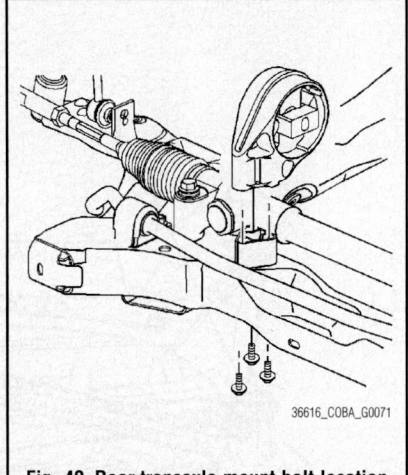

Fig. 42 Rear transaxle mount bolt location

over the engine support long bar and connect the hooks to the engine lift brackets.

9. Secure the cooling module to the upper body structure.

10. Remove the upper transaxle to mount bolts.

11. Disconnect the wiring harness retainer from the transaxle stud.

12. Remove the upper transaxle to engine stud and bolt.

13. Remove the frame. Refer to Frame in Engine Mechanical.

14. Drain the transaxle.

15. Disconnect the halfshaft and intermediate shaft from the transaxle and secure out of the way. Refer to Halfshaft and Intermediate Shaft in Front Drive Axle.

16. Remove the starter. Refer to Starter in Engine Electrical.

17. Disconnect the shift cables from the transaxle. Disconnect the backup lamp switch harness connector.

18. Disconnect the backup lamp switch harness connector and the vehicle speed sensor connector.

19. Lower the vehicle.

20. Use the engine support fixture rear hook to lower the powertrain enough to allow clearance between the side rail and powertrain.

21. Raise the vehicle.

22. Use a transaxle jack to secure the transaxle, and remove the transaxle to engine bolts.

23. Remove the transaxle from the vehicle.

24. Remove the front transaxle mount from the transaxle.

   a. Remove the front transaxle mount through bolt.

   b. Remove the front transaxle mount to transaxle bolts.

c. Remove the front transaxle mount from the vehicle.

25. Remove the rear transaxle mount and bracket from the transaxle.

   a. Remove the rear transaxle mount thru bolt and heat shield.

   b. Remove the rear transaxle mount to frame bolts.

   c. Remove the rear transaxle mount.

To install:

26. Install the rear transaxle mount to the transaxle. Tighten the thru bolt to 74 ft. lbs. (100 Nm) and the mount to frame bolts to 44 ft. lbs. (60 Nm).

27. Install the front transaxle mount to the transaxle. Tighten the thru bolt to 74 ft. lbs. (100 Nm) and the front transaxle mount to the transaxle bolts to 66 ft. lbs. (90 Nm).

➡**The front and rear transaxle mounts must be allowed to settle with the through bolts loosened. Tighten to final torque after engine and transaxle settling.**

28. Use a transaxle jack to position the transaxle to the vehicle.

29. Ensure the input shaft is engaged to the clutch disc.

30. Secure the transaxle to the engine. Tighten the bolts to 55 ft. lbs. (75 Nm).

31. Connect the backup lamp switch harness connector.

32. Connect the shift cable to the transaxle.

33. Install the starter. Refer to Starter in Engine Electrical.

34. Connect the halfshaft and intermediate shaft to the transaxle. Refer to Halfshaft and Intermediate Shaft in Front Drive Axle.

35. Lower the vehicle.

36. Use the engine support fixture in order to raise the powertrain assembly.

37. Install the left transaxle mount:

   a. Install the transaxle mount to the mid-rail.

   b. Install the transaxle mount to mid-rail bolts. Tighten the bolts to 20 ft. lbs. (27 Nm).

   c. Using a floor jack, raise the transaxle until it contacts the transaxle mount.

➡**The transaxle mount to transaxle bolts must be hand started. Do not pry the transaxle or mount to align the holes.**

   d. Hand start the transaxle mount to bracket bolts using the following sequence:
- Rear bolt
- Middle bolt
- Front bolt

   e. Using the previous sequence, tighten the transaxle mount bolts. Tighten the bolts to 48 ft. lbs. (65 Nm).

   f. Install the underhood electrical center bracket to the vehicle and install the electrical center into position on the bracket.

38. Install the frame. Refer to Frame in Engine Mechanical.

39. Remove the engine support fixture.

40. Install the top engine to transaxle bolt. Tighten the bolt to 55 ft. lbs. (75 Nm).

41. Install the top engine to transaxle stud. Tighten the stud to 55 ft. lbs. (75 Nm).

42. Connect the wiring harness retainer to the transaxle stud.

43. Connect the hydraulic clutch hose to the clutch actuator cylinder.

44. Bleed the clutch hydraulic system. Refer to Hydraulic System Bleeding in Clutch

45. Install the underhood electrical center bracket to the vehicle and install the electrical center into position on the bracket.

46. Secure the forward lamp harness retainer to the ABS modulator bracket, or the proportioning valve bracket.

47. Connect the electrical connector to the brake fluid level sensor, then press forward on the Connector Position Assurance (CPA) tab of the connector to secure.

48. Install the cover to the underhood electrical center.

49. Release the cooling module from the upper body structure.

50. Connect the negative battery cable.

51. Fill the transaxle to the proper level.

Getrag Transaxle

See Figures 41 through 45.

1. Before servicing the vehicle, refer to the Precautions Section.

2. Disconnect the negative battery cable.

3. Remove the cover from the underhood electrical center.

4. Disconnect the surge tank inlet hose from the surge tank.

5. Remove the underhood electrical center bracket nuts.

6. Loosen the underhood electrical center bracket bolt.

7. Disconnect the front wiring harness from the underhood electrical center bracket.

8. Reposition the underhood electrical center bracket aside.

9. Disconnect the hydraulic clutch hose from the clutch actuator cylinder. Refer to Clutch Actuator Assembly in Clutch.

10. Remove the front wheel and tire assemblies.

11. Secure the cooling module to the upper body structure.

12. Install the engine support fixture.

13. Remove the upper transaxle to mount bolts.

14. Remove the upper transaxle to engine bolt.

15. Remove the frame. Refer to Frame in Engine Mechanical.

16. Drain the transaxle.

17. Disconnect the drive axles from the transaxle and secure out of the way. Refer to Halfshafts in Front Drive Axle.

18. Remove the starter. Refer to Starter in Engine Electrical.

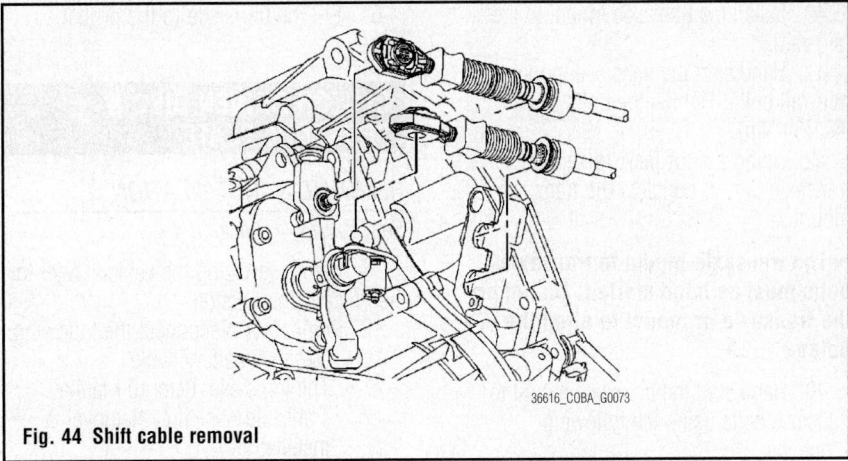

Fig. 44 Shift cable removal

19. Disconnect the shift cables from the transaxle.

20. Disconnect the backup lamp switch harness connector.

21. Disconnect the vehicle speed sensor.

22. Lower the vehicle.

23. Use the engine support fixture rear hook to lower the powertrain enough to allow clearance between the side rail and powertrain.

24. Raise the vehicle.

25. Use a transaxle jack to secure the transaxle, and remove the transaxle to engine bolts.

26. Remove the transaxle from the vehicle.

27. Remove the front transaxle mount from the transaxle.

   a. Remove the front transaxle mount through bolt.

   b. Remove the front transaxle mount to transaxle bolts.

   c. Remove the front transaxle mount from the vehicle.

28. Remove the rear transaxle mount and bracket from the transaxle.

   a. Remove the rear transaxle mount thru bolt and heat shield.

   b. Remove the rear transaxle mount to frame bolts.

   c. Remove the rear transaxle mount.

To install:

29. Install the rear transaxle mount to the transaxle. Tighten the thru bolt to 74 ft. lbs. (100 Nm) and the mount to frame bolts to 44 ft. lbs. (60 Nm).

30. Install the front transaxle mount to the transaxle. Tighten the thru bolt to 74 ft. lbs. (100 Nm) and the front transaxle mount to the transaxle bolts to 66 ft. lbs. (90 Nm).

➡**The front and rear transaxle mounts must be allowed to settle with the through bolts loosened. Tighten to final torque after engine and transaxle settling.**

31. Use a transaxle jack to position the transaxle to the vehicle.

➡**The number 3 position does not require a bolt.**

32. Secure the transaxle to the engine. Tighten the bolts to 55 ft. lbs. (75 Nm).

33. Connect the vehicle speed sensor.

34. Connect the backup lamp switch harness connector.

35. Connect the shift cable to the transaxle.

36. Install the starter. Refer to Starter in Engine Electrical.

37. Connect the halfshafts to the transaxle. Refer to Halfshafts in Front Drive Axle.

38. Lower the vehicle.

39. Use the engine support fixture in order to raise the powertrain assembly.

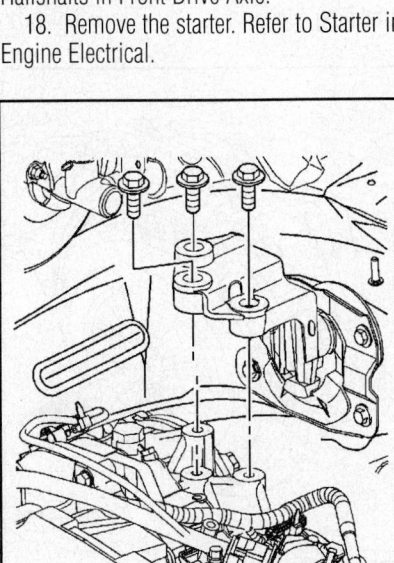

Fig. 43 Upper transaxle to mount bolts locations

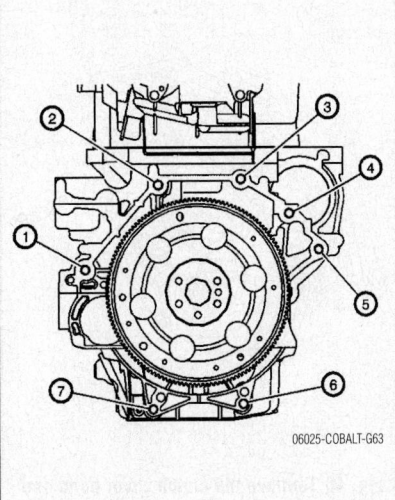

Fig. 45 Engine-to-transmission bolts— Getrag transmission

40. Install the transaxle mount to the mid-rail.

41. Hand start the transaxle mount to mid-rail bolts. Tighten the bolts to 25 ft. lbs. (34 Nm).

42. Using a floor jack, raise the transaxle until it contacts the transaxle mount.

➡ **The transaxle mount to transaxle bolts must be hand started. Do not pry the transaxle or mount to align the holes.**

43. Hand start the transaxle mount to transaxle bolts using the following sequence:
   a. Rear bolt
   b. Middle bolt
   c. Front bolt

44. Using the previous sequence, tighten the transaxle mount bolts. Tighten the bolts to 33 ft. lbs. (45 Nm).

45. Reposition the underhood electrical center.

46. Connect the wiring harness to the tray bracket.

47. Install the electrical center nuts and bolt. Tighten the nuts to 89 inch lbs. (10 Nm). Tighten the bolt to 18 ft. lbs. (25 Nm).

48. Position the underhood electrical center to the original position.

49. Install the surge tank inlet hose to the surge tank.

50. Install the front wiring harness to the junction block bracket.

51. Connect the positive battery cables to the junction block bracket.

52. Install the positive battery post to the junction block bracket.

53. Install the junction block bracket, bolt and nuts. Tighten the nuts to 89 inch lbs. (10 Nm). Tighten the bolt to 18 ft. lbs. (25 Nm).

54. Install the frame. Refer to Frame in Engine Mechanical.

55. Remove the engine support fixture.

56. Install the top engine to transaxle bolt. Tighten the bolt to 55 ft. lbs. (75 Nm).

57. Connect the hydraulic clutch hose to the clutch actuator cylinder.

58. Bleed the clutch hydraulic system. Refer to Hydraulic System Bleeding in Clutch.

59. Release the cooling module from the upper body structure.

60. Connect the negative battery cable.

61. Fill the transaxle to the proper level.

CLUTCH DRIVEN DISC & PRESSURE PLATE

REMOVAL & INSTALLATION

See Figures 46 through 49.

1. Before servicing the vehicle, refer to the Precautions Section.

2. Remove or disconnect the following:
   • Negative battery cable
   • The transaxle. Refer to Manual Transaxle Assembly Removal & Installation
   • The clutch cover bolts one turn at a time, until spring pressure is relieved
   • The clutch cover
   • The clutch driven disc and pressure plate

To install:

3. For the Getrag transaxle, align the machined side of the flywheel assembly, with the machined side of the cover.

4. Install the clutch disc and the clutch cover.

5. Hand start the clutch cover to flywheel bolts, leaving the clutch cover loose enough to reposition for alignment.

6. Install the J 43482 in order to support the clutch cover to the flywheel assembly.

✳✳ WARNING

Use the correct fastener in the correct location. Replacement fasteners

Fig. 47 Expanded view of clutch components

must be the correct part number for that application. Fasteners requiring replacement or fasteners requiring the use of thread locking compound or sealant are identified in the service procedure. Do not use paints, lubricants, or corrosion inhibitors on fasteners or fastener joint surfaces unless specified. These coatings affect fastener torque and joint clamping force and may damage the fastener. Use the correct tightening sequence and specifications when installing fasteners in order to avoid damage to parts and systems.

7. Tighten the clutch cover to flywheel bolts in the sequence shown. Tighten the bolts to 22 ft. lbs. (30 Nm).

8. Recheck each bolt torque using the tightening sequence.

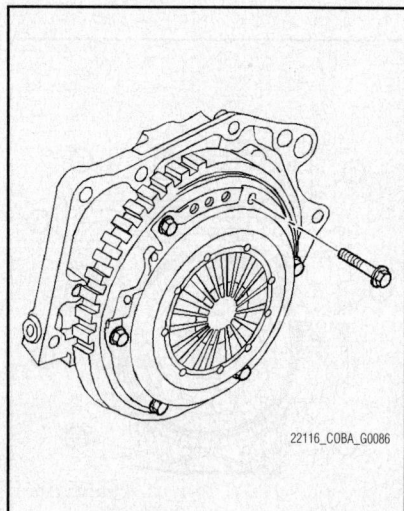
Fig. 46 Remove the clutch cover bolts one turn at a time

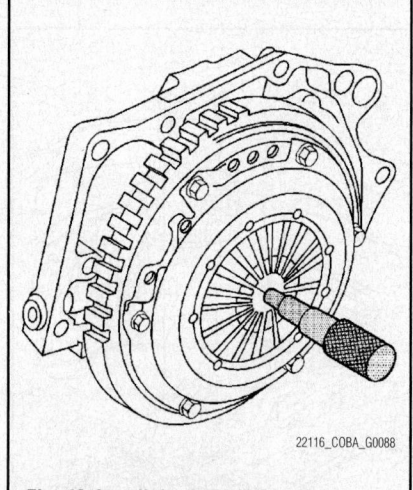
Fig. 48 Install the J 43482 in order to support the clutch cover to the flywheel assembly

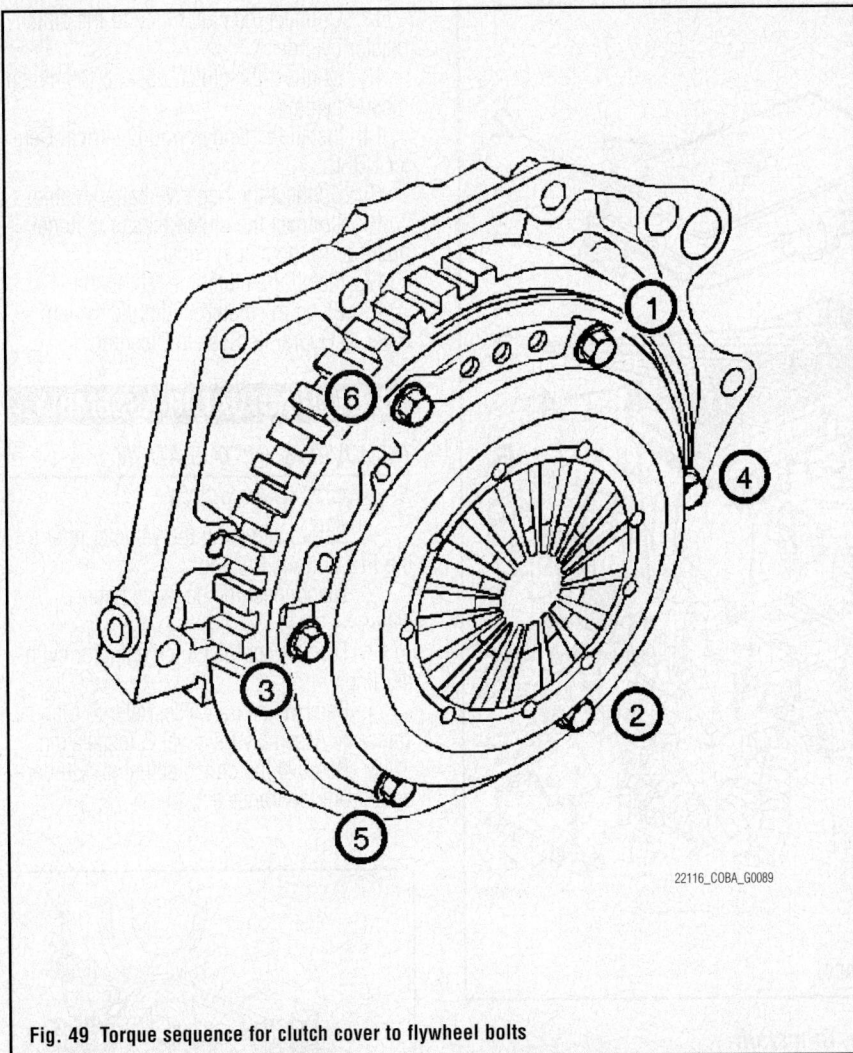

Fig. 49 Torque sequence for clutch cover to flywheel bolts

22116_COBA_G0089

9. Remove the J 43482.

➡**Excessive amounts of lubricant on the input shaft splines may contaminate the clutch disc and cause clutch shudder.**

10. Lubricate the inside diameter of the bearing.

11. Install the transaxle. Refer to Manual Transaxle Assembly Removal & Installation.

12. Bleed the hydraulic system. Refer to Clutch, Hydraulic System Bleeding.

13. Connect the negative battery cable.

ADJUSTMENTS

1. Before servicing the vehicle, refer to the Precautions Section.

The clutch has an automatic adjusting mechanism to compensate for normal wear on clutch plates no adjustment is possible, or necessary. However, clutch pedal position sensor learn is possible and necessary

✳✳ CAUTION

Replacement or reprogramming of the ECM, or replacement of the clutch pedal position sensor (CPPS) or clutch pedal requires that a CPPS learn procedure be performed. Failure to perform the CPPS learn procedure may result in personal injury or damage to the vehicle or its components if the vehicle is in gear and the starter motor is accidentally engaged.

➡**The clutch pedal position (CPP) sensor learn procedure is required when the following service procedures have been performed regardless of whether DTC P080A is set:**

- An engine control module (ECM) replacement

- A CPP sensor replacement
- Any repairs which affect the CPP sensor relationship

Clutch Pedal Position Sensor Learn

1. Before servicing the vehicle, refer to the Precautions Section.

2. Install a scan tool.

3. Monitor the ECM for DTCs with a scan tool. If other DTCs are set, except DTC P080A, refer to Diagnostic Trouble Codes.

4. With a scan tool, select Clutch Pedal Position Learn under Module Setup in Manual Transmission, and perform the following instructions displayed on the scan tool screen.

➡**The CPP sensor learn procedure cannot be performed more than once per ignition cycle. The clutch pedal needs to be fully depressed and held steady throughout this procedure in order to perform a correct learning.**

5. The scan tool will display under CPP Learn Status: Not Learned, In Process, Complete, Fail—Low Volt, Fail—High Volt, or Fail Moving. The scan tool will display under CPP Learn Status Complete if the process was successful.

6. If the scan tool indicates that DTC P080A ran and passed this ignition the CPP sensor learn procedure is complete. If the scan tool indicates DTC P080A failed or did not run this ignition, refer to DTC P080A.

7. If any other DTC is set, refer to Diagnostic Trouble Codes. If any other DTC is set, refer to Diagnostic Trouble Codes.

8. Turn OFF the ignition for 30 seconds after the learn procedure has successfully completed in order to store the CPP sensor variation values in ECM history.

CLUTCH MASTER CYLINDER

REMOVAL & INSTALLATION

See Figures 50 and 55.

1. Before servicing the vehicle, refer to the Precautions Section.

2. Remove the clutch pedal retainer from the front of the clutch pedal assembly.

3. Pull the clutch pedal upward in order to disengage the clutch master cylinder pushrod from the clutch pedal.

4. Remove the Underhood Electrical Center (UBEC).

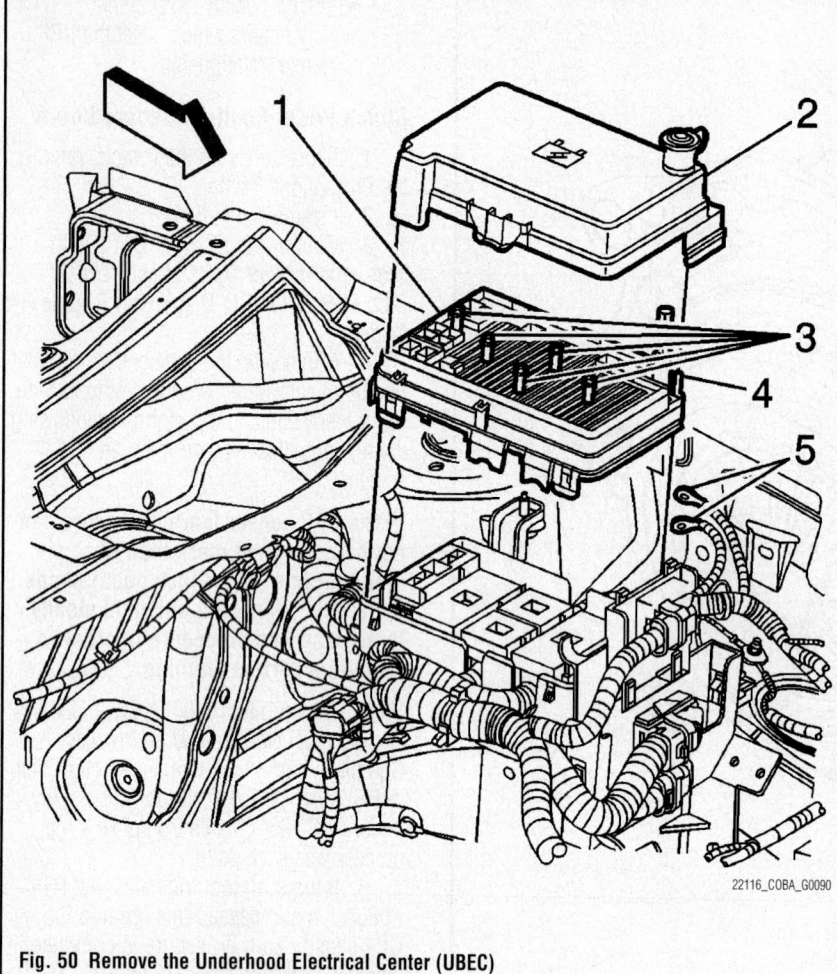

Fig. 50 Remove the Underhood Electrical Center (UBEC)

✳✳ WARNING

Avoid spilling brake fluid onto painted surfaces, electrical connections, wiring, or cables. Brake fluid will damage painted surfaces and cause corrosion to electrical components. If any brake fluid comes in contact with painted surfaces, immediately flush the area with water. If any brake fluid comes in contact with electrical connections, wiring, or cables, use a clean shop cloth to wipe away the fluid.

5. Place a shop towel under the clutch master cylinder in order to catch any fluid loss.

6. Disconnect the clutch hose from the clutch master cylinder.

7. Disconnect the clutch line from the clutch master cylinder.

8. Cap the reservoir and hydraulic lines in order to prevent fluid loss and contamination.

9. Rotate the clutch master cylinder ¼ turn clockwise and remove the cylinder from the vehicle.

To install:

➡ While installing, ensure that the clutch master cylinder pushrod is aligned with the clutch pedal.

10. Install the clutch master cylinder while rotating ¼ turn counterclockwise.

11. Uncap the reservoir and hydraulic lines.

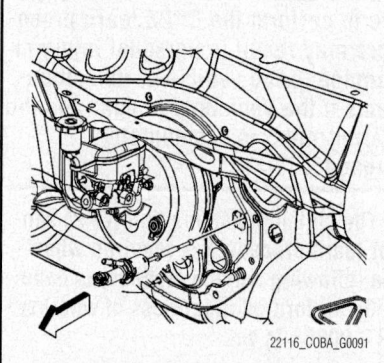

Fig. 51 Rotate the clutch master cylinder ¼ turn clockwise to remove

12. Connect the clutch line to the clutch master cylinder.

13. Connect the clutch hose to the clutch master cylinder.

14. Install the Underhood Electrical Center UBEC.

15. Connect the negative battery cable.

16. Connect the clutch master cylinder pushrod to the clutch pedal.

17. Install the clutch pedal retainer.

18. Bleed the clutch hydraulic system. Refer to Hydraulic System Bleeding.

CLUTCH ACTUATOR ASSEMBLY

REMOVAL & INSTALLATION

See Figures 52 through 54.

1. Before servicing the vehicle, refer to the Precautions Section.

2. Disconnect the negative battery cable.

3. Disconnect the clutch actuator cylinder line.

4. Remove the transaxle. Refer to Manual Transaxle Assembly Removal & Installation.

5. Remove the clutch actuator cylinder bolts from the transaxle.

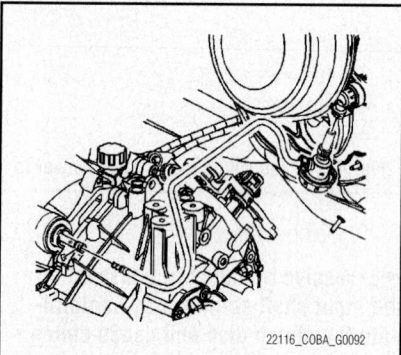

Fig. 52 Disconnect the clutch actuator cylinder line

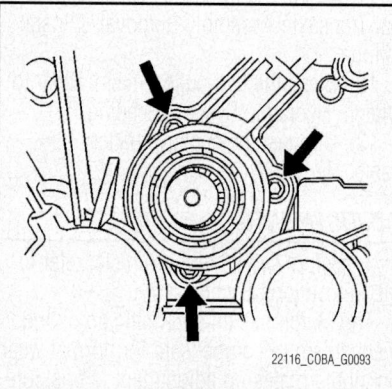

Fig. 53 Remove the clutch actuator cylinder bolts from the transmission

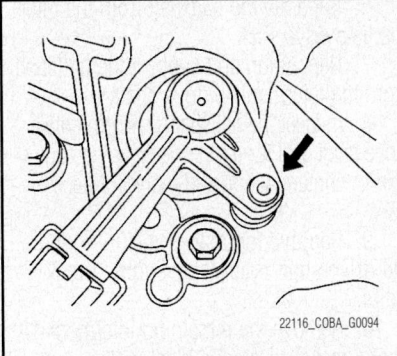

Fig. 54 Remove the upper bolt and the clutch actuator cylinder from the transaxle

6. Remove the following components from the transaxle:
   a. The upper bolt.
   b. The clutch actuator cylinder.

To install:

❋❋ WARNING

Excessive amounts of lubricant on the input shaft splines can contaminate the clutch disc and cause clutch shudder.

7. Lubricate the inside diameter of the bearing.

8. Install the clutch actuator cylinder to the transaxle.

9. Install the clutch actuator cylinder bolts. Tighten the bolts to 89 inch lbs. (10 Nm).

10. Install the upper line release bolt. Tighten the bolt to 89 inch lbs. (10 Nm).

11. Install the transaxle. Refer to Manual Transaxle Assembly Removal & Installation.

12. Connect the clutch actuator cylinder line.

13. Connect the negative battery cable.

14. Bleed the hydraulic system. Refer to Hydraulic System Bleeding.

CLUTCH HYDRAULIC SYSTEM BLEEDING

VACUUM BLEEDING

1. Before servicing the vehicle, refer to the Precautions Section.

2. Verify that all the hydraulic lines are dry and secure.

3. Clean dirt and grease from the reservoir cap in order to ensure that no foreign substances enter the system.

4. Remove the reservoir cap.

5. Fill the reservoir using DOT 3 hydraulic fluid.

❋❋ WARNING

Brake fluid will deteriorate the rubber on the adapter, use a clean shop towel to wipe away all fluid after each use.

6. Install a vacuum pump such as adapter J 43485 and pump J 35555 to the reservoir.

7. Hold the adapter to position while applying 51–68 kPa (15–20 hg) of vacuum.

8. Remove the adapter and refill the reservoir

9. Repeat previous steps.

10. If needed, refill the reservoir and continue to pull a vacuum until no more bubbles can be seen in the reservoir or until the fluid level no longer drops.

❋❋ CAUTION

The vehicle will move if started in gear before the Actuator Cylinder is refilled and operational. Start the vehicle the first time in neutral to help prevent personal injury from vehicle movement and see if the transmission will shift easily into gear.

11. Pump the clutch pedal until firm (to refill actuator cylinder).

12. Add additional fluid if needed.

13. Test drive the vehicle to ensure proper operation.

FRONT HALFSHAFTS

REMOVAL & INSTALLATION

See Figure 55.

1. Before servicing the vehicle, refer to the Precautions Section.

2. Raise and support the vehicle. Refer to Lifting and Jacking the Vehicle.

3. Remove the tire and wheel assembly. Refer to Tire and Wheel Removal & Installation.

➡**Steps 3, 4 and 5 is for standard disc brake only. For vehicles equipped with the Brembo brakes, proceed to step 6.**

4. Insert a punch or drift in the cooling fins of the brake rotor.

5. Position the punch or drift against the brake caliper mounting bracket.

6. Using a breaker bar and the appropriate size socket, loosen the wheel drive shaft nut.

7. Have an assistant apply the brakes.

8. Remove the wheel drive shaft nut (2) from the wheel drive shaft (1) and discard.

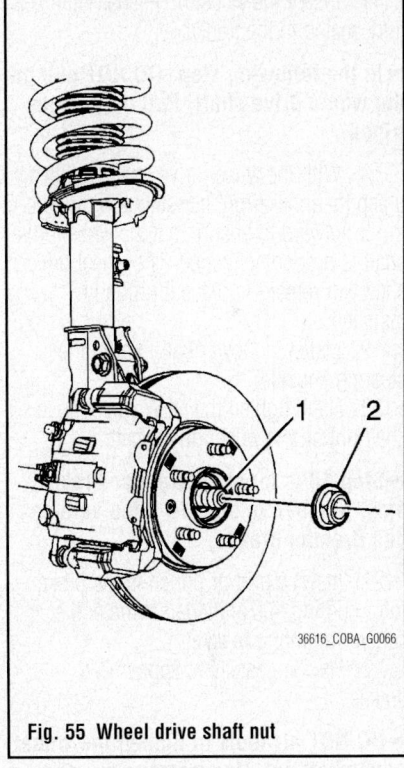

Fig. 55 Wheel drive shaft nut

DO NOT re-use the wheel drive shaft nut. Use NEW nut only.

9. Using the J 28733-B, separate the wheel drive shaft from the steering knuckle.

10. Remove the lower ball joint from the steering knuckle. Refer to Lower Control Arm in Suspension.

➡**The transmission stub staff may still be attached to the right wheel drive shaft and be removed at the same time as the wheel drive shaft. If this occurs, refer to Stub Shaft.**

11. Using the J-2619-A and the J 45341, remove the wheel drive shaft.

To install:

12. For the left wheel drive shaft, position the J 44394 in the transaxle.

13. Install the wheel drive shaft until the wheel drive shaft splines are past the axle seal.

14. Remove the J 44394 from the wheel drive shaft.

➡**The following service procedure is for those vehicles equipped with an intermediate shaft.**

15. For the right wheel drive shaft, apply a very small amount of grease, GM P/N 1051344 (Canadian P/N 993037), or equivalent to the splines of the wheel drive shaft inner joint.

16. Install the wheel drive shaft into the intermediate drive shaft.

17. Install the wheel drive shaft until it is fully seated in the transaxle.

➡ **In the following step, DO NOT pull on the wheel drive shaft. Pull only on the tripod.**

18. With the wheel drive shaft installed, grasp the inner tripot housing and pull the tripot outward to ensure that the wheel drive shaft is properly engaged. The wheel drive shaft will remain in place if properly installed.

19. Install the lower ball joint in the steering knuckle.

20. Hand tighten the NEW wheel drive shaft nut on the wheel drive shaft.

➡ **Step 10 is for standard disc brakes only, proceed to step 16 if the vehicle has Brembo brakes.**

21. Insert a drift or punch in the brake rotor cooling fins and against the brake caliper mounting bracket.

22. Have an assistant apply the brakes.

➡ **DO NOT air tools to tighten the wheel drive shaft nut. Use a torque wrench only.**

23. Using a torque wrench and the appropriate size socket, tighten the wheel drive shaft nut.

24. Tighten the wheel drive nut to 155 ft. lbs. (210 Nm).

25. Install the tire and wheel assembly.

26. Remove the support and lower the vehicle.

27. Inspect the fluid level of the transaxle.

Intermediate Shaft

See Figures 56 through 58.

1. Before servicing the vehicle, refer to the Precautions Section.

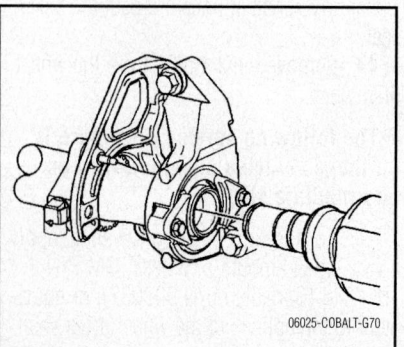

06025-COBALT-G70

Fig. 56 Separate the halfshaft from the intermediate drive shaft

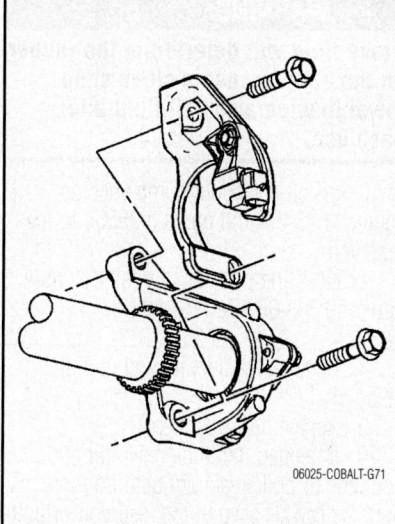

06025-COBALT-G71

Fig. 57 Remove the remaining intermediate shaft bracket-to-engine block bolts

2. Raise and support the vehicle.

3. Remove the RH tire and wheel assembly.

4. Disconnect the ball joint pinch bolt. Refer to Lower Control Arm in Suspension.

5. Rotate the steering knuckle to access the halfshaft inner joint.

6. Separate the halfshaft from the intermediate drive shaft.

7. Reposition and support the halfshaft from the intermediate drive shaft.

8. Inspect the halfshaft-to-intermediate drive shaft seal for excessive wear, damage, and/or contamination and replace if necessary.

9. Remove the rear, or LH intermediate drive shaft bracket-to-engine block bolts.

10. Remove the remaining intermediate shaft bracket-to-engine block bolts.

11. Using care to not damage the transaxle output shaft seal, remove the intermediate drive shaft assembly.

12. Inspect the transaxle output shaft seal for damage and/or contamination and replace if necessary.

To install:

13. Install tool J 44394 into the transaxle output shaft seal.

14. Install the intermediate drive shaft into the transaxle until the drive shaft splines are past the seal, remove the tool, then fully install the drive shaft.

15. Install, but do NOT tighten the intermediate drive shaft bracket-to-engine block forward, or RH bolt.

16. Tighten the intermediate drive shaft

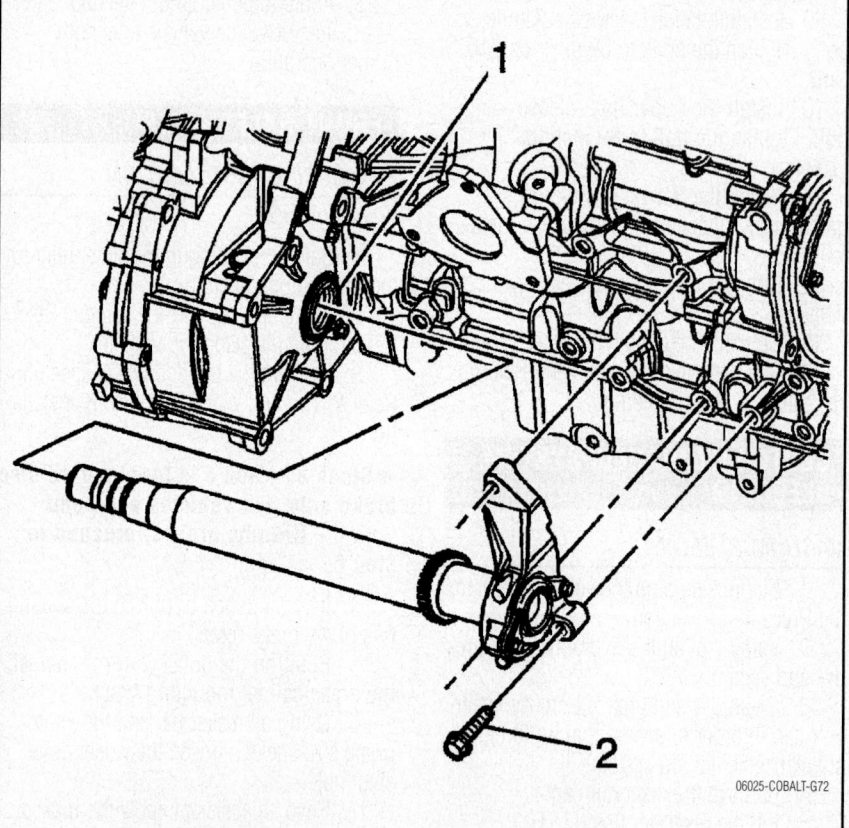

06025-COBALT-G72

Fig. 58 Intermediate shaft removal

bracket-to-engine block bolts, beginning with the upper bolt. Tighten the bolts to 37 ft. lbs. (50 Nm).

17. Apply a very small amount of grease, GM P/N 1051344 (Canadian P/N 993037), or equivalent to the splines of the halfshaft inner joint.

18. Install the halfshaft into the intermediate drive shaft.

19. Verify that the halfshaft is properly engaged:

    a. Grasp the inner tripod housing and pull the inner housing outward. Do NOT pull on the wheel drive axle shaft.

    b. The halfshaft will remain firmly in place when properly engaged.

20. Install the tire and wheel assembly.

21. Lower the vehicle.

22. Inspect the transaxle fluid level.

ENGINE COOLING

ENGINE FAN

REMOVAL & INSTALLATION

See Figures 59 through 61.

1. Before servicing the vehicle, refer to the Precautions Section.

2. Disconnect the cooling fan electrical connector.

3. Remove the cooling fan wire from the fan shroud.

4. Raise and support the vehicle.

5. Remove or disconnect the following:

- The cooling fan assembly from the radiator by pushing up on the fan shroud to unsnap the retaining features. Position the cooling fan assembly away from the radiator
- The air dam push-in retainers
- The air dam
- The right engine splash shield to radiator mount push-in retainer
- The left engine splash shield to radiator mount push-in retainer
- The lower radiator mount, brackets, and bolts. Support the radiator and condenser

6. Tilt the radiator and condenser forward in the vehicle. Remove the cooling fan assembly from the vehicle.

To install:

7. Tilt the radiator and condenser for-

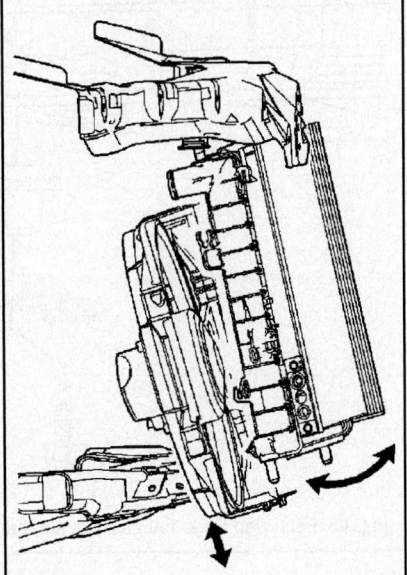

Fig. 60 Removing the engine fan assembly

ward in the vehicle. Install the cooling fan assembly into the vehicle.

8. Verify that the upper radiator mounts are installed in the vehicle.

9. Raise the radiator and condenser into position. Verify that the upper radiator

mount pins align with the upper radiator mounts.

10. Install or connect the following:

- The lower radiator mounts, brackets, and bolts. Tighten the bolts to 18 ft. lbs. (25 Nm)
- The right engine splash shield to radiator mount push-in retainer
- The left engine splash shield to radiator mount push-in retainer
- The air dam and the push-in retainers
- Align the cooling fan shroud retaining features to the radiator. Pull down on the cooling fan assembly to snap the shroud onto the radiator

11. Lower the vehicle.

12. Connect the cooling fan electrical connector.

13. Install the cooling fan wire to the fan shroud.

RADIATOR

REMOVAL & INSTALLATION

See Figures 62 through 66.

1. Before servicing the vehicle, refer to the Precautions Section.

✳✳ CAUTION

To avoid being burned, do not remove the radiator cap or surge tank cap while the engine is hot. The cooling system will release scalding fluid and steam under pressure if radiator cap or surge tank cap is removed while the engine and radiator are still hot.

2. Raise and support the vehicle.

3. Drain the cooling system.

4. Lower the vehicle.

5. Remove the air cleaner outlet resonator.

6. Remove the radiator inlet hose from the radiator using special tool, J 38185.

7. Remove the radiator outlet hose from the radiator using special tool, J 38185.

Fig. 59 Lower radiator mount, brackets, and bolts location

Fig. 61 Upper radiator mount location

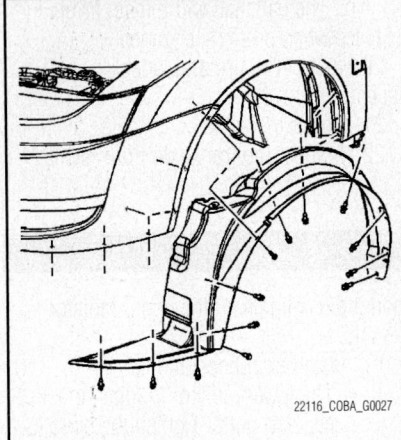

Fig. 62 Removing left front wheelhouse liner to access lower automatic transmission line

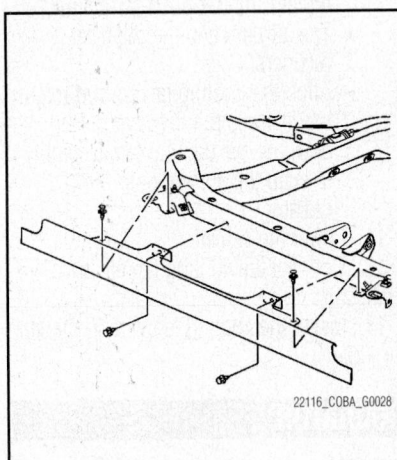

Fig. 63 Removing the air dam push-in retainer

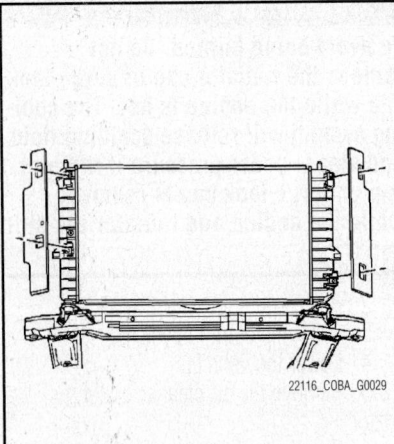

Fig. 64 Removing right and left radiator side baffles

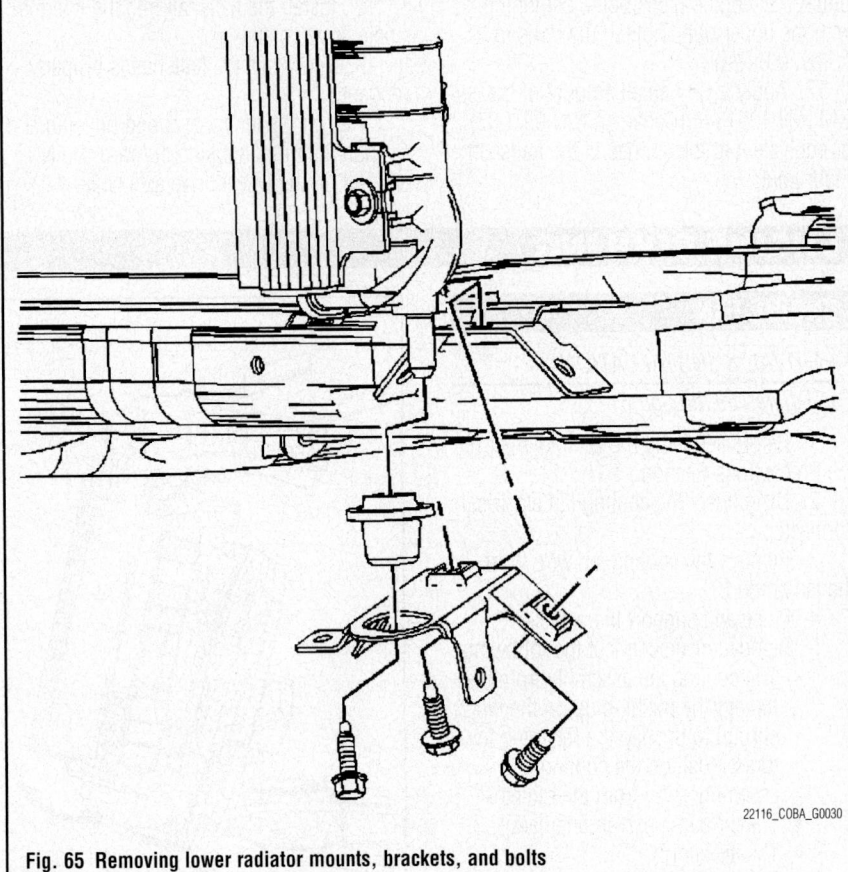

Fig. 65 Removing lower radiator mounts, brackets, and bolts

8. If equipped with an automatic transaxle, clean the upper transaxle oil cooler line connection point and remove the line from the radiator.

9. If equipped with an automatic transaxle:

   a. Remove the left front wheelhouse liner.

   b. Remove the left engine splash shield.

   c. Clean the lower transaxle oil cooler line connection point and remove the line from the radiator.

10. Remove the cooling fan assembly from the radiator by pushing up on the fan shroud to unsnap the retaining features. Position the cooling fan assembly away from the radiator and support the cooling fan assembly.

11. Remove the air dam push-in retainer.

12. Remove the air dam.

13. If equipped with air conditioning, remove the condenser bolts.

➡**You are not required to discharge the A/C system.**

14. Slide the condenser down to disengage the upper mounting tabs from the radiator. Position the condenser away

from the radiator and support the condenser.

15. Remove the right and left radiator side baffles.

16. Remove the right engine splash shield to radiator mount push-in retainer.

17. If equipped with a manual transaxle, remove the left engine splash shield to radiator mount push-in retainer.

18. Remove the lower radiator mounts, brackets, and bolts.

19. Tilt the condenser forward in the vehicle. Tilt the cooling fan assembly rearward in the vehicle.

20. Remove the radiator assembly from the vehicle.

21. Remove the upper radiator air baffle.

To install:

22. Verify that the upper radiator mounts are installed in the vehicle.

23. Install the upper radiator air baffle.

24. Tilt the condenser forward in the vehicle. Tilt the cooling fan assembly rearward in the vehicle.

25. Install the radiator assembly into the vehicle.

26. Verify that the upper radiator mount pins align with the upper radiator mounts.

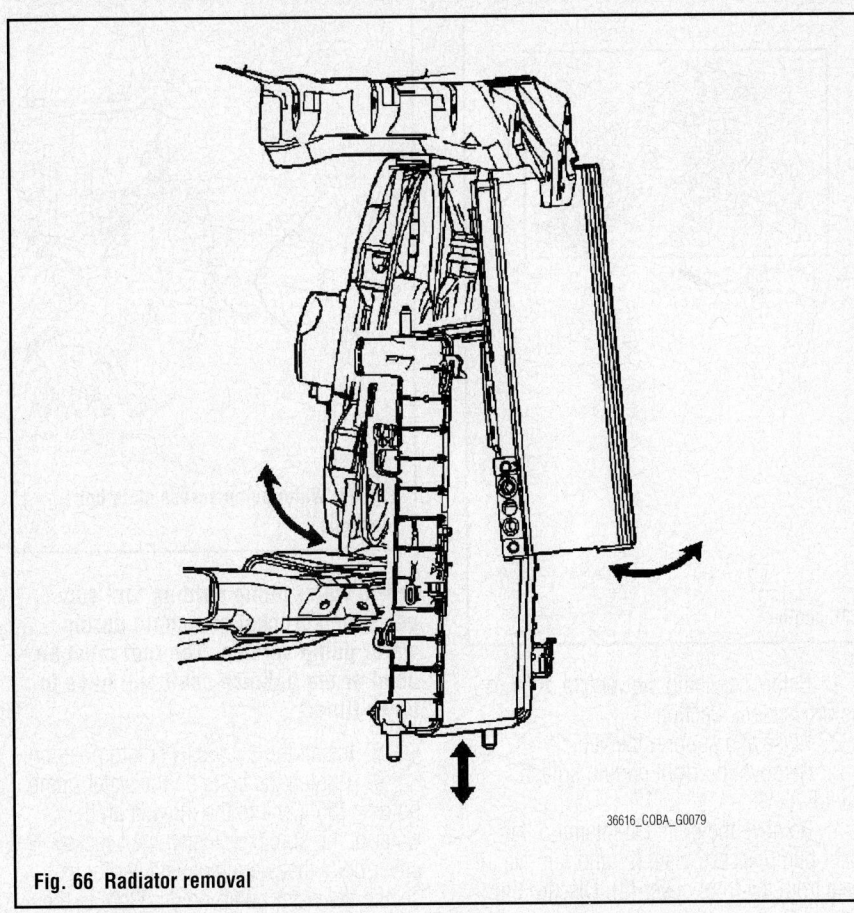

Fig. 66 Radiator removal

27. Install the lower radiator mounts, brackets, and bolts. Tighten the bolts to 18 ft. lbs. (25 Nm).

28. Install the right engine splash shield to radiator mount push-in retainer.

29. If equipped with a manual transaxle, install the left engine splash shield to radiator mount push-in retainer.

30. If equipped with air conditioning, install the right and left radiator side baffles.

31. Slide the condenser up to engage the upper mounting tabs into the radiator.

32. Install the condenser bolts. Tighten the bolts to 88 inch lbs. (10 Nm).

33. Install the charge air cooler, if equipped.

34. Install the air dam and push-in retainers.

35. Align the cooling fan shroud retaining features to the radiator. Pull down on the cooling fan assembly to snap the fan shroud onto the radiator.

36. If equipped with an automatic transaxle:

    a. Install the lower transaxle oil cooler line and seal to the radiator. Tighten the transaxle oil cooler line to 15 ft. lbs. (20 Nm).

    b. Install the left engine splash shield.

    c. Install the left front wheelhouse liner.

37. Lower the vehicle.

38. If equipped with an automatic transaxle, install the upper transaxle oil cooler line and seal to the radiator. Tighten the transaxle oil cooler line to 15 ft. lbs. (20 Nm).

39. Install the radiator outlet hose to the radiator.

40. Reposition the hose clamp to secure the hose using special tool, J 38185.

41. Install the radiator inlet hose to the radiator.

42. Reposition the hose clamp to secure the hose using special tool, J 38185.

43. Install the air cleaner outlet resonator.

44. Fill the cooling system.

45. If equipped with an automatic transaxle, add fluid to the transaxle as necessary.

THERMOSTAT

REMOVAL & INSTALLATION

See Figures 67 through 69.

1. Before servicing the vehicle, refer to the Precautions Section.

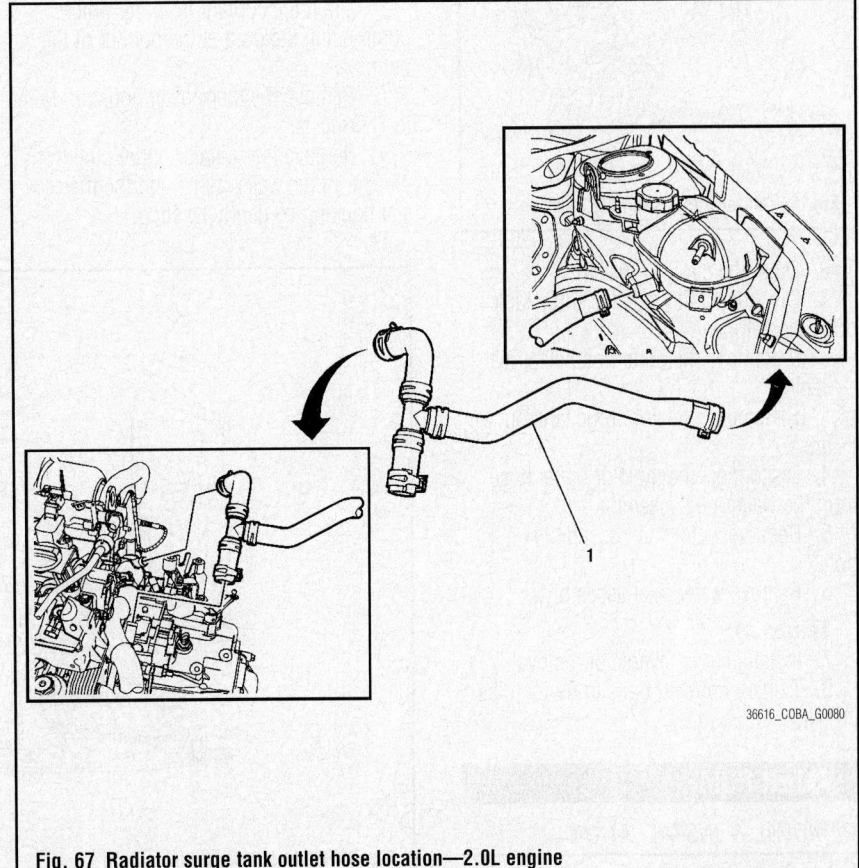

Fig. 67 Radiator surge tank outlet hose location—2.0L engine

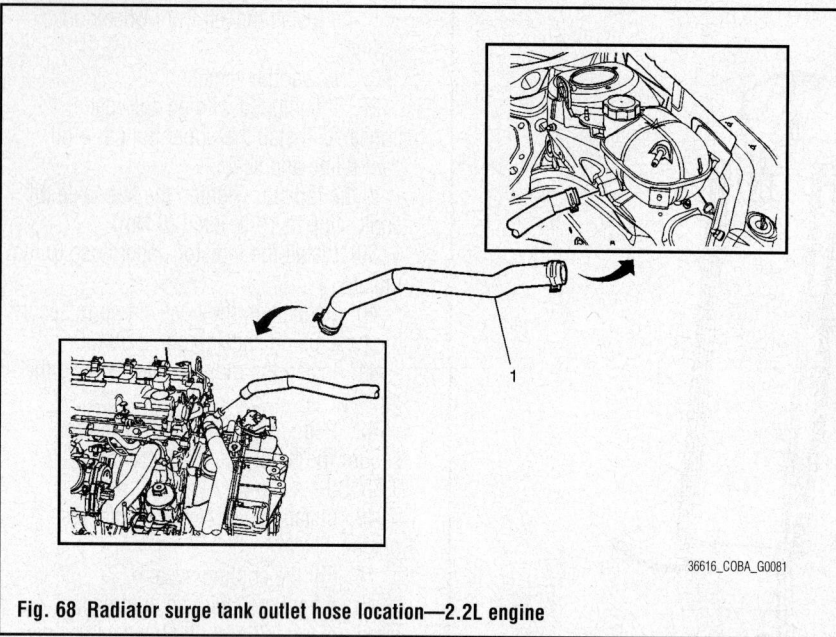

Fig. 68 Radiator surge tank outlet hose location—2.2L engine

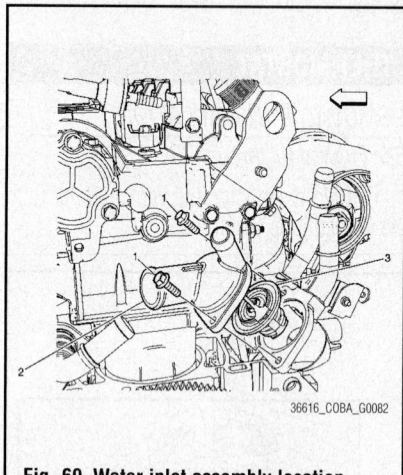

Fig. 69 Water inlet assembly location

2. Drain the cooling system.
3. Disconnect the radiator surge tank outlet hose/pipe.
  a. Remove the underhood electrical center.
  b. Remove radiator surge tank outlet hose.
4. Disconnect the radiator outlet hose from the water inlet assembly.
5. Remove water inlet assembly bolts.
6. Remove water inlet assembly.

To install:
7. Installation is reverse of removal
8. Tighten housing bolts to 89 inch lbs. (10 Nm).

WATER PUMP

REMOVAL & INSTALLATION

See Figures 70 through 75.

1. Before servicing the vehicle, refer to the Precautions Section.
2. Raise and support the vehicle.
3. Remove the right engine splash shield.
4. Remove the bolts (1) retaining the water pump access plate (2) and remove the plate from the front cover (3). Discard the seal.
5. Drain the coolant from the water pump using the plug at the bottom of the pump.
6. Remove the thermostat housing. Refer to Thermostat.
7. Remove the radiator outlet pipe from the rear of the water pump and the thermostat housing by gently twisting.

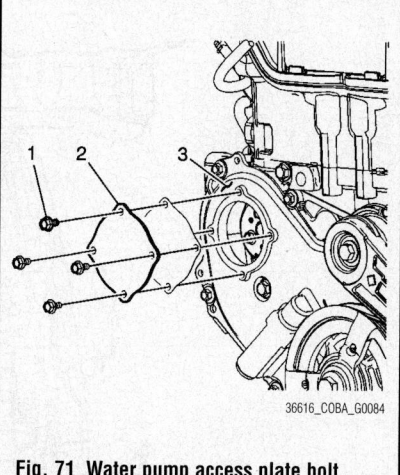

Fig. 71 Water pump access plate bolt locations

➡ **The water pump holding tool supports the sprocket and chain during water pump service. The tool must be used or the balance shaft will have to be re-timed.**

8. Install the J 43651 (1) into position.
9. Tighten the bolts on the water pump holding tool (2) into the threads on the water pump sprocket. Install the access cover bolts that were removed earlier to secure the water pump holding tool to the front cover assembly.
10. Remove the three inner water pump sprocket to water pump bolts.

➡ **Be sure to remove both front water pump bolts from the front of the engine block.**

11. Remove the two front water pump bolts.

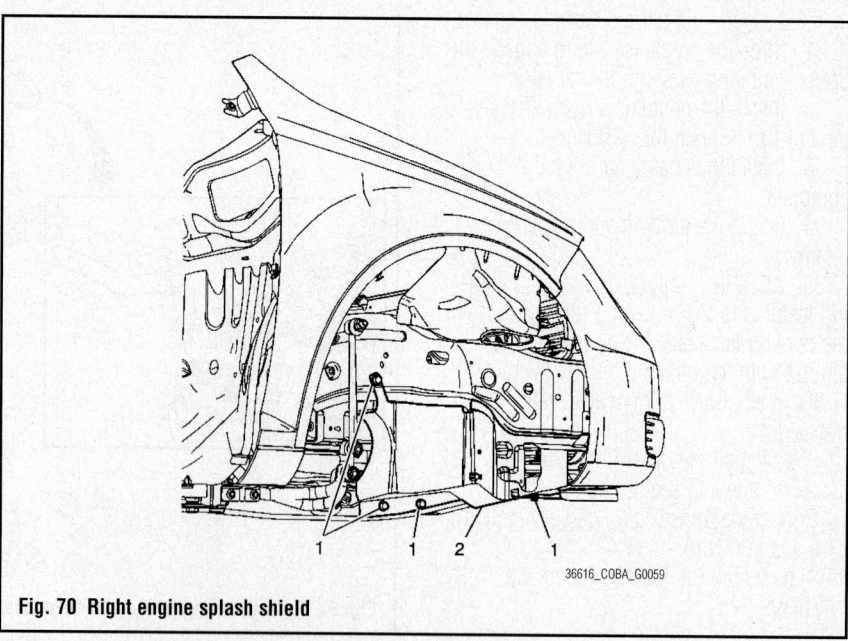

Fig. 70 Right engine splash shield

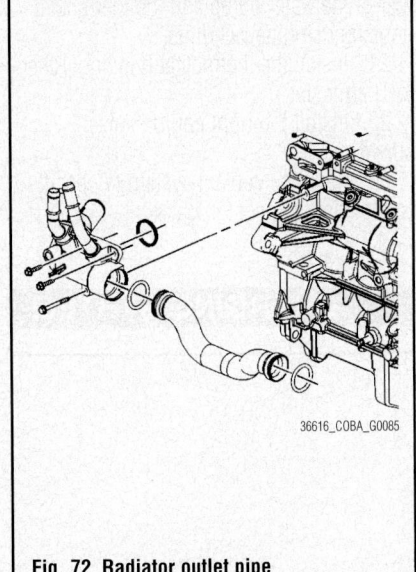

Fig. 72 Radiator outlet pipe

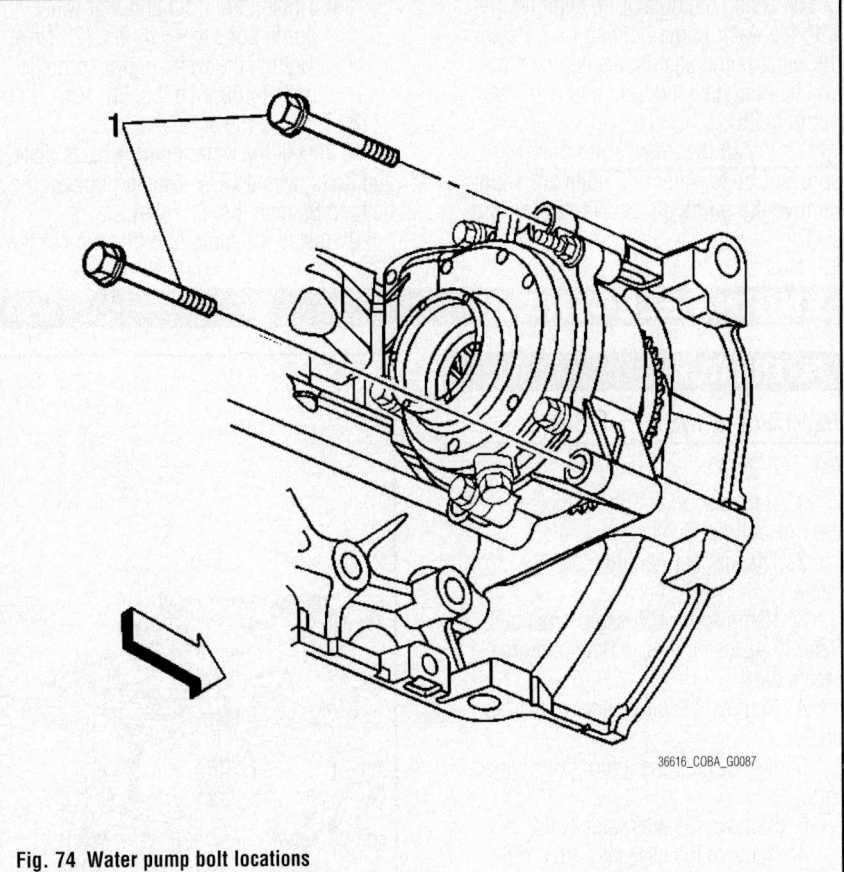

Fig. 74 Water pump bolt locations

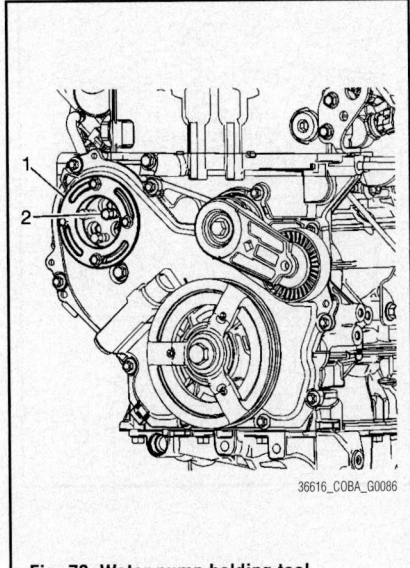

Fig. 73 Water pump holding tool

12. Remove the two rear water pump bolts.

13. Remove the water pump.

14. Remove and discard the water pump O-ring seal.

To install:

➡Prior to installing the water pump, read the entire procedure. This will help avoid balance shaft chain re-timing and ensure proper sealing.

15. Install a NEW water pump O-ring seal.

➡A guide pin can be created to aid in water pump alignment. Use a M6 m x 6 mm stud. Thread the pin into the water pump sprocket.

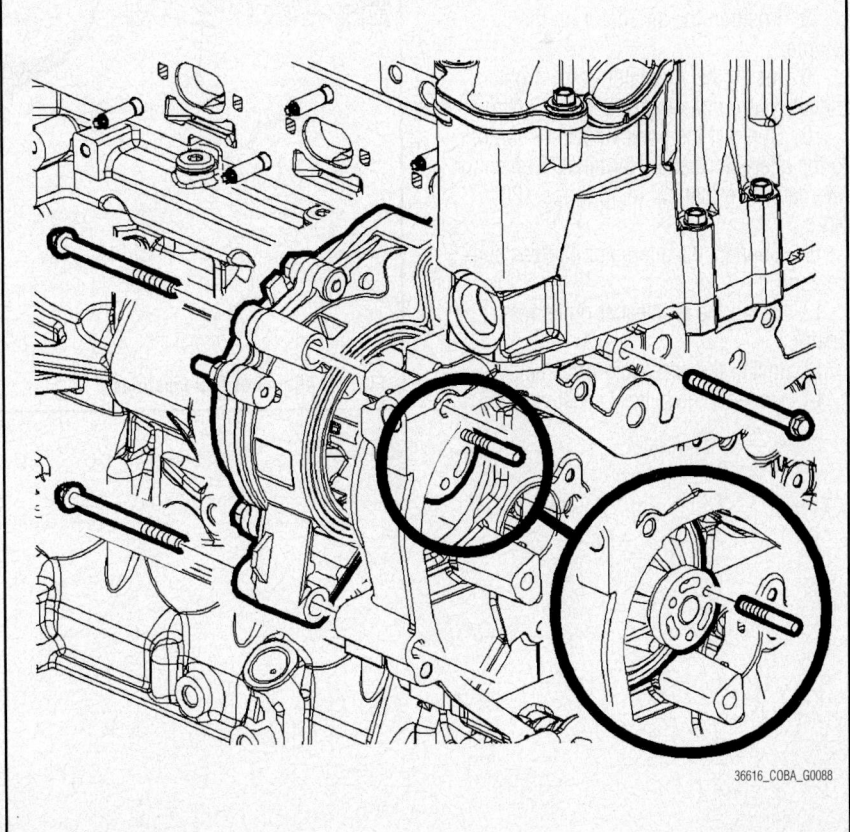

Fig. 75 Water pump bolt locations

16. Using the guide pin, align the pin with the water pump holding tool. Position the water pump against the engine block and hand tighten the front and rear water pump bolts.

17. Install the inner water pump sprocket bolts. After two bolts are snug, remove the guide pin and install the 3rd bolt.

• Tighten the front and rear water pump bolts to 18 ft. lbs. (25 Nm).
• Tighten the water pump sprocket bolts to 89 inch lbs. (10 Nm).

18. Remove the J 43651.

19. Install the water pump access plate and bolts, with a NEW seal and tighten the bolts to 89 inch lbs. (10 Nm).

20. Install the radiator outlet pipe to the rear of the water pump and the thermostat housing using new O rings.

21. Install the thermostat housing. Refer to Thermostat.

22. Install the right engine splash shield.

23. Refill the coolant system to specifications and inspect for leaks.

ENGINE ELECTRICAL   CHARGING SYSTEM

ALTERNATOR

REMOVAL & INSTALLATION

See Figure 76.

1. Before servicing the vehicle, refer to the Precautions Section.

2. Disconnect negative battery cable.

3. Remove the accessory drive belt. Refer to Accessory Drive Belt in Engine Mechanical

4. Remove the air cleaner outlet resonator.

5. Disconnect the alternator connectors.

6. Remove the alternator bolts.

7. Remove the alternator from the vehicle.

To install:

8. Position the alternator on the engine.

9. Install the alternator bolts. Tighten the alternator bolts to 16 ft. lbs. (22 Nm).

10. Connect the positive battery harness to the alternator battery terminal. Tighten the alternator terminal nut to 15 ft. lbs. (20 Nm).

11. Connect the alternator harness connectors.

12. Install the air cleaner outlet resonator.

13. Install the accessory drive belt.

14. Connect the battery negative cable.

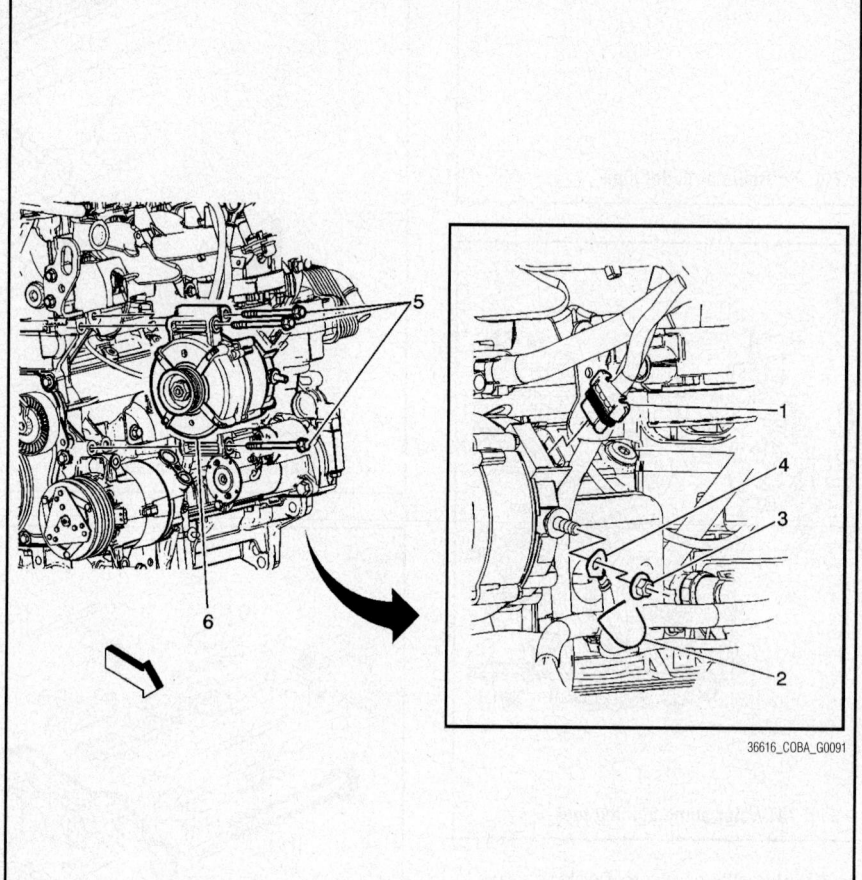

36616_COBA_G0091

Fig. 76 Alternator bolt locations

ENGINE ELECTRICAL

IGNITION SYSTEM

FIRING ORDERS

The 2.0L, 2.2L and 2.4L engines fire in this cylinder order:

- 1–3–4–2

IGNITION COIL

REMOVAL & INSTALLATION

2.0L Engine

See Figure 77.

1. Before servicing the vehicle, refer to the Precautions Section.
2. Check stored fault messages.
3. Switch off ignition.
4. Remove or disconnect the following:
   - The negative battery cable
   - The ignition coil connectors from the ignition coils
   - The retaining bolts from the ignition coils
   - The ignition coils from the engine

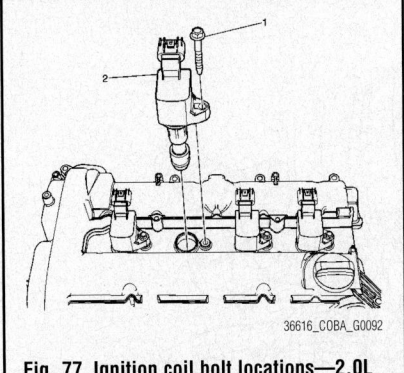

Fig. 77 Ignition coil bolt locations—2.0L engine

To install:

➡ **Make sure that the ignition coil seals are properly seated to the valve cover.**

5. Install or connect the following:
   - The ignition coil
   - The ignition coil retaining bolts, tighten to 89 inch lbs. (10 Nm)
   - the ignition coil connectors

2.2L & 2.4L Engines

See Figures 78 through 80.

1. Before servicing the vehicle, refer to the Precautions Section.
2. Check stored fault messages.
3. Switch off ignition.
4. Remove or disconnect the following:
   - The negative battery cable

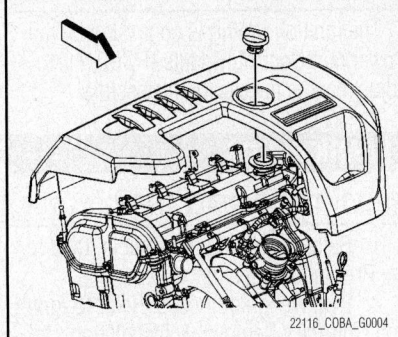

Fig. 78 Intake manifold cover removal— 2.2L and 2.4L engines

- The engine oil fill cap
- Grasp the intake manifold cover by the lower right inboard corner and pull up to disengage the cover from the stud
- Grasp the intake manifold cover by the upper left corner and pull up to disengage the cover from the stud
- Remove the intake manifold cover

5. Disconnect the ignition coil electrical connectors (1).
6. Remove the ignition coil bolts.
7. Remove the ignition coils.

To install:

8. Install or connect the following:
   - The ignition coils into position over the spark plugs
   - The ignition coil bolts and tighten to 89 inch lbs (10 Nm)
   - The ignition coil electrical connectors

9. Install the intake manifold cover:
   a. Place the intake manifold cover onto the engine over the studs.
   b. Push down on the intake manifold cover directly over the lower right stud in order to engage the cover to the stud.
   c. Push down on the intake manifold cover directly over the upper left stud in order to engage the cover to the stud.
   d. Install the engine oil fill cap.

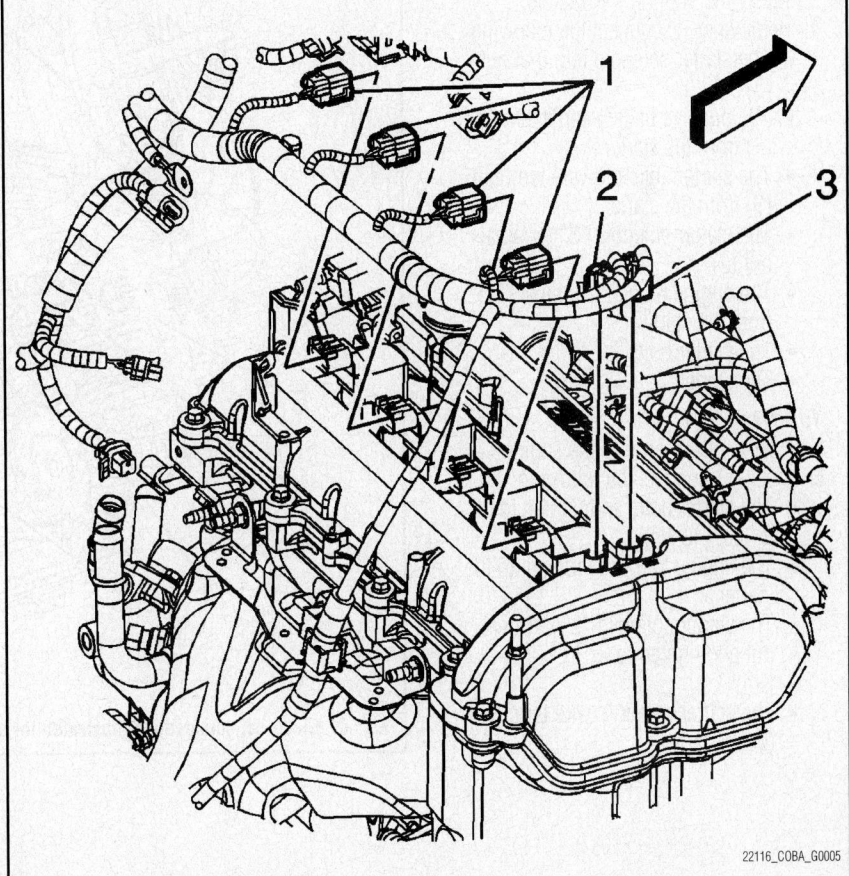

Fig. 79 Removing ignition coil electrical connectors (1)—2.2L and 2.4L engines

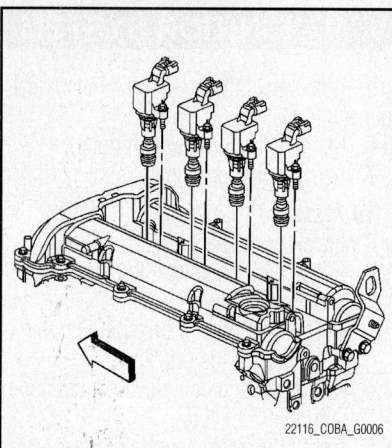

Fig. 80 Removing the ignition coils—2.2L and 2.4L engines

22116_COBA_G0006

IGNITION TIMING

ADJUSTMENT

The ignition timing is controlled by the Powertrain Control Module (PCM). No adjustment is necessary or possible.

SPARK PLUGS

REMOVAL & INSTALLATION

1. Before servicing the vehicle, refer to the Precautions Section.
2. Remove ignition coils. Refer to Ignition Coil Pack Removal & Installation.
3. Remove spark plug connector from the spark plug.
4. Clean loose debris away from area of spark plug to keep contaminants from entering engine when spark plug is removed.
5. Remove the spark plug using a spark plug socket and wrench.

To install:

6. Be sure the spark plugs are set to the proper gap:
   - 2.0L engine—0.035 inch (0.90mm)
   - 2.2L and 2.4L engines—0.042 (1.06mm)
7. Carefully install the spark plugs and tighten to 15 ft. lbs. (20 Nm).
8. Apply dielectric compound to the spark plug boots and make sure no corrosion is present.
9. Install the ignition coils. Refer to Ignition Coil Pack Removal & Installation.

ENGINE ELECTRICAL

STARTER

REMOVAL & INSTALLATION

See Figure 81.

1. Before servicing the vehicle, refer to the Precautions Section.
2. Disconnect the negative battery cable.
3. Raise and support the vehicle.
4. Remove or disconnect the following:
   - The starter solenoid terminal nut (5)
   - The positive battery cable terminal (4) from the starter
   - The starter solenoid wire terminal (3) from the starter
   - The starter solenoid "S" terminal nut (2)
   - The engine harness terminal (1) from the starter
   - The starter bolts
   - The starter

To install:

5. Position the starter to the engine.
6. Install or connect the following:
   - The starter bolts and tighten to 30 ft. lbs. (40 Nm).
   - The engine harness terminal to the starter
   - The starter solenoid "S" terminal nut and tighten to 27 inch lbs. (3 Nm)
   - The starter solenoid wire terminal to the starter

- The positive battery cable terminal to the starter

➡ **Ensure that the anti-rotational tab is correctly located into the indexing slot.**

STARTING SYSTEM

- The starter solenoid terminal nut and tighten to 13 ft. lbs. (17 Nm)
7. Lower the vehicle.
8. Connect the negative battery cable.

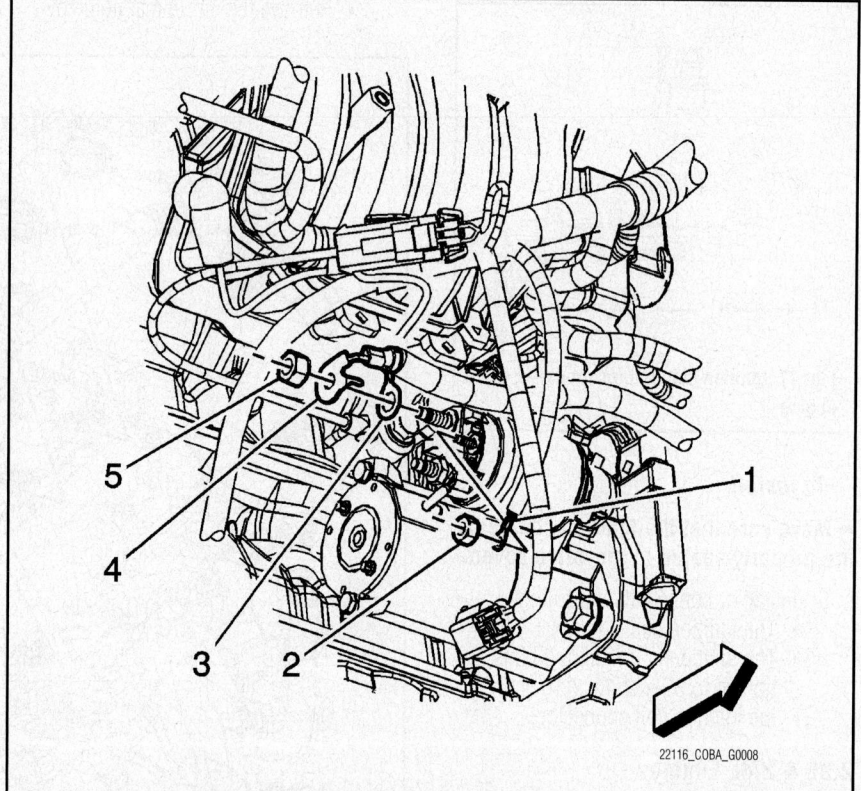

22116_COBA_G0008

Fig. 81 Electrical connections illustrated for starter removal

ENGINE MECHANICAL

ACCESSORY DRIVE BELTS

ACCESSORY BELT ROUTING

See Figure 82.

Fig. 82 Accessory drive belt routing

INSPECTION

Inspect the drive belt for signs of glazing or cracking. A glazed belt will be perfectly smooth from slippage, while a good belt will have a slight texture of fabric visible. Cracks will usually start at the inner edge of the belt and run outward. All worn or damaged drive belts should be replaced immediately.

ADJUSTMENT

The accessory drive belt adjustment is maintained by an automatic tensioner.

REMOVAL & INSTALLATION

See Figures 82 and 83.

1. Before servicing the vehicle, refer to the Precautions Section.
2. Remove the engine splash shield.
3. Install the special tool J 44811 to the accessory drive belt tensioner.
4. Rotate the tensioner counterclockwise in order to release the tension from the accessory drive belt.
5. Remove the accessory drive belt.
6. Slowly rotate special tool J 44811 and the tensioner clockwise in order to allow the tensioner to rest.
7. Remove special tool J 44811 from the drive belt tensioner.

To install:

8. Install and position the drive belt around all of the pulleys except for the drive belt tensioner.

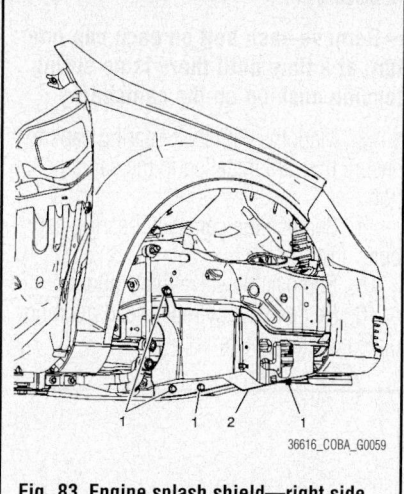

Fig. 83 Engine splash shield—right side

9. Install special tool J 44811 to the drive belt tensioner.
10. Using special tool J 44811, rotate the tensioner counterclockwise.
11. Position the drive belt under the tensioner pulley.
12. Using special tool J 44811 rotate the tensioner clockwise in order to seat the tensioner pulley onto the drive belt.
13. Install the engine splash shield.

BALANCE SHAFT

REMOVAL & INSTALLATION

See Figures 84 through 86.

1. Before servicing the vehicle, refer to the Precautions Section.
2. Remove the balance shaft bearing carrier bolts.

> ✵✵ **WARNING**
>
> **It is possible to install the intake side balance shaft into the exhaust side and vice versa. Please use care not to install the balance shafts into the wrong bores. Engine vibration will result. Do not remove the bolt holding the sprocket.**

3. Remove the balance shaft assemblies.

> ✵✵ **WARNING**
>
> **Proper centering of the tool is required on the balance shaft bushing. If the tool is not properly centered, then damage to the bearing bore and block will occur.**

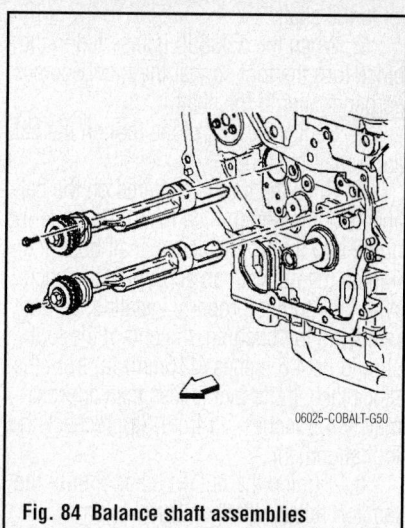

Fig. 84 Balance shaft assemblies

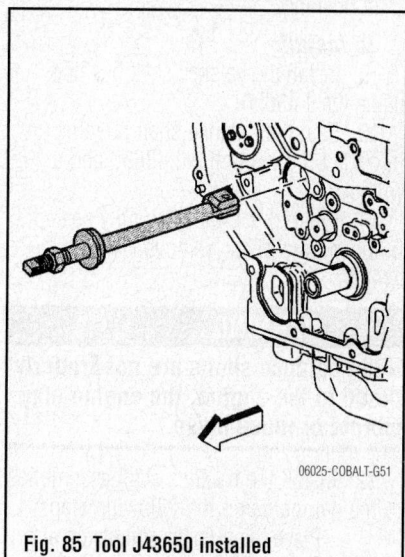

Fig. 85 Tool J43650 installed

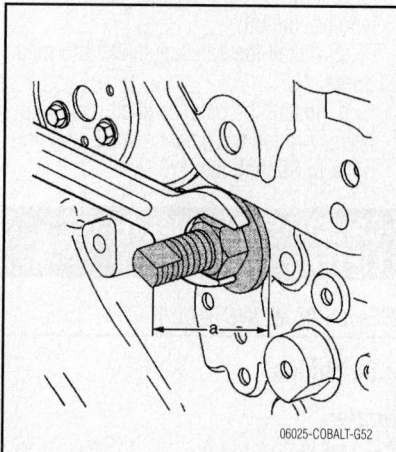

Fig. 86 When the J 43650 is inserted in the block turn the tool so that the foot becomes perpendicular to the shaft

4. Install tool J 43650 into the balance shaft hole. Insert the tool with the foot parallel to the shaft.

5. When the J 43650 is inserted in the block turn the tool so that the foot becomes perpendicular to the shaft.

6. Center the foot of the tool on the balance shaft bushing.

7. Once the tool is centered on the balance shaft bushing, then insert the centering guide into the front balance shaft bore and tighten the nut with an appropriate wrench. When the tool is properly installed, before removing the bushing, the end of the tool should be 4.6 inches (116mm) (a) from the block face. If the tool is less than approximately 4.5 inches (114mm) (a), recheck the tool alignment.

8. Tighten the nut on the tool until the tension releases. When the tension releases, remove the tool and the balance shaft bushing.

To install:

9. Install the balance shaft bushing using the J 43650.

10. Seat the balance shaft bushing into the bore using the J 43650 and a wrench.

11. When the J 43650 is fully seated in the engine block, remove it with a wrench.

✲✲ WARNING

If the balance shafts are not properly timed to the engine, the engine may vibrate or make noise.

12. Install the balance shaft assemblies to the engine using the following steps:

   a. Place the number one piston at Top Dead Center (TDC).

   b. Lubricate the balance shaft lobes with engine oil.

   c. Install the balance shafts into their bores.

   d. Install the balance shaft retaining bolts. Tighten the balance shaft retaining bolts to 89 inch lbs. (10 Nm).

CAMSHAFT AND VALVE LIFTERS

REMOVAL & INSTALLATION

2.0L Engine

Intake

See Figures 87 and 88.

1. Remove the camshaft position intake actuator. Refer to Camshaft Position Actuator.

2. Remove the high pressure fuel pump. Refer to High Pressure Fuel Pump Replacement.

➡**Remove each bolt on each cap one turn at a time until there is no spring tension pushing on the camshaft.**

3. Mark the camshaft bearing caps to ensure they are installed in the same position.

4. Remove the camshaft bearing cap bolts and caps.

5. Remove the valve lifter follower.

6. Remove the cylinder head opening plate bolts and plate.

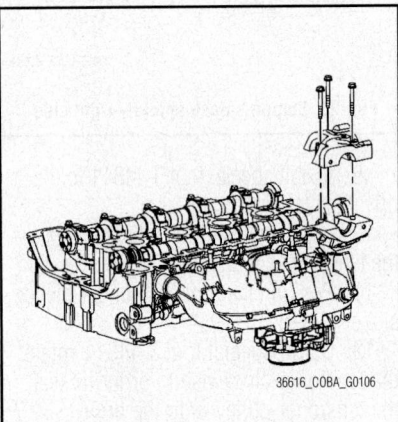

Fig. 87 Rear bearing cap bolts and cap

36616_COBA_G0106

7. Remove the rear bearing cap bolts and cap.

8. Remove the intake camshaft.

➡**Keep all of the roller followers and hydraulic valve lash adjusters in order so that they can be reinstalled in their respective locations.**

9. Remove the valve rocker arms.

10. Remove the hydraulic valve lash adjusters.

To install:

11. Install the hydraulic valve lash adjusters into their bores in the cylinder head.

12. Lubricate the hydraulic lash adjusters.

13. Lubricate the valve tips.

➡**Used valve rocker arms MUST be returned to their original position on the camshaft. If the camshaft is being replaced, the rocker arms MUST also be replaced.**

14. Position the valve rocker arms on the tip of the valve stem and on the valve lash adjuster. Lubricate the rocker arms.

15. Install the intake camshaft. Lubricate the camshaft.

16. Apply a 0.138 inches (3.5 mm) bead of sealer (1) to the cylinder head.

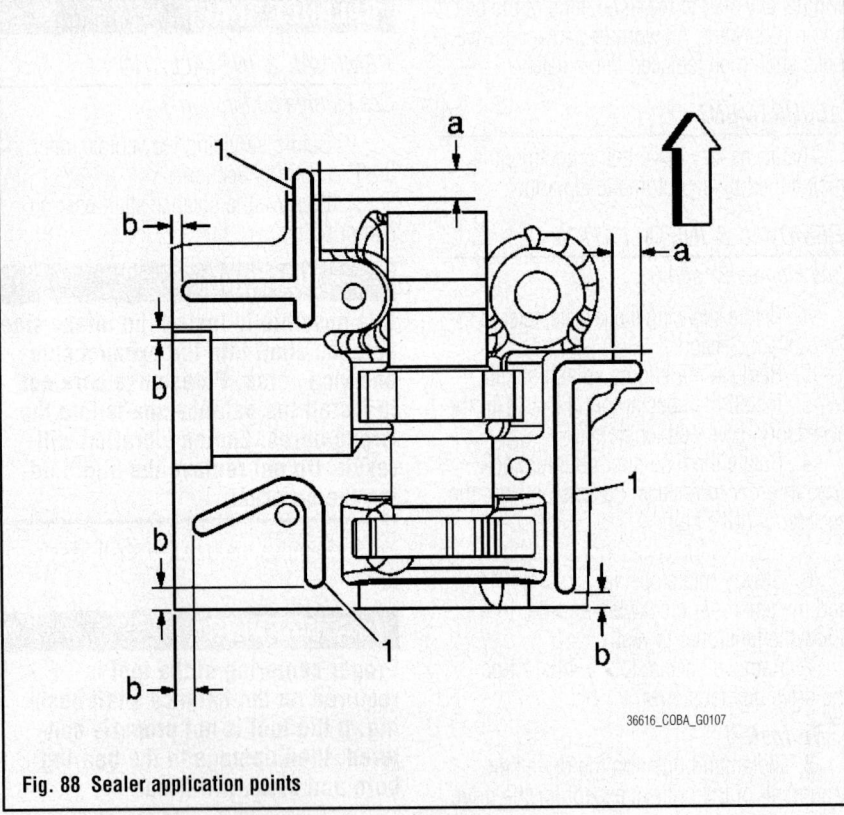

Fig. 88 Sealer application points

36616_COBA_G0107

17. In areas were the rear bearing cap ends on the perimeter rail, extend the bead of sealer 0.1575 inches (4.0 mm) beyond the edge of the cap (a).

18. Run the bead of sealer to within 4.0 mm (0.1575 in) of end points (b).

19. Install the rear bearing cap and bolts and tighten to 89 inch lbs. (10 Nm).

20. Install the cylinder head opening plate and bolts and tighten to 89 inch lbs. (10 Nm).

21. Install the valve lifter follower.

➡The caps should be installed on the cylinder head in sequence as shown on top of the bearing caps.

22. Position the camshaft bearing caps. Install the bearing cap bolts hand tight.

23. Tighten the bearing cap bolts in increments of 3 turns until they are seated and tighten to 89 inch lbs. (10 Nm).

24. Install the high pressure fuel pump. Refer to High Pressure Fuel Pump in Fuel Systems.

25. Install the camshaft position intake actuator. Refer to Camshaft Position Actuator.

Exhaust

1. Remove the camshaft position exhaust actuator. Refer to Camshaft Position Actuator.

➡Remove each bolt on each cap one turn at a time until there is no spring tension pushing on the camshaft.

2. Mark the camshaft bearing caps to ensure they are installed in the same position.

3. Remove the camshaft bearing cap bolts and cap.

4. Remove the exhaust camshaft.

➡Keep all of the rocker arms and hydraulic valve lash adjusters in order so that they can be reinstalled in their respective locations.

5. Remove the valve rocker arms.

6. Remove the hydraulic valve lash adjusters.

To install:

7. Install the hydraulic valve lash adjusters into their bores in the cylinder head.

8. Lubricate the hydraulic valve lash adjusters.

9. Lubricate the valve tips.

➡Used rocker arms MUST be returned to the original position on the camshaft. If the camshaft is being replaced, the rocker arms MUST also be replaced.

10. Position the rocker arms on the tip of the valve stem and on the valve lash adjuster. Lubricate the rocker arms.

11. Install the exhaust camshaft. Lubricate the camshaft.

➡The caps should be installed on the cylinder head in sequence as shown on top of the bearing caps.

12. Position the camshaft bearing caps. Install the bearing cap bolts hand tight.

13. Tighten the bearing cap bolts in increments of 3 turns until they are seated and tighten to 89 inch lbs. (10 Nm).

14. Install the camshaft position exhaust actuator. Refer to Camshaft Position Actuator.

2.2L & 2.4L Engines

Intake

1. Remove the intake camshaft position actuator. Refer to Camshaft Position Actuator.

➡Remove each bolt on each cap one turn at a time until there is no spring tension pushing on the camshaft.

2. Mark the bearing caps to ensure they are installed in the original position.

3. Remove the bearing cap bolts.

4. Remove the bearing caps.

5. Remove the intake camshaft.

➡Keep all of the roller followers and hydraulic adjusters in order so that they can be reinstalled in their respective locations.

6. Remove the camshaft roller followers.

7. Remove the hydraulic element lash adjusters.

To install:

8. Install the hydraulic element lash adjusters into their bores in the cylinder head.

9. Lubricate the hydraulic lash adjusters with GM P/N 12345501 (Canadian P/N 992704) or equivalent.

10. Lubricate the valve tips with GM P/N 12345501 (Canadian P/N 992704) or equivalent.

➡Used roller followers MUST be returned to their original position on the camshaft. If the camshaft is being replaced, the roller followers actuated by the camshaft must also be replaced.

11. Position the camshaft roller followers on the tip of the valve stem and on the lash adjuster. Lubricate the roller followers with GM P/N 12345501 (Canadian P/N 992704) or equivalent.

12. Install the intake camshaft. Lubricate

with GM P/N 12345501 (Canadian P/N 992704) or equivalent.

13. Install the camshaft bearing caps. Hand tighten the cap bolts.

14. Tighten the bearing cap bolts in increments of 3 turns until they are seated. Tighten the bolts to tighten to 89 inch lbs. (10 Nm).

15. Install the intake camshaft position actuator. Refer to Camshaft Position Actuator.

Exhaust

1. Remove the camshaft position exhaust actuator. Refer to Camshaft Position Actuator.

➡Remove each bolt on each cap one turn at a time until there is no spring tension pushing on the camshaft.

2. Mark the camshaft bearing caps to ensure they are installed in the same position.

3. Remove the camshaft bearing cap bolts and cap.

4. Remove the exhaust camshaft.

➡Keep all of the rocker arms and hydraulic valve lash adjusters in order so that they can be reinstalled in their respective locations.

5. Remove the valve rocker arms.

6. Remove the hydraulic valve lash adjusters.

To install:

7. Install the hydraulic valve lash adjusters into their bores in the cylinder head.

8. Lubricate the hydraulic valve lash adjusters.

9. Lubricate the valve tips.

➡Used rocker arms MUST be returned to the original position on the camshaft. If the camshaft is being replaced, the rocker arms MUST also be replaced.

10. Position the rocker arms on the tip of the valve stem and on the valve lash adjuster. Lubricate the rocker arms.

11. Install the exhaust camshaft. Lubricate the camshaft.

➡The caps should be installed on the cylinder head in sequence as shown on top of the bearing caps.

12. Position the camshaft bearing caps. Install the bearing cap bolts hand tight.

13. Tighten the bearing cap bolts in increments of 3 turns until they are seated and tighten to 89 inch lbs. (10 Nm).

14. Install the camshaft position exhaust actuator. Refer to Camshaft Position Actuator.

CAMSHAFT COVERS

REMOVAL & INSTALLATION

2.0L Engine

See Figures 89 and 90.

1. Remove the air cleaner.
2. Remove the air cleaner outlet duct.
3. Remove the charge air cooler inlet pipe.
4. Disconnect the engine wiring harness intake and exhaust electrical connectors from the camshaft position actuator solenoid valves.
5. Remove the engine wiring harness clips from the camshaft cover.
6. Disconnect the engine wiring harness electrical connector from the evaporative emission (EVAP) canister purge solenoid valve.
7. Remove the ignition coils. Refer to Ignition Coil.
8. Remove the engine wiring harness clip (1) from the turbocharger.
9. Disconnect the PCV hose.

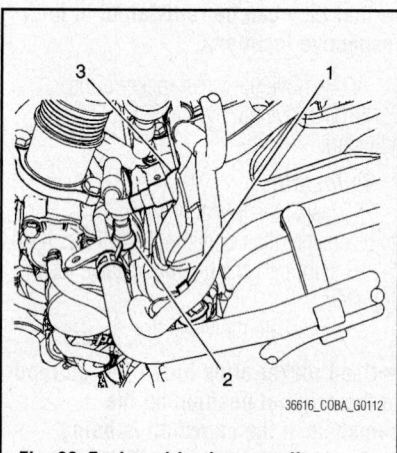

Fig. 89 Engine wiring harness clip

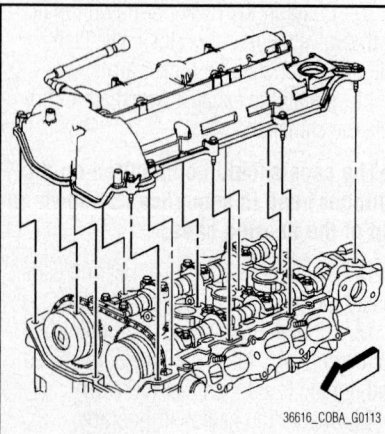

Fig. 90 Camshaft cover removal

10. Remove the engine wiring harness clips from the camshaft cover.
11. Disconnect the fuel line from the camshaft cover.

➥**The PCV hose should NOT be disconnected from the camshaft cover as damage to the hose connection will result.**

12. Remove the camshaft cover bolts.
13. Remove the camshaft cover.

To install:

14. Install the camshaft cover and bolts and tighten to 89 inch lbs. (10 Nm).
15. Connect the fuel line to the valve cover.
16. Install the engine wiring harness clips from the camshaft cover.
17. Connect the PCV hose.
18. Install the engine wiring harness clip to the turbocharger.
19. Install the ignition coils. Refer to Ignition Coil Replacement.
20. Connect the engine wiring harness electrical connector from the EVAP canister purge solenoid valve.
21. Install the engine harness clips to the camshaft cover.
22. Connect the engine wiring harness intake and exhaust electrical connectors to the camshaft position actuator solenoid valves.
23. Install the charge air cooler inlet pipe.
24. Install the air cleaner outlet duct.
25. Install the air cleaner. Refer to Air Cleaner.

2.2L & 2.4L Engines

See Figures 90 and 91.

1. Before servicing the vehicle, refer to the Precautions Section.
2. Remove the intake manifold cover.
3. Remove the air cleaner outlet duct.
4. Disconnect the intake (3) and exhaust (2) camshaft position actuator solenoid valve electrical connectors.
5. Remove the ignition coils. Refer to Ignition Coil Replacement.
6. Remove the engine harness clips from the cover.
7. Remove the fuel feed line retainers from the engine brackets.
8. Remove the camshaft cover bolts.
9. Remove the camshaft cover.

To install:

10. Install or connect the following:
   • The camshaft cover and bolts. Tighten the bolts to 89 inch lbs. (10 Nm)

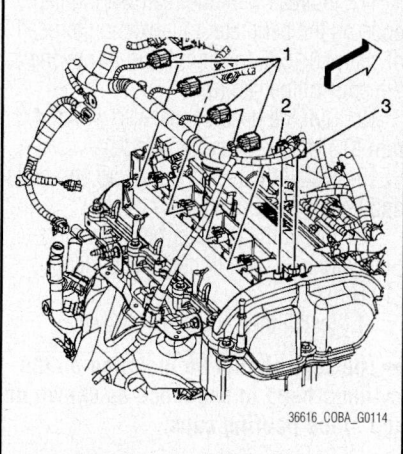

Fig. 91 Camshaft position actuator solenoid valve electrical connectors

11. Install the ignition coils. Refer to Ignition Coil Replacement.
12. Install the engine harness clips to the cover.
13. Install the feed line retainers to the engine brackets.
14. Connect the intake and exhaust camshaft position actuator solenoid valve electrical connectors.
15. Install the air cleaner outlet duct.
16. Install the intake manifold cover.

CATALYTIC CONVERTER

REMOVAL & INSTALLATION

2.0L Engine

1. Raise and support the vehicle.
2. Remove the Heated Oxygen (HO2S) sensor from the Catalytic Converter.
3. Disconnect any electrical connectors.
4. Remove turbocharger exhaust pipe nuts.
5. Remove catalytic converter nuts.
6. Remove catalytic converter.

To install:

7. Installation is reverse of removal.
8. Tighten turbocharger exhaust pipe nuts to 37 ft. lbs. (50 Nm).
9. Tighten catalytic converter nuts to 34 ft. lbs. (46 Nm).

2.2L & 2.4L Engines

1. Raise and support the vehicle.
2. Remove the wheel drive shaft heat shield.
3. Remove the Heated Oxygen (HO2S) sensor from the Catalytic Converter.
4. Disconnect any electrical connectors.

5. Remove catalytic converter to resonator nuts.

6. Remove catalytic converter to exhaust manifold nuts.

7. Remove catalytic converter.

8. Discard the exhaust gaskets.

9. Clean the flange mating surfaces of any remaining gasket material.

To install:

10. Installation is reverse of removal.

11. Install a NEW gasket onto the resonator pipe studs.

12. Install the catalytic converter to the resonator pipe nuts and tighten to 22 ft. lbs. (30 Nm).

13. Install the wheel drive shaft heat shield.

CRANKSHAFT DAMPER

REMOVAL & INSTALLATION

See Figure 92.

1. Before servicing the vehicle, refer to the Precautions Section.

2. Remove the accessory drive belt. Refer to Accessory Drive Belt Removal & Installation.

3. Use tool J 38122-A, or equivalent, to prevent the crankshaft from rotating while loosening the crankshaft damper bolt.

4. Remove the crankshaft damper bolt. Discard the bolt.

5. Remove the crankshaft damper.

To install:

6. Install the crankshaft damper.

7. Install a NEW crankshaft damper bolt.

8. Use J 38122-A to prevent the crankshaft from rotating while tightening the crankshaft damper bolt. Tighten the bolt to 74 ft. lbs. (100 Nm) plus 75°.

9. Install the accessory drive belt. Refer to Accessory Drive Belts Removal & Installation.

CRANKSHAFT FRONT SEAL

REMOVAL & INSTALLATION

See Figures 93 and 94.

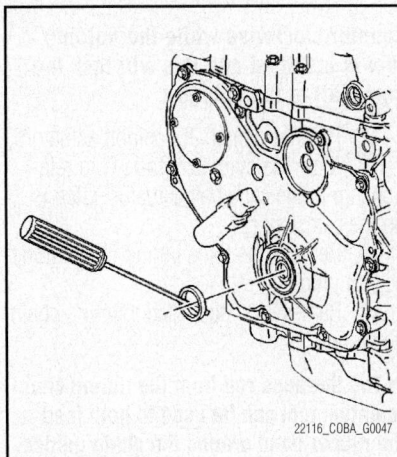

22116_COBA_G0047

Fig. 93 Using a flat-bladed tool to remove the front seal

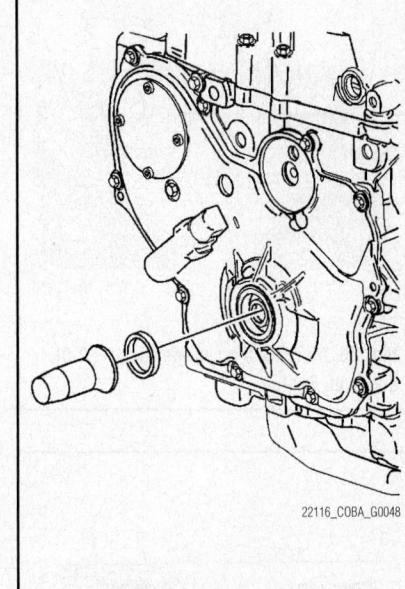

22116_COBA_G0048

Fig. 94 Using the J 35268-A to install the crankshaft front oil seal

1. Before servicing the vehicle, refer to the Precautions Section.

2. Remove the crankshaft damper. Refer to Crankshaft Damper.

3. Use a flat-bladed tool to remove the seal from the front cover.

To install:

4. Use the J 35268-A to install the crankshaft front oil seal to the engine front cover.

5. Install the crankshaft damper. Refer to Crankshaft Damper.

CYLINDER HEAD

REMOVAL & INSTALLATION

See Figures 95 through 101.

1. Drain the cooling system.

2. Remove the exhaust manifold. Refer to Exhaust Manifold.

3. Remove the intake manifold. Refer to Intake Manifold.

4. Reposition the radiator surge tank air bleed hose clamp.

5. Remove the radiator surge tank air bleed hose from the cylinder head.

6. Reposition the radiator inlet hose clamp using the J 38185.

7. Remove the radiator inlet hose from the cylinder head.

8. Disconnect all electrical connectors as necessary.

9. Remove the spark plugs. Refer to Spark Plugs

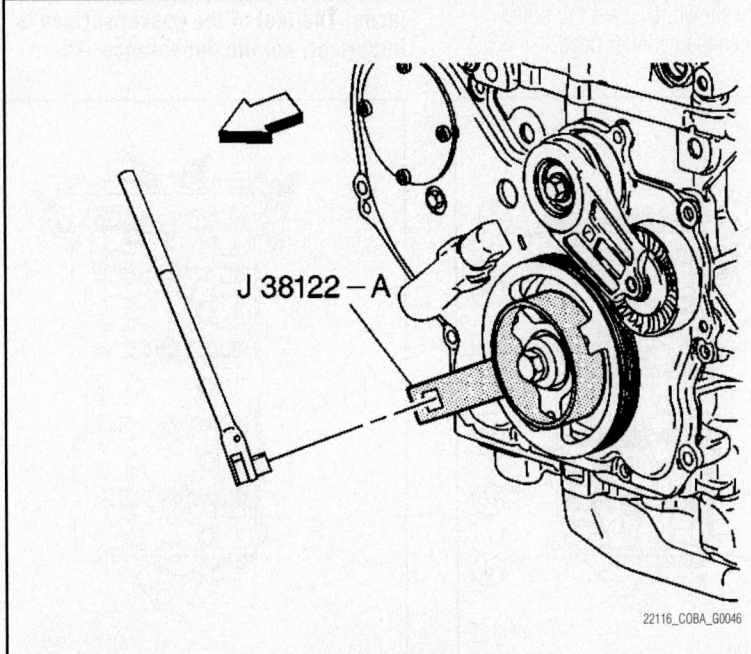

J 38122-A

22116_COBA_G0046

Fig. 92 Crankshaft damper holding tool installed

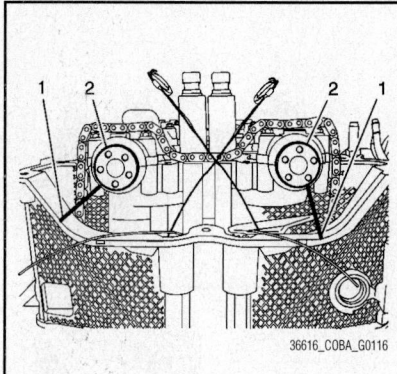

Fig. 95 Marking the cylinder head—2.0L and 2.4L Engine

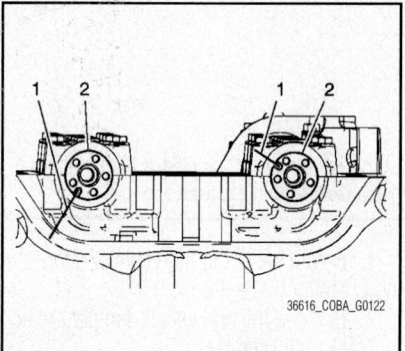

Fig. 96 Marking the cylinder head—2.2L Engine

10. Remove the camshaft cover.

➡**If the intake camshaft actuator is moving independently of the camshaft, this means the camshaft is not locked to the actuator. Rotate the camshaft**

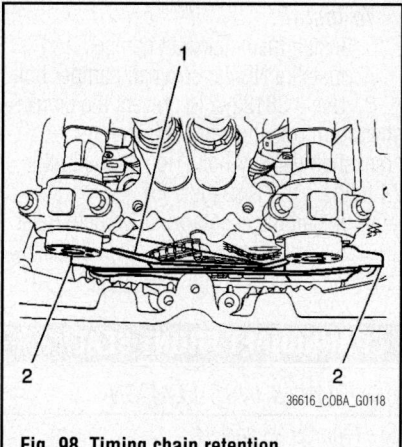

Fig. 98 Timing chain retention

counter-clockwise while the holding tool is installed and this will lock the camshaft to the actuator.

11. Remove camshaft position actuators.

12. Mark the cylinder head (1) in relationship to the camshaft actuator notch is on the camshaft (2).

13. Remove the fixed timing chain guide access plug.

14. Remove the upper fixed timing chain guide bolt.

➡**The threaded rod from the timing chain retention tool can be used to help feed the rubber band around the chain guides.**

15. Install a rubber band (1) around the top of the upper timing chain guides (2) in order to pull the guides together.

16. Remove the cylinder head bolts in the sequence shown. Discard the bolts.

17. Remove the cylinder head.

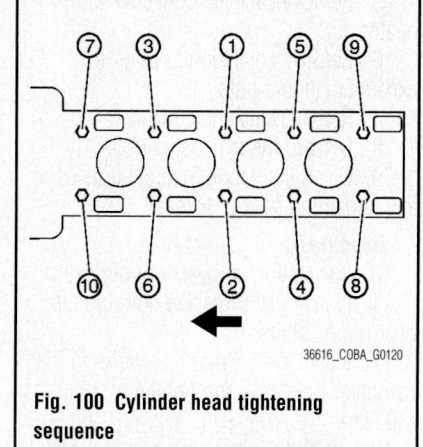

Fig. 100 Cylinder head tightening sequence

18. Remove the cylinder head gasket.

19. Clean all of the gasket surfaces.

20. Use the following steps when cleaning the cylinder head and cylinder block surfaces:

a. Use a razor blade gasket scraper to clean the cylinder head and cylinder block gasket surfaces. Do not scratch or gouge either surface.

➡**DO NOT use any other method or technique to clean these gasket surfaces.**

b. Use a NEW razor blade on the cylinder head and a NEW blade on the cylinder block.

➡**Be careful not to gouge or scratch the gasket surfaces. DO NOT gouge or scrape the combustion chamber surfaces. The feel of the gasket surface is important, not the appearance. There**

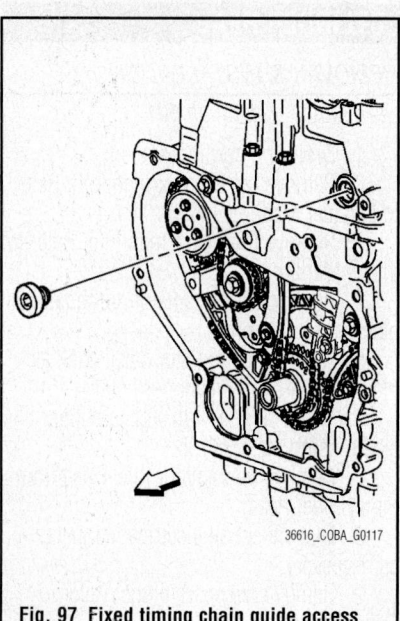

Fig. 97 Fixed timing chain guide access plug

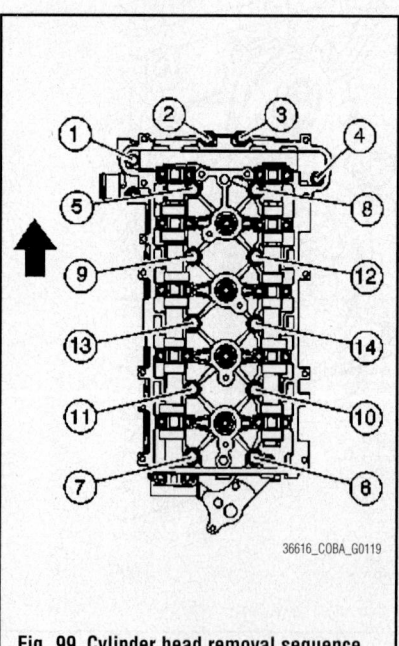

Fig. 99 Cylinder head removal sequence

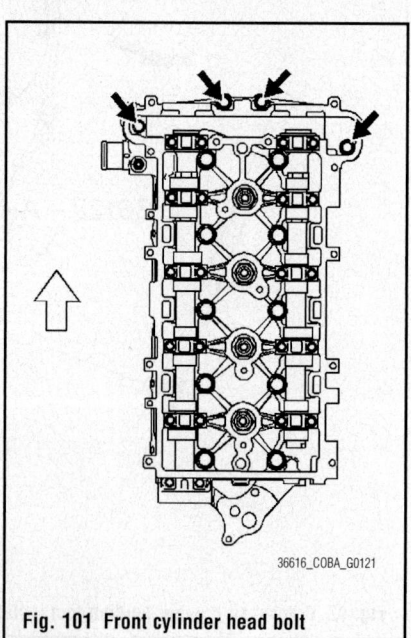

Fig. 101 Front cylinder head bolt locations

will be indentations from the gasket left in the cylinder head after all of the gasket material is removed. These small indentations will be filled in by the NEW gasket.

    c. Hold the razor blade as parallel to the gasket surface as possible.

    d. Clean the old sealer/lube and any dirt from around the bolt holes.

➡**DO NOT use a tap to clean the cylinder head bolt holes.**

    e. Clean the bolts holes with a nylon bristle brush.

    f. When cleaning the cylinder head bolt holes use suitable commercial spray liquid solvent and compressed air from an extended-tip blow gun in order to reach the bottom of the holes.

    g. If replacing the cylinder head, transfer all parts as necessary.

To install:

➡**DO NOT use any sealing material.**

21. Install the cylinder head gasket.
22. Install the cylinder head.
23. Install NEW cylinder head bolts.
24. Install and tighten the cylinder head bolts in the sequence shown.

    a. Tighten the bolts to 22 ft. lbs. (30 Nm) plus an additional 155 degrees using the J 45059 .

25. Install the NEW front cylinder head bolts and tighten to 26 ft. lbs. (35 Nm).
26. Ensure the cylinder head and the camshaft are correctly aligned. Use match-marks.
27. Remove the rubber band from around the top of the upper timing chain guides.
28. Install the fixed guide bolt into the cylinder head and tighten to 106 inch lbs. (12 Nm).
29. Apply sealant compound to thread and install the timing chain guide bolt access hole plug.
30. Install the fixed timing chain guide access plug and tighten to 59 ft. lbs. (90 Nm).

➡**Ensure that the alignment mark made previously on the intake camshaft actuator is still aligned properly with the mark on the timing chain. If the mark made previously on the intake camshaft actuator is not aligned properly, refer to Camshaft Timing Chain and Sprockets.**

31. Install camshaft position actuators, Refer to Camshaft Position Actuator.
32. Install the camshaft cover. Refer to Camshaft Cover.
33. Install the spark plugs. Refer to Spark Plug.
34. Connect all electrical connectors as necessary.
35. Install the radiator inlet hose to the cylinder head.
36. Position the radiator inlet hose clamp using the J 38185 .
37. Install the radiator surge tank air bleed hose to the cylinder head.
38. Position the radiator surge tank air bleed hose clamp.
39. Install the exhaust manifold. Refer to Exhaust Manifold.
40. Install the intake manifold. Refer to Intake Manifold.
41. Fill the cooling system.

ENGINE ASSEMBLY

REMOVAL & INSTALLATION

2.0L Engine

See Figures 102 through 107.

1. Disconnect the negative battery cable.
2. Remove the air cleaner assembly. Refer to Air Cleaner.
3. Remove the charge air cooler inlet and outlet pipes.
4. Relieve the fuel system pressure. Refer to Fuel Pressure Relief.
5. Disconnect the evaporative emission (EVAP) canister purge solenoid tube from the valve.
6. Disconnect the fuel feed pipe from the fuel line.
7. Remove the turbocharger heat shield bolts and shield.
8. Secure the cooling module to the upper body structure.
9. Remove the engine drive belt. Refer to Accessory Drive Belt.
10. Remove the charge air cooler pipe to turbocharger bolts.
11. Remove the charge air cooler pipe and gasket from the turbocharger.
12. Cap or plug the turbocharger opening.
13. Remove the radiator inlet hose. Refer to Radiator.
14. Remove the radiator outlet hose. Refer to Radiator.
15. Lower the vehicle.
16. Reposition the surge tank outlet hose clamp at the surge tank.

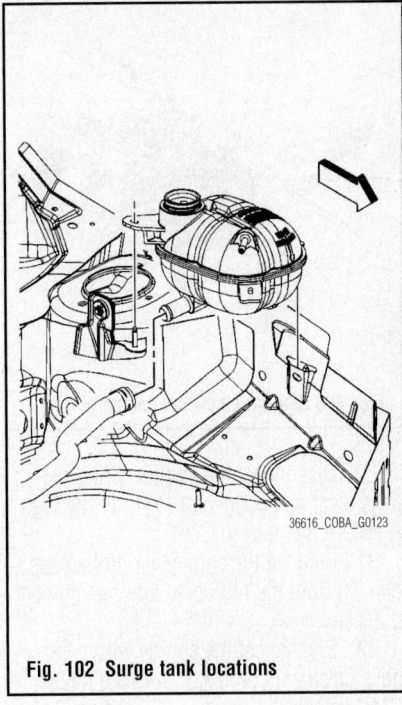

Fig. 102 Surge tank locations

36616_COBA_G0123

17. Remove the surge tank outlet hose from the surge tank.
18. Reposition the heater inlet and outlet hose clamps at the thermostat housing.
19. Remove the heater inlet and outlet hoses from the thermostat housing.
20. Disconnect the engine wiring harness electrical connector from the Crankshaft Position (CKP) sensor.
21. Disconnect the engine wiring harness electrical connector (2) from the oil pressure sensor.
22. Disconnect the engine wiring harness electrical connector from the generator. Refer to Alternator in Engine Electrical.
23. Reposition the positive battery cable terminal boot.
24. Remove the generator terminal nut.
25. Remove the positive battery cable terminal from the generator.
26. Disconnect the engine wiring harness electrical connector from the A/C compressor.
27. Disconnect the engine wiring harness electrical connector from the fuel injector jumper electrical connector.
28. Disconnect the engine wiring harness electrical connector from the knock sensor. Refer to Knock Sensor in Engine Performance & Emission Controls.
29. Disconnect the engine wiring harness electrical connector (2) from the intake camshaft position (CMP) sensor.

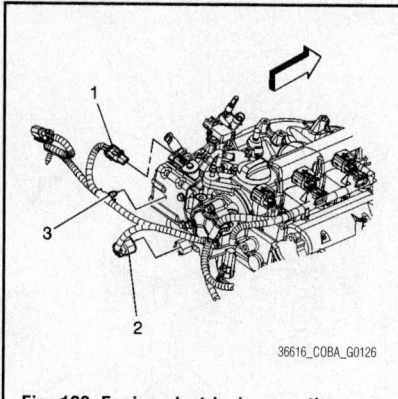

Fig. 103 Engine electrical connections

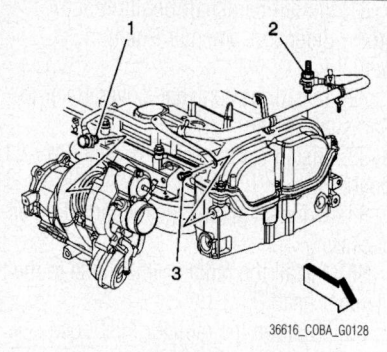

Fig. 105 Turbocharger coolant connections

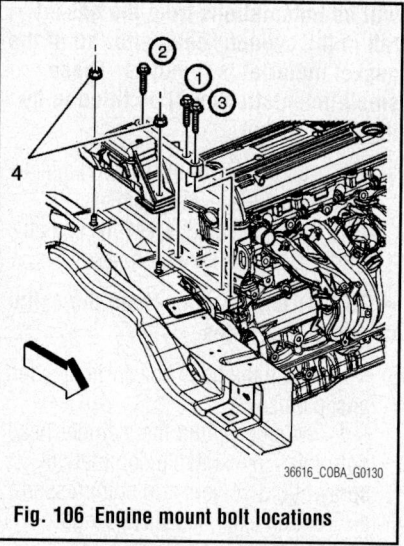

Fig. 106 Engine mount bolt locations

30. Disconnect the engine wiring harness electrical connector (1) from the high pressure fuel pump.

31. Remove the engine wiring harness clip (3) from the high pressure fuel pump bracket.

32. Disconnect the engine wiring harness electrical connector from the intake CMP actuator.

33. Disconnect the engine wiring harness electrical connector from the exhaust CMP actuator.

34. Disconnect the ignition coil electrical connectors from the ignition coils.

35. Disconnect the engine harness clips from the camshaft cover.

36. Disconnect the engine harness clip from the camshaft cover.

37. Disconnect the engine wiring harness electrical connector from the boost sensor.

38. Remove the turbocharger coolant feed pipe bolt at the turbocharger.

39. Remove the turbocharger coolant feed pipe fitting from the cylinder head.

40. Remove the turbocharger coolant feed pipe bracket bolt from the cylinder head.

41. Remove the turbocharger coolant feed pipe bracket from the vehicle.

42. Remove the A/C compressor line bolt and reposition the line off to the side.

43. Remove the engine harness clip from the camshaft cover.

44. Raise and suitably support the vehicle.

45. Disconnect the engine wiring harness electrical connector from the heated oxygen sensor (HO2S).

46. Disconnect the engine wiring harness electrical connector from the exhaust CMP sensor.

47. Remove the engine harness ground terminal bolt and reposition the engine harness ground terminal.

48. Disconnect the engine wiring harness electrical connector from the engine coolant temperature (ECT) sensor.

49. Disconnect the ECT sensor electrical connector. Refer to Engine Coolant Temperature Sensor in Engine Performance & Emission Controls.

50. Remove the CPA retainer.

51. Disconnect the engine harness electrical connector from the HO2S.

52. Disconnect the engine harness electrical connector from the VSS. Refer to Vehicle Speed sensor in Engine Performance & Emission Controls.

53. Remove the engine harness clip from the transaxle.

54. Remove the CPA retainer.

55. Remove the engine harness electrical connector clip from the transaxle rear mount bracket.

56. Disconnect the engine harness electrical connector from the HO2S.

57. Disconnect the engine harness electrical connector from the back up lamp switch.

58. Remove the engine harness clip from the transaxle.

59. Gather all engine harness branches

are reposition the harness off to the side, out of the way.

60. Disconnect the range selector and shift lever cables from the transaxle levers.

61. Remove the range selector and shift lever cables from the transaxle bracket.

62. Remove the catalytic converter. Refer to Catalytic Converter.

63. Lower the vehicle.

64. Insert blocks of wood between the powertrain and the frame, in order to support the powertrain.

65. Remove the engine mount.

66. Remove the transaxle mount to transaxle bolts.

67. Raise the vehicle.

68. Remove frame assembly with engine attached. Refer to Frame.

69. Attach the engine lift hoist to the engine lift hooks.

70. Remove the starter. Refer to Starter in Engine Electrical.

71. Remove the transaxle brace bolts and brace.

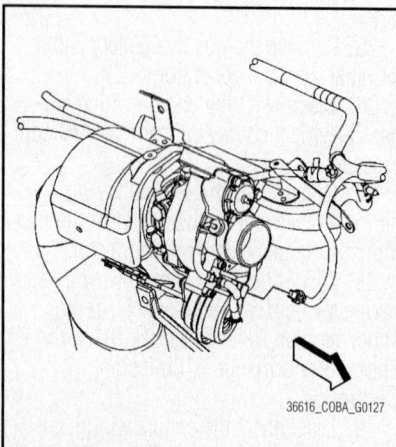

Fig. 104 Boost sensor connections

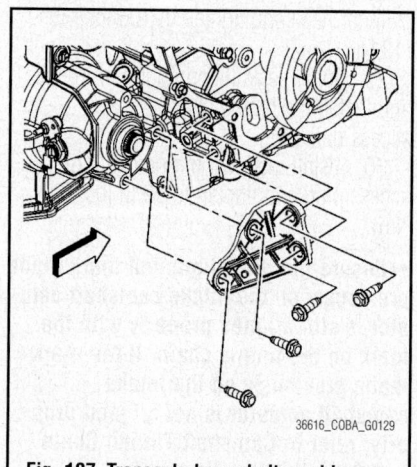

Fig. 107 Transaxle brace bolts and brace

72. Remove the transaxle to engine bolts/stud.

73. Remove the clutch pressure plate and disc. Refer to Clutch in Transmission.

74. Remove the following components:
- The engine mount bracket
- The engine block heater
- The generator

75. Using a engine hoist, install the engine to a engine stand.

To install:

76. Using a engine hoist, remove the engine from the engine stand.

77. Install the following components:
- The engine mount bracket
- The engine block heater
- The generator

78. Install the clutch pressure plate and disc. Refer to Clutch in Transmission.

79. Install the engine to the transaxle.

80. Install the transaxle to engine bolts and studs and tighten to 55 ft. lbs. (75 Nm).

81. Install the transaxle brace and bolts and tighten bolts to 37 ft. lbs. (50 Nm).

82. Install the starter. Refer to Starter in Engine Electrical.

83. Remove the engine lift hoist from the engine lift hooks.

84. Install frame assembly with engine mounted. Refer to Frame.

85. Lower the vehicle.

86. Install the transaxle mount to transaxle bolts and tighten the bolts to 33 ft. lbs. (45 Nm).

87. Install the engine mount.
    a. Tighten the engine mount to mid-rail nuts to 74 ft. lbs. (100 Nm)
    b. Tighten the engine mount to intermediate bracket bolts to 48 ft. lbs. (65 Nm).

88. Remove the blocks of wood from between the powertrain and the frame.

89. Install the catalytic converter. Refer to Catalytic Converter.

90. Lower the vehicle.

➡**Ensure that the black cable is installed in the top notch of the transaxle bracket and the white cable in installed in the bottom notch of the transaxle bracket.**

91. Install the range selector and shift lever cables to the transaxle bracket.

92. Connect the range selector and shift lever cables to the transaxle levers.

93. Gather all engine harness branches and position the harness over the engine.

94. Install the engine harness clip to the transaxle.

95. Connect the engine harness electrical connector to the backup lamp switch.

96. Connect the engine harness electrical connector to the HO2S.

97. Install the engine harness electrical connector clip to the transaxle rear mount bracket.

98. Install the engine harness clip to the transaxle.

99. Install the CPA retainer.

100. Connect the engine harness electrical connector to the VSS.

101. Connect the engine harness electrical connector to the HO2S.

102. Install the CPA retainer.

103. Connect the ECT sensor electrical connector.

104. Connect the engine wiring harness electrical connector to the exhaust CMP sensor.

105. Connect the engine wiring harness electrical connector to the ECT sensor.

106. Position the engine harness ground terminal and install the engine harness ground terminal bolt.
    a. Tighten the bolt to 18 ft. lbs. (25 Nm).

107. Connect the engine wiring harness electrical connector to the HO2S.

108. Position the A/C compressor line and install and tighten the bolts to 16 ft. lbs. (22 Nm).

109. Lower the vehicle.

110. Install the engine harness clip to the camshaft cover.

111. Position the turbocharger coolant feed pipe to the vehicle.

112. Install the turbocharger coolant feed pipe bracket bolt to the cylinder head and tighten the bolt to 89 inch lbs. (10 Nm).

113. Install the turbocharger coolant feed pipe fitting to the cylinder head and tighten the fitting to 26 ft. lbs. (35 Nm).

114. Install the turbocharger coolant feed pipe bolt (1) at the turbocharger and tighten to 26 ft. lbs. (35 Nm)

115. Install the charge air bypass valve vacuum solenoid.

116. Install the charge air bypass valve vacuum hose to the turbocharger coolant feed pipe clips.

117. Position the charge air bypass valve vacuum hose clamp at the turbocharger.

118. Place the charge air bypass valve solenoid out of the way.

119. Connect the engine wiring harness electrical connector to the boost sensor.

120. Connect the engine harness clips to the camshaft cover.

121. Connect the engine harness clip to the camshaft cover.

122. Connect the engine wiring harness electrical connectors to the ignition coils.

123. Connect the engine wiring harness electrical connector to the intake CMP actuator.

124. Connect the engine wiring harness electrical connector to the exhaust CMP actuator.

125. Connect the engine wiring harness electrical connector to the high pressure fuel pump.

126. Install the engine wiring harness clip to the high pressure fuel pump bracket.

127. Connect the engine wiring harness electrical connector to the knock sensor.

128. Connect the engine wiring harness electrical connector to the fuel injector jumper electrical connector.

129. Install the positive battery cable terminal to the generator.

130. Install the generator terminal nut and tighten the nut to 15 ft. lbs. (20 Nm).

131. Position the positive battery cable terminal boot.

132. Connect the engine wiring harness electrical connector to the A/C compressor.

133. Connect the engine wiring harness electrical connector to the generator.

134. Install the catalytic converter. Refer to Catalytic Converter.

135. Connect the engine wiring harness electrical connector to the CKP sensor.

136. Connect the engine wiring harness electrical connector to the oil pressure sensor.

137. Lower the vehicle.

138. Install the heater inlet and outlet hoses to the thermostat housing.

139. Position the heater inlet and outlet hose clamps at the thermostat housing.

140. Install the surge tank outlet hose to the surge tank.

141. Position the surge tank outlet hose clamp at the surge tank.

142. Install the radiator outlet hose.

143. Install the radiator inlet hose.

144. Remove the cap or plug from the turbocharger opening.

145. Install the charge air cooler pipe to the turbocharger.

146. Install the charge air cooler pipe to turbocharger bolts and tighten the bolts to 16 ft. lbs. (22 Nm).

147. Install the engine drive belt. Refer to Accessory Drive Belt.

148. Un-secure the cooling module from the upper body structure.

149. Fill the cooling system.

150. Install the turbocharger heat shield and bolts and tighten the bolts to 89 inch lbs. (10 Nm).

151. Connect the fuel feed pipe to the fuel line.

152. Connect the EVAP canister purge solenoid tube to the valve.

153. Install the charge air cooler inlet and outlet pipes.

154. Install the air cleaner assembly. Refer to Air Cleaner.

155. Connect the negative battery cable.

156. Fill the engine with oil.

2.2L Engine

See Figures 108 and 109.

1. Before servicing the vehicle, refer to the Precautions Section.

2. With the tires in the straight forward position, remove the key from the ignition.

3. Disconnect the negative battery cable.

4. Remove the air inlet duct and resonator.

5. Secure the cooling module to the upper body structure.

6. Relieve the fuel system pressure. Refer to Fuel System.

7. Disconnect the fuel lines from the fuel rail.

8. Drain the cooling system.

9. Remove the radiator inlet hose.

10. Remove the surge tank to cylinder head hose.

11. Remove the radiator outlet hose.

12. Remove the inlet and outlet heater hoses.

13. Disconnect the following harness connectors:

- Idle Air Control (IAC) motor
- TPS
- Manifold Absolute Pressure (MAP) sensor
- Crankshaft sensor
- Oil pressure sensor
- Purge solenoid

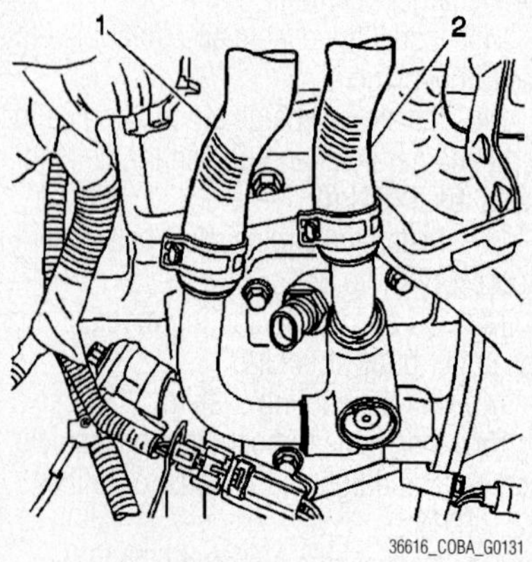

Fig. 108 Inlet and outlet heater hoses

- Ignition coil and module assembly
- Oxygen (O_2) sensor
- Vehicle speed sensor
- Engine temperature sensor
- Backup lamp switch

14. Raise and suitably support the vehicle.

15. Remove the engine accessory drive belt. Refer to Accessory Drive Belt.

16. Remove the front fender liner.

17. Rotate the drive belt tensioner counterclockwise to release the spring tension.

18. Remove the drive belt.

19. Disconnect the electrical connector from the A/C compressor.

20. Remove the A/C compressor bolts and set the compressor aside.

21. Disconnect the starter harness connectors. Refer to Starter in Engine Electrical.

22. Disconnect the generator harness connectors. Refer to Alternator in Engine Electrical.

23. Drain the engine oil.

24. Disconnect the front exhaust pipe from the exhaust manifold. Refer to Catalytic Converter.

25. Disconnect the transaxle harness connectors.

26. Disconnect the transaxle shift cable from the transaxle.

27. Use blocks of wood to support the powertrain assembly between the frame and the powertrain.

28. Support the engine with a hydraulic floor jack. Use a piece of wood between the jack and the oil pan.

29. Remove the engine mount to intermediate bracket bolts.

30. Remove the engine mount to mid-rail nuts.

31. Remove the engine mount from the engine compartment.

32. With an automatic transaxle:

a. Remove the front transaxle mount thru bolt.

b. Remove the rear transaxle mount thru bolt.

c. Lower the vehicle.

d. Remove the under hood electrical center cover.

e. Disconnect the engine control module harness connector.

f. Disconnect the positive battery cables from the underhood electrical center.

g. Disconnect the surge tank inlet hose from the surge tank.

h. Remove the under hood electrical center tray bracket nuts and bolt.

i. Disconnect the wiring harness retainer from the tray bracket.

j. Lift the electrical center up and swing it back and out of the way.

k. Support the transaxle with a hydraulic floor jack. Use a block of wood between the jack and the transaxle.

l. Remove the transaxle mount to transaxle bolts. Refer to Automatic Transaxle in Drive Train.

m. Remove the transaxle mount to mid-rail bolts.

n. Using the floor jack, slowly lower the transaxle just enough to remove the transaxle mount from the vehicle.

33. With an MU3 manual transaxle:

a. Remove the cover from the underhood electrical center.

b. Remove the underhood positive battery terminal lug.

> ### ❉❉ WARNING
> **Take note of the positioning of the positive battery cables before disconnecting the cables.**

c. Disconnect the positive battery cables from the underhood electrical center.

> ### ❉❉ WARNING
> **The underhood electrical center bolts are retained in the electrical center.**

d. Loosen all of the underhood electrical bolts.

e. Remove the underhood electrical center bracket from the vehicle and reposition the electrical center.

f. Support the transaxle with a floor jack. Use a piece of wood between the jack and the transaxle.

g. Remove the transaxle mount-to-transaxle bracket bolts. Refer to Manual Transaxle in Drive Train.

h. Remove the transaxle mount to mid-rail bolts.

i. Using a floor jack, slowly lower the transaxle enough to remove the transaxle mount from the vehicle.

34. With a Getrag 5-speed manual transaxle:

a. Remove the underhood electrical center cover.

b. Disconnect the Engine Control Module (ECM) harness connector.

c. Disconnect the positive battery cables from the underhood electrical center.

d. Disconnect the surge tank inlet hose from the surge tank.

e. Remove the underhood electrical center tray bracket nuts and bolt.

f. Disconnect the wiring harness retainer from the tray bracket.

g. Lift the electrical center up and swing it back and out of the way.

h. Support the transaxle with a floor jack. Use a piece of wood between the jack and the transaxle.

i. Remove the transaxle mount to transaxle bolts. Refer to Manual Transaxle in Drive Train

j. Remove the transaxle mount to mid-rail bolts.

k. Using a floor jack, slowly lower the transaxle enough to remove the transaxle mount from the vehicle.

l. Disconnect the control links from the stabilizer bar.

m. Disconnect the outer tie rod ends from the steering knuckles.

❉❉ WARNING

In order to prevent possible SIR system deployment, do not attempt to rotate the steering shaft.

n. Disconnect the intermediate shaft from the steering gear.

o. Disconnect the lower control arms from the steering knuckles.

p. Disconnect the drive axles from the steering knuckle.

q. Use a paint pen or magic marker in order to mark the frame to body position.

r. Lower the vehicle to about 3 feet off the ground in order to position the lift table under the frame.

s. Use wood blocks as necessary between the lift table and the frame to support the assembly.

35. Slowly remove the frame bolts using the following sequence:

a. Remove the front frame bolts.

b. Partially unscrew the rear frame bolts until 1.5 inches of bolt shank is exposed.

36. Slowly lower the table to the floor with the cradle and powertrain assembly.

37. Attach the engine lift hoist to the engine lift hooks.

38. Remove the starter.

39. If applicable, remove the torque converter to flywheel bolts.

40. Remove the transaxle to engine bolts.

41. Separate the engine from the transaxle.

42. If applicable, remove the clutch pressure plate and disk.

43. Remove the following components:

44. Remove the exhaust manifold

45. Remove the exhaust manifold studs

46. Remove the engine mount bracket

47. Remove the engine block heater

48. Remove the thermostat housing and feed pipe

49. Remove the generator

50. Remove the engine from the engine lift.

To install:

51. Attach the engine lift hoist to the engine lift hooks.

52. Install the exhaust manifold.

53. Install the intermediate bracket to the engine.

54. Hand tighten the engine mount intermediate bracket bolts in the following locations:

- The long bolts in the forward and front lower holes
- The short bolt in the rear upper hole

55. Tighten the intermediate bracket bolts to 74 ft. lbs. (100 Nm).

56. Install the fuel rail.

57. Install the engine block heater, if equipped.

58. Install the drive belt tensioner.

59. Install the thermostat and retaining sleeve with the dimple placed into the housing slot.

❉❉ WARNING

Lubricate the O-ring with soapy water or coolant before installing the O-ring in the water pump.

60. Install the feed pipe that connects the thermostat housing to the water pump.

61. Install the bolt that secures the water pump feed pipe. Tighten the bolt to 88 inch lbs. (10 Nm).

62. Install the generator.

63. Install the flywheel. Tighten the flywheel bolts to 39 ft. lbs. (53 Nm) plus 25°

64. If applicable, install the clutch pressure plate and disk.

65. Align the engine to the transaxle.

❉❉ WARNING

The number 3 bolt location is not used.

66. Secure the engine to the transaxle. Tighten the transaxle to engine bolts to 55 ft. lbs. (75 Nm).

➡**The number 3 bolt location is not used.**

67. If applicable, install the torque converter bolts. Tighten the bolts to 44 ft. lbs. (60 Nm).

68. Install the starter.

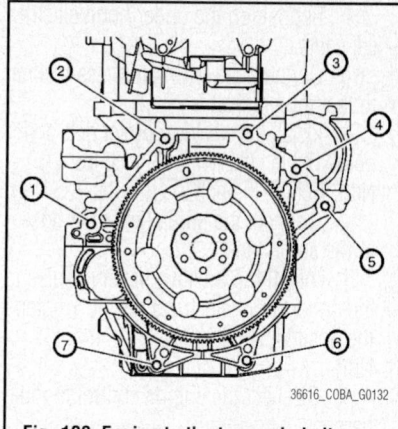

36616_COBA_G0132

Fig. 109 Engine to the transaxle bolt locations

69. Remove the engine lift from the engine.

70. Raise and position the frame and powertrain assembly to the vehicle.

71. Hand start all the frame bolts while aligning the frame to the paint marks.

72. Tighten the frame bolts. Tighten the frame bolts to 74 ft. lbs. (100 Nm) plus 180°.

73. Remove the lift table.

74. Connect the drive axles to the steering knuckles.

75. Connect the lower control arm to the steering knuckle.

76. Connect the intermediate steering shaft to the steering gear.

77. Connect the outer tie rod ends to the steering knuckles.

78. Connect the control links to the stabilizer bar.

79. With an automatic transaxle:

a. Install the transaxle mount to the mid-rail.

b. Hand start the transaxle mount to mid-rail bolts. Tighten the bolts to 25 ft. lbs. (34 Nm).

c. Using a hydraulic jack, raise the transaxle until it contacts the transaxle mount.

❉❉ WARNING

The transaxle mount to transaxle bolts must be hand started. Do not pry the transaxle or mount to align the holes.

d. Hand start the transaxle mount to transaxle bolts using the following sequence:

- Rear Bolt
- Middle Bolt
- Front Bolt

e. Using the previous sequence, tighten the transaxle mount bolts. Tighten the bolts to 37 ft. lbs. (50 Nm).

f. Reposition the under hood electrical center.

g. Connect the wiring harness retainer to the tray bracket.

h. Install the electrical center nuts and bolts. Tighten the nut to 89 inch lbs. (10 Nm). Tighten the bolt to 18 ft. lbs. (25 Nm).

i. Connect the surge tank inlet hose to the surge tank.

j. Install the positive battery cables to the under hood electrical center. Tighten the positive cable nut to 11 ft. lbs. (15 Nm).

k. Connect the engine control module harness connectors.

l. Install the under hood electrical center cover.

m. Raise the vehicle.

n. Hand tighten the front transaxle mount thru bolt

o. Hand tighten the rear transaxle mount thru bolt.

p. Tighten the front transaxle mount thru bolt. Tighten the bolt to 74 ft. lbs. (100 Nm).

q. Tighten the rear transaxle mount thru bolt. Tighten the bolt to 74 ft. lbs. (100 Nm).

80. With an MU3 manual transaxle:

a. Install the transaxle mount to the mid-rail.

b. Install the transaxle mount to mid-rail bolts. Tighten the bolts to 20 ft. lbs. (27 Nm).

c. Using a floor jack, raise the transaxle until it contacts the transaxle mount.

✼✼ WARNING

The transaxle mount to transaxle bolts must be hand started. Do not pry the transaxle or mount to align the holes.

d. Hand start the transaxle mount to bracket bolts using the following sequence:
- Rear bolt
- Middle bolt
- Front bolt

e. Using the previous sequence, tighten the transaxle mount bolts. Tighten the bolts to 37 ft. lbs. (50 Nm).

f. Install the underhood electrical center bracket to the vehicle and install the electrical center into position on the bracket.

81. With a Getrag 5-speed:

a. Install the transaxle mount to the mid-rail.

b. Hand start transaxle mount to mid-rail bolts. Tighten the bolts to.

c. Using a floor jack, raise the transaxle until it contacts the transaxle mount.

✼✼ WARNING

The transaxle mount to transaxle bolts must be hand started. Do not pry the transaxle or mount to align the holes.

d. Hand start the transaxle mount to transaxle bolts using the following sequence:
- Rear bolt
- Middle bolt
- Front bolt

e. Using the previous sequence, tighten the transaxle mount bolts. Tighten the bolts to 33 ft. lbs. (45 Nm).

82. Reposition the underhood electrical center.

83. Connect the wiring harness to the tray bracket.

84. Install the electrical center nuts and bolt. Tighten the nuts to 89 inch lbs. (10 Nm). Tighten the bolt to 18 ft. lbs. (25 Nm).

85. Connect the surge tank inlet hose to the surge tank.

86. Install the positive battery cables to the underhood electrical center. Tighten the positive cable nut to 11 ft. lbs. (15 Nm).

87. Connect the engine control module harness connectors.

88. Install the underhood electrical center cover.

89. Place the engine mount onto the mid rail and hand start the nuts.

90. Tighten the engine mount to mid-rail nuts. Tighten the nuts to 74 ft. lbs. (100 Nm).

✼✼ WARNING

The engine mount to intermediate bracket bolts must be hand started. Do not pry the engine mount to align the holes.

91. Hand start the engine mount to intermediate bracket bolts.

92. Tighten the engine mount to intermediate bracket bolts. Tighten the bolts to 37 ft. lbs. (50 Nm).

93. Remove the hydraulic floor jack.

94. Install the air cleaner assembly.

95. Remove the wood blocks between the powertrain and frame.

96. Connect the transaxle shift cable to the transaxle.

97. Connect the transaxle harness connector.

98. Connect the exhaust takedown pipe to the exhaust manifold. Tighten the nuts to 22 ft. lbs. (30 Nm).

99. Connect the generator harness connectors. Tighten the generator terminal nut to 15 ft. lbs. (20 Nm).

100. Connect the starter harness connectors. Tighten the battery terminal nut to 13 ft. lbs. (17 Nm). Tighten the S-terminal nut to 27 inch lbs. (3 Nm).

101. Install the A/C compressor to the engine. Tighten the bolts to 18 ft. lbs. (25 Nm).

102. Install the engine drive belt.

103. Connect the following harness connectors:
- IAC motor
- TPS
- MAP sensor
- Crankshaft sensor
- Oil pressure sensor
- Purge solenoid
- Ignition coil and module assembly
- O_2 sensor
- Vehicle speed sensor
- Engine temperature sensor

104. Install the inlet heater hose and outlet heater hose.

105. Install the radiator outlet hose.

106. Connect the fuel line to the fuel rail.

107. Connect the brake booster hose at the brake booster.

108. Release the cooling module from the upper body structure.

109. Install the air inlet duct and resonator.

110. Connect the negative battery cable.

111. Fill the engine with engine oil to the proper level.

112. Fill the cooling system.

113. Road test the vehicle.

2.4L Engine

See Figures 110 through 119.

1. Before servicing the vehicle, refer to the Precautions Section.

2. With the tires in the straight forward position, remove the key from the ignition.

3. Disconnect the negative battery cable.

4. Relieve fuel system pressure.

5. Disconnect the fuel feed line quick connect fitting from the fuel rail.

6. Disconnect the Evaporative Emission (EVAP) line quick connect fitting from the EVAP purge solenoid.

7. Remove the fuel line clips from the engine brackets.

8. Drain the cooling system.

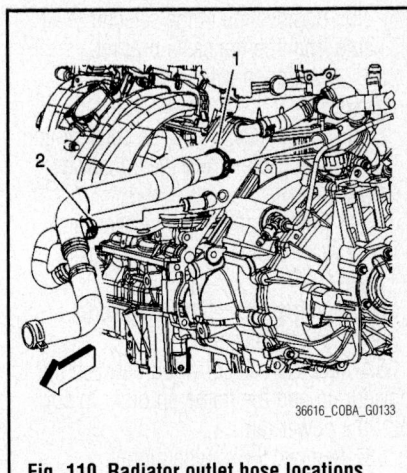

Fig. 110 Radiator outlet hose locations

9. Secure the cooling module to the upper body structure.

10. Remove the accessory drive belt. Refer to Accessory Drive Belts.

11. Disconnect the cooling fan electrical connector.

12. Reposition the radiator inlet hose clamp at the engine.

13. Remove the radiator inlet hose from the engine.

14. If the vehicle is equipped with an engine oil cooler, perform the following steps, otherwise proceed to step 19.

15. Reposition the radiator outlet hose clamp at the water outlet.

16. Reposition the radiator outlet hose clamp at the oil cooler.

17. Remove the radiator outlet hose from the water outlet.

18. Remove the radiator outlet hose from the oil cooler. Proceed to step 23.

19. If the vehicle is not equipped with an engine oil cooler, reposition the surge tank outlet hose clamp at the surge tank.

20. Remove the surge tank outlet hose from the surge tank.

21. Reposition the radiator outlet hose clamp at the thermostat cover.

22. Remove the radiator outlet hose from the thermostat cover.

23. Reposition the heater inlet and outlet hose clamps at the thermostat housing.

24. Remove the heater inlet and outlet hoses from the thermostat housing.

25. Reposition the brake booster vacuum hose clamp at the intake manifold.

26. Remove the brake booster vacuum hose from the intake manifold. Reposition the hose.

27. Disconnect the following electrical connectors:
- Throttle Actuator Control (TAC)
- Manifold Absolute Pressure (MAP) sensor
- Fuel injector harness
- Alternator

28. Remove or disconnect the following:
- The engine harness clip from the oil level indicator tube
- The engine harness clips from the intake manifold
- The ignition coils electrical connectors
- The intake and exhaust camshaft position actuator electrical connectors
- The engine harness clips from the camshaft cover
- The negative battery cable ground nut
- The engine harness ground terminal from the stud
- The negative battery cable ground terminal from the stud

29. Disconnect the following engine harness electrical connectors:

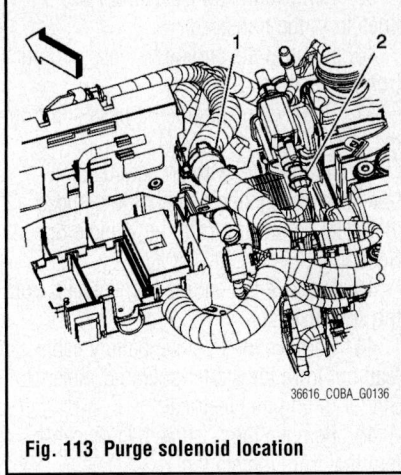

Fig. 113 Purge solenoid location

- Oil pressure sensor
- Crankshaft Position (CKP) sensor
- Knock sensor
- The EVAP purge solenoid electrical connector

30. Remove the engine harness clip from the purge solenoid bracket.

31. Remove the engine harness ground bolt.

32. Reposition the engine harness ground terminal.

33. Disconnect the engine harness electrical connector from the Air Conditioning (A/C) pressure switch.

34. Disconnect the engine harness electrical connector from A/C compressor.

35. Unbolt and reposition the A/C compressor to one side.

36. Raise and suitably support the vehicle.

37. Drain the engine oil.

38. Remove the transaxle fluid cooler bracket nut.

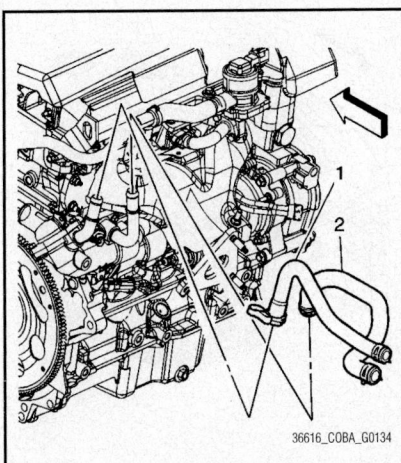

Fig. 111 Heater inlet and outlet hoses

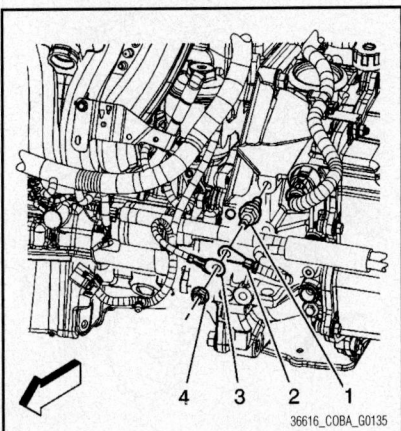

Fig. 112 Negative battery cable ground terminal location

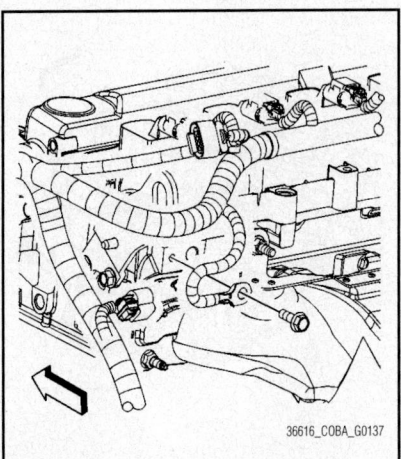

Fig. 114 Engine harness ground location

39. Remove the transaxle fluid cooler lines from the transaxle.

40. Remove the engine harness clip nut from the engine stud.

41. Remove the engine harness clip from the stud.

42. If equipped with an automatic transaxle, disconnect the engine harness electrical connector from the Vehicle Speed Sensor (VSS).

43. Remove the engine harness clip from the speed sensor.

44. Remove the positive battery cable lead nut from the starter solenoid. Refer to Starter in Engine Electrical.

45. Remove the positive battery cable terminal from the starter.

46. Remove the engine harness terminal from the starter.

47. Remove the engine harness to starter solenoid "S" terminal nut.

48. Remove the engine harness lead terminals from the starter solenoid.

49. Lower the vehicle.

50. If equipped with an automatic transaxle, disconnect the engine harness from the transaxle.

51. If equipped with a automatic transaxle, perform the following steps.

    a. Disconnect the engine harness electrical connector (2) from the engine coolant temperature (ECT) sensor.

    b. Remove the heated oxygen sensor (HO2S) connector position assurance (CPA) retainers.

    c. Disconnect the engine harness electrical connectors (2, 4) from the HO2S.

    d. Remove the HO2S connector clips from the thermostat housing and engine bracket.

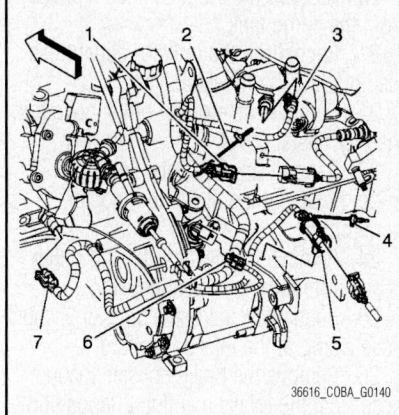

Fig. 116 Manual Transaxle harness locations

    e. Disconnect the engine harness electrical connector (1) from the park neutral position switch.

52. If equipped with a manual transaxle, disconnect the engine harness electrical connector (6) from the VSS.

    a. Disconnect the engine harness electrical connector (7) from the back up lamp switch.

    b. Remove the HO2S CPA retainers (2, 4).

    c. Disconnect the engine harness electrical connectors (1, 5) from the HO2S.

    d. Remove the HO2S clips from the engine brackets.

    e. Gather all engine harness branches are reposition the harness off to the side, out of the way.

53. If equipped with an automatic transaxle:

    a. Disconnect the range selector lever cable from the transaxle lever.

    b. Remove the range selector lever cable from the transaxle bracket.

54. If equipped with a manual transaxle:

    a. Disconnect the range selector and shift lever cables from the transaxle levers.

    b. Remove the range selector and shift lever cables from the transaxle bracket.

55. Remove the catalytic converter.

56. Lower the vehicle.

57. Insert blocks of wood between the powertrain and the frame, in order to support the powertrain.

58. Remove the engine mount.

59. Remove the transaxle mount to transaxle bolts.

60. Raise the vehicle.

61. Disconnect the control links from the stabilizer bar.

62. Disconnect the outer tie rod ends from the steering knuckles.

63. Disconnect the intermediate shaft from the steering gear.

64. Disconnect the lower control arms from the steering knuckles.

65. Using a paint pen or magic marker, mark the frame to body position.

66. Lower the vehicle to about 3 feet off the ground.

67. Position a engine lift table under the frame.

68. Place wood blocks on top of the lift table between the table and the frame.

69. Lower the vehicle until the frame is resting on the blocks of wood.

70. Slowly loosen/remove the frame bolts using the following sequence:

    a. Loosen/remove the front frame bolts.

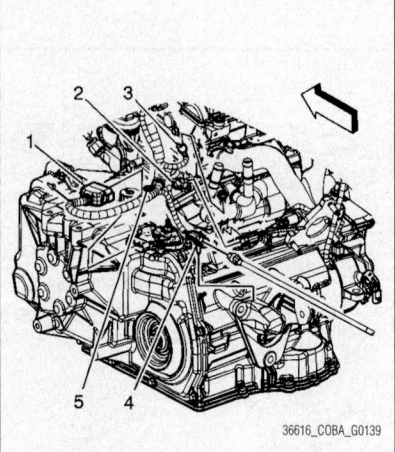

Fig. 115 Automatic Transaxle harness locations

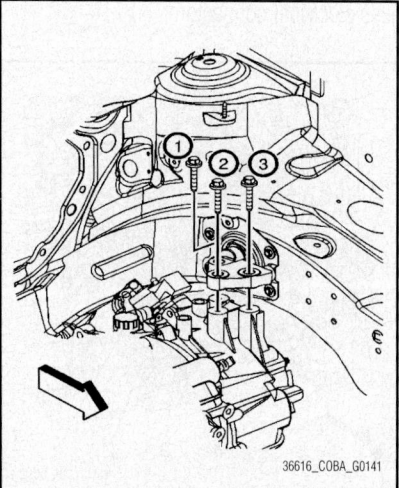

Fig. 117 Transaxle mount to transaxle bolt locations

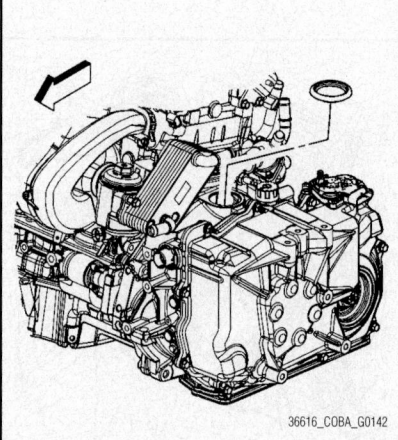

Fig. 118 Torque converter housing access plug location

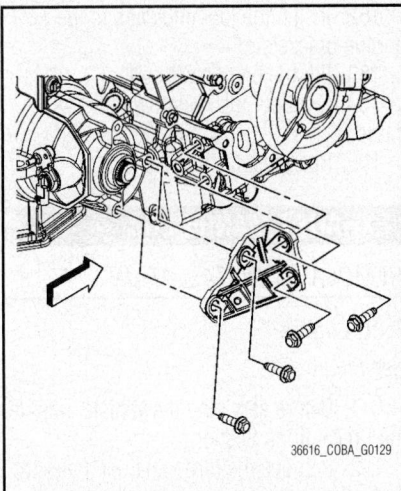

Fig. 119 Transaxle brace bolts and brace location

b. Loosen/remove the rear frame bolts.

71. Slowly raise the vehicle away from the powertrain assembly.

72. Slide the lift table out from under the vehicle.

73. Attach the engine lift hoist to the engine lift hooks.

74. Remove the starter bolts and starter.

75. If equipped with an automatic transaxle:

a. Remove the torque converter housing access plug.

b. Remove the torque converter bolts.

76. Remove the transaxle brace bolts and brace.

77. If equipped with a manual transaxle, remove the transaxle to engine bolts/stud.

78. If equipped with an automatic transaxle, remove the transaxle to engine bolts/stud.

79. Separate the engine from the transaxle.

80. If equipped with a manual transaxle, remove the clutch pressure plate and disc.

81. Remove the following components:
• The engine mount bracket
• The engine block heater
• The alternator

82. Using an engine hoist, install the engine onto an engine stand.

To install:

83. Using an engine hoist, remove the engine from the engine stand.

84. Install the following components:
• The engine mount bracket
• The engine block heater
• The alternator

85. If equipped with a manual transaxle, install the clutch pressure plate and disc.

86. Install the engine to the transaxle.

87. If equipped with an automatic transaxle, install the transaxle to engine bolts/stud. Tighten the bolts/stud to 55 ft. lbs. (75 Nm).

88. If equipped with a manual transaxle, install the transaxle to engine bolts/stud. Tighten the bolts/stud to 55 ft. lbs. (75 Nm).

89. Install the transaxle brace and bolts. Tighten the bolts to 37 ft. lbs. (50 Nm).

90. If equipped with an automatic transaxle:

a. Install the torque converter bolts. Tighten the bolts to 46 ft. lbs. (62 Nm).

b. Install the torque converter housing access plug.

91. Install the starter and bolts. Tighten the bolts to 30 ft. lbs. (40 Nm).

92. Remove the engine lift hoist from the engine lift hooks.

93. Slide the lift table under the vehicle.

94. Slowly lower the vehicle until it aligns with the alignment marks made during the removal.

95. Tighten/install the frame bolts. Tighten the bolts to 74 ft. lbs. (100 Nm) plus and additional 180°.

96. Raise the vehicle until the lift table can be removed from under the vehicle.

97. Remove the lift table.

98. Install the transaxle fluid cooler lines to the transaxle.

99. Install the transaxle fluid cooler bracket nut. Tighten the nut to 62 inch lbs. (7 Nm).

100. Connect the lower control arms to the steering knuckles. Refer to Lower Control Arm in Suspension.

101. Connect the intermediate shaft to the steering gear. Refer to Intermediate Shaft in Suspension.

102. Connect the outer tie rod ends to the steering knuckles. Refer to Tie Rod Ends in Steering.

103. Connect the control links to the stabilizer bar. Refer to Stabilizer Bar in Suspension.

104. Lower the vehicle.

105. Install the transaxle mount to transaxle bolts. Tighten the bolts to 33 ft. lbs. (45 Nm).

106. Install the engine mount.

107. Remove the blocks of wood from between the powertrain and the frame.

108. Install the catalytic converter.

109. Lower the vehicle.

➡Ensure that the black cable is installed in the top notch of the transaxle bracket and the white cable is installed in the bottom notch of the transaxle bracket.

110. If equipped with a manual transaxle:

a. Install the range selector and shift lever cables to the transaxle bracket.

b. Connect the range selector and shift lever cables to the transaxle levers.

111. If equipped with an automatic transaxle:

a. Install the range selector lever cable to the transaxle bracket.

b. Connect the range selector lever cable to the transaxle lever.

112. Gather all engine harness branches and position the harness over the engine.

113. If equipped with a manual transaxle, perform the following steps:

a. Install the HO2S clips to the engine brackets.

b. Connect the engine harness electrical connectors to the HO2S.

c. Install the HO2S CPA retainers.

114. Connect the engine harness electrical connector to the backup lamp switch.

115. Connect the engine harness electrical connector to the VSS.

116. If equipped with an automatic transaxle, perform the following steps:

a. Connect the engine harness electrical connector to the park neutral position switch.

b. Install the engine harness clips to the thermostat housing and engine brackets.

c. Connect the engine harness electrical connectors to the HO2S.

d. Install the HO2S CPA retainers.

117. Connect the ECT sensor electrical connector.

118. If equipped with an automatic transaxle, connect the engine harness to the transaxle.

119. Raise the vehicle.

120. Install the engine harness lead terminal to the starter solenoid.

121. Install the engine harness to starter solenoid "S" terminal nut. Tighten the nut to 27 inch lbs. (3 Nm).

122. Install the engine harness terminal to the starter.

123. Install the positive battery cable terminal to the starter.

124. Install the positive/negative battery cable lead nut to the starter solenoid. Tighten the nut to 13 ft. lbs. (17 Nm).

125. Install the engine harness clip to the speed sensor.

126. Connect the engine harness electrical connector to the VSS.

127. Install the engine harness clip to the stud.

128. Install the engine harness clip nut to the engine stud. Tighten the nut to 37 ft. lbs. (50 Nm).

129. Lower the vehicle.

130. Reposition and install the A/C compressor. Tighten the bolts to 37 ft. lbs. (50 Nm).

131. Connect the engine harness electrical connector to the A/C compressor.

132. Connect the engine harness electrical connector to the A/C pressure switch.

133. Position the engine harness ground terminal to the engine block.

134. Install the engine harness ground bolt. Tighten the bolt to 18 ft. lbs. (25 Nm).

135. Connect the EVAP purge solenoid electrical connector.

136. Install the engine harness clip to the EVAP purge solenoid bracket.

137. Connect the following electrical connectors:

- Knock sensor
- CKP sensor
- Oil pressure sensor

138. Install the negative battery cable ground terminal to the stud.

139. Install the engine harness ground terminal to the stud.

140. Install the negative battery cable ground nut. Tighten the nut to 89 inch lbs. (10 Nm).

141. Install the engine harness clips to the camshaft cover.

142. Connect the intake and exhaust camshaft position actuator electrical connectors.

143. Connect the ignition coils electrical connectors.

144. Connect the engine harness clips to the intake manifold.

145. Connect the engine harness clip to the oil level indicator tube.

146. Connect the following electrical connectors:

- TAC
- MAP sensor
- Fuel injector harness
- Alternator

147. Install the brake booster vacuum hose to the intake manifold.

148. Position the brake booster vacuum hose clamp at the intake manifold.

149. Install the heater inlet and outlet hoses to the thermostat housing.

150. Position the heater inlet and outlet hose clamps at the thermostat housing.

151. If the vehicle is not equipped with a engine oil cooler, perform the following steps:

a. Install the surge tank outlet hose to the surge tank.

b. Position the surge tank outlet hose clamp at the surge tank.

c. Install the radiator outlet hose to the thermostat cover.

d. Position the radiator outlet hose clamp at the thermostat cover.

152. If the vehicle is equipped with a engine oil cooler, perform the following steps:

a. Install the radiator outlet hose to the oil cooler.

b. Install the radiator outlet hose to the water outlet.

c. Position the radiator outlet hose clamp at the oil cooler.

d. Position the radiator outlet hose clamp at the water outlet.

153. Install the radiator inlet hose to the engine.

154. Position the radiator inlet hose clamp at the engine.

155. Connect the cooling fan electrical connector.

156. Install the accessory drive belt. Refer to Accessory Drive Belt.

157. Remove the cooling module from the upper body structure.

158. Fill the cooling system.

159. Check and fill the transaxle fluid as needed.

160. Connect the EVAP line quick connect fitting to the EVAP purge solenoid.

161. Connect the fuel feed line quick connect fitting to the fuel rail.

162. Install the fuel line clips to the engine brackets.

163. Fill the engine with oil.

164. Connect the negative battery cable.

165. Road test the vehicle.

EXHAUST MANIFOLD

REMOVAL & INSTALLATION

2.0L Engine

See Figure 120.

1. Before servicing the vehicle, refer to the Precautions Section.

2. Remove the turbo charger. Refer to Turbocharger.

3. Remove the exhaust manifold heat shield.

4. Remove the exhaust manifold nuts and manifold.

5. Clean and inspect all gasket mating surfaces.

To install:

6. Install new gasket.

7. Install exhaust manifold.

8. Install NEW exhaust manifold nuts.

9. Tighten nuts to 12 inch lbs. (14 Nm).

10. Install heat shield.

11. Install turbocharger. Refer to Turbocharger.

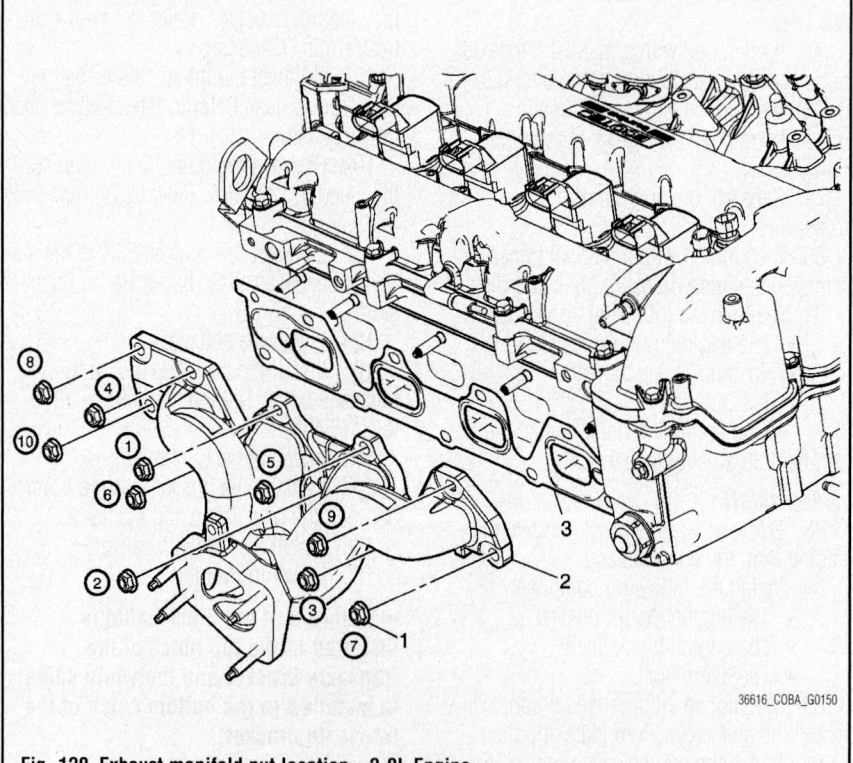

Fig. 120 Exhaust manifold nut location—2.0L Engine

36616_COBA_G0150

2.2L & 2.4L Engines

See Figure 121.

1. Remove the intake manifold cover. Refer to Intake Manifold Cover Replacement .

2. If equipped with RPO NU3, remove the secondary air injection (AIR) check valve. Refer to Secondary Air Injection Check Valve in Engine Performance & Emission Controls.

3. Remove the exhaust manifold heat shield.

4. Remove the heated oxygen sensor (HO2S). Refer to Heated Oxygen Sensor in Engine Performance & Emission Controls.

5. Raise and support the vehicle.

6. Remove the catalytic converter assembly. Refer to Catalytic Converter.

7. Lower the vehicle.

8. Remove the exhaust manifold nuts.

9. Remove the exhaust manifold and discard the exhaust manifold gasket.

10. Clean and inspect all gasket mating surfaces.

To install:

11. Install a NEW exhaust manifold gasket onto the studs.

12. Install the exhaust manifold to the engine.

13. Install NEW exhaust manifold nuts and tighten the exhaust manifold nuts in sequence to 10 ft. lbs. (14 Nm).

14. Raise and support the vehicle.

15. Install the catalytic converter assembly. Refer to Catalytic Converter.

16. Lower the vehicle.

17. Install the heated oxygen sensor HO2S. Refer to Heated Oxygen Sensor in Engine Performance & Emission Controls.

18. If equipped, install the AIR check valve. Refer to Secondary Air Injection Check Valve in Engine Performance & Emission Controls.

19. Install the intake manifold cover.

20. Inspect the exhaust system for leaks.

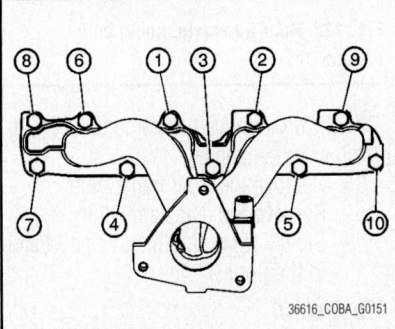

Fig. 121 Exhaust manifold nut tightening sequence—2.2L and 2.4L Engines

FLYWHEEL

REMOVAL & INSTALLATION

See Figures 122 and 123.

1. Before servicing the vehicle, refer to the Precautions Section.

2. Remove the transaxle:

a. If automatic transaxle, refer to Automatic Transaxle Assembly in Drive Train.

b. If manual transaxle, refer to Manual Transaxle Assembly in Drive Train.

3. Using the J 38122-A, hold the crankshaft damper.

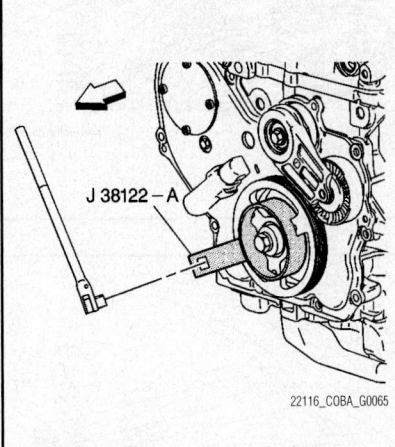

Fig. 122 Using tool J 38122-A to hold the crankshaft damper

➡ **It may be necessary to remove the chamfer (bevel) from the edge of an 18mm socket in order to get full engagement on the thin-headed flywheel bolts.**

4. Remove and discard the flywheel bolts.

➡ **Do not orientate the flywheel to the crankshaft. It is balanced separately from the engine.**

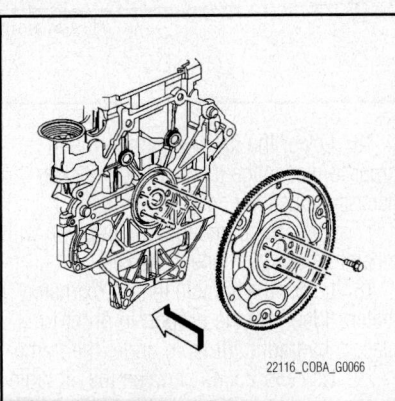

Fig. 123 Removing the flywheel

5. Remove the flywheel.

6. Clean the thread adhesive from the flywheel bolt holes. Use a nylon bristle brush to clean the holes in the crankshaft.

To install:

7. Install the flywheel.

8. Install the NEW flywheel bolts. Tighten the bolts to 39 ft. lbs. (53 Nm) plus an additional 25° using the J 45059.

9. Remove the J 38122-A tool from holding the crankshaft damper.

10. Install the transaxle:

a. If automatic transaxle, refer to Automatic Transaxle Assembly in Drive Train.

b. If manual transaxle, refer to Manual Transaxle Assembly in Drive Train.

FRAME

REMOVAL & INSTALLATION

See Figures 124 through 129.

1. With the wheels in the straight ahead position, remove the key from the ignition switch.

2. Secure the cooling module to the upper body structure.

3. Raise and support the vehicle.

4. Remove the front wheels from the vehicle.

5. Remove the left and right splash shields and the 3 screws in the inner fenders.

a. Remove front wheelhouse liner fasteners.

b. Remove rocker panel screws.

c. Lift the fender liner from the rocker molding.

6. Remove engine splash shield retainer.

7. Remove the lower radiator air deflector from the frame.

8. Remove the front transaxle mount to frame through bolt.

9. Remove the rear transaxle mount to frame bolts.

10. Remove both stabilizer link to stabilizer shaft nuts. Refer to Stabilizer Bar in Suspension.

11. Remove both tie rod to steering knuckle nuts. Refer to Tie Rod Ends in Steering.

12. Use the J 24319-B to separate the outer tie rods from the steering knuckles.

13. Remove the intermediate steering shaft to steering gear pinch bolt and discard. Refer to Intermediate Shaft in Steering.

➡ **DO NOT rotate the intermediate shaft once separated from the gear. Possible damage or a malfunction could occur.**

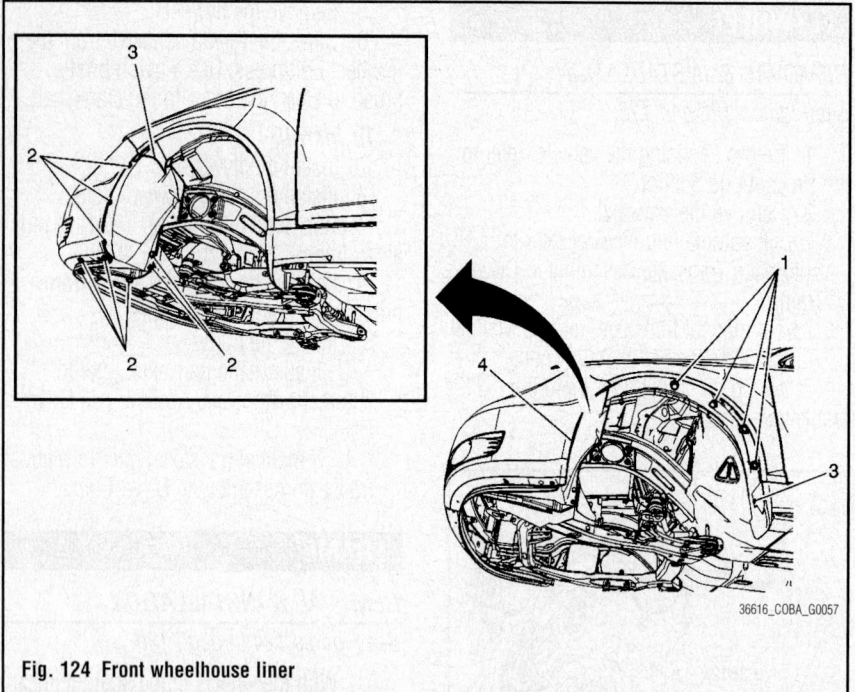

Fig. 124 Front wheelhouse liner

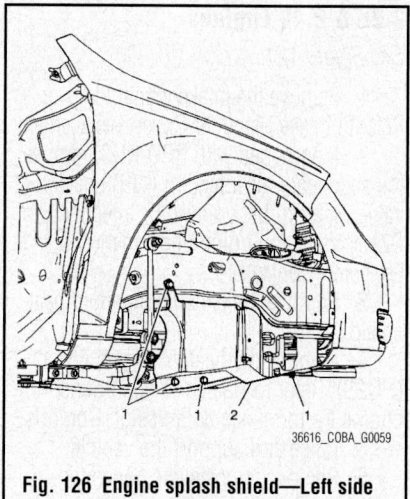

Fig. 126 Engine splash shield—Left side

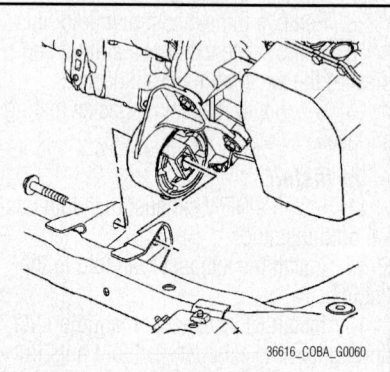

Fig. 127 Front transaxle mount bolt location

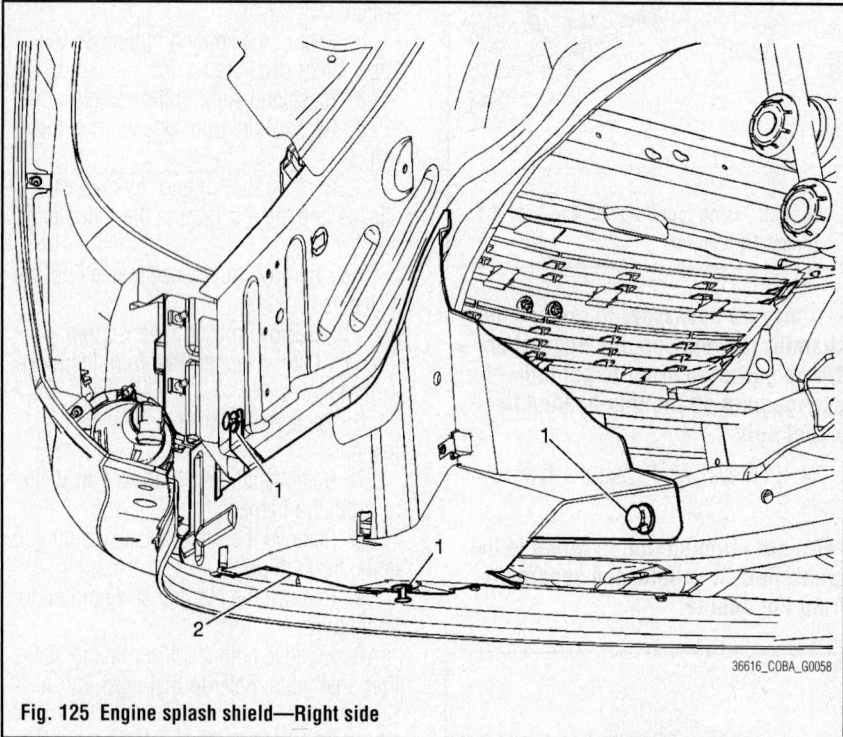

Fig. 125 Engine splash shield—Right side

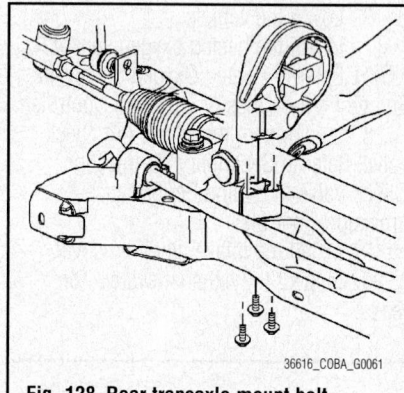

Fig. 128 Rear transaxle mount bolt location

14. Disconnect the intermediate steering shaft from the steering gear.

15. Remove both lower control arm ball stud to steering knuckle pinch bolts. Refer to Lower Control Arm in Suspension.

✳✳ WARNING

Do not free the ball stud by using a pickle fork or a wedge-type tool. Damage to the seal or bushing may result.

16. Lower the lower control arms in order to disengage the steering knuckle. If necessary, use the J43631.

17. Mark the frame to body position with a paint pen or permanent marker.

18. Lower the vehicle to approximately 1 meter (3 feet) off the ground in order to place a hydraulic lift table under the frame.

19. Use two 2 x 4s between the lift table and the frame and lift the table to the frame.

20. Slowly remove the frame bolts using the following sequence:
- Remove the front frame bolts.
- Remove the rear frame bolts.
- Slowly lower the lift table and frame to the floor.

To install:

21. With the frame on the lift table, raise the frame to the vehicle.

22. Hand start all the frame bolts

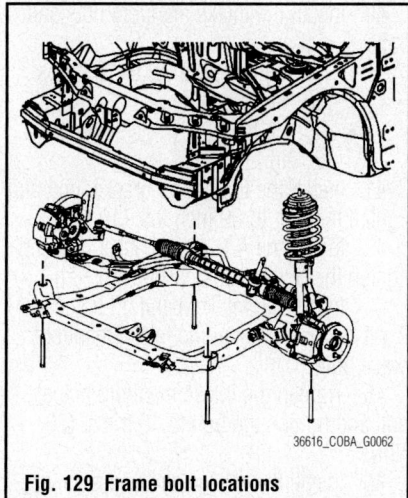

Fig. 129 Frame bolt locations

while aligning the frame to the paint marks.

23. Tighten the frame bolts to 74 ft. lbs. (100 Nm) plus 180 degrees.

24. Lower and remove the hydraulic table.

25. Connect the lower control arm to the steering knuckle.

➡ **The torque sequence must be followed in the order that is listed.**

26. Install the ball joint pinch bolt and nut.

    a. First Pass: Tighten the nut to 37 ft. lbs. (50 Nm).

    b. Reverse the nut 270 degrees.

    c. Second Pass: Tighten the nut to 37 ft. lbs. (50 Nm) plus 30 degrees.

27. The front and rear transmission mounts must be allowed to settle with the through bolts loosened.

28. Hand start the front transaxle mount through bolt.

29. Loosen the rear transmission mount through bolt.

30. Tighten the rear transaxle mount to frame bolts to 37 ft. lbs. (50 Nm).

31. Tighten the front and rear transaxle mount through bolts in the following order.

    a. Tighten the rear bolt to 74 ft. lbs. (100 Nm).

    b. Tighten the front bolt to 74 ft. lbs. (100 Nm).

32. Install the outer tie rods to the steering knuckles.

33. Install the new outer tie rod to the knuckle nuts and tighten to 18 ft. lbs. (25 Nm) plus 90 degrees.

34. Connect the stabilizer links to the stabilizer shaft. Refer to Stabilizer Shaft Link Replacement.

35. Connect the intermediate shaft to the steering gear.

36. Install a new intermediate shaft pinch bolt and tighten to 25 ft. lbs. (34 Nm).

37. Install the left and right splash shields and the 3 inner fender screws, by reversing removal procedure.

38. Install the lower radiator air deflector to the frame.

39. Install the front wheels

40. Lower the vehicle.

41. Road test the vehicle in order to test for the following conditions:

    a. Steering leads or pulls. Realign if necessary.

    b. Abnormal powertrain noise or vibration at idle, if symptoms are present; Inspect the engine and transmission mounts for proper alignment and torque.

INTAKE MANIFOLD

REMOVAL & INSTALLATION

2.0L Engine

See Figures 130 through 133.

1. Disconnect the charge air cooler outlet pipe from the throttle body.

2. Remove the oil level indicator tube.

3. Disconnect the fuel feed line quick connect fitting to the fuel rail.

4. Disconnect the charge air valve solenoid vacuum lines.

5. Mark the lines to ease installation.

6. Disconnect the charge air valve solenoid vacuum electrical connector.

7. Disconnect the evaporative emission (EVAP) electrical connector from the EVAP purge solenoid. Refer to EVAP purge solenoid in Engine Performance & Emission Controls.

8. Disconnect the evaporative emission (EVAP) line quick connect fitting from the EVAP purge solenoid.

9. Disconnect the manifold absolute pressure (MAP) sensor electrical connector. Refer to Manifold Absolute Pressure sensor in Engine Performance & Emission Controls.

10. Reposition the brake booster vacuum hose clamp at the intake manifold.

11. Remove the brake booster hose from the intake manifold.

12. Remove the knock sensor electrical connector clip from the intake manifold brace.

13. Disconnect the engine wiring harness electrical connector from the Throttle Actuator Control (TAC). Refer to Throttle Actuator Control module in Engine Performance & Emission Controls.

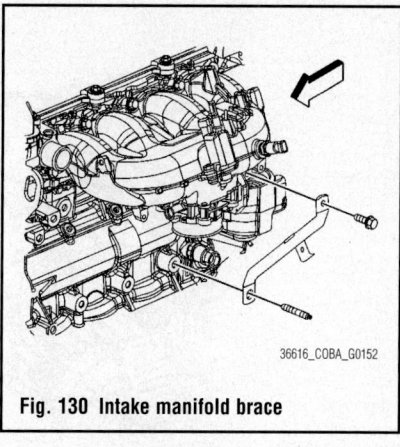

Fig. 130 Intake manifold brace

14. Remove the engine wiring harness clip from the intake manifold brace.

15. Reposition the surge tank air bleed hose clamp at the engine.

16. Reposition the surge tank air bleed hose out of the way.

17. Reposition the charge air bypass valve vacuum hose clamp at the intake manifold.

18. Remove the charge air bypass valve vacuum hose from the intake manifold.

19. Remove the charge air bypass valve solenoid bolts.

20. Reposition the charge air bypass valve solenoid assembly out of the way.

21. Disconnect the metal quick connect fitting from the fuel feed pipe.

22. Disconnect the fuel feed pipe fitting from the fuel pump.

23. Remove the fuel feed pipe bolts.

24. Remove the fuel feed pipe.

25. Inspect the fuel feed pipe nut for damaged threads.

26. Inspect the fuel feed pipe sealing bail for damage or debris.

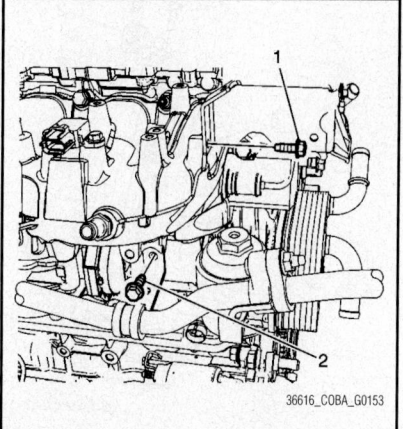

Fig. 131 Fuel pump and A/C pipe bracket bolt locations

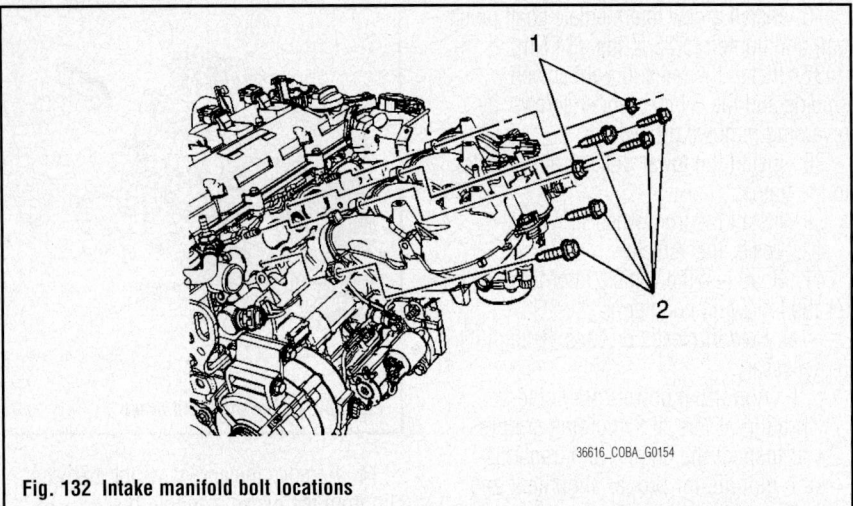

Fig. 132 Intake manifold bolt locations

27. Replace the fuel feed pipe if any damage is found.

28. Remove the charge air bypass valve vacuum tank.

29. Remove the intake manifold brace bolt.

30. Remove the intake manifold brace.

31. Remove the fuel pump bracket bolt (1).

32. Remove the A/C pipe bracket bolt (2) and reposition the bracket.

33. Remove the intake manifold nuts (1) and bolts (2).

34. Remove the intake manifold and place on a clean work surface.

35. Remove the intake manifold gasket and discard.

36. If replacing the intake manifold perform the following steps, otherwise proceed to step 2 in the installation procedure.

   a. Remove the MAP sensor bolts (1).

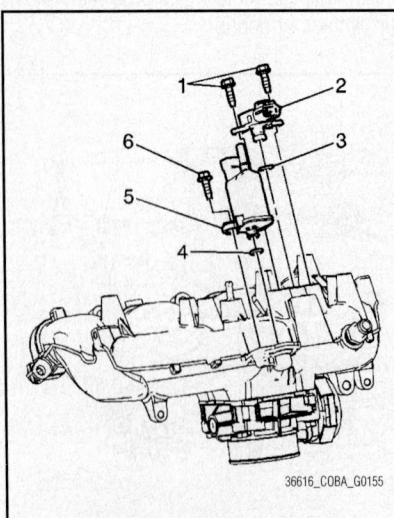

Fig. 133 Intake manifold component disassembly

   b. Remove the MAP sensor (2), ensure that the O-ring seal (3) is still attached on the sensor, if not remove the O-ring seal from the intake manifold.

   c. Remove the EVAP purge solenoid bolt (6).

   d. Remove the EVAP purge solenoid (5), ensure that the O-ring seal (4) is still attached on the sensor, if not remove the O-ring seal from the intake manifold.

   e. Turn the intake manifold upside down.

   f. Remove the throttle body bolts.

   g. Remove the throttle body and seal.

To install:

37. If replacing the intake manifold perform the following steps, otherwise proceed to step 2.

   a. Inspect the throttle body seal and replace if necessary.

   b. Install the throttle body seal and position the throttle body.

   c. Install the throttle body bolts and tighten the bolts to 89 inch lbs. (10 Nm).

   d. Turn the intake manifold right side up.

   e. Inspect the EVAP purge solenoid and MAP sensor O-ring seals, replace if necessary.

   f. Ensure that the EVAP purge solenoid O-ring seal is installed on the EVAP purge solenoid.

   g. Install the EVAP purge solenoid and bolt and tighten the bolts to 89 inch lbs. (10 Nm).

   h. Ensure that the MAP sensor O-ring seal is installed on the MAP sensor.

   i. Install the MAP sensor and bolts and tighten the bolts to 89 inch lbs. (10 Nm).

38. Install a NEW intake manifold gasket.

39. Install the intake manifold to the studs.

40. Install the intake manifold nuts and bolts.

   • Tighten the bolts (2) to 18 ft. lbs. (25 Nm).

   • Tighten the nuts (1) to 15 ft. lbs. (20 Nm).

41. Install the fuel pump bracket bolt and tighten the bolt to 89 inch lbs. (10 Nm).

42. Install the A/C pipe bracket bolt and tighten the bolt to 89 inch lbs. (10 Nm).

43. Install the intake manifold brace.

44. Loosely install the intake manifold brace bolt.

45. Tighten the intake manifold brace bolt and tighten the bolt to 16 ft lbs. (22 Nm).

46. Install the charge air bypass valve vacuum tank.

47. Lubricate the high pressure fuel pump fuel feed pipe connection threads with silicon free engine oil GM P/N 12345610 (Canadian P/N 993193) or equivalent.

48. Place the fuel feed pipe on top of the intake manifold.

49. Connect the fuel feed pipe fitting to the high pressure fuel pump.

50. Install the fuel feed pipe bolts and tighten the bolt to 89 inch lbs. (10 Nm) and the fittings to 22 ft. lbs. (30 Nm).

51. Connect the metal quick connect fitting to the fuel feed pip.

52. Position the charge air bypass valve solenoid assembly to the intake manifold.

53. Install the charge air bypass valve solenoid bolts and tighten the bolt to 89 inch lbs. (10 Nm).

54. Install the charge air bypass valve vacuum hose to the intake manifold.

55. Position the charge air bypass valve vacuum hose clamp at the intake manifold.

56. Position the surge tank air bleed hose to the engine.

57. Connect the engine wiring harness electrical connector to the TAC module.

58. Install the engine wiring harness clip to the intake manifold brace.

59. Install the knock sensor electrical connector clip to the intake manifold brace.

60. Install the brake booster hose to the intake manifold.

61. Position the brake booster vacuum hose clamp at the intake manifold.

62. Connect the EVAP line quick connect fitting to the EVAP purge solenoid.

63. Connect the charge air valve solenoid vacuum electrical connector.

64. Connect the charge air valve solenoid vacuum lines.

65. Connect the fuel feed line quick connect fitting to the fuel rail.

66. Install the oil level indicator tube.
67. Install the charge air cooler outlet pipe to the throttle body.
68. Install the air cleaner assembly. Refer to Air Cleaner Assembly.

2.2L Engine

See Figure 134.

1. Before servicing the vehicle, refer to the Precautions Section.
2. Remove the air cleaner outlet resonator.
3. Remove the throttle body. Refer to Throttle Body in Fuel System.
4. Disconnect the Positive Crankcase Ventilation (PCV) hose. Refer to Positive Crankcase Ventilation in Engine Performance & Emission Controls.
5. Disconnect the purge solenoid tube.
6. Disconnect the brake booster hose.
7. Remove the oil level indicator tube bolt.
8. Remove the fuel rail. Refer to Fuel Rail and Injectors in Fuel System.
9. Disconnect the knock sensor electrical connector. Refer to Knock Sensor in Engine Performance & Emission Controls.
10. Remove the knock sensor harness connector from the intake manifold.
11. Remove the intake manifold nuts and bolts.
12. Remove the intake manifold.

➡ **The intake manifold gasket is reusable, only replace the gasket if damage has occurred.**

13. If applicable, remove the intake manifold gasket.

To install:

14. If applicable, install the intake manifold gasket.
15. Install the intake manifold.

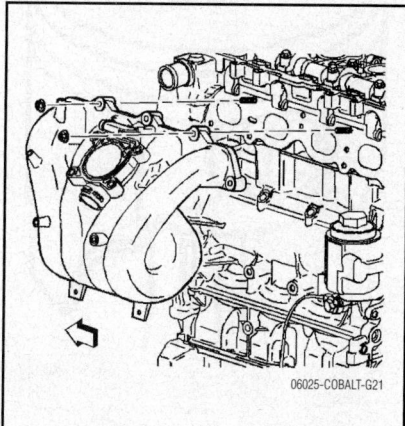

Fig. 134 Intake manifold—2.2L Engines

06025-COBALT-G21

16. Install the intake manifold nuts and bolts. Tighten the intake manifold nuts and bolts to 89 inch lbs. (10 Nm).
17. Install the knock sensor harness connector to the intake manifold.
18. Connect the knock sensor electrical connector.
19. Install the fuel rail.
20. Install the throttle body. Tighten the throttle body attaching bolts to 89 inch lbs. (10 Nm).
21. Install the oil level indicator tube bolt. Tighten the oil level indicator tube bolt to 89 inch lbs. (10 Nm).
22. Connect the brake booster hose.
23. Connect the purge solenoid tube.
24. Connect the PCV hose.
25. Install the throttle body.
26. Install the air cleaner outlet resonator.

2.4L Engine

See Figure 135.

1. Before servicing the vehicle, refer to the Precautions Section.

➡ **Never attempt to remove the intake manifold from a hot engine, allow the engine to cool to ambient temperature. The intake manifold can be damaged if it is removed when the engine is hot.**

2. Remove the evaporative emission (EVAP) canister valve tube.
3. Remove the EVAP canister valve.
4. Remove the throttle body bolts.
5. Remove the throttle body.
6. Remove fuel pipes and clip.
7. Remove the fuel rail assembly.
8. Remove the fuel injector tip insulators and discard.
9. Remove the intake manifold retaining nuts and bolts.

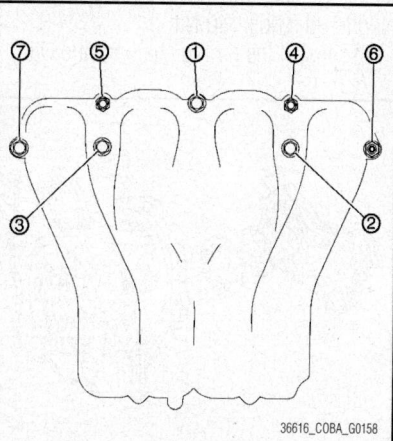

Fig. 135 Intake manifold bolt tightening sequence

36616_COBA_G0158

10. Remove the intake manifold.
11. Remove the intake manifold gasket, if necessary. The gasket can be used again if it is not damaged.
12. If the intake manifold needs to be replaced, transfer the throttle body to the new intake manifold.

To install:

13. Install the intake manifold studs in the manifold face and tighten the intake manifold studs to 53 inch lbs. (6 Nm).
14. Install a new intake manifold gasket on the intake manifold.
15. Install the intake manifold.
16. Install the intake manifold bolts and nuts finger tight. Tighten the intake manifold bolts and nuts in sequence and tighten the bolts and nuts to 89 inch lbs. (10 Nm).
17. Lubricate NEW fuel injector tip insulators with engine oil.
18. Install NEW fuel injector tip insulators.
19. Lubricate the fuel injector oil rings with engine oil.
20. Install the fuel rail assembly.
21. Install the fuel rail stud and tighten the bolts to 89 inch lbs. (10 Nm).
22. Install a new throttle body gasket.
23. Install the throttle body.
24. Install the throttle body bolts and tighten the bolts to 89 inch lbs. (10 Nm).
25. Install the EVAP canister valve and tighten the bolts and nuts to 16 ft. lbs. (22 Nm).
26. Install the EVAP canister valve tube.

OIL PAN

REMOVAL & INSTALLATION

See Figures 136 through 138.

1. Install the engine support fixture.
2. Remove the engine mount.
3. Raise the engine enough to allow clearance for the oil pan removal.
4. Raise and support the vehicle.
5. Place a drain pan under the oil pan drain plug.
6. Remove the oil pan drain plug.
7. Drain the engine oil.
8. Remove the engine drive belt. Refer to Accessory Drive Belt.
9. Remove the lower A/C compressor bolt and loosen the upper bolts.
10. Remove the 4 oil pan to transaxle bolts (1).
11. Remove the oil pan bolts.
12. Remove the oil pan
13. Remove any old oil pan sealant.

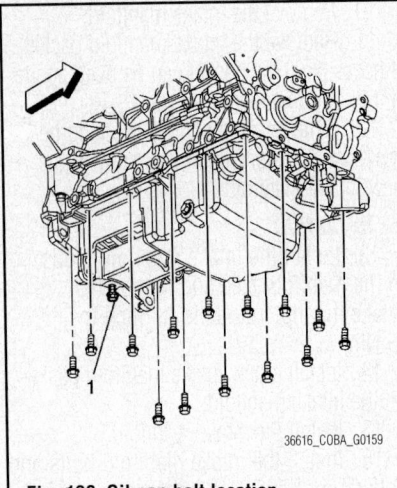

Fig. 136 Oil pan bolt location

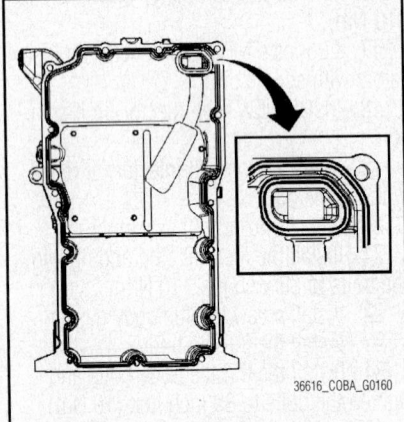

Fig. 137 Oil pan bolt sealant application

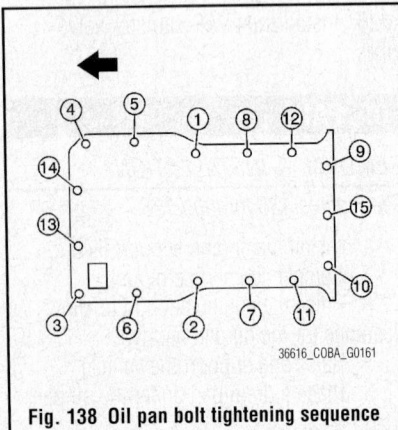

Fig. 138 Oil pan bolt tightening sequence

To install:

14. Make sure that the oil pan and mounting surface on the lower crankcase are free of all oil and debris.

15. Apply a 2 mm bead of GM P/N 123785251 (Canadian P/N 88901148) around the perimeter of the oil pan and the oil suction port opening. Do not over apply the RTV. More than a 2 mm bead is not required.

16. Install the oil pan.

17. Install the oil pan bolts in sequence. Tighten the oil pan bolts to 18 ft. lbs. (25 Nm).

18. Install the A/C compressor bolts. Tighten the bolts to 18 ft. lbs. (25 Nm).

19. Install the engine drive belt. Refer to Accessory Drive Belt.

20. Lower the vehicle.

21. Fill the engine oil to the proper level.

OIL PUMP

REMOVAL & INSTALLATION

See Figure 139.

1. Before servicing the vehicle, refer to the Precautions Section.

2. Remove the timing chain front cover. Refer to Timing Chain Cover and Seal Removal & Installation.

3. Disassemble the pressure relief valve.

4. Remove the oil pump gerotor cover and bolts.

To assemble:

5. Lubricate all oil pump parts with engine oil.

6. Install the inner gear into the outer gear.

✳✳ WARNING

If gears are improperly installed in the front cover, the gerotor cover will not bolt on.

7. Install the gears together into the front cover with the hub of the center gear facing the front cover.

8. Install the oil pump gerotor cover and bolts. Tighten the oil pump gerotor bolts to 53 inch lbs. (6 Nm).

9. Install the pressure relief valve piston.

10. Install the pressure relief valve spring. Tighten the pressure relief valve plug to 30 ft. lbs. (40 Nm).

11. Install the timing chain front cover.

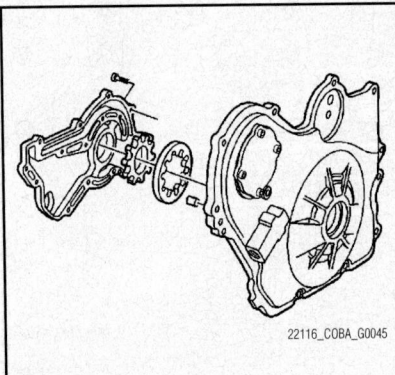

Fig. 139 Exploded view of the disassembled oil pump

Refer to Timing Chain Cover and Seal Removal & Installation.

PISTON AND RING

POSITIONING

See Figure 140.

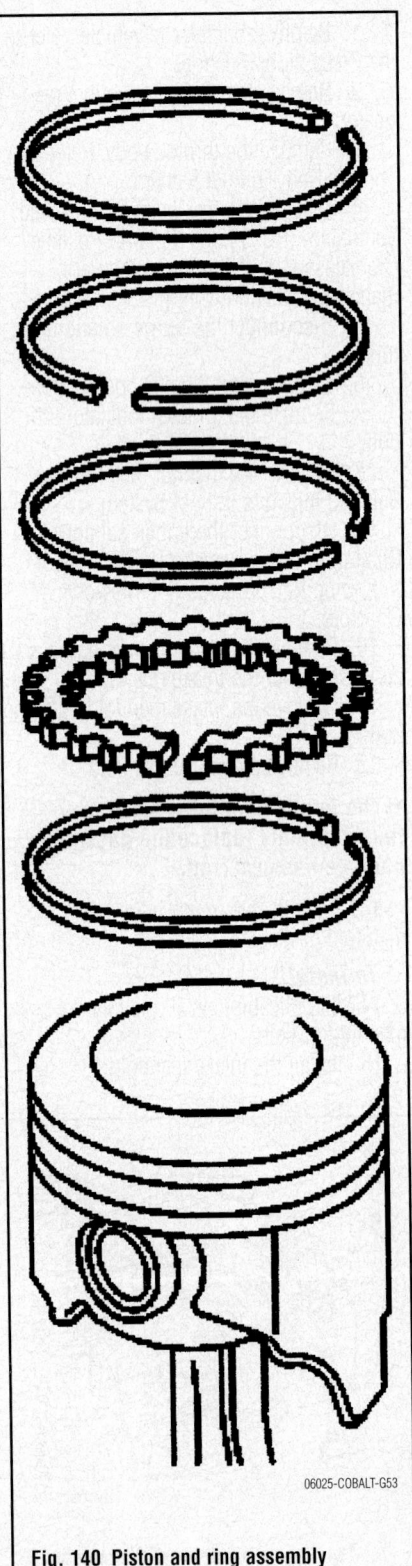

Fig. 140 Piston and ring assembly

REAR MAIN SEAL

REMOVAL & INSTALLATION

See Figures 141 and 142.

1. Before servicing the vehicle, refer to the Precautions Section.

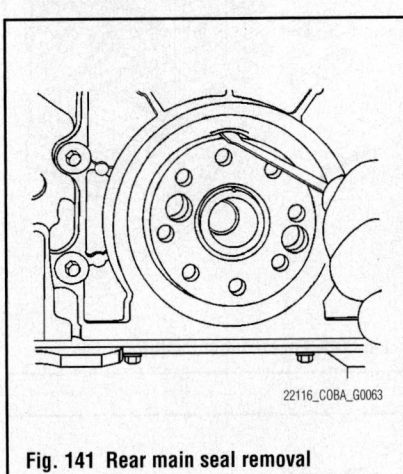

Fig. 141 Rear main seal removal

2. Remove the transaxle. Refer to Transaxle in Drive Train.
3. Remove the flywheel. Refer to Flywheel.

➡**Do not damage the outside diameter of the crankshaft or chamber with any tool.**

4. Pry the crankshaft rear oil seal with a flat-bladed tool.

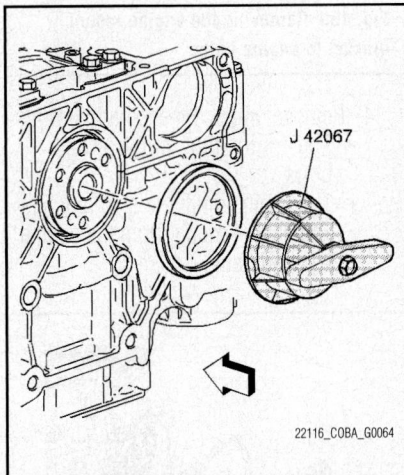

Fig. 142 Rear main seal installation using tool J 42067

To install:

5. Use a seal driver such as J 42067 and install the seal.
6. Install the flywheel. Tighten the flywheel bolts to 39 ft. lbs. (53 Nm) plus 25°.
7. Install the transaxle.

TIMING CHAIN COVER AND SEAL

REMOVAL & INSTALLATION

See Figures 143 through 151.

1. Before servicing the vehicle, refer to the Precautions Section.
2. Remove or disconnect the following:

- The drive belt tensioner
- The crankshaft damper
- The air cleaner assembly.
- The windshield washer solvent reservoir

3. Install the engine support fixture:

a. Place the engine support fixture legs (1) from the J 28467-B across the engine compartment.

b. Install the engine support fixture legs (1) from the J 28467-500 on the engine support fixture long bar (2).

c. Install the radiator shelf tube J-28467-2A (1) on top of the strut tower tube J-28467-3 (2) above the engine front (right back) lift hook bracket.

d. Install the round tube of the front support assembly J-28467-4A (3) through the large hole in the radiator shelf tube J-28467-2A.

e. Position the J-28467-4A front support assembly on to the upper tie bar.

f. Install the J-28467-9 ⁷/₁₆ inch x 2.0 inch quick-release pin (4) through the top hole in the J-28467-4A front support assembly.

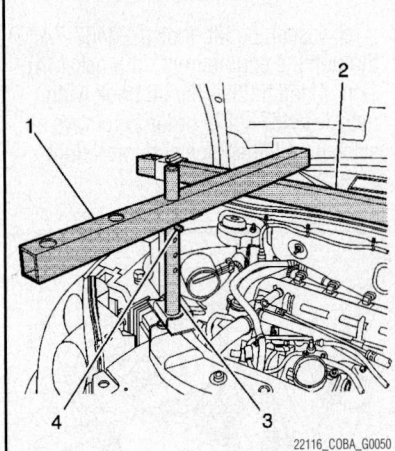

Fig. 143 Place the engine support fixture legs (1) from the J 28467-B across the engine compartment and install the engine support fixture legs (1) from the J 28467-500 on the engine support fixture long bar.

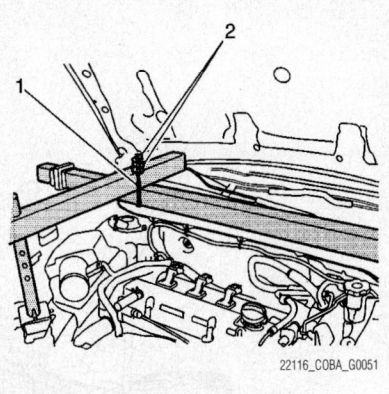

Fig. 144 Install the J-28467-1A cross bracket assembly (1) and hand tighten the J-28467-1A cross bracket wing nuts (2).

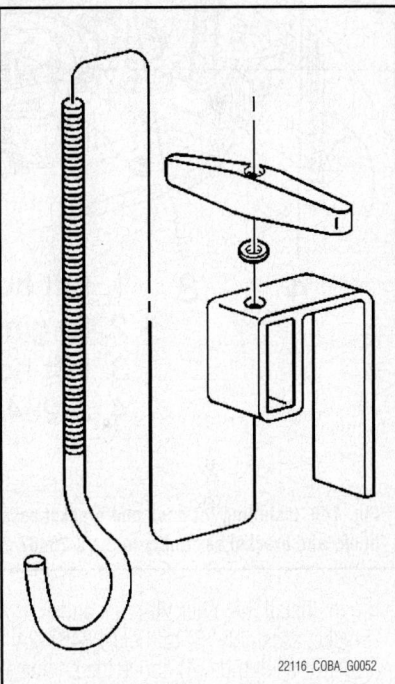

Fig. 145 View of the J-28467-7A bolt hook and the J-28467-34 lift hook wing nut and washer for installing the engine support fixture.

g. Install the J-28467-1A cross bracket assembly (1).

h. Hand tighten the J-28467-1A cross bracket wing nuts (2).

i. Install the J-28467-7A bolt hook through the J-28467-6A bracket.

j. Install the J-28467-34 lift hook wing nut and washer to the J-28467-7A lift hook.

k. Repeat the previous 2 steps in order to assemble 2 lift hooks and brackets.

l. Install one of the lift hook and bracket assemblies (1) to the engine support fixture long bar (2).

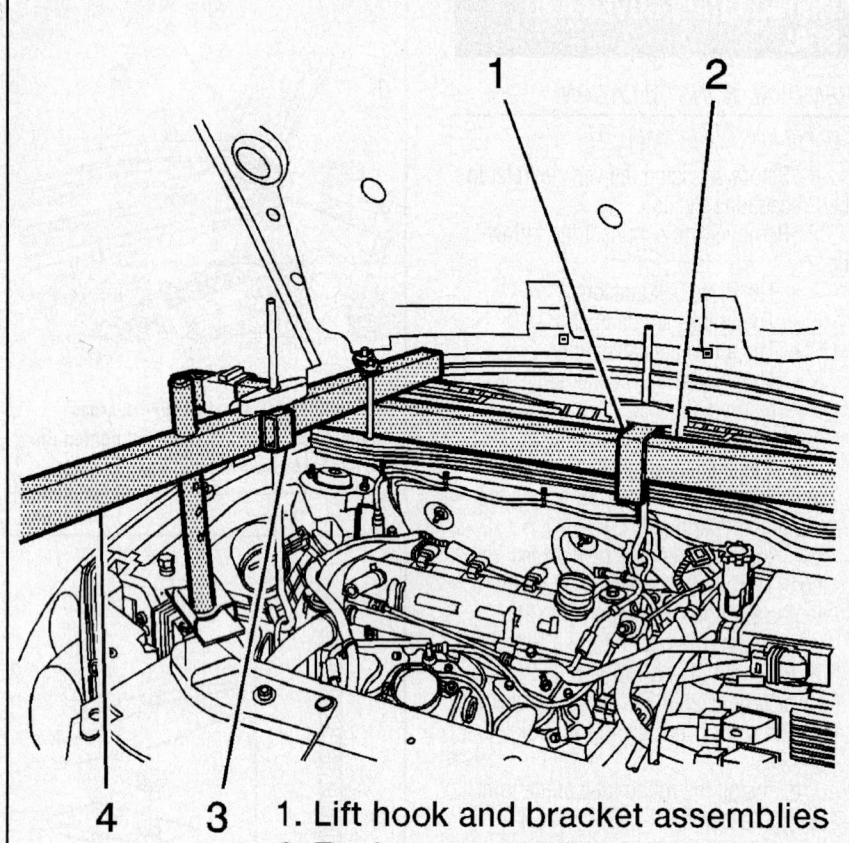

1. Lift hook and bracket assemblies
2. Engine support fixture long bar
3. Lift hook and bracket assembly
4. J-28467-2A radiator shelf tube

22116_COBA_G0053

Fig. 146 Installing lift hook and bracket assemblies to the engine support fixture long bar, lift hook, and bracket assembly to the J-28467-2A radiator shelf tube.

m. Install the other lift hook and bracket assembly (3) to the J-28467-2A radiator shelf tube (4) above the engine front lift bracket.

n. Install the lift hook J-28467-7A through the engine rear lift bracket (2).

o. Install the lift hook J-28467-7A (3) through the engine front lift bracket (4).

p. Hand tighten the lift hook wing nuts J-28467-34 in order to remove all slack from the engine support fixture assembly.

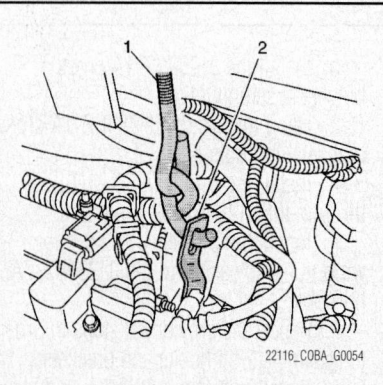

22116_COBA_G0054

Fig. 147 Install the lift hook J-28467-7A through the engine rear lift bracket (2)

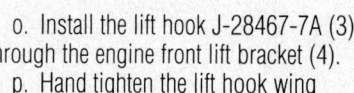

22116_COBA_G0055

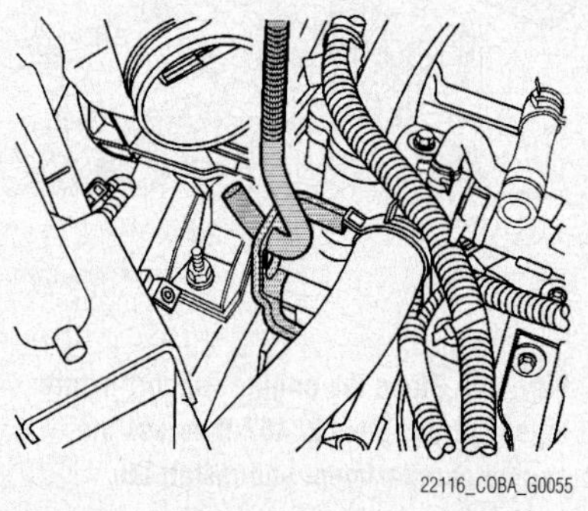

Fig. 148 Install the lift hook J-28467-7A (3) through the engine front lift bracket (4)

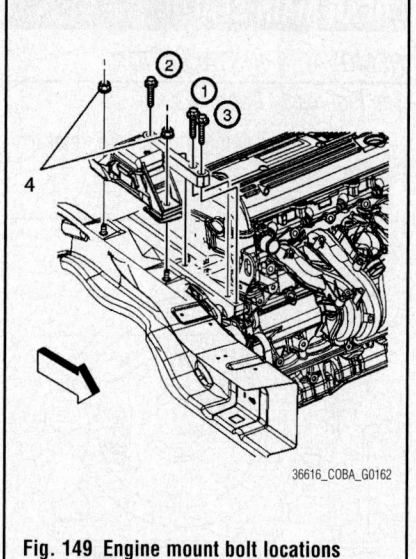

36616_COBA_G0162

Fig. 149 Engine mount bolt locations

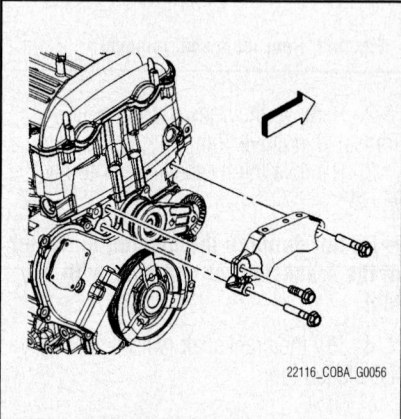

22116_COBA_G0056

Fig. 150 Removing the engine mount bracket to engine bolts

4. Remove or disconnect the following:
- The engine mount to bracket bolts
- The engine mount to side rail nuts
- The engine mount from the engine compartment

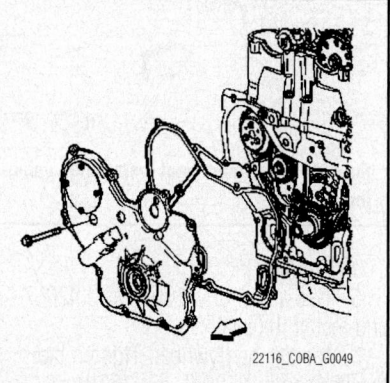

22116_COBA_G0049

Fig. 151 Removing long water pump bolt and remaining cover bolts

- The engine mount bracket to engine bolts
- The engine mount bracket
- The engine front cover to water pump bolt

5. Raise and suitably support the vehicle.

6. Remove the timing chain cover bolts.

7. Remove the timing chain cover.

8. Remove and discard the timing chain cover seal.

To install:

9. Install a NEW timing chain cover seal.

10. Install the timing chain cover.

11. Install the timing chain cover bolts. Tighten the bolts to 18 ft. lbs. (25 Nm).

12. Lower the vehicle.

13. Install the timing chain cover to water pump bolt. Tighten the bolt to 18 ft. lbs. (25 Nm).

14. Position the engine mount bracket to the engine.

15. Install the engine mount bracket bolts in the following locations:

   a. The long bolts in the forward and lower rear holes.

   b. The short bolt in the upper rear hole.

16. Tighten the engine mount bracket bolts in the following sequence:

   a. Upper rear

   b. Lower rear

   c. Forward

   d. Tighten the bolts to 37 ft. lbs. (50 Nm).

17. Install the engine mount to the engine compartment.

18. Install the engine mount to side rail nuts. Tighten the nuts to 74 ft. lbs. (100 Nm).

19. Install the engine mount to bracket bolts.

20. Tighten the engine mount to bracket bolts in the following sequence:

   a. Middle.

   b. Rear.

   c. Front.

   d. Tighten the bolts to 37 ft. lbs. (50 Nm).

21. Remove the engine support fixture. Removal is reverse of the installation.

22. Install or connect the following:

- The windshield washer solvent reservoir
- The air cleaner assembly
- The crankshaft damper. Refer to Crankshaft Damper.
- The accessory drive belt tensioner

TIMING CHAIN AND SPROCKETS

REMOVAL & INSTALLATION

2.0L Engine

See Figures 152 through 155.

1. Before servicing the vehicle, refer to the Precautions Section.

2. Remove the camshaft cover.

3. Raise and support the vehicle.

4. Remove the timing chain cover. Refer to Timing Chain Cover & Seal.

5. Lower the vehicle.

➡**To rotate the camshaft, use a 24 mm open-end wrench on the camshaft flats. Camshaft should be rotated in a clockwise direction only, facing camshaft sprockets from the passenger side of the vehicle.**

6. Locate the No. 1 piston to top dead center.

7. Remove the spark plugs. This will ease the rotation effort.

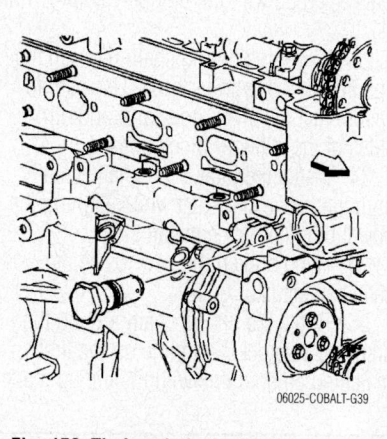

Fig. 152 Timing chain tensioner

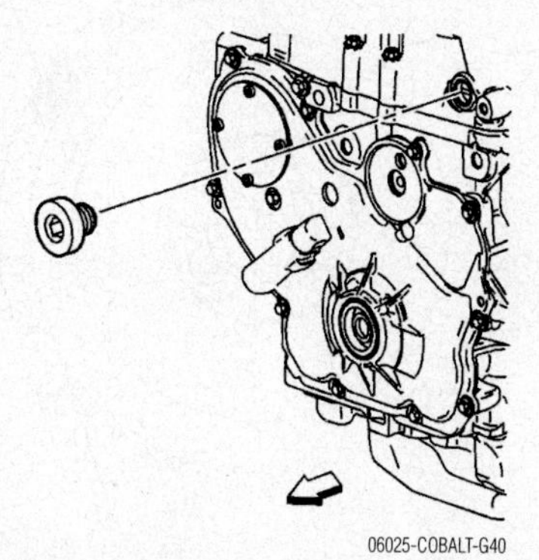

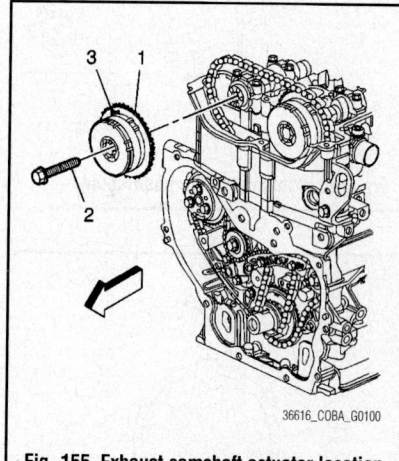

Fig. 153 Fixed timing chain guide access plug

8. Remove the timing chain tensioner.

9. Remove the fixed timing chain guide access plug.

10. Remove the fixed timing chain guide.

11. Remove the upper timing chain guide.

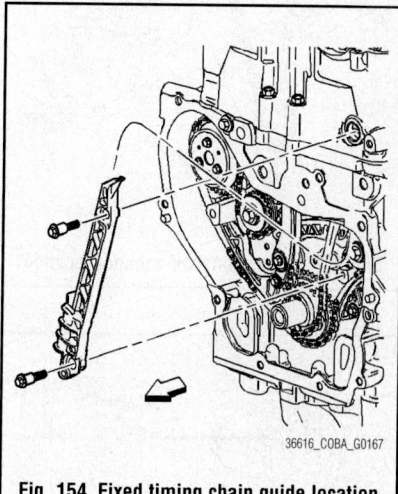

Fig. 154 Fixed timing chain guide location

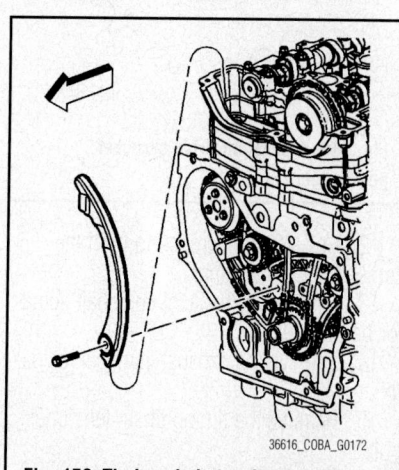

Fig. 155 Exhaust camshaft actuator location

Fig. 156 Timing chain tensioner guide

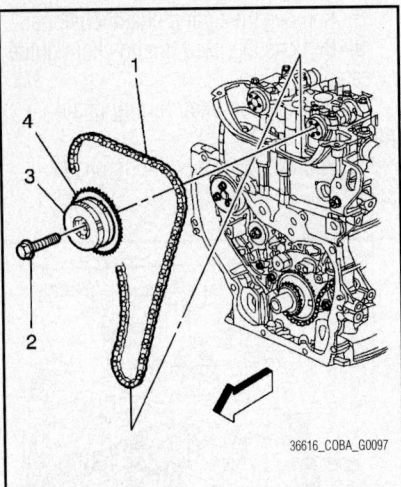

Fig. 157 Intake camshaft actuator location

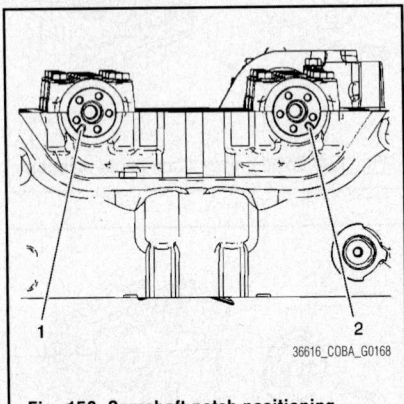

Fig. 158 Camshaft notch positioning

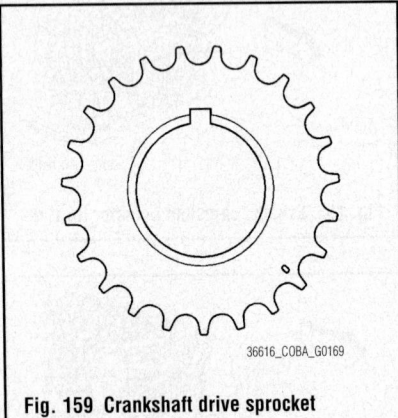

Fig. 159 Crankshaft drive sprocket positioning

12. Use a 24mm wrench to hold the camshafts from turning.

13. Remove the exhaust camshaft actuator bolt and discard.

14. Remove the exhaust camshaft actuator.

15. Remove the timing chain tensioner guide.

16. Remove the intake camshaft actuator bolt and discard.

17. Remove the intake camshaft actuator.

18. Remove the timing chain through the top of the cylinder head.

19. Remove the crankshaft sprocket.

To install:

20. Ensure the intake camshaft notch is in the 5 o'clock position (2) and the exhaust camshaft notch is in the 7 o'clock position (1). The number 1 piston should be at top dead center (TDC), crankshaft key at 12 o'clock.

21. Install the timing chain drive sprocket to the crankshaft with the timing mark in the 5 o'clock position and the front of the sprocket facing out.

➡There are 3 colored links on the timing chain. 2 links are of matching color, and 1 link is of a unique color. Use the following procedure to line up the links with the actuators. Orient the chain so that the colored links are visible.

➡Always use new actuator bolts.

22. Assemble the intake camshaft actuator into the timing chain with the timing mark lined up with the uniquely colored link (1).

23. Lower the timing chain through the opening in the cylinder head. Use care to ensure that the chain goes around both sides of the cylinder block bosses.

24. Install the intake camshaft actuator onto the intake camshaft while aligning the dowel pin into the camshaft slot.

25. Hand tighten the new intake camshaft actuator bolt.

26. Route the timing chain around the crankshaft sprocket and line up the first matching colored link with the timing mark

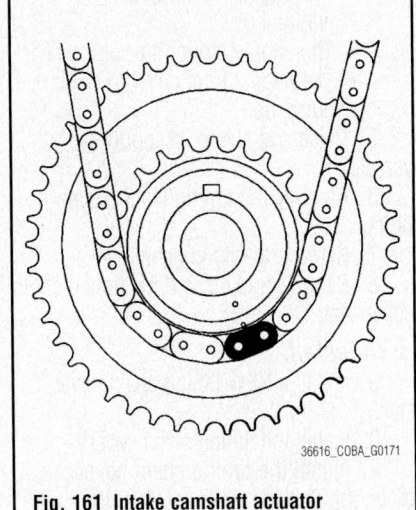

Fig. 161 Intake camshaft actuator positioning

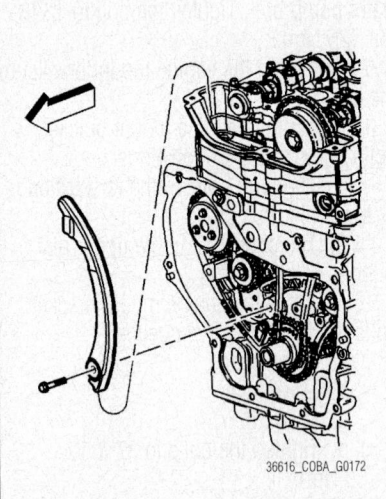

Fig. 162 Adjustable timing chain guide positioning

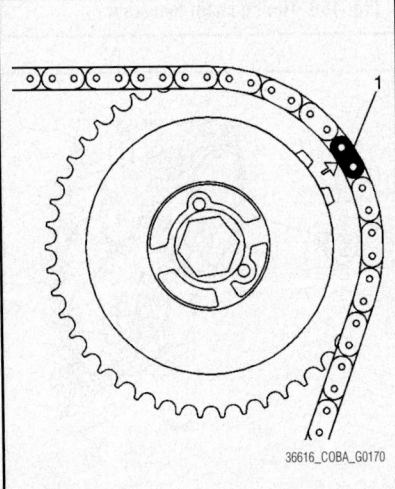

Fig. 160 Intake camshaft actuator positioning

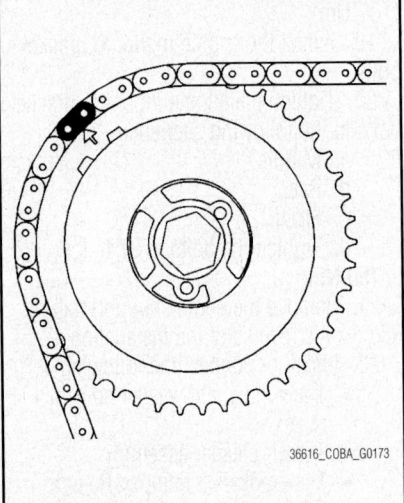

Fig. 163 Exhaust camshaft actuator positioning

on the crankshaft sprocket, in approximately the 5 o'clock position.

27. Rotate the crankshaft clockwise to remove all chain slack. Do not rotate the intake camshaft.

28. Install the adjustable timing chain guide down through the opening in the cylinder head and install the adjustable timing chain bolt and tighten the adjustable timing chain guide bolt to 89 inch lbs. (10 Nm).

29. Install the exhaust camshaft actuator into the timing chain with the timing mark lined up with the second matching colored link.

30. Install the exhaust camshaft actuator onto the exhaust camshaft, aligning the dowel pin into the camshaft slot.

31. Using a 23 mm open end wrench, rotate the exhaust camshaft approximately 45 degrees until the dowel pin in the camshaft actuator goes into the camshaft slot.

32. When the actuator seats on the cam, tighten the new exhaust camshaft actuator bolt hand tight.

33. Verify that all of the colored links and the appropriate timing marks are still aligned. If they are not aligned, repeat the portion of the procedure necessary to align the timing marks.

34. Install the fixed timing chain guide and bolts and tighten the fixed timing chain guide bolts to 106 inch lbs. (12 Nm).

35. Install the upper timing chain guide and bolts tighten the upper timing chain guide bolt to 89 inch lbs. (10 Nm).

36. Reset the timing chain tensioner by performing the following steps:

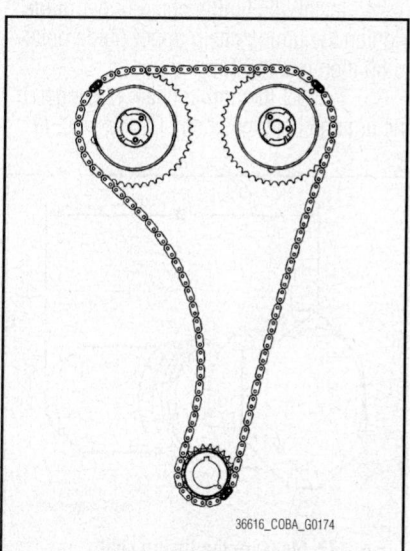

Fig. 164 Timing chain positioning

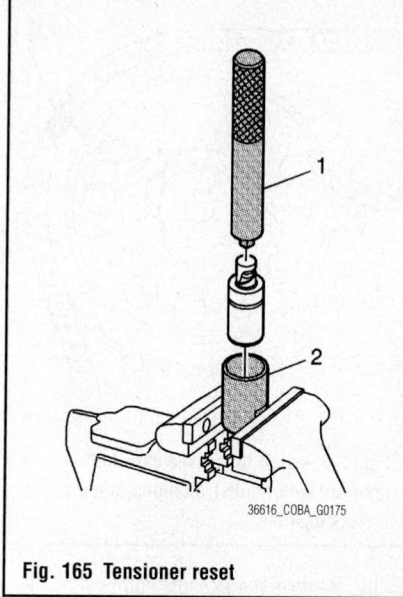

Fig. 165 Tensioner reset

- Remove the snap ring.
- Remove the piston assembly from the body of the timing chain tensioner.
- Install the J 45027-2 (2) into a vise.
- Install the notch end of the piston assembly into the J 45027-2 (2).
- Using the J 45027-1 (1), turn the ratchet cylinder into the piston.
- Reinstall the piston assembly into the body of the tensioner.
- Install the snap ring.

37. Inspect the timing chain tensioner seal for damage. If damaged, replace the seal.

38. Inspect to ensure all dirt and debris is removed from the timing chain tensioner threaded hole in the cylinder head.

➡ **Ensure the timing chain tensioner seal is centered throughout the torque procedure to eliminate the possibility of an oil leak.**

39. Install the timing chain tensioner assembly and tighten the timing chain tensioner to 55 ft. lbs. (75 Nm).

40. The timing chain tensioner is released by compressing it 2 mm (0.079 in), which will release the locking mechanism in the ratchet. To release the timing chain tensioner, use a suitable tool with a rubber tip on the end. Feed the tool down through the cam drive chest to rest on the cam chain. Then give a sharp jolt diagonally downwards to release the tensioner.

41. Using a 23 mm wrench, engage the hex on the intake camshaft, and using a torque wrench, tighten the camshaft actuator bolt and tighten the intake camshaft position

actuator bolt to 22 ft. lbs. (30 Nm), plus 100 degrees using the J 45059.

42. Using a 23 mm wrench, engage the hex on the exhaust camshaft, and using a torque wrench, tighten the camshaft actuator bolt and tighten the intake camshaft position actuator bolt to 22 ft. lbs. (30 Nm), plus 100 degrees using the J 45059.

43. Install the camshaft cover.

44. Raise the vehicle.

45. Install the engine front cover. Refer to Timing Chain Cover and Seal.

46. Lower the vehicle.

2.2L & 2.4L Engines

See Figures 166 through 173.

1. Before servicing the vehicle, refer to the Precautions Section.

2. Remove the camshaft cover.

3. Raise and support the vehicle.

4. Remove the timing chain cover. Refer to Timing Chain Cover & Seal.

5. Lower the vehicle.

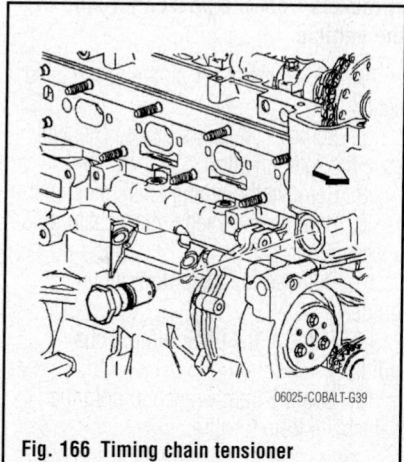

Fig. 166 Timing chain tensioner

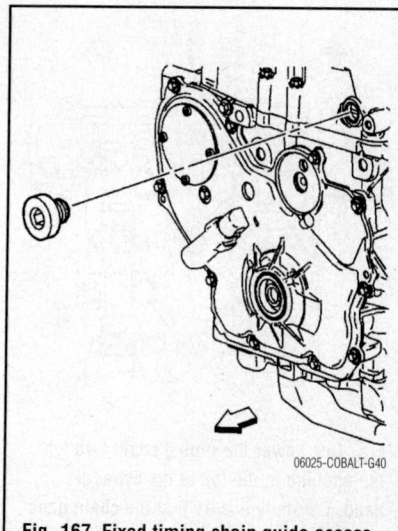

Fig. 167 Fixed timing chain guide access plug

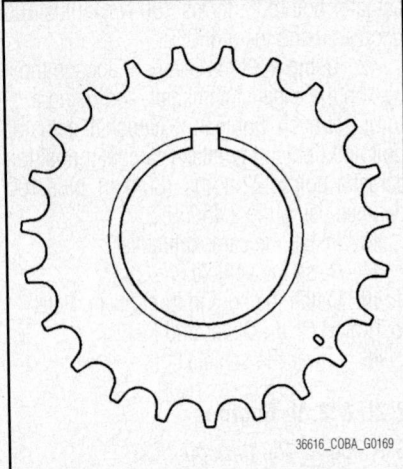

Fig. 168 Install the crankshaft sprocket with timing mark at the 5 o'clock position

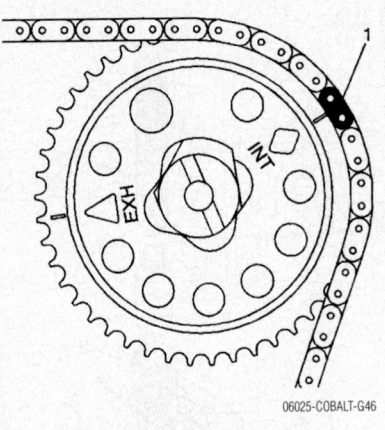

Fig. 170 Install the intake camshaft sprocket with the INT diamond at the 2 o'clock position

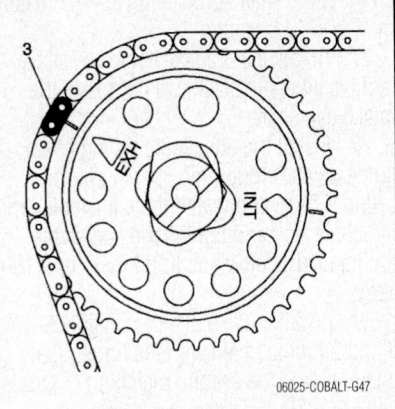

Fig. 171 Install the exhaust camshaft sprocket with the timing chain matching colored link (3) at EXH triangle aligned at the 10 o'clock position

➡ To rotate the camshaft, use a 24 mm open-end wrench on the camshaft flats. Camshaft should be rotated in a clockwise direction only, facing camshaft sprockets from the passenger side of the vehicle.

6. Locate the No. 1 piston to top dead center.

7. Remove the spark plugs. This will ease the rotation effort.

8. Remove the timing chain tensioner.

9. Remove the fixed timing chain guide access plug.

10. Remove the fixed timing chain guide.

11. Remove the upper timing chain guide.

12. Use a 24mm wrench to hold the camshafts from turning.

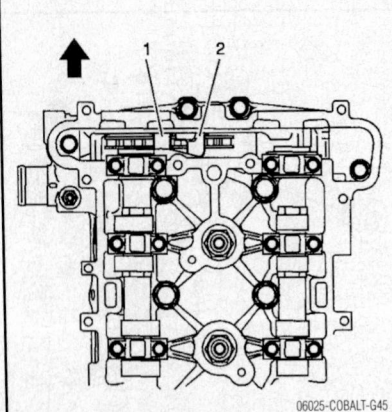

Fig. 169 Lower the timing chain through the opening in the top of the cylinder head. Carefully ensure that the chain goes around both sides of the cylinder block bosses (1, 2)

13. Remove the exhaust camshaft sprocket bolt and discard.

14. Remove the exhaust camshaft sprocket.

15. Remove the timing chain tensioner guide.

16. Remove the intake camshaft sprocket bolt and discard.

17. Remove the intake camshaft sprocket.

18. Remove the timing chain through the top of the cylinder head.

19. Remove the crankshaft sprocket.

20. Remove the oil nozzle and bolt.

To install:

21. Install the oil nozzle and bolt. Tighten the oil nozzle bolt to 89 inch lbs. (10 Nm).

22. Install the crankshaft sprocket with timing mark at the 5 o'clock position.

23. Lower the timing chain through the opening in the top of the cylinder head. Carefully ensure that the chain goes around both sides of the cylinder block bosses (1, 2).

24. Install the intake camshaft sprocket with the INT diamond at the 2 o'clock position.

➡ Always install NEW sprocket bolts.

25. Hand tighten a NEW intake camshaft sprocket bolt.

26. Route the timing chain around the crankshaft sprocket with the matching colored link aligning with the timing mark.

27. Route the timing chain around the intake camshaft sprocket with the uniquely colored link (1) aligning with the INT diamond.

28. Install the timing chain tensioner guide through the opening in the top of the

cylinder head. Tighten the timing chain tensioner guide bolt to 89 inch lbs. (10 Nm).

29. Install the exhaust camshaft sprocket with the timing chain matching colored link (3) at EXH triangle aligned at the 10 o'clock position.

30. Use a 24mm wrench to rotate the camshaft slightly, until exhaust sprocket aligns with the camshaft.

➡ Always install NEW sprocket bolts.

31. Hand-tighten the NEW exhaust camshaft sprocket bolt.

32. Install the fixed timing chain guide. Tighten the fixed timing chain bolts to 89 inch lbs. (10 Nm).

33. Apply sealant, GM P/N 12378521 (Canadian P/N 88901148) compound to thread and install the timing chain guide bolt access hole plug. Tighten the chain guide plug to 59 ft. lbs. (90 Nm).

34. Install the timing chain upper guide. Tighten the timing chain upper guide bolts to 89 inch lbs. (10 Nm).

35. Inspect the timing chain tensioner. If the timing chain tensioner, O-ring seal, or

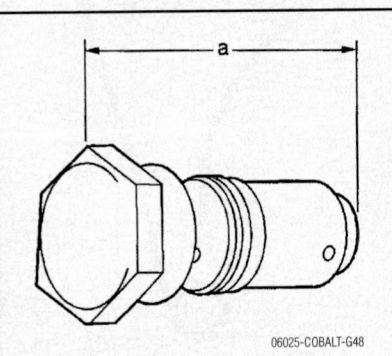

Fig. 172 Measure the timing chain tensioner assembly from end to end

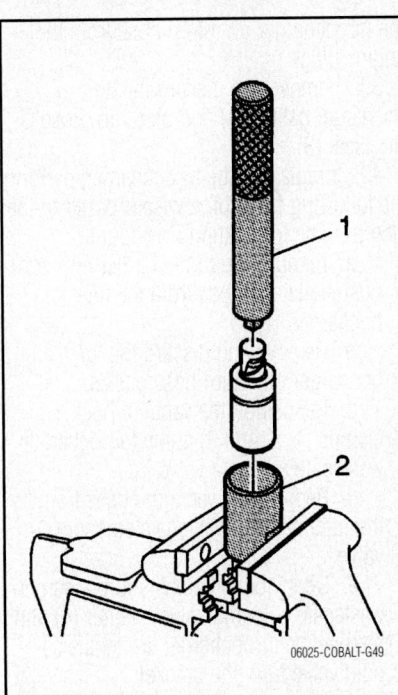

Fig. 173 Compressing the timing chain tensioner

washer is damaged, replace the timing chain tensioner.

36. Measure the timing chain tensioner assembly from end to end. A new tensioner should be supplied in the fully compressed non-active state. A tensioner in the compressed state will measure approximately 3 inches (72mm) (a) from end to end. A tensioner in the active state will measure 3 5/16 inches (85mm) (a) from end to end.

37. If the timing chain tensioner is not in the compressed state, perform the following steps:

　a. Remove the piston assembly from the body of the timing chain tensioner by pulling it out.

　b. Install the J 45027-2 (2) into a vise.

　c. Install the notch end of the piston assembly into the J 45027-2 (2).

　d. Using the J 45027-1 (1), turn the ratchet cylinder into the piston.

38. Inspect the bore of the tensioner body for dirt, debris, and damage. If any damage appears, replace the tensioner. Clean dirt or debris out with a lint-free cloth.

39. Install the compressed piston assembly back into the timing chain tensioner body until it stops at the bottom of the bore. Do not compress the piston assembly against the bottom of the bore. If the piston assembly is compressed against the bottom of the bore, it will activate the tensioner, which will then need to be reset again.

40. At this point the tensioner should measure approximately 3 inches (72mm) (a) from end to end. If the tensioner does not read approximately 3 inches (72mm) (a) from end to end repeat steps 26.1 through 26.4.

41. Install the timing chain tensioner. Tighten the timing chain tensioner to 55 ft. lbs. (75 Nm).

42. Use a suitable tool with a rubber tip on the end. Feed the tool down through the camshaft drive chain to rest on the timing chain. Then give a sharp jolt diagonally downwards to release the tensioner.

43. Use a 24mm wrench to hold the camshaft. Tighten the NEW camshaft bolts to 63 ft. lbs. (85 Nm) plus 30°.

44. Install the camshaft cover.

45. Raise the vehicle.

46. Install the engine front cover.

47. Lower the vehicle.

TURBOCHARGER

REMOVAL & INSTALLATION

See Figures 174 through 180.

1. Drain the cooling system.

2. Remove the charge air cooler inlet pipe.

3. Remove the air cleaner outlet duct.

4. Remove the charge air cooler pipe bolts at the turbocharger.

5. Remove the charge air cooler pipe from the turbocharger.

6. Remove the air conditioning (A/C) evaporator hose assembly.

7. Remove the A/C rear condenser tube.

8. Remove the brake vacuum booster vacuum hose from the booster.

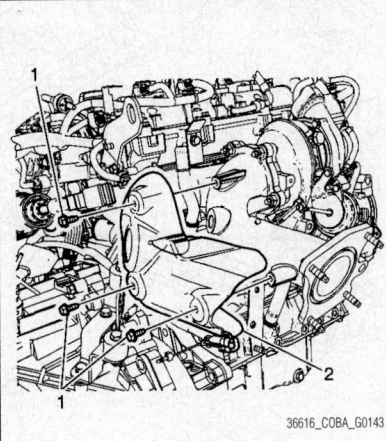

Fig. 174 Turbocharger exhaust pipe heat shield

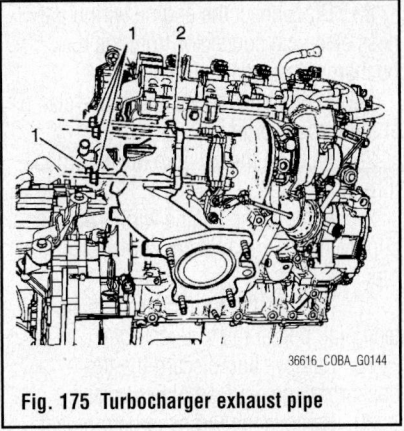

Fig. 175 Turbocharger exhaust pipe

9. Unbolt the transmission shifter bracket from the transmission and leave cables attached and position aside.

10. Remove the turbocharger heat shield bolts and shield.

11. Remove the catalytic converter. Refer to Catalytic Converter.

12. Remove the heated oxygen sensor. Refer to Heated Oxygen Sensor in Engine Performance and Emission Control.

13. Remove the turbocharger exhaust pipe heat shield bolts (1).

14. Remove the turbocharger exhaust pipe heat shield (2).

15. Raise and support the vehicle.

16. Remove the turbocharger exhaust pipe nuts (1).

17. Remove the turbocharger exhaust pipe (2).

18. Remove the turbocharger bracket bolt (1).

19. Remove the turbocharger bracket bolt (2) and bracket (3).

20. Remove the turbocharger brace bolts (4).

21. Remove the turbocharger brace nut (5) and brace (6).

22. Lower the vehicle.

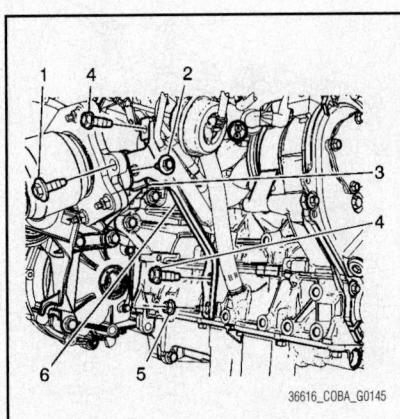

Fig. 176 Turbocharger brace and bracket bolt locations

23. Disconnect the engine wiring harness electrical connector from the turbocharger wastegate solenoid valve.

24. Reposition the vacuum hose clamp at the turbocharger.

25. Remove the vacuum hose from the turbocharger.

26. Remove the engine wiring harness clip from the turbocharger coolant feed pipe.

27. Remove the turbocharger coolant feed pipe bolt at the turbocharger.

28. Remove and discard the turbocharger coolant feed pipe gasket.

29. Remove the turbocharger coolant feed pipe bolt from the cylinder head.

30. Reposition the turbocharger coolant feed pipe out of the way.

31. Remove the positive crankcase ventilation (PCV) pipe from the turbocharger. Reposition the PCV pipe (with fitting) out of the way.

32. Remove the thermostat outlet housing and pipe. Refer to Thermostat in Engine Cooling.

➡ **Do not twist the turbocharger oil feed pipe. Twisting of the feed pipe will result in the collapse and deformation of the plastic pipe, restricting oil flow and causing turbocharger damage. During turbocharger replacement, gently push the oil feed pipe towards the front of the engine to clear the turbocharger. Assistance may be required to keep the pipes clear of the turbocharger during removal or installation.**

33. Remove the turbocharger oil feed pipe bolts and pipe (1).

34. Remove and discard the turbocharger oil feed pipe gaskets.

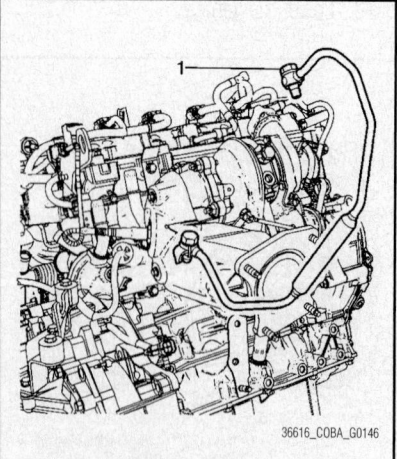

Fig. 177 Turbocharger oil feed pipe bolts and pipe locations

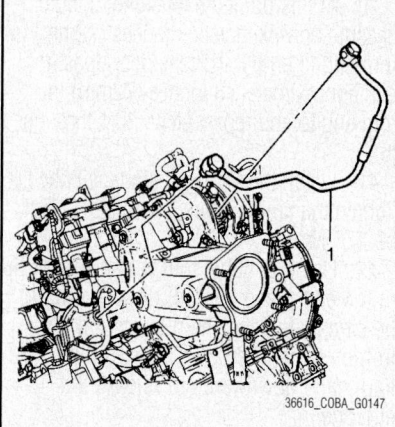

Fig. 178 Turbocharger coolant return pipe bolts and pipe locations

35. Remove the turbocharger coolant return pipe bolts and pipe (1).

36. Remove and discard the turbocharger coolant return pipe gaskets.

37. Remove the turbocharger nuts (2).

38. Remove the turbocharger from the exhaust manifold studs while also removing

the turbocharger oil return hose from the engine block.

39. Remove and discard the turbocharger gasket (1) and oil return hose O-ring seal (3).

40. If replacing the turbocharger, perform the following steps otherwise proceed to the step 2 in the Installation Procedure.

a. Remove the turbocharger oil return hose bolts and hose from the turbocharger.

b. Remove and discard the turbocharger oil return hose gasket.

c. Reposition the vacuum hose clamps (1, 2, and 3) at the turbocharger wastegate solenoid valve.

d. Remove the vacuum hoses from the turbocharger wastegate solenoid valve.

e. Gently push back the turbocharger wastegate solenoid valve retainer (4) and remove the turbocharger wastegate solenoid valve from the bracket.

To install:

41. If replacing the turbocharger, perform the following steps otherwise proceed to step 7.

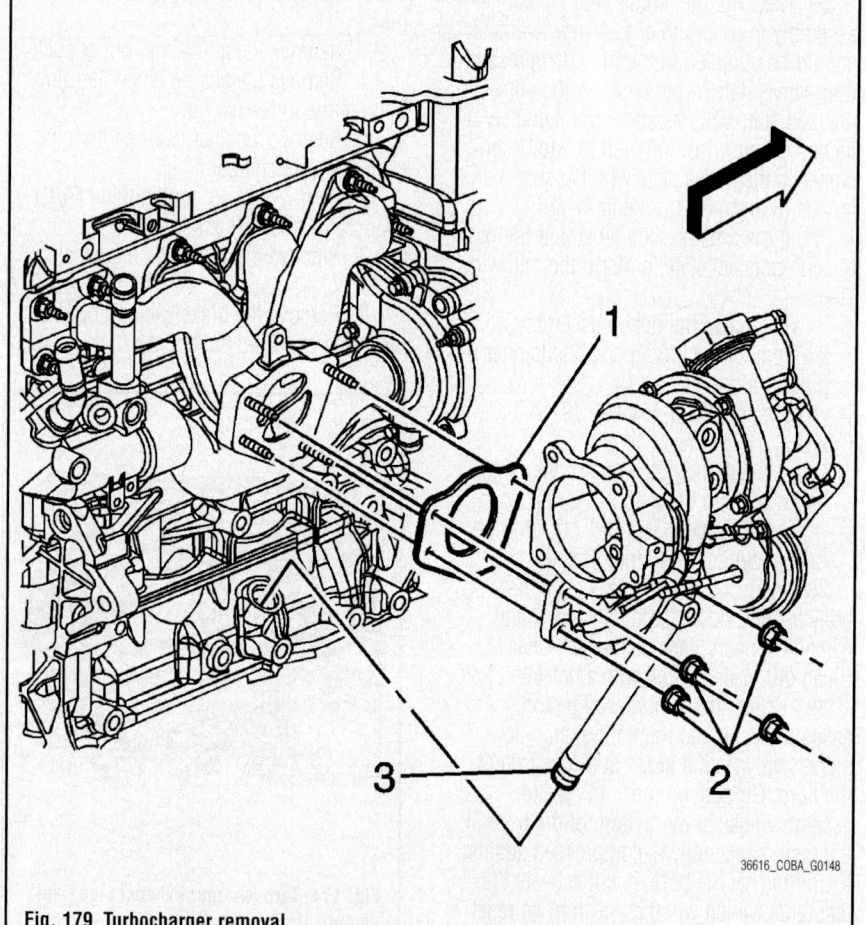

Fig. 179 Turbocharger removal

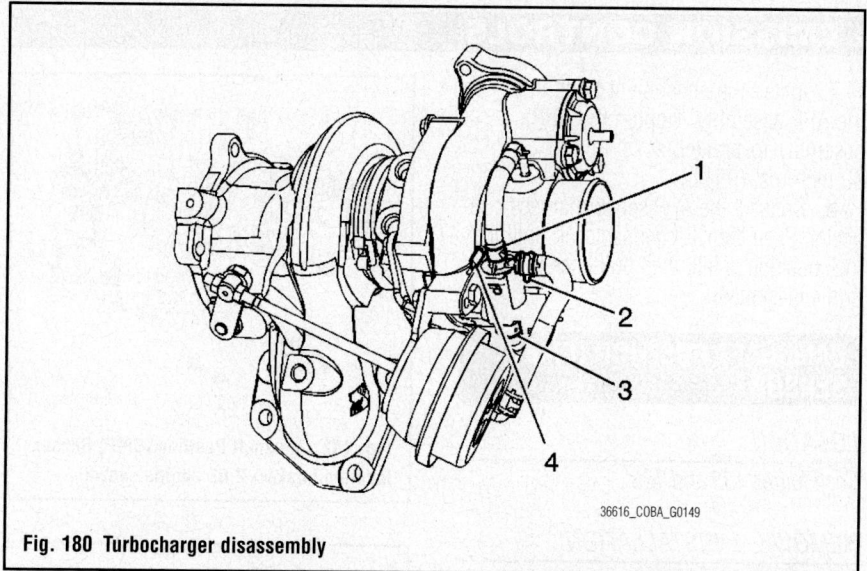

Fig. 180 Turbocharger disassembly

36616_COBA_G0149

a. Install the turbocharger wastegate solenoid valve to the bracket until the retainer clips into place.

b. Install the vacuum hoses to the turbocharger wastegate solenoid valve.

c. Position the vacuum hose clamps at the turbocharger wastegate solenoid valve.

d. Position a NEW turbocharger oil return hose gasket on the turbocharger oil return hose.

e. Install the turbocharger oil return hose and bolts and tighten the bolts to 89 inch lbs. (10 Nm).

42. Install NEW gaskets onto the turbocharger coolant return pipe fittings.

43. Install the turbocharger coolant return pipe and bolts tighten the bolts to 26 ft. lbs. (35 Nm).

44. Install the thermostat outlet housing and pipe. Refer to Thermostat in Engine Cooling.

45. Install a NEW turbocharger gasket onto the exhaust manifold studs.

46. Lubricate and install a NEW turbocharger oil return hose O-ring seal.

47. Install the turbocharger oil return hose to the engine block while also installing the turbocharger to the exhaust manifold studs.

48. Install the turbocharger nuts and tighten the nuts to 26 ft. lbs. (35 Nm).

49. Install NEW gaskets onto the turbocharger oil feed pipe fittings.

50. Install the turbocharger oil feed pipe and bolts and tighten the bolts to 24 ft. lbs. (32 Nm).

51. Position the PCV pipe (with fitting) and install the PCV fitting to the turbocharger.

52. Position the turbocharger coolant feed pipe to the turbocharger.

53. Install NEW gaskets onto the turbocharger coolant feed pipe fitting.

54. Install the turbocharger coolant feed pipe bolt at the turbocharger and tighten to 26 ft lbs. (35 Nm).

55. Install the turbocharger coolant feed pipe bolt to the cylinder head and tighten the bolt to 89 inch lbs. (10 Nm).

56. Install the engine wiring harness clip to the turbocharger coolant feed pipe.

57. Install the vacuum hose to the turbocharger.

58. Position the vacuum hose clamp at the turbocharger.

59. Connect the engine wiring harness electrical connector to the turbocharger wastegate solenoid valve.

60. Install the turbocharger brace and brace nut and tighten the nut to 37 ft. lbs. (50 Nm).

61. Install the turbocharger brace bolts and tighten the nut to 37 ft. lbs. (50 Nm).

62. Install the turbocharger bracket and bracket bolt and tighten the nut to 18 ft. lbs. (25 Nm).

63. Install the turbocharger bracket bolt and tighten to 18 ft. lbs. (25 Nm).

64. Install the turbocharger exhaust pipe.

65. Install the turbocharger exhaust pipe nuts and tighten to 37 ft. lbs. (50 Nm).

66. Install the turbocharger exhaust pipe heat shield.

67. Install the turbocharger exhaust pipe heat shield and tighten bolts to 89 inch lbs. (10 Nm).

68. Install the transmission shiftier bracket with the cables to the transmission.

69. Install the brake vacuum booster vacuum hose to the booster.

70. Install the A/C rear condenser tube.

71. Install the A/C evaporator hose assembly.

72. Raise and suitably support the vehicle.

73. Install the heated oxygen sensor.

74. Install the catalytic converter. Refer to Catalytic Converter.

75. Lower the vehicle.

76. Install the turbocharger heat shield and bolts and tighten bolts to 89 inch lbs. (10 Nm).

77. Install the charge air cooler pipe and gasket to the turbocharger.

78. Install the charge air cooler pipe bolts at the turbocharger and tighten the bolts to 16 ft. lbs. (22 Nm).

79. Install the air cleaner outlet duct.

80. Install the charge air cooler inlet pipe.

81. Fill the cooling system.

VALVE LASH

ADJUSTMENT

Valve lash is maintained by hydraulic valve lash adjusters.

ENGINE PERFORMANCE & EMISSION CONTROLS

ACCELERATOR PEDAL POSITION (APP) SENSOR

LOCATION

See Figure 181.

REMOVAL & INSTALLATION

See Figure 181.

1. Disconnect the Connector Position Assurance (CPA) from the Accelerator Pedal Position (APP) sensor connector.
2. Disconnect the APP sensor harness connector.
3. Remove the APP assembly attachment bolts from the brake pedal assembly.
4. Remove the APP assembly from the vehicle.

To install:
5. Install the upper attachment bolt into the APP assembly.
6. Install the APP assembly into the vehicle.

7. Install the attachment bolts into the APP assembly. Tighten the APP assembly-to-brake bracket bolt to 80 inch lbs. (9 Nm).
8. Connect the APP sensor harness connector. Push the CPA connector in until the lock position is felt, then pull back to confirm engagement.

CAMSHAFT POSITION (CMP) SENSOR

LOCATION

See Figures 182 and 183.

REMOVAL & INSTALLATION

Intake

See Figures 182 and 183.

1. Remove the fuel feed intermediate pipe for high pressure fuel pump—2.0L only.
2. Remove camshaft position bolt.

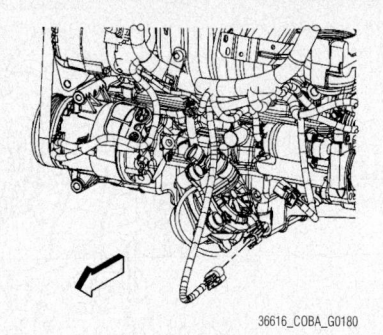

36616_COBA_G0180

Fig. 182 Camshaft Position (CMP) Sensor location intake—2.0L engine shown

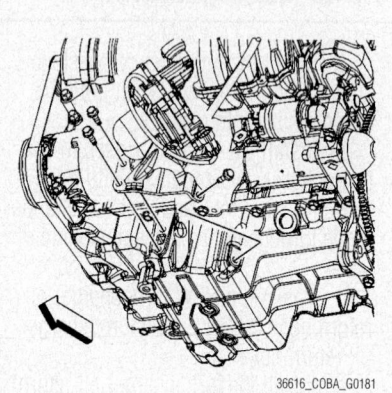

36616_COBA_G0181

Fig. 183 Camshaft Position (CMP) Sensor location exhaust—2.0L engine shown

3. Disconnect electrical connectors.
4. Remove Camshaft Position (CMP) sensor.

To install:
5. Installation is reverse of removal.
6. Lubricate the Camshaft Position (CMP) sensor O-ring seal with clean engine oil before installation.
7. Tighten bolt to 89 inch lbs. (10 Nm).

Exhaust

See Figures 182 and 183.

1. Remove camshaft position bolt.
2. Disconnect electrical connectors.
3. Remove Camshaft Position (CMP) sensor.

To install:
4. Installation is reverse of removal.
5. Lubricate the Camshaft Position (CMP) sensor O-ring seal with clean engine oil before installation.
6. Tighten bolt to 89 inch lbs. (10 Nm).

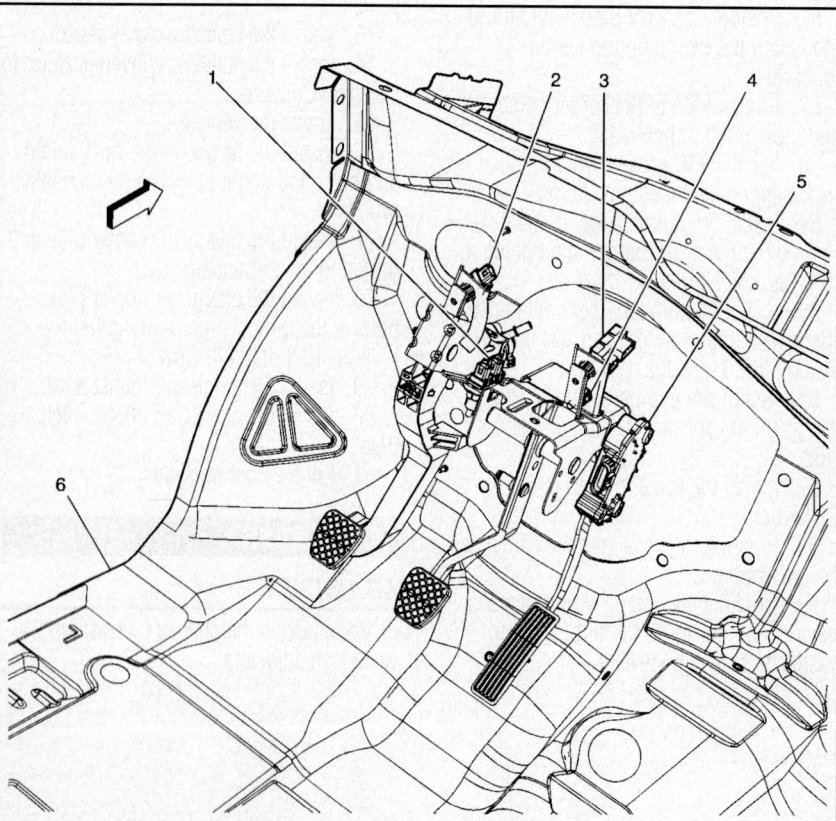

1. Clutch Pedal Position (CCP) Switch (M86)
2. Clutch Start Switch (M86)
3. Stop Lamp/TCC Switch
4. Cruise Control Cancel Switch
5. Accelerator Pedal Position (APP) Sensor
6. Floor Pan

22116_COBA_G0165

Fig. 181 Accelerator Pedal Position (APP) sensor and related components

CRANKSHAFT POSITION (CKP) SENSOR

LOCATION

See Figure 184.

REMOVAL & INSTALLATION

See Figure 184.

1. Remove the starter. Refer to Starter in Engine Electrical.
2. Disconnect the Crankshaft Position (CKP) sensor electrical connector.
3. Remove the CKP sensor bolt.
4. Remove the CKP sensor (2).

To install:

5. Inspect the CKP sensor O-ring and lubricate with a mineral based grease.
6. Gently insert the CKP sensor (2) into the block.
7. Install the CKP sensor bolt. Tighten the CKP sensor bolt to 89 inch lbs. (10 Nm).
8. Reconnect the CKP sensor electrical connector.
9. Install the starter. Tighten starter bolts to 37 ft. lbs. (50 Nm).

RELEARN PROCEDURE

➡**The Crankshaft Position (CKP) system variation learn procedure is required when the following service procedures have been performed, regardless of whether DTC P0315 is set:**

- Engine replacement
- Engine control module (ECM) replacement
- Crankshaft damper replacement
- Crankshaft replacement
- CKP sensor replacement
- Any engine repairs which disturb the crankshaft to CKP sensor relationship

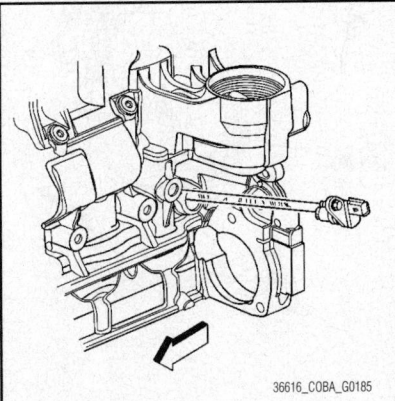

Fig. 184 CKP sensor location

➡**The scan tool monitors certain component signals to determine if all the conditions are met to continue with the CKP system variation learn procedure. The scan tool only displays the condition that inhibits the procedure. The scan tool monitors the following components:**

- CKP sensor activity, if there is a CKP sensor condition, refer to the applicable DTC that set.
- Camshaft position (CMP) signal activity, if there is a CMP signal condition, refer to the applicable DTC that set.
- Engine coolant temperature (ECT), if the engine coolant temperature is not warm enough, idle the engine until the engine coolant temperature reaches the correct temperature.

1. Install a scan tool.
2. Monitor the ECM for DTCs with a scan tool. If other DTCs are set, except DTC P0315, refer to Diagnostic Trouble Codes.
3. With a scan tool, select the CKP system variation learn procedure and perform the following:

- Observe the fuel cut-off for the applicable engine.
- Block the drive wheels.
- Set the parking brake.
- Place the vehicle's transmission in Park or Neutral.
- Turn the air conditioning (A/C) OFF.
- Cycle the ignition from OFF to ON.
- Apply and hold the brake pedal for the duration of the procedure.
- Start and idle the engine.
- Accelerate to wide open throttle (WOT). The engine should not accelerate beyond the calibrated fuel cut-off RPM value noted in step 3.1. Release the throttle immediately if the value is exceeded.

➡**While the learn procedure is in progress, release the throttle immediately when the engine starts to decelerate. The engine control is returned to the operator and the engine responds to throttle position after the learn procedure is complete.**

- Release the throttle when fuel cut-off occurs.

4. The scan tool displays Learn Status: Learned this Ignition. If the scan tool indicates that DTC P0315 ran and passed, the CKP variation learn procedure is complete. If the scan tool indicates DTC P0315 failed or did not run, refer to DTC P0315 . If any other DTCs set, refer to Diagnostic Trouble Codes.

5. Turn OFF the ignition for 30 seconds after the learn procedure is completed successfully.

ELECTRONIC CONTROL MODULE (ECM)

LOCATION

See Figure 185.

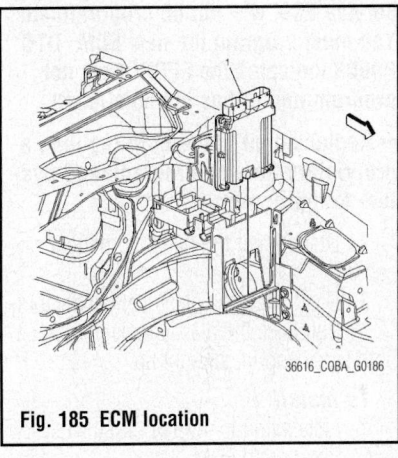

Fig. 185 ECM location

REMOVAL & INSTALLATION

See Figure 185.

➡**In order to prevent any possible electrostatic discharge damage to the ECM, do not touch the connector pins or the soldered components on the circuit board. Always turn the ignition off when installing or removing the ECM connectors in order to prevent damage to the components. It is necessary to record the remaining engine oil life. If the replacement module is not programmed with the remaining engine oil life, the engine oil life will default to 100 percent. If the replacement module is not programmed with the remaining engine oil life, the engine oil will need to be changed at 5 000 km (3,000 mi) from the last oil change.**

❊❊ CAUTION

Replacement or reprogramming of the ECM, or replacement of the clutch pedal position sensor (CPPS) or clutch pedal requires that a CPPS learn procedure be performed. Failure to perform the CPPS learn procedure may result in personal injury or damage to the vehicle or its components if the vehicle is in gear and the starter motor is accidentally engaged. Refer to Clutch Pedal Position Sensor Learn in Clutch.

➡Service of the ECM should normally consist of either replacement of the ECM or electrically erasable programmable read only memory (EEPROM) programming. If the diagnostic procedures call for ECM replacement, inspect the ECM first to see if the replacement is the correct part. If the ECM is faulty, remove the ECM and install the new service ECM. The new service ECM will not be programmed. You must program the new ECM. DTC P0602 indicates the EEPROM is not programmed or has malfunctioned.

➡Replacement of the ECM requires a proprietary Service Programming System to reprogram.

1. Disconnect the negative battery cable.
2. Disconnect the electrical connectors.
3. Pull back the plastic locking tabs on both sides and lift straight up.

To install:
4. Installation is reverse of removal.
5. Reprogram ECM.

RESET

Replacement of the ECM requires a proprietary Service Programming System to reprogram.

ENGINE COOLANT TEMPERATURE (ECT) SENSOR

REMOVAL & INSTALLATION

✳✳ WARNING

Use care when handling the coolant sensor. Damage to the coolant sensor will affect the operation of the fuel control system.

1. Turn OFF the ignition.
2. Drain the coolant system to below the Engine Coolant Temperature (ECT) sensor.
3. Disconnect the ECT sensor electrical connector.
4. Carefully remove the ECT sensor.

To install:
5. If you are reinstalling the original sensor, or if you are installing a new sensor without a sealer, coat the threads with sealer GM P/N 12346004 (Canadian P/N 10953480) or Saturn P/N 21485278 or an equivalent.
6. Install the ECT sensor. Tighten the ECT sensor to 89 inch lbs. (10 Nm).
7. Connect the ECT sensor electrical connector.

8. Refill the engine coolant system.
9. Run the engine to normal operating temperature and check for leaks.

EVAPORATIVE EMISSIONS (EVAP) CANISTER

LOCATION

See Figure 186.

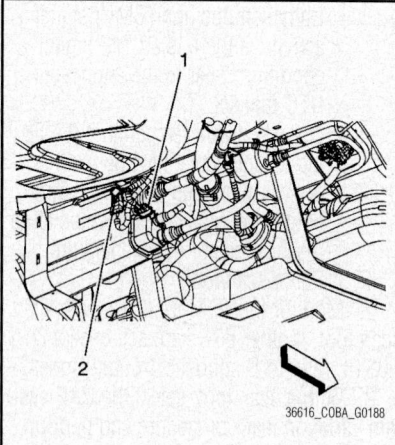

36616_COBA_G0188

Fig. 186 Evaporative Emissions (EVAP) Canister location

REMOVAL & INSTALLATION

See Figure 186.

1. Raise and suitably support the vehicle.
2. Disconnect the evaporative emission (EVAP) canister harness electrical connector from the fuel tank pressure sensor.
3. Disconnect the EVAP canister harness electrical connector from the EVAP canister vent solenoid valve.
4. Disconnect the fuel fill vent pipe quick connect fitting from the EVAP canister.
5. Disconnect the fuel tank EVAP line quick connect fittings from the EVAP canister.
6. Remove the EVAP canister bolt.
7. Slide the EVAP canister assembly toward the driver side of the vehicle in order to remove.

➡The EVAP canister may have released carbon particles which caused this part to fail and may cause damage to other components. Check the EVAP canister for loose carbon before returning the vehicle to service. If reusing the EVAP canister, inspect the canister for loose carbon particles.

To install:
8. Insert the retaining tab on the EVAP canister into the slotted bracket on the vehicle underbody.

9. Install the EVAP canister bolt and tighten to 89 inch lbs. (10 Nm).
10. Connect the fuel tank EVAP line quick connect fittings to the EVAP canister.
11. Connect the fuel fill vent pipe quick connect fitting to the EVAP canister. Connect the EVAP canister harness electrical connector to the fuel tank pressure sensor.
12. Connect the EVAP canister harness electrical connector to the EVAP canister vent solenoid valve.
13. Lower the vehicle.

HEATED OXYGEN (HO2S) SENSOR

LOCATION

See Figures 187 through 189.

REMOVAL & INSTALLATION

2.0L Engine

Heated Oxygen Sensor—1

See Figure 187.

1. Open the hood.
2. Remove the underhood junction block bracket.
3. Remove the connector position assurance (CPA) retainer.
4. Disconnect the engine wiring harness electrical connector from the HO2S electrical connector.
5. Remove the HO2S electrical connector clip from the camshaft cover.
6. Using the J 39194 , remove the HO2S.

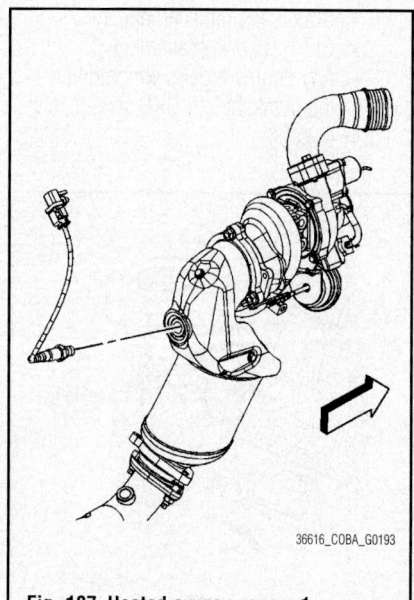

36616_COBA_G0193

Fig. 187 Heated oxygen sensor 1 location—2.0L engine

To install:

➡A special anti-seize compound is used on the HO2S threads. The compound consists of a liquid graphite and glass beads. The graphite will burn away, but the glass beads will remain, making the sensor easier to remove. New or service sensors will have the compound applied to the threads. If a sensor is removed and is to be reinstalled, the threads must have an anti-seize compound applied before installation.

➡If reinstalling the old HO2S, coat the threads with anti-seize compound GM P/N 12377953 or equivalent.

7. Using the J 39194 , install the position 1 HO2S and tighten the sensor to 31 ft. lbs. (42 Nm).

8. Connect the engine wiring harness electrical connector (1) to the HO2S electrical connector (3).

9. Install the HO2S electrical connector clip to the camshaft cover.

10. Install the CPA retainer.

11. Install the underhood junction block bracket.

12. Close the hood.

Heated Oxygen Sensor—2

See Figure 188.

1. Disconnect the electrical connector.

2. Un-crimp the heat shield from the O2 sensor wiring harness.

3. Remove the oxygen sensor using the oxygen sensor wrench, J 39194.

4. Lower the HO2S electrical harness away from the underbody.

To install:

➡A special anti-seize compound is used on the oxygen sensor threads. The compound consists of a liquid

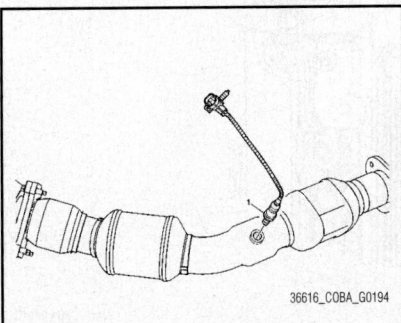

Fig. 188 Heated oxygen sensor 2 location—2.0L. 2.2L and 2.4L engines

graphite and glass beads. The graphite will burn away, but the glass beads will remain, making the sensor easier to remove. New or service sensors will have the compound applied to the threads. If a sensor is removed and is to be reinstalled, the threads must have an anti-seize compound applied before installation.

5. If reinstalling the old HO2S, coat the threads with anti-seize compound, GM P/N 12377953, or equivalent.

6. Carefully install the HO2S to the pipe.

7. Using the J 39194 , or equivalent, tighten the HO2S. Tighten the HO2S to 30 ft. lbs. (41 Nm).

8. Install the HO2S electrical harness into position as noted before removal.

❊❊ WARNING

Use care when securing the HO2S electrical harness into the channel on the exhaust heat shield, to not pinch the wires.

9. Carefully bend the edge of the channel on the LH side of the exhaust heat shield inboard, just enough to secure the HO2S electrical harness in the channel.

10. Connect the HO2S electrical connector.

11. Install the wheel drive shaft heat shield into position on the vehicle, if necessary.

12. Lower the vehicle.

2.2L & 2.4L Engines

Heated Oxygen Sensor—1

See Figure 189.

❊❊ WARNING

The oxygen sensor uses a permanently attached pigtail and connector. Do not remove the pigtail from the oxygen sensor. Damage to or removal of the pigtail connector could affect proper operation of the oxygen sensor.

❊❊ WARNING

The use of excessive force may damage the threads in the exhaust manifold/pipe.

➡The in-line connector and louvered end must be kept clear of grease, dirt or other contaminants. Avoid using cleaning solvents of any type. DO NOT drop or roughly handle the oxygen sensor.

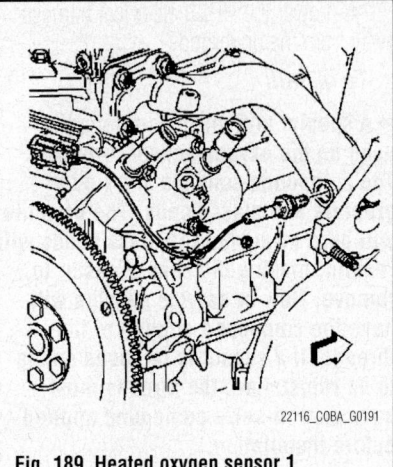

Fig. 189 Heated oxygen sensor 1 location—2.2L and 2.4L engines

➡The oxygen sensor may be difficult to remove when the engine temperature is less than 120°F (48°C).

1. Remove the exhaust manifold heat shield.

2. Disconnect the oxygen sensor harness connector.

3. Remove the oxygen sensor using the oxygen sensor wrench, J 39194-C.

To install:

➡A special anti-seize compound is used on the oxygen sensor threads. The compound consists of a liquid graphite and glass beads. The graphite will burn away, but the glass beads will remain, making the sensor easier to remove. New or service sensors will have the compound applied to the threads. If a sensor is removed and is to be reinstalled, the threads must have an anti-seize compound applied before installation.

4. Coat the threads of the oxygen sensor with anti-seize compound GM P/N 12377953, or equivalent, if necessary.

5. Install the oxygen sensor. Tighten the oxygen sensor to 30 ft. lbs. (41 Nm).

6. Connect the oxygen sensor harness connector.

7. Install the exhaust manifold heat shield. Tighten the heat shield studs to 16 ft. lbs. (22 Nm).

Heated Oxygen Sensor—2

See Figure 188.

1. Disconnect the electrical connector.

2. Un-crimp the heat shield from the O2 sensor wiring harness.

3. Remove the oxygen sensor using the oxygen sensor wrench, J 39194.

4. Lower the HO2S electrical harness away from the underbody.

To install:

➡A special anti-seize compound is used on the oxygen sensor threads. The compound consists of a liquid graphite and glass beads. The graphite will burn away, but the glass beads will remain, making the sensor easier to remove. New or service sensors will have the compound applied to the threads. If a sensor is removed and is to be reinstalled, the threads must have an anti-seize compound applied before installation.

5. If reinstalling the old HO2S, coat the threads with anti-seize compound, GM P/N 12377953, or equivalent.

6. Carefully install the HO2S to the pipe.

7. Using the J 39194 , or equivalent, tighten the HO2S. Tighten the HO2S to 30 ft. lbs. (41 Nm).

8. Install the HO2S electrical harness into position as noted before removal.

✳✳ WARNING

Use care when securing the HO2S electrical harness into the channel on the exhaust heat shield, to not pinch the wires.

9. Carefully bend the edge of the channel on the LH side of the exhaust heat shield inboard, just enough to secure the HO2S electrical harness in the channel.

10. Connect the HO2S electrical connector.

11. Install the wheel drive shaft heat shield into position on the vehicle, if necessary.

12. Lower the vehicle.

INTAKE AIR TEMPERATURE (IAT) SENSOR

LOCATION

See Figures 190 and 191.

REMOVAL & INSTALLATION

2.0L Engine

See Figure 190.

1. Disconnect the Intake Air Temperature (IAT) sensor harness connector.

2. Remove the IAT sensor bolt.

3. While twisting the IAT sensor, pull the sensor from the engine.

To install:

4. Press the IAT sensor into the engine.

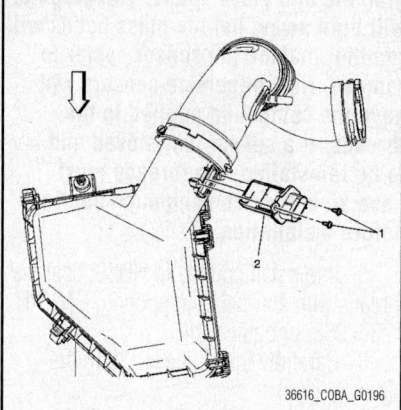

36616_COBA_G0196

Fig. 190 Mass Air Flow (MAF) and Intake Air Temperature (IAT) Sensor location—2.0L engine

5. Install the IAT sensor bolt. Tighten the bolt to 5 inch lbs. (0.6 Nm).

6. Connect the IAT sensor harness connector.

2.2L & 2.4L Engines

See Figure 191.

1. Disconnect the engine harness electrical connector from the Mass Air Flow (MAF)/Intake Air Temperature (IAT) sensor.

2. Remove the MAF/IAT sensor screws.

3. Remove the MAF/IAT sensor.

To install:

4. Install the MAF/IAT sensor.

5. Install the MAF/IAT sensor screws. Tighten the screws to 5 inch lbs. (0.6 Nm).

6. Connect the engine harness electrical connector to the MAF/IAT sensor.

KNOCK SENSOR (KS)

LOCATION

See Figures 192 and 193.

REMOVAL & INSTALLATION

2.0L Engine

See Figure 192.

1. Remove the charge air bypass tank.

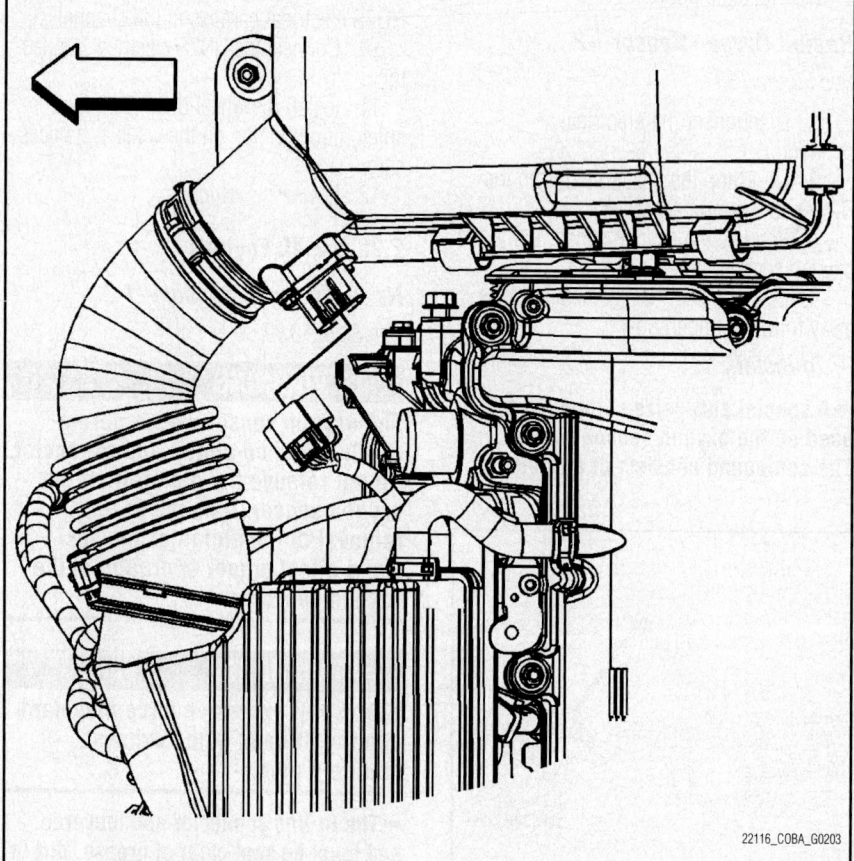

22116_COBA_G0203

Fig. 191 Mass Air Flow (MAF) and Intake Air Temperature (IAT) sensor location—2.2L and 2.4L engines

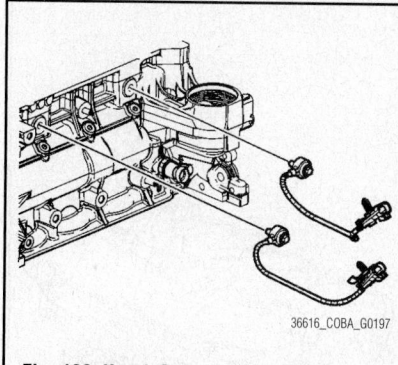

Fig. 192 Knock Sensor (KS) locations— 2.0L engine

2. Disconnect the engine wiring harness electrical connector from the front knock sensor, if required.

3. Disconnect the engine wiring harness electrical connector from the rear knock sensor, if required.

4. Remove the front knock sensor clip from the oil level indicator tube, if required.

5. Remove the rear knock sensor clip from the intake manifold brace, if required.

6. Loosen the appropriate knock sensor bolt.

7. Remove the appropriate knock sensor.

To install:

➡Rotate the pigtail 90 degrees from vertical before securing the fastener.

8. Position the appropriate knock sensor to the engine block.

9. Tighten the appropriate knock bolt and tighten the bolt to 18 ft. lbs. (25 Nm).

10. Install the front knock sensor clip to the oil level indicator tube, if required.

11. Install the rear knock sensor clip to the intake manifold brace, if required.

12. Connect the engine wiring harness electrical connector to the rear knock sensor.

13. Connect the engine wiring harness electrical connector to the front knock sensor.

14. Install the charge air bypass tank.

2.2L & 2.4L Engines

See Figure 193.

1. Disconnect the negative battery cable.

2. Remove the starter. Refer to Starter in Engine Electrical.

3. Disconnect the Knock Sensor (KS) harness connector.

4. Remove the KS retaining bolt.

5. Remove the KS.

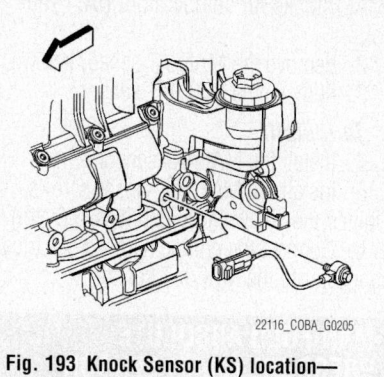

Fig. 193 Knock Sensor (KS) location— 2.2L & 2.4L engines

To install:

❊❊ WARNING

Use the correct fastener in the correct location. Replacement fasteners must be the correct part number for that application. Fasteners requiring replacement or fasteners requiring the use of thread locking compound or sealant are identified in the service procedure. Do not use paints, lubricants, or corrosion inhibitors on fasteners or fastener joint surfaces unless specified. These coatings affect fastener torque and joint clamping force and may damage the fastener. Use the correct tightening sequence and specifications when installing fasteners in order to avoid damage to parts and systems.

➡The KS threaded surfaces must be clean before installation.

6. Install the KS. Tighten the KS retaining bolt to 18 ft. lbs. (25 Nm).

7. Connect the KS harness connector.

8. Install the starter. Refer to Starter in Engine Electrical.

9. Connect the negative battery cable.

MALFUNCTION INDICATOR LIGHT (MIL)

RESET PROCEDURE

1. Proper operation of the Malfunction Indicator Lamp (MIL):
   - The MIL will illuminate with the ignition switch ON and the engine OFF
   - The MIL will turn OFF when the engine is started
   - The MIL will remain ON if the self-diagnostic system has detected a malfunction

   - The MIL may turn OFF if the malfunction is no longer present
   - If the MIL is illuminated and then the engine stalls, the MIL will remain illuminated as long as the ignition switch is ON
   - If the MIL is not illuminated and the engine stalls, the MIL will not illuminate until the ignition switch is cycled OFF, then ON

2. Resetting the MIL:
   - The control module turns OFF the MIL after 3 consecutive ignition cycles that the diagnostic system runs and does not fail
   - A current Diagnostic Trouble Code (DTC) clears when the diagnostic cycle runs and passes
   - There may still be a history of DTC's stored in the system. These will clear after 40 consecutive warm–up cycles, if no failures are reported by any other related diagnostic system
   - Manual resetting of the MIL and any DTC stored in the system, requires the use of an OBD2 scan tool connected to the data link connector for communication with the vehicle. Follow the instructions of the scan tool for both retrieval and resetting of DTC's.

➡If the error symptoms causing the MIL to illuminate have been corrected, the MIL will return to normal operation.

MASS AIR FLOW (MAF) SENSOR

LOCATION

See Figures 194 and 195.

REMOVAL & INSTALLATION

2.0L Engine

See Figure 194.

1. Disconnect the MAF/IAT sensor harness connector.

2. Remove the MAF/IAT sensor bolt.

3. While twisting the MAF/IAT sensor, pull the sensor from the engine.

To install:

4. Press the MAF/IAT sensor into the engine.

5. Install the MAF/IAT sensor bolt. Tighten the bolt to 5 inch lbs. (0.6 Nm).

6. Connect the MAF/IAT sensor harness connector.

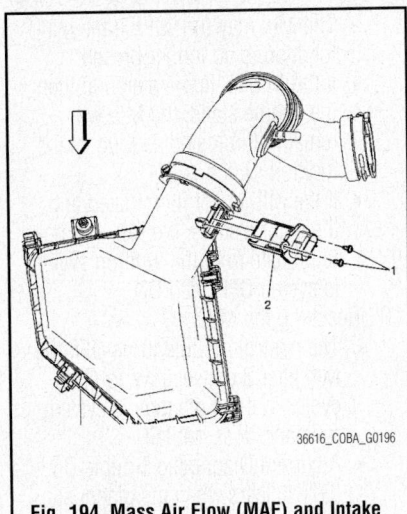

Fig. 194 Mass Air Flow (MAF) and Intake Air Temperature (IAT) Sensor location—2.0L engine

2.2L & 2.4L Engines

See Figure 195.

1. Disconnect the engine harness electrical connector from the Mass Air Flow

(MAF)/Intake Air Temperature (IAT) sensor.
2. Remove the MAF/IAT sensor screws.
3. Remove the MAF/IAT sensor.

To install:
4. Install the MAF/IAT sensor.
5. Install the MAF/IAT sensor screws. Tighten the screws to 5 inch lbs. (0.6 Nm).
6. Connect the engine harness electrical connector to the MAF/IAT sensor.

MANIFOLD ABSOLUTE PRESSURE (MAP) SENSOR

LOCATION

See Figures 196 and 197.

REMOVAL & INSTALLATION

2.0L Engine

See Figure 196.

1. Disconnect the engine wiring harness electrical connector from the manifold absolute pressure (MAP) sensor.
2. Remove the MAP sensor bolts.

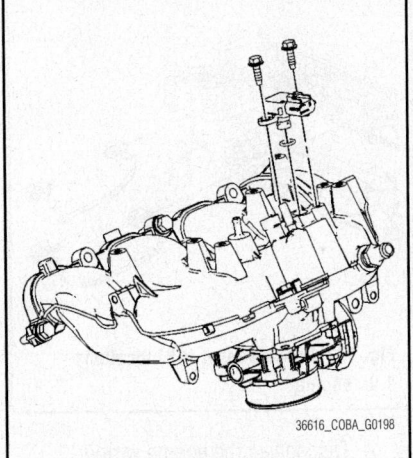

Fig. 196 Manifold Absolute Pressure (MAP) sensor location—2.0L engine

3. Remove the MAP sensor and O-ring seal from the intake manifold.

To install:
4. Lubricate the O-ring seal with clean engine oil.
5. Install the MAP sensor to the intake manifold.
6. Install the MAP sensor bolts and tighten the bolts to 89 inch lbs. (10 Nm).
7. Connect the engine wiring harness electrical connector to the MAP sensor.

2.2L & 2.4L Engines

See Figure 197.

1. Remove the throttle body. Refer to Throttle Body in Fuel System.
2. Disconnect the engine harness electrical connector from the manifold absolute pressure (MAP) sensor.
3. Remove the MAP sensor and seal.

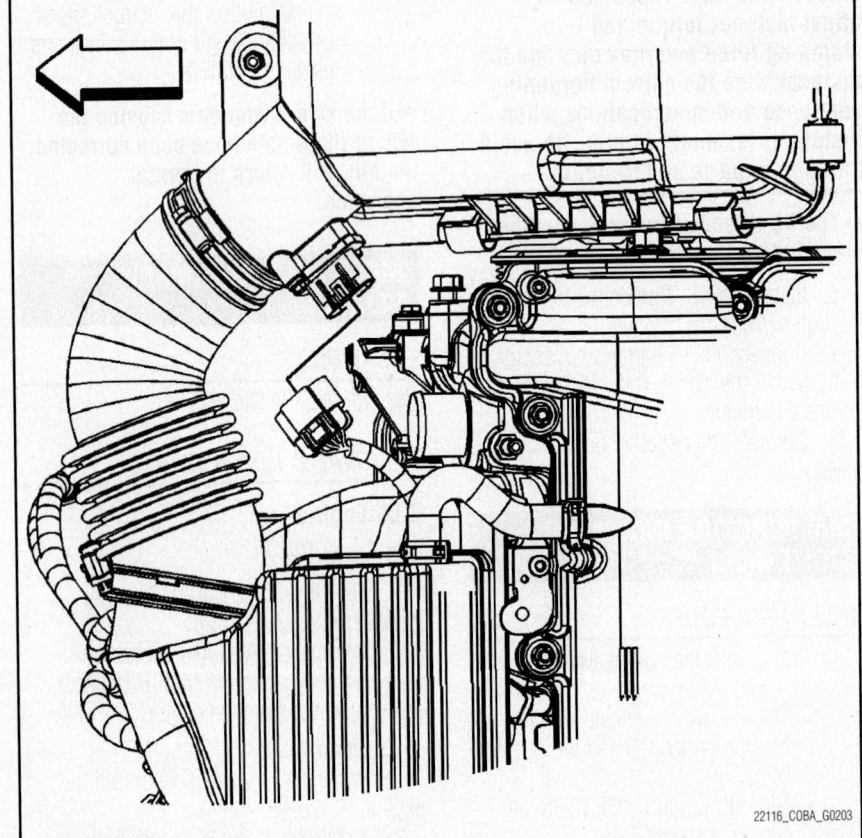

Fig. 195 Mass Air Flow (MAF) and Intake Air Temperature (IAT) sensor location—2.2L and 2.4L engines

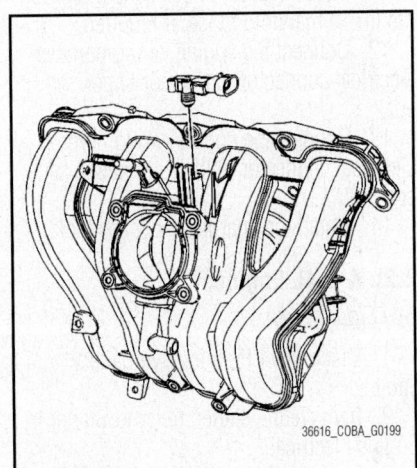

Fig. 197 Manifold Absolute Pressure (MAP) sensor location—2.2L and 2.4L engines

To install:

4. Lubricate the NEW MAP sensor seal with clean engine oil.

5. Install the MAP sensor into the intake manifold.

6. Connect the engine harness electrical connector to the MAP sensor.

7. Install the throttle body.

POSITIVE CRANKCASE VENTILATION (PCV) VALVE

LOCATION

For the 2.2L and 2.4L engines, the PCV orifice is an integral part of the camshaft cover. For the 2.0L engine, it is located in the intake manifold.

REMOVAL & INSTALLATION

1. Cleaning the orifice is possible, replacement is not specified.

THROTTLE POSITION SENSOR (TPS)

LOCATION

The Throttle Position Sensor (TPS) is integrated with the Throttle Control Actuator.

REMOVAL & INSTALLATION

2.0L Engine

> ✳✳ **WARNING**
>
> **Do not use solvent of any type when cleaning the gasket surfaces on the intake manifold and the throttle body assembly, as damage to the gasket surfaces and throttle body assembly may result. Use care in cleaning the gasket surfaces on the intake manifold and the throttle body assembly, as sharp tools may damage the gasket surfaces. Do not use any solvent that contains Methyl Ethyl Ketone (MEK). This solvent may damage fuel system components.**

1. Remove the charge air cooler outlet pipe.

2. Disconnect the engine wiring harness electrical connector from the electronic throttle control (ETC).

3. Remove the throttle body bolts.

4. Remove the throttle body and seal from the intake manifold.

To install:

5. Inspect the throttle body seal, and replace if necessary.

6. Position the throttle body to the intake manifold.

7. Install the throttle body bolts and tighten to 89 inch lbs. (10 Nm).

8. Connect the engine wiring harness electrical connector to the ETC.

9. Install the charge air cooler outlet pipe.

2.2L & 2.4L Engines

1. Remove the air cleaner outlet duct.

2. Remove the intake manifold cover.

3. Disconnect the Throttle Actuator Control (TAC) electrical connector.

4. Remove the throttle body bolts.

5. Remove the throttle body .

6. Inspect the throttle body gasket, and replace if necessary.

To install:

7. Install the throttle body.

8. Install the throttle body bolts and tighten the bolts to 89 inch lbs. (10 Nm).

9. Connect the TAC electrical connector.

10. Install the intake manifold cover.

11. Install the air cleaner outlet duct.

VEHICLE SPEED SENSOR (VSS)

LOCATION
See Figures 198 through 200.

REMOVAL & INSTALLATION

Automatic Transaxle 4T45–E
See Figure 198.

> ✳✳ **WARNING**
>
> **Unless directed otherwise, the ignition and start switch must be in the OFF or LOCK position, and all electrical loads must be OFF before servicing any electrical component. Disconnect the negative battery cable to prevent an electrical spark should a tool or equipment come in contact with an exposed electrical terminal.**

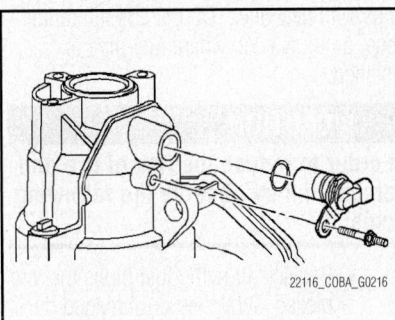

22116_COBA_G0216

Fig. 198 Location of the Vehicle Speed Sensor (VSS) on automatic transaxle 4T45–E

Failure to follow these precautions may result in personal injury and/or damage to the vehicle or its components.

1. Disconnect the negative battery cable.

2. Raise and support the vehicle.

3. Remove the electrical connector at the Vehicle Speed Sensor (VSS).

4. Remove the retaining stud and the sensor. Pull straight out in order to avoid damage to the case.

To install:

5. Clean and dry the VSS.

➡Use the correct fastener in the correct location. Replacement fasteners must be the correct part number for that application. Fasteners requiring replacement or fasteners requiring the use of thread locking compound or sealant are identified in the service procedure. Do not use paints, lubricants, or corrosion inhibitors on fasteners or fastener joint surfaces unless specified. These coatings affect fastener torque and joint clamping force and may damage the fastener. Use the correct tightening sequence and specifications when installing fasteners in order to avoid damage to parts and systems.

6. Install the VSS and the retaining bolt. Tighten the stud to 97 inch lbs. (12 Nm).

7. Install the electrical connector at the sensor.

8. Lower the vehicle.

9. Connect the negative battery cable. Tighten the terminal bolt to 11 ft. lbs. (15 Nm).

Manual Transaxle—MU3
See Figure 199.

1. Remove or disconnect the following:

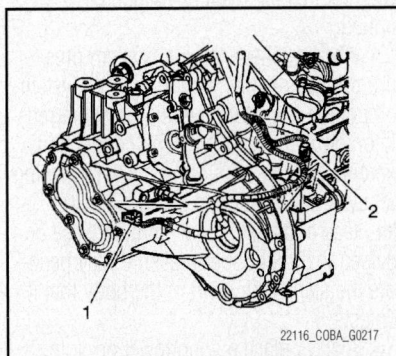

22116_COBA_G0217

Fig. 199 Location of the Vehicle Speed Sensor (VSS) on manual transaxle—MU3

- The left front wheel
- The Vehicle Speed Sensor (VSS) electrical connector (2)
- The retainer bolt
- The retainer
- The VSS
- Discard the O-ring

To install:

2. Lubricate a new O-ring with transmission fluid.

3. Install or connect the following:
- The new O-ring
- The VSS retainer
- The VSS assembly
- The VSS retainer bolt. Tighten the bolt to 80 inch lbs. (9 Nm)
- The VSS connector to the VSS
- The left front wheel. Tighten the lug nuts to 100 ft. lbs. (140 Nm)

Manual Transaxle—Getrag 5—Speed

See Figure 200.

1. Raise and safely support the vehicle.
2. Disconnect the Vehicle Speed Sensor (VSS) electrical connector.
3. Remove the retainer bolt.

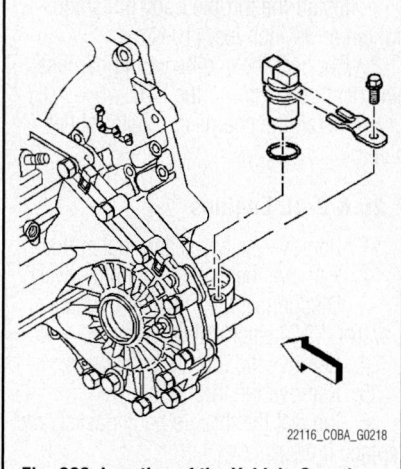

22116_COBA_G0218

Fig. 200 Location of the Vehicle Speed Sensor (VSS) on manual transaxle— Getrag 5—speed

4. Remove the retainer.
5. Pull up on the VSS in order to remove the VSS from the transaxle.
6. Remove the O-ring.

To install:

7. Lubricate a new O-ring with DEXRON III transmission fluid.

8. Install or connect the following:
- The new O-ring
- The VSS assembly
- The VSS retainer

➡**Use the correct fastener in the correct location. Replacement fasteners must be the correct part number for that application. Fasteners requiring replacement or fasteners requiring the use of thread locking compound or sealant are identified in the service procedure. Do not use paints, lubricants, or corrosion inhibitors on fasteners or fastener joint surfaces unless specified. These coatings affect fastener torque and joint clamping force and may damage the fastener. Use the correct tightening sequence and specifications when installing fasteners in order to avoid damage to parts and systems.**

- The VSS retainer bolt. Tighten the bolt to 96 inch lbs. (12 Nm)
- The VSS connector to the VSS
9. Lower the vehicle.

FUEL

GASOLINE FUEL INJECTION SYSTEM

FUEL SYSTEM SERVICE PRECAUTIONS

Safety is the most important factor when performing not only fuel system maintenance but any type of maintenance. Failure to conduct maintenance and repairs in a safe manner may result in serious personal injury or death. Maintenance and testing of the vehicle's fuel system components can be accomplished safely and effectively by adhering to the following rules and guidelines.

• To avoid the possibility of fire and personal injury, always disconnect the negative battery cable unless the repair or test procedure requires that battery voltage be applied.

• Always relieve the fuel system pressure prior to disconnecting any fuel system component (injector, fuel rail, pressure regulator, etc.), fitting or fuel line connection. Exercise extreme caution whenever relieving fuel system pressure, to avoid exposing skin, face and eyes to fuel spray. Please be advised that fuel under pressure may penetrate the skin or any part of the body that it contacts.

• Always place a shop towel or cloth around the fitting or connection prior to loosening to absorb any excess fuel due to

spillage. Ensure that all fuel spillage (should it occur) is quickly removed from engine surfaces. Ensure that all fuel soaked cloths or towels are deposited into a suitable waste container.

• Always keep a dry chemical (Class B) fire extinguisher near the work area.

• Do not allow fuel spray or fuel vapors to come into contact with a spark or open flame.

• Always use a back-up wrench when loosening and tightening fuel line connection fittings. This will prevent unnecessary stress and torsion to fuel line piping. Always follow the proper torque specifications.

• Always replace worn fuel fitting O-rings with new ones. Do not substitute fuel hose, or equivalent, where fuel pipe is installed.

✳✳ CAUTION

In order to reduce the risk of fire and personal injury observe the following items:

- Replace all nylon fuel pipes that are nicked, scratched or damaged during installation, do not attempt to repair the sections of the nylon fuel pipes
- Do not hammer directly on the fuel

harness body clips when installing new fuel pipes. Damage to the nylon pipes may result in a fuel leak.
- Always cover nylon vapor pipes with a wet towel before using a torch near them. Also, never expose the vehicle to temperatures higher than 239°F (115°C) for more than one hour, or more than 194°F (90°C) for any extended period.
- Apply a few drops of clean engine oil to the male pipe ends before connecting fuel pipe fittings. This will ensure proper reconnection and prevent a possible fuel leak. (During normal operation, the O-rings located in the female connector will swell and may prevent proper reconnection if not lubricated.)

RELIEVING FUEL SYSTEM PRESSURE

2.0L Engine

High Pressure Side

1. Install a scan tool to the vehicle and command the fuel pump relay OFF, allowing the low pressure fuel pump to shut off.

2. Start the vehicle and allow the engine to idle until the engine stops. The engine will stop in approximately 20–30 seconds.

3. Turn the ignition OFF.

4. Using the scan tool, verify that there is little to no fuel pressure, if there still is fuel pressure repeat step 2.

➡ **If a scan tool is not available, WAIT at LEAST 2 hours after the engine has been run, before removing the high pressure fuel line.**

5. Remove the high pressure fuel line.

Low Pressure Side

> ❋❋ **CAUTION**
>
> **Remove the fuel tank cap and relieve the fuel system pressure before servicing the fuel system in order to reduce the risk of personal injury. After you relieve the fuel system pressure, a small amount of fuel may be released when servicing the fuel lines, the fuel injection pump, or the connections. In order to reduce the risk of personal injury, cover the fuel system components with a shop towel before disconnection. This will catch any fuel that may leak out. Place the towel in an approved container when the disconnection is complete.**

1. If the fuel system requires repair, prevent fuel spillage by removing the fuel pump fuse. Refer to Fuses & Flashers in Chassis Electrical.

2. Loosen the fuel fill cap in order to relieve the fuel tank vapor pressure.

3. Remove the engine cover, if required.

4. Remove the fuel feed pipe service port cap.

5. Wrap a shop towel around the fuel rail service port and using a small flat-bladed tool, depress (open) the fuel feed pipe test port valve.

6. Remove the shop towel from around the fuel service port, and place in an approved gasoline container.

7. Install the fuel feed pipe service port cap.

8. Install the engine cover, if required.

9. Tighten the fuel fill cap.

2.2L & 2.4L Engines

> ❋❋ **CAUTION**
>
> **Remove the fuel tank cap and relieve the fuel system pressure before servicing the fuel system in order to reduce the risk of personal injury. After you relieve the fuel system pres-**

sure, a small amount of fuel may be released when servicing the fuel lines, the fuel injection pump, or the connections. In order to reduce the risk of personal injury, cover the fuel system components with a shop towel before disconnection. This will catch any fuel that may leak out. Place the towel in an approved container when the disconnection is complete.

1. If the fuel system requires repair, prevent fuel spillage by removing the fuel pump fuse.

2. Loosen the fuel fill cap in order to relieve the fuel tank vapor pressure.

3. Remove the engine cover, if required.

4. Remove the fuel feed pipe service port cap.

5. Wrap a shop towel around the fuel rail service port and using a small flat-bladed tool, depress (open) the fuel feed pipe test port valve.

6. Remove the shop towel from around the fuel service port, and place in an approved gasoline container.

7. Install the fuel feed pipe service port cap.

8. Install the engine cover, if required.

9. Tighten the fuel fill cap.

FUEL FILTER

REMOVAL & INSTALLATION

2.0L, 2.2L, 2.4L Engines—except 2.2L California Partial Zero Emission Vehicles (PZEV)

See Figure 201.

1. Before servicing the vehicle, refer to the Precautions Section.

2. Disconnect the negative battery cable.

➡**Keep a shop cloth and a container ready to capture any spilled fuel.**

3. Relieve the fuel system pressure. Refer to Relieving Fuel System Pressure.

4. Raise and support the vehicle.

5. Remove the fuel filter bracket bolt.

6. Disconnect the fuel filter from the engine fuel feed pipe (1).

7. Tilt the fuel filter downward and drain off the fuel into an approved fuel container.

8. Disconnect the fuel tank feed and return hose fittings from the fuel filter.

9. Drain any remaining fuel into an approved fuel container.

10. Discard the fuel filter into an approved container.

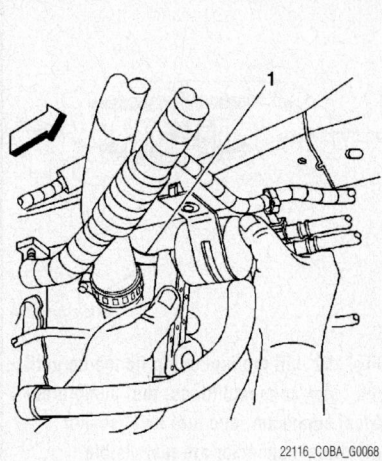

22116_COBA_G0068

Fig. 201 Location of the fuel filter, bracket bolt, and filter disconnect from the engine fuel feed pipe

To install:

11. Remove the protective caps from the new fuel filter.

12. Connect the fuel tank feed and return hose fittings to the fuel filter.

13. Connect the fuel filter to the engine feed fuel pipe.

14. Install the fuel filter bracket bolt. Tighten the bolt to 89 inch lbs. (10 Nm).

15. Lower the vehicle.

16. Connect the negative battery cable.

17. Inspect for fuel leaks using the following procedure:

a. Turn the ignition switch ON, but do not start the engine. Wait 2 seconds.

b. Turn the ignition switch OFF and wait 10 seconds.

c. Turn the ignition switch ON, but do not start the engine.

d. Inspect for fuel leaks.

2.2L Engine California Partial Zero Emission Vehicles (PZEV)

See Figures 202 through 205.

1. Before servicing the vehicle, refer to the Precautions Section.

2. Disconnect the negative battery cable.

> ❋❋ **CAUTION**
>
> **In order to reduce the risk of fire and personal injury that may result from a fuel leak, always replace the fuel sender gasket when reinstalling the fuel sender assembly.**

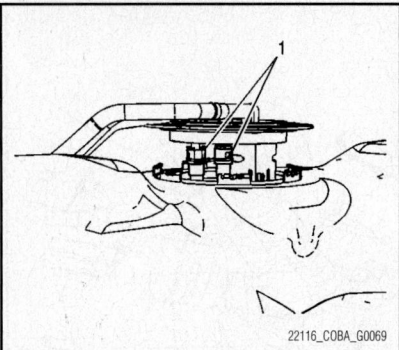

Fig. 202 Lift the fuel pump flange up until the quick connect fittings, fuel pump electrical connector, and fuel level sensor electrical connector are just visible

3. Remove the fuel tank. Refer to Fuel Tank Removal & Installation.

4. Using tool J 45722, unlock the fuel sender lock ring.

5. Slowly lift the fuel pump flange up until the quick connect fittings (1), fuel pump electrical connector, and fuel level sensor electrical connector are just visible.

6. Disconnect the fuel level sensor electrical connector from the fuel pump flange.

7. Disconnect the fuel tank vent valve and the fuel filter quick connect fittings (1) from the fuel pump flange.

8. Disconnect the fuel pump electrical connector from the fuel pump by depressing the lock tab on top of the electrical connector.

9. Remove the fuel pump flange lock ring (1) and fuel pump flange (2). If required, remove the lock ring from the flange.

10. Remove and discard the fuel pump flange seal (3).

11. Squeeze the sides of the fuel pump fuel reservoir pump fuel strainer quick connect fitting together in order to remove the fitting from the fuel filter.

12. Reposition the fuel pump fuel reservoir pump fuel strainer line.

13. Squeeze the fuel pump quick connect fitting retainer (3) together in order to remove the fitting from the fuel filter.

14. Reposition the fuel pump line.

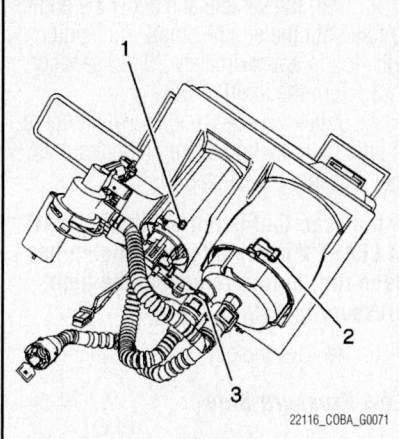

Fig. 204 Squeeze the fuel pump quick connect fitting retainer (3) together to remove the fitting from the fuel filter. Reposition the fuel pump line and rotate the fuel filter to the left until the tab (2) is aligned with the opening in the fuel pump module

15. Rotate the fuel filter to the left until the tab (2) is aligned with the opening in the fuel pump module.

16. Remove the fuel filter from the fuel pump module.

To install:

17. Align the fuel filter tab with the opening in the fuel pump module.

18. Install the fuel filter to the fuel pump module.

19. Rotate the fuel filter to the right until the tab is locked into the fuel pump module.

20. Position the fuel pump line and install the fuel pump quick connect fitting to the fuel filter.

21. Install the fuel pump fuel reservoir pump fuel strainer quick connect fitting to the fuel filter.

22. Position a NEW fuel pump flange seal onto the fuel tank.

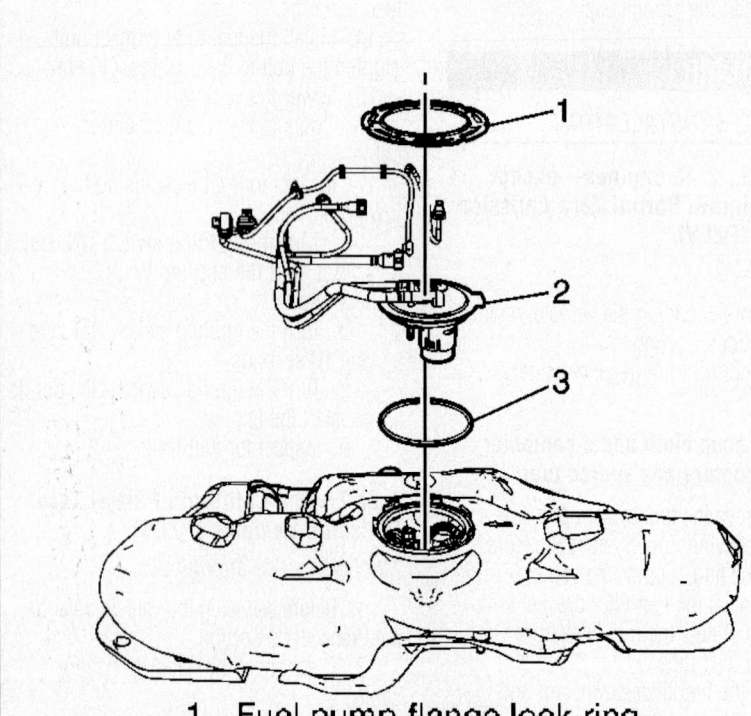

1. Fuel pump flange lock ring
2. Fuel pump flange
3. Fuel pump flange seal

Fig. 203 Exploded view of fuel tank with fuel pump flange lock and seal

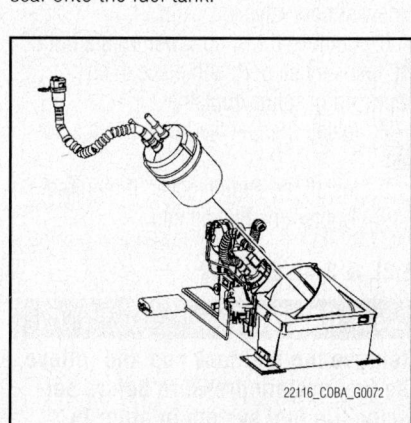

Fig. 205 Remove the fuel filter from the fuel pump module—2.2L Engine (PZEV)

23. If required, install the lock ring onto the flange. Position the fuel pump flange and lock ring over the fuel tank opening.

24. Ensure that the fuel pump flange tab is aligned with the arrow on the fuel tank.

25. Connect the fuel tank vent valve and the fuel filter quick connect fittings to the fuel pump flange.

26. Connect the fuel pump electrical connector to the fuel pump.

27. Connect the fuel level sensor electrical connector to the fuel pump flange.

28. Slowly lower the fuel pump flange into the fuel tank.

29. Using tool J 45722, lock the fuel sender lock ring.

30. Install the fuel tank. Refer to Fuel Tank Removal & Installation.

FUEL PUMP MODULE

REMOVAL & INSTALLATION

See Figures 203 and 206.

➡The fuel level sending unit is integral with the fuel pump module in the fuel tank. See Fuel Pump Removal & Installation in the Fuel section.

1. Before servicing the vehicle, refer to the Precautions Section.

2. Relieve the fuel system pressure. Refer to Relieving Fuel System Pressure

3. Disconnect the negative battery cable.

4. Remove the fuel tank.

5. Using the special tool J 45722, unlock the fuel sender lock ring.

6. Slowly lift the fuel pump flange up until the quick connect fittings and fuel level sensor electrical connector are just visible.

7. Disconnect the fuel level sensor electrical connector from the fuel pump flange.

8. Disconnect the fuel tank vent valve and the fuel filter quick connect fittings from the fuel pump flange.

9. Remove the fuel pump flange lock ring (1) and fuel pump flange (2). If required, remove the lock
ring from the flange.

10. Remove and discard the fuel pump flange seal (3).

11. Squeeze the sides of the fuel level sensor retainer (2) together in order to remove the fuel level sensor.

12. Remove the fuel level sensor from the fuel pump module by sliding the sensor up.

To install:

13. Position the fuel level sensor into the fuel pump module and slide the sensor down.

14. Ensure that the fuel level sensor retainer (2) is fully engaged with the fuel pump module.

15. Position a NEW fuel pump flange seal onto the fuel tank.

16. Position the fuel pump flange and lock ring over the fuel tank opening.

17. Ensure that the fuel pump flange tab is aligned with the arrow on the fuel tank.

18. Connect the fuel tank vent valve and the fuel filter quick connect fittings to the fuel pump flange.

19. Connect the fuel level sensor electrical connector to the fuel pump flange.

20. Slowly lower the fuel pump flange into the fuel tank.

21. Using the special tool, J 45722, lock the fuel sender lock ring.

22. Install the fuel tank.

FUEL RAIL & INJECTORS

REMOVAL & INSTALLATION

2.0L Engine

See Figures 207 through 212.

1. Before servicing the vehicle, refer to the Precautions Section.

2. Relieve the high side fuel system pressure. Refer to Fuel Pressure Relief.

3. Disconnect the engine wiring harness electrical connector from the fuel injector wiring harness electrical connector.

4. Remove the intake manifold. Refer to Intake Manifold in Engine Mechanical.

5. Remove the fuel injector insulator.

6. Disconnect the engine wiring harness electrical connector from the high pressure fuel pump.

7. Remove the intermediate fuel pipe. Refer to Fuel Feed Intermediate Pipe.

8. Disconnect the fuel injector wiring

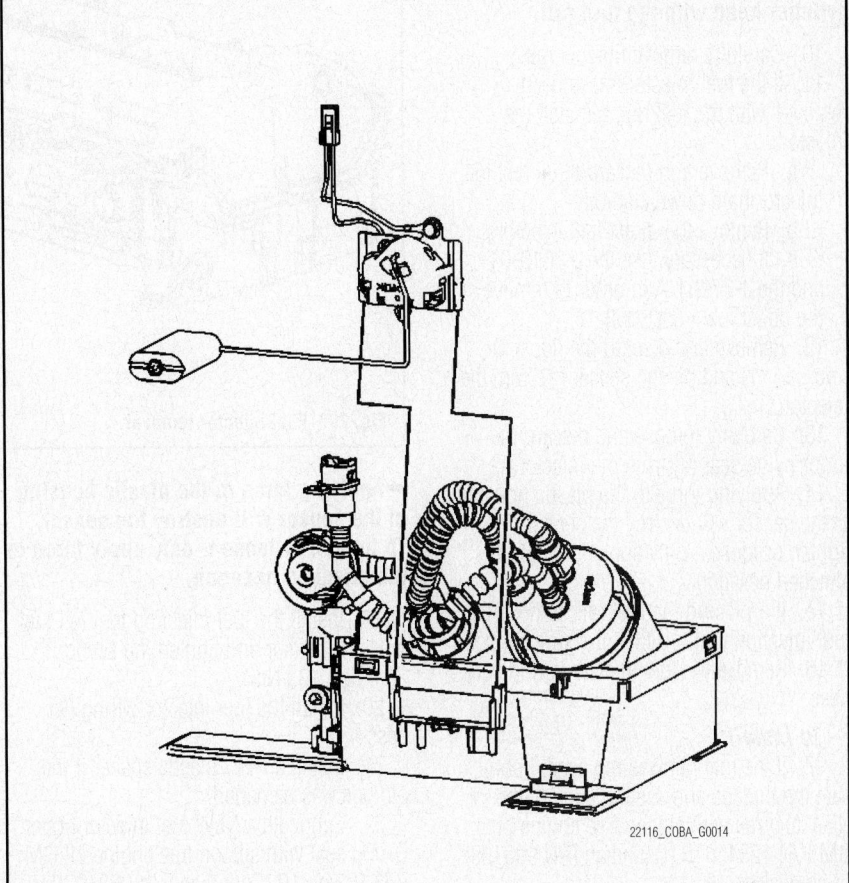

Fig. 206 Fuel level sensor retainer (2) squeezed together in order to remove the fuel level sensor—PZEV shown.

22116_COBA_G0014

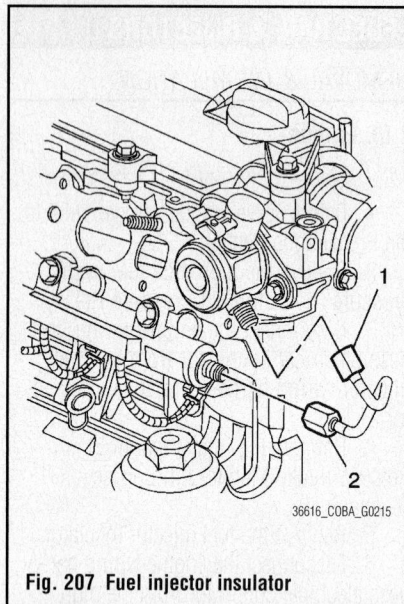

Fig. 207 Fuel injector insulator

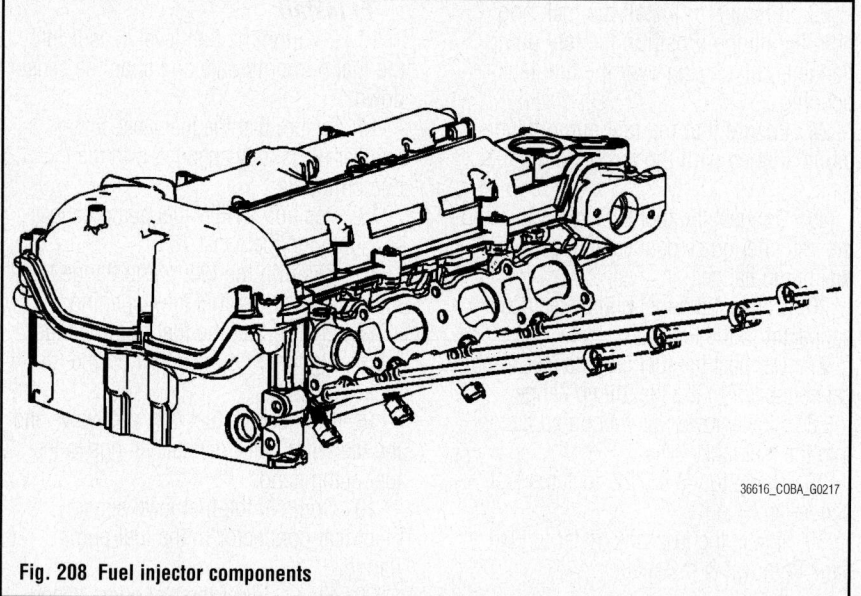

Fig. 208 Fuel injector components

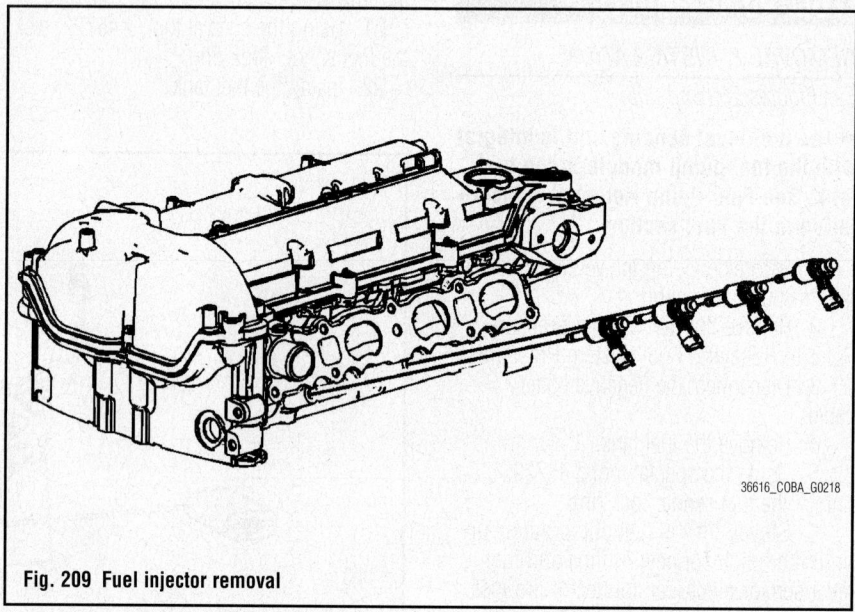

Fig. 209 Fuel injector removal

harness electrical connectors from the fuel injectors.

9. Remove the fuel rail bolts.

➡**Carefully remove the fuel rail. The fuel injectors may come out of the cylinder head with the fuel rail.**

10. Carefully remove the fuel rail.

11. If the fuel injectors have been removed with the fuel rail, reinstall the injectors.

    a. Remove and discard the direct fuel injector hold down clamps.

    b. Remove the direct fuel injectors.

    c. If necessary, use the J 2619-01 and the J-37281-A in order to remove the direct fuel injector(s).

12. Remove and discard the upper O-ring seal (1) and plastic spacer (2) from the injector(s).

13. Carefully remove and discard the lower nylon seal (4) from the injector(s).

14. Applying force to the plastic housing of the sensor will destroy the sensor. To tighten or loosen, only apply force to the attached hexagon.

15. If replacing the fuel rail, remove the fuel injection fuel rail fuel pressure sensor.

16. Remove the fuel injector wiring harness.

To install:

17. If the fuel rail was replaced, Lubricate the threads and sealing cone of the NEW fuel rail with silicon free engine oil GM P/N 12345610 (Canadian P/N 993193) or equivalent.

18. Lubricate the threads and sealing cone of the sensor with silicon free engine oil GM P/N 12345610 (Canadian P/N 993193) or equivalent.

➡**Applying force to the plastic housing of the sensor will destroy the sensor. To tighten or loosen, only apply force to the attached hexagon.**

19. Install the fuel injection fuel rail fuel pressure sensor and tighten the sensor to 25 ft. lbs. (33 Nm).

20. Install the fuel injector wiring harness.

21. Install a NEW plastic spacer if the old one was damaged.

22. Lubricate a NEW fuel injector upper O-ring seal with silicon free engine oil GM P/N 12345610 (Canadian P/N 993193) or equivalent.

23. Install the NEW fuel injector upper O-ring seal.

24. Place the fuel rail into position.

25. Install the 2 outer fuel rail bolts first hand tight, and then install the remaining 2 bolts, hand tight.

26. Connect the fuel injector wiring harness electrical connectors to the fuel injectors.

27. Tighten the fuel rail bolts in the sequence shown.

    a. Tighten the bolts a first pass to 16 ft. lbs. (22 Nm).

    b. Tighten the bolts a final pass to 16 ft. lbs. (22 Nm).

28. Install the intermediate fuel pipe. Refer to Fuel Feed Intermediate Pipe.

29. Connect the engine wiring harness electrical connector to the high pressure fuel pump.

30. Install the fuel injector insulator.

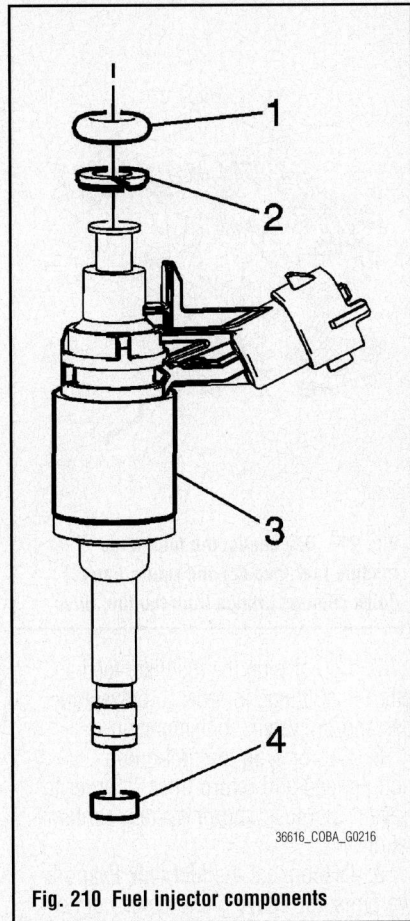

Fig. 210 Fuel injector components

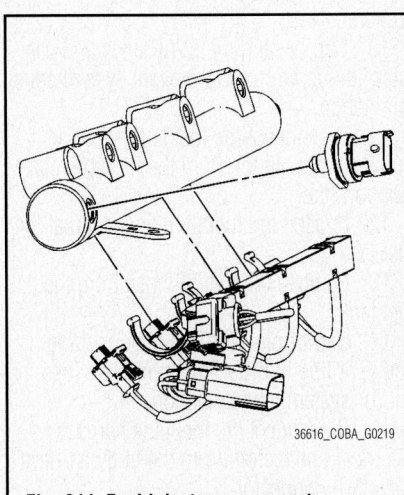

Fig. 211 Fuel injector components

31. Install the intake manifold. Refer to Intake Manifold.

32. Connect the engine wiring harness electrical connector to the fuel injector wiring harness electrical connector.

33. Inspect for leaks using the following procedure:

- Turn ON the ignition, with the engine OFF for 2 seconds.
- Turn OFF the ignition, for 10 seconds.

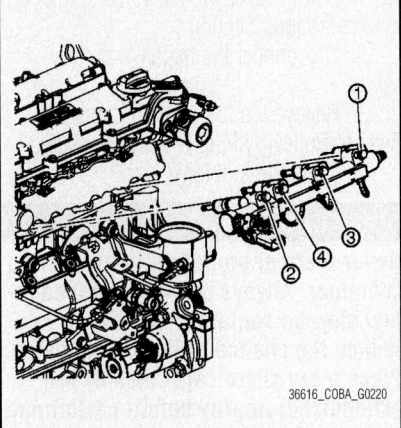

Fig. 212 Fuel rail bolts tightening sequence

- Turn ON the ignition, with the engine OFF.
- Inspect for fuel leaks.

34. Install the low side fuel pressure service port cap.

35. Tighten the fuel fill cap.

36. Install the air cleaner assembly. Refer to Air Cleaner in Engine in Engine Mechanical.

2.2L & 2.4L Engines

See Figures 213 and 214.

1. Before servicing the vehicle, refer to the Precautions Section.

2. Relieve the fuel system pressure. Refer to Relieving Fuel System Pressure.

3. Remove the air cleaner outlet resonator.

4. Disconnect the fuel line fitting.

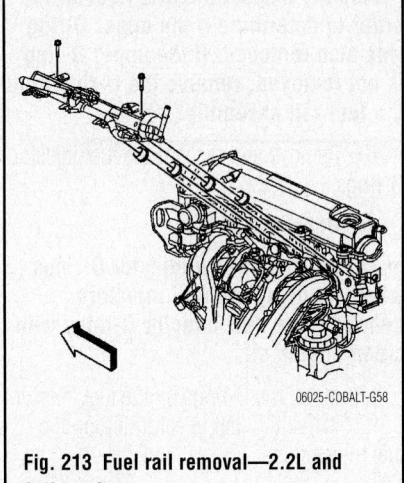

Fig. 213 Fuel rail removal—2.2L and 2.4L engines

5. Disconnect the fuel injector harness connectors.

6. Remove the fuel rail attaching studs.

➡**Use care when removing the fuel rail assembly in order to prevent damage to the fuel injectors electrical connector terminals and spray tips.**

7. Remove the fuel rail using the following procedure:

a. Pull the fuel rail back and upward to remove the fuel injectors from the cylinder head ports.

b. Rotate the fuel rail in order to position the injectors downward.

c. Remove the fuel rail.

8. Remove the fuel injector retainer clip.

9. Remove the fuel injectors from the fuel rail.

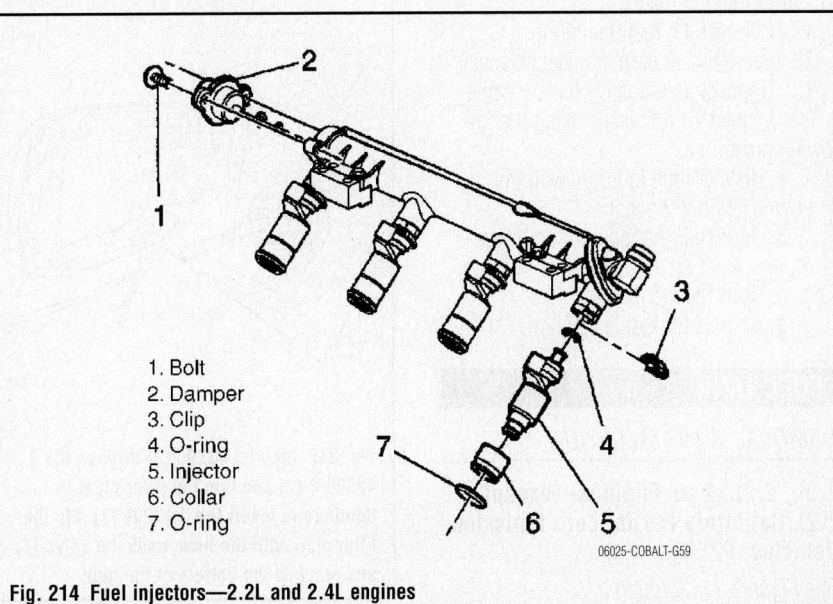

1. Bolt
2. Damper
3. Clip
4. O-ring
5. Injector
6. Collar
7. O-ring

Fig. 214 Fuel injectors—2.2L and 2.4L engines

➡Visually inspect the fuel injector in order to determine if the upper O-ring was also removed. If the upper O-ring is not removed, remove the O-ring from the fuel rail assembly.

10. Remove and discard the fuel injector O-rings.

To install:

➡Always install new injector O-rings when servicing the fuel injectors. Lubricate the new injector O-rings with clean engine oil.

11. Install the O-rings on the fuel injector.
12. Install the fuel injector clip on the fuel injector.

➡The fuel injector will click when the injector is installed correctly.

13. Install the fuel injector in the fuel rail with the connector facing upward.

➡Install new lower O-rings when reusing fuel injectors. Lubricate the injector tip O-rings prior to installing the injectors into the intake manifold.

14. Install the fuel rail using the following procedure:
   a. With the fuel injectors positioned downward, lower the fuel injectors into the cylinder head ports.
   b. Align the injectors by rotating the fuel rail forward.
   c. Carefully push the fuel injectors into the cylinder head ports.
15. Install the fuel rail attaching studs. Tighten the fuel rail studs to 89 inch lbs. (10 Nm).
16. Connect the fuel injector harness connectors. Pull back to insure the connectors are locked in place.
17. Connect the fuel line fitting.
18. Install the air cleaner outlet resonator.
19. Connect the negative battery cable.
20. Inspect for fuel leaks using the following procedure:
   a. Turn ON the ignition, with the engine OFF for 2 seconds.
   b. Turn OFF the ignition for 10 seconds.
   c. Turn ON the ignition.
   d. Inspect for fuel leaks.

FUEL TANK

REMOVAL & INSTALLATION

2.0L, 2.2L, 2.4L Engines—except 2.2L California Partial Zero Emission Vehicles (PZEV)

See Figures 215 through 219.

1. Before servicing the vehicle, refer to the Precautions Section.
2. Disconnect the negative battery cable.
3. Relieve the fuel system pressure. Refer to Relieving Fuel System Pressure.
4. Drain the fuel tank:

✳✳ CAUTION

Never drain or store fuel in an open container. Always use an approved fuel storage container in order to reduce the chance of fire or explosion. Place a dry chemical (Class B) fire extinguisher nearby before performing any on-vehicle service procedures. Failure to follow these precautions may result in personal injury.

   a. Remove the fuel filler cap.
   b. Install J 42960-2, or equivalent, into the fuel fill pipe in order to hold the door open.
   c. Insert J 43290 (2) through the J 42960-2 (1) and into the filler pipe.
   d. Continue to insert the J 43290 (2) into the filler pipe until the hose exits the valve (1) and reaches the bottom of the tank.
   e. Use an air operated pump device in order to drain as much fuel through the J 43290 (1) as possible.
5. Raise and safely support the vehicle.
6. Disconnect the fuel pump module fuel feed (2) and return line (1) quick connect fittings from the fuel filter.

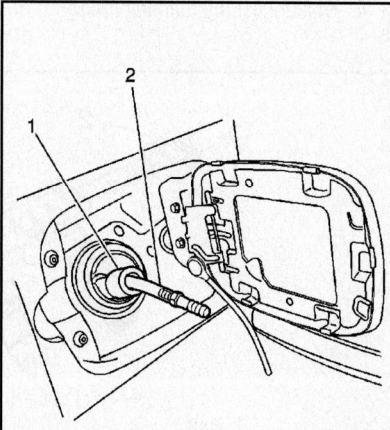

Fig. 215 Insert J 43290 (2) through the J 42960-2 (1) and into the filler pipe. Continue to insert the J 43290 (2) into the filler pipe until the hose exits the valve (1) and reaches the bottom of the tank

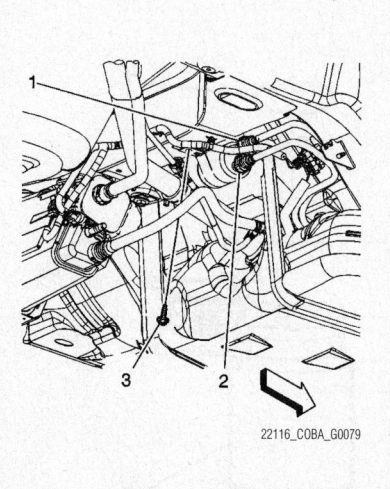

22116_COBA_G0079

Fig. 216 Disconnect the fuel pump module fuel feed (2) and return line (1) quick connect fittings from the fuel filter

7. Cap or plug the fuel filter feed and return line fittings in order to prevent fuel loss and/or system contamination.
8. Cap or plug the fuel pump module feed and return lines in order to prevent fuel loss and/or system contamination.
9. Disconnect the fuel tank Evaporative Emission (EVAP) line quick connect fittings (2) and (3) from the EVAP canister.
10. Cap or plug the EVAP lines and canister fittings in order to prevent system contamination.
11. Disconnect the fuel tank vent line quick connect fitting from the fill pipe recirculation line.
12. Loosen the fuel fill hose clamp at the fuel tank.
13. Remove the fuel fill hose from the fuel tank.
14. Cap or plug the fuel tank opening and vent line in order to prevent fuel loss and/or system contamination.
15. Disconnect the fuel tank harness electrical connectors from the body harness pass thru connector.
16. Disconnect the fuel tank harness electrical connector from the fuel tank pressure sensor.
17. Disconnect the fuel tank harness electrical connector from the EVAP canister vent solenoid valve.
18. Remove the harness retainers from the underbody.
19. Release the exhaust muffler assembly insulators from the underbody hangers and slowly lower the exhaust, allowing it to rest on the rear axle beam.

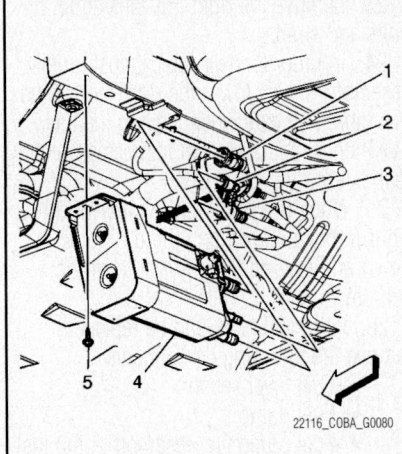

Fig. 217 Disconnect the fuel tank Evaporative Emission (EVAP) line quick connect fittings (2) and (3) from the EVAP canister

20. Use a suitable jack to support the fuel tank during the fuel tank strap and tank removal.

21. Remove the left fuel tank strap bolts and strap.

22. Remove the right fuel tank strap bolts and strap.

23. In order to clear the exhaust muffler assembly, slowly lower the right side of the fuel tank. Use care when feeding the fuel, EVAP lines, and electrical harness around rear axle.

24. Once the fuel tank is clear of the right frame rail, remove the fuel tank down and toward the right side of the vehicle.

25. If the fuel tank is to be replaced, remove the fuel pump module. Refer to Fuel Pump Module.

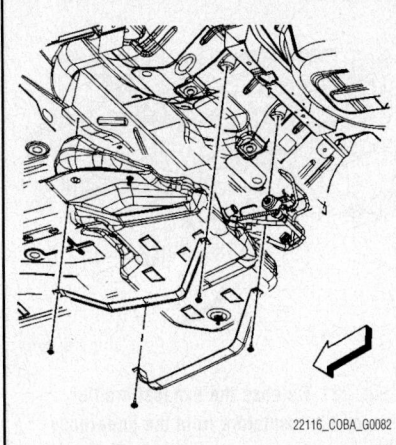

Fig. 219 Remove fuel tank straps and remove the fuel tank down and toward the right side of the vehicle

To install:

26. If the fuel tank was replaced, install the fuel pump module. Refer to Fuel Pump Module.

27. Use a suitable jack to support the fuel tank during the fuel tank and strap installation.

28. Install the left side of the fuel tank over the exhaust muffler assembly.

29. Raise the right side of the fuel tank into position inboard of the right frame rail. Use care when feeding the fuel, EVAP lines, and electrical harness over the rear axle.

30. Install the right fuel tank strap and bolts.

31. Install the left fuel tank strap and bolts.

32. Tighten the fuel tank strap bolts. Tighten the bolts to 18 ft. lbs. (25 Nm).

33. Raise the exhaust muffler assembly into position and install the insulators to the underbody hanger.

34. Connect the fuel tank harness electrical connector to the fuel tank pressure sensor.

35. Connect the fuel tank harness electrical connector to the EVAP canister vent solenoid valve.

36. Install the harness retainers to the underbody.

37. Connect the fuel tank harness electrical connectors to the body harness pass thru connector.

38. Remove the cap or plug from the fuel tank and vent line openings.

39. Connect the fuel fill hose to the fuel tank. Align the "D" notch on the fill hose with the "D" notch on the fuel tank.

40. Tighten the fuel fill hose clamp to 40 inch lbs. (5 Nm).

41. Connect the fuel tank vent line quick connect fitting to the fill pipe recirculation line.

42. Remove the caps or plugs from the EVAP lines.

43. Connect the fuel tank EVAP line quick connect fittings to the EVAP canister.

44. Remove the caps or plugs from the fuel pump module fuel feed and return lines.

45. Remove the caps or plugs from the fuel filter feed and return line fittings.

46. Connect the fuel pump module fuel feed and return line quick connect fittings to the fuel filter.

47. Lower the vehicle.

48. Refill the fuel tank.

49. Connect the negative battery cable.

50. Inspect for fuel leaks using the following procedure:

   a. Turn the ignition switch ON, but do not start the engine. Wait 2 seconds.

   b. Turn the ignition switch OFF and wait 10 seconds.

   c. Turn the ignition switch ON, but do not start the engine.

   d. Inspect for fuel leaks.

2.2L Engine California Partial Zero Emission Vehicles (PZEV)

See Figures 220 through 222.

1. Before servicing the vehicle, refer to the Precautions Section.

2. Disconnect the negative battery cable.

3. Relieve the fuel system pressure. Refer to Relieving Fuel System Pressure.

4. Drain the fuel tank:

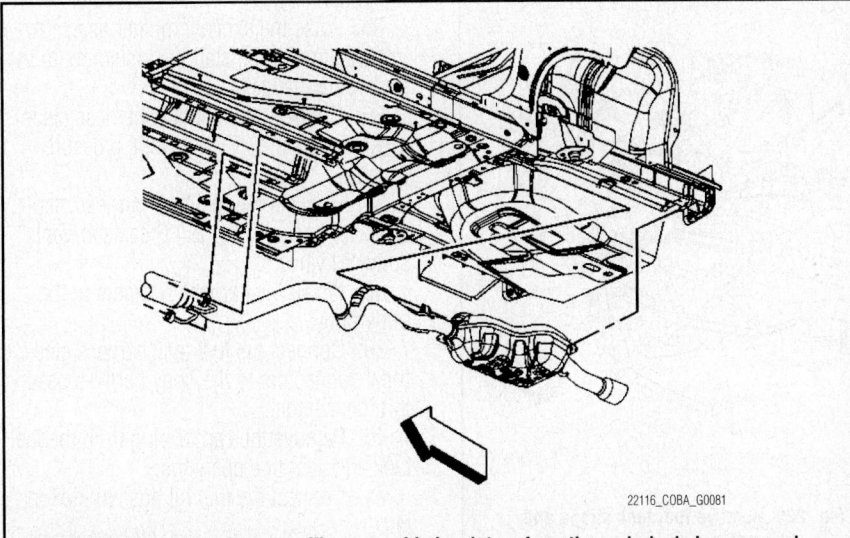

Fig. 218 Release the exhaust muffler assembly insulators from the underbody hangers and slowly lower the exhaust

5. Raise and safely support the vehicle.

6. Disconnect the fuel tank line quick connect fitting from the fuel feed line.

7. Cap or plug the fuel feed line and the fuel tank line in order to prevent fuel loss and/or system contamination.

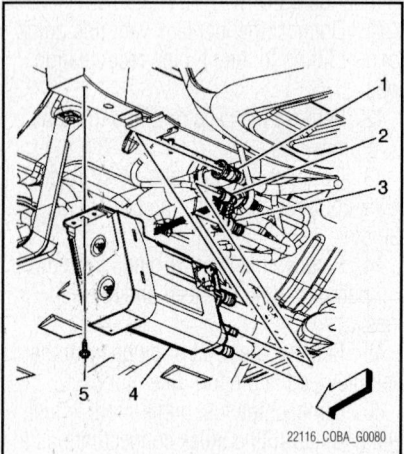

Fig. 220 Disconnect the fuel tank Evaporative Emission (EVAP) line quick connect fittings (2) and (3) from the EVAP canister

8. Disconnect the fuel tank Evaporative Emission (EVAP) line quick connect fitting (3) from the EVAP canister.

9. Disconnect the fuel fill pipe fresh air line quick connect fitting (2) from the EVAP canister.

10. Cap or plug the EVAP/fresh air lines and canister fittings in order to prevent system contamination.

11. Disconnect the fuel tank vent line quick connect fitting (1) from the fill pipe recirculation line.

12. Loosen the fuel fill hose clamp at the fuel tank.

13. Remove the fuel fill hose from the fuel tank.

14. Cap or plug the fuel tank opening and vent line in order to prevent fuel loss and/or system contamination.

15. Disconnect the fuel tank harness

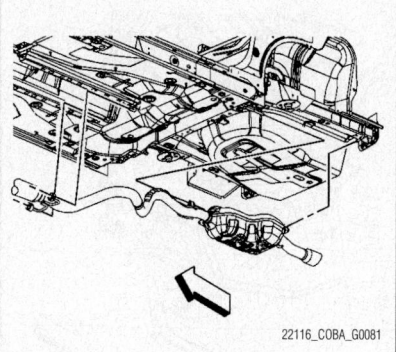

Fig. 221 Release the exhaust muffler assembly insulators from the underbody hangers and slowly lower the exhaust

electrical connectors from the body harness pass thru connector.

16. Disconnect the fuel tank harness electrical connector from the fuel tank pressure sensor.

17. Disconnect the fuel tank harness electrical connector from the EVAP canister vent solenoid valve.

18. Remove the harness retainers from the underbody.

19. Release the exhaust muffler assembly insulators from the underbody hangers and slowly lower the exhaust, allowing it to rest on the rear axle beam.

20. Remove the fuel tank harness clips from the underbody.

21. Use a suitable jack to support the fuel tank during the fuel tank strap and tank removal.

22. Remove the left fuel tank strap bolts and strap.

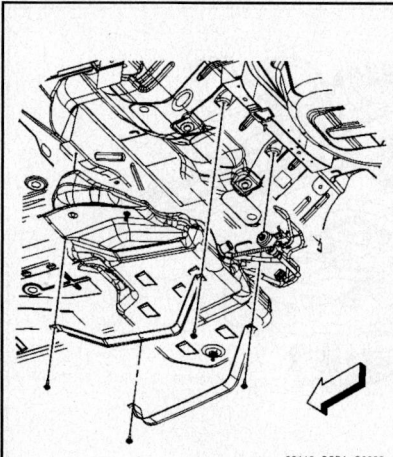

Fig. 222 Remove fuel tank straps and remove the fuel tank down and toward the right side of the vehicle

23. Remove the right fuel tank strap bolts and strap.

24. In order to clear the exhaust muffler assembly, slowly lower the right side of the fuel tank. Use care when feeding the fuel, EVAP lines, and electrical harness around rear axle.

25. Once the fuel tank is clear of the right frame rail, remove the fuel tank down and toward the right side of the vehicle.

26. If the fuel tank is to be replaced, remove the following components:
- Fuel level sensor
- Fuel pump
- Fuel pump fuel reservoir pump fuel strainer

To install:

27. If the fuel tank was replaced, install the following components:
- Fuel pump fuel reservoir pump fuel strainer
- Fuel level sensor
- Fuel pump

28. Use a suitable jack to support the fuel tank during the fuel tank and strap installation.

29. Install the left side of the fuel tank over the exhaust muffler assembly.

30. Raise the right side of the fuel tank into position inboard of the right frame rail. Use care when feeding the fuel, EVAP lines, and electrical harness over the rear axle.

31. Install the right fuel tank strap and bolts.

32. Install the left fuel tank strap and bolts.

33. Tighten the fuel tank strap bolts to 18 ft. lbs. (25 Nm).

34. Install the fuel tank harness clips to the underbody.

35. Raise the exhaust muffler assembly into position and install the insulators to the underbody hanger.

36. Connect the fuel tank harness electrical connector to the fuel tank pressure sensor.

37. Connect the fuel tank harness electrical connector to the EVAP canister vent solenoid valve.

38. Install the harness retainers to the underbody.

39. Connect the fuel tank harness electrical connectors to the body harness pass thru connector.

40. Remove the cap or plug from the fuel tank and vent line openings.

41. Connect the fuel fill hose to the fuel tank.

42. Tighten the fuel fill hose clamp. Tighten the clamp to 40 inch lbs. (5 Nm).

43. Connect the fuel tank vent line quick connect fitting to the fill pipe recirculation line.

44. Remove the caps or plug from the EVAP/fresh air lines and canister fittings.

45. Connect the fuel fill pipe fresh air line quick connect fitting to the EVAP canister.

46. Connect the fuel tank EVAP line quick connect fitting to the EVAP canister.

47. Remove the cap or plug from the fuel feed line and the fuel tank line.

48. Connect the fuel tank line quick connect fitting to the fuel feed line.

49. Lower the vehicle.

50. Refill the fuel tank.

51. Connect the negative battery cable.

52. Inspect for fuel leaks using the following procedure:

    a. Turn the ignition switch ON, but do not start the engine. Wait 2 seconds.

    b. Turn the ignition switch OFF and wait 10 seconds.

    c. Turn the ignition switch ON, but do not start the engine.

    d. Inspect for fuel leaks.

IDLE SPEED

ADJUSTMENT

Idle speed is maintained by the Powertrain Control Module (PCM). No adjustment is necessary or possible.

THROTTLE BODY

REMOVAL & INSTALLATION

2.0L Engine

See Figure 223.

1. Before servicing the vehicle, refer to the Precautions Section.

❋❋ WARNING

Do not use solvents of any type when cleaning the gasket surfaces on the intake manifold and the throttle body assembly, as damage to the gasket surfaces and throttle body assembly may result. Use care in cleaning the gasket surfaces on the intake manifold and the throttle body assembly, as sharp tools may damage the gasket surfaces. Solvents that contain Methyl Ethyl Ketone (MEK) may damage fuel system components.

2. Remove the air cleaner outlet duct.

3. Disconnect the Evaporative Emission (EVAP) purge line.

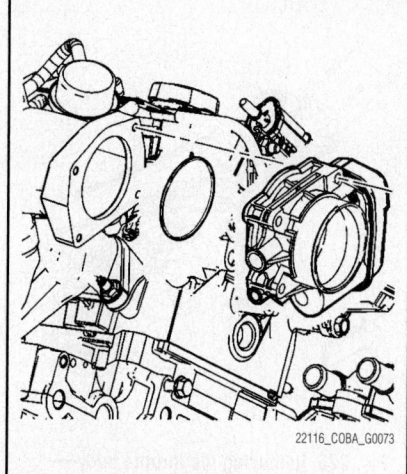

Fig. 223 Removing the throttle body—2.0L Engine

4. Disconnect the throttle body control harness connector.

5. Remove the throttle body attaching bolts.

6. Remove the throttle body and gasket from the supercharger.

To install:

7. Inspect the throttle body gasket and replace if necessary.

8. Install the throttle body to the supercharger.

9. Install the throttle body attaching bolts. Tighten the throttle body attaching bolts to 89 inch lbs. (10 Nm).

10. Connect the throttle body control harness connector.

11. Connect the EVAP purge line.

12. Install the air cleaner outlet duct.

2.2L & 2.4L Engines

See Figures 224 and 225.

1. Before servicing the vehicle, refer to the Precautions Section.

❋❋ WARNING

Do not use solvents of any type when cleaning the gasket surfaces on the intake manifold and the throttle body assembly, as damage to the gasket surfaces and throttle body assembly may result. Use care in cleaning the gasket surfaces on the intake manifold and the throttle body assembly, as sharp tools may damage the gasket surfaces. Solvents that contain Methyl Ethyl Ketone (MEK) may damage fuel system components.

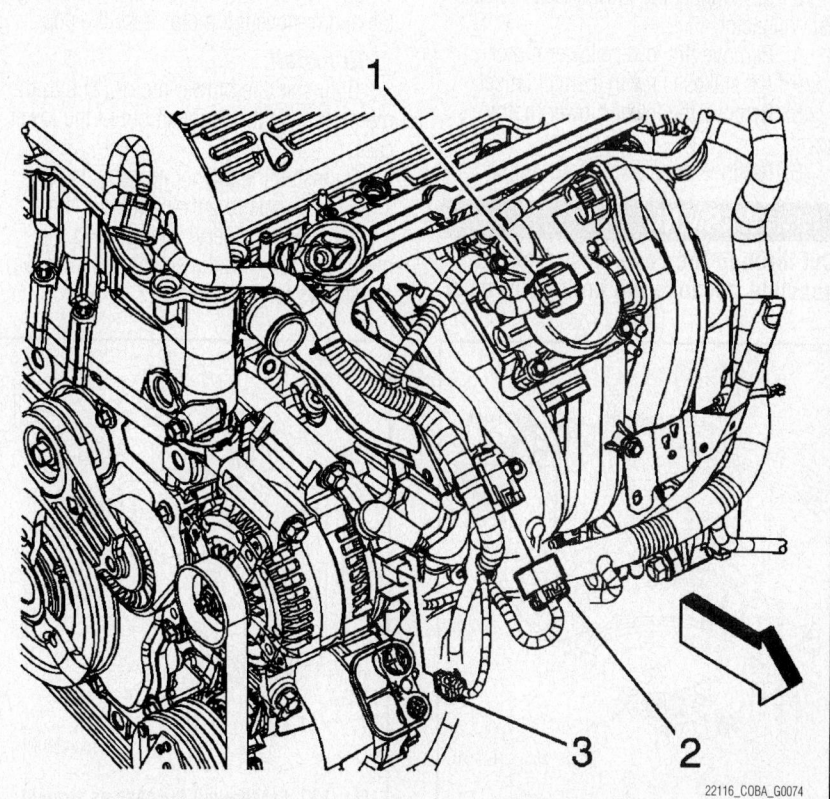

Fig. 224 Location of the Throttle Actuator Control (TAC) electrical connector (1)

➡ DO NOT prop open the throttle blade with the ignition key in the ON position as it may set a Diagnostic Trouble Code (DTC).

2. Remove the air cleaner outlet duct.

3. Remove the intake manifold cover:

    a. Remove the engine oil fill cap.

    b. Grasp the intake manifold cover by the lower right inboard corner and pull up to disengage the cover from the stud.

    c. Grasp the intake manifold cover by the upper left corner and pull up to disengage the cover from the stud.

    d. Remove the intake manifold cover.

4. Disconnect the Throttle Actuator Control (TAC) electrical connector (1).

5. Remove the throttle body bolts.

6. Remove the throttle body.

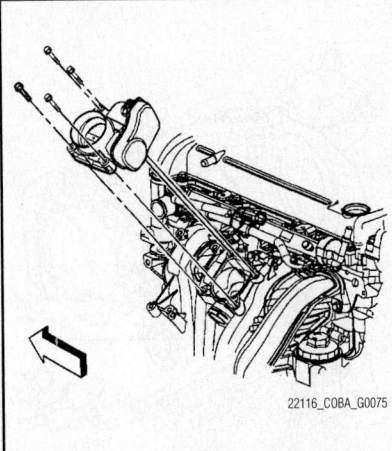

Fig. 225 Removing the throttle body— 2.2L and 2.4L Engines

To install:

7. Inspect the throttle body gasket, and replace if necessary.

8. Install the throttle body.

9. Install the throttle body bolts. Tighten the bolts to 89 inch lbs. (10 Nm).

10. Connect the TAC electrical connector (1).

11. Install the intake manifold cover:

    a. Place the intake manifold cover onto the engine over the studs.

    b. Push down on the intake manifold cover directly over the lower right stud in order to engage the cover to the stud.

    c. Push down on the intake manifold cover directly over the upper left stud in order to engage the cover to the stud.

    d. Install the engine oil fill cap.

12. Install the air cleaner outlet duct.

HEATING & AIR CONDITIONING SYSTEM

BLOWER MOTOR

REMOVAL & INSTALLATION

See Figures 226 through 228.

1. Before servicing the vehicle, refer to the Precautions Section.

2. Disconnect the negative battery cable.

3. Disconnect the blower motor electrical connector.

4. Remove the lower blower motor cover heat stakes (1) with a small chisel.

5. Remove the lower blower motor cover.

6. Remove the blower motor nuts.

❋❋ WARNING

Cut through the case as straight as possible because the motor cup must be reused. In order to prevent damage to the component, do not cut any deeper than necessary to remove the motor cup.

7. Remove the blower motor and cup from the lower case by cutting through the case between the circular ribs around the motor with a sharp utility knife.

8. Release the blower motor retaining tab and remove the motor from the cup.

To install:

9. Install the blower motor (1) into the motor cup (2) that was cut out of the lower case.

10. Install the blower motor nuts (3). Tighten the nuts to 21 inch lbs. (2 Nm).

11. Attach the service ring (4) to the motor cup (2) with the screws (5). Tighten the screws to 15 inch lbs. (2 Nm).

12. Install the blower motor and service ring into the HVAC module using the screws (5). Make certain the blower motor electrical connector is pointing rearward in the vehicle. Tighten the screws to 15 inch lbs. (2 Nm).

13. Install the lower blower motor cover.

14. Install the lower blower motor cover

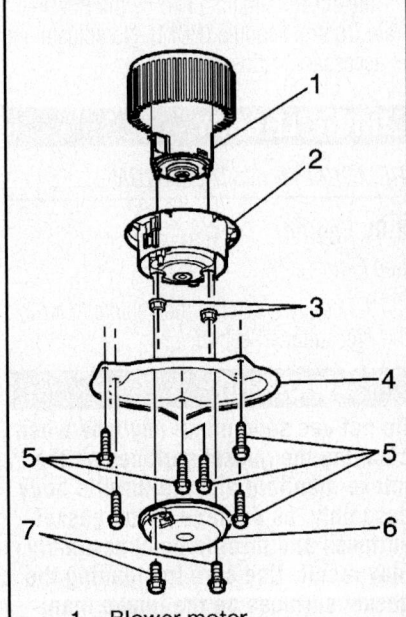

1. Blower motor
2. Motor cup
3. Blower motor nuts
4. Service ring
5. Blower motor screws

Fig. 228 Expanded view of the blower motor

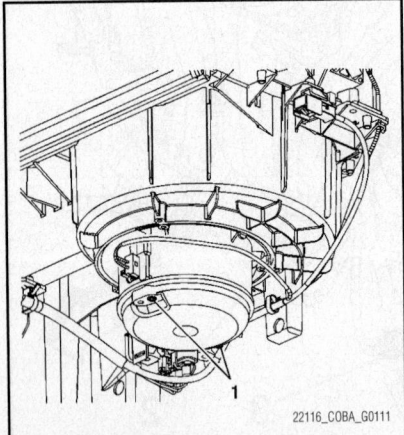

Fig. 226 Remove the lower blower motor cover heat stakes (1) with a small chisel

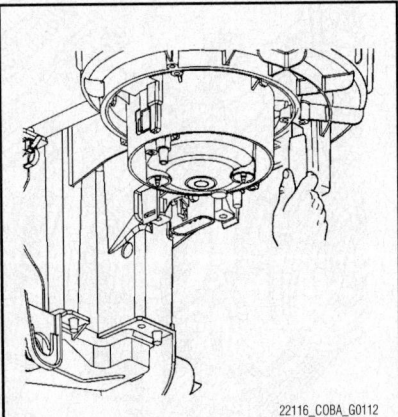

Fig. 227 Cut through the case as straight as possible to remove the blower motor and cup from the lower case

retaining screws and tighten to 15 inch lbs. (2 Nm).

15. Connect the blower motor electrical connector.

16. Connect the negative battery cable.

HEATER CORE

REMOVAL & INSTALLATION

See Figures 229 through 231.

✳✳ CAUTION

With a pressurized cooling system, the coolant temperature in the radiator can be considerably higher than the boiling point of the solution at atmospheric pressure. Removal of the surge tank cap, while the cooling system is hot and under high pressure, causes the solution to boil instantaneously with explosive force. This will cause the solution to spew out over the engine, the fenders, and the person removing the cap. Serious bodily injury may result.

1. Before servicing the vehicle, refer to the Precautions Section.

2. Drain the cooling system.

3. Raise and support the vehicle.

4. Place a drain pan under the water pump drain port.

5. Loosen the water pump drain bolt and drain the coolant from the water pump.

6. Close and tighten the water pump drain bolt to 88 inch lbs. (10 Nm).

7. Lower the vehicle.

8. Reposition the heater outlet hose clamp at the heater core using J 38185.

9. Remove the heater outlet hose from the heater core.

10. Reposition the heater inlet hose clamp at the heater core using J 38185.

11. Remove the heater inlet hose from the heater core.

12. Remove the right console extension panel.

13. Remove the Body Control Module (BCM) from the vehicle.

14. Remove the front floor console left side extension panel.

15. Pull back the carpet at the bottom of the left Instrument Panel (I/P) center support bracket and remove the left I/P center support bracket nuts.

16. Remove the left I/P center support bracket.

17. Remove the accelerator control pedal from the front of the dash and position out of the way. Refer to Accelerator Pedal Position Sensor in Engine Performance & Emission Controls.

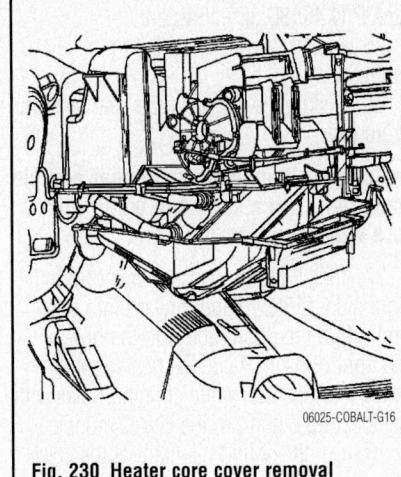

Fig. 230 Heater core cover removal

18. Raise the center floor outlet duct while pushing the floor ducts down to disengage the ducts.

19. Rotate the center floor outlet duct forward in the vehicle and pull down to disengage it from the HVAC module.

20. Remove the heater core cover heat stakes with a small chisel.

21. Loosen the nut that is behind the fuel line bracket and remove the stud from the dash panel at the heater hoses.

➡**Make certain that all of the heater core cover screws are removed before attempting to remove the heater core cover.**

22. Pull the heater core cover down just enough to clear the locating pins from the HVAC module. Slide the heater core cover rearward until the drain tube clears the front of dash. Slide the heater core cover down, rearward, and to the right to remove.

23. Remove the heater core.

To install:

24. Inspect the foam heater core seal on the lower HVAC case. If damaged, replace

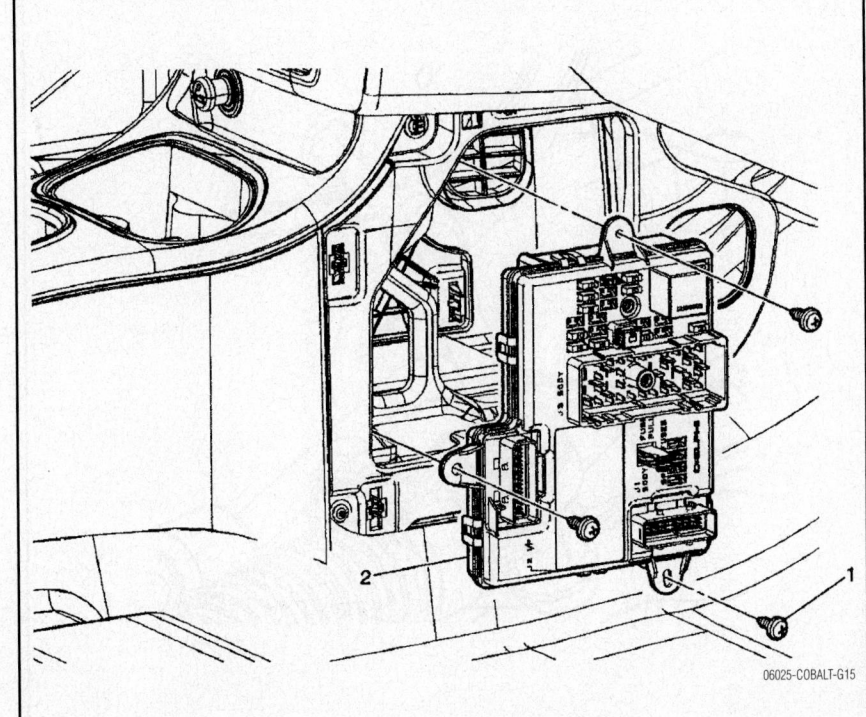

Fig. 229 Body control module

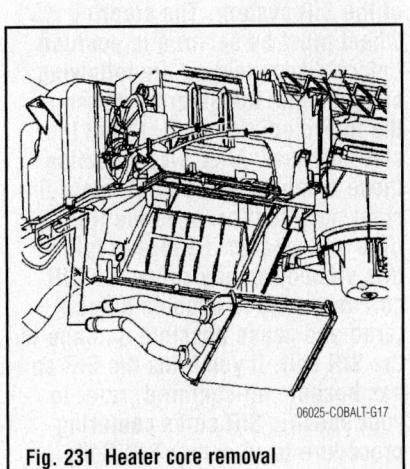

Fig. 231 Heater core removal

using Kent Industries adhesive black foam tape P/N 46480, or equivalent.

25. Install the heater core into the HVAC module.

26. Install a new drain tube seal onto the drain tube.

➡ **Spraying the heater core seal and the dash mat with a soap and water mixture will ease installation.**

27. Install the heater core cover from the right side. Slide up and forward into position. Align the drain tube with the hole in the front of dash. Raise the heater core cover into position while aligning holes with the locating pins from the HVAC module.

28. Cut the sound insulator at the cowl near the center screw approximately 3 inches (76mm) and fold the sound insulator back to ease in installation of the screw. Ensure the sound insulator is positioned back after the screws are tightened.

➡ **Make certain that the heater core cover is properly positioned and is fully seated on the HVAC module before installing the screws. Be sure to install all heater core cover screws.**

29. Install the heater core cover screws. Tighten the heater core cover screws to 15 inch lbs. (2 Nm).

30. Install the stud into the dash panel at the heater hoses and tighten the nut that is behind the fuel line bracket.

31. Align the center floor duct with the HVAC module.

32. Push the center floor duct up while rotating rearward in the vehicle to install on the HVAC module.

33. Push down on the floor duct while rotating the center floor outlet ducts to align the ducts.

34. Slide the center floor outlet duct down into position in the floor ducts.

35. Install the accelerator control pedal. Refer to Accelerator Pedal Position Sensor in Engine Performance & Emission Controls.

36. Pull back the carpet and place the left center support bracket into position.

37. Install the left center support bracket nuts and tighten to 89 inch lbs. (10 Nm).

38. Install the left side front floor console extension panel.

39. Install the BCM to the vehicle.

40. Install the heater outlet hose to the heater core.

41. Install the hose clamp to secure the hose using J 38185.

42. Install the heater inlet hose to the heater core.

43. Install the hose clamp to secure the hose using J 38185.

44. Fill the cooling system.

STEERING

POWER RACK & PINION STEERING GEAR

REMOVAL & INSTALLATION

See Figures 232 and 233.

1. Before servicing the vehicle, refer to the Precautions Section.

2. Turn the steering wheel to the straight ahead position and lock it in place.

✳✳ WARNING

With wheels of the vehicle facing straight ahead, secure the steering wheel utilizing steering column anti-rotation pin, steering column lock, or a strap to prevent rotation. Locking of the steering column will prevent damage and a possible malfunction of the SIR system. The steering wheel must be secured in position before disconnecting the following components: the steering column, the intermediate shaft(s), and the steering gear. After disconnecting these components, do not rotate the steering wheel or move the front tires and wheels. Failure to follow this procedure may cause the SIR coil assembly to become un-centered and cause possible damage to the SIR coil. If you think the SIR coil has became un-centered, refer to your specific SIR coil's centering procedure to re-center SIR Coil.

3. Raise and support the vehicle.

4. Remove the front wheels.

5. Remove the intermediate steering shaft bolt at the steering gear and discard it.

6. Disconnect the intermediate steering shaft from the steering gear.

7. Remove both rack and pinion outer tie rod end nuts and discard them.

✳✳ WARNING

Do not attempt to separate the rack and pinion outer tie rod ends using a wedge type tool.

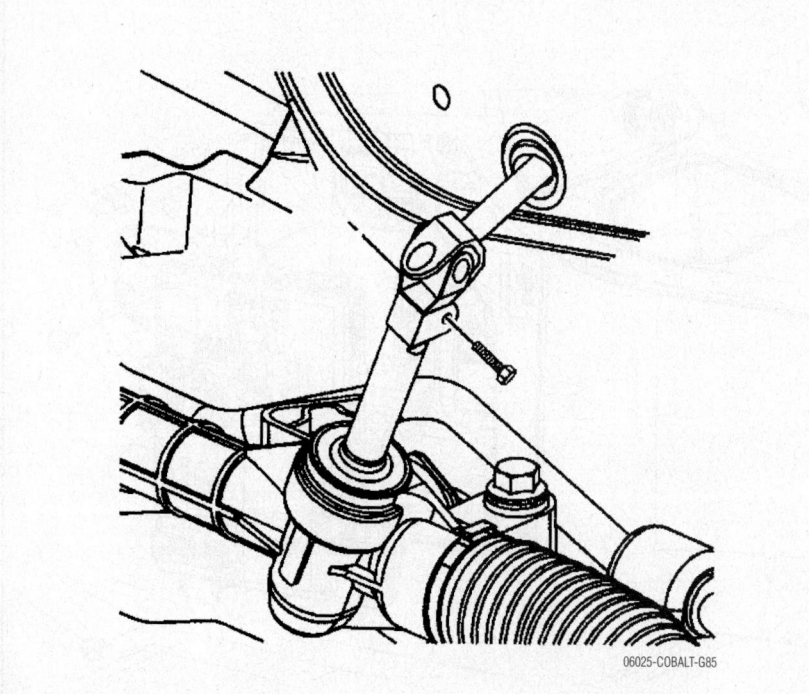

Fig. 232 Steering shaft pinch bolt

06025-COBALT-G85

8. Use puller J 24319-B to separate the rack and pinion outer tie rod ends from the steering knuckles.

9. Remove the steering gear bolts.

10. Remove the rear transaxle mount. Refer to Transaxle, in the Drive Train section.

11. Carefully remove the steering gear from the vehicle through the left wheelhouse opening.

To install:

12. Install the steering gear to the vehicle through the left wheelhouse opening.

13. Install the steering gear bolts and tighten to 81 ft. lbs. (110 Nm).

14. Install the rear transaxle mount. Refer to Transaxle, in the Drive Train section.

15. Connect the intermediate steering shaft to the steering gear.

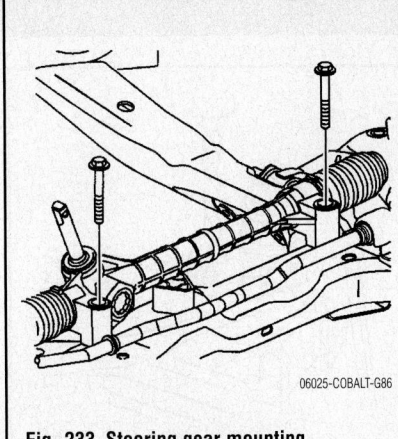

06025-COBALT-G86

Fig. 233 Steering gear mounting

16. Install a new intermediate steering shaft bolt and tighten to 25 ft. lbs. (34 Nm).

17. Install the rack and pinion outer tie rod ends to the steering knuckles.

18. Install new rack and pinion outer tie rod end nuts. Tighten the bolts to 18 ft. lbs. (25 Nm) plus 90°.

19. Install the front wheels.

20. Lower the vehicle.

21. Inspect the front toe.

22. If equipped with RPO JL4, calibrate the steering angle sensor:

   a. Keep the steering wheel centered and the wheels facing forward.

   b. With a scan tool, perform the special functions steering position sensor calibration and follow the on screen instructions.

POWER STEERING PUMP

REMOVAL & INSTALLATION

See Figure 234.

This vehicle uses electronic power steering.

1. Turn signal/multifunction switch
2. Inflatable restraint steering wheel module coil
3. Windshield wiper/washer switch
4. Steering wheel
5. Steering wheel controls—right UK3/K34
6. Horn switches
7. Steering wheel controls—left UK3/K34
8. Electronic Power Steering (EPS) control module
9. Electronic Power Steering (EPS) control motor
10. Ignition switch
11. Ignition lock cylinder control solenoid

22116_COBA_G0157

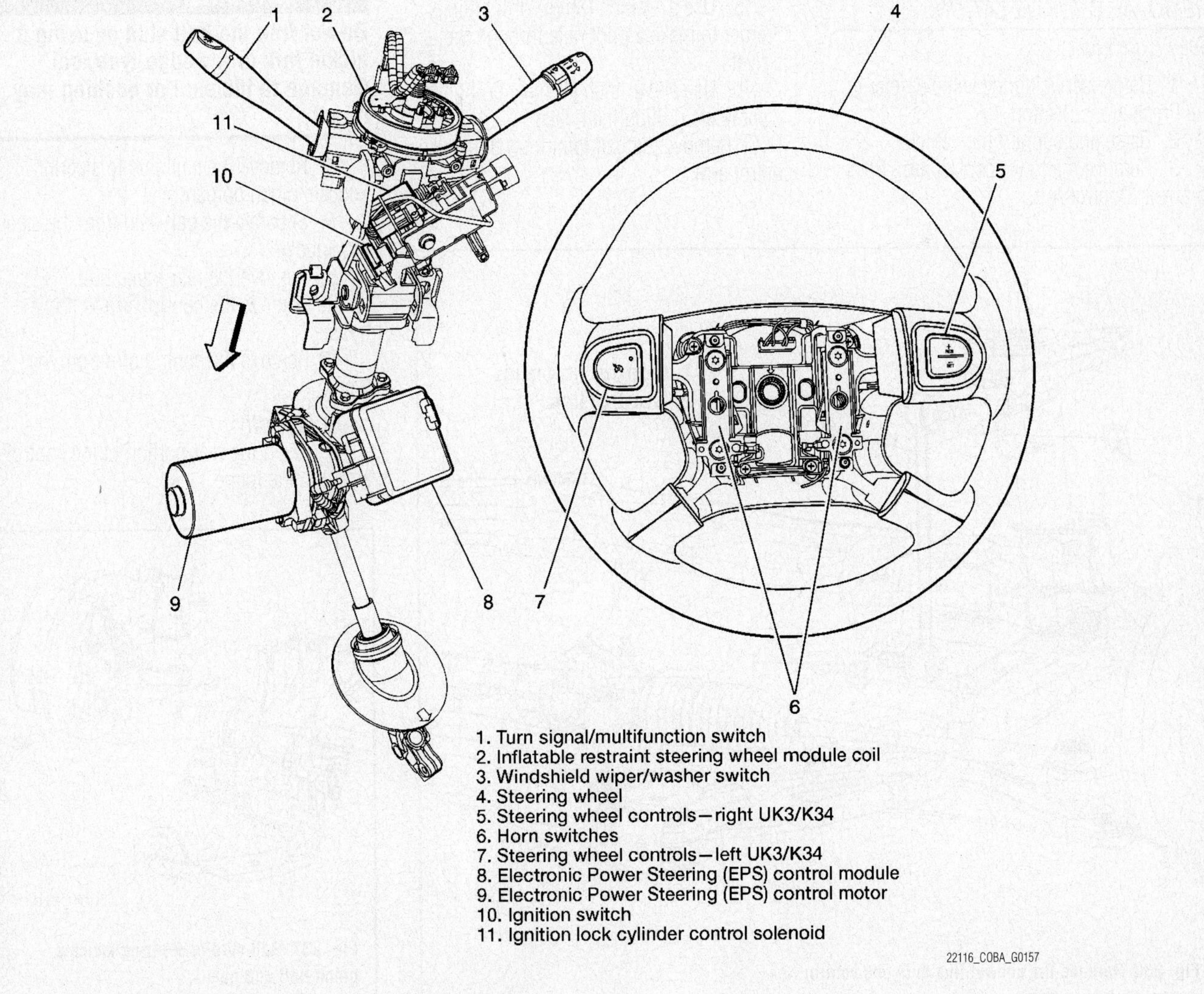

Fig. 234 Expanded view of power steering and related components

CONTROL LINKS

REMOVAL & INSTALLATION

See Figure 235.

1. Before servicing the vehicle, refer to the Precautions Section.
2. Raise and safely support the vehicle.
3. Remove the front tire and wheel assembly.
4. Remove the control link nuts (1) at the stabilizer bar and strut assembly.
5. Remove the control link (2) from the vehicle.

To install:

6. Connect the control link and tighten the control link nuts to 48 ft. lbs. (65 Nm).
7. Install the front wheel.
8. Lower the vehicle.

LOWER BALL JOINT

REMOVAL & INSTALLATION

See Figure 236.

1. Before servicing the vehicle, refer to the Precautions Section.
2. Raise and support the vehicle.
3. Remove the lower control arm. Refer to Lower Control Arm.

Fig. 236 Drilling out the lower ball joint rivets

4. Place the lower control arm in a vise.
5. Remove the ball joint to control arm rivets using the following procedure:
   a. Use a ⅛ inch (3mm) drill bit in order to make a pilot hole through the rivets.
   b. Use a ³¹⁄₆₄ inch (13mm) drill bit to complete drilling the rivets.
6. Remove the ball joint from the lower control arm.

To install:

7. Install the ball joint to the lower control arm.
8. Install the ball joint bolts and the nuts. Follow the instructions in the ball joint kit.
9. Tighten the ball joint bolts to 50 ft. lbs. (68 Nm).
10. Install the lower control arm. Refer to Lower Control Arm.
11. Lower the vehicle.

LOWER CONTROL ARM

REMOVAL & INSTALLATION

See Figures 237 through 239.

1. Before servicing the vehicle, refer to the Precautions Section.
2. Raise and support the vehicle.
3. Remove the wheel.

✳✳ WARNING

Do not free the ball stud by using a pickle fork or a wedge-type tool. Damage to the seal or bushing may result.

4. Remove the ball stud to steering knuckle pinch bolt and nut.
5. Separate the ball stud from the steering knuckle.
6. Remove the rear frame bolt.
7. Remove the control arm to frame bolts.
8. Remove the control arm from the frame.

To install:

9. Insert the rear portion of the control arm into the frame.

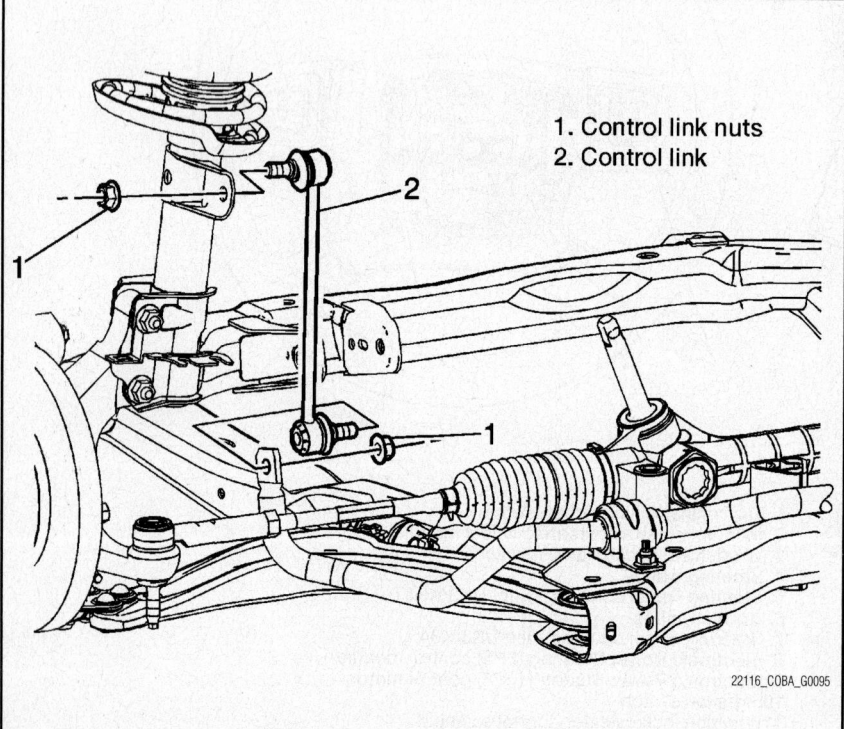

1. Control link nuts
2. Control link

Fig. 235 Remove the control link nuts and control link

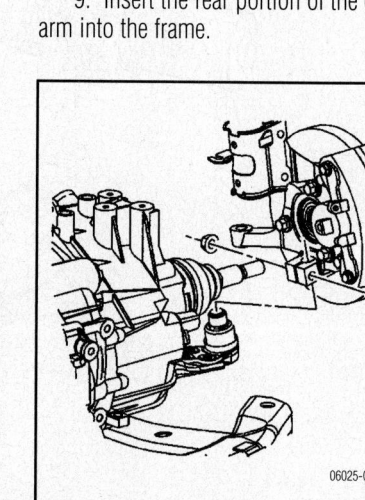

Fig. 237 Ball stud to steering knuckle pinch bolt and nut

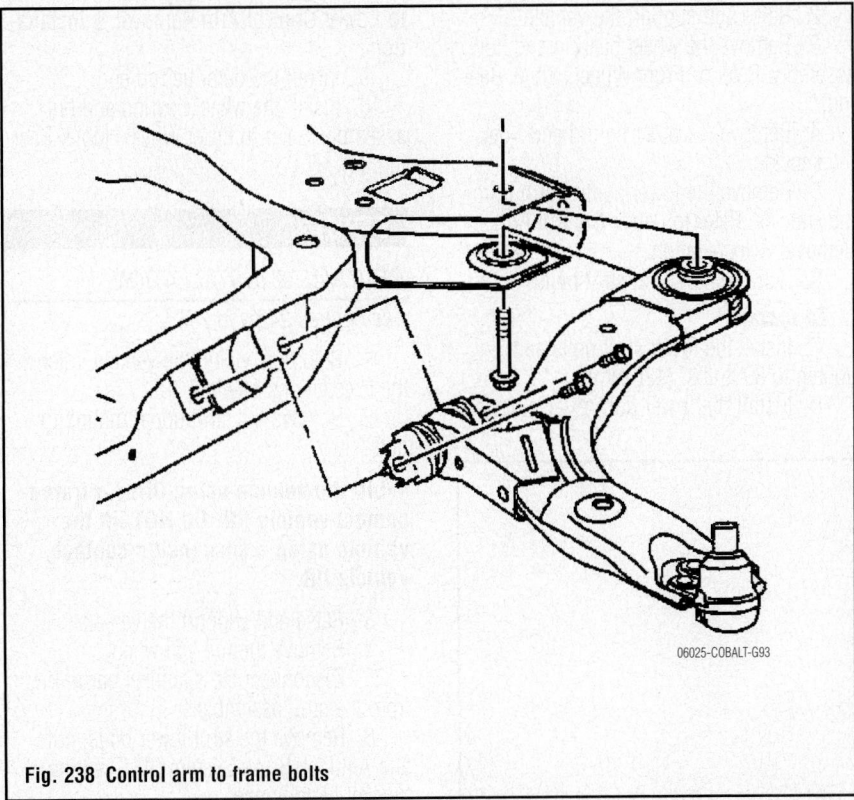

Fig. 238 Control arm to frame bolts

10. Loosely install the rear frame bolt.
11. Lower the control arm and insert the ball stud into the steering knuckle.

✳✳ WARNING

The control arm contains 2 fore/aft movement limiting brackets. Failure to install these brackets will result in abnormal handling characteristics.

12. Install the fore/aft movement limiting brackets onto the control arm forward bushing.
13. Install both control arm to frame bolts. Tighten the bolts to 41 ft. lbs. (55 Nm).
14. Tighten the rear frame bolt to 74 ft. lbs. (100 Nm), plus 180°.

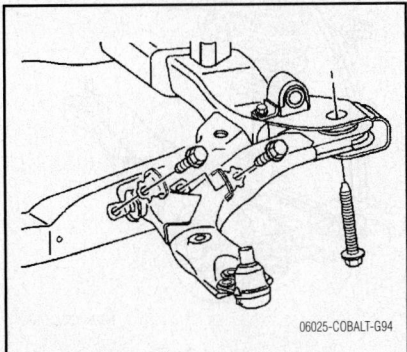

Fig. 239 Fore/aft movement limiting brackets

✳✳ WARNING

The torque sequence must be followed in the order that is listed.

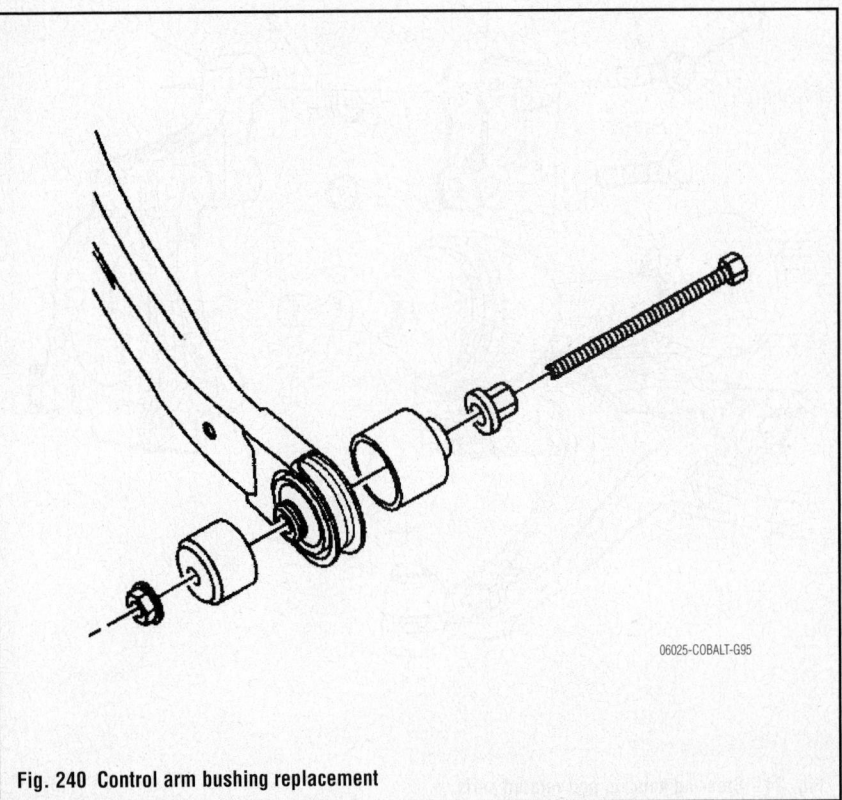

Fig. 240 Control arm bushing replacement

15. Install the ball stud pinch bolt and nut.
   a. First Pass: Tighten the nut to 37 ft. lbs. (50 Nm).
   b. Back off the nut ¾ turn.
   c. Second Pass: Tighten the nut to 37 ft. lbs. (50 Nm), plus 30°.
16. Install the wheel.
17. Lower the vehicle.
18. Road test the vehicle in order to test for leads or pulls. Align as needed.

LOWER CONTROL ARM BUSHING REPLACEMENT

See Figure 240.

1. Before servicing the vehicle, refer to the Precautions Section.
2. Raise and support the vehicle.
3. Remove the lower control arm. Refer to Lower Control Arm.
4. Wrap the control arm with a shop towel and place it in a vise.

➡**Note the depth and orientation of the old bushing before removal.**

5. Using tool J 41211, remove the control arm bushing from the lower control arm.
6. Disassemble the tools and remove the bushing.

To install:
7. Place the NEW bushing to the tapered side of the control arm.

8. Using the tool, install the control arm bushing in the lower control arm.

9. Install the bushing to the same depth and orientation as noted during removal.

10. Remove the tool from the control arm.

11. Install the lower control arm. Refer to Lower Control Arm.

STEERING KNUCKLE

REMOVAL & INSTALLATION

See Figure 241.

1. Before servicing the vehicle, refer to the Precautions Section.

2. Raise and support the vehicle.

3. Remove the wheel bearing and hub assembly. Refer to Front Wheel Hub & Bearing.

4. Remove the outer tie rod end from the knuckle.

5. Remove the lower control arm from the knuckle. Refer to Lower Control Arm Removal & Installation.

6. Remove the lower strut bolts.

To install:

7. Install the lower strut bolts and tighten to 89 ft. lbs. (120 Nm).

8. Install the lower control arm. Refer to Lower Control Arm Removal & Installation.

9. Install the outer tie rod end.

10. Install the wheel bearing and hub assembly. Refer to Front Wheel Hub & Bearing.

STRUT

REMOVAL & INSTALLATION

See Figures 242 and 243.

1. Before servicing the vehicle, refer to the Precautions Section.

2. Remove the strut upper mounting nuts.

➡ **Lift the vehicle using ONLY a frame-contact vehicle lift. Do NOT lift the vehicle using a suspension-contact vehicle lift.**

3. Raise and support the vehicle.

4. Remove the tire and wheel.

5. Disconnect the stabilizer bar link from the strut assembly.

6. Remove the strut lower bolts, nuts and Antilock Brake System (ABS) wiring bracket, if equipped.

7. Remove the strut.

To install:

8. Install the strut.

9. Install the strut upper mounting nuts and tighten to 15 ft. lbs. (20 Nm).

➡ **This is a prevailing torque type fastener. This fastener may be reused**

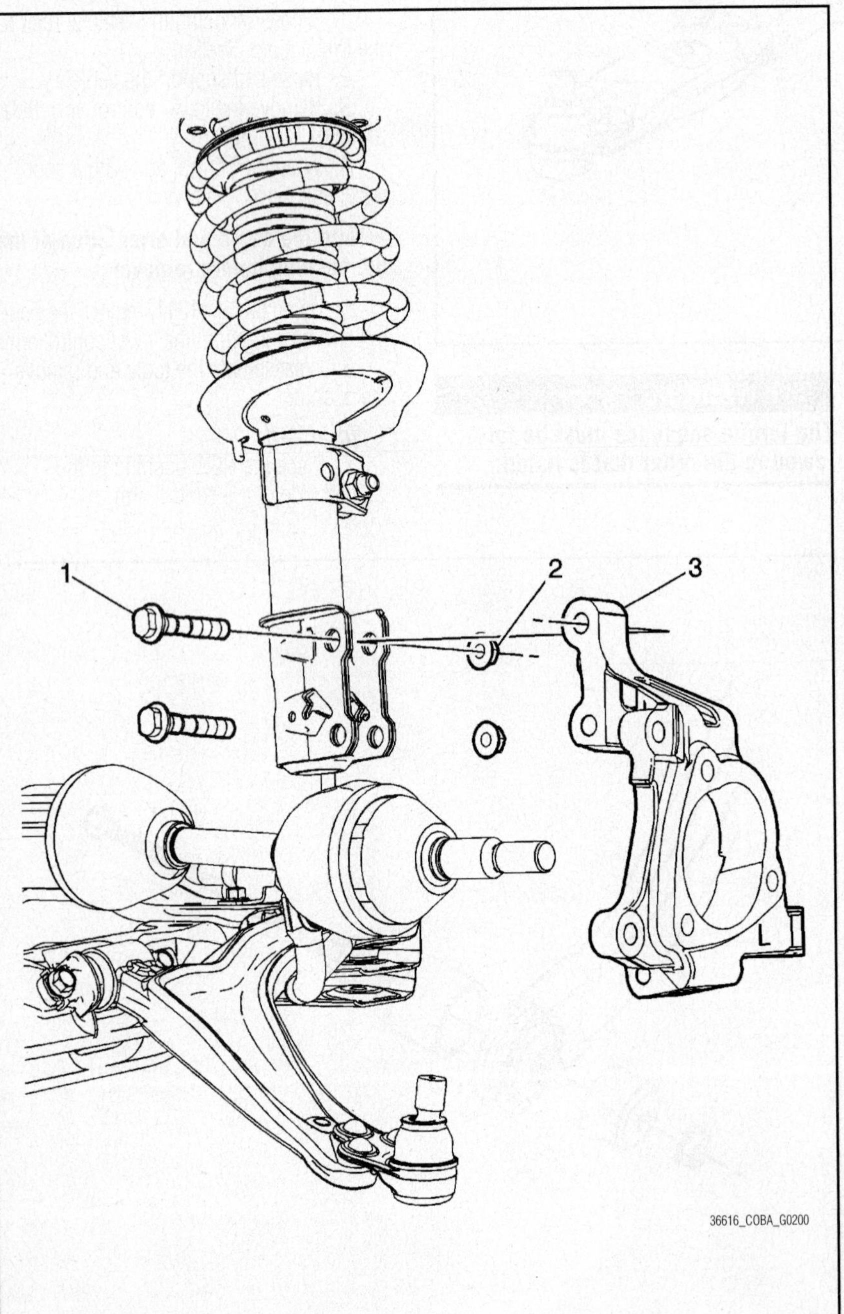

Fig. 241 Steering knuckle and related parts

36616_COBA_G0200

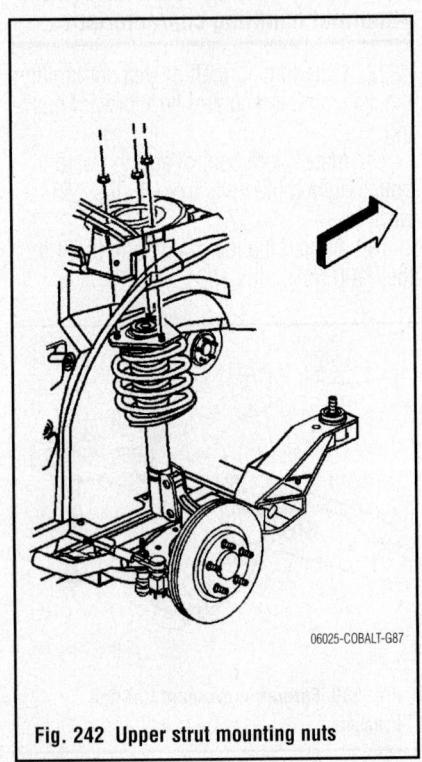

06025-COBALT-G87

Fig. 242 Upper strut mounting nuts

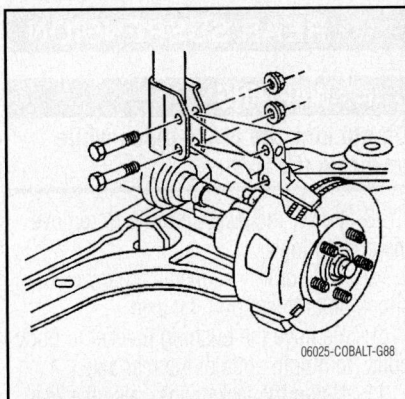

Fig. 243 Lower strut mount bolts/nuts

ONLY if: The fastener and its counterpart are clean and free from rust. The fastener develops 27 inch lbs. (3 Nm) of torque/drag against its counterpart prior to the fastener seating. If the fastener does not meet these criteria, REPLACE the fastener.

10. Install the strut lower bolts, nuts and ABS wiring bracket, if equipped. Tighten the strut lower nuts to 89 ft. lbs. (120 Nm).

11. Connect the stabilizer bar link to the strut assembly. Tighten the stabilizer bar link nut to 48 ft. lbs. (65 Nm).

12. Install the tire and wheel.

13. Lower the vehicle.

14. Inspect the front wheel alignment.

STABILIZER BAR

REMOVAL & INSTALLATION

See Figure 244.

1. Before servicing the vehicle, refer to the Precautions Section.

2. Raise and support the vehicle.

3. Remove the front wheels.

4. Remove the rear transaxle mount. Refer to Transaxle in the Drive Train section.

5. If necessary, remove the steering gear. Refer to Power Rack & Pinion Steering Gear in the Steering section.

6. Disconnect the control links from the stabilizer bar. Refer to Control Links.

7. Remove the stabilizer bar mounting clamp bolts and clamps from both sides of the vehicle.

8. Remove the bushings from the stabilizer bar.

9. Lift and rotate the stabilizer bar up and to the right.

10. Carefully remove the stabilizer bar from the right side of the vehicle.

To install:

11. Move the stabilizer bar into position from the right side of the vehicle.

12. Install the stabilizer bushings on the

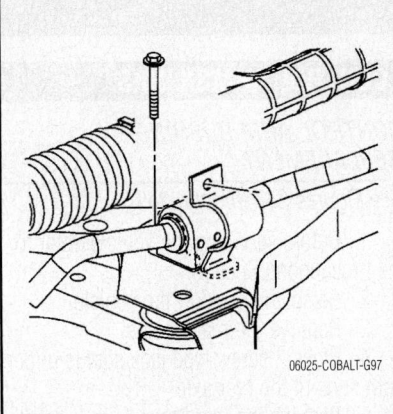

Fig. 244 Front stabilizer bar mounting clamps

stabilizer bar with the cut line facing rearward.

13. Install the stabilizer bar clamps and bolts. Tighten the bolts to 37 ft. lbs. (50 Nm).

14. Connect the control links to the stabilizer bar. Refer to Control Links.

15. If removed, install the steering gear. Refer to Power Rack & Pinion Steering Gear in the Steering section.

16. Install the rear transaxle mount. Refer to Transaxle in the Drive Train section.

17. Install the front wheels.

18. Lower the vehicle.

WHEEL HUB & BEARING

REMOVAL & INSTALLATION

See Figure 245.

1. Before servicing the vehicle, refer to the Precautions Section.

2. Raise and support the vehicle.

3. Remove the tire and wheel assembly.

4. Remove the front brake rotor. Refer to Front Disc Brake Rotor in the Brake section.

5. Remove the halfshaft nut. Refer to Halfshaft in the Drive Train section.

6. Remove the wheel speed sensor connector.

7. Remove the wheel hub and bearing bolts.

8. Remove the wheel hub and bearing assembly.

9. Remove the wheel hub and bearing spacer.

To install:

10. Installation is the reverse of removal. Tighten the wheel hub and bearing bolts to 85 ft. lbs. (115 Nm).

ADJUSTMENT

All models use sealed wheel bearings that are pre-adjusted. If the bearing needs replacing, replace the front wheel hub/bearing assembly.

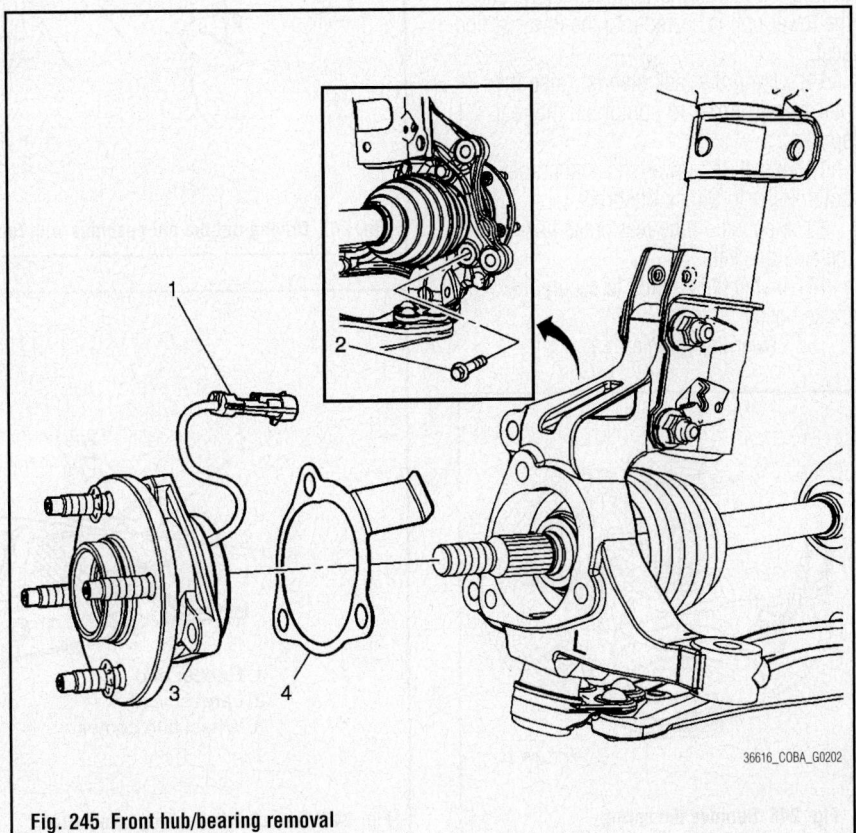

Fig. 245 Front hub/bearing removal

COIL SPRING

REMOVAL & INSTALLATION

See Figure 246.

1. Before servicing the vehicle, refer to the Precautions Section.
2. Raise and support the vehicle.
3. Support the rear axle with tall jack stands near each rear shock absorber.
4. Remove the U-clips from the rear brake hose brackets at the rear axle.
5. Remove the lower shock bolts. Refer to Shock Absorber.
6. Using the tall jack stands, slowly lower the rear axle in order to remove tension from the rear springs.
7. Remove the spring.
8. Remove the upper spring seat/jounce bumper from the spring, while leaving the lower spring seat on the axle.

To install:

→ **The rear springs are indexed with the colored tag toward the rear of the vehicle. No up/down or side to side orientation is required.**

9. Install the upper spring seat/jounce bumper on the spring.
10. Install the spring with the spring tag toward the rear of the vehicle, making sure the lower coil is seated into the lower spring seat.
11. Using the jack stands, raise the rear axle in order to compress the rear springs.
12. Install the lower shock absorber bolts. Refer to Shock Absorber.
13. Reposition the rear brake hoses in the axle brackets.
14. Install the U-clips to secure the brake hoses.
15. Lower the vehicle.

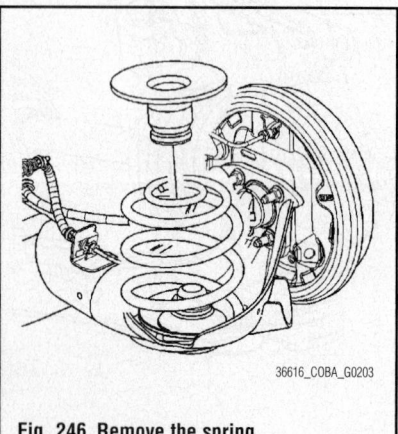

Fig. 246 Remove the spring

CONTROL ARMS/LINKS

CONTROL ARM BUSHING REPLACEMENT

See Figures 247 through 249.

1. Before servicing the vehicle, refer to the Precautions Section.
2. Raise and support the vehicle.
3. Remove the rear wheels.
4. Place 2 screw type jack stands under both ends of the rear axle.
5. Remove the rear brake hose bracket attaching nuts from the body.
6. Detach the rear brake hose brackets from the body allowing the lines to hang free.
7. Remove the lower shock bolts.

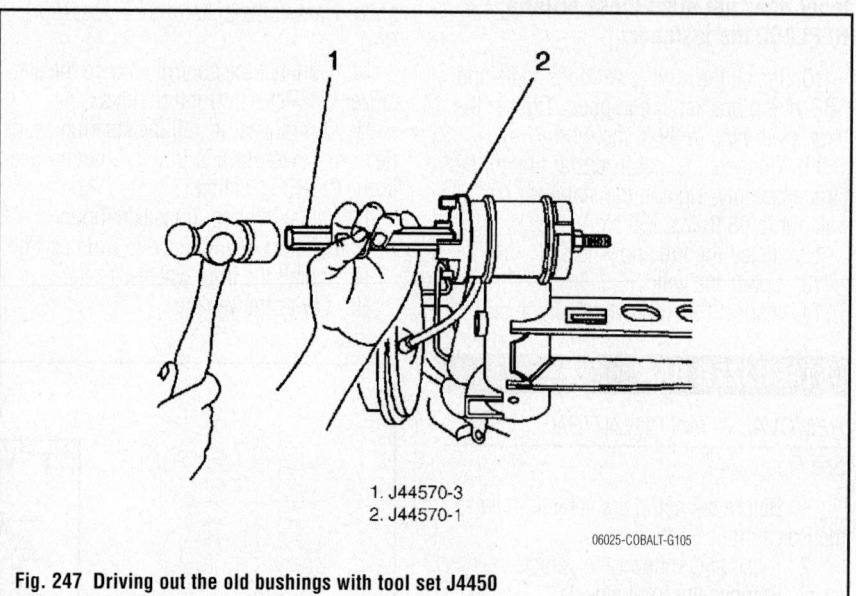

1. J44570-3
2. J44570-1

06025-COBALT-G105

Fig. 247 Driving out the old bushings with tool set J4450

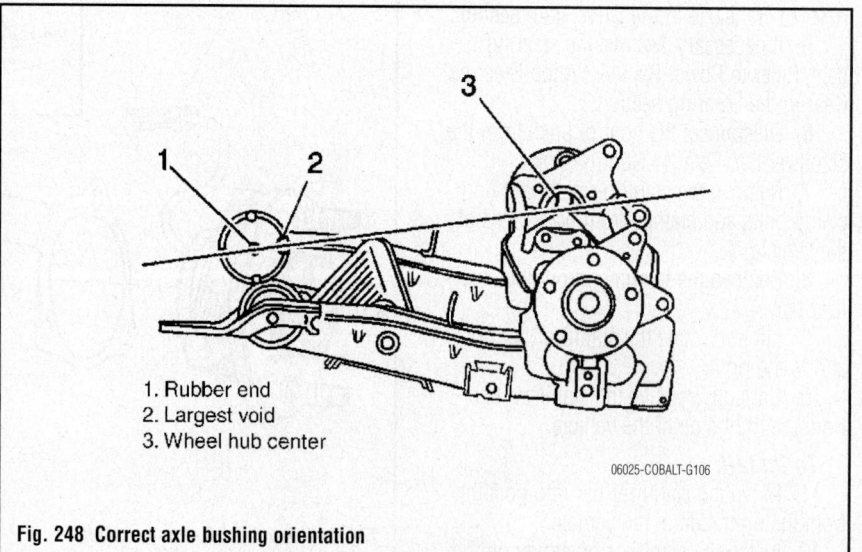

1. Rubber end
2. Largest void
3. Wheel hub center

06025-COBALT-G106

Fig. 248 Correct axle bushing orientation

✳✳ WARNING

Do not kink the brake pipes while lowering the axle.

8. Lower the jacks in order to remove the coil springs.
9. Temporarily re-install the lower shock bolts to support the axle.
10. Remove the bushing bracket to body bolts from both ends of the rear axle.
11. Using the jackstands, raise the rear of the axle until the bushing brackets pivot away from the body.
12. Remove the axle bushing through bolts and remove the bushing brackets.

→ **Note the depth and orientation of the old bushing before removal.**

13. Using tool J 44570 , install tool J 44570-1 with the lip between the axle sleeve and bushing flange. It may require tapping with a hammer to fully seat the tool.

14. Insert J 44570-3 through tool J 44570-1 and the axle bushing.

15. Install the washer and nut by hand, tightening until the tool is snug.

16. Using a hammer, drive the bushing from the axle sleeve.

17. Disassemble the tool and remove the bushing.

To install:

➡ **The axle bushings must be installed in the correct orientation as shown.**

18. Slide the new bushings into the axle sleeve in the same orientation noted during removal. Make sure the rubber end is facing inboard and the largest void is in line with the wheel hub center.

19. Place the J 44570-1 onto the bushing. Make sure the bushing is still oriented correctly.

20. Insert the J 44570-3 through the J 44570-1 and the axle bushing.

21. Install the J 44570-2 bearing, washer, and nut.

22. Pull the bushing into the axle sleeve by holding the hex end of the threaded shaft while turning the nut.

23. Disassemble and remove the bushing installation tool from the axle.

24. Install the axle brackets to the axle bushings with the alignment slot on the outboard side.

➡ **The axle bushing through bolts must be installed with the bolt head facing inboard.**

25. Loosely install the bushing bolts, park brake cable brackets and nuts .

26. Using the jack stands, lower the rear

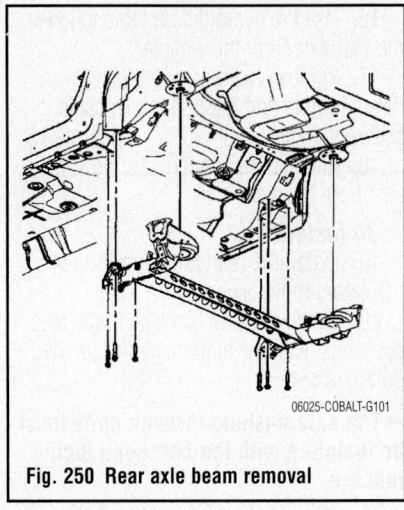

1. J44570-2
2. J44570-1
3. J44570-3

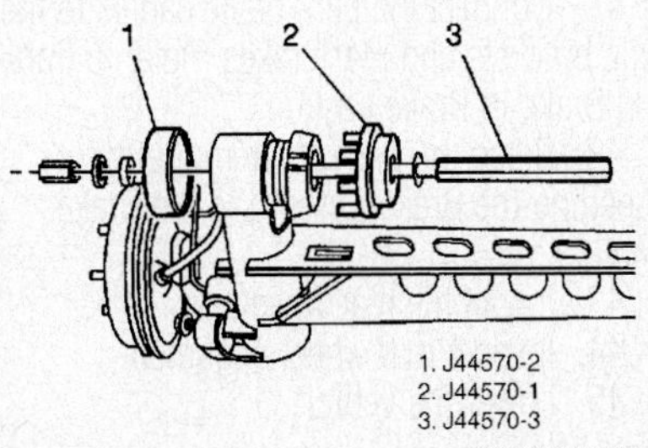

06025-COBALT-G107

Fig. 249 Axle bushing installation

of the axle until the bushing brackets contact the body.

27. Hand tighten the axle bracket to body bolts just enough to hold the brackets flush to the body.

➡ **The axle through bolts must be tightened with the axle at the correct trim height and prior to tightening the axle bracket to body bolts.**

28. Using the jack stands, raise the axle to the proper trim height specification by measuring the vertical distance between the bottom edge of the upper spring seat and the bottom of the notch in the lower spring seat. Refer to Rear Axle Beam for the D height measurement.

29. Tighten the axle bushing through bolts to 66 ft. lbs. (90 Nm) plus 60°

30. Insert two 12mm diameter pins through the axle brackets into the underbody.

31. Align the left side axle bracket and snug down the bolts.

32. Align the right side axle bracket and snug down the bolts.

33. Tighten all of the bracket-to-body bolts to 66 ft. lbs. (90 Nm) plus 30°.

34. With the axle supported by the jack stands, remove the lower shock bolts.

35. Lower the jacks in order to install the coil springs.

36. Install the coil springs, making sure the colored tag is facing the rear of the vehicle.

37. Raise the jacks until the springs are slightly compressed in order to install the lower shock bolts. Tighten the lower bolts to 81 ft. lbs. (110 Nm). Refer to Shock Absorber.

38. Remove the jack stands.

39. Reposition the rear brake hose brackets to the body.

40. Install the brake hose bracket attaching nuts.

41. Install the rear wheels.

42. Lower the vehicle.

REAR AXLE BEAM

REMOVAL & INSTALLATION

See Figures 250 through 253.

1. Before servicing the vehicle, refer to the Precautions Section.

2. Raise and support the vehicle.

3. Remove the rear wheels.

4. Disconnect the left and right rear brake pipes from the rear brake hoses at the axle.

5. Disconnect the brake hoses from the axle brake hose bracket.

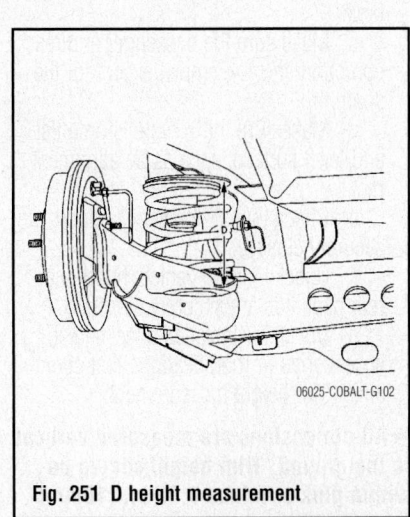

06025-COBALT-G101

Fig. 250 Rear axle beam removal

6. Plug the brake pipes and hoses in order to prevent additional brake fluid loss.

7. Disconnect both rear parking brake cables at the rear brake. Refer to Parking Brake in the Brake section.

8. If applicable, disconnect the Antilock Brake System (ABS) harness connectors and disconnect from the axle.

9. Support the rear axle with a hydraulic lift table.

10. Remove the lower shock bolts. Refer to Shock Absorber.

11. Lower the hydraulic lift table and remove the rear coil springs. Refer to Coil Springs.

12. Disconnect the park brake cables from the cable brackets.

13. Remove the wheel bearing/hub retaining nuts from both sides.

14. Remove the wheel bearing/hubs, with the brakes and backing plate as an assembly.

15. Remove all rear axle bushing bracket bolts.

06025-COBALT-G102

Fig. 251 D height measurement

16. Use the hydraulic lift table to lower the rear axle from the vehicle.

17. Remove the rear axle bushing through bolts and the park brake cable brackets.

18. Remove the rear coil spring lower seat from the axle.

To install:

19. Install the rear coil spring lower insulators to the axle.

20. Install the axle brackets to the axle bushings, with the alignment slot on the outboard side.

➡ **The axle bushing through bolts must be installed with the bolt head facing inboard.**

21. Loosely install the bushing bolts and nuts.

22. Place the axle on the hydraulic lift table.

23. Raise the axle into position.

24. Hand tighten the axle bracket to body bolts just enough to hold the brackets flush to the body.

➡ **The axle through bolts must be tightened with the axle at the correct trim height and prior to tightening the axle bracket to body bolts.**

25. Using the lift table, raise the axle to the proper trim height specification by measuring the vertical distance between the bottom edge of the upper spring seat and the bottom of the notch in the lower spring seat.

26. Before setting the D height measurement:

a. Set the tire pressure to the specifications shown on the certification label.

b. Check the fuel level. Add additional weight if necessary to simulate a full tank.

c. Make sure the passenger and rear compartments are empty, except for the spare tire.

d. Make sure the vehicle is on a flat and level surface, such as an alignment rack.

e. Check that all the vehicle doors are securely closed.

f. Check that the vehicle hood and rear deck lids are securely closed.

g. Check for installed after market accessories or modifications that could affect trim height measurement.

➡ **All dimensions are measured vertical to the ground. Trim height should be within plus or minus 0.39 in. (10mm) to be considered correct.**

The D height dimension measurement determines the proper rear end ride height. There is no adjustment procedure. Repair may require replacement of suspension components.

27. Use the following procedure to check the D dimension:

a. With the vehicle on a flat level surface, lift upward on the rear bumper 1½ inches (38mm).

b. Gently remove your hands and allow the vehicle to settle.

c. Repeat the jouncing operation 2 more times.

d. Measure the D height for the left and right side of the vehicle. Measure the vertical distance between the bottom edge of the upper spring seat to the bottom of the notch in the lower spring seat.

e. Using your hands, jounce the front of the vehicle downward approximately 1 ½ inches (38mm).

f. Gently remove your hands and allow the vehicle to settle .

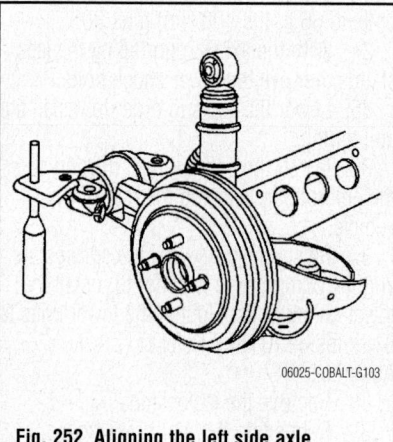

Fig. 252 Aligning the left side axle bracket

Fig. 253 Aligning the right side axle bracket

g. Repeat the jouncing operation 2 more times.

h. Measure the D height dimension.

i. The true D height dimension number is the average of the high and the low measurements:

- 2.0L engine: 8.6 inches (219mm)
- 2.2L engine with P195/60R15 tires: 9.5 inches (242mm)
- 2.2L engine with P205/55R16 tires: 9 inches (228mm)
- 2.4L engine: 8.8 inches (224mm)

j. If these measurements are out of specifications, inspect for worn or damaged suspension components and/or collision damage.

28. Tighten the axle bushing through bolts to 66 ft. lbs. (90 Nm) plus 60°.

29. Insert two 12mm diameter pins through the axle brackets into the underbody.

30. Align the left side axle bracket and snug down the bolts.

31. Align the right side axle bracket and snug down the bolts.

32. Tighten all the bracket to body bolts to 66 ft. lbs. (90 Nm) plus 45°.

33. Install the wheel bearing/hubs, with the brakes and backing plate assemblies.

34. Install the bearing/hub nuts and tighten to 33 ft. lbs. (45 Nm) plus 30°.

35. Connect the brake hoses to the rear axle brackets.

36. Connect the brake pipes to the brake hoses at the axle. Tighten the brake pipe fittings to 14 ft. lbs. (19 Nm).

37. Install the rear coil springs. Refer to Coil Springs.

38. Install the lower shock bolts. Refer to Shock Absorber.

39. Lower and remove the hydraulic lift table.

40. If applicable, connect the ABS sensor harness connector and harness to axle retainer.

41. Connect the park brake cables to the axle brackets and rear brakes. Refer to Parking Brake in Brake section.

42. Bleed the brake system. Refer to Bleeding the Brake System, in the Brake section.

43. Install the rear wheels.

44. Inspect rear wheel alignment.

45. Lower the vehicle.

SHOCK ABSORBER

REMOVAL & INSTALLATION

See Figure 254.

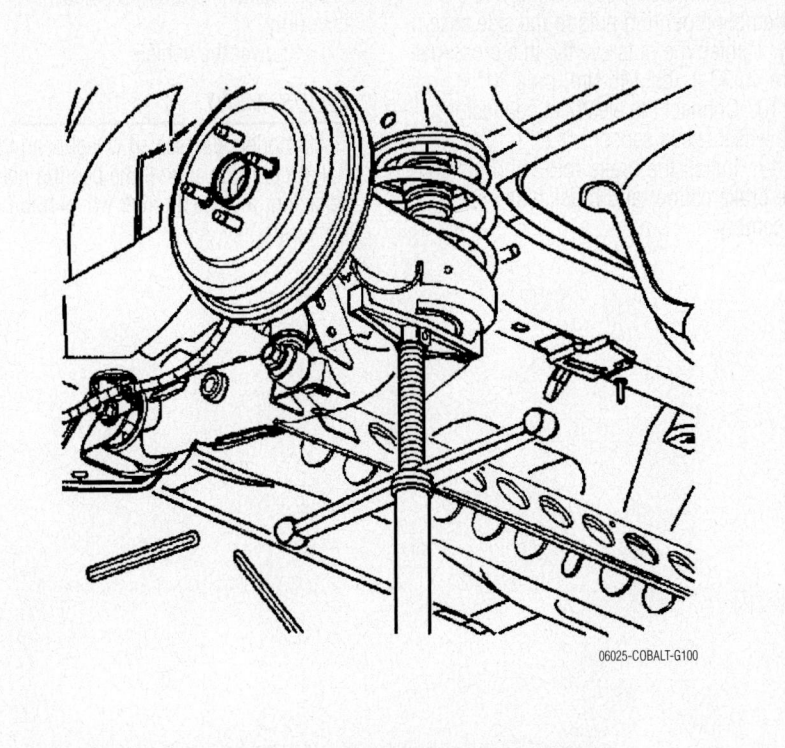

Fig. 254 Support the rear axle with a tall jackstand near the shock absorber

1. Before servicing the vehicle, refer to the Precautions Section.

2. Raise and support the vehicle.

3. Remove the wheel.

4. Support the rear axle with a tall jackstand near the shock absorber.

5. Remove the upper and lower shock bolts.

6. Remove the shock from the vehicle.

To install:

7. Position the shock absorber to the vehicle.

8. Install NEW upper and lower shock bolts. Tighten the upper bolt to 66 ft. lbs. (90 Nm). Tighten the lower bolt to 81 ft. lbs. (110 Nm).

9. Remove the jackstand.

10. Install the wheel.

11. Lower the vehicle.

WHEEL HUB & BEARING

REMOVAL & INSTALLATION

With Drum Brakes

See Figure 255.

1. Before servicing the vehicle, refer to the Precautions Section.

2. Raise and support the vehicle.

3. Remove the tire and wheel assembly.

4. Remove the brake drum. Refer to Brake Drum, in Rear Drum Brakes, within the Brake section.

5. Remove the plug from the drum brake actuator access hole in the backing plate. Using the access hole, install a support for the brake backing plate.

6. Disconnect the electrical connector from the wheel speed sensor, if equipped with ABS.

7. Remove the wheel bearing/hub assembly mounting nuts.

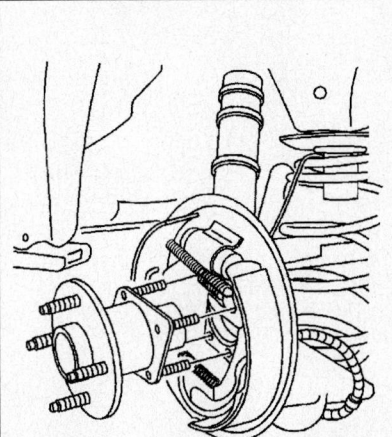

Fig. 255 Rear wheel bearing removal with drum brakes

8. Remove the wheel bearing/hub assembly from the rear axle assembly and brake backing plate.

To install:

9. Install the wheel bearing/hub assembly to the brake backing plate and the rear axle assembly.

10. Install the wheel bearing/hub assembly mounting nuts to the axle assembly. Tighten the nuts evenly, in a cross-pattern, to 33 ft. lbs. (45 Nm) plus 30°.

11. Connect the electrical connector to the wheel speed sensor, if equipped with ABS.

12. Remove the support from the brake backing plate.

13. Install the plug to the drum brake actuator access hole in the backing plate.

14. Install the brake drum. Refer to Brake Drum, in Rear Drum Brakes, within the Brake section.

15. Install the tire and wheel assembly.

16. Lower the vehicle.

With Disc Brakes

See Figure 256.

1. Before servicing the vehicle, refer to the Precautions Section.

2. Raise and support the vehicle.

3. Remove the tire and wheel assembly.

4. Without disconnecting the hydraulic brake flex hose, remove and support the rear brake caliper and bracket as an assembly, and remove the rear brake rotor.

5. Disconnect the electrical connector from the wheel speed sensor.

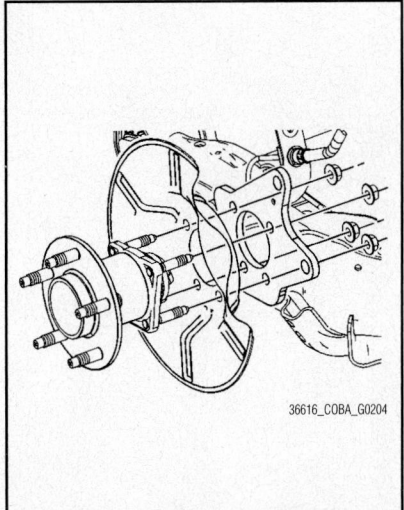

Fig. 256 Rear wheel bearing removal with disc brakes

6. Remove the wheel bearing/hub assembly mounting nuts.

7. Remove the wheel bearing/hub assembly and the disc brake backing plate from the rear axle assembly.

To install:

8. Install the wheel bearing/hub assembly and the brake backing plate to the rear axle assembly.

9. Install the wheel bearing/hub assembly mounting nuts to the axle assembly. Tighten the nuts evenly, in a cross-pattern, to 33 ft. lbs. (45 Nm) plus 30°.

10. Connect the electrical connector to the wheel speed sensor.

11. Install the brake rotor, and install the brake caliper and bracket as an assembly.

12. Install the tire and wheel assembly.

13. Lower the vehicle.

ADJUSTMENT

All models use sealed wheel bearings that are pre-adjusted. If the bearing needs replacing, replace the rear wheel hub/bearing assembly.

CHEVROLET

Corvette

11

SPECIFICATIONS AND MAINTENANCE CHARTS

ENGINE AND VEHICLE IDENTIFICATION

			Engine				Model Year	
Code ①	Liters (cc)	Cu. In.	Cyl.	Fuel Sys.	Engine Type	Eng. Mfg.	Code ②	Year
W	6.2 (6162)	376	8	SFI	OHV	GM	9	2009
E	7.0 (6997)	427	8	SFI	OHV	GM		

① 8th position of VIN

② 10th position of VIN

36616_CORV_C0001

GENERAL ENGINE SPECIFICATIONS

Year	Model	Engine Displacement Liters	Engine Series (ID/VIN)	Fuel System	Net Horsepower @ rpm	Net Torque @ rpm (ft. lbs.)	Bore x Stroke (in.)	Compression Ratio	Oil Pressure @ rpm
2009	Corvette	6.2	W	SFI	430@5900	424@4600	4.007x3.62	10.7:1	18@2000
		7.0	E	SFI	505@6300	470@4800	4.125x4.00	11.0:1	18@2000

SFI: Sequential Fuel Injection

36616_CORV_C0002

ENGINE TUNE-UP SPECIFICATIONS

Year	Engine Displacement Liters	Engine ID/VIN	Spark Plug Gap (in.)	Ignition Timing (deg.) MT	AT	Fuel Pump (psi)	Idle Speed (rpm) MT	AT	Valve Clearance In.	Ex.
2009	6.2	W	0.040	①	①	55-62	①	①	HYD	HYD
	7.0	E	0.040	①	①	55-62	①	①	HYD	HYD

NOTE: The Vehicle Emission Control Information label often reflects specification changes made during production.

The label figures must be used if they differ from those in this chart.

HYD: Hydraulic

① Refer to Vehicle Emission Control Information label

36616_CORV_C0003

CAPACITIES

Year	Model	Engine Displacement Liters	Engine ID/VIN	Engine Oil with Filter (qts.)	Transmission (pts.) 6-Spd	Transmission (pts.) Auto.	Drive Axle (pts.)	Fuel Tank (gal.)	Cooling System (qts.)
2009	Corvette	6.2	W	6.0	①	13.0	②	18.0	11.9
		7.0	E	10.5	①	13.0	②	18.0	11.9

NOTE: All capacities are approximate. Add fluid gradually and ensure a proper fluid level is obtained.

① Base - 7.2 pts.

With Standard Package - 8.4 pts.

With Z06 Package - 9.0 pts.

② Base - 4.2 pts. plus friction modifier

With Z06 Package - 5.9 pts. plus friction modifier

36616_CORV_C0004

FLUID SPECIFICATIONS

Year	Model	Engine Displacement Liters	Engine ID/VIN	Engine Oil	Auto. Transmission	Drive Axle	Power Steering Fluid	Brake Master Cylinder
2009	Corvette	6.2	W	5W-30	Dexron VI	②	③	DOT-3
		7.0	E	①	Dexron VI	②	③	DOT-3

DOT: Department Of Transportation

① 5W-30 Synthetic GM Standard GM4718M (Mobil 1)

② Dextron LS Gear Oil or equivalent

Plus Differential Friction Modifier

③ Refer to owners manual for fluid requirements

36616_CORV_C0012

VALVE SPECIFICATIONS

Year	Engine Displacement Liters	Engine ID/VIN	Seat Angle (deg.)	Face Angle (deg.)	Spring Test Pressure (lbs. @ in.)	Spring Installed Height (in.)	Stem-to-Guide Clearance (in.) Intake	Stem-to-Guide Clearance (in.) Exhaust	Stem Diameter (in.) Intake	Stem Diameter (in.) Exhaust
2009	6.2	W	46	45	90@1.80 264@1.30	1.80	0.0010- 0.0026	0.0010- 0.0026	0.3130- 0.3140	0.3130- 0.3140
	7.0	E	45	45	101@1.96 310@1.37	1.96	0.0010- 0.0024	0.0010- 0.0026	0.3130- 0.3140	0.3130- 0.3140

36616_CORV_C0005

22116_corv_specs.xls

CAMSHAFT AND BEARING SPECIFICATIONS CHART

All measurements are given in inches.

Year	Engine Displacement Liters	Engine VIN	Journal Dia.	Brg. Oil Clearance	Shaft End-play	Runout	Journal Bore	Lobe Height	
								Intake	Exhaust
2009	6.2	W	2.164-2.166	0.0009-0.0038	0.001-0.012	0.002	2.1678-2.1688	0.324	0.306
	7.0	E	2.164-2.166	0.0009-0.0038	0.001-0.012	0.002	2.1678-2.1688	0.331	0.328

36616_CORV_C0013

CRANKSHAFT AND CONNECTING ROD SPECIFICATIONS

All measurements are given in inches.

Year	Engine Displacement Liters	Engine ID/VIN	Crankshaft				Connecting Rod		
			Main Brg. Journal Dia.	Main Brg. Oil Clearance	Shaft End-play	Thrust on No.	Journal Diameter	Oil Clearance	Side Clearance
2009	6.2	W	2.558-2.559	0.0008-0.0021	0.0015-0.0078	3	2.0991-2.0999	0.0009-0.0025	0.0043-0.0200
	7.0	E	2.558-2.559	0.0008-0.0021	0.0015-0.0078	3	2.0991-2.0999	0.0009-0.0025	0.0043-0.0200

36616_CORV_C0006

PISTON AND RING SPECIFICATIONS

All measurements are given in inches.

Year	Engine Displacement Liters	Engine ID/VIN	Piston Clearance	Ring Gap			Ring Side Clearance		
				Top Compression	Bottom Compression	Oil Control	Top Compression	Bottom Compression	Oil Control
2009	6.2	W	-0.0019 +0.0000	0.0067-0.0173	0.0126-0.0272	0.0086-0.0335	0.0012-0.0033	0.0016-0.0033	0.0005-0.0079
	7.0	E	-0.0010 +0.0010	0.0075-0.0220	0.0146-0.0295	0.0086-0.0335	0.0010-0.0033	0.0008-0.0024	0.0009-0.0081

36616_CORV_C0007

TORQUE SPECIFICATIONS
All readings in ft. lbs.

Year	Engine Displacement Liters	Engine ID/VIN	Cylinder Head Bolts	Main Bearing Bolts	Rod Bearing Bolts	Crankshaft Damper Bolts	Flywheel Bolts	Manifold Intake	Manifold Exhaust	Spark Plugs	Oil Pan Drain Plug
2009	6.2	W	①	②	③	④	⑤	⑥	⑦	11	18
	7.0	E	①	②	⑧	④	⑨	⑥	⑦	11	18

① M11 bolts: 22 ft. lbs. in sequence
   M11 bolts: plus 90 degrees in sequence
   M11 bolts: plus 70 degrees in sequence
   M8 bolts: 22 ft. lbs. in sequence

② M10 bolts 15 ft. lbs. in sequence
   M10 bolts rotate 80 degrees in sequence
   M10 studs 15 ft. lbs. in sequence
   M10 studs rotate 51 degrees in sequence
   Side bolts 18 ft. lbs. in sequence

③ Step 1: 15 ft. lbs.
   Step 2: Rotate 85 degrees

④ Step 1: 111 ft. lbs.
   Step 2: Rotate 360 degrees
   Step 3: Loosen completely
   Step 4: 37 ft. lbs.
   Step 2: Rotate 230 degrees

⑤ Step 1: 15 ft. lbs.
   Step 2: 37 ft. lbs.
   Step 3: 74 ft. lbs.

⑥ Step 1: 44 inch lbs. in sequence
   Step 2: 89 inch lbs. in sequence

⑦ Step 1: 11 ft. lbs.
   Step 2: 15 ft. lbs.

⑧ Step 1: 15 ft. lbs.
   Step 2: Rotate 110 degrees

⑧ Step 1: 22 ft. lbs.
   Step 2: Rotate 40 degrees

36616_CORV_C0008

WHEEL ALIGNMENT

Year	Model		Caster Range (+/-Deg.)	Caster Preferred Setting (Deg.)	Camber Range (+/-Deg.)	Camber Preferred Setting (Deg.)	Toe-in (Deg.)
2009	Corvette	F	0.60	①	②	③	0.10 +/- 0.20
		R	—	—	0.60	④	⑤

① With FE1, FE2 or FE3 Suspension 7.50 degrees
   With FE4 Suspension 7.60 degrees
   With FE5 Suspension 7.70 degrees

② With FE1, FE2 or FE3 Suspension .60 degrees
   With FE4 Suspension .50 degrees
   With FE5 Suspension .50 degrees

③ With FE1, FE2 or FE3 Suspension -0.45 degrees
   With FE4 Suspension -1.00 degrees
   With FE5 Suspension -1.00 degrees

④ With FE1, FE2 or FE3 Suspension -0.45 degrees
   With FE4 Suspension -1.20 degrees
   With FE5 Suspension -1.25 degrees

⑤ With FE1, FE2 or FE3 Suspen
   With FE4 Suspension 0.00 +/- 0.20 degrees
   With FE5 Suspension 0.10 +/- 0.20 degrees

36616_CORV_C0009

TIRE, WHEEL AND BALL JOINT SPECIFICATIONS

Year	Model	OEM Tires Standard	OEM Tires Optional	Tire Pressures (psi) Front	Tire Pressures (psi) Rear	Wheel Size	Ball Joint Inspection	Lug Nut (ft. lbs.)
2009	Corvette	F: P245/40ZR18 R: P285/35ZR19	F: P275/35ZR18 R: P335/30ZR19	NA	NA	①	U: 0.005 in. L: 0.020 in.	②

NA: Not available

① Wheel options QX1, QG6 & QG7 F: 18x8.5 R: 19x10
   Wheel options QL9, Q10, Q44 & Q76 F: 18x9.5 R: 19x12

② Wheel lug nut torque: 100 ft. lbs.

36616_CORV_C0010

BRAKE SPECIFICATIONS

All measurements in inches unless noted

Year	Model		Brake Disc Original Thickness	Brake Disc Minimum Thickness	Brake Disc Maximum Runout	Minimum Lining Thickness Front	Minimum Lining Thickness Rear	Brake Caliper Bracket Bolts (ft. lbs.)	Brake Caliper Guide Pin Bolts (ft. lbs.)
2009	Corvette	F	1.26	1.19	0.002	0.030	0.030	①	23
		R	1.02	0.965	0.002	0.030	0.030	①	23

① JL9, J55 bracket bolts tighten to 129 ft. lbs.
   J56 caliper bolts tighten to 129 ft. lbs.

36616_CORV_C0011

MAINTENANCE I AND II SERVICE SCHEDULES
Chevrolet Corvette

When the CHANGE ENGINE OIL light appears, certain services and inspections are required.

Required services are described as Maintenance I and Maintenance II.

The first service on a vehicle should be Maintenance I, and the second service should be Maintenance II.

Alternate between the 2 thereafter. However, in some cases, Maintenance II may be required more often.

Maintenance I: Use Maintenance I if the CHANGE ENGINE OIL light comes on within 10 months since vehicle was purchased or, if Maintenance II was performed.

Maintenance II: Use Maintenance II if the previous service performed was Maintenance I. Always use Maintenance II whenever the CHANGE ENGINE OIL light comes on 10 months or more since the last service, or, if the CHANGE ENGINE OIL light has not come on at all for one year.

Service	Maintenance	Maintenance II
Change the engine oil and filter. Reset the oil life system.	✓	✓
Visually inspect the vehicle for leaks or damage. A fluid loss in the vehicle system could indicate a problem. Inspected, repair and add fluid to the system if necessary.	✓	✓
Inspect the engine air cleaner filter. If necessary, replace the filter.	--	✓
Inspect the tire inflation pressures and the tire wear.	✓	✓
Visually inspect brake lines and hoses for proper hook-up, binding, leaks, cracks, chafing, etc. Inspect disc brake pads for wear and rotors for surface condition. Inspect other brake parts, including calipers, parking brake, etc.	✓	✓
Inspect the engine coolant and the windshield washer fluid levels.	✓	✓
Visually inspect front and rear suspension and steering system for damaged, loose, or missing parts or signs of wear. Inspect power steering lines and hoses for proper hook-up, binding, leaks, cracks, chafing, etc. For ZO6 models and vehicles with the Z51 performance package, lubricate the outer ends of rear toe-links.	--	✓
Visually inspect the coolant hoses and replace the hoses if they are cracked, swollen or deteriorated. Inspect all pipes, fittings and clamps. To help ensure proper operation, a pressure test of the cooling system and pressure cap and cleaning the outside of the radiator and air conditioning condenser is recommended at least once a year.	--	✓
Inspect wiper blades for wear, cracking, or contamination. Clean the windshield and wiper blades, if contaminated. Replace wiper blades that are worn or damaged..	--	✓
Inspect restraint system components. Make sure the safety belt reminder light and safety belt assemblies are working properly. Look for any other loose or damaged safety belt system parts. If you see anything that might keep a safety belt system from doing its job, have it repaired. Have any torn	--	✓
Lubricate all key lock cylinders and body door hinges. Lubricate all hinges and latches, including those for the hood, rear compartment, console door, and any folding seat hardware. More frequent lubrication may be required when exposed to a corrosive environment. Applying silicone grease on weatherstrips with a clean cloth will make them last longer, seal better, and not stick or squeak.	--	✓
Replace the passenger compartment air filter.	--	✓

To reset the CHANGE ENGINE OIL message after an oil change, do the following:

1. Turn the ignition to ON, with the engine off.
2. Press the TRIP button so the OIL LIFE percentage is displayed.
3. Press RESET and hold for two seconds. OIL LIFE REMAIN 100% will appear.

36616_CORV_C0014

ADDITIONAL MAINTENANCE SERVICES
Chevrolet Corvette

TO BE SERVICED	TYPE OF SERVICE	VEHICLE MILEAGE INTERVAL (x1000)					
		25	50	75	100	125	150
Air cleaner filter	R		✓		✓		✓
Accessory drive belt	I						✓
Auto. Trans. Fluid and Filter ①	R		✓		✓		✓
Clutch hydraulic fluid ②	R						
Cooling system hoses and clamps	S/I						✓
Engine coolant	R						✓
Fuel system	I	✓	✓	✓	✓	✓	✓
Exhaust system & heat shields	S/I	✓	✓	✓	✓	✓	✓
Spark plugs and wires	R				✓		

R: Replace   S/I: Inspect and service, if necessary

① Replace if any of the following conditions are met:

  Heavy city traffic where the outside temperature regularly reaches 32°C (90°F) or higher

  Hilly or mountainous terrain

  Frequent trailer towing

  Taxi, police or delivery service

  Otherwise, change every 100,000 miles

② Change clutch hydraulic fluid at a regular maintenance service every two years.

36616_CORV_C0015

PRECAUTIONS

Before servicing any vehicle, please be sure to read all of the following precautions, which deal with personal safety, prevention of component damage, and important points to take into consideration when servicing a motor vehicle:

• Never open, service or drain the radiator or cooling system when the engine is hot; serious burns can occur from the steam and hot coolant.

• Observe all applicable safety precautions when working around fuel. Whenever servicing the fuel system, always work in a well-ventilated area. Do not allow fuel spray or vapors to come in contact with a spark, open flame, or excessive heat (a hot drop light, for example). Keep a dry chemical fire extinguisher near the work area. Always keep fuel in a container specifically designed for fuel storage; also, always properly seal fuel containers to avoid the possibility of fire or explosion. Refer to the additional fuel system precautions later in this section.

• Fuel injection systems often remain pressurized, even after the engine has been turned **OFF**. The fuel system pressure must be relieved before disconnecting any fuel lines. Failure to do so may result in fire and/or personal injury.

• Brake fluid often contains polyglycol ethers and polyglycols. Avoid contact with the eyes and wash your hands thoroughly after handling brake fluid. If you do get brake fluid in your eyes, flush your eyes with clean, running water for 15 minutes. If eye irritation persists, or if you have taken brake fluid internally, IMMEDIATELY seek medical assistance.

• The EPA warns that prolonged contact with used engine oil may cause a number of skin disorders, including cancer. You should make every effort to minimize your exposure to used engine oil. Protective gloves should be worn when changing oil. Wash your hands and any other exposed skin areas as soon as possible after exposure to used engine oil. Soap and water, or waterless hand cleaner should be used.

• All new vehicles are now equipped with an air bag system, often referred to as a Supplemental Restraint System (SRS) or Supplemental Inflatable Restraint (SIR) system. The system must be disabled before performing service on or around system components, steering column, instrument panel components, wiring and sensors. Failure to follow safety and disabling procedures could result in accidental air bag deployment, possible personal injury and unnecessary system repairs.

• Always wear safety goggles when working with, or around, the air bag system. When carrying a non-deployed air bag, be sure the bag and trim cover are pointed away from your body. When placing a non-deployed air bag on a work surface, always face the bag and trim cover upward, away from the surface. This will reduce the motion of the module if it is accidentally deployed. Refer to the additional air bag system precautions later in this section.

• Clean, high quality brake fluid from a sealed container is essential to the safe and proper operation of the brake system. You should always buy the correct type of brake fluid for your vehicle. If the brake fluid becomes contaminated, completely flush the system with new fluid. Never reuse any brake fluid. Any brake fluid that is removed from the system should be discarded. Also, do not allow any brake fluid to come in contact with a painted surface; it will damage the paint.

• Never operate the engine without the proper amount and type of engine oil; doing so WILL result in severe engine damage.

• Timing belt maintenance is extremely important. Many models utilize an interference-type, non-freewheeling engine. If the timing belt breaks, the valves in the cylinder head may strike the pistons, causing potentially serious (also time-consuming and expensive) engine damage. Refer to the maintenance interval charts for the recommended replacement interval for the timing belt, and to the timing belt section for belt replacement and inspection.

• Disconnecting the negative battery cable on some vehicles may interfere with the functions of the on-board computer system(s) and may require the computer to undergo a relearning process once the negative battery cable is reconnected.

• When servicing drum brakes, only disassemble and assemble one side at a time, leaving the remaining side intact for reference.

• Only an MVAC-trained, EPA-certified automotive technician should service the air conditioning system or its components.

BRAKES

ANTI-LOCK BRAKE SYSTEM (ABS)

GENERAL INFORMATION

PRECAUTIONS

• Certain components within the ABS system are not intended to be serviced or repaired individually.

• Do not use rubber hoses or other parts not specifically specified for and ABS system. When using repair kits, replace all parts included in the kit. Partial or incorrect repair may lead to functional problems and require the replacement of components.

• Lubricate rubber parts with clean, fresh brake fluid to ease assembly. Do not use shop air to clean parts; damage to rubber components may result.

• Use only DOT 3 brake fluid from an unopened container.

• If any hydraulic component or line is removed or replaced, it may be necessary to bleed the entire system.

• A clean repair area is essential. Always clean the reservoir and cap thoroughly before removing the cap. The slightest amount of dirt in the fluid may plug an orifice and impair the system function. Perform repairs after components have been thoroughly cleaned; use only denatured alcohol to clean components. Do not allow ABS components to come into contact with any substance containing mineral oil; this includes used shop rags.

• The Anti-Lock control unit is a microprocessor similar to other computer units in the vehicle. Ensure that the ignition switch is **OFF** before removing or installing controller harnesses. Avoid static electricity discharge at or near the controller.

• If any arc welding is to be done on the vehicle, the control unit should be unplugged before welding operations begin.

WHEEL SPEED SENSORS

REMOVAL & INSTALLATION

1. Before servicing the vehicle, refer to the Precautions Section.

The wheel speed sensors are integral with the hub and bearing assemblies. If a speed sensor needs replacement, you must replace the entire hub and bearing assembly. Do not try to service the harness pigtail individually because the harness pigtail is part of the sensor. Refer to Front or Rear Wheel Bearing & Hub Removal & Installation in the Suspension Section.

BLEEDING PROCEDURE

1. Before servicing the vehicle, refer to the Precautions Section.

✳✳ CAUTION

Brake fluid may irritate eyes and skin.

✳✳ WARNING

Never reuse brake fluid. Any brake fluid that is removed from the system should be discarded. Also, do not allow any brake fluid to come in contact with a painted surface; it will damage the paint.

2. Place a clean shop cloth beneath the brake master cylinder to prevent brake fluid spills.

3. With the ignition OFF and the brakes cool, apply the brakes 3–5 times, or until the brake pedal effort increases significantly, in order to deplete the brake booster power reserve.

4. If you have performed a brake master cylinder bench bleeding on this vehicle, or if you disconnected the brake pipes from the master cylinder, you must perform the following steps:

a. Ensure that the brake master cylinder reservoir is full to the maximum-fill level. If necessary, add GM approved brake fluid from a clean, sealed brake fluid container. If removal of the reservoir cap and diaphragm is necessary, clean the outside of the reservoir on and around the cap prior to removal.

b. With the rear brake pipe installed securely to the master cylinder, loosen and separate the front brake pipe from the front port of the brake master cylinder.

c. Allow a small amount of brake fluid to gravity bleed from the open port of the master cylinder.

d. Reconnect the brake pipe to the master cylinder port and tighten securely.

e. Have an assistant slowly depress the brake pedal fully and maintain steady pressure on the pedal.

f. Loosen the same brake pipe to purge air from the open port of the master cylinder.

g. Tighten the brake pipe, then have the assistant slowly release the brake pedal.

h. Wait 15 seconds, then repeat the above 5 steps until all air is purged from the same port of the master cylinder.

i. With the front brake pipe installed securely to the master cylinder, after all air has been purged from the front port of the master cylinder, loosen and separate the rear brake pipe from the master cylinder, then repeat the above 6 steps.

j. After completing the final master cylinder port bleeding procedure, ensure that both of the brake pipe-to-master cylinder fittings are properly tightened.

5. Fill the brake master cylinder reservoir with GM approved brake fluid from a clean, sealed brake fluid container. Ensure that the brake master cylinder reservoir remains at least half-full during this bleeding procedure. Add fluid as needed to maintain the proper level. Clean the outside of the reservoir on and around the reservoir cap prior to removing the cap and diaphragm.

6. Install a proper box-end wrench onto the RIGHT REAR wheel hydraulic circuit bleeder valve.

7. Install a transparent hose over the end of the bleeder valve.

8. Submerge the open end of the transparent hose into a transparent container partially filled with GM approved brake fluid from a clean, sealed brake fluid container.

9. Have an assistant slowly depress the brake pedal fully and maintain steady pressure on the pedal.

10. Loosen the bleeder valve to purge air from the wheel hydraulic circuit.

11. Tighten the bleeder valve, then have the assistant slowly release the brake pedal.

12. Wait 15 seconds, then repeat steps 9–11 until all air is purged from the same wheel hydraulic circuit.

13. With the right rear wheel hydraulic circuit bleeder valve tightened securely, after all air has been purged from the right rear hydraulic circuit, install a proper box-end wrench onto the LEFT FRONT wheel hydraulic circuit bleeder valve.

14. Install a transparent hose over the end of the bleeder valve, then repeat steps 8–12.

15. With the left front wheel hydraulic circuit bleeder valve tightened securely, after all air has been purged from the left front hydraulic circuit, install a proper box-end wrench onto the LEFT REAR wheel hydraulic circuit bleeder valve.

16. Install a transparent hose over the end of the bleeder valve, then repeat steps 8–12.

17. With the left rear wheel hydraulic circuit bleeder valve tightened securely, after all air has been purged from the left rear hydraulic circuit, install a proper box-end wrench onto the RIGHT FRONT wheel hydraulic circuit bleeder valve.

18. Install a transparent hose over the end of the bleeder valve, then repeat steps 8–12.

19. After completing the final wheel hydraulic circuit bleeding procedure, ensure that each of the 4 wheel hydraulic circuit bleeder valves are properly tightened.

20. Fill the brake master cylinder reservoir to the maximum-fill level with GM approved brake fluid from a clean, sealed brake fluid container.

21. Slowly depress and release the brake pedal. Observe the feel of the brake pedal.

➡ **If it is determined that air was inducted into the system upstream of the ABS modulator prior to servicing, the Antilock Brake System Automated Bleed Procedure must be performed.**

22. If the brake pedal feels spongy, repeat the bleeding procedure again. If the brake pedal still feels spongy after repeating the bleeding procedure, perform the following steps:

a. Inspect the brake system for external leaks.

b. Pressure bleed the hydraulic brake system in order to purge any air that may still be trapped in the system.

23. Turn the ignition key ON, with the engine OFF. Check to see if the brake system warning lamp remains illuminated.

✳✳ CAUTION

DO NOT allow the vehicle to be driven until it is diagnosed and repaired.

24. If the brake system warning lamp remains illuminated, refer to Diagnostic Trouble Codes.

BLEEDING THE ABS SYSTEM

1. Before servicing the vehicle, refer to the Precautions Section.

2. Raise the vehicle on a suitable support.

3. Remove all four tire and wheel assemblies.

4. Inspect the brake system for leaks and visual damage.

5. Inspect the battery state of charge.

6. Install a scan tool.

7. Turn ON the ignition, with the engine OFF.

8. With the scan tool, establish communications with the Electronic Brake Control Module (EBCM). Select Special Functions. Select Automated Bleed from the Special Functions menu.

9. Bleed the base brake system.

10. Follow the scan tool directions until the desired brake pedal height is achieved.

11. If the bleed procedure is aborted, a malfunction exists. Perform the following steps before resuming the bleed procedure:

   a. If a DTC is detected, check for the cause and repair as necessary.

   b. If the brake pedal feels spongy, perform the conventional brake bleed procedure again.

12. When the desired pedal height is achieved, press the brake pedal in order to inspect for firmness.

13. Remove the scan tool.

14. Install the tire and wheel assemblies.

15. Inspect the brake fluid level.

16. Road test the vehicle while inspecting that the pedal remains high and firm.

BRAKES
FRONT DISC BRAKES

✳✳ CAUTION

Dust and dirt accumulating on brake parts during normal use may contain asbestos fibers from production or aftermarket brake linings. Breathing excessive concentrations of asbestos fibers can cause serious bodily harm. Exercise care when servicing brake parts. Do not sand or grind brake lining unless equipment used is designed to contain the dust residue. Do not clean brake parts with compressed air or by dry brushing. Cleaning should be done by dampening the brake components with a fine mist of water, then wiping the brake components clean with a dampened cloth. Dispose of cloth and all residue containing asbestos fibers in an impermeable container with the appropriate label. Follow practices prescribed by the Occupational Safety and Health Administration (OSHA) and the Environmental Protection Agency (EPA) for the handling, processing, and disposing of dust or debris that may contain asbestos fibers.

BRAKE CALIPER

REMOVAL & INSTALLATION

JL9 & J55 Brake System

See Figures 1 and 2.

1. Before servicing the vehicle, refer to the Precautions Section.

✳✳ CAUTION

Brake fluid may irritate eyes and skin.

✳✳ WARNING

Avoid spilling brake fluid onto painted surfaces, electrical connections, wiring, or cables. Brake fluid will damage painted surfaces and

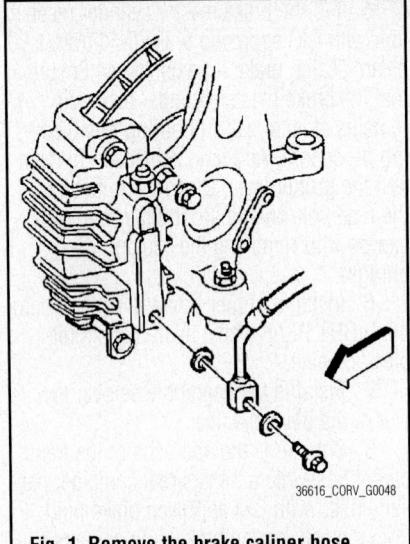

Fig. 1 Remove the brake caliper hose

cause corrosion to electrical components. If any brake fluid comes in contact with painted surfaces, immediately flush the area with water. If any brake fluid comes in contact with electrical connections, wiring, or cables, use a clean shop cloth to wipe away the fluid.**

2. Inspect the fluid level in the brake master cylinder reservoir.

   a. If the brake fluid level is midway between the maximum-full point and the minimum allowable level, no brake fluid needs to be removed from the reservoir before proceeding.

   b. If the brake fluid level is higher than midway between the maximum-full point and the minimum allowable level, remove brake fluid to the midway point before proceeding.

3. Raise and support the vehicle.

4. Remove the tire and wheel assembly.

5. Remove the brake caliper inlet fitting bolt from the caliper.

6. Remove the brake hose from the brake caliper.

7. Remove and discard the 2 copper

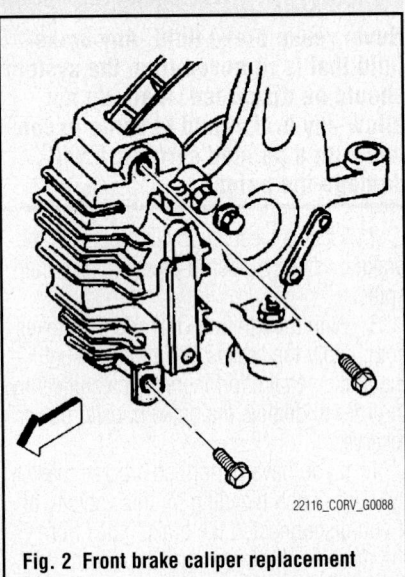

Fig. 2 Front brake caliper replacement

brake hose gaskets. These gaskets may be stuck to the brake caliper and/or the brake hose end.

8. Plug the opening in the brake caliper and the brake hose to prevent fluid loss and contamination.

9. Remove the brake caliper guide pin bolts.

10. Remove the brake caliper from the caliper mounting bracket.

To install:

11. Inspect the caliper slide boots for cuts, tears, or deterioration. If damaged, replace the slides and the boots.

12. Install the brake caliper to the caliper mounting bracket.

13. Install the brake caliper guide pin bolts and tighten to 23 ft. lbs. (31 Nm).

14. Remove the plug from the brake caliper opening and the brake hose.

➡ Install NEW copper brake hose gaskets.

15. Assemble the NEW copper brake hose gaskets, and the brake caliper inlet fitting bolt to the brake hose.

16. Install the brake hose and the brake caliper inlet fitting bolt to the brake caliper and tighten to 30 ft. lbs. (40 Nm).

17. Bleed the hydraulic brake system.
18. Install the tire and wheel assembly.

J56 Brake System
See Figure 3.

1. Before servicing the vehicle, refer to the Precautions Section.

※※ CAUTION

Brake fluid may irritate eyes and skin.

※※ WARNING

Avoid spilling brake fluid onto painted surfaces, electrical connections, wiring, or cables. Brake fluid will damage painted surfaces and cause corrosion to electrical components. If any brake fluid comes in contact with painted surfaces, immediately flush the area with water. If any brake fluid comes in contact with electrical connections, wiring, or cables, use a clean shop cloth to wipe away the fluid.

---

2. Disconnect the negative battery cable.
3. Inspect the fluid level in the brake master cylinder reservoir.

a. If the brake fluid level is midway between the maximum-full point and the minimum allowable level, no brake fluid needs to be removed from the reservoir before proceeding.

b. If the brake fluid level is higher than midway between the maximum-full point and the minimum allowable level, remove brake fluid to the midway point before proceeding.

4. Raise and support the vehicle.
5. Remove the tire and wheel assembly.
6. Remove the brake hose from the brake caliper. Discard the brake hose fitting gaskets.
7. If removing the caliper to service the brake system, support the caliper with heavy mechanics wire or equivalent.
8. Plug the brake hose fitting to prevent brake fluid leakage and contamination.
9. Remove the brake pads. Refer to Brake Pad Removal & Installation.
10. Remove caliper mounting bolts.
11. Remove the brake caliper.

To install:

➡**Inspect the caliper slide boots for damage and replace if necessary.**

12. Compress the pistons using a suitable tool, if necessary.
13. Install the caliper over the brake rotor and into the caliper mounting bracket. Make sure the shoe lining guiding surfaces are correctly seated in the bracket. Tighten the bolts to 30 ft. lbs. (40 Nm).
14. Install the brake hose inlet fitting using two NEW copper washers and the inlet fitting bolt. Torque the bolt to 33 ft. lbs. (45 Nm).
15. Properly bleed the entire brake system.

16. Check the brake fluid and add as necessary.
17. Install the wheel.
18. Connect the negative battery cable, start the engine and pump the brake pedal slowly and firmly 3 times to seat the shoe and lining assemblies.

DISC BRAKE PADS

REMOVAL & INSTALLATION

JL9 & J55 Brake Systems
See Figures 4 through 6.

1. Before servicing the vehicle, refer to the Precautions Section.
2. Inspect the fluid level in the brake master cylinder reservoir.

a. If the brake fluid level is midway between the maximum-full point and the minimum allowable level, no brake fluid needs to be removed from the reservoir before proceeding.

b. If the brake fluid level is higher than midway between the maximum-full point and the minimum allowable level, remove brake fluid to the midway point before proceeding.

3. Raise and suitably support the vehicle.

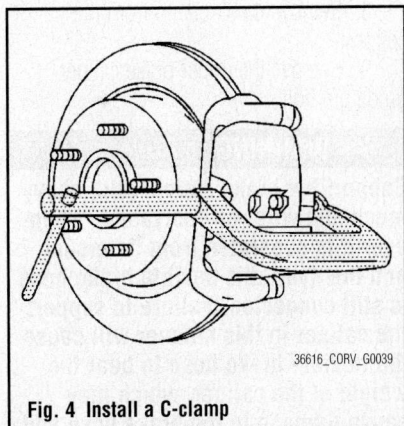

36616_CORV_G0039

Fig. 4 Install a C-clamp

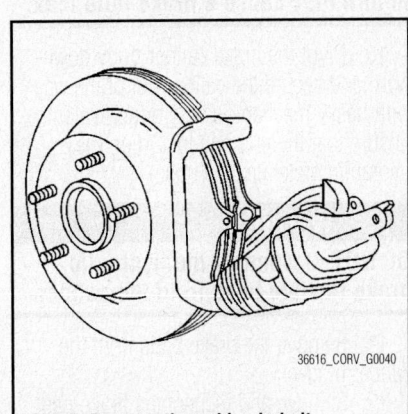

36616_CORV_G0040

Fig. 5 Remove the guide pin bolt

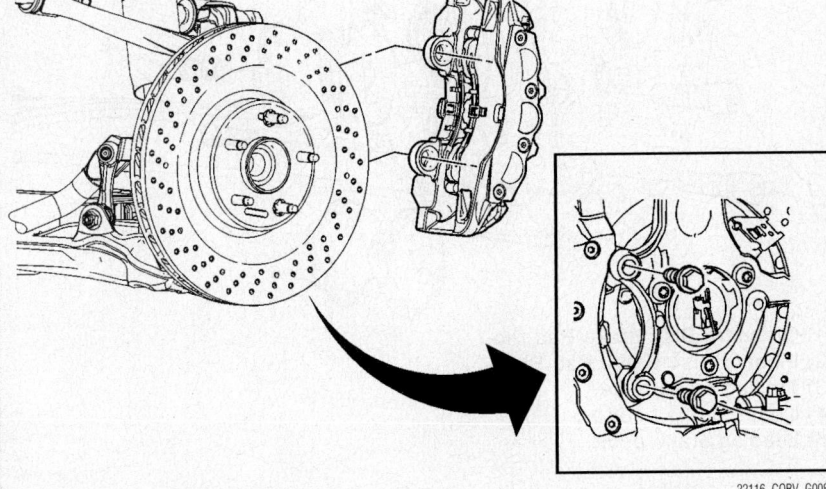

22116_CORV_G0087

Fig. 3 Front brake caliper replacement—J56

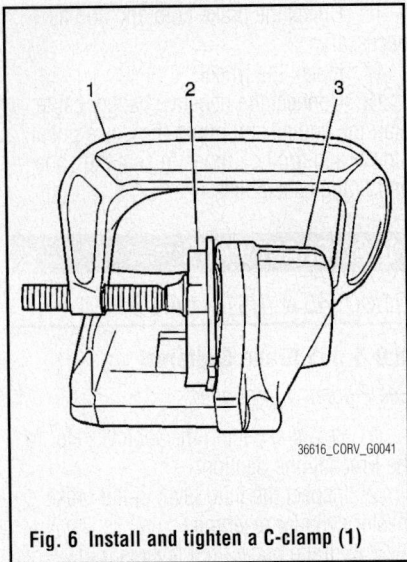

Fig. 6 Install and tighten a C-clamp (1)

4. Remove the tire and wheel assembly.

5. Hand tighten a wheel lug nut to a wheel stud to secure the rotor to the hub.

6. Install a large C-clamp over the body of the brake caliper with the C-clamp ends against the rear of the caliper body and against the outboard brake pad.

7. Tighten the C-clamp evenly until the caliper pistons are compressed into the caliper bores enough to allow the caliper to slide past the brake rotor.

8. Remove the C-clamp from the caliper.

9. Remove the upper brake caliper guide pin bolt.

> ⁂ **WARNING**
>
> **Support the brake caliper with heavy mechanic wire, or equivalent, whenever it is separated from its mount and the hydraulic flexible brake hose is still connected. Failure to support the caliper in this manner will cause the flexible brake hose to bear the weight of the caliper, which may cause damage to the brake hose and in turn may cause a brake fluid leak.**

10. Pivot the brake caliper body downward and secure the caliper out of the way with heavy mechanic's wire or equivalent. Ensure that there is no tension on the hydraulic brake flexible hose.

> ⁂ **WARNING**
>
> **Do NOT disconnect the hydraulic brake flexible hose from the caliper.**

11. Remove the brake pads from the caliper bracket.

12. Remove and inspect the brake pad retainers from the caliper bracket.

To install:

13. Inspect the caliper slide boots for cuts, tears, or deterioration. If damaged, replace the slides and the boots.

14. Install a large C-clamp (1) over the body of the brake caliper (3) with the C-clamp ends against the rear of the caliper body and against an old inboard brake pad (2) or a wood block installed against the caliper pistons.

15. Tighten the C-clamp (1) evenly until the caliper pistons are compressed completely into the caliper bores.

16. Remove the C-clamp and the old brake pad or wood block from the caliper.

17. Install the brake pad retainers to the caliper bracket.

18. Install the brake pads to the caliper bracket. The brake pad wear sensor, mounted on the inboard brake pad, must be positioned so that it is in the leading bottom position during forward rotation of the brake rotor.

19. Pivot the brake caliper upward, over the brake pads and into the caliper bracket.

20. Install the upper brake caliper guide pin bolt.

21. Tighten the brake caliper guide pin bolt to 23 ft. lbs.(31 Nm).

22. Install the tire and wheel assembly.

23. Lower the vehicle.

24. With the engine OFF:

a. Gradually apply the brake pedal to approximately ⅔ of its travel distance.

b. Slowly release the brake pedal.

c. Wait 15 seconds, then repeat the above 2 steps until a firm brake pedal apply is obtained. This will properly seat the brake caliper pistons and brake pads.

25. Fill the brake master cylinder reservoir to the proper level.

26. Burnish the pads and rotors.

J56 Brake System

See Figure 7.

1. Before servicing the vehicle, refer to the Precautions Section.

2. Inspect the fluid level in the brake master cylinder reservoir.

a. If the brake fluid level is midway between the maximum-full point and the minimum allowable level, no brake fluid needs to be removed from the reservoir before proceeding.

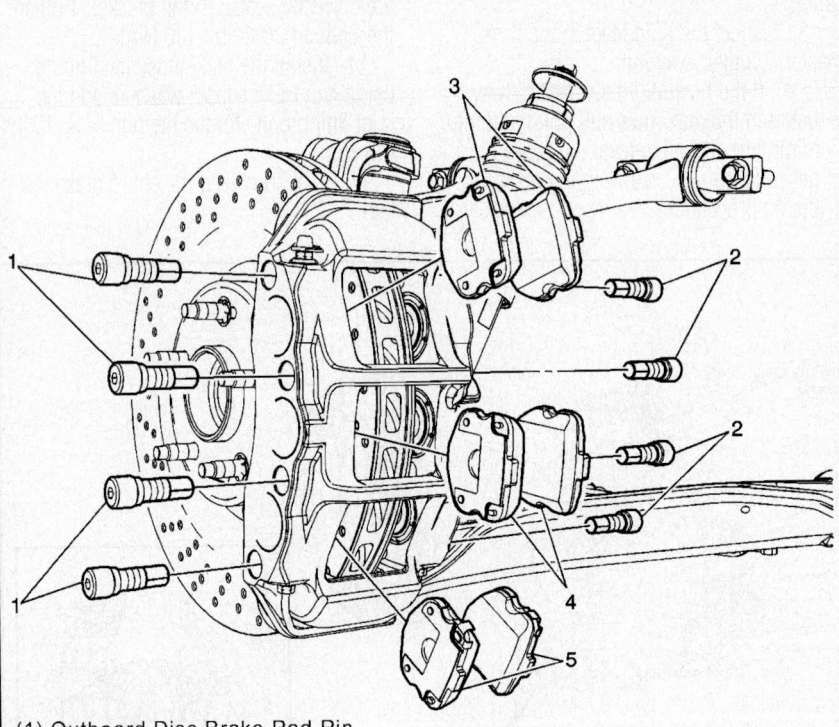

(1) Outboard Disc Brake Pad Pin
(2) Inboard Disc Brake Pad Pin
(3) Trailing brake pads
(4) Center brake pads
(5) Leading brake pads

Fig. 7 Front disc brake pads replacement—J56

b. If the brake fluid level is higher than midway between the maximum-full point and the minimum allowable level, remove brake fluid to the midway point before proceeding.

3. Raise and suitably support the vehicle.

4. Remove the tire and wheel assembly.

5. Remove the disc brake pad pins.

6. Remove the pads from the housing.

To install:

7. Using a brake pad spreader tool, compress the brake caliper pistons into the caliper bores.

8. Install the leading disc brake pads with the wear sensors on the trailing edge of the brake pad during forward wheel rotation, if equipped.

9. Hand install the disc brake pad pins while gently rocking the disc brake pads. The pins should require little effort to install.

    a. Repeat previous 2 steps to install the center and trailing pads.

10. Tighten brake pad pins to 30 ft. lbs. (40 Nm).

11. Install the tire and wheel assembly.

12. Lower the vehicle.

13. With the engine OFF:

    a. Gradually apply the brake pedal to approximately ⅔ of its travel distance.

    b. Slowly release the brake pedal.

    c. Wait 15 seconds, then repeat the above 2 steps until a firm brake pedal apply is obtained. This will properly seat the brake caliper pistons and brake pads.

14. Fill the brake master cylinder reservoir to the proper level.

15. Burnish the pads and rotors.

BRAKES

REAR DISC BRAKES

❊❊ CAUTION

Dust and dirt accumulating on brake parts during normal use may contain asbestos fibers from production or aftermarket brake linings. Breathing excessive concentrations of asbestos fibers can cause serious bodily harm. Exercise care when servicing brake parts. Do not sand or grind brake lining unless equipment used is designed to contain the dust residue. Do not clean brake parts with compressed air or by dry brushing. Cleaning should be done by dampening the brake components with a fine mist of water, then wiping the brake components clean with a dampened cloth. Dispose of cloth and all residue containing asbestos fibers in an impermeable container with the appropriate label. Follow practices prescribed by the Occupational Safety and Health Administration (OSHA) and the Environmental Protection Agency (EPA) for the handling, processing, and disposing of dust or debris that may contain asbestos fibers.

BRAKE CALIPER

REMOVAL & INSTALLATION

JL9 & J55 Brake Systems

See Figures 8 and 9.

1. Before servicing the vehicle, refer to the Precautions Section.

❊❊ CAUTION

Brake fluid may irritate eyes and skin.

2. Inspect the fluid level in the brake master cylinder reservoir.

    a. If the brake fluid level is midway

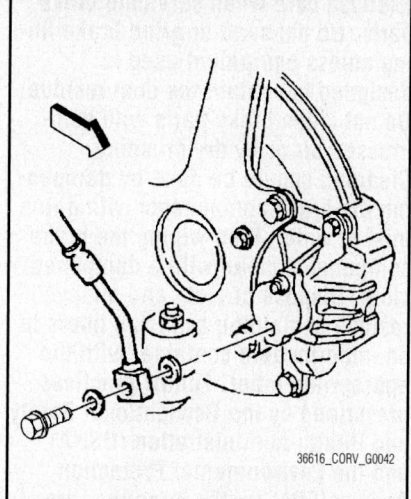

Fig. 8 Remove the brake caliper hose

between the maximum-full point and the minimum allowable level, no brake fluid needs to be removed from the reservoir before proceeding.

    b. If the brake fluid level is higher than midway between the maximum-full point and the minimum allowable level, remove brake fluid to the midway point before proceeding.

3. Raise and support the vehicle.

4. Remove the tire and wheel assembly.

5. Remove the brake caliper inlet fitting bolt from the caliper.

6. Remove the brake hose from the brake caliper.

7. Remove and discard the 2 copper brake hose gaskets. These gaskets may be stuck to the brake caliper and/or the brake hose end.

8. Plug the opening in the brake caliper and the brake hose to prevent fluid loss and contamination.

9. Remove the brake caliper guide pin bolts.

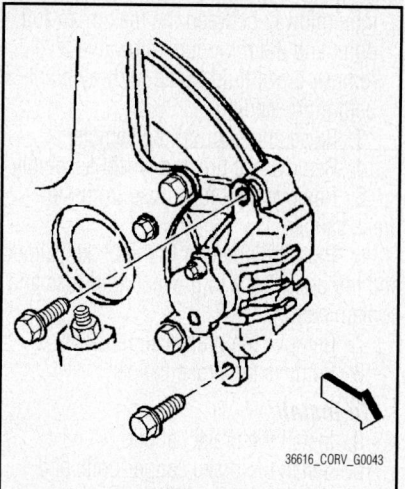

Fig. 9 Remove the brake caliper guide pin bolts

10. Remove the brake caliper from the caliper mounting bracket.

To install:

11. Inspect the caliper slide boots for cuts, tears, or deterioration. If damaged, replace the slides and the boots.

12. Install the brake caliper to the caliper mounting bracket.

13. Install the brake caliper guide pin bolts and tighten to 23 ft. lbs. (31 Nm).

14. Remove the plug from the brake caliper opening and the brake hose.

➡**Install NEW copper brake hose gaskets.**

15. Assemble the NEW copper brake hose gaskets, and the brake caliper inlet fitting bolt to the brake hose.

16. Install the brake hose and the brake caliper inlet fitting bolt to the brake caliper and tighten to 30 ft. lbs. (40 Nm).

17. Bleed the hydraulic brake system.

18. Install the tire and wheel assembly.

J56 Brake System

See Figure 10.

1. Before servicing the vehicle, refer to the Precautions Section.

> ※※ **CAUTION**
>
> **Brake fluid may irritate eyes and skin.**

2. Inspect the fluid level in the brake master cylinder reservoir.

   a. If the brake fluid level is midway between the maximum-full point and the minimum allowable level, no brake fluid needs to be removed from the reservoir before proceeding.

   b. If the brake fluid level is higher than midway between the maximum-full point and the minimum allowable level, remove brake fluid to the midway point before proceeding.

3. Raise and support the vehicle.

4. Remove the tire and wheel assembly.

5. Remove the brake hose from the brake caliper.

6. Plug the opening in the brake caliper and the brake hose to prevent fluid loss and contamination.

7. Remove the brake caliper bolts.

8. Remove the brake caliper.

To install:

9. Install the brake caliper.

10. Install the brake caliper bolts and tighten to 129 ft. lbs. (175 Nm).

11. Remove the plug from the brake caliper opening and the brake hose.

➡ **Install NEW copper brake hose gaskets.**

12. Assemble the NEW copper brake hose gaskets, and the brake caliper inlet fitting bolt to the brake hose.

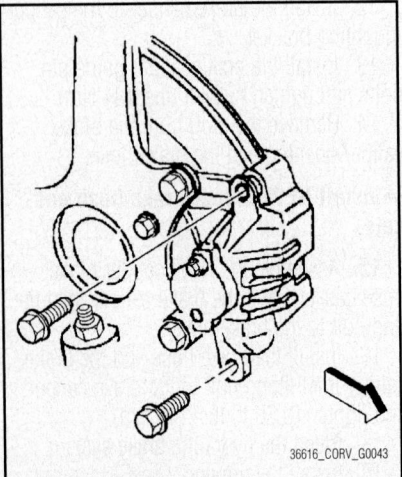

Fig. 10 Rear brake caliper

13. Install the brake hose and the brake caliper inlet fitting bolt to the brake caliper and tighten to 30 ft. lbs. (40 Nm).

14. Bleed the hydraulic brake system.

15. Install the tire and wheel assembly.

DISC BRAKE PADS

REMOVAL & INSTALLATION

> ※※ **CAUTION**
>
> **Dust and dirt accumulating on brake parts during normal use may contain asbestos fibers from production or aftermarket brake linings. Breathing excessive concentrations of asbestos fibers can cause serious bodily harm. Exercise care when servicing brake parts. Do not sand or grind brake lining unless equipment used is designed to contain the dust residue. Do not clean brake parts with compressed air or by dry brushing. Cleaning should be done by dampening the brake components with a fine mist of water, then wiping the brake components clean with a dampened cloth. Dispose of cloth and all residue containing asbestos fibers in an impermeable container with the appropriate label. Follow practices prescribed by the Occupational Safety and Health Administration (OSHA) and the Environmental Protection Agency (EPA) for the handling, processing, and disposing of dust or debris that may contain asbestos fibers.**

JL9 & J55 Brake Systems

See Figures 11 through 13.

1. Before servicing the vehicle, refer to the Precautions Section.

2. Inspect the fluid level in the brake master cylinder reservoir.

   a. If the brake fluid level is midway between the maximum-full point and the minimum allowable level, no brake fluid needs to be removed from the reservoir before proceeding.

   b. If the brake fluid level is higher than midway between the maximum-full point and the minimum allowable level, remove brake fluid to the midway point before proceeding.

3. Raise and suitably support the vehicle.

4. Remove the tire and wheel assembly.

5. Hand tighten a wheel lug nut to a wheel stud to secure the rotor to the hub.

6. Install a large C-clamp over the body

of the brake caliper with the C-clamp ends against the rear of the caliper body and against the outboard brake pad.

7. Tighten the C-clamp evenly until the caliper pistons are compressed into the caliper bores enough to allow the caliper to slide past the brake rotor.

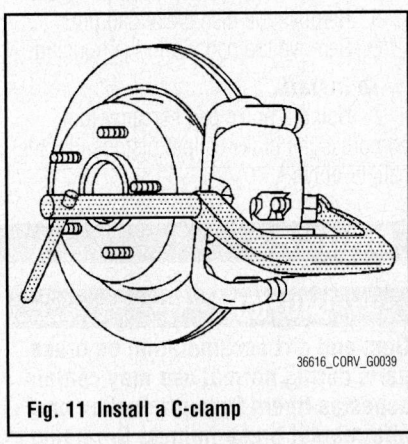

Fig. 11 Install a C-clamp

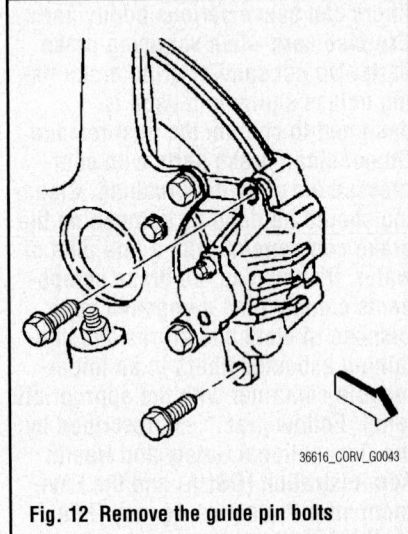

Fig. 12 Remove the guide pin bolts

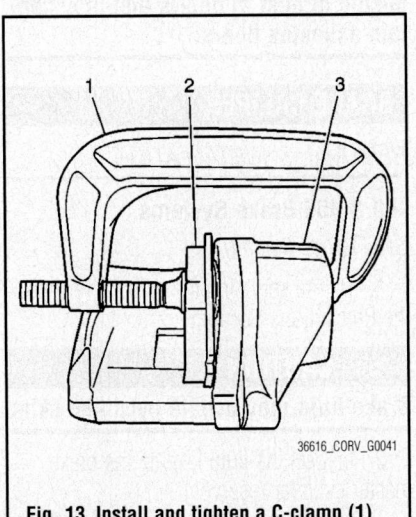

Fig. 13 Install and tighten a C-clamp (1)

8. Remove the C-clamp from the caliper.

9. Remove the upper brake caliper guide pin bolts.

✳✳ WARNING

Support the brake caliper with heavy mechanic wire, or equivalent, whenever it is separated from its mount and the hydraulic flexible brake hose is still connected. Failure to support the caliper in this manner will cause the flexible brake hose to bear the weight of the caliper, which may cause damage to the brake hose and in turn may cause a brake fluid leak.

10. Remove the brake caliper from the caliper bracket and support the caliper out of the way with heavy mechanic's wire or equivalent. Ensure that there is no tension on the hydraulic brake flexible hose.

✳✳ WARNING

Do NOT disconnect the hydraulic brake flexible hose from the caliper.

11. Remove the brake pads from the caliper bracket.

12. Remove and inspect the brake pad retainers from the caliper bracket.

To install:

13. Inspect the caliper slide boots for cuts, tears, or deterioration. If damaged, replace the slides and the boots.

14. Install a large C-clamp (1) over the body of the brake caliper (3) with the C-clamp ends against the rear of the caliper body and against an old inboard brake pad (2) or a wood block installed against the caliper pistons.

15. Tighten the C-clamp (1) evenly until the caliper pistons are compressed completely into the caliper bores.

16. Remove the C-clamp and the old brake pad or wood block from the caliper.

17. Install the brake pad retainers to the caliper bracket.

18. Install the brake pads to the caliper bracket. The brake pad wear sensor, mounted on the inboard brake pad, must be positioned so that it is in the leading bottom position during forward rotation of the brake rotor.

19. Install the brake caliper to the caliper bracket.

20. Tighten the brake caliper guide pin bolts to 23 ft. lbs.(31 Nm).

21. Install the tire and wheel assembly.

22. Lower the vehicle.

23. With the engine OFF:

a. Gradually apply the brake pedal to approximately ⅔ of its travel distance.

b. Slowly release the brake pedal.

c. Wait 15 seconds, then repeat the above 2 steps until a firm brake pedal apply is obtained. This will properly seat the brake caliper pistons and brake pads.

24. Fill the brake master cylinder reservoir to the proper level.

25. Burnish the pads and rotors.

J56 Brake System

See Figure 14.

1. Before servicing the vehicle, refer to the Precautions Section.

✳✳ CAUTION

Some models or aftermarket brake parts may contain asbestos fibers which can become airborne in dust. Breathing dust with asbestos fibers may cause serious bodily harm. Use a water-dampened cloth in order to remove any dust on brake parts. Equipment is available commercially in order to perform this washing function. These wet methods prevent

fibers from becoming airborne. Avoid taking the following actions when you service wheel brake parts: Do not grind brake linings. Do not sand brake linings. Do not clean wheel brake parts with a dry brush or with compressed air.

2. Inspect the fluid level in the brake master cylinder reservoir.

a. If the brake fluid level is midway between the maximum-full point and the minimum allowable level, no brake fluid needs to be removed from the reservoir before proceeding.

b. If the brake fluid level is higher than midway between the maximum-full point and the minimum allowable level, remove brake fluid to the midway point before proceeding.

3. Raise and suitably support the vehicle.

4. Remove the tire and wheel assembly.

5. Remove the disc brake pad pins.

6. Remove the pads from the housing.

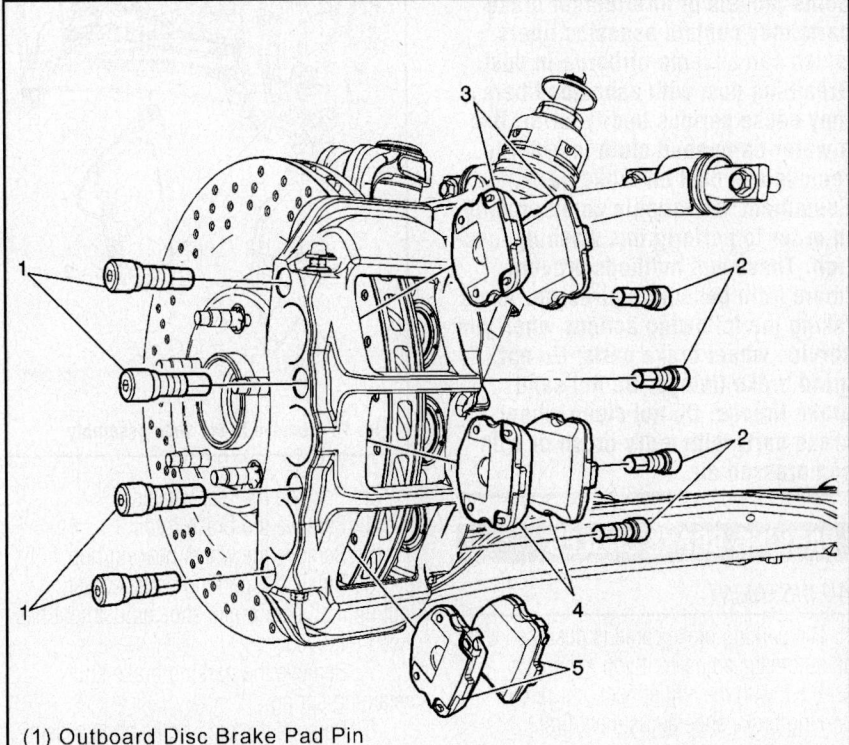

(1) Outboard Disc Brake Pad Pin
(2) Inboard Disc Brake Pad Pin
(3) Trailing brake pads
(4) Center brake pads
(5) Leading brake pads

22116_CORV_G0069

Fig. 14 Rear disc brake pads replacement—J56

To install:

7. Using a brake pad spreader tool, compress the brake caliper pistons into the caliper bores.

8. Install the leading disc brake pads with the wear sensors on the trailing edge of the brake pad during forward wheel rotation, if equipped.

9. Hand install the disc brake pad pins while gently rocking the disc brake pads. The pins should require little effort to install.

a. Repeat previous 2 steps to install the center and trailing pads.

10. Tighten brake pad pins to 30 ft. lbs. (40 Nm).

11. Install the tire and wheel assembly.

12. Lower the vehicle.

13. With the engine OFF:

a. Gradually apply the brake pedal to approximately ⅔ of its travel distance.

b. Slowly release the brake pedal.

c. Wait 15 seconds, then repeat the above 2 steps until a firm brake pedal apply is obtained. This will properly seat the brake caliper pistons and brake pads.

14. Fill the brake master cylinder reservoir to the proper level.

15. Burnish the pads and rotors.

BRAKE PAD & ROTOR BURNISHING PROCEDURE

⁂ CAUTION

Road test a vehicle under safe conditions and while obeying all traffic laws. Do not attempt any maneuvers that could jeopardize vehicle control. Failure to adhere to these precautions could lead to serious personal injury and vehicle damage.

Burnishing the brake pads and brake rotors is necessary in order to ensure that the braking surfaces are properly prepared after service has been performed on the disc brake system. This procedure should be performed whenever the disc brake rotors have been refinished or replaced, and/or whenever the disc brake pads have been replaced.

1. Select a smooth road with little or no traffic.

2. Accelerate the vehicle to 30 mph (48 km/h).

➡Use care to avoid overheating the brakes while performing this step.

3. Using moderate to firm pressure, apply the brakes to bring the vehicle to a stop. Do not allow the brakes to lock.

4. Repeat steps 2 and 3 until approximately 20 stops have been completed. Allow sufficient cooling periods between stops in order to properly burnish the brake pads and rotors.

BRAKES — PARKING BRAKE

⁂ CAUTION

Some models or aftermarket brake parts may contain asbestos fibers which can become airborne in dust. Breathing dust with asbestos fibers may cause serious bodily harm. Use a water-dampened cloth in order to remove any dust on brake parts. Equipment is available commercially in order to perform this washing function. These wet methods prevent fibers from becoming airborne. Avoid taking the following actions when you service wheel brake parts: Do not grind brake linings. Do not sand brake linings. Do not clean wheel brake parts with a dry brush or with compressed air.

PARKING BRAKE CABLES

ADJUSTMENT

The parking brake cable is designed with an automatic adjuster. If you suspect a problem with the adjustment, check the parking brake shoe adjustment first.

PARKING BRAKE SHOES

REMOVAL & INSTALLATION

See Figure 15.

1. Before servicing the vehicle, refer to the Precautions Section.

2. Raise and support the vehicle.

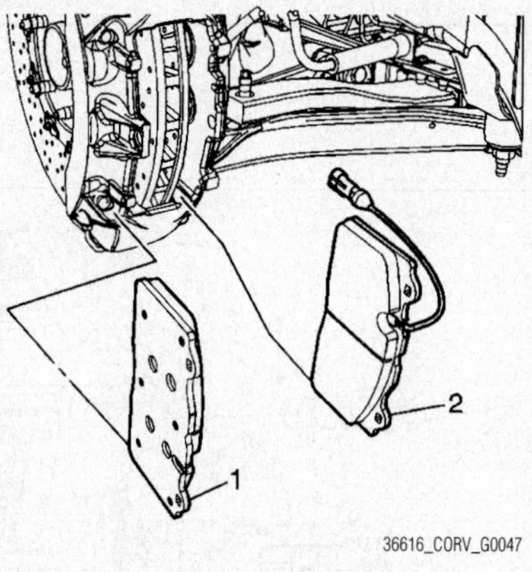
2
1
36616_CORV_G0047

Fig. 15 Remove brake shoe assembly

3. Remove the rear wheels.

4. Remove the brake rotor.

5. Remove the wheel bearing/hub.

6. Rotate the parking brake adjusting nut until all park brake shoe adjustment has been removed.

7. Remove the parking brake shoe retaining spring.

8. Remove the park brake shoe assembly by grasping the shoe and spreading slightly while pulling the shoe from the actuator assembly.

To install:

9. Install the park brake shoe assembly by grasping the shoe and spreading slightly while pulling the shoe over the actuator assembly.

10. Install the parking brake shoe retaining spring.

11. Adjust the parking brake shoe-to-drum clearance.

12. Install the wheel bearing/hub.

13. Install the brake rotor.

14. Install the wheels.

ADJUSTMENT

1. Before servicing the vehicle, refer to the Precautions Section.

2. Apply and fully release the parking brake three times.

3. Verify that the parking brake lever releases completely.

4. Turn ON the ignition. Verify that the red BRAKE warning indicator lamp is off.

5. Turn OFF the ignition.

6. Raise and support the vehicle.

7. Remove the rear tire and wheel assemblies.

➡Do not operate the park brake lever with the rear disc brake rotor removed.

8. Remove the rear disc brake rotors.

9. Place the inside measurement contacts of the with a suitable brake caliper at the widest point of the drum portion of the brake rotor.

10. Tighten the set screw on the tool in order to ensure the proper measurement when removing the tool from the drum.

11. Position the outside measurement contacts of the tool over the park brake shoe at the widest point.

➡️If the gap between the adjuster nut and the adjuster screw exceeds 0.25 in. (5 mm) during the adjustment procedure, the park brake shoe must be replaced.

12. Adjust the park brake shoe-to-drum clearance by rotating the adjustment nut on the park brake actuator. Correct specifications is 0.015 in. (0.38 mm).

13. Install the rear brake rotors.

14. Install the rear tire and wheel assemblies.

15. Apply and release the park brake lever three times.

16. Apply the park brake lever. Inspect the rotation of the rear wheels: the wheels should not rotate forward, drag, or rotate rearward.

17. If the rear tire and wheel assemblies rotate forward or do not exhibit drag rearward, repeat the adjustment procedure.

18. Release the parking lever. Verify that the wheels rotate freely.

19. Lower the vehicle.

CHASSIS ELECTRICAL

GENERAL INFORMATION

✳✳ CAUTION

These vehicles are equipped with an air bag system. The system must be disarmed before performing service on, or around, system components, the steering column, instrument panel components, wiring and sensors. Failure to follow the safety precautions and the disarming procedure could result in accidental air bag deployment, possible injury and unnecessary system repairs.

SERVICE PRECAUTIONS

Disconnect and isolate the battery negative cable before beginning any airbag system component diagnosis, testing, removal, or installation procedures. Allow system capacitor to discharge for two minutes before beginning any component service. This will disable the airbag system. Failure to disable the airbag system may result in accidental airbag deployment, personal injury, or death.

When carrying an undeployed inflator module:

• Do not carry the inflator module by the wires or connector.

• Make sure the air bag opening points away from you. Failure to observe these guidelines may result in personal injury.

When storing an undeployed inflator module:

• Make sure the air bag opening points away from the surface on which the inflator module rests.

• Provide free space for the air bag to expand in case of an accidental deployment.

• When storing a steering column, do not rest the column with the air bag opening facing down and the column vertical. Lay the column on its side. Failure to observe these guidelines may result in personal injury.

• Do not place an intact undeployed airbag face down on a solid surface. The airbag will propel into the air if accidentally

AIR BAG (SUPPLEMENTAL RESTRAINT SYSTEM)

deployed and may result in personal injury or death

Take special care when handling or storing an undeployed inflator module. An inflator module deployment produces a rapid generation of gas. This may cause the inflator module, or an object in front of the inflator module, to project through the air in the event of an unlikely deployment.

The following are general service instructions which must be followed in order to properly repair the vehicle and return it to its original integrity:

• Do not expose inflator modules to temperatures above 150°F (65°C).

  • Verify the correct replacement part number. Do not substitute a component from a different vehicle.

  • Use only original GM replacement parts available from your authorized GM dealer. Substitute parts may appear interchangeable, but internal differences may result in inferior occupant protection. Failure to do so may result in occupant personal injury or death.

  • Do not use salvaged parts for repairs to the SIR system.

Wear safety glasses, rubber gloves, and long sleeved clothing when cleaning powder residue from vehicle after an airbag deployment. Powder residue emitted from a deployed airbag can cause skin irritation. Flush affected area with cool water if irritation is experienced. If nasal or throat irritation is experienced, exit the vehicle for fresh air until the irritation ceases. If irritation continues, see a physician.

Discard any of the following components if it has been dropped from a height of 3 feet (91 cm) or greater:

• Inflatable restraint Sensing and Diagnostic Module (SDM)

• Inflatable restraint I/P module

• Inflatable restraint steering wheel module

• Inflatable restraint steering wheel module coil

• Inflatable restraint side impact modules

• Inflatable restraint Side Impact Sensors (SIS)

• Inflatable restraint seat belt pretensioners

• Inflatable restraint front end sensors

Dual stage inflator modules have two deployment stages. If stage 1 was used to deploy a dual stage inflator module, stage 2 may still be active. Therefore, a deployed dual stage inflator module must be treated as an active module. If disposal of a dual stage module is required, both deployment loops must be energized to deploy the air bag.

Do not use a replacement airbag that is not in the original packaging. This may result in improper deployment, personal injury, or death.

The factory installed fasteners, screws and bolts used to fasten airbag components have a special coating and are specifically designed for the airbag system. Do not use substitute fasteners. Use only original equipment fasteners listed in the parts catalog when fastener replacement is required.

During, and following, any child restraint anchor service, due to impact event or vehicle repair, carefully inspect all mounting hardware, tether straps, and anchors for proper installation, operation, or damage. If a child restraint anchor is found damaged in any way, the anchor must be replaced. Failure to do this may result in personal injury or death.

Deployed and non-deployed airbags may or may not have live pyrotechnic material within the airbag inflator.

Do not dispose of driver/passenger/curtain airbags or seat belt tensioners unless you are sure of complete deployment. Refer to the Hazardous Substance Control System for proper disposal.

Dispose of deployed airbags and tensioners consistent with state, provincial, local, and federal regulations.

After any airbag component testing or service, do not connect the battery negative cable. Personal injury or death may result if the system test is not performed first.

If the vehicle is equipped with the Occupant Classification System (OCS), do not connect the battery negative cable before performing the OCS Verification Test using the scan tool and the appropriate diagnostic information. Personal injury or death may result if the system test is not performed properly.

Never replace both the Occupant Restraint Controller (ORC) and the Occupant Classification Module (OCM) at the same time. If both require replacement, replace one, then perform the Airbag System test before replacing the other.

Both the ORC and the OCM store Occupant Classification System (OCS) calibration data, which they transfer to one another when one of them is replaced. If both are replaced at the same time, an irreversible fault will be set in both modules and the OCS may malfunction and cause personal injury or death.

If equipped with OCS, the Seat Weight Sensor is a sensitive, calibrated unit and must be handled carefully. Do not drop or handle roughly. If dropped or damaged, replace with another sensor. Failure to do so may result in occupant injury or death.

If equipped with OCS, the front passenger seat must be handled carefully as well. When removing the seat, be careful when setting on floor not to drop. If dropped, the sensor may be inoperative, could result in occupant injury, or possibly death.

If equipped with OCS, when the passenger front seat is on the floor, no one should sit in the front passenger seat. This uneven force may damage the sensing ability of the seat weight sensors. If sat on and damaged, the sensor may be inoperative, could result in occupant injury, or possibly death.]]

➡The air bag indicator light may remain ON after the Body Control Module (BCM), or Sensing and Diagnostic Module (SDM) is replaced, and during the programming procedure for the BCM until after the procedure is completed, and the ignition key is cycled OFF and ON.

If the SDM is replaced you must setup the new SDM part number in the BCM. With a scan tool, select the SIR module setup. Select setup SDM Part Number in BCM and follow the on-screen instructions.

DISARMING THE SYSTEM

Disabling Procedure—Air Bag Fuse

❊❊ CAUTION

Observe all SIR precautions. Failure to follow the correct safety procedures could cause air bag deployment, which can result in personal injury or death.

1. Turn the steering wheel so that the vehicles wheels are pointing straight ahead.
2. Place the ignition in the OFF position.

❊❊ CAUTION

Important: The SDM may have more than one fused power input. To ensure there is no unwanted SIR deployment, personal injury, or unnecessary SIR system repairs, remove all fuses supplying power to the SDM. With all SDM fuses removed and the ignition switch in the ON position, the AIR BAG warning indicator illuminates. This is normal operation, and does not indicate a SIR system malfunction.

3. Locate and remove the fuse(s) supplying power to the SDM.
4. Wait 1 minute before working on the system.

Disabling Procedure—Negative Battery Cable

❊❊ CAUTION

Observe all SIR precautions. Failure to follow the correct safety procedures could cause air bag deployment, which can result in personal injury or death.

1. Turn the steering wheel so that the vehicles wheels are pointing straight ahead.
2. Place the ignition in the OFF position.
3. Disconnect the negative battery cable from the battery.
4. Wait 1 minute before working on system.

ARMING THE SYSTEM

Enabling Procedure—Air Bag Fuse

❊❊ CAUTION

Observe all SIR precautions. Failure to follow the correct safety procedures could cause air bag deployment, which can result in personal injury or death.

1. Place the ignition in the OFF position.
2. Install the fuse(s) supplying power to the SDM.
3. Turn the ignition switch to the ON position.

➡The AIR BAG indicator will flash then turn OFF.

4. Perform the Diagnostic System Check if the AIR BAG warning indicator does not operate as described. Refer to Diagnostic

System Check in the General Information Section.

Enabling Procedure—Negative Battery Cable

❊❊ CAUTION

Observe all SIR precautions. Failure to follow the correct safety procedures could cause air bag deployment, which can result in personal injury or death.

1. Place the ignition in the OFF position.
2. Connect the negative battery cable to the battery.
3. Turn the ignition switch to the ON position.

➡The AIR BAG indicator will flash then turn OFF.

4. Perform the Diagnostic System Check if the AIR BAG warning indicator does not operate as described. Refer to Diagnostic System Check in the General Information Section.

CLOCKSPRING CENTERING

See Figure 16.

❊❊ CAUTION

Observe all SIR precautions. Failure to follow the correct safety procedures could cause air bag deployment, which can result in personal injury or death.

❊❊ CAUTION

The new SIR coil assembly will be centered. Improper alignment of the SIR coil assembly may damage the unit, causing an inflatable restraint malfunction.

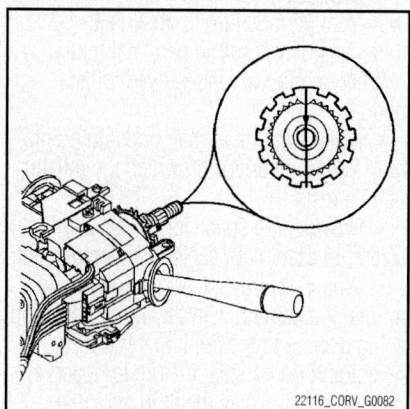

22116_CORV_G0082

Fig. 16 Position the block tooth of the steering shaft assembly in the 12 O'clock position as shown

With Type 1 System

See Figure 17.

❋❋ CAUTION

Observe all SIR precautions. Failure to follow the correct safety procedures could cause air bag deployment, which can result in personal injury or death.

If the front (5) of the SIR coil has a centering window (4), and the back side (2) has a spring service lock (1), perform the following steps:

1. Verify the following conditions before centering the SIR coil:

    a. The wheels on the vehicle are straight ahead.

    b. The block tooth (1) of the steering shaft assembly is in the 12 O'clock position.

    c. The ignition switch assembly is in the LOCK position.

2. Hold the coil with the face up.

3. While depressing the spring service lock, rotate the coil hub clockwise until the coil ribbon stops.

4. Rotate the coil hub slowly, counterclockwise, until the centering window appears yellow and both arrows (3) line up.

5. Release the spring service lock between the locking tab. The SIR coil is now centered.

6. Align the centered SIR coil with the horn tower and slide onto the steering shaft assembly.

❋❋ WARNING

Improper routing of the wire harness assembly may damage the inflatable restraint steering wheel module coil. This may result in a malfunction of the coil, which may cause personal injury.

With Type 2 System

See Figure 18.

❋❋ CAUTION

Observe all SIR precautions. Failure to follow the correct safety procedures could cause air bag deployment, which can result in personal injury or death.

If the front (4) of the SIR coil has a centering window (3) and the back side (1) has NO spring service lock, perform the following steps:

1. Verify the following conditions before centering the SIR coil:

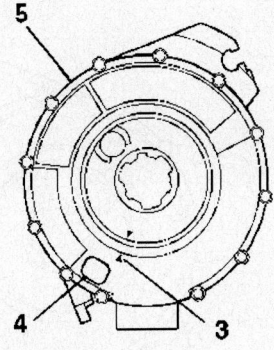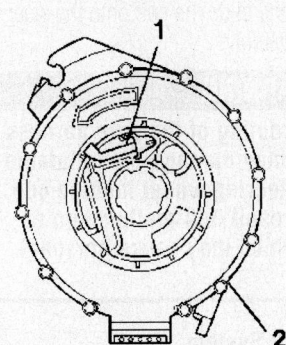

(1) Spring service lock
(2) Back side of the SIR coil
(3) Align arrows
(4) Centering window
(5) Front side of the SIR coil

22116_CORV_G0083

Fig. 17 Type 1 System Identification

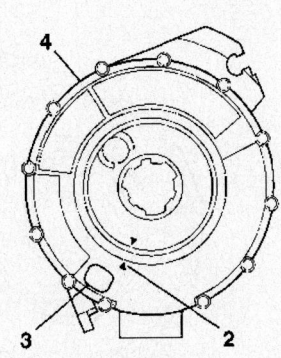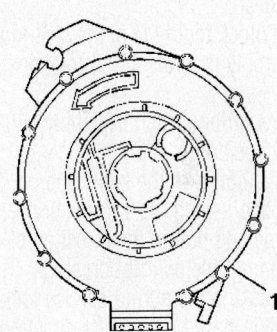

(1) Back side of the SIR coil
(2) Centering arrows
(3) Centering window
(4) Front side of the SIR coil

22116_CORV_G0084

Fig. 18 Type 2 System Identification

    a. The wheels on the vehicle are straight ahead.

    b. The block tooth (1) of the steering shaft assembly is in the 12 O'clock position.

    c. The ignition switch assembly is in the LOCK position.

2. Hold the coil with the face up.

3. Rotate the coil hub clockwise until the coil ribbon stops.

4. Rotate the coil hub slowly, counterclockwise until the centering window appears yellow and both arrows (2) line up. This is the CENTER position.

5. While holding the coil hub in the CENTER position, align the coil with the horn tower and slide the coil onto the steering shaft assembly.

✳✳ WARNING

Improper routing of the wire harness assembly may damage the inflatable restraint steering wheel module coil. This may result in a malfunction of the coil, which may cause personal injury.

With Type 3 System

See Figure 19.

✳✳ CAUTION

Observe all SIR precautions. Failure to follow the correct safety procedures could cause air bag deployment, which can result in personal injury or death.

If no centering window is present on the front side (3) of the SIR coil, but a spring service lock (1) is on the back side (2), perform the following steps:

1. Verify the following conditions before centering the SIR coil:

   a. The wheels on the vehicle are straight ahead.

   b. The block tooth (1) of the steering shaft assembly is in the 12 O'clock position.

   c. The ignition switch assembly is in the LOCK position.

2. Hold the coil with the back side up.

3. While depressing the spring service lock, rotate the coil hub in the direction of the arrow (4) until the coil ribbon stops.

4. Still pressing the spring service lock, rotate the coil hub in the opposite direction 2½ revolutions.

5. Release the spring service lock between the locking tabs. The SIR coil is now centered.

6. Align the centered coil with the horn tower and slide the coil onto the steering shaft assembly.

✳✳ WARNING

Improper routing of the wire harness assembly may damage the inflatable restraint steering wheel module coil. This may result in a malfunction of the coil, which may cause personal injury.

With Type 4 System

See Figure 20.

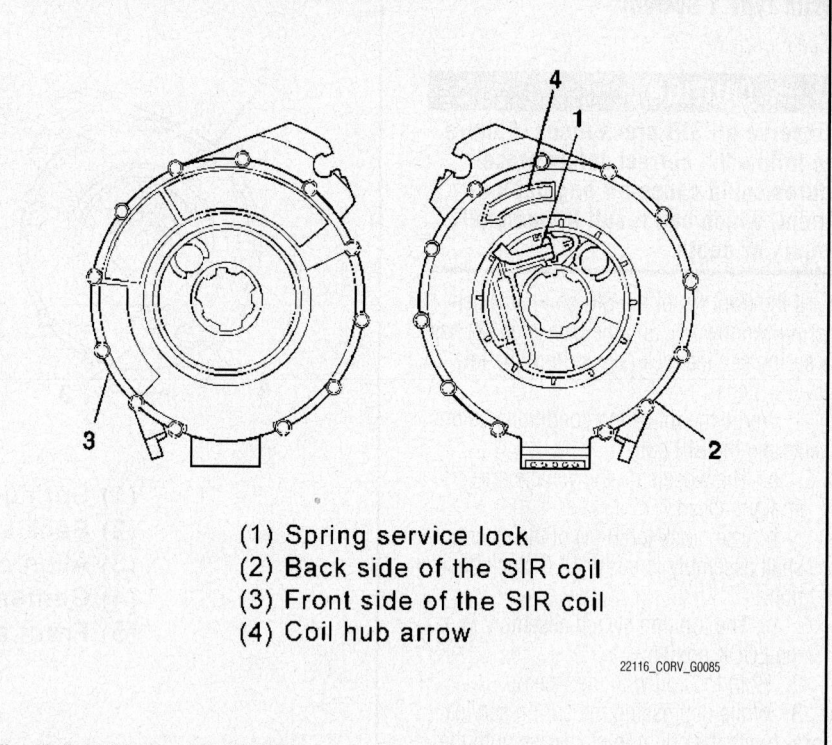

(1) Spring service lock
(2) Back side of the SIR coil
(3) Front side of the SIR coil
(4) Coil hub arrow

22116_CORV_G0085

Fig. 19 Type 3 System Identification

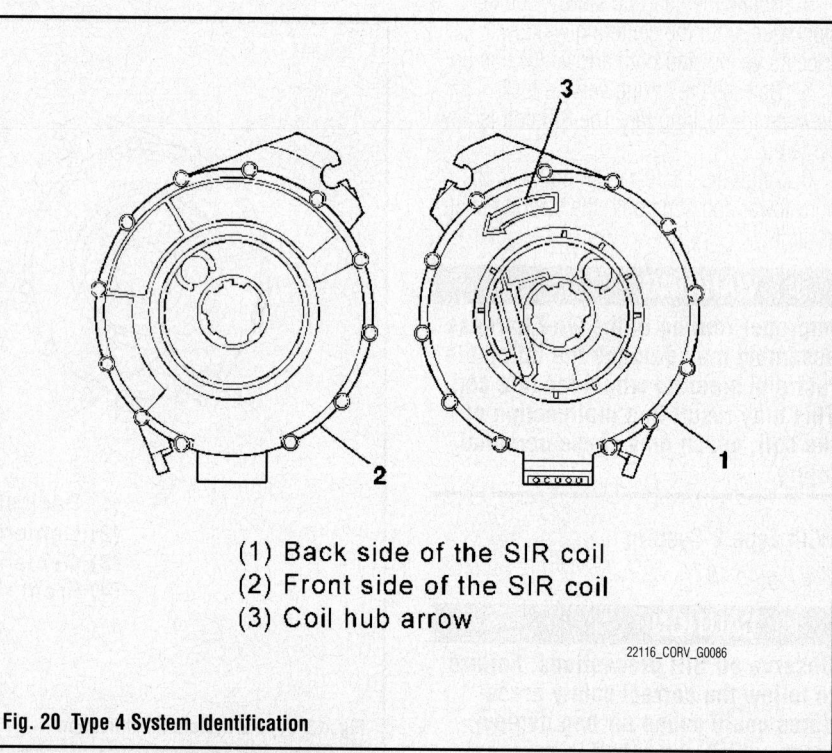

(1) Back side of the SIR coil
(2) Front side of the SIR coil
(3) Coil hub arrow

22116_CORV_G0086

Fig. 20 Type 4 System Identification

✳✳ CAUTION

Observe all SIR precautions. Failure to follow the correct safety procedures could cause air bag deployment, which can result in personal injury or death.

If no centering window appears on the front side (2) of the SIR coil and no spring service lock exists on the back side (1), perform the following steps:

1. Verify the following conditions before centering the SIR coil:

   a. The wheels on the vehicle are straight ahead.

b. The block tooth (1) of the steering shaft assembly is in the 12 O'clock position.

c. The ignition switch assembly is in the LOCK position.

2. Hold the coil with the face up.

3. Rotate the coil hub in the direction of the arrow (3) until the coil ribbon stops.

4. Rotate the coil hub, slowly, counter-clockwise, for 2½ revolutions. This is the CENTER position.

5. While maintaining the coil hub in the CENTER position, align the centered coil with the horn tower and slide the coil onto the steering shaft assembly.

✳✳ WARNING

Improper routing of the wire harness assembly may damage the inflatable restraint steering wheel module coil. This may result in a malfunction of the coil, which may cause personal injury.

DRIVE TRAIN

AUTOMATIC TRANSMISSION ASSEMBLY

REMOVAL & INSTALLATION
See Figures 21 through 29.

✳✳ WARNING

When tilting down the rear of the driveline, observe the clearance between the rear of the engine and the composite dash panel. Do not allow the engine to rest unsupported against the composite dash panel, or vehicle damage may result.

✳✳ WARNING

When lowering and removing the rear of the driveline, observe the clearance between the rear of the Transmission assembly and the underbody to prevent damage.

➡Before servicing the vehicle, refer to the Precautions Section.

✳✳ WARNING

Failure to follow the proper removal and installation procedures may

result in damage to the engine crankshaft thrust bearing.

1. Disconnect the negative battery cable.

✳✳ CAUTION

Unless directed otherwise, the ignition and start switch must be in the OFF or LOCK position, and all electrical loads must be OFF before servic-

ing any electrical component. Disconnect the negative battery cable to prevent an electrical spark should a tool or equipment come in contact with an exposed electrical terminal. Failure to follow these precautions may result in personal injury and/or damage to the vehicle or its components.

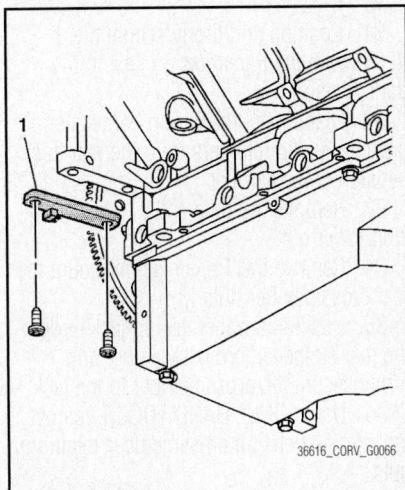

Fig. 22 Install the J 42386-A (1) to the engine flywheel

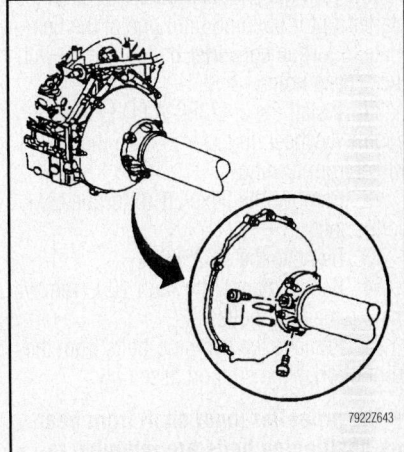

Fig. 24 Remove the plugs and install two M10 x 1.5 x 55mm or longer bolts into the bolt holes to secure the bearing

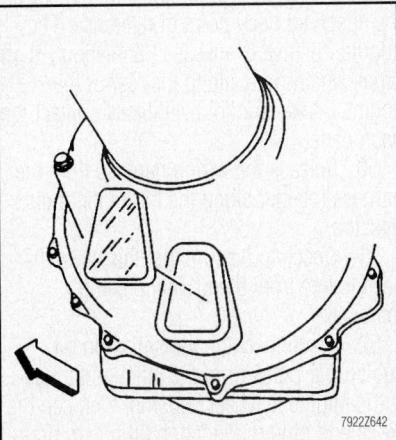

Fig. 21 Remove the inspection plug, then remove the flexplate-to-torque converter bolts

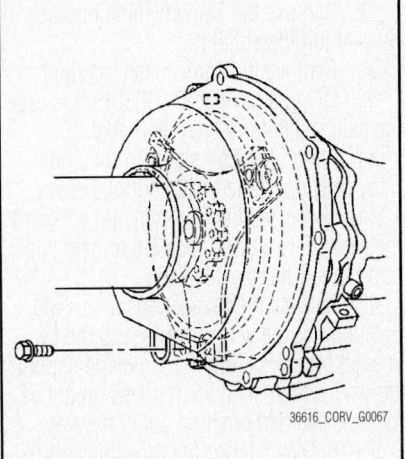

Fig. 23 Flexplate to torque converter bolt location

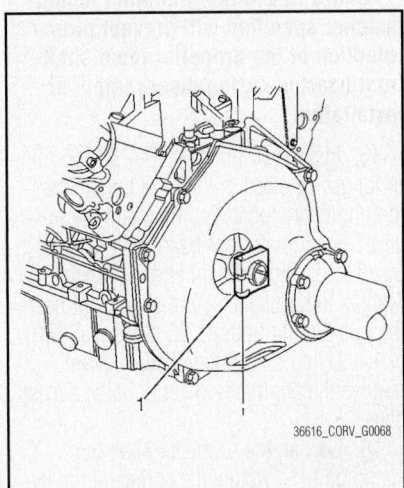

Fig. 25 Loosen the propeller shaft hub clamp bolt (1)

2. Raise and suitably support the vehicle.

3. Remove the rear tire and wheel assemblies.

4. Remove the intermediate pipe assembly.

5. Tie off the left-hand muffler assembly to the underbody to support the muffler out of the way.

6. Remove the right-hand muffler assembly.

7. Remove the floor panel tunnel reinforcement.

8. Using a flat-bladed screwdriver, remove the rear bellhousing access plug.

➡**The following step must be performed to assure proper torque converter balance during installation.**

9. Matchmark the transmission flexplate to the transmission torque converter through the access hole in the rear bellhousing.

10. Turn the engine flywheel through the starter motor opening until one of the flexplate to torque converter bolts lines up with the access hole.

11. Install the J 42386-A (1) to the engine flywheel, in order to keep the flywheel from turning.

12. Remove the flexplate to torque converter bolt.

13. Remove the J 42386-A.

14. Repeat steps 7 through 10 to remove the 2 remaining bolts.

15. Remove the two plug bolts from the front of driveline support assembly.

➡**The propeller input shaft front bearing positioning bolts are intended to remain torqued to specification and in place UNTIL INSTRUCTED in the installation procedure.**

➡**Failure to use the minimum length fastener specified will prevent proper retention of the propeller input shaft front bearing during disassembly or installation.**

16. Install two bolts, M10-1.5 X 55 mm, or longer, in place of the plug bolts. The long bolts are located to maintain the propeller input shaft front bearing in original position during removal and installation. Tighten the propeller input shaft front bearing positioning bolts to 26 ft. lbs. (35 Nm).

17. Using a flat-bladed screwdriver, remove the engine flywheel housing access plug.

18. Loosen the propeller shaft hub clamp bolt (1). Rotate the engine at the flywheel, if necessary for alignment.

19. Remove the nuts retaining the transmission shift cable bracket to the transmission.

20. Disconnect the transmission shift control cable from the transmission shift lever. Unsnap to release the cable.

21. Position the transmission shift cable and bracket aside.

22. Remove the rear transverse spring.

23. Support the lower control arm with a straight jack.

24. Disconnect the outer tie rod end from the suspension knuckle.

25. Remove the shock absorber lower mounting bolt.

26. Disconnect the lower ball joint from the suspension knuckle.

27. Remove the straight jack from the control arm.

28. Repeat steps 21 through 25 for the other side of the vehicle.

29. Assemble the J 42055.

30. Install the J 42055 to a transmission jack.

31. Position and firmly secure the J 42055 with the transmission jack to the transmission.

32. Disconnect the wiring harness and brake pipe clip retainers from the rear suspension crossmember.

33. Remove the differential to transmission lower nut.

34. Remove the Transmission mount to rear crossmember nuts (3).

35. Position a transmission jack under the rear suspension crossmember and firmly secure the crossmember to the jack.

36. Using ONLY HAND TOOLS, remove the rear suspension crossmember retaining nuts.

37. With the aid of an assistant, slowly lower the rear suspension crossmember away from the vehicle frame rails and remove the crossmember.

38. Remove the Transmission mount bracket to differential nuts.

39. Remove the Transmission mount.

40. Using a pry bar, CAREFULLY release the axle shafts from the differential.

41. Tie off the axle shafts to the underbody to support the shafts out of the way. The left-hand muffler assembly pipe toward the rear offers a good location to help support the left-hand axle shaft.

42. Release the retainer securing (and positioning) the wiring harness to the L-shaped brackets along the driveline support assembly, then slide the harness up out of the brackets and position out of the way.

43. SLOWLY lower the driveline approximately 2 in. (5 cm), while simultaneously adjusting the angle of tilt, in order to access the electrical connectors.

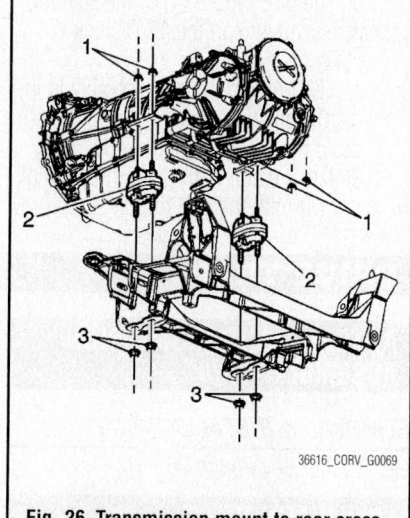

Fig. 26 Transmission mount to rear crossmember nuts (3)

44. Disconnect the Vehicle Speed Sensor (VSS) electrical connector.

45. Disconnect the wiring harness retainer from the stud at the differential rear cover.

46. Disconnect the wiring harness retainer clip from the top of the differential.

47. Disconnect the transmission harness 20-way connector. Depress both tabs on the connector and pull straight up; do not pry the connector.

48. Remove the bolt retaining the transmission wiring harness to the left-hand side of the transmission case.

49. SLOWLY lower the driveline, while simultaneously adjusting the angle of tilt, and observe the relationship between the top rear of the differential and the lowest part of the rear compartment panel floor (the center storage compartment between the frame rails). The differential should not be lowered more than approximately EVEN with the specified body point of reference. The engine Positive Crankcase Ventilation (PCV) pipes which route along the rear of the engine intake manifold will likely contact the dash panel.

50. Release the wiring harness from the harness retainer along the top of the transmission.

51. Check to be sure that the wiring harness is free from the driveline being removed.

52. Disconnect the transmission oil cooler rear pipes from the junction fittings at the engine flywheel housing, then cap the pipes and plug the junction fittings to prevent contamination.

53. Using a block of wood to protect the engine oil pan, place a straight jack under the rear of the engine oil pan to support the

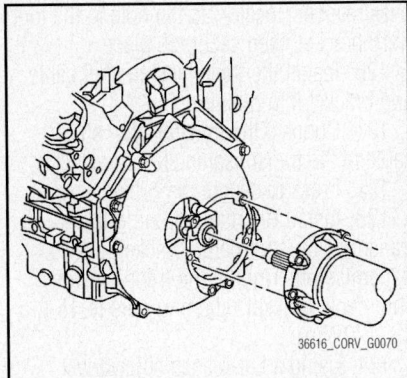

Fig. 27 Remove driveline from vehicle

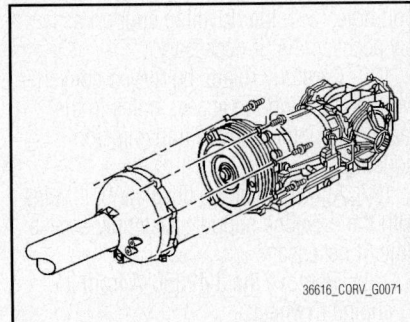

Fig. 28 Remove the transmission to driveline support assembly bolts/studs

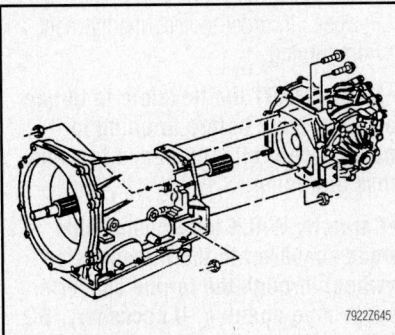

Fig. 29 Transmission-to-differential mounting bolt locations

engine from stressing the composite dash panel.

54. Remove the five driveline support assembly to engine flywheel housing bolts.

55. Carefully bend the wiring harness bracket away from the driveline, toward the driveline tunnel wall in order to make a clear removal path for the driveline.

➡**The aid of an assistant will be necessary for the remaining steps.**

56. Have an assistant insert a flat bladed screwdriver, or similar tool, between the

edge of the driveline support assembly and the engine flywheel housing, then begin to pry the driveline loose from the engine.

57. Have an assistant guide the front of the driveline during the removal of the driveline from the vehicle.

58. SLOWLY lower the driveline, while simultaneously adjusting the angle of tilt and pulling the driveline away from the engine UNTIL the propeller input shaft at the front of the driveline support assembly just clears the engine flywheel housing.

59. SLOWLY lower the driveline completely out of the vehicle.

60. Position the chainfall, or equivalent, of a lift device in a way which will protect the transmission oil cooler rear pipes and the rear exhaust hangers located on the driveline support assembly.

61. Using the lift device, raise the driveline to relieve the weight from the transmission jack.

62. Disconnect the J 42055 from the transmission jack ONLY, the J 42055 will provide stability to the driveline components while working on a bench.

63. Position the driveline on a workbench with the lift device still attached.

64. Support the driveline support assembly and the differential for additional balance.

65. Remove the lift device from the driveline.

66. Disconnect the transmission oil cooler rear pipes from the fittings on the transmission, then cap the pipes and plug the transmission fittings to prevent contamination.

67. Remove the transmission to driveline support assembly bolts/studs.

68. Insert a flat-bladed screwdriver, or similar tool, between the edge of the driveline support assembly and the transmission, then begin to pry the driveline support assembly loose from the transmission.

69. Slowly slide the driveline support assembly away from the transmission while supporting the transmission torque converter.

70. Using a strap positioned from side to side, secure the transmission torque converter to the transmission.

71. Remove the differential to transmission bolts and nuts.

➡**Use care when separating the differential from the transmission to not damage the transmission output shaft seal in the differential plate.**

72. SLOWLY slide the differential from the transmission.

To install:

✶✶ WARNING

Failure to follow the proper removal and installation procedures may result in damage to the engine crankshaft thrust bearing.

✶✶ WARNING

Use the correct fastener in the correct location. Replacement fasteners must be the correct part number for that application. Fasteners requiring replacement or fasteners requiring the use of thread locking compound or sealant are identified in the service procedure. Do not use paints, lubricants, or corrosion inhibitors on fasteners or fastener joint surfaces unless specified. These coatings affect fastener torque and joint clamping force and may damage the fastener. Use the correct tightening sequence and specifications when installing fasteners in order to avoid damage to parts and systems.

73. Install the differential to transmission bolts and nuts. Tighten the differential to transmission bolts and nuts to 37 ft. lbs. (50 Nm).

74. Remove the strap retaining the transmission torque converter.

75. Slowly slide the driveline support assembly to the transmission, while supporting the transmission torque converter.

76. Install the transmission to driveline support assembly bolts/studs. Tighten the transmission to driveline support assembly bolts/studs to 37 ft. lbs. (50 Nm).

77. Remove the caps from the rear of the transmission oil cooler rear pipes and remove the plugs from the fittings on the transmission.

78. Position the chainfall, or equivalent, of a lift device in a way which will protect the transmission oil cooler rear pipes and the rear exhaust hangers located on the driveline support assembly.

➡**The aid of an assistant will be necessary for the following steps until the driveline is installed into the vehicle.**

79. Using the lift device, raise the driveline off the workbench and position the driveline with the J 42055 onto a transmission jack.

80. Connect the J 42055 to the transmission jack.

81. Remove the lift device from the driveline.

82. Position the driveline under the vehicle.

83. Begin to raise the driveline at the approximate angle used during removal.

84. Position the wiring harness along the driveline support assembly and LOOSELY install the harness into the harness retaining slots.

85. Have an assistant guide the front of the driveline so the propeller input shaft is just to the rear of the engine flywheel housing, then raise the driveline to the PROPER HEIGHT and the PROPER ANGLE to install to the engine.

✳✳ WARNING

Use care not to use too much force to install the propeller input shaft into the propeller shaft hub. The propeller input shaft front bearing positioning system is designed to withstand an insertion force not greater than 130 lbs. (582 Nm).

86. Have an assistant begin to insert the propeller input shaft into the propeller shaft hub while maintaining the proper angle of the driveline, if necessary use a screwdriver to rotate the shaft slightly to bring the splines into alignment.

87. SLOWLY seat the driveline to the engine flywheel housing while maintaining the proper angle of the driveline.

88. Reposition the wiring harness bracket from near the driveline tunnel wall to align with the appropriate driveline support assembly bolt hole.

89. Install the five driveline support assembly to engine flywheel housing bolts. Tighten the driveline support assembly to engine flywheel housing bolts to 37 ft. lbs. (50 Nm).

90. Install the wiring harness to the wiring harness retainer along the top of the transmission.

91. SLOWLY raise the driveline to approximately 2 in. (5 cm) BELOW the final installed height.

92. Remove the caps from the front of the transmission oil cooler rear pipes and remove the plugs from the junction fittings at the engine flywheel housing.

93. Connect the transmission harness 20-way connector.

94. Align the arrows on each half of the connector and insert straight down.

95. Connect the wiring harness clip to the top of the differential.

96. Connect the wiring harness retainer to the stud at the differential rear cover.

97. Connect the Vehicle Speed Sensor (VSS) electrical connector.

98. Slowly raise the driveline to final installation height.

99. Remove the jack which supported the engine.

100. Remove the tie-off retainers from the axle shafts.

101. CAREFULLY align and seat the axle shafts to the differential.

102. Install the Transmission mount to the differential.

103. Install the Transmission mount nuts. Tighten the Transmission mount nuts to 37 ft. lbs. (50 Nm).

104. With the aid of an assistant, begin to raise the rear suspension crossmember (still firmly attached to a transmission jack), to the vehicle frame rails.

105. Guide the rear suspension crossmember alignment pins into the alignment holes in the vehicle frame rails, and guide the Transmission mount studs into the mounting holes in the crossmember, then raise the crossmember to seat to the frame rails.

106. Using ONLY HAND TOOLS, install NEW rear suspension crossmember mounting nuts. Tighten the rear suspension crossmember mounting nuts to 81 ft. lbs. (110 Nm).

107. Remove the transmission jack from the rear suspension crossmember.

108. Release the J 42055 from the transmission, then remove the J 42055 and transmission jack.

109. Install the Transmission mount to rear suspension crossmember nuts. Tighten the nuts to 37 ft. lbs. (50 Nm).

110. Install the differential to transmission lower nut. Tighten the differential to transmission lower nut to 37 ft. lbs. (50 Nm).

111. Connect the wiring harness and brake pipe clip retainers to the rear suspension crossmember.

112. Support the lower control arm with a straight jack.

113. Connect the lower ball joint to the suspension knuckle.

114. Install the shock absorber lower mounting bolt. Tighten the rear shock absorber lower mounting bolt to 162 ft. lbs. (220 Nm).

115. Connect the outer tie rod end to the suspension knuckle.

116. Remove the straight jack from the suspension control arm.

117. Repeat steps 45 through 49 for the other side of the vehicle.

118. Install the rear transverse spring.

119. Carefully pull the wiring harness down into the L-shaped brackets along the driveline support assembly, align the har-ness retainer (locator) to the hole in the forward bracket, then secure in place.

120. Install the transmission shift cable and bracket into position.

121. Connect the transmission shift cable to the transmission shift lever.

122. Press to secure the cable.

123. Install the nuts retaining the transmission shift cable bracket to the transmission. Tighten the transmission shift cable bracket retaining nuts to 15 ft. lbs. (20 Nm).

124. Using a flat-bladed screwdriver, remove the transmission torque converter access plug.

125. Align one of the torque converter bolt holes with the driveline support assembly access hole, if necessary.

126. Carefully rotate the torque converter, working through the access holes in the rear bellhousing and the transmission housing.

127. Align one of the flexplate bolt holes with the driveline support assembly access hole, if necessary.

   a. Remove the J 42386-A from the engine flywheel.

   b. Slowly turn the engine flywheel through the starter motor opening until the desired flexplate bolt hole lines up with the torque converter bolt hole.

   c. Install the J 42386-A to the engine flywheel, in order to keep the flywheel from turning.

➡ **HAND-START the flexplate to torque converter bolts before torquing to ensure proper alignment and to avoid cross threading.**

➡ **Carefully WALK the transmission torque converter to the transmission flywheel through the torque converter access plug opening, if necessary. DO NOT use the bolts to draw the torque converter to the flexplate.**

128. Install the flexplate to torque converter bolt through the driveline support assembly access hole. HAND-TIGHTEN until FINGER-TIGHT, then torque to specification. Tighten the flexplate to torque converter bolt to 47 ft. lbs. (63 Nm).

129. Remove the J 42386-A from the engine flywheel.

130. Turn the engine flywheel slowly until the next bolt holes line up with the rear bellhousing access hole.

131. Install the J 42386-A to the engine flywheel, in order to keep the flywheel from turning.

132. Repeat steps 4 through 7 to install the 2 remaining bolts.

133. Remove the J 42386-A from the engine flywheel.

134. Install the torque converter access plug.

135. Install the rear bellhousing access plug.

136. HAND-TIGHTEN the propeller shaft hub clamp bolt until FINGER-TIGHT.

137. Remove the propeller input shaft front bearing positioning bolts (M10-1.5 X 55 mm) from the driveline support assembly.

138. Install the two plug bolts to the front of the driveline support assembly. Tighten the driveline support assembly front plug bolts to 37 ft. lbs. (50 Nm).

139. Install the floor panel tunnel reinforcement.

140. Remove the tie-off retainer from the left-hand muffler assembly.

141. Install the right-hand muffler assembly.

142. Install the intermediate pipe assembly.

143. Install the rear tire and wheel assemblies.

144. Lower the vehicle.

145. Connect the negative battery cable. Tighten the negative battery cable bolt to 11 ft. lbs. (15 Nm).

146. Program the transmitters.

❊❊ WARNING

The following steps MUST be performed in order to provide proper alignment of the propeller shaft hub, the propeller input shaft and the propeller input shaft front bearing.

147. Start and run the engine at idle until normal operating temperatures are reached. Idle or drive for at least 10 minutes.

148. Turn off the engine and allow the powertrain to cool to ROOM temperature.

149. Raise the vehicle.

150. Tighten the propeller shaft hub clamp bolt. Tighten the propeller shaft hub clamp bolt to 96 ft. lbs. (130 Nm).

151. Install the engine flywheel housing access plug.

152. Flush the transmission oil cooler.

153. Lower the vehicle.

MANUAL TRANSMISSION ASSEMBLY

REMOVAL & INSTALLATION

See Figures 30 through 40.

➡**Before servicing the vehicle, refer to the Precautions Section.**

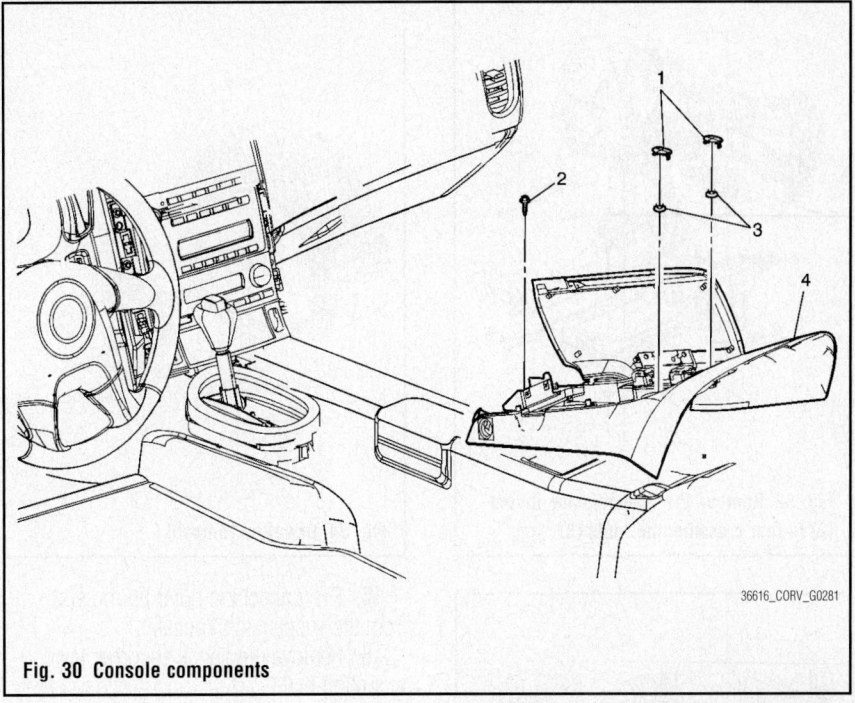

Fig. 30 Console components

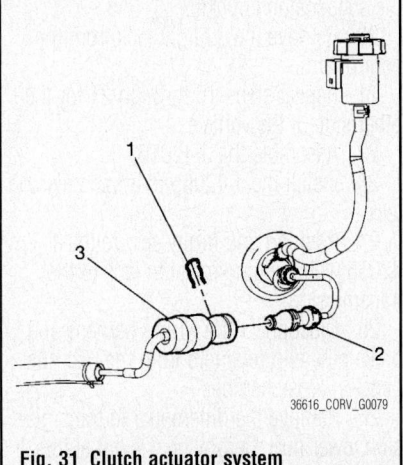

Fig. 31 Clutch actuator system

❊❊ WARNING

When tilting down the rear of the driveline, observe the clearance between the rear of the engine and the composite dash panel. Do not allow the engine to rest unsupported against the composite dash panel, or vehicle damage may result.

❊❊ WARNING

When lowering and removing the rear of the driveline, observe the clearance between the rear of the Transmission assembly and the underbody to prevent damage.

❊❊ WARNING

When tilting down the rear of the driveline, insert a putty knife or similar tool between the shift control bracket on the driveline support assembly and the brake pipe retainer on the driveline tunnel wall to prevent damage.

1. Disconnect the negative battery cable.

❊❊ CAUTION

Unless directed otherwise, the ignition and start switch must be in the OFF or LOCK position, and all electrical loads must be OFF before servicing any electrical component. Disconnect the negative battery cable to prevent an electrical spark should a tool or equipment come in contact with an exposed electrical terminal. Failure to follow these precautions may result in personal injury and/or damage to the vehicle or its components.

2. Remove the console:

a. Remove the instrument panel accessory trim plate and center console trim plate.

b. Remove the console compartment fillers (1), bolt (2), and nuts (3).

c. Disconnect the electrical connectors.

d. Remove the console assembly (4).

3. Remove the shift control closeout boot.

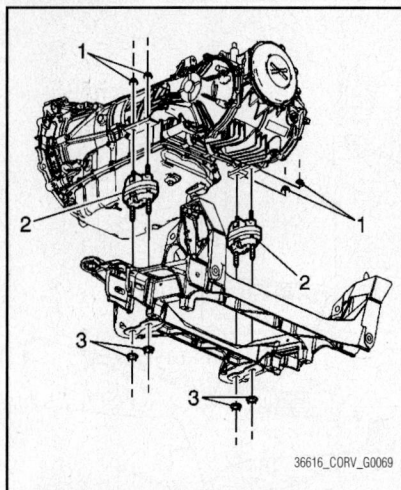

Fig. 32 Remove the Transmission mount (2) to rear crossmember nuts (3)

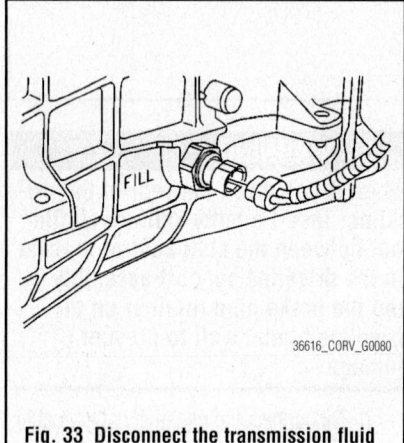

Fig. 33 Disconnect the transmission fluid temperature sensor electrical connector

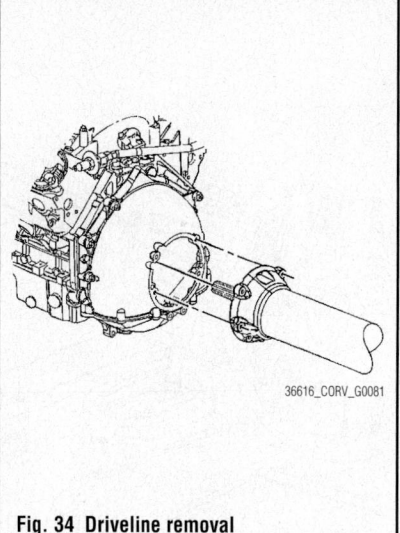

Fig. 34 Driveline removal

4. Remove the shift control assembly.

5. Remove the left I/P lower insulator panel.

6. Remove the clutch master cylinder pushrod retainer.

7. Disconnect the clutch master cylinder pushrod from the clutch pedal.

8. Raise and suitably support the vehicle.

9. Remove the clutch actuator cylinder hose (3) from the hose retaining clip below the power brake booster.

10. Remove the hose retaining clip (1) then separate the hoses (2, 3).

11. Remove the rear tire and wheel assemblies.

12. Remove the intermediate pipe.

13. Tie off the muffler assemblies to the underbody to support out of the way.

14. Remove the floor panel tunnel reinforcement.

15. Install J 33432-A transverse spring compressor.

16. Compress the rear traverse spring.

17. Disconnect the outer tie rod end from the suspension knuckle.

18. Remove the shock absorber lower mounting bolt.

19. Disconnect the lower ball joint from the suspension knuckle.

20. Remove the straight jack from the control arm.

21. Repeat steps 16 through 21 for the other side of the vehicle.

22. Assemble the J 42055.

23. Install the J 42055 to a transmission jack.

24. Position and firmly secure the J 42055 with the transmission jack to the transmission.

25. Disconnect the wiring harness and brake pipe clip retainers from the rear suspension crossmember.

26. Remove the differential to transmission lower nut. (Removing the nut at this time will aid in separating the differential from the transmission after the driveline has been removed from the vehicle.)

27. Remove the Transmission mount (2) to rear crossmember nuts (3).

28. Position a transmission jack under the rear suspension crossmember and firmly secure the crossmember to the jack.

29. Using ONLY HAND TOOLS, remove the rear suspension crossmember retaining nuts.

30. With the aid of an assistant, slowly lower the rear suspension crossmember away from the vehicle frame rails and remove the crossmember.

31. Remove the Transmission mount to differential nuts.

32. Using a pry bar, CAREFULLY release the axle shafts from the differential. Tie off the axle shafts to the underbody to support out of the way.

33. The muffler assembly pipes toward the rear offer a good location to help support the axle shafts.

34. Release the retainer (1) securing (and positioning) the wiring harness to the L-shaped brackets along the driveline support assembly, then slide the harness up out of the brackets and position out of the way.

35. SLOWLY lower the driveline approximately 2 in. (5 cm), while simultaneously adjusting the angle of tilt, in order to access the electrical connectors.

36. Disconnect the Vehicle Speed Sensor (VSS) electrical connector.

37. Disconnect the wiring harness retainer from the stud at the differential rear cover.

38. Disconnect the wiring harness retainer clip from the top of the differential.

39. Disconnect the backup lamp switch electrical connector.

40. Disconnect the reverse lockout solenoid electrical connector.

41. Disconnect the gear select (skip shift) solenoid electrical connector.

42. Disconnect the transmission fluid temperature sensor electrical connector, if equipped.

43. Insert a putty knife, or similar tool, between the edge of the shifter bracket on the side of the driveline support assembly and the brake pipe retainer on the wall of the driveline tunnel.

44. SLOWLY lower the driveline, while simultaneously adjusting the angle of tilt, and observe the relationship between the top rear of the differential and the lowest part of the rear compartment panel floor (the center storage compartment between the frame rails). The differential should not be lowered more than approximately EVEN with the specified body point of reference. The engine Positive Crankcase Ventilation (PCV) pipes which route along the rear of the engine intake manifold will likely contact the dash panel.

45. Release the wiring harness from the harness retainer along the top of the transmission.

46. Check to be sure that the wiring harness is free from the driveline being removed.

47. Using a block of wood to protect the engine oil pan, place a straight jack under the rear of the engine oil pan to support the engine from stressing the composite dash panel.

48. Remove the five driveline support assembly to engine flywheel housing bolts.

49. Carefully bend the wiring harness

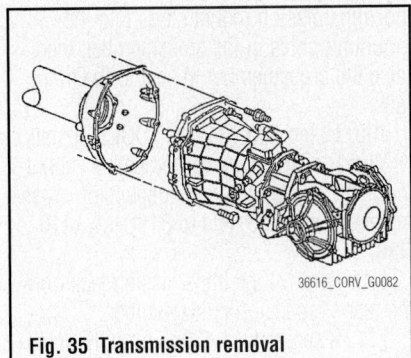

Fig. 35 Transmission removal

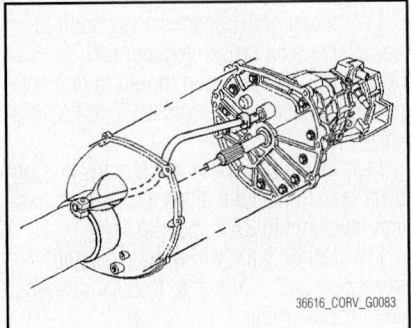

Fig. 36 Driveline support assembly removal

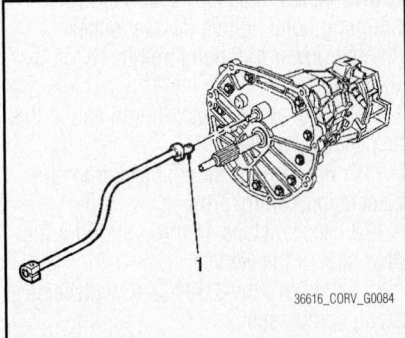

Fig. 37 Remove the transmission shift rod, roll pin (1) and shaft

bracket away from the driveline toward the driveline tunnel wall in order to make a clear removal path for the driveline.

50. The aid of an assistant will be necessary for the remaining steps.

51. Have an assistant insert a flat bladed screwdriver, or similar tool, between the edge of the driveline support assembly and the engine flywheel housing, then begin to pry the driveline loose from the engine.

52. Have an assistant guide the front of the driveline during the removal of the driveline from the vehicle.

53. SLOWLY lower the driveline, while simultaneously adjusting the angle of tilt and pulling the driveline away from the

engine UNTIL the propeller input shaft at the front of the driveline support assembly just clears the engine flywheel housing.

54. SLOWLY lower the driveline completely out of the vehicle.

55. Position the chainfall, or equivalent, of a lift device in a way which will protect the rear exhaust hangers located on the driveline support assembly.

56. Using the lift device, raise the driveline to relieve the weight from the transmission jack.

57. Disconnect the J 42055 from the transmission jack ONLY; the J 42055 will provide stability to the driveline components while working on a bench.

58. Position the driveline on a workbench with the lift device still attached.

59. Support the driveline support assembly and the differential for additional balance.

60. Remove the lift device from the driveline.

61. Remove the transmission to driveline support assembly bolts/studs.

62. Insert a flat bladed screwdriver, or similar tool, between the edge of the driveline support assembly and the transmission, then begin to pry the driveline support assembly loose from the transmission.

63. Slowly slide the driveline support assembly away from the transmission while guiding the transmission shift rod through the opening in the driveline support assembly.

64. Using a drift or punch, remove the roll pin (1) retaining the transmission shift rod to the transmission shift shaft.

65. Remove the transmission shift rod.

66. Remove the differential to transmission bolts and nuts.

67. SLOWLY slide the differential from the transmission.

68. Remove the transmission from the J 42055, if necessary.

To install:

✳✳ WARNING

When tilting down the rear of the driveline, insert a putty knife or similar tool between the shift control bracket on the driveline support assembly and the brake pipe retainer on the driveline tunnel wall to prevent damage.

✳✳ WARNING

Ensure that the clutch hydraulic hoses are positioned away from nearby vehicle components or vehicle damage may result.

69. Install the transmission to the J 42055, if removed.

70. SLOWLY slide the differential to the transmission.

71. Install the differential to transmission bolts and nuts. Tighten the differential to transmission bolts and nuts to 37 ft. lbs. (50 Nm).

72. Install the transmission shift rod to the transmission shift shaft.

73. Using a drift or punch, install the roll pin to retain the transmission shift rod to the shift shaft.

74. Slowly slide the driveline support assembly to the transmission, while guiding the transmission shift rod through the opening in the driveline support assembly.

75. Install the transmission to driveline support assembly bolts/studs. Tighten the transmission to driveline support assembly bolts/studs to 37 ft. lbs. (50 Nm).

76. Loosely install a rubber band onto the transmission shift rod and position just behind the shift rod clamp. The rubber band will be used to aid in installing the shift control assembly after the driveline has been installed.

77. Using a piece of masking tape, or similar tape which can be easily broken, affix the transmission shift rod to the driveline support assembly and position the rod just to the outside of the mounting boss used for the shift control. The tape is intended to keep the shift rod in position to aid in shift control installation after the driveline has been installed.

78. Position the chainfall, or equivalent, of a lift device in a way which will protect the rear exhaust hangers located on the driveline support assembly.

➡**The aid of an assistant will be necessary for the following steps until the driveline is installed into the vehicle.**

79. Using the lift device, raise the driveline off the workbench and position the driv-

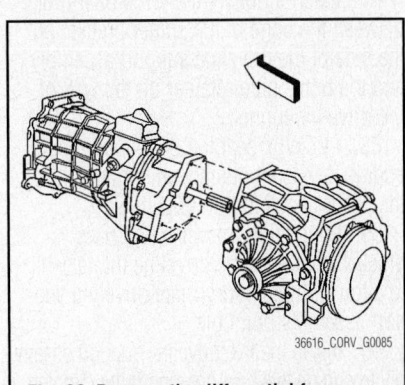

Fig. 38 Remove the differential from transmission

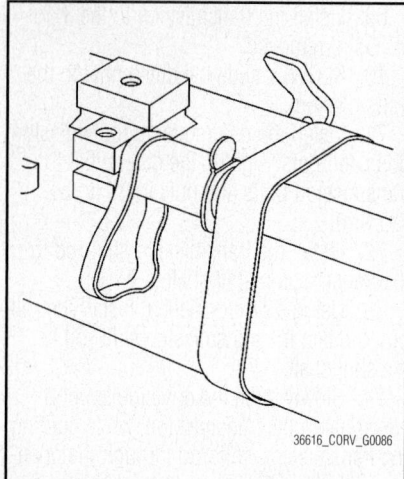

36616_CORV_G0086

Fig. 39 Install a rubber band onto the transmission shift rod

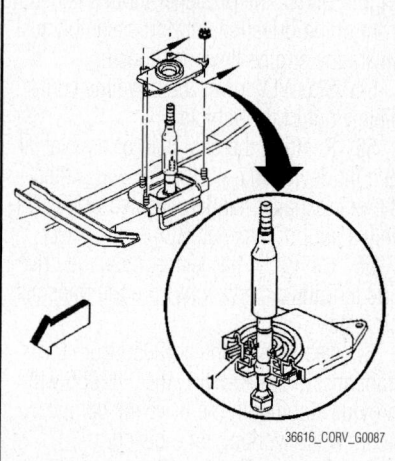

36616_CORV_G0087

Fig. 40 Install the shift control closeout boot

eline with the J 42055 onto a transmission jack.

80. Connect the J 42055 to the transmission jack.

81. Remove the lift device from the driveline.

82. Position the driveline under the vehicle.

83. Begin to raise the driveline at the approximate angle used during removal.

84. Position the wiring harness along the driveline support assembly and LOOSELY install the harness into the harness retaining slots.

85. Have an assistant guide the front of the driveline so the propeller input shaft is just to the rear of the engine flywheel housing, then raise the driveline to the PROPER HEIGHT and the PROPER ANGLE to install to the engine.

86. Have an assistant begin to insert the propeller input shaft into the clutch driven plate hub while maintaining the proper angle of the driveline; if necessary, use a screwdriver to rotate the shaft slightly to bring the splines into alignment.

87. Insert a putty knife, or similar tool, between the edge of the shifter bracket on the side of the driveline support assembly and the brake pipe retainer on the wall of the driveline tunnel.

88. SLOWLY seat the driveline to the engine flywheel housing while maintaining the proper angle of the driveline.

89. Reposition the wiring harness bracket from near the driveline tunnel wall to align with the appropriate driveline support assembly bolt hole.

90. Install the five driveline support assembly to engine flywheel housing bolts. Tighten the driveline support assembly to engine flywheel housing bolts to 37 ft. lbs. (50 Nm).

91. Install the wiring harness to the wiring harness retainer along the top of the transmission.

92. SLOWLY raise the driveline to approximately 2 in. (5 cm) BELOW the final installed height.

93. Connect the transmission fluid temperature sensor electrical connector, if equipped.

94. Connect the gear select (skip shift) solenoid electrical connector.

95. Connect the reverse lockout solenoid electrical connector.

96. Connect the backup lamp switch electrical connector.

97. Connect the wiring harness clip to the top of the differential.

98. Connect the wiring harness retainer to the stud at the differential rear cover.

99. Connect the VSS electrical connector.

100. Slowly raise the driveline to final installation height.

101. Remove the putty knife, if still in position.

102. Remove the jack which supported the rear of the engine.

103. Remove the tie-off retainers from the axle shafts.

104. CAREFULLY align and seat the axle shafts to the differential.

105. Install the Transmission mount to the differential.

106. Install the Transmission mount nuts. Tighten the Transmission mount nuts to 37 ft. lbs. (50 Nm).

107. With the aid of an assistant, begin to raise the rear suspension crossmember (still firmly attached to a transmission jack), to the vehicle frame rails.

108. Guide the rear suspension crossmember alignment pins into the alignment holes in the vehicle frame rails, and guide the Transmission mount studs into the mounting holes in the crossmember, then raise the crossmember to seat to the frame rails.

109. Using ONLY HAND TOOLS, install NEW rear suspension crossmember mounting nuts. Tighten the rear suspension crossmember mounting nuts to 81 ft. lbs. (110 Nm).

110. Remove the transmission jack from the rear suspension crossmember.

111. Release the J 42055 from the transmission, then remove the J 42055 and transmission jack.

112. Install the Transmission mount to rear suspension crossmember nuts (3). Tighten the Transmission mount to rear suspension crossmember nuts to 37 ft. lbs. (50 Nm).

113. Install the differential to transmission lower nut. Tighten the differential to transmission lower nut to 37 ft. lbs. (50 Nm).

114. Connect the wiring harness and brake pipe clip retainers to the rear suspension crossmember.

115. Support the lower control arm with a straight jack.

116. Connect the lower ball joint to the suspension knuckle.

117. Install the shock absorber lower mounting bolt. Tighten the rear shock absorber lower mounting bolt to 162 ft. lbs. (220 Nm).

118. Connect the outer tie rod end to the suspension knuckle.

119. Remove the straight jack from the suspension control arm.

120. Repeat steps 46 through 50 for the other side of the vehicle.

121. Remove the J 33432-A, transverse spring compressor.

122. Carefully pull the wiring harness down into the L-shaped brackets along the driveline support assembly, align the harness retainer (locator) to the hole in the forward bracket, then secure in place.

➡️**DO NOT rely on an audible click or a visual verification of the clutch hydraulic hose quick connect fitting connection.**

123. Install the hose retaining clip then connect the clutch actuator cylinder hose to the clutch master cylinder hose. Push together the clutch hydraulic hose quick connect fittings, then pull back on the fittings to verify engagement.

124. Check the clutch hydraulic hoses for twists or kinks.

125. Install the clutch actuator cylinder hose to the hose retaining clip below the power brake booster.

126. Install the floor panel tunnel reinforcement.

127. Remove the tie-off retainers from the muffler assemblies.

128. Install the intermediate pipe.

129. Install the rear tire and wheel assemblies.

130. Check and, if necessary, add transmission fluid.

131. Lower the vehicle.

132. Connect the clutch master cylinder pushrod to the clutch pedal.

133. Install the clutch master cylinder pushrod retainer.

134. Install the left I/P lower insulator panel.

135. Grasp the transmission shift rod and pull up to break the masking tape installed earlier to maintain position during installation.

136. Stretch the rubber band, while still installed onto the transmission shift rod, over the rear stud on top of the driveline tunnel to aid in shift control installation.

137. Install the shift control assembly.

138. Break and remove the rubber band.

139. Install the shift control closeout boot. Check that the closeout boot fully seats to the shift control lever seal and the base of the shift control assembly.

140. Install the shift control closeout boot retaining nuts. Tighten the shift control closeout boot retaining nuts to 106 inch lbs. (12 Nm).

141. Install the shift control boot and knob.

142. Install the console:
   a. Position the console assembly.
   b. Connect the electrical connectors.
   c. Install the console compartment fillers, bolt, and nuts. Tighten the bolt to 106 inch lbs. (12 Nm), and the nuts to 88 inch lbs. (10 Nm).
   d. Install the instrument panel accessory trim plate and center console trim plate.

143. Connect the negative battery cable.

144. Tighten the negative battery cable bolt to 11 ft. lbs. (15 Nm).

145. Program the transmitters.

146. Bleed the clutch hydraulic system.

CLUTCH DRIVEN DISC & PRESSURE PLATE

REMOVAL & INSTALLATION

See Figures 41 through 43.

1. Before servicing the vehicle, refer to the Precautions Section.

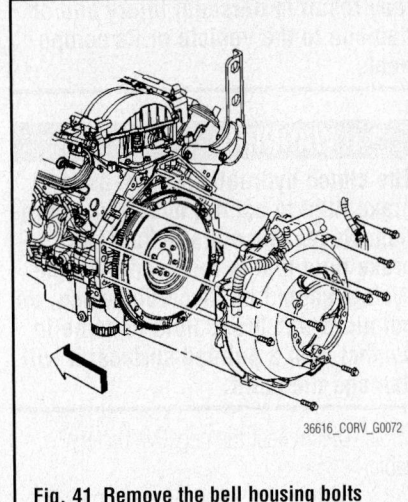

Fig. 41 Remove the bell housing bolts

Fig. 42 Clutch assembly removal

2. Disconnect the negative battery cable.

3. Raise and suitably support the vehicle.

4. Remove the driveline support assembly with the transaxle. Refer to Automatic Transmission Removal & Installation.

5. Remove the bell housing bolts. The upper bolts can be accessed by lowering the engine cradle approximately 1 in. (25 mm) and tipping the engine back.

6. Mark the clutch pressure plate and flywheel with adjacent alignment marks before removing the pressure plate.

7. Loosen the visible clutch pressure plate bolts.

8. Rotate the engine flywheel.

9. Repeat the above 2 steps all the bolts have been loosened.

10. Remove the visible clutch pressure plate bolts.

11. Rotate the engine flywheel.

12. Repeat the above 2 steps until all the bolts have been removed.

13. Remove the clutch pressure plate bolts from the flywheel.

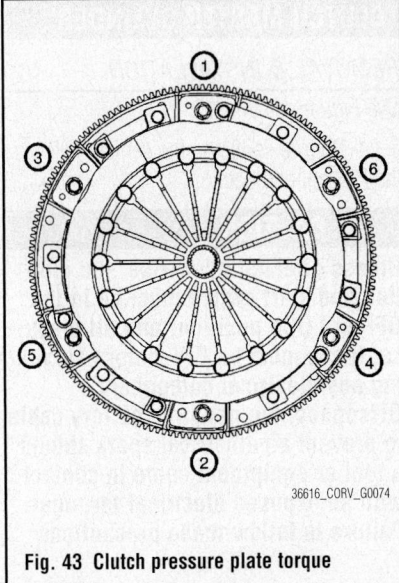

Fig. 43 Clutch pressure plate torque sequence

14. Remove the clutch pressure plate and the clutch driven plate.

To install:

15. Inspect the clutch pressure plate and the clutch driven plate for wear or damage. Repair or replace as necessary.

16. Inspect the engine flywheel. Refer to Flywheel Removal & Installation in the Engine Mechanical Section.

17. Adjust the clutch pressure plate, if necessary.

18. If reusing the clutch pressure plate, align the previously created mark on the flywheel with the alignment mark on the pressure plate.

19. Install the clutch driven plate and clutch pressure plate to the engine flywheel.

20. Install the visible clutch pressure plate bolts finger tight.

21. Rotate the engine flywheel.

22. Repeat previous steps until all the bolts are installed finger-tight.

23. Using the J-38836, align the clutch driven plate to the pilot bearing.
   a. Install J-42386-A and bolts. Use one M10 1.5 X 120 mm and one M10 1.5 X 45 mm bolt for proper tool operation. Tighten the J-42386-A bolts to 37 ft. lbs. (50 Nm).

24. Tighten the clutch pressure plate bolts in sequence and evenly over 3 increments with the fourth increment to 52 ft. lbs. (70 Nm).

25. Install the bell housing bolts and tighten to 37 ft. lbs. (50 Nm).

26. Install the driveline support assembly with the transaxle.

27. Connect the negative battery cable.

28. Lower the vehicle.

CLUTCH MASTER CYLINDER

REMOVAL & INSTALLATION

See Figures 44 and 45.

1. Before servicing the vehicle, refer to the Precautions Section.

✳ CAUTION

Unless directed otherwise, the ignition and start switch must be in the OFF or LOCK position, and all electrical loads must be OFF before servicing any electrical component. Disconnect the negative battery cable to prevent an electrical spark should a tool or equipment come in contact with an exposed electrical terminal. Failure to follow these precautions

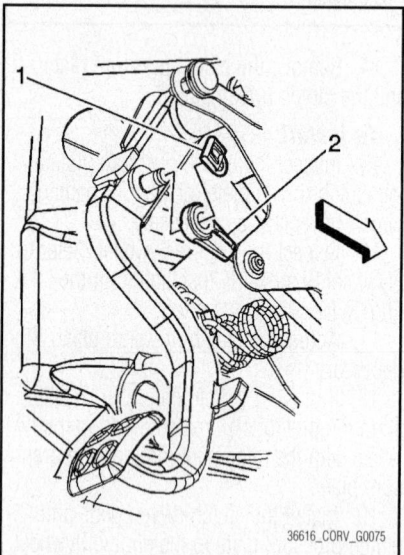

Fig. 44 Clutch master cylinder rod (2) and rod retainer (1)

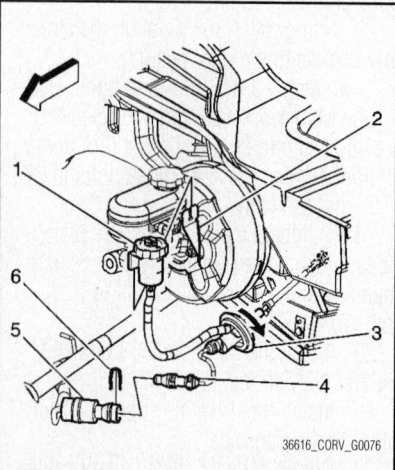

Fig. 45 Clutch master cylinder removal

may result in personal injury and/or damage to the vehicle or its components.

✳ WARNING

The clutch hydraulic system uses brake fluid to control hydraulic operation. Never reuse brake fluid. Any brake fluid that is removed from the system should be discarded. Also, do not allow any brake fluid to come in contact with a painted surface; it will damage the paint.

2. Disconnect the negative battery cable.
3. Remove the left instrument panel lower insulator panel.
4. Remove the clutch master cylinder rod retainer (1).
5. Remove the clutch master cylinder rod (2) from the clutch pedal.
6. Remove the windshield washer solvent container.
7. Raise and suitably support the vehicle.
8. Remove the clutch actuator cylinder hose from the hose retaining clip, under the brake master cylinder.
9. Remove the clutch hose connection retaining clip (6).
10. Separate the clutch hose (5) from the clutch master cylinder connection (4).
11. Protect both hose coupling ends from dirt and damage.
12. Lower the vehicle. Leave the vehicle on the hoist.
13. Remove the clutch master cylinder reservoir (1) from the reservoir bracket (2).
14. Rotate the clutch master cylinder 45 degrees.
15. Release the clutch master cylinder (3) from the dash panel.
16. Remove the clutch master cylinder (3) and reservoir (1) from the vehicle.

To install:

17. Install the clutch master cylinder and the reservoir into position.
18. Install the clutch master cylinder to the dash panel.
   a. Orientate the clutch master cylinder at a 45 degree angle.
   b. Insert the clutch master cylinder into the dash panel.
   c. Rotate the master cylinder counterclockwise to secure. DO NOT over-rotate the master cylinder.
19. Install the clutch master cylinder reservoir to the reservoir bracket.
20. Install the windshield washer solvent container.

21. Raise the vehicle.
22. Install the clutch hose connection retaining clip.

➡ DO NOT rely on an audible click or a visual verification of the clutch hydraulic hose quick connect fitting connection.

23. Connect the clutch actuator cylinder hose to the clutch master cylinder hose. Push together the clutch hydraulic hose quick connect fittings, then pull back on the fittings to verify engagement.
24. Check the clutch hydraulic hoses for twists or kinks.
25. Install the clutch actuator cylinder hose to the hose retaining clip, under the brake master cylinder
26. Lower the vehicle.
27. Install the clutch master cylinder rod to the clutch pedal.
28. Install the clutch master cylinder rod retainer.
29. Install the left lower insulator panel.
30. Connect the negative battery cable.
31. Program the transmitters.
32. Bleed the clutch hydraulic system.

CLUTCH SLAVE CYLINDER

REMOVAL & INSTALLATION

See Figures 44 through 47.

✳ WARNING

The clutch hydraulic system uses brake fluid to control hydraulic operation. Never reuse brake fluid. Any brake fluid that is removed from the system should be discarded. Also, do not allow any brake fluid to come in contact with a painted surface; it will damage the paint.

1. Disconnect the negative battery cable.

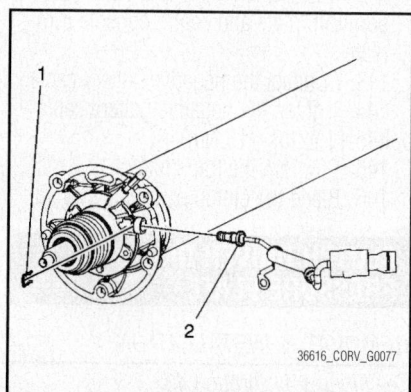

Fig. 46 Clutch hose (2) and hose connection retaining clip (1)

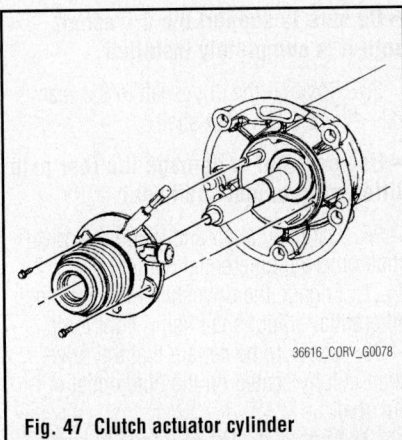

Fig. 47 Clutch actuator cylinder

❊❊ CAUTION

Unless directed otherwise, the ignition and start switch must be in the OFF or LOCK position, and all electrical loads must be OFF before servicing any electrical component. Disconnect the negative battery cable to prevent an electrical spark should a tool or equipment come in contact with an exposed electrical terminal. Failure to follow these precautions may result in personal injury and/or damage to the vehicle or its components.

2. Remove the left instrument panel lower insulator panel.

3. Remove the clutch master cylinder rod retainer (1).

4. Remove the clutch master cylinder rod (2) from the clutch pedal.

5. Remove the windshield washer solvent container.

6. Raise and suitably support the vehicle.

7. Remove the clutch hose connection retaining clip (1).

8. Separate the clutch hose (3) from the clutch master cylinder connection (2).

9. Protect both hose coupling ends from dirt and damage.

10. Remove the driveline support assembly and Transmission from the vehicle.

11. Remove the clutch hose connection retaining clip (1).

12. Separate the clutch hose (2) from the clutch actuator cylinder.

13. Protect both hose coupling ends from dirt and damage.

14. Remove the clutch actuator cylinder mounting bolts.

15. Remove the clutch actuator cylinder from the driveline support assembly.

To install:

16. Install the clutch actuator cylinder into position on the driveline support assembly.

17. Install the actuator cylinder mounting bolts and tighten to 106 inch lbs. (12 Nm).

18. Install the clutch hose connection retaining clip.

➡**DO NOT rely on an audible click or a visual verification of the clutch hydraulic hose quick connect fitting connection.**

19. Connect the clutch hose to the clutch actuator cylinder. Firmly push the clutch hydraulic hose to the clutch actuator cylinder, then pull back on the fittings to verify engagement.

20. Install the driveline support assembly and Transmission to the vehicle.

21. Install the clutch hose connection retaining clip.

➡**DO NOT rely on an audible click or a visual verification of the clutch hydraulic hose quick connect fitting connection.**

22. Connect the clutch actuator cylinder hose to the clutch master cylinder hose. Push together the clutch hydraulic hose quick connect fittings, then pull back on the fittings to verify engagement.

23. Check the hydraulic hoses for twists of kinks.

24. Install the clutch actuator cylinder hose to the hose retaining clip, under the brake master cylinder.

25. Lower the vehicle.

26. Install the windshield washer solvent container.

27. Install the clutch master cylinder rod to the clutch pedal.

28. Install the clutch master cylinder rod retainer.

29. Install the left lower insulator panel.

30. Connect the negative battery cable.

31. Program the transmitters.

32. Bleed the clutch hydraulic system.

CLUTCH HYDRAULIC SYSTEM BLEEDING

❊❊ WARNING

DO NOT use fluid which has been bled from a hydraulic clutch system, in order to fill the clutch master cylinder reservoir, due to the possibility that the fluid may be aerated, have too much moisture content, or be contaminated and may cause system or vehicle damage.

Bleeding the hydraulic clutch system is necessary whenever the level of fluid in the clutch master cylinder reservoir has been allowed to fall so low that air has been drawn into the master cylinder.

1. Before servicing the vehicle, refer to the Precautions Section.

2. Clean all dirt and debris from the clutch master cylinder cap to ensure that no foreign substances will enter the system.

3. Remove the clutch master cylinder reservoir cap with diaphragm.

4. Fill the clutch master cylinder with clean clutch hydraulic fluid.

5. Raise and safely support the vehicle with an assistant in it.

6. Remove the catalytic converters. Refer to Catalytic Converter Removal & Installation in the Engine Mechanical Section.

7. Remove the floor panel tunnel reinforcement.

8. Have an assistant depress the clutch pedal fully and hold.

9. Loosen the bleeder screw on the clutch actuator cylinder to purge air.

10. Tighten the screw.

11. Release the clutch pedal.

12. Repeat the prior four steps until all air is completely evacuated. Check and refill the clutch master cylinder reservoir with clutch hydraulic fluid as necessary in order to prevent air from being drawn through the clutch master cylinder

13. Fill the clutch master cylinder reservoir with clutch hydraulic fluid.

14. Install the floor panel tunnel reinforcement.

15. Install the catalytic converters.

16. Lower the vehicle.

REAR HALFSHAFTS

REMOVAL & INSTALLATION

See Figures 48 through 51.

1. Before servicing the vehicle, refer to the Precautions Section.

2. Raise and suitably support the vehicle.

3. Remove the tire and wheel assembly.

4. Insert a drift or punch into the brake rotor cooling fins and against the brake caliper to prevent the wheel hub and bearing from turning.

5. Remove the spindle nut retaining the rear wheel driveshaft to the hub.

6. Remove the drift or punch.

➡**Do not loosen the outer tie rod jam nut.**

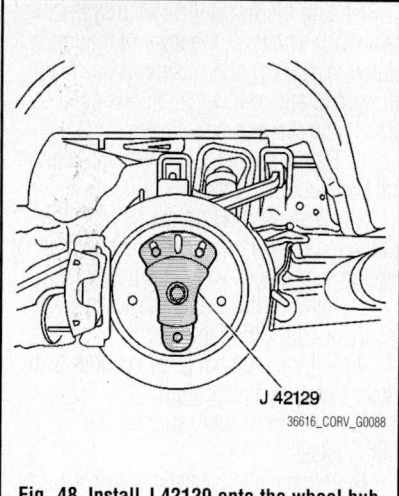

Fig. 48 Install J 42129 onto the wheel hub

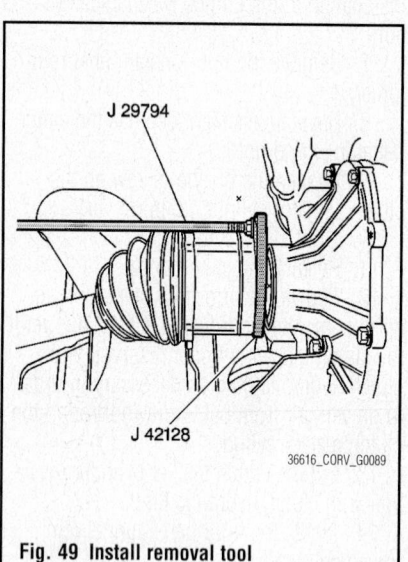

Fig. 49 Install removal tool

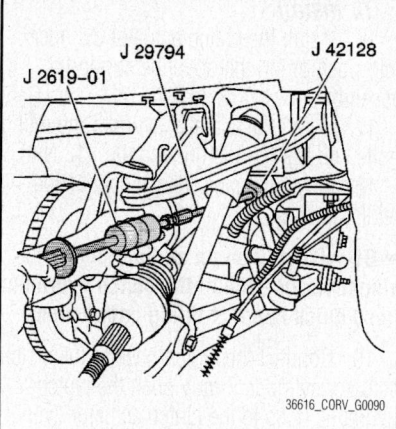

Fig. 50 Disengage the driveshaft from the rear axle differential

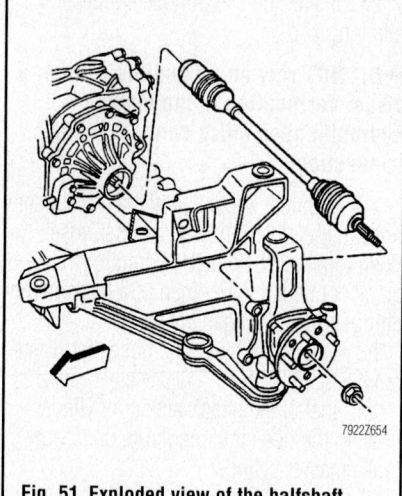

Fig. 51 Exploded view of the halfshaft mounting

7. Separate the outer tie rod end from the knuckle and reposition the tie rod toward the rear of the vehicle.

8. Disconnect the wheel speed sensor electrical connector.

9. Remove the parking brake cable from the bracket.

10. Disconnect the parking brake cable from the parking brake lever and reposition the cable toward the rear.

11. Remove the parking brake cable from the bracket and reposition toward the rear.

12. Install J 42129 onto the wheel hub and secure with wheel nuts.

13. Begin to disengage the driveshaft from the wheel hub and bearing.

14. Remove the lower shock nut and bolt.

15. Separate the upper ball joint from the suspension knuckle.

16. Disengage the driveshaft completely from the wheel hub and bearing.

➡**Be sure to support the driveshaft until it is removed.**

17. Support the driveshaft.

18. Support the suspension knuckle and upper control arm and reposition the knuckle toward the front of the vehicle.

19. Assemble the J 42128, J 29794, and J 2619-01.

20. Install the J 42128 evenly onto the rear beveled surface of the driveshaft inner joint housing.

21. Disengage the driveshaft from the rear axle differential using the J 42128, J 29794, and J 2619-01, then remove the tool assembly.

22. Remove the driveshaft from the vehicle.

23. Remove J 42129 from the wheel hub.

To install:

24. Clean and inspect the journal on the axle shaft prior to installation.

➡**Be sure to support the driveshaft until it is completely installed.**

25. Position the driveshaft to the rear axle differential output shaft.

➡**Use care not to damage the rear axle differential output shaft seal.**

26. Carefully align and guide the driveshaft onto the differential output shaft.

27. Engage the driveshaft fully onto the differential output shaft using light force.

28. Check to be certain that the driveshaft is fully seated on the differential output shaft.

29. Align and carefully guide the driveshaft into the wheel hub and bearing.

30. Connect the upper ball joint to the suspension knuckle.

31. Install the lower shock bolt and nut.

32. Connect the parking brake cable to the parking brake lever.

33. Install the parking brake cable into the bracket.

34. Connect the wheel speed sensor electrical connector.

35. Connect the outer tie rod end to the suspension knuckle.

36. Insert a drift or punch into the brake rotor cooling fins and against the caliper to prevent the wheel hub and bearing from turning.

37. Begin to install the driveshaft retaining nut onto the driveshaft by hand.

38. Slowly tighten the nut to draw the driveshaft to the wheel hub and bearing. Tighten the drive axle spindle nut to 151 ft. lbs. (205 Nm).

39. Remove the drift or punch.

40. Install the tire and wheel assembly.

41. Lower the vehicle.

OUTPUT SHAFT SEAL

REMOVAL & INSTALLATION

See Figure 52.

1. Before servicing the vehicle, refer to the Precautions Section.

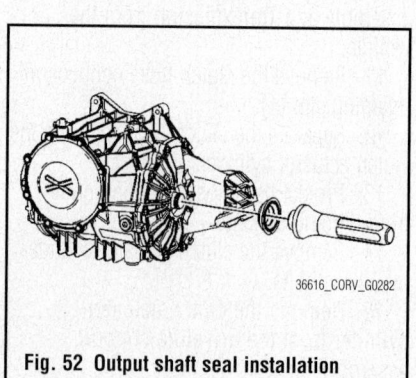

Fig. 52 Output shaft seal installation

2. Raise and suitably support the vehicle.

3. Remove the appropriate rear tire and wheel assembly.

4. Remove the appropriate driveshaft.

5. Remove the differential output shaft seal.

To install:

6. Using a seal installer, install the differential output shaft seal.

7. Install the driveshaft.

8. Install the rear tire and wheel assembly.

9. Lower the vehicle.

ENGINE COOLING

ENGINE FAN

REMOVAL & INSTALLATION

See Figure 53.

1. Before servicing the vehicle, refer to the Precautions Section.

> ✳✳ **CAUTION**
>
> **An electric fan under the hood can start up even when the engine is not running and can injure you. Keep hands, clothing and tools away from any underhood electric fan.**

> ✳✳ **CAUTION**
>
> **To help avoid personal injury or damage to the vehicle, a bent, cracked, or damaged fan blade or housing should always be replaced.**

> ✳✳ **CAUTION**
>
> **Unless directed otherwise, the ignition and start switch must be in the OFF or LOCK position, and all electrical loads must be OFF before servicing any electrical component. Disconnect the negative battery cable to prevent an electrical spark should a tool or equipment come in contact with an exposed electrical terminal. Failure to follow these precautions may result in personal injury and/or damage to the vehicle or its components.**

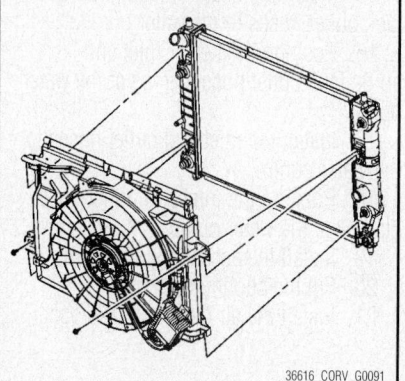

36616_CORV_G0091

Fig. 53 Cooling fan and shroud

2. Remove the radiator support.

3. Disconnect the engine wiring harness from the cooling fan shroud.

4. Disconnect the surge tank outlet hose from the retaining clips on the cooling fan shroud and position aside.

5. Raise and support the vehicle.

6. Remove the stabilizer bar.

7. Disconnect the cooling fan electrical connector.

8. Vehicles equipped with transmission fluid cooler, disconnect the lower transmission oil cooler line from the radiator.

9. Vehicles equipped with an engine oil cooler, disconnect the upper and lower engine oil cooler pipes.

10. Remove the cooling fan shroud retaining bolts.

11. Remove the cooling fan and shroud.

To install:

➡ **Ensure the cooling fan and shroud is properly seated on the radiator.**

12. Install the cooling fan and shroud.

13. Install the cooling fan shroud retaining bolts and tighten to 80 inch lbs. (9 Nm).

14. Vehicles equipped with transmission fluid cooler, connect the lower transmission oil cooler line to the radiator.

15. Vehicles equipped with an engine oil cooler, connect the upper and lower engine oil cooler pipes.

16. Connect the cooling fan electrical connector.

17. Install the stabilizer bar.

18. Lower the vehicle.

19. Connect the surge tank outlet hose to the retaining clips on the cooling fan shroud.

20. Connect the engine wiring harness to the cooling fan shroud.

21. Install the radiator support.

RADIATOR

REMOVAL & INSTALLATION

See Figure 54.

1. Before servicing the vehicle, refer to the Precautions Section.

2. Recover the refrigerant from the A/C system.

3. Drain the cooling system.

4. Remove the A/C condenser.

5. Disengage tension on the radiator inlet hose clamp at the radiator using J 38185 Hose Clamp Pliers.

6. Disconnect the radiator inlet hose from the radiator.

➡ **Lift up on the cooling fan and shroud assembly to disengage the tabs from the radiator slots.**

7. Remove the cooling fan and shroud assembly from the radiator.

8. Disengage tension and reposition the surge tank inlet hose clamp at the radiator.

9. Disconnect the surge tank inlet hose from the radiator.

10. Vehicles equipped with a transmission oil cooler, disconnect the upper transmission oil cooler line from the radiator.

11. Vehicles equipped with a engine oil cooler, disconnect the upper engine oil cooler line from the radiator.

12. Raise and support the vehicle.

13. Disengage tension on the radiator outlet hose clamp at the radiator using the J 38185 Hose Clamp Pliers

14. Disconnect the radiator outlet hose from the radiator.

15. Vehicles equipped with a transmission oil cooler, disconnect the lower transmission oil cooler line from the radiator.

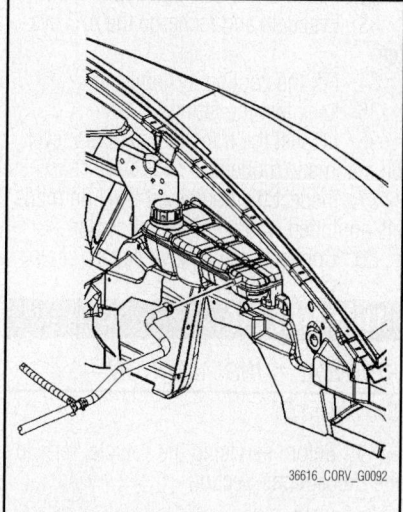

36616_CORV_G0092

Fig. 54 Disconnect the surge tank inlet hose

16. Vehicles equipped a with engine oil cooler, disconnect the lower engine oil cooler line from the radiator.

17. Remove the radiator from the vehicle.

To install:

18. Install the radiator to the vehicle.

19. Raise the vehicle.

20. Vehicles equipped with a engine oil cooler, connect the lower engine oil cooler line to the radiator.

21. Vehicles equipped with a transmission oil cooler, connect the lower transmission oil cooler line to the radiator.

22. Connect the radiator outlet hose to the radiator.

23. Engage tension on the radiator outlet hose clamp at the radiator.

24. Lower the vehicle.

25. Vehicle equipped with a transmission oil cooler, connect the upper transmission oil cooler line to the radiator.

26. Vehicles equipped with a engine oil cooler, connect the upper engine oil cooler line to the radiator.

27. Connect the surge tank inlet hose to the radiator.

28. Engage tension on the surge tank inlet hose clamp at the radiator using J 38185 Hose Clamp Pliers.

➡Lift up on the cooling fan and shroud assembly and engage the tabs to the radiator slots.

29. Install the cooling fan and shroud assembly to the radiator.

30. Connect the radiator inlet hose to the radiator.

31. Engage tension on the radiator inlet hose clamp at the radiator using J 38185 Hose Clamp Pliers

32. Install the A/C condenser.

33. Evacuate and recharge the A/C system.

34. Fill the cooling system.

35. Leak test the fittings.

36. Inspect the transmission fluid level on automatic models.

37. Inspect the engine oil level on models equipped with a engine oil cooler.

38. Connect the negative battery cable.

THERMOSTAT

REMOVAL & INSTALLATION

See Figure 55.

1. Before servicing the vehicle, refer to the Precautions Section.

Fig. 55 Thermostat housing mounting location

➡The engine cooling system thermostat and water pump will not function correctly if oil is present in the cooling system. The cooling system MUST be flushed, the water pump and thermostat replaced if oil is found in the cooling system

2. Drain the cooling system.

3. Reposition the outlet hose clamp at the water pump inlet.

4. Remove the outlet hose from the water pump inlet.

5. Remove the water pump inlet bolts.

6. Remove the water pump inlet.

7. The O-ring seal is integral to the thermostat housing.

8. Remove the thermostat housing.

To install:

9. Install the thermostat housing.

10. Ensure the thermostat housing has an O-ring seal and is in the groove correctly.

11. Install the water pump inlet (with thermostat).

12. Install the water pump inlet bolts and tighten to 11 ft. lbs. (15 Nm).

13. Install the outlet hose to the water pump inlet.

14. Position the outlet hose clamp at the water outlet.

15. Fill the cooling system.

16. Start the vehicle and check for leaks.

WATER PUMP

REMOVAL & INSTALLATION

See Figure 56.

1. Before servicing the vehicle, refer to the Precautions Section.

Fig. 56 Exploded view of the water pump mounting assembly

2. Remove the air cleaner intake duct.

3. Remove the accessory drive belt. Refer to Accessory Drive Belt Removal & Installation in the Engine Mechanical Section.

4. Drain the cooling system.

5. Reposition the inlet and outlet hose clamps at the water pump.

6. Remove the inlet and outlet hoses from the water pump.

7. Reposition the heater inlet and surge tank outlet hose clamps at the water pump.

8. Remove the heater inlet and surge tank outlet hoses from the water pump.

9. Remove the water pump bolts.

10. Remove the water pump.

11. Remove the water pump gaskets.

12. Clean and inspect the water pump.

To install:

13. Install the water pump and gaskets to the engine block.

14. Install the water pump bolts. Tighten the water pump bolts a first pass to 11 ft. lbs. (15 Nm). Tighten the water pump bolts a final pass to 22 ft. lbs. (30 Nm).

15. Install the heater inlet and surge tank outlet hoses to the water pump.

16. Position the heater inlet and surge tank outlet hose clamps at the water pump.

17. Install the inlet and outlet hoses to the water pump.

18. Position the inlet and outlet hose clamps at the water pump.

19. Install the accessory drive belt.

20. Fill the cooling system.

21. Install the air cleaner intake duct.

ENGINE ELECTRICAL

CHARGING SYSTEM

ALTERNATOR

REMOVAL & INSTALLATION

See Figures 57 and 58.

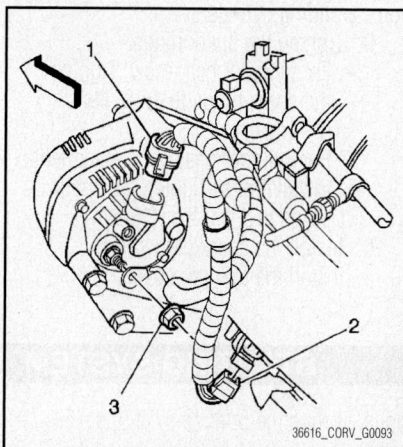

Fig. 57 Disconnect the alternator electrical connector (1 and 2) and battery feed terminal nut (3)

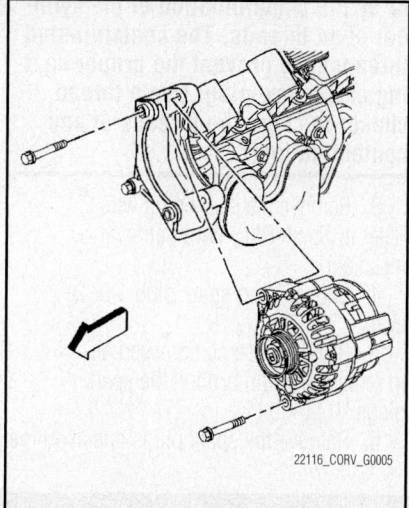

Fig. 58 Remove alternator as shown

1. Before servicing the vehicle, refer to the Precautions Section.
2. Remove the drive belt. Refer to Accessory Drive Belt Removal & Installation in the Engine Mechanical Section.

3. Disconnect the negative battery cable.
4. Disconnect the alternator electrical connector (1 and 2).
5. Remove the battery feed terminal nut (3) from the alternator.
6. Remove the battery feed cable.
7. Remove the alternator mounting bolts.
8. Remove the alternator.

To install:

9. Position the alternator on the mounting bracket.
10. Install the alternator bolts and tighten to 37 ft. lbs. (50 Nm).
11. Connect the alternator electrical connector.
12. Install the battery feed cable.
13. Install the battery feed terminal nut and tighten to 9 ft. lbs. (13 Nm).
14. Install the drive belt.
15. Connect the negative battery cable.

ENGINE ELECTRICAL

IGNITION SYSTEM

FIRING ORDERS

See Figure 59.

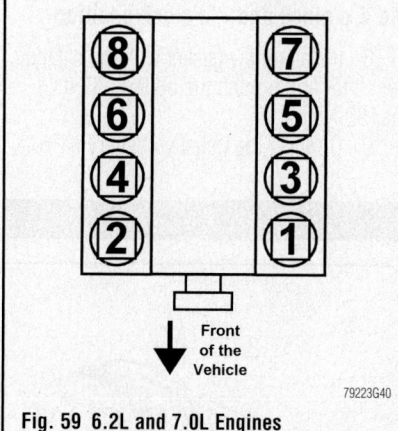

**Fig. 59 6.2L and 7.0L Engines
Firing order: 1–8–7–2–6–5–4–3**

IGNITION COIL

REMOVAL & INSTALLATION

See Figure 60.

1. Before servicing the vehicle, refer to the Precautions Section.
2. Disconnect the negative battery cable.
3. Remove the intake manifold sight shield.

Fig. 60 Ignition coil removal and installation

4. Remove the ignition coil mounting bolts.
5. Disconnect the ignition coil electrical connector.
6. Remove the ignition coil.

To install:

7. Installation is the reverse of removal procedure. Tighten the ignition coil mounting bolts to 106 inch lbs. (12 Nm).

IGNITION TIMING

ADJUSTMENT

Ignition timing is controlled by the ECM; adjustment is not necessary or possible.

SPARK PLUGS

REMOVAL & INSTALLATION

See Figure 61.

1. Before servicing the vehicle, refer to the Precautions Section.
2. Remove the fuel rail covers.

✳✳ WARNING

Allow the engine to cool before removing the spark plugs. Attempting to remove the spark plugs from a hot engine may cause the plug threads to seize, causing damage to cylinder head threads.

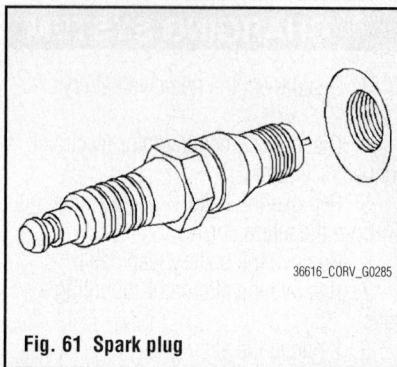

Fig. 61 Spark plug

✳✳ WARNING

Clean the spark plug recess area before removing the spark plug. Failure to do so could result in engine damage because of dirt or foreign material entering the cylinder head, or by the contamination of the cylinder head threads. The contaminated threads may prevent the proper seating of the new plug. Use a thread chaser to clean the threads of any contamination.

3. Remove the spark plug wires. Refer to Spark Plug Wire Removal & Installation.

4. Loosen each spark plug 1 or 2 turns.

5. Brush or use compressed air to remove any dirt around the spark plugs.

6. Remove the spark plugs one at a time and place each plug in a tray marked with the corresponding cylinder numbers.

To install:

7. Inspect each spark plug gap. Adjust each plug as needed. Spark plug gap: 0.040 in. (1.016 mm).

8. Hand start the spark plugs in the corresponding cylinders.

9. Tighten the spark plugs:
- For cylinder head-new: Tighten the spark plugs to 15 ft. lbs. (20 Nm).
- For cylinder head-all subsequent installations: Tighten the spark plugs to 11 ft. lbs. (15 Nm).

10. Install the spark plug wires.
11. Install the fuel rail covers.

ENGINE ELECTRICAL

STARTER

REMOVAL & INSTALLATION

See Figure 62.

1. Before servicing the vehicle, refer to the Precautions Section.

2. Disconnect the negative battery cable.

3. Remove the catalytic converter for access. Refer to Catalytic Converter Removal & Installation in the Engine Mechanical Section.

4. Disconnect the electrical connectors from the starter.

5. Remove the starter mounting bolts and remove the starter assembly from the vehicle.

To install:

6. Position the starter motor to the engine block and secure with the mounting

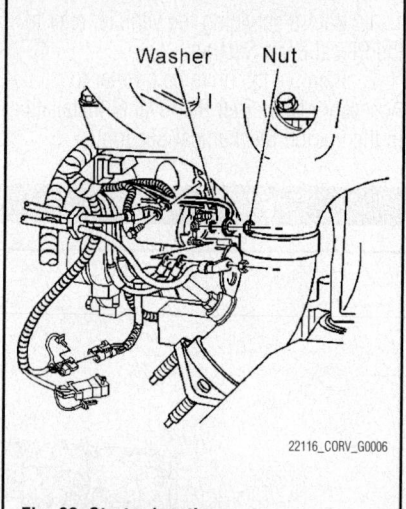

Fig. 62 Starter location

STARTING SYSTEM

bolts. Torque the bolts to 37 ft. lbs. (50 Nm).

7. Connect the starter electrical connectors as follows:

a. Install the starter motor S terminal washer and purple lead wire.

➡**Orient the purple lead wire to the 10 o'clock position when installing.**

b. Install the S terminal and tighten the S terminal nut to 71 inch lbs. (8 Nm).

➡**Orient gray and rust harness leads to the 6 o'clock and 7 o'clock position.**

8. Install a new gasket with the catalytic converter and tighten the bolts to 37 ft. lbs.(50 Nm).

9. Connect the negative battery cable.

ENGINE MECHANICAL

ACCESSORY DRIVE BELTS

ACCESSORY BELT ROUTING

See Figures 63 and 64.

INSPECTION

Inspect the drive belt for signs of glazing or cracking. A glazed belt will be perfectly smooth from slippage, while a good belt will have a slight texture of fabric visible. Cracks will usually start at the inner edge of the belt and run outward. All worn or damaged drive belts should be replaced immediately.

ADJUSTMENT

Belt tension is automatically adjusted by the drive belt tensioner.

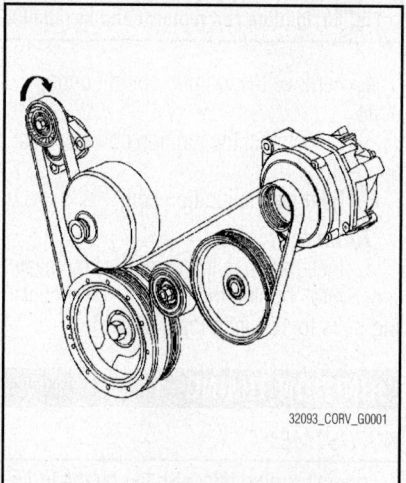

Fig. 63 Serpentine drive belt routing

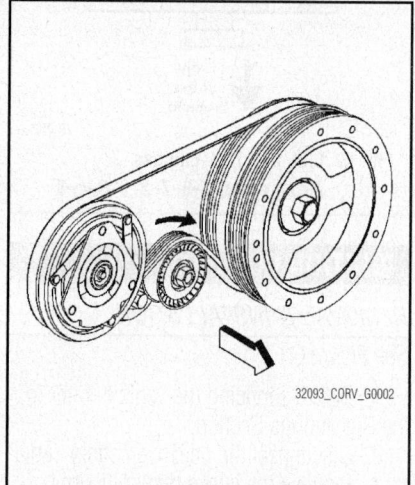

Fig. 64 Air conditioning belt routing

REMOVAL & INSTALLATION

Accessory Drive Belt

See Figure 65.

1. Before servicing the vehicle, refer to the Precautions Section.

➡ **Do not use belt dressing on the drive belt. Belt dressing causes the breakdown of the composition of the drive belt. Failure to follow this recommendation will damage the drive belt.**

2. Remove the air intake duct, if necessary.

3. Install the appropriate tool to the drive belt tensioner bolt.

4. Using the appropriate tool, rotate the drive belt tensioner clockwise to relieve the tension on the accessory drive belt.

5. Remove the accessory drive belt from the pulleys and tensioner.

6. Slowly release tension on the drive belt tensioner.

7. Remove the breaker bar and socket from the drive belt tensioner bolt.

8. Clean and inspect the drive belt surfaces of all the pulleys.

To install:

9. Route the accessory drive belt around all the pulleys except the water pump pulley and tensioner.

10. Install the appropriate tool to the drive belt tensioner.

11. Using the appropriate tool, rotate the drive belt tensioner clockwise to relieve tension on the drive belt tensioner.

12. Install the accessory drive belt under the water pump pulley.

13. Install the accessory drive belt onto the drive belt tensioner.

14. Slowly release the tension.

15. Remove the tool from the drive belt tensioner.

16. Install the air intake duct, if necessary.

17. Inspect the accessory drive belt for correct alignment.

A/C Drive Belt

See Figure 66.

1. Before servicing the vehicle, refer to the Precautions Section.

2. Remove the accessory drive belt. Refer to Accessory Drive Belt Removal & Installation.

3. Raise the vehicle.

4. Using the appropriate tool, rotate the Air Conditioning (A/C) belt tensioner clockwise in order to relieve tension on the belt.

5. Remove the A/C belt from the pulleys.

6. Slowly release the tension on the A/C belt tensioner.

7. Remove the wrench and or socket from the A/C belt tensioner.

8. Clean and inspect the belt surfaces of all the pulleys.

To install:

9. Install the A/C belt around the crankshaft balancer.

10. Using the appropriate wrench or socket, rotate the A/C belt tensioner clockwise in order to relieve tension on the belt.

11. Rotate the A/C belt tensioner clockwise in order to relieve tension on the belt.

12. Install the A/C belt over the idler pulley.

13. Install the A/C belt around the A/C compressor pulley.

14. Slowly release the tension on the A/C belt tensioner.

15. Remove the appropriate tool from the A/C belt tensioner.

16. Inspect the A/C belt for proper installation and alignment.

17. Lower the vehicle.

18. Install the accessory drive belt.

CAMSHAFT AND VALVE LIFTERS

REMOVAL & INSTALLATION

See Figures 67 through 73.

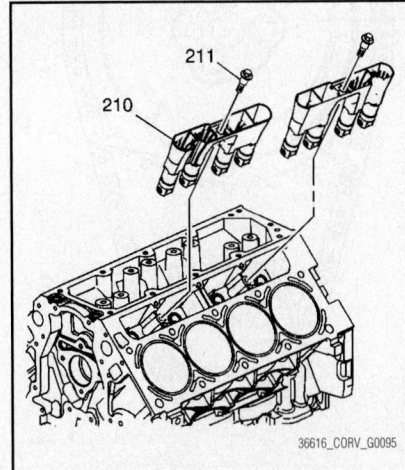

Fig. 67 Remove the guides (210) and guide bolts (211)

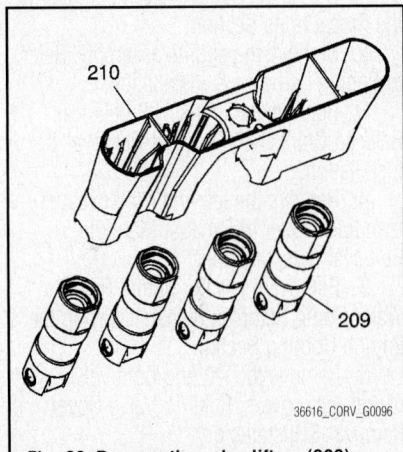

Fig. 68 Remove the valve lifters (209) from the guide (210)

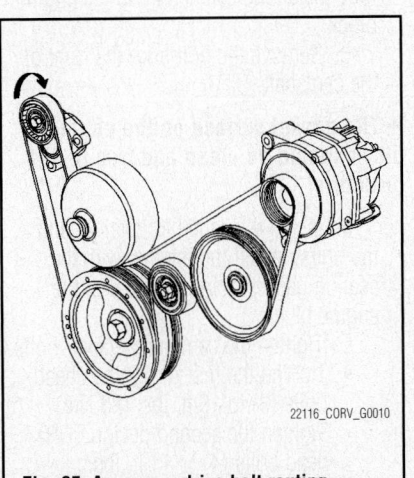

Fig. 65 Accessory drive belt routing

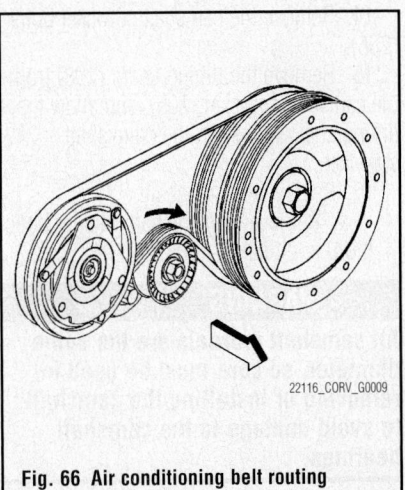

Fig. 66 Air conditioning belt routing

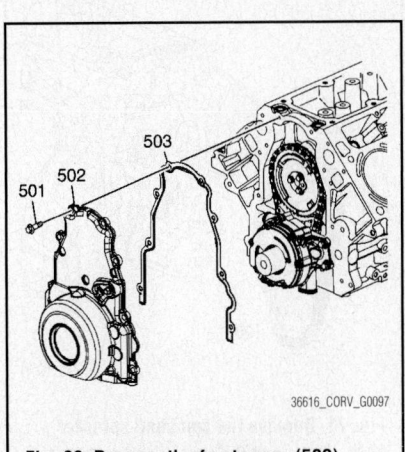

Fig. 69 Remove the front cover (502), bolts (501), and gasket (503)

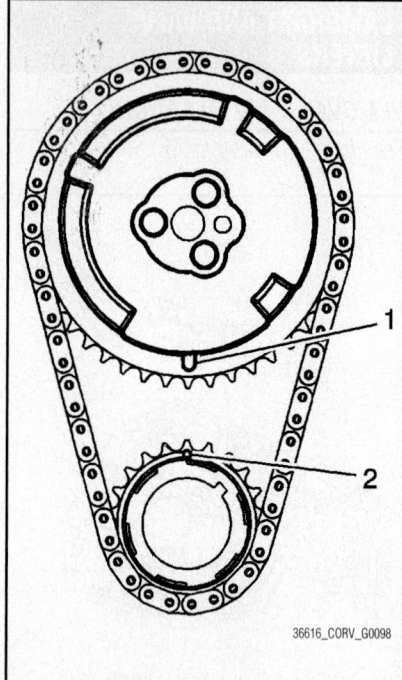

Fig. 70 Align the timing marks (1, 2)

1. Before servicing the vehicle, refer to the Precautions Section.

2. Remove the engine assembly. Refer to Engine Removal & Installation.

3. Remove the crankshaft balancer. Refer to Crankshaft Balancer Removal & Installation.

4. Remove the left and right exhaust manifolds Refer to Exhaust Manifold Removal & Installation.

5. Remove the water pump. Refer to Water Pump Removal & Installation in the Engine Cooling Section.

6. Remove the left and right valve rocker arm covers. Refer to Valve Cover Removal & Installation.

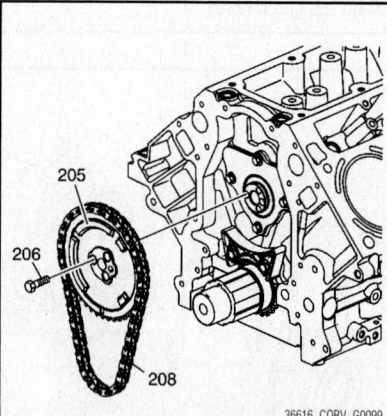

Fig. 71 Remove the camshaft sprocket bolts (206), and the timing chain (208) from the camshaft sprocket (205)

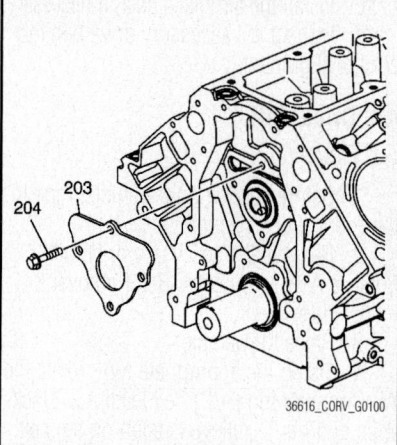

Fig. 72 Remove the camshaft retainer bolts (204) and retainer (203)

7. Remove the valve rocker arms and push rods. Refer to Valve Rocker Arm Removal & Installation.

8. Remove the left and right cylinder heads. Refer to Cylinder Head Removal & Installation.

9. Remove the valve lifters, as follows:
   a. Remove the guide bolts (211).
   b. Remove the guides (210) with lifters.
   c. Note the installed position of the guides. The notched area of the guide is to align with the locating tab on the block.
   d. Remove the valve lifters (209) from the guide (210).
   e. Organize or mark the components so they can be installed in the same location from which they were removed.

10. Remove the oil pan-to-front cover bolts.

11. Remove the front cover bolts (501).

12. Remove the front cover (502) and gasket (503). Discard the old gasket.

13. Rotate the engine in order to align the timing marks (1, 2).

14. Remove the camshaft sprocket bolts (206).

15. Remove the timing chain (208) from the camshaft sprocket (205), and allow the timing chain to rest on the crankshaft sprocket.

16. Remove the camshaft:
   a. Remove the camshaft retainer bolts (204) and retainer (203).

✷✷ WARNING

All camshaft journals are the same diameter, so care must be used in removing or installing the camshaft to avoid damage to the camshaft bearings.

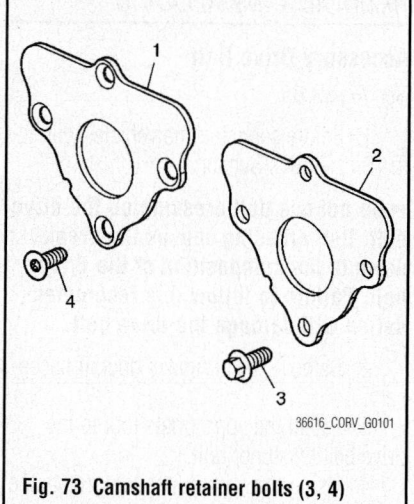

Fig. 73 Camshaft retainer bolts (3, 4)

   b. Install the camshaft sprocket bolt(s) into the camshaft front bolt hole.
   c. Using the bolt as a handle, carefully rotate and pull the camshaft out of the engine block.
   d. Remove the bolt from the front of the camshaft.

To install:
17. Install the camshaft:

➥**If camshaft replacement is required, the valve lifters must also be replaced.**

   a. Lubricate the camshaft journals and the bearings with clean engine oil.
   b. Install the camshaft sprocket bolt(s) into the camshaft front bolt hole.

✷✷ WARNING

All camshaft journals are the same diameter, so care must be used in removing or installing the camshaft to avoid damage to the camshaft bearings.

   c. Using the bolt as a handle, carefully install the camshaft into the engine block.
   d. Remove the bolt from the front of the camshaft.

➥**The gasket surface on the engine block should be clean and free of dirt or debris.**

   e. Install the camshaft retainer and the bolts. Install the retainer with the sealing gasket facing the front of the engine block.
   f. Tighten the camshaft retainer bolts:
   • Tighten the first design hex head bolts (3) to 18 ft. lbs. (25 Nm).
   • Tighten the second design TORX® head bolts (4) to 11 ft. lbs. (15 Nm).

18. Align the camshaft sprocket alignment mark in the 6 o'clock position.

19. Install the camshaft sprocket and timing chain.

20. Recheck the alignment of the timing marks.

21. Install the camshaft sprocket bolts and tighten to 22 ft. lbs. (30 Nm).

22. Apply a 0.2 in. (5 mm) bead of sealant 0.8 in. (20 mm) long to the oil pan to engine block junction.

23. Install the front cover and a new gasket.

24. Install the front cover bolts until snug.

25. Install the oil pan-to-front cover bolts until snug.

26. Install the EN-47812 over the bolt to the crankshaft.

27. Install the EN-47813.

28. Insert the tapered surface of the tool into the oil seal bore of the cover EN-47812 washer and nut.

29. Tighten the nut by hand until snug. Do not overtighten. Tighten the engine front cover bolts to 22 ft. lbs. (30 Nm).

30. Remove the tools.

31. Install a NEW crankshaft front oil seal.

32. Install the valve lifters.

33. Install the right and left cylinder heads.

34. Install the valve rocker arms and push rods.

35. Install the right and left valve rocker arm covers.

36. Install the water pump.

37. Install the left and right exhaust manifolds.

38. Install the crankshaft balancer.

39. Install the engine assembly.

CATALYTIC CONVERTER

REMOVAL & INSTALLATION

See Figure 74.

> ✳✳ **CAUTION**
>
> **In order to avoid being burned, do not service the exhaust system while it is still hot. Service the system when it is cool.**

> ✳✳ **CAUTION**
>
> **Always wear protective goggles and gloves when removing exhaust parts as falling rust and sharp edges from worn exhaust components could result in serious personal injury.**

1. Before servicing the vehicle, refer to the Precautions Section.

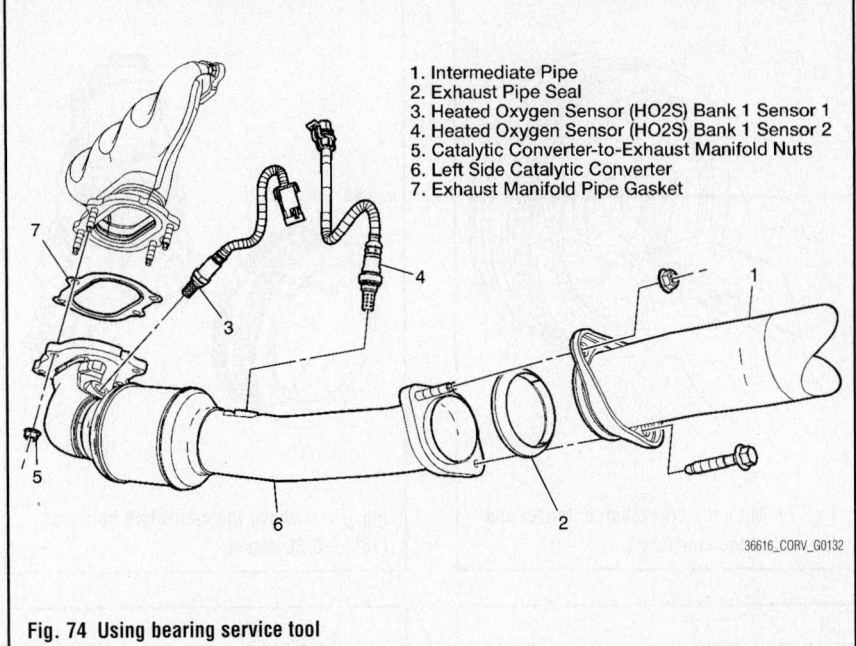

1. Intermediate Pipe
2. Exhaust Pipe Seal
3. Heated Oxygen Sensor (HO2S) Bank 1 Sensor 1
4. Heated Oxygen Sensor (HO2S) Bank 1 Sensor 2
5. Catalytic Converter-to-Exhaust Manifold Nuts
6. Left Side Catalytic Converter
7. Exhaust Manifold Pipe Gasket

36616_CORV_G0132

Fig. 74 Using bearing service tool

2. Remove the engine mount-to-engine mount bracket nuts. Refer to Engine Mount Removal & Installation.

3. Raise the vehicle.

4. Remove the intermediate pipe. Refer to Intermediate Pipe Removal & Installation.

5. Remove the exhaust pipe seal.

6. Remove the Heated Oxygen Sensors (HO2S). Refer to HO2S Removal & Installation in the Engine Performance and Emission Control Section.

7. Remove the catalytic converter-to-exhaust manifold nuts.

8. Raise the engine sufficiently for the catalytic converter to clear the exhaust manifold mounting studs.

9. Remove the left-side catalytic converter.

10. Remove the right-side catalytic converter.

11. Remove the exhaust manifold pipe gasket.

To install:

12. Installation is the reverse of removal. Tighten the catalytic converter-to-exhaust manifold nuts to 37 ft. lbs. (50 Nm).

> ✳✳ **WARNING**
>
> **Improperly installed and/or leaking exhaust gaskets may affect vehicle emissions and/or On-Board Diagnostics (OBD) II system performance.**

CRANKSHAFT BALANCER

REMOVAL & INSTALLATION

See Figures 75 through 84.

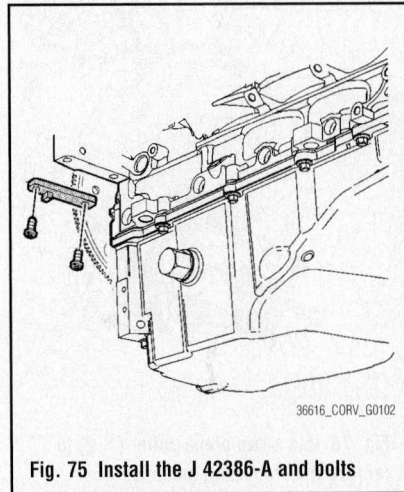

36616_CORV_G0102

Fig. 75 Install the J 42386-A and bolts

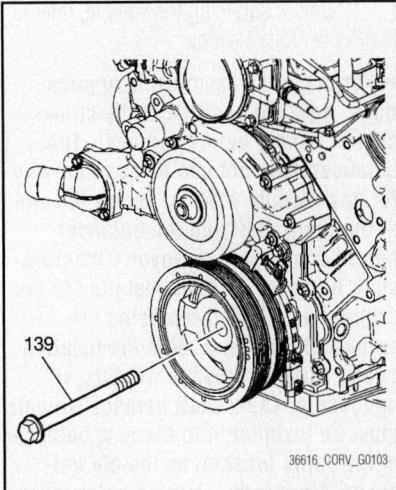

36616_CORV_G0103

Fig. 76 Remove the crankshaft balancer bolt (139)

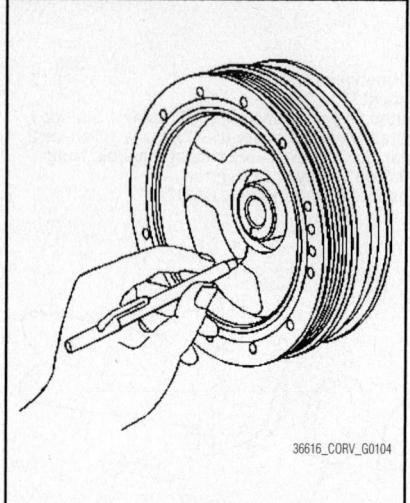

Fig. 77 Mark the crankshaft balancer and the end of the crankshaft

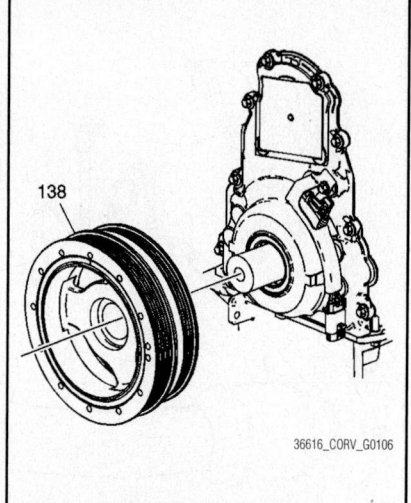

Fig. 79 Remove the crankshaft balancer (138)—6.2L engine

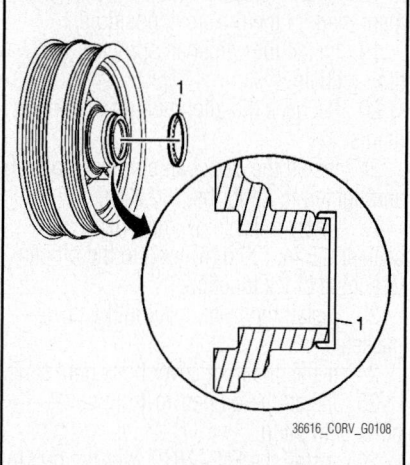

Fig. 81 Install the crankshaft balancer washer—7.0L engine

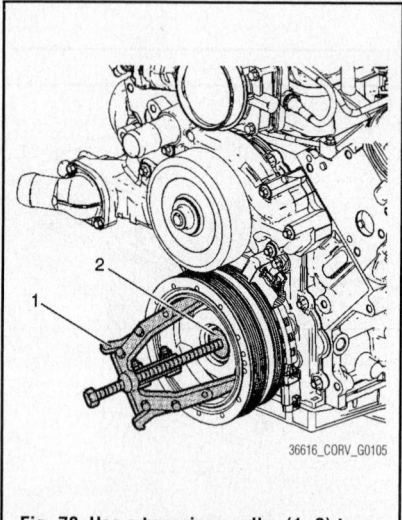

Fig. 78 Use a two-piece puller (1, 2) to remove the crankshaft balancer

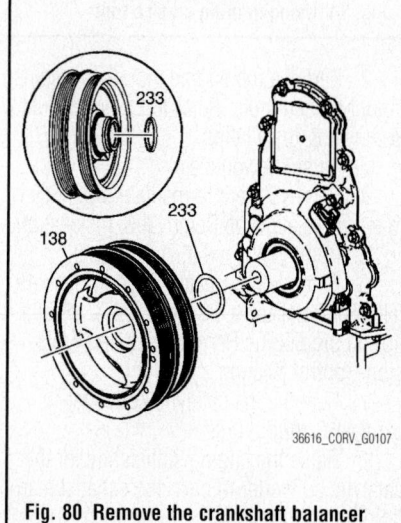

Fig. 80 Remove the crankshaft balancer (138) and washer—7.0L engine

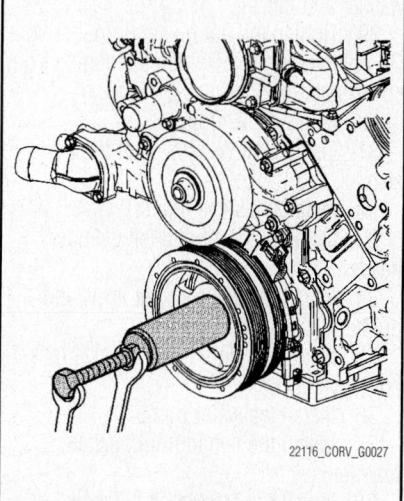

Fig. 82 Install the balancer using the J-41665—6.2L engine

1. Before servicing the vehicle, refer to the Precautions Section.

➡**For manual transmission applications, note the position of the crankshaft balancer before removal. The balancer does not use a key or keyway for positioning. Mark or scribe the end of the crankshaft and the balancer before component removal. The crankshaft balancer must be installed to the original position. If replacing the crankshaft balancer, note the location of any existing balance weights, if applicable. Crankshaft balance weights must be installed into the new balancer in the same location as the old balancer. A properly installed balance weight will be either flush or below flush with the face of the balancer.**

2. Remove the A/C drive belt.
3. Remove the power steering gear. Refer to Power Steering Gear Removal & Installation in the Steering Section.
4. Remove the starter motor. Refer to Starter Removal & Installation in the Engine Electrical Section.
5. Remove the right transmission cover and bolt.
6. Install the J 42386-A and bolts. Use one M10 - 1.5 x 120 mm and one M10 - 1.5 x 45 mm bolt for proper tool operation. Tighten the J 42386-A bolts to 37 ft. lbs. (50 Nm).
7. Remove the crankshaft balancer bolt (139). Do not discard the crankshaft balancer bolt.
8. Mark or scribe the crankshaft balancer and the end of the crankshaft.
9. Use the J 41816 (1) and the J

41816-2 (2) in order to remove the crankshaft balancer.
10. Remove the crankshaft balancer.
11. Remove the crankshaft balancer washer, if applicable.
12. Note the position of the crankshaft balance weights, if applicable.

To install:

➡**The crankshaft balancer installation and bolt tightening involves a four stage tightening process. The first pass ensures that the balancer is installed completely onto the crankshaft. The second, third and fourth passes tighten the NEW bolt to the proper torque.**

➡**The used crankshaft balancer bolt is used only during the first pass of the balancer installation procedure. Install a NEW crankshaft balancer bolt and**

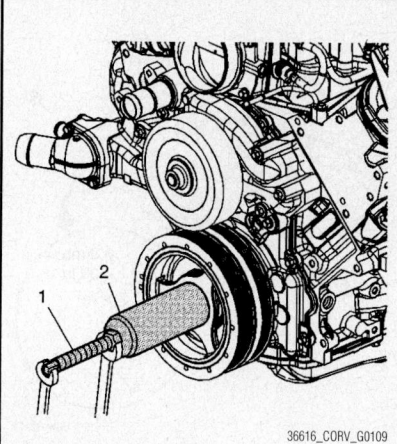

Fig. 83 Install the balancer using the J 41665 (2) and the EN-47812 (1)—7.0L engine

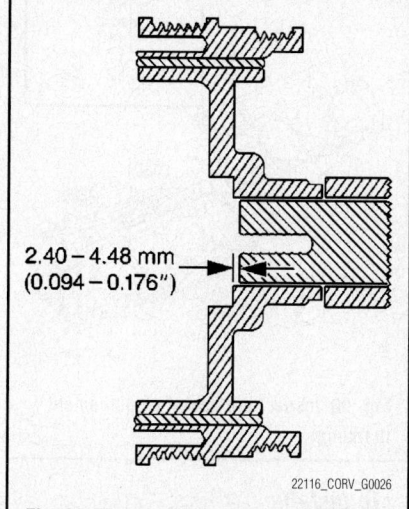

2.40 – 4.48 mm
(0.094 – 0.176")

Fig. 84 The crankshaft should be recessed into the balancer bore

tighten as described in the second, third and fourth passes of the balancer bolt tightening procedure.

13. Install the J 42386-A and bolts. Use one M10 - 1.5 x 120 mm and one M10 - 1.5 x 45 mm bolt for proper tool operation. Tighten the J 42386-A bolts to 37 ft. lbs. (50 Nm).

14. Using the old balancer as a reference, mark or scribe the new balancer in the same location, if applicable.

15. Install balance weights into the new balancer, if applicable.

16. Install the crankshaft balancer washer onto the crankshaft balancer, if applicable.

➡The balancer should be positioned onto the end of the crankshaft as straight as possible prior to tool installation.

17. Position the balancer onto the end of the crankshaft.

18. For the 6.2L engine, use the J 41665 in order to install the balancer:

   a. Assemble the threaded rod, nut, washer and installer. Insert the smaller end of the installer into the front of the balancer.

   b. Use a wrench and hold the hex end of the threaded rod.

   c. Use a second wrench and rotate the installation tool nut clockwise until the balancer is started onto the crankshaft.

   d. Remove the tool and reverse the installation tool. Position the larger end of the installer against the front of the balancer.

   e. Use a wrench and hold the hex end of the threaded rod.

   f. Use a second wrench and rotate the installation tool nut clockwise until the balancer is installed onto the crankshaft.

   g. Remove the balancer installation tool.

19. For the 7.0L engine, use the J 41665 (2) and the EN-47812 (1) in order to install the balancer:

   a. Assemble the EN-47812 (1), nut, washer and the J 41665 (2). Insert the smaller end of the J 41665 (2) into the front of the balancer.

   b. Use a wrench and hold the hex end of the EN-47812 (1).

   c. Use a second wrench and rotate the installation tool nut clockwise until the balancer is started onto the crankshaft.

   d. Remove the J 41665 (2) and reverse the installation tool. Position the larger end of the J 41665 (2) against the front of the balancer.

   e. Use a wrench and hold the end of the EN-47812 (1).

   f. Use a second wrench and rotate the installation tool nut clockwise until the balancer is installed onto the crankshaft.

   g. Remove the balancer installation tool.

20. Install the used crankshaft balancer bolt and tighten to 240 ft. lbs. (330 Nm).

21. Remove the used crankshaft balancer bolt.

➡Ensure the nose of the crankshaft should be recessed 0.094–0.176 in. (2.4–4.48 mm) into the balancer bore.

22. Measure for a correctly installed balancer. If the balancer is not installed to the proper dimensions, repeat the installation procedure.

23. Install the NEW crankshaft balancer bolt and tighten the crankshaft balancer bolt a first pass to 37 ft. lbs. (50 Nm), then a second pass to 140 degrees using the J 45059.

24. Remove the J 42386-A.

25. Install the starter motor.

26. Install the power steering gear.

27. Install the A/C drive belt.

28. Perform the Crankshaft Position (CKP) system variation learn procedure, as outlined under Crankshaft Position (CKP) sensor in the Engine Performance & Emission Controls Section.

CRANKSHAFT FRONT SEAL

REMOVAL & INSTALLATION

See Figures 85 and 86.

1. Before servicing the vehicle, refer to the Precautions Section.

2. Remove the crankshaft balancer. Refer to Crankshaft Balancer Removal & Installation.

3. Gently pry the crankshaft oil seal (1) from the front cover.

To install:

➡Do not lubricate the oil seal sealing surface.

➡Do not reuse the crankshaft oil seal.

4. Lubricate the outer edge of the oil seal with clean engine oil.

5. Lubricate the front cover oil seal bore with clean engine oil.

6. Install the crankshaft front oil seal onto the J-41478 guide.

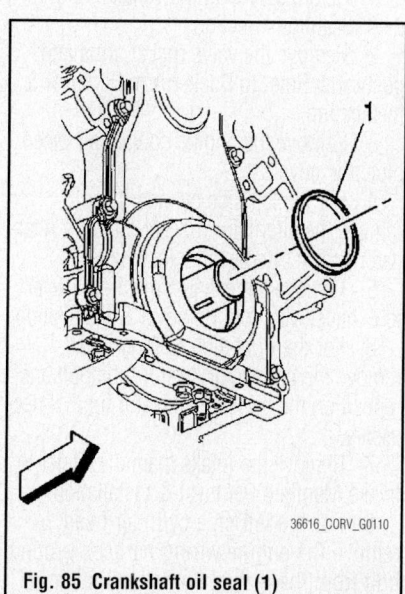

Fig. 85 Crankshaft oil seal (1)

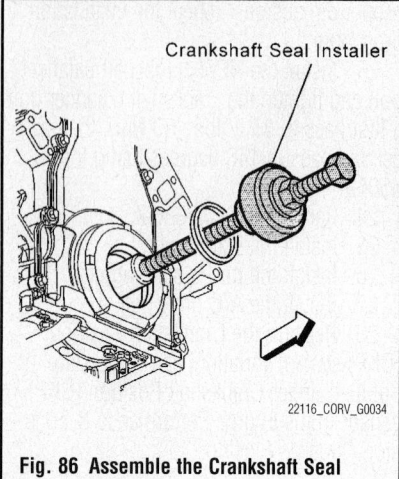

Fig. 86 Assemble the Crankshaft Seal Installer J-41478

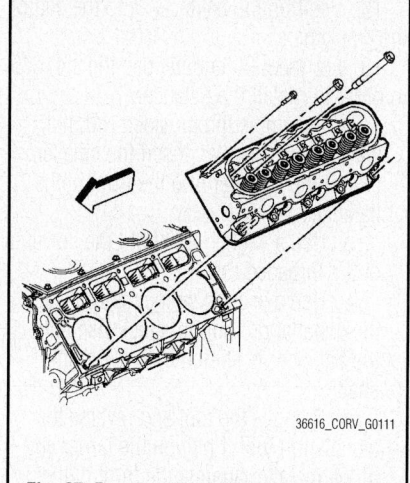

Fig. 87 Remove the cylinder head bolts

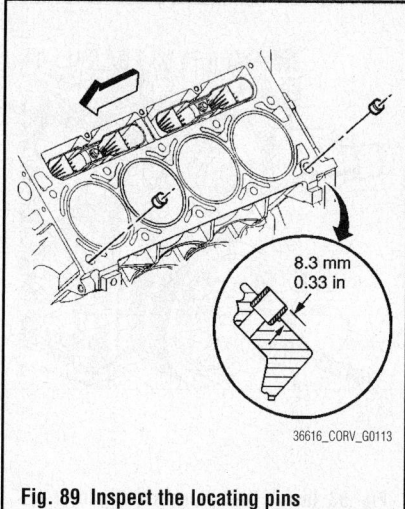

Fig. 89 Inspect the locating pins

7. Install the J 41478 threaded rod (with nut, washer, guide, and oil seal) into the end of the crankshaft.

8. Use the J 41478 in order to install the oil seal into the cover bore:

a. Use a wrench and hold the hex on the installer tool.

b. Use a second wrench and rotate the installer nut clockwise until the seal bottoms in the cover bore.

c. Remove the tool.

d. Inspect the oil seal for proper installation. The oil seal should be installed evenly and completely into the front cover bore.

9. Install the crankshaft balancer.

CYLINDER HEAD

REMOVAL & INSTALLATION

See Figures 87 through 92.

1. Before servicing the vehicle, refer to the Precautions Section.

2. Remove the valve rocker arms and pushrods. Refer to Rocker Arm Removal & Installation.

3. Remove the engine coolant air bleed pipe and covers.

4. For the left side cylinder head, remove the alternator bracket. Refer to Alternator Bracket Removal & Installation.

5. Remove the exhaust manifold. Refer to Exhaust Manifold Removal & Installation.

6. For the right side cylinder head, remove the oil level indicator tube bolt and reposition the oil level indicator tube, if necessary.

7. Remove the intake manifold. Refer to Intake Manifold Removal & Installation.

8. For the left side cylinder head, remove the engine wiring harness ground bolt from the rear of the left cylinder

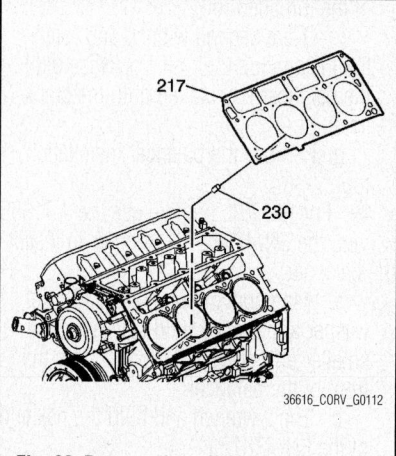

Fig. 88 Remove the cylinder head gasket (217)

head, and reposition the engine wire harness ground strap away from the cylinder head.

9. For the right side cylinder head, remove the wiring harness from the clip at the rear of the cylinder head.

➡The cylinder head bolts are NOT reusable.

10. Remove the cylinder head bolts.

✷✷ WARNING

After removal, place the cylinder head on 2 wood blocks in order to prevent damage to the sealing surfaces.

11. Remove the cylinder head.

12. Remove the cylinder head gasket (217).

13. Discard the gasket.

14. Discard all cylinder head bolts.

15. Clean and inspect the cylinder head.

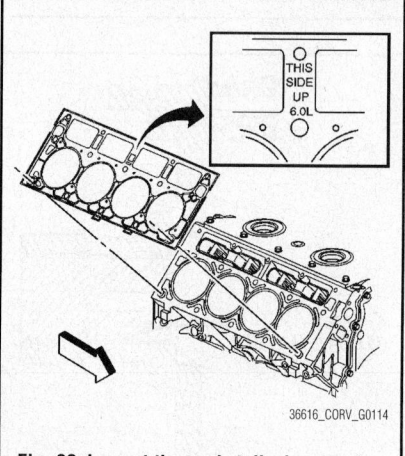

Fig. 90 Inspect the gasket displacement markings

To install:

✷✷ CAUTION

Wear safety glasses in order to avoid eye damage.

✷✷ WARNING

Clean all dirt, debris, and coolant from the engine block cylinder head bolt holes. Failure to remove all foreign material may result in damaged threads, improperly tightened fasteners or damage to components.

➡If installing a new cylinder head it is necessary to install a new engine coolant air bleed plug into the rear coolant passage of the cylinder head.

➡Do not use the cylinder head bolts again. Install NEW cylinder head bolts during assembly.

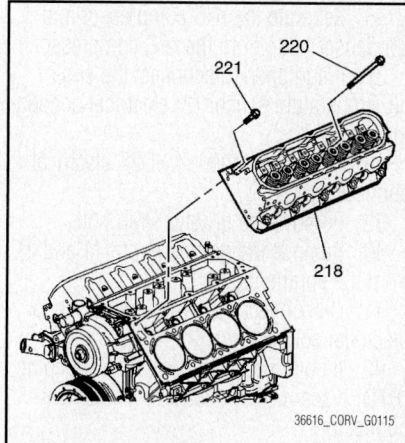

Fig. 91 Install the cylinder head (218) and NEW bolts (220, 221)

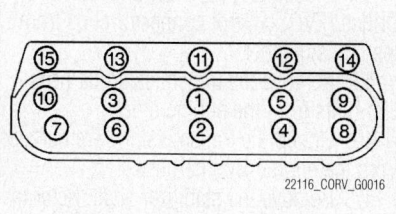

Fig. 92 Cylinder head bolt torque sequence

➡ **Do not use any type of sealant on the cylinder head gasket, unless specified.**

➡ **The cylinder head gaskets must be installed in the proper direction and position.**

16. Clean the engine block cylinder head bolt holes, if required. Thread repair tool J 42385-107 may be used to clean the threads of old threadlocking material.

17. Spray cleaner into the hole.

18. Clean the cylinder head bolt holes with compressed air.

19. Install the cylinder head locating pins.

20. Inspect the locating pins for proper installation.

21. Inspect the displacement markings on the gasket for proper usage.

22. Install the NEW cylinder head gasket onto the locating pins.

23. Install the cylinder head (218) onto the locating pins and the gasket.

24. Install the NEW cylinder head bolts (220, 221).

25. Tighten the cylinder head bolts:
- Tighten the M11 cylinder head bolts (1–10) a first pass in sequence to 22 ft. lbs. (30 Nm).
- Tighten the M11 cylinder head

bolts (1–10) a second pass in sequence to 90 degrees using the J 45059.
- Tighten the M11 cylinder head bolts (1–10) a final pass in sequence to 70 degrees using the J 45059.
- Tighten the M8 cylinder head bolts (11–15) to 22 ft. lbs. (30 Nm). Begin with the center bolt (11) and alternating side-to-side, work outward tightening all of the bolts.

26. For the right side cylinder head, install the wiring harness to the clip at the rear of the cylinder head.

27. Install the intake manifold.

28. For the right side cylinder head, position the oil level indicator tube into place and install the bolt and tighten to 18 ft. lbs. (25 Nm).

29. For the left side cylinder head, position the engine wire harness ground strap against the cylinder head, and then install the engine wiring harness ground bolt to the rear of the left cylinder head. Tighten the bolt to 24 ft. lbs. (32 Nm).

30. Install the exhaust manifold.

31. For the left side cylinder head, install the alternator bracket.

32. Install the engine coolant air bleed pipe.

33. Install the valve rocker arms and pushrods.

ENGINE ASSEMBLY

REMOVAL & INSTALLATION

See Figures 93 through 99.

1. Before servicing the vehicle, refer to the Precautions Section.

❊❊ **WARNING**

The steps in the following procedure are in a specific order. Follow these steps in this order and do not ignore any details.

2. Recover the Air Conditioning (A/C) refrigerant.

3. Remove the radiator. Refer to Radiator Removal & Installation in the Engine Cooling Section.

4. Remove the Brake Pressure Modulator Valve (BPMV) bracket.

5. Reposition the brake pipes.

6. Remove the accessory drive belt. Refer to Accessory Drive Belt Removal & Installation.

7. Remove the right fuel injection rail cover.

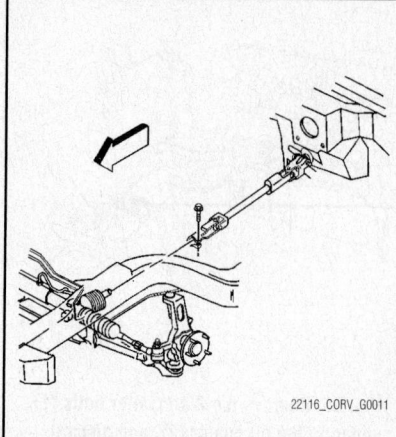

Fig. 93 Remove the intermediate steering shaft bolt to the steering gear

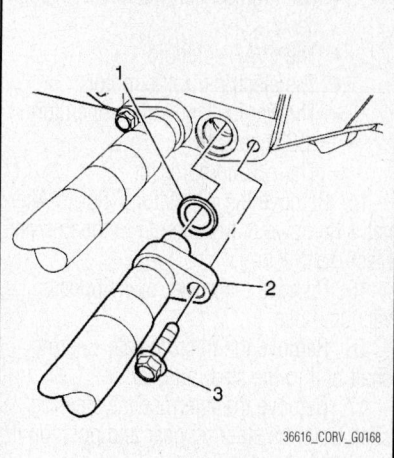

Fig. 94 Remove the oil inlet hose to oil pan bolt (3) and disconnect the hose (2)—7.0L engine

8. Relieve the fuel system pressure. Refer to Fuel System Section for the correct procedure.

9. Disconnect the Evaporative Emission (EVAP) canister purge hose at the fuel line.

10. Remove the fuel feed hose.

❊❊ **WARNING**

Cap the hoses and inlets when separating the cooling system components, this prevents dirt and other contaminants from entering the cooling system.

11. Remove the radiator hoses from the water pump.

12. Remove the heater hoses from the water pump.

13. Disconnect the following electrical connectors from the engine:

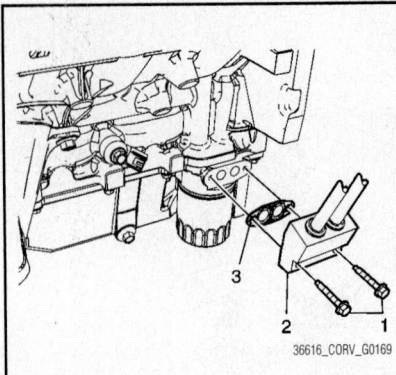

Fig. 95 Remove the 2 oil cooler bolts (1), separate the oil cooler (2), and discard seal (3)

- The fuel injectors
- The ignition coil main harness connectors
- The EVAP solenoid
- The electric throttle motor
- The Engine Coolant Temperature (ECT) sensor
- The A/C compressor

14. Remove the alternator. Refer to Alternator Removal & Installation in the Engine Electrical Section.

15. Remove the power brake booster vacuum hose.

16. Remove the intermediate steering shaft bolt to the steering gear.

17. Remove the intermediate steering shaft from the steering gear and position it to the left onto the frame rail.

18. Remove the front tires and wheels.

19. Remove the intermediate pipe. Refer to Intermediate Pipe Removal & Installation.

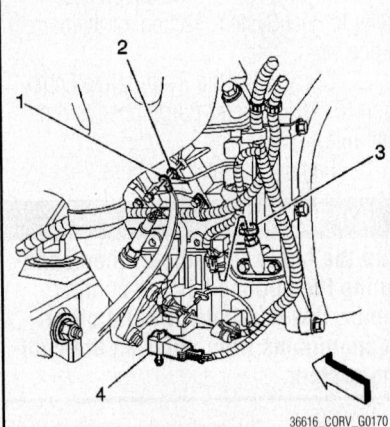

Fig. 96 Disconnect the engine oil temperature sensor (3) electrical connector, left HO2S electrical connector, and remove ground straps (1 and 2)

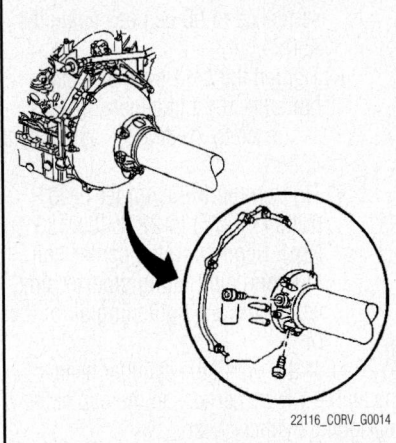

Fig. 97 On automatic transmission vehicles, remove the plugs from the driveline support assembly and install 2 M10 x 1.5 bolts into the plug holes

20. Remove the driveline tunnel close-out panel bolts.

21. Remove the driveline tunnel close-out panel.

22. Remove the starter motor. Refer to Starter Removal & Installation in the Engine Electrical Section.

23. On 7.0L engine, remove the oil inlet hose to oil pan bolt (3) and disconnect the hose (2) from the oil pan. Discard the oil seal (1).

24. If the engine failed and debris was created, remove the oil tank inlet hose and discard.

25. Remove the oil tank outlet hose to oil pan bolt and disconnect the hose from the oil pan. Discard the oil seal.

26. If the engine failed and debris was created, remove the oil tank outlet hose and discard.

27. Remove the transmission lines from the rear of the oil pan.

28. Remove the transmission lines from the front of the oil pan.

29. Remove the 2 oil cooler bolts (1) and separate the oil cooler (2) from the pan.

30. Discard the oil cooler seal (3).

31. If the engine failed and debris was created, remove the oil cooler hoses and discard.

32. On all engines, disconnect the Crankshaft Position (CKP) sensor electrical connector.

33. Disconnect the oil level sensor electrical connector.

34. Disconnect the right Heated Oxygen Sensor (HO2S) electrical connector.

35. Remove the A/C compressor and condenser hose bolt at the compressor.

36. Separate the A/C compressor and condenser hose from the A/C compressor.

37. If equipped, disconnect the engine oil temperature sensor (3) electrical connector.

38. Disconnect the left HO2S electrical connector.

39. Remove the ground strap bolt.

40. Remove the ground straps (1 and 2) from the engine block.

41. Disconnect the wheel speed sensor electrical connectors.

42. If equipped with Real Time Damping (RTD) disconnect the following electrical connectors:
- Shock absorber damper
- Position sensor pigtail

43. Unclip the transmission wire harness from the crossmember.

44. Disconnect the Electronic Variable Orifice (EVO) control connector clips from the crossmember.

45. Remove the transmission harness clip bolts from the engine block.

46. Unclip the transmission wire harness from the engine wire harness.

47. Remove the stabilizer shaft. Refer to Stabilizer Shaft Removal & Installation in the Suspension Section.

48. Loosen, do not remove, the steering knuckle nut from the lower control arm ball stud.

49. Install the J 42188 between the steering knuckle and the lower control arm ball stud.

50. Tighten the nut on the J 42188 until the steering knuckle and the lower control arm ball stud separate.

51. Disconnect the Antilock Brake System (ABS) electrical connector clips from the crossmember, if equipped.

52. Remove the front transverse leaf spring. Refer to Front Transverse Spring Removal & Installation.

53. Disconnect the automatic transmission fluid cooler pipe clip from the front of the engine oil pan, if equipped.

54. Disconnect the front automatic transmission fluid cooler pipes from the rear pipes.

55. Disconnect the automatic transmission cooler pipe clip at the right transmission cover, if equipped.

✳✳ WARNING

Use the correct fastener in the correct location. Replacement fasteners must be the correct part number for that application. Fasteners requiring replacement or fasteners requiring the use of thread locking compound or sealant are identified in the

service procedure. Do not use paints, lubricants, or corrosion inhibitors on fasteners or fastener joint surfaces unless specified. These coatings affect fastener torque and joint clamping force and may damage the fastener. Use the correct tightening sequence and specifications when installing fasteners in order to avoid damage to parts and systems

✳✳ WARNING

Failure to use the minimum fastener length specified will prevent proper retention of the propeller shaft during disassembly.

56. With automatic transmission vehicles, use the following steps:

a. Remove the 2 driveline support hole plug bolts.

b. Install a M10.0-1.5 x 55 mm bolt or longer in each plug location and tighten to 26 ft. lbs. (35 Nm).

57. If equipped with an automatic transmission, remove the flywheel housing plug.

58. If equipped with an automatic transmission perform the following:

a. Orientate the prop shaft hub clamp for access to the bolt.

b. Position the clamp bolt facing downward.

c. Loosen the prop shaft hub clamp bolt.

59. Remove bolts attaching the transmission wire harness bracket to the flywheel housing.

60. Remove the transmission wire harness from its mounting location, rearward toward the driveline support.

61. Lay the harness on the driveline support. Secure if necessary.

✳✳ WARNING

The weight of the engine should never be supported by the J 42203.

62. Install the J 42203 to the close-out panel flange.

63. If equipped with a manual transmission, disconnect the clutch actuator hose from the master cylinder hose.

64. Install the J 42203 to the close-out panel flange.

65. Slowly lower the vehicle onto the J 39580 and the J 39580-500.

66. Support the engine and crossmember on the J 39580 and the J 39580-500.

67. Using HAND TOOLS ONLY, remove the front and rear crossmember nuts.

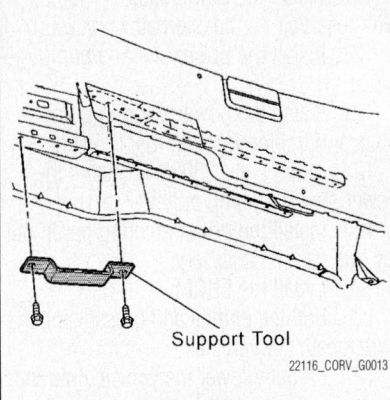

Fig. 98 Install a Driveline Support tool J-42203 to the undercover flange

22116_CORV_G0013

68. Partially raise the vehicle.

69. Disconnect the Manifold Absolute Pressure (MAP) sensor electrical connector.

70. Disconnect the Camshaft Position (CMP) sensor electrical connector.

71. Remove the ground strap bolt.

72. Remove the ground strap from the left rear cylinder head.

73. Disconnect the engine oil pressure sensor electrical connector from the back of the engine.

74. Disconnect the electrical connector for the knock sensor, left side.

75. Disconnect the electrical connector for the knock sensor, right side.

76. Remove the driveline support bolts.

➡**Visually inspect the transmission wiring harness to ensure detachment from the engine.**

77. Insert a flat-bladed screwdriver, or similar tool, between the edge of the driveline support and the flywheel housing, then separate the flywheel housing from the driveline support.

78. Slowly pull the engine away from the propeller shaft.

79. As soon as the propeller input shaft clears the flywheel housing, slowly raise the vehicle.

80. Slide the engine and crossmember forward in order to clear the propeller shaft spline.

81. Remove the Electronic Brake Control Module (EBCM). Refer to Electronic Brake Control Module Removal & Installation.

➡**Visually inspect the wiring harness clearances while raising the vehicle.**

82. Raise the vehicle completely off of the engine and crossmember.

83. Remove the power steering pump pulley hub cap, if necessary.

84. Using the J 25034-C, remove the power steering pump pulley.

➡**It is not necessary to open the power steering system during the engine removal procedure.**

85. Remove the power steering pump bolts.

86. Remove the power steering pump brace.

87. Remove the power steering pump, with reservoir, from the engine, and reposition them to the crossmember.

88. Remove the power steering pump assembly. Refer to Power Steering Pump Removal & Installation.

89. Remove the alternator bracket bolts.

90. Remove the alternator bracket and power steering pump bracket.

91. Install the J 41798 to the engine.

92. Remove the spark plugs. Refer to Spark Plug Removal & Installation.

93. Remove the engine mount nuts.

94. Using a engine hoist and the J 41798, slowly raise the engine.

95. Remove the engine from the crossmember.

96. Remove the flywheel housing bolts.

97. Remove the flywheel housing from the engine block.

98. Install the engine onto an engine stand and prepare for disassembly.

99. Remove the engine hoist.

100. Remove the J 41798 from the engine.

101. Remove the engine mount bracket bolts.

102. Remove the engine mount brackets from the engine block.

✳✳ WARNING

Avoid engine damage. Debris in the engine oil tank, oil tank hoses and engine oil cooler may be pulled back into the engine causing severe engine damage. You must clean the engine oil tank, and replace the engine oil hoses and engine oil cooler.

103. On 7.0L engine, if the engine failed and debris was created, the engine oil tank must be cleaned and the oil tank hoses and engine oil cooler must be replaced:

a. Remove the engine oil tank.

b. Disassemble the engine oil tank.

c. Clean and inspect the engine oil tank.

d. Assemble the engine oil tank.

e. Replace the engine oil cooler.

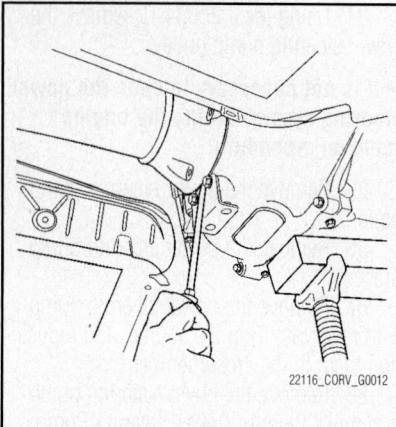

Fig. 99 Separate the flywheel housing from the driveline support

To install:

✳✳ WARNING

The steps in the following procedure are in a specific order. Follow these steps in this order and ignore no details.

104. Prepare the engine for installation.

105. Install the engine mount brackets to the engine block.

106. Install the engine mount bracket bolts and tighten to 37 ft. lbs. (50 Nm).

107. Install the J 41798 to the engine.

108. Using an engine hoist and the J 41798, raise the engine slightly.

109. Remove the engine from the engine stand.

110. Install the flywheel housing to the engine block.

111. Install the flywheel housing bolts and tighten to 37 ft. lbs. (50 Nm).

112. Using an engine hoist and the J 41798, lower the engine onto the cross-member.

113. Install the engine mount nuts and tighten to 48 ft. lbs. (65 Nm).

114. Install the spark plugs.

115. Remove the J 41798 from the engine.

116. Install the A/C compressor bracket.

117. Install the alternator bracket and power steering pump bracket.

118. Install the alternator bracket bolts until snug.

119. Tighten the alternator bracket bolts in the following order:
- Inner power steering pump reservoir bracket bolt
- Upper alternator bracket bolt
- Outer power steering pump reservoir bracket bolt
- Lower alternator bracket bolt and tighten to 37 ft. lbs. (50 Nm)

120. Install the power steering pump, with reservoir, to the alternator bracket.

121. Install the power steering pump brace.

122. Install the power steering pump bolts and tighten to 18 ft. lbs. (25 Nm).

123. Using the J 25033-C, install the power steering pump pulley.

124. Install the power steering pump pulley hub cap, if necessary.

125. Install the EBCM.

126. Roll the engine and crossmember underneath the vehicle.

127. Partially lower the vehicle onto the engine and crossmember.

128. Install the ground strap and ground strap bolt to the rear of the left cylinder head and tighten the ground strap bolt to 24 ft. lbs. (32 Nm).

129. Connect the engine oil pressure sensor electrical connector.

130. Connect the MAP sensor electrical connector.

131. Connect the CMP sensor electrical connector.

132. Reconnect the electrical connector for the knock sensor, left side.

133. Reconnect the electrical connector for the knock sensor, right side.

134. Vehicles equipped with a manual transmission, slide the engine and cross-member rearward. Do not force the engine onto the propeller spline.

135. Position the engine to the proper height and angle in order to install the propeller input shaft.

136. Insert the propeller input shaft into the clutch driven plate hub while maintaining the proper angle, DO NOT force. Rotate the shaft slightly to bring the 2 splines into alignment, if necessary.

137. Slowly seat the flywheel housing to the driveline.

138. Install the driveline support bolts and tighten to 37 ft. lbs. (50 Nm).

139. Connect the master cylinder hose to the clutch actuator hose.

➡DO NOT tighten the flywheel hub collar bolt at this time.

140. Vehicles equipped with an automatic transmission, slide the engine and crossmember rearward. Do not force the engine onto the propeller spline.

141. Position the engine to the proper height and angle in order to install the propeller input shaft.

142. Install the driveline support bolts and tighten to 37 ft. lbs. (50 Nm).

143. Hand tighten the flywheel hub collar bolt.

144. Lower the vehicle onto the cross-member and align the dowels.

➡Use only hand tools when tightening or torquing crossmember nuts.

145. By HAND, install new crossmember nuts until snug. Tighten the crossmember nuts to 81 ft. lbs. (110 Nm).

146. Raise and suitably support the vehicle.

147. Remove the J 39580 and the J 39580-500.

148. Remove the J 42203 from the vehicle.

149. Route the transmission wire harness into place.

150. Install the transmission wire harness bracket bolts and tighten to 37 ft. lbs. (50 Nm).

151. Vehicles equipped with an automatic transmission, remove the previously installed M10-1.5 x 55 mm bolts from the front of the driveline support.

152. Install 2 plugs in the driveline support and tighten to 37 ft. lbs. (50 Nm).

153. Connect the front automatic transmission fluid cooler pipes to the rear pipes, if equipped. Tighten the automatic transmission fluid cooler pipes to 18 ft. lbs. (25 Nm).

154. Install the automatic transmission cooler pipe clamp bolt, at the transmission cover, if equipped, and tighten to 22 inch lbs. (2.2 Nm).

155. Install the automatic transmission fluid cooler pipe clamp bolt, at the oil pan, if equipped, and tighten to 106 inch lbs. (12 Nm).

156. Install the front transverse leaf spring.

157. Install the lower control arm stud to the steering knuckle.

158. Install a NEW steering knuckle nut:
a. Tighten the steering knuckle nut to 15 ft. lbs. (20 Nm) to seat the ball joint stud.
b. Torque the steering knuckle nut an additional 210 degrees using J 36660-A.
c. Check the steering knuckle nut for a final torque of 41 ft. lbs. (55 Nm)

159. Connect the ABS electrical connector clips to the crossmember, if equipped.

160. Install the front stabilizer shaft.

161. Clip the transmission wire harness the engine wire harness, at the white tape.

162. Install the transmission wire harness clip bolts to the engine block:
a. Tighten the transmission wire harness clip bolt, near the harness ground, to 24 ft. lbs. (32 Nm).
b. Tighten the transmission wire harness clip bolt, near the oil pan, to 18 ft. lbs. (25 Nm).

163. Install the EVO electrical connector clips to the crossmember.

164. Clip the transmission wire harness to the crossmember.

165. If equipped with RTD connect the following electrical connectors:

- Position sensor pigtail
- Shock absorber damper

166. Position the ground straps to the engine block.

167. Install the engine ground strap bolt and tighten to 24 ft. lbs. (32 Nm).

168. Connect the left HO2S electrical connector.

169. If equipped, connect the engine oil temperature sensor electrical connector.

170. Install the AC compressor and condenser hose to the A/C compressor.

171. Install the A/C compressor and condenser hose bolt at the compressor and tighten to 20 ft. lbs. (27 Nm).

172. Connect the right front HO2S sensor electrical connector.

173. Connect the oil level sensor electrical connector.

174. Connect the CKP sensor electrical connector.

175. On 7.0L engine, using a new oil cooler seal, install the oil cooler and 2 bolts. Tighten the oil cooler bolts to 106 inch lbs. (12 Nm).

176. If the oil cooler hoses were discarded, install new hoses.

177. Install the front transmission cooler line retainer and bolt and tighten to 106 inch lbs. (12 Nm).

178. Install the rear transmission cooler lines retainer and bolt and tighten to 106 inch lbs. (12 Nm).

179. Using a new oil seal install the oil tank outlet hose and bolt to the oil pan. Tighten the outlet hose to oil pan bolt to 16 ft. lbs. (22 Nm).

180. If the oil tank outlet hose was discarded install a new hose.

181. Using a new oil seal install the oil tank inlet hose and bolt to the oil pan. Tighten the inlet hose to oil pan bolt to 16 ft. lbs. (22 Nm).

182. If the oil tank inlet hose was discarded, install a new hose.

183. On all engines, install the starter motor.

184. Install the driveline close-out panel.

185. Install the driveline close-out panel bolts and tighten to 106 inch lbs. (12 Nm).

186. Install the intermediate pipe.

187. Install the front tires and wheels.

188. Lower the vehicle.

189. Install the intermediate steering shaft to the steering gear.

190. Install the intermediate steering shaft bolt and tighten to 35 ft. lbs. (48 Nm).

191. Install the power brake booster vacuum hose.

192. Install the alternator.

193. Connect the following electrical connectors to the engine:

- The fuel injectors
- The ignition coil main harness connectors
- The EVAP solenoid
- The electric throttle motor
- The ECT sensor
- The A/C compressor

194. Install the heater hoses to the water pump.

195. Install the radiator hoses to the water pump.

196. Install the fuel feed hose.

197. Connect the EVAP emission canister purge hose at the fuel line.

198. Install the right fuel injection rail cover.

199. Install the accessory drive belt.

200. Install the BPMV bracket.

201. Install the radiator.

202. Recharge the A/C system.

203. Program the transmitters. Refer to Transmitter Programming in the Chassis Electrical Section.

204. Bleed the clutch hydraulic system, if equipped. Refer to Clutch Hydraulic System Bleeding within the Drive Train Section.

205. Perform the CKP system variation learn procedure. Refer to Crankshaft Position System Variation Learn Procedure under Crankshaft Balancer.

206. Fill the crankcase with the proper quantity and grade of engine oil.

207. Disable the ignition system.

208. Crank the engine several times. Listen for any unusual noises or evidence that parts are binding.

209. Enable the ignition system.

210. Start the engine and listen for unusual noises.

211. Check the vehicle oil pressure gage and confirm that the engine has acceptable oil pressure.

212. If necessary, install an oil pressure gage and measure the engine oil pressure.

213. Stop the engine and add oil to the engine oil tank as needed to bring the oil level to the FULL mark (approximately 2.5 quarts (2.4 liters).

214. Start the engine and run the engine speed at about 1,000 RPM until the engine has reached normal operating temperature.

215. Listen for sticking lifters and other unusual noises.

216. Inspect for fuel, oil, and/or other coolant leaks while the engine is running.

217. With automatic transmission vehicles perform the following steps:

    a. Shut off the engine.

    b. Allow the engine to cool to room temperature.

    c. Raise the vehicle.

    d. Tighten the prop shaft hub collar bolt to 92 ft. lbs. (125 Nm).

218. Install the engine flywheel housing inspection plug.

219. Perform a final inspection for the proper engine oil and coolant levels.

ENGINE FRONT COVER

REMOVAL & INSTALLATION

See Figures 100 through 104.

1. Before servicing the vehicle, refer to the Precautions Section.

2. Remove the accessory drive belt. Refer to Accessory Drive Belt Removal & Installation.

3. Remove the crankshaft balancer. Refer to Crankshaft Balancer Removal & Installation.

4. Remove the 2 front oil pan to front cover M8 bolts.

5. Remove the water pump. Refer to

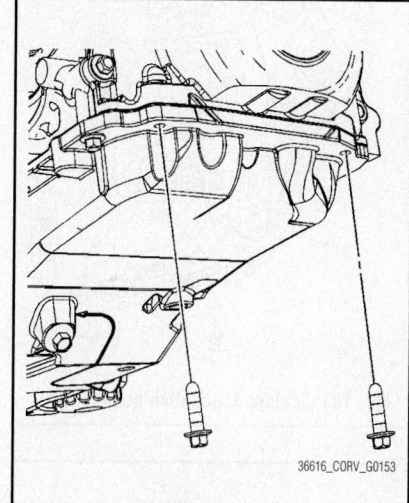

36616_CORV_G0153

Fig. 100 Remove the 2 front oil pan to front cover M8 bolts

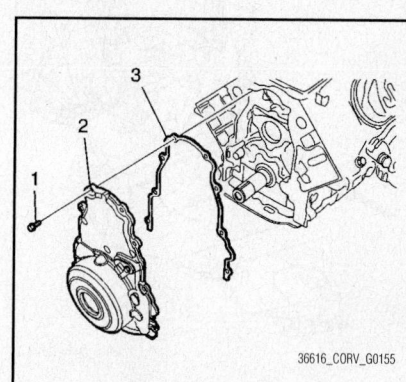

36616_CORV_G0155

Fig. 101 Remove the front cover (2), bolts (1), and gasket (3)

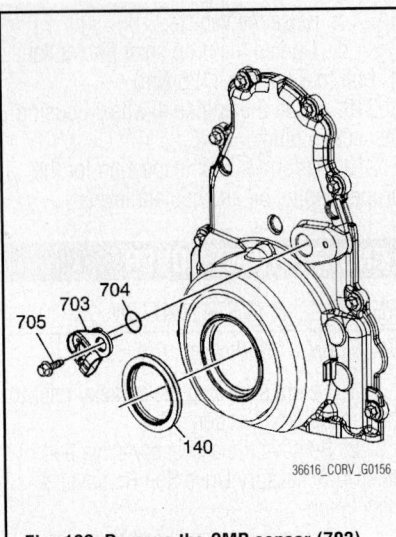

Fig. 102 Remove the CMP sensor (703), bolt (705), and O-ring (704)

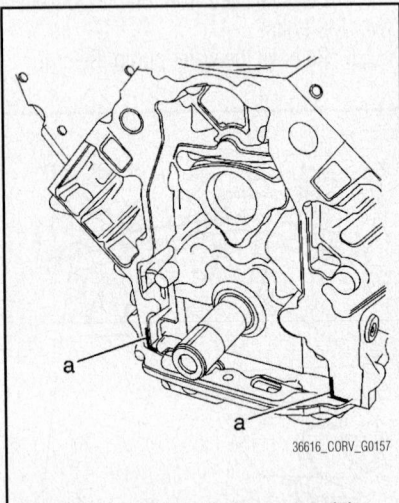

Fig. 103 Sealant application points (a)

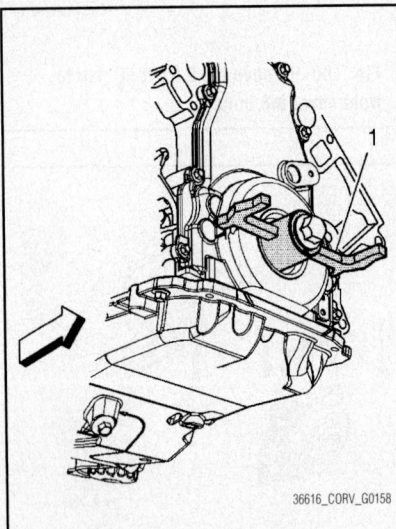

Fig. 104 Install the EN-48853 (1) onto the crankshaft

Water Pump Removal & Installation in the Engine Cooling Section.

6. Disconnect the Camshaft Position (CMP) sensor electrical connector.

7. Remove the front cover bolts (1).

8. Remove the front cover (2) and gasket (3).

9. Discard the front cover gasket.

10. Clean and inspect the engine front cover.

11. Remove the oil seal (140).

12. Remove the CMP sensor (703), bolt (705), and remove the O-ring (704) from the sensor, as required.

To install:

13. Apply a 0.2 in. (5 mm) bead of sealant 0.8 in. (20 mm) long to the engine block. Apply the sealant to the T joint location (a) where the oil pan meets the front of the engine block.

➡ Do not use the crankshaft oil seal or the engine front cover gasket again. Do not apply any type of sealant to the front cover gasket, unless specified.

❄ WARNING

The special tools in this procedure are used to properly align the engine front cover at the oil pan surface and to center the crankshaft front oil seal. All gasket surfaces should be free of oil or other foreign material during assembly. The crankshaft front oil seal MUST be centered in relation to the crankshaft. The oil pan sealing surface at the front cover and engine block MUST be aligned within specifications. An improperly aligned front cover may cause premature front oil seal wear and/or engine assembly oil leaks.

14. Install a NEW crankshaft front oil seal.

15. Install the front cover gasket, front cover, and bolts.

➡ Start the tool-to-front cover bolts. Do not tighten the bolts at this time.

16. Tighten the cover bolts finger tight. Do not overtighten. Tighten the tool-to-engine block bolts to 18 ft. lbs. (25 Nm).

17. Install the EN-48853 onto the crankshaft.

18. Tighten the crankshaft balancer bolt by hand until snug. Do not overtighten.

19. Install the front cover.

➡ Align the tapered legs of the tool with the machined alignment surfaces on the front cover.

20. Remove the tool.

21. Inspect the CMP sensor O-ring seal for cuts or damage. If the seal is not cut or damaged, it may be used again.

22. Lubricate the O-ring seal with clean engine oil.

23. Install the O-ring seal onto the sensor.

24. Install the sensor to the cover.

25. Install the CMP sensor and bolt and tighten to 106 inch lbs. (12 Nm).

26. Install the new crankshaft front oil seal.

27. Connect the CMP sensor electrical connector.

28. Install the water pump.

29. Install the crankshaft balancer.

30. Install the accessory drive belt.

ENGINE MOUNT

REMOVAL & INSTALLATION

See Figure 105.

1. Before servicing the vehicle, refer to the Precautions Section.

2. Remove the front suspension crossmember.

3. Remove the engine mount-to-engine mount bracket nut.

4. Remove the engine mount.

5. Remove the engine mount heat shield from the engine mount, if necessary.

To install:

6. Install the engine mount heat shield to the engine mount, if necessary.

7. Install the engine mount.

8. Install the engine mount-to-engine mount bracket nut and tighten to 48 ft. lbs. (65 Nm).

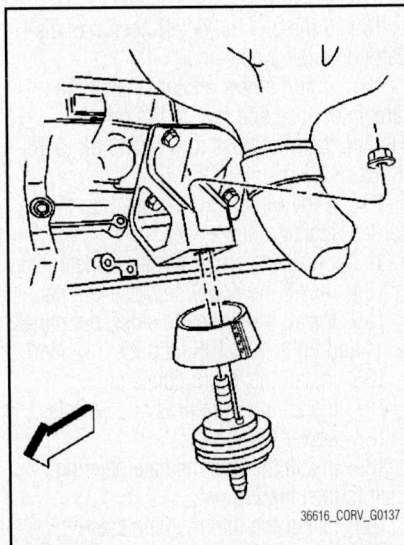

Fig. 105 Engine mount—left side shown, right side similar

9. Install the front suspension cross-member.

EXHAUST MANIFOLD

REMOVAL & INSTALLATION

Left Side

See Figures 106 through 108.

1. Before servicing the vehicle, refer to the Precautions Section.

2. Remove the oil filler cap (1), if necessary.

3. Remove the left engine sight shield (3).

4. Remove the alternator. Refer to Alternator Removal & Installation in the Engine Electrical Section.

5. Remove the bank 1, sensor 1 oxygen sensor from the exhaust manifold. Refer to Heated Oxygen Sensor (HO2S) Removal & Installation in Engine Performance & Emission Controls.

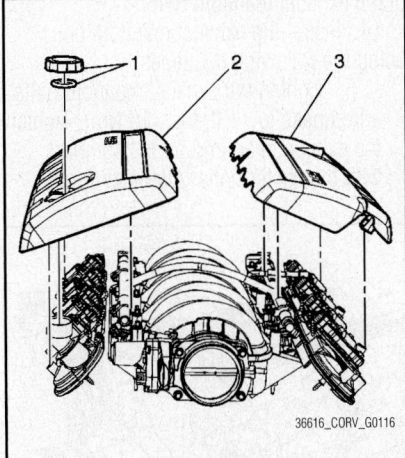

Fig. 106 Oil filler cap (1) and left engine sight shield (3)

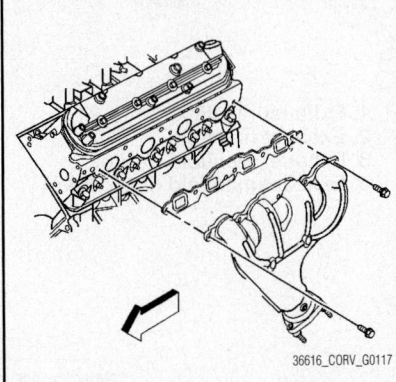

Fig. 107 Exhaust manifold removal and installation—6.2L engine, left side

6. Remove the spark plugs. Refer to Spark Plugs Removal & Installation.

7. Remove the catalytic converter. Refer to Catalytic Converter Removal & Installation.

8. Remove the exhaust manifold bolts.

➡It may be necessary to remove the heat assembly from the exhaust manifold to gain enough clearance to remove the exhaust manifold.

9. Remove the exhaust manifold.

To install:

➡The cylinder head exhaust manifold bolt hole threads must be cleaned and free of debris or threadlocking material.

➡In the following service procedure, position the catalytic converter on the intermediate pipe, but DO NOT tighten the clamp. Leave it loose to allow the alignment of the exhaust manifold on the cylinder head. Install the catalytic converter.

✴✴ WARNING

Use the correct fastener in the correct location. Replacement fasteners must be the correct part number for that application. Fasteners requiring replacement or fasteners requiring the use of thread locking compound or sealant are identified in the service procedure. Do not use paints, lubricants, or corrosion inhibitors on fasteners or fastener joint surfaces unless specified. These coatings affect fastener torque and joint clamping force and may damage the fastener. Use the correct tightening sequence and specifications when installing fasteners in order to avoid damage to parts and systems.

10. Apply a 0.2 in. (5 mm) wide band of threadlock GM P/N 12345493 (Canadian P/N 10953489), or equivalent to the threads of the exhaust manifold bolts.

11. Position the exhaust manifold and a NEW gasket into place.

12. Install the exhaust manifold bolts using the following sequence:

a. Tighten the exhaust manifold bolts a first pass to 11 ft. lbs. (15 Nm). Tighten the exhaust manifold bolts beginning with the center bolts. Alternate from side-to-side, working toward the outside bolts.

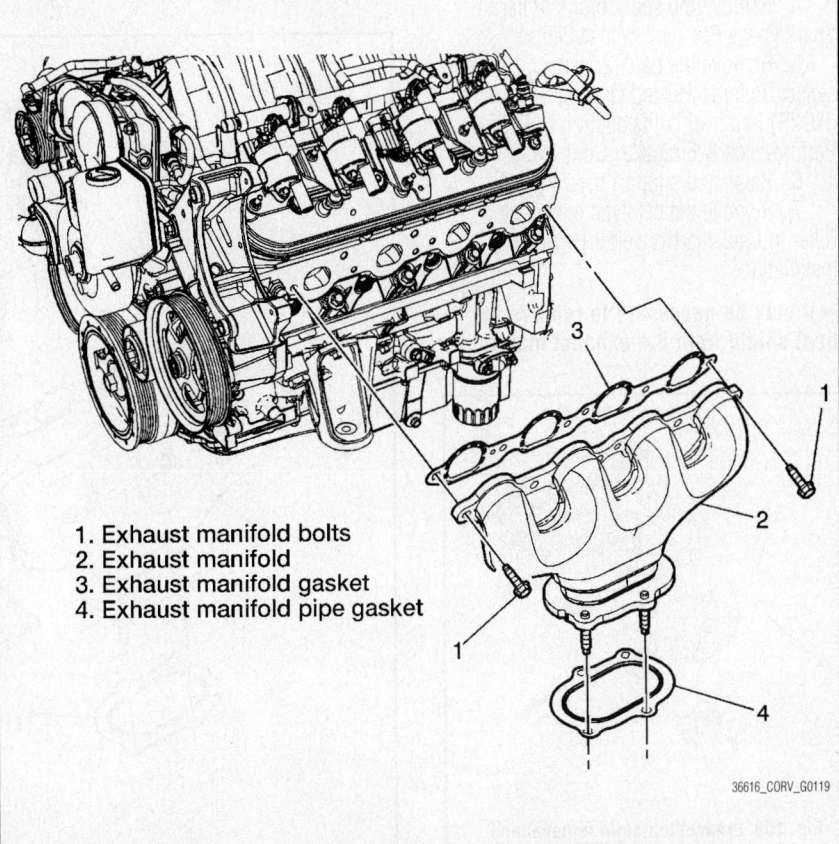

1. Exhaust manifold bolts
2. Exhaust manifold
3. Exhaust manifold gasket
4. Exhaust manifold pipe gasket

Fig. 108 Exhaust manifold removal and installation—7.0L engine, left side

b. Tighten the exhaust manifold bolts a final pass to 18 ft. lbs. (25 Nm). Tighten the exhaust manifold bolts beginning with the center bolts. Alternate from side-to-side, working toward the outside bolts.

✳✳ WARNING

Improperly installed and/or leaking exhaust manifold gaskets may affect vehicle emissions and/or On-Board Diagnostics (OBD) II system performance.

13. Install the bank 1, sensor 1 oxygen sensor in the exhaust manifold oxygen sensor.
14. Install the spark plugs.
15. Install the alternator.
16. Install the oil filler cap, if necessary.
17. Install the left engine sight shield.
18. Install the catalytic converter.

Right Side

See Figures 106, 109 and 110.

1. Before servicing the vehicle, refer to the Precautions Section.
2. Remove the oil filler cap (1), if necessary.
3. Remove the right engine sight shield (2).
4. Remove the spark plugs. Refer to Spark Plugs Removal & Installation.
5. Remove the bank 2, sensor 1 oxygen sensor. Refer to Heated Oxygen Sensor (HO2S) Removal & Installation in Engine Performance & Emission Controls.
6. Raise and support the vehicle.
7. Remove the catalytic converter. Refer to Catalytic Converter Removal & Installation.

➡**It may be necessary to remove the heat shield from the exhaust manifold.**

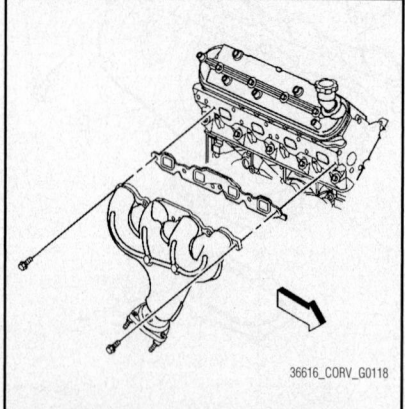

Fig. 109 Exhaust manifold removal and installation—6.2L engine, right side

8. Remove the exhaust manifold mounting nuts.
9. Remove the exhaust manifold and gasket.

To install:

➡**Tighten the exhaust manifold bolts as specified in the service procedure. Improperly installed and/or leaking exhaust manifold gaskets may affect vehicle emissions and/or On-Board Diagnostics (OBD) II system performance.**

➡**The cylinder head exhaust manifold bolt hole threads must be clean and free of debris or threadlocking material.**

✳✳ WARNING

Use the correct fastener in the correct location. Replacement fasteners must be the correct part number for that application. Fasteners requiring replacement or fasteners requiring the use of thread locking compound or sealant are identified in the service procedure. Do not use paints, lubricants, or corrosion inhibitors on fasteners or fastener joint surfaces unless specified. These coatings affect fastener torque and joint

clamping force and may damage the fastener. Use the correct tightening sequence and specifications when installing fasteners in order to avoid damage to parts and systems.

10. If necessary, install the exhaust manifold heat shield and bolts and tighten to 80 inch lbs. (9 Nm).

➡**In the following service procedure, DO NOT tighten the exhaust clamp. Leave it loosened so that the exhaust manifold and gasket can be aligned on the cylinder head.**

11. Install the catalytic converter to the intermediate pipe.

➡**Use one or two bolts to hold the manifold and gasket in place.**

12. Install the exhaust manifold and gasket.
13. Apply a 0.2 in. (5 mm) wide band of threadlock GM P/N 12345493 (Canadian P/N 10953488) or equivalent to the threads of the exhaust manifold bolts.
14. Install the exhaust manifold bolts using the following sequence:
a. Tighten the exhaust manifold bolts a first pass to 11 ft. lbs. (15 Nm). Tighten the exhaust manifold bolts beginning with the center bolts. Alternate from

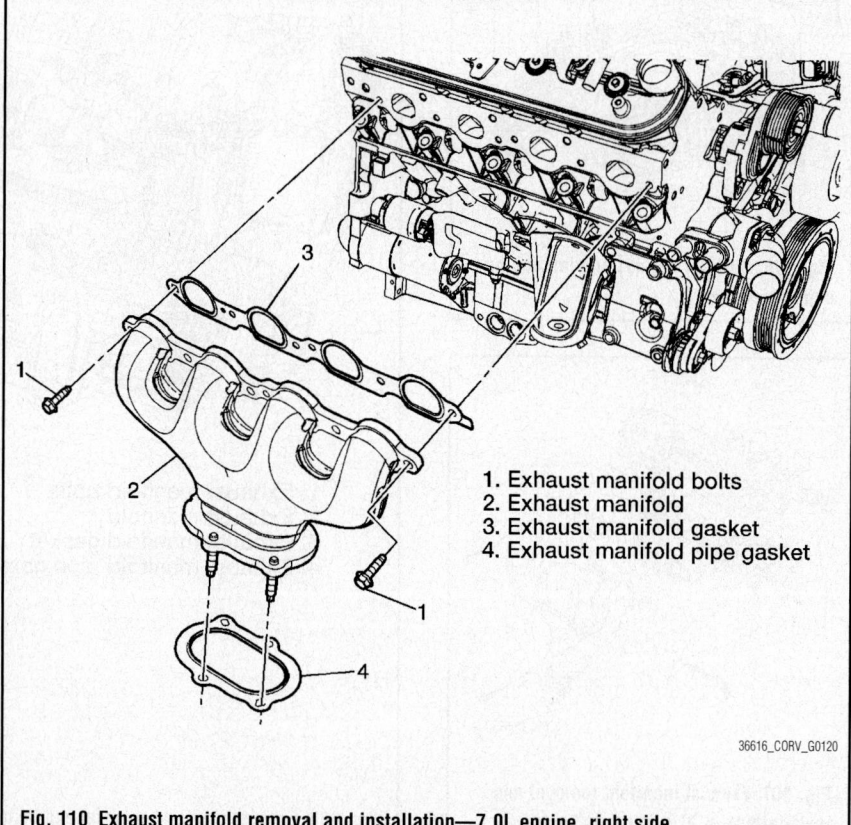

1. Exhaust manifold bolts
2. Exhaust manifold
3. Exhaust manifold gasket
4. Exhaust manifold pipe gasket

Fig. 110 Exhaust manifold removal and installation—7.0L engine, right side

side-to-side, working toward the outside bolts.

b. Tighten the exhaust manifold bolts a final pass to 18 ft. lbs. (25 Nm). Tighten the exhaust manifold bolts beginning with the center bolts. Alternate from side-to-side, working toward the outside bolts.

15. Install the spark plugs.

16. Install the oil filler cap, if necessary.

17. Install the right engine sight shield.

18. Install the bank 2, sensor 1 oxygen sensor.

19. Install the catalytic converter to the exhaust manifold nuts.

FLYWHEEL

REMOVAL & INSTALLATION

See Figures 111 through 114.

> ✴✴ **WARNING**
>
> **Failure to follow the proper removal and installation procedures may result in damage to the engine crankshaft thrust bearing.**

> ✴✴ **WARNING**
>
> **When tilting down the rear of the driveline, observe the clearance between the rear of the engine and the composite dash panel. Do not allow the engine to rest unsupported against the composite dash panel, or vehicle damage may result.**

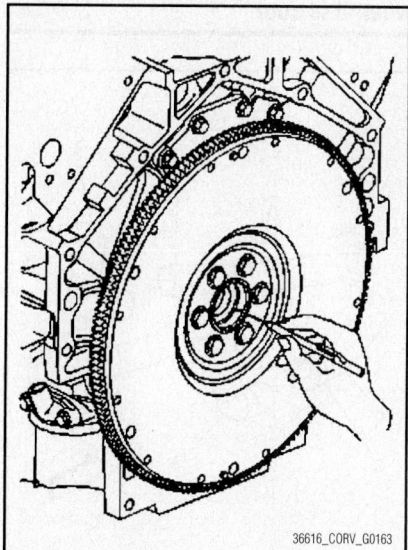

Fig. 111 Mark or scribe the end of the crankshaft and the flywheel

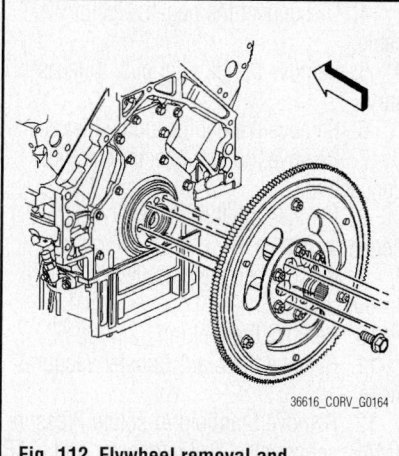

Fig. 112 Flywheel removal and installation—automatic transmission

> ✴✴ **WARNING**
>
> **When lowering and removing the rear of the driveline, observe the clearance between the rear of the Transmission assembly and the underbody to prevent damage.**

➡ **For manual transmission applications, note the position and direction of the engine flywheel before removal. The flywheel does not use a locating pin for alignment. Mark or scribe the end of the crankshaft and the flywheel before component removal. The engine flywheel must be reinstalled to the original position and direction. The engine flywheel will not initially seat against the crankshaft flange, but will be pulled onto the crankshaft by the engine flywheel bolts. This procedure requires a 3 stage tightening process.**

> ✴✴ **WARNING**
>
> **DO NOT remove the prop shaft hub or flex plate from the automatic transmission engine flywheel. The flywheel, prop shaft hub, and flex plate are balanced as an assembly. If service is required, the entire flywheel assembly should be replaced.**

1. Before servicing the vehicle, refer to the Precautions Section.

2. Remove the catalytic converter. Refer to Catalytic Converter Removal & Installation.

3. If equipped with automatic transmission, remove the driveline support. Refer to Automatic Transmission Removal & Installation, in the Drive Train Section.

4. If equipped with manual transmission, remove the clutch assembly. Refer to Clutch Driven Disc & Pressure Plate Removal & Installation, in the Drive Train Section.

5. Mark or scribe the end of the crankshaft and the manual transmission flywheel.

6. Remove the flywheel bolts.

7. Remove the flywheel.

To install:

8. If equipped with manual transmission, align the mark or scribe on the crankshaft with the mark or scribe on the existing flywheel.

9. Install the engine flywheel.

10. Apply threadlock to the threads of the flywheel bolts.

11. Install the flywheel bolts until snug. Torque the bolts in sequence as follows:

- Tighten the engine flywheel bolts a first pass in sequence to 15 ft. lbs. (20 Nm)
- Tighten the engine flywheel bolts a second pass in sequence to 37 ft. lbs. (50 Nm)
- Tighten the engine flywheel bolts a final pass in sequence to 74 ft. lbs. (100 Nm)

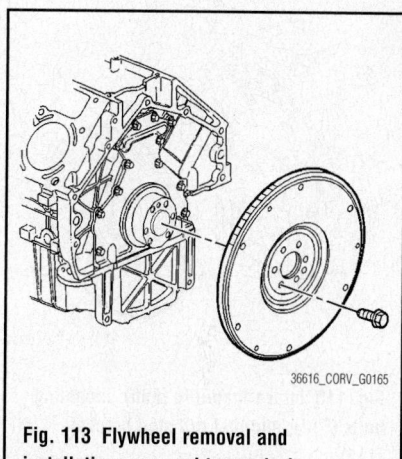

Fig. 113 Flywheel removal and installation—manual transmission

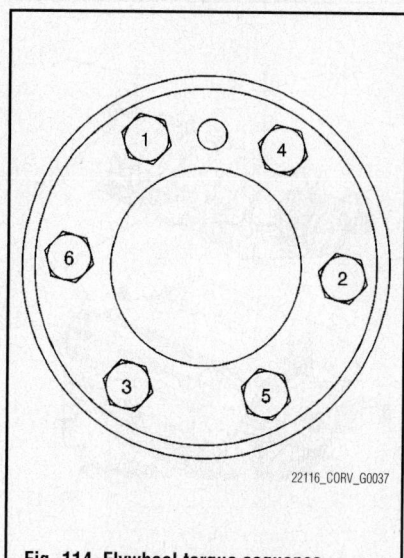

Fig. 114 Flywheel torque sequence

12. Install the driveline support, if equipped with an automatic transmission.

13. Install the clutch assembly, if equipped with a manual transmission.

14. Install the transmission.

15. Install the catalytic converter.

INTAKE MANIFOLD

REMOVAL & INSTALLATION

See Figures 106, 115 through 117.

➡The intake manifold, throttle body, fuel injection rail, and injectors may be removed as an assembly. If not servicing the individual components, remove the manifold as a complete assembly.

1. Before servicing the vehicle, refer to the Precautions Section.

2. Relieve the fuel system pressure.

3. Drain the cooling system.

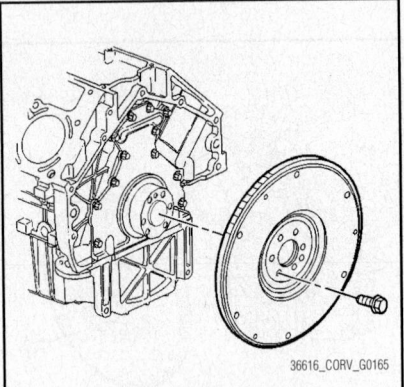

36616_CORV_G0165

Fig. 115 Intake manifold (500), mounting bolts (512), and fuel rail stop bracket (712)

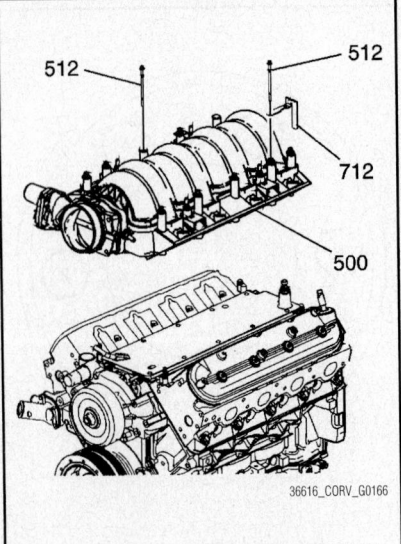

36616_CORV_G0166

Fig. 116 Intake manifold gaskets (514)

4. Disconnect the negative battery cable.

5. Remove the oil filler cap, if necessary.

6. Remove the engine sight shields.

7. Remove the fuel injector electrical connectors.

8. Remove the throttle body electrical connectors.

9. Remove the fuel supply line for the fuel injectors.

10. Remove the fuel rail.

11. Remove the brake booster vacuum hose.

12. Remove Manifold Absolute Pressure (MAP) sensor electrical connector and MAP sensor. Refer to MAP Sensor Removal & Installation in the Engine Performance & Emission Control Section.

13. Remove the grommet from the MAP sensor, as required.

14. Remove the Evaporative Emission (EVAP) clip, bolt, bracket, valve and tubes. Refer to EVAP Sensor Removal & Installation in the Engine Performance & Emission Control Section.

15. Remove the intake manifold mounting bolts (512) and fuel rail stop bracket (712).

16. Remove the intake manifold (500).

17. Remove the intake manifold gaskets (514).

To install:

✳✳ WARNING

Do not reuse the intake manifold gaskets.

18. Install new intake manifold gaskets.

19. Install the intake manifold.

20. Install the fuel rail stop bracket.

21. Apply a 0.2 in.(5 mm) band of threadlocker to the threads of the intake manifold bolts.

22. Install the fuel rail stop bracket.

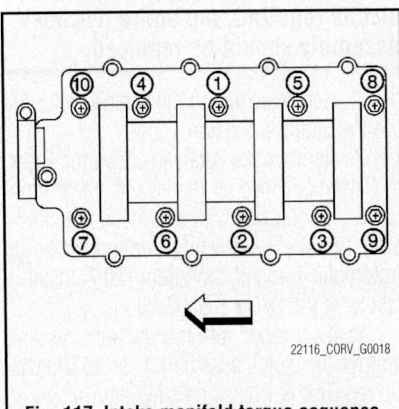

22116_CORV_G0018

Fig. 117 Intake manifold torque sequence

23. Install the intake manifold bolts and tighten in sequence as follows:
- Step 1: Tighten to 44 inch lbs. (5 Nm).
- Step 2: Tighten to 89 inch lbs. (10 Nm).

24. Lubricate the MAP sensor grommet with clean engine oil.

25. Install the MAP sensor and grommet.

26. Install the EVAP valve, bracket, and bolt. Tighten the mounting bolt to 37 ft. lbs. (50 Nm).

27. Install the EVAP tubes.

28. Install the fuel rail and fuel supply hose.

29. Connect the MAP sensor electrical connector.

30. Install the brake booster vacuum hose.

31. Connect the throttle body electrical connectors.

32. Connect the fuel injector electrical connectors.

33. Refill the cooling system to the correct level.

34. Install the engine sight shields and oil filler cap, if necessary.

35. Connect the negative battery cable.

36. Start the engine and check for leaks.

INTERMEDIATE PIPE

REMOVAL & INSTALLATION

See Figures 118 through 121.

✳✳ CAUTION

In order to avoid being burned, do not service the exhaust system while it is still hot. Service the system when it is cool.

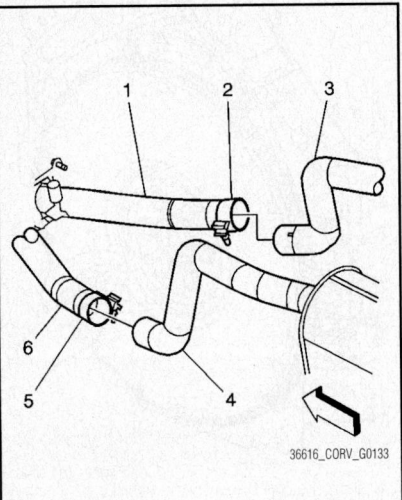

36616_CORV_G0133

Fig. 118 Loosen the exhaust muffler band clamps (2, 5)

1. Before servicing the vehicle, refer to the Precautions Section.

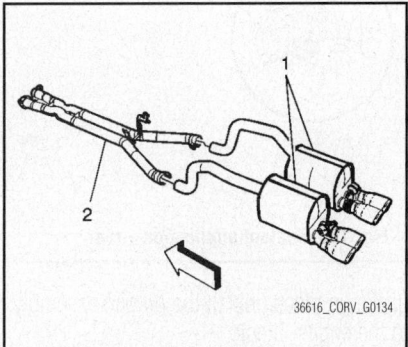

Fig. 119 Separate the exhaust mufflers (1) from the intermediate pipe (2)

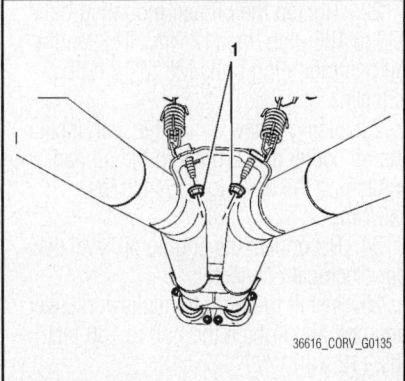

Fig. 120 Remove the exhaust pipe hanger lower nuts (1)

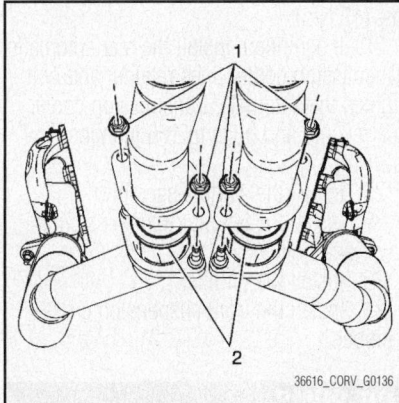

Fig. 121 Remove the intermediate pipe-to-catalytic converter pipe nuts (1) and the exhaust pipe seals (2)

2. Raise and suitably support the vehicle.

3. Install adjustable jack stands under the front and rear of the intermediate pipe.

4. Loosen the exhaust muffler band clamps (2, 5).

5. Separate the exhaust mufflers (1) from the intermediate pipe (2).

6. Remove the exhaust pipe hanger lower nuts (1).

7. Remove the intermediate pipe-to-catalytic converter pipe nuts (1) and the exhaust pipe seals (2).

8. Lower the jack stands.

9. Remove the intermediate pipe from the jack stands.

To install:

➡️**If reinstalling the original intermediate pipe, the tail pipe/muffler band clips must be replaced. Mark the position of the band clips on the intermediate exhaust pipe. Remove the band clips by grinding the welds. Install new band clips on the intermediate pipe. Position the new band clips using the alignment mark created previously.**

10. Using a wire brush, clean the contact area of the left and right mufflers to the intermediate pipe.

11. Apply a small amount of lubricant on the intermediate pipes and the left and right mufflers.

12. Position the intermediate pipe on the jack stands.

13. Raise the intermediate pipe and install the intermediate pipe.

14. Install the exhaust pipe seal.

15. Install the intermediate pipe to the exhaust mufflers.

➡️**When install the retaining nuts, hand tighten them. This will allow the proper alignment of the exhaust system for the final assembly procedure.**

16. Install the retaining nuts.

17. Remove the adjustable jack stands.

18. Tighten the exhaust muffler clamp bolts to 32 ft. lbs. (44 Nm).

19. Tighten the intermediate pipe-to-catalytic converter pipe nuts and bolts to 18 ft. lbs. (25 Nm).

20. Tighten the exhaust pipe hanger lower nuts to 37 ft. lbs. (50 Nm).

OIL PAN

REMOVAL & INSTALLATION
See Figures 122 through 128.

1. Before servicing the vehicle, refer to the Precautions Section.

2. Remove the front suspension crossmember. Refer to Crossmember Removal & Installation in the Front Suspension Section.

3. Remove the oil filter.

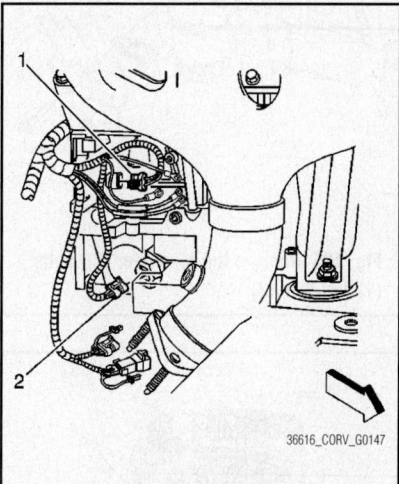

Fig. 122 Disconnect the engine oil level sensor electrical connector (2)

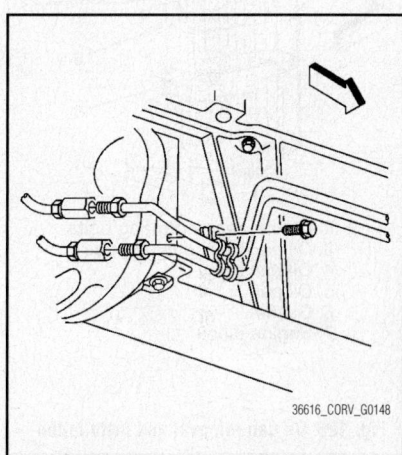

Fig. 123 Remove the transmission lines from the rear of the oil pan

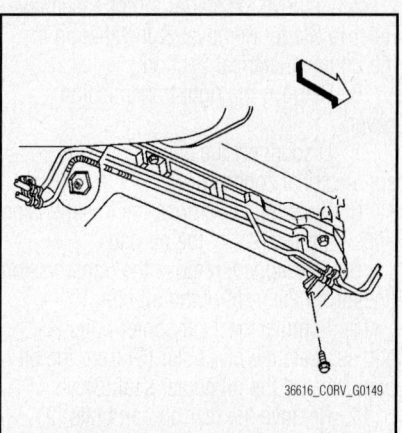

Fig. 124 Remove the transmission lines from the front of the oil pan

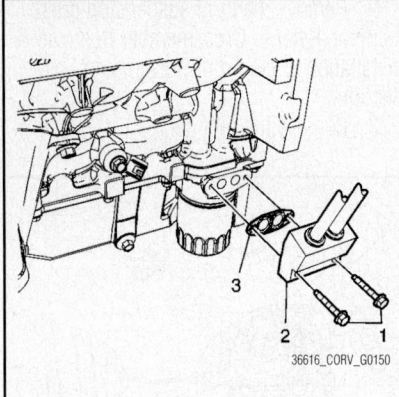

Fig. 125 Remove the oil cooler (2), bolts (1) and seal (3)

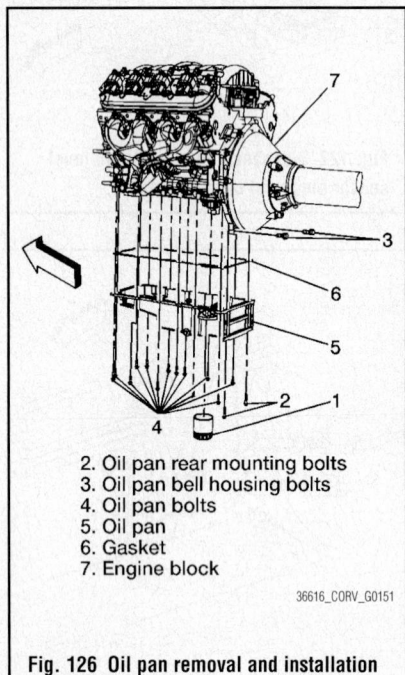

2. Oil pan rear mounting bolts
3. Oil pan bell housing bolts
4. Oil pan bolts
5. Oil pan
6. Gasket
7. Engine block

36616_CORV_G0151

Fig. 126 Oil pan removal and installation

4. Remove the left rear transmission cover.

5. Remove the starter motor assembly. Refer to Starter Removal & Installation in the Engine Electrical Section.

6. Remove the right transmission cover.

7. Disconnect the engine oil level sensor electrical connector (2).

8. If equipped, remove the transmission lines from the rear of the oil pan.

9. If equipped, remove the transmission lines from the front of the oil pan.

10. Remove the 2 oil cooler bolts (1) and separate the oil cooler (2) from the oil pan. Discard the oil cooler seal (3).

11. Remove the rear oil pan bolts (2).

12. Remove the bolts from the bell housing to the oil pan (3).

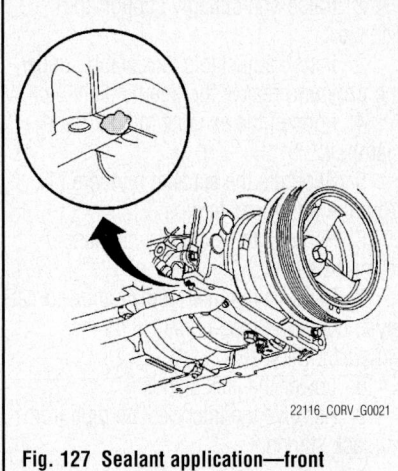

22116_CORV_G0021

Fig. 127 Sealant application—front

13. Remove the remaining oil pan bolts (4).

14. Remove the oil pan (5) from the engine block (7).

➡️It may be necessary to rotate the oil pan to remove to gain enough clearance to clear the oil pump pick up tube.

15. Remove the oil pan gasket (6) from the engine block (7).

To install:

✳️ WARNING

The alignment of the structural oil pan is critical. The rear bolt hole locations of the oil pan provide mounting points for the transmission housing. To ensure the rigidity of the powertrain and correct transmission alignment, it is important that the rear of the block and the rear of the oil pan are flush, or even. The rear of the oil pan must NEVER protrude beyond the engine block and transmission housing plane.

➡️Do not use the oil pan gasket again. It is not necessary to rivet the NEW gasket to the oil pan.

16. Apply a 0.2 in. (5 mm) bead of sealant 0.8 in. (20 mm) long to the engine block. Apply the sealant directly onto the tabs of the front cover gasket that protrude into the oil pan surface.

17. Apply a 0.2 in. (5 mm) bead of sealant 0.8 in. (20 mm) long to the engine block. Apply the sealant directly onto the tabs of the rear cover gasket that protrude into the oil pan surface.

18. Position the oil pan gasket on the oil pan.

19. Using 2 bolts to hold the oil pan

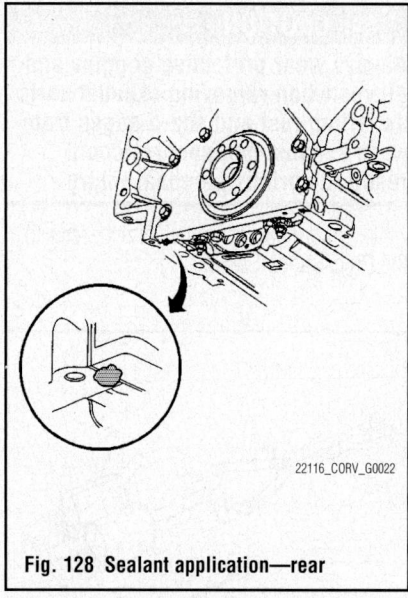

22116_CORV_G0022

Fig. 128 Sealant application—rear

gasket in place, install the oil pan assembly to the engine block.

20. Finger tighten the 2 bolts to hold the oil pan assembly in place.

21. Install the mounting bolts for the oil pan assembly.

22. Tighten the oil pan mounting bolts M6 to 106 inch lbs. (12 Nm). Tighten the oil pan mounting bolts M8 to 18 ft. lbs. (25 Nm).

23. Using a new oil cooler seal, install the oil cooler and 2 bolts to the oil pan, tightening the bolts to 106 inch lbs. (12 Nm).

24. Reconnect the engine oil level sensor electrical connector.

25. Install the right transmission cover and bolt and tighten the bolt to 106 inch lbs. (12 Nm).

26. If equipped, install the front automatic transmission cooler line retainer and bolt. Tighten the automatic transmission cooler line retainer and bolts to 106 inch lbs. (12 Nm).

27. If equipped, install the rear automatic transmission cooler lines retainer and bolt. Tighten the automatic transmission cooler line retainer and bolts to 106 inch lbs. (12 Nm).

28. Install the starter assembly.

29. Install the left rear transmission cover and bolt.

30. Install the oil filter.

31. Install the front suspension crossmember.

OIL PUMP

REMOVAL & INSTALLATION

See Figures 129 through 132.

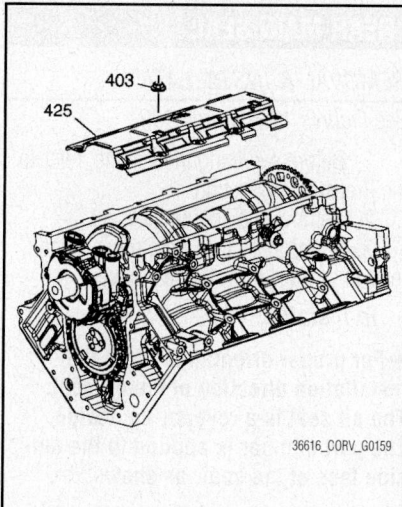

Fig. 129 Remove the crankshaft oil deflector (425) and nuts (403)

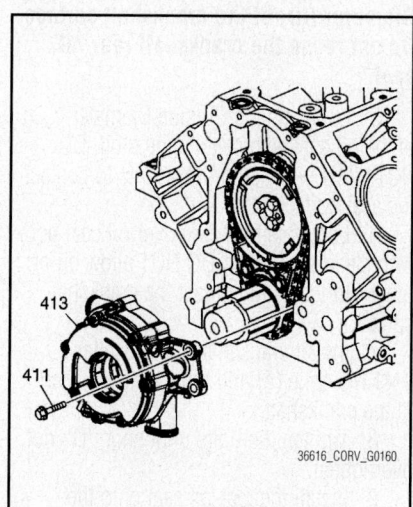

Fig. 130 Oil pump (413) removal and installation

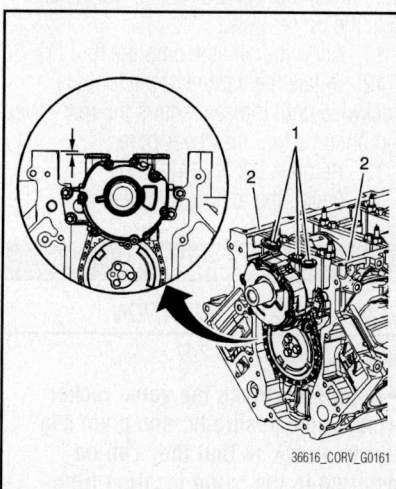

Fig. 131 Oil pump (1) and engine block (2) alignment

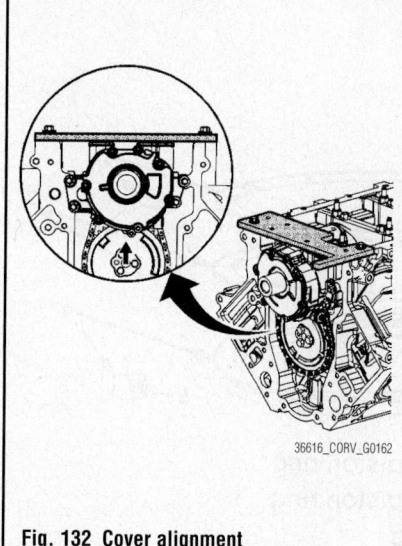

Fig. 132 Cover alignment

1. Before servicing the vehicle, refer to the precautions in the beginning of this section.

2. Remove the engine front cover. Refer to Engine Front Cover Removal & Installation.

3. Remove the engine oil pan. Refer to Engine Oil Pan Removal & Installation.

4. Remove the crankshaft oil deflector nuts (403).

5. Remove the crankshaft oil deflector (425).

6. Remove the oil pump bolts.

➡**Do not allow dirt or debris to enter the oil pump assembly. Cap ends, as necessary.**

7. Remove the oil pump (413).

8. Clean and inspect the oil pump.

To install:

➡**Inspect the engine block oil gallery passages. These surfaces must be clear and free of debris or restrictions.**

9. Align the splines of the crankshaft sprocket and the oil pump drive gears, and install the oil pump.

10. Install the oil pump onto the crankshaft sprocket until the pump housing contacts the face of the engine block.

11. Install the oil pump bolts. Do not tighten the bolts at this time.

12. Align the oil pump surfaces (1) with the engine block surfaces (2). The oil pump must be aligned flush or no greater than 0.04 in. (0.1 mm) below the engine block oil pan rail.

13. Install the EN-48853 cover alignment and bolts to the engine block. Tighten the

EN-48853 cover alignment bolts to 18 ft. lbs.(25 Nm).

14. Firmly push the oil pump until the pump surfaces contact the J 41480 cover alignment. Continue to retain the pump to the J 41480 cover alignment. Tighten the oil pump bolts to 18 ft. lbs. (25 Nm).

15. Install the crankshaft oil deflector and nuts. Install the deflector onto the engine with the word "Rear" at the back of the engine block. Tighten the crankshaft oil deflector nuts to 18 ft. lbs. (25 Nm).

16. Install the engine oil pan.

17. Install the engine front cover.

MAIN BEARING TORQUE SEQUENCE

See Figure 133.

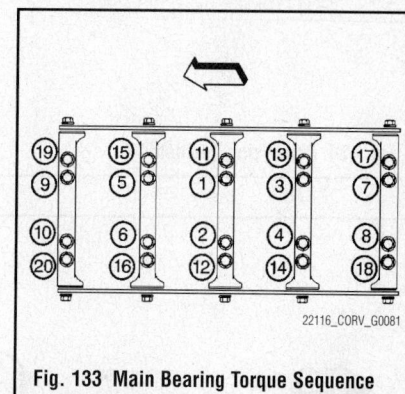

Fig. 133 Main Bearing Torque Sequence

PISTON AND RING

POSITIONING

See Figures 134 through 136.

❋❋ **WARNING**

Important: For 7.0L engine, do not attempt to disassemble or assemble the piston, pin, and connecting rod. The piston, pin, and connecting rod should be serviced as an assembly.

1. Using piston ring pliers, install the piston rings onto the piston. The dimple or mark on the piston ring should face the top of the piston. If no dimple or mark can be found on the top compression ring, it may be installed in either direction.

2. Position the oil control ring end gaps a minimum of 1.0 inch (25 mm) from each other.

3. Position the compression ring end gaps 180 degrees opposite each other.

4. Install the connecting rod bearings to the rod and cap.

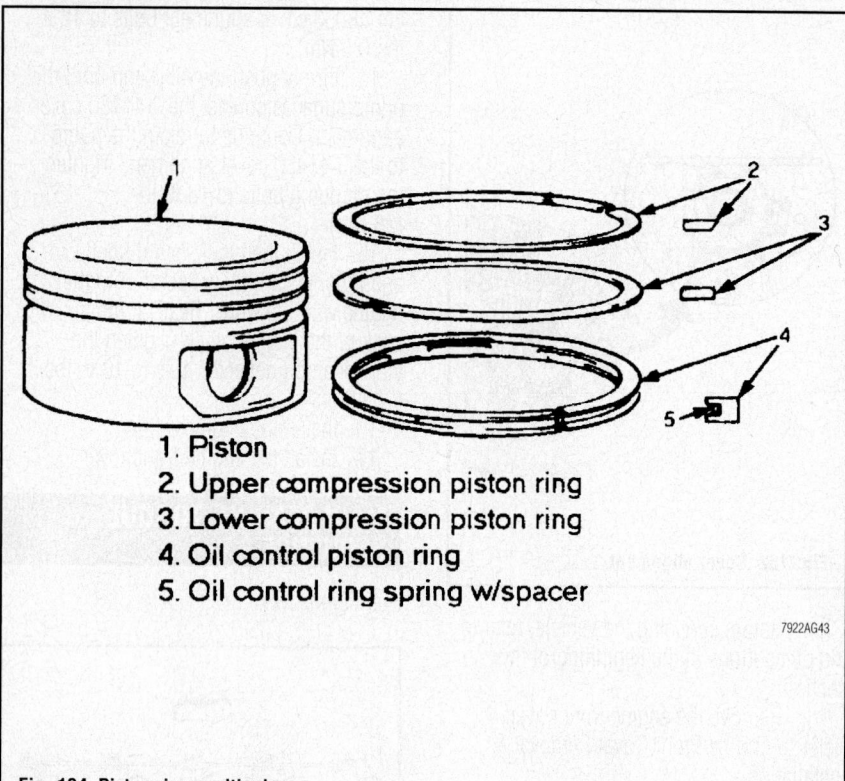

1. Piston
2. Upper compression piston ring
3. Lower compression piston ring
4. Oil control piston ring
5. Oil control ring spring w/spacer

7922AG43

Fig. 134 Piston ring positioning

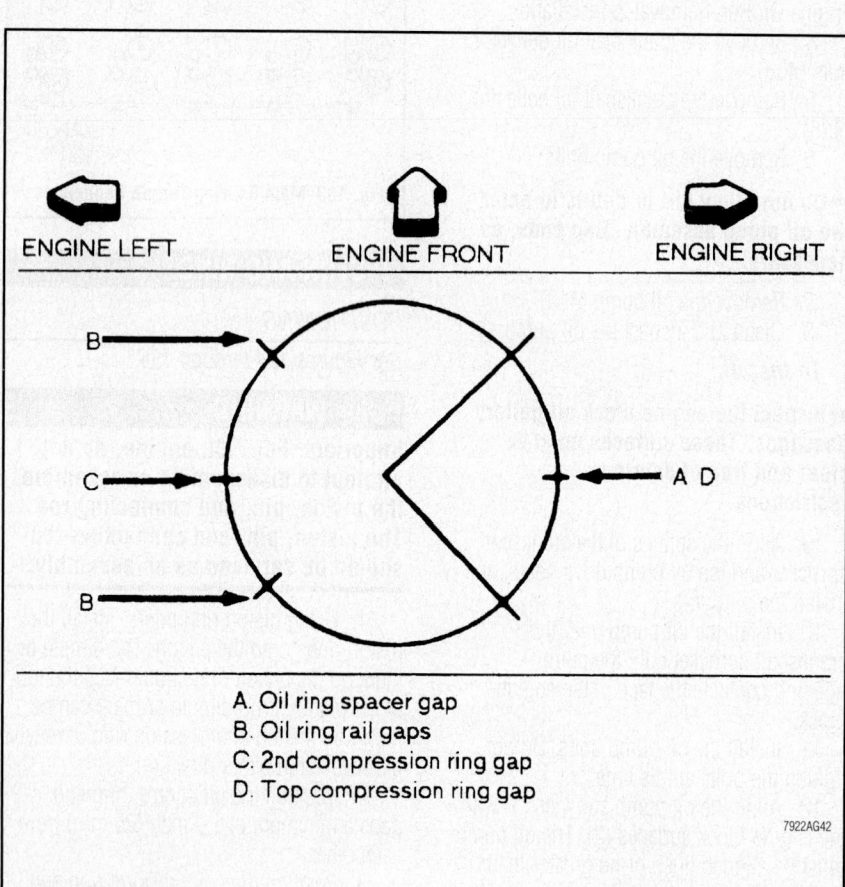

ENGINE LEFT   ENGINE FRONT   ENGINE RIGHT

A. Oil ring spacer gap
B. Oil ring rail gaps
C. 2nd compression ring gap
D. Top compression ring gap

7922AG42

Fig. 135 Piston ring end-gap spacing

REAR MAIN SEAL

REMOVAL & INSTALLATION

See Figures 137 through 139.

　1. Before servicing the vehicle, refer to the Precautions Section.
　2. Remove the engine flywheel.
　3. Using a pry tool, carefully pry the rear oil seal (1) from the rear cover.

To install:

➡**For proper orientation, note the installation direction of the oil seal. The oil seal is a reverse-lip design. The part number is applied to the outside face of the seal, as shown.**

　4. Inspect the seal and identify the part number markings for proper orientation.

➡**Do not lubricate the oil seal Inside Diameter (ID) of the crankshaft surface. Do not reuse the crankshaft rear oil seal.**

　5. Lubricate the Outside Diameter (OD) of the oil seal with clean engine oil. DO NOT allow oil or other lubricants to contact the seal surface.
　6. Lubricate the rear cover oil seal bore with clean engine oil. DO NOT allow oil or other lubricants to contact the crankshaft surface.
　7. Install crankshaft seal installer J-41479 cone (2) and bolts onto the rear of the crankshaft.
　8. Tighten the bolts until snug. Do not overtighten.
　9. Install the rear oil seal onto the tapered cone (2) and push the seal to the rear cover bore.
　10. Thread the J-41479 threaded rod into the tapered cone until the tool (1) contacts the oil seal.
　11. Align the oil seal onto the tool (1).
　12. Rotate the handle of the tool (1) clockwise until the seal enters the rear cover and bottoms into the cover bore.
　13. Remove the J-41479 tool.
　14. Install the engine flywheel.

ROCKER ARMS/SHAFTS

REMOVAL & INSTALLATION

See Figures 140 and 141.

➡**Important: Place the valve rocker arms, valve pushrods, and pivot support in a rack so that they can be installed in the same location from which they were removed.**

　1. Before servicing the vehicle, refer to the Precautions Section.

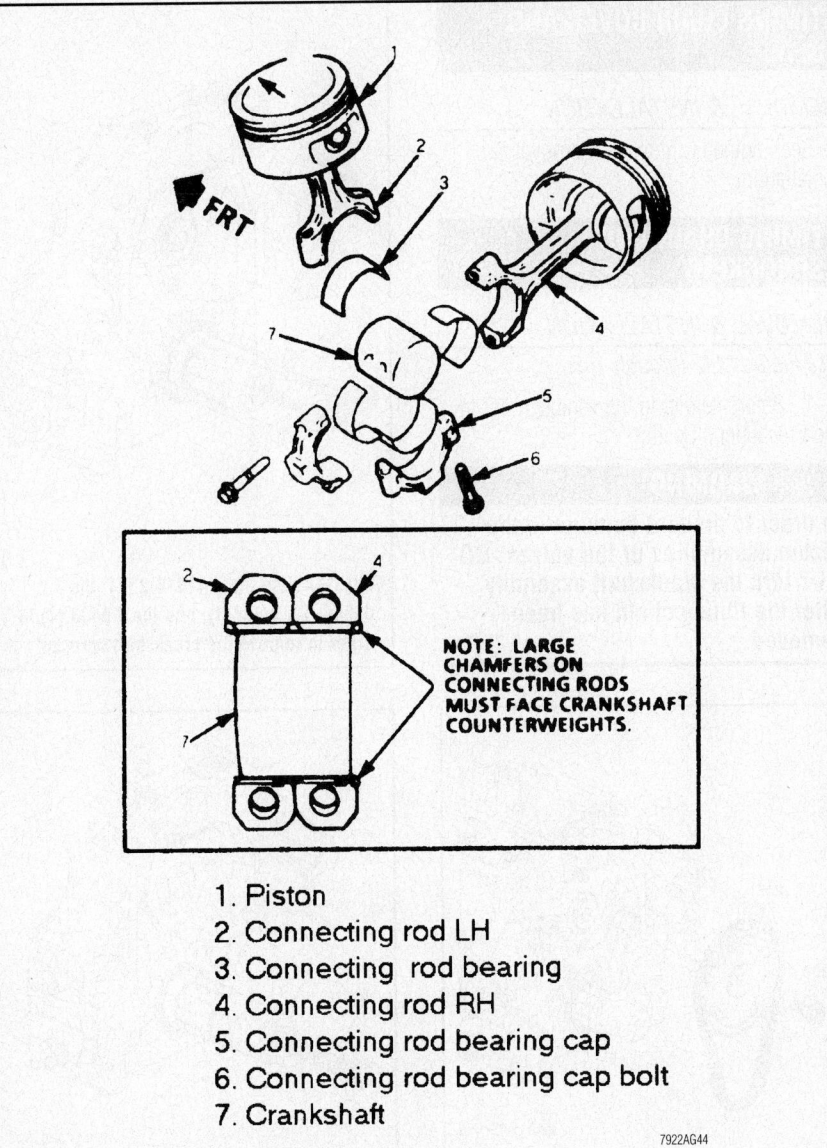

NOTE: LARGE CHAMFERS ON CONNECTING RODS MUST FACE CRANKSHAFT COUNTERWEIGHTS.

1. Piston
2. Connecting rod LH
3. Connecting rod bearing
4. Connecting rod RH
5. Connecting rod bearing cap
6. Connecting rod bearing cap bolt
7. Crankshaft

7922AG44

Fig. 136 Piston and connecting rod positioning

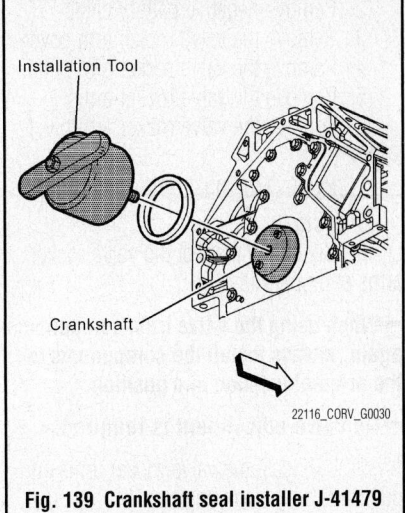

Fig. 139 Crankshaft seal installer J-41479

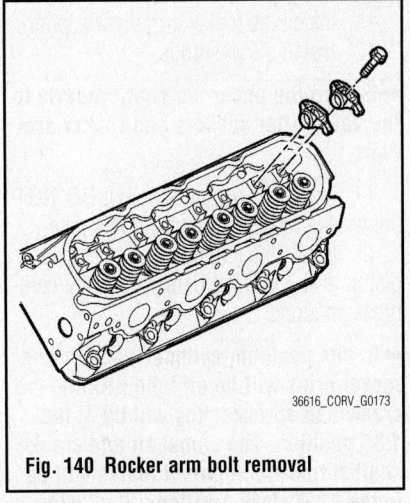

Fig. 140 Rocker arm bolt removal

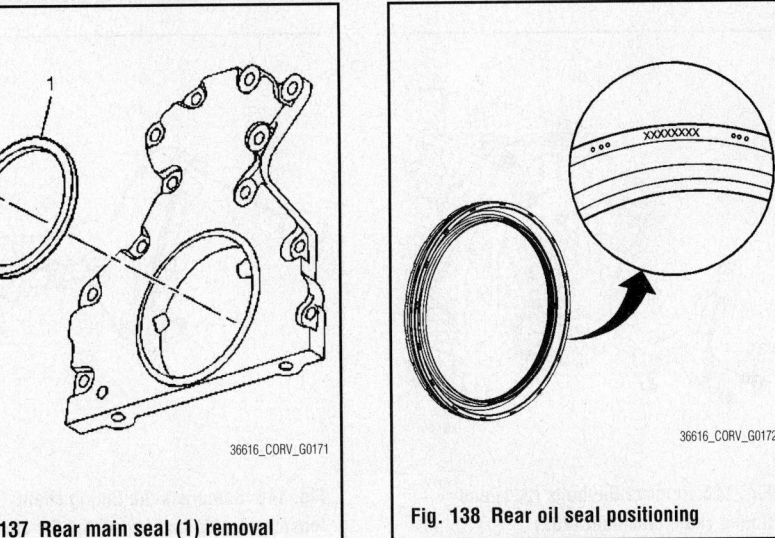

36616_CORV_G0171

Fig. 137 Rear main seal (1) removal

36616_CORV_G0172

Fig. 138 Rear oil seal positioning

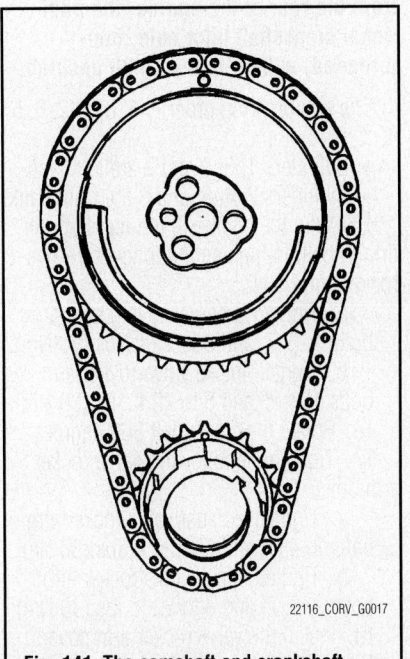

22116_CORV_G0017

Fig. 141 The camshaft and crankshaft sprocket alignment marks

2. Remove negative battery cable

3. Remove the valve rocker arm covers.

4. Remove the valve rocker arm bolts.

5. Remove the valve rocker arms.

6. Remove the valve rocker arm pivot support.

7. Remove the pushrods.

To install:

8. Clean and inspect the valve rocker arms and pushrods.

➡When using the valve train components again, always install the components to the original location and position.

➡No valve adjustment is required.

9. Lubricate the valve rocker arms and pushrods with clean engine oil.

10. Lubricate the flange of the valve rocker arm bolts with clean engine oil.

11. Install the rocker arm pivot support.

12. Install the pushrods.

➡Ensure the pushrods seat properly to the valve lifter sockets and rocker arm ends.

13. Install the rocker arms but **DO NOT** tighten the rocker arm bolts at this time.

14. Rotate the crankshaft until the No. 1 piston is at Top Dead Center (TDC) of compression stroke.

➡In this position, cylinder number one rocker arms will be off lobe lift, and the crankshaft sprocket key will be at the 1:30 position. The camshaft and crankshaft sprocket alignment marks will be in the 12 O'clock positions. If viewing from the rear of the engine, the additional crankshaft pilot hole, non-threaded, will be in the 10:30 position.

The engine firing order is 1, 8, 7, 2, 6, 5, 4, 3.

• Cylinders 1, 3, 5 and 7 are left bank.

• Cylinders 2, 4, 6, and 8 are right bank.

15. With the engine in the number one firing position, tighten the following valve rocker arm bolts:

   a. Tighten exhaust valve rocker arm bolts 1, 2, 7, and 8 to 22 ft. lbs.(30 Nm).

   b. Tighten intake valve rocker arm bolts 1, 3, 4, and 5 to 22 ft. lbs.(30 Nm).

16. Rotate the crankshaft 360 degrees.

17. Tighten the following valve rocker arm bolts:

   a. Tighten exhaust valve rocker arm bolts 3, 4, 5, and 6 to 22 ft. lbs.(30 Nm).

   b. Tighten intake valve rocker arm bolts 2, 6, 7, and 8 to 22 ft. lbs.(30 Nm).

18. Install the valve rocker arm covers.

19. Connect the negative battery cable.

20. Start the vehicle and check for leaks.

TIMING CHAIN COVER AND SEAL

REMOVAL & INSTALLATION

See Engine Front Cover Removal & Installation.

TIMING CHAIN AND SPROCKETS

REMOVAL & INSTALLATION

See Figures 142 through 148.

1. Before servicing the vehicle, refer to the Precautions Section.

✱✱ WARNING

In order to prevent damage to the piston assemblies or the valves, DO NOT turn the crankshaft assembly after the timing chain has been removed.

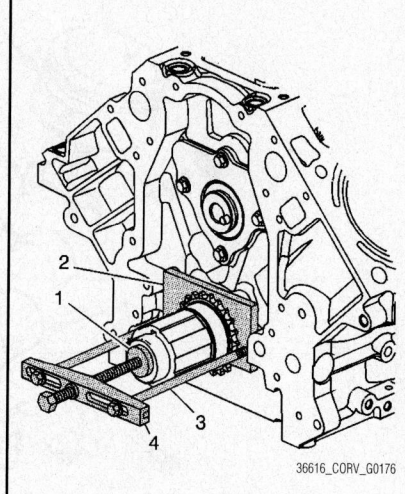

Fig. 144 Use the J 41816-2 (1), the J 41558 (2), bolts (3), and the J 8433 (4) in order to remove the crankshaft sprocket

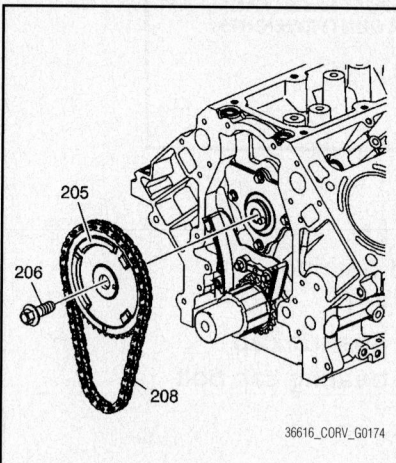

Fig. 142 Remove camshaft sprocket (205), bolt (206), and timing chain (208)

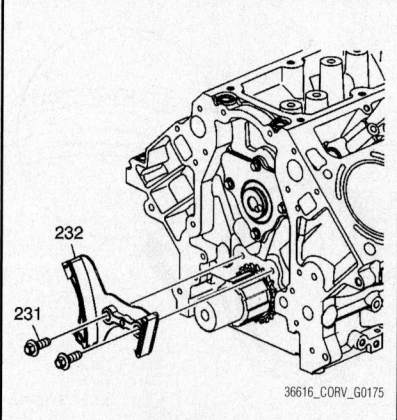

Fig. 143 Remove the bolts (231) and timing chain tensioner (232)

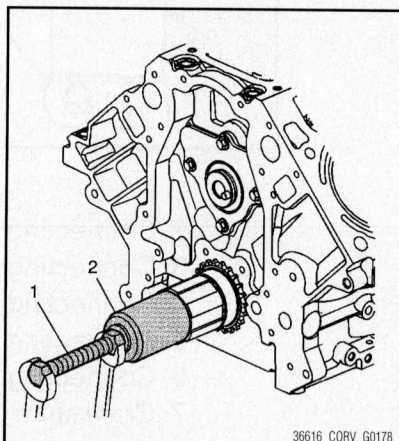

Fig. 145 Crankshaft sprocket installation, using the J 41478 (1) and the J 41665 (2)

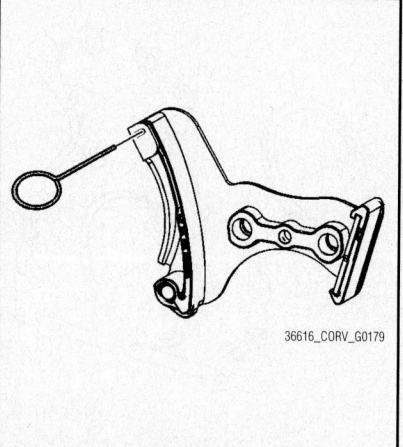

Fig. 146 Compress the timing chain tensioner guide and install the EN 46330

2. Remove the oil pump. Refer to Oil Pump Removal & Installation.

3. Remove and discard the camshaft sprocket bolt (206).

4. Remove the camshaft sprocket (205) and timing chain (208).

5. Remove the bolts (231) and timing chain tensioner (232).

6. Use the J 41816-2 (1), the J 41558 (2), bolts (3), and the J 8433 (4) in order to remove the crankshaft sprocket.

7. Remove the crankshaft sprocket.

8. Remove the crankshaft sprocket key, as required.

To install:

9. Install the key into the crankshaft keyway, if previously removed.

10. Tap the key into the keyway until both ends of the key bottom onto the crankshaft.

11. Install the crankshaft sprocket onto the front of the crankshaft. Align the crank-

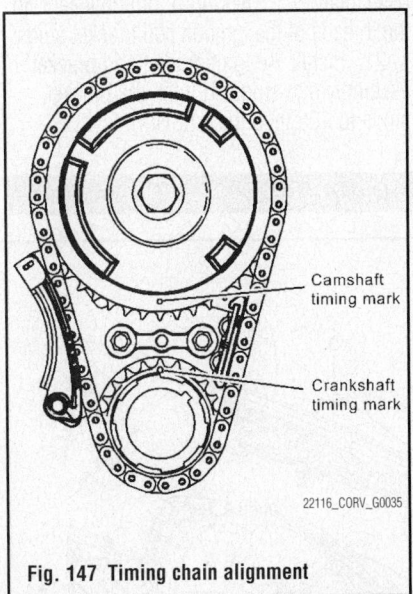

Fig. 147 Timing chain alignment

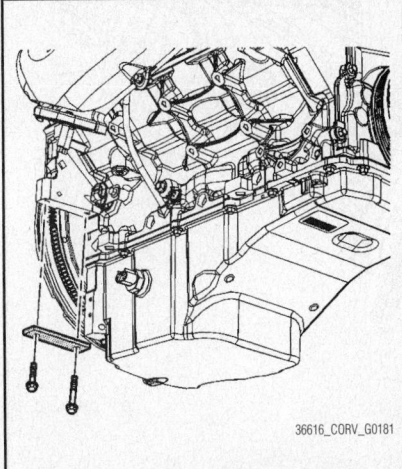

Fig. 148 Install the J 42386-A and bolts

shaft key with the crankshaft sprocket keyway.

12. Use the J 41478 (1) and the J 41665 (2) in order to install the crankshaft sprocket. Install the sprocket onto the crankshaft until fully seated against the crankshaft flange.

13. Rotate the crankshaft sprocket until the alignment mark is in the 12 o'clock position.

14. Compress the timing chain tensioner guide and install the EN 46330.

15. Install the timing chain tensioner and bolts. Tighten the bolts to 18 ft. lbs. (25 Nm).

➡**The sprocket teeth and timing chain must mesh.**

➡**The camshaft and the crankshaft sprocket alignment marks MUST be aligned properly.**

16. Install the camshaft sprocket, timing chain, and bolt.

17. Inspect the sprockets for proper alignment. The mark on the camshaft sprocket should be located in the 6 o'clock position and the mark on the crankshaft sprocket should be located in the 12 o'clock position.

18. Remove the EN 46330.

➡**Do not apply threadlock to the flex plate bolts at this time.**

19. Temporarily install the automatic transmission flex plate or manual transmission flywheel and bolts.

20. Install the J 42386-A and bolts. Use 1 M10-1.5 x 120 mm bolt and 1 M10-1.5 x 45 mm bolt for proper tool operation. Tighten the J 42386-A bolts to 37 ft. lbs. (50 Nm).

21. Tighten the camshaft sprocket bolt. Tighten the camshaft sprocket bolt a first pass to 55 ft. lbs. (75 Nm). Tighten the camshaft sprocket bolt a final pass an additional 50 degrees using the J 45059.

22. Remove the J 42386-A and bolts.

23. Remove the automatic transmission flex plate or manual transmission flywheel and bolts.

24. Install the oil pump.

VALVE COVERS

REMOVAL & INSTALLATION

See Figures 149 through 151.

1. Before servicing the vehicle, refer to the Precautions Section.

2. Remove the spark plug wires, as required.

3. Remove the ignition coil bracket studs.

4. Remove the ignition coil and bracket assembly.

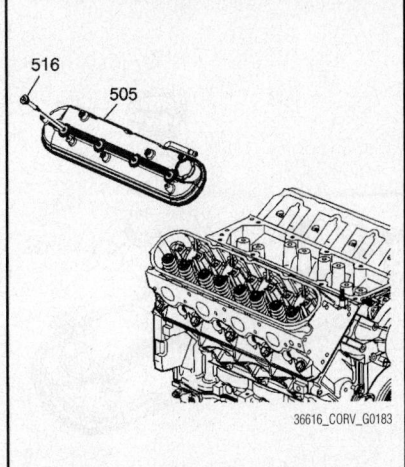

Fig. 149 Remove the valve rocker arm cover bolts (516) and cover (505)—7.0L engine, right side shown; left side similar

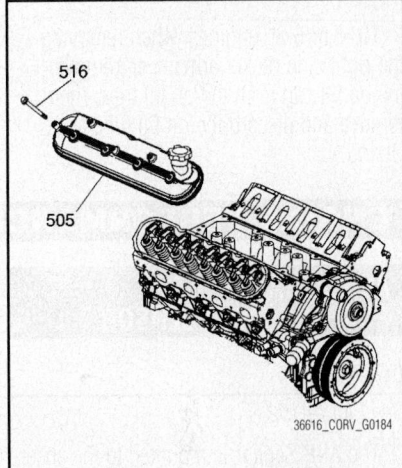

Fig. 150 Remove the valve rocker arm cover bolts (516) and cover (505)—6.2L engine, right side shown; left side similar

5. Disconnect the ignition coil electrical connectors.

6. Remove the bolts, coils, and wire harness from the bracket, as required.

7. Remove the valve rocker arm cover bolts (516) and cover (505).

8. Remove and discard the valve rocker arm cover gasket, valve rocker arm cover grommets and valve rocker arm cover bolts if they are serviced with the grommet.

9. Remove the gasket from the cover.

✳✳ WARNING

For 6.2L engines, do not remove the oil fill tube from the cover unless service is required. If the oil fill tube has been removed from the cover, install a NEW tube during assembly.

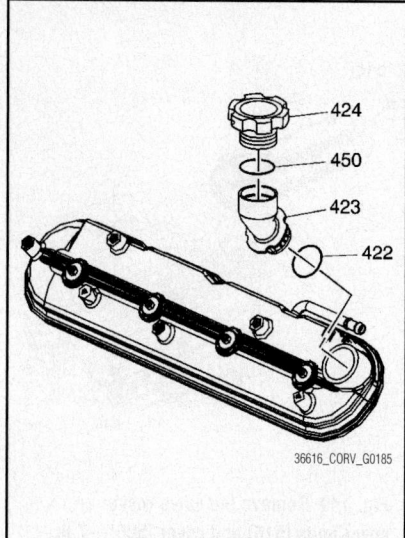

Fig. 151 Install a NEW oil fill tube (423) and seal (422)—6.2L engine, right side

10. For 6.2L engines, when removing the right side rocker arm cover, remove the oil fill cap from the oil fill tube, then remove and discard the oil fill tube and O-ring.

✳✳ WARNING

For 7.0L engines, do not remove the oil cap from the cover, unless service is required. If the oil cap has been removed from the cover, the locking features of the cap will be damaged and no longer functional. If the cap has been removed, install a NEW cap during assembly.

11. For 7.0L engines, when removing the right side rocker arm cover, remove the oil cap and seal from the cover, but only if replacement is required. Discard the oil cap.

To install:

➡All gasket surfaces should be free of oil or other foreign material during assembly.

✳✳ WARNING

DO NOT use the valve rocker arm cover gasket again.

12. Install NEW valve rocker arm cover grommets and use NEW valve rocker arm

cover bolts if they are serviced with the grommet.

13. Install a NEW gasket into the valve rocker arm cover.

14. For 6.2L engines, install a NEW oil fill tube (423) and seal (422) to the right side valve rocker arm cover, as required.

15. For 7.0L engines, install a NEW oil cap and seal to the right side valve rocker arm cover, as required.

16. Install the valve rocker arm cover onto the cylinder head.

17. Install the cover bolts with grommets and tighten the bolts to 106 inch lbs. (12 Nm).

18. Apply threadlock GM P/N 12345382 (Canadian P/N 10953489), or equivalent, to the threads of the ignition coil bolts.

19. Install the ignition coils, wire harness, and bolts to the bracket. Tighten the bolts to 89 inch lbs. (10 Nm).

20. Apply threadlock GM P/N 12345382 (Canadian P/N 10953489), or equivalent, to the threads of the ignition coil bracket studs.

21. Install the ignition coil and bracket assembly and studs. Tighten the bracket studs to 106 inch lbs. (12 Nm).

ENGINE PERFORMANCE & EMISSION CONTROLS

ACCELERATOR PEDAL POSITION (APP) SENSOR

LOCATION

See Figure 152.

The APP Sensor is mounted to the accelerator pedal, in the left footwell at the top of the accelerator pedal.

REMOVAL & INSTALLATION

See Figures 153 and 154.

1. Before servicing the vehicle, refer to the Precautions Section.

✳✳ WARNING

Handle the electronic throttle control components carefully. Use cleanliness in order to prevent damage. Do not drop the electronic throttle control components. Do not roughly handle the electronic throttle control components. Do not immerse the electronic throttle control components in cleaning solvents of any type.

2. Remove the left Instrument Panel (I/P) on the lower closeout insulator panel.

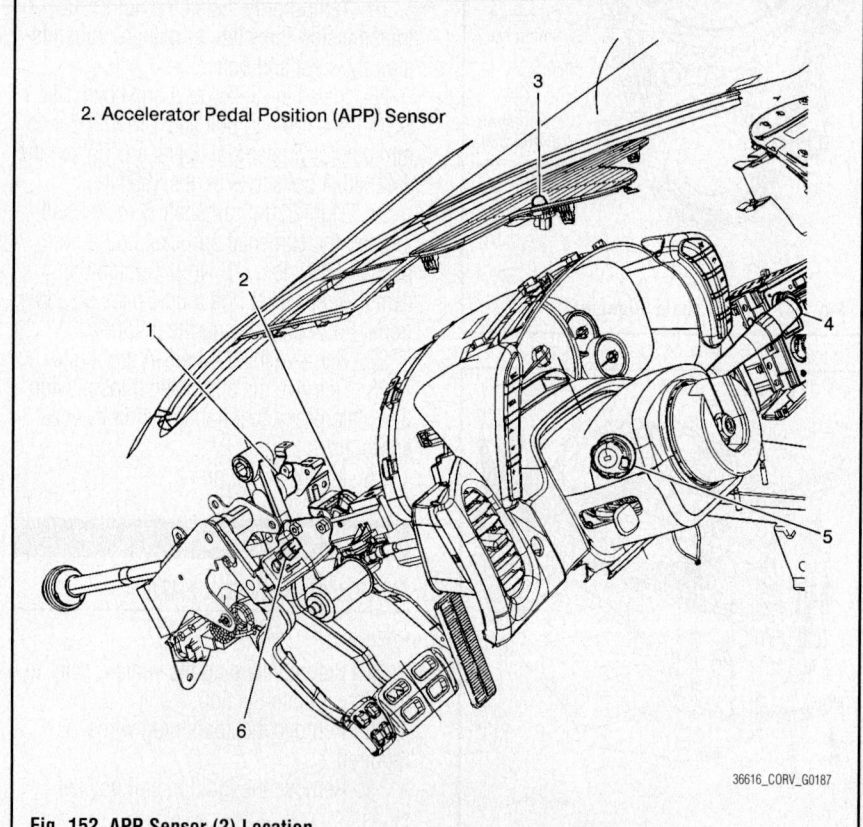

Fig. 152 APP Sensor (2) Location

3. Disconnect the electrical connector of the accelerator pedal sensor module.

4. Remove the accelerator pedal mounting bolts.

5. Remove the accelerator pedal.

To install:

6. Install the accelerator pedal to the steering column support bracket.

➡**Always use a torque wrench in order to obtain the proper torque.**

7. Install the accelerator pedal mounting bolts. Tighten the bolts to 15 ft. lbs. (20 Nm).

8. Connect the accelerator pedal sensor module electrical connector.

9. Inspect for correct carpet fit under the accelerator pedal.

10. Install the left I/P on the lower close-out insulator panel.

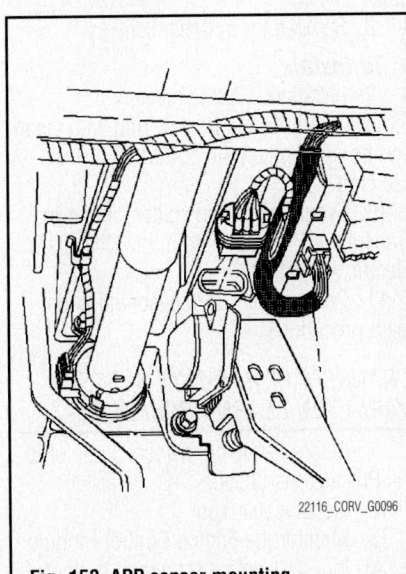

Fig. 153 APP sensor mounting

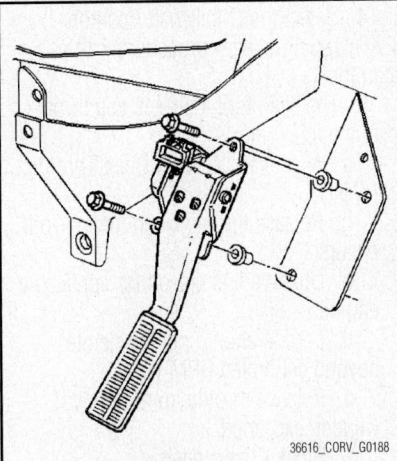

Fig. 154 Accelerator pedal removal and installation

CAMSHAFT POSITION (CMP) SENSOR

LOCATION

The CMP sensor is located at the front center of the engine, behind the water pump.

REMOVAL & INSTALLATION

See Figures 155 and 156.

1. Before servicing the vehicle, refer to the Precautions Section.

2. Remove the alternator bracket assembly:

a. Remove the alternator. Refer to Alternator Removal & Installation in the Engine Electrical Section.

b. Remove the power steering pump. Refer to Power Steering Pump Removal & Installation.

c. Remove the alternator bracket bolts, bracket, and power steering reservoir bracket.

3. Remove the camshaft position sensor mounting bolts (1).

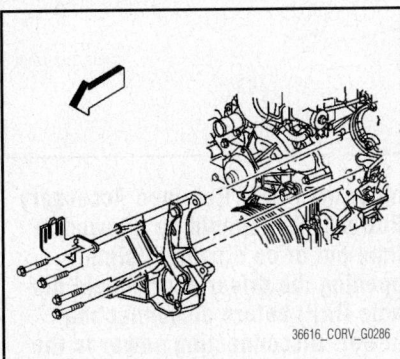

Fig. 155 Alternator bracket removal and installation

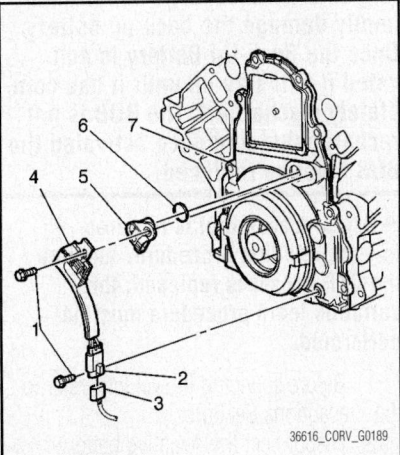

Fig. 156 Camshaft Position (CMP) Sensor removal and installation

4. Remove the camshaft position sensor assembly (4, 5, 6) from the front cover (7).

5. Disconnect the camshaft position sensor jumper harness (2) and the engine harness (3) electrical connectors.

6. Remove the camshaft sensor assembly (4, 5, 6).

7. Disconnect camshaft position sensor (5) from the jumper harness (4).

To install:

8. Reconnect the camshaft sensor and the jumper harness.

9. Install the O-ring on the camshaft sensor assembly.

10. Reconnect the camshaft position sensor assembly and the engine harness connector.

➡**Before installing the camshaft sensor assembly, apply a small amount of clean motor oil to the O-ring.**

11. Install the camshaft position sensor assembly in the front cover.

12. Install the camshaft position sensor mounting bolts. Tighten the camshaft position mounting bolts 18 ft. lbs. (25 Nm).

13. Install the alternator bracket assembly:

a. Install the alternator bracket, power steering reservoir bracket and generator bracket bolts to the cylinder head. Tighten the alternator bracket bolts to 37 ft. lbs. (50 Nm).

b. Install the power steering pump.

c. Install the alternator.

CRANKSHAFT POSITION (CKP) SENSOR

LOCATION

See Figure 157.

The CKP is located at the lower right rear of engine block, behind the starter.

REMOVAL & INSTALLATION

See Figure 158.

✳✳ CAUTION

Unless directed otherwise, the ignition and start switch must be in the OFF or LOCK position, and all electrical loads must be OFF before servicing any electrical component. Disconnect the negative battery cable to prevent an electrical spark should a tool or equipment come in contact with an exposed electrical terminal. Failure to follow these precautions may result in personal injury and/or damage to the vehicle or its components.

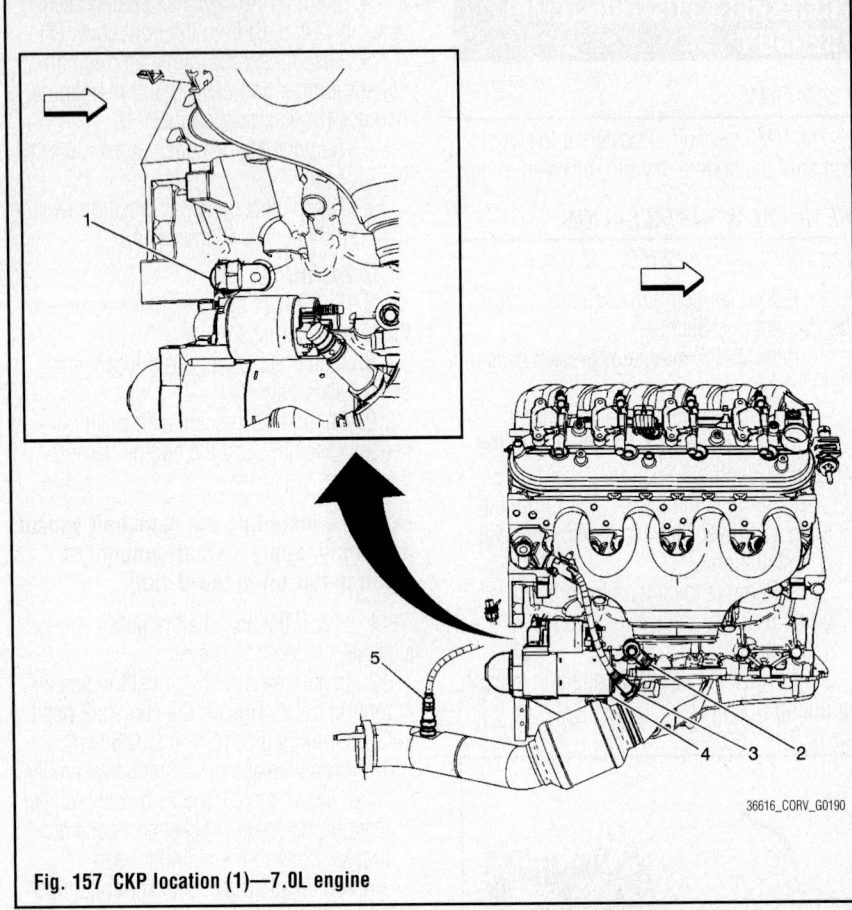

Fig. 157 CKP location (1)—7.0L engine

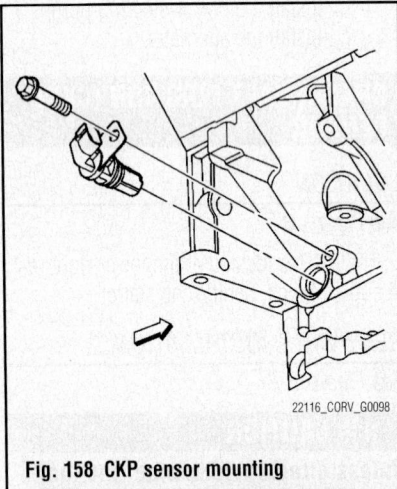

Fig. 158 CKP sensor mounting

✳✳ WARNING

For Vehicles equipped with OnStar® (UE1) with Back Up Battery: The Back Up Battery is a redundant power supply to allow limited OnStar® functionality in the event of a main vehicle battery power disruption to the VCIM (OnStar®module). Do not disconnect the main vehicle battery or remove the OnStar® fuse with the ignition key in any position

other than OFF. Retained Accessory Power (RAP) should be allowed to time out or be disabled (simply opening the driver door should disable RAP) before disconnecting power. Disconnecting power to the OnStar® module in any way while the ignition is On or with RAP activated may cause activation of the OnStar® Back-Up Battery (BUB) system and will discharge and permanently damage the back-up battery. Once the Back-Up Battery is activated it will stay on until it has completely discharged. The BUB is not rechargeable and once activated the BUB must be replaced.

➡Use of a scan tool is required to complete this procedure. Anytime the CKP sensor is replaced, the variation learn procedure must be performed.

1. Before servicing the vehicle, refer to the Precautions Section.
2. Disconnect the negative battery cable.
3. Raise and safely support the vehicle.

✳✳ CAUTION

To avoid any vehicle damage, serious personal injury or death when major components are removed from the vehicle and the vehicle is supported by a hoist, support the vehicle with jack stands at the opposite end from which the components are being removed and strap the vehicle to the hoist.

4. Remove the starter. Refer to Starter Removal & Installation in the Engine Electrical Section.
5. Disconnect the CKP sensor electrical connector.
6. Clean the area around the CKP before removal in order to avoid debris from entering the engine.
7. Remove the CKP sensor retaining bolt.
8. Remove the CKP sensor.

To install:

9. Installation is the reverse of removal. Lubricate a new O–ring with clean engine oil. Tighten the bolt to 18 ft. lbs. (25 Nm).
10. Program the transmitters. Refer to Transmitter Programming in the Chassis Electrical Section.
11. Perform the CKP sensor variation learn procedure.

CRANKSHAFT POSITION SYSTEM VARIATION LEARN PROCEDURE

1. Before servicing the vehicle, refer to the Precautions Section.
2. Install a scan tool.
3. Monitor the Engine Control Module (ECM) for DTCs with a scan tool. If other DTCs are set, except DTC P0315, refer to DTC list.
4. Select the Crankshaft Position (CKP) variation learn procedure with a scan tool.
5. The scan tool instructs you to perform the following:
   a. Accelerate to Wide Open Throttle (WOT).
   b. Release throttle when fuel cut-off occurs.
   c. Observe fuel cut-off for applicable engine.
   d. Engine should not accelerate beyond calibrated RPM value.
   e. Release throttle immediately if value is exceeded.
   f. Block drive wheels.
   g. Set parking brake.
   h. DO NOT apply brake pedal.
   i. Cycle ignition from OFF to ON.

j. Apply and hold brake pedal.

k. Start and idle engine.

l. Turn A/C OFF.

m. Vehicle must remain in Park or Neutral.

n. The scan tool monitors certain component signals to determine if all the conditions are met to continue with the procedure. The scan tool only displays the condition that inhibits the procedure. The scan tool monitors the following components:

- CKP sensors activity: If there is a CKP sensor condition, refer to the applicable DTC that set
- Camshaft Position (CMP) sensor activity: If there is a CMP sensor condition, refer to the applicable DTC that set
- Engine Coolant Temperature (ECT): If the ECT is not warm enough, idle the engine until the engine coolant temperature reaches the correct temperature

6. Enable the CKP System Variation Learn Procedure with a scan tool.

➡️**While the learn procedure is in progress, release the throttle immediately when the engine starts to decelerate. The engine control is returned to the operator and the engine responds to throttle position after the learn procedure is complete.**

7. Accelerate to WOT.

8. Release when the fuel cut-off occurs.

9. Test in progress.

10. The scan tool displays Learn Status: Learned this ignition. If the scan tool indicates that DTC P0315 ran and passed, the CKP Variation Learn Procedure is complete. If the scan tool indicates DTC P0315 failed or did not run, refer to DTC P0315 . If any other DTCs set, refer to DTC list.

11. Turn OFF the ignition for 30 seconds after the learn procedure is completed successfully.

12. The CKP Variation Learn Procedure is also required when the following service procedures have been performed, regardless of whether DTC P0315 is set:

- A CKP sensor replacement
- An engine replacement
- A ECM replacement
- A harmonic balancer replacement
- A crankshaft replacement
- Any engine repairs which disturb the CKP sensor relationship

ELECTRONIC CONTROL MODULE (ECM)

LOCATION

The ECM is located on the right front side of the vehicle behind the front wheel-house liner.

REMOVAL & INSTALLATION

See Figures 159 and 160.

✳✳ WARNING

In order to prevent internal ECM damage, the ignition must be OFF when you disconnect or reconnect the power to the ECM. For example, disconnect the power when you work with the following components: a battery cable, the ECM pigtail, the ECM fuse, the jumper cables.

➡️**When you diagnose or replace the ECM, remove any debris from the ECM connector surfaces before servicing the ECM module connector gaskets. Ensure that the gaskets are installed correctly. The gaskets prevent intrusion into the ECM.**

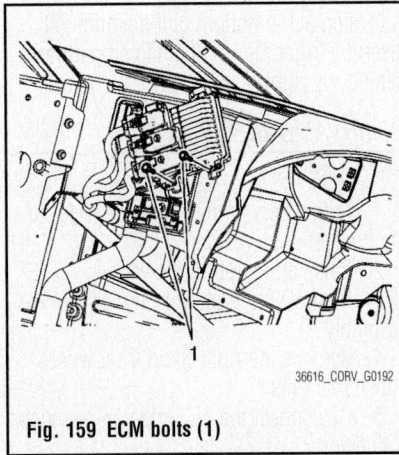

Fig. 159 ECM bolts (1)

➡️**The replacement ECM MUST be programmed.**

➡️**It is necessary to record the remaining engine oil life. If the replacement module is not programmed with the remaining engine oil life, the engine oil life will default to 100 percent. If the replacement module is not programmed with the remaining engine oil life, the engine oil must be changed at 3,000 miles (5,000 km) from the last oil change. A scan tool must be used to retrieve the ECM data. This information must be transferred to the new ECM.**

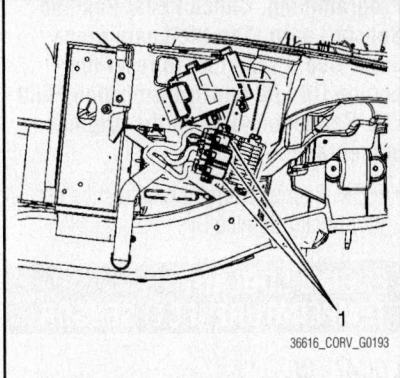

Fig. 160 ECM engine wiring harness electrical connectors (1)

1. Before servicing the vehicle, refer to the Precautions Section.

2. Using a scan tool, retrieve the percentage of remaining engine oil. Record the remaining engine oil life.

3. Disconnect the negative battery cable.

4. Remove the wheelhouse filler panel.

5. Remove the ECM bolts (1).

6. Remove the ECM from the bracket and allow the ECM to hang down from the engine wiring harness.

7. Disconnect the engine wiring harness electrical connectors as shown (1) from the ECM.

8. Remove the ECM.

To install:

9. Position the ECM.

10. Connect the engine wiring harness electrical connectors to the ECM and position the ECM into the bracket.

11. Install the ECM bolts and tighten to 89 inch lbs. (10 Nm).

12. Install the wheelhouse filler panel.

13. If a new ECM is being installed, program the ECM.

RESET

✳✳ CAUTION

Replacement or reprogramming of the ECM, or replacement of the Clutch Pedal Position Sensor (CPPS) or clutch pedal requires that a CPPS learn procedure be performed. Failure to perform the CPPS learn procedure may result in personal injury or damage to the vehicle or its components if the vehicle is in gear and the starter motor is accidentally engaged.

➡️**If the ECM is replaced, the following procedures must be performed: ECM Reprogramming, Crankshaft Position System Variation Learn, Theft Deterrent**

Programming, Clutch Pedal Position Sensor Learn, Throttle Learn procedure. Use a scan tool to reset the Engine Oil Life and Transmission Fluid Life Remaining back to the original percentage recorded.

ECM Reprogramming requires the use of a Proprietary Service System.

ENGINE COOLANT TEMPERATURE (ECT) SENSOR

LOCATION

The ECT sensor is threaded into the left side cylinder head near the front.

REMOVAL & INSTALLATION

See Figure 161.

1. Before servicing the vehicle, refer to the Precautions Section.
2. Raise the vehicle.
3. Drain the cooling system to a level below the ECT sensor.
4. Lower the vehicle.
5. Disconnect the harness connector from the ECT sensor.
6. Remove the ECT sensor from the engine.

✳✳ WARNING

Use care when handling the coolant sensor. Damage to the coolant sensor will affect the operation of the fuel control system.

To install:

✳✳ WARNING

Replacement components must be the correct part number for the application. Components requiring the use of the thread locking compound, lubricants, corrosion inhibitors, or sealants are identified in the service procedure. Some replacement components may come with these coatings already applied. Do not use these coatings on components unless specified. These coatings can affect the final torque, which may affect the operation of the component. Use the correct torque specification when installing components in order to avoid damage.

✳✳ WARNING

Use care when handling the coolant sensor. Damage to the coolant sensor will affect the operation of the fuel control system.

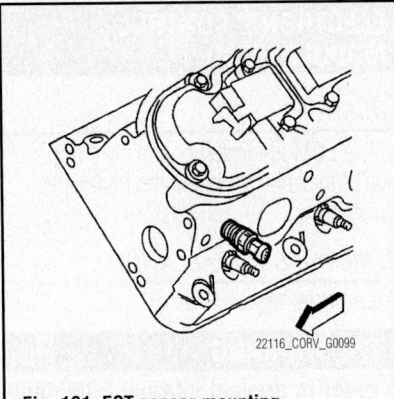

Fig. 161 ECT sensor mounting

7. Coat the ECT sensor threads with sealer P/N 12346004 (Canadian P/N 10953480) or the equivalent.
8. Install the ECT sensor, and tighten to 15 ft. lbs. (20 Nm).
9. Connect the ECT sensor electrical connector.
10. Refill the cooling system.

ENGINE OIL TEMPERATURE (EOT) SENSOR

LOCATION

1. Engine Oil Temperature (EOT) Sensor is located at the bottom of the engine oil reservoir, right rear of engine compartment, behind the right front wheel.

REMOVAL & INSTALLATION

See Figure 162.

1. Before servicing the vehicle, refer to the Precautions Section.
2. Raise and support the vehicle.
3. Remove the right front tire and wheel assembly.
4. Remove the right-hand front wheel-house rear liner.
5. Disconnect the oil temperature sensor connector.
6. Remove the oil temperature sensor.

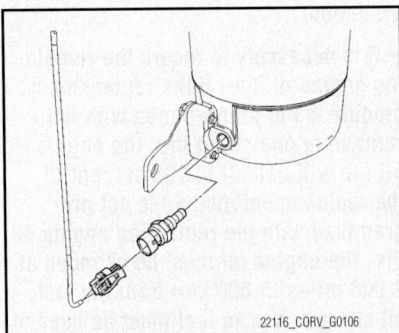

Fig. 162 Location of Oil Temperature Sensor

To install:

7. Installation is the reverse of removal. Tighten the oil temperature sensor to 15 ft. lbs. (20 Nm).

EVAPORATIVE EMISSIONS (EVAP) CANISTER

LOCATION

See Figure 163.

The EVAP canister is located in the right rear fender well.

REMOVAL & INSTALLATION

See Figure 163.

1. Before servicing the vehicle, refer to the Precautions Section.
2. Remove the right fuel tank. Refer to Fuel Tank Removal & Installation in the Fuel System Section.
3. Disconnect the vent hose from the Evaporative Emission (EVAP) canister.
4. Disconnect the purge pipe at the EVAP canister.
5. Remove the EVAP canister bracket bolt (3).
6. Remove the EVAP canister (1) from the EVAP canister bracket (2).

To install:

7. Install the new EVAP canister to the EVAP canister bracket.
8. Install the EVAP canister bracket bolt. Tighten the EVAP canister bracket bolt to 62 inch lbs. (7 Nm).
9. Connect the purge pipe at the EVAP canister.
10. Connect the vent hose to the EVAP canister.
11. Install the right fuel tank.

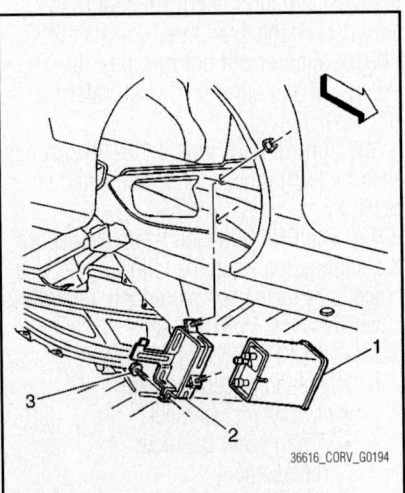

Fig. 163 Remove the EVAP canister bracket bolt (3), bracket (2). And EVAP canister (1)

HEATED OXYGEN (HO2S) SENSOR

LOCATION

See Figure 164.

REMOVAL & INSTALLATION

See Figure 164.

✳✳ WARNING

Do not remove the pigtail from either the Heated Oxygen Sensor (HO2S) or the Oxygen Sensor (O2S). Removing the pigtail or the connector will affect sensor operation. Handle the oxygen sensor carefully. Do not drop the HO2S. Keep the in-line electrical connector and the louvered end free of grease, dirt, or other contaminants. Do not use cleaning solvents of any type. Do not repair the wiring, connector or terminals. Replace the oxygen sensor if the pigtail wiring, connector, or terminal is damaged. This external clean air reference is obtained by way of the oxygen sensor signal and heater wires. Any attempt to repair the wires, connectors, or terminals could result in the obstruction of the air reference and degraded sensor performance.

The following guidelines should be used when servicing the heated oxygen sensor:

• Do not apply contact cleaner or other materials to the sensor or vehicle harness connectors. These materials may get into the sensor causing poor performance.

• Do not damage the sensor pigtail and harness wires in such a way that the wires inside are exposed. This could provide a path for foreign materials to enter the sensor and cause performance problems.

• Ensure the sensor or vehicle lead wires are not bent sharply or kinked. Sharp bends or kinks could block the reference air path through the lead wire.

• Do not remove or defeat the oxygen sensor ground wire, where applicable. Vehicles that utilize the ground wired sensor may rely on this ground as the only ground contact to the sensor. Removal of the ground wire will cause poor engine performance.

• Ensure that the peripheral seal remains intact on the vehicle harness connector in order to prevent damage due to water intrusion. The engine harness may be repaired using Packard's Crimp and Splice Seals Terminal Repair Kit. Under no circumstances should repairs be soldered since this could result in the air reference being obstructed.

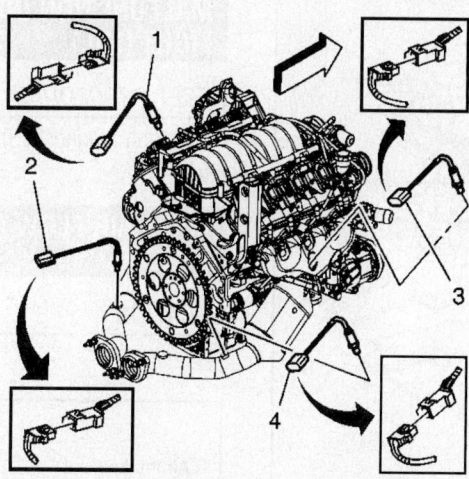

1. Bank 1, Sensor 1 (Under the vehicle, on the left exhaust pipe, forward of the catalytic converter)
2. Bank 1, Sensor 2 (Under the vehicle, on the left exhaust pipe, rearward of the catalytic converter)
3. Bank 2, Sensor 1 (Under the vehicle, on the right exhaust pipe, forward of the catalytic converter)
4. Bank 2, Sensor 2 (Under the vehicle, on the right exhaust pipe, rearward of the catalytic converter)

36616_CORV_G0198

Fig. 164 HO2S sensor locations

✳✳ WARNING

The oxygen sensor may be difficult to remove when the engine temperature is below 120° F (48° C). Excessive force may damage threads in the exhaust manifold or the exhaust pipe.

1. Before servicing the vehicle, refer to the Precautions Section.
2. Raise the vehicle.
3. Disconnect the oxygen sensor electrical connector from the engine wiring harness electrical connector.
4. Remove the oxygen sensor.

To install:

➡**Use special anti-seize compound on the heated oxygen sensor threads. The compound consists of graphite suspended in fluid and glass beads. The graphite burns away, but the glass beads remain, making the sensor easier to remove. New or service sensors already have the compound applied to the threads. If you remove an oxygen sensor and if for any reason you must reinstall the same oxygen sensor, apply the anti-seize compound to the threads before reinstallation.**

5. Coat the threads of the heated oxygen sensor with the anti-seize compound P/N 5613695, or the equivalent if necessary.
6. Install the heated oxygen sensor and tighten the sensor to 30 ft. lbs. (41 Nm).
7. Reconnect the oxygen sensor electrical connector to the engine wiring harness electrical connector.
8. Lower the vehicle.

KNOCK SENSOR (KS)

LOCATION

See Figures 165 and 166.

REMOVAL & INSTALLATION

See Figures 165 and 166.

1. Before servicing the vehicle, refer to the Precautions Section.
2. Disconnect the negative battery cable, if necessary.
3. Raise and safely support the vehicle.
4. Remove the catalytic converter. Refer to Catalytic Converter Removal & Installation in the Engine Mechanical Section.
5. Remove the exhaust manifold. Refer to Exhaust Manifold Removal & Installation in the Engine Mechanical Section.

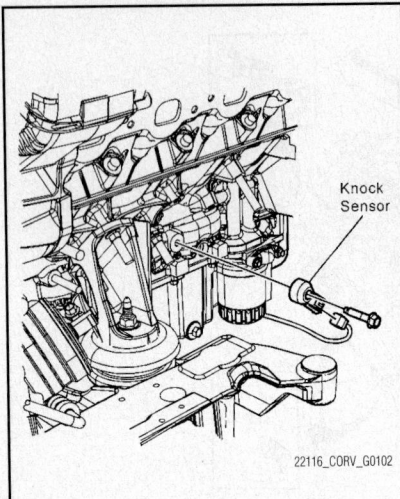

Fig. 165 Knock sensor location—left side

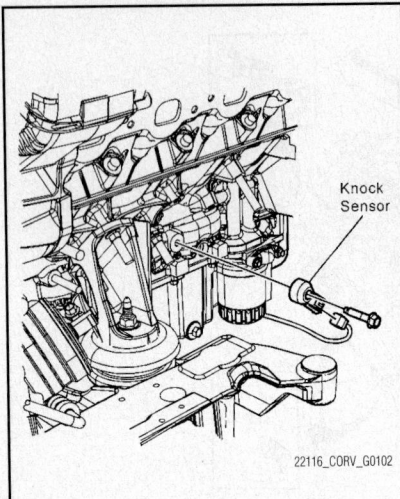

**Fig. 166 Knock sensor location—
right side**

6. Remove the starter assembly, ONLY IF NEEDED to gain enough clearance to remove the knock sensor. Refer to Starter Removal & Installation in the Engine Electrical Section.

7. Remove the mounting bolt.

8. Disconnect the knock sensor electrical connector from the engine harness.

9. Remove the knock sensor from the engine block.

To install:

10. Installation is the reverse of removal. Tighten the bolt to 15 ft. lbs. (20 Nm).

11. If battery was disconnected, program the transmitters. Refer to Transmitter Programming in the Chassis Electrical Section.

MALFUNCTION INDICATOR LIGHT (MIL)

RESET PROCEDURE

Clearing Diagnostic Trouble Codes resets the MIL.

MASS AIR FLOW (MAF) SENSOR

LOCATION

See Figure 167.

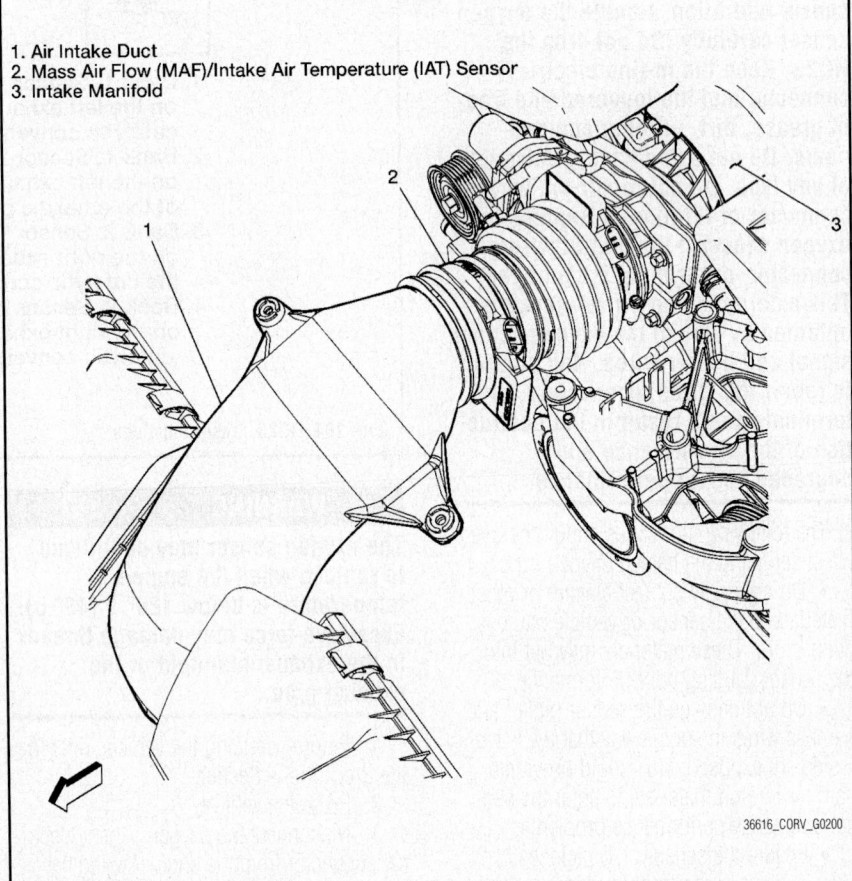

1. Air Intake Duct
2. Mass Air Flow (MAF)/Intake Air Temperature (IAT) Sensor
3. Intake Manifold

Fig. 167 MAF/IAT sensor location

REMOVAL & INSTALLATION

See Figure 168.

1. Before servicing the vehicle, refer to the Precautions Section.

2. Disconnect the Mass Air Flow (MAF)/Air Intake Temperature (IAT) sensor electrical connector.

3. Remove the 2 screws and the MAF/IAT sensor from the air cleaner housing.

To install:

4. Installation is the reverse of removal.

MANIFOLD ABSOLUTE PRESSURE (MAP) SENSOR

LOCATION

See Figure 169.

REMOVAL & INSTALLATION

See Figure 169.

1. Before servicing the vehicle, refer to the Precautions Section.

2. Remove the oil filler cap (1).

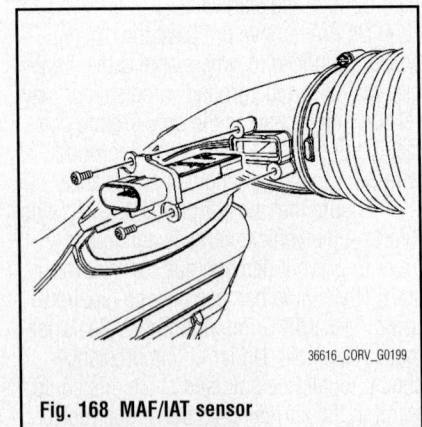

Fig. 168 MAF/IAT sensor

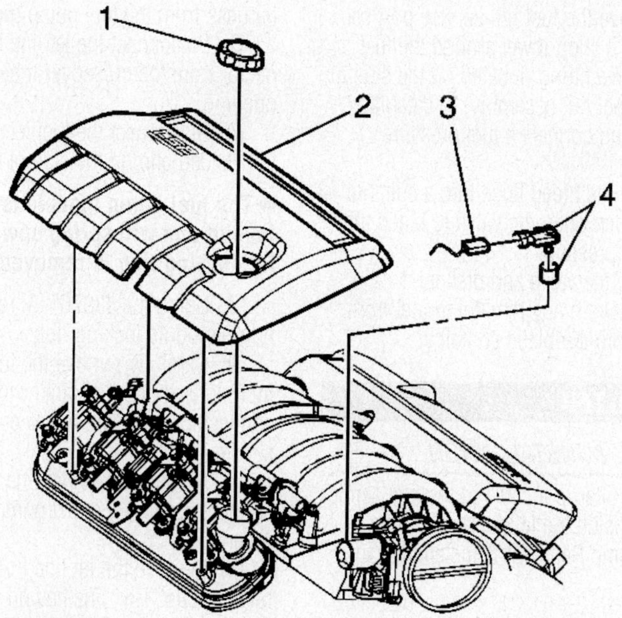

(1) Oil filler cap
(2) Right engine sight shield
(3) Electrical connector
(4) MAP sensor

22116_CORV_G0104

Fig. 169 MAP sensor location

3. Remove the right engine sight shield (2).

4. Remove the Manifold Absolute Pressure (MAP) sensor (4).

5. Disconnect the electrical connector (3) for the MAP sensor.

To install:

6. Installation is the reverse of removal. If reusing the sensor, replace the seal.

THROTTLE CONTROL ACTUATOR (TAC)

LOCATION

The Throttle Control Actuator (TAC) is part of the throttle body assembly.

REMOVAL & INSTALLATION

See Throttle Body Removal & Installation in the Fuel System Section.

THROTTLE POSITION SENSOR (TPS)

LOCATION

The Throttle Position Sensor (TPS) is part of the throttle body assembly.

REMOVAL & INSTALLATION

See Throttle Body Removal & Installation in the Fuel System Section.

VEHICLE SPEED SENSOR (VSS)

REMOVAL & INSTALLATION

See Figure 170.

1. Before servicing the vehicle, refer to the Precautions Section.

2. Raise and suitably support the vehicle.

3. Clean any dirt from around the Vehicle Speed Sensor (VSS).

4. Disconnect the electrical connector from the VSS.

5. Remove the bolt retaining the VSS to the rear differential case.

6. Remove the VSS from the differential case.

To install:

7. Installation is the reverse of removal. Tighten the vehicle speed sensor retaining bolt to 89 inch lbs. (10 Nm).

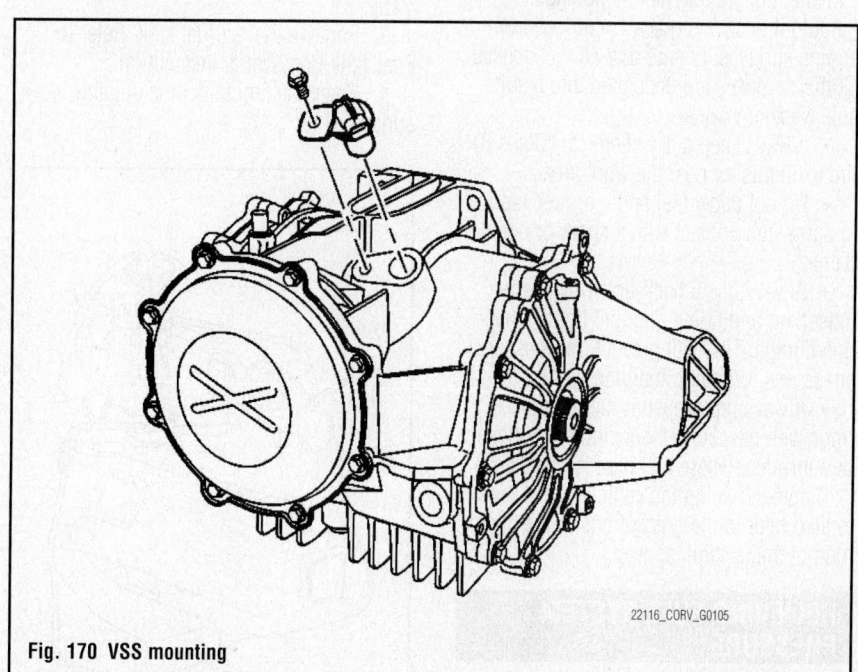

22116_CORV_G0105

Fig. 170 VSS mounting

FUEL SYSTEM SERVICE PRECAUTIONS

Safety is the most important factor when performing not only fuel system maintenance but any type of maintenance. Failure to conduct maintenance and repairs in a safe manner may result in serious personal injury or death. Maintenance and testing of the vehicle's fuel system components can be accomplished safely and effectively by adhering to the following rules and guidelines.

• To avoid the possibility of fire and personal injury, always disconnect the negative battery cable unless the repair or test procedure requires that battery voltage be applied.

• Always relieve the fuel system pressure prior to disconnecting any fuel system component (injector, fuel rail, pressure regulator, etc.), fitting or fuel line connection. Exercise extreme caution whenever relieving fuel system pressure to avoid exposing skin, face and eyes to fuel spray. Please be advised that fuel under pressure may penetrate the skin or any part of the body that it contacts.

• Always place a shop towel or cloth around the fitting or connection prior to loosening to absorb any excess fuel due to spillage. Ensure that all fuel spillage (should it occur) is quickly removed from engine surfaces. Ensure that all fuel soaked cloths or towels are deposited into a suitable waste container.

• Always keep a dry chemical (Class B) fire extinguisher near the work area.

• Do not allow fuel spray or fuel vapors to come into contact with a spark or open flame.

• Always use a back-up wrench when loosening and tightening fuel line connection fittings. This will prevent unnecessary stress and torsion to fuel line piping.

• Always replace worn fuel fitting O-rings with new Do not substitute fuel hose or equivalent where fuel pipe is installed.

Before servicing the vehicle, make sure to also refer to the precautions in the beginning of this section as well.

RELIEVING FUEL SYSTEM PRESSURE

1. Before servicing the vehicle, refer to the Precautions Section.
2. Disconnect the negative battery cable.
3. Loosen the fuel filler cap to relieve the tank pressure.

4. Remove the left fuel rail cover.
5. Remove the fuel rail service port cap.
6. Wrap a shop towel around the fuel pressure valve fitting (located on the side or end of the fuel rail assembly) to catch any fuel spray and connect a fuel pressure gauge.
7. Place the bleed hose into a suitable container, then open the valve to bleed the fuel system pressure.
8. Close the valve and disconnect the fuel gauge. Drain any remaining fuel from the gauge into the bleed container.

FUEL FILTER

REMOVAL & INSTALLATION

The fuel filter is located in the fuel sender assembly inside the left fuel tank. Refer to the Fuel Pump Removal & Installation for removal.

FUEL PUMP MODULE

REMOVAL & INSTALLATION

Left Side

See Figure 171.

1. Before servicing the vehicle, refer to the Precautions Section.
2. Disconnect the negative battery cable.
3. Remove the left fuel tank. Refer to Fuel Tank Removal & Installation.
4. Place the fuel tank on a suitable work surface.

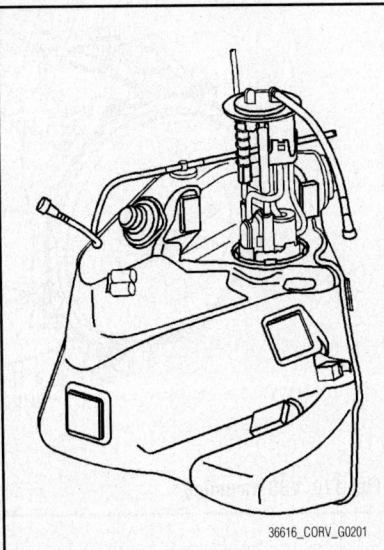

36616_CORV_G0201

Fig. 171 Fuel pump module removal and installation

5. Disconnect the fuel pump jumper harness from the fuel pump module.
6. Disconnect the jet line insert connector from the crossover tube to fuel tank opening.
7. Disconnect the fuel feed line from the welded clip on the side of the fuel tank.

➡ **The fuel pump module is spring loaded and will spring upward when the locking ring is removed.**

8. Using the J39765-A, remove the fuel pump module locking ring.
9. Carefully remove the fuel pump module from the fuel tank, with the jet lines connected. Take care not to damage the fuel sender float arm.
10. Disconnect the jet line quick-connect connectors from the fuel pump module inner port.
11. Remove the jet line from the module retainer cup. This line has no attached connector.
12. Remove the fuel pump module O-ring from the fuel tank opening.
13. Remove the jet line insert through the crossover tube to fuel tank opening.

To install:

14. Inspect the jet line insert for damage and replace if necessary.
15. Install the jet line insert through the crossover tube to fuel tank opening.
16. Install a new fuel pump module O-ring to the fuel tank opening.
17. Place tape around the jet line with the connector. This will permit line access once the pump module is inserted into the fuel tank.
18. Install the pump module into the fuel tank half way, taking care not to damage the float arm.
19. Using the tape as a guide, gently pull the jet line up through the fuel pump module opening.
20. Place the jet line with no connector in the module retainer cup.
21. Secure the line into the module retaining clip.
22. Remove the tape from the jet line with a connector.

➡ **Important: Pull on each connector to ensure that the connectors are properly latched.**

23. Connect the jet line quick-connect connectors to the fuel pump module inner port.
24. Compress and align the fuel pump module into the fuel tank, while taking care not to damage the float arm.

25. Install the fuel pump module lock ring.

26. Using the J39765-A , fully lock the fuel pump module lock ring in place.

27. Connect the fuel supply line into the weld clip on the side of the fuel tank.

28. Using a DMM, verify the full and empty readings resistance reading of the fuel pump module. Turn the fuel tank upside down to achieve the full tank reading. Empty tank reading: 247–253 ohms resistance. Full tank reading: 38.5–41.05 ohms resistance

➡ **Important: Pull the jet line insert connector to ensure that the insert is properly attached.**

29. Connect the jet line insert connector into the crossover tube to fuel tank opening.

30. Connect the fuel pump jumper harness to the fuel pump module.

31. Install the left fuel tank.

32. Connect the negative battery cable.

Right Side

See Figures 172 and 173.

1. Before servicing the vehicle, refer to the Precautions Section.

2. Disconnect the negative battery cable.

3. Remove the right fuel tank. Refer to Fuel Tank Removal & Installation.

4. Place the fuel tank on a suitable work surface.

5. Disconnect the Evaporative Emission (EVAP) purge line (4) from the fuel pump module.

6. Disconnect the fuel pump module harness connector (5).

7. Disconnect the Fuel Tank Pressure (FTP) sensor harness connector (1).

8. If replacing the fuel pump module, remove the FTP sensor (2).

9. Disconnect the jet line insert connector from the crossover tube to fuel tank opening.

➡ **Important: The fuel pump module is spring loaded and will spring upward when the locking ring is removed.**

10. Using the J39765-A, remove the fuel pump module locking ring.

11. Carefully remove the fuel pump module from the fuel tank, with the jet lines connected. Take care not to damage the fuel sender float arm.

12. Disconnect the jet line quick-connect connectors from the fuel pump module, noting the location of the lines for installation.

13. Remove the fuel pump module O-ring from the fuel tank opening.

14. Remove the jet line insert through the crossover tube to fuel tank opening.

To install:

15. Inspect the jet line insert for damage and replace if necessary.

16. Install the jet line insert through the crossover tube to fuel tank opening.

17. Install a new fuel pump module O-ring to the fuel tank opening.

➡ **Important: Pull on each connector to ensure that the connectors are properly latched.**

18. Pull the jet line quick-connectors up through the pump module opening, connecting the lines to the pump module as previously noted.

19. Install the pump module into the fuel tank, taking care not to damage the float arm.

20. Compress and align the fuel pump module, while installing the lock ring.

21. Using the J39765-A, fully lock the fuel pump module lock ring in place.

22. Using a DMM, verify the full and empty readings resistance reading of the fuel pump module. Turn the fuel tank upside down to achieve the full tank reading. Empty tank reading: 247–253 ohms resistance. Full tank reading: 38.5–41.05 ohms resistance

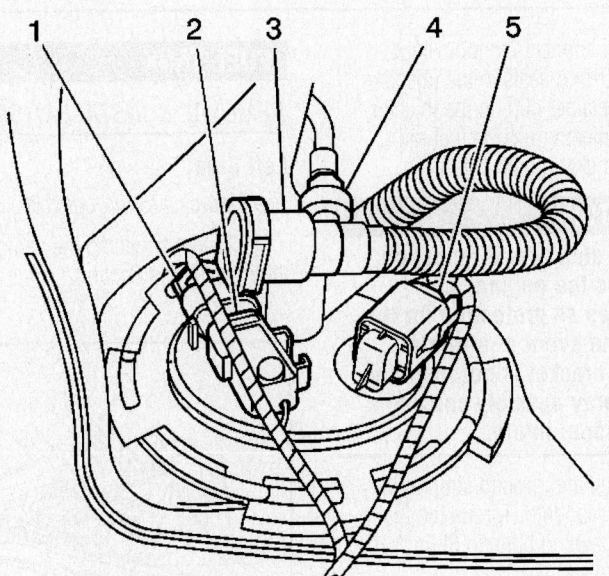

1. **Fuel Tank Pressure (FTP) sensor harness connector**
2. **FTP sensor**
4. **Evaporative Emission (EVAP) purge line**
5. **Fuel pump module harness connector**

36616_CORV_G0202

Fig. 172 Fuel pump module components

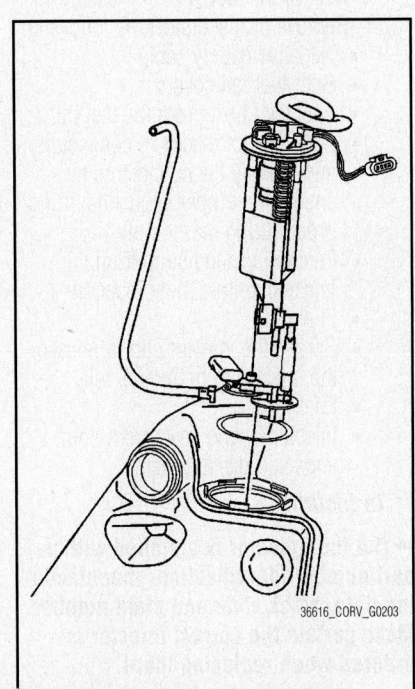

36616_CORV_G0203

Fig. 173 Fuel pump module removal and installation

➡ Pull the jet line insert connector to ensure that the insert is properly attached.

23. Connect the jet line insert connector into the crossover tube to fuel tank opening.

24. If replacing the fuel pump module, install the FTP sensor.

25. Connect the FTP sensor harness connector.

26. Connect the fuel pump module harness connector.

27. Connect the EVAP purge line from the fuel pump module.

28. Install the right fuel tank.

29. Connect the negative battery cable.

FUEL PRESSURE REGULATOR

REMOVAL & INSTALLATION

The fuel pressure regulators (both primary and secondary) are contained within the fuel pump module located in the fuel tanks. Refer to Fuel Pump Module Removal & Installation.

FUEL RAIL & INJECTORS

REMOVAL & INSTALLATION

See Figure 174.

1. Before servicing the vehicle, refer to the Precautions Section.

2. Remove the engine sight shield covers.

3. Relieve the fuel system pressure.

4. Remove or disconnect the following:
- Negative battery cable
- Both fuel rail covers
- Fuel feed hose from the fuel rail
- Fuel injector electrical connectors and identify the connectors to ensure the proper sequential firing order during reassembly
- Fuel rail ground strap from the intake manifold, note location
- Fuel rail
- Spread the injector clip to release the injector from the fuel rail
- Fuel injector
- Injector O-ring seals from both ends and discard them

To install:

➡ The fuel injector is stamped with a part number identification, manufacturing date, week code and plant number. Make certain the correct injector is ordered when replacing them.

5. Lubricate the new injector seals with clean engine oil.

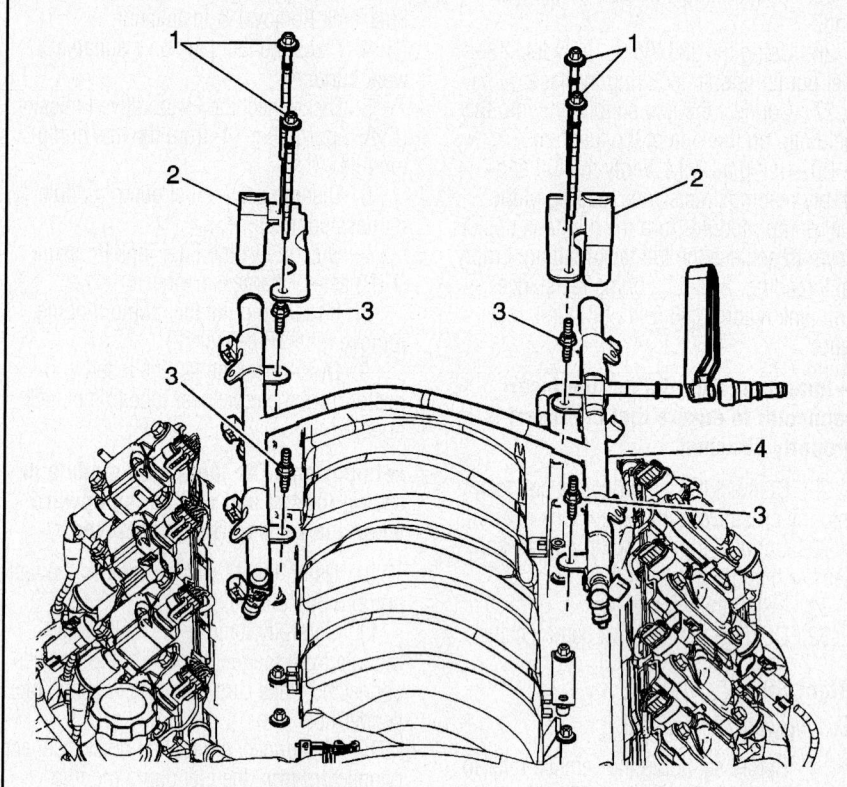

1. Intake Manifold Bolts
2. Stop Brackets
3. Fuel Rail Bolts
4. Fuel Rail

36616_CORV_G0287

Fig. 174 Fuel rail and injector removal and installation

6. Install or connect the following:
- New O-ring seals to the injectors
- New retainer clip on the injector
- Fuel injector into the fuel rail socket facing outward

✳✳ CAUTION

The fuel rail stop bracket must be installed onto the engine. The bracket serves as protection for the fuel rail in the event of a frontal crash. If the bracket is not installed, fuel could spray possibly causing a fire and personal injury.

- Fuel rail and ground strap to the intake manifold. Torque the fuel rail; attaching bolts to 89 inch lbs. (10 Nm)
- Electrical connectors to the injectors
- Fuel feed hose to the fuel rail
- Negative battery cable
- Left and right fuel rail covers

7. Turn the ignition **ON** for 2 seconds, **OFF** for 10 seconds, then **ON** again and inspect the system for leaks.

FUEL TANK

REMOVAL & INSTALLATION

Left Side

See Figures 175 through 180.

1. Before servicing the vehicle, refer to the Precautions Section.

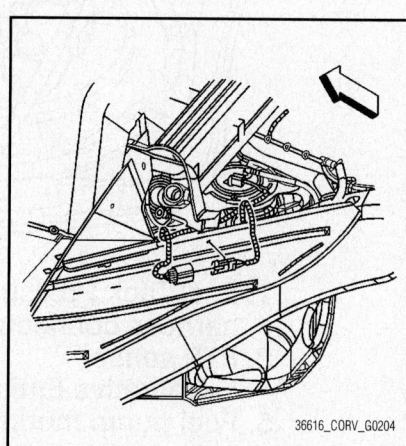

36616_CORV_G0204

Fig. 175 Disconnect the fuel pump jumper harness connector

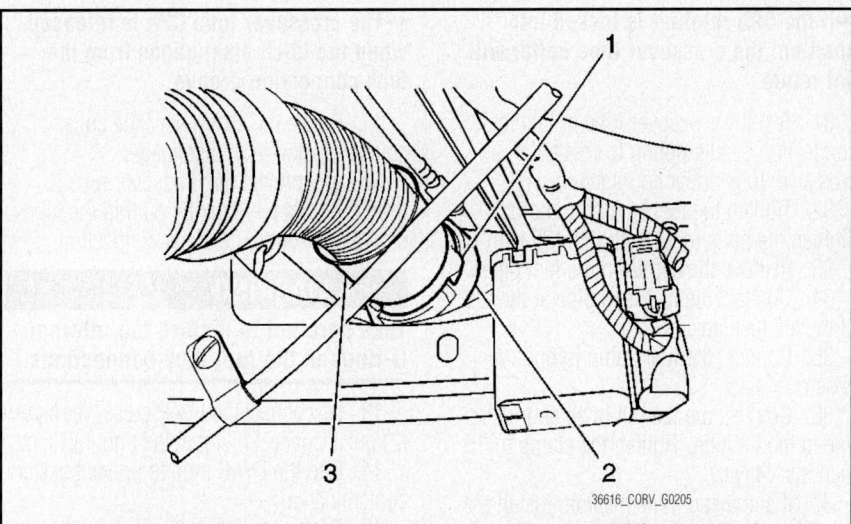

Fig. 176 Disengage the crossover tube CPA retainer by pulling the tab (1) outward and rotate

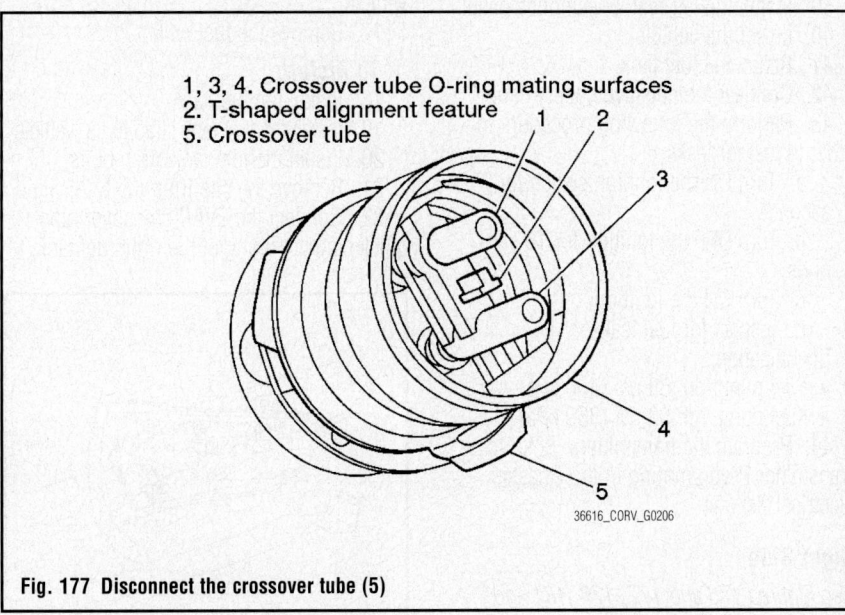

1, 3, 4. Crossover tube O-ring mating surfaces
2. T-shaped alignment feature
5. Crossover tube

Fig. 177 Disconnect the crossover tube (5)

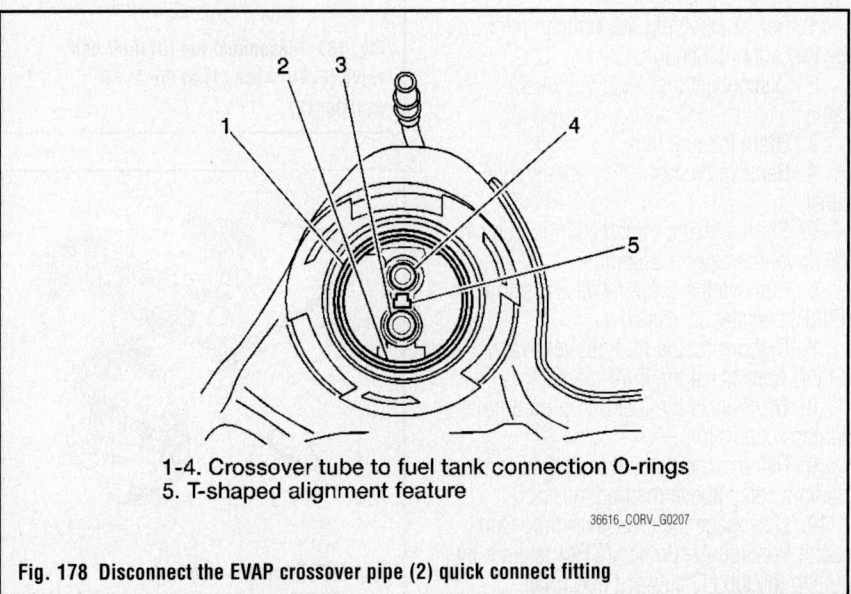

1-4. Crossover tube to fuel tank connection O-rings
5. T-shaped alignment feature

Fig. 178 Disconnect the EVAP crossover pipe (2) quick connect fitting

2. Disconnect the negative battery cable.

3. Drain the fuel tank.

4. Remove the left rear wheelhouse panel.

5. Remove both mufflers.

6. For automatic transmissions, remove the driveline support assembly.

7. Disconnect the fuel fill hose and recirc line from the fill pipe.

8. Disconnect the fuel pump jumper harness connector.

9. Disconnect the fuel feed pipe at the rear of the left fuel tank.

10. Cap the fuel pipes to prevent fuel system contamination.

11. Loosen the fuel tank strap in order to drop the tank approximately 1 inch.

12. Disengage the crossover tube Connector Position Assurance (CPA) retainer by pulling the tab (1) outward and rotate.

➡**The crossover tube CPA is released when the latch disengages from the tank connection groove.**

13. Rotate the collar counterclockwise to disengage.

14. Disconnect the crossover tube (5) from the left fuel tank.

✵✵ WARNING

Take care not to disturb the internal O-rings in the fuel tank connections.

15. Disconnect the Evaporative Emission (EVAP) crossover pipe (2) quick connect fitting at the left fuel tank.

16. Cap the EVAP pipes to prevent system contamination.

17. Remove the fuel tank strap mount bolts.

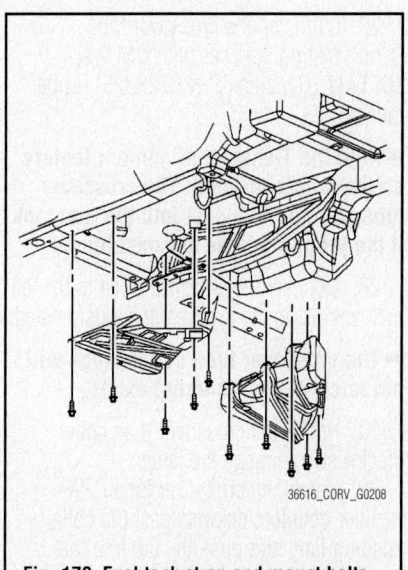

Fig. 179 Fuel tank strap and mount bolts

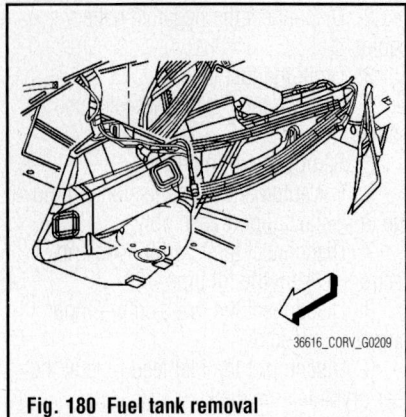

Fig. 180 Fuel tank removal

18. Remove the fuel tank strap from the vehicle.

19. Remove the fuel tank.

20. If the fuel pump sending unit is being removed and installed into the new tank, refer to Fuel Tank Fuel Pump Module Removal & Installation.

To install:

21. Install the fuel tank.

22. Install the fuel tank strap to the vehicle.

23. Install the fuel tank strap bolts loosely leaving the tank hanging approximately one inch.

24. Remove the caps from the EVAP pipes.

25. Connect the EVAP crossover pipe quick connect fitting at the left fuel tank.

26. Lubricate the crossover tube to fuel tank connection O-rings with GM P/N 1051717 (Canadian P/N 5728223) rubber lubricant.

➡️**Note the location of the T-shaped alignment feature between the jet pump feed/return pipes connector.**

27. Lubricate the crossover tube O-ring mating surfaces with GM P/N 1051717 (Canadian P/N 5728223) rubber lubricant.

➡️**Note the T-shaped alignment feature on the crossover tube. The crossover tube will not fully seat into the fuel tank if the jet pump lines are misaligned.**

28. Connect the crossover tube to the left fuel tank using the features previously noted.

➡️**The crossover tube collar tangs will not latch if misalignment exists.**

29. Rotate the crossover tube collar clockwise to engage the tangs.

30. Rotate the crossover tube CPA retainer counterclockwise past the collar latching tang and push the tab into the locked position.

➡️**If the CPA retainer is locked into position, the crossover tube collar will not rotate.**

31. Test the crossover tube to fuel tank connection by attempting to rotate the crossover tube collar counterclockwise.

32. Tighten the fuel tank strap bolts. Tighten the bolts to 18 inch lbs. (25 Nm).

33. Remove the cap from the fuel pipes.

34. Connect the fuel feed pipe at the rear of the left fuel tank.

35. Connect the fuel pump jumper harness connector.

36. Connect the fuel fill hose and recirc line to the fill tube. Tighten the clamp to 35 inch lbs. (4 Nm).

37. If automatic transmission, install the driveline support assembly.

38. Install both mufflers.

39. Install the left rear wheelhouse panel.

40. Lower the vehicle.

41. Refuel the fuel tank.

42. Connect the negative battery cable.

43. Perform the following procedure in order to test for leaks:

   a. Turn ON the ignition switch for 2 seconds.

   b. Turn OFF the ignition for 10 seconds.

   c. Turn ON the ignition.

   d. Inspect for fuel leaks.

Specification:

- Fuel pump on: 58 psi (400 kPa)
- Fuel pump off: 52 psi (359 kPa)

44. Program the transmitters. Refer to Transmitter Programming in the Chassis Electrical Section.

Right Side

See Figures 176 and 177, 179, 181 and 182.

1. Before servicing the vehicle, refer to the Precautions Section.

2. Disconnect the negative battery cable.

3. Drain the fuel tank.

4. Remove the right rear wheelhouse panel.

5. For automatic transmissions, remove the driveline support assembly.

6. Remove the Evaporative Emission (EVAP) canister access cover.

7. Disconnect the fill limit vent valve (FLVV) hose (1) at the EVAP canister (2).

8. Disconnect the fuel pump module harness connector.

9. Remove the crossover tube from the clamp located above the transmission.

10. Disengage the crossover tube Connector Position Assurance (CPA) retainer by pulling the tab (1) outward and rotate.

➡️**The crossover tube CPA is released when the latch disengages from the tank connection groove.**

11. Rotate the crossover tube collar counterclockwise to disengage.

12. Disconnect the crossover tube (5) from the right fuel tank by pulling the tube straight out of the fuel tank connection.

✳✳ WARNING

Take care not to disturb the internal O-rings in the fuel tank connections.

13. Disconnect the EVAP crossover pipe (2) quick connect fitting at the right fuel tank.

14. Cap the EVAP pipe to prevent system contamination.

15. Remove the fuel tank strap mount bolts.

16. Remove the fuel tank strap from the vehicle.

17. Remove the fuel tank.

To install:

18. Install the fuel tank.

19. Install the fuel tank strap to the vehicle.

20. Install the fuel tank strap bolts.

21. Remove the cap from the EVAP pipe.

22. Connect the EVAP crossover pipe quick connect fitting at the right fuel tank.

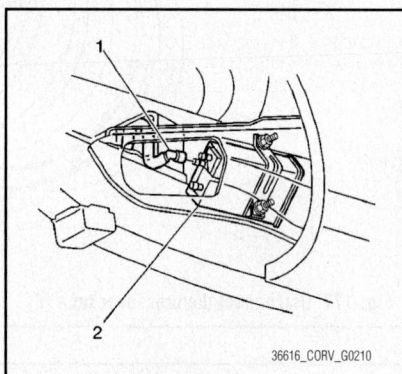

Fig. 181 Disconnect the fill limit vent valve (FLVV) hose (1) at the EVAP canister (2)

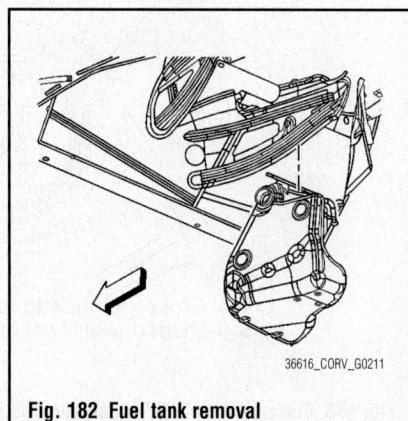

Fig. 182 Fuel tank removal

23. Inspect the O-rings for damage.

24. Lubricate the crossover tube to fuel tank connection O-rings with GM P/N 1051717 (Canadian P/N 5728223) rubber lubricant.

➡**Note the location of the T-shaped alignment feature between the jet pump feed/return pipes connector.**

25. Lubricate the crossover tube O-ring mating surfaces with GM P/N 1051717 (Canadian P/N 5728223) rubber lubricant.

➡**Note the T-shaped alignment feature on the crossover tube. The crossover tube will not fully seat into the fuel tank if the jet pump lines are mis-aligned.**

26. Connect the crossover tube to the right fuel tank using the features previously noted.

➡**The crossover tube collar tangs will not latch if misalignment exists.**

27. Rotate the crossover tube collar clockwise to engage the tangs.

28. Rotate the crossover tube CPA retainer counterclockwise past the collar latching tang and push the tab into the locked position.

➡**If the CPA retainer is locked into position, the crossover tube collar will not rotate.**

29. Test the crossover tube to fuel tank connection by attempting to rotate the crossover tube collar counterclockwise.

30. Tighten the fuel tank strap bolts. Tighten the bolts to 18 inch lbs. (25 Nm).

31. Snap the crossover tube into the clamp located above the transmission.

32. Connect the fuel pump module harness connector.

33. Connect the FLVV hose at the EVAP canister.

34. Install the EVAP canister access cover.

35. If automatic transmission, install the driveline support assembly.

36. Install the right rear wheelhouse panel.

37. Lower the vehicle.

38. Refuel the fuel tank.

39. Connect the negative battery cable.

40. Perform the following procedure in order to test for leaks:

    a. Turn ON the ignition switch for 2 seconds.

    b. Turn OFF the ignition for 10 seconds.

    c. Turn ON the ignition.

    d. Inspect for fuel leaks.

Specification:
- Fuel pump on: 58 psi (400 kPa)
- Fuel pump off: 52 psi (359 kPa)

41. Program the transmitters. Refer to Transmitter Programming in the Chassis Electrical Section.

THROTTLE BODY

REMOVAL & INSTALLATION
See Figure 183.

✳✳ WARNING

Handle the electronic throttle control components carefully. Use cleanliness in order to prevent damage. Do not drop the electronic throttle control components. Do not roughly handle the electronic throttle control components. Do not immerse the electronic throttle control components in cleaning solvents of any type.

➡**Cover or plug any openings when servicing the throttle body in order to prevent possible contamination.**

1. Before servicing the vehicle, refer to the Precautions Section.

2. An 8-digit part identification number is stamped on the throttle body casting. Refer to this number if servicing, or if a part replacement is required.

3. Remove the air cleaner assembly.

4. Disconnect the air control valve electrical connector.

5. Remove the 4 throttle body bolts.

6. Remove the throttle body and the gasket.

7. Discard the throttle body gasket.

To install:

8. Install a new throttle body gasket.

9. Install the throttle body assembly.

➡**Always use a torque wrench in order to obtain the proper torque.**

10. Install the 4 throttle body bolts and tighten to 89 inch lbs. (10 Nm).

➡**Ensure that the air control valve electrical connector and the connector seal are properly installed and no damage present.**

11. Connect the air control valve electrical connector.

12. Install the air cleaner assembly.

13. Perform the throttle learn procedure.

THROTTLE LEARN PROCEDURES

Reset Procedure (Performed after the throttle body is cleaned or replaced)

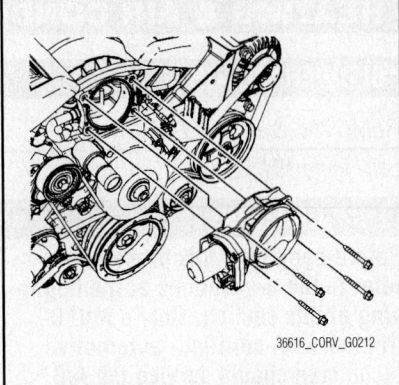

Fig. 183 Throttle body removal and installation

1. Ignition ON, engine OFF, perform the Idle Learn Reset in Module Setup with a scan tool.

2. Start the engine and monitor the TB Idle Airflow Compensation parameter. The TB Idle Airflow Compensation value should equal 0 percent and the engine should be idling at a normal idle speed.

3. Clear the DTCs and return to the diagnostic that referred you here.

Learn Procedure (Performed after the ECM is flashed or replaced)

➡**Do NOT perform this procedure if DTCs are set. Refer to Diagnostic Trouble Codes.**

1. Start and idle the engine for 3 minutes.

2. With a scan tool, monitor the Desired Idle Speed and the actual Engine Speed.

3. The ECM will start to learn the new idle cells and Desired Idle Speed should start to decrease.

4. Ignition OFF for 60 seconds.

5. Start and idle the engine for 3 minutes.

6. After the 3 minute run time the engine should be idling normal.

➡ **During the drive cycle the check engine light may come on with idle speed DTCs. If idle speed codes are set, clear codes so the ECM can continue to learn. If the engine idle speed has not been learned the vehicle will need to be driven at speeds above 44 mph (70 km/h) with several decelerations and extended idles.**

7. After the drive cycle, the engine should be idling normally. If the engine idle speed has not been learned, turn OFF the ignition for 60 seconds and repeat step 6.

8. Once the engine speed has returned to normal, clear DTCs and return to the diagnostic that referred you here.

HEATING & AIR CONDITIONING SYSTEM

BLOWER MOTOR

REMOVAL & INSTALLATION
See Figure 184.

❊❊ CAUTION

Before beginning this procedure, refer to the precautions at the beginning of this section. Only a MVAC-trained, EPA-certified, automotive technician should service the A/C system or its components.

❊❊ CAUTION

Unplug the blower motor before removal. Blower motor case contact with any ground may start the fan and cause personal injury.

➡The blower motor resistor is internal to the blower motor assembly and is not serviced separately.

1. Remove the right-hand insulator panel.
2. Disconnect the blower motor electrical connector.
3. Remove the blower motor retaining screws.
4. Remove the blower motor from the HVAC module.

To install:
5. Install the blower motor to the HVAC module.
6. Install the blower motor retaining screws and tighten to 14 inch lbs. (1.6 Nm).
7. Connect the blower motor electrical connector.
8. Install the right-hand insulator panel.

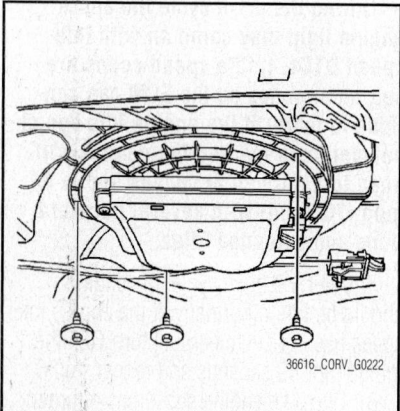

Fig. 184 Blower motor removal and installation

HEATER CORE

REMOVAL & INSTALLATION
See Figures 185 through 187.

❊❊ CAUTION

Before beginning this procedure, refer to the precautions at the beginning of this section. Only a MVAC-trained, EPA-certified, automotive technician should service the A/C system or its components.

1. Remove the HVAC module. Refer to HVAC Module Removal & Installation.
2. Remove and discard the HVAC module assembly foam seal.
3. Disconnect the Discharge Temperature Management (DTM) sensor electrical connectors.
4. Disconnect the HVAC module wiring harness retainer pin (2) from the HVAC module.
5. Disconnect the wiring harness from the heater core cover wire harness retainers (1 and 3) and reposition the wiring harness aside.
6. Remove the heater cover screws.
7. Remove the heater cover from the HVAC module.
8. Remove the heater core from the HVAC module.

To install:

➡Always install new heater core seals onto the heater core.

9. Install a new foam seal to the heater core.
10. Install the heater core to the HVAC module.
11. Install the heater cover to the HVAC

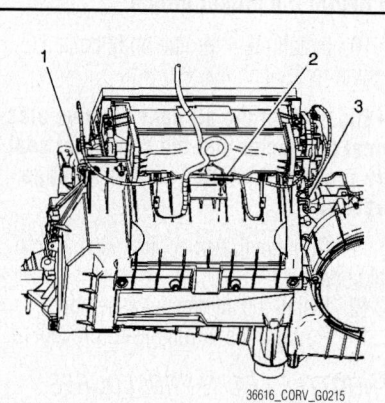

Fig. 185 Wire harness retainers (1 and 3) and pin (2)

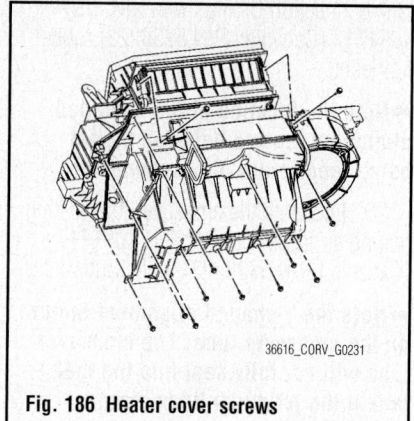

Fig. 186 Heater cover screws

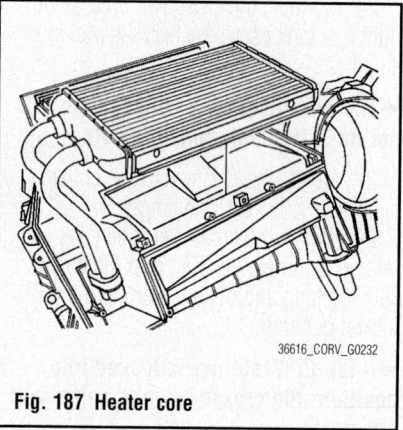

Fig. 187 Heater core

module and tighten the heater cover screws to 14 inch lbs. (1.6 Nm).
12. Reposition the HVAC wiring harness and connect the wiring harness to the heater core cover wiring harness retainer.
13. Reposition the HVAC wiring harness and connect the wiring harness to the heater core cover wiring harness retainer.
14. Connect the HVAC module wiring harness retainer pin to the HVAC module.
15. Connect the DTM sensor electrical connectors.
16. Install the HVAC module.

HVAC MODULE

REMOVAL & INSTALLATION
See Figures 188 through 200.

❊❊ CAUTION

Before beginning this procedure, refer to SIR Precautions. Failure to observe SIR Precautions can lead to serious injury or death.

⁂ **CAUTION**

When performing service on or near the SIR components or the SIR wiring, the SIR system must be disabled. Failure to observe the correct procedure could cause deployment of the SIR components. Serious injury can occur. Failure to observe the correct procedure could also result in unnecessary SIR system repairs.

⁂ **CAUTION**

Before beginning this procedure, refer to the precautions at the beginning of this section. Only a MVAC-trained, EPA-certified, automotive technician should service the A/C system or its components.

1. Recover the refrigerant from the A/C system.
2. Drain the cooling system.
3. Remove the heater pipe assembly.
4. Remove the evaporator drain tube (1) from the HVAC module.
5. Remove the Instrument Panel (I/P) assembly.
6. Remove the air distribution duct.

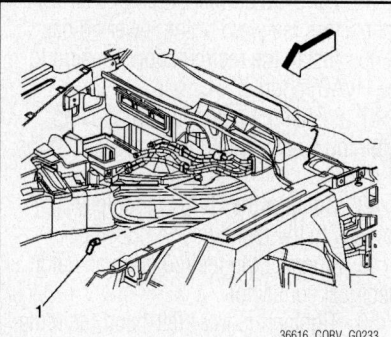
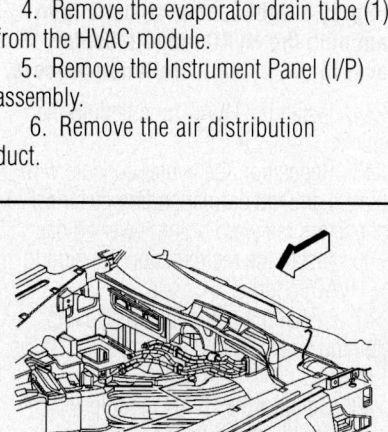

Fig. 188 Remove the evaporator drain tube (1) from the HVAC module

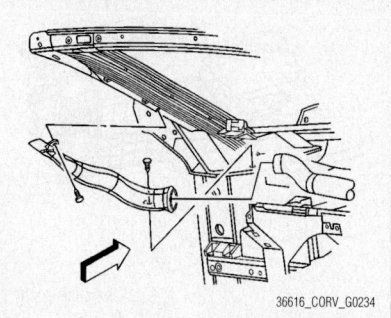

Fig. 189 Remove the retainers from the upper defogger duct on the left side window

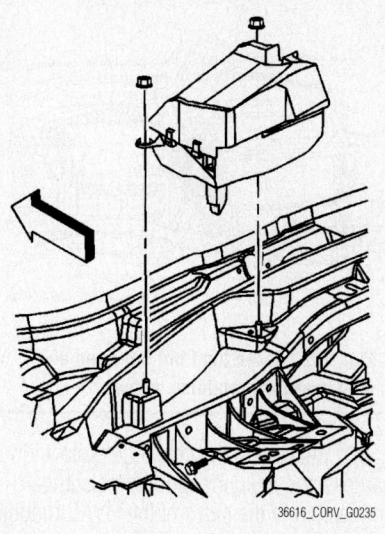

Fig. 190 Disconnect the Head-Up Display (HUD) electrical connector

7. Remove the retainers from the upper defogger duct on the left side window.
8. Disconnect and remove the upper defogger outlet duct.
9. Disconnect the Head-Up Display (HUD) electrical connector.
10. Remove the HUD retaining nuts.
11. Remove the screw that secures the HUD to the steering column bracket.
12. Remove the retainer from the lower defogger outlet duct.
13. Disconnect and remove the outlet duct from the defroster duct.
14. Remove the retaining screws from the floor air outlet duct.
15. Remove the outlet duct.
16. Remove the retainers from the upper outlet duct on the right side window defogger.
17. Disconnect and remove the defogger

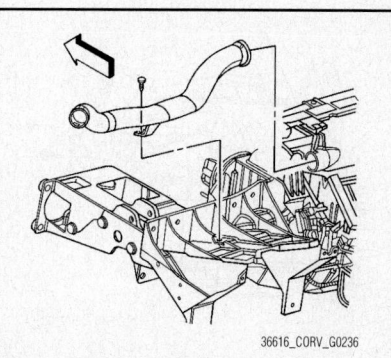

Fig. 191 Remove the retainer from the lower defogger outlet duct

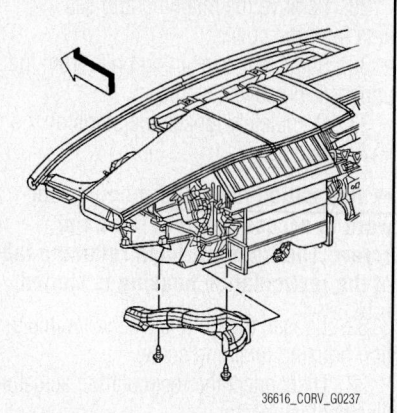

Fig. 192 Remove the retaining screws from the floor air outlet duct

upper outlet duct from the defogger lower outlet duct.
18. Disconnect the defogger lower outlet duct from the knee bolster bracket.
19. Disconnect the defogger lower outlet duct from the defroster duct.
20. Remove the defogger lower outlet duct.
21. Remove the SIR bracket.
22. Remove the retaining screws from the floor air outlet duct.
23. Remove the air outlet duct.
24. Remove the defroster duct retaining screws.
25. Remove the defroster duct.
26. Disconnect the blower motor electrical connector.
27. Remove the blower motor retaining screws.
28. Remove the blower motor from the HVAC module. Refer to Blower Motor Removal & Installation.

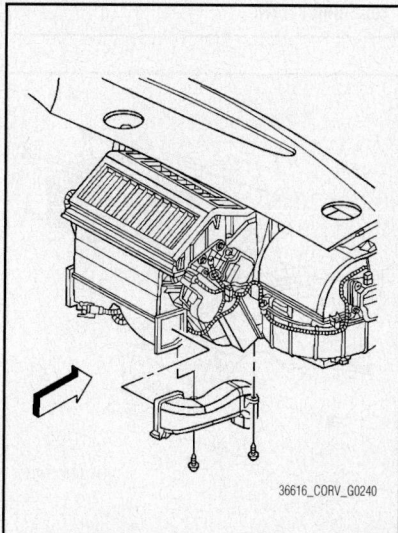

Fig. 193 Remove the air outlet duct and retaining screws

29. Remove the retaining and sealing nuts from the cowl.

30. Remove the retaining bolts from the upper I/P cross vehicle beam.

31. Completely loosen the studs on the HVAC module.

➡ **Reposition the HVAC module rearward to access the front left-hand screw. The front left-hand retaining tab of the recirculation housing is slotted.**

32. Loosen the front left-hand recirculation housing retaining screw.

33. Disconnect the recirculation actuator electrical connector.

34. Disconnect the HVAC module wiring harness from the recirculation housing.

35. Remove the remaining recirculation housing retaining screws.

36. Remove the recirculation housing from the HVAC module.

➡**Reposition the center console wiring harness that runs beneath the HVAC module to aid in HVAC module removal.**

Fig. 194 Remove the defroster duct retaining screws

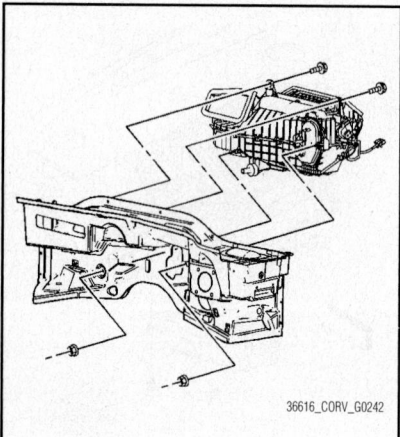

Fig. 195 Remove the retaining and sealing nuts from the cowl

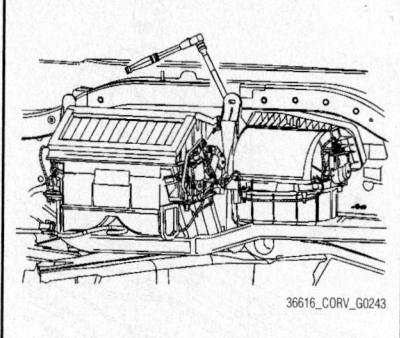

Fig. 196 Loosen the front left-hand air inlet assembly retaining screw

37. Reposition the center console wiring harness and the corresponding electrical connectors to the sides of the HVAC module and forward of the lower tie bar.

38. Carefully remove the HVAC module from the vehicle.

39. Remove and discard the air inlet, drain and plumbing seals from the HVAC module.

To install:

40. If a new HVAC module is being installed, add the specified amount of PAG oil to the evaporator core.

41. Install the HVAC module studs and tighten to 35 inch lbs. (4 Nm).

42. Install new air inlet, drain and plumbing seals to the HVAC module.

➡**Ensure that the cut-outs on the dash-mat are properly aligned so that the drain and plumbing seals are seated directly against the cowl and the air inlet seal is seated directly against the dash-mat. The opening in the dash mat for the HVAC module drain should be aligned so that the drain opening in the cowl is approximately centered in the dash-mat opening; allowing ample room for the module drain seal to fully seat against the cowl.**

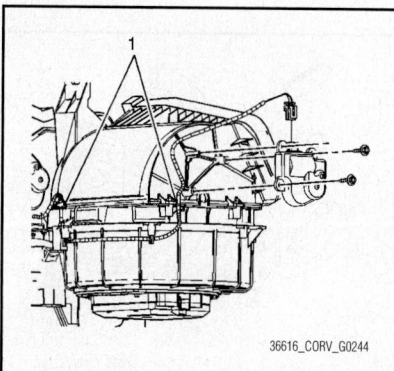

Fig. 197 Disconnect the recirculation actuator electrical connector

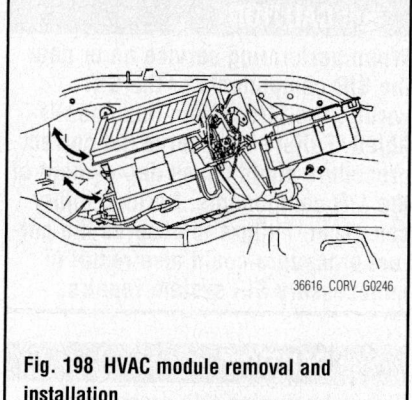

Fig. 198 HVAC module removal and installation

43. Inspect the dash-mat for proper alignment to the cowl. Align if necessary.

✳✳ WARNING

Do not force the HVAC module between upper I/P and lower I/P cross vehicle beams. Damage to the HVAC module can result.

➡**Spray a light coat of silicone lubricant onto the HVAC module heater cover to aid in the installation process.**

44. Install the HVAC module into the vehicle.

45. Reposition the center console wire harness and the corresponding electrical connectors rearward of the lower tie bar.

46. Install the recirculation housing to the HVAC module.

47. Install the recirculation housing retaining screws and tighten to 14 inch lbs. (1.6 Nm).

48. Connect the HVAC module wiring harness to the recirculation housing.

49. Connect the recirculation actuator electrical connector.

50. Tighten the front left-hand recirculation housing retaining screw to 14 inch lbs. (1.6 Nm).

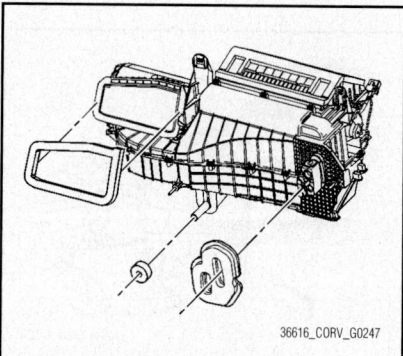

Fig. 199 Remove and discard the air inlet, drain and plumbing seals from the HVAC module

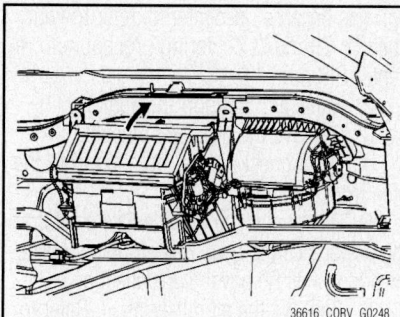

Fig. 200 Align the heater core block fitting, evaporator block fitting, HVAC module drain and studs

➡ **If necessary, gently rotate the HVAC module forward to engage the HVAC module studs through the corresponding holes on the cowl.**

51. Align the following components to the corresponding openings on the cowl:
- The heater core block fitting
- The evaporator block fitting
- The HVAC module drain
- The HVAC module studs

52. Install the bolts retaining the HVAC module to the upper I/P cross vehicle beam. Tighten the bolts to 44 inch lbs. (5 Nm).

➡ **To prevent possible water leaks or wind/road noise from entering the vehicle passenger compartment, do not reuse the old HVAC module retaining and sealing nuts.**

53. Install new HVAC module retaining and sealing nuts and tighten to 89 inch lbs. (10 Nm).

54. Install the blower motor to the HVAC module.

55. Install the blower motor retaining screws and tighten the screws to 14 inch lbs. (1.6 Nm).

56. Connect the blower motor electrical connector.

57. Install the defroster duct to the HVAC module.

58. Install the defroster duct retaining screws and tighten to 89 inch lbs. (10 Nm).

59. Install the right floor air outlet duct.

60. Install the floor air outlet duct retaining screws and tighten to 14 inch lbs. (1.6 Nm).

61. Install the lower outlet duct to the side window defogger.

62. Connect the lower outlet duct on the side window defogger to the defroster duct.

63. Install the SIR bracket.

64. Connect the defogger lower outlet duct to the knee bolster bracket.

65. Connect the defogger upper outlet duct to the defogger lower outlet duct.

66. Install the retainers to the defogger upper outlet duct.

67. Install the left rear floor air outlet duct.

68. Install the floor air outlet duct retaining screws and tighten to 14 inch lbs. (1.6 Nm).

69. Connect the window defogger lower outlet duct to the defroster duct.

70. Install the defogger lower outlet duct retainer.

71. Install the screw that secures the HUD to the steering column bracket, and tighten the screw to 27 inch lbs. (3 Nm).

72. Install the HUD retaining nuts and tighten to 44 inch lbs. (5 Nm).

73. Connect the HUD electrical connector.

74. Connect the defogger upper outlet duct.

75. Install the retainers to the upper defogger duct.

76. Install the air distribution duct.

77. Install the I/P assembly.

➡ **Ensure that the evaporator drain tube is fully seated to the HVAC module.**

78. Install the evaporator drain tube to the HVAC module.

79. Install the heater pipe assembly.

80. Fill the cooling system.

81. Evacuate and recharge the A/C system.

82. Install the air inlet assembly to the HVAC module.

83. Leak test the fittings of the components.

STEERING

INTERMEDIATE STEERING SHAFT

REMOVAL & INSTALLATION

See Figures 201 through 203.

1. Before servicing the vehicle, refer to the Precautions Section.

2. Turn the steering wheel far enough to the left to gain access to the upper coupling bolt.

3. Remove the upper coupling bolt.

✳✳ CAUTION

With wheels of the vehicle facing straight ahead, secure the steering wheel utilizing steering column anti-rotation pin, steering column lock, or a strap to prevent rotation. Locking of the steering column will prevent damage and a possible malfunction of the SIR system. The steering wheel must be secured in position before disconnecting the following components: the steering column, the intermediate shaft(s), the steering gear. After disconnecting these components, do not rotate the steering wheel or move the front tires and wheels. Failure to follow this procedure may cause the SIR coil assembly to become un-centered and cause possible damage to the SIR coil. If you think the SIR coil has became un-centered, refer to your specific SIR coil's centering procedure to re-center SIR Coil.

4. Insert the J 42640 lock pin into the steering column access hole in order to lock the steering column. This will maintain the correct orientation.

5. Remove the lower coupling shield.

6. Remove the lower coupling retaining bolt.

7. Install the J 42640 to the steering column.

8. Remove the lower coupling from the steering gear.

9. Slide the upper coupling from the steering column shaft.

10. Remove the intermediate shaft from the vehicle.

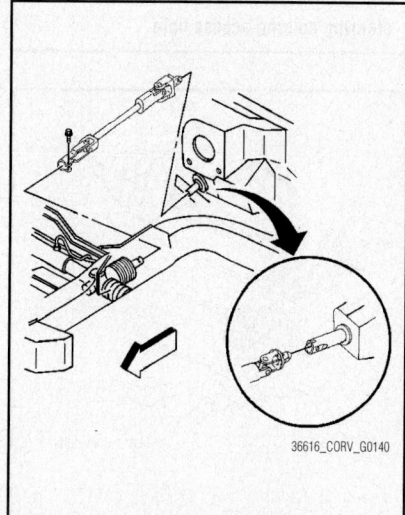

Fig. 201 Intermediate shaft bolt

To install:

11. Place the intermediate shaft into vehicle.

12. Slide the upper coupling into the steering column shaft.

13. Connect the lower coupling onto the steering gear.

14. Install the lower coupling retaining bolt into the lower coupling and tighten the bolt to 20 ft. lbs. (27 Nm).

15. Remove the J 42640 from the steering column.

16. Unlock the steering column.

17. Turn the steering wheel far enough to the left to gain access to the upper coupling bolt hole.

18. Install the upper coupling bolt into the upper coupling and tighten the bolt to 35 ft. lbs. (48 Nm).

19. Turn the steering wheel back to the right until the wheels are in a straight ahead position, then lock the steering column.

20. Install the lower steering coupling shield and tighten the screw to 31 inch lbs. (3.5 Nm).

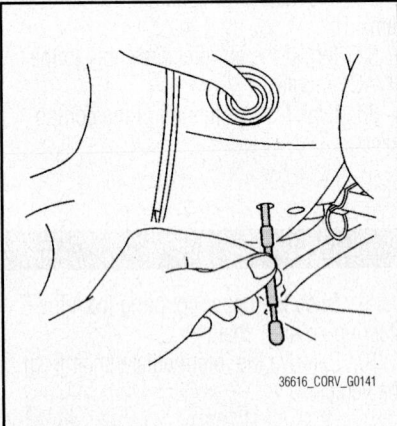

Fig. 202 Insert the J 42640 into the steering column access hole

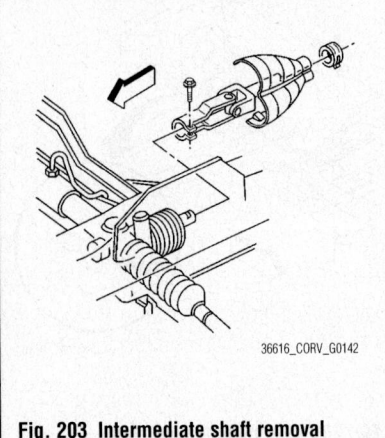

Fig. 203 Intermediate shaft removal

POWER RACK & PINION STEERING GEAR

REMOVAL & INSTALLATION

See Figure 204.

1. Before servicing the vehicle, refer to the Precautions Section.

> **✳✳ CAUTION**
>
> **Before beginning this procedure, refer to SIR Precautions. Failure to observe SIR Precautions can lead to serious injury or death.**

> **✳✳ CAUTION**
>
> **When performing service on or near the SIR components or the SIR wiring, the SIR system must be disabled. Failure to observe the correct procedure could cause deployment of the SIR components. Serious injury can occur. Failure to observe the correct procedure could also result in unnecessary SIR system repairs.**

With wheels of the vehicle facing straight ahead, secure the steering wheel utilizing steering column anti-rotation pin, steering column lock, or a strap to prevent rotation. Locking of the steering column will prevent damage and a possible malfunction of the SIR system. The steering wheel must be secured in position before disconnecting the following components:

- The steering column
- The intermediate shaft(s)
- The steering gear

After disconnecting these components, do not rotate the steering wheel or move the front tires and wheels. Failure to follow this procedure may cause the SIR coil assembly to become un-centered and cause possible damage to the SIR coil. If you think the SIR

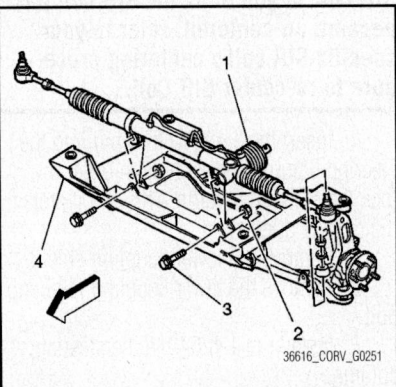

Fig. 204 Power steering gear removal and installation

coil has became un-centered, refer to your specific SIR coil's centering procedure to re-center SIR coil.

2. Raise and support the vehicle.

3. Remove the tires and wheels.

4. Disconnect the tie rod ends from the steering knuckles.

5. Disconnect the intermediate shaft from the power steering gear. Refer to Intermediate Steering Shaft Removal & Installation.

6. Remove the stabilizer shaft. Refer to Stabilizer Shaft Removal & Installation in the Suspension Section.

7. Remove the power steering pressure and return hoses from the power steering gear.

8. Remove the power steering line hold-downs from the crossmember.

9. Remove the Brake Pressure Modulator Valve (BPMV) bracket.

10. Remove the 2 front crossmember mounting nuts.

11. Using hand tools only, LOOSEN, Do Not Remove, the 2 rear crossmember mounting nuts 0.394 in. (10 mm).

12. Disconnect the height sensor arm from the control arm.

13. Use a utility stand to support the front of the crossmember.

14. Using the J 33432-A Compressor, compress the coil spring, in order to allow the crossmember to lower enough to properly remove the gear.

15. Remove the lower shock mounting bolts.

16. Remove the brake pipe bracket for the left front brake caliper from the crossmember.

17. Remove the plastic brake pipe hold-down for the right front brake pipe.

18. Remove the power steering gear mounting bolts (3) and nuts (2).

19. Maneuver the power steering gear (1) around the brake lines from the vehicle through the left wheelhouse opening.

To install:

➡ **For Z06 model applications, replace the crossmember-to-steering gear insulators.**

20. Install the power steering gear into the vehicle through the left wheelhouse opening.

21. Install the power steering gear mounting bolts and nuts and tighten the nuts to 74 ft. lbs. (100 Nm).

22. Install the lower shock mounting bolts.

23. Raise the crossmember by the utility stand and remove the J 33432-A spring compressor.

24. Install all of the crossmember mounting nuts and tighten the nuts, using hand tools only, to 81 ft. lbs. (110 Nm).

25. Install the brake pipe bracket for the left front brake caliper to the crossmember.

26. Install the plastic brake pipe hold-down for the right front brake pipe.

27. Install the brake BPMV bracket.

28. Install the power steering pressure hose to the power steering gear and tighten the fittings to 20 ft. lbs. (27 Nm).

29. Install the power steering return hose to the power steering gear and tighten the fittings to 29 ft. lbs. (27 Nm).

30. Install the power steering hold-downs to the crossmember.

31. Install the stabilizer shaft to the crossmember.

32. Connect the intermediate shaft to the power steering gear.

33. Connect the height sensor arm to the control arm.

34. Connect the tie rod ends to the steering knuckles.

35. Install the tires and wheels.

36. Lower the vehicle.

37. Bleed the power steering system.

38. Check and adjust the front end alignment.

POWER STEERING PUMP

REMOVAL & INSTALLATION

See Figures 205 through 207.

1. Before servicing the vehicle, refer to the Precautions Section.

2. Remove the power steering fluid reservoir.

3. Remove the power steering pump pulley:

    a. Remove the accessory drive belt. Refer to Accessory Drive Belt Removal & Installation the Engine Mechanical Section.

    b. Remove the BPMV bracket.

    c. Install the puller J-25034-C or equivalent on the power steering pump pulley and remove the pulley.

4. Remove the power steering reservoir outlet pipe/hose from the power steering pump. Refer to the Power Steering Reservoir Removal & Installation.

5. Remove the power steering pressure hose from the power steering pump. Refer to the Power Steering Pressure Hose Removal & Installation.

6. Remove the power steering pump mounting bolts (4) from the power steering pump (2).

7. Remove the following components from the power steering pump rear bracket (1):

    a. Remove the power steering front bracket (3).

    b. Remove the steering pump (2).

To install:

8. Install the following components to the power steering pump rear bracket:
- The power steering pump
- The power steering pump front bracket

9. Install the power steering pump mounting bolts to the power steering pump and tighten to 18 ft. lbs. (25 Nm).

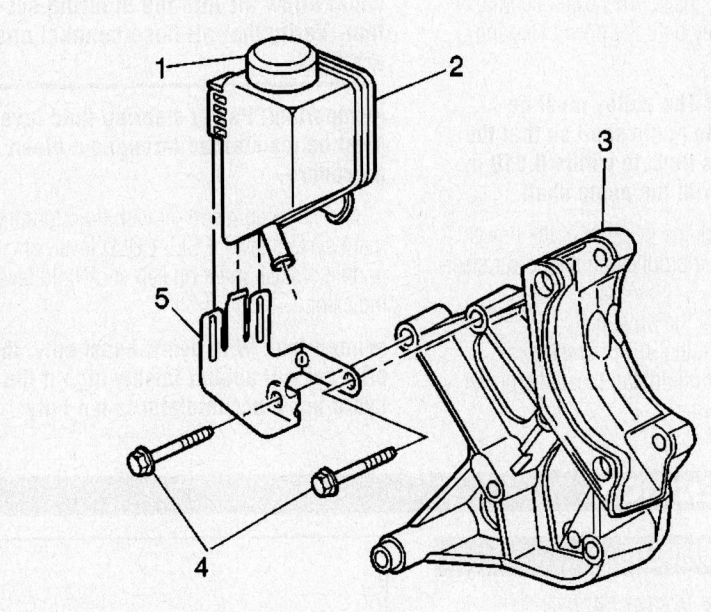

(1) Capstick
(2) Power steering fluid reservoir
(3) Power steering pump mounting bracket
(4) Mounting bolts
(5) Power steering fluid reservoir bracket

22116_CORV_G0065

Fig. 205 Remove the power steering fluid reservoir

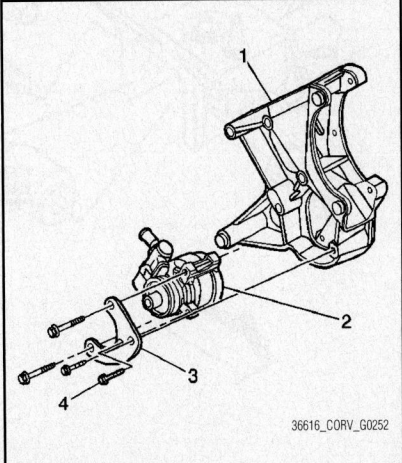

36616_CORV_G0252

Fig. 206 Power steering pump removal and installation

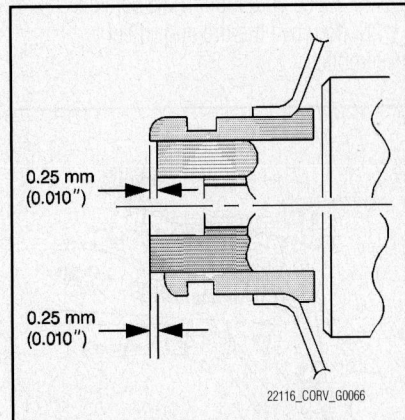

0.25 mm (0.010")

0.25 mm (0.010")

22116_CORV_G0066

Fig. 207 Important: The pulley must be installed onto pump shaft so that the pulley hub is flush to within 0.010 in. (0.25 mm) with the pump shaft

10. Install the power steering reservoir outlet pipe/hose to the power steering pump.

11. Install the power steering pressure hose to the power steering pump and tighten the fitting to 20 ft. lbs. (27 Nm).

12. Install the power steering fluid reservoir.

13. Install the power steering pump pulley:

a. Using special tool J-25033-C or equivalent, install the power steering pump pulley onto the power steering pump.

➡Important: The pulley must be installed onto pump shaft so that the pulley hub is flush to within 0.010 in. (0.25 mm) with the pump shaft.

b. Check the position of the power steering pump pulley on the power steering pump.

c. Install the drive belt.

d. Install the BPMV bracket.

14. Fill with fluid and bleed the power steering system.

BLEEDING

➡Use clean, new power steering fluid type only.

➡Hoses touching the frame, body or engine may cause system noise. Verify that the hoses do not touch any other part of the vehicle.

✳✳ WARNING

Loose connections may not leak, but could allow air into the steering system. Verify that all hose connections are tight.

➡Important: Power steering fluid level must be maintained throughout bleed procedure.

1. Fill pump reservoir with fluid to minimum system level, FULL COLD level, or middle of hash mark on cap stick fluid level indicator.

➡Important: With hydro-boost only, the oil level will appear falsely high if the hydro-boost accumulator is not fully charged. Do not apply the brake pedal with the engine OFF. This will discharge the hydro-boost accumulator.

2. If equipped with hydro-boost, fully charge the hydro-boost accumulator using the following procedure:

a. Start the engine.

b. Firmly apply the brake pedal 10–15 times.

c. Turn the engine OFF.

3. Raise the vehicle until the front wheels are off the ground.

4. With the key on, engine OFF, turn the steering wheel from stop to stop 12 times. Vehicles equipped with hydro-boost systems or longer length power steering hoses may require turns up to 15 to 20 stop to stops.

5. Verify power steering fluid level.

6. Start the engine. Rotate steering wheel from left to right. Check for sign of cavitation or fluid aeration (pump noise/whining).

7. Verify the fluid level. Repeat the bleed procedure, if necessary.

SUSPENSION

FRONT SUSPENSION

CROSSMEMBER

REMOVAL & INSTALLATION

See Figures 208 through 210.

1. Before servicing the vehicle, refer to the Precautions Section.

2. Disconnect the negative battery cable.

3. Remove the alternator. Refer to Alternator Removal & Installation in the Engine Electrical Section.

4. Install J 41803 and J 28467-B and support the engine.

5. Raise and support the vehicle.

6. Remove the tire and wheel assemblies.

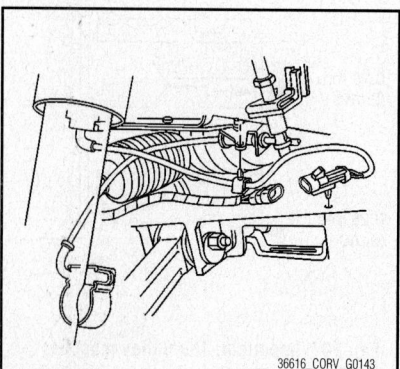

36616_CORV_G0143

Fig. 208 Disconnect the shock absorber solenoid electrical connector

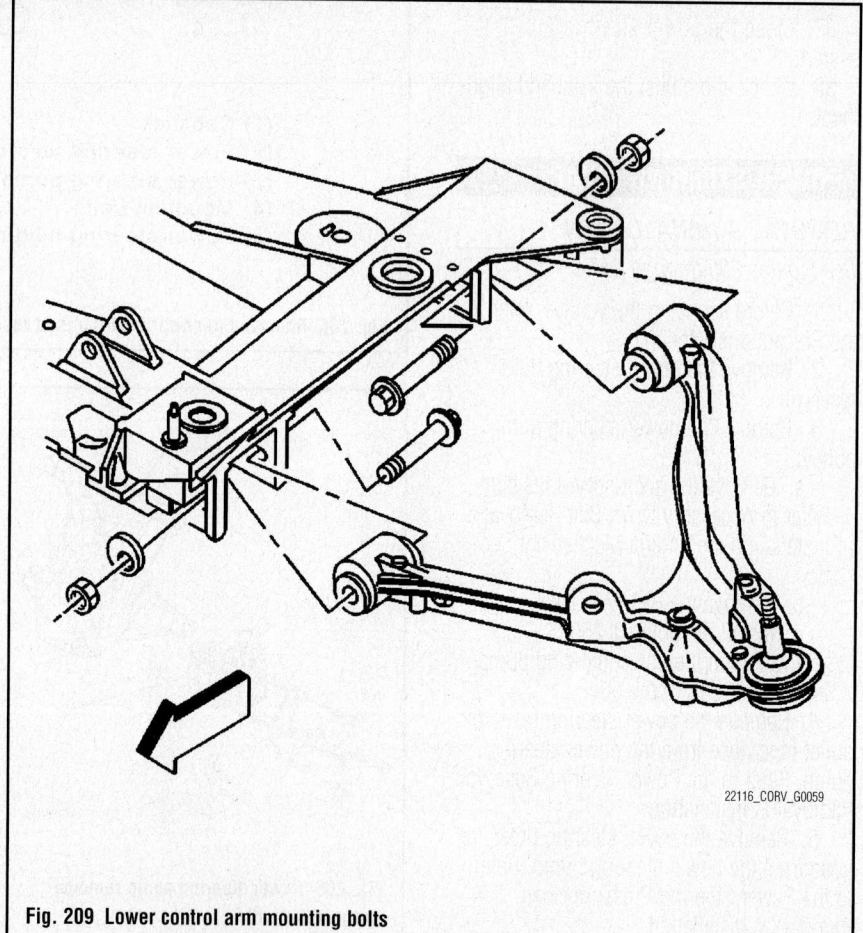

22116_CORV_G0059

Fig. 209 Lower control arm mounting bolts

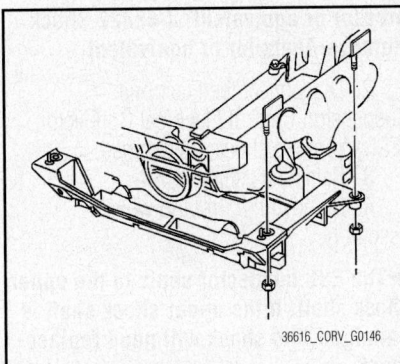

Fig. 210 Remove the crossmember mounting nuts

7. Remove the steering linkage outer tie rod end stud nuts (3). Refer to Steering Linkage Outer Tie Rod Removal & Installation in the Steering Section.

8. Disconnect the shock absorber solenoid electrical connector, if equipped.

9. Disconnect the Electronic Suspension Control (ESC) sensor links.

10. Remove the stabilizer bar from the vehicle. Refer to Stabilizer Shaft Removal & Installation in the Suspension Section.

11. Disconnect the intermediate shaft lower coupling from the steering gear. Refer to Intermediate Steering Shaft Removal & Installation in the Steering Section.

12. Remove the bolts from the Electronic Brake Control Module (EBCM)/Brake Pressure Modulator Valve (BPMV) bracket.

13. Support and reposition the EBCM/BPMV and bracket away from the crossmember.

14. Remove the power steering gear mounting bolts.

15. Remove the power steering fluid cooler from the crossmember.

16. Lift the power steering gear off of the crossmember and support.

17. Using the J 33432-A, remove the transverse spring from the vehicle. Refer to Front Transverse Spring Removal & Installation.

18. Disconnect the lower shock absorber bolts from the lower control arms.

19. Remove the lower control arm bolts from the crossmember.

20. Place a transmission jack under the crossmember.

21. Remove the engine mount lower nuts. Refer to Engine Mount Removal & Installation.

22. Disconnect the wheel speed sensor wiring harness from the crossmember.

23. Disconnect the electrical harness from the clips on the crossmember.

24. Disconnect the brake pipe from the clips on the crossmember.

25. Remove the crossmember mounting nuts.

26. Lower the crossmember out of the vehicle by removing the transmission jack from under the crossmember.

To install:

27. Raise the crossmember to the vehicle:

a. Align the crossmember dowel pins to the frame rails.

b. Align the engine mount studs.

28. Install new crossmember mounting nuts and tighten to 81 ft. lbs. (110 Nm).

29. Install the engine mount lower nuts.

30. Fasten the wheel speed sensor wiring harness retaining clips to the crossmember.

31. Fasten the brake pipe to the retaining clips on the crossmember.

32. Connect the electrical harness to the clips on the crossmember.

33. Connect the brake pipe to the clips on the crossmember.

34. Install the transverse spring, with the J 33432-A connected, to the crossmember.

35. Install the lower control arm to the crossmember.

36. Install the shock absorbers to the lower control arms. Tighten the shock absorber lower mounting nuts to 21 ft. lbs. (28 Nm).

37. Install the power steering gear to the crossmember. Tighten the mounting bolts to 74 ft. lbs. (100 Nm).

38. Install the bolts to the BPMV.

39. Connect the intermediate shaft to the steering gear.

40. Install the steering linkage outer tie rod ends to the steering knuckles.

41. Connect the Electronic Suspension Control (ESC) sensor links to the upper control arm, if equipped.

42. Connect the shock absorber solenoid electrical connector, if equipped.

43. Install the stabilizer shaft to the vehicle.

44. Install the tire and wheel assemblies.

45. Lower the vehicle.

46. Remove J 41803 and J 28467-B from the engine.

47. Install the alternator.

48. Connect the negative battery cable.

49. Align the front end of the vehicle.

LEAF SPRING

REMOVAL & INSTALLATION

See Transverse Spring Removal & Installation.

LOWER BALL JOINT

REMOVAL & INSTALLATION

The lower ball joint is replaced as part of the steering knuckle. Refer to Steering Knuckle Removal & Installation.

LOWER CONTROL ARM

REMOVAL & INSTALLATION

See Figure 209.

1. Before servicing the vehicle, refer to the Precautions Section.

2. Raise and support the vehicle.

3. Remove the tire and wheel assembly.

4. Remove the front transverse spring. Refer to Transverse Spring Removal & Installation.

5. Remove the wheel speed sensor electrical connector.

6. Disconnect the Electronic Suspension Control (ESC) electrical connector from the shock, if equipped

7. Remove the shock absorber from the lower control arm. Refer to Shock Absorber Removal & Installation.

8. Remove the stabilizer shaft link from the lower control arm. Refer to Stabilizer Shaft Link Removal & Installation.

9. Remove the lower ball joint stud from the steering knuckle.

10. Mark the position of the cam bolts for orientation when installing.

11. Remove the cam bolts, washers and nuts after matchmarking them.

➡**Important: With the Z06 model, any time the lower control arms are removed, the lower control arm-to-crossmember cam bolts must be replaced.**

12. Remove the lower control arm from the vehicle.

To install:

13. Install the lower control arm.

➡**DO NOT tighten the cam bolts to specifications until after the alignment has been performed.**

14. Install the cam bolts, washers, and nuts retaining control arm to the crossmember. Align cam bolts to the position matchmarked during the removal procedure and hand-tighten the bolts.

15. Support the lower control arm with a jackstand.

16. Install the lower ball joint in the steering knuckle.

17. Install the stabilizer shaft link to the lower control arm.

18. Install the front transverse spring.

19. Install the shock absorber to the lower control arm.

20. Connect the ESC electrical connector to the shock, if equipped

21. Connect the electrical connector to the wheel speed sensor.

22. Remove the jackstands.

23. Install the tire and wheel assembly.

24. Lower the vehicle.

25. Perform a front wheel alignment.

SHOCK ABSORBERS

REMOVAL & INSTALLATION

Without F55 Suspension

See Figure 211.

1. Before servicing the vehicle, refer to the Precautions Section.

➡**The following tools are required for removal: J-33432-A Leaf Spring Compressor or equivalent, J-43822 Shock Remover/Installer or equivalent.**

2. Raise the vehicle.

3. Remove the tire and wheel assembly.

4. Disconnect the electronic suspension control electrical connector from the shock, if equipped.

5. Remove the upper mounting nut, insulator retainer, and insulator.

6. For vehicles without heavy duty shocks, remove the shock absorber lower mounting bolts and nuts.

7. For vehicles equipped with heavy duty shocks (FE3), using a pry bar, compress the shock absorber from the bottom upward.

8. For vehicles without heavy duty

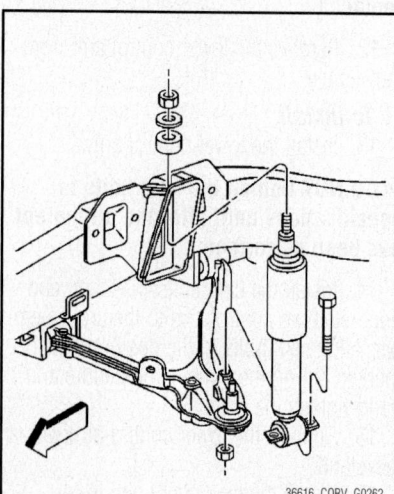

Fig. 211 Front shock absorber removal and installation—without F55 suspension

shocks, remove the shock absorber from the upper shock tower and the vehicle.

9. For vehicles equipped with heavy duty shocks (FE3), install the J 43822 to the shock absorber while the shock is compressed.

10. For vehicles without heavy duty shocks, remove the insulator and retainer from shock absorber.

11. For vehicles equipped with heavy duty shocks (FE3), remove the shock absorber from the shock tower and the vehicle, and then remove the J 43822 from the shock absorber.

To install:

12. Install the retainer and insulator to the shock absorber.

13. Install the shock absorber to the upper shock tower.

14. Install the upper insulator, retainer, and nut. Tighten the upper mounting nut to 19 ft. lbs. (26 Nm).

15. Install the shock absorber lower mounting bolts and nuts. Tighten the nuts to 21 ft. lbs. (28 Nm).

16. Connect the electronic suspension control electrical connector to the shock, if equipped.

17. Remove the J-33432-A from the spring.

18. For vehicles equipped with heavy duty shocks (FE3) perform the following steps:

a. Install the J 43822 to the shock absorber.

b. Install the shock absorber into the vehicle.

c. Install the upper insulator, retainer, and nut. Tighten the shock absorber upper mounting nut to 19 ft. lbs. (26 Nm).

d. Remove J 43822 from the shock absorber.

e. Install J 33432-A to the spring and compress.

f. Raise the lower control arm and install the shock absorber lower mounting bolts and nuts. Tighten the nuts to 21 ft. lbs. (28 Nm).

g. Remove the J 33432-A from the spring.

19. Install the tire and wheel assembly.

20. Lower the vehicle.

With F55 Suspension

See Figure 212.

1. Before servicing the vehicle, refer to the Precautions Section.

➡**The following tools are required for removal: J-33432-A Leaf Spring Com-**

pressor or equivalent, J-43822 Shock Remover/Installer or equivalent

2. Disconnect the Electronic Suspension Control Electrical Connector (ESC) from the shock, if equipped.

3. Raise the vehicle.

4. Remove the tire and wheel assembly.

➡**The ESC connector seals to the upper shock shaft. If the upper shock shaft is damaged, the shock will need replacement.**

5. Using only hand tools, remove the upper mounting nut, insulator retainer and insulator.

6. Remove the shock absorber lower mounting bolts and nuts.

7. Using a pry bar, compress the shock absorber from the bottom upward.

8. While the shock is in the compressed position, install the J-43822.

9. Remove the shock absorber from the vehicle.

10. Remove the J-43822 from the shock absorber.

11. Remove the insulator and insulator retainer from the shock absorber.

To install:

12. Install the J-43822 to the shock absorber.

13. Install the insulator and insulator retainer to the shock absorber.

14. Position the shock absorber between the upper shock support and lower control arm.

15. Install the insulator, retainer, and nut to the upper shock shaft and tighten to 19 ft. lbs. (26 Nm).

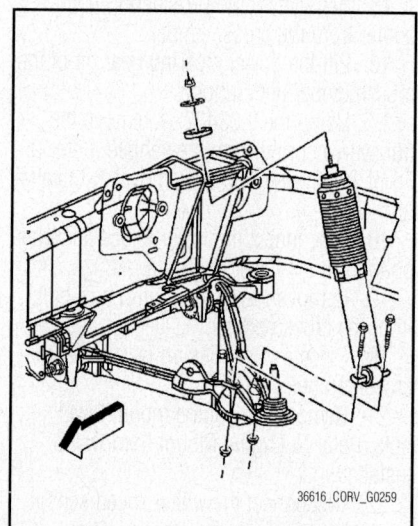

Fig. 212 Front shock absorber removal and installation—with F55 suspension

16. Remove the J-43822 from the shock absorber.

17. Install the J-33432-A to the spring and compress the spring.

18. Raise the lower control arm to the shock absorber lower mounting, install the bolts and nuts, and tighten to 21 ft. lbs. (28 Nm).

19. Remove the J-33432-A from the spring.

20. Install the tire and wheel assembly.

21. Lower the vehicle.

22. Connect the ESC harness connector. Check the connection by lightly pulling upwards on the connector.

STABILIZER SHAFT

REMOVAL & INSTALLATION

See Figure 213.

1. Before servicing the vehicle, refer to the Precautions Section.

2. Raise and support the vehicle.

3. Remove the tire and wheel assemblies.

4. Remove the stabilizer shaft link nuts from the stabilizer shaft.

5. Remove the stabilizer shaft insulator clamps from the front crossmember.

6. Remove the stabilizer shaft from the vehicle.

To install:

7. Install the stabilizer shaft, insulator clamps and bolts to the crossmember.

8. Install the stabilizer shaft links to the stabilizer shaft.

9. Install the stabilizer shaft link nuts and tighten to 56 ft. lbs. (76 Nm).

10. Install the stabilizer shaft insulator clamp bolts and tighten to 43 ft. lbs. (58 Nm).

11. Install the tire and wheel assemblies.

12. Lower the vehicle.

STABILIZER SHAFT CONTROL LINKS

REMOVAL & INSTALLATION

See Figure 213.

1. Before servicing the vehicle, refer to the Precautions Section.

2. Raise and support the vehicle.

3. Remove the tire and wheel assembly.

4. Remove the stabilizer shaft link nuts.

5. Remove the stabilizer shaft link from the stabilizer shaft and lower control arm.

To install:

6. Install the stabilizer shaft link into the stabilizer shaft and lower control arm.

7. Install the stabilizer shaft link nuts and tighten to 56 ft. lbs. (76 Nm).

8. Install the tire and wheel assembly.

9. Lower the vehicle.

STEERING KNUCKLE

REMOVAL & INSTALLATION

See Figure 214.

1. Before servicing the vehicle, refer to the Precautions Section.

2. Raise the vehicle.

3. Remove the brake caliper and rotor. Refer to Front Disc Brake Caliper Removal & Installation and Front Disc Brake Rotor Removal & Installation, in the Brake Section.

4. Remove the stabilizer shaft link from the lower control arm. Refer to Stabilizer Shaft Control Links Removal & Installation.

5. Disconnect the wheel speed sensor electrical connector.

6. Support the lower control arm using a jackstand.

7. Separate the steering linkage outer tie rod ball stud from the steering knuckle using J 42188.

8. Separate and remove the upper control arm ball joint stud from the steering knuckle using J 42188. Refer to Upper Control Arm Removal & Installation.

9. Using J 42188, separate and remove the lower ball joint stud from the steering knuckle. Refer to Lower Control Arm Removal & Installation.

10. Remove the steering knuckle from the vehicle.

To install:

11. Install the steering knuckle to the upper control arm and the lower control arm.

12. Remove the jackstand.

13. Install the steering linkage outer tie rod ball stud to the steering knuckle.

14. Install the stabilizer shaft link to the lower control arm tighten the stabilizer shaft link nut to 53 ft. lbs. (72 Nm).

15. Connect the wheel speed sensor electrical connector.

16. Install the brake rotor and caliper.

17. Install the tire and wheel assembly.

18. Lower the vehicle.

19. Check and adjust the front alignment.

TRANSVERSE SPRING

REMOVAL & INSTALLATION

See Figures 209, 215 through 218.

1. Before servicing the vehicle, refer to the Precautions Section.

2. Raise and support the vehicle.

3. Remove the tire and wheel assemblies.

4. If the transverse spring is to be replaced, measure the front spring adjuster bolt gap. This measurement will be used in the installation procedure to setup the vehicle trim height.

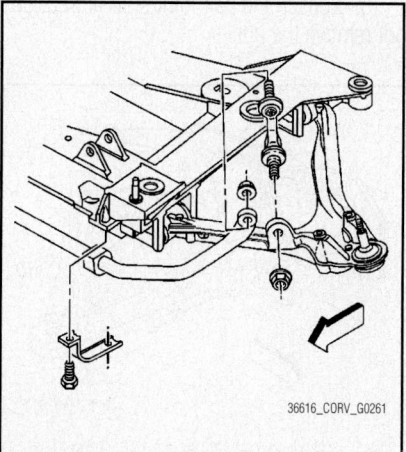

36616_CORV_G0261

Fig. 213 Stabilizer shaft

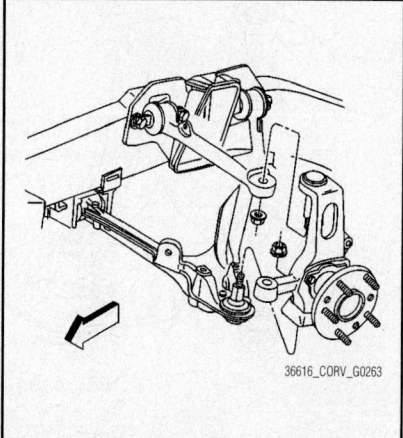

36616_CORV_G0263

Fig. 214 Steering knuckle removal and installation

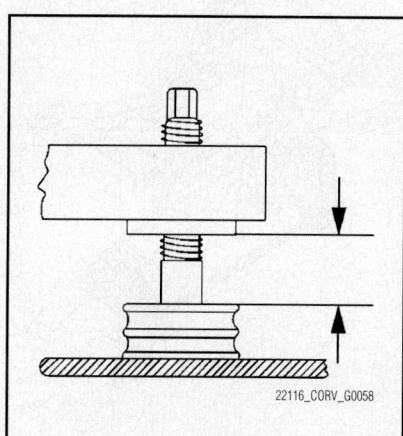

22116_CORV_G0058

Fig. 215 Measure the front spring adjuster bolt gap

→During this procedure, use care not to scratch the transverse spring.

5. Install the transverse spring compressor, J 33432-A, to the transverse spring.

6. Compress the transverse spring.

7. Remove the lower shock absorber mounting bolts from one of the lower control arms.

8. Disconnect the stabilizer shaft link from the lower control arm.

9. Loosen the lower ball joint stud nut on the lower control arm. Do not remove the nut.

10. Separate the lower ball joint from the steering knuckle using ball joint separator tool J 42188.

11. Remove the ball joint separator tool.

12. Remove the lower ball joint stud nut and discard.

13. Support the lower control arms with jackstands.

14. Mark the position of the cam bolts for reference at reinstallation.

15. Remove the cam bolts from the lower control arm.

16. Remove the lower control arm.

17. Remove the transverse spring bolts and retainers.

18. Discard the old transverse spring bolts.

19. Remove the transverse spring from the vehicle.

20. Remove the transverse spring compressor from the transverse spring, if the spring is to be replaced.

To install:

21. Install the transverse spring compressor, J 33432-A, to the transverse spring.

22. Install the transverse spring to the crossmember.

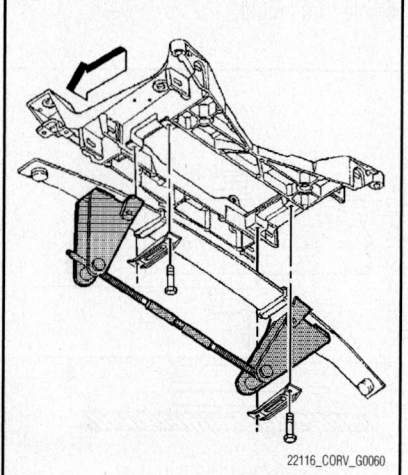

Fig. 216 Exploded view of the front transverse spring with compressor tool

✳✳ WARNING

Do not remove the transverse leaf spring compressor tool until after the shock absorber has been installed. The pad on the transverse leaf spring bolt could move out of position resulting in damage to the pad or a rattle in the suspension.

23. Install the transverse spring retainers and bolts (use new bolts) to the crossmember. Tighten the transverse spring retainer bolts (use new bolts) to 46 ft. lbs. (62 Nm).

24. Install the lower control arm to the front crossmember.

25. Install the cam bolts to the position that was marked during disassembly. Due to a required wheel alignment, tighten the cam bolts but do not set to the final torque specification at this time.

→Use a new ball joint stud nut.

26. Install the lower control arm ball joint stud to the steering knuckle and tighten the nut to 20 ft. lbs. (30 Nm) plus 180 degrees.

27. Support the lower control arm with a jackstand.

28. Install the shock absorber lower mounting bolts. Tighten the shock absorber lower mounting nuts to 21 ft. lbs. (28 Nm).

29. Connect the stabilizer shaft link to the lower control arm. Tighten the stabilizer link nut to 53 ft. lbs. (72 Nm).

30. Remove the J 33432-A, transverse spring compressor, from the transverse spring.

31. Remove the jackstands from the lower control arms.

32. Install the tire and wheel assemblies.

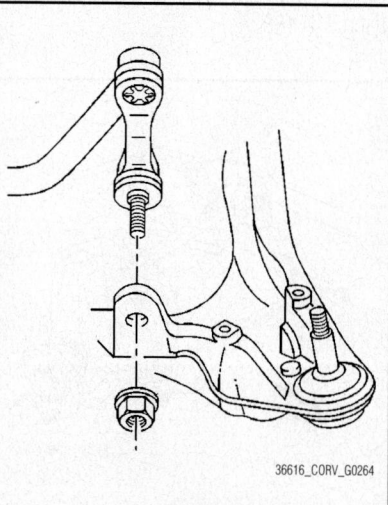

Fig. 217 Disconnect the stabilizer shaft link from the lower control arm

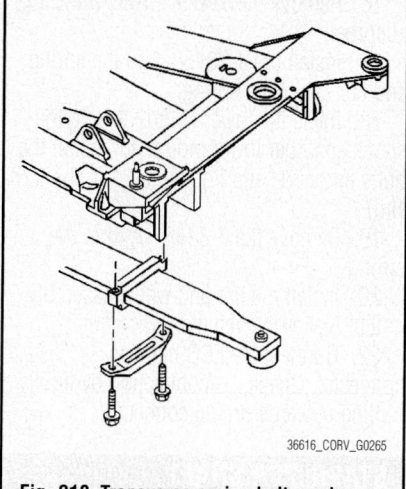

Fig. 218 Transverse spring bolts and retainers

33. Adjust the front trim height.

34. Perform a front wheel alignment.

UPPER BALL JOINT

REMOVAL & INSTALLATION

The upper ball joint is replaced as part of the steering knuckle. Refer to Steering Knuckle Removal & Installation.

UPPER CONTROL ARM

REMOVAL & INSTALLATION

See Figure 219.

1. Before servicing the vehicle, refer to the Precautions Section.

2. Raise and support the vehicle.

3. Remove the tire and wheel assembly.

4. Disconnect the Electronic Suspension Control (ESC) sensor link.

5. Support the lower control arm with a jackstand.

6. Loosen the ball joint stud nut but do not remove the nut.

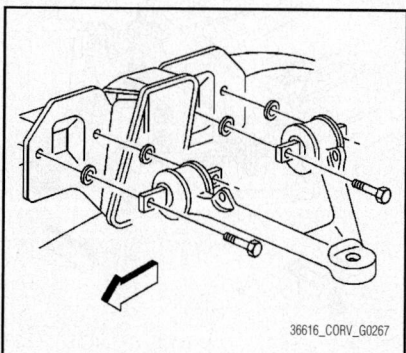

Fig. 219 Upper control arm removal and installation

7. Using tool J-42188-B, separate the upper ball joint stud from the upper control arm.

➡The upper control arm shims will have an effect on the camber and the caster. Make sure to use an equal thickness of shims on both sides of each individual upper control arm bushing.

8. Remove the upper control arm bolts and shims. Note the number and position of the shims for installation purposes.

9. Remove the upper control arm from the vehicle.

To install:

10. Install the upper control arm to the vehicle.

➡The upper control arm shims will have an effect on the camber and the caster. Make sure to use an equal thickness of shims on both sides of each individual upper control arm bushing.

11. Install the upper control arm shims.

12. Install the upper control arm mounting bolts to the upper control arm and frame rail and tighten the upper control arm mounting bolts to 48 ft. lbs. (65 Nm).

13. Install the upper ball joint stud into the upper control arm. It will be necessary to use an Allen wrench to keep the ball joint stud from spinning while tightening the ball joint stud nut and tighten the upper control arm ball joint stud nut to 15 ft. lbs. (20 Nm) plus 250 degrees.

14. Connect the ESC sensor link.

15. Remove the jackstand.

16. Install the tire and wheel assembly.

17. Lower the vehicle.

WHEEL HUB & BEARING

REMOVAL & INSTALLATION

See Figure 220.

✳ WARNING

The Front and Rear Wheel Hub/Wheel Speed Sensors are not interchangeable. When you are replacing a Wheel Hub/Wheel Speed Sensor be sure to use the correct Wheel Hub/Wheel Speed Sensor part number. Do not mount the Rear Wheel Hub/Wheel Speed Sensor in the front steering knuckle. The Rear Wheel Hub/Wheel Speed Sensor features a splined hole through the center of the bearing which mates to the drive axle. The Rear Wheel Hub/Wheel Speed Sensor requires the support of the drive axle and the drive axle nut clamped joint to properly carry the vehicle loads. Mounting the Rear Wheel Hub/Wheel Speed Sensor in the front steering knuckle can cause bearing failure and possible damage to the vehicle.

1. Before servicing the vehicle, refer to the Precautions Section.

2. Raise and support the vehicle.

3. Remove the tire and wheel assembly.

4. Disconnect the wheel speed sensor electrical connector.

5. Remove the brake rotor from the knuckle. Refer to Front Disc Brake Rotor Removal & Installation in the Brake Section.

6. Remove the stabilizer shaft link from the lower control arm. Refer to Front Transverse Spring Removal & Installation.

7. Support the lower control arm using a jackstand.

8. Separate the outer tie rod ball stud from the steering knuckle. Refer to Lower Control Arm Removal & Installation.

9. Remove the knuckle assembly from the vehicle.

10. Remove the wheel hub mounting bolts.

11. Remove the hub and bearing assembly from the steering knuckle.

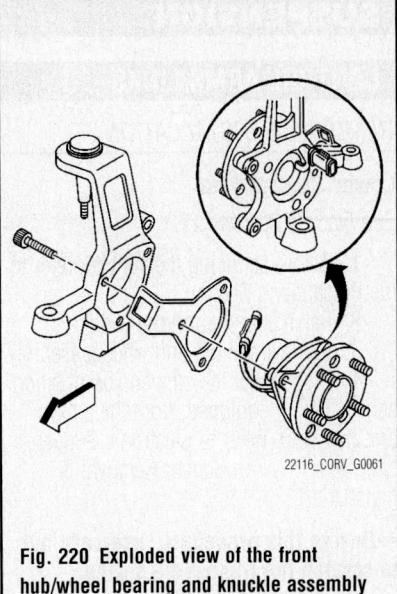

22116_CORV_G0061

Fig. 220 Exploded view of the front hub/wheel bearing and knuckle assembly

To install:

12. Install the hub and bearing assembly into the steering knuckle.

➡Note the location of the black bolt during the removal of the wheel bearing.

13. Install the wheel hub mounting bolts to 96 ft. lbs. (130 Nm).

14. Install the lower control arm ball stud to the steering knuckle.

15. Remove the jackstand.

16. Install the steering linkage outer tie rod ball stud to the steering knuckle.

17. Connect the wheel speed sensor electrical connector.

18. Install the stabilizer shaft link to the lower control arm.

19. Install the brake rotor on the knuckle.

20. Install the tire and wheel assembly.

21. Lower the vehicle.

ADJUSTMENT

No periodic wheel bearing adjustment is necessary. The wheel bearings are a sealed unit that must be replaced if loose or noisy.

SUSPENSION   REAR SUSPENSION

CONTROL ARMS/LINKS

REMOVAL & INSTALLATION

Lower Control Arm

See Figures 221 and 222.

1. Before servicing the vehicle, refer to the Precautions Section.
2. Raise and support the vehicle.
3. Remove the tire and wheel assembly.
4. Disconnect the suspension position sensor link, if equipped, from the control arm link stud. Refer to Electronic Suspension Rear Position Sensor Removal & Installation.

➡**During this procedure, use care not to scratch the transverse spring.**

5. Using the J 33432-A compressor, compress the transverse spring.
6. Disconnect the shock absorber from the lower control arm. Refer to Shock Absorber Removal & Installation.
7. Separate the lower control arm from the rear knuckle. Refer to Suspension Knuckle Removal & Installation.
8. Remove the stabilizer link from the lower control arm. Refer to Stabilizer Shaft Link Removal & Installation.
9. Support the lower control arm with a jackstand.
10. Mark the position of, and then remove the cam bolts, washers, and nuts retaining the control arm to the crossmember.
11. Remove the jack stand from under the lower control arm.

12. Remove the lower control arm from the vehicle.

To install:

✳✳ WARNING

Do not remove the transverse leaf spring compressor tool until after the shock absorber has been installed. The pad on the transverse leaf spring bolt could move out of position resulting in damage to the pad or a rattle in the suspension.

13. Install the lower control arm to the vehicle.
14. Support the lower control arm with a jack stand.

➡**Place the cam bolts at the position marked during removal.**

15. Install the lower control arm front cam bolt, washers, and nuts, and tighten bolt to 125 ft. lbs. (170 Nm), retaining the lower control arm to crossmember.
16. Install the lower control arm rear cam bolt and tighten to 44 ft. lbs. (60 Nm) plus 60 degrees.
17. Install the lower control arm ball joint stud into the suspension knuckle.
18. Install the stabilizer shaft link to the control arm.
19. Install the shock absorber to the lower control arm.
20. Remove the jackstand.
21. Release and remove J 33432-A compressor from the transverse spring.

22. Lower the vehicle.
23. Align the rear suspension.

Upper Control Arm

See Figure 223.

1. Before servicing the vehicle, refer to the Precautions Section.
2. Raise and support the vehicle.
3. Remove the tire and wheel assembly.
4. Disconnect the wheel speed sensor electrical connector.
5. Disconnect the electronic suspension control sensor link. Refer to Electronic Suspension Rear Position Sensor Removal & Installation.
6. Separate the suspension knuckle from the upper control arm using J-42188-B.
7. Support the lower control arm with a jack stand.
8. Loosen the upper ball joint stud nut, but do not remove the nut.
9. Remove J-42188 and the ball joint stud nut (2) from the ball joint stud.
10. Remove the bolts retaining the upper control arm to the frame.
11. On models with FE4 (Special Ride and Handling) or FE5 (Ride, Handling, Performance) suspension, perform the following:
    a. Remove the limiter brackets.
    b. Remove upper control arm washers, making certain to **note position of washers**.
12. Remove the upper control arm from the vehicle.

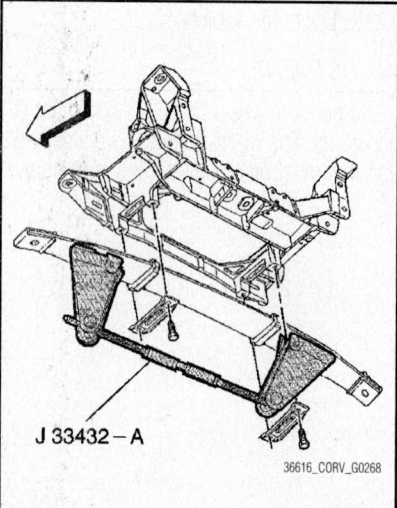

Fig. 221 Using the J 33432-A compressor, compress the transverse spring

J 33432-A

36616_CORV_G0268

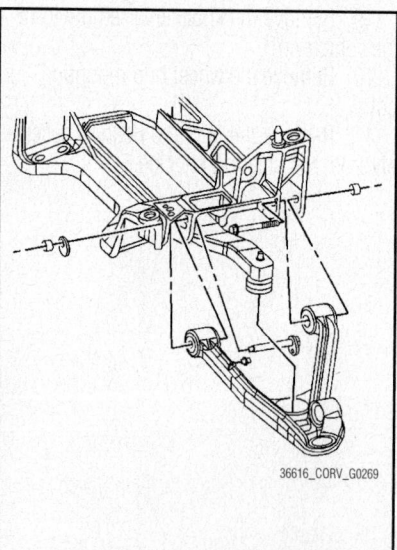

Fig. 222 Lower control arm removal and installation

36616_CORV_G0269

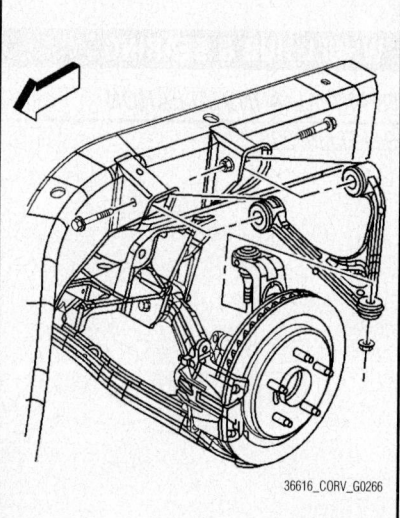

Fig. 223 Upper control arm removal and installation

36616_CORV_G0266

To install:

13. Install the upper control arm to the vehicle.

14. On Z06 models perform the following:

a. Install Upper Control Arm Washers, in their original locations as noted above.

➡**Note the following when installing the washers:**

- The washer **without insert** MUST be positioned closest to the control arm
- The washer **with insert** MUST be positioned closest to the frame
- Ensure that **only ONE washer** with a retaining insert is used on each control arm bolt
- The upper control washers will effect caster and camber. Make sure to use a equal number of washers on both sides of each upper control arm bushing.

b. Install the limiter Brackets.

➡**The limiter brackets must be installed on the inboard side of the rear upper control arm bushings.**

15. Install the upper control arm mounting bolts and to the frame.

16. Tighten the upper control arm mounting bolts as follows:

- Without FE4 or FE5 suspension: 81 ft. lbs. (110 Nm)
- With FE4 or FE5 suspension: 48 ft. lbs. (65 Nm)

17. Install the suspension knuckle upper ball joint stud into the upper control arm. It may be necessary to use an Allen wrench to keep the ball joint stud from spinning while tightening the ball joint stud nut.

18. Install the upper ball joint stud nut.

19. Tighten the suspension knuckle ball joint stud nut as follows:

- Without FE4 or FE5 suspension: 22 ft. lbs. (30 Nm) plus 195 degrees
- With FE4 or FE5 suspension: 15 ft. lbs. (20 Nm) plus 195 degrees

20. Connect the wheel speed sensor electrical connector.

21. Connect the electronic suspension control sensor link.

22. Remove the jack stand from the lower control arm.

23. Install the tire and wheel assembly.

24. Lower the vehicle.

25. Perform a rear wheel alignment.

ELECTRONIC SUSPENSION REAR POSITION SENSOR

REMOVAL & INSTALLATION

See Figures 224 and 225.

1. Before servicing the vehicle, refer to the Precautions Section.

2. Turn OFF the ignition switch.

3. Raise and support the vehicle.

4. Remove the tire and wheel assembly.

5. Disconnect the Electronic Suspension Control (ESC) position sensor harness connector.

6. Disconnect the position sensor link from the control arm link stud.

7. Remove the position sensor mounting bolt.

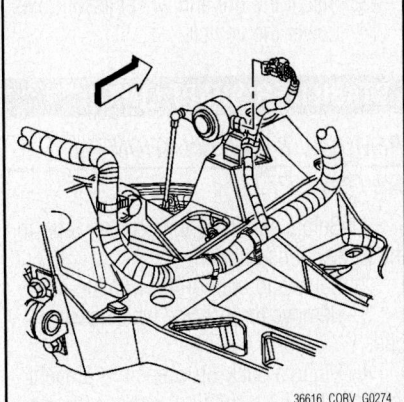

36616_CORV_G0274

Fig. 224 Disconnect the Electronic Suspension Control (ESC) position sensor harness connector

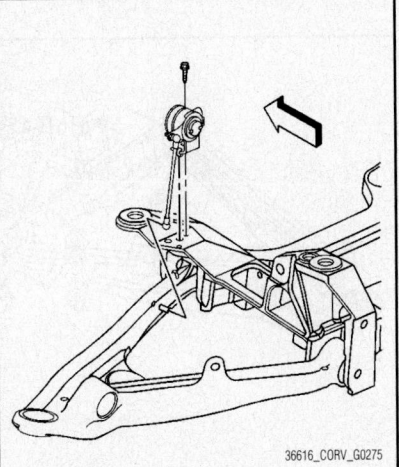

36616_CORV_G0275

Fig. 225 ESC position sensor removal and installation

8. Remove the position sensor from the vehicle.

To install:

9. Install the position sensor to the vehicle.

10. Install the position sensor mounting bolt and tighten to 62 inch lbs. (7 Nm).

11. Connect the position sensor link to the control arm link stud.

12. Connect the ESC position harness connector.

13. Install the tire and wheel assembly.

14. Lower the vehicle.

LEAF SPRING

REMOVAL & INSTALLATION

See Transverse Spring Removal & Installation.

SHOCK ABSORBER

REMOVAL & INSTALLATION

See Figure 226.

1. Before servicing the vehicle, refer to the Precautions Section.

2. Raise and support the vehicle.

3. Remove the tire and wheel assembly.

4. If equipped, disconnect the rear shock Electronic Suspension Control (ESC) harness connector. Refer to Electronic Suspension Rear Position Sensor Removal & Installation.

5. If equipped, disconnect the harness pigtail from the upper shock tower clip.

6. Remove the shock absorber to lower control arm mounting bolt.

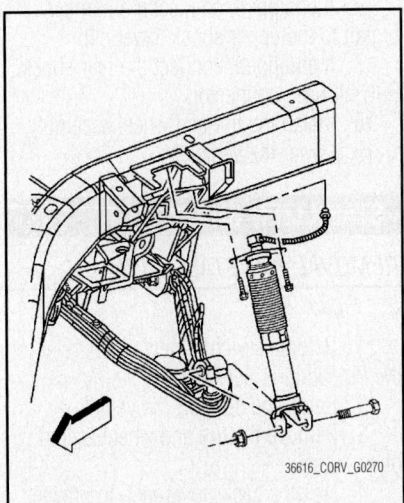

36616_CORV_G0270

Fig. 226 Rear shock absorber removal and installation

7. Remove the shock absorber upper mounting bolts.

8. Disconnect the outer tie rod from the suspension knuckle.

9. Carefully remove the shock absorber from the vehicle. If equipped, take care when routing the ESC pigtail and connector through the upper shock tower.

10. Remove the upper insulator retainer and insulator from the shock absorber.

To install:

11. Install the upper insulator retainer and insulator to the shock absorber.

➡**If equipped, the ESC connector must be installed facing the inward position, while the white paint mark on the bottom bracket must be facing outward. The bracket to ESC connector orientation is 180 degrees.**

12. Carefully install the shock absorber to the shock tower and lower control arm. If equipped, take care when routing the ESC pigtail and connector through the upper shock tower.

13. Install the shock absorber upper mounting bolts and tighten to 22 ft. lbs. (30 Nm).

✳✳ WARNING

To avoid breaking the mounting bolt that attaches the shock absorber to the lower control arm, tighten the bolt. Do NOT tighten the nut.

14. Install the shock absorber lower mounting bolt and nut and tighten to 107 ft. lbs. (145 Nm).

15. Connect the outer tie rod to the suspension knuckle.

16. If equipped, connect the harness pigtail to the upper shock tower clip.

17. If equipped, connect the rear shock ESC harness connector.

18. Install the tire and wheel assembly.

19. Lower the vehicle.

STABILIZER SHAFT

REMOVAL & INSTALLATION

See Figure 227.

1. Before servicing the vehicle, refer to the Precautions Section.

2. Raise and support the vehicle.

3. Remove the tire and wheel assemblies.

4. Using a back-up wrench to prevent the link stud from rotating, remove the stabilizer shaft link nuts from the stabilizer shaft.

5. Remove the stabilizer shaft clamps, bolts and nuts retaining the shaft to the crossmember.

6. Remove the stabilizer shaft from the vehicle.

To install:

7. Install the stabilizer shaft to the vehicle.

8. Install the stabilizer shaft insulator clamps to the stabilizer shaft and the crossmember.

9. Tighten the stabilizer shaft insulator clamp bolts to 74 ft. lbs. (100 Nm).

10. Tighten the stabilizer shaft insulator clamp nuts to 70 ft. lbs. (95 Nm).

11. Using a back-up wrench to prevent the link stud from rotating, install the stabilizer shaft links to the stabilizer shaft.

12. Tighten the stabilizer shaft link nuts to 56 ft. lbs. (76 Nm).

13. Install the tire and wheel assemblies.

14. Lower the vehicle.

STABILIZER SHAFT LINK

REMOVAL & INSTALLATION

See Figure 227.

1. Before servicing the vehicle, refer to the Precautions Section.

2. Raise and support the vehicle.

3. Remove the tire and wheel assemblies.

4. Using a back-up wrench to prevent the link stud from rotating, remove the stabilizer shaft link nuts from the lower control arms.

5. Using a back-up wrench to prevent the link stud from rotating, remove the stabilizer shaft link nuts and links from the shaft.

To install:

6. Using a back-up wrench to prevent the link stud from rotating, install the stabilizer shaft links and link nuts and tighten to 44 ft. lbs. (60 Nm) plus 30 degrees.

7. Install the tire and wheel assemblies.

8. Lower the vehicle.

SUSPENSION KNUCKLE

REMOVAL & INSTALLATION

See Figure 228.

1. Before servicing the vehicle, refer to the Precautions Section.

2. Raise and support the vehicle.

3. Remove the tire and wheel assemblies.

4. Disconnect the wheel speed sensor harness connector.

5. Disconnect the Electronic Suspension Control (ESC) position sensor link. Refer to Electronic Suspension Rear Position Sensor Removal & Installation.

6. Remove the brake rotor. Refer to Rear Disc Brake Rotor Removal & Installation in the Brake Section.

7. Separate the outer tie rod end from the suspension knuckle.

8. Remove the spindle nut retainer, the spindle nut and the washer.

9. Separate the suspension knuckle from the upper control arm. Refer to Control Arm Removal & Installation.

10. Separate the suspension knuckle from the lower control arm ball joint stud. Refer to Control Arm Removal & Installation.

11. Remove the suspension knuckle.

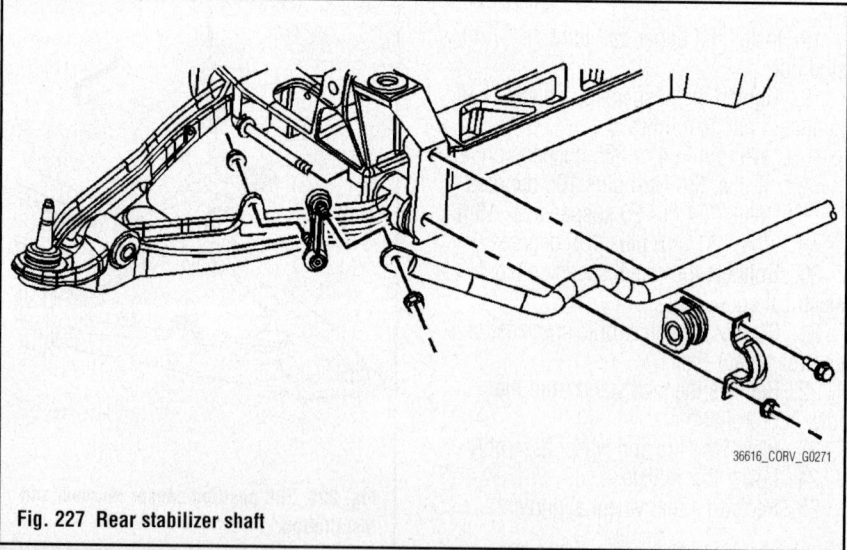

Fig. 227 Rear stabilizer shaft

36616_CORV_G0271

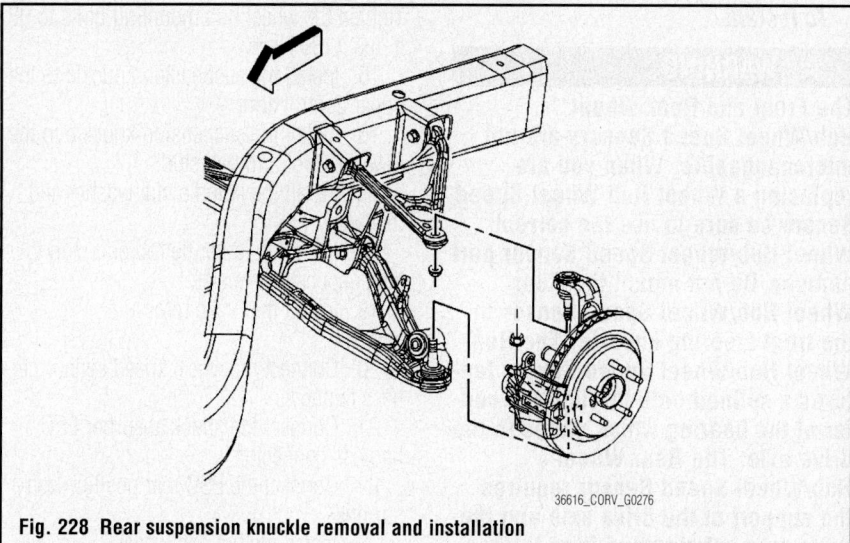

Fig. 228 Rear suspension knuckle removal and installation

To install:

12. Install the suspension knuckle to the lower control arm ball joint stud.

13. Install the suspension knuckle ball joint stud to the upper control arm.

14. Install the spindle nut, washer and retainer.

15. Install the outer tie rod end to the suspension knuckle.

16. Install the brake rotor and caliper.

17. Connect the wheel speed sensor harness connector.

18. Connect the ESC position sensor link.

19. Install the tire and wheel assembly.

20. Lower the vehicle.

21. Perform a rear wheel alignment.

TRANSVERSE SPRING

REMOVAL & INSTALLATION

See Figure 229.

1. Before servicing the vehicle, refer to the Precautions Section.

2. Raise and support the vehicle.

3. Remove the tire and wheel assemblies.

➡️**Important: During this procedure, use care not to scratch the transverse spring.**

4. Using a spring compressor tool J-33432-A, compress the transverse spring.

5. Remove one of the lower control arms. Refer to Control Arm Removal & Installation.

6. Remove the transverse spring mounting bolts and retainers.

7. Discard the old transverse spring mounting bolts.

8. Remove the transverse spring from the vehicle.

9. Remove the J 33432-A from the transverse spring, if the spring is to be replaced.

To install:

10. If installing a new transverse spring, install the J 33432-A and compress the spring.

11. Install the transverse spring to the crossmember.

✳✳ WARNING

Do not remove the transverse leaf spring compressor tool until after the shock absorber has been installed. The pad on the transverse leaf spring bolt could move out of position resulting in damage to the pad or a rattle in the suspension.

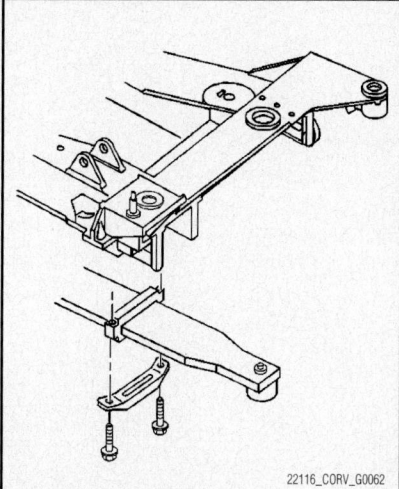

Fig. 229 Removing the transverse spring mounting bolts and insulators

➡️**Use NEW transverse spring retainer-to-crossmember bolts.**

12. Install the transverse spring retainers and NEW mounting bolts to the crossmember and tighten to 46 ft. lbs. (62 Nm).

13. Install the lower control arm to the rear crossmember.

14. Remove the J 33432-A.

15. Install the tire and wheel assemblies.

16. If a NEW transverse spring was installed, adjust the rear trim height.

17. Perform a rear wheel alignment.

WHEEL HUB & BEARING

REMOVAL & INSTALLATION

See Figures 230 and 231.

1. Raise and support the vehicle.

2. Remove the tire and wheel assembly.

3. Disconnect the wheel speed sensor harness connector.

4. Disconnect the Electronic Suspension Control (ESC) rear position sensor link. Refer to Electronic Suspension Rear Position Sensor Removal & Installation.

5. Remove the brake caliper and rotor. Refer to Rear Disc Brake Caliper Removal & Installation and Rear Disc Brake Rotor Removal & Installation in the Brake Section.

6. Disconnect the shock absorber ESC harness connector.

7. Separate the outer tie rod end from the suspension knuckle.

8. Remove the spindle nut retainer, the spindle nut and the washer.

9. Separate the upper control arm (1) from the suspension knuckle.

10. Separate the suspension knuckle from the lower control arm ball joint stud.

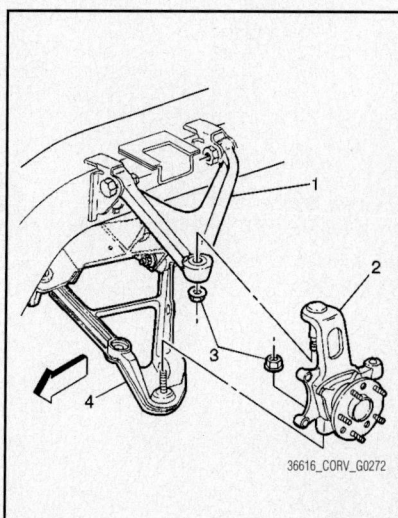

Fig. 230 Separate the upper control arm (1) from the suspension knuckle

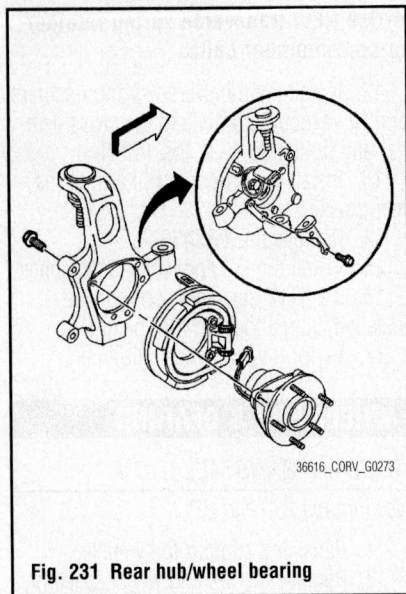

Fig. 231 Rear hub/wheel bearing

11. Remove the suspension knuckle from the vehicle.

12. Remove the wheel hub mounting bolts.

13. Remove the hub and bearing assembly from the suspension knuckle.

To install:

✳✳ WARNING

The Front and Rear Wheel Hub/Wheel Speed Sensors are not interchangeable. When you are replacing a Wheel Hub/Wheel Speed Sensor be sure to use the correct Wheel Hub/Wheel Speed Sensor part number. Do not mount the Rear Wheel Hub/Wheel Speed Sensor in the front steering knuckle. The Rear Wheel Hub/Wheel Speed Sensor features a splined hole through the center of the bearing which mates to the drive axle. The Rear Wheel Hub/Wheel Speed Sensor requires the support of the drive axle and the drive axle nut clamped joint to properly carry the vehicle loads. Mounting the Rear Wheel Hub/Wheel Speed Sensor in the front steering knuckle can cause bearing failure and possible damage to the vehicle.

14. Install the wheel hub and bearing assembly to the suspension knuckle.

Tighten the wheel hub mounting bolts to 96 ft. lbs. (130 Nm).

15. Install the suspension knuckle to the upper control arm.

16. Install the suspension knuckle to the lower control arm ball stud.

17. Install the spindle nut, washer and retainer.

18. Install the outer tie rod end stud to the suspension knuckle.

19. Install the brake rotor and caliper.

20. Connect the wheel speed sensor harness connector.

21. Connect the shock absorber ESC harness connector.

22. Connect the ESC rear position sensor link.

23. Install the tire and wheel assembly.

24. Lower the vehicle.

ADJUSTMENT

No periodic wheel bearing adjustment is necessary. The wheel bearings are a sealed unit that must be replaced if loose or noisy.

GENERAL MOTORS

Diagnostic Trouble Codes

DIAGNOSTIC TROUBLE CODES

OBD II VEHICLE APPLICATIONS

GENERAL MOTORS

Acadia
2008–2009
- 3.6L . . . . VIN 7
- 3.6L . . . . VIN D

Astra
2008–2009
- 1.8L . . . . VIN 1

Allure
2008–2009
- 3.6L . . . . VIN 7
- 3.8L . . . . VIN 2
- 5.3L . . . . VIN C
- 6.0L . . . . VIN Y

Avalanche
2008–2009
- 5.3L . . . . VIN J
- 5.3L . . . . VIN 3
- 5.3L . . . . VIN 0
- 6.0L . . . . VIN Y

Aveo, Aveo5
2008–2009
- 1.6L . . . . VIN 6
- 1.6L . . . . VIN E

Aura
2008–2009
- 2.4L . . . . VIN 5
- 2.4L . . . . VIN B
- 3.5L . . . . VIN N
- 3.6L . . . . VIN 7

Camaro
2010
- 3.6L . . . . VIN V
- 6.2L . . . . VIN J
- 6.2L . . . . VIN W

Canyon
2008–2009
- 2.9L . . . . VIN 9
- 3.7L . . . . VIN E
- 5.3L . . . . VIN L

Cobalt
2008–2009
- 2.0L . . . . VIN P
- 2.0L . . . . VIN X
- 2.2L . . . . VIN H
- 2.2L . . . . VIN F
- 2.4L . . . . VIN B

Colorado
2008–2009
- 2.9L . . . . VIN 9
- 3.7L . . . . VIN E
- 5.3L . . . . VIN L

Corvette
2008–2009
- 6.2L . . . . VIN W
- 6.2L . . . . VIN R
- 7.0L . . . . VIN E

CTS, CTS-V
2008–2009
- 3.6L . . . . VIN V
- 6.2L . . . . VIN P

DTS
2008–2009
- 4.6L . . . . VIN Y

Enclave
2008–2009
- 3.6L . . . . VIN 7
- 3.6L . . . . VIN D

Escalade/EXT/ESV
2008–2009
- 6.0L . . . . VIN 5
- 6.2L . . . . VIN 8
- 6.2L . . . . VIN 2

G3
2008–2009
- 1.6L . . . . VIN E

G5
2008–2009
- 2.2L . . . . VIN H
- 2.2L . . . . VIN F
- 2.4L . . . . VIN B

LaCrosse
2008–2009
- 3.6L . . . . VIN 7
- 3.8L . . . . VIN 2
- 5.3L . . . . VIN C

Outlook
2008–2009
- 3.6L . . . . VIN 7
- 3.6L . . . . VIN D

Suburban
2008–2009
- 5.3L . . . . VIN 3
- 5.3L . . . . VIN J
- 5.3L . . . . VIN 0
- 6.0L . . . . VIN Y
- 6.0L . . . . VIN K

Tahoe
2008–2009
- 4.8L . . . . VIN C
- 5.3L . . . . VIN 3
- 5.3L . . . . VIN J
- 5.3L . . . . VIN 0
- 6.0L . . . . VIN 5
- 6.2L . . . . VIN 2

Traverse
2009
- 3.6L . . . . VIN D

Yukon XL
2008–2009
- 5.3L . . . . VIN J
- 5.3L . . . . VIN 3
- 6.0L . . . . VIN Y
- 5.3L . . . . VIN 0
- 6.2L . . . . VIN 2
- 6.2L . . . . VIN 8

GM REFERENCE INFORMATION

OBD II TROUBLE CODE LIST

To use this information, first read and record All codes in memory along with Freeze Frame data. *If a ECM Reset function is done prior to recording this data,* All *codes and freeze frame data are lost!*

Look up the appropriate trouble code in the list on the following pages. The left hand column includes the code number, the number of trips to set the code (e.g., **1T or 2T**), the year, model description and type of OBD II Monitor that failed (e.g., **CCM or O2S**). This data can be used to determine how to drive a vehicle after a repair in order to validate the repair has been completed.

The **(N/MIL)** designator in the left hand column indicates the trouble code does not turn on the Malfunction Indicator Lamp or MIL. The **(STS Lamp)** indicator in the left column indicates a code that turns on the Service Transmission Soon lamp. This code may or may not turn "on" the MIL.

OBD II Trouble Code List (P0xxx Codes)

DTC	Trouble Code Title, Conditions & Possible Causes
DTC: P0008 **1T CCM, MIL: Yes** **Years:** 2008, 2009, 2010 **Models:** Acadia, Allure, Aura, Camaro, CTS, CTS-V, Enclave, LaCrosse, Outlook, Traverse **Engines:** 3.6L VIN 7, 3.6L VIN D, 3.6L VIN V **Transmissions:** All	**Engine Position System Performance (Bank 1)** The ECM detects that both camshafts on either bank of the engine are mis-aligned with the crankshaft, greater than 6 degrees, for greater than 4 seconds or a cumulative of 30 seconds. **Possible Causes:** • Timing chains and tensioners for excessive wear or misalignment • Crankshaft reluctor wheel for being mis-positioned
DTC: P0009 **1T CCM, MIL: Yes** **Years:** 2008, 2009, 2010 **Models:** Acadia, Allure, Aura, Camaro, CTS, CTS-V, Enclave, LaCrosse, Outlook, Traverse **Engines:** 3.6L VIN 7, 3.6L VIN D, 3.6L VIN V **Transmissions:** All	**Engine Position System Performance (Bank 2)** The ECM detects that both camshafts on either bank of the engine are mis-aligned with the crankshaft, greater than 6 degrees, for greater than 4 seconds or a cumulative of 30 seconds. **Possible Causes:** • Timing chains and tensioners for excessive wear or misalignment • Crankshaft reluctor wheel for being mis-positioned
DTC: P000A **1T CCM, MIL: Yes** **Years:** 2008, 2009 **Models:** Astra, Aura, Aveo, Aveo5, Cobalt G3, G5 **Engines:** 1.6L VIN 6, 1.6L VIN E, 1.8L VIN 1, 2.0L VIN P, 2.0L VIN X, 2.2L VIN H, 2.2L VIN F, 2.4L VIN 5, 2.4L VIN B **Transmissions:** All	**Intake Camshaft Position (CMP) System Slow Response** The engine speed is between 736-6,016 RPM and engine oil temperature is between +14 and +266°F (−10 and +130°C). The actual camshaft position does not match the commanded position. **Possible Causes:** • Engine oil low or in need of changing • CMP Actuator Solenoid ignition voltage for an open/high resistance • CMP Actuator Solenoid ignition voltage for an open/high resistance • CMP Actuator Solenoid control circuit for an open/high resistance • Engine timing components • CMP Actuator Solenoid malfunction
DTC: P000A **1T CCM, MIL: Yes** **Years:** 2008, 2009, 2010 **Models:** Acadia, Allure, Aura, Camaro, CTS, CTS-V, Enclave, LaCrosse, Outlook, Traverse **Engines:** 3.6L VIN 7, 3.6L VIN D, 3.6L VIN V **Transmissions:** All	**Intake Camshaft Position (CMP) System Slow Response (Bank 1)** The ECM detects the difference between the desired camshaft position angle and the actual camshaft position angle is greater than 6-11 degrees. Or the ECM detects a slow response, a deviation greater than 1.5 degrees in time greater than 2.5 seconds, for the actual camshaft position angle to match the desired position angle during the test. Either condition exists for greater than 1 second or a cumulative of 10 seconds **Possible Causes:** • Control circuit for an open or high resistance • Torn, restricted, mis-positioned, or missing screens at the CMP actuator solenoid • Oil leaks between the oil sealing lands of the CMP actuator solenoid • Lands of the CMP actuator solenoid for nicks • Crankshaft reluctor wheel for being mis-positioned • Oil seepage at the CMP actuator solenoind connector
DTC: P000B **1T CCM, MIL: Yes** **Years:** 2008, 2009, 2010 **Models:** Acadia, Allure, Astra, Aura, Aveo Aura, Aveo5, Cobalt G3, G5, Camaro, CTS, CTS-V, Enclave, LaCrosse, Outlook, Traverse **Engines:** All **Transmissions:** All	**Exhaust Camshaft Position (CMP) System Slow Response** The engine speed is between 736-6,016 RPM and engine oil temperature is between +14 and +266°F (−10 and +130°C). The actual camshaft position does not match the commanded position. **Possible Causes:** • Engine oil low or in need of changing • CMP Actuator Solenoid ignition voltage for an open/high resistance • CMP Actuator Solenoid ignition voltage for an open/high resistance • CMP Actuator Solenoid control circuit for an open/high resistance • Engine timing components • CMP Actuator Solenoid malfunction

DTC	Trouble Code Title, Conditions & Possible Causes
DTC: P000C **1T CCM, MIL: Yes** **Years:** 2008, 2009, 2010 **Models:** Acadia, Allure, Aura, Camaro, CTS, CTS-V, Enclave, LaCrosse, Outlook, Traverse **Engines:** 3.6L VIN 7, 3.6L VIN D, 3.6L VIN V **Transmissions:** All	**Intake Camshaft Position (CMP) System Slow Response (Bank 2)** The ECM detects the difference between the desired camshaft position angle and the actual camshaft position angle is greater than 6-11 degrees. Or the ECM detects a slow response, a deviation greater than 1.5 degrees in time greater than 2.5 seconds, for the actual camshaft position angle to match the desired position angle during the test. Either condition exists for greater than 1 second or a cumulative of 10 seconds **Possible Causes:** • Control circuit for an open or high resistance • Torn, restricted, mis-positioned, or missing screens at the CMP actuator solenoid • Oil leaks between the oil sealing lands of the CMP actuator solenoid • Lands of the CMP actuator solenoid for nicks • Crankshaft reluctor wheel for being mis-positioned • Oil seepage at the CMP actuator solenoind connector
DTC: P000D **1T CCM, MIL: Yes** **Years:** 2008, 2009, 2010 **Models:** Acadia, Allure, Aura, Camaro, CTS, CTS-V, Enclave, LaCrosse, Outlook, Traverse **Engines:** 3.6L VIN 7, 3.6L VIN D, 3.6L VIN V **Transmissions:** All	**Exhaust Camshaft Position (CMP) System Slow Response (Bank 2)** The ECM detects the difference between the desired camshaft position angle and the actual camshaft position angle is greater than 6-11 degrees. Or the ECM detects a slow response, a deviation greater than 1.5 degrees in time greater than 2.5 seconds, for the actual camshaft position angle to match the desired position angle during the test. Either condition exists for greater than 1 second or a cumulative of 10 seconds **Possible Causes:** • Control circuit for an open or high resistance • Torn, restricted, mis-positioned, or missing screens at the CMP actuator solenoid • Oil leaks between the oil sealing lands of the CMP actuator solenoid • Lands of the CMP actuator solenoid for nicks • Crankshaft reluctor wheel for being mis-positioned • Oil seepage at the CMP actuator solenoind connector
DTC: P0010 **1T CCM, MIL: Yes** **Years:** 2008, 2009 **Models:** Astra, Aveo, Aveo5, Cobalt, G3, G5 **Engines:** 1.6L VIN 6, 1.6L VIN E, 1.8L VIN 1, 2.0L VIN P, 2.0L VIN X, 2.2L VIN H, 2.2L VIN F, 2.4L VIN 5, 2.4L VIN B **Transmissions:** All	**Intake Camshaft Position (CMP) Actuator Solenoid Control Circuit** The ignition is ON. The ignition voltage is between 10-16 volts. The ECM detects an open in the CMP actuator solenoid circuits for greater than 1 second or a cumulative of 5 seconds when the solenoid is commanded OFF **Possible Causes:** • Engine oil low or in need of changing • CMP Actuator Solenoid ignition voltage for an open/high resistance • CMP Actuator Solenoid ignition voltage for an open/high resistance • CMP Actuator Solenoid control circuit for an open/high resistance • Engine timing components • CMP Actuator Solenoid malfunction • ECM has failed
DTC: P0010 **2T CCM, MIL: Yes** **Years:** 2008, 2009 **Models:** Avalanche, Escalade/EXT/ESV, Suburban, Tahoe, Yukon **Engines:** 4.8L VIN C, 5.3L VIN 0, 5.3L VIN 3, 5.3L VIN J, 5.3L VIN L, 6.0L VIN K, 6.0L VIN Y, 6.2L VIN J, 6.2L VIN W, 6.2L VIN 8, **Transmissions:** All	**Camshaft Position (CMP) Actuator Solenoid Control Circuit** The ignition switch is in the Crank or Run position. The system voltage is between 9-18 volts. The CMP actuator is command ON. DTC P0010 runs continuously when the above conditions are met. The ECM detects that the state of the high side driver and the state of the CMP solenoid control circuit does not match. The ECM will detect an open, high resistance, short to ground, or a short to voltage on the CMP solenoid control circuit, or an open on the low reference circuit, if the condition is present for more than 6 seconds. **Possible Causes:** • Solenoid control circuit for a short to voltage • Solenoid control circuit for an open/high resistance or a short to ground • Low reference circuit for an open/high resistance • Faulty CMP actuator solenoid • ECM has failed
DTC: P0010 **1T CCM, MIL: Yes** **Years:** 2008, 2009, 2010 **Models:** Acadia, Allure, Aura, Camaro, CTS, CTS-V, Enclave, LaCrosse, Outlook, Traverse **Engines:** 3.6L VIN 7, 3.6L VIN D, 3.6L VIN V **Transmissions:** All	**Intake Camshaft Position (CMP) Actuator Solenoid Control Circuit (Bank 1)** The ECM detects an open in the CMP actuator solenoid circuits for greater than 1 seconds or a cumulative of 10 seconds, when the solenoid is commanded OFF. **Possible Causes:** • Ignition circuit for a short to ground or an open/high resistance • Control circuit for a short to voltage or an open/high resistance • Control circuit for a short to ground • CMP actuator solenoid • Faulty ECM

DTC	Trouble Code Title, Conditions & Possible Causes
DTC: P0010 **1T CCM, MIL: Yes** **Years:** 2008, 2009 **Models:** Astra, Aura, Aveo, Aveo5, Cobalt G3, G5 **Engines:** 1.6L VIN 6, 1.6L VIN E, 1.8L VIN 1, 2.0L VIN P, 2.0L VIN X, 2.2L VIN H, 2.2L VIN F, 2.4L VIN 5, 2.4L VIN B **Transmissions:** All	**Intake Camshaft Position (CMP) System Performance** The engine speed is between 736-6,016 RPM and engine oil temperature is between +14 and +266°F (−10 and +130°C). The actual camshaft position does not match the commanded position. **Possible Causes:** • Engine oil low or in need of changing • CMP Actuator Solenoid ignition voltage for an open/high resistance • CMP Actuator Solenoid ignition voltage for an open/high resistance • CMP Actuator Solenoid control circuit for an open/high resistance • Engine timing components • CMP Actuator Solenoid malfunction • ECM has failed
DTC: P0011 **1T CCM, MIL: Yes** **Years:** 2008, 2009, 2010 **Models:** Acadia, Allure, Aura, Camaro, CTS, CTS-V, Enclave, LaCrosse, Outlook, Traverse **Engines:** 3.6L VIN 7, 3.6L VIN D, 3.6L VIN V **Transmissions:** All	**Intake Camshaft Position (CMP) System Performance (Bank 1)** The ECM detects the difference between the desired camshaft position angle and the actual camshaft position angle is greater than 6-11 degrees. Or the ECM detects a slow response, a deviation greater than 1.5 degrees in time greater than 2.5 seconds, for the actual camshaft position angle to match the desired position angle during the test. Either condition exists for greater than 1 second or a cumulative of 10 seconds **Possible Causes:** • Control circuit for an open or high resistance • Torn,restricted, mis-positioned, or missing screens at the CMP actuator solenoid • Oil leaks between the oil sealing lands of the CMP actuator solenoid • Lands of the CMP actuator solenoid for nicks • Crankshaft reluctor wheel for being mis-positioned • Oil seepage at the CMP actuator solenoind connector
DTC: P0011 **1T CCM, MIL: Yes** **Years:** 2008, 2009 **Models:** Astra, Aura, Aveo, Aveo5, Cobalt G3, G5 **Engines:** 1.6L VIN 6, 1.6L VIN E, 1.8L VIN 1, 2.0L VIN P, 2.0L VIN X, 2.2L VIN H, 2.2L VIN F, 2.4L VIN 5, 2.4L VIN B **Transmissions:** All	**Intake Camshaft Position (CMP) System Performance** The ECM detects the difference between the desired camshaft position angle and the actual camshaft position angle is greater than 6-11 degrees. Or the ECM detects a slow response, a deviation greater than 1.5 degrees in time greater than 2.5 seconds, for the actual camshaft position angle to match the desired position angle during the test. Either condition exists for greater than 1 second or a cumulative of 10 seconds **Possible Causes:** • Control circuit for an open or high resistance • Torn,restricted, mis-positioned, or missing screens at the CMP actuator solenoid • Oil leaks between the oil sealing lands of the CMP actuator solenoid • Lands of the CMP actuator solenoid for nicks • Crankshaft reluctor wheel for being mis-positioned • Oil seepage at the CMP actuator solenoind connector
DTC: P0013 **1T CCM, MIL: Yes** **Years:** 2008, 2009 **Models:** Astra, Aura, Aveo, Aveo5, Cobalt G3, G5 **Engines:** 1.6L VIN 6, 1.6L VIN E, 1.8L VIN 1, 2.0L VIN P, 2.0L VIN X, 2.2L VIN H, 2.2L VIN F, 2.4L VIN 5, 2.4L VIN B **Transmissions:** All	**Exhaust Camshaft Position (CMP) Actuator Solenoid Control Circuit** The ignition is ON. The ignition voltage is between 10-16 volts. The ECM detects an open in the CMP actuator solenoid circuits for greater than 1 second or a cumulative of 5 seconds when the solenoid is commanded OFF **Possible Causes:** • Engine oil low or in need of changing • CMP Actuator Solenoid ignition voltage for an open/high resistance • CMP Actuator Solenoid ignition voltage for an open/high resistance • CMP Actuator Solenoid control circuit for an open/high resistance • Engine timing components • CMP Actuator Solenoid malfunction • ECM has failed
DTC: P0013 **1T CCM, MIL: Yes** **Years:** 2008, 2009 **Models:** Canyon, Colorado **Engines:** 2.9L VIN 9, 3.7L VIN E **Transmissions:** All	**Exhaust Camshaft Position (CMP) Actuator Solenoid Control Circuit** The engine is running. The ECM has commanded the Camshaft Position Actuator Solenoid Valve ON. The system voltage is between 11-18 volts. The ECM detects that the commanded state of the driver and the actual state of the control circuit do not match for greater than 7.5 seconds. **Possible Causes:** • Engine oil low or in need of changing • CMP Actuator Solenoid ignition voltage for an open/high resistance • CMP Actuator Solenoid ignition voltage for an open/high resistance • CMP Actuator Solenoid control circuit for an open/high resistance • Engine timing components • CMP Actuator Solenoid malfunction • ECM has failed

DTC	Trouble Code Title, Conditions & Possible Causes
DTC: P0013 **1T CCM, MIL: Yes** **Years:** 2008, 2009, 2010 **Models:** Acadia, Allure, Aura, Camaro, CTS, CTS-V, Enclave, LaCrosse, Outlook, Traverse **Engines:** 3.6L VIN 7, 3.6L VIN D, 3.6L VIN V **Transmissions:** All	**Exhaust Camshaft Position (CMP) System Performance** DTC P0017, P0335, P0336, P0365, P0366 are not set.. The engine is running. The system voltage is between 9-18 volts. The ECM has enabled the CMP actuator and commanded greater than 0 degrees. DTC P0014 runs continuously when the above conditions are met. The difference between the desired CMP and the actual CMP angle is greater than 3.75 degrees for 14.5 s. **Possible Causes:** • Ignition circuit for a short to ground or an open/high resistance • Control circuit for a short to voltage or an open/high resistance • Control circuit for a short to ground • CMP actuator solenoid • Faulty ECM
DTC: P0014 **1T CCM, MIL: Yes** **Years:** 2008, 2009 **Models:** Astra, Aura, Aveo, Aveo5, Cobalt G3, G5 **Engines:** 1.6L VIN 6, 1.6L VIN E, 1.8L VIN 1, 2.0L VIN P, 2.0L VIN X, 2.2L VIN H, 2.2L VIN F, 2.4L VIN 5, 2.4L VIN B **Transmissions:** All	**Exhaust Camshaft Position (CMP) Actuator Solenoid Control Circuit (Bank 1)** The ECM detects an open in the CMP actuator solenoid circuits for greater than 1 seconds or a cumulative of 10 seconds, when the solenoid is commanded OFF. **Possible Causes:** • Engine oil low or in need of changing • CMP Actuator Solenoid ignition voltage for an open/high resistance • CMP Actuator Solenoid ignition voltage for an open/high resistance • CMP Actuator Solenoid control circuit for an open/high resistance • Engine timing components • CMP Actuator Solenoid malfunction • ECM has failed
DTC: P0014 **1T CCM, MIL: Yes** **Years:** 2008, 2009 **Models:** Canyon, Colorado **Engines:** 2.9L VIN 9, 3.7L VIN E **Transmissions:** All	**Exhaust Camshaft Position (CMP) System Performance** The engine speed is between 736-6,016 RPM and engine oil temperature is between +14 and +266°F (−10 and +130°C). The actual camshaft position does not match the commanded position. **Possible Causes:** • Engine oil low or in need of changing • CMP Actuator Solenoid ignition voltage for an open/high resistance • CMP Actuator Solenoid ignition voltage for an open/high resistance • CMP Actuator Solenoid control circuit for an open/high resistance • Engine timing components • CMP Actuator Solenoid malfunction • ECM has failed
DTC: P0014 **1T CCM, MIL: Yes** **Years:** 2008, 2009, 2010 **Models:** Acadia, Allure, Aura, Camaro, CTS, CTS-V, Enclave, LaCrosse, Outlook, Traverse **Engines:** 3.6L VIN 7, 3.6L VIN D, 3.6L VIN V **Transmissions:** All	**Exhaust Camshaft Position (CMP) System Performance (Bank 1)** The ECM detects the difference between the desired camshaft position angle and the actual camshaft position angle is greater than 6-11 degrees. Or the ECM detects a slow response, a deviation greater than 1.5 degrees in time greater than 2.5 seconds, for the actual camshaft position angle to match the desired position angle during the test. Either condition exists for greater than 1 second or a cumulative of 10 seconds **Possible Causes:** • Control circuit for an open or high resistance • Torn, restricted, mis-positioned, or missing screens at the CMP actuator solenoid • Oil leaks between the oil sealing lands of the CMP actuator solenoid • Lands of the CMP actuator solenoid for nicks • Crankshaft reluctor wheel for being mis-positioned • Oil seepage at the CMP actuator solenoind connector
DTC: P0016 **1T CCM, MIL: Yes** **Years:** 2008, 2009, 2010 **Models:** Acadia, Allure, Aura, Camaro, CTS, CTS-V, Enclave, LaCrosse, Outlook, Traverse **Engines:** 3.6L VIN 7, 3.6L VIN D, 3.6L VIN V **Transmissions:** All	**Crankshaft Position (CKP) - Intake Camshaft Position (CMP) Correlation Bank 1** The ECM detects the learned camshaft angle is greater than 10 degrees advanced or 10 degrees retarded in relationship to the crankshaft. **Possible Causes:** • Timing chain tensioner condition • Incorrectly installed timing chain • Excessive play in the timing chain • Cam actuator that is stuck in the full advance or retard position • Crankshaft reluctor wheel that has moved in relationship to top dead • Center (TDC) on the crankshaft

DTC	Trouble Code Title, Conditions & Possible Causes
DTC: P0016 **1T CCM, MIL: Yes** **Years:** 2008, 2009 **Models:** Allure, Aura, Canyon, Colorado, LaCrosse **Engines:** 2.9L VIN 9, 3.5L VIN N, 3.8L VIN 2, 5.3L VIN C, 5.3L VIN L **Transmissions:** All	**Crankshaft Position (CKP) - Intake Camshaft Position (CMP) Correlation** DTC P0335, P0336, P0340, P0341, P0641, or P0651 is not set. The engine is running. The engine speed is less than 2,000 RPM. DTC P0016 runs continuously when the above conditions are met. The ECM detects that the CMP sensor pulses occur more than 11 crank degrees before, or 11 crank degrees after, nominal position for 24 out of 30 engine cycles. **Possible Causes:** • Timing chain tensioner condition • Incorrectly installed timing chain • Excessive play in the timing chain • Cam actuator that is stuck in the full advance or retard position • Crankshaft reluctor wheel that has moved in relationship to top dead • Center (TDC) on the crankshaft
DTC: P0016 **1T CCM, MIL: Yes** **Years:** 2008, 2009 **Models:** Corvette, CTS, CTS-V, DTS **Engines:** 4.6L VIN Y, 6.2L VIN W, 6.2L VIN P, 6.2L VIN R, 7.0L VIN E **Transmissions:** All	**Crankshaft Position (CKP) - Camshaft Position (CMP) Correlation** DTC P0335, P0336, P0340, P0341, P0641, or P0651 is not set. The engine is running. The engine speed is less than 2,000 RPM. DTC P0016 runs continuously when the above conditions are met. The ECM detects that the CMP sensor pulses occur more than 11 crank degrees before, or 11 crank degrees after, nominal position for 24 out of 30 engine cycles. **Possible Causes:** • Timing chain tensioner condition • Incorrectly installed timing chain • Excessive play in the timing chain • Cam actuator that is stuck in the full advance or retard position • Crankshaft reluctor wheel that has moved in relationship to top dead • Center (TDC) on the crankshaft
DTC: P0016 **1T CCM, MIL: Yes** **Years:** 2008, 2009 **Models:** Astra, Aura, Aveo, Aveo5, Cobalt G3, G5 **Engines:** 1.6L VIN 6, 1.6L VIN E, 1.8L VIN 1, 2.0L VIN P, 2.0L VIN X, 2.2L VIN H, 2.2L VIN F, 2.4L VIN 5, 2.4L VIN B **Transmissions:** All	**Crankshaft Position (CKP) - Intake Camshaft Position (CMP) Correlation** The engine is running. The engine oil temperature is more than −10°C (+14°F). The ECM detects an incorrect CMP sensor signal for 2 seconds. **Possible Causes:** • Timing chain tensioner condition • Incorrectly installed timing chain • Excessive play in the timing chain • Cam actuator that is stuck in the full advance or retard position • Crankshaft reluctor wheel that has moved in relationship to top dead • Center (TDC) on the crankshaft
DTC: P0017 **1T CCM, MIL: Yes** **Years:** 2008, 2009 **Models:** Astra, Aura, Aveo, Aveo5, Cobalt G3, G5 **Engines:** 1.6L VIN 6, 1.6L VIN E, 1.8L VIN 1, 2.0L VIN P, 2.0L VIN X, 2.2L VIN H, 2.2L VIN F, 2.4L VIN 5, 2.4L VIN B **Transmissions:** All	**Crankshaft Position (CKP) - Exhaust Camshaft Position (CMP) Correlation** The engine is running. The engine oil temperature is more than −10°C (+14°F). The ECM detects an incorrect CMP sensor signal for 2 seconds. **Possible Causes:** • Timing chain tensioner condition • Incorrectly installed timing chain • Excessive play in the timing chain • Cam actuator that is stuck in the full advance or retard position • Crankshaft reluctor wheel that has moved in relationship to top dead • Center (TDC) on the crankshaft
DTC: P0017 **1T CCM, MIL: Yes** **Years:** 2008, 2009, 2010 **Models:** Acadia, Allure, Aura, Camaro, CTS, CTS-V, Enclave, LaCrosse, Outlook, Traverse **Engines:** 3.6L VIN 7, 3.6L VIN D, 3.6L VIN V **Transmissions:** All	**Crankshaft Position (CKP) - Exhaust Camshaft Position (CMP) Correlation (Bank1)** The ECM detects the learned camshaft angle is greater than 10 degrees advanced or 10 degrees retarded in relationship to the crankshaft. **Possible Causes:** • Timing chain tensioner condition • Incorrectly installed timing chain • Excessive play in the timing chain • Cam actuator that is stuck in the full advance or retard position • Crankshaft reluctor wheel that has moved in relationship to top dead • Center (TDC) on the crankshaft

DTC	Trouble Code Title, Conditions & Possible Causes
DTC: P0017 **1T CCM, MIL: Yes** **Years:** 2008, 2009 **Models:** Canyon, Colorado **Engines:** 2.9L VIN 9, 3.7L VIN E **Transmissions:** All	**Crankshaft Position (CKP) - Exhaust Camshaft Position (CMP) Correlation** DTCs P0335, P0336, P0365, P0366, P0641, and P0651 are not set. The engine is cranking or running. The engine speed is less than 1,200 RPM and the CMP actuator is commanded to the home or parked position. This DTC runs continuously when the above conditions are met. The ECM detects that the CMP sensor pulses occur less than 9 or more than 12 crankshaft degrees outside of the normal position for 24 out of 30 engine cycles. **Possible Causes:** • Timing chain tensioner condition • Incorrectly installed timing chain • Excessive play in the timing chain • Cam actuator that is stuck in the full advance or retard position • Crankshaft reluctor wheel that has moved in relationship to top dead • Center (TDC) on the crankshaft
DTC: P0018 **1T CCM, MIL: Yes** **Years:** 2008, 2009, 2010 **Models:** Acadia, Allure, Aura, Camaro, CTS, CTS-V, Enclave, LaCrosse, Outlook, Traverse **Engines:** 3.6L VIN 7, 3.6L VIN D, 3.6L VIN V **Transmissions:** All	**Crankshaft Position (CKP) - Intake Camshaft Position (CMP) Correlation (Bank 2)** The ECM detects the learned camshaft angle is greater than 10 degrees advanced or 10 degrees retarded in relationship to the crankshaft. **Possible Causes:** • Timing chain tensioner condition • Incorrectly installed timing chain • Excessive play in the timing chain • Cam actuator that is stuck in the full advance or retard position • Crankshaft reluctor wheel that has moved in relationship to top dead • Center (TDC) on the crankshaft
DTC: P0019 **1T CCM, MIL: Yes** **Years:** 2008, 2009, 2010 **Models:** Acadia, Allure, Aura, Camaro, CTS, CTS-V, Enclave, LaCrosse, Outlook, Traverse **Engines:** 3.6L VIN 7, 3.6L VIN D, 3.6L VIN V **Transmissions:** All	**Crankshaft Position (CKP) - Exhaust Camshaft Position (CMP) Correlation (Bank 2)** The ECM detects the learned camshaft angle is greater than 10 degrees advanced or 10 degrees retarded in relationship to the crankshaft. **Possible Causes:** • Timing chain tensioner condition • Incorrectly installed timing chain • Excessive play in the timing chain • Cam actuator that is stuck in the full advance or retard position • Crankshaft reluctor wheel that has moved in relationship to top dead • Center (TDC) on the crankshaft
DTC: P0020 **1T CCM, MIL: Yes** **Years:** 2008, 2009, 2010 **Models:** Acadia, Allure, Aura, Camaro, CTS, CTS-V, Enclave, LaCrosse, Outlook, Traverse **Engines:** 3.6L VIN 7, 3.6L VIN D, 3.6L VIN V **Transmissions:** All	**Intake Camshaft Position (CMP) Actuator Solenoid Control Circuit (Bank 2)** The ECM detects an open in the CMP actuator solenoid circuits for greater than 1 seconds or a cumulative of 10 seconds, when the solenoid is commanded OFF. **Possible Causes:** • Ignition circuit for a short to ground or an open/high resistance • Control circuit for a short to voltage or an open/high resistance • Control circuit for a short to ground • CMP actuator solenoid • Faulty ECM
DTC: P0021 **1T CCM, MIL: Yes** **Years:** 2008, 2009, 2010 **Models:** Acadia, Allure, Aura, Camaro, CTS, CTS-V, Enclave, LaCrosse, Outlook, Traverse **Engines:** 3.6L VIN 7, 3.6L VIN D, 3.6L VIN V **Transmissions:** All	**Intake Camshaft Position (CMP) System Performance (Bank 2)** The ECM detects the difference between the desired camshaft position angle and the actual camshaft position angle is greater than 6-11 degrees. Or the ECM detects a slow response, a deviation greater than 1.5 degrees in time greater than 2.5 seconds, for the actual camshaft position angle to match the desired position angle during the test. Either condition exists for greater than 1 second or a cumulative of 10 seconds **Possible Causes:** • Control circuit for an open or high resistance • Torn, restricted, mis-positioned, or missing screens at the CMP actuator solenoid • Oil leaks between the oil sealing lands of the CMP actuator solenoid • Lands of the CMP actuator solenoid for nicks • Crankshaft reluctor wheel for being mis-positioned • Oil seepage at the CMP actuator solenoind connector

DTC	Trouble Code Title, Conditions & Possible Causes
DTC: P0023 **1T CCM, MIL: Yes** **Years:** 2008, 2009, 2010 **Models:** Acadia, Allure, Aura, Camaro, CTS, CTS-V, Enclave, LaCrosse, Outlook, Traverse **Engines:** 3.6L VIN 7, 3.6L VIN D, 3.6L VIN V **Transmissions:** All	**Exhaust Camshaft Position (CMP) Actuator Solenoid Control Circuit (Bank 2)** The ECM detects an open in the CMP actuator solenoid circuits for greater than 1 seconds or a cumulative of 10 seconds, when the solenoid is commanded OFF. **Possible Causes:** • Ignition circuit for a short to ground or an open/high resistance • Control circuit for a short to voltage or an open/high resistance • Control circuit for a short to ground • CMP actuator solenoid • Faulty ECM
DTC: P0024 **1T CCM, MIL: Yes** **Years:** 2008, 2009, 2010 **Models:** Acadia, Allure, Aura, Camaro, CTS, CTS-V, Enclave, LaCrosse, Outlook, Traverse **Engines:** 3.6L VIN 7, 3.6L VIN D, 3.6L VIN V **Transmissions:** All	**Intake Camshaft Position (CMP) System Performance (Bank 2)** The ECM detects the difference between the desired camshaft position angle and the actual camshaft position angle is greater than 6-11 degrees. Or the ECM detects a slow response, a deviation greater than 1.5 degrees in time greater than 2.5 seconds, for the actual camshaft position angle to match the desired position angle during the test. Either condition exists for greater than 1 second or a cumulative of 10 seconds **Possible Causes:** • Control circuit for an open or high resistance • Torn, restricted, mis-positioned, or missing screens at the CMP actuator solenoid • Oil leaks between the oil sealing lands of the CMP actuator solenoid • Lands of the CMP actuator solenoid for nicks • Crankshaft reluctor wheel for being mis-positioned • Oil seepage at the CMP actuator solenoid connector
DTC: P0030 **1T CCM, MIL: Yes** **Years:** 2008, 2009 **Models:** Corvette, CTS, CTS-V, DTS **Engines:** 4.6L VIN Y, 6.2L VIN W, 6.2L VIN P, 6.2L VIN R, 7.0L VIN E **Transmissions:** All	**HO2S Heater Control Circuit (Bank 1 Sensor 1)** Engine started, system voltage from 9-18v, and the ECM detected the heater low control circuit current was more than the capacity of the ECM internal driver for over 20 seconds. **Possible Causes:** • HO2S low control circuit is shorted to system power (B+) • HO2S low control circuit driver is shorted inside the ECM • HO2S is damaged or it has failed • ECM has failed
DTC: P0030 **1T CCM, MIL: Yes** **Years:** 2008, 2009, 2010 **Models:** Acadia, Allure, Aura, Camaro, CTS, CTS-V, Enclave, LaCrosse, Outlook, Traverse **Engines:** 3.6L VIN 7, 3.6L VIN D, 3.6L VIN V **Transmissions:** All	**HO2S Heater Control Circuit (Bank 1 Sensor 1)** The ECM detects an open in the heater circuits of the HO2S when the heater is commanded OFF. The condition exists for greater than 4 seconds or a cumulative of 30 seconds. **Possible Causes:** • HO2S ignition circuit for a short to ground or an open/high resistance • HO2S low control circuit driver is shorted to ground • HO2S is damaged or it has failed • ECM has failed
DTC: P0030 **1T CCM, MIL: Yes** **Years:** 2008, 2009 **Models:** Astra, Aura, Aveo, Aveo5, Cobalt G3, G5 **Engines:** 1.6L VIN 6, 1.6L VIN E, 1.8L VIN 1, 2.0L VIN P, 2.0L VIN X, 2.2L VIN H, 2.2L VIN F, 2.4L VIN 5, 2.4L VIN B **Transmissions:** All	**HO2S Heater Control Circuit Sensor 1** Engine started, system voltage from 9-18v, and the ECM detected the heater low control circuit current was more than the capacity of the ECM internal driver for over 20 seconds. **Possible Causes:** • HO2S ignition circuit for a short to ground or an open/high resistance • HO2S low control circuit driver is shorted to ground • HO2S is damaged or it has failed • ECM has failed
DTC: P0030 **1T CCM, MIL: Yes** **Years:** 2008, 2009 **Models:** Allure, Aura, Canyon, Colorado, LaCrosse **Engines:** 2.9L VIN 9, 3.5L VIN N, 3.8L VIN 2, 5.3L VIN C, 5.3L VIN L **Transmissions:** All	**HO2S Heater Control Circuit Sensor 1** The ignition 1 signal is between 11-18 volts. The engine speed is more than 400 RPM. DTC P0030, P0036, P0053, P0054 runs continuously when the above conditions are met for 1 second. The ECM detects that the affected HO2S heater low control circuit is not within a specified range. DTCs P0030 or P0036 set within 3 seconds when the above condition is met. **Possible Causes:** • HO2S ignition circuit for a short to ground or an open/high resistance • HO2S low control circuit driver is shorted to ground • HO2S is damaged or it has failed • ECM has failed

DTC	Trouble Code Title, Conditions & Possible Causes
DTC: P0030 **1T CCM, MIL: Yes** **Years:** 2008, 2009 **Models:** Canyon, Colorado **Engines:** 2.9L VIN 9, 3.7L VIN E **Transmissions:** All	**HO2S Heater Control Circuit Sensor 1** The engine speed is more than 400 RPM. The Ignition 1 Signal parameter is between 11-18V. The engine speed is more than 400 RPM. DTC P0030 and P0036 runs continuously when the above conditions are met for 1 second. The ECM detects that the actual state of the affected HO2S heater low control circuit does not match the expected state. DTCs P0030 and P0036 set within 10 seconds when the above condition is met. **Possible Causes:** • HO2S ignition circuit for a short to ground or an open/high resistance • HO2S low control circuit driver is shorted to ground • HO2S is damaged or it has failed • ECM has failed
DTC: P0031 **1T CCM, MIL: Yes** **Years:** 2008, 2009 **Models:** Astra, Aura, Aveo, Aveo5, Cobalt G3, G5 **Engines:** 1.6L VIN 6, 1.6L VIN E, 1.8L VIN 1, 2.0L VIN P, 2.0L VIN X, 2.2L VIN H, 2.2L VIN F, 2.4L VIN 5, 2.4L VIN B **Transmissions:** All	**HO2S Heater Control Circuit Low Voltage Sensor 1** The ECM detects a short to ground in the heater circuits of the HO2S when the heater is commanded OFF. The condition exists for greater than 4 seconds or a cumulative of 30 seconds. **Possible Causes:** • HO2S ignition circuit for a short to ground or an open/high resistance • HO2S low control circuit driver is shorted to ground • HO2S is damaged or it has failed • ECM has failed
DTC: P0031 **1T CCM, MIL: Yes** **Years:** 2008, 2009, 2010 **Models:** Acadia, Allure, Aura, Camaro, CTS, CTS-V, Enclave, LaCrosse, Outlook, Traverse **Engines:** 3.6L VIN 7, 3.6L VIN D, 3.6L VIN V **Transmissions:** All	**HO2S Heater Control Circuit Low Voltage (Bank 1 Sensor 1)** The ECM detects a short to ground in the heater circuits of the HO2S when the heater is commanded OFF. The condition exists for greater than 4 seconds or a cumulative of 30 seconds. **Possible Causes:** • HO2S ignition circuit for a short to ground or an open/high resistance • HO2S low control circuit driver is shorted to ground • HO2S is damaged or it has failed • ECM has failed
DTC: P0032 **1T CCM, MIL: Yes** **Years:** 2008, 2009 **Models:** Astra, Aura, Aveo, Aveo5, Cobalt G3, G5 **Engines:** 1.6L VIN 6, 1.6L VIN E, 1.8L VIN 1, 2.0L VIN P, 2.0L VIN X, 2.2L VIN H, 2.2L VIN F, 2.4L VIN 5, 2.4L VIN B **Transmissions:** All	**HO2S Heater Control Circuit High Voltage Sensor 1** The ECM detects a short to voltage in the heater circuits of the HO2S when the heater is commanded ON. The condition exists for greater than 4 seconds or a cumulative of 30 seconds. **Possible Causes:** • HO2S ignition circuit for a short to ground or an open/high resistance • HO2S low control circuit driver is shorted to ground • HO2S is damaged or it has failed • ECM has failed
DTC: P0032 **1T CCM, MIL: Yes** **Years:** 2008, 2009, 2010 **Models:** Acadia, Allure, Aura, Camaro, CTS, CTS-V, Enclave, LaCrosse, Outlook, Traverse **Engines:** 3.6L VIN 7, 3.6L VIN D, 3.6L VIN V **Transmissions:** All	**HO2S Heater Control Circuit High Voltage (Bank 1 Sensor 1)** The ECM detects a short to voltage in the heater circuits of the HO2S when the heater is commanded ON. The condition exists for greater than 4 seconds or a cumulative of 30 seconds. **Possible Causes:** • HO2S ignition circuit for a short to ground or an open/high resistance • HO2S low control circuit driver is shorted to ground • HO2S is damaged or it has failed • ECM has failed
DTC: P0033 **1T CCM, MIL: Yes** **Years:** 2008, 2009 **Models:** Corvette, CTS, CTS-V, DTS **Engines:** 4.6L VIN Y, 6.2L VIN W, 6.2L VIN P, 6.2L VIN R, 7.0L VIN E **Transmissions:** All	**Supercharger Bypass Valve Solenoid Control Circuit** The ignition is ON. The engine is running. The ignition 1 voltage is between 11-18V. This DTC runs continuously within the enabling conditions. The ECM detects an improper voltage level on the boost control solenoid control circuit for greater than 20 seconds. **Possible Causes:** • ignition circuit for a short to ground or an open/high resistance • SCB solenoid control circuit terminal 2 for a short to ground • SCB solenoid control circuit terminal 2 for a short to voltage or an open/high resistance • SCB solenoid has failed • ECM has failed

DTC	Trouble Code Title, Conditions & Possible Causes
DTC: P0036 **1T CCM, MIL: Yes** **Years:** 2008, 2009 **Models:** Astra, Aura, Aveo, Aveo5, Cobalt G3, G5 **Engines:** 1.6L VIN 6, 1.6L VIN E, 1.8L VIN 1, 2.0L VIN P, 2.0L VIN X, 2.2L VIN H, 2.2L VIN F, 2.4L VIN 5, 2.4L VIN B **Transmissions:** All	**HO2S Heater Control Circuit Sensor 2** The ECM detects an open in the heater circuits of the HO2S when the heater is commanded OFF. The condition exists for greater than 4 seconds or a cumulative of 30 seconds. **Possible Causes:** • HO2S ignition circuit for a short to ground or an open/high resistance • HO2S low control circuit driver is shorted to ground • HO2S is damaged or it has failed • ECM has failed
DTC: P0036 **1T CCM, MIL: Yes** **Years:** 2008, 2009 **Models:** Canyon, Colorado **Engines:** 2.9L VIN 9, 3.7L VIN E **Transmissions:** All	**HO2S Heater Control Circuit Sensor 2** The engine speed is more than 400 RPM. The Ignition 1 Signal parameter is between 11-18V. The engine speed is more than 400 RPM. DTC P0030 and P0036 runs continuously when the above conditions are met for 1 second. The ECM detects that the actual state of the affected HO2S heater low control circuit does not match the expected state. DTCs P0030 and P0036 set within 10 seconds when the above condition is met. **Possible Causes:** • HO2S ignition circuit for a short to ground or an open/high resistance • HO2S low control circuit driver is shorted to ground • HO2S is damaged or it has failed • ECM has failed
DTC: P0036 **1T CCM, MIL: Yes** **Years:** 2008, 2009 **Models:** Corvette, CTS, CTS-V, DTS **Engines:** 4.6L VIN Y, 6.2L VIN W, 6.2L VIN P, 6.2L VIN R, 7.0L VIN E **Transmissions:** All	**Heater Control Circuit (Bank 1 Sensor 2)** The ignition 1 voltage is between 11-18 volts. The engine speed is greater than 400 RPM. The DTCs run continuously when the above conditions are met for 1 second. The ECM detects that the commanded state of the driver and the actual state of the control circuit do not match for greater than 5 seconds. **Possible Causes:** • HO2S ignition circuit for a short to ground or an open/high resistance • HO2S low control circuit driver is shorted to ground • HO2S is damaged or it has failed • ECM has failed
DTC: P0036 **1T CCM, MIL: Yes** **Years:** 2008, 2009 **Models:** Allure, Aura, Canyon, Colorado, LaCrosse **Engines:** 2.9L VIN 9, 3.5L VIN N, 3.8L VIN 2, 5.3L VIN C, 5.3L VIN L **Transmissions:** All	**HO2S Heater Control Circuit Sensor 2** The ignition 1 signal is between 11-18 volts. The engine speed is more than 400 RPM. DTC P0036 runs continuously when the above conditions are met for 1 second. The ECM detects that the affected HO2S heater low control circuit is not within a specified range. DTCs P0036 set within 3 seconds when the above condition is met. **Possible Causes:** • HO2S ignition circuit for a short to ground or an open/high resistance • HO2S low control circuit driver is shorted to ground • HO2S is damaged or it has failed • ECM has failed
DTC: P0036 **1T CCM, MIL: Yes** **Years:** 2008, 2009, 2010 **Models:** Acadia, Allure, Aura, Camaro, CTS, CTS-V, Enclave, LaCrosse, Outlook, Traverse **Engines:** 3.6L VIN 7, 3.6L VIN D, 3.6L VIN V **Transmissions:** All	**Heater Control Circuit (Bank 1 Sensor 2)** The ECM detects an open in the heater circuits of the HO2S when the heater is commanded OFF. The condition exists for greater than 4 seconds or a cumulative of 30 seconds. **Possible Causes:** • HO2S ignition circuit for a short to ground or an open/high resistance • HO2S low control circuit driver is shorted to ground • HO2S is damaged or it has failed • ECM has failed
DTC: P0037 **1T CCM, MIL: Yes** **Years:** 2008, 2009 **Models:** Astra, Aura, Aveo, Aveo5, Cobalt G3, G5 **Engines:** 1.6L VIN 6, 1.6L VIN E, 1.8L VIN 1, 2.0L VIN P, 2.0L VIN X, 2.2L VIN H, 2.2L VIN F, 2.4L VIN 5, 2.4L VIN B **Transmissions:** All	**HO2S Heater Control Circuit Low Voltage Sensor 2** The ECM detects a short to ground in the heater circuits of the HO2S when the heater is commanded OFF. The condition exists for greater than 4 seconds or a cumulative of 30 seconds. **Possible Causes:** • HO2S low control circuit is shorted to system power (B+) • HO2S low control circuit driver is shorted inside the ECM • HO2S is damaged or it has failed • ECM has failed

DTC	Trouble Code Title, Conditions & Possible Causes
DTC: P0037 **1T CCM, MIL: Yes** **Years:** 2008, 2009, 2010 **Models:** Acadia, Allure, Aura, Camaro, CTS, CTS-V, Enclave, LaCrosse, Outlook, Traverse **Engines:** 3.6L VIN 7, 3.6L VIN D, 3.6L VIN V **Transmissions:** All	**HO2S Heater Control Circuit Low Voltage (Bank 1 Sensor 2)** The ECM detects a short to ground in the heater circuits of the HO2S when the heater is commanded OFF. The condition exists for greater than 4 seconds or a cumulative of 30 seconds. **Possible Causes:** • HO2S low control circuit is shorted to system power (B+) • HO2S low control circuit driver is shorted inside the ECM • HO2S is damaged or it has failed • ECM has failed
DTC: P0038 **1T CCM, MIL: Yes** **Years:** 2008, 2009 **Models:** Astra, Aura, Aveo, Aveo5, Cobalt G3, G5 **Engines:** 1.6L VIN 6, 1.6L VIN E, 1.8L VIN 1, 2.0L VIN P, 2.0L VIN X, 2.2L VIN H, 2.2L VIN F, 2.4L VIN 5, 2.4L VIN B **Transmissions:** All	**HO2S Heater Control Circuit High Voltage Sensor 2** The ECM detects a short to voltage in the heater circuits of the HO2S when the heater is commanded ON. The condition exists for greater than 4 seconds or a cumulative of 30 seconds. **Possible Causes:** • HO2S ignition circuit for a short to ground or an open/high resistance • HO2S low control circuit driver is shorted to ground • HO2S is damaged or it has failed • ECM has failed
DTC: P0038 **1T CCM, MIL: Yes** **Years:** 2008, 2009, 2010 **Models:** Acadia, Allure, Aura, Camaro, CTS, CTS-V, Enclave, LaCrosse, Outlook, Traverse **Engines:** 3.6L VIN 7, 3.6L VIN D, 3.6L VIN V **Transmissions:** All	**HO2S Heater Control Circuit High Voltage (Bank 1 Sensor 2)** The ECM detects a short to voltage in the heater circuits of the HO2S when the heater is commanded ON. The condition exists for greater than 4 seconds or a cumulative of 30 seconds. **Possible Causes:** • HO2S ignition circuit for a short to ground or an open/high resistance • HO2S low control circuit driver is shorted to ground • HO2S is damaged or it has failed • ECM has failed
DTC: P0050 **1T CCM, MIL: Yes** **Years:** 2008, 2009, 2010 **Models:** Acadia, Allure, Aura, Camaro, CTS, CTS-V, Enclave, LaCrosse, Outlook, Traverse **Engines:** 3.6L VIN 7, 3.6L VIN D, 3.6L VIN V **Transmissions:** All	**HO2S Heater Control Circuit (Bank 2 Sensor 1)** The ECM detects an open in the heater circuits of the HO2S when the heater is commanded OFF. The condition exists for greater than 4 seconds or a cumulative of 30 seconds. **Possible Causes:** • HO2S ignition circuit for a short to ground or an open/high resistance • HO2S low control circuit driver is shorted to ground • HO2S is damaged or it has failed • ECM has failed
DTC: P0051 **1T CCM, MIL: Yes** **Years:** 2008, 2009, 2010 **Models:** Acadia, Allure, Aura, Camaro, CTS, CTS-V, Enclave, LaCrosse, Outlook, Traverse **Engines:** 3.6L VIN 7, 3.6L VIN D, 3.6L VIN V **Transmissions:** All	**HO2S Heater Control Circuit Low Voltage (Bank 2 Sensor 1)** The ECM detects a short to ground in the heater circuits of the HO2S when the heater is commanded OFF. The condition exists for greater than 4 seconds or a cumulative of 30 seconds. **Possible Causes:** • HO2S ignition circuit for a short to ground or an open/high resistance • HO2S low control circuit driver is shorted to ground • HO2S is damaged or it has failed • ECM has failed
DTC: P0052 **1T CCM, MIL: Yes** **Years:** 2008, 2009, 2010 **Models:** Acadia, Allure, Aura, Camaro, CTS, CTS-V, Enclave, LaCrosse, Outlook, Traverse **Engines:** 3.6L VIN 7, 3.6L VIN D, 3.6L VIN V **Transmissions:** All	**HO2S Heater Control Circuit High Voltage (Bank 2 Sensor 1)** The ECM detects a short to voltage in the heater circuits of the HO2S when the heater is commanded ON. The condition exists for greater than 4 seconds or a cumulative of 30 seconds. **Possible Causes:** • HO2S ignition circuit for a short to ground or an open/high resistance • HO2S low control circuit driver is shorted to ground • HO2S is damaged or it has failed • ECM has failed

DTC	Trouble Code Title, Conditions & Possible Causes
DTC: P0053 **1T CCM, MIL: Yes** **Years:** 2008, 2009 **Models:** Allure, Aura, Canyon, Colorado, LaCrosse **Engines:** 2.9L VIN 9, 3.5L VIN N, 3.8L VIN 2, 5.3L VIN C, 5.3L VIN L **Transmissions:** All	**HO2S Heater Resistance Circuit Sensor 1** DTCs P0112, P0113, P0117 and P0118 are not set. The engine is started. The ignition voltage is less than 18 volts. The ignition is OFF for more than 10 hours. The Engine Coolant Temperature (ECT) sensor is between −22 to +113°F (−30 to +45°C) at engine start-up. The ECT sensor minus the Intake Air Temperature (IAT) sensor is less than 14°F (8°C) at engine start-up. DTCs P0053 and P0054 run once per drive cycle when the above conditions are met. The ECM detects that the affected HO2S heater low control circuit is not within a specified resistance range at engine start-up. DTC P0053 sets within 3 seconds when the above condition is met. **Possible Causes:** • HO2S ignition circuit for a short to ground or an open/high resistance • HO2S low control circuit driver is shorted to ground • HO2S is damaged or it has failed • ECM has failed
DTC: P0053 **1T CCM, MIL: Yes** **Years:** 2008, 2009 **Models:** Corvette, CTS, CTS-V, DTS **Engines:** 4.6L VIN Y, 6.2L VIN W, 6.2L VIN P, 6.2L VIN R, 7.0L VIN E **Transmissions:** All	**HO2S Heater Resistance (Bank 1 Sensor 1)** DTCs P0112, P0113, P0117, P0118, or P2610 are not set. The engine run time is greater than 3 seconds. The ignition voltage is less than 18 volts. The ignition is OFF for greater than 8 hours. The Engine Coolant Temperature (ECT) is between −30 to +45°C (−22 to +113°F) at engine start-up. The ECT and the Intake Air Temperature (IAT) are within 8°C (14°F) at engine start-up. The DTCs run once per drive cycle when the above conditions are met. The ECM detects the HO2S heater is not within a specified resistance range at engine start-up for greater than 1 second. **Possible Causes:** • HO2S ignition circuit for a short to ground or an open/high resistance • HO2S control circuit for a short to voltage, or an open/high resistance • HO2S control circuit for a short to ground • HO2S is damaged or it has failed • ECM has failed
DTC: P0054 **1T CCM, MIL: Yes** **Years:** 2008, 2009 **Models:** Corvette, CTS, CTS-V, DTS **Engines:** 4.6L VIN Y, 6.2L VIN W, 6.2L VIN P, 6.2L VIN R, 7.0L VIN E **Transmissions:** All	**HO2S Heater Resistance (Bank 1 Sensor 2)** DTCs P0112, P0113, P0117, P0118, or P2610 are not set. The engine run time is greater than 3 seconds. The ignition voltage is less than 18 volts. The ignition is OFF for greater than 8 hours. The Engine Coolant Temperature (ECT) is between −30 to +45°C (−22 to +113°F) at engine start-up. The ECT and the Intake Air Temperature (IAT) are within 8°C (14°F) at engine start-up. The DTCs run once per drive cycle when the above conditions are met. The ECM detects the HO2S heater is not within a specified resistance range at engine start-up for greater than 1 second. **Possible Causes:** • HO2S ignition circuit for a short to ground or an open/high resistance • HO2S control circuit for a short to voltage, or an open/high resistance • HO2S control circuit for a short to ground • HO2S is damaged or it has failed • ECM has failed
DTC: P0056 **1T CCM, MIL: Yes** **Years:** 2008, 2009 **Models:** Corvette, CTS, CTS-V, DTS **Engines:** 4.6L VIN Y, 6.2L VIN W, 6.2L VIN P, 6.2L VIN R, 7.0L VIN E **Transmissions:** All	**HO2S Heater Control Circuit (Bank 2 Sensor 2)** Engine started, system voltage from 9-18v, and the ECM detected the heater low control circuit current was more than the capacity of the ECM internal driver for over 20 seconds. **Possible Causes:** • HO2S ignition circuit for a short to ground or an open/high resistance • HO2S control circuit for a short to voltage, or an open/high resistance • HO2S control circuit for a short to ground • HO2S is damaged or it has failed • ECM has failed
DTC: P0059 **1T CCM, MIL: Yes** **Years:** 2008, 2009 **Models:** Corvette, CTS, CTS-V, DTS **Engines:** 4.6L VIN Y, 6.2L VIN W, 6.2L VIN P, 6.2L VIN R, 7.0L VIN E **Transmissions:** All	**HO2S Heater Resistance (Bank 2 Sensor 1)** DTCs P0112, P0113, P0117, P0118, or P2610 are not set. The engine run time is greater than 3 seconds. The ignition voltage is less than 18 volts. The ignition is OFF for greater than 8 hours. The Engine Coolant Temperature (ECT) is between −30 to +45°C (−22 to +113°F) at engine start-up. The ECT and the Intake Air Temperature (IAT) are within 8°C (14°F) at engine start-up. The DTCs run once per drive cycle when the above conditions are met. The ECM detects the HO2S heater is not within a specified resistance range at engine start-up for greater than 1 second. **Possible Causes:** • HO2S ignition circuit for a short to ground or an open/high resistance • HO2S control circuit for a short to voltage, or an open/high resistance • HO2S control circuit for a short to ground • HO2S is damaged or it has failed • ECM has failed

DTC	Trouble Code Title, Conditions & Possible Causes
DTC: P0060 **1T CCM, MIL: Yes** **Years:** 2008, 2009 **Models:** Corvette, CTS, CTS-V, DTS **Engines:** 4.6L VIN Y, 6.2L VIN W, 6.2L VIN P, 6.2L VIN R, 7.0L VIN E **Transmissions:** All	**HO2S Heater Resistance (Bank 2 Sensor 2)** DTCs P0112, P0113, P0117, P0118, or P2610 are not set. The engine run time is greater than 3 seconds. The ignition voltage is less than 18 volts. The ignition is OFF for greater than 8 hours. The Engine Coolant Temperature (ECT) is between −30 to +45°C (−22 to +113°F) at engine start-up. The ECT and the Intake Air Temperature (IAT) are within 8°C (14°F) at engine start-up. The DTCs run once per drive cycle when the above conditions are met. The ECM detects the HO2S heater is not within a specified resistance range at engine start-up for greater than 1 second. **Possible Causes:** • HO2S ignition circuit for a short to ground or an open/high resistance • HO2S control circuit for a short to voltage, or an open/high resistance • HO2S control circuit for a short to ground • HO2S is damaged or it has failed • ECM has failed
DTC: P0068 **1T CCM, MIL: Yes** **Years:** 2008, 2009 **Models:** Corvette, CTS, CTS-V, DTS **Engines:** 4.6L VIN Y, 6.2L VIN W, 6.2L VIN P, 6.2L VIN R, 7.0L VIN E **Transmissions:** All	**Throttle Body Airflow Performance** DTCs P0641, P0651, P1516, P2101, P2119, P2176 are not set. The engine is running. DTC P0068 run continuously when the above conditions are met. The ECM detects that the throttle position and the indicated engine load do not correspond with the expected load and throttle position for less than 1 second. **Possible Causes:** • Throttle body for dirt, debris, and coking • Vacuum hoses for splits, kinks, and proper connections • Loose or damaged throttle blade • Broken throttle shaft • Any throttle body damage • Throttle body assembly has failed
DTC: P006D **1T CCM, MIL: Yes** **Years:** 2008, 2009 **Models:** Corvette, CTS, CTS-V, DTS **Engines:** 4.6L VIN Y, 6.2L VIN W, 6.2L VIN P, 6.2L VIN R, 7.0L VIN E **Transmissions:** All	**Supercharger Inlet Pressure (SCIP) - Barometric Pressure (BARO) Correlation** DTCs P0068, P0101, P0102, P0103, P0107, P0108, P0112, P0113, P0116, P0117, P0118, P0120, P0121, P0128, P012B, P012C, P012D, P0220, P0502, P1516, P2101, P2227, P2228, P2229 are not set. The ignition is ON. OR the engine is running. DTC P006D runs continuously when the above conditions are met. The ECM detects that during ignition ON, with the engine OFF, the calculated difference between BARO and SCIAP, whether that value is negative or positive, is greater than 12 kPa for greater than 30 seconds. Or The ECM has detected that a wide open throttle update event has occurred within the previous 2 kilometers (1.2 miles) and the difference between BARO, and a calculated BARO using the SCIAP sensor, is greater than 12 kPa for greater than 30 seconds.OrThe ECM has not detected a wide open throttle update event within the previous 2 kilometers (1.2 miles) and the difference between BARO, and a calculated BARO using the SCIAP sensor, is greater than 60 kPa for greater than 30 seconds **Possible Causes:** • SCIAP and BARO sensor, loose or improper installation • SCIAP and BARO sensor, low reference circuit for an open/high resistance • SCIAP and BARO sensor, 5V reference circuit for a short to ground or an open/high resistance. • SCIAP and BARO sensor, 5V reference circuit for a short to voltage • SCIAP and BARO sensor, signal circuit for a short to voltage • SCIAP and BARO sensor, signal circuit for an open/high resistance
DTC: P0096 **1T CCM, MIL: Yes** **Years:** 2008, 2009 **Models:** Corvette, CTS, CTS-V, DTS **Engines:** 4.6L VIN Y, 6.2L VIN W, 6.2L VIN P, 6.2L VIN R, 7.0L VIN E **Transmissions:** All	**Intake Air Temperature (IAT) Sensor 2 Performance** DTCs P0097, P0098, P0112, P0113, P0116, P0117, P0118, P0128, P0500, P0502, P0603 are not set. DTC P0116 has run and passed. The engine has been OFF for greater than 8 hours. The IAT sensor is greater than 10°C (50°F). DTC P0096 runs once per key cycle within the enabling conditions. DTC P0116 must run and pass. At start-up, after an 8 hour engine soak time, the IAT sensor 2 temperature is greater than 20°C (36°F) higher or lower than the IAT sensor. **Possible Causes:** • MAF/IAT low reference circuit for an open/high resistance • MAF/IAT low reference circuit for an open/high resistance • MAF/IAT signal circuit for an open/high resistance • MAF/IAT sensor has failed • ECM has failed
DTC: P0097 **1T CCM, MIL: Yes** **Years:** 2008, 2009 **Models:** Corvette, CTS, CTS-V **Engines:** 6.2L VIN W, 6.2L VIN P, 6.2L VIN R, 7.0L VIN E **Transmissions:** All	**Intake Air Temperature (IAT) Sensor 2 Circuit Low Voltage** The engine run has been in operation for greater than 10 seconds. The engine coolant temperature (ECT) is greater than −40°C (−40°F). The vehicle speed is greater than 1 km/h (1 mph). The MAF is less than 512 g/s. DTC P0097 and P0098 run continuously within the enabling conditionsThe IAT sensor 2 is greater than 148°C (298°F) for greater than 5 seconds. This is equal to or less than 0.24V on the IAT sensor 2 signal circuit as measured by the ECM for P0097. **Possible Causes:** • IAT signal circuit for a short to ground • IAT signal circuit terminal A for a short to voltage or an open/high resistance • IAT sensor 2 has failed • ECM has failed

DTC	Trouble Code Title, Conditions & Possible Causes
DTC: P0097 **1T CCM, MIL: Yes** **Years:** 2008, 2009 **Models:** Corvette, CTS, CTS-V **Engines:** 6.2L VIN W, 6.2L VIN P, 6.2L VIN R, 7.0L VIN E **Transmissions:** All	**Intake Air Temperature (IAT) Sensor 2 Circuit High Voltage** The engine run has been in operation for greater than 10 seconds. The engine coolant temperature (ECT) is greater than $-40°C$ ($-40°F$). The vehicle speed is greater than 1 km/h (1 mph). The MAF is less than 512 g/s. DTC P0097 and P0098 run continuously within the enabling conditionsThe IAT sensor 2 is colder than $-39°C$ ($-38°F$) for greater than 5 seconds. This is equal to or greater than 4.86V on the IAT signal circuit as measured by the ECM for P0098. **Possible Causes:** • IAT signal circuit for a short to ground • IAT signal circuit terminal A for a short to voltage or an open/high resistance • IAT sensor 2 has failed • ECM has failed
DTC: P0097 **1T CCM, MIL: Yes** **Years:** 2008, 2009 **Models:** Corvette, CTS, CTS-V **Engines:** 6.2L VIN W, 6.2L VIN P, 6.2L VIN R, 7.0L VIN E **Transmissions:** All	**Mass Air Flow (MAF) Sensor Performance** DTCs P0102, P0103, P0107, P0108, P0112, P0113, P0116, P0117, P0118, P0128, P0335, P0336 are not set. The engine speed is between 450-6,800 RPM. The IAT Sensor parameter is between -7 to $+125°C$ ($+19$ to $+257°F$). The ECT Sensor parameter is between 70-125°C (158-257°F). This DTC runs continuously when the above conditions are met. The Engine Control Module (ECM) detects that the actual measured airflow from the MAF, MAP, and TP sensors is not within range of the calculated airflow that is derived from the system of models for more than 0.5 second. **Possible Causes:** • MAF/IAT sensor for loose or improper installation • An air flow restriction • Any vacuum leak • Water intrusion • In cold climates, inspect for any snow or ice buildup • MAF sensor element for contamination • MAF/IAT sensorground circuit for an open/high resistance • MAF/IAT sensorignition circuit for a short to ground or an open/high resistance. • MAF/IAT sensorsignal circuit for a short to ground or an open/high resistance • MAF/IAT sensorsignal circuit for a short to voltage
DTC: P0097 **1T CCM, MIL: Yes** **Years:** 2008, 2009 **Models:** Corvette, CTS, CTS-V **Engines:** 6.2L VIN W, 6.2L VIN P, 6.2L VIN R, 7.0L VIN E **Transmissions:** All	**Intake Air Flow System Performance** DTCs P0102, P0103, P0107, P0108, P0112, P0113, P0116, P0117, P0118, P0128, P0335, P0336 are not set. The engine speed is between 450-6,800 RPM. The IAT Sensor parameter is between -7 to $+125°C$ ($+19$ to $+257°F$). The ECT Sensor parameter is between 70-125°C (158-257°F). This DTC runs continuously when the above conditions are met. The Engine Control Module (ECM) detects that the actual measured airflow from the MAF, MAP, and TP sensors is not within range of the calculated airflow that is derived from the system of models for more than 0.5 second. **Possible Causes:** • MAF/IAT sensor for loose or improper installation • An air flow restriction • Any vacuum leak • Water intrusion • In cold climates, inspect for any snow or ice buildup • MAF sensor element for contamination • MAF/IAT sensorground circuit for an open/high resistance • MAF/IAT sensorignition circuit for a short to ground or an open/high resistance. • MAF/IAT sensorsignal circuit for a short to ground or an open/high resistance • MAF/IAT sensorsignal circuit for a short to voltage
DTC: P009A **1T CCM, MIL: Yes** **Years:** 2008, 2009 **Models:** Astra, Aura, Aveo, Aveo5, Cobalt G3, G5 **Engines:** 1.6L VIN 6, 1.6L VIN E, 1.8L VIN 1, 2.0L VIN P, 2.0L VIN X, 2.2L VIN H, 2.2L VIN F, 2.4L VIN 5, 2.4L VIN B **Transmissions:** All	**Intake Air Temperature (IAT)-Ambient Air Temperature (AAT) Correlation** The engine is running. The ignition voltage is greater than 10 volts. The MAF Sensor parameter is between 70-500 kg/h. The ECT Sensor parameter is between 69-120°C (156-248°F). The Engine Speed parameter is between 928-6496 RPM. The vehicle speed is between 35-160 km/h (22-100 mph). The above conditions have been met for greater than 15 seconds. This DTC runs continuously within the enabling conditions. The ECM detects that the AAT sensor signal is not within a calibrated range of the modeled AAT for greater than 2 seconds. **Possible Causes:** • AAT sensor reference circuit high resistance • AAT sensor cinal circuit high resistance • AAT sensor has failed • ECM has failed

DTC	Trouble Code Title, Conditions & Possible Causes
DTC: P0102 **1T CCM, MIL: Yes** **Years:** 2008, 2009 **Models:** Corvette, CTS, CTS-V, DTS **Engines:** 4.6L VIN Y, 6.2L VIN W, 6.2L VIN P, 6.2L VIN R, 7.0L VIN E **Transmissions:** All	**Mass Air Flow (MAF) Sensor Circuit Low Frequency** The engine is running for greater than 1 second. The engine speed is greater than 300 RPM. The ignition 1 signal is greater than 8 volts. The above conditions are met for greater than 1 second. These DTCs run continuously when the above conditions are met. The ECM detects that the MAF Sensor parameter is less than 1,867 Hz for greater than 5 seconds. **Possible Causes:** • Restricted or collapsed air intake duct • Misaligned air intake duct • Dirty or deteriorating air filter element • Objects blocking the air inlet screen of the MAF/IAT sensor • Water intrusion in the induction system • Contamination or debris on the sensing elements of the MAF sensor • Any vacuum leak • MAF/IAT sensor ground circuit for an open/high resistance • MAF/IAT sensor ignition circuit terminal C for a short to ground or an open/high resistance • MAF/IAT sensor signal circuit for a short to ground or an open/high resistance. • MAF/IAT sensor signal circuit for a short to voltage • MAF/IAT sensor has failed • ECM has failed
DTC: P0103 **1T CCM, MIL: Yes** **Years:** 2008, 2009 **Models:** Corvette, CTS, CTS-V, DTS **Engines:** 4.6L VIN Y, 6.2L VIN W, 6.2L VIN P, 6.2L VIN R, 7.0L VIN E **Transmissions:** All	**Mass Air Flow (MAF) Sensor Circuit High Frequency** The engine is running for greater than 1 second. The engine speed is greater than 300 RPM. The ignition 1 signal is greater than 8 volts. The above conditions are met for greater than 1 second. These DTCs run continuously when the above conditions are met. The ECM detects that the MAF Sensor parameter is greater than 14,500 Hz for greater than 5 seconds. **Possible Causes:** • Restricted or collapsed air intake duct • Misaligned air intake duct • Dirty or deteriorating air filter element • Objects blocking the air inlet screen of the MAF/IAT sensor • Water intrusion in the induction system • Contamination or debris on the sensing elements of the MAF sensor • Any vacuum leak • MAF/IAT sensor ground circuit for an open/high resistance • MAF/IAT sensor ignition circuit terminal C for a short to ground or an open/high resistance • MAF/IAT sensor signal circuit for a short to ground or an open/high resistance. • MAF/IAT sensor signal circuit for a short to voltage • MAF/IAT sensor has failed • ECM has failed
DTC: P0106 **1T CCM, MIL: Yes** **Years:** 2008, 2009 **Models:** Corvette, CTS, CTS-V, DTS **Engines:** 4.6L VIN Y, 6.2L VIN W, 6.2L VIN P, 6.2L VIN R, 7.0L VIN E **Transmissions:** All	**Manifold Absolute Pressure (MAP) Sensor Performance** DTCs P0102, P0103, P0107, P0108, P0112, P0113, P0116, P0117, P0118, P0128, P0335, P0336 are not set. The engine is running. The IAT Sensor is between −7 and +125°C (+19 and +257°F). The ECT Sensor is between 70-125°C (158-257°F). This DTC runs continuously when the above conditions are met. The engine control module (ECM) detects that the MAP sensor pressure is not within range of the calculated pressure that is derived from the system of models for more than 0.5 second. **Possible Causes:** • MAP sensor low reference circuit for an open/high resistance • MAP sensor 5-volt reference circuit for a short to ground or an open/high resistance • MAP sensor 5-volt reference circuit for a short to voltage • MAP sensor signal circuit for a short to voltage • MAP sensor signal circuit for a short to ground or an open/high resistance • MAP sensor has failed • ECM has failed

DTC	Trouble Code Title, Conditions & Possible Causes
DTC: P0107 **1T CCM, MIL: Yes** **Years:** 2008, 2009 **Models:** Corvette, CTS, CTS-V, DTS **Engines:** 4.6L VIN Y, 6.2L VIN W, 6.2L VIN P, 6.2L VIN R, 7.0L VIN E **Transmissions:** All	**Manifold Absolute Pressure (MAP) Sensor Circuit Low Voltage** DTCs P0641, P0651, P1516, P2101, P2125, P2135, P2138, P2176 are not set. The engine speed is greater than 400 RPM. The throttle angle is greater than 0 percent when the engine speed is less than 800 RPM. Or the throttle angle is greater than 13 percent when the engine speed is greater than 800 RPM. This DTC runs continuously when the above conditions are met. The ECM detects that the MAP sensor voltage is less than 0.1 volt for more than 4 seconds. **Possible Causes:** • Intake manifold vacuum leaks • A loose or improperly installed MAP sensor • A restriction in the vacuum source of the MAP sensor • MAP sensor low reference circuit for an open/high resistance • MAP sensor 5-volt reference circuit for a short to ground or an open/high resistance • MAP sensor 5-volt reference circuit for a short to voltage • MAP sensor signal circuit for a short to voltage • MAP sensor signal circuit for a short to ground or an open/high resistance • MAP sensor has failed • ECM has failed
DTC: P0108 **1T CCM, MIL: Yes** **Years:** 2008, 2009 **Models:** Corvette, CTS, CTS-V, DTS **Engines:** 4.6L VIN Y, 6.2L VIN W, 6.2L VIN P, 6.2L VIN R, 7.0L VIN E **Transmissions:** All	**Manifold Absolute Pressure (MAP) Sensor Circuit High Voltage** DTCs P1516, P2101, P2125, P2135, P2138, P2176 are not set. The engine has been running for a period of time that is determined by the start-up engine coolant temperature (ECT). The time ranges from 8 seconds at less than −30°C (-22°F) to 3 seconds at greater than 30°C (86°F). The throttle angle is less than 1 percent when the engine speed is less than 1,200 RPM.Or the throttle angle is less than 20 percent when the engine speed is greater than 1,200 RPM. This DTC runs continuously when the above conditions are met. **Possible Causes:** • Intake manifold vacuum leaks • A loose or improperly installed MAP sensor • A restriction in the vacuum source of the MAP sensor • MAP sensor low reference circuit for an open/high resistance • MAP sensor 5-volt reference circuit for a short to ground or an open/high resistance • MAP sensor 5-volt reference circuit for a short to voltage • MAP sensor signal circuit for a short to voltage • MAP sensor signal circuit for a short to ground or an open/high resistance • MAP sensor has failed • ECM has failed
DTC: P0111 **1T CCM, MIL: Yes** **Years:** 2008, 2009 **Models:** Corvette, CTS, CTS-V **Engines:** 6.2L VIN W, 6.2L VIN P, 6.2L VIN R, 7.0L VIN E **Transmissions:** All	**Intake Air Temperature (IAT) Sensor Performance** DTCs P0112, P0113, P0117, P0118, P0128, P0502, P0503, P0601, P1621, P1627, P1680, P1681, P2610 are not set. The vehicle has had a minimum ignition OFF time of 8 hours. The ignition is ON. The start-up IAT is greater than 10°C (50°F). The Fuel Level Sensor parameter is greater than 2.5 percent. This DTC runs once per ignition cycle when the enabling conditions are met. The ECM detects a temperature difference at power-up that indicates that the IAT sensor is 20°C (68°F) greater than the IAT sensor 2.Or. The ECM detects a temperature difference at power-up that indicates that the IAT sensor is 16°C (29°F) greater than the IAT sensor 2, and the time spent cranking the engine is greater than 30 seconds, when the fuel level is greater than 2.5 percent. **Possible Causes:** • MAF/IAT sensor low reference circuit for an open or high resistance. • MAF/IAT sensor low reference circuit for high resistance • MAF/IAT sensor signal circuit open or high resistance on the signal circuit • MAF/IAT sensor has failed • ECM has failed
DTC: P0112 **1T CCM, MIL: Yes** **Years:** 2008, 2009 **Models:** Corvette, CTS, CTS-V, DTS **Engines:** 4.6L VIN Y, 6.2L VIN W, 6.2L VIN P, 6.2L VIN R, 7.0L VIN E **Transmissions:** All	**Intake Air Temperature (IAT) Sensor Circuit Low Voltage** DTCs P0116, P0117, P0118, P0128, P0502, P0503 are not set. The engine is running for greater than 10 seconds. The Engine Coolant Temperature (ECT) is less than 150°C (302°F). This DTC runs continuously when the above conditions are met. The ECM detects that the IAT is greater than 150°C (302°F) for greater than 5 seconds. **Possible Causes:** • MAF/IAT sensor low reference circuit for an open or high resistance. • MAF/IAT sensor low reference circuit for high resistance • MAF/IAT sensor signal circuit open or high resistance on the signal circuit • MAF/IAT sensor has failed • ECM has failed

DTC	Trouble Code Title, Conditions & Possible Causes
DTC: P0113 **1T CCM, MIL: Yes** **Years:** 2008, 2009 **Models:** Corvette, CTS, CTS-V, DTS **Engines:** 4.6L VIN Y, 6.2L VIN W, 6.2L VIN P, 6.2L VIN R, 7.0L VIN E **Transmissions:** All	**Intake Air Temperature (IAT) Sensor Circuit High Voltage** DTCs P0101, P0102, P0103, P0116, P0117, P0118, P0128, P0502, P0503 are not set. The engine is running for greater than 10 seconds. The ECT is greater than −40°C (-40°F). The MAF Sensor parameter is greater than 512 g/s. This DTC runs continuously when the above conditions are met. The ECM detects that the IAT is less than −39°C (-38°F) for greater than 5 seconds. **Possible Causes:** • MAF/IAT sensor low reference circuit for an open or high resistance. • MAF/IAT sensor low reference circuit for high resistance • MAF/IAT sensor signal circuit open or high resistance on the signal circuit • MAF/IAT sensor has failed • ECM has failed
DTC: P0116 **1T CCM, MIL: Yes** **Years:** 2008, 2009 **Models:** Corvette, CTS, CTS-V, DTS **Engines:** 4.6L VIN Y, 6.2L VIN W, 6.2L VIN P, 6.2L VIN R, 7.0L VIN E **Transmissions:** All	**Engine Coolant Temperature (ECT) Sensor Performance** DTCs P0112, P0113, P0117, P0118, P0502, P0503, P0601, P0603, P062F, P2610 are not set. The vehicle has had a minimum ignition OFF time of 10 hours. The ignition is ON. The start-up IAT is greater than −7°C (+19°F) The Fuel Level Sensor parameter is greater than 5 percent. This DTC runs once per ignition cycle when the above conditions are met. The ECM detects a temperature difference at power-up that indicates that the ECT sensor is 30°C (54°F) greater than the IAT sensor.Or. The ECM detects a temperature difference at power-up that indicates that the ECT sensor is 10°C (18°F) greater than the IAT sensor, and the time spent cranking the engine is greater than 10 seconds, when the fuel level is greater than 5 percent.Or. With the power-up IAT greater than −7°C (+19°F), the ECM detects a temperature difference at power-up that indicates that the ECT sensor is 20°C (36°F) greater than the IAT sensor. Then the vehicle must be driven for greater than 6 minutes and 40 seconds at greater than 40 km/h (25 mph). If the IAT sensor then decreases greater than 4°C (7°F), an engine block heater was detected and the test is aborted. If the IAT sensor does not decrease, an engine block heater was not detected and DTC P0116 will set. **Possible Causes:** • ECT sensor low reference circuit for an open/high resistance. • ECT sensor signal circuit for a short to ground • ECT sensor signal circuit for a short to voltage or an open/high resistance • ECT sensor has failed • ECM has failed
DTC: P0117 **1T CCM, MIL: Yes** **Years:** 2008, 2009 **Models:** Corvette, CTS, CTS-V, DTS **Engines:** 4.6L VIN Y, 6.2L VIN W, 6.2L VIN P, 6.2L VIN R, 7.0L VIN E **Transmissions:** All	**Engine Coolant Temperature (ECT) Sensor Circuit Low Voltage** The engine is running for greater than 10 seconds.Or. The ignition is ON when the intake air temperature (IAT) is less than 50°C (122°F). This DTC runs continuously when the above conditions are met. The ECM detects that the ECT is more than 149°C (300°F) for greater than 5 seconds. **Possible Causes:** • ECT sensor low reference circuit for an open/high resistance. • ECT sensor signal circuit for a short to ground • ECT sensor signal circuit for a short to voltage or an open/high resistance • ECT sensor has failed • ECM has failed
DTC: P0118 **1T CCM, MIL: Yes** **Years:** 2008, 2009 **Models:** Corvette, CTS, CTS-V, DTS **Engines:** 4.6L VIN Y, 6.2L VIN W, 6.2L VIN P, 6.2L VIN R, 7.0L VIN E **Transmissions:** All	**Engine Coolant Temperature (ECT) Sensor Circuit High Voltage** The engine is running for greater than 10 seconds. Or. The ignition is ON when the IAT is greater than 0°C (32°F). This DTC runs continuously when the above conditions are met. The ECM detects that the ECT is less than −39°C (−38°F) for greater than 5 seconds. **Possible Causes:** • ECT sensor low reference circuit for an open/high resistance. • ECT sensor signal circuit for a short to ground • ECT sensor signal circuit for a short to voltage or an open/high resistance • ECT sensor has failed • ECM has failed
DTC: P0120 **1T CCM, MIL: Yes** **Years:** 2008, 2009 **Models:** Corvette, CTS, CTS-V, DTS **Engines:** 4.6L VIN Y, 6.2L VIN W, 6.2L VIN P, 6.2L VIN R, 7.0L VIN E **Transmissions:** All	**Throttle Position (TP) Sensor 1 Circuit** DTCs P0601, P0602, P0603, P0604, P0606, P0607, P0641, P0651 are not set. The system voltage is more than 5.23 volts. The ignition is in the Unlock/Accessory or Run position. DTC P0120, P0122, P0123, P0220, P0222, P0223 run continuously when the above conditions are met. TP sensor 1 voltage is less than 0.325 volt or more than 4.75 volts for more than 1 second. **Possible Causes:** • TP sensor low reference circuit for an open/high resistance • TP sensor 5-volt reference circuit for a short to ground or an open/high resistance • TP sensor 5-volt reference circuit for a short to voltage • TP sensor signal circuit terminal F for a short to ground • TP sensor 1 signal circuit for a short to ground or an open/high resistance • TP sensor 2 signal circuit for a short to voltage • TP sensor 2 signal circuit for an open/high resistance. • Throttle body has failed • ECM has failed

DTC	Trouble Code Title, Conditions & Possible Causes
DTC: P0121 **1T CCM, MIL: Yes** **Years:** 2008, 2009 **Models:** Corvette, CTS, CTS-V, DTS **Engines:** 4.6L VIN Y, 6.2L VIN W, 6.2L VIN P, 6.2L VIN R, 7.0L VIN E **Transmissions:** All	**Throttle Position (TP) Sensor 1 Performance** DTCs P0102, P0103, P0107, P0108, P0112, P0113, P0116, P0117, P0118, P0128, P0315, P0335, P0336 are not set. The engine speed is more than 450 RPM. DTC P0121 run continuously when the above conditions are met. The predicted air flow and the predicted MAP combined are outside a calibrated range for more than 3 seconds. **Possible Causes:** • Loose or damaged throttle blade • Broken throttle shaft • Any throttle body damage • Throttle body assembly has failed
DTC: P0122 **1T CCM, MIL: Yes** **Years:** 2008, 2009 **Models:** Corvette, CTS, CTS-V, DTS **Engines:** 4.6L VIN Y, 6.2L VIN W, 6.2L VIN P, 6.2L VIN R, 7.0L VIN E **Transmissions:** All	**Throttle Position (TP) Sensor 1 Circuit Low Voltage** DTCs P0601, P0602, P0603, P0604, P0606, P0607, P0641, P0651 are not set. The system voltage is more than 5.23 volts. The ignition is in the Unlock/Accessory or Run position. DTC P0120, P0122, P0123, P0220, P0222, P0223 run continuously when the above conditions are met. The ECM detects that the TP sensor 1 voltage is less than 0.325 volt for more than 1 second. **Possible Causes:** • TP sensor low reference circuit for an open/high resistance • TP sensor 5-volt reference circuit for a short to ground or an open/high resistance • TP sensor 5-volt reference circuit for a short to voltage • TP sensor signal circuit terminal F for a short to ground • TP sensor 1 signal circuit for a short to ground or an open/high resistance • TP sensor 2 signal circuit for a short to voltage • TP sensor 2 signal circuit for an open/high resistance. • Throttle body has failed • ECM has failed
DTC: P0123 **1T CCM, MIL: Yes** **Years:** 2008, 2009 **Models:** Corvette, CTS, CTS-V, DTS **Engines:** 4.6L VIN Y, 6.2L VIN W, 6.2L VIN P, 6.2L VIN R, 7.0L VIN E **Transmissions:** All	**Throttle Position (TP) Sensor 1 Circuit High Voltage** DTCs P0601, P0602, P0603, P0604, P0606, P0607, P0641, P0651 are not set. The system voltage is more than 5.23 volts. The ignition is in the Unlock/Accessory or Run position. DTC P0120, P0122, P0123, P0220, P0222, P0223 run continuously when the above conditions are met. The ECM detects that the TP sensor 1 voltage is more than 4.75 volts for more than 1 second. **Possible Causes:** • TP sensor low reference circuit for an open/high resistance • TP sensor 5-volt reference circuit for a short to ground or an open/high resistance • TP sensor 5-volt reference circuit for a short to voltage • TP sensor signal circuit terminal F for a short to ground • TP sensor 1 signal circuit for a short to ground or an open/high resistance • TP sensor 2 signal circuit for a short to voltage • TP sensor 2 signal circuit for an open/high resistance. • Throttle body has failed • ECM has failed
DTC: P0128 **1T CCM, MIL: Yes** **Years:** 2008, 2009 **Models:** Corvette, CTS, CTS-V, DTS **Engines:** 4.6L VIN Y, 6.2L VIN W, 6.2L VIN P, 6.2L VIN R, 7.0L VIN E **Transmissions:** All	**Engine Coolant Temperature (ECT) Below Thermostat Regulating Temperature** DTCs P0101, P0102, P0103, P0106, P0107, P0108, P0112, P0113, P0116, P0117, P0118, P0171, P0172, P0174, P0175, P0502, P0503 are not set. The start-up IAT is more than −7°C (+19°F). The start-up ECT is less than 70°C (158°F), when the IAT is above 10°C (50°F). The start-up ECT is less than 50°C (122°F), when the IAT is below 10°C (50°F). The engine run time is between 90 seconds and 22 minutes. The vehicle has traveled more than 2.4 kilometers (1.5 miles) at greater than 8 km/h (5 mph). The accumulated airflow is between 20-75 g/s, with the minimum average airflow greater than 10 g/s. The fuel ethanol percentage is less than 85 percent. This DTC runs once per ignition cycle within the enabling conditions. The ECM detects that the minimum ECT of 75°C (167°F) has not been met, when the IAT is greater than 10°C (50°F). **Note: A critical analysis of the operation of the thermostat is necessary to properly diagnose these DTCs.** **Possible Causes:** • Open thermostat • ECT sensor low reference circuit for an open/high resistance • ECT sensor signal circuit for a short to voltage or an open/high resistance • ECT sensor signal circuit for a short to ground • ECT sensor has failed • ECM has failed

DTC	Trouble Code Title, Conditions & Possible Causes
DTC: P012B **1T CCM, MIL: Yes** **Years:** 2008, 2009 **Models:** Corvette, CTS, CTS-V **Engines:** 6.2L VIN W, 6.2L VIN P, 6.2L VIN R, 7.0L VIN E **Transmissions:** All	**Supercharger Inlet Pressure Sensor Performance** DTCs P0096, P0097, P0098, P0102, P0103, P0111, P0112, P0113, P0117, P0118, P0120, P0121, P0128, P012C, P012D, P0220, P0401, P0405, P0506, P0507, P1404, P2135 are not set. The engine is running. The engine coolant temperature (ECT) is between −7 to +129°C (+19 to +264°F). The IAT is between −7 to +125°C (+19 to +257°F). The change in the TP is less than 5 percent. The above enabling criteria must be stable for more than 5 seconds. This DTC runs continuously when the above conditions are met. The engine control module (ECM) detects that the actual measured airflow from the MAF, MAP, SC Inlet Pressure and TP sensors is not within a range of the calculated airflow that is derived from the system of models by greater than a calibrated threshold, for greater than 10 seconds. **Possible Causes:** • Restricted or collapsed air intake duct • Misaligned or damaged air intake duct • Any vacuum leak downstream of the MAF/IAT sensor • An intake manifold leak • SCIAP sensorlow reference circuit for an open/high resistance • SCIAP sensorsignal circuit terminal 3 for a short to voltage • SCIAP sensorsignal circuit for a short to ground, open/high resistance • SCIAP sensor has failed • ECM has failed
DTC: P012B **1T CCM, MIL: Yes** **Years:** 2008, 2009 **Models:** Corvette, CTS, CTS-V **Engines:** 6.2L VIN W, 6.2L VIN P, 6.2L VIN R, 7.0L VIN E **Transmissions:** All	**Supercharger Inlet Pressure (SCIP) Sensor Circuit Low Voltage** DTCs P0120, P0121, P0122, P0123, P0220, P0221, P0222, P0223, P0641, or P0651 are not set. The throttle angle is greater than 0 percent when the engine speed is less than 800 RPM. Or. The throttle angle is greater than 12 percent when the engine speed is greater than 800 RPM. This DTC runs continuously when the above enabling conditions are met. The ECM detects that the SCIAP sensor voltage is less than 0.10V for greater than 5 seconds. **Possible Causes:** • SCIAP sensor low reference circuit for an open/high resistance • SCIAP sensor 5V reference circuit for a short to ground or an open/high resistance • SCIAP sensor signal circuit terminal 3 for a short to voltage • SCIAP sensor signal circuit for a short to ground, open/high resistance • SCIAP sensor has failed • ECM has failed
DTC: P012B **1T CCM, MIL: Yes** **Years:** 2008, 2009 **Models:** Corvette, CTS, CTS-V **Engines:** 6.2L VIN W, 6.2L VIN P, 6.2L VIN R, 7.0L VIN E **Transmissions:** All	**Supercharger Inlet Pressure (SCIP) Sensor Circuit High Voltage** DTCs P0120, P0121, P0122, P0123, P0220, P0221, P0222, P0223, P0641, or P0651 are not set. The engine has been running for a period of time that is determined by the start-up Engine Coolant Temperature (ECT). The time ranges from 4 minutes at less than −30°C (−22°F) to 2 seconds at greater than 30°C (86°F). The throttle angle is less than one percent when the engine speed is less than 1,200 RPM.Or. The throttle angle is less than 20 percent when the engine speed is greater than 1,200 RPM. This DTC runs continuously when the above enabling conditions are met. The ECM detects that the SCIAP sensor voltage is more than 4.50V for greater than 5 seconds. **Possible Causes:** • SCIAP sensor low reference circuit for an open/high resistance • SCIAP sensor 5V reference circuit for a short to ground or an open/high resistance • SCIAP sensor signal circuit terminal 3 for a short to voltage • SCIAP sensor signal circuit for a short to ground, open/high resistance • SCIAP sensor has failed • ECM has failed
DTC: P0131 **1T CCM, MIL: Yes** **Years:** 2008, 2009 **Models:** Corvette, CTS, CTS-V, DTS**Engines:** 4.6L VIN Y, 6.2L VIN W, 6.2L VIN P, 6.2L VIN R, 7.0L VIN E **Transmissions:** All	**HO2S Circuit Low Voltage (Bank 1 Sensor 1)** DTCs P0068, P0101, P0102, P0103, P0106, P0107, P0108, P0112, P0113, P0116, P0117, P0118, P0120, P0121, P0122, P0123, P0128, P0201, P0202, P0203, P0204, P0205, P0206, P0207, P0208, P0220, P0222, P0223, P0442, P0443, P0446, P0449, P0455, P0496, P1516, P2101, P2119, P2135, P2176 are not set. The engine is operating in Closed Loop. The Ignition 1 voltage is between 10-18 volts. The fuel level is greater than 10 percent. The throttle position (TP) is between 3-70 percent. The DTCs run continuously when the above conditions are met for 2 seconds. The ECM detects that the HO2S voltage is less than 50 mV. The DTCs set within 100 seconds when the above condition is met. **Possible Causes:** • HO2S low reference circuit for an open/high resistance • HO2S signal circuit for a short to ground • HO2S signal circuit for a short to voltage • HO2S signal circuit for an open/high resistance • HO2S has failed • ECM has failed

DTC	Trouble Code Title, Conditions & Possible Causes
DTC: P0132 **1T CCM, MIL: Yes** **Years:** 2008, 2009 **Models:** Corvette, CTS, CTS-V, DTS **Engines:** 4.6L VIN Y, 6.2L VIN W, 6.2L VIN P, 6.2L VIN R, 7.0L VIN E **Transmissions:** All	**HO2S Circuit High Voltage (Bank 1 Sensor 1)** DTCs P0068, P0101, P0102, P0103, P0106, P0107, P0108, P0112, P0113, P0116, P0117, P0118, P0120, P0121, P0122, P0123, P0128, P0201, P0202, P0203, P0204, P0205, P0206, P0207, P0208, P0220, P0222, P0223, P0442, P0443, P0446, P0449, P0455, P0496, P1516, P2101, P2119, P2135, P2176 are not set. The engine is operating in Closed Loop. The Ignition 1 voltage is between 10-18 volts. The fuel level is greater than 10 percent. The throttle position (TP) is between 0-70 percent. The DTCs run continuously when the above conditions are met for 2 seconds. The ECM detects that the HO2S voltage is greater than 1,050 mV. The DTCs set within 15 seconds when the above condition is met. **Possible Causes:** • HO2S low reference circuit for an open/high resistance • HO2S signal circuit for a short to ground • HO2S signal circuit for a short to voltage • HO2S signal circuit for an open/high resistance • HO2S has failed • ECM has failed
DTC: P0135 **1T CCM, MIL: Yes** **Years:** 2008, 2009 **Models:** Corvette, CTS, CTS-V, DTS **Engines:** 4.6L VIN Y, 6.2L VIN W, 6.2L VIN P, 6.2L VIN R, 7.0L VIN E **Transmissions:** All	**HO2S Heater Performance (Bank 1 Sensor 1)** DTCs P0116, P0117, P0118, P0125, or P0128 are not set. The ignition 1 voltage is between 10-18 volts. The HO2S is at operating temperature. The HO2S is commanded ON. The DTCs run once per drive cycle when the above conditions are met for 120 seconds. The ECM detects that the HO2S 1 heater current is greater than 3.1 amps, or less than 0.3 amps for greater than 8 seconds. **Possible Causes:** • HO2S ignition circuit for a short to ground or an open/high resistance • HO2S control circuit for a short to voltage, or an open/high resistance • HO2S control circuit for a short to ground • HO2S is damaged or it has failed • ECM has failed
DTC: P0137 **1T CCM, MIL: Yes** **Years:** 2008, 2009 **Models:** Corvette, CTS, CTS-V, DTS **Engines:** 4.6L VIN Y, 6.2L VIN W, 6.2L VIN P, 6.2L VIN R, 7.0L VIN E **Transmissions:** All	**HO2S Circuit Low Voltage (Bank 1 Sensor 2)** DTCs P0068, P0101, P0102, P0103, P0106, P0107, P0108, P0112, P0113, P0116, P0117, P0118, P0120, P0121, P0122, P0123, P0128, P0201, P0202, P0203, P0204, P0205, P0206, P0207, P0208, P0220, P0222, P0223, P0442, P0443, P0446, P0449, P0455, P0496, P1516, P2101, P2119, P2135, P2176 are not set. The engine is operating in Closed Loop. The Ignition 1 voltage is between 10-18 volts. The fuel level is greater than 10 percent. The throttle position (TP) is between 3-70 percent. The DTCs run continuously when the above conditions are met for 2 seconds. The ECM detects that the HO2S voltage is less than 50 mV. The DTCs set within 100 seconds when the above condition is met. **Possible Causes:** • HO2S low reference circuit for an open/high resistance • HO2S signal circuit for a short to ground • HO2S signal circuit for a short to voltage • HO2S signal circuit for an open/high resistance • HO2S has failed • ECM has failed
DTC: P0138 **1T CCM, MIL: Yes** **Years:** 2008, 2009 **Models:** Corvette, CTS, CTS-V, DTS **Engines:** 4.6L VIN Y, 6.2L VIN W, 6.2L VIN P, 6.2L VIN R, 7.0L VIN E **Transmissions:** All	**HO2S Circuit High Voltage (Bank 1 Sensor 2)** DTCs P0068, P0101, P0102, P0103, P0106, P0107, P0108, P0112, P0113, P0116, P0117, P0118, P0120, P0121, P0122, P0123, P0128, P0201, P0202, P0203, P0204, P0205, P0206, P0207, P0208, P0220, P0222, P0223, P0442, P0443, P0446, P0449, P0455, P0496, P1516, P2101, P2119, P2135, P2176 are not set. The engine is operating in Closed Loop. The Ignition 1 voltage is between 10-18 volts. The fuel level is greater than 10 percent. The throttle position (TP) is between 0-70 percent. The DTCs run continuously when the above conditions are met for 2 seconds. The ECM detects that the HO2S voltage is greater than 1,050 mV. The DTCs set within 15 seconds when the above condition is met. **Possible Causes:** • HO2S low reference circuit for an open/high resistance • HO2S signal circuit for a short to ground • HO2S signal circuit for a short to voltage • HO2S signal circuit for an open/high resistance • HO2S has failed • ECM has failed

DTC	Trouble Code Title, Conditions & Possible Causes
DTC: P0140 **1T CCM, MIL: Yes** **Years:** 2008, 2009 **Models:** Corvette, CTS, CTS-V, DTS **Engines:** 4.6L VIN Y, 6.2L VIN W, 6.2L VIN P, 6.2L VIN R, 7.0L VIN E **Transmissions:** All	**HO2S Circuit Insufficient Activity (Bank 1 Sensor 2)** DTCs P0068, P0101, P0102, P0103, P0106, P0107, P0108, P0112, P0113, P0116, P0117, P0118, P0120, P0121, P0122, P0123, P0128, P0201, P0202, P0203, P0204, P0205, P0206, P0207, P0208, P0220, P0222, P0223, P0442, P0443, P0446, P0449, P0455, P0496, P1516, P2101, P2119, P2135, P2176 are not set. The Ignition 1 Signal parameter is between 10-18 volts. The Engine Run Time parameter is more than 300 seconds. The Loop Status parameter is closed. DTC P0140 runs once per drive cycle when the above conditions are met. The ECM detects that the HO2S 1 parameter is between 410-490 mV. The TP Indicated Angle parameter changes more than 5 percent 6 times. DTC P0140 sets within 100 seconds when the above conditions are met. **Possible Causes:** • HO2S low reference circuit for an open/high resistance • HO2S signal circuit for a short to ground • HO2S signal circuit for a short to voltage • HO2S signal circuit for an open/high resistance • HO2S has failed • ECM has failed
DTC: P0141 **1T CCM, MIL: Yes** **Years:** 2008, 2009 **Models:** Corvette, CTS, CTS-V, DTS **Engines:** 4.6L VIN Y, 6.2L VIN W, 6.2L VIN P, 6.2L VIN R, 7.0L VIN E **Transmissions:** All	**HO2S Heater Performance (Bank 1 Sensor 2)** DTCs P0116, P0117, P0118, P0125, or P0128 are not set. The ignition 1 voltage is between 10-18 volts. The HO2S is at operating temperature. The HO2S is commanded ON. The DTCs run once per drive cycle when the above conditions are met for 120 seconds. The ECM detects that the HO2S 2 heater current is greater than 2.9 amps, or less than 0.3 amps for greater than 8 seconds. **Possible Causes:** • HO2S ignition circuit for a short to ground or an open/high resistance • HO2S control circuit for a short to voltage, or an open/high resistance • HO2S control circuit for a short to ground • HO2S is damaged or it has failed • ECM has failed
DTC: P0151 **1T CCM, MIL: Yes** **Years:** 2008, 2009 **Models:** Corvette, CTS, CTS-V, DTS **Engines:** 4.6L VIN Y, 6.2L VIN W, 6.2L VIN P, 6.2L VIN R, 7.0L VIN E **Transmissions:** All	**HO2S Circuit Low Voltage Bank (2 Sensor 1)** DTCs P0068, P0101, P0102, P0103, P0106, P0107, P0108, P0112, P0113, P0116, P0117, P0118, P0120, P0121, P0122, P0123, P0128, P0201, P0202, P0203, P0204, P0205, P0206, P0207, P0208, P0220, P0222, P0223, P0442, P0443, P0446, P0449, P0455, P0496, P1516, P2101, P2119, P2135, P2176 are not set. The engine is operating in Closed Loop. The Ignition 1 voltage is between 10-18 volts. The fuel level is greater than 10 percent. The throttle position (TP) is between 3-70 percent. The DTCs run continuously when the above conditions are met for 2 seconds. The ECM detects that the HO2S voltage is less than 50 mV. The DTCs set within 100 seconds when the above condition is met. **Possible Causes:** • HO2S low reference circuit for an open/high resistance • HO2S signal circuit for a short to ground • HO2S signal circuit for a short to voltage • HO2S signal circuit for an open/high resistance • HO2S has failed • ECM has failed
DTC: P0152 **1T CCM, MIL: Yes** **Years:** 2008, 2009 **Models:** Corvette, CTS, CTS-V, DTS **Engines:** 4.6L VIN Y, 6.2L VIN W, 6.2L VIN P, 6.2L VIN R, 7.0L VIN E **Transmissions:** All	**HO2S Circuit High Voltage (Bank 2 Sensor 1)** DTCs P0068, P0101, P0102, P0103, P0106, P0107, P0108, P0112, P0113, P0116, P0117, P0118, P0120, P0121, P0122, P0123, P0128, P0201, P0202, P0203, P0204, P0205, P0206, P0207, P0208, P0220, P0222, P0223, P0442, P0443, P0446, P0449, P0455, P0496, P1516, P2101, P2119, P2135, P2176 are not set. The engine is operating in Closed Loop. The Ignition 1 voltage is between 10-18 volts. The fuel level is greater than 10 percent. The throttle position (TP) is between 0-70 percent. The DTCs run continuously when the above conditions are met for 2 seconds. The ECM detects that the HO2S voltage is greater than 1,050 mV. The DTCs set within 15 seconds when the above condition is met. **Possible Causes:** • HO2S low reference circuit for an open/high resistance • HO2S signal circuit for a short to ground • HO2S signal circuit for a short to voltage • HO2S signal circuit for an open/high resistance • HO2S has failed • ECM has failed

DTC	Trouble Code Title, Conditions & Possible Causes
DTC: P0154 **1T CCM, MIL: Yes** **Years:** 2008, 2009, 2010 **Models:** Acadia, Allure, Aura, Camaro, CTS, CTS-V, Enclave, LaCrosse, Outlook, Traverse **Engines:** 3.6L VIN 7, 3.6L VIN D, 3.6L VIN V **Transmissions:** All	**HO2S 21 (Bank 2 Sensor 1) Insufficient Activity** DTC P0201, P0202, P0203, P0204, P0205, P0206, P0261, P0262, P0264, P0265, P0267, P0268, P0270, P0271, P0273, P0274, P0276, P0277, P2146, P2149, P2152, P2155, P216A, or P216D is not set. The ignition voltage is greater than 10 volts. The engine speed is greater than 240 RPM. The HO2S 1 heater duty cycle is greater than 90 percent for more than 5 seconds. The HO2S 1 signal voltage is between 400-520 mV, or 400-550 mV when the calculated exhaust temperature is warmer than 800°C (1,472°F). O. the calculated internal resistance of the HO2S 1 is greater than 40,000 ohms when the calculated exhaust temperature is warmer than 600°C (1,112°F). **Possible Causes:** • HO2S damaged or has failed • Low or high fuel system pressure • Engine vacuum leaks • HO2S signal or ground circuit has a high resistance condition • HO2S signal circuit is open or shorted to system power (B+) • HO2S has failed (i.e., it is silicon, water or fuel contaminated) • ECM has failed
DTC: P0155 **1T CCM, MIL: Yes** **Years:** 2008, 2009 **Models:** Corvette, CTS, CTS-V, DTS **Engines:** 4.6L VIN Y, 6.2L VIN W, 6.2L VIN P, 6.2L VIN R, 7.0L VIN E **Transmissions:** All	**HO2S Heater Performance (Bank 2 Sensor 1)** DTCs P0116, P0117, P0118, P0125, or P0128 are not set. The ignition 1 voltage is between 10-18 volts. The HO2S is at operating temperature. The HO2S is commanded ON. The DTCs run once per drive cycle when the above conditions are met for 120 seconds. The ECM detects that the HO2S 1 heater current is greater than 3.1 amps, or less than 0.3 amps for greater than 8 seconds. **Possible Causes:** • HO2S ignition circuit for a short to ground or an open/high resistance • HO2S control circuit for a short to voltage, or an open/high resistance • HO2S control circuit for a short to ground • HO2S is damaged or it has failed • ECM has failed
DTC: P0155 **1T CCM, MIL: Yes** **Years:** 2008, 2009, 2010 **Models:** Acadia, Allure, Aura, Camaro, CTS, CTS-V, Enclave, LaCrosse, Outlook, Traverse **Engines:** 3.6L VIN 7, 3.6L VIN D, 3.6L VIN V **Transmissions:** All	**HO2S Heater Performance (Bank 2 Sensor 1)** The ECM detects that the internal resistance of the HO2S 1 heater is not within the expected range for greater than 12 seconds. The internal HO2S 1 resistance is less than 10,000 ohms. **Possible Causes:** • HO2S heater control circuit is open or it is shorted to ground • HO2S control circuit open or high resistance condition • HO2S signal circuit is open or shorted to system power (B+) • HO2S has failed (i.e., it is silicon, water or fuel contaminated) • ECM has failed
DTC: P0155 **2T O2S HTR, MIL: Yes** **Years:** 2008, 2009, 2010 **Models:** Avalanche, Camaro, Canyon, Escalade/EXT/ESV, Suburban, Tahoe, Yukon **Engines:** 4.8L VIN C, 5.3L VIN 0, 5.3L VIN 3, 5.3L VIN J, 5.3L VIN L, 6.0L VIN K, 6.0L VIN Y, 6.2L VIN J, 6.2L VIN W, 6.2L VIN 8 **Transmissions:** All	**HO2S-21 (Bank 2 Sensor 1) Heater Circuit Malfunction** DTC P0101-P0103, P0106-P0108, P0112, P0113, P0116-P0118, P0120, P0121-P0123, P0169, P0178, P0179, P0200, P0220, P0300, P0442, P0446, P0452, P0453, P0455, P0496, P1125, P1258, P1514, P1515, P1516, P1518, P2108 and P2135 not set, engine speed from 500-3000 RPM for 120 seconds, system voltage at 10-18v, ECT sensor over 122°F, MAF sensor at 3-40 g/sec, Fuel Alcohol content below 90%, and the ECM detected the HO2S heater current was below 0.25 amps or over 3.125 amps (more than 1.375 amps on 4.8L V8). **Possible Causes:** • HO2S heater low control circuit is open or shorted to ground • HO2S heater circuit is open or it is shorted to ground • HO2S heater power circuit is open (test O2A fuse in fuse block) • HO2S heater element is damaged or has failed • ECM has failed
DTC: P0157 **1T CCM, MIL: Yes** **Years:** 2008, 2009 **Models:** Corvette, CTS, CTS-V, DTS **Engines:** 4.6L VIN Y, 6.2L VIN W, 6.2L VIN P, 6.2L VIN R, 7.0L VIN E **Transmissions:** All	**HO2S Circuit Low Voltage (Bank 2 Sensor 2)** DTCs P0068, P0101, P0102, P0103, P0106, P0107, P0108, P0112, P0113, P0116, P0117, P0118, P0120, P0121, P0122, P0123, P0128, P0201, P0202, P0203, P0204, P0205, P0206, P0207, P0208, P0220, P0222, P0223, P0442, P0443, P0446, P0449, P0455, P0496, P1516, P2101, P2119, P2135, P2176 are not set. The engine is operating in Closed Loop. The Ignition 1 voltage is between 10-18 volts. The fuel level is greater than 10 percent. The throttle position (TP) is between 3-70 percent. The DTCs run continuously when the above conditions are met for 2 seconds. The ECM detects that the HO2S voltage is less than 50 mV. The DTCs set within 100 seconds when the above condition is met. **Possible Causes:** • HO2S low reference circuit for an open/high resistance • HO2S signal circuit for a short to ground • HO2S signal circuit for a short to voltage • HO2S signal circuit for an open/high resistance • HO2S has failed • ECM has failed

DTC	Trouble Code Title, Conditions & Possible Causes
DTC: P0157 **2T CCM, MIL: Yes** **Years:** 2008, 2009, 2010 **Models:** Avalanche, Camaro, Canyon, Escalade/EXT/ESV, Suburban, Tahoe, Yukon **Engines:** 4.8L VIN C, 5.3L VIN 0, 5.3L VIN 3, 5.3L VIN J, 5.3L VIN L, 6.0L VIN K, 6.0L VIN Y, 6.2L VIN J, 6.2L VIN W, 6.2L VIN 8 **Transmissions:** All	**HO2S-22 (Bank 2 Sensor 2) Circuit Low Input** DTC P0101-P0103, P0106-P0108, P0112, P0113, P0116-P0118, P0120, P0121-P0123, P0169, P0178, P0179, P0200, P0220, P0300, P0442, P0446, P0452-P0496, P1125, P1258, P1514, P1515, P1516, P1518, P2108 and P2135 not set, engine started, engine running in closed loop, system voltage from 10-18v, Fuel Alcohol content less than 90%, fuel level over 10%, TP angle from 3-70% over the idle value, Lean Test enabled, the ECM detected the HO2S signal was below 80 mv for 200 seconds or with engine runtime over 30 seconds, and during the P/E test, the ECM detected the HO2S signal was below 490 mv for 10 seconds. **Possible Causes:** • Air leaks in the exhaust system, intake manifold, vacuum lines • Engine misfire condition present (look for P0300 series codes) • Fuel system too lean (possible low fuel pressure, water in fuel) • HO2S signal circuit is shorted to the sensor or chassis ground • HO2S is damaged (i.e., cracked) or air reference hole clogged • ECM has failed
DTC: P0157 **1T CCM, MIL: Yes** **Years:** 2008, 2009, 2010 **Models:** Acadia, Allure, Aura, Camaro, CTS, CTS-V, Enclave, LaCrosse, Outlook, Traverse **Engines:** 3.6L VIN 7, 3.6L VIN D, 3.6L VIN V **Transmissions:** All	**HO2S Circuit Low Voltage (Bank 2 Sensor 2)** DTC P0036, P0037, P0038, P0056, P0057, P0058, P0116, P0117, P0118, P0119, or P0128 is not set, engine startedThe engine coolant temperature is colder than 40°C (104°F) at start-up and the engine coolant temperature was warmer than 60°C (140°F) when the ignition was turned OFF last ignition cycle. The calculated exhaust temperature at the HO2S 2 is warmer than 700°C (1,292°F) and the HO2S 2 is warmed up for greater than 90 seconds. The ECM detects the HO2S 2 signal voltage is less than 60 mV for greater than 1 seconds of for a cumulative of 10 seconds. **Possible Causes:** • Air leaks in the exhaust system, intake manifold, vacuum lines • low reference circuit for an open/high resistance or for a short to voltage • Fuel pressure that is too low or too high • HO2S signal circuit is shorted to the sensor or chassis ground • HO2S is damaged (i.e., cracked) or air reference hole clogged • Lean, rich, or leaking fuel injectors • ECM has failed
DTC: P0158 **1T CCM, MIL: Yes** **Years:** 2008, 2009 **Models:** Corvette, CTS, CTS-V, DTS **Engines:** 4.6L VIN Y, 6.2L VIN W, 6.2L VIN P, 6.2L VIN R, 7.0L VIN E **Transmissions:** All	**HO2S Circuit High Voltage (Bank 2 Sensor 2)** DTCs P0068, P0101, P0102, P0103, P0106, P0107, P0108, P0112, P0113, P0116, P0117, P0118, P0120, P0121, P0122, P0123, P0128, P0201, P0202, P0203, P0204, P0205, P0206, P0207, P0208, P0220, P0222, P0223, P0442, P0443, P0446, P0449, P0455, P0496, P1516, P2101, P2119, P2135, P2176 are not set. The engine is operating in Closed Loop. The Ignition 1 voltage is between 10-18 volts. The fuel level is greater than 10 percent. The throttle position (TP) is between 0-70 percent. The DTCs run continuously when the above conditions are met for 2 seconds. The ECM detects that the HO2S voltage is greater than 1,050 mV. The DTCs set within 15 seconds when the above condition is met. **Possible Causes:** • HO2S low reference circuit for an open/high resistance • HO2S signal circuit for a short to ground • HO2S signal circuit for a short to voltage • HO2S signal circuit for an open/high resistance • HO2S has failed • ECM has failed
DTC: P0158 **1T CCM, MIL: Yes** **Years:** 2008, 2009, 2010 **Models:** Acadia, Allure, Aura, Camaro, CTS, CTS-V, Enclave, LaCrosse, Outlook, Traverse **Engines:** 3.6L VIN 7, 3.6L VIN D, 3.6L VIN V **Transmissions:** All	**HO2S Circuit High Voltage (Bank 2 Sensor 2)** DTC P0036, P0037, P0038, P0056, P0057, P0058, P0116, P0117, P0118, P0119, or P0128 is not set, engine startedThe engine coolant temperature is colder than 40°C (104°F) at start-up and the engine coolant temperature was warmer than 60°C (140°F) when the ignition was turned OFF last ignition cycle. The calculated exhaust temperature at the HO2S 2 is warmer than 700°C (1,292°F) and the HO2S 2 is warmed up for greater than 90 seconds. The ECM detects the HO2S 2 signal voltage is less than 60 mV for greater than 1 seconds of for a cumulative of 10 seconds. **Possible Causes:** • Fuel system is too rich (fuel pressure too high, fuel pressure regulator leaking, or one or more fuel injectors sticking/leaking) • HO2S element is silicon, water or fuel contaminated • HO2S signal circuit is shorted to system power (B+) • HO2S signal tracking (water intrusion) in the connector causing a short between the HO2S signal and heater power circuits • ECM has failed

DTC	Trouble Code Title, Conditions & Possible Causes
DTC: P0158 **2T CCM, MIL: Yes** **Years:** 2008, 2009, 2010 **Models:** Avalanche, Camaro, Canyon, Escalade/EXT/ESV, Suburban, Tahoe, Yukon **Engines:** 4.8L VIN C, 5.3L VIN 0, 5.3L VIN 3, 5.3L VIN J, 5.3L VIN L, 6.0L VIN K, 6.0L VIN Y, 6.2L VIN J, 6.2L VIN W, 6.2L VIN 8 **Transmissions:** All	**HO2S-22 (Bank 2 Sensor 2) Circuit High Input** DTC P0101, P0102, P0103, P0106, P0107, P0108, P0112, P0113, P0116, P0117, P0118, P0120, P0121, P0122, P0123, P0169, P0178, P0179, P0200, P0220, P0300, P0442, P0446, P0452, P0453, P0455, P0496, P1125, P1258, P1514, P1515, P1516, P1518, P2108 and P2135 not set, engine started, engine running in closed loop, system voltage from 10-18v, Fuel Alcohol content less than 90%, fuel level over 10%, TP angle from 3-70% more than the idle value, then during the Rich Test, the ECM detected the HO2S signal was more than 950 mv for 200 seconds or with engine runtime over 30 seconds, and during the Decel Fuel Cutoff test, the ECM detected the HO2S signal was less than 250 mv for 5 seconds. **Possible Causes:** • Fuel system rich (high fuel pressure, fuel pressure regulator leaking, or injector sticking) • HO2S element is silicon, water or fuel contaminated • HO2S signal tracking (water intrusion) in the connector causing a short between the HO2S signal and heater power circuits • ECM has failed
DTC: P0160 **1T CCM, MIL: Yes** **Years:** 2008, 2009, 2010 **Models:** Acadia, Allure, Aura, Camaro, CTS, CTS-V, Enclave, LaCrosse, Outlook, Traverse **Engines:** 3.6L VIN 7, 3.6L VIN D, 3.6L VIN V **Transmissions:** All	**HO2S Circuit Insufficient Activity (Bank 2 Sensor 2)** DTC P0036, P0037, P0038, P0056, P0057, P0058, P0116, P0117, P0118, P0119, or P0128 is not set, engine startedThe engine coolant temperature is colder than 40°C (104°F) at start-up and the engine coolant temperature was warmer than 60°C (140°F) when the ignition was turned OFF last ignition cycle. The calculated exhaust temperature at the HO2S 2 is warmer than 700°C (1,292°F) and the HO2S 2 is warmed up for greater than 90 seconds. The ECM detects the HO2S 2 signal voltage is less than 60 mV for greater than 1 seconds of for a cumulative of 10 seconds. **Possible Causes:** • Fuel system is too rich (fuel pressure too high, fuel pressure regulator leaking, or one or more fuel injectors sticking/leaking) • HO2S element is silicon, water or fuel contaminated • HO2S signal circuit is shorted to system power (B+) • HO2S signal tracking (water intrusion) in the connector causing a short between the HO2S signal and heater power circuits • ECM has failed
DTC: P0160 **2T O2S, MIL: Yes** **Years:** 2008, 2009, 2010 **Models:** Avalanche, Camaro, Canyon, Escalade/EXT/ESV, Suburban, Tahoe, Yukon **Engines:** 4.8L VIN C, 5.3L VIN 0, 5.3L VIN 3, 5.3L VIN J, 5.3L VIN L, 6.0L VIN K, 6.0L VIN Y, 6.2L VIN J, 6.2L VIN W, 6.2L VIN 8 **Transmissions:** All	**HO2S-22 (Bank 2 Sensor 2) Insufficient Activity** DTC P0101, P0102, P0103, P0106, P0107, P0108, P0112, P0113, P0116, P0117, P0118, P0120, P0121, P0122, P0123, P0169, P0178, P0179, P0200, P0220, P0300, P0442, P0446, P0452, P0453, P0455, P0496, P1125, P1258, P1514, P1515, P1516, P1518, P2108 and P2135 not set, engine runtime over 300 seconds, system voltage from 10-18v, Fuel Alcohol content less than 90%, then after the TP indicated angle changed more than 5% within one seconds six times on models with a TAC system, the ECM detected the HO2S signal remained between 410-490 mv for 150 seconds. **Possible Causes:** • HO2S heater is damaged or it has failed • HO2S signal or ground circuit has a high resistance condition • HO2S has failed (i.e., it is silicon, water or fuel contaminated) • ECM has failed
DTC: P0161 **1T CCM, MIL: Yes** **Years:** 2008, 2009 **Models:** Corvette, CTS, CTS-V, DTS **Engines:** 4.6L VIN Y, 6.2L VIN W, 6.2L VIN P, 6.2L VIN R, 7.0L VIN E **Transmissions:** All	**HO2S Heater Performance (Bank 2 Sensor 2)** DTCs P0116, P0117, P0118, P0125, or P0128 are not set. The ignition 1 voltage is between 10-18 volts. The HO2S is at operating temperature. The HO2S is commanded ON. The DTCs run once per drive cycle when the above conditions are met for 120 seconds. The ECM detects that the HO2S 2 heater current is greater than 2.9 amps, or less than 0.3 amps for greater than 8 seconds. **Possible Causes:** • HO2S ignition circuit for a short to ground or an open/high resistance • HO2S control circuit for a short to voltage, or an open/high resistance • HO2S control circuit for a short to ground • HO2S is damaged or it has failed • ECM has failed
DTC: P0161 **1T CCM, MIL: Yes** **Years:** 2008, 2009, 2010 **Models:** Acadia, Allure, Aura, Camaro, CTS, CTS-V, Enclave, LaCrosse, Outlook, Traverse **Engines:** 3.6L VIN 7, 3.6L VIN D, 3.6L VIN V **Transmissions:** All	**HO2S Heater Performance (Bank 2 Sensor 2)** The ECM detects that the internal resistance of the HO2S 1 heater is not within the expected range for greater than 12 seconds. The internal HO2S 1 resistance is less than 10,000 ohms. **Possible Causes:** • HO2S heater control circuit is open or it is shorted to ground • HO2S control circuit open or high resistance condition • HO2S signal circuit is open or shorted to system power (B+) • HO2S has failed (i.e., it is silicon, water or fuel contaminated) • ECM has failed

DTC	Trouble Code Title, Conditions & Possible Causes
DTC: P0161 **2T O2S HTR, MIL: Yes** **Years:** 2008, 2009, 2010 **Models:** Avalanche, Camaro, Canyon, Escalade/EXT/ESV, Suburban, Tahoe, Yukon **Engines:** 4.8L VIN C, 5.3L VIN 0, 5.3L VIN 3, 5.3L VIN J, 5.3L VIN L, 6.0L VIN K, 6.0L VIN Y, 6.2L VIN J, 6.2L VIN W, 6.2L VIN 8 **Transmissions:** All	**HO2S-22 (Bank 2 Sensor 2) Heater Circuit Malfunction** DTC P0101, P0102, P0103, P0106, P0107, P0108, P0112, P0113, P0116, P0117, P0118, P0120, P0121, P0122, P0123, P0169, P0178, P0179, P0200, P0220, P0300, P0442, P0446, P0452, P0453, P0455, P0496, P1125, P1258, P1514, P1515, P1516, P1518, P2108 and P2135 not set, engine runtime 2 minutes, engine speed from 500-3000 RPM, system voltage from 10-18v, ECT sensor more than 122°F, MAF sensor from 3-40 g/sec, Fuel Alcohol content less than 90%, and the ECM detected the HO2S heater current was less than 0.25 amps, or over 3.125 amps (over 1.375 amps on 4.8L). **Possible Causes:** • HO2S heater low control circuit is open or shorted to ground • HO2S heater circuit is open or it is shorted to ground • HO2S heater power circuit is open (test O2A fuse in fuse block) • HO2S heater element is damaged or has failed • ECM has failed
DTC: P0167D **1T CCM, MIL: Yes** **Years:** 2008, 2009, 2010 **Models:** Acadia, Allure, Aura, Camaro, CTS, CTS-V, Enclave, LaCrosse, Outlook, Traverse **Engines:** 3.6L VIN 7, 3.6L VIN D, 3.6L VIN V **Transmissions:** All	**Control Module Ignition Coil Internal Circuit** The ECM detects a condition with the integrated circuits of the fuel injector driver module for greater than 4 seconds, or a cumulative of 30 seconds. **Possible Causes:** • The ECM must be replaced to correct this problem. A new ECM must be programmed with the correct software/calibration.
DTC: P0171 **1T CCM, MIL: Yes** **Years:** 2008, 2009 **Models:** Corvette, CTS, CTS-V, DTS **Engines:** 4.6L VIN Y, 6.2L VIN W, 6.2L VIN P, 6.2L VIN R, 7.0L VIN E **Transmissions:** All	**Fuel Trim System Lean (Bank 1)** DTCs P0050, P0056, P0059, P0060, P0068, P0101, P0102, P0103, P0107, P0108, P0112, P0113, P0120, P0122, P0123, P0128, P0151, P0152, P0153, P0154, P0155, P0157, P0158, P0160, P0201-P0208, P0220, P0222, P0223, P0300, P0301-P0308, P0442, P0443, P0446, P0449, P0451, P0452, P0453, P0454, P0455, P0496, P0506, P0507, P1153, P1516, P2101, P2119, P2120, P2125, P2135, P2138, P2A03, P2A04 are not set. The engine is in Closed Loop status. The Fuel Trim Learn is enabled. The Engine Coolant Temperature (ECT) is between −40 and +150°C (−40 and +302°F). The Intake Air Temperature (IAT) is between −40 and +150°C (−40 and +302°F). The Manifold absolute Pressure (MAP) is between 5-255 kPa (0.7-36.9 psi). The vehicle speed is less than 134 km/h (83 mph). The engine speed is between 400-6,000 RPM. The Mass Air Flow (MAF) is between 0.5-510 g/s. The Barometric Pressure (BARO) is more than 70 kPa (10.1 psi). The fuel level is more than 10 percent. This diagnostic runs continuously when the above conditions have been met. **Possible Causes:** • Malfunctioning MAF • Low fuel pressure • Fuel contamination • Malfunctioning fuel injectors • Leaking exhaust components from the HO2S forward • Vacuum leaks at the intake manifold, the throttle body, and the injector O-rings • Air induction system and the air intake ducts for leaks or for a missing air filter element • Cracked or damaged EVAP canister • Crankcase ventilation system for leaks • HO2S signal circuit open, shorted to ground, or shorted to the low reference circuit • HO2S sensor 1 low signal circuit for an open circuit or high resistance • HO2S has failed • ECM has failed

DTC	Trouble Code Title, Conditions & Possible Causes
DTC: P0171 **1T CCM, MIL: Yes** **Years:** 2008, 2009 **Models:** Allure, Aura, Canyon, Colorado, LaCrosse **Engines:** 2.9L VIN 9, 3.5L VIN N, 3.8L VIN 2, 5.3L VIN C, 5.3L VIN L **Transmissions:** All	**Fuel Trim System Lean** DTCs P0030, P0036, P0068, P0101, P0102, P0103, P0106, P0107, P0108, P0117, P0118, P0120, P0121, P0128, P0130, P0131, P0132, P0133, P0134, P0135, P0137, P0138, P0140, P0141, P0201-P0208, P0220, P0300, P0301-P0308, P0442, P0443, P0446, P0449, P0452, P0453, P0455, P0496, P1106, P1107, P1114, P1115, P1133, P1153, P1516, P2101, P2119, P2120, P2125, P2135, P2138, P2176 are not set. The engine is in Closed Loop status. The Engine Coolant Temperature (ECT) is between −40 and +150°C (−40 and +302°F). The Intake Air Temperature (IAT) is between −20 and +150°C (−4 and +302°F). The Manifold Absolute Pressure (MAP) is between 10-255 kPa (1.45-37 psi). The vehicle speed is less than 134 km/h (83 mph). The engine speed is between 375-7,000 RPM. The Mass Air Flow (MAF) is between 1-510 g/s. The Barometric Pressure (BARO) is more than 70 kPa (10.2 psi). The fuel level is more than 10 percent. This diagnostic runs continuously when the above conditions have been met. The average long term FT weighted average value is more or less than a calibrated value. The above condition is present for approximately 3 minutes after the conditions for running the DTC have been met. **Possible Causes:** • Low fuel pressure • Fuel contamination • Malfunctioning fuel injectors • Missing, loose, or leaking exhaust components from the HO2S forward • Vacuum leaks at the intake manifold, the throttle body, and the injector O-rings • Air induction system and the air intake ducts for leaks or for a missing air filter element • Cracked EVAP canister • Crankcase ventilation system for leaks • The HO2S signal circuit open, shorted to ground, or shorted to the low reference circuit • HO2S for improper installation and for electrical wires or connectors that may have contacted the exhaust system • Malfunctioning engine components • HO2S sensor has failed • MAP sensor • MAF sensor
DTC: P0171 **2T FUEL, MIL: Yes** **Years:** 2008, 2009, 2010 **Models:** Avalanche, Camaro, Canyon, Escalade/EXT/ESV, Suburban, Tahoe, Yukon **Engines:** 4.8L VIN C, 5.3L VIN 0, 5.3L VIN 3, 5.3L VIN J, 5.3L VIN L, 6.0L VIN K, 6.0L VIN Y, 6.2L VIN J, 6.2L VIN W, 6.2L VIN 8 **Transmissions:** All	**Fuel Trim System Lean (Bank 1)** DTC P0101-P0103, P0108, P0135, P0137, P0141, P0200, P0300, P0410, P0420, P0430, P0440, P0442, P0443, P0446, P0449, P0506, P0507 and P1441 not set, engine started, ECT sensor from 167-239°F, IAT sensor from 4-194°F, engine speed from 400-3000 RPM, BARO sensor over 74 kPa, MAF sensor from 5-90 gm/s, TP angle less than 90%, VSS less than 85 MPH, and the ECM detected the Long Term fuel trim value was more than 23% for 6 seconds (i.e., indicating that a lean A/F mixture was present). **Possible Causes:** • Air leaks in intake manifold, exhaust pipes or exhaust manifold • Fuel control sensor is out of calibration (ECT, IAT or MAF) • Low fuel pressure (fuel filter clogged, pressure regulator failure) • One or more injectors restricted or pressure regulator has failed • HO2S element is contaminated, deteriorated or has failed • Vacuum hose is disconnected, broken, leaking or loose
DTC: P0172 **1T CCM, MIL: Yes** **Years:** 2008, 2009 **Models:** Corvette, CTS, CTS-V, DTS **Engines:** 4.6L VIN Y, 6.2L VIN W, 6.2L VIN P, 6.2L VIN R, 7.0L VIN E **Transmissions:** All	**Fuel Trim System Rich (Bank 1)** DTCs P0050, P0056, P0059, P0060, P0068, P0101, P0102, P0103, P0107, P0108, P0112, P0113, P0120, P0122, P0123, P0128, P0151, P0152, P0153, P0154, P0155, P0157, P0158, P0160, P0201-P0208, P0220, P0222, P0223, P0300, P0301-P0308, P0442, P0443, P0446, P0449, P0451, P0452, P0453, P0454, P0455, P0496, P0506, P0507, P1153, P1516, P2101, P2119, P2120, P2125, P2135, P2138, P2A03, P2A04 are not set. The engine is in Closed Loop status. The Fuel Trim Learn is enabled. The Engine Coolant Temperature (ECT) is between −40 and +150°C (−40 and +302°F). The Intake Air Temperature (IAT) is between −40 and +150°C (−40 and +302°F). The Manifold absolute Pressure (MAP) is between 5-255 kPa (0.7-36.9 psi). The vehicle speed is less than 134 km/h (83 mph). The engine speed is between 400-6,000 RPM. The Mass Air Flow (MAF) is between 0.5-510 g/s. The Barometric Pressure (BARO) is more than 70 kPa (10.1 psi). The fuel level is more than 10 percent. This diagnostic runs continuously when the above conditions have been met. **Possible Causes:** • Malfunctioning MAF • Excessive fuel pressure • Fuel contamination • Malfunctioning fuel injectors • Vacuum hoses for splits, kinks, and improper connections • Air duct for being collapsed or restricted element • Objects blocking the throttle body • Excessive fuel in the crankcase • Evaporative emissions control system for improper operation • HO2S signal circuit open, shorted to ground, or shorted to the low reference circuit • HO2S sensor 1 low signal circuit for an open circuit or high resistance • HO2S has failed • ECM has failed

DTC	Trouble Code Title, Conditions & Possible Causes
DTC: P0172 **1T CCM, MIL: Yes** **Years:** 2008, 2009 **Models:** Allure, Aura, Canyon, Colorado, LaCrosse **Engines:** 2.9L VIN 9, 3.5L VIN N, 3.8L VIN 2, 5.3L VIN C, 5.3L VIN L **Transmissions:** All	**Fuel Trim System Rich** DTCs P0030, P0036, P0068, P0101, P0102, P0103, P0106, P0107, P0108, P0117, P0118, P0120, P0121, P0128, P0130, P0131, P0132, P0133, P0134, P0135, P0137, P0138, P0140, P0141, P0201-P0208, P0220, P0300, P0301-P0308, P0442, P0443, P0446, P0449, P0452, P0453, P0455, P0496, P1106, P1107, P1114, P1115, P1133, P1153, P1516, P2101, P2119, P2120, P2125, P2135, P2138, P2176 are not set. The engine is in Closed Loop status. The Engine Coolant Temperature (ECT) is between −40 and +150°C (−40 and +302°F). The Intake Air Temperature (IAT) is between −20 and +150°C (−4 and +302°F). The Manifold Absolute Pressure (MAP) is between 10-255 kPa (1.45-37 psi). The vehicle speed is less than 134 km/h (83 mph). The engine speed is between 375-7,000 RPM. The Mass Air Flow (MAF) is between 1-510 g/s. The Barometric Pressure (BARO) is more than 70 kPa (10.2 psi). The fuel level is more than 10 percent. This diagnostic runs continuously when the above conditions have been met. The average long term FT weighted average value is more or less than a calibrated value. The above condition is present for approximately 3 minutes after the conditions for running the DTC have been met. **Possible Causes:** • Vacuum hoses for splits, kinks, and improper connections • Air intake duct for being collapsed or restricted • Air filter for being dirty or restricted • Objects blocking the throttle body • Excessive fuel in the crankcase due to leaking fuel injectors • evaporative emissions control system for improper operation • Excessive fuel pressure– • Malfunctioning fuel injectors • Fuel contamination • The HO2S for improper installation and for electrical wires or connectors that may have contacted the exhaust system • HO2S signal circuit shorted to voltage • HO2S sensor has failed • MAP sensor • MAF sensor
DTC: P0172 **1T CCM, MIL: Yes** **Years:** 2008, 2009 **Models:** Astra, Aura, Aveo, Aveo5, Cobalt G3, G5 **Engines:** 1.6L VIN 6, 1.6L VIN E, 1.8L VIN 1, 2.0L VIN P, 2.0L VIN X, 2.2L VIN H, 2.2L VIN F, 2.4L VIN 5, 2.4L VIN B **Transmissions:** All	**Fuel Trim System Rich** DTCs P0030, P0031, P0032, P0068, P0071, P0072, P0073, P0074, P009A, P0101, P0102, P0103, P0111, P0112, P0113, P0114, P0116, P0117, P0118, P0119, P0122, P0123, P0130, P0131, P0132, P0133, P0134, P0135, P0201, P0202, P0203, P0204, P0222, P0223, P0261, P0262, P0264, P0265, P0267, P0268, P0270, P0271, P0301, P0302, P0303, P0304, P0335, P0336, P0340, P0341, P0365, P0366, P0443, P0458, P0459, P0496, P1101, P2227, P2228, P2229, P2297, P2A00 are not set. The engine is in CL status. The engine coolant temperature (ECT) is warmer than 65.3°C (149.5°F). The intake air temperature (IAT) is warmer than −9.8°C (+14.4°F). The engine speed is greater than 608 RPM. The mass air flow (MAF) is within a calibrated range. The barometric pressure (BARO) is more than 70 kPa. The long term FT weighted average value is more or less than a calibrated value. The above condition is present for approximately 3 minutes after the conditions for running the DTC have been met. **Possible Causes** • Base engine "mechanical" fault affecting one or more cylinders • EVAP system component has failed or canister fuel saturated • Fuel control sensor is out of calibration (i.e., ECT, IAT or MAP) • Fuel system supplying too much fuel at idle speed or at cruise • Fuel injector(s) is leaking or stuck partially open (one or more) • HO2S is contaminated, deteriorated or it has failed
DTC: P0172 **2T FUEL, MIL: Yes** **Years:** 2008, 2009, 2010 **Models:** Avalanche, Camaro, Canyon, Escalade/EXT/ESV, Suburban, Tahoe, Yukon **Engines:** 4.8L VIN C, 5.3L VIN 0, 5.3L VIN 3, 5.3L VIN J, 5.3L VIN L, 6.0L VIN K, 6.0L VIN Y, 6.2L VIN J, 6.2L VIN W, 6.2L VIN 8 **Transmissions:** All	**Fuel Trim System Rich (Bank 1)** DTC P0101-P0103, P0108, P0135, P0137, P0141, P0200, P0300, P0410, P0420, P0430, P0440, P0442, P0443, P0446, P0449, P0506, P0507 and P1441 not set, engine started, ECT sensor from 167-239°F, IAT sensor from 4-194°F, engine speed from 400-3000 RPM, BARO sensor over 74 kPa, MAF sensor from 5-90 gm/s, TP angle less than 90%, VSS less than 85 MPH, and the ECM detected the Long Term fuel trim value was less than −13% for 6 seconds (i.e., indicating that a rich A/F mixture was present). **Possible Causes:** • Base engine "mechanical" fault affecting one or more cylinders • Excess fuel vapors in crankcase (the oil needs to be changed) • EVAP system component has failed or canister fuel saturated • Fuel control sensor is out of calibration (i.e., ECT, IAT or MAF) • Fuel delivery system supplying too much fuel during cruise or idle periods (e.g., faulty fuel pump, or faulty pressure regulator) • Fuel injector(s) is leaking or stuck partially open (one or more) • HO2S is contaminated, deteriorated or it has failed

DTC	Trouble Code Title, Conditions & Possible Causes
DTC: P0174 **1T CCM, MIL: Yes** **Years:** 2008, 2009 **Models:** Corvette, CTS, CTS-V, DTS **Engines:** 4.6L VIN Y, 6.2L VIN W, 6.2L VIN P, 6.2L VIN R, 7.0L VIN E **Transmissions:** All	**Fuel Trim System Lean (Bank 2)** DTCs P0050, P0056, P0059, P0060, P0068, P0101, P0102, P0103, P0107, P0108, P0112, P0113, P0120, P0122, P0123, P0128, P0151, P0152, P0153, P0154, P0155, P0157, P0158, P0160, P0201-P0208, P0220, P0222, P0223, P0300, P0301-P0308, P0442, P0443, P0446, P0449, P0451, P0452, P0453, P0454, P0455, P0496, P0506, P0507, P1153, P1516, P2101, P2119, P2120, P2125, P2135, P2138, P2A03, P2A04 are not set. The engine is in Closed Loop status. The Fuel Trim Learn is enabled. The Engine Coolant Temperature (ECT) is between −40 and +150°C (−40 and +302°F). The Intake Air Temperature (IAT) is between −40 and +150°C (−40 and +302°F). The Manifold absolute Pressure (MAP) is between 5-255 kPa (0.7-36.9 psi). The vehicle speed is less than 134 km/h (83 mph). The engine speed is between 400-6,000 RPM. The Mass Air Flow (MAF) is between 0.5-510 g/s. The Barometric Pressure (BARO) is more than 70 kPa (10.1 psi). The fuel level is more than 10 percent. This diagnostic runs continuously when the above conditions have been met. **Possible Causes:** • Malfunctioning MAF • Low fuel pressure • Fuel contamination • Malfunctioning fuel injectors • Leaking exhaust components from the HO2S forward • Vacuum leaks at the intake manifold, the throttle body, and the injector O-rings • Air induction system and the air intake ducts for leaks or for a missing air filter element • Cracked or damaged EVAP canister • Crankcase ventilation system for leaks • HO2S signal circuit open, shorted to ground, or shorted to the low reference circuit • HO2S sensor 1 low signal circuit for an open circuit or high resistance • HO2S has failed • ECM has failed
DTC: P0174 **2T FUEL, MIL: Yes** **Years:** 2008, 2009, 2010 **Models:** Avalanche, Camaro, Canyon, Escalade/EXT/ESV, Suburban, Tahoe, Yukon **Engines:** 4.8L VIN C, 5.3L VIN 0, 5.3L VIN 3, 5.3L VIN J, 5.3L VIN L, 6.0L VIN K, 6.0L VIN Y, 6.2L VIN J, 6.2L VIN W, 6.2L VIN 8 **Transmissions:** All	**Fuel Trim System Lean (Bank 2)** DTC P0101-P0103, P0108, P0135, P0137, P0141, P0200, P0300, P0410, P0420, P0430, P0440, P0442, P0443, P0446, P0449, P0506, P0507 and P1441 not set, engine started, ECT sensor from 167-239°F, IAT sensor from 4-194°F, engine speed from 400-3000 RPM, BARO sensor over 74 kPa, MAF sensor from 5-90 gm/s, TP angle less than 90%, VSS less than 85 MPH, and the ECM detected the Long Term fuel trim value was more than 23% for 6 seconds (i.e., indicating that a lean A/F mixture was present). **Possible Causes:** • Air leaks in intake manifold, exhaust pipes or exhaust manifold • Fuel control sensor is out of calibration (ECT, IAT or MAF) • Low fuel pressure (fuel filter clogged, pressure regulator failure) • One or more injectors restricted or pressure regulator has failed • HO2S element is contaminated, deteriorated or has failed • Vacuum hose is disconnected, broken, leaking or loose
DTC: P0175 **1T CCM, MIL: Yes** **Years:** 2008, 2009 **Models:** Corvette, CTS, CTS-V, DTS **Engines:** 4.6L VIN Y, 6.2L VIN W, 6.2L VIN P, 6.2L VIN R, 7.0L VIN E **Transmissions:** All	**Fuel Trim System Rich (Bank 2)** DTCs P0050, P0056, P0059, P0060, P0068, P0101, P0102, P0103, P0107, P0108, P0112, P0113, P0120, P0122, P0123, P0128, P0151, P0152, P0153, P0154, P0155, P0157, P0158, P0160, P0201-P0208, P0220, P0222, P0223, P0300, P0301-P0308, P0442, P0443, P0446, P0449, P0451, P0452, P0453, P0454, P0455, P0496, P0506, P0507, P1153, P1516, P2101, P2119, P2120, P2125, P2135, P2138, P2A03, P2A04 are not set. The engine is in Closed Loop status. The Fuel Trim Learn is enabled. The Engine Coolant Temperature (ECT) is between −40 and +150°C (−40 and +302°F). The Intake Air Temperature (IAT) is between −40 and +150°C (−40 and +302°F). The Manifold absolute Pressure (MAP) is between 5-255 kPa (0.7-36.9 psi). The vehicle speed is less than 134 km/h (83 mph). The engine speed is between 400-6,000 RPM. The Mass Air Flow (MAF) is between 0.5-510 g/s. The Barometric Pressure (BARO) is more than 70 kPa (10.1 psi). The fuel level is more than 10 percent. This diagnostic runs continuously when the above conditions have been met. **Possible Causes:** • Malfunctioning MAF • Excessive fuel pressure • Fuel contamination • Malfunctioning fuel injectors • Vacuum hoses for splits, kinks, and improper connections • Air duct for being collapsed or restricted element • Objects blocking the throttle body • Excessive fuel in the crankcase • Evaporative emissions control system for improper operation • HO2S signal circuit open, shorted to ground, or shorted to the low reference circuit • HO2S sensor 1 low signal circuit for an open circuit or high resistance • HO2S has failed • ECM has failed

DTC	Trouble Code Title, Conditions & Possible Causes
DTC: P0175 **2T FUEL, MIL: Yes** **Years:** 2008, 2009, 2010 **Models:** Avalanche, Camaro, Canyon, Escalade/EXT/ESV, Suburban, Tahoe, Yukon **Engines:** 4.8L VIN C, 5.3L VIN 0, 5.3L VIN 3, 5.3L VIN J, 5.3L VIN L, 6.0L VIN K, 6.0L VIN Y, 6.2L VIN J, 6.2L VIN W, 6.2L VIN 8 **Transmissions:** All	**Fuel Trim System Rich (Bank 2)** DTC P0101-P0103, P0108, P0135, P0137, P0141, P0200, P0300, P0410, P0420, P0430, P0440, P0442, P0443, P0446, P0449, P0506, P0507 and P1441 not set, engine speed from 400-3000 RPM, ECT sensor from 167-239°F, IAT sensor from 4-194°F, BARO sensor over 74 kPa, MAF sensor from 5-90 gm/s, TP angle under 90%, VSS below 85 MPH, and the ECM detected the LT fuel trim was less than −13% for 6 seconds (i.e., a possible rich A/F mixture). **Possible Causes:** • Air leaks in intake manifold, exhaust pipes or exhaust manifold • Fuel control sensor is out of calibration (ECT, IAT or MAF) • Low fuel pressure (fuel filter clogged, pressure regulator failure) • One or more injectors restricted or pressure regulator has failed • HO2S element is contaminated, deteriorated or has failed • Vacuum hose is disconnected, broken, leaking or loose
DTC: P0191 **1T CCM, MIL: Yes** **Years:** 2008, 2009 **Models:** Corvette, CTS, CTS-V **Engines:** 6.2L VIN W, 6.2L VIN P, 6.2L VIN R, 7.0L VIN E **Transmissions:** All	**Fuel Rail Pressure (FRP) Sensor Performance** The engine is running. DTC P0192, P0193, or P1255 are not active. DTC P0641 has not failed this ignition cycle. Fuel pump control is enabled and the fuel pump control state is normal. The engine has been running for at least 5 seconds. The FPCM does not detect a change in the fuel rail pressure of at least 30 kPa (4.4 psi). **Note: Verify that the fuel tank is not empty. Only perform this diagnostic if there is at least 2 gallons of fuel in the fuel tank. Clear the DTC, and start and run the engine. Verify that the DTC P0191 resets before proceeding with the circuit system testing. If the DTC does not reset, refer to diagnostic aids.** **Possible Causes:** • FRP sensor low reference circuit for an open/high resistance • FRP sensor 5-V reference circuit for a short to ground or an open/high resistance • FRP sensor 5-V reference circuit for a short to voltage • FRP sensor signal circuit for a short to ground or an open/high resistance • Fuel pump flow control module has failed • Fuel pressure sensor has failed
DTC: P0191 **1T CCM, MIL: Yes** **Years:** 2008, 2009, 2010 **Models:** Acadia, Allure, Aura, Camaro, CTS, CTS-V, Enclave, LaCrosse, Outlook, Traverse **Engines:** 3.6L VIN 7, 3.6L VIN D, 3.6L VIN V **Transmissions:** All	**Fuel Rail Pressure (FRP) Sensor Performance** DTC P0087, P2187, or P2188 is set, and the fuel pressure at ignition ON is less than 120 kPa (17.4 psi) for greater than 4 seconds or for a cumulative of 30 seconds. Or DTC P0088, P2177, or P2187 is set, and the fuel pressure at ignition ON is greater than 1500 kPa (218 psi) for greater than 4 seconds or for a cumulative of 30 seconds. Or the fuel pressure at ignition ON is greater than 1500 kPa (218 psi) and a fuel pressure increase of greater than 385 kPa (56 psi) occurs during the fuel pump prime. The condition exists for greater than 4 seconds or for a cumulative of 30 seconds. **Possible Causes:** • (A condition with the fuel tank module or the fuel pump control module (FECM) will set this DTC) • low reference circuit for an open/high resistance • 5-volt reference circuit for a short to ground or an open/high resistance • 5-volt reference circuit for a short to voltage • signal circuit terminal 12 for a short to ground • FRP sensor is damaged or it has failed • ECM has failed
DTC: P0192 **1T CCM, MIL: Yes** **Years:** 2008, 2009 **Models:** Corvette, CTS, CTS-V **Engines:** 6.2L VIN W, 6.2L VIN P, 6.2L VIN R, 7.0L VIN E **Transmissions:** All	**Fuel Rail Pressure (FRP) Sensor Circuit Low Voltage** The ignition is on. The FPCM detects that the Fuel Rail Pressure (FRP) sensor signal circuit is above 4.9 V or below 0.1 V. **Note: Using the Failure Records data may help locate an intermittent condition. If you cannot duplicate the DTC, the information in the Failure Records can help determine how many miles since the DTC set. The Fail Counter and Pass Counter can help determine how many ignition cycles that the diagnostic test reported a pass and/or a fail.** **Possible Causes:** • FRP sensor low reference circuit for an open/high resistance • FRP sensor 5-V reference circuit for a short to ground or an open/high resistance • FRP sensor 5-V reference circuit for a short to voltage • FRP sensor signal circuit for a short to ground or an open/high resistance • Fuel pump flow control module has failed • Fuel pressure sensor has failed

DTC	Trouble Code Title, Conditions & Possible Causes
DTC: P0192 **1T CCM, MIL: Yes** **Years:** 2008, 2009, 2010 **Models:** Acadia, Allure, Aura, Camaro, CTS, CTS-V, Enclave, LaCrosse, Outlook, Traverse **Engines:** 3.6L VIN 7, 3.6L VIN D, 3.6L VIN V **Transmissions:** All	**Fuel Rail Pressure (FRP) Sensor Circuit Low Voltage** Key on or engine running; and the ECM detected the FRP sensor was less than 0.45v for 5 seconds. The fuel rail pressure (FRP) sensor is a pressure sensor. The fuel injector control module (FICM) supplies 5v on the FRP sensor reference voltage circuit. The FICM also supplies a ground circuit and a signal circuit to the FRP sensor. When the fuel rail pressure is normal, the FRP signal voltage rises to near 2.5v. If the fuel rail pressure increases, the FRP signal voltage increases. The FICM monitors the FRP sensor and communicates the data to the ECM by a dedicated pulse width modulated (PWM) circuit. **Possible Causes:** • FRP sensor 5-volt power circuit is open or shorted to ground • FRP Sensor signal circuit is shorted to ground • FRP Sensor is damaged or has failed • ECM has failed
DTC: P0193 **1T CCM, MIL: Yes** **Years:** 2008, 2009 **Models:** Corvette, CTS, CTS-V **Engines:** 6.2L VIN W, 6.2L VIN P, 6.2L VIN R, 7.0L VIN E **Transmissions:** All	**Fuel Rail Pressure (FRP) Sensor Circuit High Voltage** The ignition is on. The FPCM detects that the Fuel Rail Pressure (FRP) sensor signal circuit is above 4.9 V or below 0.1 V. **Note: Using the Failure Records data may help locate an intermittent condition. If you cannot duplicate the DTC, the information in the Failure Records can help determine how many miles since the DTC set. The Fail Counter and Pass Counter can help determine how many ignition cycles that the diagnostic test reported a pass and/or a fail.** **Possible Causes:** • FRP sensor low reference circuit for an open/high resistance • FRP sensor 5-V reference circuit for a short to ground or an open/high resistance • FRP sensor 5-V reference circuit for a short to voltage • FRP sensor signal circuit for a short to ground or an open/high resistance • Fuel pump flow control module has failed • Fuel pressure sensor has failed
DTC: P0193 **1T CCM, MIL: Yes** **Years:** 2008, 2009, 2010 **Models:** Acadia, Allure, Aura, Camaro, CTS, CTS-V, Enclave, LaCrosse, Outlook, Traverse **Engines:** 3.6L VIN 7, 3.6L VIN D, 3.6L VIN V **Transmissions:** All	**Fuel Rail Pressure Sensor Circuit High Voltage** Key on or engine running; and the ECM detected the Fuel Rail Pressure (FRP) sensor was more than 4.7 volts for 5 seconds. **Possible Causes:** • FRP sensor signal circuit is open between sensor and the ECM • FRP Sensor ground circuit is open between sensor and ECM • FRP sensor signal circuit is shorted to VREF or system power • FRP Sensor is damaged or has failed • ECM has failed
DTC: P0200 **2T CCM, MIL: Yes** **Years:** 2008, 2009, 2010 **Models:** Avalanche, Camaro, Canyon, Escalade/EXT/ESV, Suburban, Tahoe, Yukon **Engines:** 4.8L VIN C, 5.3L VIN 0, 5.3L VIN 3, 5.3L VIN J, 5.3L VIN L, 6.0L VIN K, 6.0L VIN Y, 6.2L VIN J, 6.2L VIN W, 6.2L VIN 8 **Transmissions:** All	**Fuel Injector Circuit Malfunction** Engine started; engine speed over 400 RPM, system voltage 6-18v, and the ECM detected an unexpected voltage on one or more of the Fuel Injector driver circuits for 5 seconds. Drive the vehicle at off-idle speeds and monitor the misfire current counters. Observe if more than one cylinder is misfiring. This may not be apparent until after a repair is completed. If an injector fuse is open on one cylinder bank, the Scan Tool may only display 2 or 3 cylinders as misfiring. **Possible Causes:** • Fuel injector control circuit is open between injector and ECM • Fuel injector control circuit is grounded between injector and ECM • Fuel injector power circuit is open (test INJ A, B in fuse block) • Fuel injector is damaged or has failed • ECM is damaged
DTC: P0201 **1T CCM, MIL: Yes** **Years:** 2008, 2009 **Models:** Allure, Aura, Canyon, Colorado, LaCrosse **Engines:** 2.9L VIN 9, 3.5L VIN N, 3.8L VIN 2, 5.3L VIN C, 5.3L VIN L **Transmissions:** All	**Injector 1 Control Circuit** The engine is running. The ignition voltage is more than 11 volts. DTC P0201-P0208 runs continuously when the above conditions are met. The control module detects an incorrect voltage on the fuel injector control circuit. The above condition is met for 1 second. **Note: Performing the Fuel Injector Diagnosis may help isolate an intermittent condition.** **Possible Causes:** • Fuel Injector ignition 1 voltage circuit for a short to ground or an open/high resistance • Fuel Injector ignition 1 voltage circuit fuse is open • Fuel Injector control circuit for a short to ground • Fuel Injector control circuit for a short to voltage or an open/high resistance • Fuel injector has failed • ECM has failed

DTC	Trouble Code Title, Conditions & Possible Causes
DTC: P0201 **2T CCM, MIL: Yes** **Years:** 2008, 2009, 2010 **Models:**, Acadia, Allure, Astra, Aura, Avalanche, Escalade/EXT/ ESV, Suburban, Tahoe, Yukon, Escalade/EXT/ESV, Suburban, Tahoe, Yukon Aveo, Aveo5, Camaro, Cobalt, Cobalt-GS, Colorado,Canyon, Corvette, CTS, CTS-V, CTS, CTS-V-V, DTS, Escalade/EXT/ESV, G.3, G5,Enclave, LaCrosse, Outlook, Suburban, Tahoe Traverse, Yukon **Engines:** All **Transmissions:** All	**Fuel Injector 1 Control Circuit Malfunction** Engine started; engine speed over 400 RPM, system voltage over 11.0v and the ECM detected an unexpected voltage condition on the Fuel Injector driver circuit for Cylinder 1 for 6 seconds. **Note: Drive the vehicle at cruise speed. Record the misfire current counters for review to detect if more than one cylinder is misfiring.** **Possible Causes:** • Injector 1 power circuit (B+) is open (check the power fuse) • Injector 1 control circuit is open between injector and ECM • Injector 1 control circuit is grounded between injector and ECM • Injector 1 is damaged or it has failed • ECM is damaged
DTC: P0202 **2T CCM, MIL: Yes** **Years:** 2008, 2009, 2010 **Models:**, Acadia, Allure, Astra, Aura, Avalanche, Escalade/EXT/ ESV, Suburban, Tahoe, Yukon, Escalade/EXT/ESV, Suburban, Tahoe, Yukon Aveo, Aveo5, Camaro, Cobalt, Cobalt-GS, Colorado,Canyon, Corvette, CTS, CTS-V, CTS, CTS-V-V, DTS, Escalade/EXT/ESV, G.3, G5,Enclave, LaCrosse, Outlook, Suburban, Tahoe Traverse, Yukon **Engines:** All **Transmissions:** All	**Fuel Injector 2 Control Circuit Malfunction** Engine started; engine speed over 400 RPM, system voltage over 11.0v and the ECM detected an unexpected voltage condition on the Fuel Injector driver circuit for Cylinder 2 for 6 seconds. **Note: Drive the vehicle at cruise speed. Record the misfire current counters for review to detect if more than one cylinder is misfiring.** **Possible Causes:** • Injector 2 power circuit (B+) is open (check the power fuse) • Injector 2 control circuit is open between injector and ECM • Injector 2 control circuit is grounded between injector and ECM • Injector 2 is damaged or it has failed • ECM is damaged
DTC: P0203 **2T CCM, MIL: Yes** **Years:** 2008, 2009, 2010 **Models:**, Acadia, Allure, Astra, Aura, Avalanche, Escalade/EXT/ ESV, Suburban, Tahoe, Yukon, Escalade/EXT/ESV, Suburban, Tahoe, Yukon Aveo, Aveo5, Camaro, Cobalt, Cobalt-GS, Colorado,Canyon, Corvette, CTS, CTS-V, CTS, CTS-V-V, DTS, Escalade/EXT/ESV, G.3, G5,Enclave, LaCrosse, Outlook, Suburban, Tahoe Traverse, Yukon **Engines:** All **Transmissions:** All	**Fuel Injector 3 Control Circuit Malfunction** Engine started; engine speed over 400 RPM, system voltage over 11.0v and the ECM detected an unexpected voltage condition on the Fuel Injector driver circuit for Cylinder 3 for 6 seconds. **Note: Drive the vehicle at cruise speed. Record the misfire current counters for review to detect if more than one cylinder is misfiring.** **Possible Causes:** • Injector 3 power circuit (B+) is open (check the power fuse) • Injector 3 control circuit is open between injector and ECM • Injector 3 control circuit is grounded between injector and ECM • Injector 3 is damaged or it has failed • ECM is damaged

DTC	Trouble Code Title, Conditions & Possible Causes
DTC: P0204 **2T CCM, MIL: Yes** **Years:** 2008, 2009, 2010 **Models:**, Acadia, Allure, Astra, Aura, Avalanche, Escalade/EXT/ESV, Suburban, Tahoe, Yukon, Escalade/EXT/ESV, Suburban, Tahoe, Yukon Aveo, Aveo5, Camaro, Cobalt, Cobalt-GS, Colorado,Canyon, Corvette, CTS, CTS-V, CTS, CTS-V-V, DTS, Escalade/EXT/ESV, G.3, G5,Enclave, LaCrosse, Outlook, Suburban, Tahoe Traverse, Yukon **Engines:** All **Transmissions:** All	**Fuel Injector 4 Control Circuit Malfunction** Engine started; engine speed over 400 RPM, system voltage over 11.0v and the ECM detected an unexpected voltage condition on the Fuel Injector driver circuit for Cylinder 4 for 6 seconds. **Note: Drive the vehicle at cruise speed. Record the misfire current counters for review to detect if more than one cylinder is misfiring.** **Possible Causes:** • Injector 4 power circuit (B+) is open (check the power fuse) • Injector 4 control circuit is open between injector and ECM • Injector 4 control circuit is grounded between injector and ECM • Injector 4 is damaged or it has failed • ECM is damaged
DTC: P0205 **2T CCM, MIL: Yes** **Years:** 2008, 2009, 2010 **Models:**, Acadia, Allure, Astra, Aura, Avalanche, Escalade/EXT/ESV, Suburban, Tahoe, Yukon, Escalade/EXT/ESV, Suburban, Tahoe, Yukon Aveo, Aveo5, Camaro, Cobalt, Cobalt-GS, Colorado,Canyon, Corvette, CTS, CTS-V, CTS, CTS-V-V, DTS, Escalade/EXT/ESV, G.3, G5,Enclave, LaCrosse, Outlook, Suburban, Tahoe Traverse, Yukon **Engines:** All **Transmissions:** All	**Fuel Injector 5 Control Circuit Malfunction** Engine started; engine speed over 400 RPM, system voltage over 11.0v and the ECM detected an unexpected voltage condition on the Fuel Injector driver circuit for Cylinder 5 for 6 seconds. **Note: Drive the vehicle at cruise speed. Record the misfire current counters for review to detect if more than one cylinder is misfiring.** **Possible Causes:** • Injector 5 power circuit (B+) is open (check the power fuse) • Injector 5 control circuit is open between injector and ECM • Injector 5 control circuit is grounded between injector and ECM • Injector 5 is damaged or it has failed • ECM is damaged
DTC: P0206 **2T CCM, MIL: Yes** **Years:** 2008, 2009, 2010 **Models:**, Acadia, Allure, Astra, Aura, Avalanche, Escalade/EXT/ESV, Suburban, Tahoe, Yukon, Escalade/EXT/ESV, Suburban, Tahoe, Yukon Aveo, Aveo5, Camaro, Cobalt, Cobalt-GS, Colorado,Canyon, Corvette, CTS, CTS-V, CTS, CTS-V-V, DTS, Escalade/EXT/ESV, G.3, G5,Enclave, LaCrosse, Outlook, Suburban, Tahoe Traverse, Yukon **Engines:** All **Transmissions:** All	**Fuel Injector 6 Control Circuit Malfunction** Engine started; engine speed over 400 RPM, system voltage over 11.0v and the ECM detected an unexpected voltage condition on the Fuel Injector driver circuit for Cylinder 6 for 6 seconds. **Note: Drive the vehicle at cruise speed. Record the misfire current counters for review to detect if more than one cylinder is misfiring.** **Possible Causes:** • Injector 6 power circuit (B+) is open (check the power fuse) • Injector 6 control circuit is open between injector and ECM • Injector 6 control circuit is grounded between injector and ECM • Injector 6 is damaged or it has failed • ECM is damaged

DTC	Trouble Code Title, Conditions & Possible Causes
DTC: P0207 **2T CCM, MIL: Yes** **Years:** 2008, 2009, 2010 **Models:**, Acadia, Allure, Astra, Aura, Avalanche, Escalade/EXT/ESV, Suburban, Tahoe, Yukon, Escalade/EXT/ESV, Suburban, Tahoe, Yukon Aveo, Aveo5, Camaro, Cobalt, Cobalt-GS, Colorado,Canyon, Corvette, CTS, CTS-V, CTS, CTS-V-V, DTS, Escalade/EXT/ESV, G.3, G5,Enclave, LaCrosse, Outlook, Suburban, Tahoe Traverse, Yukon **Engines:** All **Transmissions:** All	**Fuel Injector 7 Control Circuit Malfunction** Engine started; engine speed over 400 RPM, system voltage over 11.0v and the ECM detected an unexpected voltage condition on the Fuel Injector driver circuit for Cylinder 7 for 6 seconds. **Note: Drive the vehicle at cruise speed. Record the misfire current counters for review to detect if more than one cylinder is misfiring.** **Possible Causes:** • Injector 6 power circuit (B+) is open (check the power fuse) • Injector 6 control circuit is open between injector and ECM • Injector 6 control circuit is grounded between injector and ECM • Injector 6 is damaged or it has failed • ECM is damaged
DTC: P0208 **2T CCM, MIL: Yes** **Years:** 2008, 2009, 2010 **Models:**, Acadia, Allure, Astra, Aura, Avalanche, Escalade/EXT/ESV, Suburban, Tahoe, Yukon, Escalade/EXT/ESV, Suburban, Tahoe, Yukon Aveo, Aveo5, Camaro, Cobalt, Cobalt-GS, Colorado,Canyon, Corvette, CTS, CTS-V, CTS, CTS-V-V, DTS, Escalade/EXT/ESV, G.3, G5,Enclave, LaCrosse, Outlook, Suburban, Tahoe Traverse, Yukon **Engines:** All **Transmissions:** All	**Fuel Injector 8 Control Circuit Malfunction** Engine started; engine speed over 400 RPM, system voltage over 11.0v and the ECM detected an unexpected voltage condition on the Fuel Injector driver circuit for Cylinder 8 for 6 seconds. **Note: Drive the vehicle at cruise speed. Record the misfire current counters for review to detect if more than one cylinder is misfiring.** **Possible Causes:** • Injector 6 power circuit (B+) is open (check the power fuse) • Injector 6 control circuit is open between injector and ECM • Injector 6 control circuit is grounded between injector and ECM • Injector 6 is damaged or it has failed • ECM is damaged
DTC: P0220 **1T CCM, MIL: Yes** **Years:** 2008, 2009 **Models:** Corvette, CTS, CTS-V, DTS **Engines:** 4.6L VIN Y, 6.2L VIN W, 6.2L VIN P, 6.2L VIN R, 7.0L VIN E **Transmissions:** All	**Throttle Position (TP) Sensor 2 Circuit** DTCs P0601, P0602, P0603, P0604, P0606, P0607, P0641, P0651 are not set. The system voltage is more than 5.23 volts. The ignition is in the Unlock/Accessory or Run position. DTC P0120, P0122, P0123, P0220, P0222, P0223 run continuously when the above conditions are met. The TP sensor 2 voltage is less than 0.25 volt or more than 4.59 volts for more than 1 second. **Possible Causes:** • TP sensor low reference circuit for an open/high resistance • TP sensor 5-volt reference circuit for a short to ground or an open/high resistance • TP sensor 5-volt reference circuit for a short to voltage • TP sensor signal circuit terminal F for a short to ground • TP sensor 1 signal circuit for a short to ground or an open/high resistance • TP sensor 2 signal circuit for a short to voltage • TP sensor 2 signal circuit for an open/high resistance. • Throttle body has failed • ECM has failed
DTC: P0220 **1T CCM, MIL: Yes** **Years:** 2008, 2009 **Models:** Allure, Aura, Canyon, Colorado, LaCrosse **Engines:** 2.9L VIN 9, 3.5L VIN N, 3.8L VIN 2, 5.3L VIN C, 5.3L VIN L **Transmissions:** All	**Throttle Position Sensor 2 Circuit Malfunction** DTP P1518 and P2108 not set, engine cranking or running; system voltage over 5.23v, and the ECM detected the TP Sensor 2 signal was less than 0.28v or more than 4.60v for one second. The ECM provides the TP sensor with a 5v, low reference and signal circuit. The signal is low at closed throttle and higher as the throttle opens. **Possible Causes:** • TP Sensor 2 signal circuit is open or shorted to ground • TP Sensor 2 VREF (5v) circuit is open, or TP Sensor 2 ground circuit is open • TP Sensor 2 is damaged or has failed • ECM is damaged • TSB 03-04-06-034 contains a repair procedure for this code

DTC	Trouble Code Title, Conditions & Possible Causes
DTC: P0221 **1T CCM, MIL: Yes** **Years:** 2008, 2009, 2010 **Models:** Acadia, Allure, Aura, Camaro, CTS, CTS-V, Enclave, LaCrosse, Outlook, Traverse **Engines:** 3.6L VIN 7, 3.6L VIN D, 3.6L VIN V **Transmissions:** All	**Throttle Position (TP) Sensor 2 Circuit Low Voltage** DTC P0601, P0602, P0603, P0604, P0606, P0607, P0641, P0651 are not set. The system voltage is more than 5.23 volts. The ignition is in the Unlock/Accessory or Run position. DTC P0120, P0122, P0123, P0220, P0222, P0223 run continuously when the above conditions are met. The ECM detects that the TP sensor 2 voltage is less than 0.25 volt for greater than 1 s. **Possible Causes:** • TP sensor low reference circuit for an open/high resistance • TP sensor 5-volt reference circuit for a short to ground or an open/high resistance • TP sensor 5-volt reference circuit for a short to voltage • TP sensor signal circuit for a short to voltage • TP sensor signal circuit for a short to ground or an open/high resistance • TP sensor has failed (replace throttle body) • ECM has failed
DTC: P0222 **1T CCM, MIL: Yes** **Years:** 2008, 2009 **Models:** Corvette, CTS, CTS-V, DTS **Engines:** 4.6L VIN Y, 6.2L VIN W, 6.2L VIN P, 6.2L VIN R, 7.0L VIN E **Transmissions:** All	**Throttle Position (TP) Sensor2 Circuit Low Voltage** DTCs P0601, P0602, P0603, P0604, P0606, P0607, P0641, P0651 are not set. The system voltage is more than 5.23 volts. The ignition is in the Unlock/Accessory or Run position. DTC P0120, P0122, P0123, P0220, P0222, P0223 run continuously when the above conditions are met. The ECM detects that the TP sensor 2 voltage is less than 0.25 volt for more than 1 second. **Possible Causes:** • TP sensor low reference circuit for an open/high resistance • TP sensor 5-volt reference circuit for a short to ground or an open/high resistance • TP sensor 5-volt reference circuit for a short to voltage • TP sensor signal circuit terminal F for a short to ground • TP sensor 1 signal circuit for a short to ground or an open/high resistance • TP sensor 2 signal circuit for a short to voltage • TP sensor 2 signal circuit for an open/high resistance. • Throttle body has failed • ECM has failed
DTC: P0222 **1T CCM, MIL: Yes** **Years:** 2008, 2009 **Models:** Allure, Aura, Canyon, Colorado, LaCrosse **Engines:** 2.9L VIN 9, 3.5L VIN N, 3.8L VIN 2, 5.3L VIN C, 5.3L VIN L **Transmissions:** All	**Throttle Position (TP) Sensor 2 Circuit Low Voltage** The ignition is ON, with the engine OFF, or the engine is operating. The ignition voltage is greater than 7 volts. DTC P0122 runs continuously once the above conditions are met. The ECM detects the TP sensor 1 signal voltage is less than 0.18 volt. **Possible Causes:** • TP Sensor 2 signal circuit is open or shorted to ground • TP Sensor 2 VREF (5v) circuit is open, or TP Sensor 2 ground circuit is open • TP Sensor 2 is damaged or has failed (replace the throttle body assembly) • ECM is damaged
DTC: P0222 **1T CCM, MIL: Yes** **Years:** 2008, 2009, 2010 **Models:** Acadia, Allure, Aura, Camaro, CTS, CTS-V, Enclave, LaCrosse, Outlook, Traverse **Engines:** 3.6L VIN 7, 3.6L VIN D, 3.6L VIN V **Transmissions:** All	**Throttle Position (TP) Sensor 2 Circuit Low Voltage** The ignition is in the Unlock/Accessory or Run position. DTC P0642 or P0643 is not set. DTC P0222 runs continuously when the above conditions are met. The ECM detects that the TP sensor 2 voltage is less than 0.19 volt for more than 0.4 second. **Possible Causes:** • TP Sensor 2 signal circuit is open or shorted to ground • TP Sensor 2 VREF (5v) circuit is open, or TP Sensor 2 ground circuit is open • TP Sensor 2 is damaged or has failed (replace the throttle body assembly) • ECM is damaged
DTC: P0222 **1T CCM, MIL: Yes** **Years:** 2008, 2009 **Models:** Astra, Aura, Aveo, Aveo5, Cobalt G3, G5 **Engines:** 1.6L VIN 6, 1.6L VIN E, 1.8L VIN 1, 2.0L VIN P, 2.0L VIN X, 2.2L VIN H, 2.2L VIN F, 2.4L VIN 5, 2.4L VIN B **Transmissions:** All	**Throttle Position (TP) Sensor 2 Circuit High Voltage** DTC P0601, P0602, P0603, P0604, P0606, P0607, P0641, P0651 are not set. The system voltage is more than 5.23 volts. The ignition is in the Unlock/Accessory or Run position. DTC P0120, P0122, P0123, P0220, P0222, P0223 run continuously when the above conditions are met. The ECM detects that the TP sensor 2 voltage is greater than 4.59 volts for greater than 1 s. **Possible Causes:** • TP sensor low reference circuit for an open/high resistance • TP sensor 5-volt reference circuit for a short to ground or an open/high resistance • TP sensor 5-volt reference circuit for a short to voltage • TP sensor signal circuit for a short to voltage • TP sensor signal circuit for a short to ground or an open/high resistance • TP sensor has failed (replace throttle body) • ECM has failed

DTC	Trouble Code Title, Conditions & Possible Causes
DTC: P0223 **1T CCM, MIL: Yes** **Years:** 2008, 2009 **Models:** Corvette, CTS, CTS-V, DTS **Engines:** 4.6L VIN Y, 6.2L VIN W, 6.2L VIN P, 6.2L VIN R, 7.0L VIN E **Transmissions:** All	**Throttle Position (TP) Sensor 2 Circuit High Voltage** DTCs P0601, P0602, P0603, P0604, P0606, P0607, P0641, P0651 are not set. The system voltage is more than 5.23 volts. The ignition is in the Unlock/Accessory or Run position. DTC P0120, P0122, P0123, P0220, P0222, P0223 run continuously when the above conditions are met. The ECM detects that the TP sensor 2 voltage is more than 4.59 volts for more than 1 second. **Possible Causes:**
DTC: P0223 **1T CCM, MIL: Yes** **Years:** 2008, 2009 **Models:** Allure, Aura, Canyon, Colorado, LaCrosse **Engines:** 2.9L VIN 9, 3.5L VIN N, 3.8L VIN 2, 5.3L VIN C, 5.3L VIN L **Transmissions:** All	**Throttle Position (TP) Sensor 2 Circuit High Voltage** The ignition voltage is greater than 7 volts. The TP sensor 2 voltage is between 0.16-4.9 volts. The TP sensor 1 disagrees greater than 9 percent from TP sensor 2, or TP sensor 1 disagrees greater than 9 percent from the predicted value for greater than 1 second or a cumulative of 10 seconds. **Possible Causes:** • TP Sensor 2 signal circuit is open or shorted to ground • TP Sensor 2 VREF (5v) circuit is open, or TP Sensor 2 ground circuit is open • TP Sensor 2 is damaged or has failed (replace the throttle body assembly) • ECM is damaged
DTC: P0223 **1T CCM, MIL: Yes** **Years:** 2008, 2009, 2010 **Models:** Acadia, Allure, Aura, Camaro, CTS, CTS-V, Enclave, LaCrosse, Outlook, Traverse **Engines:** 3.6L VIN 7, 3.6L VIN D, 3.6L VIN V **Transmissions:** All	**Throttle Position (TP) Sensor 2 Circuit High Voltage** The ignition is in the Unlock/Accessory or Run position. DTC P0642 or P0643 is not set. DTC P0222 runs continuously when the above conditions are met. The ECM detects that the TP sensor 2 voltage is more than 4.82 volts for more than 0.4 second. **Possible Causes:** • TP Sensor 2 signal circuit is open or shorted to ground • TP Sensor 2 VREF (5v) circuit is open, or TP Sensor 2 ground circuit is open • TP Sensor 2 is damaged or has failed (replace the throttle body assembly) • ECM is damaged
DTC: P0223 **1T CCM, MIL: Yes** **Years:** 2008, 2009 **Models:** Astra, Aura, Aveo, Aveo5, Cobalt G3, G5 **Engines:** 1.6L VIN 6, 1.6L VIN E, 1.8L VIN 1, 2.0L VIN P, 2.0L VIN X, 2.2L VIN H, 2.2L VIN F, 2.4L VIN 5, 2.4L VIN B **Transmissions:** All	**Fuel Pump Relay Control Circuit** The ignition voltage is between 9-18 volts. DTC P0230 runs continuously when the above conditions are met. The control module detects that the commanded state of the driver and the actual state of the control circuit do not match. The above condition is met for a minimum of 2.5 seconds. **Possible Causes:** • Fuel pump relay shorted to ground • Fuel pump relay shorted to Voltage • Fuel pump relay open condition • Fuel pump relay has failed • ECM has failed
DTC: P0230 **1T CCM, MIL: Yes** **Years:** 2008, 2009 **Models:** Corvette, CTS, CTS-V, DTS **Engines:** 4.6L VIN Y, 6.2L VIN W, 6.2L VIN P, 6.2L VIN R, 7.0L VIN E **Transmissions:** All	**Fuel Pump Relay Control Circuit (with LS9 engine)** The ignition voltage is between 9-18 volts. DTC P0230 runs continuously when the above condition is met. The control module detects that the commanded state of the driver and the actual state of the control circuit do not match. The above condition is met for a minimum of 2.5 seconds. **Possible Causes:** • Fuel pump relay control circuit for a short to ground • Fuel pump relay control circuit for an open/high resistance • Fuel pump relay control circuit for an short to voltage • Fuel pump control module (FPCM) has failed • ECM has failed
DTC: P0230 **1T CCM, MIL: Yes** **Years:** 2008, 2009 **Models:** Corvette, CTS, CTS-V **Engines:** 6.2L VIN W, 6.2L VIN P, 6.2L VIN R, 7.0L VIN E **Transmissions:** All	**Fuel Pump Relay Control Circuit (with out LS9 engine)** The ignition voltage is between 9-18 volts. DTC P0230 runs continuously when the above condition is met. The control module detects that the commanded state of the driver and the actual state of the control circuit do not match. The above condition is met for a minimum of 2.5 seconds. **Possible Causes:** • Fuel pump relay control circuit for a short to ground • Fuel pump relay control circuit for an open/high resistance • Fuel pump relay control circuit for an short to voltage • Fuel pump relay has failed • ECM has failed

DTC	Trouble Code Title, Conditions & Possible Causes
DTC: P0230 **1T CCM, MIL: Yes** **Years:** 2008, 2009 **Models:** Allure, Aura, Canyon, Colorado, LaCrosse **Engines:** 2.9L VIN 9, 3.5L VIN N, 3.8L VIN 2, 5.3L VIN C, 5.3L VIN L **Transmissions:** All	**Fuel Pump Relay Control Circuit Malfunction** Engine started; engine speed more than 400 RPM, system voltage from 6-18v, and the ECM detected the Actual state and the Commanded state of the Fuel Pump control circuit did not match for 2.5 seconds. **Possible Causes:** • Fuel pump relay control circuit is open or shorted to ground • Fuel pump relay power circuit is open (ECM Fuse B fuse block) • Fuel pump relay is damaged or it has failed • ECM is damaged
DTC: P0230 **2T CCM, MIL: Yes** **Years:** 2008, 2009, 2010 **Models:** Avalanche, Camaro, Canyon, Escalade/EXT/ESV, Suburban, Tahoe, Yukon **Engines:** 4.8L VIN C, 5.3L VIN 0, 5.3L VIN 3, 5.3L VIN J, 5.3L VIN L, 6.0L VIN K, 6.0L VIN Y, 6.2L VIN J, 6.2L VIN W, 6.2L VIN 8 **Transmissions:** All	**Fuel Pump Control Circuit Malfunction** Engine started; engine speed over 400 RPM, system voltage over 10.0v and the ECM detected that the Actual and Commanded state of the Fuel Pump driver control circuit did not match for 2.5 seconds. **Possible Causes:** • Fuel pump relay power circuit is open (test B+ from fuse box) • Fuel pump control circuit is open or shorted to ground • Fuel pump control circuit is shorted to system power • ECM has failed • TSB 00-06-04-023 contains a repair procedure for this code
DTC: P0230 **2T CCM, MIL: Yes** **Years:** 2008, 2009 **Models:** Aveo, Aveo5, Cobalt, CTS, CTS-V, CTS, CTS-V-V, DTS, Equinox, G5, , Impala, , **Engines:** All **Transmissions:** All	**Fuel Pump Control Circuit Malfunction** Engine started; system voltage from 6-18v, and the ECM detected that the Commanded state and the Actual state of the Fuel Pump control circuit did not match for 2-5 continuous seconds. **Possible Causes:** • Fuel pump relay power circuit is open (test B+ from fuse box) • Fuel pump control circuit is open or shorted to ground • Fuel pump control circuit is shorted to system power • ECM has failed
DTC: P0231 **1T CCM, MIL: Yes** **Years:** 2008, 2009 **Models:** CTS, CTS-V **Engines:** 6.2L VIN P **Transmissions:** All	**Fuel Pump Control Circuit Low Voltage** The ignition voltage is between 9-18 volts. The FPCM detects a fault on the fuel pump voltage circuit that is above or below a predetermined voltage threshold. **Possible Causes:** • FPCM control circuit for a short to voltage • FPCM control circuit for a short to ground or an open/high resistance • FPCM control circuit terminal A for a short to voltage or an open/high resistance • Fuel pump tank module has failed • FPCM has failed
DTC: P0231 **1T CCM, MIL: Yes** **Years:** 2008, 2009, 2010 **Models:** Acadia, Allure, Aura, Camaro, CTS, CTS-V, Enclave, LaCrosse, Outlook, Traverse **Engines:** 3.6L VIN 7, 3.6L VIN D, 3.6L VIN V **Transmissions:** All	**Fuel Pump Control Circuit High Voltage** The control enable voltage signal supplied for the ECM to FECM is inactive for 4 seconds after engine has been shut off. The FECM detects a fault on the fuel pump voltage circuit that is above or below a predetermined voltage threshold. **Possible Causes:** • ECM fuel pump output control circuit for a short to voltage. • ECM fuel pump output control circuit for a short to ground or an open/high resistance • FECM control circuit terminal 2 for a short to voltage or an open/high resistance • Faulty FECM • Faulty fuel tank fuel pump module
DTC: P0232 **1T CCM, MIL: Yes** **Years:** 2008, 2009 **Models:** CTS, CTS-V **Engines:** 6.2L VIN P **Transmissions:** All	**Fuel Pump Control Circuit High Voltage** The control enable voltage signal supplied for the ECM to FPCM is inactive for 4 seconds after engine has been shut off. The FPCM detects a fault on the fuel pump voltage circuit that is above or below a predetermined voltage threshold. **Possible Causes:** • FPCM control circuit for a short to voltage • FPCM control circuit for a short to ground or an open/high resistance • FPCM control circuit terminal A for a short to voltage or an open/high resistance • Fuel pump tank module has failed • FPCM has failed

DTC	Trouble Code Title, Conditions & Possible Causes
DTC: P0232 **1T CCM, MIL: Yes** **Years:** 2008, 2009, 2010 **Models:** Acadia, Allure, Aura, Camaro, CTS, CTS-V, Enclave, LaCrosse, Outlook, Traverse **Engines:** 3.6L VIN 7, 3.6L VIN D, 3.6L VIN V **Transmissions:** All	**Fuel Pump Control Circuit** The ignition voltage is between 9-18 volts. The FECM detects a fault on the fuel pump voltage circuit that is above or below a predetermined voltage threshold. **Possible Causes:** • ECM fuel pump output control circuit for a short to voltage. • ECM fuel pump output control circuit for a short to ground or an open/high resistance • FECM control circuit terminal 2 for a short to voltage or an open/high resistance • Faulty FECM • Faulty fuel tank fuel pump module
DTC: P023A **1T CCM, MIL: Yes** **Years:** 2008, 2009 **Models:** Corvette, CTS, CTS-V **Engines:** 6.2L VIN W, 6.2L VIN P, 6.2L VIN R, 7.0L VIN E **Transmissions:** All	**Charge Air Cooler (CAC) Coolant Pump Relay Control Circuit** The Intake Air Temperature (IAT) sensor 2 is greater than 0°C (32°F). The battery voltage is between 9-18V. The engine run time is greater than 10 seconds. The Charge Air Cooler (CAC) pump relay has been commanded ON. The IAT is greater than −25°C (−13°F). This DTC runs continuously when the above conditions are met. The ECM detects an improper voltage on the supercharger (SC) intercooler pump relay circuit for greater than 30 seconds. **Possible Causes:** • CAC relay control circuit for a short to voltage. • CAC relay control B+ coil supply circuit for a short to ground or an open/high resistance • CAC relay control B+ switch supply circuit for an open/high resistance • CAC pump voltage supply circuit for a short to ground • CAC pump ground circuit for an open/high resistance • CAC pump voltage supply circuit for an open/high resistance • CAC pump control circuit for a short to ground • CAC coolant pump relay has failed • CAC coolant pump has failed • ECM has failed
DTC: P023F **1T CCM, MIL: Yes** **Years:** 2008, 2009 **Models:** CTS, CTS-V **Engines:** 6.2L VIN P **Transmissions:** All	**Fuel Pump Control Circuit** The ignition voltage is between 9-18 volts. The FPCM detects a fault on the fuel pump voltage circuit that is above or below a predetermined voltage threshold. **Possible Causes:** • FPCM control circuit for a short to voltage • FPCM control circuit for a short to ground or an open/high resistance • FPCM control circuit terminal A for a short to voltage or an open/high resistance • Fuel pump tank module has failed • FPCM has failed
DTC: P023F **1T CCM, MIL: Yes** **Years:** 2008, 2009, 2010 **Models:** Acadia, Allure, Aura, Camaro, CTS, CTS-V, Enclave, LaCrosse, Outlook, Traverse **Engines:** 3.6L VIN 7, 3.6L VIN D, 3.6L VIN V **Transmissions:** All	**Supercharger Boost Solenoid Control Circuit Malfunction** Key on or engine running; and the ECM detected an unexpected voltage on the Boost Control Solenoid control circuit for 30 seconds. The ECM uses an output driver module (ODM) to enable several current-driven devices that are needed to control various engine and transaxle functions. Each ODM can control several output device functions. **Possible Causes:** • Boost solenoid circuit is open between the solenoid and ECM • Boost solenoid circuit is shorted to ground • Boost solenoid power circuit is open to system power • Boost solenoid is damaged or has failed • ECM has failed
DTC: P025A **1T CCM, MIL: Yes** **Years:** 2008, 2009 **Models:** Corvette, CTS, CTS-V **Engines:** 6.2L VIN W, 6.2L VIN P, 6.2L VIN R, 7.0L VIN E **Transmissions:** All	**Fuel Pump Control Module Enable Circuit** The ignition is ON. The serial data message from the ECM to the FPCM does not agree with the state of the control enable circuit voltage supplied from the ECM to the FPCM for more than 2 seconds. **Possible Causes:** • FPCM has failed • ECM has failed

DTC	Trouble Code Title, Conditions & Possible Causes
DTC: P0261 **1T CCM, MIL: Yes** **Years:** 2008, 2009, 2010 **Models:** Acadia, Allure, Aura, Camaro, CTS, CTS-V, Enclave, LaCrosse, Outlook, Traverse, Astra, Aura, Aveo, Aveo5, Cobalt G3, G5 **Engines:** 3.6L VIN 7, 3.6L VIN D, 3.6L VIN V, 1.6L VIN 6, 1.6L VIN E, 1.8L VIN 1, 2.0L VIN P, 2.0L VIN X, 2.2L VIN H, 2.2L VIN F, 2.4L VIN 5, 2.4L VIN B **Transmissions:** All	**Injector 1 Control Circuit High Voltage** The engine speed is greater than 80 RPM. The ignition voltage is between 8-18 volts. The injector has been commanded ON and OFF at least once. The DTCs run continuously once the above conditions are met. The ECM detects the injector low voltage control circuit is shorted to ground for greater than 4 seconds or for a cumulative of 30 seconds. **Possible Causes:** • High voltage control circuit shorted to voltage • High voltage control circuit short to ground or an open/high resistance • Low voltage control circuit shorted to voltage • Low voltage control circuit short to ground or an open/high resistance • Faulty fuel injector • ECM has failed.
DTC: P0262 **1T CCM, MIL: Yes** **Years:** 2008, 2009, 2010 **Models:** Acadia, Allure, Aura, Camaro, CTS, CTS-V, Enclave, LaCrosse, Outlook, Traverse, Astra, Aura, Aveo, Aveo5, Cobalt G3, G5 **Engines:** 3.6L VIN 7, 3.6L VIN D, 3.6L VIN V, 1.6L VIN 6, 1.6L VIN E, 1.8L VIN 1, 2.0L VIN P, 2.0L VIN X, 2.2L VIN H, 2.2L VIN F, 2.4L VIN 5, 2.4L VIN B **Transmissions:** All	**Injector 2 Control Circuit Low Voltage** The engine speed is greater than 80 RPM. The ignition voltage is between 8-18 volts. The injector has been commanded ON and OFF at least once. The DTCs run continuously once the above conditions are met. The ECM detects the injector low voltage control circuit is shorted to ground for greater than 4 seconds or for a cumulative of 30 seconds. **Possible Causes:** • High voltage control circuit shorted to voltage • High voltage control circuit short to ground or an open/high resistance • Low voltage control circuit shorted to voltage • Low voltage control circuit short to ground or an open/high resistance • Faulty fuel injector • ECM has failed.
DTC: P0264 **1T CCM, MIL: Yes** **Years:** 2008, 2009, 2010 **Models:** Acadia, Allure, Aura, Camaro, CTS, CTS-V, Enclave, LaCrosse, Outlook, Traverse, Astra, Aura, Aveo, Aveo5, Cobalt G3, G5 **Engines:** 3.6L VIN 7, 3.6L VIN D, 3.6L VIN V, 1.6L VIN 6, 1.6L VIN E, 1.8L VIN 1, 2.0L VIN P, 2.0L VIN X, 2.2L VIN H, 2.2L VIN F, 2.4L VIN 5, 2.4L VIN B **Transmissions:** All	**Injector 2 Control Circuit High Voltage** The engine speed is greater than 80 RPM. The ignition voltage is between 8-18 volts. The injector has been commanded ON and OFF at least once. The DTCs run continuously once the above conditions are met. The ECM detects the injector low voltage control circuit is shorted to ground for greater than 4 seconds or for a cumulative of 30 seconds. **Possible Causes:** • High voltage control circuit shorted to voltage • High voltage control circuit short to ground or an open/high resistance • Low voltage control circuit shorted to voltage • Low voltage control circuit short to ground or an open/high resistance • Faulty fuel injector • ECM has failed.
DTC: P0265 **1T CCM, MIL: Yes** **Years:** 2008, 2009, 2010 **Models:** Acadia, Allure, Aura, Camaro, CTS, CTS-V, Enclave, LaCrosse, Outlook, Traverse, Astra, Aura, Aveo, Aveo5, Cobalt G3, G5 **Engines:** 3.6L VIN 7, 3.6L VIN D, 3.6L VIN V, 1.6L VIN 6, 1.6L VIN E, 1.8L VIN 1, 2.0L VIN P, 2.0L VIN X, 2.2L VIN H, 2.2L VIN F, 2.4L VIN 5, 2.4L VIN B **Transmissions:** All	**Injector 3 Control Circuit Low Voltage** The engine speed is greater than 80 RPM. The ignition voltage is between 8-18 volts. The injector has been commanded ON and OFF at least once. The DTCs run continuously once the above conditions are met. The ECM detects the injector low voltage control circuit is shorted to ground for greater than 4 seconds or for a cumulative of 30 seconds. **Possible Causes:** • High voltage control circuit shorted to voltage • High voltage control circuit short to ground or an open/high resistance • Low voltage control circuit shorted to voltage • Low voltage control circuit short to ground or an open/high resistance • Faulty fuel injector • ECM has failed.

DTC	Trouble Code Title, Conditions & Possible Causes
DTC: P0267 **1T CCM, MIL: Yes** **Years:** 2008, 2009, 2010 **Models:** Acadia, Allure, Aura, Camaro, CTS, CTS-V, Enclave, LaCrosse, Outlook, Traverse, Astra, Aura, Aveo, Aveo5, Cobalt G3, G5 **Engines:** 3.6L VIN 7, 3.6L VIN D, 3.6L VIN V, 1.6L VIN 6, 1.6L VIN E, 1.8L VIN 1, 2.0L VIN P, 2.0L VIN X, 2.2L VIN H, 2.2L VIN F, 2.4L VIN 5, 2.4L VIN B **Transmissions:** All	**Injector 3 Control Circuit High Voltage** The engine speed is greater than 80 RPM. The ignition voltage is between 8-18 volts. The injector has been commanded ON and OFF at least once. The DTCs run continuously once the above conditions are met. The ECM detects the injector low voltage control circuit is shorted to ground for greater than 4 seconds or for a cumulative of 30 seconds. **Possible Causes:** • High voltage control circuit shorted to voltage • High voltage control circuit short to ground or an open/high resistance • Low voltage control circuit shorted to voltage • Low voltage control circuit short to ground or an open/high resistance • Faulty fuel injector • ECM has failed.
DTC: P0268 **1T CCM, MIL: Yes** **Years:** 2008, 2009, 2010 **Models:** Acadia, Allure, Aura, Camaro, CTS, CTS-V, Enclave, LaCrosse, Outlook, Traverse, Astra, Aura, Aveo, Aveo5, Cobalt G3, G5 **Engines:** 3.6L VIN 7, 3.6L VIN D, 3.6L VIN V, 1.6L VIN 6, 1.6L VIN E, 1.8L VIN 1, 2.0L VIN P, 2.0L VIN X, 2.2L VIN H, 2.2L VIN F, 2.4L VIN 5, 2.4L VIN B **Transmissions:** All	**Injector 4 Control Circuit Low Voltage** The engine speed is greater than 80 RPM. The ignition voltage is between 8-18 volts. The injector has been commanded ON and OFF at least once. The DTCs run continuously once the above conditions are met. The ECM detects the injector low voltage control circuit is shorted to ground for greater than 4 seconds or for a cumulative of 30 seconds. **Possible Causes:** • High voltage control circuit shorted to voltage • High voltage control circuit short to ground or an open/high resistance • Low voltage control circuit shorted to voltage • Low voltage control circuit short to ground or an open/high resistance • Faulty fuel injector • ECM has failed.
DTC: P0270 **1T CCM, MIL: Yes** **Years:** 2008, 2009, 2010 **Models:** Acadia, Allure, Aura, Camaro, CTS, CTS-V, Enclave, LaCrosse, Outlook, Traverse, Astra, Aura, Aveo, Aveo5, Cobalt G3, G5 **Engines:** 3.6L VIN 7, 3.6L VIN D, 3.6L VIN V, 1.6L VIN 6, 1.6L VIN E, 1.8L VIN 1, 2.0L VIN P, 2.0L VIN X, 2.2L VIN H, 2.2L VIN F, 2.4L VIN 5, 2.4L VIN B **Transmissions:** All	**Injector 4 Control Circuit High Voltage** The engine speed is greater than 80 RPM. The ignition voltage is between 8-18 volts. The injector has been commanded ON and OFF at least once. The DTCs run continuously once the above conditions are met. The ECM detects the injector low voltage control circuit is shorted to ground for greater than 4 seconds or for a cumulative of 30 seconds. **Possible Causes:** • High voltage control circuit shorted to voltage • High voltage control circuit short to ground or an open/high resistance • Low voltage control circuit shorted to voltage • Low voltage control circuit short to ground or an open/high resistance • Faulty fuel injector • ECM has failed.
DTC: P0271 **1T CCM, MIL: Yes** **Years:** 2008, 2009, 2010 **Models:** Acadia, Allure, Aura, Camaro, CTS, CTS-V, Enclave, LaCrosse, Outlook, Traverse, Astra, Aura, Aveo, Aveo5, Cobalt G3, G5 **Engines:** 3.6L VIN 7, 3.6L VIN D, 3.6L VIN V, 1.6L VIN 6, 1.6L VIN E, 1.8L VIN 1, 2.0L VIN P, 2.0L VIN X, 2.2L VIN H, 2.2L VIN F, 2.4L VIN 5, 2.4L VIN B **Transmissions:** All	**Injector 5 Control Circuit Low Voltage** The engine speed is greater than 80 RPM. The ignition voltage is between 8-18 volts. The injector has been commanded ON and OFF at least once. The DTCs run continuously once the above conditions are met. The ECM detects the injector low voltage control circuit is shorted to ground for greater than 4 seconds or for a cumulative of 30 seconds. **Possible Causes:** • High voltage control circuit shorted to voltage • High voltage control circuit short to ground or an open/high resistance • Low voltage control circuit shorted to voltage • Low voltage control circuit short to ground or an open/high resistance • Faulty fuel injector • ECM has failed.

DTC	Trouble Code Title, Conditions & Possible Causes
DTC: P0273 **1T CCM, MIL: Yes** **Years:** 2008, 2009, 2010 **Models:** Acadia, Allure, Aura, Camaro, CTS, CTS-V, Enclave, LaCrosse, Outlook, Traverse **Engines:** 3.6L VIN 7, 3.6L VIN D, 3.6L VIN V **Transmissions:** All	**Injector 5 Control Circuit High Voltage** The engine speed is greater than 80 RPM. The ignition voltage is between 8-18 volts. The injector has been commanded ON and OFF at least once. The DTCs run continuously once the above conditions are met. The ECM detects the injector low voltage control circuit is shorted to ground for greater than 4 seconds or for a cumulative of 30 seconds. **Possible Causes:** • High voltage control circuit shorted to voltage • High voltage control circuit short to ground or an open/high resistance • Low voltage control circuit shorted to voltage • Low voltage control circuit short to ground or an open/high resistance • Faulty fuel injector • ECM has failed.
DTC: P0274 **1T CCM, MIL: Yes** **Years:** 2008, 2009, 2010 **Models:** Acadia, Allure, Aura, Camaro, CTS, CTS-V, Enclave, LaCrosse, Outlook, Traverse **Engines:** 3.6L VIN 7, 3.6L VIN D, 3.6L VIN V **Transmissions:** All	**Injector 6 Control Circuit Low Voltage** The engine speed is greater than 80 RPM. The ignition voltage is between 8-18 volts. The injector has been commanded ON and OFF at least once. The DTCs run continuously once the above conditions are met. The ECM detects the injector low voltage control circuit is shorted to ground for greater than 4 seconds or for a cumulative of 30 seconds. **Possible Causes:** • High voltage control circuit shorted to voltage • High voltage control circuit short to ground or an open/high resistance • Low voltage control circuit shorted to voltage • Low voltage control circuit short to ground or an open/high resistance • Faulty fuel injector • ECM has failed.
DTC: P0276 **1T CCM, MIL: Yes** **Years:** 2008, 2009, 2010 **Models:** Acadia, Allure, Aura, Camaro, CTS, CTS-V, Enclave, LaCrosse, Outlook, Traverse **Engines:** 3.6L VIN 7, 3.6L VIN D, 3.6L VIN V **Transmissions:** All	**Injector 6 Control Circuit High Voltage** The engine speed is greater than 80 RPM. The ignition voltage is between 8-18 volts. The injector has been commanded ON and OFF at least once. The DTCs run continuously once the above conditions are met. The ECM detects the injector low voltage control circuit is shorted to ground for greater than 4 seconds or for a cumulative of 30 seconds. **Possible Causes:** • High voltage control circuit shorted to voltage • High voltage control circuit short to ground or an open/high resistance • Low voltage control circuit shorted to voltage • Low voltage control circuit short to ground or an open/high resistance • Faulty fuel injector • ECM has failed.
DTC: P0277 **1T CCM, MIL: Yes** **Years:** 2008, 2009, 2010 **Models:** Acadia, Allure, Aura, Camaro, CTS, CTS-V, Enclave, LaCrosse, Outlook, Traverse **Engines:** 3.6L VIN 7, 3.6L VIN D, 3.6L VIN V **Transmissions:** All	**Injector 1 Leak** The engine speed is between 1,520-6,000 RPM The engine load is less than 100 percent. The misfire monitor is enabled. DTC P029D runs continuously once the conditions above have been met for approximately 20 seconds. The ECM detects a specific cylinder misfire rate of greater than 100 counts in less than 17 engine revolutions, and P0087 is set. The condition exists for greater than 4 seconds or for a cumulative of 30 seconds. **Possible Causes:** • Test or replace the appropriate fuel injector
DTC: P029D **1T CCM, MIL: Yes** **Years:** 2008, 2009, 2010 **Models:** Acadia, Allure, Aura, Camaro, CTS, CTS-V, Enclave, LaCrosse, Outlook, Traverse **Engines:** 3.6L VIN 7, 3.6L VIN D, 3.6L VIN V **Transmissions:** All	**Injector 2 Leak** The engine speed is between 1,520-6,000 RPM The engine load is less than 100 percent. The misfire monitor is enabled. DTC P02A5 runs continuously once the conditions above have been met for approximately 20 seconds. The ECM detects a specific cylinder misfire rate of greater than 100 counts in less than 17 engine revolutions, and P0087 is set. The condition exists for greater than 4 seconds or for a cumulative of 30 seconds. **Possible Causes:** • Test or replace the appropriate fuel injector
DTC: P02A5 **1T CCM, MIL: Yes** **Years:** 2008, 2009, 2010 **Models:** Acadia, Allure, Aura, Camaro, CTS, CTS-V, Enclave, LaCrosse, Outlook, Traverse **Engines:** 3.6L VIN 7, 3.6L VIN D, 3.6L VIN V **Transmissions:** All	**Injector 3 Leak** The engine speed is between 1,520-6,000 RPM The engine load is less than 100 percent. The misfire monitor is enabled. DTC P02A9 runs continuously once the conditions above have been met for approximately 20 seconds. The ECM detects a specific cylinder misfire rate of greater than 100 counts in less than 17 engine revolutions, and P0087 is set. The condition exists for greater than 4 seconds or for a cumulative of 30 seconds. **Possible Causes:** • Test or replace the appropriate fuel injector

DTC	Trouble Code Title, Conditions & Possible Causes
DTC: P02A9 **1T CCM, MIL: Yes** **Years:** 2008, 2009, 2010 **Models:** Acadia, Allure, Aura, Camaro, CTS, CTS-V, Enclave, LaCrosse, Outlook, Traverse **Engines:** 3.6L VIN 7, 3.6L VIN D, 3.6L VIN V **Transmissions:** All	**Injector 4 Leak** The engine speed is between 1,520-6,000 RPM The engine load is less than 100 percent. The misfire monitor is enabled. DTC P02AD runs continuously once the conditions above have been met for approximately 20 seconds. The ECM detects a specific cylinder misfire rate of greater than 100 counts in less than 17 engine revolutions, and P0087 is set. The condition exists for greater than 4 seconds or for a cumulative of 30 seconds. **Possible Causes:** • Test or replace the appropriate fuel injector
DTC: P02AD **1T CCM, MIL: Yes** **Years:** 2008, 2009, 2010 **Models:** Acadia, Allure, Aura, Camaro, CTS, CTS-V, Enclave, LaCrosse, Outlook, Traverse **Engines:** 3.6L VIN 7, 3.6L VIN D, 3.6L VIN V **Transmissions:** All	**Injector 6 Leak** The engine speed is between 1,520-6,000 RPM The engine load is less than 100 percent. The misfire monitor is enabled. DTC P02B1 runs continuously once the conditions above have been met for approximately 20 seconds. The ECM detects a specific cylinder misfire rate of greater than 100 counts in less than 17 engine revolutions, and P0087 is set. The condition exists for greater than 4 seconds or for a cumulative of 30 seconds. **Possible Causes:** • Test or replace the appropriate fuel injector
DTC: P02B1 **1T CCM, MIL: Yes** **Years:** 2008, 2009, 2010 **Models:** Acadia, Allure, Aura, Camaro, CTS, CTS-V, Enclave, LaCrosse, Outlook, Traverse **Engines:** 3.6L VIN 7, 3.6L VIN D, 3.6L VIN V **Transmissions:** All	**Multiple Engine Misfire Detected** The ECM detects a crankshaft rotation speed variation indicating a single cylinder misfire rate sufficient to cause emissions levels to exceed mandated standards. The ECM disables the fuel injector of the misfiring cylinder when a misfire is present. **Possible Causes:** • Base engine mechanical fault that affects one or more cylinders • Fuel metering fault (high fuel pressure or fuel contaminated) • EVAP system problem or the EVAP canister is fuel saturated • EGR valve is stuck open or the PCV system has a vacuum leak • Ignition system fault (a coil) that affects more than one cylinder • MAF sensor contamination (it can cause a very lean condition)
DTC: P0300 **2T CCM, MIL: Yes** **Years:** 2008, 2009, 2010 **Models:**, Acadia, Allure, Astra, Aura, Avalanche, Escalade/EXT/ESV, Suburban, Tahoe, Yukon, Escalade/EXT/ESV, Suburban, Tahoe, Yukon Aveo, Aveo5, Camaro, Cobalt, Cobalt-GS, Colorado,Canyon, Corvette, CTS, CTS-V, CTS, CTS-V-V, DTS, Escalade/EXT/ESV, G.3, G5,Enclave, LaCrosse, Outlook, Suburban, Tahoe Traverse, Yukon **Engines:** All **Transmissions:** All	**Multiple Engine Misfire Detected** DTC P0101-P0103, P0116-P0118, P0121-P0123, P0125, P0335, P0336, P0341-P0343, P0500-P0503 and P1258 not set, engine speed from 450-3000 RPM, system voltage over 10.0v, ECT sensor from 19-230°F, fuel level over 10%, TP angle steady (1%), ABS and Traction Control inactive, ABS signal not indicating rough road thresholds, transmission not shifting, A/C clutch stable, AIR Test and DFCO "off", and the PCM detected a crankshaft speed variation in two or more cylinders characteristic of a misfire condition. **Note: If the misfire is severe, the MIL will flash on/off on the 1st trip!** **Possible Causes:** • Base engine mechanical fault that affects one or more cylinders • Fuel metering fault that affects more than one cylinder • Fuel pressure too low or too high, fuel supply contaminated • EVAP system problem or the EVAP canister is fuel saturated • EGR valve is stuck open or the PCV system has a vacuum leak • IC control circuit is shorted to ground (an intermittent fault) • Ignition system fault (a coil) that affects more than one cylinder • MAF sensor contamination (it can cause a very lean condition)
DTC: P0301 **2T CCM, MIL: Yes** **Years:** 2008, 2009, 2010 **Models:**, Acadia, Allure, Astra, Aura, Avalanche, Escalade/EXT/ESV, Suburban, Tahoe, Yukon, Escalade/EXT/ESV, Suburban, Tahoe, Yukon Aveo, Aveo5, Camaro, Cobalt, Cobalt-GS, Colorado,Canyon, Corvette, CTS, CTS-V, CTS, CTS-V-V, DTS, Escalade/EXT/ESV, G.3, G5,Enclave, LaCrosse, Outlook, Suburban, Tahoe Traverse, Yukon **Engines:** All **Transmissions:** All	**Cylinder 1 Misfire Detected** The ECM detects a crankshaft rotation speed variation indicating a single cylinder misfire rate sufficient to cause emissions levels to exceed mandated standards. The ECM disables the fuel injector of the misfiring cylinder when a misfire is present. **Note: A misfire DTC could be caused by an excessive vibration from sources other than the engine. If the misfire is severe, the MIL will flash on/off on the 1st trip!** **Possible Causes:** • Air leak in the intake manifold, or in the EGR or PCV system • Base engine mechanical fault that affects only Cylinder 1 • Fuel delivery component fault that affects only Cylinder 1 (i.e., a contaminated, dirty or sticking fuel injector) • Ignition system problem (coil, plug) that affects only Cylinder 1

DTC	Trouble Code Title, Conditions & Possible Causes
DTC: P0302 **2T CCM, MIL: Yes** **Years:** 2008, 2009, 2010 **Models:**, Acadia, Allure, Astra, Aura, Avalanche, Escalade/EXT/ESV, Suburban, Tahoe, Yukon, Escalade/EXT/ESV, Suburban, Tahoe, Yukon Aveo, Aveo5, Camaro, Cobalt, Cobalt-GS, Colorado,Canyon, Corvette, CTS, CTS-V, CTS, CTS-V-V, DTS, Escalade/EXT/ESV, G.3, G5,Enclave, LaCrosse, Outlook, Suburban, Tahoe Traverse, Yukon **Engines:** All **Transmissions:** All	**Cylinder 2 Misfire Detected** The ECM detects a crankshaft rotation speed variation indicating a single cylinder misfire rate sufficient to cause emissions levels to exceed mandated standards. The ECM disables the fuel injector of the misfiring cylinder when a misfire is present. **Note: A misfire DTC could be caused by an excessive vibration from sources other than the engine. If the misfire is severe, the MIL will flash on/off on the 1st trip!** **Possible Causes:** • Air leak in the intake manifold, or in the EGR or PCV system • Base engine mechanical fault that affects only Cylinder 2 • Fuel delivery component fault that affects only Cylinder 2 (i.e., a contaminated, dirty or sticking fuel injector) • Ignition system problem (coil, plug) that affects only Cylinder 2
DTC: P0303 **2T CCM, MIL: Yes** **Years:** 2008, 2009, 2010 **Models:**, Acadia, Allure, Astra, Aura, Avalanche, Escalade/EXT/ESV, Suburban, Tahoe, Yukon, Escalade/EXT/ESV, Suburban, Tahoe, Yukon Aveo, Aveo5, Camaro, Cobalt, Cobalt-GS, Colorado,Canyon, Corvette, CTS, CTS-V, CTS, CTS-V-V, DTS, Escalade/EXT/ESV, G.3, G5,Enclave, LaCrosse, Outlook, Suburban, Tahoe Traverse, Yukon **Engines:** All **Transmissions:** All	**Cylinder 3 Misfire Detected** The ECM detects a crankshaft rotation speed variation indicating a single cylinder misfire rate sufficient to cause emissions levels to exceed mandated standards. The ECM disables the fuel injector of the misfiring cylinder when a misfire is present. **Note: A misfire DTC could be caused by an excessive vibration from sources other than the engine. If the misfire is severe, the MIL will flash on/off on the 1st trip!** **Possible Causes:** • Air leak in the intake manifold, or in the EGR or PCV system • Base engine mechanical fault that affects only Cylinder 3 • Fuel delivery component fault that affects only Cylinder 3 (i.e., a contaminated, dirty or sticking fuel injector) • Ignition system problem (coil, plug) that affects only Cylinder 3
DTC: P0304 **2T CCM, MIL: Yes** **Years:** 2008, 2009, 2010 **Models:**, Acadia, Allure, Astra, Aura, Avalanche, Escalade/EXT/ESV, Suburban, Tahoe, Yukon, Escalade/EXT/ESV, Suburban, Tahoe, Yukon Aveo, Aveo5, Camaro, Cobalt, Cobalt-GS, Colorado,Canyon, Corvette, CTS, CTS-V, CTS, CTS-V-V, DTS, Escalade/EXT/ESV, G.3, G5,Enclave, LaCrosse, Outlook, Suburban, Tahoe Traverse, Yukon **Engines:** All **Transmissions:** All	**Cylinder 4 Misfire Detected** The ECM detects a crankshaft rotation speed variation indicating a single cylinder misfire rate sufficient to cause emissions levels to exceed mandated standards. The ECM disables the fuel injector of the misfiring cylinder when a misfire is present. **Note: A misfire DTC could be caused by an excessive vibration from sources other than the engine. If the misfire is severe, the MIL will flash on/off on the 1st trip!** **Possible Causes:** • Air leak in the intake manifold, or in the EGR or PCV system • Base engine mechanical fault that affects only Cylinder 4 • Fuel delivery component fault that affects only Cylinder 4 (i.e., a contaminated, dirty or sticking fuel injector) • Ignition system problem (coil, plug) that affects only Cylinder 4

DTC	Trouble Code Title, Conditions & Possible Causes
DTC: P0305 **2T CCM, MIL: Yes** **Years:** 2008, 2009, 2010 **Models:** Acadia, Allure, Astra, Aura, Avalanche, Escalade/EXT/ESV, Suburban, Tahoe, Yukon, Escalade/EXT/ESV, Suburban, Tahoe, Yukon Aveo, Aveo5, Camaro, Cobalt, Cobalt-GS, Colorado,Canyon, Corvette, CTS, CTS-V, CTS, CTS-V-V, DTS, Escalade/EXT/ESV, G.3, G5,Enclave, LaCrosse, Outlook, Suburban, Tahoe Traverse, Yukon **Engines:** All **Transmissions:** All	**Cylinder 5 Misfire Detected** The ECM detects a crankshaft rotation speed variation indicating a single cylinder misfire rate sufficient to cause emissions levels to exceed mandated standards. The ECM disables the fuel injector of the misfiring cylinder when a misfire is present. **Note: A misfire DTC could be caused by an excessive vibration from sources other than the engine. If the misfire is severe, the MIL will flash on/off on the 1st trip!** **Possible Causes:** • Air leak in the intake manifold, or in the EGR or PCV system • Base engine mechanical fault that affects only Cylinder 5 • Fuel delivery component fault that affects only Cylinder 5 (i.e., a contaminated, dirty or sticking fuel injector) • Ignition system problem (coil, plug) that affects only Cylinder 5
DTC: P0306 **2T CCM, MIL: Yes** **Years:** 2008, 2009, 2010 **Models:** Acadia, Allure, Astra, Aura, Avalanche, Escalade/EXT/ESV, Suburban, Tahoe, Yukon, Escalade/EXT/ESV, Suburban, Tahoe, Yukon Aveo, Aveo5, Camaro, Cobalt, Cobalt-GS, Colorado,Canyon, Corvette, CTS, CTS-V, CTS, CTS-V-V, DTS, Escalade/EXT/ESV, G.3, G5,Enclave, LaCrosse, Outlook, Suburban, Tahoe Traverse, Yukon **Engines:** 6 & 8 Cylinders **Transmissions:** All	**Cylinder 6 Misfire Detected** The ECM detects a crankshaft rotation speed variation indicating a single cylinder misfire rate sufficient to cause emissions levels to exceed mandated standards. The ECM disables the fuel injector of the misfiring cylinder when a misfire is present. **Note: A misfire DTC could be caused by an excessive vibration from sources other than the engine. If the misfire is severe, the MIL will flash on/off on the 1st trip!** **Possible Causes:** • Air leak in the intake manifold, or in the EGR or PCV system • Base engine mechanical fault that affects only Cylinder 6 • Fuel delivery component fault that affects only Cylinder 6 (i.e., a contaminated, dirty or sticking fuel injector) • Ignition system problem (coil, plug) that affects only Cylinder 6
DTC: P0307 **2T CCM, MIL: Yes** **Years:** 2008, 2009, 2010 **Models:** Acadia, Allure, Astra, Aura, Avalanche, Escalade/EXT/ESV, Suburban, Tahoe, Yukon, Escalade/EXT/ESV, Suburban, Tahoe, Yukon Aveo, Aveo5, Camaro, Cobalt, Cobalt-GS, Colorado,Canyon, Corvette, CTS, CTS-V, CTS, CTS-V-V, DTS, Escalade/EXT/ESV, G.3, G5,Enclave, LaCrosse, Outlook, Suburban, Tahoe Traverse, Yukon **Engines:** 6 & 8 Cylinders **Transmissions:** All	**Cylinder 7 Misfire Detected** The ECM detects a crankshaft rotation speed variation indicating a single cylinder misfire rate sufficient to cause emissions levels to exceed mandated standards. The ECM disables the fuel injector of the misfiring cylinder when a misfire is present. **Note: A misfire DTC could be caused by an excessive vibration from sources other than the engine. If the misfire is severe, the MIL will flash on/off on the 1st trip!** **Possible Causes:** • Air leak in the intake manifold, or in the EGR or PCV system • Base engine mechanical fault that affects only Cylinder 7 • Fuel delivery component fault that affects only Cylinder 7 (i.e., a contaminated, dirty or sticking fuel injector) • Ignition system problem (coil, plug) that affects only Cylinder 7

DTC	Trouble Code Title, Conditions & Possible Causes
DTC: P0308 **2T CCM, MIL: Yes** **Years:** 2008, 2009, 2010 **Models:**, Acadia, Allure, Astra, Aura, Avalanche, Escalade/EXT/ESV, Suburban, Tahoe, Yukon, Escalade/EXT/ESV, Suburban, Tahoe, Yukon Aveo, Aveo5, Camaro, Cobalt, Cobalt-GS, Colorado,Canyon, Corvette, CTS, CTS-V, CTS, CTS-V-V, DTS, Escalade/EXT/ESV, G.3, G5,Enclave, LaCrosse, Outlook, Suburban, Tahoe Traverse, Yukon **Engines:** All 8 Cylinders **Transmissions:** All	**Cylinder 8 Misfire Detected** The ECM detects a crankshaft rotation speed variation indicating a single cylinder misfire rate sufficient to cause emissions levels to exceed mandated standards. The ECM disables the fuel injector of the misfiring cylinder when a misfire is present. **Note: A misfire DTC could be caused by an excessive vibration from sources other than the engine. If the misfire is severe, the MIL will flash on/off on the 1st trip!** **Possible Causes:** • Air leak in the intake manifold, or in the EGR or PCV system • Base engine mechanical fault that affects only Cylinder 8 • Fuel delivery component fault that affects only Cylinder 8 (i.e., a contaminated, dirty or sticking fuel injector) • Ignition system problem (coil, plug) that affects only Cylinder 8
DTC: P0313 **2T CCM, MIL: Yes** **Years:** 2008, 2009, 2010 **Models:**, Acadia, Allure, Astra, Aura, Avalanche, Escalade/EXT/ESV, Suburban, Tahoe, Yukon, Escalade/EXT/ESV, Suburban, Tahoe, Yukon Aveo, Aveo5, Camaro, Cobalt, Cobalt-GS, Colorado,Canyon, Corvette, CTS, CTS-V, CTS, CTS-V-V, DTS, Escalade/EXT/ESV, G.3, G5,Enclave, LaCrosse, Outlook, Suburban, Tahoe Traverse, Yukon **Engines:** All 8 Cylinders **Transmissions:** All	**Misfire Detected With Low Fuel Level** DTCs P0016, P0101, P0102, P0103, P0121, P0122, P0123, P0221, P0222, P0223, P0335, P0336 or P1101 are not set. The engine speed is between 600-6,528 RPM. The ECM is not in fuel cut-off mode. DTCs P0313 runs continuously when the above conditions are met. **Possible Causes:** • Damaged reluctor wheel • Damaged accessory drive component or belt • Certain rough road conditions • Variable thickness brake rotors • Tire or wheel that is out of round or out of balance • Engine vacuum leaks • Fuel pressure that is too low or too high • Contaminated fuel • Restricted exhaust system
DTC: P0313 **1T CCM, MIL: Yes** **Years:** 2008, 2009 **Models:** Astra, Aura, Aveo, Aveo5, Cobalt G3, G5 **Engines:** 1.6L VIN 6, 1.6L VIN E, 1.8L VIN 1, 2.0L VIN P, 2.0L VIN X, 2.2L VIN H, 2.2L VIN F, 2.4L VIN 5, 2.4L VIN B **Transmissions:** All	**Crankshaft Position (CKP) System Variation Not Learned** The diagnostic runs continuously. The ECM detects that the CKP system variation values are not stored in memory. **Possible Causes:** • Any worn crankshaft main bearings • Damaged or misaligned reluctor wheel • Excessive crankshaft runout • A damaged crankshaft • Interference in the signal circuit of the CKP sensor • Ignition switch is left in the ON position, until the battery is discharged • ECM power disconnect, with the ignition ON, that may have erased the CKP system variation values • Debris between the CKP sensor and the reluctor wheel • CKP System lost Variation Learn Procedure • ECM has failed
DTC: P0315 **1T CCM, MIL: Yes** **Years:** 2008, 2009 **Models:** Corvette, CTS, CTS-V, DTS **Engines:** 4.6L VIN Y, 6.2L VIN W, 6.2L VIN P, 6.2L VIN R, 7.0L VIN E **Transmissions:** All	**Crankshaft Position (CKP) System Variation Not Learned** The diagnostic runs continuously. The ECM detects that the CKP system variation values are not stored in memory. **Possible Causes:** • Worn crankshaft main bearings • Damaged or misaligned reluctor wheel • Excessive crankshaft runout • Damaged crankshaft • Interference in the signal circuit of the CKP sensor • The ignition switch is left in the ON position, until the battery is discharged • An ECM power disconnect, with the ignition ON, that may have erased the CKP system variation values and set DTC P0315 • Any debris between the CKP sensor and the reluctor wheel • ECM has failed

DTC	Trouble Code Title, Conditions & Possible Causes
DTC: P0315 **1T CCM, MIL: Yes** **Years:** 2008, 2009 **Models:** Allure, Aura, Canyon, Colorado, LaCrosse **Engines:** 2.9L VIN 9, 3.5L VIN N, 3.8L VIN 2, 5.3L VIN C, 5.3L VIN L **Transmissions:** All	**Crankshaft Position Sensor Variation Not Learned** DTC P0335, P0336, P0341, P0342 and P0343 not set, engine started, ECT sensor more than 149°F, and the ECM determined the CKP sensor variation values were not stored in memory. The CKP System variation "learning" feature is used to calculate reference period errors caused by slight tolerance variations in the crankshaft and the CKP sensor. The calculated error Allows the ECM to accurately compensate for reference period variations. The ECM stores CKP variation values after a learn procedure is done. **Possible Causes:** • CKP sensor signal circuit has an interference condition (EMI) • Crankshaft main bearings worn or reluctor wheel is damaged • Crankshaft run-out is excessive or the crankshaft is damaged • ECT sensor not within the conditions for running the code test • Ignition switch is on, but the battery has insufficient voltage • ECM power disconnected with key on (erases learned values) • Debris that passes between the CKP sensor and reluctor wheel
DTC: P0324 **1T CCM, MIL: Yes** **Years:** 2008, 2009 **Models:** Corvette, CTS, CTS-V, DTS **Engines:** 4.6L VIN Y, 6.2L VIN W, 6.2L VIN P, 6.2L VIN R, 7.0L VIN E **Transmissions:** All	**Knock Sensor (KS) Module Performance** DTC P0325, P0326, P0327, P0328, P0330, P0332, or P0333 is not set. The engine speed is greater than 300 RPM. The engine air flow is greater than 50 mg/cylinder. DTC P0324 runs continuously when the above conditions are met. The ECM has detected an internal circuitry fault. **Possible Causes:** • KS sensor signal circuit for a short to ground or an open/high resistance • KS sensor signal circuit for a short to voltage • KS sensor low reference circuit for a short to ground or an open/high resistance • KS sensor • KS sensor has failed • ECM has failed
DTC: P0324 **1T CCM, MIL: Yes** **Years:** 2008, 2009 **Models:** Allure, Aura, Canyon, Colorado, LaCrosse **Engines:** 2.9L VIN 9, 3.5L VIN N, 3.8L VIN 2, 5.3L VIN C, 5.3L VIN L **Transmissions:** All	**Knock Sensor (KS) Module Performance** The ECM is controlling spark. The engine coolant temperature is warmer than 60°C (140°F). DTC P0324 runs continuously once the above conditions are met. The ECM detects an incorrect response to the self tests performed on the internal KS circuitry. The condition exists for greater than 1 seconds or for a cumulative of 10 seconds. **Note: If you can hear an engine knock, repair the engine mechanical condition before proceeding with this diagnostic.** **Possible Causes:** • Knock sensor signal circuit is open, shorted to ground or power • Knock sensor ground circuit is open (i.e., not mounted properly) • Knock sensor is damaged or has failed • ECM has failed.
DTC: P0324 **1T CCM, MIL: Yes** **Years:** 2008, 2009, 2010 **Models:** Acadia, Allure, Aura, Camaro, Corvette, CTS, CTS-V, DTS, Enclave, LaCrosse, Outlook, Traverse **Engines:** 3.6L VIN 7, 3.6L VIN D, 3.6L VIN V 4.6L VIN Y, 6.2L VIN P, 7.0L VIN E **Transmissions:** All	**Knock Sensor (KS) Circuit (Bank 1)** DTC P0324, P0326, P0327, P0328, P0330, P0332, or P0333 is not set. The engine speed is greater than 400 RPM. The Engine Coolant Temperature (ECT) is greater than −40°C (−40°F). The engine run time is greater than 2 minutes. DTCs P0325 and P0330 run continuously when the above conditions are met. **Possible Causes:** • KS circuits A and B for a short to ground or an open/high resistance • KS circuits A and B for a short to voltage • KS sensor has failed • ECM has failed
DTC: P0325 **1T CCM, MIL: Yes** **Years:** 2008, 2009 **Models:** Corvette, CTS, CTS-V, DTS **Engines:** 4.6L VIN Y, 6.2L VIN W, 6.2L VIN P, 6.2L VIN R, 7.0L VIN E **Transmissions:** All	**Knock Sensor (KS) Circuit (Bank 1)** DTC P0324, P0325, P0326, P0327, P0328, P0330, P0332, or P0333 is not set. The engine speed is greater than 400 RPM. The Engine Coolant Temperature (ECT) is greater than −40°C (−40°F). The engine run time is greater than 2 minutes. DTCs P0325 and P0330 run continuously when the above conditions are met. The KS signal circuits are open or shorted together for 5 seconds. **Possible Causes:** • KS sensor signal circuit for a short to ground or an open/high resistance • KS sensor signal circuit for a short to voltage • KS sensor low reference circuit for a short to ground or an open/high resistance • KS sensor • KS sensor has failed • ECM has failed

DTC	Trouble Code Title, Conditions & Possible Causes
DTC: P0325 **1T CCM, MIL: Yes** **Years:** 2008, 2009 **Models:** Allure, Aura, Canyon, Colorado, LaCrosse **Engines:** 2.9L VIN 9, 3.5L VIN N, 3.8L VIN 2, 5.3L VIN C, 5.3L VIN L **Transmissions:** All	**Knock Sensor (KS) Circuit** DTCs P0335, P0336, P0340, P0341, P0365, P0366, P0601, P0602, or P0604 are not set. The engine speed is greater than 2,500 RPM. The mass air flow (MAF) is greater than 20 g/s. The engine is NOT in decel fuel cut-off. The KS signal voltage is above or below a calibrated range for 20 engine revolutions. **Note: If the KS lead is damaged in any way, replace the KS.** **Possible Causes:** • Knock sensor signal circuit is open, shorted to ground or power • Knock sensor ground circuit is open (i.e., not mounted properly) • Knock sensor is damaged or has failed • ECM has failed.
DTC: P0325 **1T CCM, MIL: Yes** **Years:** 2008, 2009 **Models:** Astra, Aura, Aveo, Aveo5, Cobalt G3, G5 **Engines:** 1.6L VIN 6, 1.6L VIN E, 1.8L VIN 1, 2.0L VIN P, 2.0L VIN X, 2.2L VIN H, 2.2L VIN F, 2.4L VIN 5, 2.4L VIN B **Transmissions:** All	**Knock Sensor Circuit Malfunction** DTC P0122 and P0123 not set, engine started, vehicle driven at an engine speed of 1600-6400 RPM for 20 seconds, ECT sensor over 131°F, MAP sensor more than 60 kPa, and the ECM detected the KS sensor signal variation was out of normal range for 15 seconds. **Possible Causes:** • Knock sensor signal circuit is open, shorted to ground or power • Knock sensor ground circuit is open (not mounted properly) • Knock sensor is damaged or has failed • On modules with an integrated sensor, clear the codes and retest for codes. If the same code resets, the ECM has failed.
DTC: P0325 **1T CCM, MIL: Yes** **Years:** 2008, 2009, 2010 **Models:** Acadia, Allure, Aura, Camaro, Corvette, CTS, CTS-V, DTS, Enclave, LaCrosse, Outlook, Traverse **Engines:** 3.6L VIN 7, 3.6L VIN D, 3.6L VIN V 4.6L VIN Y, 6.2L VIN P, 7.0L VIN E **Transmissions:** All	**Knock Sensor Circuit Malfunction** DTC P0327 not set, engine started, engine runtime from 10 seconds to 2 minutes, system voltage over 10.0v and the ECM detected an unexpected voltage condition for a period of 5-25 seconds on the diagnostic circuit used during diagnosis of the Knock sensor. **Possible Causes:** • Knock sensor signal circuit is open, shorted to ground or power • Knock sensor ground circuit is open (i.e., not mounted properly) • Knock sensor is damaged or has failed • On modules with an integrated sensor, clear the codes and retest for codes. If the same code resets, the ECM has failed.
DTC: P0325 **2T CCM, MIL: Yes** **Years:** 2008, 2009, 2010 **Models:** Avalanche, Camaro, Canyon, Escalade/EXT/ESV, Suburban, Tahoe, Yukon **Engines:** 4.8L VIN C, 5.3L VIN 0, 5.3L VIN 3, 5.3L VIN J, 5.3L VIN L, 6.0L VIN K, 6.0L VIN Y, 6.2L VIN J, 6.2L VIN W, 6.2L VIN 8 **Transmissions:** All	**Knock Sensor Circuit Malfunction** DTC P0101, P0102, P0103, P0116, P0117, P0118, P0121, P0122, P0123, P0125, P0336, P0341, P0502, P0503, P1114, P1115, P1121, P1122 and P1336 are not set, engine speed from 1000-5000 RPM for 30 seconds, TP sensor over 15%, engine load over 45%, ECT sensor over 140°F, spark retard less than 15 degrees, and the ECM detected an unexpected voltage condition on the Knock Sensor circuit used by the ECM to test the sensor. **Possible Causes:** • Knock sensor signal circuit is open, shorted to ground or power • Knock sensor ground circuit is open (i.e., not mounted properly) • Knock sensor is damaged or has failed • On modules with an integrated sensor, clear the codes and retest for codes. If the same code resets, the ECM has failed.
DTC: P0326 **1T CCM, MIL: Yes** **Years:** 2008, 2009 **Models:** Corvette, CTS, CTS-V, DTS **Engines:** 4.6L VIN Y, 6.2L VIN W, 6.2L VIN P, 6.2L VIN R, 7.0L VIN E **Transmissions:** All	**Knock Sensor (KS) Performance** DTC P0068, P0120, P0121, P0122, P0123, P0220, P0222, P0223, P0606, P1516, P2101, P2135, or P2176 is not set. The engine speed is greater than 400 RPM. The Manifold Air Pressure (MAP) is greater than 10 kPa. DTC P0326 runs continuously when the above conditions are met. The KS signal indicates an engine knock is present. The ECM has commanded the spark retard to a value which is more than the calibrated valve, for a specific engine load and speed. The above conditions exist for more than 5 seconds. **Possible Causes:** • KS sensor signal circuit for a short to ground or an open/high resistance • KS sensor signal circuit for a short to voltage • KS sensor low reference circuit for a short to ground or an open/high resistance • KS sensor • KS sensor has failed • ECM has failed

DTC	Trouble Code Title, Conditions & Possible Causes
DTC: P0326 **1T CCM, MIL: Yes** **Years:** 2008, 2009 **Models:** Allure, Aura, Canyon, Colorado, LaCrosse **Engines:** 2.9L VIN 9, 3.5L VIN N, 3.8L VIN 2, 5.3L VIN C, 5.3L VIN L **Transmissions:** All	**Knock Sensor (KS) System Performance (Bank 1)** The Engine Coolant Temperature (ECT) sensor is warmer than 60°C (140°F). The engine speed is greater than 2,200 RPM. DTC P0326 runs continuously once the above conditions are met for approximately 20 seconds. The ECM detects a short to ground or a voltage on the KS signal circuits in 25 of 250 test samples. The condition exists for greater than 1 second or for a cumulative of 10 seconds. **Possible Causes:** • Knock sensor signal circuit is open, shorted to ground or power • Knock sensor ground circuit is open (check for proper torque) • Knock sensor is damaged or has failed • ECM has failed
DTC: P0326 **1T CCM, MIL: Yes** **Years:** 2008, 2009, 2010 **Models:** Acadia, Allure, Aura, Camaro, Corvette, CTS, CTS-V, DTS, Enclave, LaCrosse, Outlook, Traverse **Engines:** 3.6L VIN 7, 3.6L VIN D, 3.6L VIN V 4.6L VIN Y, 6.2L VIN P, 7.0L VIN E **Transmissions:** All	**Knock Sensor (KS) System Performance** DTCs P0335, P0336, P0340, P0341, P0365, P0366, P0601, P0602, or P0604 are not set. The engine speed is greater than 2,500 RPM. The mass air flow (MAF) is greater than 20 g/s. The engine is NOT in decel fuel cut-off. The KS signal is not present for 20 engine revolutions. **Possible Causes:** • Knock sensor signal circuit is open, shorted to ground or power • Knock sensor ground circuit is open (check for proper torque) • Knock sensor is damaged or has failed • ECM has failed
DTC: P0326 **1T CCM, MIL: Yes** **Years:** 2008, 2009 **Models:** Astra, Aura, Aveo, Aveo5, Cobalt G3, G5 **Engines:** 1.6L VIN 6, 1.6L VIN E, 1.8L VIN 1, 2.0L VIN P, 2.0L VIN X, 2.2L VIN H, 2.2L VIN F, 2.4L VIN 5, 2.4L VIN B **Transmissions:** All	**Knock Sensor (KS) Circuit Low Voltage (Bank 1)** The KS signal circuits are shorted to voltage or ground. The ignition timing is retarded to reduce the potential of engine damaging spark knock. **Possible Causes:** • KS circuits A and B for a short to ground or an open/high resistance • KS circuits A and B for a short to voltage • KS sensor has failed • ECM has failed
DTC: P0327 **1T CCM, MIL: Yes** **Years:** 2008, 2009 **Models:** Corvette, CTS, CTS-V, DTS **Engines:** 4.6L VIN Y, 6.2L VIN W, 6.2L VIN P, 6.2L VIN R, 7.0L VIN E **Transmissions:** All	**Knock Sensor (KS) Circuit Low Voltage (Bank 1)** DTC P0112, P0113, P0116, P0117, P0118, or P0128 is not set. The Engine Coolant Temperature (ECT) is greater than −40°C (−40°F). The engine oil temperature is less than 256°C (492.8°F). The engine run time is greater than 2 minutes. DTCs P0327, P0328, P0332, and P0333 run continuously when the above conditions are met. The KS signal circuits are shorted to voltage or ground. **Possible Causes:** • KS sensor signal circuit for a short to ground or an open/high resistance • KS sensor signal circuit for a short to voltage • KS sensor low reference circuit for a short to ground or an open/high resistance • KS sensor • KS sensor has failed • ECM has failed
DTC: P0327 **1T CCM, MIL: Yes** **Years:** 2008, 2009 **Models:** Allure, Aura, Canyon, Colorado, LaCrosse **Engines:** 2.9L VIN 9, 3.5L VIN N, 3.8L VIN 2, 5.3L VIN C, 5.3L VIN L **Transmissions:** All	**Knock Sensor (KS) System Performance (Bank 1)** The Engine Coolant Temperature (ECT) sensor is warmer than 60°C (140°F). The increase in engine speed is less than a range of 500-2300 RPM per second. The engine speed is greater than 2,200 RPM. DTC P0326 runs continuously once the above conditions are met for approximately 20 seconds. The ECM detects a short to ground or a voltage on the KS signal circuits in 25 of 250 test samples. The condition exists for greater than 1 second or for a cumulative of 10 seconds. **Possible Causes:** • Knock sensor signal circuit is open, shorted to ground or power • Knock sensor ground circuit is open (check for proper torque) • Knock sensor is damaged or has failed • ECM has failed

DTC	Trouble Code Title, Conditions & Possible Causes
DTC: P0327 **1T CCM, MIL: Yes** **Years:** 2008, 2009, 2010 **Models:** Acadia, Allure, Aura, Camaro, CTS, CTS-V, Enclave, LaCrosse, Outlook, Traverse **Engines:** 3.6L VIN 7, 3.6L VIN D, 3.6L VIN V **Transmissions:** All	**Knock Sensor Circuit Low Input (Bank 1)** DTC P0117, P0118, P0121, P0122, P0123, P0125, P1114, P1115, P1121, P1122 and P1258 not set, engine speed from 475-975 for 10 seconds, ECT sensor over 140°F, system voltage over 10.0v, minimum noise level learned, then with the engine speed from 1500-3000 RPM for 10 seconds, the MAP sensor less than 49 kPa, TP angle over 0%, and the ECM detected the Knock sensor was within an assigned average range for 9 seconds. **Possible Causes:** • Knock sensor signal circuit is open, shorted to ground or power • Knock sensor ground circuit is open (check for proper torque) • Knock sensor is damaged or has failed • ECM has failed
DTC: P0328 **1T CCM, MIL: Yes** **Years:** 2008, 2009 **Models:** Corvette, CTS, CTS-V, DTS **Engines:** 4.6L VIN Y, 6.2L VIN W, 6.2L VIN P, 6.2L VIN R, 7.0L VIN E **Transmissions:** All	**Knock Sensor (KS) Circuit High Voltage (Bank 1)** DTC P0112, P0113, P0116, P0117, P0118, or P0128 is not set. The Engine Coolant Temperature (ECT) is greater than −40°C (−40°F). The engine oil temperature is less than 256°C (492.8°F). The engine run time is greater than 2 minutes. DTCs P0327, P0328, P0332, and P0333 run continuously when the above conditions are met. The KS signal circuits are shorted to voltage or ground. **Possible Causes:** • KS sensor signal circuit for a short to ground or an open/high resistance • KS sensor signal circuit for a short to voltage • KS sensor low reference circuit for a short to ground or an open/high resistance • KS sensor • KS sensor has failed • ECM has failed
DTC: P0328 **1T CCM, MIL: Yes** **Years:** 2008, 2009 **Models:** Allure, Aura, Canyon, Colorado, LaCrosse **Engines:** 2.9L VIN 9, 3.5L VIN N, 3.8L VIN 2, 5.3L VIN C, 5.3L VIN L **Transmissions:** All	**Knock Sensor (KS) System Performance (Bank 1)** The Engine Coolant Temperature (ECT) sensor is warmer than 60°C (140°F). The increase in engine speed is less than a range of 500-2300 RPM per second.The engine speed is greater than 2,200 RPM. DTC P0326 runs continuously once the above conditions are met for approximately 20 seconds. The ECM detects a short to ground or a voltage on the KS signal circuits in 25 of 250 test samples. The condition exists for greater than 1 second or for a cumulative of 10 seconds. **Possible Causes:** • Knock sensor signal circuit is open, shorted to ground or power • Knock sensor ground circuit is open (check for proper torque) • Knock sensor is damaged or has failed • ECM has failed
DTC: P0328 **1T CCM, MIL: Yes** **Years:** 2008, 2009, 2010 **Models:** Acadia, Allure, Aura, Camaro, CTS, CTS-V, Enclave, LaCrosse, Outlook, Traverse **Engines:** 3.6L VIN 7, 3.6L VIN D, 3.6L VIN V **Transmissions:** All	**Knock Sensor Circuit Low Input (Bank 1)** DTC P0117, P0118 and P0125 not set, engine runtime 10 seconds, minimum noise level learned with the engine speed from 475-975 RPM, then with the engine speed from 1500-3000, ECT sensor more than 140°F, MAP sensor under 49 kPa, TP angle over 0%, system voltage over 10.0v, the ECM detected the Knock Sensor signal was within a calculated voltage range or no signal existed for 9 seconds. **Possible Causes:** • Knock sensor signal circuit is open, shorted to ground or power • Knock sensor ground circuit is open (check for proper torque) • Knock sensor is damaged or it has failed • ECM has failed
DTC: P0328 **2T CCM, MIL: Yes** **Years:** 2008, 2009, 2010 **Models:** Avalanche, Camaro, Canyon, Escalade/EXT/ESV, Suburban, Tahoe, Yukon **Engines:** 4.8L VIN C, 5.3L VIN 0, 5.3L VIN 3, 5.3L VIN J, 5.3L VIN L, 6.0L VIN K, 6.0L VIN Y, 6.2L VIN J, 6.2L VIN W, 6.2L VIN 8 **Transmissions:** All	**Knock Sensor (KS) Circuit (Bank 2)** DTC P0324, P0325, P0326, P0327, P0328, P0332, or P0333 is not set. The engine speed is greater than 400 RPM. The Engine Coolant Temperature (ECT) is greater than −40°C (−40°F). The engine run time is greater than 2 minutes. DTC P0330 runs continuously when the above conditions are met. **Possible Causes:** • KS circuits A and B for a short to ground or an open/high resistance • KS circuits A and B for a short to voltage • KS sensor has failed • ECM has failed

DTC	Trouble Code Title, Conditions & Possible Causes
DTC: P0330 **1T CCM, MIL: Yes** **Years:** 2008, 2009 **Models:** Corvette, CTS, CTS-V, DTS **Engines:** 4.6L VIN Y, 6.2L VIN W, 6.2L VIN P, 6.2L VIN R, 7.0L VIN E **Transmissions:** All	**Knock Sensor (KS) Circuit (Bank 2)** DTC P0324, P0325, P0326, P0327, P0328, P0330, P0332, or P0333 is not set. The engine speed is greater than 400 RPM. The Engine Coolant Temperature (ECT) is greater than −40°C (−40°F). The engine run time is greater than 2 minutes. DTCs P0325 and P0330 run continuously when the above conditions are met. The KS signal circuits are open or shorted together for 5 seconds. **Possible Causes:** • KS sensor signal circuit for a short to ground or an open/high resistance • KS sensor signal circuit for a short to voltage • KS sensor low reference circuit for a short to ground or an open/high resistance • KS sensor • KS sensor has failed • ECM has failed
DTC: P0330 **1T CCM, MIL: Yes** **Years:** 2008, 2009 **Models:** Allure, Aura, Canyon, Colorado, LaCrosse **Engines:** 2.9L VIN 9, 3.5L VIN N, 3.8L VIN 2, 5.3L VIN C, 5.3L VIN L **Transmissions:** All	**Knock Sensor (KS) System Performance (Bank 1)** The engine coolant temperature (ECT) sensor is warmer than 60°C (140°F). The engine speed is greater than 2,200 RPM. DTC P0326 runs continuously once the above conditions are met for approximately 20 seconds. The ECM detects a short to ground or a voltage on the KS signal circuits in 25 of 250 test samples. The condition exists for greater than 1 second or for a cumulative of 10 seconds. **Possible Causes:** • Knock sensor signal circuit is open, shorted to ground or power • Knock sensor ground circuit is open (check for proper torque) • Knock sensor is damaged or has failed • ECM has failed
DTC: P0331 **1T CCM, MIL: Yes** **Years:** 2008, 2009 **Models:** Corvette, CTS, CTS-V, DTS **Engines:** 4.6L VIN Y, 6.2L VIN W, 6.2L VIN P, 6.2L VIN R, 7.0L VIN E **Transmissions:** All	**Knock Sensor (KS) System Performance (Bank 2)** Before the ECM can report DTC P0326 or P0331 failed, DTCs P0324, P0335, P0336, and P0338 must run and pass. DTC P0341, P0342, P0343, P0346, P0347, P0348, P0366, P0367, P0368, P0391, P0392, or P0393 is not set. The Engine Coolant Temperature (ECT) sensor is warmer than 60°C (140°F). The engine speed is greater than 2,200 RPM. DTCs P0331 runs continuously once the above conditions are met for approximately 20 seconds. The ECM detects a short to ground or a voltage on the KS signal circuits in 25 of 250 test samples. The condition exists for greater than 1 second or for a cumulative of 10 seconds. **Possible Causes:** • KS sensor signal circuit for a short to ground or an open/high resistance • KS sensor signal circuit for a short to voltage • KS sensor low reference circuit for a short to ground or an open/high resistance • KS sensor • KS sensor has failed • ECM has failed
DTC: P0331 **1T CCM, MIL: Yes** **Years:** 2008, 2009, 2010 **Models:** Acadia, Allure, Aura, Camaro, CTS, CTS-V, Enclave, LaCrosse, Outlook, Traverse **Engines:** 3.6L VIN 7, 3.6L VIN D, 3.6L VIN V **Transmissions:** All	**Knock Sensor (KS) Circuit Low Voltage (Bank 2)** The KS signal circuits are shorted to voltage or ground. The ignition timing is retarded to reduce the potential of engine damaging spark knock. **Possible Causes** • KS circuits A and B for a short to ground or an open/high resistance • KS circuits A and B for a short to voltage • KS sensor has failed • ECM has failed
DTC: P0332 **1T CCM, MIL: Yes** **Years:** 2008, 2009 **Models:** Corvette, CTS, CTS-V, DTS **Engines:** 4.6L VIN Y, 6.2L VIN W, 6.2L VIN P, 6.2L VIN R, 7.0L VIN E **Transmissions:** All	**Knock Sensor (KS) Circuit Low Voltage (Bank 2)** DTC P0112, P0113, P0116, P0117, P0118, or P0128 is not set. The Engine Coolant Temperature (ECT) is greater than −40°C (−40°F). The engine oil temperature is less than 256°C (492.8°F). The engine run time is greater than 2 minutes. DTCs P0327, P0328, P0332, and P0333 run continuously when the above conditions are met. The KS signal circuits are shorted to voltage or ground. **Possible Causes:** • KS sensor signal circuit for a short to ground or an open/high resistance • KS sensor signal circuit for a short to voltage • KS sensor low reference circuit for a short to ground or an open/high resistance • KS sensor • KS sensor has failed • ECM has failed

DTC	Trouble Code Title, Conditions & Possible Causes
DTC: P0332 **1T CCM, MIL: Yes** **Years:** 2008, 2009 **Models:** Allure, Aura, Canyon, Colorado, LaCrosse **Engines:** 2.9L VIN 9, 3.5L VIN N, 3.8L VIN 2, 5.3L VIN C, 5.3L VIN L **Transmissions:** All	**Knock Sensor (KS) System Performance (Bank 1)** The Engine Coolant Temperature (ECT) sensor is warmer than 60°C (140°F). The increase in engine speed is less than a range of 500-2300 RPM per second.The engine speed is greater than 2,200 RPM. DTC P0326 runs continuously once the above conditions are met for approximately 20 seconds. The ECM detects a short to ground or a voltage on the KS signal circuits in 25 of 250 test samples. The condition exists for greater than 1 second or for a cumulative of 10 seconds. . **Possible Causes:** • Knock sensor signal circuit is open, shorted to ground or power • Knock sensor ground circuit is open (check for proper torque) • Knock sensor is damaged or has failed • ECM has failed
DTC: P0332 **1T CCM, MIL: Yes** **Years:** 2008, 2009, 2010 **Models:** Acadia, Allure, Aura, Camaro, CTS, CTS-V, Enclave, LaCrosse, Outlook, Traverse **Engines:** 3.6L VIN 7, 3.6L VIN D, 3.6L VIN V **Transmissions:** All	**Knock Sensor Circuit Malfunction (Bank 2)** DTC P0101-P0103, P0116-P0118, P0121-P0123, P0125, P0128, P0336, P0341, P0502, P0503, P1114, P1115, P1121 and P1336 not set, engine started, engine speed at 1000-4000 RPM for 30 seconds, system voltage over 10.0v, ECT sensor over 140°F, TP angle from 3-15%, engine load 20-45%, spark retard less than 15 degrees, and the ECM detected an invalid voltage on the Knock sensor circuit. **Possible Causes:** • Knock sensor signal circuit is open, shorted to ground or power • Knock sensor ground circuit is open (i.e., not mounted properly) • Knock sensor is damaged or has failed • On modules with an integrated sensor, clear the codes and retest for codes. If the same code resets, the ECM has failed.
DTC: P0332 **2T CCM, MIL: Yes** **Years:** 2008, 2009, 2010 **Models:** Avalanche, Camaro, Canyon, Escalade/EXT/ESV, Suburban, Tahoe, Yukon **Engines:** 4.8L VIN C, 5.3L VIN 0, 5.3L VIN 3, 5.3L VIN J, 5.3L VIN L, 6.0L VIN K, 6.0L VIN Y, 6.2L VIN J, 6.2L VIN W, 6.2L VIN 8 **Transmissions:** All	**Knock Sensor Circuit Malfunction (Bank 2)** DTC P0117, P0118, P0121-P0123, P0125, P1114, P1115, P1120 and P1122 not set, engine started, engine speed from 475-975 for 10 seconds, system voltage from 10-18v, ECT sensor more than 140°F, minimum noise level learned, then with the engine speed from 1500-3000 RPM, MAP sensor less than 49 kPa, TP angle more than 0% for 10 seconds, the ECM detected the KS signal was less than or more than the expected amount for 9 seconds. **Possible Causes:** • Knock sensor signal circuit is open, shorted to ground or power • Knock sensor ground circuit is open (check for proper torque) • Knock sensor is damaged or has failed • ECM has failed • TSB 02-06-04-023A contains a repair procedure for this code
DTC: P0333 **1T CCM, MIL: Yes** **Years:** 2008, 2009 **Models:** Corvette, CTS, CTS-V, DTS **Engines:** 4.6L VIN Y, 6.2L VIN W, 6.2L VIN P, 6.2L VIN R, 7.0L VIN E **Transmissions:** All	**Knock Sensor (KS) Circuit High Voltage (Bank 2)** DTC P0112, P0113, P0116, P0117, P0118, or P0128 is not set. The Engine Coolant Temperature (ECT) is greater than −40°C (−40°F). The engine oil temperature is less than 256°C (492.8°F). The engine run time is greater than 2 minutes. DTCs P0327, P0328, P0332, and P0333 run continuously when the above conditions are met. The KS signal circuits are shorted to voltage or ground. **Possible Causes:** • KS sensor signal circuit for a short to ground or an open/high resistance • KS sensor signal circuit for a short to voltage • KS sensor low reference circuit for a short to ground or an open/high resistance • KS sensor • KS sensor has failed • ECM has failed
DTC: P0333 **1T CCM, MIL: Yes** **Years:** 2008, 2009 **Models:** Allure, Aura, Canyon, Colorado, LaCrosse **Engines:** 2.9L VIN 9, 3.5L VIN N, 3.8L VIN 2, 5.3L VIN C, 5.3L VIN L **Transmissions:** All	**Knock Sensor (KS) System Performance (Bank 1)** The Engine Coolant Temperature (ECT) sensor is warmer than 60°C (140°F). The increase in engine speed is less than a range of 500-2300 RPM per second.The engine speed is greater than 2,200 RPM. DTC P0326 runs continuously once the above conditions are met for approximately 20 seconds. The ECM detects a short to ground or a voltage on the KS signal circuits in 25 of 250 test samples. The condition exists for greater than 1 second or for a cumulative of 10 seconds. **Possible Causes:** • Knock sensor signal circuit is open, shorted to ground or power • Knock sensor ground circuit is open (check for proper torque) • Knock sensor is damaged or has failed • ECM has failed

DTC	Trouble Code Title, Conditions & Possible Causes
DTC: P0333 **1T CCM, MIL: Yes** **Years:** 2008, 2009, 2010 **Models:** Acadia, Allure, Aura, Camaro, CTS, CTS-V, Enclave, LaCrosse, Outlook, Traverse **Engines:** 3.6L VIN 7, 3.6L VIN D, 3.6L VIN V **Transmissions:** All	**Crankshaft Position (CKP) Sensor Circuit** DTC P0340, P0341, P0641, or P0651 is not set. The engine is cranking or running. DTC P0335 runs continuously when the above conditions are met. DTC P0335 runs continuously when the above conditions are met. Or the ECM detects that the engine is running, but has not received a CKP sensor pulse for 2 of 10 engine cycles. **Possible Causes:** • CKP sensor low reference circuit for an open/high resistance • CKP sensor 5-volt reference circuit for an open/high resistance or short to ground • CKP sensor 5-volt reference circuit for a short to voltage • CKP sensor signal circuit for an open/high resistance or short to ground • CKP sensor signal circuit for a short to voltage • CKP sensor has failed • ECM has failed
DTC: P0335 **1T CCM, MIL: Yes** **Years:** 2008, 2009 **Models:** Corvette, CTS, CTS-V, DTS **Engines:** 4.6L VIN Y, 6.2L VIN W, 6.2L VIN P, 6.2L VIN R, 7.0L VIN E **Transmissions:** All	**Crankshaft Position (CKP) Sensor Circuit** DTC P0340, P0341, P0641, or P0651 is not set. The engine is cranking or running. DTC P0335 runs continuously when the above conditions are met. The ECM detects that the starter is commanded on and the engine has been cranking for more than 4 seconds without a CKP sensor pulse. The ECM detects that the engine is running, but has not received a CKP sensor pulse for 2 of 10 engine cycles. **Possible Causes:** • CKP sensor low reference circuit for an open/high resistance • CKP sensor 5-volt reference circuit for an open/high resistance or short to ground • CKP sensor 5-volt reference circuit for a short to voltage. • CKP sensor signal circuit for an open/high resistance or short to ground • CKP sensor signal circuit for a short to voltage • CKP sensor has failed • ECM has failed
DTC: P0335 **1T CCM, MIL: Yes** **Years:** 2008, 2009 **Models:** Allure, Aura, Canyon, Colorado, LaCrosse **Engines:** 2.9L VIN 9, 3.5L VIN N, 3.8L VIN 2, 5.3L VIN C, 5.3L VIN L **Transmissions:** All	**Crankshaft Position (CKP) Sensor Circuit** The engine is cranking or operating. The ECM has detected greater than 12 camshaft revolutions. The ECM does not detect a signal from the CKP sensor. Or the ECM detects a CKP signal without a reference pulse for greater than 6 revolutions. **Possible Causes:** • Physical damage to the CKP sensor or the reluctor wheel • 5 volt reference circuit for a short to ground or for an open/high resistance. • 5 volt reference circuit for a short to voltage • Short to voltage in the signal circuit • Short to ground or an open/high resistance in the signal circuit • CKP has failed • ECM has failed
DTC: P0335 **1T CCM, MIL: Yes** **Years:** 2008, 2009, 2010 **Models:** Acadia, Allure, Aura, Camaro, CTS, CTS-V, Enclave, LaCrosse, Outlook, Traverse **Engines:** 3.6L VIN 7, 3.6L VIN D, 3.6L VIN V **Transmissions:** All	**CKP Sensor Circuit Malfunction** DTC P0101, P0102, P0103, P0341, P0342 and P0343 not set; engine cranking, CMP signal varying, MAF sensor more than 3 g/sec, and the ECM did not detect any signals from the CKP sensor for less than 8 seconds during the CCM test period. **Possible Causes:** • CKP sensor signal circuit is open or shorted to ground • CKP sensor ground (low reference) circuit is open • CKP sensor power circuit is open between sensor and the ECM • Crankshaft reluctor wheel is damaged or improper installation • ECM has failed
DTC: P0335 **1T CCM, MIL: Yes** **Years:** 2008, 2009, 2010 **Models:** Avalanche, Camaro, Canyon, Escalade/EXT/ESV, Suburban, Tahoe, Yukon **Engines:** 4.8L VIN C, 5.3L VIN 0, 5.3L VIN 3, 5.3L VIN J, 5.3L VIN L, 6.0L VIN K, 6.0L VIN Y, 6.2L VIN J, 6.2L VIN W, 6.2L VIN 8 **Transmissions:** All	**Crankshaft Position Sensor Circuit Malfunction** DTC P0101, P0102, P0103, P0341, P0342 and P0343 not set, engine cranking, CMP sensor signals transitioning, MAF sensor more than 3 g/sec, and the ECM did not detect any signals from the CKP sensor (Hall Effect) for up 4-8 seconds during the CCM test. **Possible Causes:** • CKP sensor signal circuit is open or shorted to ground • CKP sensor VREF circuit is open between the sensor and ECM • CKP sensor ground (Low Reference) circuit is open • CKP sensor is damaged or it failed (check crankshaft reluctor) • ECM has failed

DTC	Trouble Code Title, Conditions & Possible Causes
DTC: P0335 **1T CCM, MIL: Yes** **Years:** 2008, 2009 **Models:** Astra, Aura, Aveo, Aveo5, Cobalt G3, G5 **Engines:** 1.6L VIN 6, 1.6L VIN E, 1.8L VIN 1, 2.0L VIN P, 2.0L VIN X, 2.2L VIN H, 2.2L VIN F, 2.4L VIN 5, 2.4L VIN B **Transmissions:** All	**Crankshaft Position Sensor Circuit Malfunction** DTC P0562 not set, engine started; system voltage less than 18v, and the ECM did not detect any CKP sensor signals. **Possible Causes:** • CKP sensor signal (+) circuit or (−) circuit is open or shorted to ground • CKP sensor is damaged or has failed • ECM has failed
DTC: P0336 **1T CCM, MIL: Yes** **Years:** 2008, 2009 **Models:** Corvette, CTS, CTS-V, DTS **Engines:** 4.6L VIN Y, 6.2L VIN W, 6.2L VIN P, 6.2L VIN R, 7.0L VIN E **Transmissions:** All	**Crankshaft Position (CKP) Sensor Performance** DTC P0340, P0341, P0641, or P0651 is not set. The engine is cranking or running. DTC P0336 runs continuously when the above conditions are met. The ECM detects that the engine is running, but receives less than 53 or more than 63 CKP sensor pulses, during each engine revolution, for 8 of 10 engine revolutions. The ECM detects that the engine is running, but more than 25 crankshaft resyncs have occurred within 20 seconds. The ECM detects that the engine has been running, but the crankshaft does not sync for 0.4 second. **Possible Causes:** • Crankshaft reluctor wheel for damage • Timing chain, tensioner, and sprockets for wear or damage • CKP sensor for correct installation • Harness connector to the CKP sensor • CKP sensor has failed
DTC: P0336 **1T CCM, MIL: Yes** **Years:** 2008, 2009 **Models:** Allure, Aura, Canyon, Colorado, LaCrosse **Engines:** 2.9L VIN 9, 3.5L VIN N, 3.8L VIN 2, 5.3L VIN C, 5.3L VIN L **Transmissions:** All	**Crankshaft Position (CKP) Sensor Performance** The engine is cranking or operating. The ECM has detected greater than 12 camshaft revolutions The ECM re-syncs the engine position greater than 2,600 times during an ignition cycle. The ECM detects 28 or more interruptions in the engine speed signal during an ignition cycle. **Possible Causes:** • Physical damage to the CKP sensor or the reluctor wheel • 5 volt reference circuit for a short to ground or for an open/high resistance. • 5 volt reference circuit for a short to voltage • Short to voltage in the signal circuit • Short to ground or an open/high resistance in the signal circuit • CKP has failed • ECM has failed
DTC: P0336 **1T CCM, MIL: Yes** **Years:** 2008, 2009, 2010 **Models:** Acadia, Allure, Aura, Camaro, CTS, CTS-V, Enclave, LaCrosse, Outlook, Traverse **Engines:** 3.6L VIN 7, 3.6L VIN D, 3.6L VIN V **Transmissions:** All	**Crankshaft Reference 24X Circuit Malfunction** Engine started; 3X signals detected for 3 seconds, and the ECM detected an invalid ratio of 24X to 3X CKP REF pulses. The circuit uses 2 different types of crankshaft position (CKP) sensors. The CKP Sensor 'A' connects directly to the ECM through the 12v VREF, Medium Resolution engine speed signal and the low reference circuits. The CKP Sensor 'B' connects directly to the ignition control (IC) module via the CKP 'B' signal and low reference circuits. **Possible Causes:** • CKP sensor signal circuit is open or shorted to ground • CKP sensor ground (Low Reference) circuit is open • CKP sensor is damaged or it failed (check crankshaft reluctor) • ECM has failed
DTC: P0336 **1T CCM, MIL: Yes** **Years:** 2008, 2009 **Models:** Astra, Aura, Aveo, Aveo5, Cobalt G3, G5 **Engines:** 1.6L VIN 6, 1.6L VIN E, 1.8L VIN 1, 2.0L VIN P, 2.0L VIN X, 2.2L VIN H, 2.2L VIN F, 2.4L VIN 5, 2.4L VIN B **Transmissions:** All	**Crankshaft Reference 18X Circuit Malfunction** Engine started; 3X REF signals detected, and the ECM did not detect any 18X pulses, or the ratio of 18X REF pulses to 3X REF pulses did not equal 6:1, or ratio of 3X REF pulses to CMP pulses equaled 6:1, conditions met for 290 of 300 samples. The Crankshaft Position Sensor (CKP) circuit uses two types of CKP sensors. CKP Sensor 'B' is connected directly to the ignition control module (ICM), while CKP sensor 'A' connects directly to the ECM. **Possible Causes:** • CKP sensor signal circuit is open or shorted to ground • CKP sensor VREF circuit is open, or the ground (Low Reference) circuit is open • CKP sensor is damaged or it failed (check the crankshaft reluctor) • CKP sensor wiring routed close to spark plug wires (EMI/RFI) • ECM has failed

DTC	Trouble Code Title, Conditions & Possible Causes
DTC: P0336 **2T CCM, MIL: Yes** **Years:** 2008, 2009, 2010 **Models:** Avalanche, Camaro, Canyon, Escalade/EXT/ESV, Suburban, Tahoe, Yukon **Engines:** 4.8L VIN C, 5.3L VIN 0, 5.3L VIN 3, 5.3L VIN J, 5.3L VIN L, 6.0L VIN K, 6.0L VIN Y, 6.2L VIN J, 6.2L VIN W, 6.2L VIN 8 **Transmissions:** All	**Crankshaft Position Sensor Range/Performance** Engine cranking or running; and the ECM detected the CKP sensor signal was out-of-range for 2 seconds during the CCM test. **Possible Causes:** • CKP sensor signal circuit has a high resistance condition • CKP sensor ground (Low Reference) circuit has high resistance • CKP sensor is damaged or it failed (check crankshaft reluctor) • ECM has failed • Vehicle have been driven while very low on fuel
DTC: P0338 **1T CCM, MIL: Yes** **Years:** 2008, 2009, 2010 **Models:** Acadia, Allure, Aura, Camaro, CTS, CTS-V, Enclave, LaCrosse, Outlook, Traverse **Engines:** 3.6L VIN 7, 3.6L VIN D, 3.6L VIN V **Transmissions:** All	**Camshaft Position (CMP) Sensor Circuit** DTC P0335, P0336, P0641, or P0651 is not set. The engine is cranking or running. DTC P0340 runs continuously when the above conditions are met. The ECM detects that the starter is commanded on and the engine has been cranking for more than 4 seconds without a CMP sensor pulse. The ECM detects that the engine has started, but did not receive a CMP sensor pulse during the first engine revolution. The ECM detects that the engine is running, but does not receive a CMP sensor pulse for 800 of 1000 engine cycles. **Possible Causes:** • CMP sensor 5-volt reference circuit for an open/high resistance or short to ground • CMP sensor 5-volt reference circuit for a short to voltage • CMP sensor signal circuit for an open/high resistance or short to ground • CMP sensor signal circuit for a short to voltage • CKP sensor has failed • ECM has failed
DTC: P0340 **1T CCM, MIL: Yes** **Years:** 2008, 2009 **Models:** Corvette, CTS, CTS-V, DTS **Engines:** 4.6L VIN Y, 6.2L VIN W, 6.2L VIN P, 6.2L VIN R, 7.0L VIN E **Transmissions:** All	**Camshaft Position (CMP) Sensor Circuit** DTC P0335, P0336, P0641, or P0651 is not set. The engine is cranking or running. DTC P0340 runs continuously when the above conditions are met. The ECM detects that the starter is commanded on and the engine has been cranking for more than 4 seconds without a CMP sensor pulse. The ECM detects that the engine has started, but did not receive a CMP sensor pulse during the first engine revolution. The ECM detects that the engine is running, but does not receive a CMP sensor pulse for 800 of 1000 engine cycles. **Possible Causes:** • Close routing of aftermarket electrical equipment. • Close to solenoids, motors, and relays. • CMP sensor low reference circuit for an open/high resistance • CMP sensor 5-volt reference circuit for an open/high resistance or short to ground • CMP sensor 5-volt reference circuit for a short to voltage • CMP sensor signal circuit for an open/high resistance or short to ground • CMP sensor signal circuit for a short to voltage • CMP sensor has failed • ECM has failed
DTC: P0340 **1T CCM, MIL: Yes** **Years:** 2008, 2009 **Models:** Allure, Aura, Canyon, Colorado, LaCrosse **Engines:** 2.9L VIN 9, 3.5L VIN N, 3.8L VIN 2, 5.3L VIN C, 5.3L VIN L **Transmissions:** All	**Intake Camshaft Position (CMP) Sensor Circuit** The engine is running. DTCs P0340 and P0365 run continuously when the above condition is met. The ECM does not receive 2 camshaft pulses within 3 seconds. **Possible Causes:** • CMP sensor signal circuit is open, shorted to ground or shorted to VREF between the sensor and the ECM • CMP sensor VREF circuit is open between sensor and ECM • CMP sensor ground circuit or "shielded" ground circuit is open • CMP sensor is cracked or damaged (check the reluctor wheel) • ECM has failed
DTC: P0340 **1T CCM, MIL: Yes** **Years:** 2008, 2009 **Models:** Astra, Aura, Aveo, Aveo5, Cobalt G3, G5 **Engines:** 1.6L VIN 6, 1.6L VIN E, 1.8L VIN 1, 2.0L VIN P, 2.0L VIN X, 2.2L VIN H, 2.2L VIN F, 2.4L VIN 5, 2.4L VIN B **Transmissions:** All	**CMP Sensor Circuit Malfunction** Engine started; and the ECM detected the CMP sensor (Hall Effect) Active Counter did not increment (i.e., no change detected in the CMP sensor activity for 30 crankshaft revolutions). **Possible Causes:** • CMP sensor signal circuit is open, shorted to ground or shorted to VREF between the sensor and the ECM • CMP sensor VREF circuit is open between sensor and ECM • CMP sensor ground circuit or "shielded" ground circuit is open • CMP sensor is cracked or damaged (check the reluctor wheel) • ECM has failed

DTC	Trouble Code Title, Conditions & Possible Causes
DTC: P0341 **1T CCM, MIL: Yes** **Years:** 2008, 2009 **Models:** Corvette, CTS, CTS-V, DTS **Engines:** 4.6L VIN Y, 6.2L VIN W, 6.2L VIN P, 6.2L VIN R, 7.0L VIN E **Transmissions:** All	**Camshaft Position (CMP) Sensor Performance** DTC P0335, P0336, P0641, or P0651 is not set. The engine is cranking or running. DTC P0341 runs continuously when the above conditions are met. The ECM detects that the engine was started, but has received less than 2 or more than 8 CMP sensor pulses during the first engine resolution. The ECM detects that the engine has started and is running, but receives less than 398 or more than 402 CMP pulses per 100 engine cycles in 800 of 1000 engine cycles. **Possible Causes:** • Engine oil for debris • CMP sensor is loose, • Camshaft reluctor wheel for damage • timing chain, timing chain tensioner, and sprockets for wear or damage • Harness connector to the CMP sensor • CMP sensor has failed
DTC: P0341 **1T CCM, MIL: Yes** **Years:** 2008, 2009 **Models:** Allure, Aura, Canyon, Colorado, LaCrosse **Engines:** 2.9L VIN 9, 3.5L VIN N, 3.8L VIN 2, 5.3L VIN C, 5.3L VIN L **Transmissions:** All	**Intake Camshaft Position (CMP) Sensor Performance (Bank 1)** The ECM detects greater than 10 crankshaft revolutions. The engine speed is less than 2,520 RPM The DTCs run continuously once the above condition is met. The ECM detects a signal from the CMP sensor, but the number of pulses are less than or greater than what is expected for one crankshaft revolution. Or the CMP sensor does NOT correlate to the crankshaft position. Either condition must exist for greater than 1 second, or cumulative of 10 seconds. **Note: The control module or the sensor may be damaged if the circuit is shorted to B+ voltage.** **Possible Causes:** • Low reference circuit for an open/high resistance or for a short to voltage • 5 volt reference circuit for an open/high resistance • Short to voltage in the signal circuit • Short to ground or an open/high resistance in the signal circuit. • CMP has failed • ECM has failed
DTC: P0341 **1T CCM, MIL: Yes** **Years:** 2008, 2009, 2010 **Models:** Acadia, Allure, Aura, Camaro, CTS, CTS-V, Enclave, LaCrosse, Outlook, Traverse **Engines:** 3.6L VIN 7, 3.6L VIN D, 3.6L VIN V **Transmissions:** All	**Intake Camshaft Position (CMP) Sensor Performance** The engine is cranking or running. DTCs P0335, P0336, and P0365 are not set. DTC P0341 runs continuously when the above conditions are met. The ECM detects the incorrect number of CMP sensor pulses in 2 revolutions of the crankshaft, which is usually within 1 second. **Note: Inspect the CMP sensor for correct installation. Remove the CMP sensor from the engine and inspect the sensor and the O-ring for damage.** **Possible Causes:** • Camshaft reluctor wheel for damage • Timing chain, tensioner, and sprockets for wear or damage. • CMP has failed • ECM has failed
DTC: P0341 **1T CCM, MIL: Yes** **Years:** 2008, 2009 **Models:** Astra, Aura, Aveo, Aveo5, Cobalt G3, G5 **Engines:** 1.6L VIN 6, 1.6L VIN E, 1.8L VIN 1, 2.0L VIN P, 2.0L VIN X, 2.2L VIN H, 2.2L VIN F, 2.4L VIN 5, 2.4L VIN B **Transmissions:** All	**CMP Sensor Signal Range/Performance** Engine started; and the ECM detected more than 15 CMP sensor resynchronizations during a 4 minute 16 second period. **Possible Causes:** • CMP sensor signal circuit is open, shorted to ground or VREF • CMP sensor signal wire is routed to close to the Generator, spark plug wires or any other possible cause of EMI/RFI under the hood (check for high power receivers causing interference) • CMP sensor "shield" ground circuit is open (intermittent fault) • CMP sensor is cracked or damaged (check the reluctor wheel) • ECM has failed
DTC: P0341 **2T CCM, MIL: Yes** **Years:** 2008, 2009, 2010 **Models:** Avalanche, Camaro, Canyon, Escalade/EXT/ESV, Suburban, Tahoe, Yukon **Engines:** 4.8L VIN C, 5.3L VIN 0, 5.3L VIN 3, 5.3L VIN J, 5.3L VIN L, 6.0L VIN K, 6.0L VIN Y, 6.2L VIN J, 6.2L VIN W, 6.2L VIN 8 **Transmissions:** All	**CMP Sensor Signal Range/Performance** Engine started; at less than 4000 RPM, and the ECM detected incorrect correlation between the CKP and CMP signals. **Possible Causes:** • CMP sensor signal circuit is open, shorted to ground or VREF • CMP sensor signal wire is routed to close to the Generator, spark plug wires or any other possible cause of EMI/RFI • CMP sensor is cracked, damaged or has failed • ECM has failed • TSB 02-06-04-008 contains a repair procedure for this code

DTC	Trouble Code Title, Conditions & Possible Causes
DTC: P0342 **1T CCM, MIL: Yes** **Years:** 2008, 2009, 2010 **Models:** Acadia, Allure, Aura, Camaro, CTS, CTS-V, Enclave, LaCrosse, Outlook, Traverse **Engines:** 3.6L VIN 7, 3.6L VIN D, 3.6L VIN V **Transmissions:** All	**CMP Sensor Circuit Low Input** Engine started; at less than 4000 RPM, and the ECM detected the CMP sensor signal was in a low state (when the signal should have been in a high state) for 1.5 seconds in the test. **Possible Causes:** • Camshaft reluctor wheel is damaged or foreign material present • CMP sensor signal circuit is open, shorted to ground or VREF • CMP sensor is contacting the reluctor wheel or is damaged • ECM has failed
DTC: P0343 **1T CCM, MIL: Yes** **Years:** 2008, 2009, 2010 **Models:** Acadia, Allure, Aura, Camaro, CTS, CTS-V, Enclave, LaCrosse, Outlook, Traverse **Engines:** 3.6L VIN 7, 3.6L VIN D, 3.6L VIN V **Transmissions:** All	**CMP Sensor Circuit High Input** Engine started; engine speed less than 4000 RPM and the ECM detected the CMP sensor signal was stuck high (when the signal should have been in a low state) for 1.5 seconds in the CCM test. **Possible Causes:** • CMP sensor connector is damaged, loose or shorted • CMP sensor low reference circuit is open or shorted to VREF • Camshaft reluctor wheel is damaged or foreign material present • CMP sensor is contacting the reluctor wheel or is damaged • ECM has failed
DTC: P0346 **1T CCM, MIL: Yes** **Years:** 2008, 2009, 2010 **Models:** Acadia, Allure, Aura, Camaro, CTS, CTS-V, Enclave, LaCrosse, Outlook, Traverse **Engines:** 3.6L VIN 7, 3.6L VIN D, 3.6L VIN V **Transmissions:** All	**Intake Camshaft Position (CMP) Sensor Circuit Low Voltage Bank 2** The CMP sensor signal voltage is always high and the ECM detects no pulses from the CMP sensor for greater than 1 second or cumulative of 10 seconds. **Note: The control module or the sensor may be damaged if the circuit is shorted to B+ voltage.** **Possible Causes:** • Low reference circuit for an open/high resistance or for a short to voltage • 5 volt reference circuit for an open/high resistance • Short to voltage in the signal circuit • Short to ground or an open/high resistance in the signal circuit. • CMP has failed • ECM has failed
DTC: P0347 **1T CCM, MIL: Yes** **Years:** 2008, 2009, 2010 **Models:** Acadia, Allure, Aura, Camaro, CTS, CTS-V, Enclave, LaCrosse, Outlook, Traverse **Engines:** 3.6L VIN 7, 3.6L VIN D, 3.6L VIN V **Transmissions:** All	**Intake Camshaft Position (CMP) Sensor Circuit High Voltage (Bank 2)** The CMP sensor signal voltage is always high and the ECM detects no pulses from the CMP sensor for greater than 1 second or cumulative of 10 seconds. **Note: The control module or the sensor may be damaged if the circuit is shorted to B+ voltage.** **Possible Causes:** • Low reference circuit for an open/high resistance or for a short to voltage • 5 volt reference circuit for an open/high resistance • Short to voltage in the signal circuit • Short to ground or an open/high resistance in the signal circuit. • CMP has failed • ECM has failed
DTC: P0348 **1T CCM, MIL: Yes** **Years:** 2008, 2009, 2010 **Models:** Acadia, Allure, Aura, Camaro, CTS, CTS-V, Enclave, LaCrosse, Outlook, Traverse **Engines:** 3.6L VIN 7, 3.6L VIN D, 3.6L VIN V **Transmissions:** All	**Ignition Coil 1 Control Circuit** The ignition is ON. DTC P0351-P0358 runs continuously when the above condition is met. The ECM detects an open, short to ground, short to voltage on the IC circuit. **Note: An IC circuit fault condition will result in an engine misfire, and under certain driving conditions could possibly overheat the 3-way catalytic converter.** **Possible Causes:** • Ignition coil • ECM has failed
DTC: P0351 **1T CCM, MIL: Yes** **Years:** 2008, 2009 **Models:** Allure, Aura, Canyon, Colorado, LaCrosse **Engines:** 2.9L VIN 9, 3.5L VIN N, 3.8L VIN 2, 5.3L VIN C, 5.3L VIN L **Transmissions:** All	**Ignition Coil 1 Control Circuit Malfunction** Engine started; and the ECM detected an unexpected voltage condition on the Coil Near Plug Ignition Control (IC) 1 circuit for less than one second during the CCM test period. **Possible Causes:** • IC circuit is open, shorted to ground or shorted to power (B+) • IC ground (Low REF) circuit or Module ground circuit is open • IC power circuit is open (check the INJ fuse in U/H fuse block) • Ignition Coil 1 is damaged or it has failed • ECM has failed

DTC	Trouble Code Title, Conditions & Possible Causes
DTC: P0351 **2T CCM, MIL: Yes** **Years:** 2008, 2009, 2010 **Models:**, Acadia, Allure, Astra, Aura, Avalanche, Escalade/EXT/ESV, Suburban, Tahoe, Yukon, Escalade/EXT/ESV, Suburban, Tahoe, Yukon Aveo, Aveo5, Camaro, Cobalt, Cobalt-GS, Colorado,Canyon, Corvette, CTS, CTS-V, CTS, CTS-V-V, DTS, Escalade/EXT/ESV, G.3, G5,Enclave, LaCrosse, Outlook, Suburban, Tahoe Traverse, Yukon **Engines:** All **Transmissions:** All	**Ignition Coil 1 Control Circuit Malfunction** Engine started; and the ECM detected an unexpected low or high voltage condition on Coil On Plug (COP) Ignition Control circuit for less than one second during the CCM test. **Note: Watch the Scan Tool Misfire Counters to identify the fault.** **Possible Causes:** • IC circuit is open, shorted to ground or shorted to power • Ignition coil (COP) is damaged or has failed • ECM has failed
DTC: P0352 **1T CCM, MIL: Yes** **Years:** 2008, 2009 **Models:** Allure, Aura, Canyon, Colorado, LaCrosse **Engines:** 2.9L VIN 9, 3.5L VIN N, 3.8L VIN 2, 5.3L VIN C, 5.3L VIN L **Transmissions:** All	**Ignition Coil 2 Control Circuit Malfunction** Engine started; and the ECM detected an unexpected voltage condition on the Coil Near Plug Ignition Control (IC) 2 circuit for less than one second during the CCM test period. **Possible Causes:** • IC circuit is open, shorted to ground or shorted to power (B+) • IC ground (Low REF) circuit or Module ground circuit is open • IC power circuit is open (check the INJ fuse in U/H fuse block) • Ignition Coil 2 is damaged or it has failed • ECM has failed
DTC: P0352 **2T CCM, MIL: Yes** **Years:** 2008, 2009, 2010 **Models:**, Acadia, Allure, Astra, Aura, Avalanche, Escalade/EXT/ESV, Suburban, Tahoe, Yukon, Escalade/EXT/ESV, Suburban, Tahoe, Yukon Aveo, Aveo5, Camaro, Cobalt, Cobalt-GS, Colorado,Canyon, Corvette, CTS, CTS-V, CTS, CTS-V-V, DTS, Escalade/EXT/ESV, G.3, G5,Enclave, LaCrosse, Outlook, Suburban, Tahoe Traverse, Yukon **Engines:** All **Transmissions:** All	**Ignition Coil 2 Control Circuit Malfunction** Engine started; and the ECM detected an unexpected low or high voltage condition on Coil On Plug (COP) Ignition Control circuit for less than one second during the CCM test. **Note: Watch the Scan Tool Misfire Counters to identify the fault.** **Possible Causes:** • IC circuit is open, shorted to ground or shorted to power • Ignition coil (COP) is damaged or has failed • ECM has failed
DTC: P0353 **1T CCM, MIL: Yes** **Years:** 2008, 2009 **Models:** Allure, Aura, Canyon, Colorado, LaCrosse **Engines:** 2.9L VIN 9, 3.5L VIN N, 3.8L VIN 2, 5.3L VIN C, 5.3L VIN L **Transmissions:** All	**Ignition Coil 3 Control Circuit Malfunction** Engine started; and the ECM detected an unexpected voltage condition on the Coil Near Plug Ignition Control (IC) 3 circuit for less than one second during the CCM test period. **Possible Causes:** • IC circuit is open, shorted to ground or shorted to power (B+) • IC ground (Low REF) circuit or Module ground circuit is open • IC power circuit is open (check the INJ fuse in U/H fuse block) • Ignition Coil 3 is damaged or it has failed • ECM has failed

DTC	Trouble Code Title, Conditions & Possible Causes
DTC: P0353 **2T CCM, MIL: Yes** **Years:** 2008, 2009, 2010 **Models:**, Acadia, Allure, Astra, Aura, Avalanche, Escalade/EXT/ESV, Suburban, Tahoe, Yukon, Escalade/EXT/ESV, Suburban, Tahoe, Yukon Aveo, Aveo5, Camaro, Cobalt, Cobalt-GS, Colorado,Canyon, Corvette, CTS, CTS-V, CTS, CTS-V-V, DTS, Escalade/EXT/ESV, G.3, G5,Enclave, LaCrosse, Outlook, Suburban, Tahoe Traverse, Yukon **Engines:** All **Transmissions:** All	**Ignition Coil 3 Control Circuit Malfunction** Engine started; and the ECM detected an unexpected low or high voltage condition on Coil On Plug (COP) Ignition Control circuit for less than one second during the CCM test. **Note: Watch the Scan Tool Misfire Counters to identify the fault.** **Possible Causes:** • IC circuit is open, shorted to ground or shorted to power between the coil and the ECM • Ignition coil (COP) is damaged or has failed • ECM has failed
DTC: P0354 **1T CCM, MIL: Yes** **Years:** 2008, 2009 **Models:** Allure, Aura, Canyon, Colorado, LaCrosse **Engines:** 2.9L VIN 9, 3.5L VIN N, 3.8L VIN 2, 5.3L VIN C, 5.3L VIN L **Transmissions:** All	**Ignition Coil 4 Control Circuit Malfunction** Engine started; and the ECM detected an unexpected voltage condition on the Coil Near Plug Ignition Control (IC) 4 circuit for less than one second during the CCM test period. **Possible Causes:** • IC circuit is open, shorted to ground or shorted to power (B+) • IC ground (Low REF) circuit or Module ground circuit is open • IC power circuit is open (check the INJ fuse in U/H fuse block) • Ignition Coil 4 is damaged or it has failed • ECM has failed
DTC: P0354 **2T CCM, MIL: Yes** **Years:** 2008, 2009, 2010 **Models:**, Acadia, Allure, Astra, Aura, Avalanche, Escalade/EXT/ESV, Suburban, Tahoe, Yukon, Escalade/EXT/ESV, Suburban, Tahoe, Yukon Aveo, Aveo5, Camaro, Cobalt, Cobalt-GS, Colorado,Canyon, Corvette, CTS, CTS-V, CTS, CTS-V-V, DTS, Escalade/EXT/ESV, G.3, G5,Enclave, LaCrosse, Outlook, Suburban, Tahoe Traverse, Yukon **Engines:** All **Transmissions:** All	**Ignition Coil 4 Control Circuit Malfunction** Engine started; and the ECM detected an unexpected low or high voltage condition on Coil On Plug (COP) Ignition Control circuit for less than one second during the CCM test. **Note: Watch the Scan Tool Misfire Counters to identify the fault.** **Possible Causes:** • IC circuit is open, shorted to ground or shorted to power between the coil and the ECM • Ignition coil (COP) is damaged or has failed, or the ECM has failed
DTC: P0355 **1T CCM, MIL: Yes** **Years:** 2008, 2009 **Models:** Allure, Aura, Canyon, Colorado, LaCrosse **Engines:** 2.9L VIN 9, 3.5L VIN N, 3.8L VIN 2, 5.3L VIN C, 5.3L VIN L **Transmissions:** All	**Ignition Coil 5 Control Circuit Malfunction** Engine started; and the ECM detected an unexpected voltage condition on the Coil Near Plug Ignition Control (IC) 5 circuit for less than one second during the CCM test period. **Possible Causes:** • IC circuit is open, shorted to ground or shorted to power (B+) • IC ground (Low REF) circuit or Module ground circuit is open • IC power circuit is open (check the INJ fuse in U/H fuse block) • Ignition Coil 5 is damaged or it has failed • ECM has failed

DTC	Trouble Code Title, Conditions & Possible Causes
DTC: P0355 **2T CCM, MIL: Yes** **Years:** 2008, 2009, 2010 **Models:**, Acadia, Allure, Astra, Aura, Avalanche, Escalade/EXT/ESV, Suburban, Tahoe, Yukon, Escalade/EXT/ESV, Suburban, Tahoe, Yukon Aveo, Aveo5, Camaro, Cobalt, Cobalt-GS, Colorado,Canyon, Corvette, CTS, CTS-V, CTS, CTS-V-V, DTS, Escalade/EXT/ESV, G.3, G5,Enclave, LaCrosse, Outlook, Suburban, Tahoe Traverse, Yukon **Engines:** 6 & 8 Cylinders **Transmissions:** All	**Ignition Coil 5 Control Circuit Malfunction** Engine started; and the ECM detected an unexpected low or high voltage condition on Coil On Plug (COP) Ignition Control circuit for less than one second during the CCM test. **Note: Watch the Scan Tool Misfire Counters to identify the fault.** **Possible Causes:** • IC circuit is open, shorted to ground or shorted to power between the coil and the ECM • Ignition coil (COP) is damaged or has failed • ECM has failed
DTC: P0356 **1T CCM, MIL: Yes** **Years:** 2008, 2009 **Models:** Allure, Aura, Canyon, Colorado, LaCrosse **Engines:** 2.9L VIN 9, 3.5L VIN N, 3.8L VIN 2, 5.3L VIN C, 5.3L VIN L **Transmissions:** All	**Ignition Coil 6 Control Circuit Malfunction** Engine started; and the ECM detected an unexpected voltage condition on the Coil Near Plug Ignition Control (IC) 6 circuit for less than one second during the CCM test period. **Possible Causes:** • IC circuit is open, shorted to ground or shorted to power (B+) • IC ground (Low REF) circuit or Module ground circuit is open • IC power circuit is open (check the INJ fuse in U/H fuse block) • Ignition Coil 6 is damaged or it has failed • ECM has failed
DTC: P0356 **2T CCM, MIL: Yes** **Years:** 2008, 2009, 2010 **Models:**, Acadia, Allure, Astra, Aura, Avalanche, Escalade/EXT/ESV, Suburban, Tahoe, Yukon, Escalade/EXT/ESV, Suburban, Tahoe, Yukon Aveo, Aveo5, Camaro, Cobalt, Cobalt-GS, Colorado,Canyon, Corvette, CTS, CTS-V, CTS, CTS-V-V, DTS, Escalade/EXT/ESV, G.3, G5,Enclave, LaCrosse, Outlook, Suburban, Tahoe Traverse, Yukon **Engines:** 6 & 8 Cylinders **Transmissions:** All	**Ignition Coil 6 Control Circuit Malfunction** Engine started; and the ECM detected an unexpected low or high voltage condition on Coil On Plug (COP) Ignition Control circuit for less than one second during the CCM test. **Note: Watch the Scan Tool Misfire Counters to identify the fault.** **Possible Causes:** • IC circuit is open, shorted to ground or shorted to power between the coil and the ECM • Ignition coil (COP) is damaged or has failed • ECM has failed
DTC: P0357 **2T CCM, MIL: Yes** **Years:** 2008, 2009, 2010 **Models:**, Acadia, Allure, Astra, Aura, Avalanche, Escalade/EXT/ESV, Suburban, Tahoe, Yukon, Escalade/EXT/ESV, Suburban, Tahoe, Yukon Aveo, Aveo5, Camaro, Cobalt, Cobalt-GS, Colorado,Canyon, Corvette, CTS, CTS-V, CTS, CTS-V-V, DTS, Escalade/EXT/ESV, G.3, G5,Enclave, LaCrosse, Outlook, Suburban, Tahoe Traverse, Yukon **Engines:** 8 Cylinders **Transmissions:** All	**Ignition Coil 8 Control Circuit** The ignition is ON. DTC P0351-P0358 runs continuously when the above condition is met. The ECM detects an open, short to ground, short to voltage on the IC circuit. **Note: An IC circuit fault condition will result in an engine misfire, and under certain driving conditions could possibly overheat the 3-way catalytic converter.** **Possible Causes:** • Ignition coil • ECM has failed

DTC	Trouble Code Title, Conditions & Possible Causes
DTC: P0358 **1T CCM, MIL: Yes** **Years:** 2008, 2009 **Models:** Allure, Aura, Canyon, Colorado, LaCrosse **Engines:** 2.9L VIN 9, 3.5L VIN N, 3.8L VIN 2, 5.3L VIN C, 5.3L VIN L **Transmissions:** All	**Ignition Coil 8 Control Circuit Malfunction** Engine started; and the ECM detected an unexpected voltage condition on the Coil Near Plug Ignition Control (IC) 8 circuit for less than one second during the CCM test period. **Possible Causes:** • IC circuit is open, shorted to ground or shorted to power (B+) • IC ground (Low REF) circuit or Module ground circuit is open • IC power circuit is open (check the INJ fuse in U/H fuse block) • Ignition Coil 8 is damaged or it has failed • ECM has failed
DTC: P0358 **2T CCM, MIL: Yes** **Years:** 2008, 2009, 2010 **Models:**, Acadia, Allure, Astra, Aura, Avalanche, Escalade/EXT/ESV, Suburban, Tahoe, Yukon, Escalade/EXT/ESV, Suburban, Tahoe, Yukon Aveo, Aveo5, Camaro, Cobalt, Cobalt-GS, Colorado,Canyon, Corvette, CTS, CTS-V, CTS, CTS-V-V, DTS, Escalade/EXT/ESV, G.3, G5,Enclave, LaCrosse, Outlook, Suburban, Tahoe Traverse, Yukon **Engines:** 8 Cylinders **Transmissions:** All	**Ignition Coil 8 Control Circuit Malfunction** Engine started; and the ECM detected an unexpected low or high voltage condition on Coil On Plug (COP) Ignition Control circuit for less than one second during the CCM test. **Note: Watch the Scan Tool Misfire Counters to identify the fault.** **Possible Causes:** • IC circuit is open, shorted to ground or shorted to power between the coil and the ECM • Ignition coil (COP) is damaged or has failed • ECM has failed
DTC: P0365 **1T CCM, MIL: Yes** **Years:** 2008, 2009 **Models:** Astra, Aura, Aveo, Aveo5, Cobalt G3, G5 **Engines:** 1.6L VIN 6, 1.6L VIN E, 1.8L VIN 1, 2.0L VIN P, 2.0L VIN X, 2.2L VIN H, 2.2L VIN F, 2.4L VIN 5, 2.4L VIN B **Transmissions:** All	**Exhaust Camshaft Position (CMP) Sensor Performance** The engine is cranking or running. The medium resolution is less than or equal to 10 counts. DTC P0366 runs continuously when the above conditions are met. The ECM detects the incorrect number of CMP sensor pulses in 2 revolutions of the crankshaft, which is usually within 1 second. **Note: Inspect the CMP sensor for correct installation. Remove the CMP sensor from the engine and inspect the sensor and the O-ring for damage.** **Possible Causes:** • Camshaft reluctor wheel for damage • Engine oil for debris • Timing chain, tensioner, and sprockets for wear or damage. • CMP has failed • ECM has failed
DTC: P0366 **1T CCM, MIL: Yes** **Years:** 2008, 2009 **Models:** Astra, Aura, Aveo, Aveo5, Cobalt G3, G5 **Engines:** 1.6L VIN 6, 1.6L VIN E, 1.8L VIN 1, 2.0L VIN P, 2.0L VIN X, 2.2L VIN H, 2.2L VIN F, 2.4L VIN 5, 2.4L VIN B **Transmissions:** All	**Exhaust Camshaft Position (CMP) Sensor Performance (Bank 1)** The ECM detects greater than 10 crankshaft revolutions. The engine speed is less than 2,520 RPM. The DTCs run continuously once the above condition is met. The ECM detects a signal from the CMP sensor, but the number of pulses are less than or greater than what is expected for one crankshaft revolution. Or the CMP sensor does NOT correlate to the crankshaft position. Either condition must exist for greater than 1 second, or cumulative of 10 seconds. **Possible Causes:** • Low reference circuit for an open/high resistance or for a short to voltage • 5 volt reference circuit for an open/high resistance • Short to voltage in the signal circuit • Short to ground or an open/high resistance in the signal circuit. • CMP has failed • ECM has failed
DTC: P0366 **1T CCM, MIL: Yes** **Years:** 2008, 2009, 2010 **Models:** Acadia, Allure, Aura, Camaro, CTS, CTS-V, Enclave, LaCrosse, Outlook, Traverse **Engines:** 3.6L VIN 7, 3.6L VIN D, 3.6L VIN V **Transmissions:** All	**Exhaust Camshaft Position (CMP) Sensor Circuit Low Voltage (Bank 1)** The ECM detects greater than 10 crankshaft revolutions. The engine speed is less than 2,520 RPM. The DTCs run continuously once the above condition is met. The CMP sensor signal voltage is always high and the ECM detects no pulses from the CMP sensor for greater than 1 second or cumulative of 10 seconds. **Possible Causes:** • Low reference circuit for an open/high resistance or for a short to voltage • 5 volt reference circuit for an open/high resistance • Short to voltage in the signal circuit • Short to ground or an open/high resistance in the signal circuit. • CMP has failed • ECM has failed

DTC	Trouble Code Title, Conditions & Possible Causes
DTC: P0367 **1T CCM, MIL: Yes** **Years:** 2008, 2009, 2010 **Models:** Acadia, Allure, Aura, Camaro, CTS, CTS-V, Enclave, LaCrosse, Outlook, Traverse **Engines:** 3.6L VIN 7, 3.6L VIN D, 3.6L VIN V **Transmissions:** All	**Exhaust Camshaft Position (CMP) Sensor Circuit High Voltage (Bank 1)** The ECM detects greater than 10 crankshaft revolutions. The engine speed is less than 2,520 RPM. The DTCs run continuously once the above condition is met. The CMP sensor signal voltage is always high and the ECM detects no pulses from the CMP sensor for greater than 1 second or cumulative of 10 seconds. **Possible Causes:** • Low reference circuit for an open/high resistance or for a short to voltage • 5 volt reference circuit for an open/high resistance • Short to voltage in the signal circuit • Short to ground or an open/high resistance in the signal circuit. • CMP has failed • ECM has failed
DTC: P0368 **1T CCM, MIL: Yes** **Years:** 2008, 2009, 2010 **Models:** Acadia, Allure, Aura, Camaro, CTS, CTS-V, Enclave, LaCrosse, Outlook, Traverse **Engines:** 3.6L VIN 7, 3.6L VIN D, 3.6L VIN V **Transmissions:** All	**Exhaust Camshaft Position (CMP) Sensor Performance (Bank 2)** The ECM detects greater than 10 crankshaft revolutions. The engine speed is less than 2,520 RPM. The DTCs run continuously once the above condition is met. The ECM detects a signal from the CMP sensor, but the number of pulses are less than or greater than what is expected for one crankshaft revolution. Or the CMP sensor does NOT correlate to the crankshaft position. Either condition must exist for greater than 1 second, or cumulative of 10 seconds. **Possible Causes:** • Low reference circuit for an open/high resistance or for a short to voltage • 5 volt reference circuit for an open/high resistance • Short to voltage in the signal circuit • Short to ground or an open/high resistance in the signal circuit. • CMP has failed • ECM has failed
DTC: P0391 **1T CCM, MIL: Yes** **Years:** 2008, 2009, 2010 **Models:** Acadia, Allure, Aura, Camaro, CTS, CTS-V, Enclave, LaCrosse, Outlook, Traverse **Engines:** 3.6L VIN 7, 3.6L VIN D, 3.6L VIN V **Transmissions:** All	**Exhaust Camshaft Position (CMP) Sensor Circuit Low Voltage (Bank 2)** The ECM detects greater than 10 crankshaft revolutions. The engine speed is less than 2,520 RPM. The DTCs run continuously once the above condition is met. The CMP sensor signal voltage is always high and the ECM detects no pulses from the CMP sensor for greater than 1 second or cumulative of 10 seconds. **Possible Causes:** • Low reference circuit for an open/high resistance or for a short to voltage • 5 volt reference circuit for an open/high resistance • Short to voltage in the signal circuit • Short to ground or an open/high resistance in the signal circuit. • CMP has failed • ECM has failed
DTC: P0392 **1T CCM, MIL: Yes** **Years:** 2008, 2009, 2010 **Models:** Acadia, Allure, Aura, Camaro, CTS, CTS-V, Enclave, LaCrosse, Outlook, Traverse **Engines:** 3.6L VIN 7, 3.6L VIN D, 3.6L VIN V **Transmissions:** All	**Exhaust Camshaft Position (CMP) Sensor Circuit High Voltage (Bank 2)** The ECM detects greater than 10 crankshaft revolutions. The engine speed is less than 2,520 RPM. The DTCs run continuously once the above condition is met. The CMP sensor signal voltage is always high and the ECM detects no pulses from the CMP sensor for greater than 1 second or cumulative of 10 seconds. **Possible Causes:** • Low reference circuit for an open/high resistance or for a short to voltage • 5 volt reference circuit for an open/high resistance • Short to voltage in the signal circuit • Short to ground or an open/high resistance in the signal circuit. • CMP has failed • ECM has failed
DTC: P0393 **1T CCM, MIL: Yes** **Years:** 2008, 2009, 2010 **Models:** Acadia, Allure, Aura, Camaro, CTS, CTS-V, Enclave, LaCrosse, Outlook, Traverse **Engines:** 3.6L VIN 7, 3.6L VIN D, 3.6L VIN V **Transmissions:** All	**Insufficient EGR Flow Detected** DTC P0101, P0102, P0103, P0107, P0108, P0112, P0113, P0116, P0117, P0118, P0121, P0122, P0123, P0403, P0404, P0405, P0502, P0503, P0506, P0507, P0641, P0651, P1374, P1404 not set, engine started, ECT sensor more than 167°F, IAT sensor from 32-212°F, system voltage 11-18v, BARO sensor more than 74 kPa, IAC steady (5 counts), A/C Clutch and TR signals stable, then vehicle driven to over 50 MPH at an engine speed of 1050-1300 RPM, MAP sensor from 15-70 kPa, followed by a deceleration period with the TP angle less than 1.3%, and the ECM detected the amount of MAP sensor change monitored with the valve open and then closed during deceleration indicated insufficient EGR flow. The EGR flow test is enabled by the ECM during deceleration. A change from 0 to a value over +0 in the Desired EGR and Actual EGR Position PID will appear on a Scan Tool. The ECM Allows one EGR flow test in each key cycle. To verify a repair, the ECM will Allow up to 12 EGR flow test counts during the first key cycle after codes are cleared. From 9-12 EGR flow tests are enough to detect adequate EGR flow. **Possible Causes:** • Base engine problem (e.g., a severely restricted exhaust) • EGR vacuum hoses damaged, loose or routed incorrectly • EGR passages or intake passages clogged or restricted • EGR solenoid valve is clogged (carbon), damaged or has failed • TSB 87-65-22 contains a repair procedure for this code

DTC	Trouble Code Title, Conditions & Possible Causes
DTC: P0403 **1T CCM, MIL: Yes** **Years:** 2008, 2009 **Models:** DTS **Engines:** 4.6L VIN Y **Transmissions:** All	**Exhaust Gas Recirculation (EGR) Solenoid Control Circuit** The Ignition 1 Signal parameter is between 9-18 volts. The engine is cranking or running. The DTC P0401 intrusive test is not active. These DTCs run continuously once the above conditions are met. **Possible Causes:** • EGR valve low control circuit for an open/high resistance • EGR valve high control circuit for a short to voltage • EGR valve low reference circuit and ground • EGR valve low reference circuit for an open/high resistance • EGR valve 5-volt reference circuit for a short to ground • EGR valve 5-volt reference circuit for a short to voltage • EGR valve signal circuit for a short to voltage • EGR valve signal circuit for a short to ground or an open/high resistance • EGR sensor has failed • ECM has failed
DTC: P0404 **1T CCM, MIL: Yes** **Years:** 2008, 2009 **Models:** DTS **Engines:** 4.6L VIN Y **Transmissions:** All	**Exhaust Gas Recirculation (EGR) Open Position Performance** The Ignition 1 Signal parameter is between 9-18 volts. The engine is cranking or running. The DTC P0401 intrusive test is not active. These DTCs run continuously once the above conditions are met. The EGR valve is commanded open. DTC P0641 and P0651 are not set. **Possible Causes:** • EGR valve low control circuit for an open/high resistance • EGR valve high control circuit for a short to voltage • EGR valve low reference circuit and ground • EGR valve low reference circuit for an open/high resistance • EGR valve 5-volt reference circuit for a short to ground • EGR valve 5-volt reference circuit for a short to voltage • EGR valve signal circuit for a short to voltage • EGR valve signal circuit for a short to ground or an open/high resistance • EGR sensor has failed • ECM has failed
DTC: P0405 **1T CCM, MIL: Yes** **Years:** 2008, 2009 **Models:** DTS **Engines:** 4.6L VIN Y **Transmissions:** All	**Exhaust Gas Recirculation (EGR) Position Sensor Circuit Low Voltage** The Ignition 1 Signal parameter is between 9-18 volts. The engine is cranking or running. The DTC P0401 intrusive test is not active. These DTCs run continuously once the above conditions are met. DTC P0641 and P0651 are not set. **Possible Causes:** • EGR valve low control circuit for an open/high resistance • EGR valve high control circuit for a short to voltage • EGR valve low reference circuit and ground • EGR valve low reference circuit for an open/high resistance • EGR valve 5-volt reference circuit for a short to ground • EGR valve 5-volt reference circuit for a short to voltage • EGR valve signal circuit for a short to voltage • EGR valve signal circuit for a short to ground or an open/high resistance • EGR sensor has failed • ECM has failed
DTC: P0405 **2T CCM, MIL: Yes** **Years:** 2008, 2009, 2010 **Models:** Avalanche, Camaro, Canyon, Escalade/EXT/ESV, Suburban, Tahoe, Yukon **Engines:** 4.8L VIN C, 5.3L VIN 0, 5.3L VIN 3, 5.3L VIN J, 5.3L VIN L, 6.0L VIN K, 6.0L VIN Y, 6.2L VIN J, 6.2L VIN W, 6.2L VIN 8 **Transmissions:** All	**Secondary AIR System Performance** DTC P0030, P0036, P0101-P0103, P0112, P0113, P0116-P0118, P0121-P0123, P0125, P0131-P0138, P0140, P0141, P0171, P0172, P0300, P0440, P0442, P0446, P0449, P0502-P0503, P1111-P1115, P1121-P1122, P1133, P1134, P1380, P1381 and P1441 not set, engine started, vehicle driven to over 25 MPH at over 1200 RPM for 10 seconds, BARO sensor over 75 kPa, ECT sensor from 41-230°F, MAF sensor at 2-25 g/sec, IAT sensor from 41-158°F, A/F Ratio over 13.0:1, engine load from 0-50%, and the ECM detected the HO2S signal was too high and the SHRTFT did not increase a calibrated amount with the AIR system "on" (test must fail 3 times). **Possible Causes:** • AIR solenoid power circuit is open (check the U/H IGN fuse) • AIR pump is damaged or has failed (inspect air pump for water) • AIR system check valves and/or pipes are damaged or leaking • AIR system hoses or lines are damaged, pinched or kinked • Base engine problem (e.g., excessive exhaust back pressure) • ECM has failed • TSB 99-06-04-048 contains a repair procedure for this code

DTC	Trouble Code Title, Conditions & Possible Causes
DTC: P0406 **1T CCM, MIL: Yes** **Years:** 2008, 2009 **Models:** DTS **Engines:** 4.6L VIN Y **Transmissions:** All	**Exhaust Gas Recirculation (EGR) Position Sensor Circuit High Voltage** The Ignition 1 Signal parameter is between 9-18 volts. The engine is cranking or running. The DTC P0401 intrusive test is not active. These DTCs run continuously once the above conditions are met. DTC P0641 and P0651 are not set. The EGR valve is not being commanded with a scan tool. **Possible Causes:** • EGR valve low control circuit for an open/high resistance • EGR valve high control circuit for a short to voltage • EGR valve low reference circuit and ground • EGR valve low reference circuit for an open/high resistance • EGR valve 5-volt reference circuit for a short to ground • EGR valve 5-volt reference circuit for a short to voltage • EGR valve signal circuit for a short to voltage • EGR valve signal circuit for a short to ground or an open/high resistance • EGR sensor has failed • ECM has failed
DTC: P0411 **1T CCM, MIL: Yes** **Years:** 2008, 2009 **Models:** DTS **Engines:** 4.6L VIN Y **Transmissions:** All	**Secondary Air Injection (AIR) System Incorrect Air Flow Detected** DTCs P0068, P0101, P0102, P0103, P0106, P0107, P0108, P0112, P0113, P0116, P0117, P0118, P0128, P0201-P0208, P0300, P0301-P0308, P0351-P0358, P0412, P0418, P0420, P0606, P0641, P0651, P2430, P2431, P2432, P2433, P2440, 2444 are not set. The system voltage is between 11-18V. The start-up intake air temperature (IAT) is greater than 5°C (41°F). The start-up engine coolant temperature (ECT) is between 5-80°C (41-176°F). The AIR system is commanded ON. The conditions are stable for greater than 5 seconds. DTC P0411 runs once per trip start-up when the above conditions are met and AIR pump operation is requested. The ECM determines that the difference between the predicted system pressure and the actual system pressure is greater than 6 kPa.Or. The ECM determines that the difference between the predicted system pressure and the actual system pressure is less than −5 kPa. DTC P0411 sets during phase 1 and within 22 seconds when the above conditions are met. **Possible Causes:** • AIR pump relay has failed • AIR pump has failed • AIR solenoid relay has failed • AIR solenoid valve has failed • Test or inspect the AIR solenoid valve outlet pipe and exhaust manifold for a restriction • Air injection check valve
DTC: P0412 **1T CCM, MIL: Yes** **Years:** 2008, 2009 **Models:** DTS **Engines:** 4.6L VIN Y **Transmissions:** All	**Secondary Air Injection (AIR) Solenoid Control Circuit** The system voltage is between 9-18V. The ignition is ON. These DTCs run on a 250 ms loop. DTCs P0412 and P0418 run continuously when the above conditions are met. The ECM determines that the actual and expected states of the AIR solenoid and AIR pump relay control circuits do not match. DTCs P0412 or P0418 set when the above condition exists for greater than 4 seconds. **Possible Causes:** • AIR pump relay has failed • AIR pump has failed • AIR solenoid relay has failed • AIR solenoid valve has failed • Test or inspect the AIR solenoid valve outlet pipe and exhaust manifold for a restriction • Air injection check valve
DTC: P0418 **1T CCM, MIL: Yes** **Years:** 2008, 2009 **Models:** DTS **Engines:** 4.6L VIN Y **Transmissions:** All	**Secondary Air Injection (AIR) Pump Control Circuit** The system voltage is between 9-18V. The ignition is ON. These DTCs run on a 250 ms loop. DTCs P0412 and P0418 run continuously when the above conditions are met. The ECM determines that the actual and expected states of the AIR solenoid and AIR pump relay control circuits do not match. DTCs P0412 or P0418 set when the above condition exists for greater than 4 seconds. **Possible Causes:** • AIR pump relay has failed • AIR pump has failed • AIR solenoid relay has failed • AIR solenoid valve has failed • Test or inspect the AIR solenoid valve outlet pipe and exhaust manifold for a restriction • Air injection check valve

DTC	Trouble Code Title, Conditions & Possible Causes
DTC: P0420 **1T CCM, MIL: Yes** **Years:** 2008, 2009 **Models:** Corvette, CTS, CTS-V, DTS **Engines:** 4.6L VIN Y, 6.2L VIN W, 6.2L VIN P, 6.2L VIN R, 7.0L VIN E **Transmissions:** All	**Catalyst System Low Efficiency (Bank 1)** DTCs P0030, P0031, P0036, P0037, P0038, P0068, P0106, P0107, P0108, P0112, P0113, P0117, P0118, P0120, P0121, P0122, P0123, P0125, P0128, P0130, P0131, P0132, P0133, P0134, P0135, P0136, P0137, P0138, P0140, P0141, P0171, P0172, P0201, P0202, P0203, P0204, P0205, P0206, P0207, P0208, P0220, P0300, P0315, P0326, P0327, P0336, P0340, P0341, P0442, P0446, P0452, P0453, P0455, P0496, P0500 (manual transmission only), P0502, P0506, P0507, P0601, P0602, P0606, P0641, P0722, P0723, P1133, P1134, P1516, P1621, P2135, P2138, P2176 are not set. The engine has been running for greater than 2 minutes. The vehicle has been driven at greater than 1,000 RPM with the mass air flow (MAF) greater than 18 g/s for greater than 30 seconds. The vehicle is in Closed Loop. The vehicle has Fuel Trim Learn enabled. The Engine Coolant Temperature (ECT) parameter is between 45-128°C (113-262°F). The Barometric Pressure (BARO) parameter is greater than 70 kPa. The Catalytic Converter Calculated Temperature parameter is greater than or equal to 420°C (788°F). The Intake Air Temperature (IAT) parameter is between −20 and +85°C (−4 and +185°F). The battery voltage is more than 11 volts. The ECM has determined the catalyst efficiency has degraded below a calibrated threshold. This diagnostic may conclude in one test attempt. However, this diagnostic may require as many as 18 test attempts, which would require at least 3 drive cycles. Each test attempt may conclude within approximately 1 minute. **Possible Causes:** • Engine misfire • High engine oil or high coolant consumption • Retarded spark timing • A weak or poor spark • A lean fuel mixture • A rich fuel mixture • A damaged oxygen sensor or wiring harness • Catalytic converter
DTC: P0420 **1T CCM, MIL: Yes** **Years:** 2008, 2009 **Models:** Allure, Aura, Canyon, Colorado, LaCrosse **Engines:** 2.9L VIN 9, 3.5L VIN N, 3.8L VIN 2, 5.3L VIN C, 5.3L VIN L **Transmissions:** All	**Catalyst System Bank 1 Low Efficiency** DTC P0030, P0101-P0103, P0107, P0108, P0112, P0113, P0116-P0118, P0121-P0123, P0128, P0130-P0138, P0140, P0141, P0171, P0172, P0201-P0206, P0300, P0336, P0341, P0404, P0405, P0410, P0440, P0442, P0443, P0502, P0503, P0506, P0507, P1133, P1134, P1351, P1352, P1361, P1362 and P1441 not set, engine runtime over 10 minutes, system voltage over 10.0v, BARO sensor more than 75 kPa, ECT sensor from 169-255°F, IAT sensor from −4°F to 212°F, engine running in closed loop, and the ECM detected the catalyst oxygen storage capacity had degraded. Test Instructions: To activate the test, return to idle and place vehicle in Drive (depress the clutch pedal for manual transmission vehicles). Then within 60 seconds, the A/F ratio will go below 14.1 for up to 8 seconds (and may go to above 15.3 for up to 10 seconds). Use a Scan Tool to monitor DTC P0420 to determine if the current trip passes or fails. The catalytic catalyst promotes a chemical reaction that oxidizes the amount of HC and CO in the exhaust gas to convert them into water vapor and CO2. It also reduces NOx by converting it to nitrogen. The converter has the ability to store excess oxygen and then release it. **Possible Causes:** • Air leaks at the exhaust manifold or in the exhaust pipes • Base engine problems (i.e., high engine oil or coolant usage) • Catalytic converter is damaged, contaminated or has failed • Continuous engine misfire conditions, or weak or low coil output • Front HO2S or rear HO2S is contaminated with fuel or moisture • Rear HO2S is loose in the mounting hole (check it for a leak) • Front HO2S older (aged) than the rear HO2S (HO2S-12 is lazy)
DTC: P0420 **1T CCM, MIL: Yes** **Years:** 2008, 2009, 2010 **Models:** Acadia, Allure, Aura, Camaro, CTS, CTS-V, Enclave, LaCrosse, Outlook, Traverse **Engines:** 3.6L VIN 7, 3.6L VIN D, 3.6L VIN V **Transmissions:** All	**Catalyst System Low Efficiency (Bank 1)** DTC P0101-P0103, P0106-P0108, P0112, P0113, P0117, P0118, P0120, P0121-123, P0125, P0128, P0131-P0138, P0140, P0141, P0171-P0172, P0177-P0179, P0200, P0220, P0300, P0325, P0327, P0332, P0335, P0336, P0341-P0343, P0351-P0358, P0442-P0446, P0452-P0453, P0455, P0496, P0502-P0503, P1125, P1133, P1153, P1258, P1514- P1518, P2108 or P2135 not set, engine started, ECT sensor from 158-248°F, BARO sensor over 74 kPa, IAT sensor at 5-185°F, vehicle driven in closed loop at cruise speed for 40-45 seconds, and the ECM detected that the Oxygen storage capability of the Catalyst was degraded. **Possible Causes:** • Air leaks at the exhaust manifold or in the exhaust pipes • Base engine problems (i.e., high engine oil or coolant usage) • Catalytic converter is damaged, contaminated or has failed • Continuous engine misfire conditions, or weak or low coil output • Front HO2S or rear HO2S is contaminated with fuel or moisture • Rear HO2S is loose in the mounting hole (check it for a leak) • TSB 81-65-37 contains a repair procedure for this code

DTC	Trouble Code Title, Conditions & Possible Causes
DTC: P0420 **2T CAT, MIL: Yes** **Years:** 2008, 2009, 2010 **Models:** Avalanche, Camaro, Canyon, Escalade/EXT/ESV, Suburban, Tahoe, Yukon **Engines:** 4.8L VIN C, 5.3L VIN 0, 5.3L VIN 3, 5.3L VIN J, 5.3L VIN L, 6.0L VIN K, 6.0L VIN Y, 6.2L VIN J, 6.2L VIN W, 6.2L VIN 8 **Transmissions:** All	**Catalyst System Low Efficiency** DTCs P000A, P000B, P0010, P0013, P0016, P0017, P0030, P0031, P0032, P0036, P0053, P0038, P0068, P0101, P0102, P0103, P0116, P0117, P0118, P0119, P0121, P0122, P0123, P0130, P0131, P0132, P0133, P0134, P0135, P0136, P0137, P0138, P0139, P0140, P0141, P0171, P0201, P0202, P0203, P0204, P0221, P0222, P0223, P0261, P0262, P0264, P0265, P0267, P0268, P0270, P0271, P0301, P0302, P0303, P0304, P0335, P0336, P0340, P0365, P0366, P0443, P0446, P0458, P0459, P0496, P0562, P0563, P0642, P0643, P0652, P0653, P065E, P0661, P0662, P1101, P2088, P2089, P2090, P2091, P2096, P2097, P2100, P2101, P2122, P2123, P2127, P2128, P2176, P2227, P2228, P2229, P2297, P2301, P2303, P2304, P2306, P2307, P2309, P2310, P2A00, P2A01 are not set. The engine speed is between 1,040-2,760 RPM. The engine load is between 15-50 percent. The vehicle is in Closed Loop. The calculated exhaust mass gas flow is between 5-55.56 g/sec, and stable. The calculated catalyst temperature is between 400-850°C (852-1,562°F), and stable. The ambient temperature is more than −15°C (+5°F). The rear HO2S has exceeded the dew point for more than 60 seconds. This diagnostic attempts one test during each period when the above conditions have been met. This diagnostic attempts up to 4 tests during each drive cycle. The ECM has determined the catalyst efficiency has degraded below a calibrated thresholdThis diagnostic may conclude in 6 test attempts which will require at least 2 drive cycles. However, this diagnostic may require as many as 8 test attempts. Depending on driving conditions, more than 2 drive cycles may be required. Each test attempt may conclude within approximately 1 minute. **Note: A new converter with less than 100 miles on it may set DTC P0420 due to out-gassing of the internal matting. Operating the vehicle at highway speeds for approximately 1 hour may correct the condition.** **Possible Causes:** • Air leaks at the exhaust manifold or in the exhaust pipes • Base engine problems (i.e., high engine oil or coolant usage) • Catalytic converter is damaged, contaminated or has failed • Continuous engine misfire conditions, or weak or low coil output • Front HO2S or rear HO2S is contaminated with fuel or moisture • Rear HO2S is loose in the mounting hole (check it for a leak) • Front HO2S older (aged) than the rear HO2S (HO2S-12 is lazy)
DTC: P0420 **1T CCM, MIL: Yes** **Years:** 2008, 2009 **Models:** Astra, Aura, Aveo, Aveo5, Cobalt G3, G5 **Engines:** 1.6L VIN 6, 1.6L VIN E, 1.8L VIN 1, 2.0L VIN P, 2.0L VIN X, 2.2L VIN H, 2.2L VIN F, 2.4L VIN 5, 2.4L VIN B **Transmissions:** All	**Catalyst System Low Efficiency (Bank 1)** DTC P0101-P0103, P0106-P0108, P0112-P0118, P0128, P0131-P0137, P0140, P0141, P0151-P0158, P0160, P0161, P0171-P0175, P0200, P0300, P0335, P0336, P0341-P0343, P0351-P0358, P0410, P0440, P0502-P0503, P0506-P0507, P0606, P1120, P1133, P1134, P1153, P1154, P1220, P1336, P1415, P1416 and P1441 not set, engine speed over 850 RPM for 230 seconds since last idle, VSS under 85 MPH, BARO sensor over 75 kPa, ECT sensor over 167°F, IAT sensor at 19-167°F, MAF sensor at 14-40 g/sec, MAP sensor from 25-80 kPa, and the ECM detected the Catalyst was degraded. **Possible Causes:** • Air leaks at the exhaust manifold or in the exhaust pipes • Base engine problems (i.e., high engine oil or coolant usage) • Catalytic converter is damaged, contaminated or has failed • Continuous engine misfire conditions, or weak or low coil output • Front HO2S or rear HO2S is contaminated with fuel or moisture • Rear HO2S is loose in the mounting hole (check it for a leak) • Front HO2S older (aged) than the rear HO2S (HO2S-12 is lazy)
DTC: P042E **1T CCM, MIL: Yes** **Years:** 2008, 2009 **Models:** DTS **Engines:** 4.6L VIN Y **Transmissions:** All	**Exhaust Gas Recirculation (EGR) Closed Position Performance** The Ignition 1 Signal parameter is between 9-18 volts. The engine is cranking or running. The DTC P0401 intrusive test is not active. These DTCs run continuously once the above conditions are met. DTC P0641 and P0651 are not set. **Possible Causes:** • EGR valve low control circuit for an open/high resistance • EGR valve high control circuit for a short to voltage • EGR valve low reference circuit and ground • EGR valve low reference circuit for an open/high resistance • EGR valve 5-volt reference circuit for a short to ground • EGR valve 5-volt reference circuit for a short to voltage • EGR valve signal circuit for a short to voltage • EGR valve signal circuit for a short to ground or an open/high resistance • EGR sensor has failed • ECM has failed

DTC	Trouble Code Title, Conditions & Possible Causes
DTC: P0430 **1T CCM, MIL: Yes** **Years:** 2008, 2009 **Models:** Corvette, CTS, CTS-V **Engines:** 6.2L VIN W, 6.2L VIN P, 6.2L VIN R, 7.0L VIN E **Transmissions:** All	**Catalyst System Low Efficiency (Bank 2)** DTCs P0030, P0031, P0036, P0037, P0038, P0068, P0106, P0107, P0108, P0112, P0113, P0117, P0118, P0120, P0121, P0122, P0123, P0125, P0128, P0130, P0131, P0132, P0133, P0134, P0135, P0136, P0137, P0138, P0140, P0141, P0171, P0172, P0201, P0202, P0203, P0204, P0205, P0206, P0207, P0208, P0220, P0300, P0315, P0326, P0327, P0336, P0340, P0341, P0442, P0446, P0452, P0453, P0455, P0496, P0500 (manual transmission only), P0502, P0506, P0507, P0601, P0602, P0606, P0641, P0722, P0723, P1133, P1134, P1516, P1621, P2135, P2138, P2176 are not set. The engine has been running for greater than 2 minutes. The vehicle has been driven at greater than 1,000 RPM with the mass air flow (MAF) greater than 18 g/s for greater than 30 seconds. The vehicle is in Closed Loop. The vehicle has Fuel Trim Learn enabled. The Engine Coolant Temperature (ECT) parameter is between 45-128°C (113-262°F). The Barometric Pressure (BARO) parameter is greater than 70 kPa. The Catalytic Converter Calculated Temperature parameter is greater than or equal to 420°C (788°F). The Intake Air Temperature (IAT) parameter is between −20 and +85°C (−4 and +185°F). The battery voltage is more than 11 volts. The ECM has determined the catalyst efficiency has degraded below a calibrated threshold. This diagnostic may conclude in one test attempt. However, this diagnostic may require as many as 18 test attempts, which would require at least 3 drive cycles. Each test attempt may conclude within approximately 1 minute. **Possible Causes:** • Engine misfire • High engine oil or high coolant consumption • Retarded spark timing • A weak or poor spark • A lean fuel mixture • A rich fuel mixture • A damaged oxygen sensor or wiring harness • Catalytic converter
DTC: P0430 **1T CCM, MIL: Yes** **Years:** 2008, 2009, 2010 **Models:** Acadia, Allure, Aura, Camaro, CTS, CTS-V, Enclave, LaCrosse, Outlook, Traverse **Engines:** 3.6L VIN 7, 3.6L VIN D, 3.6L VIN V **Transmissions:** All	**Catalyst System Low Efficiency (Bank 2)** DTC P0101-P0103, P0106-P0108, P0112-P0118, P0125, P0131, P0132-P0138, P0140, P0141, P0151-P0158, P0160, P0161, P0171-P0175, P0200, P0300, P0325, P0327, P0335, 336, P0341, P0343, P0351-P0358, P0443-P0449, P0502, P0503, P0506, P0507, P1120, P1125, P1133, P1134, P1153, P1154, P1220, P1221, P1275, P1276, P1280-P1286, P1441, P1514-P1518 not set, engine runtime over 6 minutes, ECT sensor over 167°F, BARO sensor over 72 kPa, IAT sensor over 16°F, MAF sensor from 15-50 g/sec, Catalyst Temperature over 840°F, engine running at idle speed for 2 minutes with Actual idle speed within 100-125 RPM of the Desired idle speed, vehicle driven to 22-85 MPH, less than a 10% change in engine load, fuel trim stable, and the ECM detected the Catalyst was degraded. **Possible Causes:** • Air leaks at the exhaust manifold or in the exhaust pipes • Base engine problems (i.e., high engine oil or coolant usage) • Catalytic converter is damaged, contaminated or has failed • Continuous engine misfire conditions, or weak or low coil output • Front HO2S or rear HO2S is contaminated with fuel or moisture • Rear HO2S is loose in the mounting hole (check it for a leak)
DTC: P0430 **2T CAT, MIL: Yes** **Years:** 2008, 2009, 2010 **Models:** Avalanche, Camaro, Canyon, Escalade/EXT/ESV, Suburban, Tahoe, Yukon **Engines:** 4.8L VIN C, 5.3L VIN 0, 5.3L VIN 3, 5.3L VIN J, 5.3L VIN L, 6.0L VIN K, 6.0L VIN Y, 6.2L VIN J, 6.2L VIN W, 6.2L VIN 8 **Transmissions:** All	**Catalyst System Low Efficiency (Bank 2)** DTC P0101-P0103, P0107, P0108, P0112-P0118, P0121-P0123, P0125, P0171-P0175, P0200, P0230, P0300, P0325-P0327, P0332-P0336, P0341-P0343, P0351-P0358, P0401-P0405, P0410, P0412, P0418, P0440-P0449, P0500, P0704, P0801-0803, P1258, P1336, P1404, P1415, P1416, P1441, no HO2S codes set, engine started, engine speed over 1000 RPM for a period of 37-44 seconds, BARO sensor more than 75 kPa, ECT sensor from 167-248°F, IAT sensor from 64-176°F, MAF sensor from 12-32 g/sec, and the ECM detected the Bank 2 Catalyst was degraded below a calibrated level. **Possible Causes:** • Air leaks at the exhaust manifold or in the exhaust pipes • Base engine problems (i.e., high engine oil or coolant usage) • Catalytic converter is damaged, contaminated or has failed • Continuous engine misfire conditions, or weak or low coil output • Front HO2S or rear HO2S is contaminated with fuel or moisture • Rear HO2S is loose in the mounting hole (check it for a leak) • Front HO2S older (aged) than the rear HO2S (HO2S-12 is lazy)

DTC	Trouble Code Title, Conditions & Possible Causes
DTC: P0442 **1T CCM, MIL: Yes** **Years:** 2008, 2009 **Models:** Corvette, CTS, CTS-V, DTS **Engines:** 4.6L VIN Y, 6.2L VIN W, 6.2L VIN P, 6.2L VIN R, 7.0L VIN E **Transmissions:** All	**Evaporative Emission (EVAP) System Small Leak Detected** DTCs P0106, P0107, P0108, P0112, P0113, P0116, P0117, P0118, P0120, P0121, P0122, P0123, P0222, P0223, P0443, P0446, P0449, P0451, P0452, P0453, P0454, P0455, P0461, P0462, P0463, P0464, P0496, P0502, P0503, P0608, P0641, P0651, P1516, P2101, P2119, P2120, P2122, P2123, P2125, P2127, P2128, P2135, P2138 are not set. The ignition 1 voltage is between 10-16 volts. The Barometric Pressure (BARO) is greater than 74 kPa. No fuel filling during the EONV test period. The fuel level is between 15-85 percent. The start-up Engine Coolant Temperature (ECT) and the start-up Intake Air Temperature (IAT) are between 0-40°C (32-104°F). The Barometric Pressure (BARO) is more than 74 kPa. The engine run time before engine shut-off was greater than 10 minutes. The drive distance before engine shut-off was more than 5 kilometers (3.1 miles). The ignition is OFF. The ambient air temperature at the end of the drive cycle is between 0-32°C (32-93°F). DTC P0442 runs once per drive cycle during the hot soak period after the ignition is turned OFF and may require up to 45 minutes to complete. The controller will not make more than 2 test attempts per day. The time since the last completed EONV test must be at least 17 hours. The ECM detects a leak in the EVAP system that is greater than a calibrated amount. **Note: Inject smoke in less than 2-minute cycles for optimum tester performance.** **Possible Causes:** • Small leak in the EVAP system
DTC: P0442 **1T CCM, MIL: Yes** **Years:** 2008, 2009 **Models:** Allure, Aura, Canyon, Colorado, LaCrosse **Engines:** 2.9L VIN 9, 3.5L VIN N, 3.8L VIN 2, 5.3L VIN C, 5.3L VIN L **Transmissions:** All	**EVAP System Small Leak (0.040") Detected** DTC P0107, P0108, P0112, P0113, P0116, P0117, P0118, P0125, P0440, P0443, P0455, P0449, P0452, P0453, P1111, P1112, P1114, P1115, P1120, P1220 and P1221 not set, ECT and IAT sensors from 39-86°F and within 16°F at startup, engine started, vehicle driven at less than 75 MPH, system voltage over 10.0v, BARO sensor over 75 kPa, fuel level from 15-85%, DTC P0125 not active, and the ECM detected the EVAP system was able to achieve proper vacuum, but that a vacuum decay condition was detected. **Possible Causes:** • Charcoal canister is loaded with fuel or moisture • Fuel filler cap is loose, cross-threaded, damaged or wrong part • Fuel tank, fuel filler neck or fuel sending unit 'O' ring is leaking • Fuel tank pressure sensor is damaged, disconnected or it failed • Fuel tank vapor line(s) is clogged, damaged or disconnected • Purge valve vapor line is clogged, damaged, or disconnected • Purge solenoid or Vent solenoid has a small leaking (sticking) • ECM has failed
DTC: P0442 **2T EVAP, MIL: Yes** **Years:** 2008, 2009, 2010 **Models:** Avalanche, Camaro, Canyon, Escalade/EXT/ESV, Suburban, Tahoe, Yukon **Engines:** 4.8L VIN C, 5.3L VIN 0, 5.3L VIN 3, 5.3L VIN J, 5.3L VIN L, 6.0L VIN K, 6.0L VIN Y, 6.2L VIN J, 6.2L VIN W, 6.2L VIN 8 **Transmissions:** All	**EVAP System Small Leak (0.040") Detected** DTC P0107, P0108, P0112-P0118, P0121-P0123, P0125, P0443, P0449, P0452, P0453, P1111-P1115, P1121 and P1122 not set, engine started, ECT and IAT sensors from 39-86°F and within 16°F at startup, BARO sensor over 75 kPa, system voltage over 10.0v, vehicle speed less than 75 MPH and steady, fuel level at 15-85%, and the ECM detected the EVAP system achieved proper vacuum, but a vacuum decay condition was detected in the test. **Possible Causes:** • Charcoal canister is loaded with fuel or moisture • Fuel filler cap is loose, cross-threaded, damaged or wrong part • Fuel tank, fuel filler neck or fuel sending unit 'O' ring is leaking • Fuel tank pressure sensor is damaged, disconnected or it failed • Fuel tank vapor line(s) is clogged, damaged or disconnected • Purge valve vapor line is clogged, damaged, or disconnected • Purge solenoid or Vent solenoid has a small leaking (sticking) • ECM has failed
DTC: P0442 **1T CCM, MIL: Yes** **Years:** 2008, 2009 **Models:** Astra, Aura, Aveo, Aveo5, Cobalt G3, G5 **Engines:** 1.6L VIN 6, 1.6L VIN E, 1.8L VIN 1, 2.0L VIN P, 2.0L VIN X, 2.2L VIN H, 2.2L VIN F, 2.4L VIN 5, 2.4L VIN B **Transmissions:** All	**Evaporative Emission (EVAP) System Small Leak Detected** The control module detects approximately 6 vacuum/pressure changes significantly less than a calibrated amount. The condition exists during the engine OFF test, then a 5 second delay for the MIL after engine start up **Note: Introduce smoke at 15 second intervals while testing the system.** **Possible Causes:** • Damaged EVAP purge solenoid • Damaged EVAP vent valve or EVAP canister • Incorrectly routed, kinked, or damaged EVAP pipes and hoses
DTC: P0442 **1T CCM, MIL: Yes** **Years:** 2008, 2009, 2010 **Models:** Acadia, Allure, Aura, Camaro, CTS, CTS-V, Enclave, LaCrosse, Outlook, Traverse **Engines:** 3.6L VIN 7, 3.6L VIN D, 3.6L VIN V **Transmissions:** All	**Evaporative Emission (EVAP) System Small Leak Detected** The control module detects approximately 6 vacuum/pressure changes significantly less than a calibrated amount. The condition exists during the engine OFF test, then a 5 second delay for the MIL after engine start up **Note: Introduce smoke at 15 second intervals while testing the system.** **Possible Causes:** • Damaged EVAP purge solenoid • Damaged EVAP vent valve or EVAP canister • Incorrectly routed, kinked, or damaged EVAP pipes and hoses

DTC	Trouble Code Title, Conditions & Possible Causes
DTC: P0442 **1T CCM, MIL: Yes** **Years:** 2008, 2009, 2010 **Models:** Acadia, Allure, Aura, Camaro, CTS, CTS-V, Enclave, LaCrosse, Outlook, Traverse **Engines:** 3.6L VIN 7, 3.6L VIN D, 3.6L VIN V **Transmissions:** All	**Evaporative Emission (EVAP) Purge Solenoid Control Circuit** The ignition is ON. The system voltage is between 9-18 volts. DTCs P0443 and P0449 run continuously when the above conditions are met. The ECM detects that the commanded state of the driver and the actual state of the control circuit do not match for a minimum of 5 seconds. **Possible Causes:** • EVAP canister purge or vent solenoid valve voltage supply circuit for a short to ground or an open/high resistance • EVAP canister purge or vent solenoid valve control circuit for a short to ground • EVAP canister purge or vent solenoid valve control circuit for a short to voltage or an open/high resistance • EVAP canister purge or vent solenoid valve • ECM has failed
DTC: P0443 **1T CCM, MIL: Yes** **Years:** 2008, 2009 **Models:** Corvette, CTS, CTS-V, DTS **Engines:** 4.6L VIN Y, 6.2L VIN W, 6.2L VIN P, 6.2L VIN R, 7.0L VIN E **Transmissions:** All	**Evaporative Emission (EVAP) Purge Solenoid Control Circuit** The ignition is ON. The system voltage is between 9-18 volts. DTCs P0443 and P0449 run continuously when the above conditions are met. The ECM detects that the commanded state of the driver and the actual state of the control circuit do not match for a minimum of 5 seconds. **Possible Causes:** • EVAP canister purge or vent solenoid valve voltage supply circuit for a short to ground or an open/high resistance • EVAP canister purge or vent solenoid valve control circuit for a short to ground • EVAP canister purge or vent solenoid control circuit for a short to voltage or an open/high resistance • EVAP canister purge or vent solenoid valve has failed • ECM has failed
DTC: P0443 **1T CCM, MIL: Yes** **Years:** 2008, 2009 **Models:** Allure, Aura, Canyon, Colorado, LaCrosse **Engines:** 2.9L VIN 9, 3.5L VIN N, 3.8L VIN 2, 5.3L VIN C, 5.3L VIN L **Transmissions:** All	**EVAP Purge Solenoid Control Circuit Malfunction** Engine started; system voltage from 6-18v, and the ECM detected the Actual and Commanded state of the EVAP Purge solenoid driver control circuit did not match for over 5 seconds during the CCM test. **Possible Causes:** • Purge solenoid control circuit is open or shorted to ground • Purge solenoid control circuit is shorted to system power (B+) • Purge solenoid power circuit is open (test the ENG1 fuse) • Purge solenoid is damaged or has failed • ECM has failed
DTC: P0443 **1T CCM, MIL: Yes** **Years:** 2008, 2009 **Models:** Astra, Aura, Aveo, Aveo5, Cobalt G3, G5 **Engines:** 1.6L VIN 6, 1.6L VIN E, 1.8L VIN 1, 2.0L VIN P, 2.0L VIN X, 2.2L VIN H, 2.2L VIN F, 2.4L VIN 5, 2.4L VIN B **Transmissions:** All	**EVAP Purge Solenoid Control Circuit Malfunction** Engine started; system voltage over 10.0v and the ECM detected the Actual state and the Commanded state of the Purge Solenoid driver control circuit did not match for 30 seconds. An ignition voltage is supplied directly to the EVAP canister purge solenoid valve. The EVAP canister purge solenoid is driven by a pulse width modulated (PWM) signal. The Scan Tool displays the amount of signal on-time as a percentage. The ECM monitors the status of the solenoid driver. The ECM controls the EVAP canister purge valve on-time by grounding the control circuit via an internal switch called a driver. If the ECM detects an incorrect voltage for the commanded state of the driver, it will set this trouble code (P0443). **Possible Causes:** • Purge solenoid control circuit is open or shorted to ground • Purge solenoid control circuit is shorted to system power (B+) • Purge solenoid power circuit is open (test the IGN1 fuse) • Purge solenoid is damaged or has failed • ECM has failed
DTC: P0443 **1T CCM, MIL: Yes** **Years:** 2008, 2009, 2010 **Models:** Acadia, Allure, Aura, Camaro, CTS, CTS-V, Enclave, LaCrosse, Outlook, Traverse **Engines:** 3.6L VIN 7, 3.6L VIN D, 3.6L VIN V **Transmissions:** All	**EVAP Purge Solenoid Control Circuit Malfunction** Engine started; system voltage at 6-18v, and the ECM detected the Actual and Commanded state of the EVAP Purge solenoid driver control circuit did not match for over 5 seconds during the CCM test period. **Possible Causes:** • Purge solenoid control circuit is open or shorted to ground • Purge solenoid control circuit is shorted to system power (B+) • Purge solenoid power circuit is open (test the ENG1 fuse) • Purge solenoid is damaged or has failed • ECM has failed

DTC	Trouble Code Title, Conditions & Possible Causes
DTC: P0443 **2T CCM, MIL: Yes** **Years:** 2008, 2009, 2010 **Models:** Avalanche, Camaro, Canyon, Escalade/EXT/ESV, Suburban, Tahoe, Yukon **Engines:** 4.8L VIN C, 5.3L VIN 0, 5.3L VIN 3, 5.3L VIN J, 5.3L VIN L, 6.0L VIN K, 6.0L VIN Y, 6.2L VIN J, 6.2L VIN W, 6.2L VIN 8 **Transmissions:** All	**Evaporative Emissions (EVAP) Vent System Performance** DTCs P0106, P0107, P0108, P0116, P0117, P0118, P0120, P0121, P0122, P0123, P0220, P0222, P0223, P0442, P0443, P0449, P0451, P0452, P0453, P0454, P0464, P0496, P0608, P0609, P0641, P0651, P1516, P2101, P2119, P2120, P2122, P2123, P2125, P2127, P2128, P2135, P2138 are not set. The ignition voltage is between 11-18 volts. The barometric pressure (BARO) is more than 74 kPa. The fuel level is between 15-85 percent. The engine coolant temperature (ECT) is less than 35°C (95°F). The intake air temperature (IAT) is between 4-30°C (39-86°F). DTC P0446 runs once per cold start when the above conditions are met. The fuel tank vacuum is greater than 12 inches H2O vacuum for 5 seconds.Or the FTP is less than −2.5 inches H2O or more than +5 inches for 60 seconds after a cold start. **Possible Causes:** • EVAP canister filter that is restricted • Damaged EVAP vent housing • Blockage at the EVAP canister vent solenoid valve inlet, or a pinched vent hose • FTP sensor • EVAP canister purge solenoid valve • EVAP canister vent solenoid valve
DTC: P0446 **1T CCM, MIL: Yes** **Years:** 2008, 2009 **Models:** Corvette, CTS, CTS-V, DTS **Engines:** 4.6L VIN Y, 6.2L VIN W, 6.2L VIN P, 6.2L VIN R, 7.0L VIN E **Transmissions:** All	**Evaporative Emissions (EVAP) Vent System Performance** Before the engine control module (ECM) can report DTC P0446 failed, DTCs P0442 and P0496 must run and pass. DTCs P0107, P0108, P0112, P0113, P0116, P0117, P0118, P0125, P0128, P0443, P0449, P0451, P0453, P0454, P1106, P1107, P1111, P1112, P1114, P1115, P1125, P1516, P2101, P2108, P2119, P2120, P2125, P2138 are not set. The ignition voltage is between 10-18 volts. The Barometric Pressure (BARO) is more than 74 kPa. The fuel level is between 15-85 percent. The start-up Engine Coolant Temperature (ECT) is less than 30°C (86°F). The start-up Intake Air Temperature (IAT) is less than 30°C (86°F). The start-up ECT and IAT are within 9°C (16°F) of each other. DTC P0446 runs once per trip when the above conditions have been met. The Fuel Tank Pressure (FTP) sensor is more than 8 inches H2O vacuum for 2 seconds during the 13 minute test.Or. The FTP is less than −2.5 inches H2O or more than +5 inches H2O for 3 seconds after a cold start ignition ON. The fuel tank vacuum is greater than a calibrated amount for a calibrated period of time. **Possible Causes:** • FTP sensor low reference circuit for an open/high resistance • FTP sensor has failed
DTC: P0446 **1T CCM, MIL: Yes** **Years:** 2008, 2009 **Models:** Allure, Aura, Canyon, Colorado, LaCrosse **Engines:** 2.9L VIN 9, 3.5L VIN N, 3.8L VIN 2, 5.3L VIN C, 5.3L VIN L **Transmissions:** All	**EVAP Vent System Performance** DTC P0106, P0107, P0108, P0112, P0113, P0116-P0118, P0125, P0440-P0453, P1111-P1115, P1120, P1220 and P1221 not set, engine started, ECT and IAT sensors from 39-86°F and within 16°F at startup, BARO over 75 kPa, fuel level from 15-85%, vehicle driven to a speed of less than 75 MPH, and the ECM detected the fuel tank pressure sensor indicated less than −10 inches H2O for 20 seconds. **Possible Causes:** • EVAP vent fresh air hose is clogged, kinked or restricted • EVAP Vent solenoid is contaminated, damaged or has failed • EVAP Canister plugged or severely restricted • Fuel Cap or EVAP Service Port leaking • Fuel vapor lines or purge lines damaged or leaking • FTP sensor is out-of-calibration, damaged or "skewed" • ECM has failed • TSB 02-06-04-037 contains a repair procedure for this code
DTC: P0446 **2T EVAP, MIL: Yes** **Years:** 2008, 2009, 2010 **Models:** Avalanche, Camaro, Canyon, Escalade/EXT/ESV, Suburban, Tahoe, Yukon **Engines:** 4.8L VIN C, 5.3L VIN 0, 5.3L VIN 3, 5.3L VIN J, 5.3L VIN L, 6.0L VIN K, 6.0L VIN Y, 6.2L VIN J, 6.2L VIN W, 6.2L VIN 8 **Transmissions:** All	**EVAP Vent System Performance** DTC P0107. P0108, P0112, P0113, P0116, P0117, P0118, P0121, P0122, P0123, P0125, P0440, P0442, P0443, P0449, P0452, P0453, P1111, P1112, P1114, P1115, P1121, and P1122 not set, engine started, ECT and IAT sensors from 39-86°F and within 16°F at startup, system voltage over 10.0v, BARO sensor over 75 kPa, fuel level from 15-85%, vehicle driven to a speed of less than 75 MPH, and the ECM detected the fuel tank pressure (from the FTP sensor signal) was less than −10" H2O for up to 30 seconds. **Note: This trouble code does not report a first failed test. A first fail of this code will show the Scan Tool status as Not Run.** **Possible Causes:** • EVAP vent fresh air hose is clogged, kinked or restricted • EVAP Vent solenoid is contaminated, damaged or has failed • FTP sensor is out-of-calibration, damaged or "skewed" • ECM has failed

DTC	Trouble Code Title, Conditions & Possible Causes
DTC: P0446 **1T CCM, MIL: Yes** **Years:** 2008, 2009 **Models:** Astra, Aura, Aveo, Aveo5, Cobalt G3, G5 **Engines:** 1.6L VIN 6, 1.6L VIN E, 1.8L VIN 1, 2.0L VIN P, 2.0L VIN X, 2.2L VIN H, 2.2L VIN F, 2.4L VIN 5, 2.4L VIN B **Transmissions:** All	**Evaporative Emissions (EVAP) Vent System Performance** The Fuel Tank Pressure (FTP) is less than −7.5 mm Hg (−4.0 in. H2O). The condition is present for greater than 5 seconds during the test. **Note: An intermittent condition could be caused by a damaged EVAP vent housing, a temporary blockage at the EVAP canister vent solenoid valve inlet, or a pinched vent hose. A blockage in the vent system may also cause a poor fuel fill condition** **Possible Causes:** • EVAP vent fresh air hose is clogged, kinked or restricted • EVAP Vent solenoid is contaminated, damaged or has failed • FTP sensor is out-of-calibration, damaged or "skewed" • ECM has failed
DTC: P0446 **1T CCM, MIL: Yes** **Years:** 2008, 2009, 2010 **Models:** Acadia, Allure, Aura, Camaro, CTS, CTS-V, Enclave, LaCrosse, Outlook, Traverse **Engines:** 3.6L VIN 7, 3.6L VIN D, 3.6L VIN V **Transmissions:** All	**Evaporative Emission (EVAP) Vent Solenoid Control Circuit** The ignition is ON. The system voltage is between 9-18 volts. DTCs P0443 and P0449 run continuously when the above conditions are met. The ECM detects that the commanded state of the driver and the actual state of the control circuit do not match for a minimum of 5 seconds. **Possible Causes:** • EVAP canister purge or vent solenoid valve voltage supply circuit for a short to ground or an open/high resistance • EVAP canister purge or vent solenoid valve control circuit for a short to ground • EVAP canister purge or vent solenoid valve control circuit for a short to voltage or an open/high resistance • EVAP canister purge or vent solenoid valve • ECM has failed
DTC: P0449 **1T CCM, MIL: Yes** **Years:** 2008, 2009 **Models:** Corvette, CTS, CTS-V, DTS **Engines:** 4.6L VIN Y, 6.2L VIN W, 6.2L VIN P, 6.2L VIN R, 7.0L VIN E **Transmissions:** All	**Evaporative Emission (EVAP) Vent Solenoid Control Circuit** The ignition is ON. The system voltage is between 9-18 volts. DTCs P0443 and P0449 run continuously when the above conditions are met. The ECM detects that the commanded state of the driver and the actual state of the control circuit do not match for a minimum of 5 seconds. **Possible Causes:** • EVAP canister purge or vent solenoid valve voltage supply circuit for a short to ground or an open/high resistance • EVAP canister purge or vent solenoid valve control circuit for a short to ground • EVAP canister purge or vent solenoid control circuit for a short to voltage or an open/high resistance • EVAP canister purge or vent solenoid valve has failed • ECM has failed
DTC: P0449 **1T CCM, MIL: Yes** **Years:** 2008, 2009 **Models:** Allure, Aura, Canyon, Colorado, LaCrosse **Engines:** 2.9L VIN 9, 3.5L VIN N, 3.8L VIN 2, 5.3L VIN C, 5.3L VIN L **Transmissions:** All	**EVAP Vent Solenoid Control Circuit Malfunction** Engine started; system voltage from 6-18v, and the ECM detected the Actual and Commanded state of the Vent Solenoid driver control circuit did not match for over 5 seconds. **Possible Causes:** • Vent solenoid control circuit is open or shorted to ground • Vent solenoid control circuit is shorted to system power (B+) • Vent solenoid power circuit is open (test the ENG1 fuse) • Vent solenoid is damaged or has failed • ECM has failed
DTC: P0449 **1T CCM, MIL: Yes** **Years:** 2008, 2009 **Models:** Astra, Aura, Aveo, Aveo5, Cobalt G3, G5 **Engines:** 1.6L VIN 6, 1.6L VIN E, 1.8L VIN 1, 2.0L VIN P, 2.0L VIN X, 2.2L VIN H, 2.2L VIN F, 2.4L VIN 5, 2.4L VIN B **Transmissions:** All	**EVAP Vent Solenoid Control Circuit Malfunction** Engine started; system voltage from 6-18v, and the ECM detected the Actual and Commanded state of the Vent Solenoid driver control circuit did not match for over 5 seconds during the CCM test period. **Possible Causes:** • Vent solenoid control circuit is open or shorted to ground • Vent solenoid control circuit is shorted to system power (B+) • Vent solenoid power circuit is open (test the ENG1 fuse) • Vent solenoid is damaged or has failed • ECM has failed
DTC: P0449 **2T CCM, MIL: Yes** **Years:** 2008, 2009, 2010 **Models:** Avalanche, Camaro, Canyon, Escalade/EXT/ESV, Suburban, Tahoe, Yukon **Engines:** 4.8L VIN C, 5.3L VIN 0, 5.3L VIN 3, 5.3L VIN J, 5.3L VIN L, 6.0L VIN K, 6.0L VIN Y, 6.2L VIN J, 6.2L VIN W, 6.2L VIN 8 **Transmissions:** All	**EVAP Vent Solenoid Control Circuit Malfunction** Engine started; system voltage 10-18 volts The ECM detects the voltage on the EVAP canister vent valve control circuit is between 2.6-4.6 volts when the driver is commanded OFF. The condition exists for less than 4 seconds or for a cumulative of 30 seconds. **Possible Causes:** • Vent solenoid control circuit is open or shorted to ground • Vent solenoid control circuit is shorted to system power (B+) • Vent solenoid power circuit is open • Vent solenoid is damaged or has failed • ECM has failed

DTC	Trouble Code Title, Conditions & Possible Causes
DTC: P0449 **1T CCM, MIL: Yes** **Years:** 2008, 2009, 2010 **Models:** Acadia, Allure, Aura, Camaro, CTS, CTS-V, Enclave, LaCrosse, Outlook, Traverse **Engines:** 3.6L VIN 7, 3.6L VIN D, 3.6L VIN V **Transmissions:** All	**Fuel Tank Pressure (FTP) Sensor Circuit** The ECM detects that the FTP sensor signal oscillates greater than 6.09 mm/Hg (3.26 in. H2O) for 4 seconds, or for a cumulative of 30 seconds. **Possible Causes:** • EVAP purge solenoid valve • FTP sensor • EVAP canister vent solenoid valve and vent pipe for a blockage or restriction
DTC: P0450 **1T CCM, MIL: Yes** **Years:** 2008, 2009, 2010 **Models:** Acadia, Allure, Aura, Camaro, CTS, CTS-V, Enclave, LaCrosse, Outlook, Traverse **Engines:** 3.6L VIN 7, 3.6L VIN D, 3.6L VIN V **Transmissions:** All	**Fuel Tank Pressure (FTP) Sensor Performance** DTC P0451 runs only when the engine-off natural vacuum small leak test, P0442, executes. The number of times this test runs can range from 0-2 per engine-off period. The length of the test can be up to 10 minutes. This DTC will set if the controller is unable to re-zero the FTP sensor voltage within a calibrated range during the engine-off small leak test, P0442. **Possible Causes:** • FTP sensor low reference circuit for an open/high resistance • FTP sensor 5-volt reference circuit for a short to ground or an open/high resistance. • FTP sensor 5-volt reference circuit for a short to voltage • FTP sensor signal circuit for short to ground or an open/high resistance • FTP sensor has failed • ECM has failed
DTC: P0451 **1T CCM, MIL: Yes** **Years:** 2008, 2009 **Models:** Corvette, CTS, CTS-V, DTS **Engines:** 4.6L VIN Y, 6.2L VIN W, 6.2L VIN P, 6.2L VIN R, 7.0L VIN E **Transmissions:** All	**Fuel Tank Pressure (FTP) Sensor Performance** DTC P0451 runs only when the engine-off natural vacuum small leak test, P0442, executes. The number of times this test runs can range from 0-2 per engine-off period. The length of the test can be up to 10 minutes. This DTC will set if the controller is unable to re-zero the FTP sensor voltage within a calibrated range during the engine-off small leak test, P0442. **Possible Causes:** • FTP sensor 5-volt reference circuit for a short to ground or an open/high resistance • FTP sensor low reference circuit for an open/high resistance • FTP sensor 5-volt reference circuit for a short to ground or an open/high resistance • FTP sensor 5-volt reference circuit for a short to voltage • FTP sensor signal circuit terminal B for a short to voltage • FTP sensor signal circuit for a short to ground or an open/high resistance • FTP sensor has failed • ECM has failed
DTC: P0451 **1T CCM, MIL: Yes** **Years:** 2008, 2009 **Models:** Allure, Aura, Canyon, Colorado, LaCrosse **Engines:** 2.9L VIN 9, 3.5L VIN N, 3.8L VIN 2, 5.3L VIN C, 5.3L VIN L **Transmissions:** All	**Fuel Tank Pressure (FTP) Sensor Performance** DTCs P0452, P0453, P0642, P0643 are not set. The engine has been running for more than 10 seconds. The FTP signal is between 0.2-4.9 volts. The vehicle speed reached once during drive cycle of 20 kph (14.2 mph). The EVAP system has reached full purge and no purge once during drive cycle. The EVAP system is purging. DTC P0451 runs continuously when the above conditions have been met. The maximum minus the minimum FTP signal voltage is less than 0.039 volt for 5 seconds. **Possible Causes:** • EVAP purge solenoid valve • FTP sensor • EVAP canister vent solenoid valve and vent pipe for a blockage or restriction
DTC: P0451 **1T CCM, MIL: Yes** **Years:** 2008, 2009 **Models:** Astra, Aura, Aveo, Aveo5, Cobalt G3, G5 **Engines:** 1.6L VIN 6, 1.6L VIN E, 1.8L VIN 1, 2.0L VIN P, 2.0L VIN X, 2.2L VIN H, 2.2L VIN F, 2.4L VIN 5, 2.4L VIN B **Transmissions:** All	**Fuel Tank Pressure (FTP) Sensor Performance** The ECM detects that the FTP is less than −26.2 mm/Hg (−14.1 in. H2O) or greater than 11.0 mm/Hg (5.9 in. H2O) for 4 seconds or for a cumulative of 30 seconds. Or the ECM detects a change in the zero point of FTP sensor signal greater than +/−5.16 mm/Hg (2.76 in. H2O) from the zero point at start up for 4 seconds, or a cumulative of 30 seconds. **Possible Causes:** • EVAP purge solenoid valve • FTP sensor • EVAP canister vent solenoid valve and vent pipe for a blockage or restriction

DTC	Trouble Code Title, Conditions & Possible Causes
DTC: P0451 **1T CCM, MIL: Yes** **Years:** 2008, 2009, 2010 **Models:** Acadia, Allure, Aura, Camaro, CTS, CTS-V, Enclave, LaCrosse, Outlook, Traverse **Engines:** 3.6L VIN 7, 3.6L VIN D, 3.6L VIN V **Transmissions:** All	**Fuel Tank Pressure (FTP) Sensor Circuit High Voltage** Key on or engine running; and the ECM detected the Fuel Tank Pressure (FTP) sensor signal was over 4.90v for 5 seconds during the CCM test period. The FTP sensor measures the difference between the air pressure and vacuum in the EVAP system. The ECM supplies a 5v VREF and a low reference circuit to the FTP sensor. The FTP sensor signal varies depending on EVAP system pressure or vacuum. **Possible Causes:** • FTP sensor signal circuit is shorted to VREF or system power • FTP sensor ground circuit is open between sensor and ECM • FTP sensor is damaged or has failed • ECM has failed
DTC: P0451 **1T CCM, MIL: Yes** **Years:** 2008, 2009, 2010 **Models:** Acadia, Allure, Aura, Camaro, CTS, CTS-V, Enclave, LaCrosse, Outlook, Traverse **Engines:** 3.6L VIN 7, 3.6L VIN D, 3.6L VIN V **Transmissions:** All	**Fuel Tank Pressure (FTP) Sensor Circuit Low Voltage** DTC P0452 and P0453 run continuously when the ignition is ON. The FTP sensor voltage is less than 0.1 volt for more than 5 seconds. **Possible Causes:** • FTP sensor low reference circuit for an open/high resistance • FTP sensor 5-volt reference circuit for a short to ground or an open/high resistance. • FTP sensor 5-volt reference circuit for a short to voltage • FTP sensor signal circuit for short to ground or an open/high resistance • FTP sensor has failed • ECM has failed
DTC: P0452 **1T CCM, MIL: Yes** **Years:** 2008, 2009 **Models:** Corvette, CTS, CTS-V, DTS **Engines:** 4.6L VIN Y, 6.2L VIN W, 6.2L VIN P, 6.2L VIN R, 7.0L VIN E **Transmissions:** All	**Fuel Tank Pressure (FTP) Sensor Circuit Low Voltage** DTC P0452 runs continuously when the ignition is ON. The FTP sensor voltage is less than 0.1 volt. **Possible Causes:** • FTP sensor 5-volt reference circuit for a short to ground or an open/high resistance • FTP sensor low reference circuit for an open/high resistance • FTP sensor 5-volt reference circuit for a short to ground or an open/high resistance • FTP sensor 5-volt reference circuit for a short to voltage • FTP sensor signal circuit terminal B for a short to voltage • FTP sensor signal circuit for a short to ground or an open/high resistance • FTP sensor has failed • ECM has failed
DTC: P0452 **1T CCM, MIL: Yes** **Years:** 2008, 2009 **Models:** Allure, Aura, Canyon, Colorado, LaCrosse **Engines:** 2.9L VIN 9, 3.5L VIN N, 3.8L VIN 2, 5.3L VIN C, 5.3L VIN L **Transmissions:** All	**Fuel Tank Pressure Sensor Circuit Low Input** Key on or engine running; and the ECM detected the Fuel Tank Pressure (FTP) sensor circuit was less than 0.10v for 5 seconds during the CCM test period. **Possible Causes:** • FTP sensor connector is damaged or shorted • FTP sensor signal circuit is open or shorted to ground • FTP sensor VREF circuit is open or shorted to ground • FTP sensor is damaged or has failed • ECM has failed
DTC: P0452 **2T CCM, MIL: Yes** **Years:** 2008, 2009, 2010 **Models:** Avalanche, Camaro, Canyon, Escalade/EXT/ESV, Suburban, Tahoe, Yukon **Engines:** 4.8L VIN C, 5.3L VIN 0, 5.3L VIN 3, 5.3L VIN J, 5.3L VIN L, 6.0L VIN K, 6.0L VIN Y, 6.2L VIN J, 6.2L VIN W, 6.2L VIN 8 **Transmissions:** All	**Fuel Tank Pressure Sensor Circuit Low Input** Key on or engine running; and the ECM detected the Fuel Tank Pressure (FTP) sensor circuit was less than 0.1v for 5 seconds. **Possible Causes:** • FTP sensor signal circuit is open or shorted to ground • FTP sensor VREF circuit is open or shorted to ground • FTP sensor is damaged or has failed • ECM has failed
DTC: P0452 **1T CCM, MIL: Yes** **Years:** 2008, 2009, 2010 **Models:** Acadia, Allure, Aura, Camaro, CTS, CTS-V, Enclave, LaCrosse, Outlook, Traverse **Engines:** 3.6L VIN 7, 3.6L VIN D, 3.6L VIN V **Transmissions:** All	**Fuel Tank Pressure (FTP) Sensor Circuit High Voltage** DTC P0452 and P0453 run continuously when the ignition is ON. The FTP sensor voltage is more than 4.9 volts for more than 5 seconds. **Possible Causes:** • FTP sensor low reference circuit for an open/high resistance • FTP sensor 5-volt reference circuit for a short to ground or an open/high resistance. • FTP sensor 5-volt reference circuit for a short to voltage • FTP sensor signal circuit for short to ground or an open/high resistance • FTP sensor has failed • ECM has failed

DTC	Trouble Code Title, Conditions & Possible Causes
DTC: P0453 **1T CCM, MIL: Yes** **Years:** 2008, 2009 **Models:** Corvette, CTS, CTS-V, DTS **Engines:** 4.6L VIN Y, 6.2L VIN W, 6.2L VIN P, 6.2L VIN R, 7.0L VIN E **Transmissions:** All	**Fuel Tank Pressure (FTP) Sensor Circuit High Voltage** DTC P0453 runs continuously when the ignition is ON. The FTP sensor voltage is more than 4.9 volts. **Possible Causes:** • FTP sensor 5-volt reference circuit for a short to ground or an open/high resistance • FTP sensor low reference circuit for an open/high resistance • FTP sensor 5-volt reference circuit for a short to ground or an open/high resistance • FTP sensor 5-volt reference circuit for a short to voltage • FTP sensor signal circuit terminal B for a short to voltage • FTP sensor signal circuit for a short to ground or an open/high resistance • FTP sensor has failed • ECM has failed
DTC: P0453 **1T CCM, MIL: Yes** **Years:** 2008, 2009 **Models:** Allure, Aura, Canyon, Colorado, LaCrosse **Engines:** 2.9L VIN 9, 3.5L VIN N, 3.8L VIN 2, 5.3L VIN C, 5.3L VIN L **Transmissions:** All	**Fuel Tank Pressure Sensor Circuit High Input** Key on or engine running; and the ECM detected the Fuel Tank Pressure (FTP) sensor circuit was more than 4.85v for 4 seconds during the CCM test period. **Possible Causes:** • FTP sensor connector is damaged, loose or open • FTP sensor signal circuit is shorted to VREF (5v) • FTP sensor ground circuit is open between sensor and ECM • FTP sensor is damaged or has failed • ECM has failed
DTC: P0453 **2T CCM, MIL: Yes** **Years:** 2008, 2009, 2010 **Models:** Avalanche, Camaro, Canyon, Escalade/EXT/ESV, Suburban, Tahoe, Yukon **Engines:** 4.8L VIN C, 5.3L VIN 0, 5.3L VIN 3, 5.3L VIN J, 5.3L VIN L, 6.0L VIN K, 6.0L VIN Y, 6.2L VIN J, 6.2L VIN W, 6.2L VIN 8 **Transmissions:** All	**Fuel Tank Pressure Sensor Circuit High Input** Key on or engine running; and the ECM detected an unexpected "high" voltage condition (more than 4.90v) on the Fuel Tank Pressure sensor signal circuit for 5 seconds in the test. **Possible Causes:** • FTP sensor signal circuit is shorted to VREF or system power • FTP sensor ground circuit is open between sensor and ECM • FTP sensor is damaged or has failed • ECM has failed
DTC: P0454 **1T CCM, MIL: Yes** **Years:** 2008, 2009 **Models:** Corvette, CTS, CTS-V, DTS **Engines:** 4.6L VIN Y, 6.2L VIN W, 6.2L VIN P, 6.2L VIN R, 7.0L VIN E **Transmissions:** All	**Fuel Tank Pressure (FTP) Sensor Intermittent** DTC P0454 runs only when the engine-off natural vacuum small leak test, P0442, executes. This test can run once per engine-off period. The length of the test can be up to 10 minutes. A refueling event is not detected. **Possible Causes:** • FTP sensor 5-volt reference circuit for a short to ground or an open/high resistance • FTP sensor low reference circuit for an open/high resistance • FTP sensor 5-volt reference circuit for a short to ground or an open/high resistance • FTP sensor 5-volt reference circuit for a short to voltage • FTP sensor signal circuit terminal B for a short to voltage • FTP sensor signal circuit for a short to ground or an open/high resistance • FTP sensor has failed • ECM has failed

DTC	Trouble Code Title, Conditions & Possible Causes
DTC: P0454 **1T CCM, MIL: Yes** **Years:** 2008, 2009 **Models:** Allure, Aura, Canyon, Colorado, LaCrosse **Engines:** 2.9L VIN 9, 3.5L VIN N, 3.8L VIN 2, 5.3L VIN C, 5.3L VIN L **Transmissions:** All	**Fuel Tank Pressure (FTP) Sensor Intermittent** DTCs P000A, P000B, P0010, P0013, P0016, P0017, P0030, P0031, P0032, P0068, P0072, P0073, P0074, P009A, P0101, P0102, P0103, P0111, P0112, P0113, P0114, P0116, P0117, P0118, P0119, P0121, P0122, P0123, P0130, P0131, P0132, P0133, P0134, P0135, P0171, P0172, P0201, P0202, P0203, P0204, P0221, P0222, P0223, P0261, P0262, P0264, P0265, P0267, P0268, P0270, P0271, P0300, P0301, P0302, P0303, P0304, P0335, P0336, P0340, P0341, P0365, P0366, P0442, P0443, P0446, P0449, P0451, P0452, P0453, P0454, P0455, P0456, P0458, P0459, P0496, P0498, P0499, P0500, P0501, P0506, P0507, P0562, P0563, P0601, P0602, P0603, P0604, P0605, P0606, P0607, P061A, P061B, P061C, P0642, P0643, P1101, P2088, P2089, P2090, P2091, P2100, P2101, P2119, P2176, P2227, P2228, P2229, P2297, P2301, P2304, P2307, P2310, and P2A00 are not set. The ignition is ON. The Barometric Pressure (BARO) is more than 75 kPa. The Engine Coolant Temperature (ECT) is less than 110°C (230°F). The engine has been running between 1-10 minutes. The engine is idling. The vehicle speed is 0 kph (0 mph). The fuel level is between 6-40 liters (2-10 gallons). The fuel tank pressure is between −3 and +1 kPa (−2 and +4 H2O). The intake air temperature (IAT) is between −8.25 and +70°C (+17 and +158°F). The battery voltage is more than 10 volts. The engine is operating in Closed Loop fuel control. DTC P0454 runs once per drive cycle when the above conditions have been met. The maximum minus the minimum fuel tank pressure is more than 0.1 kPa (0.4 in H2O) for 5 seconds. **Possible Causes:** • FTP sensor • FTP sensor 5-volt reference circuit shorted to ground or an open/high resistance • FTP sensor signal circuit terminal 1 for a short to voltage • FTP sensor signal circuit for short to ground or an open/high resistance • FTP sensor has failed • ECM has failed
DTC: P0454 **1T CCM, MIL: Yes** **Years:** 2008, 2009 **Models:** Astra, Aura, Aveo, Aveo5, Cobalt G3, G5 **Engines:** 1.6L VIN 6, 1.6L VIN E, 1.8L VIN 1, 2.0L VIN P, 2.0L VIN X, 2.2L VIN H, 2.2L VIN F, 2.4L VIN 5, 2.4L VIN B **Transmissions:** All	**Evaporative Emission (EVAP) System Large Leak Detected** Before the ECM can report DTC P0455 failed, DTC P0496 must run and pass. DTCs P0106, P0107, P0108, P0116, P0117, P0118, P0120, P0121, P0122, P0123, P0220, P0222, P0223, P0442, P0443, P0449, P0451, P0452, P0453, P0454, P0464, P0496, P0608, P0609, P0641, P0651, P1516, P2101, P2119, P2120, P2122, P2123, P2125, P2127, P2128, P2135, P2138 are not set. The ignition voltage is between 11-18 volts. The Barometric Pressure (BARO) is more than 74 kPa. The fuel level is between 15-85 percent. The Engine Coolant temperature (ECT) is less than 35°C (95°F). The Intake Air Temperature (IAT) is between 4-30°C (39-86°F). DTC P0455 runs once per cold start when the above conditions are met. The EVAP system is not able to achieve or maintain a calibrated level of vacuum within a set amount of time. **Possible Causes:** • Inspect for a damaged fuel filler neck seal surface. • Blockage or restriction in the EVAP purge solenoid valve, purge pipe, EVAP canister, or vapor pipe, • Inspect for a loose, missing, damaged, or incorrect fuel fill cap • FTP sensor has failed
DTC: P0455 **1T CCM, MIL: Yes** **Years:** 2008, 2009 **Models:** Corvette, CTS, CTS-V, DTS **Engines:** 4.6L VIN Y, 6.2L VIN W, 6.2L VIN P, 6.2L VIN R, 7.0L VIN E **Transmissions:** All	**Evaporative Emission (EVAP) System Large Leak Detected** Before the ECM can report DTC P0455 failed, DTC P0496 must run and pass. DTCs P0106, P0107, P0108, P0116, P0117, P0118, P0120, P0121, P0122, P0123, P0220, P0222, P0223, P0442, P0443, P0449, P0451, P0452, P0453, P0454, P0464, P0496, P0608, P0609, P0641, P0651, P1516, P2101, P2119, P2120, P2122, P2123, P2125, P2127, P2128, P2135, P2138 are not set. The ignition voltage is between 11-18 volts. The Barometric Pressure (BARO) is more than 74 kPa. The fuel level is between 15-85 percent. The Engine Coolant Temperature (ECT) is less than 35°C (95°F). The Intake Air Temperature (IAT) is between 4-30°C (39-86°F). DTC P0455 runs once per cold start when the above conditions are met. The EVAP system is not able to achieve or maintain a calibrated level of vacuum within a set amount of time. **Possible Causes:** • Fuel cap damaged or missing • Large leak in the EVAP sytem • FTP sensor has failed

DTC	Trouble Code Title, Conditions & Possible Causes
DTC: P0455 **1T CCM, MIL: Yes** **Years:** 2008, 2009 **Models:** Allure, Aura, Canyon, Colorado, LaCrosse **Engines:** 2.9L VIN 9, 3.5L VIN N, 3.8L VIN 2, 5.3L VIN C, 5.3L VIN L **Transmissions:** All	**EVAP System Large Leak (0.080") Detected** DTC P0106-P0108, P0112, P0113, P0116-P0118, P0120-P0123, P0125, P0131-P0138, P0140, P0141, P0147, P0151-P0158, P0160, P0161, P0167, P0220, P0442-P0443, P0449, P0452-P0453, P0455, P0502, P0503, P1111, P1112, P1114, P1115, P1120 not set, engine started, ECT and IAT sensors from 39-167°F and within 16°F at startup, system voltage from 10-18v, BARO sensor more than 75 kPa, Fuel Level from 15-85%, and the ECM detected it was unable to achieve or maintain vacuum during the EVAP system. The ECM monitors the FTP sensor signal to determine the EVAP system vacuum level. Once conditions are correct, the ECM commands the Purge valve open and the EVAP vent valve closed to Allow engine vacuum to enter the system. After a calibrated time or vacuum level, the ECM commands the Purge valve closed to seal the system, and monitors the FTP sensor to determine the EVAP system vacuum level. If the system is unable to achieve the correct vacuum level, or the vacuum level decreases too rapidly, the ECM will set this code. **Possible Causes:** • Fuel filler cap is very loose, missing or the wrong part • Fuel tank, fuel filler neck or fuel sending unit 'O' ring is leaking • Fuel tank pressure sensor is damaged, disconnected or it failed • Fuel tank vapor line(s) is clogged, damaged or disconnected • Purge valve vapor line is clogged, damaged, or disconnected • Purge solenoid is not opening (it may be damaged or sticking) • Vent solenoid is not closing (it may be damaged or sticking) • ECM has failed
DTC: P0455 **2T EVAP, MIL: Yes** **Years:** 2008, 2009, 2010 **Models:** Avalanche, Camaro, Canyon, Escalade/EXT/ESV, Suburban, Tahoe, Yukon **Engines:** 4.8L VIN C, 5.3L VIN 0, 5.3L VIN 3, 5.3L VIN J, 5.3L VIN L, 6.0L VIN K, 6.0L VIN Y, 6.2L VIN J, 6.2L VIN W, 6.2L VIN 8 **Transmissions:** All	**Evaporative Emission (EVAP) System Large Leak Detected** The ECM detects the EVAP system is not able to achieve or maintain vacuum during the diagnostic test. The condition exists for greater than 4 seconds or for a cumulative of 30 seconds. **Possible Causes:** • Fuel filler cap is very loose, missing or the wrong part • Fuel tank, fuel filler neck or fuel sending unit 'O' ring is leaking • Fuel tank pressure sensor is damaged, disconnected or it failed • Fuel tank vapor line(s) is clogged, damaged or disconnected • Purge valve vapor line is clogged, damaged, or disconnected • Purge solenoid is not opening (it may be damaged or sticking) • Vent solenoid is not closing (it may be damaged or sticking) • ECM has failed
DTC: P0455 **1T CCM, MIL: Yes** **Years:** 2008, 2009, 2010 **Models:** Acadia, Allure, Aura, Camaro, CTS, CTS-V, Enclave, LaCrosse, Outlook, Traverse **Engines:** 3.6L VIN 7, 3.6L VIN D, 3.6L VIN V **Transmissions:** All	**Evaporative Emission (EVAP) System Large Leak Detected** DTCs P000A, P000B, P0010, P0013, P0016, P0017, P0030, P0031, P0032, P0068, P0072, P0073, P0074, P009A, P0101, P0102, P0103, P0111, P0112, P0113, P0114, P0116, P0117, P0118, P0119, P0121, P0122, P0123, P0130, P0131, P0132, P0133, P0134, P0135, P0171, P0172, P0201, P0202, P0203, P0204, P0221, P0222, P0223, P0261, P0262, P0264, P0265, P0267, P0268, P0270, P0271, P0300, P0301, P0302, P0303, P0304, P0335, P0336, P0340, P0341, P0365, P0366, P0436, P0442, P0443, P0446, P0449, P0451, P0452, P0453, P0454, P0456, P0458, P0459, P0496, P0498, P0499, P0500, P0506, P0507, P0562, P0563, P0601, P0602, P0604, P0605, P0606, P0607, P061A, P061B, P061C, P0642, P0643, P1101, P2088, P2089, P2090, P2091, P2100, P2101, P2119, P2176, P2227, P2228, P2229, P2297, P2301, P2304, P2307, P2310, P2610, and P2A00 are not set. The Ignition is ON. The Barometric Pressure (BARO) is more than 75 kPa. The Engine Coolant Temperature (ECT) is less than 110°C (230°F). The engine has been running between 1-10 minutes. The engine is idling. The fuel level is between 6-40 liters (2-10 gallons). The Fuel Tank Pressure (FTP) is between −3 and +1 kPa (−12 and +4 in H2O). The vehicle speed is 0 kph (0 mph). The Intake Air Temperature (IAT) is between −8 and +70°C (+17 and +158°F). The battery voltage is more than 10 volts. The engine is operating in Closed Loop fuel control. DTC P0455 runs once per drive cycle when the above conditions are met. The EVAP system is not able to achieve or maintain vacuum before purge has reached a calibrated volume. **Possible Causes:** • Fuel filler cap is very loose, missing or the wrong part • Fuel tank, fuel filler neck or fuel sending unit 'O' ring is leaking • Fuel tank pressure sensor is damaged, disconnected or it failed • Fuel tank vapor line(s) is clogged, damaged or disconnected • Purge valve vapor line is clogged, damaged, or disconnected • Purge solenoid is not opening (it may be damaged or sticking) • Vent solenoid is not closing (it may be damaged or sticking) • ECM has failed

DTC	Trouble Code Title, Conditions & Possible Causes
DTC: P0455 **1T CCM, MIL: Yes** **Years:** 2008, 2009 **Models:** Astra, Aura, Aveo, Aveo5, Cobalt G3, G5 **Engines:** 1.6L VIN 6, 1.6L VIN E, 1.8L VIN 1, 2.0L VIN P, 2.0L VIN X, 2.2L VIN H, 2.2L VIN F, 2.4L VIN 5, 2.4L VIN B **Transmissions:** All	**Evaporative Emissions (EVAP) System Very Small Leak Detected** DTCs P000A, P000B, P0010, P0013, P0016, P0017, P0030, P0031, P0032, P0068, P0072, P0073, P0074, P009A, P0101, P0102, P0103, P0111, P0112, P0113, P0114, P0116, P0117, P0118, P0119, P0121, P0122, P0123, P0130, P0131, P0132, P0133, P0134, P0135, P0171, P0172, P0201, P0202, P0203, P0204, P0221, P0222, P0223, P0261, P0262, P0264, P0265, P0267, P0268, P0270, P0271, P0300, P0301, P0302, P0303, P0304, P0335, P0336, P0340, P0341, P0365, P0366, P0442, P0443, P0446, P0449, P0451, P0452, P0453, P0454, P0455, P0456, P0458, P0459, P0496, P0498, P0499, P0501, P0506, P0507, P0562, P0563, P0601, P0603, P0604, P0605, P0606, P0607, P061A, P061B, P061C, P0642, P0643, P1101, P2088, P2089, P2090, P2091, P2100, P2101, P2119, P2176, P2227, P2228, P2297, P2301, P2304, P2307, P2310, P2610, and P2A00 are not set. The ignition is ON. The barometric pressure (BARO) is more than 75 kPa. The engine coolant temperature (ECT) is less than 110°C (230°F). The engine has been running between 1-10 minutes. The engine is idling. The fuel level is between 6-40 liters (2-10 gallons). The fuel tank pressure (FTP) is between −3 and +1 kPa (−12 and +4 in H2O). The vehicle speed is 0 kph (0 mph). The intake air temperature (IAT) is between −8 and +70°C (+17 and +158°F). The battery voltage is more than 10 volts. DTC P0456runs once per drive cycle when the above conditions have been met. DTC P0456 sets when a leak between 0.85-0.39 mm (0.033-0.015 in) is detected. **Possible Causes:** • Damaged EVAP purge solenoid • Damaged EVAP vent valve or EVAP canister • Incorrectly routed, kinked, or damaged EVAP pipes and hoses
DTC: P0456 **1T CCM, MIL: Yes** **Years:** 2008, 2009 **Models:** Astra, Aura, Aveo, Aveo5, Cobalt G3, G5 **Engines:** 1.6L VIN 6, 1.6L VIN E, 1.8L VIN 1, 2.0L VIN P, 2.0L VIN X, 2.2L VIN H, 2.2L VIN F, 2.4L VIN 5, 2.4L VIN B **Transmissions:** All	**Evaporative Emission (EVAP) Purge Solenoid Control Circuit Low Voltage** The engine speed is greater than 80 RPM. The ignition voltage is between 10-18 volts. The ECM has commanded the EVAP canister purge valve ON and OFF at least once during the ignition cycle. The DTCs run continuously once the above conditions are met. The ECM detects the EVAP canister purge solenoid control circuit is shorted to ground. The condition exists for 4 seconds or a cumulative of 30 seconds. **Possible Causes:** • EVAP purge solenoid control circuit for a shorted to ground. • EVAP purge solenoid shorted to voltage or an open/high resistance • Faulty EVAP purge solenoid. • ECM has failed
DTC: P0458 **1T CCM, MIL: Yes** **Years:** 2008, 2009, 2010 **Models:** Acadia, Allure, Aura, Camaro, CTS, CTS-V, Enclave, LaCrosse, Outlook, Traverse **Engines:** 3.6L VIN 7, 3.6L VIN D, 3.6L VIN V **Transmissions:** All	**Evaporative Emission (EVAP) Purge Solenoid Control Circuit Low Voltage** DTCs P0606, P0628, or P0629 are not set. The ignition is ON. The engine is running. The battery voltage is more than 10 volts. The EVAP canister purge solenoid valve is commanded between 8-91 percent. DTC P0458 runs continuously when the above conditions are met. This DTC sets when a short to ground is detected on the EVAP canister purge solenoid valve control circuit for 3 seconds. **Possible Causes:** • EVAP purge solenoid control circuit for a shorted to ground. • EVAP purge solenoid shorted to voltage or an open/high resistance • Faulty EVAP purge solenoid. • ECM has failed
DTC: P0458 **1T CCM, MIL: Yes** **Years:** 2008, 2009 **Models:** Astra, Aura, Aveo, Aveo5, Cobalt G3, G5 **Engines:** 1.6L VIN 6, 1.6L VIN E, 1.8L VIN 1, 2.0L VIN P, 2.0L VIN X, 2.2L VIN H, 2.2L VIN F, 2.4L VIN 5, 2.4L VIN B **Transmissions:** All	**Evaporative Emission (EVAP) Purge Solenoid Control Circuit High Voltage** The engine speed is greater than 80 RPM. The ignition voltage is between 10-18 volts. The ECM has commanded the EVAP canister purge valve ON and OFF at least once during the ignition cycle. The DTCs run continuously once the above conditions are met. The ECM detects the EVAP canister purge solenoid control circuit is shorted to voltage. The condition exists for 4 seconds or a cumulative of 30 seconds. **Possible Causes:** • EVAP purge solenoid control circuit for a shorted to ground. • EVAP purge solenoid shorted to voltage or an open/high resistance • Faulty EVAP purge solenoid. • ECM has failed
DTC: P0459 **1T CCM, MIL: Yes** **Years:** 2008, 2009, 2010 **Models:** Acadia, Allure, Aura, Camaro, CTS, CTS-V, Enclave, LaCrosse, Outlook, Traverse **Engines:** 3.6L VIN 7, 3.6L VIN D, 3.6L VIN V **Transmissions:** All	**Evaporative Emission (EVAP) Purge Solenoid Control Circuit High Voltage** DTCs P0606, P0628, or P0629 are not set. The ignition is ON. The engine is running. The battery voltage is more than 10 volts. The EVAP canister purge solenoid valve is commanded between 8-91 percent. DTC P0458 runs continuously when the above conditions are met. This DTC sets when an open circuit is detected on the EVAP canister vent solenoid valve control circuit for 3 seconds. **Possible Causes:** • EVAP purge solenoid control circuit for a shorted to ground. • EVAP purge solenoid shorted to voltage or an open/high resistance • Faulty EVAP purge solenoid. • ECM has failed

DTC	Trouble Code Title, Conditions & Possible Causes
DTC: P0459 **1T CCM, MIL: Yes** **Years:** 2008, 2009 **Models:** Astra, Aura, Aveo, Aveo5, Cobalt G3, G5 **Engines:** 1.6L VIN 6, 1.6L VIN E, 1.8L VIN 1, 2.0L VIN P, 2.0L VIN X, 2.2L VIN H, 2.2L VIN F, 2.4L VIN 5, 2.4L VIN B **Transmissions:** All	**Fuel Level Sensor High Input** Engine started; system voltage over 10.0v and the ECM detected the Fuel Level sensor signal indicated more than 2.90v for 6 minutes under these conditions during the CCM test. **Possible Causes:** • Fuel level sensor signal circuit is shorted to system power • Fuel level sensor ground circuit is open • Fuel level sender is damaged, binding or not aligned properly • ECM has failed
DTC: P0463 **1T CCM, MIL: No** **Years:** 2008, 2009, 2010 **Models:** Avalanche, Camaro, Canyon, Escalade/EXT/ESV, Suburban, Tahoe, Yukon **Engines:** 4.8L VIN C, 5.3L VIN 0, 5.3L VIN 3, 5.3L VIN J, 5.3L VIN L, 6.0L VIN K, 6.0L VIN Y, 6.2L VIN J, 6.2L VIN W, 6.2L VIN 8 **Transmissions:** All	**Cooling Fan Relay 1 Control Circuit Malfunction** Key on or engine running; system voltage from 9-18v, and the ECM detected the Actual state and Commanded state of the Fan Relay 1 control circuit (Low Speed Fan) did not match for 30 seconds. **Possible Causes:** • Fan control relay control circuit is open or shorted to ground • Fan control relay control circuit is shorted to system power • Fan control relay power circuit is open (check Cool Fan 1 fuse) • Fan control relay is damaged or has failed • ECM has failed
DTC: P0496 **1T CCM, MIL: Yes** **Years:** 2008, 2009 **Models:** Corvette, CTS, CTS-V, DTS **Engines:** 4.6L VIN Y, 6.2L VIN W, 6.2L VIN P, 6.2L VIN R, 7.0L VIN E **Transmissions:** All	**Evaporative Emission System Flow During Non-Purge** DTCs P0106, P0107, P0108, P0116, P0117, P0118, P0120, P0121, P0122, P0123, P0220, P0222, P0223, P0442, P0443, P0446, P0449, P0451, P0452, P0453, P0454, P0464, P0608, P0609, P0641, P0651, P1516, P2101, P2119, P2120, P2122, P2123, P2125, P2127, P2128, P2135, P2138 are not set. The ignition voltage is between 11-18 volts. The Barometric Pressure (BARO) is more than 74 kPa. The fuel level is between 15-85 percent. The engine coolant temperature (ECT) is less than 35°C (95°F). The Intake Air Temperature (IAT) is between 4-30°C (39-86°F). DTC P0496 runs once per cold start when the above conditions are met. The ECM detects more than 10 inch H2O vacuum for 5 seconds during a non-purge condition. **Possible Causes:** • EVAP canister purge solenoid valve
DTC: P0496 **1T CCM, MIL: Yes** **Years:** 2008, 2009 **Models:** Allure, Aura, Canyon, Colorado, LaCrosse **Engines:** 2.9L VIN 9, 3.5L VIN N, 3.8L VIN 2, 5.3L VIN C, 5.3L VIN L **Transmissions:** All	**EVAP Canister Purge System High Purge Flow** DTC P0106-P0108, P0112, P0113, P0116-P0118, P0120-P0123, P0125, P0131-P0138, P0140, P0141, P0147, P0151-P0158, P0160, P0161, P0167, P0220, P0442-P0443, P0449, P0452-P0453, P0455, P0502, P0503, P1111, P1112, P1114, P1115, P1120 not set, engine started, ECT and IAT sensors from 39-86°F and within 16°F at startup, system voltage from 10-18v, BARO sensor more than 75 kPa, fuel level at 15-85%, and the ECM detected a continuous open purge flow condition in the system (FTP less than −11 H2O). This diagnostic test is designed to test for undesired intake manifold vacuum flow to the EVAP system. During this test, the ECM seals the EVAP system by commanding the EVAP Purge valve closed and the EVAP canister vent valve closed. The ECM monitors the FTP sensor signal in order to determine if a vacuum is being drawn on the EVAP system. If vacuum in the EVAP system is more than a predetermined value within a certain time, this code is set. **Possible Causes:** • EVAP charcoal canister is damaged or restricted • EVAP purge pipe is damaged or restricted • FTP sensor is damaged or it has failed • Purge solenoid is damaged (it may be sticking) • Purge solenoid valve has failed
DTC: P0496 **2T EVAP, MIL: Yes** **Years:** 2008, 2009, 2010 **Models:** Avalanche, Camaro, Canyon, Escalade/EXT/ESV, Suburban, Tahoe, Yukon **Engines:** 4.8L VIN C, 5.3L VIN 0, 5.3L VIN 3, 5.3L VIN J, 5.3L VIN L, 6.0L VIN K, 6.0L VIN Y, 6.2L VIN J, 6.2L VIN W, 6.2L VIN 8 **Transmissions:** All	**Evaporative Emissions (EVAP) System Flow During Non-Purge** The control module detects vacuum during a non-purge condition. The condition exists for greater than 4 seconds or for a cumulative of 30 seconds. **Possible Causes:** • EVAP charcoal canister is damaged or restricted • EVAP purge pipe is damaged or restricted • FTP sensor is damaged or it has failed • Purge solenoid is damaged (it may be sticking) • Purge solenoid valve has failed

DTC	Trouble Code Title, Conditions & Possible Causes
DTC: P0496 **1T CCM, MIL: Yes** **Years:** 2008, 2009 **Models:** Acadia, Allure, Aura, Astra, Aura, Aveo, Aveo5, Cobalt G3, G5, Enclave, LaCrosse, Outlook, Traverse **Engines:** 1.6L VIN 6, 1.6L VIN E, 1.8L VIN 1, 2.0L VIN P, 2.0L VIN X, 2.2L VIN H, 2.2L VIN F, 2.4L VIN 5, 2.4L VIN B, 3.6L VIN 7, 3.6L VIN D, 3.6L VIN V **Transmissions:** All	**Evaporative Emission (EVAP) System No Flow During Purge** The ECM detects the EVAP system is not able to achieve or maintain vacuum during the diagnostic test. The condition exists for greater than 4 seconds or for a cumulative of 30 seconds. **Possible Causes:** • Fuel filler cap is very loose, missing or the wrong part • Fuel tank, fuel filler neck or fuel sending unit 'O' ring is leaking • Fuel tank pressure sensor is damaged, disconnected or it failed • Fuel tank vapor line(s) is clogged, damaged or disconnected • Purge valve vapor line is clogged, damaged, or disconnected • Purge solenoid is not opening (it may be damaged or sticking) • Vent solenoid is not closing (it may be damaged or sticking) • ECM has failed
DTC: P0497 **1T CCM, MIL: Yes** **Years:** 2008, 2009, 2010 **Models:** Acadia, Allure, Aura, Camaro, CTS, CTS-V, Enclave, LaCrosse, Outlook, Traverse **Engines:** 3.6L VIN 7, 3.6L VIN D, 3.6L VIN V **Transmissions:** All	**Evaporative Emission (EVAP) Vent Solenoid Valve Control Circuit Low Voltage** The ECM detects the voltage on the EVAP canister vent valve control circuit is less than 2.6 volts when the driver is commanded OFF. The condition is present for greater than 4 seconds or for a cumulative of 30 seconds. **Possible Causes:** • Vent solenoid control circuit is open or shorted to ground • Vent solenoid control circuit is shorted to system power (B+) • Vent solenoid power circuit is open • Vent solenoid is damaged or has failed • ECM has failed
DTC: P0498 **1T CCM, MIL: Yes** **Years:** 2008, 2009 **Models:** Acadia, Allure, Aura, Astra, Aura, Aveo, Aveo5, Cobalt G3, G5, Enclave, LaCrosse, Outlook, Traverse **Engines:** 1.6L VIN 6, 1.6L VIN E, 1.8L VIN 1, 2.0L VIN P, 2.0L VIN X, 2.2L VIN H, 2.2L VIN F, 2.4L VIN 5, 2.4L VIN B, 3.6L VIN 7, 3.6L VIN D, 3.6L VIN V **Transmissions:** All	**Evaporative Emission (EVAP) Vent Solenoid Valve Control Circuit High Voltage** The ECM detects the voltage on the EVAP canister vent valve control circuit is greater than 4.6 volts when the driver is commanded ON. The condition is present for greater than 4 seconds or for a cumulative of 30 seconds. **Possible Causes:** • Vent solenoid control circuit is open or shorted to ground • Vent solenoid control circuit is shorted to system power (B+) • Vent solenoid power circuit is open • Vent solenoid is damaged or has failed • ECM has failed
DTC: P0499 **1T CCM, MIL: Yes** **Years:** 2008, 2009 **Models:** Acadia, Allure, Aura, Astra, Aura, Aveo, Aveo5, Cobalt G3, G5, Enclave, LaCrosse, Outlook, Traverse **Engines:** 1.6L VIN 6, 1.6L VIN E, 1.8L VIN 1, 2.0L VIN P, 2.0L VIN X, 2.2L VIN H, 2.2L VIN F, 2.4L VIN 5, 2.4L VIN B, 3.6L VIN 7, 3.6L VIN D, 3.6L VIN V **Transmissions:** All	**Vehicle Speed Sensor Circuit Malfunction** DTC P0106, P0107, P0108, P0335, P0336, P1120, P1125, P1128, P1220, P1221, P1514, P1515, P1516, P1517 and P1518 not set, engine started, vehicle driven at a speed over 1000 RPM, ECT sensor more than 95°F, MAP sensor from 40-100 kPa (Turbo Boost Pressure from 40-100 kPa on Diesel) TP angle from 5-95%, and the ECM did not detect any VSS signals for from 50-100 seconds. **Possible Causes:** • Output shaft rotor is chipped or damaged • Output shaft rotor is not aligned properly with the VSS unit • VSS tip contains debris or metal shavings (an intermittent fault) • VSS positive (+) signal circuit is open or shorted to ground • VSS negative (−) signal circuit is open or shorted to ground • VSS is damaged or has failed
DTC: P0500 **2T CCM, MIL: Yes** **Years:** 2008, 2009, 2010 **Models:** Avalanche, Camaro, Canyon, Escalade/EXT/ESV, Suburban, Tahoe, Yukon **Engines:** 4.8L VIN C, 5.3L VIN 0, 5.3L VIN 3, 5.3L VIN J, 5.3L VIN L, 6.0L VIN K, 6.0L VIN Y, 6.2L VIN J, 6.2L VIN W, 6.2L VIN 8 **Transmissions:** All	**VSS Circuit Low Input** DTC P0106, P0107, P0108, P1106, P1107, P0121, P0122, P0123, P1121 and P1122 not set, engine started, Input Shaft Speed signal over 1500 RPM, MAP sensor from 12-15 kPa, transaxle not in P/N, TP angle over 12%, engine torque more than 25-150 lb ft., and the ECM detected the OSS signal was less than 150 RPM for 3 seconds. **Possible Causes:** • Output shaft rotor is chipped or damaged • OSS tip contains debris or metal shavings (an intermittent fault) • OSS positive (+) signal circuit is open or shorted to ground • OSS negative (−) signal circuit is open or shorted to ground • OSS is damaged or has failed

DTC	Trouble Code Title, Conditions & Possible Causes
DTC: P0502 **2T CCM, MIL: Yes** **Years:** 2008, 2009, 2010 **Models:** Avalanche, Camaro, Canyon, Escalade/EXT/ESV, Suburban, Tahoe, Yukon **Engines:** 4.8L VIN C, 5.3L VIN 0, 5.3L VIN 3, 5.3L VIN J, 5.3L VIN L, 6.0L VIN K, 6.0L VIN Y, 6.2L VIN J, 6.2L VIN W, 6.2L VIN 8 **Transmissions:** All	**VSS Circuit Malfunction** DTC P0502 and P1810 not set, engine running, at least 6 seconds have passed since the last gear change, Decel Fuel Cutoff inactive, Transmission output shaft speed did not increase over 250 RPM for 2 seconds, and the ECM detected the OSS signal dropped more than 1500 RPM in 2 seconds during the CCM test. **Possible Causes:** • OSS assembly connector is damaged, loose or shorted • Output shaft rotor is chipped or damaged (intermittent fault) • OSS tip contains debris or metal shavings (an intermittent fault) • OSS (+) signal circuit is open or shorted to ground (intermittent) • OSS (-) signal circuit is open or shorted to ground (intermittent) • OSS is damaged or has failed (an intermittent fault)
DTC: P0503 **2T CCM, MIL: Yes** **Years:** 2008, 2009, 2010 **Models:** Avalanche, Camaro, Canyon, Escalade/EXT/ESV, Suburban, Tahoe, Yukon **Engines:** 4.8L VIN C, 5.3L VIN 0, 5.3L VIN 3, 5.3L VIN J, 5.3L VIN L, 6.0L VIN K, 6.0L VIN Y, 6.2L VIN J, 6.2L VIN W, 6.2L VIN 8 **Transmissions:** All	**Idle Speed Low** DTCs P0068, P0101, P0102, P0103, P0106, P0107, P0108, P0112, P0113, P0117, P0118, P0120, P0122, P0123, P0171, P0172, P0201, P0202, P0203, P0204, P0205, P0206, P0207, P0208, P0220, P0221, P0222, P0223, P0230, P0300, P0336, P0442, P0446, P0449, P0452, P0453, P0455, P0462, P0463, P0496, P1516, P2101, P2135, P2176 are not set. The engine is operating for at least 60 seconds. The Engine Coolant Temperature (ECT) is more than −60°C (-140°F). The Intake Air Temperature (IAT) is more than −10°C (−14°F). The Barometric Pressure (BARO) is more than 65 kPa. The system voltage is between 9-18 volts. The vehicle speed is less than 1.6 km/h (1 mph). DTC P0506 and P0507 run continuously when the above conditions are met.. The actual idle speed is approximately 150 RPM lower than the desired idle speed. The above condition is present for 15 seconds. **Possible Causes:** • Incorrect torque converter clutch (TCC) operation • Accessories that require additional torque to operate • Excessive deposits in the throttle bod • Restricted exhaust • Mechanical conditions that limit engine speed
DTC: P0506 **1T CCM, MIL: Yes** **Years:** 2008, 2009 **Models:** Corvette, CTS, CTS-V, DTS **Engines:** 4.6L VIN Y, 6.2L VIN W, 6.2L VIN P, 6.2L VIN R, 7.0L VIN E **Transmissions:** All	**Idle Speed Low** DTCs P0068, P0101, P0102, P0103, P0106, P0107, P0108, P0112, P0113, P0117, P0118, P0120, P0122, P0123, P0171, P0172, P0201, P0202, P0203, P0204, P0205, P0206, P0207, P0208, P0220, P0221, P0222, P0223, P0230, P0300, P0336, P0442, P0446, P0449, P0452, P0453, P0455, P0462, P0463, P0496, P1516, P2101, P2135, P2176 are not set. The engine has been running for greater than 60 seconds. The engine is idling for greater than 10 seconds. The AC mode state has not changed. The power steering load state has not changed. The transmission gear selector state has not changed. The engine coolant temperature (ECT) is greater than −60°C (−76°F). The system voltage is between 11-18 volts. The vehicle speed is less than 4.8 km/h (2 mph). The actual idle speed is approximately 100 RPM lower than the desired idle speed. The above condition is present for 15 seconds. **Possible Causes:** • Incorrect Torque Converter Clutch (TCC) operation • Dirty throttle body • Accessories that require additional torque to operate • Excessive deposits in the throttle body • Restricted exhaust
DTC: P0506 **1T CCM, MIL: Yes** **Years:** 2008, 2009 **Models:** Allure, Aura, Canyon, Colorado, LaCrosse **Engines:** 2.9L VIN 9, 3.5L VIN N, 3.8L VIN 2, 5.3L VIN C, 5.3L VIN L **Transmissions:** All	**Idle Speed Too Low** DTC P0105, P0107, P0108, P0112, P0113, P0117, P0118, P0122, P0123, P0125, P0128, P0130-P0134, P0171, P0172, P0201-P0204, P0300, P0301-P0304, P0336, P0440, P0442, P0446, P0452, P0453, P0502, P0503, P1133 and P1441 not set, engine started, engine runtime over 20 seconds, system voltage over 10.0v, ECT sensor more than 104°F, BARO sensor more than 72 kPa, and the ECM detected the Actual idle speed was 60 RPM less than Desired idle speed for 13 seconds with the IAC position over 145 counts. **Possible Causes:** • Air inlet duct is collapsed, loose or air filter element is clogged • Base engine problem (i.e., compression or misfire condition) • Idle air inlet passage or throttle bore is dirty or full of deposits • IAC solenoid control circuit has a high resistance condition • IAC valve is damaged or has failed • MAF sensor is dirty, out-of-calibration or it is "skewed" • Throttle plate, throttle shaft or linkage is damaged or sticking • ECM has failed

DTC	Trouble Code Title, Conditions & Possible Causes
DTC: P0506 **2T CCM, MIL: Yes** **Years:** 2008, 2009, 2010 **Models:** Avalanche, Camaro, Canyon, Escalade/EXT/ESV, Suburban, Tahoe, Yukon **Engines:** 4.8L VIN C, 5.3L VIN 0, 5.3L VIN 3, 5.3L VIN J, 5.3L VIN L, 6.0L VIN K, 6.0L VIN Y, 6.2L VIN J, 6.2L VIN W, 6.2L VIN 8 **Transmissions:** All	**Idle Speed Too Low** DTC P0107, P0108, P0112, P0113, P0117, P0118, P0125, P0171, P0172, P0200, P0300, P0336, P0440, P0442, P0446, P0452, P0453, P0502, P0503, P1120, P1220, P1221, P1514, P1515, P1516, P1635 and P1639 not set, engine runtime over 2 seconds, ECT sensor more than −40°F, IAT sensor more than −40°F, BARO sensor more than 65 kPa, system voltage from 6-18v, VSS less than 3 MPH, and the ECM detected the Actual idle speed was more than 105 RPM less than the Desired idle speed for 15 seconds. **Possible Causes:** • Air inlet duct is collapsed, loose or air filter element is clogged • Base engine problem (i.e., compression or misfire condition) • IAC valve is damaged or has failed • Idle air inlet passage or throttle bore is dirty or full of deposits • MAF sensor is dirty, out-of-calibration or it is "skewed" • Throttle plate, throttle shaft or linkage is damaged or sticking • ECM has failed
DTC: P0507 **1T CCM, MIL: Yes** **Years:** 2008, 2009 **Models:** Corvette, CTS, CTS-V, DTS **Engines:** 4.6L VIN Y, 6.2L VIN W, 6.2L VIN P, 6.2L VIN R, 7.0L VIN E **Transmissions:** All	**Idle Speed High** DTCs P0068, P0101, P0102, P0103, P0106, P0107, P0108, P0112, P0113, P0117, P0118, P0120, P0122, P0123, P0171, P0172, P0201, P0202, P0203, P0204, P0205, P0206, P0207, P0208, P0220, P0221, P0222, P0223, P0230, P0300, P0336, P0442, P0446, P0449, P0452, P0453, P0455, P0462, P0463, P0496, P1516, P2101, P2135, P2176 are not set. The engine has been running for greater than 60 seconds. The engine is idling for greater than 10 seconds. The AC mode state has not changed. The power steering load state has not changed. The transmission gear selector state has not changed. The Engine Coolant Temperature (ECT) is greater than −60°C (−76°F). The system voltage is between 11-18 volts. The vehicle speed is less than 4.8 km/h (2 mph). The actual idle speed is approximately 200 RPM greater than the desired idle speed. The above condition is present for 15 seconds. **Possible Causes:** • Vacuum leaks • A faulty Positive Crankcase Ventilation (PCV) valve • Dirty throttle body
DTC: P0507 **1T CCM, MIL: Yes** **Years:** 2008, 2009 **Models:** Allure, Aura, Canyon, Colorado, LaCrosse **Engines:** 2.9L VIN 9, 3.5L VIN N, 3.8L VIN 2, 5.3L VIN C, 5.3L VIN L **Transmissions:** All	**Idle Speed Too High** DTC P0105, P0107, P0108, P0112, P0113, P0117, P0118, P0122, P0123, P0125, P0128, P0130-P0134, P0171, P0172, P0201-P0204, P0300, P0301-P0304, P0336, P0440, P0442, P0446, P0452, P0453, P0502, P0503, P1133 and P1441 not set, engine started, engine runtime over 20 seconds, system voltage over 10.0v, ECT sensor more than 104°F, BARO sensor more than 72 kPa, and the ECM detected the Actual idle speed was 60 RPM more than Desired idle speed for 13 seconds with the IAC position under 2 counts. **Possible Causes:** • Engine vacuum leaks, ECM valve is leaking or the wrong valve • Idle air inlet passage or throttle bore is dirty or full of deposits • IAC valve is damaged or has failed • MAF sensor is dirty, "skewed" or installed improperly • Throttle plate, throttle shaft or linkage is damaged or sticking • TP sensor is out-of-range or "skewed" high • ECM has failed
DTC: P0507 **2T CCM, MIL: Yes** **Years:** 2008, 2009, 2010 **Models:** Avalanche, Camaro, Canyon, Escalade/EXT/ESV, Suburban, Tahoe, Yukon **Engines:** 4.8L VIN C, 5.3L VIN 0, 5.3L VIN 3, 5.3L VIN J, 5.3L VIN L, 6.0L VIN K, 6.0L VIN Y, 6.2L VIN J, 6.2L VIN W, 6.2L VIN 8 **Transmissions:** All	**Idle Speed Too High** DTC P0107, P0108, P0112, P0113, P0117, P0118, P0125, P0171, P0172, P0200, P0300, P0336, P0440, P0442, P0446, P0452, P0453, P0502, P0503, P1120, P1220, P1221, P1514, P1515, P1516, P1635 and P1639 not set, engine runtime over 2 seconds, ECT sensor more than −40°F, IAT sensor more than −40°F, BARO sensor more than 65 kPa, system voltage from 6-18v, VSS less than 3 MPH, and the ECM detected the Actual idle speed was more than 100 RPM more than the Desired idle speed for 15 seconds. **Possible Causes:** • Air inlet duct is collapsed, loose or air filter element is clogged • Base engine problem (i.e., compression or misfire condition) • IAC valve is damaged or has failed • Idle air inlet passage or throttle bore is dirty or full of deposits • MAF sensor is dirty, out-of-calibration or it is "skewed" • Throttle plate, throttle shaft or linkage is damaged or sticking • ECM has failed

DTC	Trouble Code Title, Conditions & Possible Causes
DTC: P0507 **1T CCM, MIL: Yes** **Years:** 2008, 2009 **Models:** Acadia, Allure, Aura, Astra, Aura, Aveo, Aveo5, Cobalt G3, G5, Enclave, LaCrosse, Outlook, Traverse **Engines:** 1.6L VIN 6, 1.6L VIN E, 1.8L VIN 1, 2.0L VIN P, 2.0L VIN X, 2.2L VIN H, 2.2L VIN F, 2.4L VIN 5, 2.4L VIN B, 3.6L VIN 7, 3.6L VIN D, 3.6L VIN V **Transmissions:** All	**Idle Speed Too High** The actual engine speed is greater than the desired idle speed by at least 200 RPM for greater than 4 seconds or for a cumulative of 30 seconds. The ECM detects 3 fuel cut-offs due to an engine over speed condition while the vehicle speed is zero. **Possible Causes:** • Air inlet duct is collapsed, loose or air filter element is clogged • A parasitic load on the engine • Base engine problem (i.e., compression or misfire condition) • MAF sensor is dirty, out-of-calibration or it is "skewed" • Throttle plate, throttle shaft or linkage is damaged or sticking • ECM has failed
DTC: P0508 **1T CCM, MIL: Yes** **Years:** 2008, 2009 **Models:** Acadia, Allure, Aura, Astra, Aura, Aveo, Aveo5, Cobalt G3, G5, Enclave, LaCrosse, Outlook, Traverse **Engines:** 1.6L VIN 6, 1.6L VIN E, 1.8L VIN 1, 2.0L VIN P, 2.0L VIN X, 2.2L VIN H, 2.2L VIN F, 2.4L VIN 5, 2.4L VIN B, 3.6L VIN 7, 3.6L VIN D, 3.6L VIN V **Transmissions:** All	**Cold Start Idle Air Control System Performance** DTCs P000A, P0010, P0016, P0068, P0071, P0072, P0073, P0101, P0102, P0103, P0116, P0117, P0118, P0119, P0121, P0123, P0171, P0172, P0201, P0202, P0203, P0204, P0222, P0261, P0262, P0264, P0265, P0267, P0268, P0270, P0271, P0335, P0336, P0340, P0341, P0365, P0366, P0443, P0459, P0496, P0501, P061A, P1101, P2088, P2089, P2100, P2101, P2122, P2123, P2127, P2128, P2138, P2227, P2228, P2229, P2301, P2304, P2307, P2310 are not set. The battery voltage is more than 10 volts. The engine speed is at idle. The vehicle speed equals 0 kph (0 mph). The Engine Coolant Temperature (ECT) is more than −9.75°C (+14.45°F). The Mass Air Flow (MAF) is within the calibrated range. The Pulse Width Modulated (PWM) signal for the canister purge solenoid is less than 90 percent. DTC P050A runs continuously when the above conditions are met. The actual idle speed is 175 RPM lower than the desired idle speed or 175 RPM greater than the desired idle speed during a cold start. The above condition is present for 3 seconds. **Possible Causes:** • Faulty Positive Crankcase Ventilation (PCV) system • Vacuum leaks • Mechanical conditions that limit engine speed • Restricted exhaust • Excessive deposits in the throttle body • Accessories that require additional torque to operate
DTC: P050A **2T CCM, MIL: Yes** **Years:** 2008, 2009 **Models:** Astra, Aura, Aveo, Aveo5, Cobalt G3, G5 **Engines:** 1.6L VIN 6, 1.6L VIN E, 1.8L VIN 1, 2.0L VIN P, 2.0L VIN X, 2.2L VIN H, 2.2L VIN F, 2.4L VIN 5, 2.4L VIN B **Transmissions:** All	**Cold Start Idle Air Control (IAC) System Performance** The actual engine speed is greater than the desired idle speed by at least 200 RPM for greater than 4 seconds or for a cumulative of 30 seconds. The ECM detects 3 fuel cut-offs due to an engine over speed condition while the vehicle speed is zero. **Possible Causes:** • Air inlet duct is collapsed, loose or air filter element is clogged • A parasitic load on the engine • Base engine problem (i.e., compression or misfire condition) • MAF sensor is dirty, out-of-calibration or it is "skewed" • Throttle plate, throttle shaft or linkage is damaged or sticking • ECM has failed
DTC: P050A **1T CCM, MIL: Yes** **Years:** 2008, 2009, 2010 **Models:** Acadia, Allure, Aura, Camaro, CTS, CTS-V, Enclave, LaCrosse, Outlook, Traverse **Engines:** 3.6L VIN 7, 3.6L VIN D, 3.6L VIN V **Transmissions:** All	**Engine Oil Pressure Sensor Circuit Low Input** DTC P1635 not set, engine started, and the ECM detected the Engine Oil Pressure (EOP) signal was less than 0.48v for 9 seconds. The sensor range is 0.5v (0 psi) to 4.5v (128 psi). **Possible Causes:** • Engine oil level it too low • EOP sensor signal circuit is open or shorted to ground • EOP sensor VREF circuit is open • EOP sensor is damaged or has failed • Instrument Cluster or ECM has failed
DTC: P0601 **1T CCM, MIL: Yes** **Years:** 2008, 2009 **Models:** Allure, Aura, Canyon, Colorado, LaCrosse **Engines:** 2.9L VIN 9, 3.5L VIN N, 3.8L VIN 2, 5.3L VIN C, 5.3L VIN L **Transmissions:** All	**Control Module ROM Malfunction** Key in crank or the run position, and the ECM detected more than 3 incorrect checksums during its initial self-test. The ECM uses an EEPROM to store software and calibration data. The ECM uses a checksum to verify the integrity of the information. At the time of programming, the ECM calculates a checksum and stores the value in the EEPROM. The ECM retrieves this data, performs a checksum test to compare the key "on" value to the value stored in EEPROM. If these two values do not match at key "on", it sets DTC P0601. **Possible Causes:** • The ECM must be replaced to correct this problem. A new ECM must be programmed with the correct software/calibration. • TSB 67-65-23 contains a repair procedure for this code

DTC	Trouble Code Title, Conditions & Possible Causes
DTC: P0601 **1T ECM, MIL: Yes** **Years:** 2008, 2009, 2010 **Models:** All **Engines:** All **Transmissions:** All	**Control Module Torque Performance** The ignition switch is in the Run or Crank position. DTC P061A runs continuously when the above condition is met. The ECM detects an internal failure or incomplete programming for more than 10 seconds. **Possible Causes:** • Voltage and ground inputs to the ECM • High resistance, short or open condition to the ECM • ECM is not properly programmed • ECM has failed
DTC: P0601A **2T CCM, MIL: Yes** **Years:** 2008, 2009 **Models:** Astra, Aura, Aveo, Aveo5, Cobalt G3, G5 **Engines:** 1.6L VIN 6, 1.6L VIN E, 1.8L VIN 1, 2.0L VIN P, 2.0L VIN X, 2.2L VIN H, 2.2L VIN F, 2.4L VIN 5, 2.4L VIN B **Transmissions:** All	**Control Module Torque Calculation Performance** The engine is running or cranking. DTC P061B runs continuously when the above condition is met. **Possible Causes:** • Voltage and ground inputs to the ECM • High resistance, short or open condition to the ECM • ECM is not properly programmed • ECM has failed
DTC: P0601B **2T CCM, MIL: Yes** **Years:** 2008, 2009 **Models:** Astra, Aura, Aveo, Aveo5, Cobalt G3, G5 **Engines:** 1.6L VIN 6, 1.6L VIN E, 1.8L VIN 1, 2.0L VIN P, 2.0L VIN X, 2.2L VIN H, 2.2L VIN F, 2.4L VIN 5, 2.4L VIN B **Transmissions:** All	**Control Module Engine Speed Performance** The engine is running and the engine speed is more than 1,760 RPM. DTC P061C runs continuously when the above condition is met. **Possible Causes:** • Voltage and ground inputs to the ECM • High resistance, short or open condition to the ECM • ECM is not properly programmed • ECM has failed
DTC: P0601C **2T CCM, MIL: Yes** **Years:** 2008, 2009 **Models:** Astra, Aura, Aveo, Aveo5, Cobalt G3, G5 **Engines:** 1.6L VIN 6, 1.6L VIN E, 1.8L VIN 1, 2.0L VIN P, 2.0L VIN X, 2.2L VIN H, 2.2L VIN F, 2.4L VIN 5, 2.4L VIN B **Transmissions:** All	**Control Module Not Programmed** The ignition switch is in Run or Crank. DTC P0602 runs once per ignition cycle. The ECM detects an internal failure or incomplete programming for more than 10 seconds. **Note: Attempt to program the ECM before replacing the ECM.** **Possible Causes:** • Check the voltage and ground inputs to the ECM for a, short, open or high resistance • ECM has failed
DTC: P0602 **1T CCM, MIL: Yes** **Years:** 2008, 2009 **Models:** Allure, Aura, Canyon, Colorado, LaCrosse **Engines:** 2.9L VIN 9, 3.5L VIN N, 3.8L VIN 2, 5.3L VIN C, 5.3L VIN L **Transmissions:** All	**Control Module Not Programmed** Key on, and the ECM detected it did not have the correct program to operate or that the EEPROM had been programmed incorrectly. **Possible Causes:** • Reprogram the ECM with the correct software and calibration. If this step does not correct the problem, the ECM must be replaced and programmed with the correct software/calibration.
DTC: P0602 **1T ECM, MIL: Yes** **Years:** 2008, 2009, 2010 **Models:** All **Engines:** All **Transmissions:** All	**Control Module Long Term Memory Reset** The ignition switch is in Run or Crank. DTC P0603 runs once per ignition cycle. The ECM detects an internal failure or incomplete programming for more than 10 seconds. **Possible Causes:** • Check the voltage and ground inputs to the ECM for a, short, open or high resistance • ECM has failed
DTC: P0603 **1T CCM, MIL: Yes** **Years:** 2008, 2009 **Models:** Allure, Aura, Canyon, Colorado, LaCrosse **Engines:** 2.9L VIN 9, 3.5L VIN N, 3.8L VIN 2, 5.3L VIN C, 5.3L VIN L **Transmissions:** All	**Control Module Long Term Memory Reset** DTC P0604 not set, and then with the key on, the ECM detected the calculated checksum that did not match the previous checksum. **Possible Causes:** • An interruption to the ECM main power and/or ground circuits • Check the ECM power and ground circuits and make repairs as necessary. Clear the codes and recheck. If it resets, the ECM must be replaced and programmed with the correct software.

DTC	Trouble Code Title, Conditions & Possible Causes
DTC: P0603 **1T ECM, MIL: Yes** **Years:** 2008, 2009, 2010 **Models:** All **Engines:** All **Transmissions:** All	**Control Module Random Access Memory (RAM)** The ignition switch is in Run or Crank. DTC P0604 runs continuously when the above condition is met. The ECM detects an internal failure or incomplete programming for more than 10 seconds. **Note: Attempt to program the ECM before replacing the ECM.** **Possible Causes:** • Check the voltage and ground inputs to the ECM for a, short, open or high resistance • ECM has failed
DTC: P0604 **1T CCM, MIL: Yes** **Years:** 2008, 2009 **Models:** Allure, Aura, Canyon, Colorado, LaCrosse **Engines:** 2.9L VIN 9, 3.5L VIN N, 3.8L VIN 2, 5.3L VIN C, 5.3L VIN L **Transmissions:** All	**Control Module Random Access Memory (RAM) Failure** Key on for 5 seconds, and the ECM detected the internal data test of its RAM failed. The ECM copies the program information stored in the RAM. This Allows the ECM to work with, and make any updates to this data. The ECM checks for problems in All areas of the RAM. **Possible Causes:** • The ECM must be replaced to correct this problem. A new ECM must be programmed with the correct software/calibration.
DTC: P0604 **1T ECM, MIL: Yes** **Years:** 2008, 2009, 2010 **Models:** All **Engines:** All **Transmissions:** All	**Control Module Programming Read Only Memory (ROM)** Key on, and the ECM detected the data checksum did not match the expected value, or that it was unable to read its flash memory data. **Possible Causes:** • The ECM must be replaced to correct this problem. A new ECM must be programmed with the correct software/calibration.
DTC: P0605 **1T ECM, MIL: Yes** **Years:** 2008, 2009, 2010 **Models:** Avalanche, Camaro, Canyon, Escalade/EXT/ESV, Suburban, Tahoe, Yukon **Engines:** 4.8L VIN C, 5.3L VIN 0, 5.3L VIN 3, 5.3L VIN J, 5.3L VIN L, 6.0L VIN K, 6.0L VIN Y, 6.2L VIN J, 6.2L VIN W, 6.2L VIN 8 **Transmissions:** All	**Control Module Programming Read Only Memory** Key on, and the ECM detected the data checksum did not match the expected value, or that it was unable to read its flash memory data. **Possible Causes:** • The ECM must be replaced to correct this problem. A new ECM must be programmed with the correct software/calibration.
DTC: P0605 **1T ECM, MIL: Yes** **Years:** 2008, 2009, 2010 **Models:** Avalanche, Camaro, Canyon, Escalade/EXT/ESV, Suburban, Tahoe, Yukon **Engines:** 4.8L VIN C, 5.3L VIN 0, 5.3L VIN 3, 5.3L VIN J, 5.3L VIN L, 6.0L VIN K, 6.0L VIN Y, 6.2L VIN J, 6.2L VIN W, 6.2L VIN 8 **Transmissions:** All	**Control Module Internal Performance** The ignition switch is in the Unlock/Accessory, Run, or Crank positions. The system voltage is more than 5.23 volts. DTC P0606 runs continuously when the above conditions are met. The ECM detects an internal failure or incomplete programming for more than 10 seconds. **Possible Causes:** • Check the voltage and ground inputs to the ECM for a, short, open or high resistance • ECM has failed
DTC: P0606 **1T CCM, MIL: Yes** **Years:** 2008, 2009 **Models:** Allure, Aura, Canyon, Colorado, LaCrosse **Engines:** 2.9L VIN 9, 3.5L VIN N, 3.8L VIN 2, 5.3L VIN C, 5.3L VIN L **Transmissions:** All	**Control Module Internal Performance** DTC P0601 and P0604 not set, key on, and the ECM determined that an internal performance problem existed within its controller. **Possible Causes:** • The ECM must be replaced to correct this problem. A new ECM must be programmed with the correct software/calibration.
DTC: P0606 **1T ECM, MIL: Yes** **Years:** 2008, 2009, 2010 **Models:** All **Engines:** All **Transmissions:** All	**Control Module Performance** The ignition switch is in Unlock, Accessory, Run or Crank. The system voltage is more than 5.23 volts. DTCs P0601, P0602, P0603, P0604, P0606, P062F, P0641, P0651, P2610 are not set. DTC P0607 runs continuously when the above conditions are met. The ECM detects an internal failure or incomplete programming for more than 10 seconds. **Note: Attempt to program the ECM before replacing the ECM.** **Possible Causes:** • Check the voltage and ground inputs to the ECM for a, short, open or high resistance • ECM has failed

DTC	Trouble Code Title, Conditions & Possible Causes
DTC: P0607 **1T CCM, MIL: Yes** **Years:** 2008, 2009 **Models:** Allure, Aura, Canyon, Colorado, LaCrosse **Engines:** 2.9L VIN 9, 3.5L VIN N, 3.8L VIN 2, 5.3L VIN C, 5.3L VIN L **Transmissions:** All	**Control Module Performance** Key on or engine running; then after the initial ECM power up sequence, the ECM detected an internal performance problem. **Possible Causes:** • The ECM must be replaced to correct this problem. A new ECM must be programmed with the correct software/calibration.
DTC: P0607 **1T ECM, MIL: Yes** **Years:** 2008, 2009, 2010 **Models:** All **Engines:** All **Transmissions:** All	**Vehicle Speed Output Circuit Malfunction** Engine started, engine speed over 600 RPM, and the ECM detected the Actual and Commanded state of the VSS output circuit did not match for 5 seconds. The ECM creates the VSS output signal by causing the circuit to pulse to ground, and monitoring the operation. **Possible Causes:** • VSS output signal circuit is open, shorted to ground or to power • VSS output signal problem related to the Instrument Cluster or the Electronic Suspension Control Module (internal problem) • ECM has failed
DTC: P060D **1T ECM, MIL: Yes** **Years:** 2008, 2009, 2010 **Models:** All **Engines:** All **Transmissions:** All	**Control Module Vehicle Options Incorrect** The ignition is ON. The ECM detects that programming for vehicle options is incorrect. **Possible Causes:** • ECM is not properly programmed • ECM has failed
DTC: P0610 **2T CCM, MIL: Yes** **Years:** 2008, 2009 **Models:** Astra, Aura, Aveo, Aveo5, Cobalt G3, G5 **Engines:** 1.6L VIN 6, 1.6L VIN E, 1.8L VIN 1, 2.0L VIN P, 2.0L VIN X, 2.2L VIN H, 2.2L VIN F, 2.4L VIN 5, 2.4L VIN B **Transmissions:** All	**Generator Signal Range/Performance** Engine started, the Voltage Telltale lamp is on, or less than 1000 RPM for the low duty cycle test, or more than 1000 RPM for high duty cycle test, and the ECM detected the 'L' terminal voltage was low with the Generator commanded "on", or the 'F' terminal PWM was less than 5% with the engine speed below 2500 RPM for 30 seconds. **Note: Refer to the Freeze Frame Records for additional information.** **Possible Causes:** • Generator 'L' terminal circuit is open, shorted to ground or B+ • Generator 'F' terminal circuit is open, shorted to ground or B+ • ECM has failed
DTC: P0627 **1T CCM, MIL: Yes** **Years:** 2008, 2009, 2010 **Models:** Acadia, Allure, Aura, Camaro, CTS, CTS-V, Enclave, LaCrosse, Outlook, Traverse **Engines:** 3.6L VIN 7, 3.6L VIN D, 3.6L VIN V **Transmissions:** All	**Fuel Pump Enable Circuit Low Voltage** The ECM detects the fuel pump enable circuit voltage is less than 2.21 volts when the enable circuit is commanded OFF. The condition exists for greater than 4 seconds, or a cumulative of 30 seconds. **Possible Causes:** • Short to voltage on the enable circuit • Fuel Pump Control Module (FECM) • ECM has failed
DTC: P0628 **1T CCM, MIL: Yes** **Years:** 2008, 2009, 2010 **Models:** Acadia, Allure, Aura, Camaro, CTS, CTS-V, Enclave, LaCrosse, Outlook, Traverse **Engines:** 3.6L VIN 7, 3.6L VIN D, 3.6L VIN V **Transmissions:** All	**Fuel Pump Relay Control Circuit Low Voltage** The ignition is ON and the engine is running. The fuel pump is running. The ignition voltage is more than 9 volts. These DTCs run continuously when the above conditions are met. The ECM detects the fuel pump relay control circuit is shorted to ground. **Possible Causes:** • Fuel pump relay has failed • ECM has failed
DTC: P0628 **2T CCM, MIL: Yes** **Years:** 2008, 2009 **Models:** Astra, Aura, Aveo, Aveo5, Cobalt G3, G5 **Engines:** 1.6L VIN 6, 1.6L VIN E, 1.8L VIN 1, 2.0L VIN P, 2.0L VIN X, 2.2L VIN H, 2.2L VIN F, 2.4L VIN 5, 2.4L VIN B **Transmissions:** All	**Fuel Pump Enable Circuit High Voltage** The ECM detects the fuel pump enable circuit voltage is greater than 2.74 volts when the enable circuit is commanded OFF. The condition exists for greater than 4 seconds, or a cumulative of 30 seconds. **Possible Causes:** • Short to voltage on the enable circuit • Fuel Pump Control Module (FECM) • ECM has failed

DTC	Trouble Code Title, Conditions & Possible Causes
DTC: P0629 **1T CCM, MIL: Yes** **Years:** 2008, 2009, 2010 **Models:** Acadia, Allure, Aura, Camaro, CTS, CTS-V, Enclave, LaCrosse, Outlook, Traverse **Engines:** 3.6L VIN 7, 3.6L VIN D, 3.6L VIN V **Transmissions:** All	**Fuel Pump Enable Circuit High Voltage** The ignition is ON and the engine is running. The fuel pump is running. The ignition voltage is more than 9 volts. These DTCs run continuously when the above conditions are met. The ECM detects the fuel pump relay control circuit is open or shorted to voltage. **Possible Causes:** • Short to voltage on the enable circuit • Fuel pump relay • ECM has failed
DTC: P0629 **2T CCM, MIL: Yes** **Years:** 2008, 2009 **Models:** Astra, Aura, Aveo, Aveo5, Cobalt G3, G5 **Engines:** 1.6L VIN 6, 1.6L VIN E, 1.8L VIN 1, 2.0L VIN P, 2.0L VIN X, 2.2L VIN H, 2.2L VIN F, 2.4L VIN 5, 2.4L VIN B **Transmissions:** All	**Control Module Fuel Injector Control Performance** The engine speed is greater than 80 RPM. The ignition voltage is between 8-18 volts. DTC P062B runs continuously when the above condition is met for greater than 500 The ECM detects a condition with the integrated circuits of the fuel injector driver module for greater than 4 seconds, or a cumulative of 30 seconds. **Note: Verify that the battery cables are clean and tight and the battery is fully charged.** **Possible Causes:** • Module not properly programmed • ECM has failed
DTC: P062B **1T CCM, MIL: Yes** **Years:** 2008, 2009, 2010 **Models:** Acadia, Allure, Aura, Camaro, CTS, CTS-V, Enclave, LaCrosse, Outlook, Traverse **Engines:** 3.6L VIN 7, 3.6L VIN D, 3.6L VIN V **Transmissions:** All	**Control Module Long Term Memory Performance** The ignition is ON. DTC P062F runs once per ignition cycle. The ECM detects an internal failure or incomplete programming for more than 10 seconds. **Note: Attempt to program the ECM before replacing the ECM.** **Possible Causes:** • Check the voltage and ground inputs to the ECM for a, short, open or high resistance • ECM has failed
DTC: P062F **1T ECM, MIL: Yes** **Years:** 2008, 2009, 2010 **Models:** All **Engines:** All **Transmissions:** All	**Throttle Actuator Control (TAC) Command Performance** The ECM detects that the commanded duty cycle for the range test high is greater than 80 percent. Or the ECM detects that the commanded duty cycle for the range test low is greater than 80 percent. Either condition exists for greater than 1 second, or a cumulative of 10 seconds. **Note: Use a scan tool to help diagnose the condition.** **Possible Causes:** • Throttle blade that is not in the rest position • Throttle valve that is binding open or closed • Throttle valve that opens or closes without spring pressure • Throttle body has failed • ECM has failed
DTC: P0638 **1T CCM, MIL: Yes** **Years:** 2008, 2009, 2010 **Models:** Acadia, Allure, Aura, Camaro, CTS, CTS-V, Enclave, LaCrosse, Outlook, Traverse **Engines:** 3.6L VIN 7, 3.6L VIN D, 3.6L VIN V **Transmissions:** All	**5-Volt Reference 1 Circuit** The ignition is in Unlock, Accessory, Run, or Crank. The ignition voltage is more than 5.23 volts. DTCs P0641 and P0651 run continuously when the above conditions are met. The ECM detects a voltage out of tolerance condition on the 5-volt reference 1 or 2 circuit for more than 0.5 second. The 5-volt reference 1 circuit provides 5 volts to the following sensors, Fuel tank pressure (FTP) sensor, Accelerator Pedal Position (APP) sensor 2, Engine Oil Pressure (EOP) sensor and Camshaft Position (CMP) sensor. **Possible Causes:** • 5v VREF circuit is shorted to chassis or sensor ground • 5v VREF circuit to FTP. APP, EOP, and CMP sensors circuit is shorted to (B+) • ECM has failed
DTC: P0641 **1T CCM, MIL: Yes** **Years:** 2008, 2009 **Models:** Allure, Aura, Canyon, Colorado, LaCrosse **Engines:** 2.9L VIN 9, 3.5L VIN N, 3.8L VIN 2, 5.3L VIN C, 5.3L VIN L **Transmissions:** All	**5-Volt Reference Circuit (FECM)** The ignition is on. The Fuel Pump Control Module (FECM) detects that the fuel pressure 5-volt reference is above or below a predetermined voltage threshold. **Possible Causes:** • Fuel line pressure sensor, 5v VREF circuit shorted to ground or an open/high resistance • Fuel line pressure sensor, 5v VREF circuit for a shorted to voltage • Fuel line pressure sensor, low reference circuit for an open/high resistance • FECM has failed • ECM has failed

DTC	Trouble Code Title, Conditions & Possible Causes
DTC: P0641 **1T CCM, MIL: Yes** **Years:** 2008, 2009, 2010 **Models:** Acadia, Allure, Aura, Camaro, Corvette, CTS, CTS-V, DTS, Enclave, LaCrosse, Outlook, Traverse **Engines:** All **Transmissions:** All	**5-Volt Reference 1 Circuit Low Voltage** Key on or engine running; and the ECM detected the 5v Reference circuit was out of tolerance for 10 seconds. The 5v VREF 1 circuit from the ECM is used to provide power to the The Fuel Tank Pressure (FTP) sensor. The air conditioning (A/C) refrigerant pressure sensorThe Accelerator Pedal Position (APP) sensor 1. The exhaust Camshaft Position (CMP) sensor. The intake CMP sensor. The Throttle Position (TP) sensor 2. The Intake Manifold Tuning Valve (IMTV) sensorThe ECM detects a voltage out of range condition on the 5-volt reference 1 or 2 buss for more than 0.5 second. **Possible Causes:** • 5v VREF circuit is shorted to chassis or sensor ground • 5v VREF circuit to FTP. CMP IMTV or TP sensor circuit is shorted to (B+) • Component failure • ECM has failed
DTC: P0642 **2T CCM, MIL: Yes** **Years:** 2008, 2009, 2010 **Models:** All **Engines:** All **Transmissions:** All	**5-Volt Reference 1 Circuit High Voltage** Key on or engine running; and the ECM detected the 5v Reference circuit was out of tolerance for 10 seconds. The 5v VREF 1 circuit from the ECM is used to provide power to the The Fuel Tank Pressure (FTP) sensor. The air conditioning (A/C) refrigerant pressure sensorThe Accelerator Pedal Position (APP) sensor 1. The exhaust Camshaft Position (CMP) sensor. The intake CMP sensor. The Throttle Position (TP) sensor 2. The Intake Manifold Tuning Valve (IMTV) sensorThe ECM detects a voltage out of range condition on the 5-volt reference 1 or 2 buss for more than 0.5 second. **Possible Causes:** • 5v VREF circuit is shorted to chassis or sensor ground • 5v VREF circuit to FTP. CMP IMTV or TP sensor circuit is shorted to (B+) • Component failure • ECM has failed
DTC: P0643 **2T CCM, MIL: Yes** **Years:** 2008, 2009, 2010 **Models:** All **Engines:** All **Transmissions:** All	**Air Conditioning Clutch Relay Control Circuit Malfunction** Engine started, engine speed over 400 RPM, system voltage over 10.0v, and the ECM detected the Actual and Commanded state of the A/C Relay Control circuit did not match for 5 seconds. **Possible Causes:** • A/C relay control circuit is open, shorted to ground or to power • A/C relay power circuit is open (test the A/C CRUISE mini fuse) • A/C relay is damaged or has failed • ECM has failed
DTC: P064A **1T CCM, MIL: Yes** **Years:** 2008, 2009, 2010 **Models:** Acadia, Allure, Aura, Camaro, CTS, CTS-V, Enclave, LaCrosse, Outlook, Traverse **Engines:** 3.6L VIN 7, 3.6L VIN D, 3.6L VIN V **Transmissions:** All	**Malfunction Indicator Lamp (MIL) Control Circuit** The ignition is in the Run or Crank position. The ignition voltage is between 9-18 volts. DTC P0650 runs continuously when the ignition is ON. The control module detects that the commanded state of the MIL driver and the actual state of the control circuit do not match for more than 5 seconds. **Possible Causes:** • IPC ignition circuit fuse is open, • IPC control circuit for a short to ground • IPC control circuit for a short to voltage or high resistance • IPC has failed • ECM has failed
DTC: P0650 **1T CCM, MIL: Yes** **Years:** 2008, 2009 **Models:** Allure, Aura, Canyon, Colorado, LaCrosse **Engines:** 2.9L VIN 9, 3.5L VIN N, 3.8L VIN 2, 5.3L VIN C, 5.3L VIN L **Transmissions:** All	**Malfunction Indicator Lamp (MIL) Control Circuit** The ECM detects an open, a short to ground, or a short to voltage on the circuit that controls the MIL. The condition exists for at least 4 seconds. **Possible Causes:** • MIL control circuit is open or shorted to ground • MIL control circuit is shorted to system power • MIL control power circuit is open in the Instrument Cluster • MIL (the lamp) is damaged or has failed • Instrument Control Panel (IPC) has failed • ECM has failed
DTC: P0650 **2T CCM, MIL: Yes** **Years:** 2008, 2009, 2010 **Models:** All **Engines:** All **Transmissions:** All	**5-Volt Reference 2 Circuit** The ignition is in Unlock, Accessory, Run, or Crank. The ignition voltage is more than 5.23 volts. DTCs P0641 and P0651 run continuously when the above conditions are met. The ECM detects a voltage out of tolerance condition on the 5-volt reference 1 or 2 circuit for more than 0.5 second. The 5-volt reference 2 circuit provides 5 volts to the following sensors, APP sensor 1, Throttle Position (TP) sensor 1 and 2, Crankshaft Position (CKP) and brake booster vacuum sensor. **Possible Causes:** • 5v VREF circuit is shorted to chassis or sensor ground • 5v VREF circuit to APP. CKP, and CMP brake booster vacuum sensor circuit is shorted to (B+) • ECM has failed

DTC	Trouble Code Title, Conditions & Possible Causes
DTC: P0651 **1T CCM, MIL: Yes** **Years:** 2008, 2009 **Models:** Allure, Aura, Canyon, Colorado, LaCrosse **Engines:** 2.9L VIN 9, 3.5L VIN N, 3.8L VIN 2, 5.3L VIN C, 5.3L VIN L **Transmissions:** All	**5-Volt Reference 2 Circuit Malfunction** Key on or engine running; and the ECM detected the 5v Reference circuit was out of tolerance for 10 seconds. The 5v VREF 2 circuit is used to provide power to the Fuel Tank Pressure (FTP) sensor on this vehicle application. **Possible Causes:** • 5v VREF circuit is shorted to chassis or sensor ground • 5v VREF circuit to MAP or TP sensor circuit is shorted to (B+) • ECM has failed
DTC: P0651 **1T CCM, MIL: No** **Years:** 2008, 2009, 2010 **Models:** Avalanche, Camaro, Canyon, Escalade/EXT/ESV, Suburban, Tahoe, Yukon **Engines:** 4.8L VIN C, 5.3L VIN 0, 5.3L VIN 3, 5.3L VIN J, 5.3L VIN L, 6.0L VIN K, 6.0L VIN Y, 6.2L VIN J, 6.2L VIN W, 6.2L VIN 8 **Transmissions:** All	**5-Volt Reference 2 Circuit Malfunction** The 5-volt reference circuit voltage is greater or less than a predetermined threshold. The condition exists, then a 5 second delay for MIL ONThe 5-volt reference 2 circuit provides 5 volts to the following sensors. All four camshaft position (CMP) sensors and the Accelerator pedal position (APP) sensor 1 **Possible Causes:** • 5v VREF circuit is shorted to chassis or sensor ground • 5v VREF circuit to CMP or APP sensor circuit is shorted to (B+) • Component failure • ECM has failed
DTC: P0651 **1T CCM, MIL: Yes** **Years:** 2008, 2009, 2010 **Models:** Acadia, Allure, Aura, Camaro, Corvette, CTS, CTS-V, DTS, Enclave, LaCrosse, Outlook, Traverse **Engines:** 3.6L VIN 7, 3.6L VIN D, 3.6L VIN V **Transmissions:** All	**5-Volt Reference 2 Circuit Low Voltage** The 5-volt reference circuit voltage is greater or less than a predetermined threshold. The condition exists, then a 5 second delay for MIL ONThe 5-volt reference 2 circuit provides 5 volts to the following sensors. All four camshaft position (CMP) sensors and the Accelerator pedal position (APP) sensor 1 **Possible Causes:** • 5v VREF circuit is shorted to chassis or sensor ground • 5v VREF circuit to CMP or APP sensor circuit is shorted to (B+) • Component failure • ECM has failed
DTC: P0652 **1T CCM, MIL: Yes** **Years:** 2008, 2009, 2010 **Models:** Acadia, Allure, Aura, Camaro, CTS, CTS-V, Enclave, LaCrosse, Outlook, Traverse **Engines:** 3.6L VIN 7, 3.6L VIN D, 3.6L VIN V **Transmissions:** All	**5-Volt Reference 2 Circuit Low Voltage** The 5-volt reference circuit voltage is greater or less than a predetermined threshold. The condition exists, then a 5 second delay for MIL ONThe 5-volt reference 2 circuit provides 5 volts to the following sensors. The APP sensor 2. The Throttle Position (TP) sensor 1. The Crankshaft Position (CKP) sensor **Possible Causes:** • 5v VREF circuit is shorted to chassis or sensor ground • 5v VREF circuit to TP, CKP or APP sensor circuit is shorted to (B+) • ECM has failed
DTC: P0652 **2T CCM, MIL: Yes** **Years:** 2008, 2009 **Models:** Astra, Aura, Aveo, Aveo5, Cobalt G3, G5 **Engines:** 1.6L VIN 6, 1.6L VIN E, 1.8L VIN 1, 2.0L VIN P, 2.0L VIN X, 2.2L VIN H, 2.2L VIN F, 2.4L VIN 5, 2.4L VIN B **Transmissions:** All	**5-Volt Reference 2 Circuit High Voltage** The 5-volt reference circuit voltage is greater or less than a predetermined threshold. The condition exists, then a 5 second delay for MIL ON. The 5-volt reference 2 circuit provides 5 volts to the following sensors. The APP sensor 2. The Throttle Position (TP) sensor 1. The Crankshaft Position (CKP) sensor **Possible Causes:** • 5v VREF circuit is shorted to chassis or sensor ground • 5v VREF circuit to APP TP or CKP sensor circuit is shorted to (B+) • Component failure • ECM has failed
DTC: P0653 **1T CCM, MIL: Yes** **Years:** 2008, 2009, 2010 **Models:** Acadia, Allure, Aura, Camaro, CTS, CTS-V, Enclave, LaCrosse, Outlook, Traverse **Engines:** 3.6L VIN 7, 3.6L VIN D, 3.6L VIN V **Transmissions:** All	**5-Volt Reference 2 Circuit High Voltage** DTCs P0601, P0602, P0603, P0604, P0605, P0606, P0607, and P2610 are not set. The ignition is in Unlock, Accessory, Run, or Crank. The ignition voltage is more than 5.23 volts. DTCs P0653 runs continuously when the above conditions are met.The APP sensor 2. The Throttle Position (TP) sensor 1. The Crankshaft Position (CKP) sensor. **Possible Causes:** • 5v VREF circuit is shorted to chassis or sensor ground • 5v VREF circuit to APP TP or CKP sensor circuit is shorted to (B+) • Component failure • ECM has failed

DTC	Trouble Code Title, Conditions & Possible Causes
DTC: P0653 **2T CCM, MIL:** Yes **Years:** 2008, 2009 **Models:** Astra, Aura, Aveo, Aveo5, Cobalt G3, G5 **Engines:** 1.6L VIN 6, 1.6L VIN E, 1.8L VIN 1, 2.0L VIN P, 2.0L VIN X, 2.2L VIN H, 2.2L VIN F, 2.4L VIN 5, 2.4L VIN B **Transmissions:** All	**Intake Manifold Tuning (IMT) Valve Performance.** DTC P0111, P0112, P0113, P0114, P0116, P0117, P0118, P0119, P0642, P0643, P0652, P0653, P0652, P0653, P0661, P0662, P2227, P2228, or P2229 is not set. The engine is running for greater than 3 seconds. The engine speed is between 608-6,208 RPM. The Intake Air Temperature (IAT) is warmer than −10°C (14°F). This DTC runs continuously within the enabling conditions. The commanded ON or OFF position of the IMT valve is stable for greater than 0.5 second, and the ECM detects less than 1 volt on the IMT valve position sensor signal circuit, when the IMT valve is commanded OFF. Or The commanded ON or OFF position of the IMT valve is stable for greater than 0.5 second, and the ECM detects greater than 4 volts on the IMT valve position sensor signal circuit, when the IMT valve is commanded ON. **Possible Causes:** • IMT low reference circuit for an open/high resistance • IMT 5-volt reference circuit for a short to ground or an open/high resistance • IMT 5-volt reference circuit for a short to voltage • IMT signal circuit for an open/high resistance • IMT signal circuit for a short to ground or an open/high resistance • IMT signal circuit for a short to voltage • IMT has failed • ECM has failed
DTC: P065E **2T CCM, MIL:** Yes **Years:** 2008, 2009 **Models:** Astra, Aura, Aveo, Aveo5, Cobalt G3, G5 **Engines:** 1.6L VIN 6, 1.6L VIN E, 1.8L VIN 1, 2.0L VIN P, 2.0L VIN X, 2.2L VIN H, 2.2L VIN F, 2.4L VIN 5, 2.4L VIN B **Transmissions:** All	**Intake Manifold Tuning (IMT) Valve Solenoid Control Circuit Low Voltage.** DTC P0606 is not set. The ignition is ON, or the engine is running. The battery voltage is greater than 9 volts. This DTC runs continuously within the enabling conditions. The ECM detects a short to ground or an open on the IMT valve actuator solenoid control circuit for greater than 2 seconds. **Possible Causes:** • IMT ignition circuit for a short to ground or an open/high resistance. • IMT control circuit for a short to ground • IMT control circuit for a short to voltage or an open/high resistance • IMT component failure • ECM has failed
DTC: P0661 **2T CCM, MIL:** Yes **Years:** 2008, 2009 **Models:** Astra, Aura, Aveo, Aveo5, Cobalt G3, G5 **Engines:** 1.6L VIN 6, 1.6L VIN E, 1.8L VIN 1, 2.0L VIN P, 2.0L VIN X, 2.2L VIN H, 2.2L VIN F, 2.4L VIN 5, 2.4L VIN B **Transmissions:** All	**Intake Manifold Tuning (IMT) Valve Solenoid Control Circuit High Voltage.** DTC P0606 is not set. The ignition is ON, or the engine is running. The battery voltage is greater than 9 volts. This DTC runs continuously within the enabling conditions. The ECM detects a short to voltage on the IMT valve actuator solenoid control circuit for greater than 2 seconds. **Possible Causes:** • IMT ignition circuit for a short to ground or an open/high resistance. • IMT control circuit for a short to ground • IMT control circuit for a short to voltage or an open/high resistance • IMT component failure • ECM has failed
DTC: P0662 **2T CCM, MIL:** Yes **Years:** 2008, 2009 **Models:** Astra, Aura, Aveo, Aveo5, Cobalt G3, G5 **Engines:** 1.6L VIN 6, 1.6L VIN E, 1.8L VIN 1, 2.0L VIN P, 2.0L VIN X, 2.2L VIN H, 2.2L VIN F, 2.4L VIN 5, 2.4L VIN B **Transmissions:** All	**Engine Controls Ignition Relay Control Circuit** The ignition is ON. The battery voltage is between 9-16 volts. The commanded state of the ODM and the actual state of the control circuit do not match. The condition is present for more than 5 seconds. **Possible Causes:** • Powertrain relay shorted to ground on the control circuit • Powertrain relay shorted to voltage or an open/high resistance • Powertrain relay has failed • ECM has failed
DTC: P0685 **1T CCM, MIL:** Yes **Years:** 2008, 2009 **Models:** Allure, Aura, Canyon, Colorado, LaCrosse **Engines:** 2.9L VIN 9, 3.5L VIN N, 3.8L VIN 2, 5.3L VIN C, 5.3L VIN L **Transmissions:** All	**Engine Controls Ignition Relay Control Circuit** The ignition voltage is between 10-18 volts. The engine speed is greater than 80 RPM. The powertrain relay has been commanded ON and OFF. The commanded state of the ODM and the actual state of the control circuit do not match. **Possible Causes:** • Powertrain relay shorted to ground on the control circuit • Powertrain relay shorted to voltage or an open/high resistance • Powertrain relay has failed • ECM has failed

DTC	Trouble Code Title, Conditions & Possible Causes
DTC: P0685 **1T CCM, MIL: Yes** **Years:** 2008, 2009, 2010 **Models:** Acadia, Allure, Aura, Camaro, Corvette CTS, CTS-V, DTS, Enclave, LaCrosse, Outlook, Traverse **Engines:** All **Transmissions:** All	**Engine Controls Ignition Relay Control Circuit Low Voltage** The ignition voltage is between 10-18 volts. The engine speed is greater than 80 RPM. The powertrain relay has been commanded ON and OFF. The commanded state of the ODM and the actual state of the control circuit do not match. **Possible Causes:** • Powertrain relay shorted to ground on the control circuit • Powertrain relay shorted to voltage or an open/high resistance • Powertrain relay has failed • ECM has failed
DTC: P0686 **1T CCM, MIL: Yes** **Years:** 2008, 2009 **Models:** Acadia, Allure, Aura, Astra, Aura, Aveo, Aveo5, Cobalt G3, G5, Enclave, LaCrosse, Outlook, Traverse **Engines:** 1.6L VIN 6, 1.6L VIN E, 1.8L VIN 1, 2.0L VIN P, 2.0L VIN X, 2.2L VIN H, 2.2L VIN F, 2.4L VIN 5, 2.4L VIN B, 3.6L VIN 7, 3.6L VIN D, 3.6L VIN V **Transmissions:** All	**Engine Controls Ignition Relay Control Circuit High Voltage** The ignition voltage is between 10-18 volts. The engine speed is greater than 80 RPM. The powertrain relay has been commanded ON and OFF. The commanded state of the ODM and the actual state of the control circuit do not match. **Note: The ignition voltage circuit is between the powertrain relay and the ECM. The ignition voltage is a feedback circuit** **Possible Causes:** • Powertrain relay shorted to ground on the control circuit • Powertrain relay shorted to voltage or an open/high resistance • Powertrain relay has failed • ECM has failed
DTC: P0687 **1T CCM, MIL: Yes** **Years:** 2008, 2009 **Models:** Acadia, Allure, Aura, Astra, Aura, Aveo, Aveo5, Cobalt G3, G5, Enclave, LaCrosse, Outlook, Traverse **Engines:** 1.6L VIN 6, 1.6L VIN E, 1.8L VIN 1, 2.0L VIN P, 2.0L VIN X, 2.2L VIN H, 2.2L VIN F, 2.4L VIN 5, 2.4L VIN B, 3.6L VIN 7, 3.6L VIN D, 3.6L VIN V **Transmissions:** All	**Engine Controls Relay Feedback Circuit Low Voltage** The ignition is ON. The powertrain relay is commanded ON. DTC P0685 is not set. The ECM detects less than 5 volts on the ignition 1 voltage circuit to the ECM. The condition is present for more than 5 seconds. **Possible Causes:** • Powertrain relay shorted to ground on the control circuit • Powertrain relay shorted to voltage or an open/high resistance • Powertrain relay has failed • ECM has failed
DTC: P0689 **1T CCM, MIL: Yes** **Years:** 2008, 2009 **Models:** Allure, Aura, Canyon, Corvette, CTS, CTS-V, Colorado, DTS, LaCrosse **Engines:** All **Transmissions:** All	**Engine Controls Ignition Relay Feedback Circuit Low Voltage** The ignition voltage is between 10-18 volts. The ignition is ON. The DTCs runs continuously once the above condition is met. The ECM detects that powertrain relay feedback voltage is less than 6 volts for greater than 500 mS. **Possible Causes:** • Powertrain relay shorted to ground on the control circuit • Powertrain relay shorted to voltage or an open/high resistance • Powertrain relay has failed • ECM has failed
DTC: P0689 **1T CCM, MIL: Yes** **Years:** 2008, 2009 **Models:** Acadia, Allure, Aura, Astra, Aura, Aveo, Aveo5, Cobalt G3, G5, Enclave, LaCrosse, Outlook, Traverse **Engines:** 1.6L VIN 6, 1.6L VIN E, 1.8L VIN 1, 2.0L VIN P, 2.0L VIN X, 2.2L VIN H, 2.2L VIN F, 2.4L VIN 5, 2.4L VIN B, 3.6L VIN 7, 3.6L VIN D, 3.6L VIN V **Transmissions:** All	**Engine Controls Ignition Relay De-energized Too Late** The ignition is ON. The relay has been commanded ON. These DTCs run continuously when the above conditions have been met. The commanded state of the ODM and the actual state of the control circuit do not match. The ECM detects that the feedback voltage is not within a predicted range when the relay is commanded ON and OFF. Either condition is present for more than 2 seconds. **Possible Causes:** • Powertrain relay shorted to ground on the control circuit • Powertrain relay shorted to voltage or an open/high resistance • Powertrain relay has failed • ECM has failed

DTC	Trouble Code Title, Conditions & Possible Causes
DTC: P068B **2T CCM, MIL: Yes** **Years:** 2008, 2009 **Models:** Astra, Aura, Aveo, Aveo5, Cobalt G3, G5 **Engines:** 1.6L VIN 6, 1.6L VIN E, 1.8L VIN 1, 2.0L VIN P, 2.0L VIN X, 2.2L VIN H, 2.2L VIN F, 2.4L VIN 5, 2.4L VIN B **Transmissions:** All	**Engine Controls Relay Feedback Circuit High Voltage** This DTC will run with the ignition ON or OFF. This DTC will run when the powertrain relay is commanded ON or OFF. DTC P0685 is not set. The ECM detects more than 16 volts on the ignition 1 voltage circuit to the ECM when the relay is commanded ON. The ECM detects more than 2 volts on the ignition 1 voltage circuit to the ECM when the relay is commanded OFF. The condition is present for more than 2 seconds. **Possible Causes:** • Powertrain relay shorted to ground on the control circuit • Powertrain relay shorted to voltage or an open/high resistance • Powertrain relay has failed • ECM has failed
DTC: P0690 **1T CCM, MIL: Yes** **Years:** 2008, 2009 **Models:** Allure, Aura, Canyon, Corvette, CTS, CTS-V, Colorado, DTS, LaCrosse **Engines:** All **Transmissions:** All	**Engine Controls Ignition Relay Feedback Circuit High Voltage** The ignition voltage is between 10-18 volts. The ignition is ON. The DTCs runs continuously once the above condition is met. The ECM detects that powertrain relay feedback voltage is less than 6 volts for greater than 500 mS. **Possible Causes:** • Powertrain relay shorted to ground on the control circuit • Powertrain relay shorted to voltage or an open/high resistance • Powertrain relay has failed • ECM has failed
DTC: P0690 **1T CCM, MIL: Yes** **Years:** 2008, 2009, 2010 **Models:** Acadia, Allure, Aura, Camaro, Enclave, LaCrosse, Outlook, Traverse **Engines:** 3.6L VIN 7, 3.6L VIN D, 3.6L VIN V **Transmissions:** All	**5-Volt Reference 3 Circuit** The 5-volt reference circuit voltage is greater or less than a predetermined threshold. The condition exists, then a 5 second delay for MIL ONThe 5-volt reference 2 circuit provides 5 volts to the following sensors. The Throttle position sensor (TPS) 1 and 2, Crankshaft position (CKP) sensorand the Accelerator pedal position (APP) sensor 2. **Possible Causes:** • 5v VREF circuit is shorted to chassis or sensor ground • 5v VREF circuit to TPS, CKP or APP sensor circuit is shorted to (B+) • ECM has failed
DTC: P0697 **1T CCM, MIL: Yes** **Years:** 2008, 2009, 2010 **Models:** Acadia, Allure, Aura, Camaro, CTS, CTS-V, Enclave, LaCrosse, Outlook, Traverse **Engines:** 3.6L VIN 7, 3.6L VIN D, 3.6L VIN V **Transmissions:** All	**5-Volt Reference 3 Circuit Low Voltage** The 5-volt reference circuit voltage is greater or less than a predetermined threshold. The condition exists,then a 5 second delay for MIL ONThe 5-volt reference 2 circuit provides 5 volts to the following sensors. The Throttle position sensor (TPS) 1 and 2, Crankshaft position (CKP) sensorand the Accelerator pedal position (APP) sensor 2. **Possible Causes:** • 5v VREF circuit is shorted to chassis or sensor ground • 5v VREF circuit to TPS, CKP or APP sensor circuit is shorted to (B+) • ECM has failed
DTC: P0698 **1T CCM, MIL: Yes** **Years:** 2008, 2009, 2010 **Models:** Acadia, Allure, Aura, Camaro, CTS, CTS-V, Enclave, LaCrosse, Outlook, Traverse **Engines:** 3.6L VIN 7, 3.6L VIN D, 3.6L VIN V **Transmissions:** All	**5-Volt Reference 3 Circuit High Voltage** The 5-volt reference circuit voltage is greater or less than a predetermined threshold. The condition exists,then a 5 second delay for MIL ONThe 5-volt reference 2 circuit provides 5 volts to the following sensors. The Throttle position sensor (TPS) 1 and 2, Crankshaft position (CKP) sensorand the Accelerator pedal position (APP) sensor 2. **Possible Causes:** • 5v VREF circuit is shorted to chassis or sensor ground • 5v VREF circuit to TPS, CKP or APP sensor circuit is shorted to (B+) • ECM has failed
DTC: P0699 **1T CCM, MIL: Yes** **Years:** 2008, 2009, 2010 **Models:** Acadia, Allure, Aura, Camaro, CTS, CTS-V, Enclave, LaCrosse, Outlook, Traverse **Engines:** 3.6L VIN 7, 3.6L VIN D, 3.6L VIN V **Transmissions:** All	**Fuel Pump Control Module Requested MIL Illumination** The ignition is ON, or the engine is running. The fuel pump control module requests the ECM to illuminate the MIL. **Possible Causes:** • Emissions failure in fuel pump control system

DTC	Trouble Code Title, Conditions & Possible Causes
DTC: P069E **1T CCM, MIL: Yes** **Years:** 2008, 2009 **Models:** Corvette, CTS, CTS-V, DTS **Engines:** 4.6L VIN Y, 6.2L VIN W, 6.2L VIN P, 6.2L VIN R, 7.0L VIN E **Transmissions:** All	**Fuel Pump Control Module Requested MIL Illumination** The ignition is ON, or the engine is running. The fuel pump control module requests the ECM to illuminate the MIL. **Possible Causes:** • Fuel line pressure sensor, 5v VREF circuit shorted to ground or an open/high resistance • Fuel line pressure sensor, 5v VREF circuit for a shorted to voltage • Fuel line pressure sensor, low reference circuit for an open/high resistance • FECM has failed
DTC: P069E **1T CCM, MIL: Yes** **Years:** 2008, 2009, 2010 **Models:** Acadia, Allure, Aura, Camaro, Enclave, LaCrosse, Outlook, Traverse **Engines:** 3.6L VIN 7, 3.6L VIN D, 3.6L VIN V **Transmissions:** All	**5-Volt Reference Performance** The ignition is on. The Fuel Pump Control Module (FECM) detects that the fuel pressure 5-volt reference is above or below a predetermined voltage threshold **Possible Causes:** • Fuel line pressure sensor, 5v VREF circuit shorted to ground or an open/high resistance • Fuel line pressure sensor, 5v VREF circuit for a shorted to voltage • Fuel line pressure sensor, low reference circuit for an open/high resistance • FECM has failed
DTC: P06A6 **2T CCM, MIL: Yes** **Years:** 2008, 2009, 2010 **Models:** All **Engines:** All **Transmissions:** All	**Transmission Control Module (TCM) Requested MIL Illumination** The ignition is ON. The TCM is requesting MIL illumination. **Note: DTC P0700 can not be cleared from the ECM until the related TCM codes have been cleared.** **Possible Causes:** • MIL control circuit is shorted to ground • Check the TCM for any trouble codes in memory that are responsible for the request to turn on the MIL • TCM has failed
DTC: P0700 **1T CCM, MIL: Yes** **Years:** 2008, 2009, 2010 **Models:** All **Engines:** All **Transmissions:** All	**Clutch Switch Circuit Malfunction (M49/MM6)** DTC P0500, P0502 and P0503 not set, engine started, engine load and vehicle acceleration indicate vehicle is in gear and moving, and the ECM detected a VSS signal indicating the vehicle went from 0 to over 24 MPH and then back to 0 MPH within 2 seconds without the ECM detecting a change in the Clutch Anticipate switch circuit. **Note: This fault must occur 7 times before ECM will set this code.** **Possible Causes:** • Clutch switch circuit is open, shorted to ground or to power • Clutch switch power circuit is open (test the ENG IGN fuse) • Clutch switch is out of adjustment, damaged or has failed • ECM has failed
DTC: P0706 **1T CCM, MIL: No** **Years:** 2008, 2009, 2010 **Models:** Avalanche, Camaro, Canyon, Escalade/EXT/ESV, Suburban, Tahoe, Yukon **Engines:** 4.8L VIN C, 5.3L VIN 0, 5.3L VIN 3, 5.3L VIN J, 5.3L VIN L, 6.0L VIN K, 6.0L VIN Y, 6.2L VIN J, 6.2L VIN W, 6.2L VIN 8 **Transmissions:** All	**Transaxle Range Switch (PRNDL) Performance** Engine started, system voltage over 10.0v, and the ECM detected the Transaxle Range switch signal indicated a range other than P/N during startup. **Note: This test must fail 2 out of 4 consecutive tests in order to set this trouble code.** **Possible Causes:** • TR switch circuit is or shorted to ground • TR switch circuit is shorted to another PRNDL circuit • TR switch is damaged or out of adjustment • ECM has failed
DTC: P0711 **1T CCM, MIL: No** **Years:** 2008, 2009, 2010 **Models:** Avalanche, Camaro, Canyon, Escalade/EXT/ESV, Suburban, Tahoe, Yukon **Engines:** 4.8L VIN C, 5.3L VIN 0, 5.3L VIN 3, 5.3L VIN J, 5.3L VIN L, 6.0L VIN K, 6.0L VIN Y, 6.2L VIN J, 6.2L VIN W, 6.2L VIN 8 **Transmissions:** A/T	**TFT Sensor Circuit Low Input** DTC P0560 not set, engine started, engine running and the ECM detected the TFT sensor was more than 298°F for 10 seconds. **Possible Causes:** • TFT sensor signal circuit is shorted to sensor or chassis ground • TFT sensor is damaged or has failed (it may be shorted) • ECM has failed

DTC	Trouble Code Title, Conditions & Possible Causes
DTC: P0712 **1T CCM, MIL: No** **Years:** 2008, 2009, 2010 **Models:** Avalanche, Camaro, Canyon, Escalade/EXT/ESV, Suburban, Tahoe, Yukon **Engines:** 4.8L VIN C, 5.3L VIN 0, 5.3L VIN 3, 5.3L VIN J, 5.3L VIN L, 6.0L VIN K, 6.0L VIN Y, 6.2L VIN J, 6.2L VIN W, 6.2L VIN 8 **Transmissions:** All	**TFT Sensor Circuit High Input** DTC P0117, P0118 and P0560 not set, engine started, and the ECM detected the TFT sensor was less than −33°F (a voltage of 4.92v or higher) for 10 seconds during the CCM test. **Possible Causes:** • TFT sensor signal circuit is open between the sensor and ECM • TFT sensor signal circuit is shorted to VREF or system power • TFT sensor is damaged or has failed (it may be open) • ECM has failed • TSB 02-07-30-15 contains a repair procedure for this code
DTC: P0713 **1T CCM, MIL: No** **Years:** 2008, 2009, 2010 **Models:** Avalanche, Camaro, Canyon, Escalade/EXT/ESV, Suburban, Tahoe, Yukon **Engines:** 4.8L VIN C, 5.3L VIN 0, 5.3L VIN 3, 5.3L VIN J, 5.3L VIN L, 6.0L VIN K, 6.0L VIN Y, 6.2L VIN J, 6.2L VIN W, 6.2L VIN 8 **Transmissions:** All	**A/T Input Speed Sensor Circuit Malfunction** DTC P0121, P0122, P0123, P0502, P0503, P0717, P0751, P0752, P0753, P0756, P0757 and P0758 not set, DTC P0717 test passed this key cycle, engine started, engine speed over 500 RPM for 5 seconds, Fuel Cutoff inactive, TP angle more than 14%, VSS over 5 MPH, and the ECM detected the Input Shaft Sensor speed changed by more than 1300 RPM within 800 ms during the CCM test. **Possible Causes:** • ISS positive (+) circuit is open, shorted to ground or to power • ISS negative (-) circuit is open, shorted to ground or to power • ISS is damaged or has failed • ECM has failed • TSB 02-07-30-022A contains a repair procedure for this code
DTC: P0716 **2T CCM, MIL: Yes** **Years:** 2008, 2009, 2010 **Models:** Avalanche, Camaro, Canyon, Escalade/EXT/ESV, Suburban, Tahoe, Yukon **Engines:** 4.8L VIN C, 5.3L VIN 0, 5.3L VIN 3, 5.3L VIN J, 5.3L VIN L, 6.0L VIN K, 6.0L VIN Y, 6.2L VIN J, 6.2L VIN W, 6.2L VIN 8 **Transmissions:** All	**A/T Input Speed Sensor Circuit Malfunction** DTC P0502, P0503, P0717, P0751, P0752, P1820, P1822, P1823, P1825, P1842 and P1843 not set, engine started, engine runtime over 5 seconds, Fuel Cutoff inactive, gearshift not in P/N, VSS over 10 MPH, and the ECM detected the ISS indicated less than 51 RPM for 6 seconds during the CCM test. **Possible Causes:** • ISS positive (+) or negative (-) circuit is open, shorted to ground or to power • ISS is damaged or has failed • ECM has failed • TSB 77-71-72 contains a repair procedure for this code
DTC: P0717 **2T CCM, MIL: Yes** **Years:** 2008, 2009, 2010 **Models:** Avalanche, Camaro, Canyon, Escalade/EXT/ESV, Suburban, Tahoe, Yukon **Engines:** 4.8L VIN C, 5.3L VIN 0, 5.3L VIN 3, 5.3L VIN J, 5.3L VIN L, 6.0L VIN K, 6.0L VIN Y, 6.2L VIN J, 6.2L VIN W, 6.2L VIN 8 **Transmissions:** All	**A/T Input Speed Sensor Circuit Low Input** DTC P0502, P0503 and P1810 not set, engine started, TFP manual valve position switch not indicating Park or Neutral, system voltage over 10.0v, vehicle driven to a speed of over 5 MPH, Fuel Cutoff inactive, and the ECM detected the Input Shaft Speed sensor signal was less than 50 RPM for over 5 seconds during the CCM test. **Possible Causes:** • ISS positive (+) circuit is open, shorted to ground or to power • ISS negative (-) circuit is open, shorted to ground or to power • ISS is damaged or has failed • ECM has failed • TSB 02-07-30-022A contains a repair procedure for this code
DTC: P0719 **1T CCM, MIL: No** **Years:** 2008, 2009, 2010 **Models:** Avalanche, Camaro, Canyon, Escalade/EXT/ESV, Suburban, Tahoe, Yukon **Engines:** 4.8L VIN C, 5.3L VIN 0, 5.3L VIN 3, 5.3L VIN J, 5.3L VIN L, 6.0L VIN K, 6.0L VIN Y, 6.2L VIN J, 6.2L VIN W, 6.2L VIN 8 **Transmissions:** All	**TCC Brake Switch Circuit Low Input** DTC P0502, P0503 and P0719 not set, Key on or engine running; Brake switch status is open and DTC P0719 has not passed, and the ECM detected the Brake switch or circuit indicated open (0v) for 15 minutes without changing for 2 seconds, and the following events occurred (7) times: vehicle speed less than 5 MPH, then the vehicle speed from 5-20 MPH for 4 seconds; and then the vehicle speed was more than 20 MPH for 6 seconds during the test. **Possible Causes:** • TCC brake switch circuit is open or shorted to ground • TCC brake switch power circuit is open (test ABS or ERL fuse) • TCC brake switch is out of adjustment or damaged • ECM has failed

DTC	Trouble Code Title, Conditions & Possible Causes
DTC: P0724 **1T CCM, MIL: No** **Years:** 2008, 2009, 2010 **Models:** Avalanche, Camaro, Canyon, Escalade/EXT/ESV, Suburban, Tahoe, Yukon **Engines:** 4.8L VIN C, 5.3L VIN 0, 5.3L VIN 3, 5.3L VIN J, 5.3L VIN L, 6.0L VIN K, 6.0L VIN Y, 6.2L VIN J, 6.2L VIN W, 6.2L VIN 8 **Transmissions:** All	**Incorrect Gear Ratio** DTC P0121, P0122, P0123, P0502, P0503, P0716, P0717 and P1810 not set, engine started, vehicle driven to over 7 MPH, Fuel Cutoff inactive, Transmission not in Park or Neutral, time since last gear select lever change over 6 seconds, TP angle over 14%, TFT sensor more than 68°F, engine torque from 50-300 ft lbs, and the ECM detected one of these conditions occurred for 7 seconds: - The gear ratio was more than 2.97:1 or it was 1.62:1 to 2.33:1 - The gear ratio was 1.05:1 to 1.52:1 or it was 0.75:1 to 0.95:1 **Possible Causes:** • ATF level is too low, or the fluid is burnt or contaminated • ISS or OSS signal circuit has an intermittent fault condition • Inspect for debris in the transmission pan or internal damaged • Possible vehicle overloading, exceeding the trailer towing limit, or towing in overdrive events occurred (discuss with customer) • TSB 02-07-30-022A contains a repair procedure for this code
DTC: P0730 **1T CCM, MIL: No** **Years:** 2008, 2009, 2010 **Models:** Avalanche, Camaro, Canyon, Escalade/EXT/ESV, Suburban, Tahoe, Yukon **Engines:** 4.8L VIN C, 5.3L VIN 0, 5.3L VIN 3, 5.3L VIN J, 5.3L VIN L, 6.0L VIN K, 6.0L VIN Y, 6.2L VIN J, 6.2L VIN W, 6.2L VIN 8 **Transmissions:** All	**TCC Solenoid Circuit Malfunction** Engine started, system voltage over 10.0v, Fuel Cutoff inactive, and the ECM detected the TCC feedback voltage was high with the TCC Solenoid commanded "on", or it was "low" with the TCC Solenoid commanded "off" for 5 seconds. **Possible Causes:** • TCC solenoid control circuit is open, shorted to ground or to B+ • TCC solenoid power circuit is open (test the TRANS fuse) • TCC solenoid is damaged or has failed • ECM has failed • TSB 01-07-30-002C contains a repair procedure for this code
DTC: P0740 **2T CCM, MIL: Yes** **Years:** 2008, 2009, 2010 **Models:** Avalanche, Camaro, Canyon, Escalade/EXT/ESV, Suburban, Tahoe, Yukon **Engines:** 4.8L VIN C, 5.3L VIN 0, 5.3L VIN 3, 5.3L VIN J, 5.3L VIN L, 6.0L VIN K, 6.0L VIN Y, 6.2L VIN J, 6.2L VIN W, 6.2L VIN 8 **Transmissions:** All	**TCC System Stuck Off - Mechanical** DTC P0121-P0123, P0502, P0503, P0716, P0717, P0742, P1820, P1860 and P1887 not set, engine started, Fuel Cutoff inactive, Transmission gear range was D2, D3 or D4, time since last gear select lever change more than 6 seconds, TFT sensor from 68-266°F, TP angle from 4-35%, TCC PWM solenoid commanded "on" for over 500 ms, TCC commanded to maximum apply pressure, and the ECM detected the TCC slip speed was more than 180 RPM twice during a 7 second period during this key cycle. **Possible Causes:** • ATF level is too low, or the fluid is burnt or contaminated • Inspect transmission lines to radiator for bends or restrictions • Oil pressure screen is clogged or debris in the oil pan • TCC control valve is stuck "off" due to sediment or binding • TCC regulator valve is stuck "off" due to sediment or binding • TCC solenoid valve O-ring or turbine shaft seals leaking or cut • TSB 00-07-30-007A contains a repair procedure for this code
DTC: P0741 **2T CCM, MIL: Yes** **Years:** 2008, 2009, 2010 **Models:** Avalanche, Camaro, Canyon, Escalade/EXT/ESV, Suburban, Tahoe, Yukon **Engines:** 4.8L VIN C, 5.3L VIN 0, 5.3L VIN 3, 5.3L VIN J, 5.3L VIN L, 6.0L VIN K, 6.0L VIN Y, 6.2L VIN J, 6.2L VIN W, 6.2L VIN 8 **Transmissions:** All	**TCC System Mechanically Stuck Off** DTC P0502, P0503, P0740, P0742, P0753, P1120, P1220 and P1810 not set, engine runtime over 5 seconds, not in Fuel Cutoff mode, TFT sensor from 68-302°F, TP angle from 20-99%, speed ratio from 0.89-1.02, gear range is D2, D3 or D4 with no gear change for over 6 seconds, then with the TCC commanded "on" at over 75% for 5 seconds, the ECM detected the TCC slip speed was over 130 RPM for 20 seconds (fault detected 3 times). The TCC solenoid valve is a N.O. exhaust valve used with the TCC PWM solenoid to control fluid acting on the converter clutch apply valve. When the TCC solenoid is grounded, the valve stops converter signal oil from exhausting. This causes converter signal oil pressure to increase and move the converter clutch apply valve against spring force to the apply position. In this position, release fluid is open to an exhaust port and converter feed fluid fills the apply circuit. The converter feed fluid applies the TCC. **Possible Causes:** • Converter clutch apply valve stuck in "off" (release) position • Misaligned or damaged valve body gasket • Restricted apply valve passage • TCC PWM valve exhaust orifice in damaged or it has failed • TCC solenoid valve mechanically stuck in "off" position

DTC	Trouble Code Title, Conditions & Possible Causes
DTC: P0742 **2T CCM, MIL: Yes** **Years:** 2008, 2009, 2010 **Models:** Avalanche, Camaro, Canyon, Escalade/EXT/ESV, Suburban, Tahoe, Yukon **Engines:** 4.8L VIN C, 5.3L VIN 0, 5.3L VIN 3, 5.3L VIN J, 5.3L VIN L, 6.0L VIN K, 6.0L VIN Y, 6.2L VIN J, 6.2L VIN W, 6.2L VIN 8 **Transmissions:** All	**TCC System Mechanically Stuck Off** DTC P0120, P0220, P0502, P0503, P0740, P0742, P0753, P0758, P1810 and P1860 not set, engine runtime over 6 seconds, not in Fuel Cutoff mode, TP angle from 17-45%, engine torque at 50-400 lb ft., engine vacuum 0-105 kPa (0-15 psi), speed ratio at 0.64-1.35, TFT sensor from 68-266°F, gear range is D4 with no gear change for over 6 seconds, engine speed from 1,000-3,000 RPM, vehicle speed from 15-50 MPH, then with the TCC commanded "off", the ECM detected the TCC slip speed was −20 to +20 RPM for 5 seconds (fault occurs twice during one trip). The TCC solenoid valve is a normally open (N.O.) exhaust valve that is used with the TCC PWM solenoid to control the fluid that acts on the converter clutch apply valve. The TCC solenoid valve attaches to the transmission case assembly extending into the pump cover. When the TCC solenoid is grounded, the valve stops converter signal oil from exhausting. This causes converter signal oil pressure to increase and move the converter clutch apply valve against spring force to the apply position. In this position, release fluid is open to an exhaust port and converter feed fluid fills the apply circuit. The converter feed fluid applies the TCC. **Possible Causes:** • Apply valve passage is restricted • Converter clutch apply valve stuck in "off" (release) position • Misaligned or damaged valve body gasket • TCC PWM valve exhaust orifice in damaged or it has failed • TCC solenoid valve is mechanically stuck in the "off" position
DTC: P0751 **2T CCM, MIL: Yes** **Years:** 2008, 2009, 2010 **Models:** Avalanche, Camaro, Canyon, Escalade/EXT/ESV, Suburban, Tahoe, Yukon **Engines:** 4.8L VIN C, 5.3L VIN 0, 5.3L VIN 3, 5.3L VIN J, 5.3L VIN L, 6.0L VIN K, 6.0L VIN Y, 6.2L VIN J, 6.2L VIN W, 6.2L VIN 8 **Transmissions:** All	**A/T 1-2 Shift Solenoid - No 1st or 4th Gear** DTC P0122, P0123, P0502, P0503, P0740, P0742, P0753, P0758, P0785, P1810 and P1860 not set, engine started, vehicle driven to over 5 MPH, Fuel Cutoff inactive, TP angle more than 9%, TFT sensor from 68-266°F, gear range is D4, D3, D2 or D1, engine torque was 50-400 lb ft., transmission output speed was more than 150 RPM, then with 1st Gear "on" for 2 seconds, the ECM detected the engine speed was more than 2.44 times the TCC slip speed with an estimated gear ratio of 1.2-1.85 for 2 seconds; or with 4th Gear "on" for 1 second, the ECM detected the engine speed was 2.44 times the TCC slip speed with an estimated gear ratio of 0.95-1.15 for 6 seconds during the CCM test. **Possible Causes:** • ATF is burnt or contaminated, or the level is incorrect • Transmission has an internal damage to the torque converter • Shift solenoid valve seals are damaged or leaking • Transmission is damaged or it has failed
DTC: P0752 **1T CCM, MIL: Yes** **Years:** 2008, 2009, 2010 **Models:** Avalanche, Camaro, Canyon, Escalade/EXT/ESV, Suburban, Tahoe, Yukon **Engines:** 4.8L VIN C, 5.3L VIN 0, 5.3L VIN 3, 5.3L VIN J, 5.3L VIN L, 6.0L VIN K, 6.0L VIN Y, 6.2L VIN J, 6.2L VIN W, 6.2L VIN 8 **Transmissions:** All	**A/T 1-2 Shift Solenoid - No 2nd Or 3rd Gear** DTC P0122, P0123, P0502, P0503, P0740, P0742, P0753, P0758, P0785, P1810 and P1860 not set, vehicle driven to over 5 MPH, Fuel Cutoff inactive, TP angle more than 10%, gear range is D4, TFT sensor from 68-266°F, engine torque from 50-400 lb ft., transmission output speed more than 150 RPM, Transfer Case low ratio in 4WD Low at 0.9-1.2 or in 4WD High at 2.6-2.85; engine torque from 25-650 lb ft., then with 2nd Gear commanded "on" for 1 second, the ECM detected the estimated gear ratio was 3.0-3.3 for 2 seconds; or with 3rd Gear commanded "on" for 1 second, the gear ratio was 0.65-0.95 for 3 seconds. **Possible Causes:** • ATF is burnt or contaminated, or the level is incorrect • Transmission has an internal damage to the torque converter • Shift solenoid valve seals are damaged or leaking • Transmission has failed
DTC: P0752 **2T CCM, MIL: Yes** **Years:** 2008, 2009, 2010 **Models:** Avalanche, Camaro, Canyon, Escalade/EXT/ESV, Suburban, Tahoe, Yukon **Engines:** 4.8L VIN C, 5.3L VIN 0, 5.3L VIN 3, 5.3L VIN J, 5.3L VIN L, 6.0L VIN K, 6.0L VIN Y, 6.2L VIN J, 6.2L VIN W, 6.2L VIN 8 **Transmissions:** All	**A/T 1-2 Shift Solenoid - No 2nd or 3rd Gear** DTC P0101-P0103, P0107, P0108, P0122, P0123, P0502, P0503, P0740, P1810 and P1860 not set, engine speed at 1000-3000 RPM, VSS at 20-75 MPH, Fuel Cutoff "off", TP angle from 13-99%, TFT sensor at 68-266°F, engine torque at 50-400 lb ft., vacuum at 0-15 kPa, gear range is D4 with no gear change for 6 seconds, transmission speed ratio at 0.95-1.7, not in 1st Gear, TCC off and the ECM detected the TCC slip speed was −20 to +58 for 3.8 seconds. **Possible Causes:** • ATF is burnt or contaminated, or the level is incorrect • Transmission has an internal damage to the torque converter • Shift solenoid valve seals are damaged or leaking • Transmission has failed
DTC: P0753 **2T CCM, MIL: Yes** **Years:** 2008, 2009, 2010 **Models:** Avalanche, Camaro, Canyon, Escalade/EXT/ESV, Suburban, Tahoe, Yukon **Engines:** 4.8L VIN C, 5.3L VIN 0, 5.3L VIN 3, 5.3L VIN J, 5.3L VIN L, 6.0L VIN K, 6.0L VIN Y, 6.2L VIN J, 6.2L VIN W, 6.2L VIN 8 **Transmissions:** All	**A/T 1-2 Shift Solenoid Circuit Malfunction** Engine started, Fuel Cutoff inactive, system voltage over 10.0v, and the ECM detected an unexpected voltage condition on the 1-2 Shift Solenoid control circuit during the CCM continuous test. **Possible Causes:** • 1-2 shift solenoid control circuit is open or shorted to ground • 1-2 shift solenoid control circuit is shorted to system power • 1-2 shift solenoid is damaged or has failed • ECM has failed • TSB 01-07-30-002C contains a repair procedure for this code

DTC	Trouble Code Title, Conditions & Possible Causes
DTC: P0753 **2T CCM, MIL: Yes** **Years:** 2008, 2009, 2010 **Models:** Avalanche, Camaro, Canyon, Escalade/EXT/ESV, Suburban, Tahoe, Yukon **Engines:** 4.8L VIN C, 5.3L VIN 0, 5.3L VIN 3, 5.3L VIN L, 6.0L VIN K, 6.0L VIN Y, 6.2L VIN J, 6.2L VIN W, 6.2L VIN 8 **Transmissions:** All	**A/T 1-2 Shift Solenoid Circuit Malfunction** Engine started, Fuel Cutoff inactive, system voltage over 10.0v, and the ECM detected an unexpected voltage condition on the 1-2 Shift Solenoid control circuit during the CCM test. **Possible Causes:** • 1-2 shift solenoid control circuit is open or shorted to ground • 1-2 shift solenoid control circuit is shorted to system power • 1-2 shift solenoid is damaged or has failed • ECM has failed
DTC: P0756 **1T CCM, MIL: Yes** **Years:** 2008, 2009, 2010 **Models:** Avalanche, Camaro, Canyon, Escalade/EXT/ESV, Suburban, Tahoe, Yukon **Engines:** 4.8L VIN C, 5.3L VIN 0, 5.3L VIN 3, 5.3L VIN J, 5.3L VIN L, 6.0L VIN K, 6.0L VIN Y, 6.2L VIN J, 6.2L VIN W, 6.2L VIN 8 **Transmissions:** All	**2-3 Shift Solenoid - No 2nd Or 3rd Gear** DTC P0122, P0123, P0502, P0503, P0740, P0742, P0753, P0758, P0785, P1810 and P1860 not set, engine started, system voltage over 10.0v, vehicle speed over 5 MPH, TP angle over 10%, gear range is D4, TFT sensor from 68-266°F, engine torque from 50-400 lb ft., transmission output shaft speed more than 150 RPM, Fuel Cutoff inactive, then with 1st Gear commanded "on", the ECM detected the gear ratio indicated 4th Gear for 2.5 seconds; or with 2nd Gear commanded "on" for 1 second, the ECM detected the estimate gear ratio was 0.9-1.2 for 2 seconds during the CCM test **Possible Causes:** • ATF is burnt or contaminated • Transmission has plugged or restricted fluid circuits • Shift solenoid valve seals are leaking or damaged • Transmission has failed • TSB 01-07-30-036A contains a repair procedure for this code
DTC: P0756 **2T CCM, MIL: Yes** **Years:** 2008, 2009, 2010 **Models:** Avalanche, Camaro, Canyon, Escalade/EXT/ESV, Suburban, Tahoe, Yukon **Engines:** 4.8L VIN C, 5.3L VIN 0, 5.3L VIN 3, 5.3L VIN J, 5.3L VIN L, 6.0L VIN K, 6.0L VIN Y, 6.2L VIN J, 6.2L VIN W, 6.2L VIN 8 **Transmissions:** All	**A/T 2-3 Shift Solenoid - No 2nd or 3rd Gear** DTC P0101-P0103, P0107, P0108, P0122, P0123, P0502, P0503, P0740, P0742, P0753, P0758, P0785, P1810, P1860 and P1870 not set, engine started, vehicle driven to a speed of over 5 MPH, system voltage over 10.0v, Fuel Cutoff inactive, TP angle more than 9%, TFT sensor from 68-266°F, gear range is D4, no gear change for 6 seconds, engine torque from 50-400 lb ft., engine vacuum from 0-15 kPa, A/T output speed over 150 RPM, gear range is D4, D3, D2 or D1, then with 1st Gear commanded "on", engine speed more than the TCC slip speed and the Output speed over 300 RPM, the ECM detected the gear ratio was 0.0-0.895 for 1 second; or with 2nd Gear commanded "on", engine speed 5.26 times more than the TCC slip speed, the ECM detected the gear ratio was 0.9-1.2 for 2 seconds. **Possible Causes:** • ATF is burnt or contaminated • Transmission has plugged or restricted fluid circuits • Shift solenoid valve seals are leaking or damaged • Transmission has failed
DTC: P0757 **1T CCM, MIL: No** **Years:** 2008, 2009, 2010 **Models:** Avalanche, Camaro, Canyon, Escalade/EXT/ESV, Suburban, Tahoe, Yukon **Engines:** 4.8L VIN C, 5.3L VIN 0, 5.3L VIN 3, 5.3L VIN J, 5.3L VIN L, 6.0L VIN K, 6.0L VIN Y, 6.2L VIN J, 6.2L VIN W, 6.2L VIN 8 **Transmissions:** All	**A/T 2-3 Shift Solenoid Circuit Malfunction** DTC P0560 not set, engine started, engine speed over 500 RPM for 5 seconds, 2-3 Shift Solenoid commanded "on" and then "off", and the ECM detected an unexpected voltage condition on the 2-3 Shift Solenoid Control circuit for 5 seconds during the CCM test. **Possible Causes:** • 2-3 shift solenoid control circuit is open or shorted to ground • 2-3 shift solenoid control circuit is shorted to system power • 2-3 shift solenoid power circuit is open (test TRANS SOL fuse) • 2-3 shift solenoid is damaged or has failed • ECM has failed • TSB 02-07-30-022A contains a repair procedure for this code
DTC: P0758 **1T CCM, MIL: Yes** **Years:** 2008, 2009, 2010 **Models:** Avalanche, Camaro, Canyon, Escalade/EXT/ESV, Suburban, Tahoe, Yukon **Engines:** 4.8L VIN C, 5.3L VIN 0, 5.3L VIN 3, 5.3L VIN J, 5.3L VIN L, 6.0L VIN K, 6.0L VIN Y, 6.2L VIN J, 6.2L VIN W, 6.2L VIN 8 **Transmissions:** All	**A/T 2-3 Shift Solenoid Circuit Malfunction (4L80-E)** Engine speed over 450 RPM for 7 seconds, system voltage over 10.0v, and the ECM detected an unexpected voltage on the 2-3 Shift Solenoid control circuit for 4-5 seconds. **Possible Causes:** • 2-3 shift solenoid control circuit is open, shorted to ground or shorted to system power • 2-3 shift solenoid power circuit is open (test the TRANS fuse) • 2-3 shift solenoid has failed, or the ECM has failed

DTC	Trouble Code Title, Conditions & Possible Causes
DTC: P0785 **1T CCM, MIL: Yes** **Years:** 2008, 2009, 2010 **Models:** Avalanche, Camaro, Canyon, Escalade/EXT/ESV, Suburban, Tahoe, Yukon **Engines:** 4.8L VIN C, 5.3L VIN 0, 5.3L VIN 3, 5.3L VIN J, 5.3L VIN L, 6.0L VIN K, 6.0L VIN Y, 6.2L VIN J, 6.2L VIN W, 6.2L VIN 8 **Transmissions:** All	**A/T 3-2 Shift Solenoid Circuit Malfunction** Engine started, engine speed over 450 RPM for 5 seconds, system voltage over 10.0v, and the ECM detected an unexpected voltage condition on the 3-2 Shift Solenoid control circuit for 4-5 seconds. **Possible Causes:** • 3-2 shift solenoid control circuit is open, shorted to ground or shorted to system power • 3-2 shift solenoid power circuit is open (check the TRANS fuse) • 3-2 shift solenoid is damaged or has failed • ECM has failed • TSB 01-07-30-002C contains a repair procedure for this code
DTC: P0785 **1T CCM, MIL: Yes** **Years:** 2008, 2009, 2010 **Models:** Avalanche, Camaro, Canyon, Escalade/EXT/ESV, Suburban, Tahoe, Yukon **Engines:** 4.8L VIN C, 5.3L VIN 0, 5.3L VIN 3, 5.3L VIN J, 5.3L VIN L, 6.0L VIN K, 6.0L VIN Y, 6.2L VIN J, 6.2L VIN W, 6.2L VIN 8 **Transmissions:** All	**A/T 2-3 Shift Solenoid Circuit Malfunction** P0560 not set, engine started, engine speed over 500 RPM for 5 seconds, and the ECM detected an unexpected voltage on the 2-3 Shift Solenoid Control circuit for 5 seconds. **Possible Causes:** • 2-3 shift solenoid control circuit is open or shorted to ground • 2-3 shift solenoid control circuit is shorted to system power • 2-3 shift solenoid power circuit is open (check ENG CTRL fuse) • 2-3 shift solenoid is damaged or has failed • ECM has failed

OBD II Trouble Code List (P1xxx Codes)

DTC	Trouble Code Title, Conditions & Possible Causes
DTC: P1111 **1T CCM, MIL: No** **Years:** 2008, 2009 **Models:** Express, Savana **Engines:** 4.3L VIN X **Transmissions:** All	**IAT Sensor Circuit Intermittent High Input** DTC P0101, P0102, P0103, P0116, P0117, P0118, P0125, P0128, P0502, P0503, P1114 and P1115 not set, engine started, engine runtime over 120 seconds, ECT sensor more than 140°F, VSS less than 7 MPH, MAF input less than 15 g/sec, and the ECM detected an intermittent high voltage condition (over 4.90v) on the IAT sensor signal circuit for 1 second during the CCM test. **Possible Causes:** • IAT sensor signal circuit is open (intermittent fault) • IAT sensor ground circuit is open (intermittent fault) • IAT sensor is damaged (an intermittent "open" condition) • ECM has failed
DTC: P1111 **1T CCM, MIL: No** **Years:** 2008, 2009, 2010 **Models:** Avalanche, Camaro, Canyon, Escalade/EXT/ESV, Suburban, Tahoe, Yukon **Engines:** 4.8L VIN C, 5.3L VIN 0, 5.3L VIN 3, 5.3L VIN J, 5.3L VIN L, 6.0L VIN K, 6.0L VIN Y, 6.2L VIN J, 6.2L VIN W, 6.2L VIN 8 **Transmissions:** All	**IAT Sensor Circuit Intermittent High Input** DTC P0101, P0102, P0103 and P0113 not set, engine runtime over 120 seconds, ECT sensor more than 140°F, VSS less than 7 MPH, MAF input less than 15 g/sec, and the ECM detected an intermittent high voltage condition (Scan Tool reads below −36°F) on the IAT sensor signal circuit during the CCM test period. **Possible Causes:** • IAT sensor signal circuit is open (intermittent fault) • IAT sensor ground circuit is open (intermittent fault) • IAT sensor is damaged (an intermittent "open" condition) • ECM has failed
DTC: P1111 **1T CCM, MIL: No** **Years:** 2008, 2009 **Models:** Corvette **Engines:** All **Transmissions:** All	**IAT Sensor Circuit Intermittent High Input** DTC P0101-P0103, P0116-P0118, P0125, P0128, P0502, P0503, P1114 and P1115 not set, engine started, engine runtime over 3 minutes, VSS under 35 MPH, MAF sensor less than 15 g/sec, ECT sensor more than 140°F, and the ECM detected an intermittent high voltage condition (Scan Tool reads −38°F) on the IAT sensor signal circuit for 5 seconds during the CCM test. **Possible Causes:** • IAT sensor signal circuit is open (intermittent fault) • IAT sensor ground circuit is open (intermittent fault) • IAT sensor is damaged (an intermittent "open" condition) • ECM has failed

DTC	Trouble Code Title, Conditions & Possible Causes
DTC: P1112 **1T CCM, MIL: No** **Years:** 2008, 2009, 2010 **Models:** Avalanche, Camaro, Canyon, Escalade/EXT/ESV, Suburban, Tahoe, Yukon **Engines:** 4.8L VIN C, 5.3L VIN 0, 5.3L VIN 3, 5.3L VIN J, 5.3L VIN L, 6.0L VIN K, 6.0L VIN Y, 6.2L VIN J, 6.2L VIN W, 6.2L VIN 8 **Transmissions:** All	**IAT Sensor Circuit Intermittent Low Input** DTC P0112, P0500, P0502 and P0503 not set, engine runtime over 45 seconds, ECT sensor less than 257°F, VSS more than 25 MPH, and the ECM detected an intermittent low voltage condition (Scan Tool reads over 262°F) on the IAT sensor signal circuit. **Possible Causes:** • IAT sensor signal circuit is open (intermittent fault) • IAT sensor ground circuit is open (intermittent fault) • IAT sensor is damaged (an intermittent "open" condition) • ECM has failed
DTC: P1112 **1T CCM, MIL: No** **Years:** 2008, 2009 **Models:** Corvette **Engines:** All **Transmissions:** All	**IAT Sensor Circuit Intermittent Low Input** DTC P0101-P0103, P0116-P0118, P0125, P0128, P0502, P0503, P1114 and P1115 not set, engine runtime over 3 minutes, VSS under 35 MPH, MAF sensor less than 15 g/sec, ECT sensor more than 140°F, and the ECM detected an intermittent low voltage condition (Scan Tool reads 282°F) on the IAT sensor signal circuit for 6 seconds during the CCM test. **Possible Causes:** • IAT sensor signal circuit is shorted to ground (intermittent fault) • IAT sensor is damaged (an intermittent "shorted" condition) • ECM has failed
DTC: P1114 **1T CCM, MIL: No** **Years:** 2008, 2009, 2010 **Models:** Avalanche, Camaro, Canyon, Escalade/EXT/ESV, Suburban, Tahoe, Yukon **Engines:** 4.8L VIN C, 5.3L VIN 0, 5.3L VIN 3, 5.3L VIN J, 5.3L VIN L, 6.0L VIN K, 6.0L VIN Y, 6.2L VIN J, 6.2L VIN W, 6.2L VIN 8 **Transmissions:** All	**ECT Sensor Circuit Intermittent Low Input** Engine started, engine runtime over 10 seconds, and the ECM detected an intermittent low voltage condition (Scan Tool reads over 280°F) on the ECT sensor signal circuit during the CCM test period. **Possible Causes:** • ECT sensor signal circuit shorted to ground (intermittent fault) • ECT sensor has failed (possible intermittent shorted condition) • ECM has failed
DTC: P1114 **1T CCM, MIL: No** **Years:** 2008, 2009 **Models:** Corvette **Engines:** All **Transmissions:** All	**ECT Sensor Circuit Intermittent Low Input** Engine started, engine runtime over 10 seconds, system voltage over 10.0v, and the ECM detected an intermittent "low" voltage condition (Scan Tool reads over 282°F) for 1 second out of a 20 second period during the CCM test. **Possible Causes:** • ECT sensor signal circuit shorted to ground (intermittent fault) • ECT sensor has failed (possible intermittent shorted condition) • ECM has failed
DTC: P1133 **1T CCM, MIL: Yes** **Years:** 2008, 2009 **Models:** Corvette, CTS, CTS-V, DTS **Engines:** 4.6L VIN Y, 6.2L VIN W, 6.2L VIN P, 6.2L VIN R, 7.0L VIN E **Transmissions:** All	**HO2S Insufficient Switching (Bank 1 Sensor 1)** DTCs P0068, P0101, P0102, P0103, P0106, P0107, P0108, P0112, P0113, P0116, P0117, P0118, P0120, P0121, P0122, P0123, P0128, P0201, P0202, P0203, P0204, P0205, P0206, P0207, P0208, P0220, P0222, P0223, P0442, P0443, P0446, P0449, P0455, P0496, P1516, P2101, P2119, P2135, P2176 are not set. The ECT Sensor parameter is more than 60°C (140°F). The Engine Speed parameter is between 1,100-2,500 RPM. The Ignition 1 Signal parameter is between 10-18 volts. The Engine Run Time parameter is more than 202 seconds. The Loop Status parameter is Closed. The TP Indicated Angle parameter is more than 5 percent. The Fuel Level Sensor parameter is more than 10 percent. The BARO parameter is more than 70 kPa. The MAF Sensor parameter is between 20-40 g/s. DTC P1133 runs once per drive cycle when the above conditions are met for 1 second. The control module detects that the HO2S 1 rich-to-lean counts, or the lean-to-rich counts are less than a calibrated value. DTC P1133 sets within 60 seconds when the above condition is met. **Possible Causes:** • HO2S low reference circuit for an open/high resistance • HO2S signal circuit for a short to ground • HO2S signal circuit for a short to voltage • HO2S signal circuit for an open/high resistance • HO2S has failed • ECM has failed

DTC	Trouble Code Title, Conditions & Possible Causes
DTC: P1133 **2T O2S, MIL: Yes** **Years:** 2008, 2009 **Models:** Corvette **Engines:** All **Transmissions:** All	**HO2S-11 (Bank 1 Sensor 1) Insufficient Switching** DTC P0101-P0103, P0106-P0108, P0112-P0118, P0131-P0135, P0151-P0155, P0200, P0300, P0410, P0440-P0446, P0452, P0453, P1120, P1125, P1220, P1221, P1258, P1415, P1416, P1441, P1514-P1518 not set, engine started, engine speed from 1000-2300 RPM for 160 seconds in closed loop, system voltage over 10.0v, fuel level over 10%, ECT sensor more than 122°F, Purge command over 0%, MAF sensor from 18-50 g/sec, TP indicated angle 5% over the idle value for 60 seconds, and the ECM less than 10 lean-to-rich or rich-lean switch counts on the HO2S signal circuit during the test. **Possible Causes:** • Air leaks present in the exhaust manifold or the exhaust pipes • Fuel pressure is too high (i.e., causing a rich air fuel mixture) • HO2S may be contaminated (due to improper fuel or silicone) • HO2S signal high or low reference circuit has high resistance • HO2S heater element has failed, or the heater circuit is open • ECM has failed
DTC: P1133 **2T O2S, MIL: Yes** **Years:** 2008, 2009, 2010 **Models:** Avalanche, Camaro, Canyon, Escalade/EXT/ESV, Suburban, Tahoe, Yukon **Engines:** 4.8L VIN C, 5.3L VIN 0, 5.3L VIN 3, 5.3L VIN J, 5.3L VIN L, 6.0L VIN K, 6.0L VIN Y, 6.2L VIN J, 6.2L VIN W, 6.2L VIN 8 **Transmissions:** All	**HO2S-11 (Bank 1 Sensor 1) Insufficient Switching** DTC P0101, P0102, P0103, P0106, P0107, P0108, P0112, P0113, P0116, P0117, P0118, P0120, P0131, P0132, P0134, P0135, P0151, P0152, P0154, P0155, P0169, P0178, P0179, P0200, P0220, P0300, P0442, P0446, P0452, P0453, P0455, P0496, P1125, P1258, P1514, P1515, P1516, P1518, P2108 and P2135 not set, engine runtime over 160 seconds, engine speed at 1200-3000 RPM in closed loop, system voltage from 10-18v, ECT sensor more than 149°F, fuel level over 10%, Purge command over 1%, MAF sensor from 23-50 g/sec, TP indicated angle more than 5% above the idle value on models with TAC, Fuel Alcohol content less than 90%, and the ECM detected the number of rich-to-lean or lean-to-rich HO2S signal transitions were less than a calibrated value. **Possible Causes:** • Air leaks present in the exhaust manifold or the exhaust pipes • Fuel pressure is too high (i.e., causing a rich air fuel mixture) • HO2S may be contaminated (due to improper fuel or silicone) • HO2S signal high or low reference circuit has high resistance • HO2S heater element has failed, or the heater circuit is open • ECM has failed
DTC: P1134 **2T O2S, MIL: Yes** **Years:** 2008, 2009, 2010 **Models:** Avalanche, Camaro, Canyon, Escalade/EXT/ESV, Suburban, Tahoe, Yukon **Engines:** 4.8L VIN C, 5.3L VIN 0, 5.3L VIN 3, 5.3L VIN J, 5.3L VIN L, 6.0L VIN K, 6.0L VIN Y, 6.2L VIN J, 6.2L VIN W, 6.2L VIN 8 **Transmissions:** All	**HO2S-11 (Bank 1 Sensor 1) Transition Time Ratio** DTC P0101-P0103, P0106-P0108, P0112-P0118, P0121-P0123, P0131-P0135, P0151-P0155, P0200, P0300, P0401-P0405, P0440-P0446, P0452, P0453, P1120, P1125, P1220, P1221, P1258, P1404, P1441and P01514, and P1518 not set, engine speed from 1200-3000 RPM for over 3 minutes in closed loop, system voltage over 10.0v, ECT sensor over 149°F, fuel level over 10%, Purge command over 1%, MAF sensor from 23-50 g/sec, TP angle at 5% over idle value on models with TAC, Intrusive and Scan Tool tests "off" for 100 seconds, and the ECM detected the HO2S time ratio value was not within the calibrated range. **Possible Causes:** • Air leaks present in the exhaust manifold or the exhaust pipes • HO2S may be contaminated (due to improper fuel or silicone) • HO2S signal low reference circuit has high resistance • HO2S heater element has failed, or the heater circuit is open • ECM has failed
DTC: P1134 **2T O2S, MIL: Yes** **Years:** 2008, 2009 **Models:** Corvette **Engines:** All **Transmissions:** All	**HO2S-11 (Bank 1 Sensor 1) Transition Time Ratio** DTC P0101-P0103, P0106-P0108, P0112-P0118, P0131-P0135, P0151-P0155, P0200, P0300, P0410, P0440-P0446, P0452, P0453, P1120, P1125, P1220, P1221, P1258, P1415, P1416, P1441, P1514 and P1518 not set, engine speed at 1000-2300 RPM for 160 seconds in closed loop, system voltage over 10.0v, fuel level over 10%, ECT sensor over 122°F, Purge over 0%, MAF sensor from 18-50 g/sec, TP angle 5% above idle value for 60 seconds (TAC models), and the ECM detected the HO2S transition time ratio value was out-of-range. **Possible Causes:** • Air leaks present in the exhaust manifold or the exhaust pipes • HO2S may be contaminated (due to improper fuel or silicone) • HO2S signal low reference circuit has high resistance • HO2S heater element has failed, or the heater circuit is open • ECM has failed

DTC	Trouble Code Title, Conditions & Possible Causes
DTC: P1153 **2T O2S, MIL: Yes** **Years:** 2008, 2009, 2010 **Models:** Avalanche, Camaro, Canyon, Escalade/EXT/ESV, Suburban, Tahoe, Yukon **Engines:** 4.8L VIN C, 5.3L VIN 0, 5.3L VIN 3, 5.3L VIN J, 5.3L VIN L, 6.0L VIN K, 6.0L VIN Y, 6.2L VIN J, 6.2L VIN W, 6.2L VIN 8 **Transmissions:** All	**HO2S-21 (Bank 2 Sensor 1) Insufficient Switching** DTC P0101, P0102, P0103, P0106, P0107, P0108, P0112, P0113, P0116, P0117, P0118, P0120, P0131, P0132, P0134, P0135, P0151, P0152, P0154-P0155, P0169, P0178-P0179, P0200, P0220, P0300, P0442, P0446, P0452-P0453, P0455-P0496, P1125, P1258, P1404, P1514, P1515, P1516, P1518, P2108 and P2135 not set, engine runtime over 160 seconds, engine speed at 1200-3000 RPM in closed loop, system voltage from 10-18v, ECT sensor more than 149°F, Fuel Level over 10%, Purge command over 1%, MAF sensor from 23-50 g/sec, TP indicated angle more than 5% above the idle value on models with TAC, Fuel Alcohol content less than 90%, and the ECM detected the number of rich-to-lean or lean-to-rich HO2S signal transitions were less than a calibrated value. **Possible Causes:** • Air leaks present in the exhaust manifold or the exhaust pipes • Fuel pressure is too high (i.e., causing a rich air fuel mixture) • HO2S may be contaminated (due to improper fuel or silicone) • HO2S signal high or low reference circuit has high resistance • HO2S heater element has failed, or the heater circuit is open • ECM has failed
DTC: P1153 **2T O2S, MIL: Yes** **Years:** 2008, 2009 **Models:** Corvette **Engines:** All **Transmissions:** All	**HO2S-21 (Bank 2 Sensor 1) Insufficient Switching** DTC P0101-P0103, P0106-P0108, P0112-P0118, P0131-P0135, P0151-P0155, P0200, P0300, P0410, P0440-P0446, P0452, P0453, P1120, P1125, P1220, P1221, P1258, P1415, P1416, P1441, P1514-P1518 not set, engine started, engine speed from 1000-2300 RPM for 160 seconds in closed loop, system voltage over 10.0v, fuel level over 10%, ECT sensor more than 122°F, Purge command over 0%, MAF sensor from 18-50 g/sec, TP indicated angle 5% over the idle value for 60 seconds, and the ECM less than 10 lean-to-rich or rich-lean switch counts on the HO2S signal circuit during the test. **Possible Causes:** • Air leaks present in the exhaust manifold or the exhaust pipes • Fuel pressure is too high (i.e., causing a rich air fuel mixture) • HO2S may be contaminated (due to improper fuel or silicone) • HO2S signal high or low reference circuit has high resistance • HO2S heater element has failed, or the heater circuit is open • ECM has failed
DTC: P1154 **2T O2S, MIL: Yes** **Years:** 2008, 2009, 2010 **Models:** Avalanche, Camaro, Canyon, Escalade/EXT/ESV, Suburban, Tahoe, Yukon **Engines:** 4.8L VIN C, 5.3L VIN 0, 5.3L VIN 3, 5.3L VIN J, 5.3L VIN L, 6.0L VIN K, 6.0L VIN Y, 6.2L VIN J, 6.2L VIN W, 6.2L VIN 8 **Transmissions:** All	**HO2S-21 (Bank 2 Sensor 1) Transition Time Ratio** DTC P0101-P0103, P0106-P0108, P0112-P0118, P0121-P0123, P0131-P0135, P0151-P0155, P0200, P0300, P0401-P0405, P0440-P0446, P0452, P0453, P1120, P1125, P1220, P1221, P1258, P1404, P1441and P01514, and P1518 not set, engine speed from 1200-3000 RPM for over 3 minutes in closed loop, system voltage over 10.0v, ECT sensor over 149°F, fuel level over 10%, Purge command over 1%, MAF sensor from 23-50 g/sec, TP angle at 5% over idle value on models with TAC, Intrusive and Scan Tool tests "off" for 100 seconds, and the ECM detected the HO2S time ratio value was not within the calibrated range. **Possible Causes:** • Air leaks present in the exhaust manifold or the exhaust pipes • HO2S may be contaminated (due to improper fuel or silicone) • HO2S signal low reference circuit has high resistance • HO2S heater element has failed, or the heater circuit is open • ECM has failed
DTC: P1154 **2T O2S, MIL: Yes** **Years:** 2008, 2009 **Models:** Corvette **Engines:** All **Transmissions:** All	**HO2S-21 (Bank 2 Sensor 1) Transition Time Ratio** DTC P0101-P0103, P0106-P0108, P0112-P0118, P0131-P0135, P0151-P0155, P0200, P0300, P0410, P0440-P0446, P0452, P0453, P1120, P1125, P1220, P1221, P1258, P1415, P1416, P1441, P1514-P1518 not set, engine speed from 1000-2300 RPM for 160 seconds in closed loop, system voltage over 10.0v, fuel level over 10%, ECT sensor over 122°F, Purge over 0%, MAF sensor from 18-50 g/sec, TP angle over 5% over the idle value for 1 minute (TAC models), and the ECM detected the HO2S transition time ratio was out of range. **Possible Causes:** • Air leaks present in the exhaust manifold or the exhaust pipes • HO2S may be contaminated (due to improper fuel or silicone) • HO2S signal low reference circuit has high resistance • HO2S heater element has failed, or the heater circuit is open • ECM has failed

DTC	Trouble Code Title, Conditions & Possible Causes
DTC: P1174 **1T CCM, MIL: Yes** **Years:** 2008, 2009 **Models:** Corvette, CTS, CTS-V **Engines:** 6.2L VIN W, 6.2L VIN P, 6.2L VIN R, 7.0L VIN E **Transmissions:** All	**Fuel Trim Cylinder Balance (Bank 1)** DTCs P0030, P0036, P0050, P0053, P0059, P0101, P0102, P0103, P0106, P0107, P0108, P0117, P0118, P0128, P0131, P0132, P0133, P0134, P0135, P0151, P0152, P0153, P0154, P0155, P0201-P0206, P0300, P0301-P0306, P0411, P0412, P0418, P0442, P0443, P0446, P0449, P0452, P0453, P0454, P0455, P0496, P1133, P1153, P1516, P2101, P2119, P2120, P2125, P2135, P2138, P2176, P2431, P2432, P2433, P2440, P2A00, P2A03 are not set. The device control is not active. The intrusive diagnostics are not active. The engine overspeed protection is not active. The Power Take-Off (PTO) is not active. The traction control is not active. The fuel control is in air-fuel Closed Loop. The system voltage is more than 10 volts, or less than 18 volts. The engine run time is greater than 100 seconds. The Engine Coolant Temperature (ECT) is greater than −20°C (−4°F). The engine speed is greater than 425 RPM, but less than 6,000 RPM. The mass air flow is greater than 25 g/s, but less than 510 g/s Multiple samples of the pre-catalyst HO2S accumulated voltage are consistently greater than the desired value. **Possible Causes:** • Vacuum hoses for splits, kinks, and improper connections. • Crankcase ventilation system for improper operation • Air induction system for modified, damaged, leaking, or restricted components. • Restricted, damaged, leaking, or modified exhaust system from the catalytic converter forward • Fuel injectors for improper operation • Ignition system for improper operation
DTC: P1175 **1T CCM, MIL: Yes** **Years:** 2008, 2009 **Models:** Corvette, CTS, CTS-V **Engines:** 6.2L VIN W, 6.2L VIN P, 6.2L VIN R, 7.0L VIN E **Transmissions:** All	**Fuel Trim Cylinder Balance (Bank 2)** DTCs P0030, P0036, P0050, P0053, P0059, P0101, P0102, P0103, P0106, P0107, P0108, P0117, P0118, P0128, P0131, P0132, P0133, P0134, P0135, P0151, P0152, P0153, P0154, P0155, P0201-P0206, P0300, P0301-P0306, P0411, P0412, P0418, P0442, P0443, P0446, P0449, P0452, P0453, P0454, P0455, P0496, P1133, P1153, P1516, P2101, P2119, P2120, P2125, P2135, P2138, P2176, P2431, P2432, P2433, P2440, P2A00, P2A03 are not set. The device control is not active. The intrusive diagnostics are not active. The engine overspeed protection is not active. The Power Take-Off (PTO) is not active. The traction control is not active. The fuel control is in air-fuel Closed Loop. The system voltage is more than 10 volts, or less than 18 volts. The engine run time is greater than 100 seconds. The Engine Coolant Temperature (ECT) is greater than −20°C (−4°F). The engine speed is greater than 425 RPM, but less than 6,000 RPM. The mass air flow is greater than 25 g/s, but less than 510 g/s Multiple samples of the pre-catalyst HO2S accumulated voltage are consistently greater than the desired value. **Possible Causes:** • Vacuum hoses for splits, kinks, and improper connections. • Crankcase ventilation system for improper operation • Air induction system for modified, damaged, leaking, or restricted components. • Restricted, damaged, leaking, or modified exhaust system from the catalytic converter forward • Fuel injectors for improper operation • Ignition system for improper operation
DTC: P1220 **1T CCM, MIL: Yes** **Years:** 2008, 2009, 2010 **Models:** Avalanche, Camaro, Canyon, Escalade/EXT/ESV, Suburban, Tahoe, Yukon **Engines:** 4.8L VIN C, 5.3L VIN 0, 5.3L VIN 3, 5.3L VIN J, 5.3L VIN L, 6.0L VIN K, 6.0L VIN Y, 6.2L VIN J, 6.2L VIN W, 6.2L VIN 8 **Transmissions:** All	**TP Sensor 2 Circuit Malfunction** DTC P1517 and P1518 not set, key in crank or run position, system voltage over 5.23v, and the ECM detected the TP2 signal was less than 0.13v or more than 4.87v for 1 second during the CCM test. **Possible Causes:** • TP2 sensor signal circuit is open, shorted to ground or to power • TP2 sensor VREF circuit is open, shorted to ground or shorted to system power (B+) • TP2 sensor ground circuit has a high resistance condition • TP2 sensor is damaged or has failed
DTC: P1220 **1T CCM, MIL: Yes** **Years:** 2008, 2009 **Models:** Corvette **Engines:** All **Transmissions:** All	**TP Sensor 2 Circuit Malfunction** DTC P0606, P1517 and P1518 not set, key in crank or run mode, system voltage over 5.23v, Electronic Throttle Control serial data operating, and the ECM detected the TP Sensor 2 signal was less than 0.13v or more than 4.87v during the CCM test. **Possible Causes:** • TP2 sensor signal circuit is open, shorted to ground or to power • TP2 sensor VREF circuit is open or shorted to ground • TP2 sensor VREF circuit is shorted to system power (B+) • TP2 sensor ground circuit has a high resistance condition • TP2 sensor is damaged or has failed

DTC	Trouble Code Title, Conditions & Possible Causes
DTC: P1221 **1T CCM, MIL: Yes** **Years:** 2008, 2009, 2010 **Models:** Avalanche, Camaro, Canyon, Escalade/EXT/ESV, Suburban, Tahoe, Yukon **Engines:** 4.8L VIN C, 5.3L VIN 0, 5.3L VIN 3, 5.3L VIN J, 5.3L VIN L, 6.0L VIN K, 6.0L VIN Y, 6.2L VIN J, 6.2L VIN W, 6.2L VIN 8 **Transmissions:** All	**TP Sensor 2 Signal Correlation** DTC P1517 and P1518 not set, key in crank or run position TP Sensor 1 (TP1) and TP Sensor 2 (TP2) more than 15% for 140ms, and the ECM detected the TP2 signal disagreed with the TP1 signal by more than 7.5% for 1 second. The TP sensor has two separate signal, ground, and 5 volt reference circuits that are used to connect the TP sensor to the TAC module. These sensors have opposite functionality. The TP1 voltage increases from below 1.0v at 0% throttle to above 3.5v at 100% throttle opening. The TP2 voltage decreases from around 3.8v at 0 percent throttle to below 1.0v at 100% throttle opening. The TP1 signal circuit is pulled up to 5.0v and the TP2 signal circuit is pulled to ground in the TAC module. **Possible Causes:** • TP2 sensor connector is contaminated, dirty or contains water • TP2 sensor signal, ground or VREF circuit has high resistance • TP2 sensor VREF circuit has a high resistance condition • TP2 sensor ground circuit has a high resistance condition • TP2 sensor is damaged or has failed • TAC controller or the throttle body is damaged or has failed • TSB 02-06-04-005 contains a repair procedure for this code
DTC: P1221 **1T CCM, MIL: Yes** **Years:** 2008, 2009 **Models:** Corvette **Engines:** All **Transmissions:** All	**TP Sensor 1-2 Signal Correlation** DTC P0606, P1517 and P1518 not set, key in crank or run mode, ETC serial data normal, and the ECM detected the TP1 disagreed with the TP2 input by over 7.5% for 1 second. **Possible Causes:** • TP1, 2 sensor signal circuit has a high resistance condition • TP1, 2 sensor VREF circuit has a high resistance condition • TP1, 2 sensor ground circuit has a high resistance condition • TP1, 2 sensor is damaged or has failed • TAC controller or the throttle body is damaged or has failed • TSB 02-06-04-005 contains a repair procedure for this code
DTC: P1255 **1T CCM, MIL: Yes** **Years:** 2008, 2009 **Models:** Acadia, Allure, Aura, Camaro, Corvette CTS, CTS-V, Enclave, LaCrosse, Outlook, Traverse **Engines:** All **Transmissions:** All	**Fuel Pump Control Module Driver Overtemperature** The engine is running. The FECM detects an overtemperature fault. **Note: Verify that DTC P0231, P0232 or P023F are not set as current or history before performing this diagnostic. If any of those codes are, diagnose first.** **Possible Causes:** • Dirty build up on FECM housing • FECM has failed
DTC: P1275 **1T CCM, MIL: No** **Years:** 2008, 2009, 2010 **Models:** Avalanche, Camaro, Canyon, Escalade/EXT/ESV, Suburban, Tahoe, Yukon **Engines:** 4.8L VIN C, 5.3L VIN 0, 5.3L VIN 3, 5.3L VIN J, 5.3L VIN L, 6.0L VIN K, 6.0L VIN Y, 6.2L VIN J, 6.2L VIN W, 6.2L VIN 8 **Transmissions:** All	**Accelerator Pedal Position Sensor 1 Circuit Malfunction** DTC P0601, P0602, P0606, P1517 and P1518 not set, key in crank or run position, system voltage over 5.23v, and the ECM detected the APP1 sensor signal voltage ranged between 0.25v and 4.22v for less than 1 second during the test. **Possible Causes:** • APP1 sensor connector is contaminated, oily or contains water • APP1 sensor signal, ground or VREF circuit high resistance • APP1 sensor VREF circuit is open, shorted to ground or to B+ • APP1 sensor signal or ground circuit has high resistance • APP1 sensor is damaged or has failed • TAC module is damaged or has failed
DTC: P1276 **1T CCM, MIL: No** **Years:** 2008, 2009, 2010 **Models:** Avalanche, Camaro, Canyon, Escalade/EXT/ESV, Suburban, Tahoe, Yukon **Engines:** 4.8L VIN C, 5.3L VIN 0, 5.3L VIN 3, 5.3L VIN J, 5.3L VIN L, 6.0L VIN K, 6.0L VIN Y, 6.2L VIN J, 6.2L VIN W, 6.2L VIN 8 **Transmissions:** All	**Accelerator Pedal Position Sensor 1 Range/Performance** DTC P0606, P1517 and P1518 not set, key in crank or run position, system voltage over 5.23v, and the ECM detected the APP Sensor 1 and the APP Sensor 2 signals disagreed by more than 10%, or the APP Sensor 1 and APP Sensor 3 signals disagreed by over 13%. **Note: Refer to the information in the Failure Records as needed.** **Possible Causes:** • APP1 sensor connector is contaminated, oily or contains water • APP1 sensor signal circuit is open or shorted to ground • APP1 sensor signal circuit is shorted to VREF or system power • APP1 sensor ground circuit is open or has high resistance • APP1 sensor VREF circuit is open or shorted to ground • APP1 sensor is damaged or has failed

DTC	Trouble Code Title, Conditions & Possible Causes
DTC: P1280 **1T CCM, MIL: No** **Years:** 2008, 2009, 2010 **Models:** Avalanche, Camaro, Canyon, Escalade/EXT/ESV, Suburban, Tahoe, Yukon **Engines:** 4.8L VIN C, 5.3L VIN 0, 5.3L VIN 3, 5.3L VIN J, 5.3L VIN L, 6.0L VIN K, 6.0L VIN Y, 6.2L VIN J, 6.2L VIN W, 6.2L VIN 8 **Transmissions:** All	**Accelerator Pedal Position Sensor 2 Circuit Malfunction** DTC P0601, P0602, P0606, P1517 and P1518 not set, key in crank or run position, system voltage over 5.23v, and the ECM detected the TP2 signal was less than 0.83v, or it was more than 4.81v for 1 second during the test. **Possible Causes:** • APP2 sensor connector is contaminated, oily or contains water • APP2 sensor signal, ground or VREF circuit high resistance • APP2 sensor VREF circuit is open, shorted to ground or to B+ • APP2 sensor signal or ground circuit has high resistance • APP2 sensor is damaged or has failed • TAC module is damaged or has failed
DTC: P1336 **2T CCM, MIL: Yes** **Years:** 2008, 2009, 2010 **Models:** All **Engines:** All **Transmissions:** All	**CKP Sensor System Variation Not Learned** DTC P0336, P0341and P1374 not set, engine started, ECT sensor more than 158°F, and the ECM did not detect any CKP variation values. The Crankshaft Position system variation-learning feature is used to calculate reference period errors caused by slight tolerance variations in the crankshaft, and the CKP sensor(s). The calculated error Allows the ECM to accurately compensate for reference period variations to enhance the Misfire Detection capability of the system. **Possible Causes:** • Set the parking brake and block the drive wheels for safety. • Verify the hood is closed. • Read the trouble codes. If a code is set, refer to that code. • Start the engine. Allow engine temperature to reach at least 158°F (70°C). Then key off. • Select Crankshaft Position Variation Learn procedure on Scan Tool & start the vehicle. • Apply the brake pedal firmly and verify the selector is in Park. • Increase accelerator pedal position until fuel cutoff is reached at the test RPM (e.g., 5150). Quickly release the accelerator pedal after fuel cutoff is reached. The CKP system variation compensating values are learned when the engine speed (RPM) decreases back to idle speed and the procedure terminates. • Read the trouble codes and recheck for DTC P1336. • If DTC P1336 runs and passes, the CKP system variation "learn" procedure is complete. If not, look for other codes. If no codes are set, repeat the test procedure.
DTC: P1362 **2T CCM, MIL: Yes** **Years:** 2008, 2009, 2010 **Models:** All **Engines:** All **Transmissions:** All	**ICM Control Circuit High Input** Engine started; and the ECM detected an intermittent high voltage condition on the IC timing signal circuit for 300 3X reference periods (100 crankshaft revolutions). The ICM has independent power and ground circuits that connect it to the ECM. Both the CMP sensor and CKP sensor signals are input directly to the ICM. The ICM sends 3X signals to the ECM, and controls the timing advance during engine cranking. The timing advance changes to ECM control after the ECM receives the second 3X signal. At this point, the ECM applies a 5v signal to the to the ignition control (IC) timing signal circuit. **Possible Causes:** • IC timing signal is shorted to system power • IC timing control circuit and IC timing signal circuits are shorted • IC module is damaged or it has failed • ECM has failed
DTC: P1380 **2T CCM, MIL: Yes** **Years:** 2008, 2009, 2010 **Models:**, Acadia, Allure, Astra, Aura, Avalanche, Escalade/EXT/ESV, Suburban, Tahoe, Yukon, Escalade/EXT/ESV, Suburban, Tahoe, Yukon Aveo, Aveo5, Camaro, Cobalt, Cobalt-GS, Colorado,Canyon, Corvette, CTS, CTS-V, CTS, CTS-V-V, DTS, Escalade/EXT/ESV, G.3, G5,Enclave, LaCrosse, Outlook, Suburban, Tahoe Traverse, Yukon **Engines:** All **Transmissions:** All	**Misfire Detected, Rough Road Data Not Available** DTC P0101, P0102, P0103, P0120, P0335, P0336 and P0742 not set, engine started, vehicle driven to over 10 MPH at an engine load over 60%, engine speed less than 3200 RPM, Misfire code (P0300) set with MIL requested "on", and the ECM detected a malfunction occurred that prevented it from receiving rough road detection data from the EBCM. The ECM detects engine misfire events by monitoring variations in the crankshaft rotation speed. Wheel speed changes caused by rough road conditions can cause changes in crankshaft speed. The ABS (system) monitors the wheel speed sensors to determine when the vehicle is operating on a rough road. **Possible Causes:** • Use the Freeze Frame/Failure Records data to help find the cause on an intermittent fault. If the code cannot be duplicated, the data in the Freeze Frame/Failure Records can determine how many miles since the code set. The Fail Counter and Pass Counter can also help determine how many ignition cycles the diagnostic reported a pass or a fail. Operate the vehicle within the Freeze Frame conditions (i.e., load, engine and vehicle speed, temperature etc.). This will isolate when the code set. • Service the ABS before diagnosing a misfire because an actual engine misfire may or may not exist. Also, an actual engine misfire may have occurred during an ABS malfunction. • Determine if the vehicle was driven on a rough road, and the ABS could not detect this due to a malfunction. The ECM may interpret variations in crankshaft speed caused by the rough road as a misfire without an actual engine misfire present. • Refer to Diagnostic System Check for Antilock Brake System • Refer to Diagnostic System Check for the Engine Controls

DTC	Trouble Code Title, Conditions & Possible Causes
DTC: P1381 **2T CCM, MIL: Yes** **Years:** 2008, 2009, 2010 **Models:**, Acadia, Allure, Astra, Aura, Avalanche, Escalade/EXT/ESV, Suburban, Tahoe, Yukon, Escalade/EXT/ESV, Suburban, Tahoe, Yukon Aveo, Aveo5, Camaro, Cobalt, Cobalt-GS, Colorado,Canyon, Corvette, CTS, CTS-V, CTS, CTS-V-V, DTS, Escalade/EXT/ESV, G.3, G5,Enclave, LaCrosse, Outlook, Suburban, Tahoe Traverse, Yukon **Engines:** All **Transmissions:** All	**Misfire Detected - No Communication with Brake Control Module** The vehicle speed is greater than 8 km/h (5 mph). The engine speed is less than 7,000 RPM. The engine load is less than 60 percent. Engine misfire is detected and DTC P0300 sets with the MIL illuminated. DTCs P1381 run continuously when the above conditions are met. An ABS malfunction exists for more than 10 seconds, preventing the ECM from receiving rough road detection data. Engine misfire is detected and DTC P0300 set. **Possible Causes:** • If any ABS DTCs are set, diagnose those first • ABS module
DTC: P1400 **2T CCM, MIL: Yes** **Years:** 2008, 2009, 2010 **Models:**, Acadia, Allure, Astra, Aura, Avalanche, Escalade/EXT/ESV, Suburban, Tahoe, Yukon, Escalade/EXT/ESV, Suburban, Tahoe, Yukon Aveo, Aveo5, Camaro, Cobalt, Cobalt-GS, Colorado,Canyon, Corvette, CTS, CTS-V, CTS, CTS-V-V, DTS, Escalade/EXT/ESV, G.3, G5,Enclave, LaCrosse, Outlook, Suburban, Tahoe Traverse, Yukon **Engines:** All **Transmissions:** All	**Cold Start Emission Reduction Control System** The engine is running, and a cold start has been detected. Vehicle speed is less than 2 km/h (1 mph). The engine is at idle with no input from the accelerator pedal. DTCs P0068, P0101, P0102, P0103, P0106, P0107, P0108, P0112, P0113, P0116, P0117, P0118, P0120, P0121, P0122, P0123, P0220, P0222, P0223, P0201, P0202, P0203, P0204, P0205, P0206, P0300, P0335, P0336, P0351, P0352, P0353, P0501, P0502, P0506, P0507, P0601, P0602, P0603, P0604, P0606, P0607, P060D, P062F, P0641, P0651, P1101, P1516, P1682, P2101, P2119, P2120, P2122, P2123, P2125, P2127, P2128, P2135, P2138, P2176, P2610 are not set. This DTC runs for 15 seconds within the first 2 minutes of start-up. This diagnostic runs once per trip when a cold start has been determined. The actual exhaust energy model does not match the expected exhaust energy model. **Possible Causes:** • Air intake system for Damage, restriction, or modification • Dirty or deteriorating air filter element • Crankcase ventilation system for correct operation • Vacuum leak and other un-metered air downstream of the Mass Air Flow (MAF) sensor • Intake manifold leak • Damaged, restricted, modified or enhanced exhaust system • Exhaust leaks
DTC: P1404 **2T EGR, MIL: Yes** **Years:** 2008, 2009, 2010 **Models:** Avalanche, Camaro, Canyon, Escalade/EXT/ESV, Suburban, Tahoe, Yukon **Engines:** 4.8L VIN C, 5.3L VIN 0, 5.3L VIN 3, 5.3L VIN J, 5.3L VIN L, 6.0L VIN K, 6.0L VIN Y, 6.2L VIN J, 6.2L VIN W, 6.2L VIN 8 **Transmissions:** All	**EGR Valve Closed Position Performance** Engine started; system voltage from 11-18v, EGR valve enabled at least (6) times, and the ECM detected the EGR position sensor was 0.29v more than the EGR learned minimum position when the desired EGR position was commanded to 0% for over 2 seconds, or the EGR position sensor command is over 30% and steady for 2 seconds after a test failure and before the next test. **Possible Causes:** • EGR sensor signal circuit is shorted to VREF (5v) • EGR sensor ground circuit is open or has high resistance • EGR sensor is damaged or has failed (sensor/solenoid unit) • EGR valve pintle or valve seat contains carbon deposits • ECM has failed • TSB 01-06-04-043 contains a repair procedure for this code
DTC: P1415 **2T AIR, MIL: Yes** **Years:** 2008, 2009, 2010 **Models:** Avalanche, Camaro, Canyon, Escalade/EXT/ESV, Suburban, Tahoe, Yukon **Engines:** 4.8L VIN C, 5.3L VIN 0, 5.3L VIN 3, 5.3L VIN J, 5.3L VIN L, 6.0L VIN K, 6.0L VIN Y, 6.2L VIN J, 6.2L VIN W, 6.2L VIN 8 **Transmissions:** All	**Secondary Air Injection System (Bank 1) Malfunction** DTC P0137, 0138 P0140-P0147, P0151-P0158, P0160, P0161, P0171, P0172, P0174, P0175, P0300, P0500, P1106, P1107, P1111-P1115, P1121, P1122, P1133, P1134, P1153, P1154, P1351 and P1361 not set, engine started, vehicle driven to an engine speed over 900 RPM at an engine load less than 33.25%, airflow less than 22 g/sec, A/F ratio at 13.125:1, ECT sensor from 158-230°F, system voltage over 10.0v, and the ECM detected the Bank 1 HO2S signal was less than 222 mv for 1 second with the AIR pump on while in closed loop. A secondary air injection (AIR) pump is used to reduce the tailpipe emissions during startup. The ECM supplies a ground to the AIR pump relay control circuit, and this action energizes the AIR pump. The ECM monitors the front HO2S signal in order to diagnose the AIR system. During the AIR test, the ECM activates the AIR pump during closed loop operation. Once the AIR pump is "on", the ECM monitors the HO2S signal and the Short Term fuel trim values of both banks of the engine. If the AIR system is operating properly, the HO2S signal should go low, and the Short Term fuel trim value should go high. If the ECM detects the HO2S signals for both banks did not respond as expected during the tests, it will set DTC P0410. If only one sensor responds, the ECM sets either a DTC P1415 or P1416 to indicate the bank where the AIR system failed. **Possible Causes:** • Air hoses disconnected, loose, kinked or failed (a burnt hose) • AIR pump is damaged or has failed (inspect air pump for water) • AIR system check valves and/or pipes are damaged or leaking • ECM has failed

DTC	Trouble Code Title, Conditions & Possible Causes
DTC: P1416 **2T AIR, MIL: Yes** **Years:** 2008, 2009, 2010 **Models:** Avalanche, Camaro, Canyon, Escalade/EXT/ESV, Suburban, Tahoe, Yukon **Engines:** 4.8L VIN C, 5.3L VIN 0, 5.3L VIN 3, 5.3L VIN J, 5.3L VIN L, 6.0L VIN K, 6.0L VIN Y, 6.2L VIN J, 6.2L VIN W, 6.2L VIN 8 **Transmissions:** All	**Secondary Air Injection System (Bank 2) Malfunction** DTC P0137, 0138 P0140-P0147, P0151-P0158, P0160, P0161, P0171, P0172, P0174, P0175, P0300, P0500, P1106, P1107, P1111-P1115, P1121, P1122, P1133, P1134, P1153, P1154, P1351 and P1361 not set, engine started, vehicle driven to an engine speed over 900 RPM at an engine load less than 33.25%, airflow less than 22 g/sec, A/F ratio at 13.125:1, ECT sensor from 158-230°F, system voltage over 10.0v, and the ECM detected the Bank 2 HO2S signal was less than 222 mv for 1 second with the AIR pump on while in closed loop. The ECM supplies a ground to the AIR pump relay control circuit, and this action energizes the AIR pump. The ECM monitors the front HO2S signal in order to diagnose the AIR system. During the AIR test, the ECM activates the AIR pump during closed loop operation. Once the AIR pump is "on", the ECM monitors the HO2S signal and the Short Term fuel trim values of both banks of the engine. If the AIR system is operating properly, the HO2S signal should go low, and the Short Term fuel trim value should go high. If the ECM detects the HO2S signals for both banks did not respond as expected during the tests, it will set DTC P0410. If only one sensor responds, the ECM sets either a DTC P1415 or P1416 to indicate the bank where the AIR system failed. **Possible Causes:** • Air hoses disconnected, loose, kinked or failed (a burnt hose) • AIR pump is damaged or has failed (inspect air pump for water) • AIR system check valves and/or pipes are damaged or leaking • ECM has failed
DTC: P1514 **1T CCM, MIL: Yes** **Years:** 2008, 2009, 2010 **Models:** Avalanche, Camaro, Canyon, Escalade/EXT/ESV, Suburban, Tahoe, Yukon **Engines:** 4.8L VIN C, 5.3L VIN 0, 5.3L VIN 3, 5.3L VIN J, 5.3L VIN L, 6.0L VIN K, 6.0L VIN Y, 6.2L VIN J, 6.2L VIN W, 6.2L VIN 8 **Transmissions:** All	**Throttle Body Performance** DTC P0601, P0602, P0606, P1515, P1516, P1517 and P1518 not set, P1120, P1220 and P1221 not active at the time this code set, or P1120 and P1220 not set at the same time, engine speed over 500 RPM, and the ECM detected the difference between Actual (MAF) airflow and Speed Density Calculated airflow was more than expected for 1 second. The Reduced Engine Power message displays on the Driver Information Center if this code sets. **Possible Causes:** • Inspect the throttle blade for damage and/or proper installation • Inspect the TAC module connectors for signs of water intrusion. When water intrusion occurs, multiple codes can set with no circuit or component faults apparent during diagnostic testing. • Physically and visually inspect the throttle body assembly, and throttle position sensor for damage and/or a loose mounting. Move the throttle blade from closed to wide open position without applying too much force. The throttle blade should move smoothly through the full range and should return to a slightly open position on its own. • If the TAC module detects a fault in the system, it may set more than one related code because of the many redundant tests that run continuously on this system. Locating and repairing one individual condition may fix more than one code.
DTC: P1515 **1T CCM, MIL: Yes** **Years:** 2008, 2009, 2010 **Models:** Avalanche, Camaro, Canyon, Escalade/EXT/ESV, Suburban, Tahoe, Yukon **Engines:** 4.8L VIN C, 5.3L VIN 0, 5.3L VIN 3, 5.3L VIN J, 5.3L VIN L, 6.0L VIN K, 6.0L VIN Y, 6.2L VIN J, 6.2L VIN W, 6.2L VIN 8 **Transmissions:** All	**Control Module Throttle Actuator Position Performance** DTC P0601, P0602, P0606, P1515, P1516, P1517 and P1518 not set, P1120, P1220 and P1221 not active at the time this code set, or P1120 and P1220 not set at the same time, key in crank or run mode, ETC or TAC system not in Battery Saver Mode, and the ECM detected the Actual and Commanded throttle positions were out-of-range for under 1 second. **Possible Causes:** • Throttle actuator motor CKT 1 is open, shorted to ground or B+ • Throttle actuator motor CKT 2 is open, shorted to ground or B+ • Throttle actuator motor is damaged or has failed • Throttle actuator motor control module has failed • TSB 00-06-04-035 contains a repair procedure for this code
DTC: P1516 **1T CCM, MIL: Yes** **Years:** 2008, 2009 **Models:** Allure, Aura, Canyon, Colorado, LaCrosse **Engines:** 2.9L VIN 9, 3.5L VIN N, 3.8L VIN 2, 5.3L VIN C, 5.3L VIN L **Transmissions:** All	**Throttle Actuator Control (TAC) Module Throttle Actuator Position Performance** The ignition is ON. The ignition voltage is more than 8 volts. The system is not in the Battery Save mode. The engine is running. DTC P0068 is not set. DTC P1516 and P2101 run continuously when the above conditions are met. The indicated throttle position does not match the predicted throttle position for more than 0.5 second. **Note: Disconnecting the throttle body harness connector causes additional DTCs to set.** **Possible Causes:** • TAC motor control circuit for a short to voltage • TAC motor control circuit for a short to voltage • TAC motor control circuit for a short to ground • TAC motor control circuit for a short to ground • Throttle body has failed • ECM has failed

DTC	Trouble Code Title, Conditions & Possible Causes
DTC: P1516 **2T CCM, MIL: Yes** **Years:** 2008, 2009, 2010 **Models:**, Acadia, Allure, Astra, Aura, Avalanche, Escalade/EXT/ESV, Suburban, Tahoe, Yukon, Escalade/EXT/ESV, Suburban, Tahoe, Yukon Aveo, Aveo5, Camaro, Cobalt, Cobalt-GS, Colorado, Canyon, Corvette, CTS, CTS-V, CTS, CTS-V-V, DTS, Escalade/EXT/ESV, G.3, G5, Enclave, LaCrosse, Outlook, Suburban, Tahoe Traverse, Yukon **Engines:** All **Transmissions:** All	**TAC Module Throttle Actuator Position Performance** DTC P1518 not set, key in crank or run mode, ETC or TAC system not in Battery Saver Mode, then the ETC/TAC module detected the predicted and actual throttle positions were not within a calibrated range of each other or the ECM and ETC/TAC could not determine the throttle position or that both TP sensors signals were invalid. **Possible Causes:** • TAC motor CKT 1 or CKT 2 is open, shorted to ground or B+ • Throttle actuator motor CKT 1 is shorted to CKT 2 • Throttle actuator motor control module has failed • TSB 03-04-06-032 contains a repair procedure for this code
DTC: P1517 **1T CCM, MIL: Yes** **Years:** 2008, 2009, 2010 **Models:** Avalanche, Camaro, Canyon, Escalade/EXT/ESV, Suburban, Tahoe, Yukon **Engines:** 4.8L VIN C, 5.3L VIN 0, 5.3L VIN 3, 5.3L VIN J, 5.3L VIN L, 6.0L VIN K, 6.0L VIN Y, 6.2L VIN J, 6.2L VIN W, 6.2L VIN 8 **Transmissions:** All	**Throttle Actuator Control Module Performance** DTC P1518 not set, key in the crank or run mode, system voltage over 5.23v, and the ETC or TAC module detected that an internal data test failed (did not pass) for a time period of less than 1 second. **Possible Causes:** • Test the charging system output (low voltage can set this code) • Inspect the TAC module connectors for signs of water intrusion. If water intrusion occurs, multiple codes may set without any circuit or component conditions found during diagnostic testing. • When the TAC module detects a fault condition, several TAC related codes set because there are redundant tests running. • TAC module has failed
DTC: P1517 **1T CCM, MIL: Yes** **Years:** 2008, 2009 **Models:** Corvette **Engines:** All **Transmissions:** All	**Throttle Actuator Control Module Performance** DTC P1518 not set, key in crank or run mode, system voltage over 5.23v, and the ETC or TAC module detected that an internal data test failed (did not pass) for less than 1 second. **Possible Causes:** • Test the charging system output (low voltage can set this code) • Inspect the TAC module connectors for signs of water intrusion. If water intrusion occurs, multiple codes may set without any circuit or component conditions present. • When the TAC module detects a fault condition, several TAC related codes set because there are redundant tests running. • TAC module has failed
DTC: P1518 **1T CCM, MIL: Yes** **Years:** 2008, 2009, 2010 **Models:** Avalanche, Camaro, Canyon, Escalade/EXT/ESV, Suburban, Tahoe, Yukon **Engines:** 4.8L VIN C, 5.3L VIN 0, 5.3L VIN 3, 5.3L VIN J, 5.3L VIN L, 6.0L VIN K, 6.0L VIN Y, 6.2L VIN J, 6.2L VIN W, 6.2L VIN 8 **Transmissions:** All	**Throttle Actuator Control Module Serial Data Malfunction** Key in the crank or run mode, system voltage over 5.23v, and the ETC or TAC module detected invalid or missing serial data present for a specified amount of time, condition met for less than 1 second. **Possible Causes:** • DTC P1518 sets if the battery voltage is low. If the customer's concern is slow cranking or no crank due to low battery voltage, ignore the DTC P1518. Clear codes and retest. • DTC P1518 also sets when there is a short to B+ on the TAC module ground circuit. Inspect the Brake & Cruise fuses first. • TSB 03-04-06-032 contains a repair procedure for this code
DTC: P1551 **1T CCM, MIL: Yes** **Years:** 2008, 2009 **Models:** Acadia, Allure, Aura, Camaro, CTS, CTS-V, Enclave, LaCrosse, Outlook, Traverse **Engines:** 3.6L VIN 7, 3.6L VIN D, 3.6L VIN V **Transmissions:** All	**Throttle Valve Rest Position Not Reached During Learn** The ECM detects the TP sensor angle is less than 10 percent or greater than 40 percent when the throttle actuator control motor is deactivated. The condition exists, and then a 5 second delay for MIL ON. **Possible Causes:** • Faulty throttle body, (binding, sticking or no spring pressure) • Throttle body has failed

DTC	Trouble Code Title, Conditions & Possible Causes
DTC: P1585 **1T CCM, MIL: No** **Years:** 2008, 2009, 2010 **Models:**All **Engines:** All **Transmissions:** All	**Cruise Control Inhibit Output Circuit Malfunction** Engine started; system voltage over 10.0v and the ECM detected an unexpected voltage condition on the Cruise Control Inhibit driver circuit for at least 30 seconds. **Possible Causes:** • Cruise control inhibit circuit is shorted to system voltage • Cruise control inhibit circuit is open or shorted to ground • Cruise control module power circuit is open (test CR CNT fuse) • Cruise control module is damaged or has failed • ECM has failed
DTC: P1631 **1T CCM, MIL: No** **Years:** 2008, 2009, 2010 **Models:** Avalanche, Camaro, Canyon, Escalade/EXT/ESV, Suburban, Tahoe, Yukon **Engines:** 4.8L VIN C, 5.3L VIN 0, 5.3L VIN 3, 5.3L VIN J, 5.3L VIN L, 6.0L VIN K, 6.0L VIN Y, 6.2L VIN J, 6.2L VIN W, 6.2L VIN 8 **Transmissions:** All	**Theft Deterrent - Start Enable Signal Not Correct** DTC P1626 not active, engine cranking with the ECM not in "password learn mode", VTD (Pass Lock) system enabled, and the ECM did not receive a valid password before the fuel disable decision point was reached. When the Passlock portion of the VTD system has sensed the proper operation of the ignition switch and lock, or determined that the switch and lock have not been tampered with, the VTD (Passlock) module transmits a password to the ECM. Fuel delivery is enabled if this password matches the password stored in the ECM memory. If a component in the Theft Deterrent system has been replaced, the two modules need to relearn the password of the new components. If the relearn procedure has not been performed, DTC P1631 will set. If a VTD failure occurs during an ignition cycle on which the ECM has enabled fuel, then the ECM will enter Fail Safe mode (VTD System Failure with Fuel Enabled). The ECM remains in Fail Enable Mode for the current and future ignition cycles, until the fault is corrected, a valid password is received, or until the battery is disconnected. If the codes are cleared, the vehicle will lose its Fail Enable status and will not start until the fault is corrected or the ten minute timer expires. At this point, the ECM receives the correct fuel delivery password. **Possible Causes:** • Refer to Diagnostic System Check for Theft Deterrent Module • Perform the Powertrain Onboard Diagnostic System Check • TSB 77-65-31 contains a repair procedure for this code
DTC: P1637 **1T CCM, MIL: No** **Years:** 2008, 2009, 2010 **Models:** Avalanche, Camaro, Canyon, Escalade/EXT/ESV, Suburban, Tahoe, Yukon **Engines:** 4.8L VIN C, 5.3L VIN 0, 5.3L VIN 3, 5.3L VIN J, 5.3L VIN L, 6.0L VIN K, 6.0L VIN Y, 6.2L VIN J, 6.2L VIN W, 6.2L VIN 8 **Transmissions:** All	**Generator 'L' Terminal Circuit Malfunction** Engine started; and the ECM detected an incorrect voltage on the Generator 'L' terminal during the CCM test. The ECM supplies the ignition voltage to the generator lamp feed. This voltage is pulled low by the generator once the circuit is supplied voltage. Once the generator begins to turn, the ECM detects ignition voltage. If there are no Charging system faults, the lamp terminal circuit will be low (0 volts) with the ignition switch "on" and then change to the system voltage after engine startup. If the Charging system detects this circuit is shorted to ground) the IPC will display a fault message. **Possible Causes:** • A Scan Tool should display Inactive for the 'L' Terminal and 10-40% for the 'F' Terminal with the ignition "on". With the engine running, the display should indicate the 'L' Terminal is Active and the 'F' Terminal is higher than 5% on the tool display. • Generator 'L terminal circuit shorted to ground or to power (B+) • Generator 'F' terminal circuit is open or shorted to ground • Generator is damaged or has failed or the ECM has failed
DTC: P1638 **1T CCM, MIL: No** **Years:** 2008, 2009, 2010 **Models:** Avalanche, Camaro, Canyon, Escalade/EXT/ESV, Suburban, Tahoe, Yukon **Engines:** 4.8L VIN C, 5.3L VIN 0, 5.3L VIN 3, 5.3L VIN J, 5.3L VIN L, 6.0L VIN K, 6.0L VIN Y, 6.2L VIN J, 6.2L VIN W, 6.2L VIN 8 **Transmissions:** All	**Generator 'F' Terminal Circuit Malfunction** No CKP, CMP or Generator codes set, key on and the ECM detected the PWM signal was from 10-40% for over 6 seconds; or with the engine speed under 3000 RPM, the ECM detected the PWM signal was less than 5% for 6 seconds. The ECM uses the generator field duty cycle signal circuit to monitor the duty cycle of the generator. The generator field duty cycle signal circuit connects to the high side of the field winding in the generator. A pulse width modulated (PWM) high side driver in the voltage regulator turns the field winding on/off. When the key is in run position and the engine is off, the ECM should detect a duty cycle near 0%. However, when the engine is running, the duty cycle should be from 5-100%. The ECM monitors the PWM signal using a key on test and a run test. During the tests, if the ECM detects an out of range PWM signal, DTC P1638 will set. When the DTC sets, the ECM will send a class 2 serial data message to the IPC to illuminate the charge indicator. **Possible Causes:** • Generator connector is damaged or has high resistance • Generator field duty cycle signal circuit is open or shorted • Generator is damaged or has failed • ECM has failed

DTC	Trouble Code Title, Conditions & Possible Causes
DTC: P1639 **1T CCM, MIL: Yes** **Years:** 2008, 2009, 2010 **Models:** Avalanche, Camaro, Canyon, Escalade/EXT/ESV, Suburban, Tahoe, Yukon **Engines:** 4.8L VIN C, 5.3L VIN 0, 5.3L VIN 3, 5.3L VIN J, 5.3L VIN L, 6.0L VIN K, 6.0L VIN Y, 6.2L VIN J, 6.2L VIN W, 6.2L VIN 8 **Transmissions:** All	**5-Volt Reference 2 Circuit Malfunction** Key on or engine running; and the ECM detected the 5v Reference No. 2 circuit was out of tolerance for 2 seconds during the CCM test. This circuit is connected to the Fuel Tank Pressure (FTP) and TP sensor. **Possible Causes:** • 5v VREF circuit is shorted to sensor ground or chassis ground • 5v VREF circuit, FTP or TP sensor circuit is shorted to (B+) • 5v VREF circuit shorted to FTP or TP sensor signal circuit • FTP sensor or TP sensor is damaged or ECM has failed
DTC: P1682 **2T CCM, MIL: Yes** **Years:** 2008, 2009, 2010 **Models:**, Acadia, Allure, Astra, Aura, Avalanche, Escalade/EXT/ESV, Suburban, Tahoe, Yukon, Escalade/EXT/ESV, Suburban, Tahoe, Yukon Aveo, Aveo5, Camaro, Cobalt, Cobalt-GS, Colorado,Canyon, Corvette, CTS, CTS-V, CTS, CTS-V-V, DTS, Escalade/EXT/ESV, G.3, G5,Enclave, LaCrosse, Outlook, Suburban, Tahoe Traverse, Yukon **Engines:** All **Transmissions:** All	**Ignition 1 Switch Circuit 2** The ignition is ON. System voltage is more than 7 volts. The powertrain relay is commanded ON. DTC P1682 runs continuously when the above conditions are met. The ECM detects that the voltage level difference is greater than 3 volts between the 2 ignition 1 voltage circuits for less than 1 second. **Possible Causes:** • Powertrain relay controlled output circuit for a short to voltage • Powertrain relay coil voltage supply circuit for a short to ground or an open/high resistance. • Powertrain relay switch voltage supply circuit for an open/high resistance. • Ignition 1 relay controlled output circuit for a short to ground or open/high resistance • Powertrain relay • ECM has failed
DTC: P1810 **2T CCM, MIL: Yes** **Years:** 2008, 2009, 2010 **Models:** Avalanche, Camaro, Canyon, Escalade/EXT/ESV, Suburban, Tahoe, Yukon **Engines:** 4.8L VIN C, 5.3L VIN 0, 5.3L VIN 3, 5.3L VIN J, 5.3L VIN L, 6.0L VIN K, 6.0L VIN Y, 6.2L VIN J, 6.2L VIN W, 6.2L VIN 8 **Transmissions:** All	**TFP Valve Position Switch Assembly** DTC P0502 and P0503 not set, system voltage over 10.0v, engine running for 5 seconds, Fuel Cutoff inactive, engine torque from 40-400 ft-lbs, engine vacuum from 0-105 kPa, then during Condition 1 the ECM detected an illegal TFP manual valve position switch state for 60 seconds; or during Condition 2 with the engine speed less than 80 RPM for 0.1 second, then the engine speed from 80-550 RPM for 100ms, then the engine speed was greater than 550 RPM; then the vehicle speed was less than 2 MPH, and the ECM detected the gear range was D2, D4 or Reverse during startup for 5 seconds; or during Condition 3 with the TP angle from 10-50%, fourth gear commanded "on", TCC engaged, speed ratio from 0.6-0.75, and the ECM detected the gear range indicated Park or Neutral with the vehicle is operating in D4 for 10 seconds. The TFP manual valve position switch assembly cannot distinguish between P/N because the monitored valve body pressures are identical in both cases. **Possible Causes:** • TFP valve position switch signal circuit is open, grounded or shorted to another signal • TFP valve position switch is damaged or has failed • This code can set during fluid refilling. After refilling the fluid, cycle the key "off", then idle the engine for 20 seconds. Turn the key "off" and Allow the ECM to power down. • This code can set due to low pump pressure or due to a stuck pressure regulator. • This code can set due to a rolled forward clutch piston seal. It may Allow the ECM to see a 2.08:1 ratio (reverse) when the manual valve position is actually indicated in D4. • ECM has failed
DTC: P1860 **1T CCM, MIL: Yes** **Years:** 2008, 2009, 2010 **Models:** Avalanche, Camaro, Canyon, Escalade/EXT/ESV, Suburban, Tahoe, Yukon **Engines:** 4.8L VIN C, 5.3L VIN 0, 5.3L VIN 3, 5.3L VIN J, 5.3L VIN L, 6.0L VIN K, 6.0L VIN Y, 6.2L VIN J, 6.2L VIN W, 6.2L VIN 8 **Transmissions:** All	**TCM PWM Solenoid Circuit Malfunction** Engine started, engine runtime over 5 seconds, system voltage over 10.0v, Fuel Cutoff inactive, 1st gear commanded "on", and the ECM detected a high voltage with the TCC solenoid commanded to 90%, or a low voltage with the TCC commanded to 0%. The TCC PWM solenoid controls fluid acting on the converter clutch valve that controls the application and release of the torque converter clutch. The solenoid attaches to the control valve body in the transmission. **Possible Causes:** • TCC solenoid control circuit is open or shorted to ground • TCC solenoid control circuit is shorted to system power (B+) • TCC solenoid power circuit is open (test TRANS or IGN fuse) • TCC solenoid is damaged or has failed • ECM has failed

DTC	Trouble Code Title, Conditions & Possible Causes
DTC: P1870 **1T CCM, MIL: Yes** **Years:** 2008, 2009, 2010 **Models:** Avalanche, Camaro, Canyon, Escalade/EXT/ESV, Suburban, Tahoe, Yukon **Engines:** 4.8L VIN C, 5.3L VIN 0, 5.3L VIN 3, 5.3L VIN J, 5.3L VIN L, 6.0L VIN K, 6.0L VIN Y, 6.2L VIN J, 6.2L VIN W, 6.2L VIN 8 **Transmissions:** All	**Transmission Component Slipping** DTC P0122, P0123, P0502, P0503, P0711-P0713, P0740, P0753, P0758, P1810 and P1860 not set, vehicle driven at a speed of 30-70 MPH at an engine speed of 1500-3000 RPM, Fuel Cutoff inactive, TP angle from 9-35%, engine vacuum 0-150 kPa, speed ratio is 0.69-0.88, Transmission not 1st gear, gear range is D4, TFT sensor from 68°F-266°F, shift solenoid diagnostic counter at zero, then with the TCC solenoid commanded "on" at a 95% duty cycle for 5 seconds, the ECM detected the TCC slip speed was 130-180 RPM for 7 seconds. The fault must be detected three times with the TCC commanded "off" each time between cycles. **Possible Causes:** • 1-2 shift solenoid valve has sediment, damage or leaking seals • 2-3 shift solenoid valve has sediment, damage or leaking seals • 3-2 shift solenoid valve has sediment, damage or leaking seals • Valve body regulator apply valve stuck or regulator is scored • Torque converter front stator shaft bushing is worn, the stator roller clutch is not holding or it has external damage/leaks • Converter clutch valve is stuck or it is installed backwards • Converter clutch valve retaining ring is not positioned properly • Converter clutch outer valve spring is cocked • Pump to case gasket is not positioned properly • Orifice cup plugs are restricted or damaged • Over-tightened, or unevenly tightened pump body to cover bolts • TSB 02-07-30-001 contains a repair procedure for this code
DTC: P1875 **2T CCM, MIL: Yes** **Years:** 2008, 2009, 2010 **Models:** Avalanche, Camaro, Canyon, Escalade/EXT/ESV, Suburban, Tahoe, Yukon **Engines:** 4.8L VIN C, 5.3L VIN 0, 5.3L VIN 3, 5.3L VIN J, 5.3L VIN L, 6.0L VIN K, 6.0L VIN Y, 6.2L VIN J, 6.2L VIN W, 6.2L VIN 8 **Transmissions:** All	**4WD Low Switch Circuit Fault** DTC P0122, P0123, P0502, P0503, P0740, P0742, P0751, P0752, P0756, P0758, P1810, P1860 and P1870 not set, engine started, vehicle driven to a speed over 7 MPH for 5 seconds, gear range is D4, Fuel Cutoff not active, TP angle from 17-50%, engine torque from 50-400 lb ft, engine vacuum from 0-105 kPa, shift solenoid performance counters at zero, TFT sensor from 68-266°F, then during Condition 1 with the 4WD Low switch in 4WD low, transfer case not in 4WD low, TCC slip speed from −3000 to −50 RPM, the ECM detected the speed ratio was 0.8-1.2; or during Condition 2 with the 4WD Low switch not in 4WD low, transfer case in 4WD low, TCC commanded "on", TCC slip speed was 100 to 3000 RPM, the ECM detected the speed ratio was 2.5-2.9 for 10 seconds. **Possible Causes:** • 4WD low switch signal circuit is open, shorted to ground or B+ • 4WD low switch is damaged or has failed • ECM has failed
DTC: P1887 **2T CCM, MIL: Yes** **Years:** 2008, 2009 **Models:** , Impala, **Engines:** 3.4L VIN X, 3.4L VIN E, 3.5L VIN N, 3.8L VIN 1, 3.8L VIN K **Transmissions:** A/T	**TCC Release Switch Circuit Malfunction** DTC P0716, P0717, P0741, P0742 and P1810 not set, engine started, Fuel Cutoff inactive, engine driven to a speed of 30-70 MPH, engine torque from 30-300 lb ft, Transmission gear is D4 with the TCC commanded "on", TCC pressure from 15-120 psi, TCC slip speed from −20 to +60 RPM, and the ECM detected the pressure switch was open for 6 seconds. The fault must occur twice in 1 trip to set this code. The TCC release switch is normally closed (N.C.) switch that signals the ECM that the TCC is released. This is accomplished by torque converter release fluid pressure acting on the switch contacts that open the circuit. When the circuit voltage is high, the ECM detects the TCC is no longer engaged. If the ECM determines the TCC release switch is open (indicating the TCC is not applied) and the TCC slip speed indicates the TCC is applied, then DTC P1887 sets **Possible Causes:** • TCC release switch signal circuit is open • Turbine shaft O-ring seal leaks, oil seal rings missing/damaged. • TCC control valve damaged or No. 1 check ball is damaged • Spacer plate release exhaust blocked or case cover or spacer plate gaskets damaged • TSB 02-07-30-022A contains a repair procedure for this code

OBD II Trouble Code List (P2xxx Codes)

DTC	Trouble Code Title, Conditions & Possible Causes
DTC: P2088 **2T CCM, MIL: Yes** **Years:** 2008, 2009 **Models:** Astra, Aura, Aveo, Aveo5, Cobalt G3, G5 **Engines:** 1.6L VIN 6, 1.6L VIN E, 1.8L VIN 1, 2.0L VIN P, 2.0L VIN X, 2.2L VIN H, 2.2L VIN F, 2.4L VIN 5, 2.4L VIN B **Transmissions:** All	**Intake Camshaft Position (CMP) Actuator Solenoid Control Circuit Low Voltage** DTC P0606 is not set. The ignition is ON. The ignition voltage is between 10-16 volts. The ECM detects a short to ground in the CMP actuator solenoid circuits for greater than 1 second or a cumulative of 5 seconds when the solenoid is commanded OFF. **Possible Causes:** • Ignition circuit for a short to ground or an open/high resistance • Control circuit for a short to voltage or an open/high resistance • Control circuit for a short to ground • CMP actuator solenoid • Faulty ECM

DTC	Trouble Code Title, Conditions & Possible Causes
DTC: P2088 **1T CCM, MIL: Yes** **Years:** 2008, 2009, 2010 **Models:** Acadia, Allure, Aura, Camaro, CTS, CTS-V, Enclave, LaCrosse, Outlook, Traverse **Engines:** 3.6L VIN 7, 3.6L VIN D, 3.6L VIN V **Transmissions:** All	**Intake Camshaft Position (CMP) Actuator Solenoid Control Circuit Low Voltage (Bank 1)** The ECM detects a short to ground in the CMP actuator solenoid circuits for greater than 1 seconds or a cumulative of 10 seconds, when the solenoid is commanded OFF. **Possible Causes:** • Ignition circuit for a short to ground or an open/high resistance • Control circuit for a short to voltage or an open/high resistance • Control circuit for a short to ground • CMP actuator solenoid • Faulty ECM
DTC: P2089 **2T CCM, MIL: Yes** **Years:** 2008, 2009 **Models:** Astra, Aura, Aveo, Aveo5, Cobalt G3, G5 **Engines:** 1.6L VIN 6, 1.6L VIN E, 1.8L VIN 1, 2.0L VIN P, 2.0L VIN X, 2.2L VIN H, 2.2L VIN F, 2.4L VIN 5, 2.4L VIN B **Transmissions:** All	**Intake Camshaft Position (CMP) Actuator Solenoid Control Circuit High Voltage** DTC P0606 is not set. The ignition is ON. The ignition voltage is between 10-16 volts The ECM detects a short to voltage in the CMP actuator solenoid circuits for greater than 1 seconds or a cumulative of 10 seconds, when the solenoid is commanded OFF. **Possible Causes:** • Ignition circuit for a short to ground or an open/high resistance • Control circuit for a short to voltage or an open/high resistance • Control circuit for a short to ground • CMP actuator solenoid • Faulty ECM
DTC: P2089 **1T CCM, MIL: Yes** **Years:** 2008, 2009, 2010 **Models:** Acadia, Allure, Aura, Camaro, CTS, CTS-V, Enclave, LaCrosse, Outlook, Traverse **Engines:** 3.6L VIN 7, 3.6L VIN D, 3.6L VIN V **Transmissions:** All	**Intake Camshaft Position (CMP) Actuator Solenoid Control Circuit High Voltage (Bank 1)** The ECM detects a short to voltage in the CMP actuator solenoid circuits for greater than 1 seconds or a cumulative of 10 seconds, when the solenoid is commanded OFF. **Possible Causes:** • Ignition circuit for a short to ground or an open/high resistance • Control circuit for a short to voltage or an open/high resistance • Control circuit for a short to ground • CMP actuator solenoid • Faulty ECM
DTC: P2090 **1T CCM, MIL: Yes** **Years:** 2008, 2009, 2010 **Models:** Acadia, Allure, Aura, Camaro, CTS, CTS-V, Enclave, LaCrosse, Outlook, Traverse **Engines:** 3.6L VIN 7, 3.6L VIN D, 3.6L VIN V **Transmissions:** All	**Exhaust Camshaft Position (CMP) Actuator Solenoid Control Circuit Low Voltage (Bank 1)** The ECM detects a short to ground in the CMP actuator solenoid circuits for greater than 1 seconds or a cumulative of 10 seconds, when the solenoid is commanded OFF. **Possible Causes:** • Ignition circuit for a short to ground or an open/high resistance • Control circuit for a short to voltage or an open/high resistance • Control circuit for a short to ground • CMP actuator solenoid • Faulty ECM
DTC: P2091 **2T CCM, MIL: Yes** **Years:** 2008, 2009 **Models:** Astra, Aura, Aveo, Aveo5, Cobalt G3, G5 **Engines:** 1.6L VIN 6, 1.6L VIN E, 1.8L VIN 1, 2.0L VIN P, 2.0L VIN X, 2.2L VIN H, 2.2L VIN F, 2.4L VIN 5, 2.4L VIN B **Transmissions:** All	**Exhaust Camshaft Position (CMP) Actuator Solenoid Control Circuit High Voltage (Bank 1)** DTC P0606 is not set. The ignition is ON. The ignition voltage is between 10-16 volts. The ECM detects a short to voltage in the CMP actuator solenoid circuits for greater than 1 second or a cumulative of 5 seconds when the solenoid is commanded ON. **Possible Causes:** • Ignition circuit for a short to ground or an open/high resistance • Control circuit for a short to voltage or an open/high resistance • Control circuit for a short to ground • CMP actuator solenoid • Faulty ECM
DTC: P2091 **1T CCM, MIL: Yes** **Years:** 2008, 2009, 2010 **Models:** Acadia, Allure, Aura, Camaro, CTS, CTS-V, Enclave, LaCrosse, Outlook, Traverse **Engines:** 3.6L VIN 7, 3.6L VIN D, 3.6L VIN V **Transmissions:** All	**Exhaust Camshaft Position (CMP) Actuator Solenoid Control Circuit High Voltage (Bank 1)** The ECM detects a short to voltage in the CMP actuator solenoid circuits for greater than 1 seconds or a cumulative of 10 seconds, when the solenoid is commanded OFF. **Possible Causes:** • Ignition circuit for a short to ground or an open/high resistance • Control circuit for a short to voltage or an open/high resistance • Control circuit for a short to ground • CMP actuator solenoid • Faulty ECM

DTC	Trouble Code Title, Conditions & Possible Causes
DTC: P2092 **1T CCM, MIL: Yes** **Years:** 2008, 2009, 2010 **Models:** Acadia, Allure, Aura, Camaro, CTS, CTS-V, Enclave, LaCrosse, Outlook, Traverse **Engines:** 3.6L VIN 7, 3.6L VIN D, 3.6L VIN V **Transmissions:** All	**Intake Camshaft Position (CMP) Actuator Solenoid Control Circuit Low Voltage Bank (Bank 2)** The ECM detects a short to ground in the CMP actuator solenoid circuits for greater than 1 seconds or a cumulative of 10 seconds, when the solenoid is commanded OFF. **Possible Causes:** • Ignition circuit for a short to ground or an open/high resistance • Control circuit for a short to voltage or an open/high resistance • Control circuit for a short to ground • CMP actuator solenoid • Faulty ECM
DTC: P2093 **1T CCM, MIL: Yes** **Years:** 2008, 2009, 2010 **Models:** Acadia, Allure, Aura, Camaro, CTS, CTS-V, Enclave, LaCrosse, Outlook, Traverse **Engines:** 3.6L VIN 7, 3.6L VIN D, 3.6L VIN V **Transmissions:** All	**Intake Camshaft Position (CMP) Actuator Solenoid Control Circuit High Voltage (Bank 2)** The ECM detects a short to ground in the CMP actuator solenoid circuits for greater than 1 seconds or a cumulative of 10 seconds, when the solenoid is commanded OFF. **Possible Causes:** • Ignition circuit for a short to ground or an open/high resistance • Control circuit for a short to voltage or an open/high resistance • Control circuit for a short to ground • CMP actuator solenoid • Faulty ECM
DTC: P2094 **1T CCM, MIL: Yes** **Years:** 2008, 2009, 2010 **Models:** Acadia, Allure, Aura, Camaro, CTS, CTS-V, Enclave, LaCrosse, Outlook, Traverse **Engines:** 3.6L VIN 7, 3.6L VIN D, 3.6L VIN V **Transmissions:** All	**Exhaust Camshaft Position (CMP) Actuator Solenoid Control Circuit Low Voltage (Bank 2)** The ECM detects a short to ground in the CMP actuator solenoid circuits for greater than 1 seconds or a cumulative of 10 seconds, when the solenoid is commanded OFF. **Possible Causes:** • Ignition circuit for a short to ground or an open/high resistance • Control circuit for a short to voltage or an open/high resistance • Control circuit for a short to ground • CMP actuator solenoid • Faulty ECM
DTC: P2095 **1T CCM, MIL: Yes** **Years:** 2008, 2009, 2010 **Models:** Acadia, Allure, Aura, Camaro, CTS, CTS-V, Enclave, LaCrosse, Outlook, Traverse **Engines:** 3.6L VIN 7, 3.6L VIN D, 3.6L VIN V **Transmissions:** All	**Exhaust Camshaft Position (CMP) Actuator Solenoid Control Circuit High Voltage (Bank 2)** The ECM detects a short to ground in the CMP actuator solenoid circuits for greater than 1 seconds or a cumulative of 10 seconds, when the solenoid is commanded OFF. **Possible Causes:** • Ignition circuit for a short to ground or an open/high resistance • Control circuit for a short to voltage or an open/high resistance • Control circuit for a short to ground • CMP actuator solenoid • Faulty ECM
DTC: P2096 **1T CCM, MIL: Yes** **Years:** 2008, 2009, 2010 **Models:** Acadia, Allure, Aura, Camaro, CTS, CTS-V, Enclave, LaCrosse, Outlook, Traverse **Engines:** 3.6L VIN 7, 3.6L VIN D, 3.6L VIN V **Transmissions:** All	**Post Catalyst Fuel Trim System Low Limit (Bank 1)** The lean correction limit for a condition causing a rich air/fuel ratio has been exceeded for greater than 4 seconds or for a cumulative of 30 seconds. **Possible Causes:** • Malfunctioning fuel injectors • High fuel system pressure • Fuel that is contaminated • Fuel saturation of the evaporative emissions (EVAP) canister • Stuck open or leaking EVAP purge valve • Restricted exhaust • Incorrect PCV system operation

DTC	Trouble Code Title, Conditions & Possible Causes
DTC: P2096 **2T CCM, MIL: Yes** **Years:** 2008, 2009 **Models:** Astra, Aura, Aveo, Aveo5, Cobalt G3, G5 **Engines:** 1.6L VIN 6, 1.6L VIN E, 1.8L VIN 1, 2.0L VIN P, 2.0L VIN X, 2.2L VIN H, 2.2L VIN F, 2.4L VIN 5, 2.4L VIN B **Transmissions:** All	**Post Catalyst Fuel Trim System Low Limit** DTCs P000A, P000B, P0010, P0011, P0013, P0014, P0016, P0017, P0030, P0031, P0032, P0036, P0037, P0038, P0068, P0101, P0102, P0103, P0116, P0117, P0118, P0119, P0121, P0122, P0123, P0130, P0131, P0132, P0133, P0137, P0138, P0139, P0140, P0141, P0171, P0172, P0201, P0202, P0203, P0204, P0221, P0222, P0223, P0261, P0262, P0264, P0265, P0267, P0268, P0270, P0271, P0300, P0301, P0302, P0303, P0304, P0313, P0335, P0336, P0340, P0341, P0365, P0366, P0420, P0443, P0458, P0459, P1101, P2088, P2089, P2090, P2091, P2100, P2101, P2176, P2270, P2271, P2297, P2300, P2301, P2303, P2304, P2306, P2307, P2309, P2310, P2A00, P2A01 are not set. The ignition is ON. The EVAP system is not purging. The post catalyst fuel trim is enabled. These DTCs run continuously when the above conditions have been met. The long term FT has reached its limit while the HO2S voltage is still trying to move the adjustment further in the same direction. **Possible Causes:** • Malfunctioning fuel injectors • Low fuel system pressure • Fuel that is contaminated • Missing, loose, or leaking exhaust components from the HO2S forward • Vacuum leaks • Ethanol concentration greater than 15 percent • Incorrect PCV system operation
DTC: P2096 **1T CCM, MIL: Yes** **Years:** 2008, 2009, 2010 **Models:** Acadia, Allure, Aura, Camaro, CTS, CTS-V, Enclave, LaCrosse, Outlook, Traverse **Engines:** 3.6L VIN 7, 3.6L VIN D, 3.6L VIN V **Transmissions:** All	**Post Catalyst Fuel Trim System Low Limit (Bank 1)** The lean correction limit for a condition causing a rich air/fuel ratio has been exceeded for greater than 4 seconds or for a cumulative of 30 seconds. **Possible Causes:** • Rich fuel injectors • High fuel system pressure • Fuel that is contaminated • Fuel saturation of the evaporative emissions (EVAP) canister • Stuck open or leaking EVAP purge valve • Restricted exhaust • Incorrect PCV system operation
DTC: P2097 **1T CCM, MIL: Yes** **Years:** 2008, 2009, 2010 **Models:** Acadia, Allure, Aura, Camaro, CTS, CTS-V, Enclave, LaCrosse, Outlook, Traverse **Engines:** 3.6L VIN 7, 3.6L VIN D, 3.6L VIN V **Transmissions:** All	**Post Catalyst Fuel Trim System High Limit (Bank 1)** The rich correction limit for a condition causing a lean air/fuel ratio has been exceeded for greater than 4 seconds or for a cumulative of 30 seconds. **Possible Causes:** • Malfunctioning fuel injectors • High fuel system pressure • Fuel that is contaminated • Fuel saturation of the evaporative emissions (EVAP) canister • Stuck open or leaking EVAP purge valve • Restricted exhaust • Incorrect PCV system operation
DTC: P2098 **1T CCM, MIL: Yes** **Years:** 2008, 2009, 2010 **Models:** Acadia, Allure, Aura, Camaro, CTS, CTS-V, Enclave, LaCrosse, Outlook, Traverse **Engines:** 3.6L VIN 7, 3.6L VIN D, 3.6L VIN V **Transmissions:** All	**Post Catalyst Fuel Trim System Low Limit (Bank 2)** The lean correction limit for a condition causing a rich air/fuel ratio has been exceeded for greater than 4 seconds or for a cumulative of 30 seconds. **Possible Causes:** • Malfunctioning fuel injectors • Low fuel system pressure • Fuel that is contaminated • Missing, loose, or leaking exhaust components from the HO2S forward • Vacuum leaks • Ethanol concentration greater than 15 percent • Incorrect PCV system operation
DTC: P2098 **1T CCM, MIL: Yes** **Years:** 2008, 2009, 2010 **Models:** Acadia, Allure, Aura, Camaro, CTS, CTS-V, Enclave, LaCrosse, Outlook, Traverse **Engines:** 3.6L VIN 7, 3.6L VIN D, 3.6L VIN V **Transmissions:** All	**Post Catalyst Fuel Trim System Low Limit (Bank 2)** The lean correction limit for a condition causing a rich air/fuel ratio has been exceeded for greater than 4 seconds or for a cumulative of 30 seconds. **Possible Causes:** • Rich fuel injectors • High fuel system pressure • Fuel that is contaminated • Fuel saturation of the evaporative emissions (EVAP) canister • Stuck open or leaking EVAP purge valve • Restricted exhaust • Incorrect PCV system operation

DTC	Trouble Code Title, Conditions & Possible Causes
DTC: P2099 **1T CCM, MIL: Yes** **Years:** 2008, 2009, 2010 **Models:** Acadia, Allure, Aura, Camaro, CTS, CTS-V, Enclave, LaCrosse, Outlook, Traverse **Engines:** 3.6L VIN 7, 3.6L VIN D, 3.6L VIN V **Transmissions:** All	**Post Catalyst Fuel Trim System High Limit (Bank 2)** The rich correction limit for a condition causing a lean air/fuel ratio has been exceeded for greater than 4 seconds or for a cumulative of 30 seconds. **Possible Causes:** • Exhaust system leaks • Engine vacuum leaks • Low fuel system pressure • Fuel that is contaminated • Malfunctioning fuel injectors
DTC: P2100 **1T CCM, MIL: Yes** **Years:** 2008, 2009 **Models:** Acadia, Allure, Aura, Astra, Aura, Aveo, Aveo5, Cobalt G3, G5, Enclave, LaCrosse, Outlook, Traverse **Engines:** 1.6L VIN 6, 1.6L VIN E, 1.8L VIN 1, 2.0L VIN P, 2.0L VIN X, 2.2L VIN H, 2.2L VIN F, 2.4L VIN 5, 2.4L VIN B, 3.6L VIN 7, 3.6L VIN D, 3.6L VIN V **Transmissions:** All	**Throttle Actuator Control (TAC) Motor Control Circuit** The ECM is active. The ECM detects the output circuit for the TAC motor is open, shorted to ground, or shorted to a voltage. The condition exists, then a 5 second delay for MIL ON. **Possible Causes:** • Throttle blade that is not in the rest position • Throttle valve that is binding open or closed • Throttle valve that opens or closes without spring pressure • Throttle body malfunction • ECM has failed
DTC: P2100 **1T CCM, MIL: Yes** **Years:** 2008, 2009, 2010 **Models:** Acadia, Allure, Aura, Camaro, CTS, CTS-V, Enclave, LaCrosse, Outlook, Traverse **Engines:** 3.6L VIN 7, 3.6L VIN D, 3.6L VIN V **Transmissions:** All	**Throttle Actuator Control (TAC) Motor Control Circuit** The ECM is active. The ECM detects the output circuit for the TAC motor is open, shorted to ground, or shorted to a voltage. The condition exists, then a 5 second delay for MIL ON. **Possible Causes:** • Throttle blade that is not in the rest position • Throttle valve that is binding open or closed • Throttle valve that opens or closes without spring pressure • Throttle body malfunction • ECM has failed
DTC: P2101 **1T CCM, MIL: Yes** **Years:** 2008, 2009 **Models:** Acadia, Allure, Aura, Astra, Aura, Aveo, Aveo5, Cobalt G3, G5, Enclave, LaCrosse, Outlook, Traverse **Engines:** 1.6L VIN 6, 1.6L VIN E, 1.8L VIN 1, 2.0L VIN P, 2.0L VIN X, 2.2L VIN H, 2.2L VIN F, 2.4L VIN 5, 2.4L VIN B, 3.6L VIN 7, 3.6L VIN D, 3.6L VIN V **Transmissions:** All	**Control Module Throttle Actuator Position Performance** The ECM detects a 4-50 percent difference between the commanded and the actual throttle plate position, dependant upon the rate of commanded throttle movement. The condition exists, then a 5 second delay for MIL ON. **Possible Causes:** • Throttle blade that is not in the rest position • Throttle valve that is binding open or closed • Throttle valve that opens or closes without spring pressure • Throttle body malfunction • ECM has failed
DTC: P2101 **1T CCM, MIL: Yes** **Years:** 2008, 2009 **Models:** Acadia, Allure, Aura, Astra, Aura, Aveo, Aveo5, Cobalt G3, G5, Enclave, LaCrosse, Outlook, Traverse **Engines:** 1.6L VIN 6, 1.6L VIN E, 1.8L VIN 1, 2.0L VIN P, 2.0L VIN X, 2.2L VIN H, 2.2L VIN F, 2.4L VIN 5, 2.4L VIN B, 3.6L VIN 7, 3.6L VIN D, 3.6L VIN V **Transmissions:** All	**Throttle Closed Position Performance** The ECM determines that the throttle valve did not return to the rest position within 1 second. The condition exists, and then a 5 second delay for MIL ON. **Possible Causes:** • Throttle blade that is not in the rest position • Throttle valve that is binding open or closed • Throttle valve that opens or closes without spring pressure • Throttle body malfunction • ECM has failed

DTC	Trouble Code Title, Conditions & Possible Causes
DTC: P2101 **1T CCM, MIL: Yes** **Years:** 2008, 2009, 2010 **Models:** Acadia, Allure, Aura, Camaro, CTS, CTS-V, Enclave, LaCrosse, Outlook, Traverse **Engines:** 3.6L VIN 7, 3.6L VIN D, 3.6L VIN V **Transmissions:** All	**Control Module Throttle Actuator Position Performance** The ECM detects a 4-50 percent difference between the commanded and the actual throttle plate position, dependant upon the rate of commanded throttle movement. The condition exists, then a 5 second delay for MIL ON. **Possible Causes:** • Throttle blade that is not in the rest position • Throttle valve that is binding open or closed • Throttle valve that opens or closes without spring pressure • Throttle body malfunction • ECM has failed
DTC: P2101 **1T CCM, MIL: Yes** **Years:** 2008, 2009 **Models:** Allure, Aura, Canyon, Colorado, LaCrosse **Engines:** 2.9L VIN 9, 3.5L VIN N, 3.8L VIN 2, 5.3L VIN C, 5.3L VIN L **Transmissions:** All	**Throttle Actuator Position Performance** The ignition is ON. The ignition voltage is more than 8 volts. The system is not in the Battery Save mode. The engine is running. DTC P0068 is not set. DTC P1516 and P2101 run continuously when the above conditions are met. The indicated throttle position does not match the predicted throttle position for more than 0.3 second. **Possible Causes:** • TAC motor control circuit for a short to voltage • TAC motor control circuit for a short to voltage • TAC motor control circuit for a short to ground • TAC motor control circuit for a short to ground • Throttle body has failed • ECM has failed
DTC: P2105 **1T CCM, MIL: Yes** **Years:** 2008, 2009, 2010 **Models:** Acadia, Allure, Aura, Camaro, CTS, CTS-V, Enclave, LaCrosse, Outlook, Traverse **Engines:** 3.6L VIN 7, 3.6L VIN D, 3.6L VIN V **Transmissions:** All	**Throttle Actuator Control (TAC) System - Forced Engine Shutdown** The ECM detects an incorrect voltage level at the ignition voltage supply circuits. Or the ECM detects an internal communication error. The condition exists, and then a 5 second delay for MIL ON. **This DTC will only set if the fuse is open and the circuits are not grounded. The ignition voltage circuits must be tested thoroughly for an intermittent short to ground.** **Possible Causes:** • Open ignition suppl fuse • Ignition voltage supply open or high resistance • ECM has failed
DTC: P2105 **1T CCM, MIL: Yes** **Years:** 2008, 2009, 2010 **Models:** Acadia, Allure, Aura, Camaro, CTS, CTS-V, Enclave, LaCrosse, Outlook, Traverse **Engines:** 3.6L VIN 7, 3.6L VIN D, 3.6L VIN V **Transmissions:** All	**Throttle Actuator Control (TAC) System - Forced Engine Shutdown** The ECM detects an incorrect voltage level at the ignition voltage supply circuits. Or the ECM detects an internal communication error. The condition exists, and then a 5 second delay for MIL ON. **This DTC will only set if the fuse is open and the circuits are not grounded. The ignition voltage circuits must be tested thoroughly for an intermittent short to ground.** **Possible Causes:** • Open ignition suppl fuse • Ignition voltage supply open or high resistance • ECM has failed
DTC: P2108 **2T CCM, MIL: Yes** **Years:** 2008, 2009 **Models:** Astra, Aura, Aveo, Aveo5, Cobalt G3, G5 **Engines:** 1.6L VIN 6, 1.6L VIN E, 1.8L VIN 1, 2.0L VIN P, 2.0L VIN X, 2.2L VIN H, 2.2L VIN F, 2.4L VIN 5, 2.4L VIN B **Transmissions:** All	**Throttle Actuator Control (TAC) Module Performance** The ignition is ON. DTCs P0121, P0122, P0123, P0221, P0222, P0223, P2176 are not set. DTC P2176 run continuously when the above conditions are met. The indicated throttle position does not match the predicted throttle position for more than 0.3 second. **Possible Causes:** • Throttle blade that is not in the rest position • Throttle valve that is binding open or closed • Throttle valve that opens or closes without spring pressure • Throttle body malfuntion • ECM has failed
DTC: P2108 **1T CCM, MIL: Yes** **Years:** 2008, 2009, 2010 **Models:** Avalanche, Camaro, Canyon, Escalade/EXT/ESV, Suburban, Tahoe, Yukon **Engines:** 4.8L VIN C, 5.3L VIN 0, 5.3L VIN 3, 5.3L VIN J, 5.3L VIN L, 6.0L VIN K, 6.0L VIN Y, 6.2L VIN J, 6.2L VIN W, 6.2L VIN 8 **Transmissions:** All	**Throttle Actuator Control Module Internal Data Test Failed** DTCP1518 not set, engine cranking or running, system voltage over 6.0v, and the TAC determined that its internal data test did not pass, condition met for 1 second. The TAC module contains data that is essential for proper TAC system operation. The TAC module continuously tests the integrity of this data. When the TAC module is unable to write or read data to and from random access memory, or the TAC module was unable to correctly read data from the flash memory or internal TAC processor fault is detected, it sets P2108. **Possible Causes:** • TAC module is damaged or it has failed

DTC	Trouble Code Title, Conditions & Possible Causes
DTC: P2119 **2T CCM, MIL: Yes** **Years:** 2008, 2009 **Models:** Astra, Aura, Aveo, Aveo5, Cobalt G3, G5 **Engines:** 1.6L VIN 6, 1.6L VIN E, 1.8L VIN 1, 2.0L VIN P, 2.0L VIN X, 2.2L VIN H, 2.2L VIN F, 2.4L VIN 5, 2.4L VIN B **Transmissions:** All	**Throttle Closed Position Performance** The ignition is ON. DTCs P2101, P2119 and P2176 run continuously when the above conditions are met. The ECM determines that the throttle blade did not return to the rest position within 720 milliseconds. **Possible Causes:** • Throttle blade that is not in the rest position • Throttle valve that is binding open or closed • Throttle valve that opens or closes without spring pressure • Throttle body malfuntion • ECM has failed
DTC: P2119 **1T CCM, MIL: Yes** **Years:** 2008, 2009, 2010 **Models:** Acadia, Allure, Aura, Camaro, CTS, CTS-V, Enclave, LaCrosse, Outlook, Traverse **Engines:** 3.6L VIN 7, 3.6L VIN D, 3.6L VIN V **Transmissions:** All	**Throttle Closed Position Performance** The ECM determines that the throttle valve did not return to the rest position within 1 second. The condition exists, and then a 5 second delay for MIL ON. **Possible Causes:** • Throttle blade that is not in the rest position • Throttle valve that is binding open or closed • Throttle valve that opens or closes without spring pressure • Throttle body malfuntion • ECM has failed
DTC: P2119 **1T CCM, MIL: Yes** **Years:** 2008, 2009 **Models:** Allure, Aura, Canyon, Colorado, LaCrosse **Engines:** 2.9L VIN 9, 3.5L VIN N, 3.8L VIN 2, 5.3L VIN C, 5.3L VIN L **Transmissions:** All	**Throttle Closed Position Performance** The ignition is ON. The ignition voltage is more than 8 volts. The system is in the Battery Save mode. DTC P2119 runs continuously when the above conditions are met. The ECM determines that the throttle blade did not return to the rest position within 720 milliseconds. **Possible Causes:** • TAC motor control circuit for a short to voltage • TAC motor control circuit for a short to voltage • TAC motor control circuit for a short to ground • TAC motor control circuit for a short to ground • Throttle body has failed • ECM has failed
DTC: P2120 **2T CCM, MIL: Yes** **Years:** 2008, 2009, 2010 **Models:**, Acadia, Allure, Astra, Aura, Avalanche, Escalade/EXT/ESV, Suburban, Tahoe, Yukon, Escalade/EXT/ESV, Suburban, Tahoe, Yukon Aveo, Aveo5, Camaro, Cobalt, Cobalt-GS, Colorado,Canyon, Corvette, CTS, CTS-V, CTS, CTS-V-V, DTS, Escalade/EXT/ESV, G.3, G5,Enclave, LaCrosse, Outlook, Suburban, Tahoe Traverse, Yukon **Engines:** All **Transmissions:** All	**Accelerator Pedal Position Sensor 1 Signal Performance** DTC P0601, P0602, P0606, P1518 and P2108 not set; engine cranking or running, system voltage more than 5.23v, and the ECM detected the APP Sensor 1 signal circuit voltage was less than 0.24v or more than 4.49v, or that the APP VREF (5v) circuit was less than 4.54v or more than 5.21v. The ECM provides the APP sensor with a 5v reference circuit and a low reference circuit. The APP sensor provides the control module a signal voltage proportional to pedal movement. The APP sensor 1 signal voltage is low at rest and increases as the pedal is depressed. When the control module detects that the APP sensor 1 signal or APP sensor 5-volt reference voltage is outside the predetermined range, it sets DTC P2120. **Possible Causes:** • APP sensor connector is damaged, open or shorted • APP1 sensor signal circuit is open or shorted to ground • APP1 sensor signal circuit is shorted to APP sensor 2 circuit • APP1 sensor signal circuit is open or shorted to VREF (5v) • APP sensor is damaged or it has failed • TAC module is damaged or it has failed
DTC: P2122 **2T CCM, MIL: Yes** **Years:** 2008, 2009, 2010 **Models:**, Acadia, Allure, Astra, Aura, Avalanche, Escalade/EXT/ESV, Suburban, Tahoe, Yukon, Escalade/EXT/ESV, Suburban, Tahoe, Yukon Aveo, Aveo5, Camaro, Cobalt, Cobalt-GS, Colorado,Canyon, Corvette, CTS, CTS-V, CTS, CTS-V-V, DTS, Escalade/EXT/ESV, G.3, G5,Enclave, LaCrosse, Outlook, Suburban, Tahoe Traverse, Yukon **Engines:** All **Transmissions:** All	**Accelerator Pedal Position (APP) Sensor 1 Circuit Low Voltage** The ignition is ON or the engine is operating. The ignition voltage is greater than 7 volts. The DTCs run continuously once the above conditions are met for greater than 200 ms. The APP sensor 1 voltage is less than 0.74 volt, then a 5 second delay for MIL ON. **Possible Causes:** • Low reference circuit of the APP sensor for a short to voltage, or an open/high resistance. • 5-volt reference circuit for a short to ground or open/high resistance. • Faulty APP Sensor • ECM has failed

DTC	Trouble Code Title, Conditions & Possible Causes
DTC: P2123 **2T CCM, MIL: Yes** **Years:** 2008, 2009, 2010 **Models:**, Acadia, Allure, Astra, Aura, Avalanche, Escalade/EXT/ESV, Suburban, Tahoe, Yukon, Escalade/EXT/ESV, Suburban, Tahoe, Yukon Aveo, Aveo5, Camaro, Cobalt, Cobalt-GS, Colorado,Canyon, Corvette, CTS, CTS-V, CTS, CTS-V-V, DTS, Escalade/EXT/ESV, G.3, G5,Enclave, LaCrosse, Outlook, Suburban, Tahoe Traverse, Yukon **Engines:** All **Transmissions:** All	**Accelerator Pedal Position (APP) Sensor 1 Circuit High Voltage** The ignition is ON or the engine is operating. The ignition voltage is greater than 7 volts. The DTCs run continuously once the above conditions are met for greater than 200 ms. The APP sensor 1 voltage is greater than 4.82 volts, then a 5 second delay for MIL ON. **Possible Causes:** • Low reference circuit of the APP sensor for a short to voltage, or an open/high resistance. • 5-volt reference circuit for a short to ground or open/high resistance. • Faulty APP Sensor • ECM has failed
DTC: P2125 **2T CCM, MIL: Yes** **Years:** 2008, 2009, 2010 **Models:**, Acadia, Allure, Astra, Aura, Avalanche, Escalade/EXT/ESV, Suburban, Tahoe, Yukon, Escalade/EXT/ESV, Suburban, Tahoe, Yukon Aveo, Aveo5, Camaro, Cobalt, Cobalt-GS, Colorado,Canyon, Corvette, CTS, CTS-V, CTS, CTS-V-V, DTS, Escalade/EXT/ESV, G.3, G5,Enclave, LaCrosse, Outlook, Suburban, Tahoe Traverse, Yukon **Engines:** All **Transmissions:** All	**Accelerator Pedal Position (APP) Sensor 2 Circuit Low Voltage** The ignition is ON or the engine is operating. The ignition voltage is greater than 7 volts. The DTCs run continuously once the above conditions are met for greater than 200 ms. The APP sensor 2 voltage is less than 0.63 volt, then a 5 second delay for MIL ON. **Possible Causes:** • Low reference circuit of the APP sensor for a short to voltage, or an open/high resistance. • 5-volt reference circuit for a short to ground or open/high resistance. • Faulty APP Sensor • ECM has failed
DTC: P2127 **2T CCM, MIL: Yes** **Years:** 2008, 2009, 2010 **Models:**, Acadia, Allure, Astra, Aura, Avalanche, Escalade/EXT/ESV, Suburban, Tahoe, Yukon, Escalade/EXT/ESV, Suburban, Tahoe, Yukon Aveo, Aveo5, Camaro, Cobalt, Cobalt-GS, Colorado,Canyon, Corvette, CTS, CTS-V, CTS, CTS-V-V, DTS, Escalade/EXT/ESV, G.3, G5,Enclave, LaCrosse, Outlook, Suburban, Tahoe Traverse, Yukon **Engines:** All **Transmissions:** All	**Accelerator Pedal Position (APP) Sensor 2 Circuit Low Voltage** The ignition is ON or the engine is operating. The ignition voltage is greater than 7 volts. The DTCs run continuously once the above conditions are met for greater than 200 ms. The APP sensor 2 voltage is less than 0.63 volt, then a 5 second delay for MIL ON. **Possible Causes:** • Low reference circuit of the APP sensor for a short to voltage, or an open/high resistance. • 5-volt reference circuit for a short to ground or open/high resistance. • Faulty APP Sensor • ECM has failed

DTC	Trouble Code Title, Conditions & Possible Causes
DTC: P2128 **2T CCM, MIL: Yes** **Years:** 2008, 2009, 2010 **Models:**, Acadia, Allure, Astra, Aura, Avalanche, Escalade/EXT/ESV, Suburban, Tahoe, Yukon, Escalade/EXT/ESV, Suburban, Tahoe, Yukon Aveo, Aveo5, Camaro, Cobalt, Cobalt-GS, Colorado,Canyon, Corvette, CTS, CTS-V, CTS, CTS-V-V, DTS, Escalade/EXT/ESV, G.3, G5,Enclave, LaCrosse, Outlook, Suburban, Tahoe Traverse, Yukon **Engines:** All **Transmissions:** All	**Accelerator Pedal Position (APP) Sensor 2 Circuit High Voltage** The ignition is ON or the engine is operating. The ignition voltage is greater than 7 volts. The DTCs run continuously once the above conditions are met for greater than 200 ms. The APP sensor 2 voltage is greater than 4.82 volts, then a 5 second delay for MIL ON. **Possible Causes:** • Low reference circuit of the APP sensor for a short to voltage, or an open/high resistance. • 5-volt reference circuit for a short to ground or open/high resistance. • Faulty APP Sensor • ECM has failed
DTC: P2129 **1T CCM, MIL: Yes** **Years:** 2008, 2009 **Models:** Acadia, Allure, Aura, Astra, Aura, Aveo, Aveo5, Cobalt G3, G5, Enclave, LaCrosse, Outlook, Traverse **Engines:** 1.6L VIN 6, 1.6L VIN E, 1.8L VIN 1, 2.0L VIN P, 2.0L VIN X, 2.2L VIN H, 2.2L VIN F, 2.4L VIN 5, 2.4L VIN B, 3.6L VIN 7, 3.6L VIN D, 3.6L VIN V **Transmissions:** All	**Barometric Pressure (BARO) Sensor Circuit High Voltage** The ignition is ON, or the engine is running. The ignition voltage is greater than 9 volts. The ECM detects that the BARO sensor voltage is greater than 4.87 volts for 1 second or for a cumulative of 10 seconds. **Possible Causes:** • Moisture in the vent inlet • Debris in the vent inlet
DTC: P2135 **1T CCM, MIL: Yes** **Years:** 2008, 2009 **Models:** Corvette, CTS, CTS-V, DTS **Engines:** 4.6L VIN Y, 6.2L VIN W, 6.2L VIN P, 6.2L VIN R, 7.0L VIN E **Transmissions:** All	**Throttle Position (TP) Sensor 1-2 Correlation** The system voltage is more than 5.23 volts. The ignition is in the Unlock/Accessory or Run position. DTC P0120, P0220, P0641, P0651 are not set. DTC P2135 runs continuously when the above conditions are met. The difference between the TP sensor 1 and TP sensor 2 exceeds a predetermined value for more than 2 seconds. **Possible Causes:** • TP sensor low reference circuit for an open/high resistance • TP sensor 5-volt reference circuit for a short to ground or an open/high resistance • TP sensor 5-volt reference circuit for a short to voltage • TP sensor signal circuit terminal F for a short to ground • TP sensor 1 signal circuit for a short to ground or an open/high resistance • TP sensor 2 signal circuit for a short to voltage • TP sensor 2 signal circuit for an open/high resistance. • Throttle body has failed • ECM has failed
DTC: P2135 **1T CCM, MIL: Yes** **Years:** 2008, 2009 **Models:** Acadia, Allure, Aura, Astra, Aura, Aveo, Aveo5, Cobalt G3, G5, Enclave, LaCrosse, Outlook, Traverse **Engines:** 1.6L VIN 6, 1.6L VIN E, 1.8L VIN 1, 2.0L VIN P, 2.0L VIN X, 2.2L VIN H, 2.2L VIN F, 2.4L VIN 5, 2.4L VIN B, 3.6L VIN 7, 3.6L VIN D, 3.6L VIN V **Transmissions:** All	**Throttle Position Sensor 1-2 Correlation Error** DTC P1518 and P2108 not set, key in crank or run mode, system voltage more than 5.23v, and the ECM detected the TP Sensor 2 signal disagreed with the TP Sensor 1 signal by more than 7.5% for one second. The TP sensors are used to determine the throttle plate angle for various engine management systems. The TP sensor signals are both low at closed throttle and increase as the throttle opens. When the ECM detects that TP sensor 1 and TP sensor 2 signals disagree or signal voltages are too far apart, this code is set. **Possible Causes:** • TP1 sensor signal circuit shorted to TP sensor signal 2 circuit • TP1 sensor signal circuit is shorted to the low reference circuit • TP2 sensor signal circuit is shorted to the low reference circuit • Throttle body assembly is damaged or it has failed

DTC	Trouble Code Title, Conditions & Possible Causes
DTC: P2138 **1T CCM, MIL: Yes** **Years:** 2008, 2009 **Models:** Acadia, Allure, Aura, Astra, Aura, Aveo, Aveo5, Cobalt G3, G5, Enclave, LaCrosse, Outlook, Traverse **Engines:** 1.6L VIN 6, 1.6L VIN E, 1.8L VIN 1, 2.0L VIN P, 2.0L VIN X, 2.2L VIN H, 2.2L VIN F, 2.4L VIN 5, 2.4L VIN B, 3.6L VIN 7, 3.6L VIN D, 3.6L VIN V **Transmissions:** All	**Accelerator Pedal Position (APP) Sensor 1-2 Correlation** The ignition is ON or the engine is operating. The ignition voltage is greater than 7 volts. The DTCs run continuously once the above conditions are met for greater than 200 ms. The ECM detects that the voltage difference between APP sensor 1 and the calculated idle range is greater than 0.25 volts, with a released pedal. The ECM detects that the voltage difference between APP sensor 2 and the calculated idle range is greater than 0.31 volts, with a released pedal. The ECM detects that the voltage difference between APP sensor 1 and 2 is greater than 0.31 volts with a partially pressed pedal. The ECM detects that the voltage difference between APP sensor 1 and 2 is greater than 1.70 volts with a fully pressed pedal. Any of the above conditions exist, then a 5 second delay for MIL ON. **Possible Causes:** • Low reference circuit of the APP sensor for a short to voltage, or an open/high resistance. • 5-volt reference circuit for a short to ground or open/high resistance. • Faulty APP Sensor • ECM has failed
DTC: P2146 **1T CCM, MIL: Yes** **Years:** 2008, 2009, 2010 **Models:** Acadia, Allure, Aura, Camaro, CTS, CTS-V, Enclave, LaCrosse, Outlook, Traverse **Engines:** 3.6L VIN 7, 3.6L VIN D, 3.6L VIN V **Transmissions:** All	**Injector Positive Voltage Control Circuit (Group 1)** The ECM detects the injector high voltage control circuit is shorted to ground or shorted to a voltage for greater than 4 seconds or for a cumulative of 30 seconds. **Possible Causes:** • High voltage control circuit shorted to voltage • High voltage control circuit short to ground or an open/high resistance • Low voltage control circuit shorted to voltage • Low voltage control circuit short to ground or an open/high resistance • Faulty fuel injector • ECM has failed.
DTC: P2146 **1T CCM, MIL: Yes** **Years:** 2008, 2009, 2010 **Models:** Acadia, Allure, Aura, Camaro, CTS, CTS-V, Enclave, LaCrosse, Outlook, Traverse **Engines:** 3.6L VIN 7, 3.6L VIN D, 3.6L VIN V **Transmissions:** All	**Injector Positive Voltage Control Circuit (Group 1)** The ECM detects the injector high voltage control circuit is shorted to ground or shorted to a voltage for greater than 4 seconds or for a cumulative of 30 seconds. **Possible Causes:** • High voltage control circuit shorted to voltage • High voltage control circuit short to ground or an open/high resistance • Low voltage control circuit shorted to voltage • Low voltage control circuit short to ground or an open/high resistance • Faulty fuel injector • ECM has failed.
DTC: P2149 **1T CCM, MIL: Yes** **Years:** 2008, 2009, 2010 **Models:** Acadia, Allure, Aura, Camaro, CTS, CTS-V, Enclave, LaCrosse, Outlook, Traverse **Engines:** 3.6L VIN 7, 3.6L VIN D, 3.6L VIN V **Transmissions:** All	**Injector Positive Voltage Control Circuit (Group 2)** The ECM detects the injector high voltage control circuit is shorted to ground or shorted to a voltage for greater than 4 seconds or for a cumulative of 30 seconds. **Possible Causes:** • High voltage control circuit shorted to voltage • High voltage control circuit short to ground or an open/high resistance • Low voltage control circuit shorted to voltage • Low voltage control circuit short to ground or an open/high resistance • Faulty fuel injector • ECM has failed.
DTC: P2149 **1T CCM, MIL: Yes** **Years:** 2008, 2009, 2010 **Models:** Acadia, Allure, Aura, Camaro, CTS, CTS-V, Enclave, LaCrosse, Outlook, Traverse **Engines:** 3.6L VIN 7, 3.6L VIN D, 3.6L VIN V **Transmissions:** All	**Injector Positive Voltage Control Circuit (Group 2)** The ECM detects the injector high voltage control circuit is shorted to ground or shorted to a voltage for greater than 4 seconds or for a cumulative of 30 seconds. **Possible Causes:** • High voltage control circuit shorted to voltage • High voltage control circuit short to ground or an open/high resistance • Low voltage control circuit shorted to voltage • Low voltage control circuit short to ground or an open/high resistance • Faulty fuel injector • ECM has failed.

DTC	Trouble Code Title, Conditions & Possible Causes
DTC: P2152 **1T CCM, MIL: Yes** **Years:** 2008, 2009, 2010 **Models:** Acadia, Allure, Aura, Camaro, CTS, CTS-V, Enclave, LaCrosse, Outlook, Traverse **Engines:** 3.6L VIN 7, 3.6L VIN D, 3.6L VIN V **Transmissions:** All	**Injector Positive Voltage Control Circuit (Group 3)** The ECM detects the injector high voltage control circuit is shorted to ground or shorted to a voltage for greater than 4 seconds or for a cumulative of 30 seconds. **Possible Causes:** • High voltage control circuit shorted to voltage • High voltage control circuit short to ground or an open/high resistance • Low voltage control circuit shorted to voltage • Low voltage control circuit short to ground or an open/high resistance • Faulty fuel injector • ECM has failed.
DTC: P2152 **1T CCM, MIL: Yes** **Years:** 2008, 2009, 2010 **Models:** Acadia, Allure, Aura, Camaro, CTS, CTS-V, Enclave, LaCrosse, Outlook, Traverse **Engines:** 3.6L VIN 7, 3.6L VIN D, 3.6L VIN V **Transmissions:** All	**Injector Positive Voltage Control Circuit (Group 3)** The ECM detects the injector high voltage control circuit is shorted to ground or shorted to a voltage for greater than 4 seconds or for a cumulative of 30 seconds. **Possible Causes:** • High voltage control circuit shorted to voltage • High voltage control circuit short to ground or an open/high resistance • Low voltage control circuit shorted to voltage • Low voltage control circuit short to ground or an open/high resistance • Faulty fuel injector • ECM has failed.
DTC: P2155 **1T CCM, MIL: Yes** **Years:** 2008, 2009, 2010 **Models:** Acadia, Allure, Aura, Camaro, CTS, CTS-V, Enclave, LaCrosse, Outlook, Traverse **Engines:** 3.6L VIN 7, 3.6L VIN D, 3.6L VIN V **Transmissions:** All	**Injector Positive Voltage Control Circuit (Group 4)** The ECM detects the injector high voltage control circuit is shorted to ground or shorted to a voltage for greater than 4 seconds or for a cumulative of 30 seconds. **Possible Causes:** • High voltage control circuit shorted to voltage • High voltage control circuit short to ground or an open/high resistance • Low voltage control circuit shorted to voltage • Low voltage control circuit short to ground or an open/high resistance • Faulty fuel injector • ECM has failed.
DTC: P2155 **1T CCM, MIL: Yes** **Years:** 2008, 2009, 2010 **Models:** Acadia, Allure, Aura, Camaro, CTS, CTS-V, Enclave, LaCrosse, Outlook, Traverse **Engines:** 3.6L VIN 7, 3.6L VIN D, 3.6L VIN V **Transmissions:** All	**Injector Positive Voltage Control Circuit (Group 4)** The ECM detects the injector high voltage control circuit is shorted to ground or shorted to a voltage for greater than 4 seconds or for a cumulative of 30 seconds. **Possible Causes:** • High voltage control circuit shorted to voltage • High voltage control circuit short to ground or an open/high resistance • Low voltage control circuit shorted to voltage • Low voltage control circuit short to ground or an open/high resistance • Faulty fuel injector • ECM has failed.
DTC: P216A **1T CCM, MIL: Yes** **Years:** 2008, 2009, 2010 **Models:** Acadia, Allure, Aura, Camaro, CTS, CTS-V, Enclave, LaCrosse, Outlook, Traverse **Engines:** 3.6L VIN 7, 3.6L VIN D, 3.6L VIN V **Transmissions:** All	**Injector Positive Voltage Control Circuit (Group 5)** The ECM detects the injector high voltage control circuit is shorted to ground or shorted to a voltage for greater than 4 seconds or for a cumulative of 30 seconds. **Possible Causes:** • High voltage control circuit shorted to voltage • High voltage control circuit short to ground or an open/high resistance • Low voltage control circuit shorted to voltage • Low voltage control circuit short to ground or an open/high resistance • Faulty fuel injector • ECM has failed.
DTC: P216A **1T CCM, MIL: Yes** **Years:** 2008, 2009, 2010 **Models:** Acadia, Allure, Aura, Camaro, CTS, CTS-V, Enclave, LaCrosse, Outlook, Traverse **Engines:** 3.6L VIN 7, 3.6L VIN D, 3.6L VIN V **Transmissions:** All	**Injector Positive Voltage Control Circuit (Group 5)** The ECM detects the injector high voltage control circuit is shorted to ground or shorted to a voltage for greater than 4 seconds or for a cumulative of 30 seconds. **Possible Causes:** • High voltage control circuit shorted to voltage • High voltage control circuit short to ground or an open/high resistance • Low voltage control circuit shorted to voltage • Low voltage control circuit short to ground or an open/high resistance • Faulty fuel injector • ECM has failed.

DTC	Trouble Code Title, Conditions & Possible Causes
DTC: P216D **1T CCM, MIL: Yes** **Years:** 2008, 2009, 2010 **Models:** Acadia, Allure, Aura, Camaro, CTS, CTS-V, Enclave, LaCrosse, Outlook, Traverse **Engines:** 3.6L VIN 7, 3.6L VIN D, 3.6L VIN V **Transmissions:** All	**Injector Positive Voltage Control Circuit (Group 6)** The ECM detects the injector high voltage control circuit is shorted to ground or shorted to a voltage for greater than 4 seconds or for a cumulative of 30 seconds. **Possible Causes:** • High voltage control circuit shorted to voltage • High voltage control circuit short to ground or an open/high resistance • Low voltage control circuit shorted to voltage • Low voltage control circuit short to ground or an open/high resistance • Faulty fuel injector • ECM has failed.
DTC: P216D **1T CCM, MIL: Yes** **Years:** 2008, 2009, 2010 **Models:** Acadia, Allure, Aura, Camaro, CTS, CTS-V, Enclave, LaCrosse, Outlook, Traverse **Engines:** 3.6L VIN 7, 3.6L VIN D, 3.6L VIN V **Transmissions:** All	**Injector Positive Voltage Control Circuit (Group 6)** The ECM detects the injector high voltage control circuit is shorted to ground or shorted to a voltage for greater than 4 seconds or for a cumulative of 30 seconds. **Possible Causes:** • High voltage control circuit shorted to voltage • High voltage control circuit short to ground or an open/high resistance • Low voltage control circuit shorted to voltage • Low voltage control circuit short to ground or an open/high resistance • Faulty fuel injector • ECM has failed.
DTC: P2176 **1T CCM, MIL: Yes** **Years:** 2008, 2009 **Models:** Acadia, Allure, Aura, Astra, Aura, Aveo, Aveo5, Cobalt G3, G5, Enclave, LaCrosse, Outlook, Traverse **Engines:** 1.6L VIN 6, 1.6L VIN E, 1.8L VIN 1, 2.0L VIN P, 2.0L VIN X, 2.2L VIN H, 2.2L VIN F, 2.4L VIN 5, 2.4L VIN B, 3.6L VIN 7, 3.6L VIN D, 3.6L VIN V **Transmissions:** All	**Minimum Throttle Position Not Learned** The ECM detects that the TP sensor 1 voltage is not between 4.12-4.55 volts after the throttle learn procedure, with the throttle at rest. The ECM detects that the TP sensor 2 voltage is not between 0.34-0.99 volts after the throttle learn procedure, with the throttle at rest. The minimum throttle position is not learned after an ECM replacement. I f either condition exists, then a 5 second delay for MIL ON. **Possible Causes:** • Perform the throttle learn procedure • Throttle body has failed.
DTC: P2176 **1T CCM, MIL: Yes** **Years:** 2008, 2009, 2010 **Models:** Acadia, Allure, Aura, Camaro, CTS, CTS-V, Enclave, LaCrosse, Outlook, Traverse **Engines:** 3.6L VIN 7, 3.6L VIN D, 3.6L VIN V **Transmissions:** All	**Minimum Throttle Position Not Learned** The ECM detects that the TP sensor 1 voltage is not between 4.12-4.55 volts after the throttle learn procedure, with the throttle at rest. The ECM detects that the TP sensor 2 voltage is not between 0.34-0.99 volts after the throttle learn procedure, with the throttle at rest. The minimum throttle position is not learned after an ECM replacement. I f either condition exists, then a 5 second delay for MIL ON. **Possible Causes:** • Perform the throttle learn procedure • Throttle body has failed.
DTC: P2176 **1T CCM, MIL: Yes** **Years:** 2008, 2009 **Models:** Allure, Aura, Canyon, Colorado, LaCrosse **Engines:** 2.9L VIN 9, 3.5L VIN N, 3.8L VIN 2, 5.3L VIN C, 5.3L VIN L **Transmissions:** All	**Minimum Throttle Position Not Learned** The ignition is ON. The ignition voltage is more than 8 volts. The system is not in the Battery Save mode. The engine is running. DTCs P0068, P0120, P0122, P0123, P0220, P0222, P0223 are not set. DTC P2176 runs continuously when the above conditions are met. The difference between the predicted and the actual throttle position is more than a calibrated amount for more than 1.5 seconds. **Possible Causes:** • TAC motor control circuit for a short to voltage • TAC motor control circuit for a short to voltage • TAC motor control circuit for a short to ground • TAC motor control circuit for a short to ground • Throttle body has failed • ECM has failed

DTC	Trouble Code Title, Conditions & Possible Causes
DTC: P2177 **1T CCM, MIL: Yes** **Years:** 2008, 2009, 2010 **Models:** Acadia, Allure, Aura, Camaro, CTS, CTS-V, Enclave, LaCrosse, Outlook, Traverse **Engines:** 3.6L VIN 7, 3.6L VIN D, 3.6L VIN V **Transmissions:** All	**Fuel Trim System Lean at Cruise or Accel (Bank1)** The Long Term Fuel Trim Cruise/Accel is greater than 32 percent for 4 seconds or for a cumulative time of 30 seconds. **Possible Causes:** • Leaking crankcase ventilation system • Fuel system is operating lean • Vacuum leaks that only affect one bank of the engine • Lean injectors • Fuel contamination • Engine mechanical conditions • High engine oil level condition • engine control module grounds for being clean, tight, and in the correct locations • Mass Air Flow (MAF) sensor signal that is skewed • Air intake system after the MAF sensor for vacuum leaks • Missing, restricted, or leaking exhaust components • Heated oxygen sensor (HO2S)
DTC: P2178 **1T CCM, MIL: Yes** **Years:** 2008, 2009, 2010 **Models:** Acadia, Allure, Aura, Camaro, CTS, CTS-V, Enclave, LaCrosse, Outlook, Traverse **Engines:** 3.6L VIN 7, 3.6L VIN D, 3.6L VIN V **Transmissions:** All	**Fuel Trim System Rich at Cruise or Accel (Bank 1)** The Long Term Fuel Trim Cruise/Accel is less than −22 percent for 4 seconds or for a cumulative of 30 seconds. **Possible Causes:** • Mass Air Flow (MAF) sensor signal that is skewed • Collapsed air intake duct • Restricted air filter element • Excessive fuel in the crankcase • Fuel contamination • Engine control module grounds for being clean, tight, and in the correct locations • Rich injectors • Engine mechanical conditions • Restricted exhaust system
DTC: P2179 **1T CCM, MIL: Yes** **Years:** 2008, 2009, 2010 **Models:** Acadia, Allure, Aura, Camaro, CTS, CTS-V, Enclave, LaCrosse, Outlook, Traverse **Engines:** 3.6L VIN 7, 3.6L VIN D, 3.6L VIN V **Transmissions:** All	**Fuel Trim System Lean at Cruise or Accel (Bank 2)** The Long Term Fuel Trim Cruise/Accel is greater than 32 percent for 4 seconds or for a cumulative time of 30 seconds. **Possible Causes:** • Leaking crankcase ventilation system • Fuel system is operating lean • Vacuum leaks that only affect one bank of the engine • Lean injectors • Fuel contamination • Engine mechanical conditions • High engine oil level condition • engine control module grounds for being clean, tight, and in the correct locations • Mass Air Flow (MAF) sensor signal that is skewed • Air intake system after the MAF sensor for vacuum leaks • Missing, restricted, or leaking exhaust components • Heated oxygen sensor (HO2S)
DTC: P2180 **1T CCM, MIL: Yes** **Years:** 2008, 2009, 2010 **Models:** Acadia, Allure, Aura, Camaro, CTS, CTS-V, Enclave, LaCrosse, Outlook, Traverse **Engines:** 3.6L VIN 7, 3.6L VIN D, 3.6L VIN V **Transmissions:** All	**Fuel Trim System Rich at Cruise or Accel Bank 2** The Long Term Fuel Trim Cruise/Accel is less than −22 percent for 4 seconds or for a cumulative of 30 seconds. **Possible Causes:** • Mass Air Flow (MAF) sensor signal that is skewed • Collapsed air intake duct • Restricted air filter element • Excessive fuel in the crankcase • Fuel contamination • Engine control module grounds for being clean, tight, and in the correct locations • Rich injectors • Engine mechanical conditions • Restricted exhaust system

DTC	Trouble Code Title, Conditions & Possible Causes
DTC: P2187 **1T CCM, MIL: Yes** **Years:** 2008, 2009, 2010 **Models:** Acadia, Allure, Aura, Camaro, CTS, CTS-V, Enclave, LaCrosse, Outlook, Traverse **Engines:** 3.6L VIN 7, 3.6L VIN D, 3.6L VIN V **Transmissions:** All	**Fuel Trim System Lean at Idle (Bank 1)** The Long Term Fuel Trim Idle/Decel is greater than 6 percent for 4 seconds or for a cumulative of 30 seconds. **Possible Causes:** • Leaking crankcase ventilation system • Fuel system is operating lean • Vacuum leaks that only affect one bank of the engine • Lean injectors • Fuel contamination • Engine mechanical conditions • High engine oil level condition • engine control module grounds for being clean, tight, and in the correct locations • Mass Air Flow (MAF) sensor signal that is skewed • Air intake system after the MAF sensor for vacuum leaks • Missing, restricted, or leaking exhaust components • Heated oxygen sensor (HO2S)
DTC: P2188 **1T CCM, MIL: Yes** **Years:** 2008, 2009, 2010 **Models:** Acadia, Allure, Aura, Camaro, CTS, CTS-V, Enclave, LaCrosse, Outlook, Traverse **Engines:** 3.6L VIN 7, 3.6L VIN D, 3.6L VIN V **Transmissions:** All	**Fuel Trim System Rich at Idle Bank 1** The Long Term Fuel Trim Idle/Decel is less than −6 percent for 4 seconds or for a cumulative of 30 seconds. **Possible Causes:** • Mass Air Flow (MAF) sensor signal that is skewed • Collapsed air intake duct • Restricted air filter element • Excessive fuel in the crankcase • Fuel contamination • Engine control module grounds for being clean, tight, and in the correct locations • Rich injectors • Engine mechanical conditions • Restricted exhaust system
DTC: P2189 **1T CCM, MIL: Yes** **Years:** 2008, 2009, 2010 **Models:** Acadia, Allure, Aura, Camaro, CTS, CTS-V, Enclave, LaCrosse, Outlook, Traverse **Engines:** 3.6L VIN 7, 3.6L VIN D, 3.6L VIN V **Transmissions:** All	**Fuel Trim System Lean at Idle (Bank 2)** **Possible Causes:** • Leaking crankcase ventilation system • Fuel system is operating lean • Vacuum leaks that only affect one bank of the engine • Lean injectors • Fuel contamination • Engine mechanical conditions • High engine oil level condition • Engine control module grounds for being clean, tight, and in the correct locations • Mass Air Flow (MAF) sensor signal that is skewed • Air intake system after the MAF sensor for vacuum leaks • Missing, restricted, or leaking exhaust components • Heated oxygen sensor (HO2S)
DTC: P2190 **1T CCM, MIL: Yes** **Years:** 2008, 2009, 2010 **Models:** Acadia, Allure, Aura, Camaro, CTS, CTS-V, Enclave, LaCrosse, Outlook, Traverse **Engines:** 3.6L VIN 7, 3.6L VIN D, 3.6L VIN V **Transmissions:** All	**Fuel Trim System Rich at Idle Bank 2** The Long Term Fuel Trim Idle/Decel is less than −6 percent for 4 seconds or for a cumulative of 30 seconds. **Possible Causes:** • Mass Air Flow (MAF) sensor signal that is skewed • Collapsed air intake duct • Restricted air filter element • Excessive fuel in the crankcase • Fuel contamination • Engine control module grounds for being clean, tight, and in the correct locations • Rich injectors • Engine mechanical conditions • Restricted exhaust system

DTC	Trouble Code Title, Conditions & Possible Causes
DTC: P2227 **2T CCM, MIL: Yes** **Years:** 2008, 2009, 2010 **Models:**, Acadia, Allure, Astra, Aura, Avalanche, Escalade/EXT/ESV, Suburban, Tahoe, Yukon, Escalade/EXT/ESV/ESV, Suburban, Tahoe, Yukon Aveo, Aveo5, Camaro, Cobalt, Cobalt-GS, Colorado,Canyon, Corvette, CTS, CTS-V, CTS, CTS-V-V, DTS, Escalade/EXT/ESV, G.3, G5,Enclave, LaCrosse, Outlook, Suburban, Tahoe Traverse, Yukon **Engines:** All **Transmissions:** All	**Barometric Pressure (BARO) Sensor Performance** DTCs P0068, P0101, P0102, P0103, P0107, P0108, P0112, P0113, P0116, P0117, P0118, P0120, P0128, P0220, P0502, P0503, P2135, P2228, P2229 are not set. The engine run time is greater than 10 seconds. The ECM detects that 80 out of 100 consecutive BARO sensor samples vary greater than 10 kPa between each sample, for 10 seconds. **Possible Causes:** • Vacuum leaks • BARO sensor low reference circuit for an open/high resistance • BARO sensor 5V reference circuit for an open/high resistance or a short to ground • BARO sensor 5V reference circuit for a short to voltage • BARO sensor signal circuit terminal 3 for a short to voltage • BARO sensor signal circuit for an open/high resistance or a short to ground • BARO sensor has failed
DTC: P2228 **2T CCM, MIL: Yes** **Years:** 2008, 2009, 2010 **Models:**, Acadia, Allure, Astra, Aura, Avalanche, Escalade/EXT/ESV, Suburban, Tahoe, Yukon, Escalade/EXT/ESV, Suburban, Tahoe, Yukon Aveo, Aveo5, Camaro, Cobalt, Cobalt-GS, Colorado,Canyon, Corvette, CTS, CTS-V, CTS, CTS-V-V, DTS, Escalade/EXT/ESV, G.3, G5,Enclave, LaCrosse, Outlook, Suburban, Tahoe Traverse, Yukon **Engines:** All **Transmissions:** All	**Barometric Pressure (BARO) Sensor Circuit Low Voltage** DTCs P0120, P0121, P0122, P0123, P0220, P0222 or P0223 are not set. The ignition is ON. This DTC runs continuously when the above conditions are met. The BARO is less than 50 kPa for less than 1 minute. **Possible Causes:** • Vacuum leaks • BARO sensor low reference circuit for an open/high resistance • BARO sensor 5V reference circuit for an open/high resistance or a short to ground • BARO sensor 5V reference circuit for a short to voltage • BARO sensor signal circuit terminal 3 for a short to voltage • BARO sensor signal circuit for an open/high resistance or a short to ground • BARO sensor has failed
DTC: P2229 **2T CCM, MIL: Yes** **Years:** 2008, 2009, 2010 **Models:**, Acadia, Allure, Astra, Aura, Avalanche, Escalade/EXT/ESV, Suburban, Tahoe, Yukon, Escalade/EXT/ESV, Suburban, Tahoe, Yukon Aveo, Aveo5, Camaro, Cobalt, Cobalt-GS, Colorado,Canyon, Corvette, CTS, CTS-V, CTS, CTS-V-V, DTS, Escalade/EXT/ESV, G.3, G5,Enclave, LaCrosse, Outlook, Suburban, Tahoe Traverse, Yukon **Engines:** All **Transmissions:** All	**Barometric Pressure (BARO) Sensor Circuit High Voltage** DTCs P0120, P0121, P0122, P0123, P0220, P0222, or P0223 are not set. The engine is running. The engine run time is greater than 4 minutes. The startup coolant temperature is between −30°C and +30°C (−22°F and +86°F). The throttle position is less than 1 percent. The engine speed is greater than 1,200 RPM. This DTC runs continuously when the above conditions are met. **Possible Causes:** • Vacuum leaks • BARO sensor low reference circuit for an open/high resistance • BARO sensor 5V reference circuit for an open/high resistance or a short to ground • BARO sensor 5V reference circuit for a short to voltage • BARO sensor signal circuit terminal 3 for a short to voltage • BARO sensor signal circuit for an open/high resistance or a short to ground • BARO sensor has failed
DTC: P2232 **1T CCM, MIL: Yes** **Years:** 2008, 2009, 2010 **Models:** Acadia, Allure, Aura, Camaro, CTS, CTS-V, Enclave, LaCrosse, Outlook, Traverse **Engines:** 3.6L VIN 7, 3.6L VIN D, 3.6L VIN V **Transmissions:** All	**HO2S Signal Circuit Shorted to Heater Circuit (Bank 1 Sensor 2)** The ECM detects that the HO2S signal voltage increases greater than 2 volts within 40 ms, in 4 out of 6 HO2S heater switch OFF samples. The condition exists for greater than 1 second, or for a cumulative of 10 seconds. **Possible Causes:** • Signal circuit terminal B for a short to the heater control circuit terminal E • ECM has failed • Faulty HO2S

DTC	Trouble Code Title, Conditions & Possible Causes
DTC: P2235 **1T CCM, MIL: Yes** **Years:** 2008, 2009, 2010 **Models:** Acadia, Allure, Aura, Camaro, CTS, CTS-V, Enclave, LaCrosse, Outlook, Traverse **Engines:** 3.6L VIN 7, 3.6L VIN D, 3.6L VIN V **Transmissions:** All	**HO2S Signal Circuit Shorted to Heater Circuit (Bank 2 Sensor 2)** The ECM detects that the HO2S signal voltage increases greater than 2 volts within 40 ms, in 4 out of 6 HO2S heater switch OFF samples. The condition exists for greater than 1 second, or for a cumulative of 10 seconds. **Possible Causes:** • Signal circuit terminal B for a short to the heater control circuit terminal E • ECM has failed • Faulty HO2S
DTC: P2270 **1T CCM, MIL: Yes** **Years:** 2008, 2009 **Models:** Corvette, CTS, CTS-V, DTS **Engines:** 4.6L VIN Y, 6.2L VIN W, 6.2L VIN P, 6.2L VIN R, 7.0L VIN E **Transmissions:** All	**HO2S Signal Stuck Lean (Bank 1 Sensor 2)** DTCs P0036, P0037, P0038, P0137, P0138, P0140, P0141, P0443, P0458, P0459, P2232 are not set. The Ignition 1 Signal parameter is between 10-18 volts. The Engine Run Time parameter is more than 5 minutes. The Engine Speed parameter is between 1,100-2,500 RPM. The MAF Sensor parameter is between 3-20 g/s. The Vehicle Speed parameter is between 50-120 km/h (31-75 mph). The Fuel Level Sensor parameter is more than 10 percent. The Loop Status parameter is closed. The Catalytic Converter Temperature parameter is between 550-900°C (1,022-1,652°F). DTC P2270 runs once per drive cycle when the above conditions are met. The ECM detects that the HO2S 2 voltage oscillations are slower than a calibrated value. DTC P2270 sets within 4 seconds when the above condition is met continuously, or within 50 seconds when the above condition is met cumulatively. **Possible Causes:** • HO2S low signal circuit for an open/high resistance • HO2S high signal circuit for a short to voltage • HO2S high signal circuit for a short to ground • HO2S high signal circuit for an open/high resistance • HO2S has failed • ECM has failed
DTC: P2270 **1T CCM, MIL: Yes** **Years:** 2008, 2009, 2010 **Models:** Acadia, Allure, Aura, Camaro, CTS, CTS-V, Enclave, LaCrosse, Outlook, Traverse **Engines:** 3.6L VIN 7, 3.6L VIN D, 3.6L VIN V **Transmissions:** All	**HO2S Signal Stuck Lean (Bank 1 Sensor 2)** The ECM detects that the HO2S 2 voltage is less than 629 mV for greater than 100 seconds, then an intrusive test is performed. The ECM will enrich the fuel mixture 2 percent per second up to 20 percent then hold the enrichment for 10 seconds. If the ECM detects that the HO2S 2 voltage is less than 629 mV during the intrusive test, for greater than 4 second or for a cumulative of 30 seconds, the DTC sets. **Possible Causes:** • Water intrusion in the HO2S harness connector • Signal circuit terminal B for a short to ground • Low fuel system pressure • Lean fuel injectors • Fuel that is contaminated • Vacuum hoses for splits, kinks, and proper connection • Air intake system after the Mass Air Flow (MAF) sensor for vacuum leaks • Exhaust system leaks • Contaminated HO2S – Silicon • Engine mechanical condition • Faulty HO2S • ECM has failed
DTC: P2270 **2T CCM, MIL: Yes** **Years:** 2008, 2009 **Models:** Astra, Aura, Aveo, Aveo5, Cobalt G3, G5 **Engines:** 1.6L VIN 6, 1.6L VIN E, 1.8L VIN 1, 2.0L VIN P, 2.0L VIN X, 2.2L VIN H, 2.2L VIN F, 2.4L VIN 5, 2.4L VIN B **Transmissions:** All	**HO2S Signal Stuck Lean Sensor 2** DTCs P0036, P0037, P0038, P0137, P0138, P0140, P0141, P0443, P0458, P0459, and P2232 are not set. The engine is running. The ignition voltage is more than 10.5 V. The HO2S 2 has been in Closed Loop for more than 10 s. The DFCO is inactive. The engine air flow has been between 5.56-33.33 g/s for more than 3 s, and is currently more than 9.72 g/s. DTC P2270 runs continuously when the above conditions are met for 10 min. The ECM detects that the HO2S 2 voltage oscillations are slower than a calibrated value. DTC P2270 sets within 4 s when the above condition is met continuously, or within 50 s when the above condition is met cumulatively. **Possible Causes:** • HO2S signal circuit open/high resistance • HO2S signal circuit short to voltage • HO2S signal circuit open/high resistance • HO2S is damaged • ECM has failed

DTC	Trouble Code Title, Conditions & Possible Causes
DTC: P2271 **1T CCM, MIL: Yes** **Years:** 2008, 2009 **Models:** Corvette, CTS, CTS-V, DTS **Engines:** 4.6L VIN Y, 6.2L VIN W, 6.2L VIN P, 6.2L VIN R, 7.0L VIN E **Transmissions:** All	**HO2S Signal Stuck Rich (Bank 1 Sensor 2)** DTCs P0036, P0037, P0038, P0137, P0138, P0140, P0141, P0443, P0458, P0459, P2232 are not set. The Ignition 1 Signal parameter is between 10-18 volts. The Engine Speed parameter is between 500-5,000 RPM. The MAF Sensor parameter is between 3-50 g/s. The Vehicle Speed parameter is between 24-132 km/h (15-82 mph). The Fuel Level Sensor parameter is more than 10 percent. The Loop Status parameter is closed. DTC P2270 runs once per drive cycle when the above conditions are met for 1 second. **Possible Causes:** • HO2S low signal circuit for an open/high resistance • HO2S high signal circuit for a short to voltage • HO2S high signal circuit for a short to ground • HO2S high signal circuit for an open/high resistance • HO2S has failed • ECM has failed
DTC: P2271 **2T CCM, MIL: Yes** **Years:** 2008, 2009 **Models:** Astra, Aura, Aveo, Aveo5, Cobalt G3, G5 **Engines:** 1.6L VIN 6, 1.6L VIN E, 1.8L VIN 1, 2.0L VIN P, 2.0L VIN X, 2.2L VIN H, 2.2L VIN F, 2.4L VIN 5, 2.4L VIN B **Transmissions:** All	**HO2S Signal Stuck Rich Sensor 2** DTCs P000A, P000B, P0010, P0011, P0013, P0014, P0016, P0017, P0030, P0031, P0032, P0036, P0037, P0038, P0068, P0101, P0102, P0103, P0116, P0117, P0118, P0119, P0121, P0122, P0123, P0130, P0131, P0132, P0133, P0137, P0138, P0139, P0141, P0171, P0172, P0221, P0222, P0223, P0300, P0301, P0302, P0303, P0304, P0313, P0335, P0336, P0340, P0341, P0365, P0366, P0443, P0458, P0459, P0496, P1101, P2088, P2089, P2090, P2091, P2176, P2270, P2271, P2297, P2A00, P2A01 are not set. The engine has been running for more than 5 min. The engine coolant temperature is hotter than 167°F (75°C). DTC P2271 runs continuously when the above conditions are met for 10 min. The ECM detects that the HO2S 2 voltage oscillations are faster than a calibrated value. DTC P2271 sets within 4 s when the above condition is met continuously, or within 50 s when the above condition is met cumulatively. **Possible Causes:** • HO2S signal circuit open/high resistance • HO2S signal circuit short to voltage • HO2S signal circuit open/high resistance • HO2S is damaged • ECM has failed
DTC: P2271 **1T CCM, MIL: Yes** **Years:** 2008, 2009, 2010 **Models:** Acadia, Allure, Aura, Camaro, CTS, CTS-V, Enclave, LaCrosse, Outlook, Traverse **Engines:** 3.6L VIN 7, 3.6L VIN D, 3.6L VIN V **Transmissions:** All	**HO2S Signal Stuck Rich (Bank 1 Sensor 2)** The ECM detects that the HO2S 2 voltage is greater than 629 mV for greater than 100 seconds, then an intrusive test is performed. The ECM will lean the fuel mixture −2 percent per second up to −15 percent then hold the enleanment for 10 seconds. If the ECM detects that the HO2S voltage is greater than 629 mV during the intrusive test, for greater than 4 seconds or for a cumulative of 30 seconds, the DTC sets. **Possible Causes:** • Collapsed air intake duct • Restricted air filter element • Excessive fuel in the crankcase • Fuel contamination • Rich injectors • Engine mechanical conditions • Restricted exhaust system • Faulty HO2S • ECM has failed
DTC: P2272 **1T CCM, MIL: Yes** **Years:** 2008, 2009, 2010 **Models:** Acadia, Allure, Aura, Camaro, CTS, CTS-V, Enclave, LaCrosse, Outlook, Traverse **Engines:** 3.6L VIN 7, 3.6L VIN D, 3.6L VIN V **Transmissions:** All	**HO2S Signal Stuck Lean (Bank 2 Sensor 2)** The ECM detects that the HO2S 2 voltage is less than 629 mV for greater than 100 seconds, then an intrusive test is performed. The ECM will enrich the fuel mixture 2 percent per second up to 20 percent then hold the enrichment for 10 seconds. If the ECM detects that the HO2S 2 voltage is less than 629 mV during the intrusive test, for greater than 4 second or for a cumulative of 30 seconds, the DTC sets. **Possible Causes:** • Water intrusion in the HO2S harness connector • Signal circuit terminal B for a short to ground • Low fuel system pressure • Lean fuel injectors • Fuel that is contaminated • Vacuum hoses for splits, kinks, and proper connection • Air intake system after the Mass Air Flow (MAF) sensor for vacuum leaks • Exhaust system leaks • Contaminated HO2S – Silicon • Engine mechanical condition • Faulty HO2S • ECM has failed

DTC	Trouble Code Title, Conditions & Possible Causes
DTC: P2273 **1T CCM, MIL: Yes** **Years:** 2008, 2009, 2010 **Models:** Acadia, Allure, Aura, Camaro, CTS, CTS-V, Enclave, LaCrosse, Outlook, Traverse **Engines:** 3.6L VIN 7, 3.6L VIN D, 3.6L VIN V **Transmissions:** All	**HO2S Signal Stuck Rich (Bank 1 Sensor 2)** The ECM detects that the HO2S 2 voltage is greater than 629 mV for greater than 100 seconds, then an intrusive test is performed. The ECM will lean the fuel mixture −2 percent per second up to −15 percent then hold the enleanment for 10 seconds. If the ECM detects that the HO2S voltage is greater than 629 mV during the intrusive test, for greater than 4 seconds or for a cumulative of 30 seconds, the DTC sets. **Possible Causes:** • Collapsed air intake duct • Restricted air filter element • Excessive fuel in the crankcase • Fuel contamination • Rich injectors • Engine mechanical conditions • Restricted exhaust system • Faulty HO2S • ECM has failed
DTC: P2300 **1T CCM, MIL: Yes** **Years:** 2008, 2009, 2010 **Models:** Acadia, Allure, Aura, Camaro, CTS, CTS-V, Enclave, LaCrosse, Outlook, Traverse **Engines:** 3.6L VIN 7, 3.6L VIN D, 3.6L VIN V **Transmissions:** All	**Ignition Coil 1 Control Circuit Low Voltage** The engine is running. The ignition 1 voltage signal is greater than 10 volts. The ECM detects the ignition control circuit is shorted to ground for greater than 4 seconds or a cumulative of 30 seconds. **Possible Causes:** • Ignition Coil circuit for a short to ground or an open/high resistance • Inition Coil circuit for a short to voltage • Ignition coil has failed • ECM has failed
DTC: P2301 **1T CCM, MIL: Yes** **Years:** 2008, 2009 **Models:** Acadia, Allure, Aura, Astra, Aura, Aveo, Aveo5, Cobalt G3, G5, Enclave, LaCrosse, Outlook, Traverse **Engines:** 1.6L VIN 6, 1.6L VIN E, 1.8L VIN 1, 2.0L VIN P, 2.0L VIN X, 2.2L VIN H, 2.2L VIN F, 2.4L VIN 5, 2.4L VIN B, 3.6L VIN 7, 3.6L VIN D, 3.6L VIN V **Transmissions:** All	**Ignition Coil 1 Control Circuit High Voltage** The engine is running. The ignition 1 voltage signal is greater than 10 volts. The ECM detects the ignition control circuit is shorted to ground for greater than 4 seconds or a cumulative of 30 seconds. **Possible Causes:** • Ignition Coil circuit for a short to ground or an open/high resistance • Inition Coil circuit for a short to voltage • Ignition coil has failed • ECM has failed
DTC: P2303 **1T CCM, MIL: Yes** **Years:** 2008, 2009, 2010 **Models:** Acadia, Allure, Aura, Camaro, CTS, CTS-V, Enclave, LaCrosse, Outlook, Traverse **Engines:** 3.6L VIN 7, 3.6L VIN D, 3.6L VIN V **Transmissions:** All	**Ignition Coil 2 Control Circuit Low Voltage** The engine is running. The ignition 1 voltage signal is greater than 10 volts. The ECM detects the ignition control circuit is shorted to ground for greater than 4 seconds or a cumulative of 30 seconds. **Possible Causes:** • Ignition Coil circuit for a short to ground or an open/high resistance • Inition Coil circuit for a short to voltage • Ignition coil has failed • ECM has failed
DTC: P2304 **1T CCM, MIL: Yes** **Years:** 2008, 2009 **Models:** Acadia, Allure, Aura, Astra, Aura, Aveo, Aveo5, Cobalt G3, G5, Enclave, LaCrosse, Outlook, Traverse **Engines:** 1.6L VIN 6, 1.6L VIN E, 1.8L VIN 1, 2.0L VIN P, 2.0L VIN X, 2.2L VIN H, 2.2L VIN F, 2.4L VIN 5, 2.4L VIN B, 3.6L VIN 7, 3.6L VIN D, 3.6L VIN V **Transmissions:** All	**Ignition Coil 2 Control Circuit High Voltage** The engine is running. The ignition 1 voltage signal is greater than 10 volts. The ECM detects the ignition control circuit is shorted to ground for greater than 4 seconds or a cumulative of 30 seconds. **Possible Causes:** • Ignition Coil circuit for a short to ground or an open/high resistance • Inition Coil circuit for a short to voltage • Ignition coil has failed • ECM has failed

DTC	Trouble Code Title, Conditions & Possible Causes
DTC: P2306 **1T CCM, MIL: Yes** **Years:** 2008, 2009, 2010 **Models:** Acadia, Allure, Aura, Camaro, CTS, CTS-V, Enclave, LaCrosse, Outlook, Traverse **Engines:** 3.6L VIN 7, 3.6L VIN D, 3.6L VIN V **Transmissions:** All	**Ignition Coil 3 Control Circuit Low Voltage** The engine is running. The ignition 1 voltage signal is greater than 10 volts. The ECM detects the ignition control circuit is shorted to ground for greater than 4 seconds or a cumulative of 30 seconds. **Possible Causes:** • Ignition Coil circuit for a short to ground or an open/high resistance • Inition Coil circuit for a short to voltage • Ignition coil has failed • ECM has failed
DTC: P2307 **1T CCM, MIL: Yes** **Years:** 2008, 2009 **Models:** Acadia, Allure, Aura, Astra, Aura, Aveo, Aveo5, Cobalt G3, G5, Enclave, LaCrosse, Outlook, Traverse **Engines:** 1.6L VIN 6, 1.6L VIN E, 1.8L VIN 1, 2.0L VIN P, 2.0L VIN X, 2.2L VIN H, 2.2L VIN F, 2.4L VIN 5, 2.4L VIN B, 3.6L VIN 7, 3.6L VIN D, 3.6L VIN V **Transmissions:** All	**Ignition Coil 3 Control Circuit High Voltage** The engine is running. The ignition 1 voltage signal is greater than 10 volts. The ECM detects the ignition control circuit is shorted to ground for greater than 4 seconds or a cumulative of 30 seconds. **Possible Causes:** • Ignition Coil circuit for a short to ground or an open/high resistance • Inition Coil circuit for a short to voltage • Ignition coil has failed • ECM has failed
DTC: P2309 **1T CCM, MIL: Yes** **Years:** 2008, 2009, 2010 **Models:** Acadia, Allure, Aura, Camaro, CTS, CTS-V, Enclave, LaCrosse, Outlook, Traverse **Engines:** 3.6L VIN 7, 3.6L VIN D, 3.6L VIN V **Transmissions:** All	**Ignition Coil 4 Control Circuit Low Voltage** The engine is running. The ignition 1 voltage signal is greater than 10 volts. The ECM detects the ignition control circuit is shorted to ground for greater than 4 seconds or a cumulative of 30 seconds. **Possible Causes:** • Ignition Coil circuit for a short to ground or an open/high resistance • Inition Coil circuit for a short to voltage • Ignition coil has failed • ECM has failed
DTC: P2310 **1T CCM, MIL: Yes** **Years:** 2008, 2009 **Models:** Acadia, Allure, Aura, Astra, Aura, Aveo, Aveo5, Cobalt G3, G5, Enclave, LaCrosse, Outlook, Traverse **Engines:** 1.6L VIN 6, 1.6L VIN E, 1.8L VIN 1, 2.0L VIN P, 2.0L VIN X, 2.2L VIN H, 2.2L VIN F, 2.4L VIN 5, 2.4L VIN B, 3.6L VIN 7, 3.6L VIN D, 3.6L VIN V **Transmissions:** All	**Ignition Coil 4 Control Circuit High Voltage** The engine is running. The ignition 1 voltage signal is greater than 10 volts. The ECM detects the ignition control circuit is shorted to ground for greater than 4 seconds or a cumulative of 30 seconds. **Possible Causes:** • Ignition Coil circuit for a short to ground or an open/high resistance • Inition Coil circuit for a short to voltage • Ignition coil has failed • ECM has failed
DTC: P2312 **1T CCM, MIL: Yes** **Years:** 2008, 2009, 2010 **Models:** Acadia, Allure, Aura, Camaro, CTS, CTS-V, Enclave, LaCrosse, Outlook, Traverse **Engines:** 3.6L VIN 7, 3.6L VIN D, 3.6L VIN V **Transmissions:** All	**Ignition Coil 5 Control Circuit Low Voltage** The engine is running. The ignition 1 voltage signal is greater than 10 volts. The ECM detects the ignition control circuit is shorted to ground for greater than 4 seconds or a cumulative of 30 seconds. **Possible Causes:** • Ignition Coil circuit for a short to ground or an open/high resistance • Inition Coil circuit for a short to voltage • Ignition coil has failed • ECM has failed
DTC: P2313 **1T CCM, MIL: Yes** **Years:** 2008, 2009, 2010 **Models:** Acadia, Allure, Aura, Camaro, CTS, CTS-V, Enclave, LaCrosse, Outlook, Traverse **Engines:** 3.6L VIN 7, 3.6L VIN D, 3.6L VIN V **Transmissions:** All	**Ignition Coil 5 Control Circuit High Voltage** The engine is running. The ignition 1 voltage signal is greater than 10 volts. The ECM detects the ignition control circuit is shorted to ground for greater than 4 seconds or a cumulative of 30 seconds. **Possible Causes:** • Ignition Coil circuit for a short to ground or an open/high resistance • Inition Coil circuit for a short to voltage • Ignition coil has failed • ECM has failed

DTC	Trouble Code Title, Conditions & Possible Causes
DTC: P2315 **1T CCM, MIL: Yes** **Years:** 2008, 2009, 2010 **Models:** Acadia, Allure, Aura, Camaro, CTS, CTS-V, Enclave, LaCrosse, Outlook, Traverse **Engines:** 3.6L VIN 7, 3.6L VIN D, 3.6L VIN V **Transmissions:** All	**Ignition Coil 6 Control Circuit Low Voltage** The engine is running. The ignition 1 voltage signal is greater than 10 volts. The ECM detects the ignition control circuit is shorted to ground for greater than 4 seconds or a cumulative of 30 seconds. **Possible Causes:** • Ignition Coil circuit for a short to ground or an open/high resistance • Inition Coil circuit for a short to voltage • Ignition coil has failed • ECM has failed
DTC: P2316 **1T CCM, MIL: Yes** **Years:** 2008, 2009, 2010 **Models:** Acadia, Allure, Aura, Camaro, CTS, CTS-V, Enclave, LaCrosse, Outlook, Traverse **Engines:** 3.6L VIN 7, 3.6L VIN D, 3.6L VIN V **Transmissions:** All	**Ignition Coil 6 Control Circuit High Voltage** The engine is running. The ignition 1 voltage signal is greater than 10 volts. The ECM detects the ignition control circuit is shorted to ground for greater than 4 seconds or a cumulative of 30 seconds. **Possible Causes:** • Ignition Coil circuit for a short to ground or an open/high resistance • Inition Coil circuit for a short to voltage • Ignition coil has failed • ECM has failed
DTC: P2430 **1T CCM, MIL: Yes** **Years:** 2008, 2009 **Models:** DTS **Engines:** 4.6L VIN Y **Transmissions:** All	**Secondary Air Injection (AIR) System Pressure Sensor Circuit** DTCs P0412, P0418, P0606, P1635, P1639, P2432, P2433 are not set. The engine has been OFF for greater than 60 minutes since the last cold start. The AIR pump is commanded ON. DTC P2430 runs continuously when the above conditions are met. The ECM determines that the AIR pressure sensor value change is less than a calibrated value while the AIR pump is commanded ON. Or. DTC P2430 sets during phase 1 or 2 within 1.5 seconds when the above condition is met. **Possible Causes:**
DTC: P2431 **1T CCM, MIL: Yes** **Years:** 2008, 2009 **Models:** DTS **Engines:** 4.6L VIN Y **Transmissions:** All	**Secondary Air Injection System Pressure Sensor Circuit Performance** DTCs P0106, P0107, P0108, P0412, P0418, P0606, P0641, P0651, P2432, P2433 are not set. The ignition is ON. DTC P2431 runs continuously when the above conditions are met. The ECM determines that the difference between the AIR pressure sensor and the Barometric Pressure (BARO) sensor signals is greater than 10 kPa when the AIR pump is commanded OFF. Or The ECM determines that the difference between the AIR pressure sensor and the BARO sensor signals is greater than 50 kPa when the AIR pump is commanded ON. **Possible Causes:** • AIR solenoid valvelow reference circuit for an open/high resistance • AIR solenoid valve5-volt reference circuit for a short to ground or an open/high resistance • AIR solenoid valve5-volt reference circuit for a short to voltage • AIR solenoid valvesignal circuit terminal 2 for a short to voltage • AIR solenoid valvesignal circuit for a short to ground or an open/high resistance • AIR solenoid valve has failed • ECM has failed
DTC: P2432 **1T CCM, MIL: Yes** **Years:** 2008, 2009 **Models:** DTS **Engines:** 4.6L VIN Y **Transmissions:** All	**Secondary Air Injection System Pressure Sensor Circuit Low Voltage** DTCs P0606, P0641, P0651, P1635, P1639 are not set. The ignition is ON or the engine is running. DTCs P2432 and P2433 run continuously when the above conditions are met. The ECM determines that the AIR pressure sensor signal is less than 0.2 volt for at least 12.5 seconds. **Possible Causes:** • AIR solenoid valvelow reference circuit for an open/high resistance • AIR solenoid valve5-volt reference circuit for a short to ground or an open/high resistance • AIR solenoid valve5-volt reference circuit for a short to voltage • AIR solenoid valvesignal circuit terminal 2 for a short to voltage • AIR solenoid valvesignal circuit for a short to ground or an open/high resistance • AIR solenoid valve has failed • ECM has failed

DTC	Trouble Code Title, Conditions & Possible Causes
DTC: P2433 **1T CCM, MIL: Yes** **Years:** 2008, 2009 **Models:** DTS **Engines:** 4.6L VIN Y **Transmissions:** All	**Air Injection System Pressure Sensor Circuit High Voltage** DTCs P0606, P0641, P0651, P1635, P1639 are not set. The ignition is ON or the engine is running. DTCs P2432 and P2433 run continuously when the above conditions are met. The ECM determines that the AIR pressure sensor signal is equal to or greater than 4.7 volts for at least 12.5 seconds. **Possible Causes:** • AIR solenoid valvelow reference circuit for an open/high resistance • AIR solenoid valve5-volt reference circuit for a short to ground or an open/high resistance • AIR solenoid valve5-volt reference circuit for a short to voltage • AIR solenoid valvesignal circuit terminal 2 for a short to voltage • AIR solenoid valvesignal circuit for a short to ground or an open/high resistance • AIR solenoid valve has failed • ECM has failed
DTC: P2440 **1T CCM, MIL: Yes** **Years:** 2008, 2009 **Models:** DTS **Engines:** 4.6L VIN Y **Transmissions:** All	**Secondary Air Injection (AIR) System Shut-Off Valve Stuck Open** DTCs P0068, P0101, P0102, P0103, P0106, P0107, P0108, P0112, P0113, P0116, P0117, P0118, P0128, P0201-P0208, P0300, P0351-P0358, P0411, P0412, P0418, P0420, P0606, P0641, P0651, P2430, P2431, P2432, P2433, 2444 are not set. The system voltage is between 11-18V. The BARO is greater than 70 kPa. The start-up Engine Coolant Temperature (ECT) is between 5-80°C (41-176°F). The start-up Intake Air Temperature (IAT) is between 5-80°C (41-176°F). The Mass Air Flow (MAF) sensor is less than 33 g/s. The AIR system is commanded ON. Conditions are stable for greater than 5 seconds. DTC P2440 runs once per trip start-up when the above conditions are met and AIR pump operation is requested. The ECM determines that the actual AIR system pressure is 3 kPa less than the predicted AIR system pressure. DTC P2440 sets during phase 2 and when the above condition exists for greater than 2 seconds. **Possible Causes:** • AIR pump relay has failed • AIR pump has failed • AIR solenoid relay has failed • AIR solenoid valve has failed • Test or inspect the AIR solenoid valve outlet pipe and exhaust manifold for a restriction • Air injection check valve
DTC: P2444 **1T CCM, MIL: Yes** **Years:** 2008, 2009 **Models:** Corvette, CTS, CTS-V, DTS **Engines:** 4.6L VIN Y, VIN P 6.2L **Transmissions:** All	**Secondary Air Injection (AIR) System Pump Stuck On** DTCs P0068, P0101, P0102, P0103, P0106, P0107, P0108, P0112, P0113, P0116, P0117, P0118, P0128, P0201-P0204, P0300, P0351-P0358, P0411, P0412, P0418, P0420, P0606, P0641, P0651, P1106, P1107, P2430, P2431, P2432, P2433, 2440 are not set. The system voltage is between 11-18V. The BARO is greater than 70 kPa. The start-up Engine Coolant Temperature (ECT) is between 5-80°C (41-176°F). The start-up intake air temperature (IAT) is between 5-80°C (41-176°F). The MAF sensor is less than 33 g/s. The AIR system is commanded ON. The conditions are stable for greater than 5 seconds. DTC P2444 runs once per trip start-up when the above conditions are met and AIR pump operation is requested. The ECM determines that the actual AIR system pressure is 11.2 kPa greater than the predicted AIR system pressure. DTC P2444 sets during phase 3 and when the above condition exists for greater than 2 seconds. **Possible Causes:** • AIR pump relay has failed • AIR pump has failed • AIR solenoid relay has failed • AIR solenoid valve has failed • Test or inspect the AIR solenoid valve outlet pipe and exhaust manifold for a restriction • Air injection check valve
DTC: P2534 **1T CCM, MIL: Yes** **Years:** 2008, 2009 **Models:** Corvette, CTS, CTS-V **Engines:** 6.2L VIN W, 6.2L VIN P, 6.2L VIN R, 7.0L VIN E **Transmissions:** All	**Ignition 1 Switch Circuit Low** The engine is running. The FPCM detects that the IGN voltage is less than 6.0 volts. **Possible Causes:** • FPCM relay IGN voltage circuit a short to ground or an open/high resistance • FPCM relay has failed • FPCM has failed

DTC	Trouble Code Title, Conditions & Possible Causes
DTC: P2544 **1T CCM, MIL: Yes** **Years:** 2008, 2009 **Models:** Acadia, Allure, Aura, Astra, Aura, Aveo, Aveo5, Cobalt G3, G5, Enclave, LaCrosse, Outlook, Traverse **Engines:** 1.6L VIN 6, 1.6L VIN E, 1.8L VIN 1, 2.0L VIN P, 2.0L VIN X, 2.2L VIN H, 2.2L VIN F, 2.4L VIN 5, 2.4L VIN B, 3.6L VIN 7, 3.6L VIN D, 3.6L VIN V **Transmissions:** All	**Transmission Torque Request Circuit** The engine run time is greater than 5 seconds. No other CAN errors are present. The ECM notifies the TCM that a torque reduction request has failed for 2 seconds. **Possible Causes:** • If DTC P0604 is set, replace the ECM. • If DTC P0604 is not set, replace the TCM.
DTC: P2544 **2T CCM, MIL: Yes** **Years:** 2008, 2009 **Models:** Astra, Aura, Aveo, Aveo5, Cobalt G3, G5 **Engines:** 1.6L VIN 6, 1.6L VIN E, 1.8L VIN 1, 2.0L VIN P, 2.0L VIN X, 2.2L VIN H, 2.2L VIN F, 2.4L VIN 5, 2.4L VIN B **Transmissions:** All	**Transmission Torque Request Circuit** The engine run time is greater than 5 seconds. No other CAN errors are present. The ECM notifies the TCM that a torque reduction request has failed for 2 seconds. **Possible Causes:** • If DTC P0604 is set, replace the ECM. • If DTC P0604 is not set, replace the TCM.
DTC: P2610 **2T CCM, MIL: Yes** **Years:** 2008, 2009, 2010 **Models:** All **Engines:** All **Transmissions:** All	**Control Module Ignition OFF Timer Performance** The ECM is powered down. DTC P2610 runs once per ignition cycle. Or the ECM is powered up with the ignition switch in the Run or Crank position. The engine OFF timer value is less than or greater than an internal reference counter during an 2-second interval. DTC P2610 runs continuously when the above conditions are met. The ECM detects an internal failure or incomplete programming for more than 10 seconds. **Possible Causes:** • Voltage and ground inputs to the ECM • If DTC P0602 is set, attempt to program the ECM before replacing the ECM. If DTC P0602 resets, replace the ECM.
DTC: P2635 **1T CCM, MIL: Yes** **Years:** 2008, 2009 **Models:** Corvette, CTS, CTS-V, DTS **Engines:** 4.6L VIN Y, 6.2L VIN W, 6.2L VIN P, 6.2L VIN R, 7.0L VIN E **Transmissions:** All	**Fuel Pump Flow Performance** DTC P0191, P0192, P0193, P1255 or P06A6 are not active. DTC P0641 has not failed this ignition cycle. Fuel pump control is enabled and the fuel pump control state is normal. The system voltage is greater than 11 V. The engine has been running for more than 30 seconds. This DTC sets when the FPCM detects a predetermined fuel pressure performance degradation between the desired fuel rail pressure and the current estimated fuel rail pressure. **Possible Causes:** • FPCM relaycircuit for a short to voltage • FPCM relaycircuit for a short to ground or an open/high resistance • FPCM relay
DTC: P2A00 **1T CCM, MIL: Yes** **Years:** 2008, 2009 **Models:** Corvette, CTS, CTS-V, DTS **Engines:** 4.6L VIN Y, 6.2L VIN W, 6.2L VIN P, 6.2L VIN R, 7.0L VIN E **Transmissions:** All	**HO2S Performance (Bank 1 Sensor 1)** DTCs P0068, P0101, P0102, P0103, P0106, P0107, P0108, P0112, P0113, P0116, P0117, P0118, P0120, P0121, P0122, P0123, P0125, P0128, P0201, P0202, P0203, P0204, P0205, P0206, P0207, P0208, P0220, P0222, P0223, P0442, P0443, P0446, P0449, P0455, P0496, P1516, P2101, P2119, P2135, P2176 are not set. The Engine Run Time parameter is more than 100 seconds. The Engine speed parameter is between 500-5,000 RPM. The Ignition 1 Signal parameter is between 10-18 volts. The Mass Airflow (MAF) Sensor parameter is between 3-30 g/s. The ECT Sensor parameter is more than 70°C (158°F). DTC P2A00 runs continuously when the above conditions are met for 5 seconds. The control module detects that the Loop Status parameter is open. DTC P2A00 sets within 5 seconds when the above condition is met. **Possible Causes:** • HO2S low reference circuit for an open/high resistance • HO2S signal circuit for a short to ground • HO2S signal circuit for a short to voltage • HO2S signal circuit for an open/high resistance • HO2S has failed • ECM has failed

DTC	Trouble Code Title, Conditions & Possible Causes
DTC: P2A00 **2T CCM, MIL: Yes** **Years:** 2008, 2009 **Models:** Astra, Aura, Aveo, Aveo5, Cobalt G3, G5 **Engines:** 1.6L VIN 6, 1.6L VIN E, 1.8L VIN 1, 2.0L VIN P, 2.0L VIN X, 2.2L VIN H, 2.2L VIN F, 2.4L VIN 5, 2.4L VIN B **Transmissions:** All	**HO2S Performance Sensor 1** DTCs P0030, P0031, P0032, P0130, P0131, P0132, P0133, P0134, P2297 are not set. The ignition is ON. The ECM detects that the HO2S 1 is not ready after 30 s. DTC P2A00 sets immediately after the above condition is met. **Possible Causes:** • HO2S signal circuit open/high resistance • HO2S signal circuit short to voltage • HO2S signal circuit open/high resistance • HO2S is damaged • ECM has failed
DTC: P2A01 **1T CCM, MIL: Yes** **Years:** 2008, 2009 **Models:** Corvette, CTS, CTS-V, DTS **Engines:** 4.6L VIN Y, 6.2L VIN W, 6.2L VIN P, 6.2L VIN R, 7.0L VIN E **Transmissions:** All	**HO2S Performance (Bank 1 Sensor 2)** DTCs P0030, P0036, P0053, P0054, P0068, P0101, P0102, P0103, P0106, P0107, P0108, P0112, P0113, P0116, P0117, P0118, P0120, P0121, P0122, P0123, P0128, P0131, P0132, P0133, P0134, P0135, P0137, P0138, P0140, P0141, P0171, P0172, P0174, P0175, P0201, P0202, P0203, P0204, P0205, P0206, P0207, P0208, P0220, P0222, P0223, P0300, P0301, P0302, P0303, P0304, P0305, P0306, P0307, P0308, P0442, P0443, P0446, P0449, P0455, P0496, P1133, P1516, P2101, P2119, P2135, P2176, P2A00 are not set. The engine is running. The Engine Run Time parameter is less than 260 seconds. DTC P2A01 Passive Test runs the passive test once per drive cycle when the above conditions are met for 2 seconds. The control module detects that the HO2S 2 did not transition below 299 mV and above 751 mV during the passive test. One of the following tests fail once per trip/runs until pass or fail reporting: DTC P2A01 sets within 2 minutes when the above conditions are met. **Possible Causes:** • HO2S low reference circuit for an open/high resistance • HO2S signal circuit for a short to ground • HO2S signal circuit for a short to voltage • HO2S signal circuit for an open/high resistance • HO2S has failed • ECM has failed
DTC: P2A01 **2T CCM, MIL: Yes** **Years:** 2008, 2009 **Models:** Astra, Aura, Aveo, Aveo5, Cobalt G3, G5 **Engines:** 1.6L VIN 6, 1.6L VIN E, 1.8L VIN 1, 2.0L VIN P, 2.0L VIN X, 2.2L VIN H, 2.2L VIN F, 2.4L VIN 5, 2.4L VIN B **Transmissions:** All	**HO2S Performance Sensor 2** DTCs P0036, P0037, P0038, P0068, P0101, P0102, P0103, P0136, P0137, P0138, P0139, P0140, P0141, P0171, P0172, P0201, P0202, P0203, P0204, P0261, P0262, P0264, P0265, P0267, P0268, P0270, P0271, P0300, P0301, P0302, P0303, P0304, P0313, P0443, P0458, P0459, P0496, P1101, P2270, P2271 are not set. The ignition is ON. Decel fuel cut-off is active. The mass airflow is more than 10 grams per second. DTC P2A01 runs continuously when the above conditions are met. The ECM detects that the HO2S 2 voltage is more than 0.151 V. DTC P2A01 sets when the above condition is met. **Possible Causes:** • Collapsed air intake duct • Restricted air filter element • Excessive fuel in the crankcase • Fuel contamination • Rich injectors • Engine mechanical conditions • Restricted exhaust system • Faulty HO2S • ECM has failed

OBD II Trouble Code List (P3xxx Codes)

DTC	Trouble Code Title, Conditions & Possible Causes
DTC: P3400 **1T CCM, MIL: Yes** **Years:** 2008, 2009 **Models:** Allure, Aura, Canyon, Colorado, LaCrosse **Engines:** 2.9L VIN 9, 3.5L VIN N, 3.8L VIN 2, 5.3L VIN C, 5.3L VIN L **Transmissions:** All	**Cylinder Deactivation System Performance** DTCs P0102, P0103, P0107, P0108, P0112, P0113, P0117, P0119, P0335, and P0336 are not set. The engine speed is between 450-6,400 RPM. The IAT Sensor parameter is between −7 and +125°C (+19 and +257°F). The ECT Sensor parameter is between 70- 125°C (158-257°F). Time in V8 mode is more than 2 seconds. Time in V4 mode is more than 2 seconds. This DTC runs continuously within the enabling conditions. The ECM detects that the actual measured values from the MAF sensor, MAP sensor, and TP sensor, is not within the range of the calculated values for V4 mode. The above condition is met for more than 100 milliseconds. **Possible Causes:** • Low oil pressure • Oil contamination • Ignition 1 voltage circuit powertrain relay • Valve Lifter Oil Manifold (VLOM) • Powertrain relay • ECM has failed

DTC	Trouble Code Title, Conditions & Possible Causes
DTC: P3401 **1T CCM, MIL: Yes** **Years:** 2008, 2009 **Models:** Allure, Aura, Canyon, Colorado, LaCrosse **Engines:** 2.9L VIN 9, 3.5L VIN N, 3.8L VIN 2, 5.3L VIN C, 5.3L VIN L **Transmissions:** All	**Cylinder 1 Deactivation Solenoid Control Circuit** The engine speed is greater than 400 RPM. The ignition voltage is between 9-18 volts. DTC P3401, P3425, P3441, and P3449 runs continuously when the above conditions are met. The ECM detects that the commanded state of the low side driver and the actual voltage level of the control circuit do not match. The condition is present for 20 out of 25 sample counts. **Possible Causes:** • Low oil pressure • Oil contamination • Ignition 1 voltage circuit powertrain relay • Valve Lifter Oil Manifold (VLOM) • Powertrain relay • ECM has failed
DTC: P3425 **1T CCM, MIL: Yes** **Years:** 2008, 2009 **Models:** Allure, Aura, Canyon, Colorado, LaCrosse **Engines:** 2.9L VIN 9, 3.5L VIN N, 3.8L VIN 2, 5.3L VIN C, 5.3L VIN L **Transmissions:** All	**Cylinder 4 Deactivation Solenoid Control Circuit** The engine speed is greater than 400 RPM. The ignition voltage is between 9-18 volts. DTC P3401, P3425, P3441, and P3449 runs continuously when the above conditions are met. The ECM detects that the commanded state of the low side driver and the actual voltage level of the control circuit do not match. The condition is present for 20 out of 25 sample counts. **Possible Causes:** • Low oil pressure • Oil contamination • Ignition 1 voltage circuit powertrain relay • Valve Lifter Oil Manifold (VLOM) • Powertrain relay • ECM has failed
DTC: P3441 **1T CCM, MIL: Yes** **Years:** 2008, 2009 **Models:** Allure, Aura, Canyon, Colorado, LaCrosse **Engines:** 2.9L VIN 9, 3.5L VIN N, 3.8L VIN 2, 5.3L VIN C, 5.3L VIN L **Transmissions:** All	**Cylinder 6 Deactivation Solenoid Control Circuit** The engine speed is greater than 400 RPM. The ignition voltage is between 9-18 volts. DTC P3401, P3425, P3441, and P3449 runs continuously when the above conditions are met. The ECM detects that the commanded state of the low side driver and the actual voltage level of the control circuit do not match. The condition is present for 20 out of 25 sample counts. **Possible Causes:** • Low oil pressure • Oil contamination • Ignition 1 voltage circuit powertrain relay • Valve Lifter Oil Manifold (VLOM) • Powertrain relay • ECM has failed
DTC: P3449 **1T CCM, MIL: Yes** **Years:** 2008, 2009 **Models:** Allure, Aura, Canyon, Colorado, LaCrosse **Engines:** 2.9L VIN 9, 3.5L VIN N, 3.8L VIN 2, 5.3L VIN C, 5.3L VIN L **Transmissions:** All	**Cylinder 7 Deactivation Solenoid Control Circuit** The engine speed is greater than 400 RPM. The ignition voltage is between 9-18 volts. DTC P3401, P3425, P3441, and P3449 runs continuously when the above conditions are met. The ECM detects that the commanded state of the low side driver and the actual voltage level of the control circuit do not match. The condition is present for 20 out of 25 sample counts. **Possible Causes:** • Low oil pressure • Oil contamination • Ignition 1 voltage circuit powertrain relay • Valve Lifter Oil Manifold (VLOM) • Powertrain relay • ECM has failed

OBD II Trouble Code List (U1xxx Codes)

DTC	Trouble Code Title, Conditions & Possible Causes
DTC: U0020 **1T CCM, MIL: Yes** **Years:** 2008, 2009, 2010 **Models:** Acadia, Allure, Aura, Camaro, CTS, CTS-V, Enclave, LaCrosse, Outlook, Traverse **Engines:** 3.6L VIN 7, 3.6L VIN D, 3.6L VIN V **Transmissions:** All	**Low Speed CAN Communication Bus Performance** Voltage at the modules is in the normal operating voltage range. The vehicle power mode requires serial data communication to occur. The DTC U2100 does not have a current status. A supervised periodic message that includes the transmitter module availability has not been received. **Possible Causes:** • Control modules the vehicle is equipped with • Control modules B+, ignition, ground, communication enable and serial data circuit terminals • Control module locations on the low and high speed GMLAN serial data circuits

DTC	Trouble Code Title, Conditions & Possible Causes
DTC: U0073 **1T CCM, MIL: Yes** **Years:** 2008, 2009, 2010 **Models:** Acadia, Allure, Aura, Camaro, CTS, CTS-V, Enclave, LaCrosse, Outlook, Traverse **Engines:** 3.6L VIN 7, 3.6L VIN D, 3.6L VIN V **Transmissions:** All	**Control Module Communication Bus Off** Supply voltage at the modules are in the normal operating range. The vehicle power mode requires serial data communications. The module setting the DTC has attempted to establish communications on the serial data circuits more than 3 times. **Possible Causes:** • Control modules the vehicle is equipped with • Control module locations on the low speed GMLAN serial data circuit • Each control module's low speed GMLAN serial data circuit terminals • Control modules the vehicle is equipped with • High speed GMLAN serial data circuit terminating resistors • Control module locations on the high speed GMLAN serial data circuits • Each control module's high speed GMLAN serial data circuit terminals
DTC: U1000 **1T ECM, MIL: Yes** **Years:** 2008, 2009, 2010 **Models:** All **Engines:** All **Transmissions:** All	**Class 2 Communication Malfunction** Modules connected to the Class 2 circuit monitor for serial data communications during normal vehicle operation. Operating information and commands are exchanged among the modules. When a module receives a message for a critical operating parameter, the module records the identification number of the module that sent the message. These Node Alive messages are used for State of Health monitoring. A critical operating parameter is one which, when not received, requires that the module use a default value for that parameter. When a module does not associate an identification number with at least one critical parameter within 5 seconds of starting data communication, DTC U1000 or U1255 is set. When more than one critical parameter does not have an identification number associated with it, the code will only set once. **Possible Causes:** • Class 2 circuit is open, shorted to ground or shorted to power • ECM ignition power circuit(s) has a high resistance condition • ECM main ground circuit(s) has a high resistance condition • SDM (module) could be shorted pulling the voltage low
DTC: U1016 **1T ECM, MIL: Yes** **Years:** 2008, 2009, 2010 **Models:** All **Engines:** All **Transmissions:** All	**No Communication With Powertrain Control Module** Key on, and a message from a learned ID number was not detected for the five seconds. Modules on the Class 2 circuit monitor for data communications during vehicle operation. When a module receives a message for critical data, the module records the identification number of the module sending the message for State of Health monitoring (Node Alive messages). Once a module learns an ID number, it checks for that module's Node Alive message. **Note: Look for this code in All modules. The one without the code is the module that has a problem, and it may have failed.** **Possible Causes:** • ECM Class 2 circuit is open, shorted to ground or to B+ • ECM ignition power circuit(s) has a high resistance condition • ECM main ground circuit(s) has a high resistance condition • ECM (module) may have failed and is pulling the circuit low
DTC: U1026 **1T ECM, MIL: Yes** **Years:** 2008, 2009, 2010 **Models:** Avalanche, Camaro, Canyon, Escalade/EXT/ESV, Suburban, Tahoe, Yukon **Engines:** 4.8L VIN C, 5.3L VIN 0, 5.3L VIN 3, 5.3L VIN J, 5.3L VIN L, 6.0L VIN K, 6.0L VIN Y, 6.2L VIN J, 6.2L VIN W, 6.2L VIN 8 **Transmissions:** All	**Loss of ATC Class 2 Communication** Key on or engine running; and a module detected that it could not communicate with the ATC controller for 1 second. Modules connected to the Class 2 circuit monitor for data communications during normal vehicle operation. Operating information and commands are exchanged among the modules. When a module receives a message for a critical operating parameter, the module records the identification number of the module that sent the message for State of Health monitoring (Node Alive messages). Once a module learns an identification number, it will monitor for that module's Node Alive message. Each module on the Class 2 circuit that is powered and performing functions that require detection of a communications malfunction is required to send a Node Alive message every two seconds. When no message is detected from a learned identification number for five seconds, a DTC U1xxx (XXX is equal to the 3-digit identification number) is set. **Possible Causes:** • Check for a loose connection at the ATC module • Test the main power and ground circuits to the ATC module • Check the Class 2 serial data circuit to the ATC module • ATC module may have failed

DTC	Trouble Code Title, Conditions & Possible Causes
DTC: U1041 **2T ECM, MIL: Yes** **Years:** 2008, 2009, 2010 **Models:** Avalanche, Camaro, Canyon, Escalade/EXT/ESV, Suburban, Tahoe, Yukon **Engines:** 4.8L VIN C, 5.3L VIN 0, 5.3L VIN 3, 5.3L VIN J, 5.3L VIN L, 6.0L VIN K, 6.0L VIN Y, 6.2L VIN J, 6.2L VIN W, 6.2L VIN 8 **Transmissions:** All	**Loss of Electronic Brake Controller Communication** Key on or engine running; and a module detected that it could not communicate with the EBCM controller for 1 second. Modules connected to the Class 2 circuit monitor for data communications during normal vehicle operation. Operating information and commands are exchanged among the modules. When a module receives a message for a critical operating parameter, the module records the identification number of the module that sent the message for State of Health monitoring (Node Alive messages). Once a module learns an identification number, it will monitor for that module's Node Alive message. Each module on the Class 2 circuit that is powered and performing functions that require detection of a communications malfunction is required to send a Node Alive message every two seconds. When no message is detected from a learned identification number for five seconds, a DTC U1xxx (XXX is equal to the 3-digit identification number) is set. **Possible Causes:** • Check for a loose connection at the EBCM (module) • Test the main power and ground circuits to the EBCM (module) • Check the Class 2 serial data circuit to the EBCM (module) • EBCM (module) may have failed
DTC: U1048 **2T ECM, MIL: Yes** **Years:** 2008, 2009, 2010 **Models:** All With Rear Steering **Engines:** All **Transmissions:** All	**No Communication With Rear Wheel Steering Control Module** Key on, and a message from a learned ID number was not detected for the five seconds. Modules on the Class 2 circuit monitor for data communications during vehicle operation. When a module receives a message for critical data, the module records the identification number of the module sending the message for State of Health monitoring (Node Alive messages). Once a module learns an ID number, it checks for that module's Node Alive message. **Note: Look for this code in All modules. The one without the code is the module that has a problem, and it may have failed.** **Possible Causes:** • RWSCM Class 2 circuit is open, shorted to ground or to B+ • RWSCM ignition power circuit has a high resistance condition • RESCM main ground circuit(s) has a high resistance condition • RESCM (module) may have failed and is pulling the circuit low
DTC: U1064 **2T ECM, MIL: Yes** **Years:** 2008, 2009, 2010 **Models:** All **Engines:** All **Transmissions:** All	**No Communication With Body Control Module** Key on, and a message from a learned ID number was not detected for the five seconds. Modules on the Class 2 circuit monitor for data communications during vehicle operation. When a module receives a message for critical data, the module records the identification number of the module sending the message for State of Health monitoring (Node Alive messages). Look for this code in All modules. The one without this code may have failed **Possible Causes:** • BCM Class 2 circuit is open, shorted to ground or to B+ • BCM ignition power circuit has a high resistance condition • BCM main ground circuit(s) has a high resistance condition • BCM (module) may have failed and is pulling the circuit low
DTC: U1088 **2T ECM, MIL: Yes** **Years:** 2008, 2009, 2010 **Models:** All **Engines:** All **Transmissions:** All	**No Communication With SDM (Restraint Module)** Key on, and a message from a learned ID number was not detected for the five seconds. Modules on the Class 2 circuit monitor for data communications during vehicle operation. When a module receives a message for critical data, the module records the identification number of the module sending the message for State of Health monitoring (Node Alive messages). Look for this code in All modules. The one without this code may have failed. **Possible Causes:** • SDM Class 2 circuit is open, shorted to ground or to B+ • SDM ignition power circuit has a high resistance condition • SDM main ground circuit(s) has a high resistance condition • SDM (module) may have failed and is pulling the circuit low
DTC: U1092 **2T ECM, MIL: Yes** **Years:** 2008, 2009, 2010 **Models:** Avalanche, Camaro, Canyon, Escalade/EXT/ESV, Suburban, Tahoe, Yukon **Engines:** 4.8L VIN C, 5.3L VIN 0, 5.3L VIN 3, 5.3L VIN J, 5.3L VIN L, 6.0L VIN K, 6.0L VIN Y, 6.2L VIN J, 6.2L VIN W, 6.2L VIN 8 **Transmissions:** All	**Loss of VTD (Pass Lock) Communication** Key on or engine running; and a module detected that it could not communicate with the VTD controller for 1 second. Modules connected to the Class 2 circuit monitor for data communications during normal vehicle operation. Operating information and commands are exchanged among the modules. When a module receives a message for a critical operating parameter, the module records the identification number of the module that sent the message for State of Health monitoring (Node Alive messages). Once a module learns an identification number, it will monitor for that module's Node Alive message. Each module on the Class 2 circuit that is powered and performing functions that require detection of a communications malfunction is required to send a Node Alive message every two seconds. When no message is detected from a learned identification number for five seconds, a DTC U1xxx (the X's identify the 3-digit identification number) is set. **Possible Causes:** • Check for a loose connection at the VTD module • Test the main power and ground circuits to the VTD module • Check the Class 2 serial data circuit to the VTD module • VTD module may have failed

DTC	Trouble Code Title, Conditions & Possible Causes
DTC: U1096 **2T ECM, MIL:** Yes **Years:** 2008, 2009, 2010 **Models:** All **Engines:** All **Transmissions:** All	**No Communication With Instrument Panel Cluster** Key on, and a message from a learned ID number was not detected for the five seconds. Modules on the Class 2 circuit monitor for data communications during vehicle operation. When a module receives a message for critical data, the module records the identification number of the module sending the message for State of Health monitoring (Node Alive messages). Once a module learns an ID number, it checks for that module's Node Alive message. **Note: Look for this code in All modules. The one without the code is the module that has a problem, and it may have failed.** **Possible Causes:** • IPC Class 2 circuit is open, shorted to ground or to B+ • IPC ignition power circuit has a high resistance condition • IPC main ground circuit(s) has a high resistance condition • IPC (module) may have failed and is pulling the circuit low
DTC: U1097 **2T ECM, MIL:** Yes **Years:** 2008, 2009, 2010 **Models:** All **Engines:** All **Transmissions:** All	**No Communication With Driver Information Center** Key on, and a message from a learned ID number was not detected for the five seconds. Modules on the Class 2 circuit monitor for data communications during vehicle operation. When a module receives a message for critical data, the module records the identification number of the module sending the message for State of Health monitoring (Node Alive messages). Once a module learns an ID number, it checks for that module's Node Alive message. **Note: Look for this code in All modules. The one without the code is the module that has a problem, and it may have failed.** **Possible Causes:** • DIC Class 2 circuit is open, shorted to ground or to B+ • DIC ignition power circuit has a high resistance condition • DIC main ground circuit(s) has a high resistance condition • DIC (module) may have failed and is pulling the circuit low
DTC: U1151 **2T ECM, MIL:** Yes **Years:** 2008, 2009, 2010 **Models:** All **Engines:** All **Transmissions:** All	**No Communication With Vehicle Interface Unit** Key on, and a message from a learned ID number was not detected for the five seconds. Modules on the Class 2 circuit monitor for data communications during vehicle operation. When a module receives a message for critical data, the module records the identification number of the module sending the message for State of Health monitoring (Node Alive messages). Once a module learns an ID number, it checks for that module's Node Alive message. The module without this code is the module with a problem (it has failed). **Possible Causes:** • VIU Class 2 circuit is open, shorted to ground or to B+ • VIU ignition power circuit has a high resistance condition • VIU main ground circuit(s) has a high resistance condition • VIU (module) may have failed and is pulling the circuit low
DTC: U1152 **2T ECM, MIL:** Yes **Years:** 2008, 2009, 2010 **Models:** All **Engines:** All **Transmissions:** All	**No Communication With HVAC Control Module** Key on, and a message from a learned ID number was not detected for the five seconds. Modules on the Class 2 circuit monitor for data communications during vehicle operation. When a module receives a message for critical data, the module records the identification number of the module sending the message for State of Health monitoring (Node Alive messages). Once a module learns an ID number, it checks for that module's Node Alive message. The module without this code is the module with a problem (it has failed). **Possible Causes:** • HVAC Class 2 circuit is open, shorted to ground or to B+ • HVAC ignition power circuit has a high resistance condition • HVAC main ground circuit(s) has a high resistance condition • HVAC (module) may have failed and is pulling the circuit low
DTC: U1193 **2T ECM, MIL:** Yes **Years:** 2008, 2009, 2010 **Models:** Avalanche, Camaro, Canyon, Escalade/EXT/ESV, Suburban, Tahoe, Yukon **Engines:** 4.8L VIN C, 5.3L VIN 0, 5.3L VIN 3, 5.3L VIN J, 5.3L VIN L, 6.0L VIN K, 6.0L VIN Y, 6.2L VIN J, 6.2L VIN W, 6.2L VIN 8 **Transmissions:** All	**Loss of Vehicle Immobilizer Module Communications** Key on or engine running; and a module detected that it could not communicate with the VIM controller for 1 second. Modules connected to the Class 2 circuit monitor for data communications during normal vehicle operation. Operating information and commands are exchanged among the modules. When a module receives a message for a critical operating parameter, the module records the identification number of the module that sent the message for State of Health monitoring (Node Alive messages). Once a module learns an identification number, it will monitor for that module's Node Alive message. Each module on the Class 2 circuit that is powered and performing functions that require detection of a communications malfunction is required to send a Node Alive message every two seconds. When no message is detected from a learned identification number for five seconds, a DTC U1xxx (XXX is equal to the 3-digit identification number) is set. **Possible Causes:** • Test the main power and ground circuits to the VIM module for a loose connection • Check the Class 2 serial data circuit to the VIM module • VTD module may have failed

DTC	Trouble Code Title, Conditions & Possible Causes
DTC: U1255 **2T ECM, MIL: Yes** **Years:** 2008, 2009, 2010 **Models:** All **Engines:** All **Transmissions:** All	**Class 2 Communications Malfunction** Modules connected to the Class 2 circuit monitor for serial data communications during normal vehicle operation. Operating data and commands are exchanged among modules. When a module receives a message for a critical operating parameter, the module records the identification number of the module that sent the message. These Node Alive messages are used for State of Health monitoring. A critical operating parameter is one which, when not received, requires the module use a default value for that parameter. If a module does not associate an ID number with at least one critical parameter in 5 seconds after starting communication, U1000 or U1255 is set. If two or more are missing, the code sets at once. **Possible Causes:** • Class 2 circuit is open, shorted to ground or shorted to power • ECM ignition power circuit(s) has a high resistance condition • ECM main ground circuit(s) has a high resistance condition
DTC: U1300 **1T ECM, MIL: Yes** **Years:** 2008, 2009, 2010 **Models:** All **Engines:** All **Transmissions:** All	**Class 2 Circuit Short to Ground** Key on or engine running; system voltage supplied to the module is in the normal operating voltage range, vehicle power mode requires serial data communication to occur, and the ECM did no detect any valid messages on the Class 2 circuit, or the voltage condition detected on the Class 2 circuit was low for 3 seconds. Modules connected to the Class 2 circuit check for data communications during normal vehicle operation. Operating information and commands are exchanged among the modules. Each module transmits Node Alive messages on the Class 2 data circuit once every 2 seconds. When the module detects a low voltage condition on the Class 2 serial data circuit for approximately 3 seconds, it sets U1300 or U1305 if it cannot identify the problem. **Note: This code is set by loss of communication. Look in All of the modules for this trouble code - the one without it has a problem** **Possible Causes:** • Class 2 serial data line was in a low state for 3 seconds due to a short to sensor ground or chassis ground • One or more modules on the Class 2 line has a short to ground
DTC: U1301 **1T ECM, MIL: Yes** **Years:** 2008, 2009, 2010 **Models:** All **Engines:** All **Transmissions:** All	**Class 2 Circuit Short to Battery** Key on or engine running; system voltage supplied to the module is in the normal operating voltage range, vehicle power mode requires serial data communication to occur, and the ECM did no detect any valid messages on the Class 2 circuit, or the voltage condition detected on the Class 2 circuit was low for 3 seconds. Modules connected to the Class 2 circuit check for data communications during normal vehicle operation. Operating information and commands are exchanged among the modules. In addition, each module transmits Node Alive messages on the Class 2 data circuit once every 2 seconds. If the module detects a high voltage condition on the Class 2 serial data circuit for 3 seconds, it sets U1300. **Note: This code is set by loss of communication. Look in All of the modules for this trouble code - the one without it has a problem.** **Possible Causes:** • Class 2 serial data line was in a high state for 3 seconds due to a short to VREF or system power • One or more modules on Class 2 line has an short to power
DTC: U1305 **1T ECM, MIL: Yes** **Years:** 2008, 2009, 2010 **Models:** All **Engines:** All **Transmissions:** All	**Class 2 Data Link High or Low** Key on or engine running; system voltage supplied to the module is in the normal operating voltage range, vehicle power mode requires serial data communication to occur, and the ECM did no detect any valid messages on the Class 2 circuit, or the voltage condition detected on the Class 2 circuit was low for 3 seconds. Modules connected to the Class 2 circuit check for data communications during normal vehicle operation. Operating information and commands are exchanged among the modules. In addition, each module transmits Node Alive messages on the Class 2 data circuit about once every 2 seconds. When the module detects a high voltage condition on the Class 2 serial data circuit for approximately 3 seconds, it sets U1300 or U1305 if it cannot identify the problem. **Possible Causes:** • Class 2 serial data line has either a high or low voltage condition on the circuit, and the module cannot identify the fault • One or more modules on Class 2 line has an short to power • One or more modules on the Class 2 line has a short to ground

DTC	Trouble Code Title, Conditions & Possible Causes
DTC: U2100 **1T CCM, MIL: Yes** **Years:** 2008, 2009 **Models:** Acadia, Allure, Aura, Camaro, CTS, CTS-V, Enclave, LaCrosse, Outlook, Traverse **Engines:** 3.6L VIN 7, 3.6L VIN D, 3.6L VIN V **Transmissions:** All	**Controller Area Network (CAN) Bus Communication** Supply voltage at the modules are in the normal operating range. vehicle power mode requires serial data communicationsThe module setting the DTC has attempted to establish communications on the serial data circuits more than 3 times. **Possible Causes:** • Control modules the vehicle is equipped with • Control module locations on the low speed GMLAN serial data circuit • Each control module's low speed GMLAN serial data circuit terminals • Control modules the vehicle is equipped with • High speed GMLAN serial data circuit terminating resistors • Control module locations on the high speed GMLAN serial data circuits • Each control module's high speed GMLAN serial data circuit terminals

GLOSSARY

ABS: Anti-lock braking system. An electro-mechanical braking system which is designed to minimize or prevent wheel lock-up during braking.

ABSOLUTE PRESSURE: Atmospheric (barometric) pressure plus the pressure gauge reading.

ACCELERATOR PUMP: A small pump located in the carburetor that feeds fuel into the air/fuel mixture during acceleration.

ACCUMULATOR: A device that controls shift quality by cushioning the shock of hydraulic oil pressure being applied to a clutch or band.

ACTUATING MECHANISM: The mechanical output devices of a hydraulic system, for example, clutch pistons and band servos.

ACTUATOR: The output component of a hydraulic or electronic system.

ADVANCE: Setting the ignition timing so that spark occurs earlier before the piston reaches top dead center (TDC).

ADAPTIVE MEMORY (ADAPTIVE STRATEGY): The learning ability of the TCM or PCM to redefine its decision-making process to provide optimum shift quality.

AFTER TOP DEAD CENTER (ATDC): The point after the piston reaches the top of its travel on the compression stroke.

AIR BAG: Device on the inside of the car designed to inflate on impact of crash, protecting the occupants of the car.

AIR CHARGE TEMPERATURE (ACT) SENSOR: The temperature of the airflow into the engine is measured by an ACT sensor, usually located in the lower intake manifold or air cleaner.

AIR CLEANER: An assembly consisting of a housing, filter and any connecting ductwork. The filter element is made up of a porous paper, sometimes with a wire mesh screening, and is designed to prevent airborne particles from entering the engine through the carburetor or throttle body.

AIR INJECTION: One method of reducing harmful exhaust emissions by injecting air into each of the exhaust ports of an engine. The fresh air entering the hot exhaust manifold causes any remaining fuel to be burned before it can exit the tailpipe.

AIR PUMP: An emission control device that supplies fresh air to the exhaust manifold to aid in more completely burning exhaust gases.

AIR/FUEL RATIO: The ratio of air-to-gasoline by weight in the fuel mixture drawn into the engine.

ALDL (assembly line diagnostic link): Electrical connector for scanning ECM/PCM/TCM input and output devices.

ALIGNMENT RACK: A special drive-on vehicle lift apparatus/measuring device used to adjust a vehicle's toe, caster and camber angles.

ALL WHEEL DRIVE: Term used to describe a full time four wheel drive system or any other vehicle drive system that continuously delivers power to all four wheels. This system is found primarily on station wagon vehicles and SUVs not utilized for significant off road use.

ALTERNATING CURRENT (AC): Electric current that flows first in one direction, then in the opposite direction, continually reversing flow.

ALTERNATOR: A device which produces AC (alternating current) which is converted to DC (direct current) to charge the car battery.

AMMETER: An instrument, calibrated in amperes, used to measure the flow of an electrical current in a circuit. Ammeters are always connected in series with the circuit being tested.

AMPERAGE: The total amount of current (amperes) flowing in a circuit.

AMPLIFIER: A device used in an electrical circuit to increase the voltage of an output signal.

AMP/HR. RATING (BATTERY): Measurement of the ability of a battery to deliver a stated amount of current for a stated period of time. The higher the amp/hr. rating, the better the battery.

AMPERE: The rate of flow of electrical current present when one volt of electrical pressure is applied against one ohm of electrical resistance.

ANALOG COMPUTER: Any microprocessor that uses similar (analogous) electrical signals to make its calculations.

ANODIZED: A special coating applied to the surface of aluminum valves for extended service life.

ANTIFREEZE: A substance (ethylene or propylene glycol) added to the coolant to prevent freezing in cold weather.

ANTI-FOAM AGENTS: Minimize fluid foaming from the whipping action encountered in the converter and planetary action.

ANTI-WEAR AGENTS: Zinc agents that control wear on the gears, bushings, and thrust washers.

ANTI-LOCK BRAKING SYSTEM: A supplementary system to the base hydraulic system that prevents sustained lock-up of the wheels during braking as well as automatically controlling wheel slip.

ANTI-ROLL BAR: See stabilizer bar.

ARC: A flow of electricity through the air between two electrodes or contact points that produces a spark.

ARMATURE: A laminated, soft iron core wrapped by a wire that converts electrical energy to mechanical energy as in a motor or relay. When rotated in a magnetic field, it changes mechanical energy into electrical energy as in a generator.

ATDC: After Top Dead Center.

ATF: Automatic transmission fluid.

ATMOSPHERIC PRESSURE: The pressure on the Earth's surface caused by the weight of the air in the atmosphere. At sea level, this pressure is 14.7 psi at 32°F (101 kPa at 0°C).

ATOMIZATION: The breaking down of a liquid into a fine mist that can be suspended in air.

AUXILIARY ADD-ON COOLER: A supplemental transmission fluid cooling device that is installed in series with the heat exchanger (cooler), located inside the radiator, to provide additional support to cool the hot fluid leaving the torque converter.

AUXILIARY PRESSURE: An added fluid pressure that is introduced into a regulator or balanced valve system to control valve movement. The auxiliary pressure itself can be either a fixed or a variable value. (See balanced valve; regulator valve.)

AWD: All wheel drive.

AXIAL FORCE: A side or end thrust force acting in or along the same plane as the power flow.

AXIAL PLAY: Movement parallel to a shaft or bearing bore.

AXLE CAPACITY: The maximum load-carrying capacity of the axle itself, as specified by the manufacturer. This is usually a higher number than the GAWR.

AXLE RATIO: This is a number (3.07:1, 4.56:1, for example) expressing the ratio between driveshaft revolutions and wheel revolutions. A low numerical ratio allows the engine to work easier because it doesn't have to turn as fast. A high numerical ratio means that the engine has to turn more rpm's to move the wheels through the same number of turns.

BACKFIRE: The sudden combustion of gases in the intake or exhaust system that results in a loud explosion.

BACKLASH: The clearance or play between two parts, such as meshed gears.

BACKPRESSURE: Restrictions in the exhaust system that slow the exit of exhaust gases from the combustion chamber.

BAKELITE®: A heat resistant, plastic insulator material commonly used in printed circuit boards and transistorized components.

BALANCED VALVE: A valve that is positioned by opposing auxiliary hydraulic pressures and/or spring force. Examples include mainline regulator, throttle, and governor valves. (See regulator valve.)

BAND: A flexible ring of steel with an inner lining of friction material. When tightened around the outside of a drum, a planetary member is held stationary to the transmission/transaxle case.

BALL BEARING: A bearing made up of hardened inner and outer races between which hardened steel balls roll.

BALL JOINT: A ball and matching socket connecting suspension components (steering knuckle to lower control arms). It permits rotating movement in any direction between the components that are joined.

BARO (BAROMETRIC PRESSURE SENSOR): Measures the change in the intake manifold pressure caused by changes in altitude.

BAROMETRIC MANIFOLD ABSOLUTE PRESSURE (BMAP) SENSOR: Operates similarly to a conventional MAP sensor; reads intake manifold pressure and is also responsible for determining altitude and barometric pressure prior to engine operation.

BAROMETRIC PRESSURE: (See atmospheric pressure.)

BALLAST RESISTOR: A resistor in the primary ignition circuit that lowers voltage after the engine is started to reduce wear on ignition components.

BATTERY: A direct current electrical storage unit, consisting of the basic active materials of lead and sulfuric acid, which converts chemical energy into electrical energy. Used to provide current for the operation of the starter as well as other equipment, such as the radio, lighting, etc.

BEAD: The portion of a tire that holds it on the rim.

BEARING: A friction reducing, supportive device usually located between a stationary part and a moving part.

BEFORE TOP DEAD CENTER (BTDC): The point just before the piston reaches the top of its travel on the compression stroke.

BELTED TIRE: Tire construction similar to bias-ply tires, but using two or more layers of reinforced belts between body plies and the tread.

BEZEL: Piece of metal surrounding radio, headlights, gauges or similar components; sometimes used to hold the glass face of a gauge in the dash.

BIAS-PLY TIRE: Tire construction, using body ply reinforcing cords which run at alternating angles to the center line of the tread.

BI-METAL TEMPERATURE SENSOR: Any sensor or switch made of two dissimilar types of metal that bend when heated or cooled due to the different expansion rates of the alloys. These types of sensors usually function as an on/off switch.

BLOCK: See Engine Block.

BLOW-BY: Combustion gases, composed of water vapor and unburned fuel, that leak past the piston rings into the crankcase during normal engine operation. These gases are removed by the PCV system to prevent the buildup of harmful acids in the crankcase.

BOOK TIME: See Labor Time.

BOOK VALUE: The average value of a car, widely used to determine trade-in and resale value.

BOOST VALVE: Used at the base of the regulator valve to increase mainline pressure.

BORE: Diameter of a cylinder.

BRAKE CALIPER: The housing that fits over the brake disc. The caliper holds the brake pads, which are pressed against the discs by the caliper pistons when the brake pedal is depressed.

BRAKE HORSEPOWER (BHP): The actual horsepower available at the engine flywheel as measured by a dynamometer.

BRAKE FADE: Loss of braking power, usually caused by excessive heat after repeated brake applications.

BRAKE HORSEPOWER: Usable horsepower of an engine measured at the crankshaft.

BRAKE PAD: A brake shoe and lining assembly used with disc brakes.

BRAKE PROPORTIONING VALVE: A valve on the master cylinder which restricts hydraulic brake pressure to the wheels to a specified amount, preventing wheel lock-up.

BREAKAWAY: Often used by Chrysler to identify first-gear operation in D and 2 ranges. In these ranges, first-gear operation depends on a one-way roller clutch that holds on acceleration and releases (breaks away) on deceleration, resulting in a freewheeling coast-down condition.

BRAKE SHOE: The backing for the brake lining. The term is, however, usually applied to the assembly of the brake backing and lining.

BREAKER POINTS: A set of points inside the distributor, operated by a cam, which make and break the ignition circuit.

BRINNELLING: A wear pattern identified by a series of indentations at regular intervals. This condition is caused by a lack of lube, overload situations, and/or vibrations.

BTDC: Before Top Dead Center.

BUMP: Sudden and forceful apply of a clutch or band.

BUSHING: A liner, usually removable, for a bearing; an anti-friction liner used in place of a bearing.

CALIFORNIA ENGINE: An engine certified by the EPA for use in California only; conforms to more stringent emission regulations than Federal engine.

CALIPER: A hydraulically activated device in a disc brake system,

which is mounted straddling the brake rotor (disc). The caliper contains at least one piston and two brake pads. Hydraulic pressure on the piston(s) forces the pads against the rotor.

CAPACITY: The quantity of electricity that can be delivered from a unit, as from a battery in ampere-hours, or output, as from a generator.

CAMBER: One of the factors of wheel alignment. Viewed from the front of the car, it is the inward or outward tilt of the wheel. The top of the tire will lean outward (positive camber) or inward (negative camber).

CAMSHAFT: A shaft in the engine on which are the lobes (cams) which operate the valves. The camshaft is driven by the crankshaft, via a belt, chain or gears, at one half the crankshaft speed.

CAPACITOR: A device which stores an electrical charge.

CARBON MONOXIDE (CO): A colorless, odorless gas given off as a normal byproduct of combustion. It is poisonous and extremely dangerous in confined areas, building up slowly to toxic levels without warning if adequate ventilation is not available.

CARBURETOR: A device, usually mounted on the intake manifold of an engine, which mixes the air and fuel in the proper proportion to allow even combustion.

CASTER: The forward or rearward tilt of an imaginary line drawn through the upper ball joint and the center of the wheel. Viewed from the sides, positive caster (forward tilt) lends directional stability, while negative caster (rearward tilt) produces instability.

CATALYTIC CONVERTER: A device installed in the exhaust system, like a muffler, that converts harmful byproducts of combustion into carbon dioxide and water vapor by means of a heat-producing chemical reaction.

CENTRIFUGAL ADVANCE: A mechanical method of advancing the spark timing by using flyweights in the distributor that react to centrifugal force generated by the distributor shaft rotation.

CENTRIFUGAL FORCE: The outward pull of a revolving object, away from the center of revolution. Centrifugal force increases with the speed of rotation.

CETANE RATING: A measure of the ignition value of diesel fuel. The higher the cetane rating, the better the fuel. Diesel fuel cetane rating is roughly comparable to gasoline octane rating.

CHECK VALVE: Any one-way valve installed to permit the flow of air, fuel or vacuum in one direction only.

CHOKE: The valve/plate that restricts the amount of air entering an engine on the induction stroke, thereby enriching the air/fuel ratio.

CHUGGLE: Bucking or jerking condition that may be engine related and may be most noticeable when converter clutch is engaged; similar to the feel of towing a trailer.

CIRCLIP: A split steel snaping that fits into a groove to hold various parts in place.

CIRCUIT BREAKER: A switch which protects an electrical circuit from overload by opening the circuit when the current flow exceeds a pre-determined level. Some circuit breakers must be reset manually, while most reset automatically.

CIRCUIT: Any unbroken path through which an electrical current can flow. Also used to describe fuel flow in some instances.

CIRCUIT, BYPASS: Another circuit in parallel with the major circuit through which power is diverted.

CIRCUIT, CLOSED: An electrical circuit in which there is no interruption of current flow.

CIRCUIT, GROUND: The non-insulated portion of a complete circuit used as a common potential point. In automotive circuits, the ground is composed of metal parts, such as the engine, body sheet metal, and frame and is usually a negative potential.

CIRCUIT, HOT: That portion of a circuit not at ground potential. The hot circuit is usually insulated and is connected to the positive side of the battery.

CIRCUIT, OPEN: A break or lack of contact in an electrical circuit, either intentional (switch) or unintentional (bad connection or broken wire).

CIRCUIT, PARALLEL: A circuit having two or more paths for current flow with common positive and negative tie points. The same voltage is applied to each load device or parallel branch.

CIRCUIT, SERIES: An electrical system in which separate parts are connected end to end, using one wire, to form a single path for current to flow.

CIRCUIT, SHORT: A circuit that is accidentally completed in an electrical path for which it was not intended.

CLAMPING (ISOLATION) DIODES: Diodes positioned in a circuit to prevent self-induction from damaging electronic components.

CLEARCOAT: A transparent layer which, when sprayed over a vehicle's paint job, adds gloss and depth as well as an additional protective coating to the finish.

CLUTCH: Part of the power train used to connect/disconnect power to the rear wheels.

CLUTCH, FLUID: The same as a fluid coupling. A fluid clutch or coupling performs the same function as a friction clutch by utilizing fluid friction and inertia as opposed to solid friction used by a friction clutch. (See fluid coupling.)

CLUTCH, FRICTION: A coupling device that provides a means of smooth and positive engagement and disengagement of engine torque to the vehicle powertrain. Transmission of power through the clutch is accomplished by bringing one or more rotating drive members into contact with complementing driven members.

COAST: Vehicle deceleration caused by engine braking conditions.

COEFFICIENT OF FRICTION: The amount of surface tension between two contacting surfaces; identified by a scientifically calculated number.

COIL: Part of the ignition system that boosts the relatively low voltage supplied by the car's electrical system to the high voltage required to fire the spark plugs.

COMBINATION MANIFOLD: An assembly which includes both the intake and exhaust manifolds in one casting.

COMBINATION VALVE: A device used in some fuel systems that routes fuel vapors to a charcoal storage canister instead of venting them into the atmosphere. The valve relieves fuel tank pressure and allows fresh air into the tank as the fuel level drops to prevent a vapor lock situation.

COMBUSTION CHAMBER: The part of the engine in the cylinder head where combustion takes place.

COMPOUND GEAR: A gear consisting of two or more simple gears with a common shaft.

COMPOUND PLANETARY: A gearset that has more than the three elements found in a simple gearset and is constructed by combining members of two planetary gearsets to create additional gear ratio possibilities.

COMPRESSION CHECK: A test involving removing each spark plug and inserting a gauge. When the engine is cranked, the gauge will record a pressure reading in the individual cylinder. General operating condition can be determined from a compression check.

COMPRESSION RATIO: The ratio of the volume between the piston and cylinder head when the piston is at the bottom of its stroke (bottom dead center) and when the piston is at the top of its stroke (top dead center).

COMPUTER: An electronic control module that correlates input data according to prearranged engineered instructions; used for the management of an actuator system or systems.

CONDENSER: An electrical device which acts to store an electrical charge, preventing voltage surges.
2. A radiator-like device in the air conditioning system in which refrigerant gas condenses into a liquid, giving off heat.

CONDUCTOR: Any material through which an electrical current can be transmitted easily.

CONNECTING ROD: The connecting link between the crankshaft and piston.

CONSTANT VELOCITY JOINT: Type of universal joint in a halfshaft assembly in which the output shaft turns at a constant angular velocity without variation, provided that the speed of the input shaft is constant.

CONTINUITY: Continuous or complete circuit. Can be checked with an ohmmeter.

CONTROL ARM: The upper or lower suspension components which are mounted on the frame and support the ball joints and steering knuckles.

CONVENTIONAL IGNITION: Ignition system which uses breaker points.

CONVERTER: (See torque converter.)

CONVERTER LOCKUP: The switching from hydrodynamic to direct mechanical drive, usually through the application of a friction element called the converter clutch.

COOLANT: Mixture of water and anti-freeze circulated through the engine to carry off heat produced by the engine.

CORROSION INHIBITOR: An inhibitor in ATF that prevents corrosion of bushings, thrust washers, and oil cooler brazed joints.

COUNTERSHAFT: An intermediate shaft which is rotated by a mainshaft and transmits, in turn, that rotation to a working part.

COUPLING PHASE: Occurs when the torque converter is operating at its greatest hydraulic efficiency. The speed differential between the impeller and the turbine is at its minimum. At this point, the stator freewheels, and there is no torque multiplication.

CRANKCASE: The lower part of an engine in which the crankshaft and related parts operate.

CRANKSHAFT: Engine component (connected to pistons by connecting rods) which converts the reciprocating (up and down) motion of pistons to rotary motion used to turn the driveshaft.

CURB WEIGHT: The weight of a vehicle without passengers or payload, but including all fluids (oil, gas, coolant, etc.) and other equipment specified as standard.

CURRENT: The flow (or rate) of electrons moving through a circuit. Current is measured in amperes (amp).

CURRENT FLOW CONVENTIONAL: Current flows through a circuit from the positive terminal of the source to the negative terminal (plus to minus).

CURRENT FLOW, ELECTRON: Current or electrons flow from the negative terminal of the source, through the circuit, to the positive terminal (minus to plus).

CV-JOINT: Constant velocity joint.

CYCLIC VIBRATIONS: The off-center movement of a rotating object that is affected by its initial balance, speed of rotation, and working angles.

CYLINDER BLOCK: See engine block.

CYLINDER HEAD: The detachable portion of the engine, usually fastened to the top of the cylinder block and containing all or most of the combustion chambers. On overhead valve engines, it contains the valves and their operating parts. On overhead cam engines, it contains the camshaft as well.

CYLINDER: In an engine, the round hole in the engine block in which the piston(s) ride.

DATA LINK CONNECTOR (DLC): Current acronym/term applied to the federally mandated, diagnostic junction connector that is used to monitor ECM/PC/TCM inputs, processing strategies, and outputs including diagnostic trouble codes (DTCs).

DEAD CENTER: The extreme top or bottom of the piston stroke.

DECELERATION BUMP: When referring to a torque converter clutch in the applied position, a sudden release of the accelerator pedal causes a forceful reversal of power through the drivetrain (engine braking), just prior to the apply plate actually being released.

DELAYED (LATE OR EXTENDED): Condition where shift is expected but does not occur for a period of time, for example, where clutch or band engagement does not occur as quickly as expected during part throttle or wide open throttle apply of accelerator or when manually downshifting to a lower range.

DETENT: A spring-loaded plunger, pin, ball, or pawl used as a holding device on a ratchet wheel or shaft. In automatic transmissions, a detent mechanism is used for locking the manual valve in place.

DETENT DOWNSHIFT: (See kickdown.)

DETERGENT: An additive in engine oil to improve its operating characteristics.

DETONATION: An unwanted explosion of the air/fuel mixture in the combustion chamber caused by excess heat and compression, advanced timing, or an overly lean mixture. Also referred to as "ping".

DEXRON®: A brand of automatic transmission fluid.

DIAGNOSTIC TROUBLE CODES (DTCs): A digital display from the control module memory that identifies the input, processor, or output device circuit that is related to the powertrain emission/driveability malfunction detected. Diagnostic trouble codes can be read by the MIL to flash any codes or by using a handheld scanner.

DIAPHRAGM: A thin, flexible wall separating two cavities, such as in a vacuum advance unit.

DIESELING: The engine continues to run after the car is shut off; caused by fuel continuing to be burned in the combustion chamber.

DIFFERENTIAL: A geared assembly which allows the transmission of motion between drive axles, giving one axle the ability to rotate faster than the other, as in cornering.

DIFFERENTIAL AREAS: When opposing faces of a spool valve are acted upon by the same pressure but their areas differ in size, the face with the larger area produces the differential force and valve movement. (See spool valve.)

DIFFERENTIAL FORCE: (See differential areas)

DIGITAL READOUT: A display of numbers or a combination of numbers and letters.

DIGITAL VOLT OHMMETER: An electronic diagnostic tool used to measure voltage, ohms and amps as well as several other functions, with the readings displayed on a digital screen in tenths, hundredths and thousandths.

DIODE: An electrical device that will allow current to flow in one direction only.

DIRECT CURRENT (DC): Electrical current that flows in one direction only.

DIRECT DRIVE: The gear ratio is 1:1, with no change occurring in the torque and speed input/output relationship.

DISC BRAKE: A hydraulic braking assembly consisting of a brake disc, or rotor, mounted on an axle shaft, and a caliper assembly containing, usually two brake pads which are activated by hydraulic pressure. The pads are forced against the sides of the disc, creating friction which slows the vehicle.

DISPERSANTS: Suspend dirt and prevent sludge buildup in a liquid, such as engine oil.

DOUBLE BUMP (DOUBLE FEEL): Two sudden and forceful applies of a clutch or band.

DISPLACEMENT: The total volume of air that is displaced by all pistons as the engine turns through one complete revolution.

DISTRIBUTOR: A mechanically driven device on an engine which is responsible for electrically firing the spark plug at a pre-determined point of the piston stroke.

DOHC: Double overhead camshaft.

DOUBLE OVERHEAD CAMSHAFT: The engine utilizes two camshafts mounted in one cylinder head. One camshaft operates the exhaust valves, while the other operates the intake valves.

DOWEL PIN: A pin, inserted in mating holes in two different parts allowing those parts to maintain a fixed relationship.

DRIVELINE: The drive connection between the transmission and the drive wheels.

DRIVE TRAIN: The components that transmit the flow of power from the engine to the wheels. The components include the clutch, transmission, driveshafts (or axle shafts in front wheel drive), U-joints and differential.

DRUM BRAKE: A braking system which consists of two brake shoes and one or two wheel cylinders, mounted on a fixed backing plate, and a brake drum, mounted on an axle, which revolves around the assembly.

DRY CHARGED BATTERY: Battery to which electrolyte is added when the battery is placed in service.

DVOM: Digital volt ohmmeter

DWELL: The rate, measured in degrees of shaft rotation, at which an electrical circuit cycles on and off.

DYNAMIC: An application in which there is rotating or reciprocating motion between the parts.

EARLY: Condition where shift occurs before vehicle has reached proper speed, which tends to labor engine after upshift.

EBCM: See Electronic Control Unit (ECU).

ECM: See Electronic Control Unit (ECU).

ECU: Electronic control unit.

ELECTRODE: Conductor (positive or negative) of electric current.

ELECTROLYSIS: A surface etching or bonding of current conducting transmission/transaxle components that may occur when grounding straps are missing or in poor condition.

ELECTROLYTE: A solution of water and sulfuric acid used to activate the battery. Electrolyte is extremely corrosive.

ELECTROMAGNET: A coil that produces a magnetic field when current flows through its windings.

ELECTROMAGNETIC INDUCTION: A method to create (generate) current flow through the use of magnetism.

ELECTROMAGNETISM: The effects surrounding the relationship between electricity and magnetism.

ELECTROMOTIVE FORCE (EMF): The force or pressure (voltage) that causes current movement in an electrical circuit.

ELECTRONIC CONTROL UNIT: A digital computer that controls engine (and sometimes transmission, brake or other vehicle system) functions based on data received from various sensors. Examples used by some manufacturers include Electronic Brake Control Module (EBCM), Engine Control Module (ECM), Powertrain Control Module (PCM) or Vehicle Control Module (VCM).

ELECTRONIC IGNITION: A system in which the timing and firing of the spark plugs is controlled by an electronic control unit, usually called a module. These systems have no points or condenser.

ELECTRONIC PRESSURE CONTROL (EPC) SOLENOID: A specially designed solenoid containing a spool valve and spring assembly to control fluid mainline pressure. A variable current flow, controlled by the ECM/PCM, varies the internal force of the solenoid on the spool valve and resulting mainline pressure. (See variable force solenoid.)

ELECTRONICS: Miniaturized electrical circuits utilizing semiconductors, solid-state devices, and printed circuits. Electronic circuits utilize small amounts of power.

ELECTRONIFICATION: The application of electronic circuitry to a mechanical device. Regarding automatic transmissions, electrification is incorporated into converter clutch lockup, shift scheduling, and line pressure control systems.

ELECTROSTATIC DISCHARGE (ESD): An unwanted, high-voltage electrical current released by an individual who has taken on a static charge of electricity. Electronic components can be easily damaged by ESD.

ELEMENT: A device within a hydrodynamic drive unit designed with a set of blades to direct fluid flow.

ENAMEL: Type of paint that dries to a smooth, glossy finish.

END BUMP (END FEEL OR SLIP BUMP): Firmer feel at end of shift when compared with feel at start of shift.

END-PLAY: The clearance/gap between two components that allows for expansion of the parts as they warm up, to prevent binding and to allow space for lubrication.

ENERGY: The ability or capacity to do work.

ENGINE: The primary motor or power apparatus of a vehicle, which converts liquid or gas fuel into mechanical energy.

ENGINE BLOCK: The basic engine casting containing the cylinders, the crankshaft main bearings, as well as machined surfaces for the mounting of other components such as the cylinder head, oil pan, transmission, etc.

ENGINE BRAKING: Use of engine to slow vehicle by manually downshifting during zero-throttle coast down.

ENGINE CONTROL MODULE (ECM): Manages the engine and incorporates output control over the torque converter clutch solenoid. (Note: Current designation for the ECM in late model vehicles is PCM.)

ENGINE COOLANT TEMPERATURE (ECT) SENSOR: Prevents converter clutch engagement with a cold engine; also used for shift timing and shift quality.

EP LUBRICANT: EP (extreme pressure) lubricants are specially formulated for use with gears involving heavy loads (transmissions, differentials, etc.).

ETHYL: A substance added to gasoline to improve its resistance to knock, by slowing down the rate of combustion.

ETHYLENE GLYCOL: The base substance of antifreeze.

EXHAUST MANIFOLD: A set of cast passages or pipes which conduct exhaust gases from the engine.

FAIL-SAFE (BACKUP) CONTROL: A substitute value used by the PCM/TCM to replace a faulty signal from an input sensor. The temporary value allows the vehicle to continue to be operated.

FAST IDLE: The speed of the engine when the choke is on. Fast idle speeds engine warm-up.

FEDERAL ENGINE: An engine certified by the EPA for use in any of the 49 states (except California).

FEEDBACK: A circuit malfunction whereby current can find another path to feed load devices.

FEELER GAUGE: A blade, usually metal, of precisely predetermined thickness, used to measure the clearance between two parts.

FILAMENT: The part of a bulb that glows; the filament creates high resistance to current flow and actually glows from the resulting heat.

FINAL DRIVE: An essential part of the axle drive assembly where final gear reduction takes place in the powertrain. In RWD applications and north-south FWD applications, it must also change the power flow direction to the axle shaft by ninety degrees. (Also see axle ratio).

FIRING ORDER: The order in which combustion occurs in the cylinders of an engine. Also the order in which spark is distributed to the plugs by the distributor.

FIRM: A noticeable quick apply of a clutch or band that is considered normal with medium to heavy throttle shift; should not be confused with harsh or rough.

FLAME FRONT: The term used to describe certain aspects of the fuel explosion in the cylinders. The flame front should move in a controlled pattern across the cylinder, rather than simply exploding immediately.

FLARE (SLIPPING): A quick increase in engine rpm accompanied by momentary loss of torque; generally occurs during shift.

FLAT ENGINE: Engine design in which the pistons are horizontally opposed. Porsche, Subaru and some old VW are common examples of flat engines.

FLAT RATE: A dealership term referring to the amount of money paid to a technician for a repair or diagnostic service based on that particular service versus dealership's labor time (NOT based on the actual time the technician spent on the job).

FLAT SPOT: A point during acceleration when the engine seems to lose power for an instant.

FLOODING: The presence of too much fuel in the intake manifold and combustion chamber which prevents the air/fuel mixture from firing, thereby causing a no-start situation.

FLUID: A fluid can be either liquid or gas. In hydraulics, a liquid is used for transmitting force or motion.

FLUID COUPLING: The simplest form of hydrodynamic drive, the fluid coupling consists of two look-alike members with straight radial varies referred to as the impeller (pump) and the turbine. Input torque is always equal to the output torque.

FLUID DRIVE: Either a fluid coupling or a fluid torque converter. (See hydrodynamic drive units.)

FLUID TORQUE CONVERTER: A hydrodynamic drive that has the ability to act both as a torque multiplier and fluid coupling. (See hydrodynamic drive units; torque converter.)

FLUID VISCOSITY: The resistance of a liquid to flow. A cold fluid (oil) has greater viscosity and flows more slowly than a hot fluid (oil).

FLYWHEEL: A heavy disc of metal attached to the rear of the crankshaft. It smoothes the firing impulses of the engine and keeps the crankshaft turning during periods when no firing takes place. The starter also engages the flywheel to start the engine.

FOOT POUND (ft. lbs., lbs. ft. or sometimes, ft. lb.): The amount of energy or work needed to raise an item weighing one pound, a distance of one foot.

FREEZE PLUG: A plug in the engine block which will be pushed out if the coolant freezes. Sometimes called expansion plugs, they protect the block from cracking should the coolant freeze.

FRICTION: The resistance that occurs between contacting surfaces. This relationship is expressed by a ratio called the coefficient of friction (CL).

FRICTION, COEFFICIENT OF: The amount of surface tension between two contacting surfaces; expressed by a scientifically calculated number.

FRONT END ALIGNMENT: A service to set caster, camber and toe-in to the correct specifications. This will ensure that the car steers and handles properly and that the tires wear properly.

FRICTION MODIFIER: Changes the coefficient of friction of the fluid between the mating steel and composition clutch/band surfaces during the engagement process and allows for a certain amount of intentional slipping for a good "shift-feel".

FRONTAL AREA: The total frontal area of a vehicle exposed to air flow.

FUEL FILTER: A component of the fuel system containing a porous paper element used to prevent any impurities from entering the engine through the fuel system. It usually takes the form of a canister-like housing, mounted in-line with the fuel hose, located anywhere on a vehicle between the fuel tank and engine.

FUEL INJECTION: A system replacing the carburetor that sprays fuel into the cylinder through nozzles. The amount of fuel can be more precisely controlled with fuel injection.

FULL FLOATING AXLE: An axle in which the axle housing extends through the wheel giving bearing support on the outside of the housing. The front axle of a four-wheel drive vehicle is usually a full floating axle, as are the rear axles of many larger (1 ton and over) pick-ups and vans.

FULL-TIME FOUR-WHEEL DRIVE: A four-wheel drive system that continuously delivers power to all four wheels. A differential between the front and rear driveshafts permits variations in axle speeds to control gear wind-up without damage.

FULL THROTTLE DETENT DOWNSHIFT: A quick apply of accelerator pedal to its full travel, forcing a downshift.

FUSE: A protective device in a circuit which prevents circuit overload by breaking the circuit when a specific amperage is present. The device is constructed around a strip or wire of a lower amperage rating than the circuit it is designed to protect. When an amperage higher than that stamped on the fuse is present in the circuit, the strip or wire melts, opening the circuit.

FUSIBLE LINK: A piece of wire in a wiring harness that performs the same job as a fuse. If overloaded, the fusible link will melt and interrupt the circuit.

FWD: Front wheel drive.

GAWR: (Gross axle weight rating) the total maximum weight an axle is designed to carry.

GCW: (Gross combined weight) total combined weight of a tow vehicle and trailer.

GARAGE SHIFT: initial engagement feel of transmission, neutral to reverse or neutral to a forward drive.

GARAGE SHIFT FEEL: A quick check of the engagement quality and responsiveness of reverse and forward gears. This test is done with the vehicle stationary.

GEAR: A toothed mechanical device that acts as a rotating lever to transmit power or turning effort from one shaft to another. (See gear ratio.)

GEAR RATIO: A ratio expressing the number of turns a smaller gear will make to turn a larger gear through one revolution. The ratio is found by dividing the number of teeth on the smaller gear into the number of teeth on the larger gear.

GEARBOX: Transmission

GEAR REDUCTION: Torque is multiplied and speed decreased by the factor of the gear ratio. For example, a 3:1 gear ratio changes an input torque of 180 ft. lbs. and an input speed of 2700 rpm to 540 Ft. lbs. and 900 rpm, respectively. (No account is taken of frictional losses, which are always present.)

GEARTRAIN: A succession of intermeshing gears that form an assembly and provide for one or more torque changes as the power input is transmitted to the power output.

GEL COAT: A thin coat of plastic resin covering fiberglass body panels.

GENERATOR: A device which produces direct current (DC) necessary to charge the battery.

GOVERNOR: A device that senses vehicle speed and generates a hydraulic oil pressure. As vehicle speed increases, governor oil pressure rises.

GROUND CIRCUIT: (See circuit, ground.)

GROUND SIDE SWITCHING: The electrical/electronic circuit control switch is located after the circuit load.

GVWR: (Gross vehicle weight rating) total maximum weight a vehicle is designed to carry including the weight of the vehicle, passengers, equipment, gas, oil, etc.

HALOGEN: A special type of lamp known for its quality of brilliant white light. Originally used for fog lights and driving lights.

HARD CODES: DTCs that are present at the time of testing; also called continuous or current codes.

HARSH(ROUGH): An apply of a clutch or band that is more noticeable than a firm one; considered undesirable at any throttle position.

HEADER TANK: An expansion tank for the radiator coolant. It can be located remotely or built into the radiator.

HEAT RANGE: A term used to describe the ability of a spark plug to carry away heat. Plugs with longer nosed insulators take longer to carry heat off effectively.

HEAT RISER: A flapper in the exhaust manifold that is closed when the engine is cold, causing hot exhaust gases to heat the intake manifold providing better cold engine operation. A thermostatic spring opens the flapper when the engine warms up.

HEAVY THROTTLE: Approximately three-fourths of accelerator pedal travel.

HEMI: A name given an engine using hemispherical combustion chambers.

HERTZ (HZ): The international unit of frequency equal to one cycle per second (10,000 Hertz equals 10,000 cycles per second).

HIGH-IMPEDANCE DVOM (DIGITAL VOLT-OHMMETER): This styled device provides a built-in resistance value and is capable of limiting circuit current flow to safe milliamp levels.

HIGH RESISTANCE: Often refers to a circuit where there is an excessive amount of opposition to normal current flow.

HORSEPOWER: A measurement of the amount of work; one horsepower is the amount of work necessary to lift 33,000 lbs. one foot in one minute. Brake horsepower (bhp) is the horsepower delivered by an engine on a dynamometer. Net horsepower is the power remaining (measured at the flywheel of the engine) that can be used to turn the wheels after power is consumed through friction and running the engine accessories (water pump, alternator, air pump, fan etc.)

HOT CIRCUIT: (See circuit, hot; hot lead.)

HOT LEAD: A wire or conductor in the power side of the circuit. (See circuit, hot.)

HOT SIDE SWITCHING: The electrical/electronic circuit control switch is located before the circuit load.

HUB: The center part of a wheel or gear.

HUNTING (BUSYNESS): Repeating quick series of up-shifts and downshifts that causes noticeable change in engine rpm, for example, as in a 4-3-4 shift pattern.

HYDRAULICS: The use of liquid under pressure to transfer force of motion.

HYDROCARBON (HC): Any chemical compound made up of hydrogen and carbon. A major pollutant formed by the engine as a by-product of combustion.

HYDRODYNAMIC DRIVE UNITS: Devices that transmit power solely by the action of a kinetic fluid flow in a closed recirculating path. An impeller energizes the fluid and discharges the high-speed jet stream into the turbine for power output.

HYDROMETER: An instrument used to measure the specific gravity of a solution.

HYDROPLANING: A phenomenon of driving when water builds up under the tire tread, causing it to lose contact with the road. Slowing down will usually restore normal tire contact with the road.

HYPOID GEARSET: The drive pinion gear may be placed below or above the centerline of the driven gear; often used as a final drive gearset.

IDLE MIXTURE: The mixture of air and fuel (usually about 14:1) being fed to the cylinders. The idle mixture screw(s) are sometimes adjusted as part of a tune-up.

IDLER ARM: Component of the steering linkage which is a geometric duplicate of the steering gear arm. It supports the right side of the center steering link.

IMPELLER: Often called a pump, the impeller is the power input (drive) member of a hydrodynamic drive. As part of the torque converter cover, it acts as a centrifugal pump and puts the fluid in motion.

INCH POUND (inch lbs.; sometimes in. lb. or in. lbs.): One twelfth of a foot pound.

INDUCTANCE: The force that produces voltage when a conductor is passed through a magnetic field.

INDUCTION: A means of transferring electrical energy in the form of a magnetic field. Principle used in the ignition coil to increase voltage.

INITIAL FEEL: A distinct firmer feel at start of shift when compared with feel at finish of shift.

INJECTOR: A device which receives metered fuel under relatively low pressure and is activated to inject the fuel into the engine under relatively high pressure at a predetermined time.

INPUT: In an automatic transmission, the source of power from the engine is absorbed by the torque converter, which provides the power input into the transmission. The turbine drives the input(turbine)shaft.

INPUT SHAFT: The shaft to which torque is applied, usually carrying the driving gear or gears.

INTAKE MANIFOLD: A casting of passages or pipes used to conduct air or a fuel/air mixture to the cylinders.

INTERNAL GEAR: The ring-like outer gear of a planetary gearset with the gear teeth cut on the inside of the ring to provide a mesh with the planet pinions.

ISOLATION (CLAMPING) DIODES: Diodes positioned in a circuit to prevent self-induction from damaging electronic components.

IX ROTARY GEAR PUMP: Contains two rotating members, one shaped with internal gear teeth and the other with external gear teeth. As the gears separate, the fluid fills the gaps between gear teeth, is pulled across a crescent-shaped divider, and then is forced to flow through the outlet as the gears mesh.

IX ROTARY LOBE PUMP: Sometimes referred to as a gerotor type pump. Two rotating members, one shaped with internal lobes and the other with external lobes, separate and then mesh to cause fluid to flow.

JOURNAL: The bearing surface within which a shaft operates.

JUMPER CABLES: Two heavy duty wires with large alligator clips used to provide power from a charged battery to a discharged battery mounted in a vehicle.

JUMPSTART: Utilizing the sufficiently charged battery of one vehicle to start the engine of another vehicle with a discharged battery by the use of jumper cables.

KEY: A small block usually fitted in a notch between a shaft and a hub to prevent slippage of the two parts.

KICKDOWN: Detent downshift system; either linkage, cable, or electrically controlled.

KILO: A prefix used in the metric system to indicate one thousand.

KNOCK: Noise which results from the spontaneous ignition of a portion of the air-fuel mixture in the engine cylinder caused by overly advanced ignition timing or use of incorrectly low octane fuel for that engine.

KNOCK SENSOR: An input device that responds to spark knock, caused by over advanced ignition timing.

LABOR TIME: A specific amount of time required to perform a certain repair or diagnostic service as defined by a vehicle or after-market manufacturer .

LACQUER: A quick-drying automotive paint.

LATE: Shift that occurs when engine is at higher than normal rpm for given amount of throttle.

LIGHT-EMITTING DIODE (LED): A semiconductor diode that emits light as electrical current flows through it; used in some electronic display devices to emit a red or other color light.

LIGHT THROTTLE: Approximately one-fourth of accelerator pedal travel.

LIMITED SLIP: A type of differential which transfers driving force to the wheel with the best traction.

LIMP-IN MODE: Electrical shutdown of the transmission/ transaxle output solenoids, allowing only forward and reverse gears that are hydraulically energized by the manual valve. This permits the vehicle to be driven to a service facility for repair.

LIP SEAL: Molded synthetic rubber seal designed with an outer sealing edge (lip) that points into the fluid containing area to be sealed. This type of seal is used where rotational and axial forces are present.

LITHIUM-BASE GREASE: Chassis and wheel bearing grease using lithium as a base. Not compatible with sodium-base grease.

LOAD DEVICE: A circuit's resistance that converts the electrical energy into light, sound, heat, or mechanical movement.

LOAD RANGE: Indicates the number of plies at which a tire is rated. Load range B equals four-ply rating; C equals six-ply rating; and, D equals an eight-ply rating.

LOAD TORQUE: The amount of output torque needed from the transmission/transaxle to overcome the vehicle load.

LOCKING HUBS: Accessories used on part-time four-wheel drive systems that allow the front wheels to be disengaged from the drive train when four-wheel drive is not being used. When four-wheel drive is desired, the hubs are engaged, locking the wheels to the drive train.

LOCKUP CONVERTER: A torque converter that operates hydraulically and mechanically. When an internal apply plate (lockup plate) clamps to the torque converter cover, hydraulic slippage is eliminated.

LOCK RING: See Circlip or Snapring

MAGNET: Any body with the property of attracting iron or steel.

MAGNETIC FIELD: The area surrounding the poles of a magnet that is affected by its attraction or repulsion forces.

MAIN LINE PRESSURE: Often called control pressure or line pressure, it refers to the pressure of the oil leaving the pump and is controlled by the pressure regulator valve.

MALFUNCTION INDICATOR LAMP (MIL): Previously known as a check engine light, the dash-mounted MIL illuminates and signals the driver that an emission or driveability problem with the powertrain has been detected by the ECM/PCM. When this occurs, at least one diagnostic trouble code (DTC) has been stored into the control module memory.

MANIFOLD ABSOLUTE PRESSURE (MAP) SENSOR: Reads the amount of air pressure (vacuum) in the engine's intake manifold system; its signal is used to analyze engine load conditions.

MANIFOLD VACUUM: Low pressure in an engine intake manifold formed just below the throttle plates. Manifold vacuum is highest at idle and drops under acceleration.

MANIFOLD: A casting of passages or set of pipes which connect the cylinders to an inlet or outlet source.

MANUAL LEVER POSITION SWITCH (MLPS): A mechanical switching unit that is typically mounted externally to the transmission/transaxle to inform the PCM/ECM which gear range the driver has selected.

MANUAL VALVE: Located inside the transmission/transaxle, it is directly connected to the driver's shift lever. The position of the manual valve determines which hydraulic circuits will be charged with oil pressure and the operating mode of the transmission.

MANUAL VALVE LEVER POSITION SENSOR (MVLPS): The input from this device tells the TCM what gear range was selected.

MASS AIR FLOW (MAF) SENSOR: Measures the airflow into the engine.

MASTER CYLINDER: The primary fluid pressurizing device in a hydraulic system. In automotive use, it is found in brake and hydraulic clutch systems and is pedal activated, either directly or, in a power brake system, through the power booster.

MacPherson STRUT: A suspension component combining a shock absorber and spring in one unit.

MEDIUM THROTTLE: Approximately one-half of accelerator pedal travel.

MEGA: A metric prefix indicating one million.

MEMBER: An independent component of a hydrodynamic unit such as an impeller, a stator, or a turbine. It may have one or more elements.

MERCON: A fluid developed by Ford Motor Company in 1988. It contains a friction modifier and closely resembles operating characteristics of Dexron.

METAL SEALING RINGS: Made from cast iron or aluminum, their primary application is with dynamic components involving pressure sealing circuits of rotating members. These rings are designed with either butt or hook lock end joints.

METER (ANALOG): A linear-style meter representing data as lengths; a needle-style instrument interfacing with logical numerical increments. This style of electrical meter uses relatively low impedance internal resistance and cannot be used for testing electronic circuitry.

METER (DIGITAL): Uses numbers as a direct readout to show values. Most meters of this style use high impedance internal resistance and must be used for testing low current electronic circuitry.

MICRO: A metric prefix indicating one-millionth (0.000001).

MILLI: A metric prefix indicating one-thousandth (0.001).

MINIMUM THROTTLE: The least amount of throttle opening required for upshift; normally close to zero throttle.

MISFIRE: Condition occurring when the fuel mixture in a cylinder fails to ignite, causing the engine to run roughly.

MODULE: Electronic control unit, amplifier or igniter of solid state or integrated design which controls the current flow in the ignition primary circuit based on input from the pick-up coil. When the module opens the primary circuit, high secondary voltage is induced in the coil.

MODULATED: In an electronic-hydraulic converter clutch system (or shift valve system), the term modulated refers to the pulsing of a solenoid, at a variable rate. This action controls the buildup of oil pressure in the hydraulic circuit to allow a controlled amount of clutch slippage.

MODULATED CONVERTER CLUTCH CONTROL (MCCC): A pulse width duty cycle valve that controls the converter lockup apply pressure and maximizes smoother transitions between lock and unlock conditions.

MODULATOR PRESSURE (THROTTLE PRESSURE): A hydraulic signal oil pressure relating to the amount of engine load, based on either the amount of throttle plate opening or engine vacuum.

MODULATOR VALVE: A regulator valve that is controlled by engine vacuum, providing a hydraulic pressure that varies in relation to engine torque. The hydraulic torque signal functions to delay the shift pattern and provide a line pressure boost. (See throttle valve.)

MOTOR: An electromagnetic device used to convert electrical energy into mechanical energy.

MULTIPLE-DISC CLUTCH: A grouping of steel and friction lined plates that, when compressed together by hydraulic pressure acting upon a piston, lock or unlock a planetary member.

MULTI-WEIGHT: Type of oil that provides adequate lubrication at both high and low temperatures.

needed to move one amp through a resistance of one ohm.

MUSHY: Same as soft; slow and drawn out clutch apply with very little shift feel.

MUTUAL INDUCTION: The generation of current from one wire circuit to another by movement of the magnetic field surrounding a current-carrying circuit as its ampere flow increases or decreases.

NEEDLE BEARING: A bearing which consists of a number (usually a large number) of long, thin rollers.

NITROGEN OXIDE (NOx): One of the three basic pollutants found in the exhaust emission of an internal combustion engine. The amount of NOx usually varies in an inverse proportion to the amount of HC and CO.

NONPOSITIVE SEALING: A sealing method that allows some minor leakage, which normally assists in lubrication.

O2 SENSOR: Located in the engine's exhaust system, it is an input device to the ECM/PCM for managing the fuel delivery and ignition system. A scanner can be used to observe the fluctuating voltage readings produced by an O2 sensor as the oxygen content of the exhaust is analyzed.

O-RING SEAL: Molded synthetic rubber seal designed with a circular cross-section. This type of seal is used primarily in static applications.

OBD II (ON-BOARD DIAGNOSTICS, SECOND GENERATION): Refers to the federal law mandating tighter control of 1996 and newer vehicle emissions, active monitoring of related devices, and standardization of terminology, data link connectors, and other technician concerns.

OCTANE RATING: A number, indicating the quality of gasoline based on its ability to resist knock. The higher the number, the better the quality. Higher compression engines require higher octane gas.

OEM: Original Equipment Manufactured. OEM equipment is that furnished standard by the manufacturer.

OFFSET: The distance between the vertical center of the wheel and the mounting surface at the lugs. Offset is positive if the center is outside the lug circle; negative offset puts the center line inside the lug circle.

OHM'S LAW: A law of electricity that states the relationship between voltage, current, and resistance. Volts = amperes x ohms

OHM: The unit used to measure the resistance of conductor-to-electrical flow. One ohm is the amount of resistance that limits current flow to one ampere in a circuit with one volt of pressure.

OHMMETER: An instrument used for measuring the resistance, in ohms, in an electrical circuit.

ONE-WAY CLUTCH: A mechanical clutch of roller or sprag design that resists torque or transmits power in one direction only. It is used to either hold or drive a planetary member.

ONE-WAY ROLLER CLUTCH: A mechanical device that transmits or holds torque in one direction only.

OPEN CIRCUIT: A break or lack of contact in an electrical circuit, either intentional (switch) or unintentional (bad connection or broken wire).

ORIFICE: Located in hydraulic oil circuits, it acts as a restriction. It slows down fluid flow to either create back pressure or delay pressure buildup downstream.

OSCILLOSCOPE: A piece of test equipment that shows electric impulses as a pattern on a screen. Engine performance can be analyzed by interpreting these patterns.

OUTPUT SHAFT: The shaft which transmits torque from a device, such as a transmission.

OUTPUT SPEED SENSOR (OSS): Identifies transmission/transaxle output shaft speed for shift timing and may be used to calculate TCC slip; often functions as the VSS (vehicle speed sensor).

OVERDRIVE: (1.) A device attached to or incorporated in a transmission/transaxle that allows the engine to turn less than one full revolution for every complete revolution of the wheels. The net effect is to reduce engine rpm, thereby using less fuel. A typical overdrive gear ratio would be .87:1, instead of the normal 1:1 in high gear. (2.) A gear assembly which produces more shaft revolutions than that transmitted to it.

OVERDRIVE PLANETARY GEARSET: A single planetary gearset designed to provide a direct drive and overdrive ratio. When coupled to a three-speed transmission/transaxle configuration, a four-speed/overdrive unit is present.

OVERHEAD CAMSHAFT (OHC): An engine configuration in which the camshaft is mounted on top of the cylinder head and operates the valve either directly or by means of rocker arms.

OVERHEAD VALVE (OHV): An engine configuration in which all of the valves are located in the cylinder head and the camshaft is located in the cylinder block. The camshaft operates the valves via lifters and pushrods.

OVERRUNCLUTCH: Another name for a one-way mechanical clutch. Applies to both roller and sprag designs.

OVERSTEER: The tendency of some vehicles, when steering into a turn, to over-respond or steer more than required, which could result in excessive slip of the rear wheels. Opposite of under-steer.

OXIDATION STABILIZERS: Absorb and dissipate heat. Automatic transmission fluid has high resistance to varnish and sludge buildup that occurs from excessive heat that is generated primarily in the torque converter. Local temperatures as high as 6000F (3150C) can occur at the clutch plates during engagement, and this heat must be absorbed and dissipated. If the fluid cannot withstand the heat, it burns or oxidizes, resulting in an almost immediate destruction of friction materials, clogged filter screen and hydraulic passages, and sticky valves.

OXIDES OF NITROGEN: See nitrogen oxide (NOx).

OXYGEN SENSOR: Used with a feedback system to sense the presence of oxygen in the exhaust gas and signal the computer which can use the voltage signal to determine engine operating efficiency and adjust the air/fuel ratio.

PARALLEL CIRCUIT: (See circuit, parallel.)

PARTS WASHER: A basin or tub, usually with a built-in pump mechanism and hose used for circulating chemical solvent for the purpose of cleaning greasy, oily and dirty components.

PART-TIME FOUR WHEEL DRIVE: A system that is normally in the two wheel drive mode and only runs in four-wheel drive when the system is manually engaged because more traction is desired. Two or four wheel drive is normally selected by a lever to engage the front axle, but if locking hubs are used, these must also be manually engaged in the Lock position. Otherwise, the front axle will not drive the front wheels.

PASSIVE RESTRAINT: Safety systems such as air bags or automatic seat belts which operate with no action required on the part of the driver or passenger. Mandated by Federal regulations on all vehicles sold in the U.S. after 1990.

PAYLOAD: The weight the vehicle is capable of carrying in addition to its own weight. Payload includes weight of the driver, passengers and cargo, but not coolant, fuel, lubricant, spare tire, etc.

PCM: Powertrain control module.

PCV VALVE: A valve usually located in the rocker cover that vents crankcase vapors back into the engine to be reburned.

PERCOLATION: A condition in which the fuel actually "boils," due to excessive heat. Percolation prevents proper atomization of the fuel causing rough running.

PICK-UP COIL: The coil in which voltage is induced in an electronic ignition.

PING: A metallic rattling sound produced by the engine during acceleration. It is usually due to incorrect ignition timing or a poor grade of gasoline.

PINION: The smaller of two gears. The rear axle pinion drives the ring gear which transmits motion to the axle shafts.

PINION GEAR: The smallest gear in a drive gear assembly.

PISTON: A disc or cup that fits in a cylinder bore and is free to move. In hydraulics, it provides the means of converting hydraulic pressure into a usable force. Examples of piston applications are found in servo, clutch, and accumulator units.

PISTON RING: An open-ended ring which fits into a groove on the outer diameter of the piston. Its chief function is to form a seal between the piston and cylinder wall. Most automotive pistons have three rings: two for compression sealing; one for oil sealing.

PITMAN ARM: A lever which transmits steering force from the steering gear to the steering linkage.

PLANET CARRIER: A basic member of a planetary gear assembly that carries the pinion gears.

PLANET PINIONS: Gears housed in a planet carrier that are in constant mesh with the sun gear and internal gear. Because they have their own independent rotating centers, the pinions are capable of rotating around the sun gear or the inside of the internal gear.

PLANETARY GEAR RATIO: The reduction or overdrive ratio developed by a planetary gearset.

PLANETARY GEARSET: In its simplest form, it is made up of a basic assembly group containing a sun gear, internal gear, and planet carrier. The gears are always in constant mesh and offer a wide range of gear ratio possibilities.

PLANETARY GEARSET (COMPOUND): Two planetary gearsets combined together.

PLANETARY GEARSET (SIMPLE): An assembly of gears in constant mesh consisting of a sun gear, several pinion gears mounted in a carrier, and a ring gear. It provides gear ratio and direction changes, in addition to a direct drive and a neutral.

PLY RATING: A. rating given a tire which indicates strength (but not necessarily actual plies). A two-ply/four-ply rating has only two plies, but the strength of a four-ply tire.

POLARITY: Indication (positive or negative) of the two poles of a battery.

PORT: An opening for fluid intake or exhaust.

POSITIVE SEALING: A sealing method that completely prevents leakage.

POTENTIAL: Electrical force measured in volts; sometimes used interchangeably with voltage.

POWER: The ability to do work per unit of time, as expressed in horsepower; one horsepower equals 33,000 ft. lbs. of work per minute, or 550 ft. lbs. of work per second.

POWER FLOW: The systematic flow or transmission of power through the gears, from the input shaft to the output shaft.

POWER-TO-WEIGHT RATIO: Ratio of horsepower to weight of car.

POWERTRAIN: See Drivetrain.

POWERTRAIN CONTROL MODULE (PCM): Current designation for the engine control module (ECM). In many cases, late model vehicle control units manage the engine as well as the transmission. In other settings, the PCM controls the engine and is interfaced with a TCM to control transmission functions.

Ppm: Parts per million; unit used to measure exhaust emissions.

PREIGNITION: Early ignition of fuel in the cylinder, sometimes due to glowing carbon deposits in the combustion chamber. Preignition can be damaging since combustion takes place prematurely.

PRELOAD: A predetermined load placed on a bearing during assembly or by adjustment.

PRESS FIT: The mating of two parts under pressure, due to the inner diameter of one being smaller than the outer diameter of the other, or vice versa; an interference fit.

PRESSURE: The amount of force exerted upon a surface area.

PRESSURE CONTROL SOLENOID (PCS): An output device that provides a boost oil pressure to the mainline regulator valve to control line pressure. Its operation is determined by the amount of current sent from the PCM.

PRESSURE GAUGE: An instrument used for measuring the fluid pressure in a hydraulic circuit.

PRESSURE REGULATOR VALVE: In automatic transmissions, its purpose is to regulate the pressure of the pump output and supply the basic fluid pressure necessary to operate the transmission. The regulated fluid pressure may be referred to as mainline pressure, line pressure, or control pressure.

PRESSURE SWITCH ASSEMBLY (PSA): Mounted inside the transmission, it is a grouping of oil pressure switches that inputs to the PCM when certain hydraulic passages are charged with oil pressure.

PRESSURE PLATE: A spring-loaded plate (part of the clutch) that transmits power to the driven (friction) plate when the clutch is engaged.

PRIMARY CIRCUIT: The low voltage side of the ignition system which consists of the ignition switch, ballast resistor or resistance wire, bypass, coil, electronic control unit and pick-up coil as well as the connecting wires and harnesses.

PROFILE: Term used for tire measurement (tire series), which is the ratio of tire height to tread width.

PROM (PROGRAMMABLE READ-ONLY MEMORY): The heart of the computer that compares input data and makes the engineered program or strategy decisions about when to trigger the appropriate output based on stored computer instructions.

PULSE GENERATOR: A two-wire pickup sensor used to produce a fluctuating electrical signal. This changing signal is read by the controller to determine the speed of the object and can be used to measure transmission/transaxle input speed, output speed, and vehicle speed.

PSI: Pounds per square inch; a measurement of pressure.

PULSE WIDTH DUTY CYCLE SOLENOID (PULSE WIDTH MODULATED SOLENOID): A computer-controlled solenoid that turns on and off at a variable rate producing a modulated oil pressure; often referred to as a pulse width modulated (PWM) solenoid. Employed in many electronic automatic transmissions and transaxles, these solenoids are used to manage shift control and converter clutch hydraulic circuits.

PUSHROD: A steel rod between the hydraulic valve lifter and the valve rocker arm in overhead valve (OHV) engines.

PUMP: A mechanical device designed to create fluid flow and pressure buildup in a hydraulic system.

QUARTER PANEL: General term used to refer to a rear fender. Quarter panel is the area from the rear door opening to the tail light area and from rear wheel well to the base of the trunk and roof-line.

RACE: The surface on the inner or outer ring of a bearing on which the balls, needles or rollers move.

RACK AND PINION: A type of automotive steering system using a pinion gear attached to the end of the steering shaft. The pinion meshes with a long rack attached to the steering linkage.

RADIAL TIRE: Tire design which uses body cords running at right angles to the center line of the tire. Two or more belts are used to give tread strength. Radials can be identified by their characteristic sidewall bulge.

RADIATOR: Part of the cooling system for a water-cooled engine, mounted in the front of the vehicle and connected to the engine with rubber hoses. Through the radiator, excess combustion heat is dissipated into the atmosphere through forced convection using a water and glycol based mixture that circulates through, and cools, the engine.

RANGE REFERENCE AND CLUTCH/BAND APPLY CHART: A guide that shows the application of clutches and bands for each gear, within the selector range positions. These charts are extremely useful for understanding how the unit operates and for diagnosing malfunctions.

RAVIGNEAUX GEARSET: A compound planetary gearset that features matched dual planetary pinions (sets of two) mounted in a single planet carrier. Two sun gears and one ring mesh with the carrier pinions.

REACTION MEMBER: The stationary planetary member, in a planetary gearset, that is grounded to the transmission/transaxle case through the use of friction and wedging devices known as bands, disc clutches, and one-way clutches.

REACTION PRESSURE: The fluid pressure that moves a spool valve against an opposing force or forces; the area on which the opposing force acts. The opposing force can be a spring or a combination of spring force and auxiliary hydraulic force.

REACTOR, TORQUE CONVERTER: The reaction member of a fluid torque converter, more commonly called a stator. (See stator.)

REAR MAIN OIL SEAL: A synthetic or rope-type seal that prevents oil from leaking out of the engine past the rear main crankshaft bearing.

RECIRCULATING BALL: Type of steering system in which recirculating steel balls occupy the area between the nut and worm wheel, causing a reduction in friction.

RECTIFIER: A device (used primarily in alternators) that permits electrical current to flow in one direction only.

REDUCTION: (See gear reduction.)

REGULATOR VALVE: A valve that changes the pressure of the oil in a hydraulic circuit as the oil passes through the valve by bleeding off (or exhausting) some of the volume of oil supplied to the valve.

REFRIGERANT 12 (R-12) or 134 (R-134): The generic name of the refrigerant used in automotive air conditioning systems.

REGULATOR: A device which maintains the amperage and/or voltage levels of a circuit at predetermined values.

RELAY: A switch which automatically opens and/or closes a circuit.

RELAY VALVE: A valve that directs flow and pressure. Relay valves simply connect or disconnect interrelated passages without restricting the fluid flow or changing the pressure.

RELIEF VALVE: A spring-loaded, pressure-operated valve that limits oil pressure buildup in a hydraulic circuit to a predetermined maximum value.

RELUCTOR: A wheel that rotates inside the distributor and triggers the release of voltage in an electronic ignition.

RESERVOIR: The storage area for fluid in a hydraulic system; often called a sump.

RESIN: A liquid plastic used in body work.

RESIDUAL MAGNETISM: The magnetic strength stored in a material after a magnetizing field has been removed.

RESISTANCE: The opposition to the flow of current through a circuit or electrical device, and is measured in ohms. Resistance is equal to the voltage divided by the amperage.

RESISTOR SPARK PLUG: A spark plug using a resistor to shorten the spark duration. This suppresses radio interference and lengthens plug life.

RESISTOR: A device, usually made of wire, which offers a preset amount of resistance in an electrical circuit.

RESULTANT FORCE: The single effective directional thrust of the fluid force on the turbine produced by the vortex and rotary forces acting in different planes.

RETARD: Set the ignition timing so that spark occurs later (fewer degrees before TDC).

RHEOSTAT: A device for regulating a current by means of a variable resistance.

RING GEAR: The name given to a ring-shaped gear attached to a differential case, or affixed to a flywheel or as part of a planetary gear set.

ROADLOAD: grade.

ROCKER ARM: A lever which rotates around a shaft pushing down (opening) the valve with an end when the other end is pushed up by the pushrod. Spring pressure will later close the valve.

ROCKER PANEL: The body panel below the doors between the wheel opening.

ROLLER BEARING: A bearing made up of hardened inner and outer races between which hardened steel rollers move.

ROLLER CLUTCH: A type of one-way clutch design using rollers and springs mounted within an inner and outer cam race assembly.

ROTARY FLOW: The path of the fluid trapped between the blades of the members as they revolve with the rotation of the torque converter cover (rotational inertia).

ROTOR: (1.) The disc-shaped part of a disc brake assembly, upon which the brake pads bear; also called, brake disc. (2.) The device mounted atop the distributor shaft, which passes current to the distributor cap tower contacts.

ROTARY ENGINE: See Wankel engine.

RPM: Revolutions per minute (usually indicates engine speed).

RTV: A gasket making compound that cures as it is exposed to the atmosphere. It is used between surfaces that are not perfectly machined to one another, leaving a slight gap that the RTV fills and in which it hardens. The letters RTV represent room temperature vulcanizing.

RUN-ON: Condition when the engine continues to run, even when the key is turned off. See dieseling.

SEALED BEAM: A automotive headlight. The lens, reflector and filament from a single unit.

SEATBELT INTERLOCK: A system whereby the car cannot be started unless the seatbelt is buckled.

SECONDARY CIRCUIT: The high voltage side of the ignition system, usually above 20,000 volts. The secondary includes the ignition coil, coil wire, distributor cap and rotor, spark plug wires and spark plugs.

SELF-INDUCTION: The generation of voltage in a current-carrying wire by changing the amount of current flowing within that wire.

SEMI-CONDUCTOR: A material (silicon or germanium) that is neither a good conductor nor an insulator; used in diodes and transistors.

SEMI-FLOATING AXLE: In this design, a wheel is attached to the axle shaft, which takes both drive and cornering loads. Almost all solid axle passenger cars and light trucks use this design.

SENDING UNIT: A mechanical, electrical, hydraulic or electromagnetic device which transmits information to a gauge.

SENSOR: Any device designed to measure engine operating conditions or ambient pressures and temperatures. Usually electronic in nature and designed to send a voltage signal to an on-board computer, some sensors may operate as a simple on/off switch or they may provide a variable voltage signal (like a potentiometer) as conditions or measured parameters change.

SERIES CIRCUIT: (See circuit, series.)

SERPENTINE BELT: An accessory drive belt, with small multiple v-ribs, routed around most or all of the engine-powered accessories such as the alternator and power steering pump. Usually both the front and the back side of the belt comes into contact with various pulleys.

SERVO: In an automatic transmission, it is a piston in a cylinder assembly that converts hydraulic pressure into mechanical force and movement; used for the application of the bands and clutches.

SHIFT BUSYNESS: When referring to a torque converter clutch, it is the frequent apply and release of the clutch plate due to uncommon driving conditions.

SHIFT VALVE: Classified as a relay valve, it triggers the automatic shift in response to a governor and a throttle signal by directing fluid to the appropriate band and clutch apply combination to cause the shift to occur.

SHIM: Spacers of precise, predetermined thickness used between parts to establish a proper working relationship.

SHIMMY: Vibration (sometimes violent) in the front end caused by misaligned front end, out of balance tires or worn suspension components.

SHORT CIRCUIT: An electrical malfunction where current takes the path of least resistance to ground (usually through damaged insulation). Current flow is excessive from low resistance resulting in a blown fuse.

SHUDDER: Repeated jerking or stick-slip sensation, similar to chuggle but more severe and rapid in nature, that may be most noticeable during certain ranges of vehicle speed; also used to define condition after converter clutch engagement.

SIMPSON GEARSET: A compound planetary gear train that integrates two simple planetary gearsets referred to as the front planetary and the rear planetary.

SINGLE OVERHEAD CAMSHAFT: See overhead camshaft.

SKIDPLATE: A metal plate attached to the underside of the body to protect the fuel tank, transfer case or other vulnerable parts from damage.

SLAVE CYLINDER: In automotive use, a device in the hydraulic clutch system which is activated by hydraulic force, disengaging the clutch.

SLIPPING: Noticeable increase in engine rpm without vehicle speed increase; usually occurs during or after initial clutch or band engagement.

SLUDGE: Thick, black deposits in engine formed from dirt, oil, water, etc. It is usually formed in engines when oil changes are neglected.

SNAP RING: A circular retaining clip used inside or outside a shaft or part to secure a shaft, such as a floating wrist pin.

SOFT: Slow, almost unnoticeable clutch apply with very little shift feel.

SOFTCODES: DTCs that have been set into the PCM memory but are not present at the time of testing; often referred to as history or intermittent codes.

SOHC: Single overhead camshaft.

SOLENOID: An electrically operated, magnetic switching device.

SPALLING: A wear pattern identified by metal chips flaking off the hardened surface. This condition is caused by foreign particles, overloading situations, and/or normal wear.

SPARK PLUG: A device screwed into the combustion chamber of a spark ignition engine. The basic construction is a conductive core inside of a ceramic insulator, mounted in an outer conductive base. An electrical charge from the spark plug wire travels along the conductive core and jumps a preset air gap to a grounding point or points at the end of the conductive base. The resultant spark ignites the fuel/air mixture in the combustion chamber.

SPECIFIC GRAVITY (BATTERY): The relative weight of liquid (battery electrolyte) as compared to the weight of an equal volume of water.

SPLINES: Ridges machined or cast onto the outer diameter of a shaft or inner diameter of a bore to enable parts to mate without rotation.

SPLIT TORQUE DRIVE: In a torque converter, it refers to parallel paths of torque transmission, one of which is mechanical and the other hydraulic.

SPONGY PEDAL: A soft or spongy feeling when the brake pedal is depressed. It is usually due to air in the brake lines.

SPOOLVALVE: A precision-machined, cylindrically shaped valve made up of lands and grooves. Depending on its position in the valve bore, various interconnecting hydraulic circuit passages are either opened or closed.

SPRAG CLUTCH: A type of one-way clutch design using cams or contoured-shaped sprags between inner and outer races. (See one-way clutch.)

SPRUNG WEIGHT: The weight of a car supported by the springs.

SQUARE-CUT SEAL: Molded synthetic rubber seal designed with a square- or rectangular-shaped cross-section. This type of seal is used for both dynamic and static applications.

SRS: Supplemental restraint system

STABILIZER (SWAY) BAR: A bar linking both sides of the suspension. It resists sway on turns by taking some of added load from one wheel and putting it on the other.

STAGE: The number of turbine sets separated by a stator. A turbine set may be made up of one or more turbine members. A three-element converter is classified as a single stage.

STALL: In fluid drive transmission/transaxle applications, stall refers to engine rpm with the transmission/transaxle engaged and the vehicle stationary; throttle valve can be in any position between closed and wide open.

STALL SPEED: In fluid drive transmission/transaxle applications, stall speed refers to the maximum engine rpm with the transmission/transaxle engaged and vehicle stationary, when the throttle valve is wide open. (See stall; stall test.)

STALL TEST: A procedure recommended by many manufacturers to help determine the integrity of an engine, the torque converter stator, and certain clutch and band combinations. With the shift lever in each of the forward and reverse positions and with the brakes firmly applied, the accelerator pedal is momentarily pressed to the wide open throttle (WOT) position. The engine rpm reading at full throttle can provide clues for diagnosing the condition of the items listed above.

STALL TORQUE: The maximum design or engineered torque ratio of a fluid torque converter, produced under stall speed conditions. (See stall speed.)

STARTER: A high-torque electric motor used for the purpose of starting the engine, typically through a high ratio geared drive connected to the flywheel ring gear.

STATIC: A sealing application in which the parts being sealed do not move in relation to each other.

STATOR (REACTOR): The reaction member of a fluid torque converter that changes the direction of the fluid as it leaves the turbine to enter the impeller vanes. During the torque multiplication phase, this action assists the impeller's rotary force and results in an increase in torque.

STEERING GEOMETRY: Combination of various angles of suspension components (caster, camber, toe-in); roughly equivalent to front end alignment.

STRAIGHT WEIGHT: Term designating motor oil as suitable for use within a narrow range of temperatures. Outside the narrow temperature range its flow characteristics will not adequately lubricate.

STROKE: The distance the piston travels from bottom dead center to top dead center.

SUBSTITUTION: Replacing one part suspected of a defect with a like part of known quality.

SUMP: The storage vessel or reservoir that provides a ready source of fluid to the pump. In an automatic transmission, the sump is the oil pan. All fluid eventually returns to the sump for recycling into the hydraulic system.

SUN GEAR: In a planetary gearset, it is the center gear that meshes with a cluster of planet pinions.

SUPERCHARGER: An air pump driven mechanically by the engine through belts, chains, shafts or gears from the crankshaft. Two general types of supercharger are the positive displacement and centrifugal type, which pump air in direct relationship to the speed of the engine.

SUPPLEMENTAL RESTRAINT SYSTEM: See air bag.

SURGE: Repeating engine-related feeling of acceleration and deceleration that is less intense than chuggle.

SWITCH: A device used to open, close, or redirect the current in an electrical circuit.

SYNCHROMESH: A manual transmission/transaxle that is equipped with devices (synchronizers) that match the gear speeds so that the transmission/transaxle can be downshifted without clashing gears.

SYNTHETIC OIL: Non-petroleum based oil.

TACHOMETER: A device used to measure the rotary speed of an engine, shaft, gear, etc., usually in rotations per minute.

TDC: Top dead center. The exact top of the piston's stroke.

TEFLON SEALING RINGS: Teflon is a soft, durable, plastic-like material that is resistant to heat and provides excellent sealing. These rings are designed with either scarf-cut joints or as one-piece rings. Teflon sealing rings have replaced many metal ring applications.

TERMINAL: A device attached to the end of a wire or cable to make an electrical connection.

TEST LIGHT, CIRCUIT-POWERED: Uses available circuit voltage to test circuit continuity.

TEST LIGHT, SELF-POWERED: Uses its own battery source to test circuit continuity.

THERMISTOR: A special resistor used to measure fluid temperature; it decreases its resistance with increases in temperature.

THERMOSTAT: A valve, located in the cooling system of an engine, which is closed when cold and opens gradually in response to engine heating, controlling the temperature of the coolant and rate of coolant flow.

THERMOSTATIC ELEMENT: A heat-sensitive, spring-type device that controls a drain port from the upper sump area to the lower sump. When the transaxle fluid reaches operating temperature, the port is closed and the upper sump fills, thus reducing the fluid level in the lower sump.

THROTTLE POSITION (TP) SENSOR: Reads the degree of throttle opening; its signal is used to analyze engine load conditions. The ECM/PCM decides to apply the TCC, or to disengage it for coast or load conditions that need a converter torque boost.

THROTTLE PRESSURE/MODULATOR PRESSURE: A hydraulic signal oil pressure relating to the amount of engine load, based on either the amount of throttle plate opening or engine vacuum.

THROTTLE VALVE: A regulating or balanced valve that is controlled mechanically by throttle linkage or engine vacuum. It sends a hydraulic signal to the shift valve body to control shift timing and shift quality. (See balanced valve; modulator valve.)

THROW-OUT BEARING: As the clutch pedal is depressed, the throwout bearing moves against the spring fingers of the pressure plate, forcing the pressure plate to disengage from the driven disc.

TIE ROD: A rod connecting the steering arms. Tie rods have threaded ends that are used to adjust toe-in.

TIE-UP: Condition where two opposing clutches are attempting to apply at same time, causing engine to labor with noticeable loss of engine rpm.

TIMING BELT: A square-toothed, reinforced rubber belt that is driven by the crankshaft and operates the camshaft.

TIMING CHAIN: A roller chain that is driven by the crankshaft and operates the camshaft.

TIRE ROTATION: Moving the tires from one position to another to make the tires wear evenly.

TOE-IN (OUT): A term comparing the extreme front and rear of the front tires. Closer together at the front is toe-in; farther apart at the front is toe-out.

TOP DEAD CENTER (TDC): The point at which the piston reaches the top of its travel on the compression stroke.

TORQUE: Measurement of turning or twisting force, expressed as foot-pounds or inch-pounds.

TORQUE CONVERTER: A turbine used to transmit power from a driving member to a driven member via hydraulic action, providing changes in drive ratio and torque. In automotive use, it links the driveplate at the rear of the engine to the automatic transmission.

TORQUE CONVERTER CLUTCH: The apply plate (lockup plate) assembly used for mechanical power flow through the converter.

TORQUE PHASE: Sometimes referred to as slip phase or stall phase, torque multiplication occurs when the turbine is turning at a slower speed than the impeller, and the stator is reactionary (stationary). This sequence generates a boost in output torque.

TORQUE RATING (STALL TORQUE): The maximum torque multiplication that occurs during stall conditions, with the engine at wide open throttle (WOT) and zero turbine speed.

TORQUE RATIO: An expression of the gear ratio factor on torque effect. A 3:1 gear ratio or 3:1 torque ratio increases the torque input by the ratio factor of 3. Input torque (100 ft. lbs.) x 3 = output torque (300 ft. lbs.)

TRACTION: The amount of usable tractive effort before the drive wheels slip on the road contact surface.

TORSION BAR SUSPENSION: Long rods of spring steel which take the place of springs. One end of the bar is anchored and the other arm (attached to the suspension) is free to twist. The bars' resistance to twisting causes springing action.

TRACK: Distance between the centers of the tires where they contact the ground.

TRACTION CONTROL: A control system that prevents the spinning of a vehicle's drive wheels when excess power is applied.

TRACTIVE EFFORT: The amount of force available to the drive wheels, to move the vehicle.

TRANSAXLE: A single housing containing the transmission and differential. Transaxles are usually found on front engine/front wheel drive or rear engine/rear wheel drive cars.

TRANSDUCER: A device that changes energy from one form to another. For example, a transducer in a microphone changes sound energy to electrical energy. In automotive air-conditioning controls used in automatic temperature systems, a transducer changes an electrical signal to a vacuum signal, which operates mechanical doors.

TRANSMISSION: A powertrain component designed to modify torque and speed developed by the engine; also provides direct drive, reverse, and neutral.

TRANSMISSION CONTROL MODULE (TCM): Manages transmission functions. These vary according to the manufacturer's product design but may include converter clutch operation, electronic shift scheduling, and mainline pressure.

TRANSMISSION FLUID TEMPERATURE (TFT) SENSOR: Originally called a transmission oil temperature (TOT) sensor, this input device to the ECM/PCM senses the fluid temperature and provides a resistance value. It operates on the thermistor principle.

TRANSMISSION INPUT SPEED (TIS) SENSOR: Measures turbine shaft (input shaft) rpm's and compares to engine rpm's to determine torque converter slip. When compared to the transmission output speed sensor or VSS, gear ratio and clutch engagement timing can be determined.

TRANSMISSION OIL TEMPERATURE (TOT) SENSOR: (See transmission fluid temperature (TFT) sensor.)

TRANSMISSION RANGE SELECTOR (TRS) SWITCH: Tells the module which gear shift position the driver has chosen.

TRANSFER CASE: A gearbox driven from the transmission that delivers power to both front and rear driveshafts in a four-wheel drive system. Transfer cases usually have a high and low range set of gears, used depending on how much pulling power is needed.

TRANSISTOR: A semi-conductor component which can be actuated by a small voltage to perform an electrical switching function.

TREAD WEAR INDICATOR: Bars molded into the tire at right angles to the tread that appear as horizontal bars when 1/16 in. of tread remains.

TREAD WEAR PATTERN: The pattern of wear on tires which can be "read" to diagnose problems in the front suspension.

TUNE-UP: A regular maintenance function, usually associated with the replacement and adjustment of parts and components in the electrical and fuel systems of a vehicle for the purpose of attaining optimum performance.

TURBINE: The output (driven) member of a fluid coupling or fluid torque converter. It is splined to the input (turbine) shaft of the transmission.

TURBOCHARGER: An exhaust driven pump which compresses intake air and forces it into the combustion chambers at higher than atmospheric pressures. The increased air pressure allows more fuel to be burned and results in increased horsepower being produced.

TURBULENCE: The interference of molecules of a fluid (or vapor) with each other in a fluid flow.

TYPE F: Transmission fluid developed and used by Ford Motor Company up to 1982. This fluid type provides a high coefficient of friction.

TYPE 7176: The preferred choice of transmission fluid for Chrysler automatic transmissions and transaxles. Developed in 1986, it closely resembles Dexron and Mercon. Type 7176 is the recommended service fill fluid for all Chrysler products utilizing a lockup torque converter dating back to 1978.

U-JOINT (UNIVERSAL JOINT): A flexible coupling in the drive train that allows the driveshafts or axle shafts to operate at different angles and still transmit rotary power.

UNDERSTEER: The tendency of a car to continue straight ahead while negotiating a turn.

UNIT BODY: Design in which the car body acts as the frame.

UNLEADED FUEL: Fuel which contains no lead (a common gasoline additive). The presence of lead in fuel will destroy the functioning elements of a catalytic converter, making it useless.

UNSPRUNG WEIGHT: The weight of car components not supported by the springs (wheels, tires, brakes, rear axle, control arms, etc.).

UPSHIFT: A shift that results in a decrease in torque ratio and an increase in speed.

VACUUM: A negative pressure; any pressure less than atmospheric pressure.

VACUUM ADVANCE: A device which advances the ignition timing in response to increased engine vacuum.

VACUUM GAUGE: An instrument used for measuring the existing vacuum in a vacuum circuit or chamber. The unit of measure is inches (of mercury in a barometer).

VACUUM MODULATOR: Generates a hydraulic oil pressure in response to the amount of engine vacuum.

VALVES: Devices that can open or close fluid passages in a hydraulic system and are used for directing fluid flow and controlling pressure.

VALVE BODY ASSEMBLY: The main hydraulic control assembly of the transmission/transaxle that contains numerous valves, check balls, and other components to control the distribution of pressurized oil throughout the transmission.

VALVE CLEARANCE: The measured gap between the end of the valve stem and the rocker arm, cam lobe or follower that activates the valve.

VALVE GUIDES: The guide through which the stem of the valve passes.

The guide is designed to keep the valve in proper alignment.

VALVE LASH (clearance): The operating clearance in the valve train.

VALVE TRAIN: The system that operates intake and exhaust valves, consisting of camshaft, valves and springs, lifters, pushrods and rocker arms.

VAPOR LOCK: Boiling of the fuel in the fuel lines due to excess heat. This will interfere with the flow of fuel in the lines and can completely stop the flow. Vapor lock normally only occurs in hot weather.

VARIABLE DISPLACEMENT (VARIABLE CAPACITY) VANE PUMP: Slipper-type vanes, mounted in a revolving rotor and contained within the bore of a movable slide, capture and then force fluid to flow. Movement of the slide to various positions changes the size of the vane chambers and the amount of fluid flow. **Note:** GM refers to this pump design as variable displacement, and Ford terms it variable capacity.

VARIABLE FORCE SOLENOID (VFS): Commonly referred to as the electronic pressure control (EPC) solenoid, it replaces the cable/linkage style of TV system control and is integrated with a spool valve and spring assembly to control pressure. A variable computer-controlled current flow varies the internal force of the solenoid on the spool valve and resulting control pressure.

VARIABLE ORIFICE THERMAL VALVE: Temperature-sensitive hydraulic oil control device that adjusts the size of a circuit path opening. By altering the size of the opening, the oil flow rate is adapted for cold to hot oil viscosity changes.

VARNISH: Term applied to the residue formed when gasoline gets old and stale.

VCM: See Electronic Control Unit (ECU).

VEHICLE SPEED SENSOR (VSS): Provides an electrical signal to the computer module, measuring vehicle speed, and affects the torque converter clutch engagement and release.

VESPEL SEALING RINGS: Hard plastic material that produces excellent sealing in dynamic settings. These rings are found in late versions of the 4T60 and in all 4T60-E and 4T80-E transaxles.

VISCOSITY: The ability of a fluid to flow. The lower the viscosity rating, the easier the fluid will flow. 10 weight motor oil will flow much easier than 40 weight motor oil.

VISCOSITY INDEX IMPROVERS: Keeps the viscosity nearly constant with changes in temperature. This is especially important at low temperatures, when the oil needs to be thin to aid in shifting and for cold-weather starting. Yet it must not be so thin that at high temperatures it will cause excessive hydraulic leakage so that pumps are unable to maintain the proper pressures.

VISCOUS CLUTCH: A specially designed torque converter clutch apply plate that, through the use of a silicon fluid, clamps smoothly and absorbs torsional vibrations.

VOLT: Unit used to measure the force or pressure of electricity. It is defined as the pressure needed to move one amp through the resistance of one ohm.

VOLTAGE: The electrical pressure that causes current to flow. Voltage is measured in volts (V).

VOLTAGE, APPLIED: The actual voltage read at a given point in a circuit. It equals the available voltage of the power supply minus the losses in the circuit up to that point.

VOLTAGE DROP: The voltage lost or used in a circuit by normal loads such as a motor or lamp or by abnormal loads such as a poor (high-resistance) lead or terminal connection.

VOLTAGE REGULATOR: A device that controls the current output of the alternator or generator.

VOLTMETER: An instrument used for measuring electrical force in units called volts. Voltmeters are always connected parallel with the circuit being tested.

VORTEX FLOW: The crosswise or circulatory flow of oil between the blades of the members caused by the centrifugal pumping action of the impeller.

WANKEL ENGINE: An engine which uses no pistons. In place of pistons, triangular-shaped rotors revolve in specially shaped housings.

WATER PUMP: A belt driven component of the cooling system that mounts on the engine, circulating the coolant under pressure.

WATT: The unit for measuring electrical power. One watt is the product of one ampere and one volt (watts equals amps times volts). Wattage is the horsepower of electricity (746 watts equal one horsepower).

WHEEL ALIGNMENT: Inclusive term to describe the front end geometry (caster, camber, toe-in/out).

WHEEL CYLINDER: Found in the automotive drum brake assembly, it is a device, actuated by hydraulic pressure, which, through internal pistons, pushes the brake shoes outward against the drums.

WHEEL WEIGHT: Small weights attached to the wheel to balance the wheel and tire assembly. Out-of-balance tires quickly wear out and also give erratic handling when installed on the front.

WHEELBASE: Distance between the center of front wheels and the center of rear wheels.

WIDE OPEN THROTTLE (WOT): Full travel of accelerator pedal.

WORK: The force exerted to move a mass or object. Work involves motion; if a force is exerted and no motion takes place, no work is done. Work per unit of time is called power. Work = force x distance = ft. lbs. 33,000 ft. lbs. in one minute = 1 horsepower

ZERO-THROTTLE COAST DOWN: A full release of accelerator pedal while vehicle is in motion and in drive range.

Commonly Used Abbreviations

2
2WD	Two Wheel Drive

4
4WD	Four Wheel Drive

A
A/C	Air Conditioning
ABDC	After Bottom Dead Center
ABS	Anti-lock Brakes
AC	Alternating Current
ACL	Air cleaner
ACT	Air Charge Temperature
AIR	Secondary Air Injection
ALCL	Assembly Line Communications Link
ALDL	Assembly Line Diagnostic Link
AT	Automatic Transaxle/Transmission
ATDC	After Top Dead Center
ATF	Automatic Transmission Fluid
ATS	Air Temperature Sensor
AWD	All Wheel Drive

B
BAP	Barometric Absolute Pressure
BARO	Barometric Pressure
BBDC	Before Bottom Dead Center
BCM	Body Control Module
BDC	Bottom Dead Center
BPT	Backpressure Transducer
BTDC	Before Top Dead Center
BVSV	Bimetallic Vacuum Switching Valve

C
CAC	Charge Air Cooler
CARB	California Air Resources Board
CAT	Catalytic Converter
CCC	Computer Command Control
CCCC	Computer Controlled Catalytic Converter
CCCI	Computer Controlled Coil Ignition
CCD	Computer Controlled Dwell
CDI	Capacitor Discharge Ignition
CEC	Computerized Engine Control
CFI	Continuous Fuel Injection
CIS	Continuous Injection System
CIS-E	Continuous Injection System - Electronic
CKP	Crankshaft Position
CL	Closed Loop
CMP	Camshaft Position
CPP	Clutch Pedal Position
CTOX	Continuous Trap Oxidizer System
CTP	Closed Throttle Position
CVC	Constant Vacuum Control
CYL	Cylinder

D
DBC	Dual Bed Catalyst
DC	Direct Current
DFI	Direct Fuel Injection
DIS	Distributorless Ignition System
DLC	Data Link Connector
DMM	Digital Multimeter
DOHC	Double Overhead Camshaft
DRB	Diagnostic Readout Box
DTC	Diagnostic Trouble Code
DTM	Diagnostic Test Mode
DVOM	Digital Volt/Ohmmeter

E
EBCM	Electronic Brake Control Module
ECM	Engine Control Module
ECT	Engine Coolant Temperature
ECU	Engine Control Unit or Electronic Control Unit
EDIS	Electronic Distributorless Ignition System
EEC	Electronic Engine Control
EEPROM	Electrically Erasable Programmable Read Only Memory
EFE	Early Fuel Evaporation
EGR	Exhaust Gas Recirculation
EGRT	Exhaust Gas Recirculation Temperature
EGRVC	EGR Valve Control
EPROM	Erasable Programmable Read Only Memory
EVAP	Evaporative Emissions
EVP	EGR Valve Position

F
FBC	Feedback Carburetor
FEEPROM	Flash Electrically Erasable Programmable Read Only Memory
FF	Flexible Fuel
FI	Fuel Injection
FT	Fuel Trim
FWD	Front Wheel Drive

G
GND	Ground

H
HAC	High Altitude Compensation
HEGO	Heated Exhaust Gas Oxygen sensor
HEI	High Energy Ignition
HO2 Sensor	Heated Oxygen Sensor

I
IAC	Idle Air Control
IAT	Intake Air Temperature
ICM	Ignition Control Module
IFI	Indirect Fuel Injection
IFS	Inertia Fuel Shutoff
ISC	Idle Speed Control
IVSV	Idle Vacuum Switching Valve

Commonly Used Abbreviations

K

KOEO	Key On, Engine Off
KOER	Key ON, Engine Running
KS	Knock Sensor

M

MAF	Mass Air Flow
MAP	Manifold Absolute Pressure
MAT	Manifold Air Temperature
MC	Mixture Control
MDP	Manifold Differential Pressure
MFI	Multiport Fuel Injection
MIL	Malfunction Indicator Lamp or Maintenance
MST	Manifold Surface Temperature
MVZ	Manifold Vacuum Zone

N

NVRAM	Nonvolatile Random Access Memory

O

O2 Sensor	Oxygen Sensor
OBD	On-Board Diagnostic
OC	Oxidation Catalyst
OHC	Overhead Camshaft
OL	Open Loop

P

P/S	Power Steering
PAIR	Pulsed Secondary Air Injection
PCM	Powertrain Control Module
PCS	Purge Control Solenoid
PCV	Positive Crankcase Ventilation
PIP	Profile Ignition Pick-up
PNP	Park/Neutral Position
PROM	Programmable Read Only Memory
PSP	Power Steering Pressure
PTO	Power Take-Off
PTOX	Periodic Trap Oxidizer System

R

RABS	Rear Anti-lock Brake System
RAM	Random Access Memory
ROM	Read Only Memory
RPM	Revolutions Per Minute
RWAL	Rear Wheel Anti-lock Brakes
RWD	Rear Wheel Drive

S

SBC	Single Bed Converter
SBEC	Single Board Engine Controller
SC	Supercharger
SCB	Supercharger Bypass
SFI	Sequential Multiport Fuel Injection
SIR	Supplemental Inflatible Restraint
SOHC	Single Overhead Camshaft
SPL	Smoke Puff Limiter
SPOUT	Spark Output
SRI	Service Reminder Indicator
SRS	Supplemental Restraint System
SRT	System Readiness Test
SSI	Solid State Ignition
ST	Scan Tool
STO	Self-Test Output

T

TAC	Thermostatic Air Clearner
TBI	Throttle Body Fuel Injection
TC	Turbocharger
TCC	Torque Converter Clutch
TCM	Transmission Control Module
TDC	Top Dead Center
TFI	Thick Film Ignition
TP	Throttle Position
TR Sensor	Transaxle/Transmission Range Sensor
TVV	Thermal Vacuum Valve
TWC	Three-way Catalytic Converter

V

VAF	Volume Air Flow, or Vane Air Flow
VAPS	Variable Assist Power Steering
VRV	Vacuum Regulator Valve
VSS	Vehicle Speed Sensor
VSV	Vacuum Switching Valve

W

WOT	Wide Open Throttle
WU-TWC	Warm Up Three-way Catalytic Converter

ENGLISH TO METRIC CONVERSION: TORQUE

To convert foot-pounds (ft. lbs.) to Newton-meters (Nm), multiply the number of ft. lbs. by 1.36
To convert Newton-meters (Nm) to foot-pounds (ft. lbs.), multiply the number of Nm by 0.7376

ft. lbs.	Nm	ft. lbs.	Nm	ft. lbs.	Nm	ft. lbs.	Nm
0.1	0.1	34	46.2	76	103.4	118	160.5
0.2	0.3	35	47.6	77	104.7	119	161.8
0.3	0.4	36	49.0	78	106.1	120	163.2
0.4	0.5	37	50.3	79	107.4	121	164.6
0.5	0.7	38	51.7	80	108.8	122	165.9
0.6	0.8	39	53.0	81	110.2	123	167.3
0.7	1.0	40	54.4	82	111.5	124	168.6
0.8	1.1	41	55.8	83	112.9	125	170.0
0.9	1.2	42	57.1	84	114.2	126	171.4
1	1.4	43	58.5	85	115.6	127	172.7
2	2.7	44	59.8	86	117.0	128	174.1
3	4.1	45	61.2	87	118.3	129	175.4
4	5.4	46	62.6	88	119.7	130	176.8
5	6.8	47	63.9	89	121.0	131	178.2
6	8.2	48	65.3	90	122.4	132	179.5
7	9.5	49	66.6	91	123.8	133	180.9
8	10.9	50	68.0	92	125.1	134	182.2
9	12.2	51	69.4	93	126.5	135	183.6
10	13.6	52	70.7	94	127.8	136	185.0
11	15.0	53	72.1	95	129.2	137	186.3
12	16.3	54	73.4	96	130.6	138	187.7
13	17.7	55	74.8	97	131.9	139	189.0
14	19.0	56	76.2	98	133.3	140	190.4
15	20.4	57	77.5	99	134.6	141	191.8
16	21.8	58	78.9	100	136.0	142	193.1
17	23.1	59	80.2	101	137.4	143	194.5
18	24.5	60	81.6	102	138.7	144	195.8
19	25.8	61	83.0	103	140.1	145	197.2
20	27.2	62	84.3	104	141.4	146	198.6
21	28.6	63	85.7	105	142.8	147	199.9
22	29.9	64	87.0	106	144.2	148	201.3
23	31.3	65	88.4	107	145.5	149	202.6
24	32.6	66	89.8	108	146.9	150	204.0
25	34.0	67	91.1	109	148.2	151	205.4
26	35.4	68	92.5	110	149.6	152	206.7
27	36.7	69	93.8	111	151.0	153	208.1
28	38.1	70	95.2	112	152.3	154	209.4
29	39.4	71	96.6	113	153.7	155	210.8
30	40.8	72	97.9	114	155.0	156	212.2
31	42.2	73	99.3	115	156.4	157	213.5
32	43.5	74	100.6	116	157.8	158	214.9
33	44.9	75	102.0	117	159.1	159	216.2

METRIC TO ENGLISH CONVERSION: TORQUE

To convert foot-pounds (ft. lbs.) to Newton-meters (Nm), multiply the number of ft. lbs. by 1.36
To convert Newton-meters (Nm) to foot-pounds (ft. lbs.), multiply the number of Nm by 0.7376

Nm	ft. lbs.	Nm	ft. lbs.	Nm	ft. lbs.	Nm	ft. lbs.	Nm	ft. lbs.
0.1	0.1	34	25.0	76	55.9	118	86.8	160	117.6
0.2	0.1	35	25.7	77	56.6	119	87.5	161	118.4
0.3	0.2	36	26.5	78	57.4	120	88.2	162	119.1
0.4	0.3	37	27.2	79	58.1	121	89.0	163	119.9
0.5	0.4	38	27.9	80	58.8	122	89.7	164	120.6
0.6	0.4	39	28.7	81	59.6	123	90.4	165	121.3
0.7	0.5	40	29.4	82	60.3	124	91.2	166	122.1
0.8	0.6	41	30.1	83	61.0	125	91.9	167	122.8
0.9	0.7	42	30.9	84	61.8	126	92.6	168	123.5
1	0.7	43	31.6	85	62.5	127	93.4	169	124.3
2	1.5	44	32.4	86	63.2	128	94.1	170	125.0
3	2.2	45	33.1	87	64.0	129	94.9	171	125.7
4	2.9	46	33.8	88	64.7	130	95.6	172	126.5
5	3.7	47	34.6	89	65.4	131	96.3	173	127.2
6	4.4	48	35.3	90	66.2	132	97.1	174	127.9
7	5.1	49	36.0	91	66.9	133	97.8	175	128.7
8	5.9	50	36.8	92	67.6	134	98.5	176	129.4
9	6.6	51	37.5	93	68.4	135	99.3	177	130.1
10	7.4	52	38.2	94	69.1	136	100.0	178	130.9
11	8.1	53	39.0	95	69.9	137	100.7	179	131.6
12	8.8	54	39.7	96	70.6	138	101.5	180	132.4
13	9.6	55	40.4	97	71.3	139	102.2	181	133.1
14	10.3	56	41.2	98	72.1	140	102.9	182	133.8
15	11.0	57	41.9	99	72.8	141	103.7	183	134.6
16	11.8	58	42.6	100	73.5	142	104.4	184	135.3
17	12.5	59	43.4	101	74.3	143	105.1	185	136.0
18	13.2	60	44.1	102	75.0	144	105.9	186	136.8
19	14.0	61	44.9	103	75.7	145	106.6	187	137.5
20	14.7	62	45.6	104	76.5	146	107.4	188	138.2
21	15.4	63	46.3	105	77.2	147	108.1	189	139.0
22	16.2	64	47.1	106	77.9	148	108.8	190	139.7
23	16.9	65	47.8	107	78.7	149	109.6	191	140.4
24	17.6	66	48.5	108	79.4	150	110.3	192	141.2
25	18.4	67	49.3	109	80.1	151	111.0	193	141.9
26	19.1	68	50.0	110	80.9	152	111.8	194	142.6
27	19.9	69	50.7	111	81.6	153	112.5	195	143.4
28	20.6	70	51.5	112	82.4	154	113.2	196	144.1
29	21.3	71	52.2	113	83.1	155	114.0	197	144.9
30	22.1	72	52.9	114	83.8	156	114.7	198	145.6
31	22.8	73	53.7	115	84.6	157	115.4	199	146.3
32	23.5	74	54.4	116	85.3	158	116.2	200	147.1
33	24.3	75	55.1	117	86.0	159	116.9	201	147.8

ENGLISH/METRIC CONVERSION: TEMPERATURE

To convert Fahrenheit (F°) to Celsius (C°), take F° temperature and subtract 32, multiply the result by 5 and divide the result by 9
To convert Celsius (C°) to Fahrenheit (F°), take C° temperature and multiply it by 9, divide the result by 5 and add 32

F°	C°	F°	C°	C°	F°	C°	F°
-40	-40.0	150	65.6	-38	-36.4	46	114.8
-35	-37.2	155	68.3	-36	-32.8	48	118.4
-30	-34.4	160	71.1	-34	-29.2	50	122
-25	-31.7	165	73.9	-32	-25.6	52	125.6
-20	-28.9	170	76.7	-30	-22	54	129.2
-15	-26.1	175	79.4	-28	-18.4	56	132.8
-10	-23.3	180	82.2	-26	-14.8	58	136.4
-5	-20.6	185	85.0	-24	-11.2	60	140
0	-17.8	190	87.8	-22	-7.6	62	143.6
1	-17.2	195	90.6	-20	-4	64	147.2
2	-16.7	200	93.3	-18	-0.4	66	150.8
3	-16.1	205	96.1	-16	3.2	68	154.4
4	-15.6	210	98.9	-14	6.8	70	158
5	-15.0	212	100.0	-12	10.4	72	161.6
10	-12.2	215	101.7	-10	14	74	165.2
15	-9.4	220	104.4	-8	17.6	76	168.8
20	-6.7	225	107.2	-6	21.2	78	172.4
25	-3.9	230	110.0	-4	24.8	80	176
30	-1.1	235	112.8	-2	28.4	82	179.6
35	1.7	240	115.6	0	32	84	183.2
40	4.4	245	118.3	2	35.6	86	186.8
45	7.2	250	121.1	4	39.2	88	190.4
50	10.0	255	123.9	6	42.8	90	194
55	12.8	260	126.7	8	46.4	92	197.6
60	15.6	265	129.4	10	50	94	201.2
65	18.3	270	132.2	12	53.6	96	204.8
70	21.1	275	135.0	14	57.2	98	208.4
75	23.9	280	137.8	16	60.8	100	212
80	26.7	285	140.6	18	64.4	102	215.6
85	29.4	290	143.3	20	68	104	219.2
90	32.2	295	146.1	22	71.6	106	222.8
95	35.0	300	148.9	24	75.2	108	226.4
100	37.8	305	151.7	26	78.8	110	230
105	40.6	310	154.4	28	82.4	112	233.6
110	43.3	315	157.2	30	86	114	237.2
115	46.1	320	160.0	32	89.6	116	240.8
120	48.9	325	162.8	34	93.2	118	244.4
125	51.7	330	165.6	36	96.8	120	248
130	54.4	335	168.3	38	100.4	122	251.6
135	57.2	340	171.1	40	104	124	255.2
140	60.0	345	173.9	42	107.6	126	258.8
145	62.8	350	176.7	44	111.2	128	262.4

LENGTH CONVERSION

To convert inches (in.) to millimeters (mm), multiply the number of inches by 25.4
To convert millimeters (mm) to inches (in.), multiply the number of millimeters by 0.04

Inches	Millimeters	Inches	Millimeters	Inches	Millimeters	Inches	Millimeters
0.0001	0.00254	0.005	0.1270	0.09	2.286	4	101.6
0.0002	0.00508	0.006	0.1524	0.1	2.54	5	127.0
0.0003	0.00762	0.007	0.1778	0.2	5.08	6	152.4
0.0004	0.01016	0.008	0.2032	0.3	7.62	7	177.8
0.0005	0.01270	0.009	0.2286	0.4	10.16	8	203.2
0.0006	0.01524	0.01	0.254	0.5	12.70	9	228.6
0.0007	0.01778	0.02	0.508	0.6	15.24	10	254.0
0.0008	0.02032	0.03	0.762	0.7	17.78	11	279.4
0.0009	0.02286	0.04	1.016	0.8	20.32	12	304.8
0.001	0.0254	0.05	1.270	0.9	22.86	13	330.2
0.002	0.0508	0.06	1.524	1	25.4	14	355.6
0.003	0.0762	0.07	1.778	2	50.8	15	381.0
0.004	0.1016	0.08	2.032	3	76.2	16	406.4

ENGLISH/METRIC CONVERSION: LENGTH

To convert inches (in.) to millimeters (mm), multiply the number of inches by 25.4

To convert millimeters (mm) to inches (in.), multiply the number of millimeters by 0.04

Inches Fraction	Inches Decimal	Millimeters Decimal	Inches Fraction	Inches Decimal	Millimeters Decimal	Inches Fraction	Inches Decimal	Millimeters Decimal
1/64	0.016	0.397	11/32	0.344	8.731	11/16	0.688	17.463
1/32	0.031	0.794	23/64	0.359	9.128	45/64	0.703	17.859
3/64	0.047	1.191	3/8	0.375	9.525	23/32	0.719	18.256
1/16	0.063	1.588	25/64	0.391	9.922	47/64	0.734	18.653
5/64	0.078	1.984	13/32	0.406	10.319	3/4	0.750	19.050
3/32	0.094	2.381	27/64	0.422	10.716	49/64	0.766	19.447
7/64	0.109	2.778	7/16	0.438	11.113	25/32	0.781	19.844
1/8	0.125	3.175	29/64	0.453	11.509	51/64	0.797	20.241
9/64	0.141	3.572	15/32	0.469	11.906	13/16	0.813	20.638
5/32	0.156	3.969	31/64	0.484	12.303	53/64	0.828	21.034
11/64	0.172	4.366	1/2	0.500	12.700	27/32	0.844	21.431
3/16	0.188	4.763	33/64	0.516	13.097	55/64	0.859	21.828
13/64	0.203	5.159	17/32	0.531	13.494	7/8	0.875	22.225
7/32	0.219	5.556	35/64	0.547	13.891	57/64	0.891	22.622
15/64	0.234	5.953	9/16	0.563	14.288	29/32	0.906	23.019
1/4	0.250	6.350	37/64	0.578	14.684	59/64	0.922	23.416
17/64	0.266	6.747	19/32	0.594	15.081	15/16	0.938	23.813
9/32	0.281	7.144	39/64	0.609	15.478	61/64	0.953	24.209
19/64	0.297	7.541	5/8	0.625	15.875	31/32	0.969	24.606
5/16	0.313	7.938	41/64	0.641	16.272	63/64	0.984	25.003
21/64	0.328	8.334	21/32	0.656	16.669	1/1	1.000	25.400
			43/64	0.672	17.066			

CHILTON LABOR GUIDE

Whether you are looking for labor times in print, or on CD-ROM, Chilton is your source! Chilton's editors have carefully crafted the latest edition of the famous Chilton Labor Guide to bring you the most accurate repair information available. Chilton's editors consider warranty times, component locations, component type, the environment in which technicians work, the training they receive, and the tools they use when calculating a labor time. To allow for vehicle age, operating conditions, and type of service, the Chilton Labor Guide provides standard and severe service times, plus OEM warranty times. Vehicle makes and models conform to current Automotive Aftermarket Industry Association (AAIA) standards.

978-1-1110-3608-9 Chilton 2010 Labor Guide Manual Set (Domestic & Import)

978-1-1110-3611-9 Chilton 2010 Labor Guide CD-ROM (Domestic & Import)

CD-ROM FEATURES

- access labor times for 1981-2010 import and domestic vehicle models
- save time with automatically calculated labor charges, taxes, & parts as total job is estimated
- create professional estimates for your customer and worksheets for your technicians, printing them whenever needed
- keep track of customers, prior estimates, and your own parts or package jobs with less paper
- choose part names for estimates from an industry standard database to reduce typing
- estimate and track your work status with improved forms
- communicate easily with customers using re-designed printouts which show all labor and parts in an easy-to-read format.
- simplify adding parts to your estimate or work order with a helpful parts list
- locate information quick with a keyword search engine
- quickly locate work requests by day, week and month using the calendar feature

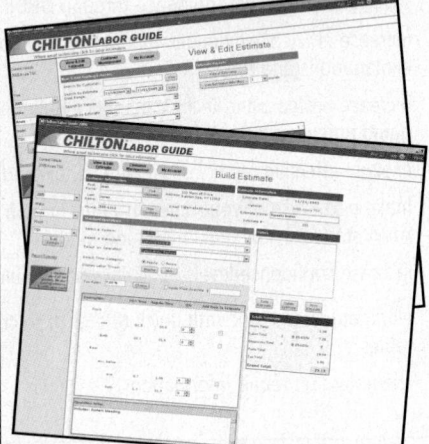

Manual FEATURES

- more than 2,500 pages of updated Chilton labor times split into two volumes includes vehicle information from 1981 to 2010
- trusted by more service professionals than any other labor guide
- less flipping though pages with separate domestic and imported vehicle manuals
- convenient tabs display contents by manufacturer and model
- easy-to-find manufacturers are arranged alphabetically within each volume
- search using two-indexes - labor operations and systems - in each model group
- page numbers include manufacturer code so you know where you are in the book

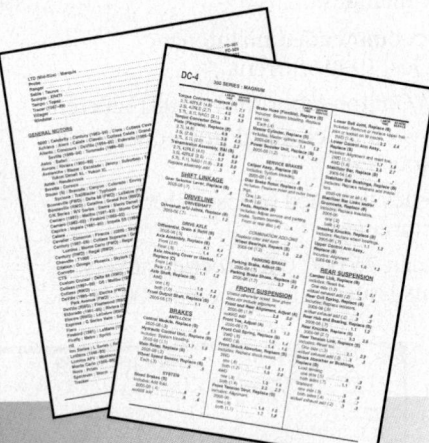

Chilton's labor times are so trusted, even a competing publisher uses them!

CHILTON®PRO.COM
Where smart technicians click for service information.

ChiltonPRO is the alternative for professional technicians who want a cost-effective electronic automotive repair system. It combines Chilton's famous automotive repair information into one solution covering more than 20 years of domestic and imported vehicles. The information is delivered online and is updated regularly throughout the year.

Online Monthly Payment
ISBN: 978-14180-3002-5

Online Annual Payment
ISBN: 978-14180-2876-3

For a free demo visit ChiltonPRO.com

ChiltonPRO FEATURES

- make repairs even easier with videos & animations which explain system operations & contribute to technician knowledge
- create better estimates using labor times developed with real-world factors
- save money by accurately identifying and solving engine performance problems
- save time with expert guidance through OBDII diagnostics
- increase efficiency by understanding system operation through detailed explanations and theory
- increase profits using Technical Service Bulletins (TSBs) to ensure that work is not going unperformed
- execute effective repairs by viewing cutaway diagrams and actual photos
- make better use of your time with information that can be found quicker using AAIA standards for year, make, and model
- increase confidence levels by always being able to print what you need
- eliminate guesswork with quick reference to critical specifications in helpful tables
- spend less on repair information

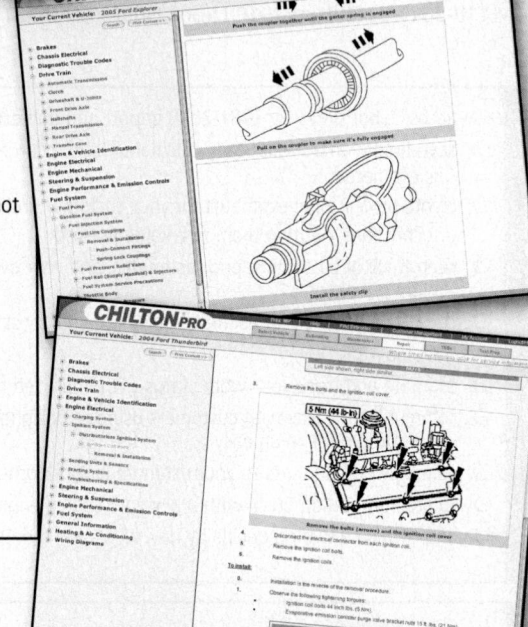

Coverage Includes:

- OEM recommended maintenance schedules, 1990–current
- trusted Chilton labor times, 1981–current
- step-by-step mechanical procedures, 1950s–current
- diagnostics designed by instructors, 1990–current
- More than 75,000 OEM Technical Service Bulletins issued during the past 20 years

System Requirements:
Web browser

- Internet Explorer 6.0 or above (recommended)
- Firefox 2 or 3, or Safari
- High-speed internet connection
- Adobe Flash Player
- Adobe Shockwave Player
- Windows XP or Vista

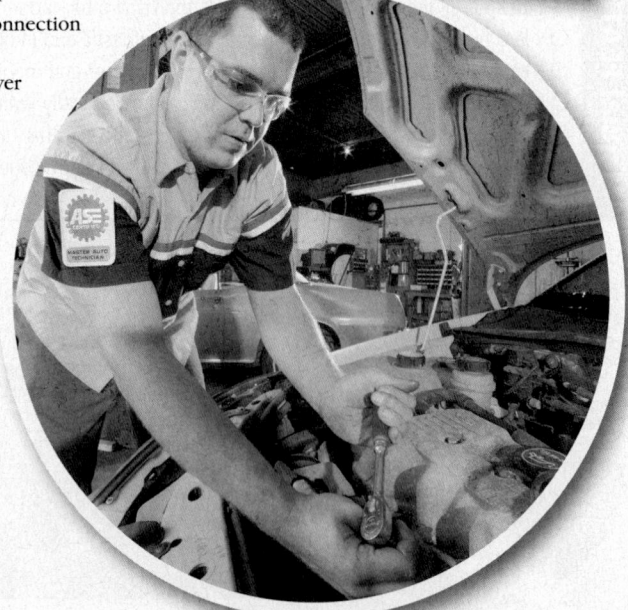

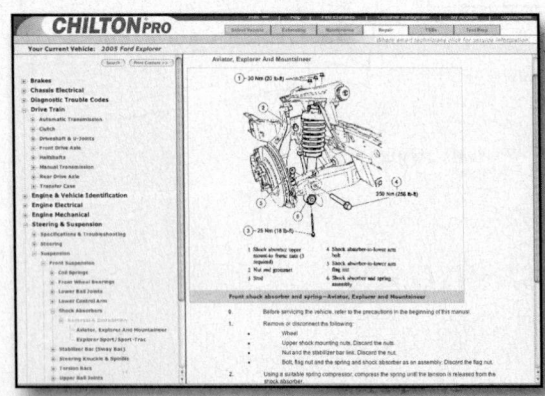

Chilton® 2010 Service Manuals

The Chilton 2010 Service Manuals now include even better graphics and expanded procedures! Chilton's editors have put together the most current automotive repair information available to assist users during daily repairs. These new manuals allow users to accurately and efficiently diagnose and repair late-model cars and trucks. Trust the step-by-step procedures and helpful illustrations that only Chilton can provide. The 2010 Service Manuals cover 2008 and 2009 models plus available 2010 models.

KEY FEATURES
- organized by vehicle manufacturer
- provides thousands of pages of expertly written content
- access new year, make, and model information without repeating previous edition's content
- comprehensive, technically detailed content, including exploded view illustrations, diagnostics and specification charts, arranged alphabetically by model group for quick, easy access

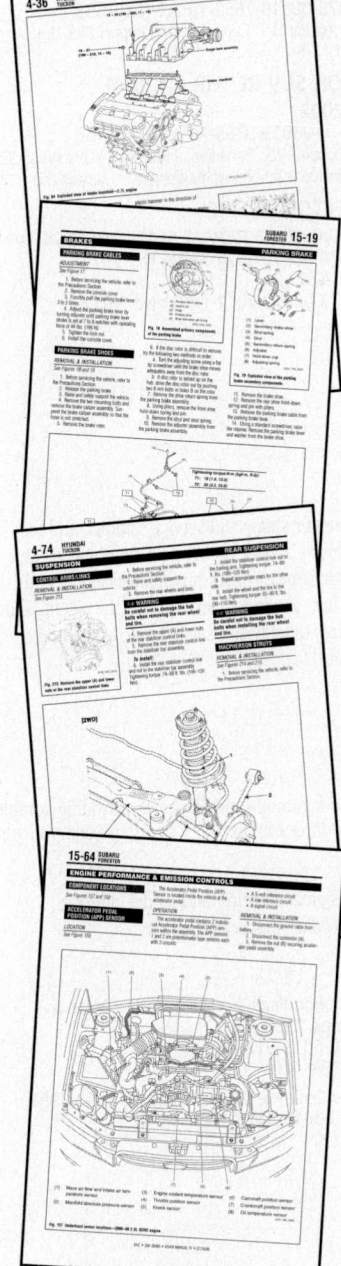

2010 EDITIONS

2010 Asian Service Manual Vol. 1*
ISBN 978-1-1110-3764-2
Part No. 163764

2010 Asian Service Manual Vol. 2*
ISBN 978-1-1110-3765-9
Part No. 163765

2010 Asian Service Manual Vol. 3*
ISBN 978-1-1110-3766-6
Part No. 163766

2010 Asian Service Manual Vol. 4*
ISBN 978-1-1110-3767-3
Part No. 163767

2010 Asian Service Manual Vol. 5*
ISBN 978-1-1110-3768-0
Part No. 163768

2010 European Service Manual*
ISBN 978-1-1110-3769-7
Part No. 163769

2010 Chrysler Service Manual, Volumes 1 & 2
ISBN 978-1-1110-3654-6
Part No. 163654

2010 Ford Service Manual, Vols. 1 & 2
ISBN 978-1-1110-3657-7
Part No. 163657

2010 General Motors Service Manuals, Vols. 1, 2, & 3
ISBN 978-1-111-03661-4
Part No. 163661

2008 EDITIONS

2008 Chrysler Service Manual, Vols. 1 & 2
ISBN 978-1-4283-2204-2
Part No. 142204

2008 Ford Service Manuals, Vols. 1 & 2
ISBN 978-1-4283-2208-0
Part No. 142208

2008 Edition General Motors Service Manuals, Vols. 1 & 2
ISBN 978-1-4283-2211-0
Part No. 142211

2008 Asian Service Manuals, Vols. 1-4
ISBN 978-1-4283-2214-1
Part No. 142214

2008 Asian Service Manual, Vol. 1
ISBN 978-1-4283-2215-8
Part No. 142215

2008 Asian Service Manual, Vol. 2
ISBN 978-1-4283-2216-5
Part No. 142216

2008 Asian Service Manual, Vol. 3
ISBN 978-1-4283-2217-2
Part No. 142217

2008 Asian Service Manual, Vol. 4
ISBN 978-1-4283-2218-9
Part No. 142218

2008 European Service Manual
ISBN 978-1-4283-2220-2
Part No. 142220

2006 EDITIONS

2006 DaimlerChrysler Diagnostic Service Manual
ISBN 978-1-4180-2118-4
Part No. 132118

2006 General Motors Diagnostic Service Manual
ISBN 978-1-4180-2120-7
Part No. 132120

2006 Asian Diagnostic Service Manual, Vol. 1
ISBN 978-1-4180-2913-5
Part No. 132913

2006 Asian Diagnostic Service Manual, Vol. 2
ISBN 978-1-4180-2914-2
Part No. 132914

2006 Asian Diagnostic Service Manual, Vol. 3
ISBN 978-1-4180-2915-9
Part No. 132915

2006 Asian Diagnostic Service Manual, 3 Vol. Set
ISBN 978-1-4180-3212-8
Part No. 132986

2006 European Diagnostic Service Manual
ISBN 978-1-4180-2924-1
Part No. 132924

2006 DaimlerChrysler Mechanical Service Manual
ISBN 978-1-4180-0600-6
Part No. 130600

2006 Asian Mechanical Service Manual, Vol. 1
ISBN 978-1-4180-0947-2
Part No. 130947

2006 Asian Mechanical Service Manual, Vol. 2
ISBN 978-1-4180-0948-9
Part No. 130948

2006 Asian Mechanical Service Manual, Vol. 3
ISBN 978-1-4180-0949-6
Part No. 130949

2006 Asian Mechanical Service Manual, 3 Vol. Set
ISBN 978-1-4180-0603-7
Part No. 130603

2006 European Mechanical Service Manual
ISBN 978-1-4180-0604-4
Part No. 130604

*Available December 2010

**Order Today–
Quantities
are Limited**

Chilton® Mechanical Service Manuals–Perennial Editions

These manuals contain repair and maintenance information for all major systems. Included are repair and overhaul procedures using thousands of illustrations.

CHILTON AUTO REPAIR MANUALS
1998-2002
ISBN 978-0-8019-9362-6/Part No. 9362
Covers all popular American and Canadian cars. An added feature includes scheduled maintenance interval charts.
1993-97
ISBN 978-0-8019-7919-4/Part No. 7919
Covers all popular American and Canadian cars.
1980-87
ISBN 978-0-8019-7670-4/Part No. 7670
Covers all popular American and Canadian cars.

CHILTON IMPORT AUTO REPAIR MANUALS
1998-2002
ISBN 978-0-8019-9363-3/Part No. 9363
Covers all popular Import cars. An added feature includes scheduled maintenance intervals charts.
1993-97
ISBN 978-0-8019-7920-0/Part No. 7920
Covers all popular Import cars.
1988-92
ISBN 978-0-8019-7907-1/Part No. 7907
Covers all popular Import cars.
1980-87
ISBN 978-0-8019-7672-8/Part No. 7672
Covers all popular Import cars.

CHILTON TRUCK AND VAN REPAIR MANUALS
1998-2002
ISBN 978-0-8019-9364-0/Part No. 9364
Covers popular U.S., Canadian, and Import Pick-Ups, Vans, and 4WDs. An added feature includes scheduled maintenance interval charts.

1993-97
ISBN 978-0-8019-7921-7/Part No. 7921
Covers popular U.S., Canadian, and Import Pick-Ups, Sport-Utilities, Vans, RVs and 4 wheel drives.
1991-95
ISBN 978-0-8019-7911-8/Part No. 7911
Covers popular U.S., Canadian, and Import Pick-Ups, Vans, RVs and 4 wheel drives.
1986-90
ISBN 978-08019-7902-6/Part No. 7902
Covers popular U.S., Canadian, and Import Pick-Us, Vans, RVs and 4 wheel drives.
1979-86
ISBN 978-08019-7655-1/Part No. 7655
Covers popular U.S., Canadian, and Import Pick-Ups, Vans, RVs and 4 wheel drives.

CHILTON SUV REPAIR MANUAL
1998-2002
ISBN 978-08019-9365-7/Part No. 9365
Covers popular U.S., Canadian, and import SUVs. An added feature includes scheduled maintenance intervals charts.

COLLECTOR'S SERIES
CHILTON AUTO REPAIR MANUAL 1964-1971
ISBN 978-08019-5974-5/Part No. 5974
1971-1978
ISBN 978-08019-7012-2/Part No. 7012

Chilton Timing Belts, 1985-2005

Timing belt procedures can represent increased profits for automotive repair shops and service stations, and this manual contains all the information automotive technicians need to properly service timing belts on domestic and imported cars, vans, and light trucks through 2005 models. Clear, straightforward procedures, illustrations, and specifications help to communicate 20 years of vehicle applications for fast, accurate inspection, replacement, and tensioning of timing belts. Users will learn how to perform key procedures quickly and safely, while learning the correct labor time to charge for the service.

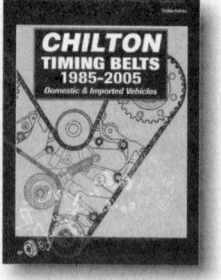

ISBN 978-1-4018-9880-9
Part No. 129880
544 pp, 8" x 11", SC, ©2006

ALSO AVAILABLE:
Quick-Reference Manuals

The Chilton Professional Series offers *Quick-Reference Manuals* for the automotive professional, providing complete coverage on repair and maintenance, adjustments, and diagnostic procedures for specific systems and components.

KEY FEATURES
- step-by-step procedures
- detailed illustrations and exploded views
- easy-to-use manufacturer and model indexing
- handy specifications or data charts

Heater Core Service 1990-2000,
ISBN 978-0-8019-9311-4
Part No. 9311

Brake Specifications and Service 1990-2000
ISBN 978-0-8019-9312-1
Part No. 9312

Electric Cooling Fans, Accessory Drive Belts & Water Pumps, 1995-1999,
ISBN 978-0-8019-9126-4
Part No. 9126

Powertrain Codes & Oxygen Sensors, 1990-1999,
ISBN 978-0-8019-9127-1
Part No. 9127

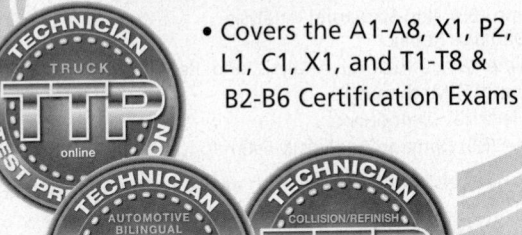
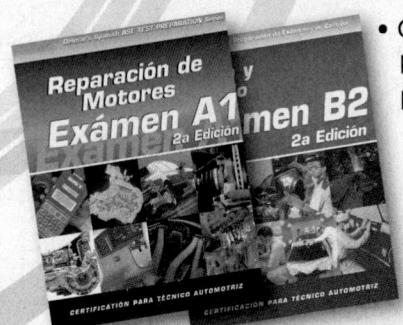

You Deserve The Best When You Are Putting Your Skills To The Test!

ASE Test Preparation Manuals

133878	(A1) Engine Repair, 4E	978-1-4180-3878-6
133879	(A2) Transmissions and Transaxles, 4E	978-1-4180-3879-3
133880	(A3) Manual Drive Train and Axles, 4E	978-1-4180-3880-9
133881	(A4) Suspension and Steering, 4E	978-1-4180-3881-6
133882	(A5) Brakes, 4E	978-1-4180-3882-3
133883	(A6) Electrical/Electronic Systems, 4E	978-1-4180-3883-0
133884	(A7) Heating and Air Conditioning, 4E	978-1-4180-3884-7
133885	(A8) Engine Performance, 4E	978-1-4180-3885-4
133888	(L1) Advanced Engine Performance, 4E	978-1-4180-3888-5
133886	(X1) Exhaust Systems, 4E	978-1-4180-3886-1
133887	(P2) Parts Specialist, 4E	978-1-4180-3887-8
133889	(C1) Service Consultant, 2E	978-1-4180-3889-2
23664	(B2) Painting and Refinishing, 3E	978-1-4018-3664-1
23665	(B3) Non Structural Analysis and Damage Repair, 3E	978-1-4018-3665-8
23666	(B4) Structural Analysis and Damage Repair, 3E	978-1-4018-3666-5
23667	(B5) Mechanical and Electrical Components, 3E	978-1-4018-3667-2
23668	(B6) Damage Analysis and Estimation, 3E	978-1-4018-3668-9
16280	(M1) Cylinder Head Specialist	978-0-7668-6280-7
16281	(M2) Cylinder Block Specialist	978-0-7668-6281-4
16282	(M3) Assembly Specialist	978-0-7668-6282-1
134828	(T1) Gasoline Engines, 4E	978-1-4180-4828-0
134829	(T2) Diesel Engines, 4E	978-1-4180-4829-7
134830	(T3) Drive Train, 4E	978-1-4180-4830-3
134831	(T4) Brakes, 4E	978-1-4180-4831-0
134832	(T5) Suspension and Steering, 4E	978-1-4180-4832-7
134834	(T6) Electrical/Electronic Systems, 4E	978-1-4180-4834-1
134835	(T7) Heating, Ventilation, and Air Conditioning, 4E	978-1-4180-4835-8
134836	(T8) Preventive Maintenance, 4E	978-1-4180-4836-5
21822	(S2) Diesel Engines	978-1-4018-1822-7
21824	(S4) Brakes	978-1-4018-1824-1
21825	(S5) Suspension and Steering	978-1-4018-1825-8
153939	(H1) Compressed Natural Gas Engines	978-1-4354-3939-9
136570	(H2) Diesel Engines	978-1-4180-6570-6
155376	(H3) Drive Train	978-1-4354-5376-0
134998	(H4) Brakes	978-1-4180-4998-0
144011	(H5) Suspension & Steering	978-1-4283-4011-4
134999	(H6) Electrical/Electronic Systems	978-1-4180-4999-7
136571	(H7) Heating, Ventilation, & Air Conditioning	978-1-4180-6571-3
153938	(H8) Preventive Maintenance	978-1-4354-3938-2
153935	(E1) Truck Equipment Installation & Repair	978-1-4354-3935-1
153936	(E2) Electronic Systems Installation & Repair	978-1-4354-3936-8
153937	(E3) Auxilary Power Systems Installation & Repair	978-1-4354-3937-5

ASE Test Preparation in Spanish

131305	Spanish (A1) Engine Repair	978-1-4018-1014-6
131305	Spanish (A2) Transmissions and Transaxles	978-1-4018-1015-3
131305	Spanish (A3) Manual Drive Train and Axles	978-1-4018-1016-0
131305	Spanish (A4) Suspension and Steering	978-1-4018-1017-7
131305	Spanish (A5) Brakes	978-1-4018-1018-4
131305	Spanish (A6) Electrical/Electronic Systems	978-1-4018-1019-1
131305	Spanish (A7) Heating and Air Conditioning	978-1-4018-1020-7
131305	Spanish (A8) Engine Performance	978-1-4018-1021-4
131305	Spanish (L1) Advanced Engine Performance	978-1-4018-1022-1
131305	Spanish (X1) Exhaust Systems	978-1-4018-1024-5
131305	Spanish (P2) Parts Specialist	978-1-4018-1023-8
29255	Spanish (B2) Painting and Refinishin	978-1-4018-9255-5
22544	Spanish (B3) Non-Structural Analysis and Damage Repair	978-1-4018-2544-7
29131	Spanish (B4) Structural Analysis and Damage Repair	978-1-4018-9131-2
27759	Spanish (B5) Mechanical and Electrical Components	978-1-4018-7759-0
26573	Spanish (B6) Damage Analysis and Estimation	978-1-4018-6573-3

Online ASE Test Preparation
Place your order online at www.techniciantestprep.com

131305	*Online (A1) Engine Repair	978-1-4180-1305-9
131306	*Online (A2) Automatic Transmissions & Transaxles	978-1-4180-1306-6
131307	*Online (A3) Manual Drive Trains & Axles	978-1-4180-1307-3
131308	*Online (A4) Suspension & Steering	978-1-4180-1308-0
131309	*Online (A5) Brakes	978-1-4180-1309-7
131310	*Online (A6) Electrical/Electronic Systems	978-1-4180-1310-3
131311	*Online (A7) Heating & Air Conditioning	978-1-4180-1311-0
131312	*Online (A8) Engine Performance	978-1-4180-1312-7
131313	*Online (X1) Exhaust Systems	978-1-4180-1313-4
131314	*Online (P2) Automobile Parts Specialist	978-1-4180-1314-1
131315	*Online (L1) Advanced Engine Performance	978-1-4180-1315-8
131316	*Online (C1) Service Consultant	978-1-4180-1316-5
127897	Online (T1) Gasoline Engines	978-1-4018-7897-9
127898	Online (T2) Diesel Engines	978-1-4018-7898-6
127900	Online (T3) Drive Train	978-1-4018-7900-6
127901	Online (T4) Brakes	978-1-4018-7901-3
127903	Online (T5) Suspension & Steering	978-1-4018-7903-7
131879	Online (T6) Electrical/Electronic Systems	978-1-4180-1879-5
131880	Online (T7) Heating, Ventilation, & Air Conditioning	978-1-4180-1880-1
127906	Online (T8) Preventive Maintenance	978-1-4018-7906-8
154748	Online (B2) Painting & Refinishing	978-1-4354-4748-6
154749	Online (B3) Non-Structural Analysis & Damage Repair	978-1-4354-4749-3
154750	Online (B4) Structural Analysis and Repair	978-1-4354-4750-9
154751	Online (B5) Mechanical & Electrical Components	978-1-4354-4751-6
154752	Online (B6) Damage Analysis & Estimating	978-1-4354-4752-3

*Switch between English & Spanish at the click of a button!

Complete Series

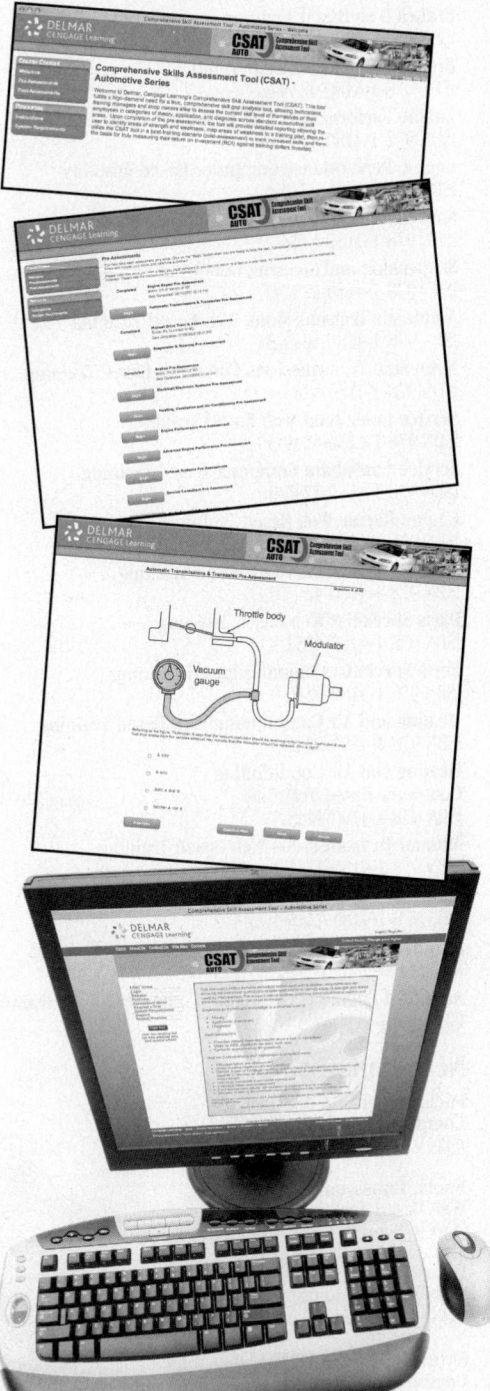

CSAT-Automotive Series

The online *Comprehensive Skill Assessment Tool-Automotive Series* helps instructors and trainers implement the necessary training programs for individual areas needing improvement over various key automotive topics. As a true skill gap analysis tool, within each key topic, strategic learning areas are measured for knowledge of theory, hands-on application, and diagnostic skill. Areas of strength and areas needing improvement are identified. The combined phases of education and training, and post-assessment allow instructors to track skill level growth and target specific areas needing development.

Courses Available in the CSAT Automotive Series

Parts Specialist
ISBN 978-1-4180-3225-8

Service Consultant
ISBN 978-1-4180-3223-4

Advanced Engine Performance
ISBN 978-1-4180-0073-8

Brakes
ISBN 978-1-4180-0069-1

Electrical/Electronic Systems
ISBN 978-1-4180-0070-7

Engine Performance
ISBN 978-1-4180-0072-1

Engine Repair
ISBN 978-1-4180-0065-3

Exhaust Systems
ISBN 978-1-4180-0074-5

Heating and Air Conditioning
ISBN 978-1-4180-0071-4

Manual Drive Train & Axles
ISBN 978-1-4180-0067-7

Suspension & Steering
ISBN 978-1-4180-0068-4

Transmissions & Transaxles
ISBN 978-1-4180-0066-0

All-in-One (contains questions from all eight core automotive areas in one product)
ISBN 978-1-4354-2825-6

FEATURES

- available tests include Engine Repair, Transmissions and Transaxles, Manual Drive Train and Axles, Suspension and Steering, Brakes, Electrical/Electronic Systems, Heating and Air Conditioning, Engine Performance, Advanced Engine Performance, and Exhaust Systems

- can be utilized by companies to measure the technical skill level of individuals against an "ideal" to identify areas of strength and creates a skill gap analysis to help users address areas needing improvement

- questions are written and reviewed by experts in the industry and offer users the opportunity to receive instant feedback

- account set-up that enables instructors and trainers to assess and track the results of individual students

- acts as a true return on investment (ROI) tool for companies to ensure they invest their training dollars in the most appropriate areas

Visit **www.skillanalysis.com**
for a free demo!

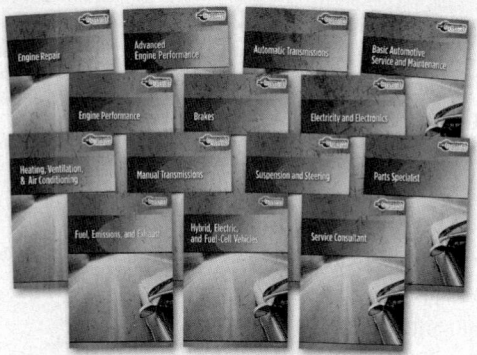

Professional Automotive Technician Training Series: PATTS
Delmar

Delmar, the leader in providing first-rate educational materials for automotive technicians, now offers this exciting self-paced learning series. Choose the delivery method that best suits your needs– CD-ROM or Web-based product – and receive more than 8.5 hours worth of quality instruction. Combining theory, diagnosis, and repair information into one easy-to-use training tool, this highly interactive product helps technicians receive the most applicable delivery method for their needs, regardless of technical infrastructure.

KEY FEATURES

- attention-grabbing animations and learner interactions keep users interested and engaged throughout the course of the program
- bookmarking technology enables users to track their progress from beginning to end
- periodic progress checks and end-of-section reviews are integrated throughout to ensure the highest level of retention
- a certificate of completion can be printed by users achieving a score of 80% or higher on the final review of the course
- all material is completely AICC and SCORM compliant
- all material follows the latest ASE and NATEF standards

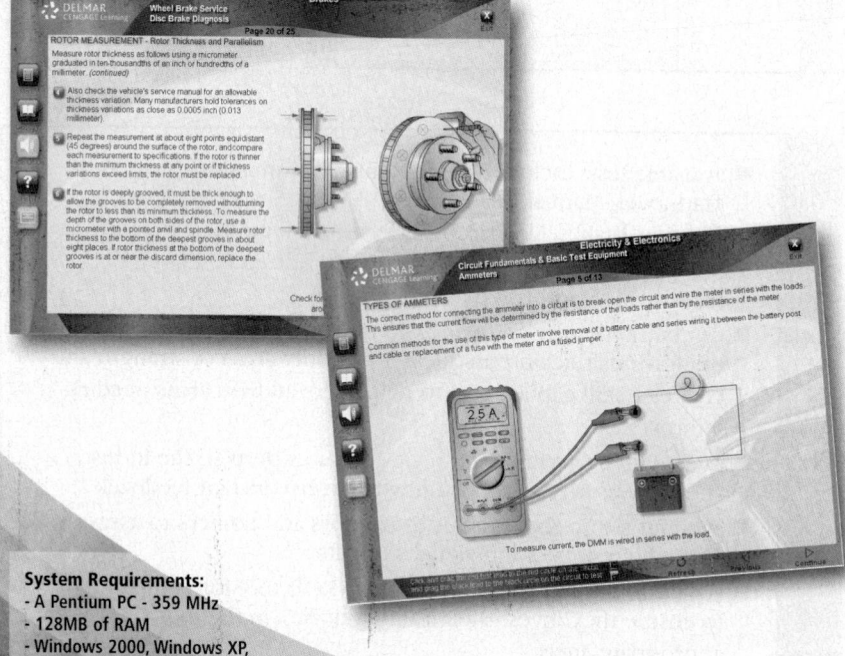

System Requirements:
- A Pentium PC - 359 MHz
- 128MB of RAM
- Windows 2000, Windows XP, Windows Vista
- Graphics adapter with Minimum 1024 x 768 display resolution, 32 bit depth
- Minimum Display Resolution 1024 x 768
- High Speed Internet Connection
- Internet Explorer 6, 7, or Firefox 2
- Not Mac Compatible

Basic Automotive Service and Maintenance Web Based Training
ISBN 978-1-4180-4101-4

Basic Automotive Service and Maintenance Computer Based Training
ISBN 978-1-4180-4100-7

Electricity and Electronics Web Based Training
ISBN 978-1-4180-4242-4

Electricity and Electronics Computer Based Training
ISBN 978-1-4180-4241-7

Brakes Web Based Training
ISBN 978-1-4180-4236-3

Brakes Computer Based Training
ISBN 978-1-4180-4235-6

Engine Performance Web Based Training
ISBN 978-1-4180-4240-0

Engine Performance Computer Based Training
ISBN 978-1-4180-4239-4

Suspension and Steering Web Based Training
ISBN 978-1-4180-4238-7

Suspension and Steering Computer Based Training
ISBN 978-1-4180-4237-0

Automatic Transmissions Web Based Training
ISBN 978-1-4180-4244-8

Automatic Transmissions Computer Based Training
ISBN 978-1-4180-4243-1

Service Consultant Web Based Training
ISBN 978-1-4180-4249-3

Service Consultant Computer Based Training
ISBN 978-1-4180-4247-9

Engine Repair Web Based Training
ISBN 978-1-4180-4254-7

Engine Repair Computer Based Training
ISBN 978-1-4180-4253-0

Parts Specialist Web Based Training
ISBN 978-1-4180-4252-3

Parts Specialist Computer Based Training
ISBN 978-1-4180-4250-9

Heating and Air Conditioning Web Based Training
ISBN 978-1-4180-4246-2

Heating and Air Conditioning Computer Based Training
ISBN 978-1-4180-4245-5

Manual Transmissions Web Based Training
ISBN 978-1-4180-4256-1

Manual Transmissions Computer Based Training
ISBN 978-1-4180-4255-4

Advanced Engine Performance Web Based Training
ISBN 978-1-4283-2098-7

Advanced Engine Performance Computer Based Training
ISBN 978-1-4283-2097-0

New Courses!

Fuels, Emissions, and Exhaust Computer Based Training
ISBN 978-1-4354-4148-4

Fuels, Emissions, and Exhaust Web Based Training
ISBN 978-1-4354-4147-7

Hybrid, Electric, and Fuel-Cell Vehicles Web Based Training
ISBN 978-1-4354-4144-6

Hybrid, Electric, and Fuel-Cell Vehicles Computer Based Training
ISBN 978-1-4354-4143-9

Visit **www.techniciantraining.com**
for a free demo!